Glencoe Science

BIOLOGY
The Dynamics of Life

JUST FOR INDIANA

Exclusively from Glencoe!

FEATURES OF THE INDIANA EDITION

- Correlation of Indiana's Academic Standards to *Biology: The Dynamics of Life*

- Correlation of *Biology: The Dynamics of Life* to Indiana's Academic Standards

- Countdown to Indiana's Academic Standards

ADDITIONAL INDIANA RESOURCES

- **Indiana Interactive Chalkboard CD-ROM** Microsoft® PowerPoint® presentations you can customize for each lesson

- **Indiana TeacherWorks™ CD-ROM** An all-in-one lesson planner and resource center that helps you customize lesson plans and reproduce classroom resources quickly and easily

- **Indiana StudentWorks™ CD-ROM** An all-in-one Interactive Student Edition and student resources—your students' backpack solution in Spanish and English

For more information, visit: in.bdol.glencoe.com

Safety Symbols

These safety symbols are used in laboratory and field investigations in this book to indicate possible hazards. Learn the meaning of each symbol and refer to this page often. *Remember to wash your hands thoroughly after completing lab procedures.*

SAFETY SYMBOLS	HAZARD	EXAMPLES	PRECAUTION	REMEDY
DISPOSAL	Special disposal procedures need to be followed.	certain chemicals, living organisms	Do not dispose of these materials in the sink or trash can.	Dispose of wastes as directed by your teacher.
BIOLOGICAL	Organisms or other biological materials that might be harmful to humans	bacteria, fungi, blood, unpreserved tissues, plant materials	Avoid skin contact with these materials. Wear mask or gloves.	Notify your teacher if you suspect contact with material. Wash hands thoroughly.
EXTREME TEMPERATURE	Objects that can burn skin by being too cold or too hot	boiling liquids, hot plates, dry ice, liquid nitrogen	Use proper protection when handling.	Go to your teacher for first aid.
SHARP OBJECT	Use of tools or glassware that can easily puncture or slice skin	razor blades, pins, scalpels, pointed tools, dissecting probes, broken glass	Practice common-sense behavior and follow guidelines for use of the tool.	Go to your teacher for first aid.
FUME	Possible danger to respiratory tract from fumes	ammonia, acetone, nail polish remover, heated sulfur, moth balls	Make sure there is good ventilation. Never smell fumes directly. Wear a mask.	Leave foul area and notify your teacher immediately.
ELECTRICAL	Possible danger from electrical shock or burn	improper grounding, liquid spills, short circuits, exposed wires	Double-check setup with teacher. Check condition of wires and apparatus.	Do not attempt to fix electrical problems. Notify your teacher immediately.
IRRITANT	Substances that can irritate the skin or mucous membranes of the respiratory tract	pollen, moth balls, steel wool, fiberglass, potassium permanganate	Wear dust mask and gloves. Practice extra care when handling these materials.	Go to your teacher for first aid.
CHEMICAL	Chemicals that can react with and destroy tissue and other materials	bleaches such as hydrogen peroxide; acids such as sulfuric acid, hydrochloric acid; bases such as ammonia, sodium hydroxide	Wear goggles, gloves, and an apron.	Immediately flush the affected area with water and notify your teacher.
TOXIC	Substance may be poisonous if touched, inhaled, or swallowed.	mercury, many metal compounds, iodine, poinsettia plant parts	Follow your teacher's instructions.	Always wash hands thoroughly after use. Go to your teacher for first aid.
OPEN FLAME	Open flame may ignite flammable chemicals, loose clothing, or hair.	alcohol, kerosene, potassium permanganate, hair, clothing	Tie back hair. Avoid wearing loose clothing. Avoid open flames when using flammable chemicals. Be aware of locations of fire safety equipment.	Notify your teacher immediately. Use fire safety equipment if applicable.

 Eye Safety Proper eye protection should be worn at all times by anyone performing or observing science activities.

 Clothing Protection This symbol appears when substances could stain or burn clothing.

 Animal Safety This symbol appears when safety of animals and students must be ensured.

 Radioactivity This symbol appears when radioactive materials are used.

The Indiana Biology Handbook

Table of Contents

Indiana Dunes State Park

Correlations to Indiana's Academic Standards

The table below will help you review the content covered in Indiana's Academic Standards. For each standard, the table shows the pages where the content can be found.

Correlations to Indiana's Academic Standards

Standard 1	Text	Biology: The Dynamics of Life page(s)
Principles of Biology *Students work with the concepts, principles, and theories that enable them to understand the living environment. They recognize that living organisms are made of cells or cell products that consist of the same components as all other matter, involve the same kinds of transformations of energy, and move using the same kinds of basic forces. Students investigate, through laboratories and fieldwork, how living things function and how they interact with one another and their environment.*		
Molecules and Cells		

B.1.1 *Recognize that and explain how the many cells in an individual can be very different from one another, even though they are all descended from a single cell and thus have essentially identical genetic instructions. Understand that different parts of the genetic instructions are used in different types of cells and are influenced by the cell's environment and past history.*

Expanded Standard	Recognize that and explain how the many cells in an individual can be very different from one another, even though they are all descended from a single cell and thus have essentially identical genetic instructions.	211, 244, 606-608, 611, 613, 629, 678-679, 688-691, 695, 697, 717, 1008, 1048
	Understand that different parts of the genetic instructions are used in different types of cells.	629, 678-679, 1048
	Understand that different parts of the genetic instructions are influenced by the cell's environment and past history.	688-691, 695, 782, 1008

B.1.2 *Explain that every cell is covered by a membrane that controls what can enter and leave the cell. Recognize that in all but quite primitive cells, a complex network of proteins provides organization and shape. In addition, understand that flagella and/or cilia may allow some Protista, some Monera, and some animal cells to move.*

Expanded Standard	Explain that every cell is covered by a membrane that controls what can enter and leave the cell.	175-181, 185-187, 193-201, 217-218, 246-247, 249, 487-488
	Recognize that in all but quite primitive cells, a complex network of proteins provides organization and shape.	185-187, 193-201, 246-247, 249, 487-488, 554-555
	Understand that flagella and/or cilia may allow some Protista, some Monera, and some animal cells to move.	187, 487-488, 503-507, 511-513, 515, 525-527, 554-555

B.1.3 *Know and describe that within the cell are specialized parts for the transport of materials, energy capture and release, protein building, waste disposal, information feedback, and movement. In addition to these basic cellular functions common to all cells, understand that most cells in multicellular organisms perform some special functions that others do not.*

Expanded Standard	Know and describe that within the cell are specialized parts for the transport of materials.	162, 190-192, 193, 218, 246-249
	Know and describe that within the cell are specialized parts for energy capture and release.	184-185, 190-192, 193, 218, 224, 226-234, 240-242, 246-249
	Know and describe that within the cell are specialized parts for protein building.	163, 180-186, 192, 193
	Know and describe that within the cell are specialized parts for information feedback.	162-163
	Know and describe that within the cell are specialized parts for movement.	505-507, 526
	Understand that most cells in multicellular organisms perform some special functions that others do not.	605-606, 975-980, 991

Standard 1	Text	*Biology: The Dynamics of Life* page(s)
	B.1.4 *Understand and describe that the work of the cell is carried out by the many different types of molecules it assembles, such as proteins, lipids, carbohydrates, and nucleic acids.*	
Expanded Standard	Understand and describe that the work of the cell is carried out by the many different types of molecules it assembles, such as proteins.	160-161, 211
	Understand and describe that the work of the cell is carried out by the many different types of molecules it assembles, such as lipids.	160, 175-178
	Understand and describe that the work of the cell is carried out by the many different types of molecules it assembles, such as carbohydrates.	228-237, 241-243
	Understand and describe that the work of the cell is carried out by the many different types of molecules it assembles, such as nucleic acids.	163, 211
	B.1.5 *Demonstrate that most cells function best within a narrow range of temperature and acidity. Note that extreme changes may harm cells, modifying the structure of their protein molecules and therefore, some possible functions.*	
Expanded Standard	Demonstrate that most cells function best within a narrow range of temperature and acidity.	150-151, 164-165, 169
	Note that extreme changes may harm cells, modifying the structure of their protein molecules and therefore, some possible functions.	164-165, 169
	B.1.6 *Show that a living cell is composed mainly of a small number of chemical elements—carbon, hydrogen, nitrogen, oxygen, phosphorous, and sulfur. Recognize that carbon can join to other carbon atoms in chains and rings to form large and complex molecules.*	
Expanded Standard	Show that a living cell is composed mainly of a small number of chemical elements—carbon, hydrogen, nitrogen, oxygen, phosphorous, and sulfur.	157-159, 160-163, 169, 176-178, 222, 245
	Recognize that carbon can join to other carbon atoms in chains and rings to form large and complex molecules.	157-159, 225
	B.1.7 *Explain that complex interactions among the different kinds of molecules in the cell cause distinct cycles of activities, such as growth and division. Note that cell behavior can also be affected by molecules from other parts of the organism, such as hormones.*	
Expanded Standard	Explain that complex interactions among the different kinds of molecules in the cell cause distinct cycles of activities, such as growth and division.	203-213, 217-219, 229, 233, 241-243, 691, 932-933, 1002-1004, 1016-1021
	Note that cell behavior can also be affected by molecules from other parts of the organism, such as hormones.	211-213, 217-219, 229, 233, 241-243, 622-623, 624-625, 629, 691, 932-933, 1002-1004, 1016-1021, 1051
	B.1.8 *Understand and describe that all growth and development is a consequence of an increase in cell number, cell size, and/or cell products. Explain that cellular differentiation results from gene expression and/or environmental influence. Differentiate between mitosis and meiosis.*	
Expanded Standard	Understand and describe that all growth and development is a consequence of an increase in cell number, cell size, and/or cell products.	201-219, 203-210, 489-490, 512-513, 515-516, 518-519, 634-635, 709, 1001
	Explain that cellular differentiation results from gene expression and/or environmental influence.	210
	Differentiate between mitosis and meiosis.	203-210, 247-249, 265-271, 273, 277-279, 361, 1001

Correlations to Indiana's Academic Standards

Correlations to Indiana's Academic Standards

Standard 1	Text	Biology: The Dynamics of Life page(s)
B.1.9 *Recognize and describe that both living and nonliving things are composed of compounds, which are themselves made up of elements joined by energy-containing bonds, such as those in ATP.*		
Expanded Standard	Recognize and describe that both living and nonliving things are composed of compounds.	140-153, 156,163, 167-169, 176-178
	Compounds are made up of elements joined by energy-containing bonds, such as those in ATP	222-225, 229, 232-237, 241-244
B.1.10 *Recognize and explain that macromolecules such as lipids contain high energy bonds as well.*		160-161

Developmental and Organismal Biology

B.1.11 *Describe that through biogenesis all organisms begin their life cycles as a single cell and that in multicellular organisms, successive generations of embryonic cells form by cell division.*		
Expanded Standard	Describe that through biogenesis all organisms begin their life cycles as a single.	8, 516, 518-519, 533, 536, 575, 635-640, 646-648, 650-652, 664, 696-697, 700-701, 1005-1006
	In multicellular organisms, successive generations of embryonic cells form by cell division.	512, 516, 518-519, 533, 536, 539, 575, 633, 635-640, 646-648, 662, 676-679, 996, 1000-1001, 1009
B.1.12 *Compare and contrast the form and function of prokaryotic and eukaryotic cells.*		
Expanded Standard	Compare and contrast the form of prokaryotic and eukaryotic cells.	172-174, 187-189, 192, 245, 499, 550
	Compare and contrast the function of prokaryotic an eukaryotic cells.	172-174, 487-489, 550
B.1.13 *Explain that some structures in the modern eukaryotic cell developed from early prokaryotes, such as mitochondria, and in plants, chloroplasts.*		
Expanded Standard	Explain that some structures in the modern eukaryotic cell developed from early prokaryotes, such as mitochondria.	467
	Explain that some structures in the modern eukaryotic cell developed from early prokaryotes such as, in plants, chloroplasts.	467
B.1.14 *Recognize and explain that communication and/or interaction are required between cells to coordinate their diverse activities.*		702, 707-710, 724-725, 739, 745, 796, 892-896, 929-935, 939-963, 967-969, 973-974, 982-984, 992, 1002-1004
B.1.15 *Understand and explain that, in biological systems, structure and function must be considered together.*		581-597, 602-604, 606-621, 629-630, 641-645, 649-655, 657, 661-669, 682-685, 689, 691-699, 701-705, 707-710, 717-718, 722-731, 737-738, 742-745, 747-749, 751-755, 759-760, 762-775, 779-803, 804, 805-807, 809, 813-816, 818, 820, 825-827, 829, 830-831, 833, 837-849, 855-857, 880-885, 887, 889, 892-896, 898-909, 913, 919, 979-987, 991, 996-1001, 1004, 1006- 1007, 1011, 1012-1013, 1021, 1032-1041, 1045, 1048-1051, 1056-1057
B.1.16 *Explain how higher levels of organization result from specific complexing and interactions of smaller units and that their maintenance requires a constant input of energy as well as new material.*		
Expanded Standard	Explain how higher levels of organization result from specific complexing and interactions of smaller units.	9, 30, 630, 673-675, 689-690, 827-828, 917-923, 1008-1011, 1019, 1056
	The maintenance of smaller units requires a contant input of energy as well as new material.	9, 30, 221-223, 909-911, 1008-1011, 1019

Standard 1	Text	Biology: The Dynamics of Life page(s)
B.1.17 *Understand that and describe how the maintenance of a relatively stable internal environment is required for the continuation of life and explain how stability is challenged by changing physical, chemical, and environmental conditions, as well as the presence of disease agents.*		
Expanded Standard	Understand that and describe how the maintenance of a relatively stable internal environment is required for the continuation of life.	9, 756-757, 828-829, 856, 886-887, 896, 913-914, 928, 987, 991, 1049
	Explain how stability is challenged by changing physical conditions.	828-829, 928
	Explain how stability is challenged by changing chemical conditions.	756-757, 909, 928, 987, 991, 1057
	Explain how stability is challenged by changing environmental conditions.	739, 756-757, 828-829, 833, 841-842, 846-847, 856, 886-887
	Explain how stability is challenged by the presence of disease agents.	713, 761, 1023-1030, 1046
B.1.18 *Explain that the regulatory and behavioral responses of an organism to external stimuli occur in order to maintain both short- and long-term equilibrium.*		
Expanded Standard	Explain that the regulatory responses of an organism to external stimuli occur in order to maintain short-term equilibrium.	9, 10, 30, 71, 624-625, 629, 667-669, 814, 828, 833, 847, 887
	Explain that the regulatory responses of an organism to external stimuli occur in order to maintain long-term equilibrium.	64-66, 71, 624-625, 629, 644-645, 654-655, 661, 667-669, 828, 833, 847, 887
	Explain that the behavioral responses of an organism to external stimuli occur in order to maintain short-term equilibrium.	9, 10, 64-66, 734-735, 803-806, 820, 859, 874-877, 887
	Explain that the behavioral responses of an organism to external stimuli occur in order to maintain long-term equilibrium.	64-66, 734-735, 803-806, 820, 859, 874-877, 887
B.1.19 *Recognize and describe that metabolism consists of the production, modification, transport, and exchange of materials that are required for the maintenance of life.*		
Expanded Standard	Recognize and describe that metabolism consists of the production of materials that are required for the maintenance of life.	54, 809, 825, 843, 890, 916-923, 924-925, 926-928, 939, 941
	Recognize and describe that metabolism consists of the modification of materials that are required for the maintenance of life.	732, 764-766, 774, 843, 916-923, 924-925, 926-928, 939
	Recognize and describe that metabolism consists of the transport of materials that are required for the maintenance of life.	724-725, 729-730, 738, 760, 764-766, 774, 778, 789, 794, 806, 843, 916-923, 924-925, 926-928, 970-989, 993, 1051, 1053-1054
	Recognize and describe that metabolism consists of the exchange of materials that are required for the maintenance of life.	724-725, 729-730, 738, 744-745, 760, 774, 794, 806, 827-828, 843, 880-882, 884, 970-989, 1007, 1053-1054, 1057
B.1.20 *Recognize that and describe how the human immune system is designed to protect against microscopic organisms and foreign substances that enter from outside the body and against some cancer cells that arise within.*		
Expanded Standard	Recognize that and describe how the human immune system is designed to protect against microscopic organisms and foreign substances that enter from outside the body.	897-898, 913, 977-980, 984, 992, 1022, 1031-1041, 1045-1047, 1055, 1057
	Recognize that and describe how the human immune system is designed to protect against some cancer cells that arise within.	1031-1041, 1045-1047

Standard 1		Text	Biology: The Dynamics of Life page(s)
Genetics			
B.1.21 Understand and explain that the information passed from parents to offspring is transmitted by means of genes which are coded in DNA molecules.			250-271, 273-296, 301-303, 305-335, 337-340, 358, 360, 362-365, 575, 660, 978-979, 1011, 1047
B.1.22 Understand and explain the genetic basis for Mendel's laws of segregation and independent assortment.			
Expanded Standard	Understand and explain the genetic basis for Mendel's law of segregation.		255-264, 270, 273, 276-277, 279, 340, 360, 363
	Understand and explain the genetic basis for Mendel's law of independent assortment.		255-264, 270, 273, 276-277, 279, 340, 360, 363
B.1.23 Understand that and describe how inserting, deleting, or substituting DNA segments can alter a gene. Recognize that an altered gene may be passed on to every cell that develops from it, and that the resulting features may help, harm, or have little or no effect on the offspring's success in its environment.			
Expanded Standard	Understand that and describe how inserting, deleting, or substituting DNA segments can alter a gene.		296-301, 305, 307, 341-348, 352-357, 359, 363, 365, 660
	Recognize that an altered gene may be passed on to every cell that develops from it, and that the resulting features may help, harm, or have little or no effect on the offspring's success in its environment.		296-301, 305, 307, 345-348, 352-357, 363, 660
B.1.24 Explain that gene mutations can be caused by such things as radiation and chemicals. Understand that when they occur in sex cells, the mutations can be passed on to offspring; if they occur in other cells, they can be passed on to descendant cells only.			
Expanded Standard	Explain that gene mutations can be caused by such things as radiation and chemicals.		296, 300-301, 406
	Understand that when mutations occur in sex cells, the mutations can be passed on to offspring.		296, 300-301, 305-306
	Understand that when mutations occur in others cells, they can be passed on to descendant cells only.		297-298, 300-301, 305-306
B.1.25 Explain that gene mutation in a cell can result in uncontrolled cell division, called cancer. Also know that exposure of cells to certain chemicals and radiation increases mutations and thus increases the chance of cancer.			
Expanded Standard	Explain that gene mutation in a cell can result in uncontrolled cell division, called cancer.		297-298, 305
	Know that exposure of cells to certain chemicals and radiation increases mutations and thus increases the chance of cancer.		297-298, 301, 305
B.1.26 Demonstrate how the genetic information in DNA molecules provides instructions for assembling protein molecules and that this is virtually the same mechanism for all life forms.			281, 284-295, 302-305, 322, 330-335, 361-362, 365
B.1.27 Explain that the similarity of human DNA sequences and the resulting similarity in cell chemistry and anatomy identify human beings as a unique species, different from all others. Likewise, understand that every other species has its own characteristic DNA sequence.			
Expanded Standard	Explain that the similarity of human DNA sequences and the resulting similarity in cell chemistry and anatomy identify human beings as a unique species, different from all others.		284-295, 306, 336, 349-353, 357-359
	Understand that every other species has its own characteristic DNA sequence.		336, 357-359

Standard 1	Text	*Biology: The Dynamics of Life* page(s)
B.1.28 *Illustrate that the sorting and recombination of genes in sexual reproduction results in a great variety of possible gene combinations from the offspring of any two parents. Recognize that genetic variation can occur from such processes as crossing over, jumping genes, and deletion and duplication of genes.*		
Expanded Standard	Illustrate that the sorting and recombination of genes in sexual reproduction results in a great variety of possible gene combinations from the offspring of any two parents.	263-275, 277-278, 322-329, 333-335, 410
	Recognize that genetic variation can occur from such processes as crossing over, jumping genes, and deletion and duplication of genes.	263-275, 277-278, 299
B.1.29 *Understand that and explain how the actions of genes, patterns of inheritance, and the reproduction of cells and organisms account for the continuity of life, and give examples of how inherited characteristics can be observed at molecular and whole-organism levels–in structure, chemistry, or behavior.*		255-271, 273-279, 308-320, 322-329, 332-335

Evolution

Standard 1	Text	*Biology: The Dynamics of Life* page(s)
B.1.30 *Understand and explain that molecular evidence substantiates the anatomical evidence for evolution and provides additional detail about the sequence in which various lines of descent branched off from one another.*		290, 306, 366-367, 404-407, 417, 429, 434-435, 440-441, 468, 672
B.1.31 *Describe how natural selection provides the following mechanism for evolution: Some variation in heritable characteristics exists within every species, and some of these characteristics give individuals an advantage over others in surviving and reproducing. Understand that the advantaged offspring, in turn, are more likely than others to survive and reproduce. Also understand that the proportion of individuals in the population that have advantageous characteristics will increase.*		
Expanded Standard	Describe how natural selection provides the following mechanism for evolution: Some variation in heritable characteristics exists within every species, and some of these characteristics give individuals an advantage over others in surviving and reproducing.	9-10, 28, 78, 392, 407, 410, 417-418, 548, 558, 560-562, 573, 798, 808-809, 814, 816, 818-819, 837
	Understand that the advantaged offspring, in turn, are more likely than others to survive and reproduce.	9-10, 28, 407, 410, 417, 548, 560, 573, 837
	Understand that the proportion of individuals in the population that have advantageous characteristics will increase.	9-10, 407, 409, 417, 468
B.1.32 *Explain how natural selection leads to organisms that are well suited for survival in particular environments, and discuss how natural selection provides scientific explanation for the history of life on Earth as depicted in the fossil record and in the similarities evident within the diversity of existing organisms.*		
Expanded Standard	Explain how natural selection leads to organisms that are well suited for survival in particular environments.	395-396, 417-418, 468, 470-471, 559-560, 586-587, 597, 602, 681, 685, 705, 733, 736-737, 755, 769, 779-780, 800, 807-808, 813, 817, 824-825, 832-833, 837-838, 850
	Discuss how natural selection provides scientific explanation for the history of life on Earth as depicted in the fossil record and in the similarities evident within the diversity of existing organisms.	370-379, 389-393, 396-403, 417-418, 420-441, 468-471, 736, 779, 800, 807, 824, 826, 832-833, 838, 850, 889

Correlations to Indiana's Academic Standards

Standard 1	Text	*Biology: The Dynamics of Life* page(s)
B.1.33 *Describe how life on Earth is thought to have begun as simple, one-celled organisms about 4 billion years ago. Note that during the first 2 billion years, only single-cell microorganisms existed, but once cells with nuclei developed about a billion years ago, increasingly complex multicellular organisms evolved.*		
Expanded Standard	Describe how life on Earth is thought to have begun as simple, one-celled organisms about 4 billion years ago.	369, 466
	Note that during the first 2 billion years, only single-cell microorganisms existed, but once cells with nuclei developed about a billion years ago, increasingly complex multicellular organisms evolved.	382-385, 389-390, 467, 484-485, 490, 499
B.1.34 *Explain that evolution builds on what already exists, so the more variety there is, the more there can be in the future. Recognize, however, that evolution does not necessitate long-term progress in some set direction.*		
Expanded Standard	Explain that evolution builds on what already exists, so the more variety there is, the more there can be in the future.	398-399, 407-409
	Recognize, however, that evolution does not necessitate long-term progress in some set direction.	408-419, 761, 822, 830
B.1.35 *Explain that the degree of kinship between organisms or species can be estimated from the similarity of their DNA sequences, which often closely matches their classification based on anatomical similarities. Know that amino acid similarities also provide clues to this kinship.*		
Expanded Standard	Explain that the degree of kinship between organisms or species can be estimated from the similarity of their DNA sequences, which often closely matches their classification based on anatomical similarities.	418, 451, 463, 520-521, 543, 555, 559, 563, 569, 573-575, 580, 587, 656, 663
	Know that amino acid similarities also provide clues to this kinship.	418, 451, 463
B.1.36 *Trace the relationship between environmental changes and changes in the gene pool, such as genetic drift and isolation of sub-populations.*		397, 399, 403, 406-407, 412-413, 417, 418, 469, 488, 830

Ecology

B.1.37 *Explain that the amount of life any environment can support is limited by the available energy, water, oxygen, and minerals, and by the ability of ecosystems to recycle the residue of dead organic materials. Recognize, therefore, that human activities and technology can change the flow and reduce the fertility of the land.*		
Expanded Standard	Explain that the amount of life any environment can support is limited by the available energy, water, oxygen, and minerals.	37, 51-57, 62-63, 87-89, 113, 133
	Explain that the amount of life any environment can support is limited by the ability of ecosystems to recycle the residue of dead organic materials.	52-57, 62-63, 72, 91, 93-94, 97-101, 113, 133
	Recognize, therefore, that human activities and technology can change the flow and reduce the fertility of the land.	55, 60, 62-63, 91, 103, 107-109, 113, 131, 631

Standard 1	Text	*Biology: The Dynamics of Life* page(s)
B.1.38 *Understand and explain the significance of the introduction of species, such as zebra mussels, into American waterways, and describe the consequent harm to native species and the environment in general.*		
Expanded Standard	Understand and explain the significance of the introduction of species, such as zebra mussels, into American waterways.	12, 97, 120, 129, 758, 815
	Describe the consequent harm to native species and the environment in general.	12, 97, 118, 120, 129, 758, 815
B.1.39 *Describe how ecosystems can be reasonably stable over hundreds or thousands of years. Understand that if a disaster such as flood or fire occurs, the damaged ecosystem is likely to recover in stages that eventually result in a system similar to the original one.*		
Expanded Standard	Describe how ecosystems can be reasonably stable over hundreds or thousands of years.	68, 87, 89
	Understand that if a disaster such as flood or fire occurs, the damaged ecosystem is likely to recover in stages that eventually result in a system similar to the original one.	68-69, 84-85, 87, 89, 135
B.1.40 *Understand and explain that like many complex systems, ecosystems tend to have cyclic fluctuations around a state of rough equilibrium. However, also understand that ecosystems can always change with climate changes or when one or more new species appear as a result of migration or local evolution.*		
Expanded Standard	Understand and explain that like many complex systems, ecosystems tend to have cyclic fluctuations around a state of rough equilibrium.	52-53, 57, 62, 64-66, 67-69, 76, 78, 83, 88-89, 97-98, 108-109, 134-136, 500, 547
	Understand that ecosystems can always change with climate changes or when one or more new species appear as a result of migration or local evolution.	64-66, 67-69, 88-89, 97-98, 108-109, 134-136, 500
B.1.41 *Recognize that and describe how human beings are part of Earth's ecosystems. Note that human activities can, deliberately or inadvertently, alter the equilibrium in ecosystems.*		
Expanded Standard	Recognize that and describe how human beings are part of Earth's ecosystems.	5, 23, 26, 35, 47, 79-80, 101, 103, 106
	Note that human activities can, deliberately or inadvertently, alter the equilibrium in ecosystems.	5, 12, 23, 26, 55, 60, 62, 79-80, 103, 106, 115-118, 120-131, 600, 836, 854, 857, 1044
B.1.42 *Realize and explain that at times, the environmental conditions are such that plants and marine organisms grow faster than decomposers can recycle them back to the environment. Understand that layers of energy-rich organic material thus laid down have been gradually turned into great coal beds and oil pools by the pressure of the overlying earth. Further understand that by burning these fossil fuels, people are passing most of the stored energy back into the environment as heat and releasing large amounts of carbon dioxide.*	55	

Standard 1	Text	Biology: The Dynamics of Life page(s)
B.1.43 *Understand that and describe how organisms are influenced by a particular combination of living and nonliving components of the environment.*		4-5, 28, 37-39, 41-57, 59-63, 66-67, 69-78, 81-83, 87-88, 90, 91-92, 96-99, 101-103, 107-110, 113-114, 118, 120-122, 127, 131-137, 238-239, 243, 472-483, 485-486, 492-495, 499-501, 509, 513-514, 516-518, 520-526, 528-529, 532-543, 546-547, 549, 550-556, 560-561, 564-566, 572-574, 577-580, 582-584, 602, 657, 667, 670-671, 704-706, 712-713, 716, 718-719, 740-741, 748, 760-761, 768, 781, 820, 831, 863-879, 888-889, 1026-1027, 1029-1030, 1045-1046

B.1.44 *Describe the flow of matter, nutrients, and energy within ecosystems.*		
Expanded Standard	Describe the flow of matter within ecosystems.	47-50, 62-63, 73, 77-78
	Describe the flow of nutrients within ecosystems.	52-57, 61-63, 73, 81, 134, 531, 547, 549
	Describe the flow of energy within ecosystems.	51-52, 61-63, 134, 220-221
B.1.45 *Recognize that and describe how the physical or chemical environment may influence the rate, extent, and nature of the way organisms develop within ecosystems.*		37, 56-57, 63, 69, 74, 83, 85, 88, 95, 111-113, 116-120, 123, 125, 130, 131, 135, 544-545, 560-561, 581, 592, 624-625
B.1.46 *Recognize and describe that a great diversity of species increases the chance that at least some living things will survive in the face of large changes in the environment.*		88, 115-117, 129
B.1.47 *Explain, with examples, that ecology studies the varieties and interactions of living things across space while evolution studies the varieties and interactions of living things across time.*		
Expanded Standard	Explain, with examples, that ecology studies the varieties and interactions of living things across space.	36-57, 59-63, 125, 132-133
	Explain, with examples, that evolution studies the varieties and interactions of living things across time.	393, 397, 400, 411, 417, 418, 423, 427

Historical Perspectives of Biology

Students gain understanding of how the scientific enterprise operates through examples of historical events. Through the study of these events, they understand that new ideas are limited by the context in which they are conceived, are often rejected by the scientific establishment, sometimes spring from unexpected findings, and grow or transform slowly through the contributions of many different investigators.

Standard 1	Text	*Biology: The Dynamics of Life* page(s)
B.2.1 *Explain that prior to the studies of Charles Darwin, the most widespread belief was that all known species were created at the same time and remained unchanged throughout history. Note that some scientists at the time believed that features an individual acquired during a lifetime could be passed on to its offspring, and the species could thereby gradually change to fit an environment better.*		
Expanded Standard	Explain that prior to the studies of Charles Darwin, the most widespread belief was that all known species were created at the same time and remained unchanged throughout history.	380-381, 385-388, 467
	Note that some scientists at the time believed that features an individual acquired during a lifetime could be passed on to its offspring, and the species could thereby gradually change to fit an environment better.	404-405
B.2.2 *Explain that Darwin argued that only biologically inherited characteristics could be passed on to offspring. Note that some of these characteristics were advantageous in surviving and reproducing. Understand that the offspring would also inherit and pass on those advantages, and over generations the aggregation of these inherited advantages would lead to a new species.*		
Expanded Standard	Explain that Darwin argued that only biologically inherited characteristics could be passed on to offspring.	394-397, 403, 417
	Note that some of these characteristics were advantageous in surviving and reproducing.	397-399, 417, 468
	Understand that the offspring would also inherit and pass on those advantages, and over generations the aggregation of these inherited advantages would lead to a new species.	397, 417
B.2.3 *Describe that the quick success of Darwin's book* Origin of Species, *published in 1859, came from the clear and understandable argument it made, including the comparison of natural selection to the selective breeding of animals in wide use at the time, and from the massive array of biological and fossil evidence it assembled to support the argument.*	393-396, 400	
B.2.4 *Explain that after the publication of Origin of Species, biological evolution was supported by the rediscovery of the genetics experiments of an Austrian monk, Gregor Mendel, by the identification of genes and how they sorted in reproduction, and by the discovery that the genetic code found in DNA is the same for almost all organisms.*		
Expanded Standard	Explain that after the publication of *Origin of Species*, biological evolution was supported by the rediscovery of the genetics experiments of an Austrian monk, Gregor Mendel.	253-260
	Explain that after the publication of *Origin of Species*, biological evolution was supported by the by the identification of genes and how they sorted in reproduction.	263-270
	Explain that after the publication of *Origin of Species*, biological evolution was supported and by the discovery that the genetic code found in DNA is the same for almost all organisms.	291-292

The table below will help you review the content covered in Indiana's Academic Standards. For each standard, the table shows the sections in *Biology: The Dynamics of Life* where the content can be found.

Section	Indiana Academic Standard
1.1 What is biology?	B.1.11, B.1.16, B.1.17, B.1.18, B.1.31, B.1.41, B.1.43
1.2 The Methods of Biology	B.1.38, B.1.41
1.3 The Nature of Biology	B.1.41
2.1 Organisms and Their Environment	B.1.32, B.1.37, B.1.41, B.1.43, B.1.45, B.1.47
2.2 Nutrition and Energy Flow	B.1.19, B.1.37, B.1.40, B.1.41, B.1.42, B.1.43, B.1.44, B.1.45, B.1.47
3.1 Communities	B.1.18, B.1.39, B.1.40, B.1.43, B.1.45
3.2 Biomes	B.1.18, B.1.31, B.1.37, B.1.39, B.1.40, B.1.41, B.1.43, B.1.44, B.1.45
4.1 Population Dynamics	B.1.37, B.1.38, B.1.40, B.1.43, B.1.45
4.2 Human Population	B.1.37, B.1.41, B.1.43
5.1 Vanishing Species	B.1.37, B.1.38, B.1.41, B.1.43, B.1.45, B.1.46
5.2 Conservation of Biodiversity	B.1.38, B.1.41, B.1.43, B.1.45, B.1.46, B.1.47
6.1 Atoms and Their Interactions	B.1.9, B.1.5
6.2 Water and Diffusion	B.1.2, B.1.5, B.1.9
6.3 Life Substances	B.1.3, B.1.4, B.1.5, B.1.6, B.1.9, B.1.10
7.1 The Discovery of Cells	B.1.3, B.1.8, B.1.12
7.2 The Plasma Membrane	B.1.2, B.1.4, B.1.6, B.1.9
7.3 Eukaryotic Cell Structure	B.1.2, B.1.3, B.1.12
8.1 Cellular Transport	B.1.2, B.1.8
8.2 Cell Growth and Reproduction	B.1.2, B.1.7, B.1.8
8.3 Control of the Cell Cycle	B.1.1, B.1.4, B.1.7, B.1.8
9.1 The Need for Energy	B.1.3, B.1.4, B.1.6, B.1.7, B.1.9, B.1.16, B.1.44
9.2 Photosynthesis: Trapping the Sun's Energy	B.1.3, B.1.4, B.1.6, B.1.7, B.1.9
9.3 Getting Energy to Make ATP	B.1.3, B.1.4, B.1.7, B.1.9, B.1.43
10.1 Mendel's Laws of Heredity	B.1.21, B.1.22, B.1.29, B.2.4
10.2 Meiosis	B.1.8, B.1.21, B.1.22, B.1.28, B.1.29, B.2.4
11.1 DNA: The Molecule of Heredity	B.1.21, B.1.26, B.1.27
11.2 From DNA to Protein	B.1.21, B.1.26, B.1.27, B.1.30
11.3 Genetic Changes	B.1.21, B.1.23, B.1.24, B.1.25, B.1.26, B.1.28
12.1 Mendelian Inheritance of Human Traits	B.1.21, B.1.29
12.2 When Heredity Follows Different Rules	B.1.21, B.1.23, B.1.24, B.1.28, B.1.29
12.3 Complex Inheritance of Human Traits	B.1.21, B.1.26, B.1.28, B.1.29
13.1 Applied Genetics	B.1.21, B.1.22, B.1.27
13.2 Recombinant DNA Technology	B.1.23
13.3 The Human Genome	B.1.23, B.1.27
14.1 The Record of Life	B.1.32, B.1.33
14.2 The Origin of Life	B.1.32, B.1.33, B.2.1
15.1 Natural Selection and the Evidence for Evolution	B.1.31, B.1.32, B.1.34, B.1.36, B.1.47, B.2.2, B.2.3
15.2 Mechanisms of Evolution	B.1.24, B.1.28, B.1.30, B.1.31, B.1.34, B.1.36
16.1 Primate Adaptation and Evolution	B.1.32, B.1.47
16.2 Human Ancestry	B.1.30, B.1.32, B.1.35
17.1 Classification	B.1.35
17.2 The Six Kingdoms	B.1.35
18.1 Viruses	B.1.43
18.2 Archaebacteria and Eubacteria	B.1.2, B.1.3, B.1.8, B.1.12, B.1.33, B.1.36, B.1.43
19.1 The World of Protists	B.1.2, B.1.3, B.1.43
19.2 Algae: Plantlike Protists	B.1.2, B.1.3, B.1.8, B.1.11, B.1.43
19.3 Slime Molds, Water Molds, and Downy Mildews	B.1.2, B.1.8, B.1.11, B.1.35, B.1.43
20.1 What is a fungus?	B.1.8, B.1.11, B.1.13, B.1.43, B.1.44

Section	Indiana Academic Standard
20.2 The Diversity of Fungi	B.1.11, B.1.35, B.1.40, B.1.43, B.1.44
21.1 Adapting to Life on Land	B.1.31, B.1.32, B.1.35, B.1.43, B.1.45
21.2 Survey of the Plant Kingdom	B.1.31, B.1.32, B.1.35, B.1.43
22.1 Nonvascular Plants	B.1.35, B.1.43
22.2 Non-Seed Vascular Plants	B.1.15, B.1.32, B.1.35, B.1.43, B.1.45
22.3 Seed Plants	B.1.15, B.1.32, B.1.41, B.1.45
23.1 Plant Cells and Tissues	B.1.1, B.1.2, B.1.3, B.1.15
23.2 Roots, Stems, and Leaves	B.1.1, B.1.15
23.3 Plant Responses	B.1.1, B.1.7, B.1.15, B.1.18, B.1.45
24.1 Life Cycles of Mosses, Ferns, and Conifers	B.1.8, B.1.11
24.2 Flowers and Flowering	B.1.15, B.1.18
24.3 The Life Cycle of a Flowering Plant	B.1.11, B.1.15, B.1.18, B.1.21, B.1.23, B.1.35, B.1.43
25.1 Typical Animal Characteristics	B.1.1, B.1.11, B.1.16, B.1.30
25.2 Body Plans and Adaptations	B.1.1, B.1.15, B.1.16, B.1.32
26.1 Sponges	B.1.1, B.1.11, B.1.15
26.2 Cnidarians	B.1.11, B.1.14, B.1.15, B.1.32, B.1.43
26.3 Flatworms	B.1.8, B.1.14, B.1.15, B.1.19
26.4 Roundworms	B.1.1, B.1.14, B.1.15, B.1.17, B.1.43
27.1 Mollusks	B.1.14, B.1.15, B.1.19, B.1.31
27.2 Segmented Worms	B.1.15, B.1.18, B.1.19, B.1.32
28.1 Characteristics of Arthropods	B.1.14, B.1.15, B.1.16, B.1.19, B.1.43
28.2 Diversity of Arthropods	B.1.11, B.1.15, B.1.17, B.1.19, B.1.31, B.1.32, B.1.38, B.1.43
29.1 Echinoderms	B.1.15, B.1.19, B.1.32, B.1.43
29.2 Invertebrate Chordates	B.1.15, B.1.19, B.1.32
30.1 Fishes	B.1.14, B.1.15, B.1.19, B.1.31, B.1.32
30.2 Amphibians	B.1.14, B.1.15, B.1.18, B.1.19, B.1.31, B.1.32
31.1 Reptiles	B.1.14, B.1.15, B.1.18, B.1.19, B.1.31, B.1.32, B.1.34, B.1.43
31.2 Birds	B.1.15, B.1.16, B.1.17, B.1.18, B.1.19, B.1.31, B.1.32, B.1.34, B.1.36, B.1.41, B.1.43
32.1 Mammal Characteristics	B.1.14, B.1.15, B.1.17, B.1.19, B.1.31
32.2 Diversity of Mammals	B.1.15, B.1.17, B.1.31, B.1.32, B.1.41
33.1 Innate Behavior	B.1.18, B.1.31, B.1.43
33.2 Learned Behavior	B.1.18, B.1.43
34.1 Skin: The Body's Protection	B.1.14, B.1.15, B.1.17, B.1.19, B.1.20
34.2 Bones: The Body's Support	B.1.14, B.1.15, B.1.16, B.1.19
34.3 Muscles for Locomotion	B.1.14, B.1.15, B.1.16, B.1.17, B.1.20
35.1 Following Digestion of a Meal	B.1.15, B.1.16, B.1.19
35.2 Nutrition	B.1.9, B.1.10, B.1.17, B.1.19
35.3 The Endocrine System	B.1.7, B.1.14
36.1 The Nervous System	B.1.14
36.2 The Senses	B.1.14
36.3 The Effects of Drugs	B.1.14
37.1 The Respiratory System	B.1.14, B.1.19
37.2 The Circulatory System	B.1.3, B.1.14, B.1.15, B.1.19, B.1.20, B.1.21
37.3 The Urinary System	B.1.3, B.1.14, B.1.15, B.1.17, B.1.19, B.1.20
38.1 Human Reproductive Systems	B.1.7, B.1.8, B1.11, B.1.14, B.1.15
38.2 Development Before Birth	B.1.1, B.1.7, B1.11, B.1.14, B.1.15, B.1.16, B.1.19, B.1.21
38.3 Birth, Growth, and Aging	B.1.7, B.1.11, B.1.15, B.1.16, B.1.19
39.1 The Nature of Disease	B.1.17, B1.20, B.1.43
39.2 Defense Against Infectious Diseases	B.1.15, B.1.20, B.1.41, B.1.43

How to...

Master the Indiana Academic Standards

Your textbook contains many opportunities for you to master **Indiana's Academic Standards**. Take advantage of these so you are prepared for tests that assess these standards. A complete list of Indiana's Academic Standards can be found on pages IN2-IN11.

■ The **Indiana Academic Standards** that are covered in that unit are indicated on the Unit Opener.

> **Unit 2 Review**
> **BioDigest & Standardized Test Practice**
>
> **Why It's Important**
> Everything on Earth—air, land, water, plants, and animals—is connected. Understanding these connections helps us keep our environment clean, healthy, and safe.
>
> **Indiana Standards**
> The following standards are covered in Unit 2:
> B.1.18, B.1.32, B.1.37, B.1.38, B.1.39, B.1.40, B.1.41, B1.42, B.1.43, B.1.44, B.1.45, B.1.46, B.1.47
>
> **Understanding the Photo**▶
> At the foot of the Elias Mountains in Glacier Bay Nati Park and Preserve in Alaska, a cold, clear stream move silently past brilliant purple dwarf fireweed and red a yellow Indian paintbrush plants growing out of a roc beach. The clouds are so low, it looks as if they coul the stream. Ecology is the study

■ At the beginning of a section, the **Indiana Academic Standard** covered in that section is listed. The **boldface** portion indicates the specific portion of the standard that is addressed in that section.

> # Organisms and Their Environment
>
> **Indiana Standards** Standard B.1.43 **Understand that and describe how organisms are** influenced by a particular combination of living and nonliving components of the environment
>
> **Where in the world am I?**
>
> **Finding the Main Idea** When you start to study a new topic in depth, it is sometimes difficult to see the big ideas and make the connections that you need to make. Learning about ecology is more than memorizing the vocabulary. Of all the subjects that you might study in biol-

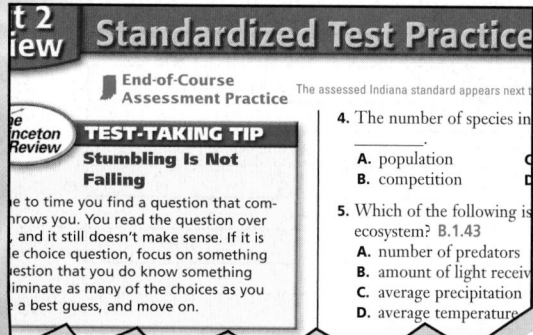

> **Standardized Test Practice**
>
> **End-of-Course Assessment Practice** The assessed Indiana standard appears next t
>
> **The Princeton Review**
> **TEST-TAKING TIP**
> **Stumbling Is Not Falling**
> e to time you find a question that com- rows you. You read the question over , and it still doesn't make sense. If it is e choice question, focus on something estion that you do know something iminate as many of the choices as you e a best guess, and move on.
>
> **4.** The number of species in
> **A.** population
> **B.** competition
>
> **5.** Which of the following is ecosystem? B.1.43
> **A.** number of predators
> **B.** amount of light receiv
> **C.** average precipitation
> **D.** average temperature

> **End-of-Course Assessment Practice**
> The assessed Indiana standard appea
> All questi
>
> **Part 1** Multiple Choice
> Use the graph below to answer questions 17 and 18 about wetland-dependent species in a northeastern state.
>
> | State Wetland Data | |
> |---|---|
> | Total number of endangered | Percent wetland dependent |
>
> **19.** A federally fu
> B.1.41 endangered s
> This probabl
> **A.** the U.S. the devel
> **B.** a reintro
> **C.** the o

The **End-of-Course Assessment Practice** at the end of each chapter and unit gives you the opportunity to benchmark your knowledge of Indiana's Academic Standards. ECA questions that assess an academic standard are indicated next to the question.

Week 1

Monday

1. Which cell part is analogous to the human skeleton? *(Section 7.3)*

A. cytoskeleton
B. lysosomes
C. cilia
D. nucleus

Tuesday

2. Which is a protein that changes the rate of a chemical reaction and is involved in nearly all metabolic processes? *(Section 6.3)*

A. amino acid
B. nucleic acid
C. enzyme
D. nucleotide

Wednesday

3. Viruses can reproduce only under which condition? *(Section 18.1)*

A. when they are outside a living organism
B. when they carry out respiration
C. when they grow or move
D. when they are inside a host cell

Thursday

4. What is the main function of the projections that cover the HIV? *(Section 18.1)*

A. They protect the virus and give it its structure.
B. They aid in respiration.
C. They help the virus invade its host.
D. They help the virus move and grow.

Friday

Normal
mRNA AUGAAGUUUGGCGCAUUGUAA
Protein Met — Lys — Phe — Gly — Ala — Leu — Stop

Replace G with A

Mutation
mRNA AUGAAGUUUAGCGCAUUGUAA
Protein Met — Lys — Phe — Ser — Ala — Leu — Stop

5. What kind of mutation is shown in the figure above? *(Section 11.3)*

A. deletion
B. insertion
C. inversion
D. translocation

End-of-Course Assessment Practice Countdown

Pages IN15–IN32 of this text include a section called **End-of-Course Assessment Practice Countdown.** Each page contains five practice questions that are similar to those you might find on most standardized tests. There are 18 weeks of assessment practice; you should plan to complete one page a week to help you master the academic standards.

These multiple choice questions address Indiana's Academic Standards. For more information for the assessed standard, refer to the section in parentheses next to the question.

Week 1 Answers
1. A
2. C
3. D
4. D
5. A

Indiana Standards

Monday	B.1.3
Tuesday	B.1.4, B.1.7
Wednesday	B.1.15, B.1.43
Thursday	B.1.15
Friday	B.1.23

Week 2 Answers

1. B
2. A
3. B
4. C
5. C

Week 2

Monday

Plankton → Fish → Bear

Bacteria of decay

1. The diagram above shows a food chain. If environmental pollution and overfishing were to decrease the number of fish in the ocean, which of the following might occur? *(Section 2.1)*

A. The bear population would increase.
B. The plankton population would increase.
C. The plankton population would decrease.
D. The bacteria population would increase.

Tuesday

2. Which best describes the role of RNA molecules that form in the nucleus? *(Section 11.2)*

A. RNA molecules carry the code from DNA to the ribosomes.
B. RNA molecules are responsible for the genetic code.
C. RNA molecules attach to ribosomes.
D. RNA molecules determine how an organism looks and acts.

Wednesday

3. What happens after ribosomes pass into the cytoplasm? *(Section 11.2)*

A. They pass through the nuclear envelope.
B. They may attach to areas of endoplasmic reticulum.
C. They replicate the DNA.
D. They sort and distribute proteins to cell organelles.

Thursday

4. Which organelle is most like a miniature stomach? *(Section 7.3)*

A. centriole
B. chloroplast
C. lysosome
D. vacuole

Friday

5. Which is referred to as a cell's "powerhouse?" *(Sections 7.3, 9.3)*

A. cytoskeleton
B. mitochondrion
C. flagellum
D. lysosome

Indiana Standards

Monday	B.1.41, B.1.43
Tuesday	B.1.26
Wednesday	B.1.3
Thursday	B.1.3
Friday	B.1.3

Week 3

Monday

Phosphate

HO—P—O—CH₂

Nitrogen base

Ribose sugar

1. Which describes the nitrogen base in the nucleotide shown to the left? *(Sections 6.3, 11.1)*

   A. a branched chain
   B. a macromolecule
   C. a ring structure
   D. a straight chain

Tuesday

2. How many carbon atoms are in this nucleotide? *(Section 6.3)*

   A. 4
   B. 5
   C. 7
   D. 9

Wednesday

3. Which stage of meiosis begins with homologous chromosomes, each with its two chromatids, separating and moving to opposite ends of the cell? *(Section 10.2)*

   A. anaphase I
   B. metaphase I
   C. prophase I
   D. telophase I

Thursday

4. When non-sister chromatids from homologous chromosomes break and exchange genetic material, what process has occurred? *(Section 10.2)*

   A. trisomy
   B. nondisjunction
   C. crossing over
   D. sexual reproduction

Friday

5. What is nondisjunction? *(Section 10.2)*

   A. failure of genes to be passed on to future generations
   B. failure of chromosomes to separate properly during meiosis
   C. A mutation most often caused by environmental factors.
   D. A duplication of genes on a chromosome.

End-of-Course Assessment Practice Countdown

Week 3 Answers
1. C
2. D
3. A
4. C
5. C

Indiana Standards

Monday	B.1.21
Tuesday	B.1.21
Wednesday	B.1.8
Thursday	B.1.8, B.1.28
Friday	B.1.28

Week 4 Answers
1. C
2. C
3. A
4. A
5. D

Week 4

Monday

1. In a certain type of corn plant, the gene for smooth seeds is a dominant trait (S), while the gene for wrinkled seeds is recessive (s). Based on the Punnett square above, what kinds of seeds will the offspring of these two corn plants have? *(Section 10.1)*

A. 100 percent will be smooth, and none will be wrinkled.
B. 50 percent will be smooth, 50 percent will be wrinkled.
C. 75 percent will be smooth, and 25 percent will be wrinkled.
D. 25 percent will be smooth, and 75 percent will be wrinkled.

Tuesday

2. What is the type of cell division where one body cell produces four gametes, each containing half the number of chromosomes as a parent's body cell? *(Section 10.2)*

A. diploid
B. gametes
C. meiosis
D. mitosis

Wednesday

3. In humans, what is the role of the 23rd pair of chromosomes? *(Section 12.2)*

A. It determines the sex of an individual.
B. It determines the eye and hair color of an individual.
C. It determines male pattern baldness in an individual.
D. It determines the blood type of an individual.

Thursday

4. A purebred animal with brown fur is crossed with a purebred animal with tan fur. The only offspring has both tan and brown fur. What type of inheritance pattern is involved? *(Section 12.1)*

A. codominance
B. incomplete dominance
C. polygenic inheritance
D. simple inheritance

Friday

5. A plant shows incomplete dominance. First generation offspring of a cross between plants with white flowers and plants with purple flowers will produce flowers with which of the following colors? *(Section 12.1)*

A. purple
B. white
C. deep purple
D. light blue

End-of-Course Assessment
Practice Countdown

Indiana Standards	
Monday	B.1.29
Tuesday	B.1.8
Wednesday	B.1.29
Thursday	B.1.29
Friday	B.1.29

Week 5

Monday

1. Which correctly sequences the main steps involved in protein synthesis? *(Section 11.2)*

A. Free RNA nucleotides form mRNA; mRNA attaches to a ribosome; tRNA molecules pair with mRNA codons as the mRNA slides along the ribosome; amino acids are joined by an enzyme.

B. mRNA attaches to a ribosome; tRNA molecules pair with mRNA codons as the mRNA slides along the ribosome; amino acids are joined by an enzyme; free RNA nucleotides form mRNA.

C. tRNA molecules pair with mRNA codons as the mRNA slides along the ribosome; amino acids are joined by an enzyme; free RNA nucleotides for mRNA; mRNA attaches to a ribosome.

D. Free RNA nucleotides form mRNA; tRNA molecules pair with mRNA codons as the mRNA slides along the ribosome; amino acids are joined by an enzyme; mRNA attaches to a ribosome.

Tuesday

2. Which describes Mendel's first law, the law of segregation? *(Section 10.1)*

A. Two organisms can have the same phenotype, but have different genotypes.

B. When gametes are produced, each gamete receives one of two possible alleles.

C. Genes for different traits are inherited independently of each other.

D. An organism's two alleles are located on different copies of a chromosome.

Wednesday

Use the figure below to answer questions 3–5.

3. Which of the following nitrogenous base sequences will complement the anticodon shown? *(Section 11.2)*

A. AUG
B. GUA
C. TCG
D. AUT

Thursday

4. This molecule plays a major role in which of the following processes? *(Section 11.2)*

A. meiosis
B. mitosis
C. replication
D. translation

Friday

5. What kind of molecule is shown? *(Section 11.2)*

A. replicated DNA
B. messenger RNA
C. transfer RNA
D. transfer DNA

Week 5 Answers
1. A
2. B
3. A
4. D
5. C

Indiana Standards

Monday	B.1.26
Tuesday	B.1.22
Wednesday	B.1.26
Thursday	B.1.8
Friday	B.1.8

Week 6 Answers
1. C
2. D
3. D
4. B
5. B

Week 6

Monday

G	G	A	T	A	C	C	T	G
C	C	T	A	T	G	?	?	?

1. The diagram shows a portion of a DNA molecule. Which sequence of bases do the question marks represent? *(Section 11.2)*

   A. CAC
   B. GCA
   C. GAC
   D. TCA

Tuesday

2. Which of these processes does NOT require DNA replication? *(Section 8.2)*

   A. mitosis
   B. meiosis
   C. cell division
   D. cell growth

Wednesday

3. Which base pairs with adenine in RNA? *(Section 11.2)*

   A. cytosine
   B. guanine
   C. thymine
   D. uracil

Thursday

4. Why can the deletion of a single nitrogen base in DNA be harmful to an organism? *(Section 11.3)*

   A. Deletion causes chromosomes to join backwards or to join the wrong chromosomes.
   B. Deletion causes nearly every amino acid in the protein to change.
   C. Deletion causes a gamete to have an extra chromosome.
   D. Deletion causes chromosomes to join with the wrong chromosome.

Friday

5. What are the genotypes of a homozygous tall pea plant and a heterozygous tall pea plant, respectively? *(Section 10.1)*

   A. tt, Tt
   B. TT, Tt
   C. Tt, tt
   D. Tt, TT

End-of-Course Assessment Practice Countdown

Indiana Standards

Monday	B.1.8
Tuesday	B.1.7
Wednesday	B.1.26
Thursday	B.1.23
Friday	B.1.29

ECA Practice Countdown

Week 7

Monday

1. Which of the following processes does NOT involve ribonucleic acid? *(Section 11.2)*

   A. replication
   B. translation
   C. transcription
   D. codon attachment to a ribosome

Tuesday

2. Which of the following analogies is TRUE? *(Sections 11.1, 11.2)*

   A. A copy of DNA is like a blueprint of the RNA code.
   B. DNA is like workers on an assembly line.
   C. Nucleotides are the building blocks of nitrogenous bases.
   D. The structure of DNA can be compared to a twisted ladder.

Wednesday

```
        ┌───┐
        │ Z │
        └───┘
          ↑
┌───┐   ┌───┐
│ X │ ← │ Y │
└───┘   └───┘
  ↖       ↗
    ┌───┐
    │ V │
    └───┘
```

3. Which organism in the figure above is a first-order consumer? *(Section 2.2)*

   A. V
   B. X
   C. both X and Y
   D. both V and Z

Thursday

4. Which processes results in an RNA copy of a DNA strand? *(Section 11.2)*

   A. translation
   B. transcription
   C. replication
   D. mitosis

Friday

5. Which does NOT describe restriction enzymes? *(Section 13.2)*

   A. They are bacterial proteins.
   B. They have the ability to cut double-stranded DNA.
   C. They can carry DNA from one species into a host cell.
   D. There are hundreds of restriction enzymes.

Indiana Standards

Day	Standard
Monday	B.1.26
Tuesday	B.1.8
Wednesday	B.1.44
Thursday	B.1.8
Friday	B.1.4

Week 8

Monday

   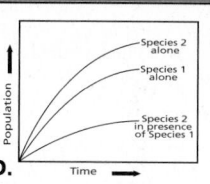

1. The graphs above illustrate the changing populations of two species in the same ecosystem over time. Which graph represents a mutualistic relationship? *(Section 2.1)*

Tuesday

2. Which series correctly sequences interactions in nature from largest to smallest? *(Section 2.1)*

A. population, ecosystem, community
B. species, organism, community
C. ecosystem, community, population
D. community, population, ecosystem

Wednesday

3. A manufacturing plant is located on the banks of a river. One day, toxic chemicals from the plant accidentally spilled into the river. Fish absorbed some of these chemicals into their bodies. Later, a hawk living near the river was found to have the same toxic chemicals in its system. Which statement best explains why? *(Section 2.2)*

A. The chemicals entered the air.
B. The chemicals entered the food chain.
C. The chemicals were contagious.
D. The chemicals commonly are found in the environment.

Thursday

4. Which terms are NOT related? *(Section 2.1)*

A. water cycle–precipitation
B. phosphorus cycle–evaporation
C. nitrogen cycle–nitrogen fixation
D. carbon cycle–photosynthesis

Friday

5. Based on what you've learned about the cycling of materials through ecosystems, predict which material would most likely be added to a chemical fertilizer to increase soil productivity. *(Section 2.2)*

A. H_2O
B. CO_2
C. N_2
D. NO_3

End-of-Course Assessment Practice Countdown

Indiana Standards

Monday	B.1.43
Tuesday	B.1.40
Wednesday	B.1.37, B.1.41
Thursday	B.1.44
Friday	B.1.44

Week 9

Monday

A.

B.

C.

1. Which best describes the bacteria shown in A at left? *(Section 18.2)*
   A. streptococci
   B. staphylococci
   C. diplococci
   D. diplobacilli

Tuesday

2. How does parasitism differ from predation? *(Section 2.1)*
   A. No organism is harmed in a parasitic relationship.
   B. No organism is harmed in a predator-prey relationship.
   C. Parasitism does not always result in the death of an organism.
   D. Parasitism does not occur among mammals.

Wednesday

3. Which model would an ecologist use to show the weight of living material in an ecosystem? *(Section 2.2)*
   A. a food web
   B. a pyramid of energy
   C. a pyramid of numbers
   D. a pyramid of biomass

Thursday

4. How does camouflage aid in the evolutionary process? *(Section 15.1)*
   A. Camouflage enables an organism to copy the appearance of another species.
   B. This anatomical adaptation helps an organism mutate.
   C. Organisms that are well camouflaged are more likely to escape predators and survive to reproduce.
   D. The ability to camouflage is lost during embryonic development.

Friday

5. Both parents carry a single recessive gene. What are the chances of their child inheriting the recessive disorder caused by the gene? *(Section 12.1)*
   A. 2 percent
   B. 25 percent
   C. 50 percent
   D. 100 percent

End-of-Course Assessment Practice Countdown

Indiana Standards	
Monday	B.1.12
Tuesday	B.1.43
Wednesday	B.1.44
Thursday	B.1.31, B.1.32
Friday	B.1.29

Week 10 Answers
1. B
2. C
3. D
4. A
5. D

Week 10

Monday

1. What is a mutation in which a single base is added to or deleted from DNA? *(Section 11.3)*

   A. chromosomal mutation
   B. frameshift mutation
   C. junction mutation
   D. point mutation

Tuesday

2. Industrialization in England in the early 1900s produced black soot that covered many tree trunks and branches. At about the same time, the number of light-colored moths in this part of the country decreased over time. Why? *(Section 15.1)*

   A. The soot killed only light-colored moths.
   B. The light-colored moths became extinct.
   C. The light-colored moths showed up against the dark tree bark and could be easily seen by the birds that fed on them.
   D. The light-colored moths became isolated from other moths and reproductive speciation occurred.

Wednesday

3. What is an alteration of allelic frequencies by chance events that greatly affects small populations? *(Section 15.2)*

   A. allelic frequency
   B. genetic equilibrium
   C. gene pool
   D. genetic drift

Thursday

4. Dolphins and fish are unrelated vertebrates with similar body shapes that are adapted for moving efficiently through water. What evolutionary process is shown by this example? *(Section 15.2)*

   A. convergent evolution
   B. divergent evolution
   C. polyploid speciation
   D. reproductive isolation

Friday

Chemicals Present	
Bacteria 1	A, G, T, C, L, E, S, H
Bacteria 2	A, G, T, C, L, D
Bacteria 3	A, G, T, C, L, D, P, U, S, R, I, V
Bacteria 4	A, G, T, C, L, D, H

5. The table above shows chemicals found in certain bacteria. Each capital letter represents a different chemical. Which bacteria are most closely related? *(Section 15.1)*

   A. bacteria 1 and 2
   B. bacteria 1 and 3
   C. bacteria 2 and 3
   D. bacteria 2 and 4

End-of-Course Assessment Practice Countdown

Indiana Standards

Monday	B.1.23
Tuesday	B.1.37, B.1.41
Wednesday	B.1.36
Thursday	B.1.32
Friday	B.1.35

Week 11

Monday

1. The circular structures on membrane C can be best compared to which of the following? *(Sections 7.3, 11.2)*

   A. workers on an assembly line
   B. storage bins
   C. scaffolding
   D. delivery trucks

Week 11 Answers
1. A
2. C
3. A
4. A
5. A

Tuesday

2. Periods of drought (absence of rain) break up a forest into smaller patches of trees. Natural selection results in tree frog populations evolving distinct gene pools. Groups of frogs can no longer produce fertile offspring. Which of the following processes occurred in this situation? *(Section 15.2)*

   A. convergent evolution
   B. extinction
   C. geographic isolation
   D. phylogenetic classification

Wednesday

3. The presence of gills and tails in the early stages of all vertebrates indicates common ancestry. Which of the following evidence from the fossil record supports this statement? *(Section 15.1)*

   A. Aquatic, gill-breathing vertebrates were the ancestors of air-breathing land species.
   B. Fossils generally are as old as the rocks in which they are found.
   C. Similarities among DNA indicate a common ancestor.
   D. Structural adaptations are not inherited from parents.

Thursday

4. What is cellular respiration? *(Section 9.3)*

   A. a process that uses oxygen to break down glucose and release energy
   B. a process that rids the body of nitrogen gases
   C. a process where cilia constantly move to filter out foreign material
   D. a process in which the muscles of the chest cavity contract and relax

Friday

5. Which describes the parasympathetic nervous system? *(Section 36.2)*

   A. It controls many of the body's internal functions when the body is at rest.
   B. It relays information between your skin, the CNS, and skeletal muscles.
   C. It carries impulses from the CNS to internal organs.
   D. It controls internal functions during times of stress.

End-of-Course Assessment Practice Countdown

Indiana Standards

Monday	B.1.3
Tuesday	B.1.31, B.1.32
Wednesday	B.1.32, B.1.35
Thursday	B.1.3
Friday	B.1.15

Week 12 Answers

1. C
2. B
3. D
4. B
5. A

Week 12

Monday

1. Which is NOT a function of the endocrine system? *(Section 35.3)*

A. Released hormones convey information to other cells in the body, controlling metabolism, growth, development, and behavior.
B. The pituitary gland releases chemicals and stimulates other glands to release their chemicals.
C. A positive feedback system controls homeostasis.
D. The hypothalamus receives messages from the brain and internal organs.

Tuesday

2. Which does NOT describe how an impulse is transmitted? *(Section 36.1)*

A. Depolarization moves like a wave down the axon.
B. Calcium diffuses across the membrane and releases synaptic chemicals.
C. Gated potassium channels open, letting K^+ ions out, repolarizing the cell.
D. Gated potassium channels close, allowing the Na^+/ K^+ pump to restore ion distribution.

Wednesday

3. What do interneurons do? *(Section 36.1)*

A. carry impulses from the body to the spinal cord and brain
B. receive impulses and carry them toward the cell body
C. carry response impulses away from the brain and spinal cord to a muscle or gland
D. process incoming impulses and pass response impulses on to motor neurons

Thursday

Nucleus

4. What is the function of the structure labeled C? *(Section 7.3)*

A. to suspend organelles
B. to produce ribosomes
C. to generate energy
D. to maintain homeostasis

Friday

5. The epidermis contains which protein that helps protect living cell layers from exposure to bacteria, heat, and chemicals? *(Section 34.1)*

A. keratin   **C.** myosin
B. melanin   **D.** vitamin D

End-of-Course Assessment Practice Countdown

Indiana Standards

Monday	B.1.15
Tuesday	B.1.15
Wednesday	B.1.15
Thursday	B.1.3
Friday	B.1.15

Week 13

Monday

1. As part of their job, a group of factory workers must handle certain chemicals every day. The workers are concerned that the chemicals are making them ill. The factory hires a researcher to investigate the situation. The researcher conducts a poll with factory workers at a different plant, and compares the results. In both cases, few people were hospitalized, so the researcher concludes there is no health problem. The workers charge that the study is biased. Which statement below does NOT reflect bias in the study? *(Section 1.2)*

A. The researcher was hired by the factory.
B. Polls are not valid.
C. Sick people do not always require hospitalization.
D. The factory workers may have handled different materials.

Tuesday

2. What is a vaccine? *(Section 39.2)*

A. an injection of antibodies from animals or humans that have immunity
B. weakened, dead, or incomplete portions of pathogens or antigens
C. venom from the bite of a snake
D. antibodies that come from a mother's milk

Wednesday

3. How does penicillin affect a bacterial cell? *(Section 39.1)*

A. It interferes with transcription.
B. It interferes with DNA replication.
C. It interferes with protein synthesis.
D. It interferes with the construction and repair of a bacterial cell wall.

Thursday

4. What is a virus? *(Section 18.1)*

A. an infectious agent with a cell wall composed of only single, circular strand of RNA
B. a disease-causing, nonliving particle composed of an inner core of nucleic acids surrounded by a capsid
C. an infectious agent with a sticky gelatinous capsule around the cell wall
D. a disease-causing plasmid with a few genes located in a small circular chromosome

Friday

Population of Unknown Organisms				
Year	Spring	Summer	Autumn	Winter
1995	564	14,598	25,762	127
1996	750	16,422	42,511	102
1997	365	14,106	36,562	136

5. Based on the data above, what can you conclude about the organism? *(Section 1.2)*

A. It has a short lifespan.
B. It has a long lifespan.
C. It thrives in even-numbered years.
D. It doesn't like hot or cold temperatures.

Week 13 Answers
1. B
2. B
3. D
4. B
5. A

Indiana Standards

Monday	B.1.41
Tuesday	B.1.20
Wednesday	B.1.20
Thursday	B.1.15
Friday	B.1.43

Week 14

Week 14 Answers

1. B
2. A
3. D
4. D
5. B

End-of-Course Assessment Practice Countdown

Monday

Aluminum Collected During Week

Mass (kg)

Monday   Wednesday   Friday
Day of collection

1. The graph shows the amount of aluminum collected during one week for recycling. Which of the following statements best describes the data shown? *(Section 1.2)*

   A. More aluminum was collected on Wednesday than Friday.
   B. Twice as much aluminum was collected on Monday than Friday.
   C. Less aluminum was collected on Monday than Friday.
   D. The most aluminum was collected on Friday.

Tuesday

2. During an experiment to test the heat absorption rates of different-colored materials, a researcher placed a white cloth in direct sunlight and a black cloth under a lamp. He then placed a thermometer under each cloth and recorded the temperature changes every five minutes for 30 minutes. When he presented his results to a colleague, the colleague told him that the experiment contained a crucial flaw. What is the flaw? *(Section 1.2)*

   A. The researcher did not control variables.
   B. The researcher did not use the proper equipment.
   C. The researcher should have used cloths of the same color.
   D. The researcher should have recorded temperature changes each minute.

Wednesday

3. What distinguishes a hypothesis from a theory? *(Section 1.2)*

   A. A theory is a scientific explanation.
   B. A theory is testable.
   C. A theory explains a natural phenomenon.
   D. A theory is backed up by repeated observations and tests.

Thursday

4. Why should quantitative experiments be repeated? *(Section 1.3)*

   A. to publish results
   B. to communicate results
   C. to clearly display information
   D. to reduce the chance of error

Friday

5. What data will a student need to collect to determine the speed of a toy car? *(Section 1.2)*

   A. distance only
   B. distance, time
   C. mass, distance, time
   D. speed only

Week 15

Monday

1. Which pair of terms is NOT related? *(Section 7.3)*

A. nucleus—DNA
B. flagella—cilia
C. chloroplasts—chlorophyll
D. nucleus—cell wall

Tuesday

2. What is the function of the leaves of a plant? *(Section 21.1)*

A. conserve gases
B. support the plant
C. obtain water
D. trap sunlight

Wednesday

3. In which of the following does one diploid cell produce four haploid cells, providing a way for offspring to have the same number of chromosomes as their parents? *(Section 10.2)*

A. meiosis
B. mitosis
C. prophase I of meiosis
D. telophase II of meiosis

Thursday

4. What are the chances of being a carrier of a defective gene if both parents are carriers? *(Section 12.1)*

A. 2 percent
B. 25 percent
C. 50 percent
D. 100 percent

Friday

5. If two heterozygous animals that have a single dominant trait mate, what is the phenotype ratio of their young? *(Section 10.1)*

A. 3:1
B. 1:2:1
C. 9:3:3:1
D. 1:6:9:1

End-of-Course Assessment Practice Countdown

Week 15 Answers
1. D
2. D
3. A
4. C
5. A

Indiana Standards

Monday	B.1.3
Tuesday	B.1.15
Wednesday	B.1.8
Thursday	B.1.28
Friday	B.1.29

Week 16

Monday

1. Plants or animals that contain functional recombinant DNA from an organism of a different genus are known as what? *(Section 13.2)*

A. recombinant organisms
B. heterozygous organisms
C. polygenic organisms
D. transgenic organisms

End-of-Course Assessment Practice Countdown

Tuesday

2. Which food chain correctly shows the path of matter and energy through an ecosystem? *(Section 2.2)*

A. deer → bear → grass
B. grass → deer → bear
C. seeds → bear → chipmunk
D. chipmunk → seeds → deer

Wednesday

3. Which is NOT a factor that contributes to natural selection? *(Section 15.1)*

A. overproduction of offspring
B. inheritance of unfavorable variations
C. inheritance of favorable variations
D. survival and reproduction of individuals with favorable variations

Thursday

4. Which is NOT true about hemoglobin? *(Section 37.2)*

A. It carries CO_2.
B. It carries O_2.
C. It is an iron-containing protein molecule in RBCs.
D. It is involved in blood clotting.

Friday

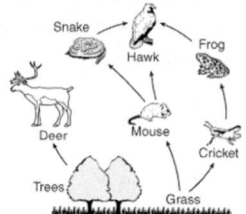

5. The food web above shows how many predators? *(Section 2.2)*

A. one
B. two
C. three
D. four

Indiana Standards

Monday	B.1.23
Tuesday	B.1.44
Wednesday	B.1.31
Thursday	B.1.15
Friday	B.1.44

Week 17

Monday

1. Bacteria and viruses both cause diseases and disorders. Antibiotics are medicines that kill bacteria. Which statement is NOT true?

A. A cold can be cured with antibiotics.
B. The best way to get over a cold is to rest, eat properly, and get plenty of fluids.
C. Cold viruses can be inhaled when someone with a cold sneezes while standing close to you.
D. You can catch a cold by shaking hands with someone who has a cold and putting your hands near your mouth.

Tuesday

2. Why are mutations important?

A. They are always passed on to future generations.
B. They are often random events.
C. They only occur in sex cells.
D. Variation that results from mutations is fundamental to the evolution of a species.

Wednesday

3. Which structure would you NOT find in your body cells?

A. mitochondria
B. cell walls
C. plasma membranes
D. ribosomes

Thursday

4. How does natural selection affect an organism in a changing environment?

A. If an organism is not suited to a change in the environment, it will not survive.
B. If an organism is not suited, it will find another niche and thrive in the new environment.
C. Changing environments do not affect individuals in a population.
D. Natural selection causes the individual to overproduce because it cannot survive in its environment.

Friday

5. Which is NOT a characteristic shared by green algae and plants?

A. cell walls and cellulose
B. root systems
C. chlorophyll
D. stored food

End-of-Course Assessment Practice Countdown

Week 17 Answers

1. A
2. D
3. B
4. A
5. B

Indiana Standards

Monday	B.1.20
Tuesday	B.1.23, B.1.24, B.1.31
Wednesday	B.1.3
Thursday	B.1.31
Friday	B.1.3

Week 18

Week 18 Answers

1. D
2. D
3. B
4. C
5. B

Monday

1. Which would be most likely to cause disease?

A. a bacterium whose cell what has ruptured
B. a relatively large bacterial cell
C. a bacterium with flagella
D. a bacterial cell with a capsule

Tuesday

2. Which of the following is a biotic factor in an ecosystem?

A. air
B. soil
C. water
D. tree

Wednesday

3. Identify two methods of nitrogen fixation.

A. decomposition and excretion
B. lightning and bacteria
C. respiration and transpiration
D. condensation and evaporation

Thursday

4. Why do plants have roots?

A. to conserve nutrients
B. to photosynthesize
C. to absorb water
D. to reproduce

Friday

5. With two alleles for a trait, there are four boxes in the Punnett square. How many boxes would there be in a Punnett square if two traits were being studied?

A. 4
B. 8
C. 12
D. 16

Indiana Standards

Day	Standard
Monday	B.1.17
Tuesday	B.1.43
Wednesday	B.1.44
Thursday	B.1.15
Friday	B.1.29

Indiana Teacher Wraparound Edition

Glencoe Science

BIOLOGY
The Dynamics of Life

• Indiana's Science Academic Standards Edition

NATIONAL GEOGRAPHIC

in.bdol.glencoe.com
- ● ECA Practice
- ● Microscopy links
- ● Self-check quizzes
- ● Vocabulary PuzzleMaker
- ● WebQuests

AUTHORS

Alton Biggs • Whitney Crispen Hagins
Chris Kapicka • Linda Lundgren • Peter Rillero
Kathleen G. Tallman • Dinah Zike
National Geographic Society

McGraw Hill **Glencoe**

New York, New York   Columbus, Ohio   Chicago, Illinois   Peoria, Illinois   Woodland Hills, California

A GLENCOE PROGRAM
BIOLOGY: THE DYNAMICS OF LIFE

Glencoe Online
SCIENCE

Visit the Glencoe Science Web site
in.bdol.glencoe.com

You'll find:
Standardized Test Practice, Interactive Tutor, Section and Chapter Self-Check Quizzes, Online Student Edition, Web Links, Microscopy Links, WebQuest Projects, Internet BioLabs, In The News, Textbook Updates, Teacher Bulletin Board, Teaching Today

and much more!

 Glencoe

The *McGraw-Hill* Companies

The "Standardized Test Practice" and "Test-Taking Tip" features in this book were aligned and verified by The Princeton Review, the nation's leader in test preparation. Through its association with McGraw-Hill, The Princeton Review offers the best way to help students excel on standardized assessments.

The Princeton Review is not affiliated with Princeton University or Educational Testing Service.

Send all inquiries to:
Glencoe/McGraw-Hill
8787 Orion Place
Columbus, OH 43240

ISBN 0-07-867562-6 (Student Edition)   ISBN 0-07-867563-4 (Teacher Edition)

Printed in the United States of America.

1 2 3 4 5 6 7 8 9 10   071   10 09 08 07 06 05

Contents in Brief

About the Authors

Alton Biggs has been a biology educator in Texas public schools for more than 30 years. He has a B.S. in natural sciences and an M.S. in biology from Texas A & M University—Commerce. Mr. Biggs received NABT's Outstanding Biology Teacher Award for Texas in 1982 and 1995, he was the founding president of the Texas Association of Biology Teachers in 1985, and in 1992 was the president of the National Association of Biology Teachers.

Whitney Crispen Hagins teaches biology at Lexington High School in Lexington, Massachusetts. She has a B.A. and an M.A. in biological sciences from Mount Holyoke College and an M.A.T. from Duke University. Since 1997, she has been an instructor for Project STIR Technology Institute. In 1999, she was awarded the NABT Outstanding Biology Teacher Award for Massachusetts, and in 1998 received NFS funding for development of molecular biology activities for high school students.

Chris Kapicka is a biology professor at Northwest Nazarene University, Nampa, Idaho, and does collaborative heart research with the Veteran's Administration Hospital in Boise, Idaho. She has a B.S. in biology from Boise State University, an M.S. in microbiology from Washington State University, and a Ph.D. in cell physiology and pharmacology from the University of Nevada—Reno. In 1986, she received the Presidential Award for Science Teaching, and in 1988 was awarded NABT's Outstanding Biology Teacher Award.

Linda Lundgren is a research associate in the Mathematics, Science, and Technology Program at The University of Colorado at Denver. She taught biology at Bear Creek High School, Lakewood, Colorado, for 10 years. Ms. Lundgren has a B.A. in journalism and zoology from the University of Massachusetts and an M.S. in zoology from The Ohio State University. In 1991, she was named Colorado Science Teacher of the Year.

Peter Rillero is a professor of science education at Arizona State University West in Phoenix. He has an M.A. in science education from Columbia University, an M.A. in biology from City University of New York, and a Ph.D. in science education from The Ohio State University. He has taught high school biology as a Peace Corps volunteer in Kenya and for four years as a public school teacher in Bronx, NY. As a Fulbright Fellow, Dr. Rillero taught science methods at Akureyri University in Iceland. As an exchange professor, he taught biology at the National University of Costa Rica.

Kathleen G. Tallman is an Assistant Professor in the Biology Department at Doane College in Crete, Nebraska. She has a B.A. in biology and chemistry from Point Loma Nazarene College and a Ph.D. in neuroscience from The Ohio State University. In 2002, Dr. Tallman was a participant with a team of faculty at Doane College who were awarded an NIH grant to fund undergraduate research in the biomedical sciences.

Dinah Zike is an international curriculum consultant and inventor who has designed and developed educational products and three-dimensional, interactive graphic organizers for over thirty years. She is frequently a featured speaker at national, regional, and state science teachers' conferences. As president and founder of Dinah-Might Adventures, L.P., Dinah is the author of over 100 award-winning educational publications including *The Big Book of Science*. Dinah has a B.S. and an M.S. in educational curriculum and instruction from Texas A & M University. Dinah Zike's *Foldables* are an exclusive feature of McGraw-Hill textbooks. www.dinah.com

National Geographic Society, founded in 1888 for the increase and diffusion of geographic knowledge, is the world's largest nonprofit scientific and educational organization. The Education Division supports the Society's mission by developing innovative educational programs. National Geographic Society wrote the *Focus On* features for *Biology: The Dynamics of Life*, which are located on pages 1060–1091.

Contributing Author
Rebecca Johnson, Science Writer, Sioux Falls, SD

Consultants & Reviewers

Teacher Reviewers

Cynthia Alsworth
Mt. Olive Attendance Center
Mount Olive, MS

Debbie Arnold
Ware County School of Agricultural,
    Forestry, and Environmental Sciences
Manor, GA

Alan Ascher
Port Richmond High School
Staten Island, NY

Janice Baulch
Midland Independent School District
Midland, TX

Donna Bettinelli
Bay Shore High School
Bay Shore, NY

Beth Bodock
Chippewa High School
Doylestown, OH

Lynn M. Buttrey
W. F. West High School
Chehalis, WA

Robert A. Di Dio, M.S. Ed., Ph.D.
Intermediate School 192
Bronx, NY

Barry Feldman
Corona Del Sol High School
Tempe, AZ

Randi Haftel
Paulsboro High School
Paulsboro, NJ

Stephanie Hansen
Redfield High School
Redfield, SD

Mitch Harrington
Slidell High School
Slidell, LA

W. J. Hayden
Hammond High School
Hammond, IN

Martin Hettrich
Holy Trinity High School
Hicksville, NY

Terri Hood
East Union High School
Blue Springs, MS

Carol Johnson
John Jay High School
San Antonio, TX

Beth Kruetzer
Hoehne High School
Hoehne, CO

Richard Lord, Jr.
Presque Isle High School
Presque Isle, ME

Mary McNeill
Hoke County Schools
Raeford, NC

Lynn Miller
Leeton High School
Leeton, MO

Donald Reid, M.S.
Cypress High School
Cypress, CA

Jo Ann Scheidt
Helias High School
Jefferson City, MO

Sidra S. Spies
Niceville Senior High School
Niceville, FL

Beverly H. St. John
Milton High School
Milton, FL

Gary Upchurch
Robert E. Lee High School
Midland, TX

Karl Walker
Carlsbad High School
Carlsbad, CA

Robert Willis
Ballou High School
Washington, DC

Content Specialists

William Ausich
Department of Geological Sciences
The Ohio State University
Columbus, OH

Richard Duhrkoph
Department of Biology
Baylor University
Waco, TX

Alan Gishlick
National Center for Science Education
Oakland, CA

Elizabeth Godrick, Ph.D.
Department of Biology
Boston University
Boston, MA

Paula Gregory, Ph.D.
Genetics Department
Louisiana State University
Health Sciences Center
New Orleans, LA

Carol Hoffman
Institute of Ecology
University of Georgia
Athens, GA

Mozell Lang
Michigan Department of Education
Michigan State University
Lansing, MI

Raymond W. McCoy, Ph.D.
Kinesiology Department
The College of William and Mary
Williamsburg, VA

Carol McFadden
Cornell University
Ithaca, NY

Dale M. J. Mueller
Department of Biological Sciences
Texas A & M University
College Station, TX

Valerie Porter
Biology Teacher
Eisenhower High School
Houston, TX

Gary Simone
Plant Pathologist
Simone's Plant Disease Solutions
Corbett, OR

Cindy Lee Van Dover
Biology Department
College of William and Mary
Williamsburg, VA

Safety Consultants

John Longo
Chemisty Department
St. Joseph's University
Philadelphia, PA

Kenneth Russell Roy, Ph.D.
K–12 Director of Science and Safety
Glastonbury Public Schools
Glastonbury, CT

Sandra West
Department of Biology
Southwest Texas State University
San Marcos, TX

Reading Consultant

William Holliday
Department of Curriculum and
    Instruction
University of Maryland
College Park, MD

Teacher & Student Advisory Board

Indiana Teacher Advisory Board

The Teacher Advisory Board gave the Glencoe team feedback on the content of the Student Edition. They were instrumental in providing valuable input toward the development of the 2005 Indiana edition of *Biology: The Dynamics of Life.*

Student Advisory Board

The Student Advisory Board gave the authors, editorial staff, and design team feedback on the design of the Student Edition. We thank these students for their hard work and creative suggestions in making the 2005 edition of *Biology: The Dynamics of Life* more student friendly.

Field Test Schools

Glencoe/McGraw-Hill wishes to thank the following schools that field-tested pre-publication manuscript. They were instrumental in providing feedback and verifying the effectiveness of this program.

Teacher Handbook

Table of Contents

Dynamic Instructional Strategies

Getting Students Involved

The consistent instructional strategies in each chapter strengthen students' learning—from the beginning of each chapter where students see "What You'll Learn," to the end where they have a chance to test the knowledge they have acquired and prepare for the next lesson.

Chapter Opener

What You'll Learn at the beginning of each chapter introduces the main concepts.

Why It's Important provides an answer to the question "Why do we have to learn this?"

Biology Online connects students to the resources available at in.bdol.glencoe.com.

Section Opener

Section Preview provides *Section Objectives* to help the students focus on the main topics of the section. *Review Vocabualry* and *New Vocabulary* also are listed here.

Section Opener Features at the beginning of each section immediately engage the students in the lesson. Students may be instructed to:

- organize concepts in *Foldables*.
- relate the section's content to information students already know by *Using Prior Knowledge*.
- compare the section's content to a familiar topic by *Using an Anology*.
- build *Concept Maps*.
- generate *Outlines*.
- summarize concepts in the section in order to practice *Finding Main Ideas*.

Student Edition, pp. 220–221

Chapter 9

Energy in a Cell

What You'll Learn
- You will recognize why organisms need a constant supply of energy and where that energy comes from.
- You will identify how cells store and release energy as ATP
- You will describe the pathways by which cells obtain energy.
- You will compare ATP production in mitochondria and in chloroplasts.

Why It's Important
Every cell in your body needs energy in order to function. The energy your cells store is the fuel for basic body functions such as walking and breathing.

Understanding the Photo ▶
This squirrel is eating seeds produced by the conifer. The conifer traps light energy and stores it in the bonds of certain molecules for later use. How do the squirrel's cells, which cannot trap light energy, use the molecules in the seeds to supply energy for the squirrel?

Biology Online

Visit in.bdol.glencoe.com to
- study the entire chapter online
- access Web Links for more information and activities on cell energy
- review content with the Interactive Tutor and self-check quizzes

220

Section 9.1

The Need for Energy

Indiana Standards Standard B.1.9 Recognize and describe that both living and nonliving things are composed of compounds. ... joined by energy-containing bonds, such as those in ATP.

SECTION PREVIEW

Objectives
Explain why organisms need a supply of energy.
Describe how energy is stored and released by ATP.

Review Vocabulary
active transport: movement of materials through a membrane against a concentration gradient; requires energy from the cell (p. 199)

New Vocabulary
ATP (adenosine triphosphate)
ADP (adenosine diphosphate)

Why ATP?

Using an Analogy A spring stores energy when it is compressed. When the compressed spring is released, energy also is released, energy that sends this smiley-faced toy flying into the air. Like this coiled spring, chemical bonds store energy that can be released when the bond is broken. Just as some springs are tighter than others, some chemical bonds store more energy than others.
Summarize Scan this section and make a list of general ways in which cells use energy.

Stored energy

Figure 9.1
Because this panda cannot trap the sun's energy for use in its body, it eats bamboo. Molecules in bamboo leaves contain energy in their chemical bonds. Some of those molecules supply energy for the panda.

Cell Energy

Energy is essential to life. All living organisms must be able to obtain energy from the environment in which they live. Plants and other green organisms are able to trap the light energy in sunlight and store it in the bonds of certain molecules for later use. Other organisms, such as the panda shown in **Figure 9.1**, cannot use sunlight directly. Instead, they eat green plants. In that way, they obtain the energy stored in plants.

Work and the need for energy

You've learned about several cell processes that require energy. Active transport, cell division, movement of flagella or cilia, and the production, transport, and storage of proteins are some examples. You can probably come up with other examples of biological work, such as muscles contracting during exercise, your

9.1   THE NEED FOR ENERGY **221**

2T

Hands-On Learning

Student Edition, pp. 988–989

Labs

BioLabs give your students an opportunity to develop their own plans for investigating a question or problem and to share their data with others. Whether they're designing investigations or following well-tested procedures, they'll be learning and practicing science processes.

To further student inquiry in a short amount of time, assign a MiniLab or Problem-Solving Lab, which are located throughout the chapters. These labs offer students quick and easy-to-do labs that further clarify concepts and reinforce skills.

Chapter Assessment

The Chapter Assessment provides three pages of review and testing to help you evaluate students' knowledge and ability to apply science concepts.

Study Guide provides the *Key Concepts* of each section. This page is designed to help students review the major concepts and vocabulary of the chapter.

Vocabulary Review,
Understanding Key Concepts,
Constructed Response, &
Thinking Critically provide questions for the students to review the lesson.

Standardized Test Practice gives students the opportunity to test their knowledge while practicing for state and national examinations. All Multiple Choice, Constructed Response, and Grid In questions have been aligned and verified by *The Princeton Review*.

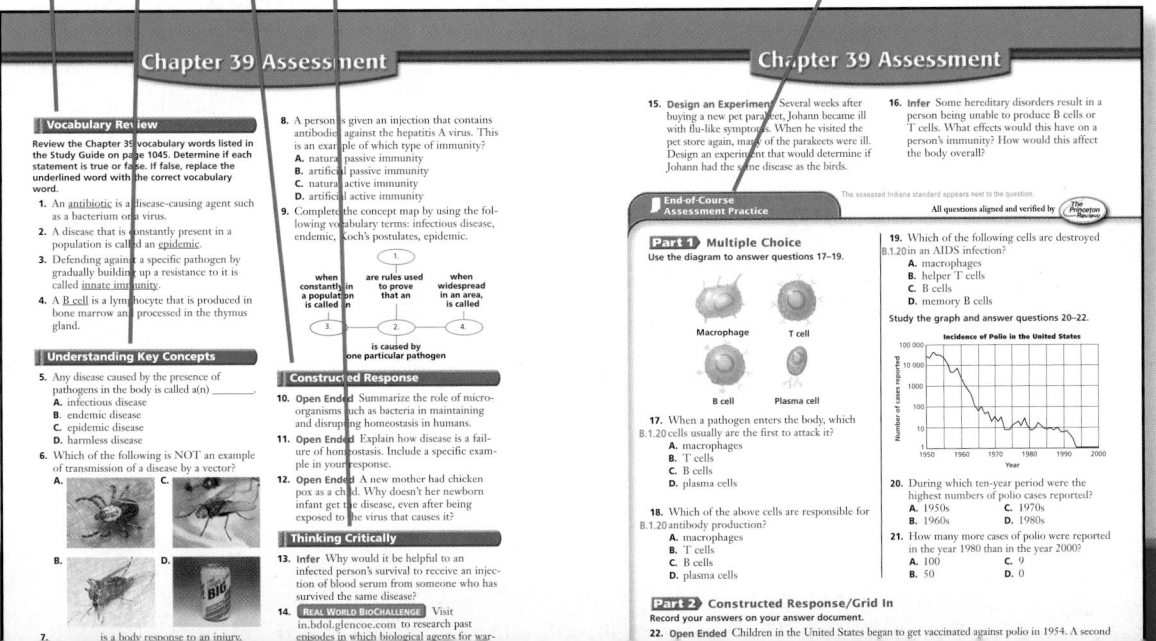

Student Edition, pp. 1046–1047

Teaching Tools

Time-Saving Teacher Resources

Biology: The Dynamics of Life provides an extensive list of support materials and resources designed to help you customize your biology course quickly and easily.

Teacher Wraparound Edition

The *Teacher Wraparound Edition* is your key to all of the teaching resources in *Biology: The Dynamics of Life*. In addition to teaching strategies and suggestions, the *Teacher Wraparound Edition* provides a guide for all of the print and software materials available for each lesson.

Transparency Books

- The *Section Focus Transparencies* book contains 97 full-color transparencies. These transparencies allow you to begin each lesson by capturing the attention of your students with simple activities as well as assess their prior knowledge.

- The *Basic Concepts Transparencies* book includes full-color transparencies designed to teach basic biology concepts.

- The *Reteaching Skills Transparencies* book helps you present, reinforce, or review key concepts developed in the text. Many of the transparencies are designed to reinforce scientific methods and processes.

- *Transparency masters and worksheets* for all three types of transparencies, in addition to answers and teaching strategies, are found in the *FAST FILE™ Unit Resources*.

FAST FILE Unit Resources

FAST FILE™ Unit Resources contain key reproducible masters along with additional teaching strategies, teacher support, and answer keys for each chapter.

Reproducible Student Resources include:

- Worksheets for all MiniLabs and BioLabs
- *Real World BioApplications* connecting biology to real world situations
- *Reinforcement and Study Guide* worksheets in English and Spanish, *Concept Mapping*, and *Critical Thinking/ Problem Solving* worksheets for each chapter
- *Section Focus, Basic Concepts,* and *Reteaching Skills Transparencies* activity masters
- *Chapter Assessment* masters
- *Student Recording Sheets* for practice using standardized test answer sheets

Teacher Support and Planning

- An additional Foldables™ Reading and Teaching Strategy for each chapter
- Answer keys and teaching strategies

Student Edition, pp. 550–551

BioDigest Unit Review

The BioDigest provided at the end of each unit can be used to:

- introduce important unit concepts.
- give students a quick overview of important information in the unit.
- review key unit concepts for quizzes and year-end exams.

Technology Support

Glencoe offers many time-saving software products to help you creatively engage your students.

Interactive Chalkboard brings Microsoft® Powerpoint® presentations right to your classroom. This tool is perfect for standardized or chapter-based test review. Use the step-by-step lessons provided to teach key concepts from each chapter or customize your own presentations. With the large number of graphics provided, students can use a visual approach to learning chapter content.

Includes:
- Image bank
- Section-check questions
- Online help and more

Virtual Labs CD-ROM Program

The Virtual Labs CD-ROM contains 22 virtual labs that allow students to complete laboratory investigations that are otherwise too dangerous, too expensive, or take too long to complete in a laboratory setting.

Teacher Works™

TeacherWorks™ is your all-in-one teacher resource center. Personalize lesson plans, access resources from the *Teacher Wraparound Edition*, connect to the Internet, or make a to-do list. These are only a few of the many features that can assist you in the planning and organizing of your lessons.

Includes:
- A calendar feature
- Access to all program blackline masters
- Standards correlations and more

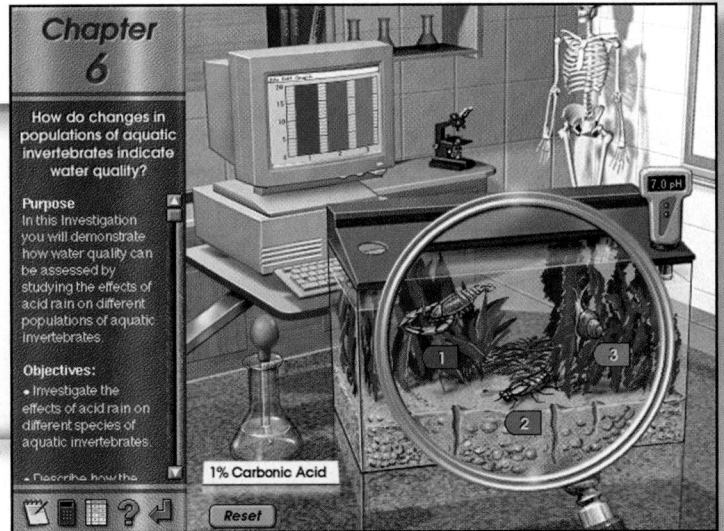

Biology: The Dynamics of Life Web Site

The *Biology: The Dynamics of Life* Web site in.bdol.glencoe.com provides both you and your students with a wide range of materials. Students can access previewed Internet sites (Web Links), which correlate to text chapters, and tutor themselves with interactive activities that review chapter concepts. Students also will have access to their entire Student Edition online. They can check their knowledge of chapter content with interactive self-check quizzes for each chapter section as well as the entire chapter. You will also find WebQuest activities, a Teacher Forum for teachers to share activities and ideas, and Internet BioLabs where students can post and share data.

Helping Students Become Fluent in the Language of Science

Biology: The Dynamics of Life is designed to increase science literacy through improving reading comprehension and deepening students' understanding of ideas and concepts. The reading strategies are active, constructive, and engaging.

Professor William Holliday with the Department of Curriculum and Instruction at the University of Maryland served as reading consultant for this edition. Dr. Holliday reviewed the text for readability and suggested strategies for improving reading fluency. In addition, he reviewed the illustrations and identified misconceptions they might introduce or reinforce.

In the Student Edition

Foldables™ in each chapter help students organize and process information as they read through the chapter.

Word Origin features enhance the understanding of biology terms. Use these *Word Origin* margin features as a pre-reading activity, or have students keep a vocabulary journal. Additional word origins can be found in *The Skill Handbook* at the back of the book.

Caption Questions throughout each chapter offer a visual approach to learning. Students are asked to recall what they have read by interpreting the visual.

Reading Checks throughout each chapter stimulate quick recall and keep the students focused on the main idea.

Student Edition, p. 3

Student Edition, p. 66

Technology Support

Vocabulary PuzzleMaker allows you to create crossword puzzles, jumble puzzles, and word searches in minutes or edit a database of key terms and puzzles to review chapter vocabulary. The puzzles can be printed or played on the computer screen.

Guided Reading Audio Summaries, available on MP3-formatted CD-ROMs, provide a comprehensive overview in Spanish and English to help auditory learners, students with reading difficulties, and English language learners (ELL) review key concepts.

Additional Teacher Resources

Reading and Writing in the Science Classroom

Dinah Zike's Teaching Science with Foldables

Foldables™

Improving Active Reading and Study Skills

Foldables are easy-to-make, three-dimensional, interactive graphic organizers that students create out of simple sheets of paper. These unique hands-on tools for studying and reviewing were created exclusively for Glencoe by education specialist Dinah Zike.

Build Prereading Skills
- Enables students to organize and process information
- Encourages students to observe and read
- Creates an interactive snapshot of the chapter

Encourage Reading and Writing
- Practices basic reading and writing skills
- Develops skills in finding and reporting main ideas
- Organizes information
- Reviews key vocabulary terms

Summarize Content for Review
- Creates a comprehensive, interactive snapshot of the chapter
- Provides preparation support for chapter, unit, and end-of-course exams, as well as standardized tests

Help with Assessment
- Probes the depth of your students' understanding of chapter concepts
- Pinpoints what your students understand
- Identifies misconceptions

Additional Resource
Dinah Zike's Teaching Science with Foldables offers
- Comprehensive presentations of Foldables instructions
- More ideas on how to incorporate Foldables into your lessons
- Easy-to-read folding instruction pages in color

Student Edition, p. 171

The Cell Theory Make the following Foldable to help you organize the ideas of the cell theory.

STEP 1 Collect 2 sheets of paper and layer them about 1.5 cm apart vertically. Keep the edges level.

STEP 2 Fold up the bottom edges of the paper to form 4 equal tabs.

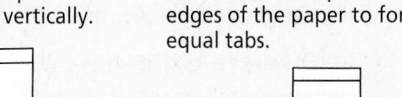

STEP 3 Fold the papers and crease well to hold the tabs in place. Staple along the fold. **Label** each tab with one of the main ideas of the cell theory.

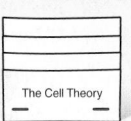

Summarize After you read Section 7.1, summarize the three main ideas of the cell theory in your own words. Review the theory using the information provided and note its strengths and weaknesses.

Laboratory Guide

Engaging Labs that Get Students Excited About Biology

Biology: The Dynamics of Life provides your students with the hands-on opportunity to plan, create, and explore biology investigations. Students will learn biology while having fun.

In the Student Edition

 Investigate BioLabs provide guided inquiry as students hypothesize, plan investigations, and collect and analyze data.

 Design Your Own BioLabs challenge your students to design their own investigation that will provide an answer to the lab problem.

 Internet BioLabs help students share and retrieve data from others around the country and world by posting data they have collected on the Glencoe Science Web site. These investigations show students the possible ranges of data, importance of collecting large amounts of data, and data analysis.

MiniLabs and Problem-Solving Labs are quick ways for students to practice specific process skills as they learn science concepts. Many of them can be classroom demonstrations or homework assignments.

In the Teacher Wraparound Edition

Additional Lab **Additional Labs** are available in each chapter and can be used as make-up labs or as alternatives to the BioLabs.

Quick Demos allow students to visualize biology concepts.

Quick Demo

Everyday Sounds To show how important each sense is, play a tape of various common sounds that students can identify. Discuss the dependence of humans on senses and the adjustments that are made if one sense is lost.

Teacher Edition, p. 952

Technology Support

Virtual Labs CD-ROM is a collection of interactive activities involving major chapter themes that allow students to understand biological concepts in a virtual setting. These labs provide a way to conduct experiments without classroom time, cost, and safety constraints.

Video Labs are instructional videos that show students step-by-step lab procedures, while emphasizing important lab safety skills. The lab videos also include teacher support, troubleshooting advice, and expected outcomes.

Additional Teacher Resources

Laboratory Manual contains activities that offer a variety of traditional laboratory experiences that reinforce the biology principles in the text.

Forensics and Biotechnology Labs present activities that offer students an opportunity to investigate high-interest topics. The labs will reinforce concepts and science process skills introduced in the student edition.

Probeware Labs present activities for students to explore scientific concepts using a probeware data collection system. Integrating technology in the classroom is made simple with step-by-step instructions for setting up and using the probeware.

Science Inquiry Labs will increase students' independence in stating hypotheses, designing and performing investigations, and collecting and analyzing data.

Effective Tools to Measure Success

Biology: The Dynamics of Life offers the Glencoe Assessment Advantage, a system designed to give you all the tools you need to prepare your students for success in any testing situation.

In the Student Edition

Standardized Test Practice questions at the end of each Chapter Assessment and Unit Review give students the opportunity to prepare for state and national tests.

Section Assessment questions and **Skill Builder Activities** appear in every chapter.

Chapter Assessment questions help you evaluate students' knowledge and ability to apply science concepts.

In the Teacher Wraparound Edition

Modified Assessment, located throughout the *Teacher Wraparound Edition*, provides an alternative method of assessing struggling learners or students with learning disabilities.

✓ MODIFIED Assessment

Performance Quiz students by having them label blank diagrams of the female and male reproductive systems. Have them indicate, using colored pencils and arrows, the pathways of sperm and eggs through these systems. **L1**

Teacher Edition, p. 1004

Rubric samples are provided throughout the book to help you assess your students' knowledge of a particular concept.

RUBRIC

Evaluating Open-Ended Questions
Open-ended assessment questions are graded by using a multilevel rubric that guides you in assessing a student's knowledge of a particular concept. The following rubric is a sample scoring device.

SCORE	CRITERIA
4	A correct solution that is supported by well-developed, accurate explanations.
3	A generally correct solution, but may contain minor flaws in reasoning.

RUBRIC

SCORE	CRITERIA
2	A partially correct interpretation and/or solution to the problem.
1	A correct solution with no supporting evidence or explanation.
0	An incorrect solution or no solution is given.

Additional Teacher Resources

Performance Assessment in the Science Classroom contains guidelines for assessing the performance of a task, reproducible activities for evaluating students' performance assessment, performance task assessment lists and rubrics, and sample rubrics and checklists.

Reviewing Biology is a flexible assessment tool created by The Princeton Review. Use the multiple-choice format tests as self-check tests with explanations for answers and text references for content review or as a comprehensive assessment of chapter concepts.

FAST FILE™ Unit Resources contain a test for every chapter. In addition, a *Student Recording Sheet* for each Student Edition chapter and unit assessment gives students practice with standardized practice answer sheets.

Technology Support

MindJogger Videoquizzes are interactive videoquizzes set in a game show context. These quizzes review core concepts from every chapter. Each is designed for the full range of student learning styles within the classroom.

ExamView® Pro Test Bank CD-ROM for Windows® and Macintosh® provides an easy way to create, edit, and customize your tests. Select your own test items by objective from two different levels of difficulty, or write and edit your own. Tests also convert to Spanish.

Meeting Student Needs

Intervention and Extension Guide

In the Teacher Wraparound Edition

Teaching Strategies, following suggested assessments and activities, supply *ability levels* to accommodate all students.

- **L1** Level 1 activities should be appropriate for students with learning difficulties.
- **L2** Level 2 activities should be within the ability range of all students.
- **L3** Level 3 activities are designed for above-average students.
- **ELL** ELL activities should be within the ability range of English Language Learners or students who speak English as a second language (ESL).
- **COOP LEARN** Cooperative Learning activities are designed for small group work.

Multiple Learning Styles are specified throughout the *Teacher Wraparound Edition* to help students learn science concepts through their preferred learning styles. Look for these italicized designations under various activities:

- *Kinesthetic* learners learn through touch, movement, and manipulating objects.
- *Visual-Spatial* learners think in terms of images, illustrations, and models.
- *Interpersonal* learners understand and work well with other people.
- *Intrapersonal* learners can analyze their own strengths and weaknesses and may prefer to work on their own.
- *Linguistic* learners write clearly and easily understand the written word.
- *Logical-Mathematical* learners understand numbers easily and have highly developed reasoning skills.
- *Naturalist* learners can distinguish among, classify, and use features of the environment.

Daily Interventions are found at the end of each chapter section. This feature is designed to intercept students who are struggling and prescribe a system to help them grasp the material. Suggested *Reading Essentials* worksheets are provided as additional daily interventions for each lesson.

Teacher Edition, p. 904

DAILY INTERVENTION

Check for Understanding
Have students fill in the names of the bones and label an example of each of the major types of joints on a diagram of the skeleton. **L2**

Reteach
Interpersonal Have students make flash cards containing the names of bones. On the opposite side of each card, have students describe where each bone is located and identify its common name. Have students work in pairs to review the information on the flash cards. **L1** **COOP LEARN**

Resources
For more practice, use *Reading Essentials for Biology,* Section 34.2.

Revealing Misconceptions recognize that students have many experiences outside the science classroom that have shaped their understandings of the natural world. Unfortunately, interpretations based on causal observation are not always accurate. This feature is designed to uncover possible misconceptions and help students understand the concepts.

Teacher Edition, p. 918

Revealing Misconceptions

Many students may believe that cavities are the greatest threat to teeth.

Uncover the Misconception

Ask students what they think is the biggest threat to teeth in the U.S. List their suggestions on the board or have them research to find the answer. periodontal disease

Demonstrate the Concept

Using either a model of the teeth and gums or a photograph, explain how periodontal disease affects the gums. Bacteria and the toxins they release irritate and inflame gums, causing them to bleed easily. As pockets of infection form, the gum begins to separate from the tooth. Left untreated, this infection can lead to destruction of the teeth and portions of the jawbone.

Assess New Knowledge

Have students work in groups to make a pamphlet they can distribute to middle or elementary grades presenting information about the dangers and prevention of periodontal disease.

Student & Teacher Editions, p. 1113

...ergy-expending process by ...s transport materials across the cell membrane against a concentration gradient.

adaptation (a dap TAY shun): (p. 9) evolution of a structure, behavior, or internal process that enables an organism to respond to environmental factors and live to produce offspring.

adaptive radiation: (p. 412) divergent evolution in which ancestral species evolve into an array of species to fit a num-... diverse habitats.

...logical and/or physiological drug

transporte... mediante el cual la célula t... membrana celular contra un gradien...

adaptación: (pág. 9) Evolución de una estru... tamiento o proceso interno que permite a un... responder a los factores ambientales y sobrevivir... ducir progenie.

radiación adaptativa: (pág. 412) Evolución... cual la especie ancestral evoluciona y... de especies adaptadas a amb...

adicción: (...

Glossary/Glosario offers side-by-side English and Spanish definitions to help English Language Learners better understand and learn biology vocablulary.

Cultural Diversity

provides insights into the unique ways in which people of different ethnicities and cultural heritage have approached science. The intent of these features is to build awareness and appreciation for the global community in which we live.

CULTURAL DIVERSITY

Carlos Monge and High-Altitude Physiology Carlos Monge (1884–1970) was a Peruvian scientist who studied the physiology of people who live at high altitudes. He was the founder of the Institute of Andean Biology and Pathology. Introduce students to Monge's research and major findings.

Discuss with students the physiological adaptations of people who live at high altitudes, such as the Aymara and Quechua Indians of South America. Have students relate these adaptations to the proper functioning of the respiratory system. **L2**

Teacher Edition, p. 976

Teacher Edition, p. 79

INCLUSION STRATEGIES

Visually Impaired: *Kinesthetic* Allow visually impaired students to feel the texture of sandy, clay, and loam soils. Have them work with peers to rank the samples in terms of decayed material present. Ask them to explain how such material contributes to the fertility of each soil. **L1**

CHALLENGE ACTIVITY

Dissection Have students who need an additional challenge prepare a labeled dissection of a sheep brain. They should prepare whole brains and half brains, labeling areas discussed in this chapter. **L3**

Teacher Edition, p. 944

Challenge Activities provide opportunities for gifted students to engage in activities and research projects that extend the chapter's concepts.

Inclusion Strategies present various teaching strategies designed to help you meet the special needs of students with learning disabilities, physical challenges, visual impairment, and hearing impairment.

Additional Teacher Resources

Reading Essentials for Biology consists of biology lessons written for inclusion students. Students are guided through the passages and asked to find key content through structured activities. The worksheets allow students to master the basic concepts of each chapter while reinforcing their reading and study skills.

BioChallenges and Enrichment provide interesting, challenging, and in-depth projects for advanced students.

FAST FILE™ Unit Resources combine key student masters and teacher resources in chapter order in convenient unit books. Everything is at hand as you teach each chapter.

Technology Support

Guided Reading Audio Summaries offer an alternative format to help English language learners, assist auditory learners, and make biology accessible to all students through the use of chapter audio summaries on MP3-formatted CD-ROMs.

WebQuests are inquiry-based activities designed to provide students with a task that they will need to research on the Internet, using specific links supplied. They are then asked questions about the information they gathered. Teachers can view the Teacher Page to determine how to grade each student's report.

Education Partners

NATIONAL GEOGRAPHIC

Some topics of biology have received more attention than others because they're unusual, informative, or just plain interesting. National Geographic Society has created visually exciting multi-page Focus On features that inform, excite, and motivate your students. Focus On features, conveniently located in the back of the book, are a great resource that can be used to get students involved in the world of biology. Assign them as a lead-in to special research projects and in-depth studies for extra credit.

Student Edition, pp. 1062–1063

Student Edition, pp. 554–555

Student Edition, p. 549

The Princeton Review

Glencoe has partnered with The Princeton Review, a nationally renowned company that helps students prepare for state and national tests. This partnership has resulted in test practice questions at the end of each Chapter Assessment and a two-page Standardized Test Practice at the end of each Unit Review.

mhln.com is an online teaching and learning space for teachers, students, and parents. mhln.com includes online textbooks along with unique learning and teaching tools.

- For students, mhln.com provides an interactive textbook accessible wherever a student can log on to the Internet. This means a lighter student backpack.

- For teachers, mhln.com provides a customizable online learning space for posting assignments,

web-based instruction, student resources, and a class calendar.

- For parents, mhln.com provides tools that parents can use at home to help their child succeed in school. Parents also have instant access to their child's progress at school and daily assignments.

mhln.com provides online textbooks and educational tools that are adaptable to all curricula. These tools are designed to make classrooms easier to manage, raise student performance with interaction, provide online tutoring and instruction, and help parents help their child in school.

Course Planning Guide

Biology: The Dynamics of Life provides a complete selection of core concepts that are presented in a way to meet the needs of all students. The following Course Planning Guide offers general suggestions for pacing your students through the book. Both standard class periods and block schedule class periods are provided to assist you in:

- designing a biology course that meets the needs of your individual students and classes.
- setting the pace at which the content is covered.
- determining what material should be given the most emphasis.

Glencoe's TeacherWorks™ provides another method for helping you plan your course. TeacherWorks allows you to:

- plan your class lessons in a calendar format.
- create lesson plans, schedule appointments, and make notes.
- import Web links.
- download state standard correlations.
- access your electronic Teacher Edition.
- hot link to the Internet.
- access all blackline masters and transparencies.

Chapter	Single-Class Schedule (160 days)	Block Scheduling (80 days)
1	3	1½
2	5	2½
3	5	2½
4	5	2
5	4	2
6	5	2
7	6	3
8	6	3½
9	6	3
10	5	4
11	6	4
12	5	4½
13	4	—
14	4	2
15	5	3
16	2	—
17	4	2
18	5	2
19	4	2½
20	3	1½
21	3	2
22	4	1½
23	4	2½
24	4	1½
25	3	2
26	3	—
27	2	1½
28	2	1½
29	2	1
30	4	1½
31	4	1½
32	3	1½
33	2	—
34	5	3
35	4	2
36	6	2½
37	5	3
38	5	3
39	3	1
TOTAL	160	80

The total number of days in each level of pacing is less than the typical 180-day school year and 90-day semester to allow for flexibility in planning due to testing, school cancellations, or shortened class periods.

National Science Content Standards

Setting the Standard for National Science Literacy

Unifying Concepts and Processes

UCP.1   Systems, order, and organization

UCP.2   Evidence, models, and explanation

UCP.3   Change, constancy, and measurement

UCP.4   Evolution and equilibrium

UCP.5   Form and function, Science as Inquiry

Science as Inquiry

A.1   Abilities necessary to do scientific inquiry

A.2   Understandings about scientific inquiry

Physical Science

B.1   Structure of atoms

B.2   Structure and properties of matter

B.3   Chemical reactions

B.4   Motions and forces

B.5   Conservation of energy and increase in disorder

B.6   Interactions of energy and matter

Life Science

C.1   The cell

C.2   Molecular basis of heredity

C.3   Biological evolution

C.4   Interdependence of organisms

C.5   Matter, energy, and organization in living systems

C.6   Behavior of organisms

Earth and Space Sciences

D.1   Energy in the earth system

D.2   Geochemical cycles

D.3   Origin and evolution of the earth system

D.4   Origin and evolution of the universe

Science and Technology

E.1   Abilities of technological design

E.2   Understandings about science and technology

Science in Personal and Social Perspectives

F.1   Personal and community health

F.2   Population growth

F.3   Natural resources

F.4   Environmental quality

F.5   Natural and human-induced hazards

F.6   Science and technology in local, national, and global challenges

History and Nature of Science

G.1   Science as a human endeavor

G.2   Nature of scientific knowledge

G.3   Historical perspectives

Managing Activities in the Biology Classroom

The activities in *Biology: The Dynamics of Life* are designed to minimize dangers in the laboratory. Careful laboratory planning and management by both the instructor and the student are essential to a safe laboratory experience. **Local, state, and federal laboratory safety laws and regulations must be strictly followed.** The information provided here is one of the many resources to which you can refer for information about laboratory safety.

Classroom and/or Laboratory Preparation

1. Label and store chemicals properly and securely. See p. 16T.
2. Store equipment properly and securely.
   a. Clean and dry all equipment before storing.
   b. Protect electronic equipment and microscopes from dust, humidity, and extreme temperatures.
   c. Number, catalog, and organize equipment.
3. Ensure adequate work space for each student.
4. Ensure adequate classroom and storeroom ventilation.
5. Explain and post safety and evacuation guidelines along with expectations of conduct.
6. Ensure that all safety equipment is functioning properly and is clearly visible.
7. Provide hot plates as a heat source whenever possible. If gas burners are used, know where the central gas supply shutoff valve is located.
8. Ensure that each workstation has a GFCI-protected electrical source.
9. Provide safety goggles consistent with ANSI Standard Z87.1 for each student, including students who wear corrective lenses.

First Day of Class (with students)

1. Distribute and discuss safety rules, safety symbols, and first aid guidelines. Have students refer to pages 1107–1109 to review safety symbols and guidelines.
2. Review safe use of equipment and chemicals.
3. Review use and location of safety equipment.
4. Discuss safe disposal of materials and laboratory cleanup policy.
5. Discuss proper laboratory attitude and conduct.
6. Document students' understanding of the preceding points. Have students sign a safety contract and return it.

Before Each MiniLab or BioLab

1. Perform each investigation yourself before assigning it.
2. Arrange the lab in such a way that equipment and supplies are clearly labeled and easily accessible.
3. Have available only equipment and supplies needed to complete the assigned investigation.
4. Review the procedure with students, emphasizing any caution statements or safety symbols that appear.
5. Be sure all students know the proper procedures to follow if an accident should occur.
6. Provide containers for disposing of chemicals, waste products, and biological specimens. Disposal methods should meet local guidelines.

During the MiniLab or BioLab

1. Make sure the lab is clean and free of clutter.
2. Insist that students wear goggles and aprons.
3. Never allow a student to work alone in the lab.
4. Never allow students to use a cutting device with more than one edge.
5. Students should not point the open end of a heated test tube toward anyone.
6. Remove broken glassware or frayed cords from use. Also clean up any spills immediately. Dilute solutions with water before removing.
7. Be sure all glassware that is to be heated is of a heat-treated type that will not shatter.
8. Remind students that hot glassware looks cool.
9. Prohibit eating and drinking in the lab.

After the MiniLab or BioLab

1. Be sure that the lab is clean.
2. Be certain that students have returned all equipment and disposed of broken glassware and chemicals properly.
3. Be sure that all hot plates and electrical connections are off.
4. Insist that each student wash his or her hands when lab work is completed.

Chemical Storage and Disposal

General Guidelines

Be sure to store all chemicals properly. The following are guidelines commonly used. Your school, city, county, or state may have additional requirements for handling chemicals. It is the responsibility of each teacher to become informed of the rules or guidelines in effect in his or her area.

1. Separate chemicals by reaction type. Strong acids should be stored together. Likewise, strong bases should be stored together and should be separated from acids. Oxidants should be stored away from easily oxidized materials, and so on.

2. Be sure all chemicals are stored in labeled containers indicating contents, concentration, source, date purchased (or prepared), any precautions for handling and storage, and expiration date.

3. Dispose of any outdated or waste chemicals properly according to accepted disposal procedures.

4. Do not store chemicals above eye level.

5. Wood shelving is preferable to metal. All shelving should be firmly attached to the wall and should have anti-roll edges.

6. Store only those chemicals that you plan to use.

7. Hazardous chemicals require special storage containers and conditions. Be sure to know which chemicals those are and the accepted practices for your area. Some substances must be stored outside the building.

8. When working with chemicals or preparing solutions, observe the same general safety precautions that you would expect from students. These include wearing an apron and goggles during lab preparation, activity, and cleanup. Wear gloves and use the fume hood when necessary.

9. If you are a new teacher in a particular laboratory, it is your responsibility to survey the chemicals stored there to be sure they are stored properly. If not, they should be disposed of. Consult the rules and laws in your area concerning which chemicals can be kept in your classroom. For disposal, consult up-to-date disposal information from state and federal governments.

Disposal of Chemicals

Local, state, and federal laws regulate the proper disposal of chemicals. These laws should be consulted before chemical disposal is attempted. Although most substances encountered in high school biology can be flushed down the drain with plenty of water, it is not safe to assume that this is always true. Teachers who use chemicals should consult the following book from the National Research Council:

Prudent Practices in the Laboratory. Washington, DC: National Academy Press, 1995. This book is useful and was revised in 1995. Current laws in your area would, of course, supersede the information in this book.

DISCLAIMER

Glencoe/McGraw-Hill makes no claims to the completeness of this discussion of laboratory safety and chemical storage. The material presented is not all-inclusive, nor does it address all of the hazards associated with handling, storing, and disposing of chemicals, or with laboratory management.

Preparation of Solutions

It is most important to use safe laboratory techniques when handling all chemicals. Many substances may appear harmless but are, in fact, toxic, corrosive, or very reactive. Always check with the supplier. Chemicals should never be ingested. Be sure to use proper techniques to smell solutions or other agents. Always wear safety goggles, gloves, and an apron. Observe the following precautions.

1. *Poisonous/corrosive liquid and/or vapor*—use in the fume hood; Examples: acetic acid, nitric acid, hydrochloric acid, ammonium hydroxide

2. *Poisonous and corrosive to eyes, lungs, and skin;* Examples: acids, limewater, iron(III) chloride, bases, silver nitrate, iodine, potassium permanganate

3. *Poisonous if swallowed, inhaled, or absorbed through the skin;* Examples: glacial acetic acid, copper compounds, barium chloride, lead compounds, chromium compounds, lithium compounds, cobalt(II) chloride, silver compounds

4. Always add acids to water, never the reverse.

5. When sulfuric acid and sodium hydroxide are added to water, a large amount of thermal energy is released. Sodium metal reacts violently with water. Use extra care when handling any of these substances.

Alcohol testing solution: Wear goggles, gloves, and an apron. In a fume hood, add 20 g of potassium dichromate powder to a glass beaker. Pour 20 mL concentrated H_2SO_4 into the beaker and stir with a glass stirring rod to dissolve most of the powder. Slowly and carefully pour the solution into 60 mL distilled water in a glass beaker and continue to stir. The solution becomes VERY HOT. Allow to cool. Powder may precipitate out after cooling. Pour only the liquid solution into dropper bottles for student use. Solution has a shelf life of one year.

Baking soda (sodium bicarbonate) solution: To prepare a 0.25% solution, dissolve 0.5 g baking soda (sodium hydrogen carbonate) in 200 mL of water.

Benedict's solution: Dissolve 173 g sodium citrate and 100 g sodium carbonate in 700 mL water over a hot plate. Filter. Dissolve 17.3 g copper sulfate in 100 mL water. Slowly add to the first solution. Add water to a total volume of 1 L.

Bromothymol blue: Add 0.5 g bromothymol blue powder to 500 mL distilled water to make a BTB stock solution. Dilute 40 mL BTB stock solution to 2 L with distilled water. Solution should be bright blue. If not, add one drop of NaOH at a time, swirling to mix. Check color.

Cola, dilute solution: Add 1 part cola to 1 part distilled water.

Congo red: Add 0.1 g Congo red powder to 50 mL distilled water.

Cough medicine, dilute: Add 2 mL of cough medicine (syrup) to 98 mL distilled water. Stir before use.

Ethyl alcohol, dilute: Add 2 mL ethyl alcohol to 98 mL distilled water. Stir.

Fertilizer solution: To make a 1% fertilizer solution, mix 1 g 5-10-5 fertilizer with 99 mL water. For a 0.1 % serial dilution, mix 1 mL 1% solution with 9 mL water. For a 0.01% serial dilution, mix 1 mL 0.1% solution with 9 mL water.

Gelatin solution: Soften 1 g gelatin in 20 mL water; then add 80 mL hot, not boiling, water to dissolve. Cool to room temperature before using.

Glucose solution: For 1% glucose solution, dissolve 1 g of glucose in 99 mL water.

Gum arabic solution: Dissolve 1 g gum arabic in 100 mL warm water. Cool to room temperature before use.

Hydrochloric acid (HCl) solution: To make a 10% solution, add 27 mL concentrated hydrochloric acid to 73 mL water while stirring. To make a 0.1M solution, add 1 mL concentrated hydrochloric acid to 100 mL water while stirring.

Iodine solution/Iodine stain: Dilute 1 part Lugol's solution with 15 parts water.

Lugol's solution: Dissolve 10 g potassium iodide in 100 mL distilled water; then add and dissolve 5 g iodine. Store in dark bottle. Keeps indefinitely.

Methylene blue stain: Dissolve 1.5 g methylene blue in 100 mL ethyl alcohol. Dilute by adding 10 mL of solution to 90 mL water.

Methylcellulose solution: Add 20 g methylcellulose to 40 mL of boiling distilled water. Let stand for 30 minutes, then add 40 mL distilled water. Stir until uniform. Solution will be very thick.

Pancreatic solution: Blend a pig or sheep pancreas with 150 mL 30% ethyl alcohol. Allow the solution to stand for 24 hours, shaking occasionally. Strain the solution through cheesecloth and then filter. Neutralize with KOH until you get near the end point, then use 0.5% sodium carbonate.

Potassium chloride (KCl) solution: To make a 0.5M solution, dissolve 3.73 g of potassium chloride in 60 mL of distilled water, then add distilled water to make 100 mL final volume.

Salt solution: For a 3.5% salt solution that simulates the concentration of ocean water, dissolve 35 g salt in 965 mL water. For a 1% solution, dissolve 1 g of salt in 99 mL of water. For a 3% solution, dissolve 3 g of salt in 97 mL of water. For a 5% solution, dissolve 5 g of salt in 95 mL of water. For a 6% solution, dissolve 6 g of salt in 94 mL of water.

Sodium hydroxide (NaOH) solution: To make a 1% solution, dissolve 1 g NaOH in 99 mL of water. For a 0.04% serial dilution, mix 4 mL 1% solution with 96 mL water.

Starch solution: Make a 1% solution by stirring a slurry of 1 g cornstarch and 50 mL cold water into 1 L boiling water. Cool before using.

Sterile pond water: Filter pond water and place it in flat pans. Boil for 15 minutes. Allow to cool before using.

Sucrose solution: For a 1% sucrose solution, dissolve 1 g sucrose in 99 mL water. For a 2% sucrose solution, dissolve 2 g sucrose in 98 mL water. For a 5% sucrose solution, dissolve 5 g sucrose with 95 mL water. For a 10% sucrose solution, dissolve 10 g of sucrose in 90 mL water. For a 20% sucrose solution, dissolve 20 g of sucrose in 80 mL of water. For a 30% sucrose solution, dissolve 30 g of sucrose in 70 mL of water. For a 40% sucrose solution, dissolve 40 g of sucrose in 60 mL of water.

Sugar solution: Add 1 tablespoon of sugar to 1 cup of warm water in a deep jar or flask. Stir to dissolve.

Tetrazolium solution: Dissolve 1 g of 2,3,5-triphenyl tetrazolium chloride in 100 mL of water. Store in dark glass bottle.

Tobacco solution: Grind tobacco from one cigarette into a fine powder. Mix the powder with 100 mL of a 1% glucose solution.

Urine (artificial) solutions: Normal: Add 1 tsp. of salt and 4 drops of yellow food coloring to 500 mL of tap water. Stir to dissolve. Abnormal: Add 1 tsp. of salt, 2 tsp. of glucose or honey, and 4 drops of yellow food coloring to 500 mL of tap water. Stir to dissolve.

Yeast culture: Add 1/5 package dry baker's yeast to 200 mL distilled water.

Equipment and Materials List

This table of equipment and inexpensive, easily accessible materials can help you prepare for your biology classes for the year. Refer to the Chapter Organizer in front of each chapter for a list of equipment and materials used for each laboratory activity in the chapter. It is assumed that goggles, laboratory aprons, tap water, textbooks, paper, pencils, and pens are available for all activities.

Non-Consumables

Item	BioLab	MiniLab	Additional Lab
aquarium	p. 686		pp. 798, 864
balance	pp. 756, 834, 936		pp. 76, 196, 608, 694, 742
beaker	pp. 58, 686, 756, 936	pp. 151, 155, 198, 634	pp. 76, 234
beaker, 100-mL		p. 226	p. 196
beaker, 150-mL			p. 694
beaker, 200-mL		p. 122	
beaker, 250-mL	p. 544		
beaker, 400-mL	p. 164		
beaker, 1000-mL	p. 238		
bowl, small			p. 234
brush, camel hair	p. 714		
bulb baster	p. 686		
Bunsen burner	p. 936		p. 408
calculator (optional)	p. 104		
cardboard pieces			p. 530
clock or stopwatch w/second hand	pp. 24, 164, 238, 910, 988	p. 683	p. 798
colored pencils 4 colors	pp. 354, 414, 658	p. 327	p. 998
container		p. 22	
cover glasses	p. 84		
coverslip	pp. 58, 188, 522, 626, 658	pp. 6, 73, 254, 506, 511, 530, 586, 608, 675, 683, 845	pp. 182, 382, 560
culture dish	p. 734		
cup			p. 118
diagrams, skull	p. 436		
dichotomous key	p. 446		
dish	p. 874	pp. 122, 860	
dropper	pp. 84, 188, 522, 626, 658, 686, 734, 874, 936, 964	pp. 73, 506, 511, 702, 987	pp. 182, 382, 920
dropper bottles	p. 936		
dropper bottle, dark			p. 654
eyedropper	p. 58		
field guides for amphibian identification	p. 810		
filter paper	p. 936		
flask, (250-mL)			p. 982
flowerpot	p. 274		
forceps	pp. 164, 188, 330, 496, 658, 776	pp. 155, 530, 586, 589, 743, 754, 773, 845, 987	pp. 182, 560, 694, 1032
funnel	p. 936		
hand lens	pp. 274, 658, 734	pp. 561, 827	p. 560
hot plate	pp. 544, 936		p. 234
glass container	pp. 84	p. 151	
glass slide	pp. 84, 626	pp. 14, 173, 182, 254, 511, 586, 608, 675, 683, 987	pp. 182, 350, 560
glass slide, chilled	p. 714		
glassware, laboratory, assorted			p. 454
golf ball	p. 834		
graduated cylinder	pp. 756, 936	p. 122	pp. 12, 38, 196, 920

Lab Preparation

Item	BioLab	MiniLab	Additional Lab
graduated cylinder, 50-mL	p. 544		
incubator, 37 degrees	p. 496		p. 1032
inoculation loop			p. 408
Internet connection	pp. 24, 126, 598, 852, 1042		
jar lid			p. 864
jars	p. 58	p. 92	pp. 12, 864
knife, kitchen	p. 164		pp. 160, 196
lamp		p. 860	pp. 724, 818
lamp, 150-watt with reflector	p. 238		
lightbulbs, incandescent 60-watt			p. 488
lightsource	pp. 274, 330		
magnifying glass		p. 327	
marker, permanent (dark color)	p. 104		
measuring spoon			p. 196
meterstick		pp. 376, 948	
microscope	pp. 58, 84, 188, 214, 522, 589, 626, 658, 675, 964	pp. 6, 67, 73, 173, 182, 209, 254, 371, 490, 506, 511, 530, 586, 608, 657, 683, 702, 712, 764, 795, 843, 845, 934,1006, 1035	pp. 182, 324, 350, 382, 560, 592, 682
microscope, binocular	p. 686		
microscope, compound			
microscope, dissecting	pp. 658, 714, 874	pp. 561, 773	
microscope slides	pp. 58, 522, 658, 964	pp. 6, 371, 845	pp. 382
mortar and pestle	p. 936		
novel		p. 350	
objects, small for burying			p. 842
paintbrushes	p. 330		
pan, glass	p. 734		
paper clips			pp. 234, 266, 948
paper hole punch		p. 398	
pennies	p. 386		p. 742
petri dish	pp. 686, 714, 776	p. 702	pp. 96, 316, 408, 518, 560, 742
petri dish, bottoms			p. 694
pipette, plastic		p. 236	
protractor	pp. 436, 834		
razor blade, single-edge	pp. 330, 626, 658, 714	p. 155	
refrigerator			p. 160
ring stand			p. 724
rubber tubing, 10 cm	p. 544		
ruler, metric	pp. 24, 436, 460, 496, 522, 626, 734, 834, 988	p. 907	pp. 432, 724, 818, 948
ruler, millimeter		p. 398	
sample keys for guidebooks	pp. 460, 810		
scissors	pp. 302, 354, 522, 1016	p. 874	pp. 266, 282
seedling flat	p. 274		
stereomicroscope	p. 734		p. 694
stirring rod			pp. 196, 382
stoppers, one-hole, with glass tube	p. 544		
table-tennis ball	p. 834		
tabletop, smooth			p. 742
tape measure			p. 432
tennis ball		p. 425	
terrarium			pp. 864, 842
test tube	p 936	pp. 54, 236, 634	pp. 382, 408, 920
test tube, large	p. 544		
test-tube racks	pp. 544, 936		
test tube, screw-top			p. 488
test tube, small	p. 544		
thermometer, Celsius, non-mercury	pp. 274, 544, 734		p. 818

Item	BioLab	MiniLab	Additional Lab
timer			p. 842
tobacco seeds	p. 274		
tongs	p. 164		
trays	p. 330	p. 122	
trowel, garden			p. 608
tweezers	p. 658		
washers	p. 238		
washers, metal		p. 236	
watch glass	p. 936	p. 702	
watering bottle, plant	p. 274		
wax marking pencil			pp. 408, 694
weights, small	p. 910		

Consumables

Item	BioLab	MiniLab	Additional Lab
Accent seasoning			p. 488
aluminum foil	p. 544		pp. 196, 530
ammonia solution, household		p. 151	
antacid tablet		p. 54	
antibiotic disks	p. 496		p. 1032
apple, fresh		p. 1028	
apple juice		p. 236	
apple, rotten		p. 1028	
apple slices			p. 864
balloon, round	p. 988		
banana		p. 92	
beans	p. 104		
bean seeds, germinated		p. 657	
bean seeds, ungerminated		p. 657	
beans, kidney canned			p. 654
beans, kidney dried			p. 654
beans, lima		p. 589	
beans, pinto	p. 414		p. 38
beans, white navy	p. 414		
bottles, plastic milk, large		p. 830	
box, 100 cm x 50 cm			p. 282
Brassica rapa seeds, normal & variegated	p. 330		
bread, bakery, fresh		p. 530	
carrot root		p. 634	
celery stalk		p. 608	
cellophane, assorted colors	p. 238		
cereal, dry	p. 936		
clay	p. 834	p. 268	pp. 76, 818
cloth		p. 92	
cloth squares, 30 cm x 30 cm			p. 76
coffee, caffeinated	p. 964		p. 12
coffee, decaffeinated			p. 12
cola	p. 964		
conifer branches	pp. 570–571		
conifer cones	pp. 570–571		
conifer twigs	pp. 570–571		
corn seeds, germinated		p. 657	p. 38
corn seeds, ungerminated		p. 657	
corn syrup, white mixture	p. 544		
cotton ball		p. 1028	
cotton swabs	pp. 496, 734		p. 1032
cough medicine	p. 964		
data sheet			p. 998
detergent, liquid		p. 151	
dinosaur eggs, artificial, from oatmeal		p. 22	
dye, purple		p. 155	

Lab Preparation

Item	BioLab	MiniLab	Additional Lab
egg, hard-boiled	p. 834		
feather, contour		p. 827	
feather, down		p. 827	
filter paper, 5 cm x 14 cm		p. 226	
filter paper disk, sterile	p. 496		
garlic bulb			
gelatin			p. 160
gloves, protective		pp. 561, 566	
glucose test paper		p. 987	p. 920
glue		p. 446	p. 266
grapes			p. 160
graph paper	pp. 386, 910		
gravel, aquarium, black and white			p. 798
hair, human			p. 350
ice	pp. 164, 734		
ice, crushed			p. 724
ice, cubes	p. 544		
index cards	p. 522	p. 895	
ink pad		p. 895	
juice containers			p. 818
juice, lemon		p. 151	
juice, red			p. 350
label	pp. 84, 330, 714, 756		pp. 12, 38, 118, 196, 234, 560, 654
macaroni			p. 530
marking pen	p. 496		p. 1032
marking pencil	pp. 714, 756		
matchbox			p. 864
mildew samples		p. 6	
milk			p. 920
mold spores			p. 530
mushrooms		p. 538	
mustard seeds			p. 560
nail polish (4 colors)			p. 864
napkins			p. 96
oatmeal			p. 864
oatmeal flakes			p. 530
onion		p. 182	
orange			p. 160
owl pellet		p. 845	
paper bag	pp. 104, 414	p. 538	
paper, black, sheet of	p. 734	pp. 398, 560	pp. 234, 818
paper, construction, black		p. 860	pp. 724, 798
paper, construction, 5 colors	p. 302		
paper cups			pp. 38, 160, 530, 654
paper, graph	p. 414		p. 998
paper, heavy	p. 1016		
paper puzzle		p. 870	
paper towels	p. 734	pp. 36, 845	pp. 38, 118, 316
paper toweling, moist		p. 860	
paper, tracing	p. 1016		
paper, white, sheet of	p. 354	pp. 398, 446, 530, 620, 730	p. 818
peanut shells		p. 407	
peas		p. 589	
pencil, dull	p. 24		
pencil, glass-marking	p. 544		
pencil, grease		p. 987	
pencil, wax marking	p. 686		p. 724
pH paper		p. 151	p. 382
pineapple, canned chunk			p. 160

Item	BioLab	MiniLab	Additional Lab
pineapple, fresh			p. 160
plastic bottles	p. 756		
plastic sandwich bags		pp. 36, 198, 530, 1028	pp. 38, 118
plastic teaspoon	p. 84		
plastic trays	p. 756		
plastic wrap	p. 84		pp. 196, 530
pond water, containing plant material	p. 84		
pond water, sterile	p. 58	p. 511	
potato	p. 164	p. 155	p. 196
potato with eye (root and stem)		p. 634	
radish seeds			p. 96
rice		p. 589	
rice, cooked, white	p. 84		
rubber band	p. 874	p. 92	
rye seeds		p. 589	
salt	p. 756		p. 196
sand			pp. 76, 842, 864
sandpaper	p. 734		p. 724
sawdust			p. 842
seeds		p. 36	p. 118
seeds, crushed wheat		p. 506	
seeds (sunflower, hulled oats, cracked corn, wheat, thistle, millet)		p. 830	
shampoo		p. 151	
shoe box with lid	p. 386		
soil, potting	p. 274, 330	p. 122	p. 76
soil samples (4 different)			p. 488
spring water, sterilized	p. 84, 874		
sponge pieces			p. 864
starch		p. 198	
sterile untreated disks			p. 1032
straw	p. 544	p. 54	p. 982
string	pp. 238, 834, 988		p. 266
T-shirt with spot of red ink			p. 350
tobacco	p. 964		
tobacco seeds, heterozygous			
tape, clear	pp. 302, 354, 874	pp. 425, 860	pp. 266, 742, 818, 1032
tape, masking			p. 798
tea	p. 964		
thread, heavy			p. 742
toothbrush bristles		p. 675	
toothpicks	pp. 522, 776	p. 634	p. 266
toweling, cloth			p. 742
tray, deli, clear plastic			p. 724
twist tie		p. 198	p. 76
water, pond		p. 511	
wax paper	p. 164		pp. 160, 654
wire		p. 830	
yarn			p. 266
yarn, skein of			p. 282
yeast	p. 544	p. 236	

Living Organisms

Item	BioLab	MiniLab	Additional Lab
Armadillidium (pill bug) or isopods	p. 24	p. 860	
bess beetles			p. 742
brine shrimp		p. 702	
brine shrimp eggs	p. 756		
Coleus plants			p. 234
crickets, male and female			p. 864
Daphnia culture	p. 964		

Lab Preparation

Item	BioLab	MiniLab	Additional Lab
Didinium culture	p. 58		
E.coli culture			p. 1032
earthworms	p. 730		
Equisetum (horsetail)		p. 566	
Elodea leaf	p. 182		
Elodea plant	p. 238		p. 182
Euglena culture	p. 522		
flower		p. 254	
flower, complete dicot	p. 658		
hydra culture		p. 702	
land snail			p. 724
lichen samples		p. 67	
Lycopodium (club moss)		p. 566	
Marchantia		p. 561	
marine plankton		p. 73	
mouse			p. 842
Paramecium culture	pp. 58, 522	p. 506	
Physarum polycephalum			p. 518
planarian culture	p. 714		
plant leaves		pp. 446, 620	
onion plant	p. 626		
rotifer culture		p. 675	
snails	p. 874		
sori from a frond		p. 586	
tropical fishes (gourami, catfish, zebra)			p. 798
vinegar eel culture		p. 683	
zebra fish	p. 686		

Chemicals

Item	BioLab	MiniLab	Additional Lab
2,3,5- triphenyl tetrazolium chloride solution			p. 654
agar dish, sterile nutrient	p. 496		
agar, nutrient, tube			pp. 408, 1032
agar, streptomycin, tube			p. 408
alcohol		pp. 14, 1027	
alcohol, 95%			p. 234
alcohol, ethyl	p. 964		
alcohol, rubbing		p. 226	
alcohol-testing chemical		p. 14	
amylase solution	p. 936		
baking soda			p. 488
baking soda solution, 0.25%	p. 238		
bromothymol blue (BTB) solution	p. 544	p. 54	
distilled water	p. 714		pp. 488, 982
ethanol			p. 1032
freshwater solution		p. 36	
gelatin solution, 1%			p. 382
glucose solution			p. 920
glycerin		p. 586	
gum arabic solution, 1%			p. 382
hydrochloric acid			p. 382
hydrogen peroxide, 3%	p. 164		
iodine solution	p. 936	p. 198	p. 234
iodine stain		pp. 182, 589	
liquid lactose digestive aid			p. 920
liquid plant fertilizer solution			p. 488
methylcellulose solution	p. 522		
NaOH solution, 0.04%			p. 982
phenolphthalein indicator			p. 982
plant solution		p. 226	
saltwater solution, 10%		p. 36	

Item	BioLab	MiniLab	Additional Lab
simulated "abnormal urine"		p. 987	
simulated "normal urine"		p. 987	
vinegar		p. 151	pp. 118, 488
Preserved Specimens			
Bacillus subtilis slides	p. 188		p. 408
bacteria slides	p. 496	p. 490	
blood cells, red and white slides		p. 1035	
conifer leaf cross-section slide			p. 592
diatomaceous earth		p. 371	
earthworm cross-section slides			p. 682
fish gill slides		p. 795	
fish mitosis slide		p. 209	
frog, adult		p. 806	
frog blood slides	p. 188		
grasshopper, life stage specimens		p. 754	
human cheek cells slides			p. 188
human cheek cells slides, male and female			pp. 324, 350
human egg slide		p. 1006	
human sperm slide		p. 1006	
human tooth cross-section slides		p. 843	
Hydra cross section slides			p. 682
lancelet slides		p. 773	p. 772
lobster		p. 743	
Marchantia		p. 561	
nematode cross-section slides			p. 682
onion root tip slide	p. 214		
planarian cross-section slides			p. 682
preserved leaves		p. 620	
sand dollar specimen	p. 776		
sea cucumber specimen	p. 776		
sea sponges, 4 types			p. 694
sea star specimen	p. 776		
sea star blastula slide		p. 1006	
sea star pedicellariae slides		p. 764	
sea urchin specimen	p. 776		
sea urchin development slides			p. 772
tadpole		p. 806	
thyroid and parathyroid endocrine gland tissue slides			p. 934
Trichinella larvae slide		p. 712	

Lab Preparation

Suppliers

Equipment Suppliers

American Science & Surplus
P.O. Box 1030
Skokie, IL 60076
1-847-647-0011
www.sciplus.com

Bio-Rad Laboratories
2000 Alfred Nobel Dr.
Life Science Group
Hercules, CA 94547
(800) 876-3425
www.biorad.com

Boreal Laboratories, Ltd.
399 Vansickle Rd.
St. Catharines, Ontario,
  L2S 3T4
Canada
(800) 387-9393
www.boreal.com

Carolina Biological Supply Co.
2700 York Road
Burlington, NC 27215
(800) 334-5551
carolina.com

Edmund Scientifics
60 Pearce Ave.
Tonawanda, NY 14150-6711
(800) 728-6999
www.scientificsonline.com

Fisher Science Education
4500 Turnberry
Hanover Park, IL 60133
(800) 955-1177
fisheredu.com

Frey Scientific, School Specialties
100 Paragon Parkway
Mansfield, OH 44903
(800) 225-3739

Nasco Science
901 Janesville Avenue
P.O. Box 901
Fort Atkinson, WI 53538-0901
(800) 558-9595
www.nascofa.com

Nebraska Scientific
3823 Leavenworth St.
Omaha, NE 68105-1180
(800) 228-7117
nebraskascientific.com

PASCO Scientific
10101 Foothills Blvd.
Roseville, CA 95747-7100
(800) 772-8700
pasco.com

Sargent-Welch/VWR Scientific Products
P.O. Box 5229
Buffalo Grove, IL 60089-5229
(800) SAR-GENT
www.sargentwelch.com

Science Kit and Boreal Laboratories
777 East Park Dr.
P.O. Box 5003
Tonawanda, NY 14150
(800) 828-7777
www.sciencekit.com

Ward's Natural Science Est.
5100 W. Henrietta Road
P.O. Box 92912
Rochester, NY 14692-9012
(800) 962-2660
www.wardsci.com

Audiovisual Distributors

Bullfrog Films
P.O. Box 149
Oley, PA 19547
(800) 543-FROG
www.bullfrogfilms.com

Coronet/MTI Film & Video
2349 Chaffee Dr.
St. Louis, MO 63146
(800) 221-1274
phoenixlearninggroup.com

Discovery Channel School
P.O. Box 6027
Florence, KY 41022-6448
school.discovery.com

Films for the Humanities and Sciences
P.O. Box 2053
Princeton, NJ 08543
(800) 257-5126
films.com

Flinn Scientific
P.O. Box 219
770 N. Raddant Rd.
Batavia, IL 60510
(800) 452-1261
www.flinnsci.com

National Geographic Society Educational Services
1145 17th Street, N.W.
Washington, DC 20036
(800) 368-2728

Optical Data School Media
512 Means St., N.W.
Atlanta, GA 30318
(800) 524-2481
www.opticaldata.com

Scholastic, Inc.
555 Broadway
New York, NY 10012-3999
(800) 325-6149
www.scholastic.com

Videodiscovery
1700 Westlake Ave., N.
Suite 600
Seattle, WA 98109-3012
(800) 548-3472
www.videodiscovery.com

Software Distributors

Cross Education Software
508 E. Kentucky Ave.
Ruston, LA 71270
(800) 768-1969

Educational Activities, Inc.
P.O. Box 87
Baldwin, NY 11510
(800) 645-3739
www.edact.com

IBM Global Education
4111 Northside Parkway
Atlanta, GA 30327-2150
(800) 426-8322
www.solutions.ibm.com/k12

J. Weston Walch, Publisher
321 Valley St.
P.O. Box 658
Portland, ME 04104-0658
(800) 341-6094
www.walch.com

Scholastic, Inc.
555 Broadway
New York, NY 10012-3999
(800) 325-6149
www.scholastic.com

Sunburst Communications
1900 S. Batavia Ave.
Geneva, IL 60134
(800) 321-7511
www.SUNBURST.com

Contents

A coral reef, p. 116

Contents

▲ An arctic fox, p. 321

Contents

Geographic isolation, p. 409

Contents

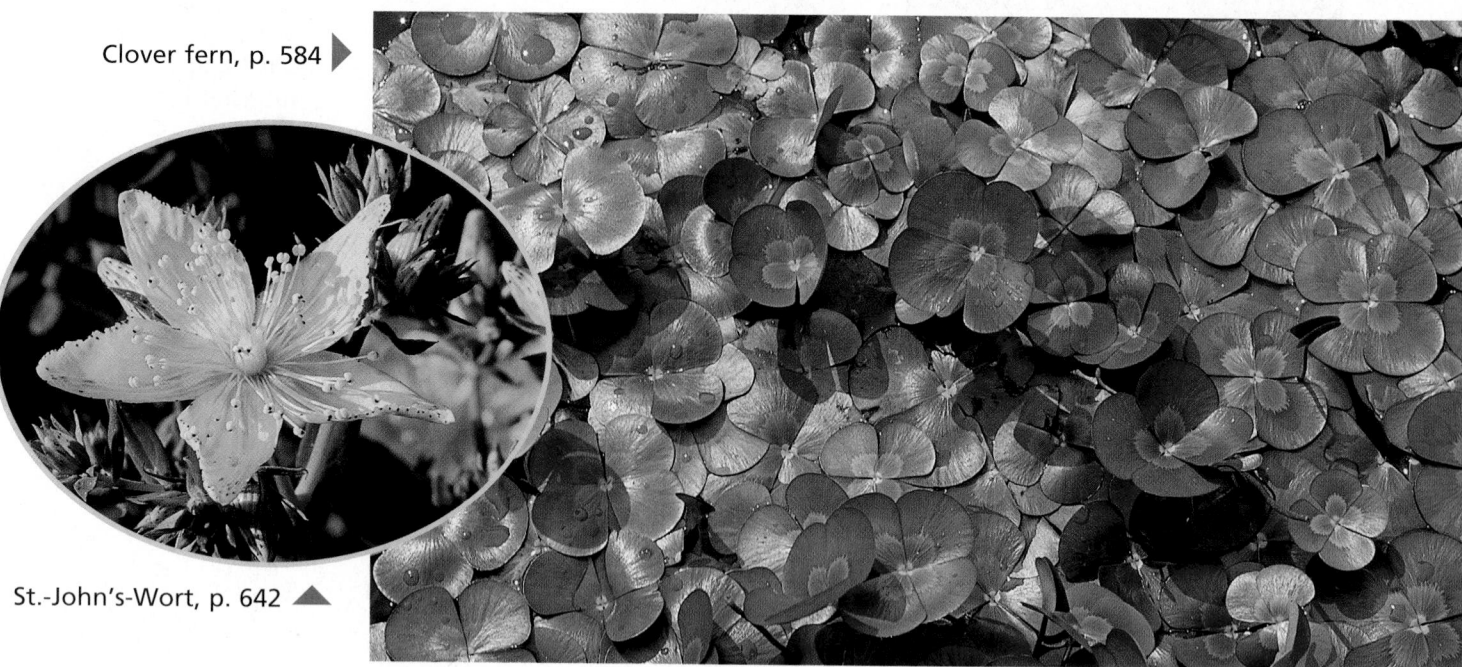

Clover fern, p. 584 ▶

St.-John's-Wort, p. 642 ▲

x

Contents

A jellyfish, p. 782 ▶

Contents

▲ A pickerel frog, p. 803

Contents

▲ Mushrooms of the genus *Psilocybe*, p. 962

Color-enhanced TEM Magnification: 57 000×

▲ The virus that causes smallpox, p. 1044

BioLab

Working in the lab is an enjoyable part of biology. BIOLABS give you an opportunity to do the work of a biologist and develop your own plans for studying a question or problem. Whether you're designing experiments or following well-tested procedures, you'll have fun doing these lab activities.

Two rabbit phenotypes, p. 415 ▶

◀ Testing enzyme reaction, p. 164

BioLab

Cones, p. 571 ▼

▲ Female spruce cone, p. 571

xv

MiniLab

Do you often ask how, what, or why about the living world around you? Sometimes it takes just a little time to find out the answers for yourself. These short activities can be tried on your own at home or with help from a teacher at school. When you're feeling inquisitive, try a MiniLab.

◀ Freshwater pond, p. 36

Anthophyte leaves, p. 446 ▶

Change Through Time

Viruses, Bacteria, Protists, and Fungi

Plants

Invertebrates

◀ Polio virus, p. 476

Color-enhanced TEM
Magnification: 180 000×

MiniLab

▲ Parathyroid and thyroid tissue, p. 934

Color-enhanced LM
Magnification: 16×

Vertebrates

The Human Body

▲ Tadpoles, p. 803

Problem-Solving Lab

Sharpen up your pencil and your wit because you'll need them to solve these PROBLEM-SOLVING LABS. These labs offer a unique opportunity to evaluate another scientist's experiments and data without lab bench cleanup.

Problem-Solving Lab

▲ Guinea pig, p. 339

Problem-Solving Lab

Orange sea cucumber, p. 768

INSIDE STORY

As you study biology, you will discover that some concepts are better explained by detailed illustrations. The INSIDE STORY features display elaborate diagrams with step-by-step explanations of complex structures or processes in biology. They are designed to help you remember some important details of biology.

▼ Snail, p. 723

Gibbon, p. 422 ▶

It may not have occurred to you that biology is connected to all your courses. In the connections, learn how biology is connected to art, literature, and other subjects. Learn more at bdol.glencoe.com.

Physical Science Connections

NATIONAL GEOGRAPHIC

FOCUS ON

Some topics of biology deserve more attention than others because they're unusual, informative, or just plain interesting. Here are several features that FOCUS ON these fascinating topics. Learn more at bdol.glencoe.com/news.

CAREERS IN BIOLOGY AND BIOTECHNOLOGY

What can you do with a knowledge of biology? Why is biology so important to you? Knowing about biology can start you on a journey into any one of these exciting careers. Learn more at bdol.glencoe.com/careers.

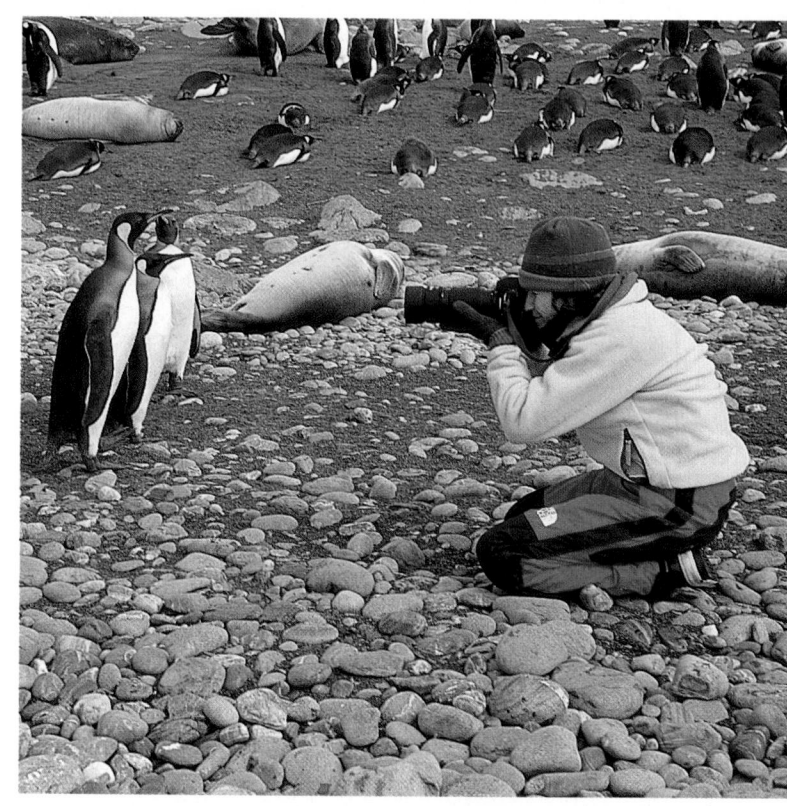

▲ Wildlife photographer, p. 822

How does biology impact our society? How does biology affect what you eat, the world around you, and your future? Take this opportunity to understand the many different sides of issues, and learn how biotechnology may affect your life. Learn more at bdol.glencoe.com/biology_society and bdol.glencoe.com/biotechnology.

▼ Healthy coral reef, p. 716

What is biology?

Unit Overview

Unit 1 includes one chapter that introduces students to the nature, excitement, and methods of biology.

Chapter 1 Students are first introduced to the characteristics of living organisms. The nature of science and methods used in science are then discussed with examples intended to spark student interest as they attempt to answer questions and solve problems concerning the world of life.

Introducing the Unit

Ask students to look at the photo and describe some of the adaptations of poppies that make them successful. Tell students that they will learn in this unit how to identify the characteristics of all living organisms, including poppies. Explain to students that during their studies in this course, they will use the methods of science described later in the chapter.

Web**Quest**

A WebQuest is an inquiry-based online project in which all information used by students is obtained from the Web. Students evaluate the information to complete the activity. Access the Unit 1 WebQuest at **in.bdol.glencoe.com/webquest**

---

600 B.C.   100 B.C.

> 105
> Tsai Lun invent
> paper as we
> know it today.

520 B.C.
Greek philosophers propose that the universe is composed of four elements: earth, air, fire, and water.

400 B.C.
Hippocrates founds the profession of physicians.

350 B.C.
The first classification of 500 species of animals is created.

What is biology?

▲ Hippocrates

What You'll Learn

Chapter 1
Biology: The Study of Life

Unit 1 Review
BioDigest & Standardized Test Practice

Why It's Important

Biologists seek answers to questions about living things. For example, a biologist might ask how plants, such as California poppies, convert sunlight into chemical energy that can be used by the plants to maintain life processes. Biologists use many methods to answer their questions about life. During this course, you will gain an understanding of the questions and answers of biology, and how the answers are learned.

Indiana Standards
The following standards are covered in Unit 1:
B.1.11, B.1.16, B.1.17, B.1.18, B.1.31, B.1.38, B.1.41, B.1.43

Understanding the Photo ▶

This field of flowers represents not only a collection of living things, but also a community. These plants interact with each other, and form a biological community that provides food, nesting materials, and oxygen for other living things.

 in.bdol.glencoe.com/webquest

Time Line

Activity Have students select a scientist from the time line and prepare a short biography on that person and his or her accomplishments. Each student should give a presentation on the person he or she selected. Have the class combine their presentation materials to create one large poster showing each scientist's contributions to the field of biology. Display the poster in your classroom. **L2**
COOP LEARN

1452
Gutenberg invents moveable type, allowing mass production of printed materials.

1863
Lincoln delivers the Gettysburg Address.

1600   1700   1800   1900

1627
Francis Bacon publishes work urging that the experimental method should play a key role in the development of scientific theories.

1687
Isaac Newton publishes *Principia,* which details the first scientific methods.

1895
X rays are discovered and the first X ray of the human body is taken.

◀ The first X ray

2000
The first draft of the Human Genome Project, sequencing all human genes, is completed.

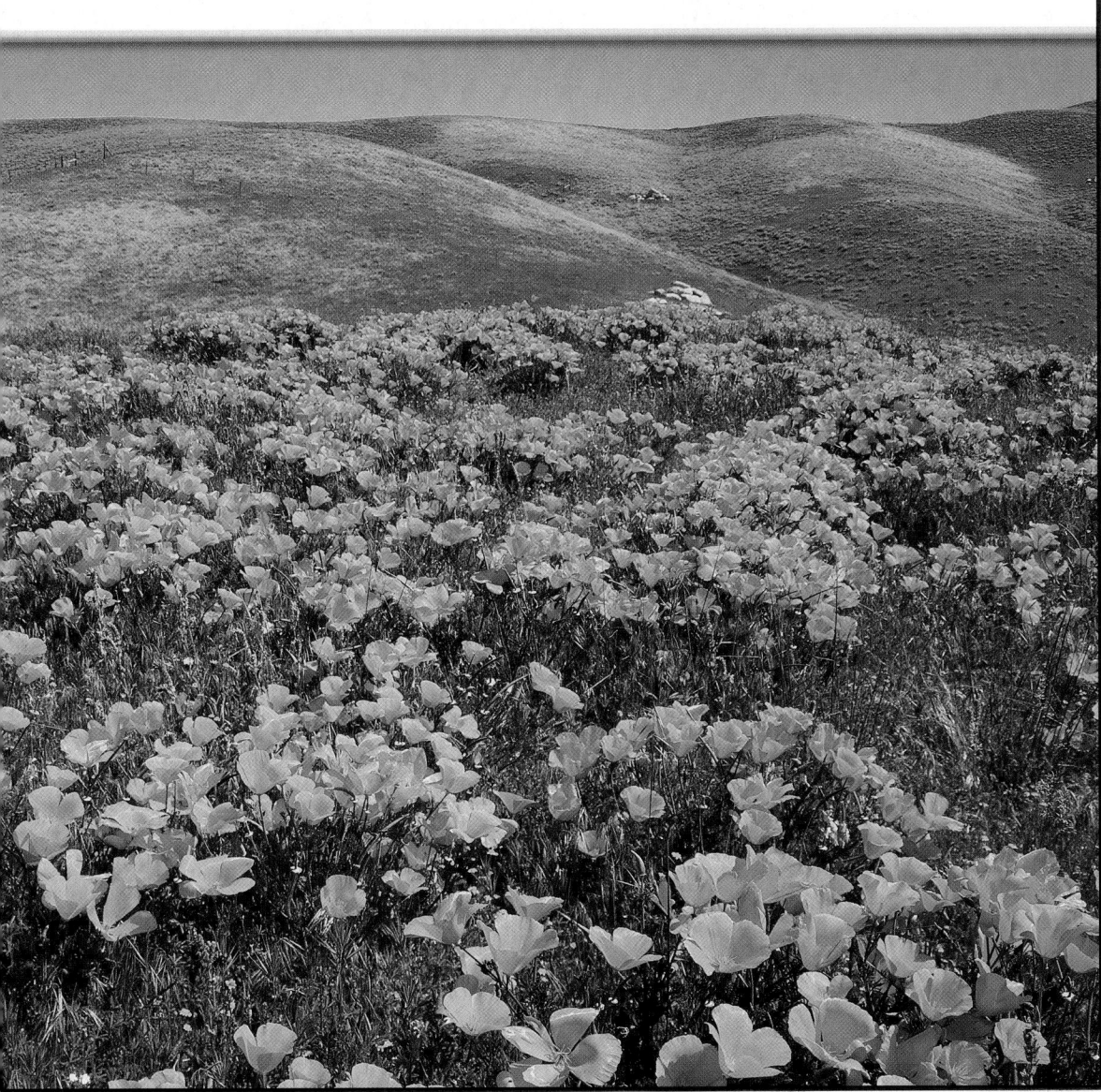

Advance Materials Planning

The following materials may need to be ordered a few weeks in advance of the planned activity.

Chapter 1

- ■ **MiniLab** (p. 6) mildew samples
- ■ **Quick Demo** (p. 7) *Lithops* plants
- ■ **Activity** (p. 7) squash seeds, bubbles, bubble wand, fresh fruit, cut flower
- ■ **Additional Lab** (p. 12) brewed coffee: caffeinated and decaffeinated
- ■ **MiniLab** (p. 14) isopropyl (rubbing) alchohol, over-the-counter products: aftershave lotion, cough syrups, mouthwash
- ■ **Quick Demo** (p. 21) pine needles
- ■ **MiniLab** (p. 22) oatmeal packets with candy dinosaur eggs
- ■ **BioLab** (pp. 24–25) pill bugs

Unit Projects

Tape Production
Visual-Spatial Have students use a video camera to make a tape cataloging and describing the living things in your area. Students may tape the same area through the seasons to show changes. **L1** **ELL**

Make a Model
Kinesthetic Students can make a three-dimensional model that depicts the kinds of living things found in your area. Alternatively, students can model another area, such as a rain forest. **L2** **ELL**

Field Investigation
Visual-Spatial Have student groups study a local pond or stream to find out what living organisms are present. Students may wish to make drawings or take photos to illustrate their findings. **L1** **ELL**
COOP LEARN

Chapter 1 Organizer

Section Objectives	National Science Standards	State/Local Standards	Advanced Lab and Demo Planning
Section 1.1 1/2 session 1. **Recognize** some possible benefits from studying biology. 2. **Summarize** the characteristics of living things.	UCP.2; A.1, A.2; C.1, C.3, C.4, C.5, C.6; E.1, E.2; F.3, F.4, F.6; G.1, G.2, G.3	**Indiana Standards** B.1.11, B.1.16, B.1.17, B.1.18, B.1.31, B.1.41, B.1.43	**Student Lab:** **MiniLab 1.1**, p. 6: mildew samples, microscope, microscope slides, coverslips **Internet BioLab**, p. 24: See materials below. **Teacher Demonstration:** **Quick Demo**, p. 7: *Lithops* plant
Section 1.2 1 session, 1/2 block 3. **Compare** different scientific methods. 4. **Differentiate** among hypothesis, theory, and principle.	UCP.2; A.1, A.2; B.2; C.6; E.2; G.1, G.2	**Indiana Standards** B.1.38, B.1.41	**Student Labs:** **MiniLab 1.2**, p. 14: glass slide, safety goggles, water, alcohol, alcohol-testing chemical **Problem-Solving Lab 1.1**, p. 16 **Additional Lab**, p. 12: 2 small jars, graduated cylinder, labels, caffeinated coffee, decaffeinated coffee **Teacher Demonstrations:** **Quick Demo**, p. 12: sugar cube, matches **Quick Demo**, p. 15: scientific journals
Section 1.3 1 session, 1 block 5. **Compare and contrast** quantitative and qualitative information. 6. **Explain** why science and technology cannot solve all problems.	UCP.2; A.1, A.2; C.6; E.1, E.2; F.3, F.4, F.6; G.1, G2	**Indiana Standards** B.1.41	**Student Labs:** **Problem Solving Lab 1.2**, p. 20 **MiniLab 1.3**, p. 22: oatmeal with candy dinosaur eggs, 2 containers, water **Teacher Demonstration:** **Quick Demo**, p. 21: metric ruler, pine needles
End of Chapter Assessment Student Edition **Study Guide**, p. 27 **Content Assessment**, pp. 28–29		**Indiana Standards** B.1.16, B.1.18, B.1.31, B.1.43	**Student Lab:** **Internet BioLab**, p. 24: *Armadillidium* (pill bug), clock or watch, container, ruler, Internet connection, dull pencil, plastic soup bowls

Key to Teaching Strategies

L1 Level 1 activities should be appropriate for students with learning difficulties.

L2 Level 2 activities should be within the ability range of all students.

L3 Level 3 activities are designed for above-average students.

ELL ELL activities should be within the ability range of English Language Learners.

COOP LEARN Cooperative Learning activities are designed for small group work.

Legend

 Transparency   CD-ROM   MP3   Videocassette   DVD

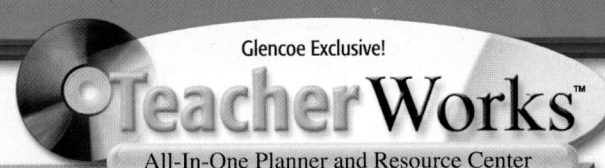
Glencoe Exclusive!
TeacherWorks™
All-In-One Planner and Resource Center

Reproducible Masters and Transparencies	Technology

Reproducible Masters and Transparencies

Unit 1 *FAST FILE* Resources
MiniLab Worksheet, p. 3
BioLab Worksheet, pp. 9–10
Reinforcement and Study Guide in English,
  pp. 13–14
Reinforcement and Study Guide in Spanish,
  pp. 17–18
Concept Mapping, p. 21
Critical Thinking/Problem Solving, p. 22
Transparency Worksheet, p. 23
Reading Essentials for Biology,
  Section 1.1
Section Focus Transparency 1

Unit 1 *FAST FILE* Resources
MiniLab Worksheet, p. 5
Real World BioApplications, pp. 11–12
Reinforcement and Study Guide in English, p.15
Reinforcement and Study Guide in Spanish, p. 19
Transparency Worksheet, p. 24
Reading Essentials for Biology,
  Section 1.2
Laboratory Manual, pp. 1–4
Section Focus Transparency 2

Unit 1 *FAST FILE* Resources
MiniLab Worksheet, p. 7
Reinforcement and Study Guide in English, p. 16
Reinforcement and Study Guide in Spanish, p. 20
Transparency Worksheet, p. 23
Reading Essentials for Biology,
  Section 1.3
Laboratory Manual, pp. 5–8
Section Focus Transparency 3

Unit 1 *FAST FILE* Resources
Chapter Assessment, pp. 27–32
Student Recording Sheet, p. 33

The Princeton Review **Reviewing Biology,** pp. 1–2

Technology

Interactive Chalkboard CD-ROM: Section 1.1 Presentation
TeacherWorks™ CD-ROM
Guided Reading Audio Summaries MP3

Interactive Chalkboard CD-ROM: Section 1.2 Presentation
TeacherWorks™ CD-ROM
Guided Reading Audio Summaries MP3
Virtual Lab CD-ROM
  Virtual Lab: *Dependent and Independent Variables*

Interactive Chalkboard CD-ROM: Section 1.3 Presentation
TeacherWorks™ CD-ROM
Guided Reading Audio Summaries MP3
Virtual Lab CD-ROM
  Virtual Lab: *Dependent and Independent Variables*

Interactive Chalkboard:
  Chapter 1 Assessment
MindJogger Videoquizzes
  DVD/VHS
Exam*View*® Pro Test Bank
  CD-ROM
TeacherWorks™ CD-ROM
Succeeding on National Standards CD-ROM

in.bdol.glencoe.com
/self_check_quiz
/vocabulary_puzzlemaker
/chapter_test
/standardized_test

Indicates materials created specifically for Indiana.

Short on Time?

BIODIGEST The BioDigest at the end of this unit can be used as a(n):

- preview to introduce important unit concepts.
- overview if time does not permit teaching the entire chapter.
- review of key unit concepts.

Understanding the Photo

Use the image to introduce the characteristics of life that all living things share. Be sure that the students understand that living things, such as moose and plants, have all of these characteristics, not just one or two of them. Additional information about these characteristics is discussed in detail on pages 6–10.

INTERACTIVE CHALKBOARD
with Image Bank

PowerPoint® Presentations

This CD-ROM is an editable Microsoft® PowerPoint® presentation that includes:

- Section presentations
- Section checks
- Image bank
- Hot links to Biology Online
- All transparencies

Biology: The Study of Life

What You'll Learn

- You will identify the characteristics of life.
- You will recognize how scientific methods are used to study living things.

Why It's Important

Recognizing life's characteristics and the methods used to study life provides a basis for understanding the living world.

Understanding ▶ the Photo

Even though the moose and plants pictured here appear to be completely different from each other, they share certain characteristics that make them both living things. Animals and plants, as well as other organisms such as mushrooms and bacteria, all exhibit the basic characteristics of life.

Biology Online

Visit **in.bdol.glencoe.com** to
- study the entire chapter online
- access Web Links for more information and activities on biology
- review content with the Interactive Tutor and self-check quizzes

2

Two-Minute Chapter Launcher

Demo To elicit students' preconceptions about the nature of biology, arrange the following materials on a desk: a grasshopper or other living insect in a cage, a potted plant, a rock, a photo of a population of organisms. Ask students: What do you think you will learn about during your study of biology? Guide students toward an understanding that, in addition to plants and animals, their study of biology will include a broad understanding of all living things.

Section 1.1

What is biology?

Indiana Standards Standard B.1.43 Understand that and describe how organisms are influenced by a particular combination of living and nonliving components of the environment.

Bellringer
Section Focus Transparency 1

SECTION PREVIEW

Objectives

Recognize some possible benefits from studying biology.

Summarize the characteristics of living things.

New Vocabulary
biology
organism
organization
reproduction
species
growth
development
environment
stimulus
response
homeostasis
energy
adaptation
evolution

Characteristics of Living Things Make the following Foldable to help you organize information about the characteristics of living things.

STEP 1 **Fold** a vertical sheet of paper in half from top to bottom, twice.

STEP 2 **Fold** the paper widthwise into six sections.

STEP 3 **Unfold,** lay the paper lengthwise, and draw lines along the folds.

STEP 4 **Label** your table as shown.

Characteristics	Organism 1	Organism 2	Organism 3

Make a Table As you read Chapter 1, list the characteristics of living things in the far left column. Choose three organisms that seem different from each other and make notes in each column describing how each organism fulfills the requirements of a living thing.

Transparency **1** Characteristics of Life

SECTION FOCUS
Use with Chapter 1,
Section 1.1

❶ What are some characteristics of living organisms?
❷ Which of these characteristics does each object have?

BIOLOGY: The Dynamics of Life   SECTION FOCUS TRANSPARENCIES

The Science of Biology

People have always been curious about living things—how many different kinds there are, where they live, what they are like, how they relate to each other, and how they behave. The concepts, principles, and theories that allow people to understand the natural environment form the core of **biology,** the study of life. What will you, as a young biologist, learn about in your study of biology?

A key aspect of biology is simply learning about the different types of living things around you. With all the facts in biology textbooks, you might think that biologists have answered almost all the questions about life. Of course, this is not true. There are undoubtedly many life forms yet to be discovered; many life forms haven't even been named yet, let alone studied. Life on Earth includes not only the common organisms you notice every day, but also distinctive life forms that have unusual behaviors.

Word Origin

biology from the Greek words *bios,* meaning "life," and *logos,* meaning "study"; Biology is the study of life.

Word Origin

Have the students find and define other words using "bio" as part of the root, such as *biohazard* and *biotechnology.*

FOLDABLES™

For an additional Foldables activity idea, see the Chapter 1 Foldables page in *Unit 1 FAST FILE Resources.*

RESOURCE MANAGER

Unit 1 *FAST FILE* Resources
MiniLab Worksheet, p. 3
BioLab Worksheet, pp. 9–10
Reinforcement and Study Guide in English, pp. 13–14
Reinforcement and Study Guide in Spanish, pp. 17–18

Concept Mapping, p. 21
Critical Thinking/Problem Solving, p. 22
Transparency Worksheet, p. 23
Reading Essentials for Biology, Section 1.1
Section Focus Transparency 1

2 Teach

When studying the different types of living things, you'll ask what, why, and how questions about life. You might ask, "Why does this living thing possess these particular features? How do these features work?" The answers to such questions lead to the development of general biological principles and rules. As strange as some forms of life may appear to be, there is order in the natural world.

Biologists study the interactions of life

One of the most general principles in biology is that living things do not exist in isolation; they are all functioning parts in the delicate balance of nature. As you can see in ***Figure 1.1,*** living things interact with their environment and depend upon other living and nonliving things to aid their survival.

Figure 1.1
Questions about living things can sometimes be answered only by finding out about their interactions with their surroundings.

A Leaf-cutter ants feed on fungus. They carry bits of leaves to their nest, then chew the bits and form them into moist balls on which the fungus grows.

B Leaves of the insect-eating pitcher plant form a lip lined with downward-pointing hairs that prevent insects from escaping. Trapped insects fall into a pool of water and digestive juices at the bottom of the tube.

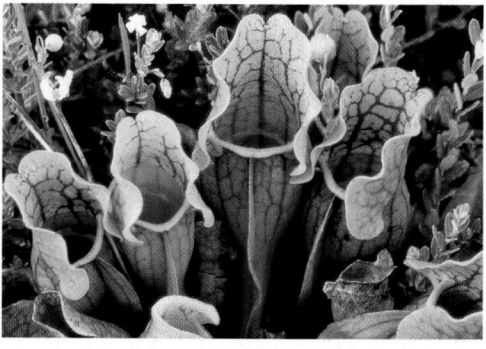

C The seahorse is well hidden in its environment. Its body shape blends in with the shapes of the seaweeds in which it lives.

D The spadefoot toad burrows underground during extended periods of dry weather and encases itself in a waterproof envelope to prevent water loss.

4 BIOLOGY: THE STUDY OF LIFE

 Indiana Academic Standards

Pages 4–5: B.1.41, B.1.43

4

Biologists Study the Diversity of Life

Many people study biology simply for the pleasure of learning about the world of living things. As you've seen, the natural world is filled with examples of living things that can be amusing or amazing, and that challenge your thinking. Through your study of biology, you will come to appreciate the great diversity of life on Earth and the way all living organisms fit into the dynamic pattern of life on our planet.

Biologists study the interactions of the environment

Because no living things, including humans, exist in isolation, the study of biology must include the investigation of living interactions. For example, learning about a population of wild rabbits would require finding out what plants they eat and what animals prey on them. The study of one living thing always involves the study of the others with which it interacts.

Human existence, too, is closely intertwined with the existence of other organisms living on Earth. Plants and animals supply us with food and with raw materials like wood, cotton, and oil. Plants also replenish the essential oxygen in the air. The students in *Figure 1.2* are studying organisms that live in a local stream. Activities like this help provide a thorough understanding of living things and the intricate web of nature. It is only through such knowledge that humans can expect to understand how to preserve the health of our planet.

✓ **Reading Check** **Explain** why scientists study an organism's environment.

Figure 1.2
By understanding the interactions of living things, you will be better able to impact the planet positively.

Biologists study problems and propose solutions

The future of biology holds many exciting promises. Biological research can lead to advances in medical treatment and disease prevention in humans and in other organisms. It can reveal ways to help preserve organisms that are in danger of disappearing, and solve other problems, like the one described in *Figure 1.3*. The study of biology will teach you how humans function and how we fit in with the rest of the natural world. It will also equip you with the knowledge you need to help sustain this planet's web of life.

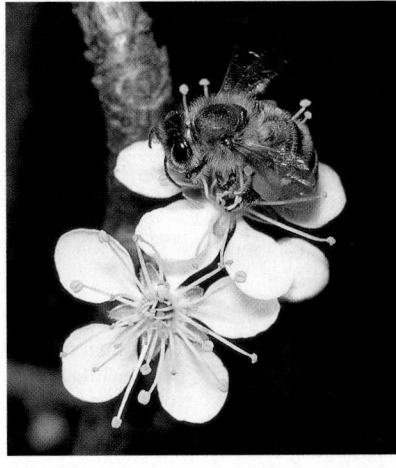

Figure 1.3
Honeybees and many other insects are important to farmers because they pollinate the flowers of crop plants, such as fruit trees. In the 1990s, populations of many pollinators declined, raising worries about reduced crop yields.

1.1 WHAT IS BIOLOGY? **5**

Revealing Misconceptions

Students often think that all organisms found in an area are native to that area.

Uncover the Misconception

Ask students to describe differences between an organism that is native to an area and one that is not. Explain that non-native organisms may be well adapted, less adapted, or may have been introduced without the limitations they had in their native area.

Demonstrate the Concept

Explain cases of introduced species, such as the red imported fire ant, which came from South America in the 1930s and has steadily spread from Alabama throughout the southern portions of the U.S. These ants are aggressive and have caused extensive damage to agriculture and wildlife in states such as Texas.

Assess New Knowledge

Ask students to suggest how they might find out if a particular plant is native to a given area. Introduced species often either die out soon or the population rapidly increases at the expense of native populations because of a lack of environmental controls.

INCLUSION STRATEGIES

Learning Disabled: *Kinesthetic* Have students make a web from string to illustrate the intricate web of nature. On the web, have students place index cards and pictures that illustrate organisms common to your area and their needs for life. **L1**

✓ **Reading Check** Scientists study an organism's environment because the existence of living things is always dependent on the environment and other living things in the environment.

Purpose

Students will look at mildew under the microscope in a well-ventilated room and decide if it is living. **CAUTION:** *Allergic students may observe mildew sealed in the plastic bag and use slides that are already prepared.*

Process Skills

predict, compare and contrast, observe and infer

Safety Precautions

Have students turn to p. 1107 for an introduction to the safety symbols used in this text.

Troubleshooting

Scrape mildew samples from shower grout or plastic shower curtains and bring them to class. Store samples in water to prevent them from drying out. **CAUTION:** *If live specimens are used, seal them in a plastic bag to protect students who might be allergic to mildew spores or whose asthma might be triggered by mildew.*

Teaching Strategies

■ Prior to the activity, ask how many students think mildew is living/not living. Post the results on the chalkboard. Poll students again after the MiniLab.

■ Preserved mildew from biological supply houses can be used in place of live specimens.

■ Instruct students on use of microscope and microscope slides.

■ Demonstrate the technique for making a wet mount. Include proper handling and cleaning of cover glasses and glass slides.

MiniLab 1.1

Observe

Predicting Whether Mildew Is Alive What is mildew? Is it alive? We see it "growing" on plastic shower curtains or on bathroom grout. Does it show the characteristics associated with living things?

Mildew

Procedure

1 Copy the data table below.

Data Table	
Prediction	**Life Characteristics**
First	None
Second	
Third	

2 Predict whether or not mildew is alive. Record your prediction in the data table under "First Prediction."

3 Obtain a sample of mildew from your teacher. Examine it for life characteristics. Make a second prediction and record it in the data table along with any observed life characteristics. **CAUTION:** *Wash hands thoroughly after handling the mildew sample. Do not handle the sample if you are allergic to mildew.*

4 Following your teacher's directions, prepare a wet mount of mildew for viewing under the microscope. **CAUTION:** *Use caution when working with a microscope, microscope slides, and coverslips.*

5 Are there any life characteristics visible through the microscope that you could not see before? Make a third prediction and include any observed life characteristics.

Analysis

1. **Describe** Which life characteristics did you observe?
2. **Interpret Data** Compare your three predictions and explain how your observations may have changed them.
3. **Observe and Infer** Explain the value of using scientific tools to extend your powers of observation.

Figure 1.4
These plants are called *Lithops* from the Greek *lithos,* meaning "stone." Although they don't appear to be so, *Lithops* are just as alive as elephants. Both species possess all of the characteristics of life.

Characteristics of Living Things

Most people feel confident that they can tell the difference between a living thing and a nonliving thing, but sometimes it's not so easy. In identifying life, you might ask, "Does it move? Does it grow? Does it reproduce?" These are all excellent questions, but consider a flame. A flame can move, it can grow, and it can produce more flames. Are flames alive?

Biologists have formulated a list of characteristics by which we can recognize living things. Sometimes, nonliving things have one or more of life's characteristics, but only when something has all of them can it then be considered living. Anything that possesses all of the characteristics of life is known as an **organism,** like the plants shown in *Figure 1.4.* All living things
• have an orderly structure
• produce offspring
• grow and develop
• adjust to changes in the environment
Practice identifying the characteristics of life by carrying out the *MiniLab* on this page.

Expected Results

Students may initially predict that mildew is not alive. During microscopic examination, students will see long filaments (hyphae) and tiny circular objects (spores). Some students may see spores enclosed in a spore sac.

Analysis

1. organization, reproduction, growth, adjusting to environment
2. Answers will vary, depending on the observations made by individual students.
3. Certain life characteristics could not have been seen without the use of a microscope.

Modified Assessment

Knowledge Have students compose a list of things that are questionable as to whether the items listed are living things or not. As a class, go through the list and discuss whether each thing should be considered alive or not.

Living things are organized

When biologists search for signs of life, one of the first things they look for is structure. That's because they know that all living things show an orderly structure, or **organization.**

The living world is filled with organisms. All of them, including the earthworm pictured in *Figure 1.5,* are composed of one or more cells. Each cell contains the genetic material, or DNA, that provides all the information needed to control the organism's life processes.

Although living things are very diverse—there may be five to ten million species, perhaps more—they are unified in having cellular organization. Whether an organism is made up of one cell or billions of cells, all of its parts function together in an orderly, living system.

Living things make more living things

One of the most obvious of all the characteristics of life is **reproduction,** the production of offspring. The litter of mice in *Figure 1.6* is just

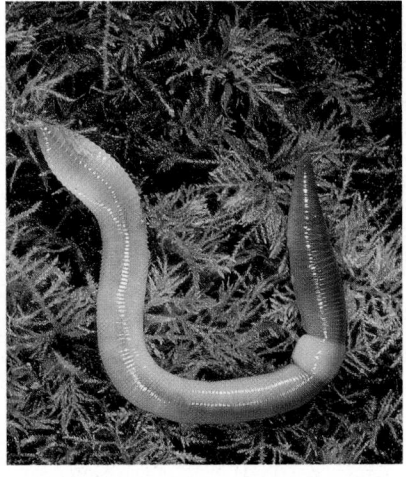

Figure 1.5
Like all organisms, earthworms are made up of cells. The cells form structures that carry out essential functions, such as feeding or digestion. The interaction of these structures and their functions result in a single, orderly, living organism.

one example. Organisms don't live forever. For life to continue, they must replace themselves.

Reproduction is not essential for the survival of an individual organism, but it is essential for the continuation of the organism's species (SPEE sheez). A **species** is a group of organisms that can interbreed and produce fertile offspring in nature. If individuals in a species never reproduced, it would mean an end to that species' existence on Earth.

Figure 1.6
A variety of mechanisms for reproduction have evolved that ensure the continuation of each species. Some organisms, including mice, produce many offspring in one lifetime.

7

Quick Demo

Living Characteristics
Show students a *Lithops* plant and ask how they might determine whether it is living or nonliving. L2

Activity

Kinesthetic Give small groups of students the following materials: a squash seed, a bottle of bubbles and a bubble wand, a fresh fruit such as a tomato, a cut flower in a test tube filled with water, and a warming candle in a jar lid. Light the candle for each group and instruct students to observe the flame. **CAUTION:** *Take extreme care with fire around the students.*

Instruct them to blow a few bubbles. Ask them to observe each of the other objects. Have students decide whether or not each item is alive and explain the reasons for their decisions. Discuss responses as a class. You may find it necessary to distinguish between nonliving things and once-living or dead things as part of the discussion. Students will probably know that bubbles and warming candles are not alive, but because they move, students may say they are alive. L2

Microscope Activity

Visual-Spatial Have students refer to the **Skill Handbook** to review the proper procedures for caring for and using a microscope. Then ask them to examine prepared slides of a variety of organisms. L2

CHALLENGE ACTIVITY

Alive or Not Set up stations around the classroom with living and nonliving items such as a rock with lichens, a bird's nest, a potted plant, seeds, and other interesting material you may have. Ask students to decide if each item is alive or not and to justify their answers. L3

Discussion

Lead students in a discussion of general developmental stages of various organisms. Examples include complete and incomplete metamorphosis in insects, or birth, infancy, childhood, puberty, adulthood, old age, and death in humans.

CAREERS IN BIOLOGY

Nature Preserve Interpreter

If you like people as much as you love nature, you can combine your skills and interests in a career as a nature preserve interpreter.

Skills for the Job

Interpreters are also called naturalists, ecologists, and environmental educators. They might work for a nature preserve or a state or national park, where they give talks, conduct tours, offer video presentations, and teach special programs. Some interpreters are required to have a degree in biology, botany, zoology, forestry, environmental science, education, or a related field. They must also be skilled in communicating with others.

Many interpreters begin as volunteers who have no degrees, just a love for what they do. Over time, volunteers may become interns and eventually be hired. Interpreters often help restore natural habitats and protect existing ones. Part of their job is to make sure visitors do not harm these habitats and to point out the wonders of these natural areas.

For example, many tidepool organisms find protection from too much sunlight by crawling under rocks. A naturalist can explain the importance of replacing rocks exactly as they were found.

For more careers in related fields, visit
in.bdol.glencoe.com/careers

Living things change during their lives

An organism's life begins as a single cell, and over time, it grows and takes on the characteristics of its species. **Growth** results in an increase in the amount of living material and the formation of new structures.

All organisms grow, with different parts of the organism growing at different rates. Organisms made up of only one cell may change little during their lives, but they do grow. On the other hand, organisms made up of numerous cells go through many changes during their lifetimes, such as the changes that will take place in the young nestlings shown in *Figure 1.7*. Think about some of the structural changes your body has already undergone since you were born. All of the changes that take place during the life of an organism are known as its **development.**

Living things adjust to their surroundings

Organisms live in a constant interface with their surroundings, or **environment,** which includes the air, water, weather, temperature, any other organisms in the area, and many other factors. For example, the fox in *Figure 1.8* feeds on small

Figure 1.7
All life begins as a single cell. As cells multiply, each organism grows and develops and begins to take on the characteristics that identify it as a member of a particular species, such as the owls shown here.

CULTURAL DIVERSITY

The History of Biological Discovery: *Interpersonal* Have students work in groups of three or four to prepare a presentation about the history of biological science in a different country. Student presentations can include a chronology of discoveries in the country, or they can be more specific accounts of a particular area of research. Presentations should include names of scientists, details about the research, and how the research may have benefited society. Encourage students to incorporate posters, models, photographs, or videos in their presentations. **L3** **COOP LEARN**

Figure 1.8
Living things respond to stimuli and make adjustments to environmental conditions.

A Trees that drop their leaves in the fall conserve water and avoid freezing during winter.

B Keen senses of smell and hearing enable a fox to find prey. Fur allows foxes and other mammals to regulate body temperature. **Describe** *What are some other examples of how feedback mechanisms help maintain homeostasis?*

The BioLab at the end of the chapter can be used at this point in the lesson.

animals such as rabbits and mice. The fox responds to the presence of a rabbit by quietly moving toward it, then pouncing. Trees adjust to cold, dry winter weather by losing their leaves. Anything in an organism's external or internal environment that causes the organism to react is a **stimulus.** A reaction to a stimulus is a **response.**

The ability to respond to stimuli in the environment is an important characteristic of living things. It's one of the more obvious ones, as well. That's because many of the structures and behaviors that you see in organisms enable them to adjust to the environment. Try the *BioLab* at the end of this chapter to find out more about how organisms respond to environmental stimuli.

Regulation of an organism's internal environment to maintain conditions suitable for its survival is called **homeostasis** (hoh mee oh STAY sus). Homeostasis is a characteristic of life because it is a process that occurs in all living things. Living things also use internal feedback to respond to internal changes. For example, organisms must make constant adjustments to maintain the correct amount of water and minerals in their cells and the proper internal temperature. Without this ability to adjust to internal changes, organisms die.

Living things reproduce themselves, grow and develop, respond to external stimuli, and maintain homeostasis by using energy. **Energy** is the ability to cause change. Organisms get their energy from food. Plants make their own food, whereas animals, fungi, and other organisms get their food from plants or from organisms that consume plants.

Living things adapt and evolve

Any inherited structure, behavior, or internal process that enables an organism to respond to environmental factors and live to produce offspring is called an **adaptation** (a dap TAY shun).

Adaptations are inherited from previous generations. There are always some differences in the adaptations of individuals within any population of organisms. As the environment changes, some adaptations are more suited to the new conditions than others. Individuals with more suitable adaptations are more likely to

Caption Question Answer
Figure 1.8 Bears hibernate when air temperatures drop and food becomes unavailable; butterflies metamorphose from caterpillars to pupae at a time when leafy food may become scarce; and resurrection plants open and close their leaves depending on water availability. Students may list many others. Make certain that students understand that these changes are part of the organisms' adaptations. These activities are not conscious decisions on the part of the organism.

Portfolio

Stimulus and Response Have students cut five pictures from magazines that show organisms responding to stimuli. Ask students to mount each picture on a clean sheet of paper and label the stimulus and response. Have students place their labeled illustrations in their portfolios. **L1 ELL**

USING MODELS

Model Homeostasis Use a model of a human torso to identify organ systems, and relate how the systems help to maintain homeostasis. Some examples could include sweating and shivering. **L2**

 Indiana Academic Standards

Pages 8–9: B.1.11, B.1.16, B.1.17, B.1.18, B.1.31

3 Assess

Extension

Ask students working in groups to investigate the latest developments in robotics. Have them list the characteristics of robots and compare and contrast these characteristics with those of living organisms. Have them point out key characteristics that distinguish robots as nonliving. **L3**

Assessment

Skill Ask students to explain how they would test to see which color of light would cause a bean plant to grow faster. **L2**

Figure 1.9
Living things adapt to their environments in a variety of ways.

A The desert Ocotillo has leaves only during the rainy season. Lacking leaves during the dry season is an adaptation which helps conserve water.

B Many nocturnal animals, such as this owl, possess large eyes for efficient vision at night.

survive and reproduce. As a result, individuals with these adaptations become more numerous in the population. *Figure 1.9* shows some examples of adaptation.

The gradual change in a species through adaptations over time is **evolution** (e vuh LEW shun). Clues to the way the present diversity of life came about may be understood through the study of evolution. You will study how the theory of evolution can help answer many of the questions people have about living things.

As you learn more about Earth's organisms in this book, reflect on the general characteristics of life. Rather than simply memorizing facts about organisms or the vocabulary terms, try to see how these facts and vocabulary are related to the characteristics of living things.

Section Assessment

Understanding Main Ideas
1. What are some important reasons for studying biology?
2. Identify and describe how an organism could respond to an external stimulus. Describe a response to an internal stimulus.
3. Why is energy required for living things? How do living things obtain energy?
4. Describe how biologists' research contributes to our understanding of the world.

Thinking Critically
5. Describe how energy and homeostasis are related in living organisms.

SKILL REVIEW

6. **Observe and Infer** Suppose you discover an unidentified object on your way home from school. What characteristics would you study to determine whether the object is a living or nonliving thing? For more help, refer to *Observe and Infer* in the **Skill Handbook**.

 in.bdol.glencoe.com/self_check_quiz

Section Assessment

1. for the pleasure of learning about living things, or to appreciate the diversity of species and the way each fits into the dynamic patterns of life on Earth
2. A stimulus is anything in the environment that requires an organism to adjust. The adjustment made is the response. Sweating in humans is a response to the stimulus of high temperature.
3. Energy is required for organisms to carry on all life processes. Organisms, such as plants, obtain energy from sunlight, but most organisms obtain their energy by consuming living or dead organisms.
4. Biology research expands understanding of how the natural world works

and aids development of helpful technology.
5. A transfer of energy is often necessary to maintain homeostasis.
6. Examine its organization and see if it is cellular or not; see if it grows or develops; see if it responds to stimuli or adapts to a change in its environment; see if it maintains homeostasis.

The Methods of Biology

Why does rain bring out the worms?

Using an Analogy Have you noticed that moss grows only in shady, moist locations? Or that earthworms crawl to the surface after a rain? If you have ever wondered why moss grows in certain locations, or why earthworms appear after a rain, then you have used methods like scientists use to develop experiments. You might examine locations such as the one in the photo and make notes on the environment in which moss grows. Scientists use many different methods to answer questions, but all scientific inquiries share some common methods.

Experiment *As you read the section, use your new knowledge of scientific methods to plan an investigative procedure to learn why moss grows only in shady, moist locations.*

Mosses are tiny plants that grow in dense clumps.

1 Focus

Bellringer
Section Focus Transparency 2

Using an Analogy

Experiment Encourage students to develop a controlled experiment that they might carry out by having them do research, make a testable hypothesis, define a control group, an independent variable, and a dependent variable. If practical, students may carry out their experiment.

Observing and Hypothesizing

Curiosity is often what motivates biologists to try to answer simple questions about everyday observations, such as why earthworms leave their burrows after it rains. Earthworms obtain oxygen through their skin, and will drown in waterlogged soil. Sometimes, answers to questions like these also provide better understanding of general biological principles and may even lead to practical applications, such as the discovery that a certain plant can be used as a medicine. The knowledge obtained when scientists answer one question often generates other questions or proves useful in solving other problems.

The methods biologists use

To answer questions, biologists may use many different approaches, yet there are some steps that are common to all approaches. The common steps that biologists and other scientists use to gather information and answer questions are collectively known as **scientific methods.**

Scientific methods do not suggest a rigid approach to investigating and solving problems. There are no fixed steps to follow, yet scientific

2 Teach

Brainstorming

Ask students to brainstorm a list of questions they have that relate to biology. Write the questions as a list on the board. Allow students to give examples of how they might find answers to their questions if they were given access to any equipment or technology they can imagine. **L2**

Caption Question Answer
Figure 1.11 (p. 13) The amount of fertilizer is the independent variable.

Figure 1.10
Brown tree snakes *(Boiga irregularis)* were introduced to Guam more than 50 years ago. Since then, their numbers have increased dramatically, and they have severely reduced the native bird population of the island.

investigations generally involve making observations and collecting relevant information as well as using logical reasoning and imagination to make predictions and form explanations. Scientific methods usually begin with scientists identifying a problem to solve by observing the world around them.

The question of brown tree snakes

Have you ever been told that you have excellent powers of observation? This is one trait that is required of biologists. The story of the brown tree snake in *Figure 1.10* serves as an example. During the 1940s, this species of snake was accidentally introduced to the island of Guam from the Admiralty Islands in the Pacific Ocean. In 1965, it was reported in a local newspaper that the snake might be considered beneficial to the island because it is a predator that feeds on rats, mice, and other small rodents. Rodents are often considered pests because they carry disease and contaminate food supplies.

Shortly after reading the newspaper report, a young biologist walking through the forests of Guam made an important observation. She noted that there were no bird songs echoing through the forest. Looking into the trees, she saw a brown tree snake hanging from a branch. After learning that the bird population of Guam had declined rapidly since the introduction of the snake, she hypothesized that the snake might be eating the birds. A **hypothesis** (hi PAHTH us sus) is an explanation for a question or a problem that can be formally tested. Hypothesizing is one of the methods most frequently used by scientists. A scientist who forms a hypothesis must be certain that it can be tested. Until then, he or she may propose suggestions to explain observations.

As you can see from the brown tree snake example, a hypothesis is not a random guess. Before a scientist makes a hypothesis, he or she has developed some idea of what the answer to a question might be through personal observations, extensive reading, or previous investigations.

After stating a hypothesis, a scientist may continue to make observations and form additional hypotheses to account for the collected data. Eventually, the scientist may test a hypothesis by conducting an experiment. The results of the experiment will help the scientist draw a conclusion about whether or not the hypothesis is correct.

Experimenting

People do not always use the word *experiment* in their daily lives in the same way scientists use it in their work. As an example, you may have heard someone say that he or she was going to experiment with a cookie recipe. Perhaps the person is planning to substitute raisins for chocolate chips, use margarine instead of butter, add cocoa powder, reduce the amount of sugar, and bake the cookies for a longer time. This is not an experiment in the scientific sense because there is no way to know what effect any one of the changes alone has on the resulting cookies. To a scientist, an **experiment** is an investigation that tests a hypothesis by the process of collecting information under controlled conditions.

What is a controlled experiment?

Some experiments involve two groups: the control group and the experimental group. A **control** is the part of an experiment that is the standard against which results are compared. The control receives no experimental treatment. The experimental group is the test group that receives experimental treatment.

Suppose you wanted to learn how fertilizer affects the growth of different varieties of soybean plants. Your hypothesis might state that the presence of fertilizer will increase the growth rate of each plant variety. An experimental setup designed to test this hypothesis is shown in *Figure 1.11*. Fertilizer is present in the soil of the experimental plants, but not the controls. All other conditions—including soil, light, and water—are the same for both groups of plants.

Designing an experiment

In a controlled experiment, only one condition is changed at a time. The condition in an experiment that is tested is the **independent variable,** because it is the only factor that affects the outcome of the experiment. In the case of the soybeans, the presence of fertilizer is the independent variable. While testing the independent variable, the scientist observes or measures a second condition that results from the change. This condition is the **dependent variable,** because any changes in it depend on changes made to the independent variable. In the soybean experiment, the dependent variable

Figure 1.11
This experiment tested the effect of fertilizer on the growth of several varieties of soybeans. For each experiment there are three rows of each variety. The center rows are the experimental plants. The outer rows are the controls. **Infer** *What is the independent variable in this experiment?*

is the growth rate of the plants. Controlled experiments are most often used in laboratory settings.

However, not all investigations are controlled. Suppose you were on a group of islands in the Pacific that is the only nesting area for a large seabird known as a waved albatross, shown in *Figure 1.12*. Watching the nesting birds, you observe that the female leaves the nest when her mate flies back from a foraging trip. The birds take turns sitting on the eggs or caring for the chicks, often for two weeks at a time. You might hypothesize that the birds fly around the island, or that they fly to some distant location, in search of food. To test these hypotheses, you might attach a satellite transmitter to some of the birds and record their travels.

Figure 1.12
The waved albatross is a large bird that nests mainly on Hood Island in the Galápagos Islands. By tagging the birds with satellite transmitters, scientists have learned where these birds travel.

1.2 THE METHODS OF BIOLOGY **13**

Virtual Lab

CD-ROM Have students experiment with plants by altering conditions in *Dependent and Independent Variables.*

Visual Learning

Figure 1.12 Ask students to explain how a satellite transmitter is useful in tracking waved albatrosses. Because albatrosses fly long distances over open ocean, a transmitter is useful because it can continuously relay information that would be difficult or impossible to attain in any other way.

Tying to Prior Knowledge

Logical-Mathematical Present the following hypothesis to your students: "Yeast, in its dry state, appears lifeless. If yeast produces carbon dioxide and is made up of cells, then it is alive." Ask students to: (a) Describe experimental procedures that would need to be used to verify this hypothesis. Give yeast a source of food and water and watch to see if it produces carbon dioxide. Then look at it under the microscope to see if it is made up of cells. (b) Describe reasoning that was used to form the hypothesis. Organisms that are made up of cells and produce carbon dioxide are described as being alive. If yeast meets these requirements, then it is also alive.

Indiana Academic Standards

Pages 12–13: B.1.38, B.1.41

4. Place both jars, uncovered, in the same location.
5. Make daily observations of your jars for one week. Check for the presence of mold.
6. Record your observations in a suitable data table by making diagrams of the coffee liquid surfaces.

Analysis
1. Which type of coffee allows mold to grow? both
2. Was your hypothesis supported by your data? will depend on hypothesis
3. What was the control, independent variable, and dependent variable? decaffeinated coffee, caffeinated coffee, mold growth

Assessment
Portfolio Have students write a report of their experimental findings. Ask them to record any other questions that arose during this experiment and explain how they might be answered. Use the Performance Task Assessment List for Lab Report in **PASC**, p. 119. **L2**

Purpose

Students will experiment to determine which products contain alcohol.

Process Skills

draw a conclusion, experiment, interpret data, observe and infer

Safety Precautions

See Safety Symbol chart on p. 1107. Review safety precautions regarding goggles, hand washing, and the use of an acid solution.

Teaching Strategies

■ For preparation instructions for the alcohol-testing reagent, see page 17T.

■ Label three separate slides *A*, *B*, and *C*. Make one circle on each slide with a China marking or eyebrow pencil. (Students could use small test tubes rather than glass slides.) Use caution when cleaning glassware.

■ For circle *C*, use isopropyl (rubbing) alcohol. Products to be tested may include aftershave lotion, cough syrups, mouthwash.

Expected Results

Student data will vary with the products tested. Circle *A* will appear yellow-orange, circle *B* green to blue, and circle *C* yellow.

Analysis

1. to determine which colors indicate the presence or absence of alcohol
2. Answers will depend on products tested.

Assessment

Performance Provide students with several different types of alcohol (rubbing, ethyl, methyl), and ask them to determine which types the alcohol-testing chemical can detect. Use the Performance Task Assessment List for Carrying Out a Strategy and Collecting Data in **PASC**, p. 97. **L2** **ELL**

MiniLab 1.2

Investigate

Testing for Alcohol Promotional claims for certain over-the-counter products may not tell you that one of the ingredients is alcohol. How can you verify whether or not a certain product contains alcohol? One way is to simply rely on the information provided on a product label or an advertisement. Another way is to investigate and find out for yourself.

Procedure

Data Table		
	Color of Liquid	**Alcohol Present**
Circle A		
Circle B		
Circle C		
Product name		
Product name		

1 Copy the data table.

2 Draw three circles on a glass slide. Label them *A*, *B*, and *C*. **CAUTION: *Put on safety goggles.***

3 Add one drop of water to circle A, one drop of alcohol to circle B, and one drop of alcohol-testing chemical to circles A, B, and C. **CAUTION: *Rinse immediately with water if testing chemical gets on skin or clothing.***

4 Wait 2–3 minutes. Note in the data table the color of each liquid and the presence or absence of alcohol.

5 Record the name of the first product to be tested.

6 Draw a circle on a clean glass slide. Add one drop of the product to the circle.

7 Add a drop of the alcohol-testing chemical to the circle. Wait 2–3 minutes. Record the color of the liquid.

8 Repeat steps 5–7 for each product to be tested. **CAUTION: *Wash your hands with soap and water immediately after using the alcohol-testing chemical.***

9 Complete the last column of the data table. If alcohol is present, the liquid turns green, deep green, or blue. A yellow or orange color means no alcohol is present.

Analysis

1. **Infer** Explain the purpose of using the alcohol-testing chemical with water, with a known alcohol, and by itself.

2. **Evaluate** Which products did contain alcohol? No alcohol?

An investigation such as this, which has no control, is the type of biological investigation most often used in fieldwork.

The design of the procedure that is selected depends on what other investigators have done and what information the biologist hopes to gain. Sometimes, a biologist will design a second investigation even while a first one is being conducted, to answer the question. Try your hand at investigation in the *MiniLab* on this page.

✔ **Reading Check** **Describe** the roles of a control, independent variable, and dependent variable.

Using tools

To carry out investigations, scientists need tools that enable them to record information. The growth rate of plants and the information from satellite transmitters placed on albatrosses are examples of important information gained from investigations.

Biologists use a variety of tools to obtain information in an investigation. Common tools include beakers, test tubes, hot plates, petri dishes, thermometers, balances, metric rulers, and graduated cylinders. More complex tools include microscopes, centrifuges, radiation detectors, spectrophotometers, DNA analyzers, and gas chromatographs. *Figure 1.13* shows some complex tools.

Maintaining safety

Safety is another important factor that scientists consider when carrying out investigations. Biologists try to minimize hazards to themselves, the people working around them, and the organisms they are studying.

In the investigations in this textbook, you will be alerted to possible safety hazards by the safety symbols shown in *Table 1.1* and precautions.

✔ **Reading Check** The control provides a comparison for the experimental group. The independent variable is the single condition that is changed in the experiment, and the dependent variable is the condition that is measured as a result of the change.

INCLUSION STRATEGIES

Learning Disabled: *Interpersonal*
Have students plan scientific methods to alter a cookie recipe, such as replacing chocolate chips with nuts. Ask students to name the control to be used, the independent variable, and the dependent variable. **L1** **ELL** **COOP LEARN**

A Gel electrophoresis can be used to produce a DNA fingerprint as shown. Comparing DNA reveals how closely related two species are.

B The optical microscope makes small details visible.

Figure 1.13
Biologists use many tools in their studies.

A **safety symbol** is a symbol that warns you about a danger that may exist from chemicals, electricity, heat, or procedures you will use. Refer to the safety symbols at the back of this book before beginning any field investigation or lab activity in this text. It is your responsibility to maintain the highest safety standards to protect yourself as well as your classmates.

Data gathering

To answer their questions about scientific problems, scientists seek information from their investigations. Information obtained from investigations is called **data.** Sometimes, these data are referred to as experimental results.

Often, data are in numerical form, such as the distance covered in an albatross's trip or the height that soybean plants grow per day. Numerical data may be measurements of time, temperature, length, mass, area, volume, or other factors. Numerical data may also be counts, such as the number of bees that visit a flower per day or the number of wheat seeds that germinate at different soil temperatures.

Sometimes data are expressed in verbal form, using words to describe observations made during an investigation. Scientists who first observed the behavior of pandas in China obtained data by recording what these animals do in their natural habitat and how they respond to their environment. Learning that pandas are solitary animals with large territories helped scientists understand how to provide better care for them in zoos and research centers.

Having the data from an investigation does not end the scientific process. See how data collection relates to other important aspects of research on pages 1060–1061 in the *Focus On*.

Table 1.1 Safety Symbols

 Sharp Object Safety This symbol appears when a danger of cuts or punctures caused by the use of sharp objects exists.

 Clothing Protection Safety This symbol appears when substances used could stain or burn clothing.

 Eye Safety This symbol appears when a danger to the eyes exists. Safety goggles should be worn when this symbol appears.

 Chemical Safety This symbol appears when chemicals used can cause burns or are poisonous if absorbed through the skin.

Science Journals Bring copies of scientific journals to class and allow students to examine them. Ask students to speculate as to which branch of science each journal addresses. (Other science magazines, available on newsstands, explain science in more common terms, but are not science journals.)

Brainstorming

A student repeats an investigation several times and each time records different data. Have students offer possible reasons why an experiment might yield different data for different trials. Reasons include failure to keep all factors but one the same, errors in data recording, errors in mathematical treatment of the data, or naturally occurring variability in experimental outcome. **L2**

Inquiry

Activity Call all students' attention to Table 1.1, the Safety Symbols. Shown here are some of the most commonly used symbols in this program. Students should always wear an apron and safety goggles and wash their hands thoroughly after handling laboratory materials. Have students turn to page 1107 and study each of the symbols shown. Then have them look through the text for examples of these symbols. **L1**

INCLUSION STRATEGIES

Hearing Impaired: *Interpersonal* Supply students with the following data showing how many seeds were germinated by three laboratory groups over a three-day period. Group A had two seeds germinate on day 1, four seeds on day 2, and four seeds on day 3. Group B had one seed germinate on day 1, six on day 2, and five on day 3. Group C had two seeds germinate on day 1, four on day 2, and three on day 3. Have students work in groups to prepare a class graph of the number of seeds germinating each day for all three groups. **L2**

Purpose

Students will analyze the claims made in a commercial.

Process Skills

analyze information, draw a conclusion, experiment, think critically

Teaching Strategies

You may wish to have the entire class analyze the same commercial. Tape a specific commercial and play it back to the class. Or provide students with the printed dialogue from a radio commercial. **L2**

Thinking Critically

1. Student answers will vary. Many commercials make claims without specifying any scientific backing.
2. Student answers will vary. Many commercials appear to use inference. However, according to the Federal Food, Drug, and Cosmetic Act of 1938, drugs must be safe and effective for their intended use. According to the Federal Trade Commission Act, advertisers of products used nationwide must be able to back up their claims with evidence and must not be deceptive.
3. Students should describe a hypothesis, control, dependent and independent variables, trials, data accumulation, and a conclusion based on data.

Assessment

Portfolio Ask students to design a video commercial that bases its claims on experimental data. Have them include their data and analyses as part of the commercial. Use the Performance Task Assessment List for Video in **PASC**, p. 153. **L2**

Problem-Solving Lab 1.1

Analyze Information

Are promotional claims valid?
"Our product is new and improved." "Use this mouthwash and your mouth will feel clean all day." Sound familiar? TV and radio commercials constantly tell us how great certain products are. Are these claims always based on facts?

Solve the Problem

Listen to or view a commercial for a product that addresses a medical problem such as heartburn, allergies, or bad breath. If possible, tape the commercial so that you can replay it as often as needed. Record the following information:

1. What is the major claim made in the commercial?
2. Is the claim based on experimentation?
3. What data, if any, are used to support the claim?

Thinking Critically

1. **Evaluate** In general, was the promotional claim based on scientific methods? Explain your answer.
2. **Evaluate** In general, are promotional claims made in advertisements based on experimental evidence? Explain your answer.
3. **Experiment** Plan an investigative procedure that could be conducted to establish promotional claims made for the product in your advertisement.

Thinking about what happened

Often, the thinking that goes into analyzing data takes the greatest amount of a scientist's time. After careful review of the results, the scientist must come to a conclusion: Was the hypothesis supported by the data? Was it not supported? Are more data needed? Data from an investigation may be considered confirmed only if repeating that investigation several times yields similar results. To review how scientific methods are used in investigations, see *Figure 1.14* on the next page.

After analyzing the data, scientists often have more questions than they had before the investigation. They compare their results and conclusions with the results of other studies by researching the published literature for more information. They also begin to think of other experiments they might carry out. Are all the claims you hear on TV commercials based on data gathered by scientific methods? Find out by conducting the *Problem-Solving Lab* here.

Reporting results

Results and conclusions of investigations are reported in scientific journals, where they are available for examination by other scientists. Hundreds of scientific journals are published weekly or monthly. In fact, scientists usually spend a large part of their time reading journal articles to keep up with new information as it is reported. The amount of information published every day in scientific journals is more than any single scientist could read. Fortunately, scientists also have access to computer databases that contain summaries of scientific articles, both old and new.

Verifying results

Data and conclusions are shared with other scientists for an important reason. After results of an investigation have been published, other scientists can try to verify the results by repeating the procedure. If they obtain similar results, there is even more support for the hypothesis. When a hypothesis is supported by data from additional investigations, it is considered valid and is generally accepted by the scientific community. When a scientist publishes the results of his or her investigation, other scientists can relate their own work to the published data.

PROJECT

Recognizing Technology: *Visual-Spatial* Ask students to work in co-operative groups to prepare a time line that shows the technological advances in one area of biology, such as genetics, biotechnology, or oceanography. **L2** **COOP LEARN**

Scientific Methods

Figure 1.14
Scientific methods are used by scientists to answer questions and solve problems. The development of the cell theory, one of the most useful theories in biological science, illustrates how the methods of science work. In 1665, Robert Hooke first observed cells in cork. He made the drawing on the right, showing what he saw. **Critical Thinking** *What is the function of other scientists in the scientific process?*

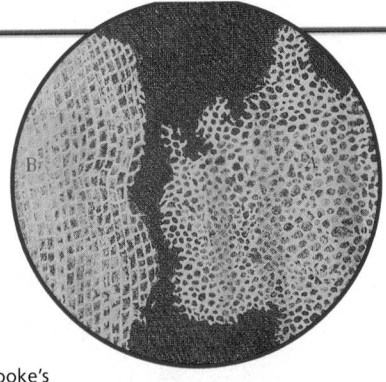

Cork cells as drawn by Robert Hooke

A **Observing** The first step toward scientific discovery often takes place when a scientist observes something no one has noticed before. After Hooke's discovery, other scientists observed cells in a variety of organisms.

B **Making a hypothesis** A hypothesis is a testable explanation or answer to a question. In 1824, René Dutrochet hypothesized that cells are the basic unit of life.

C **Collecting data** Investigations and experiments test a hypothesis. Data must be thoroughly analyzed to determine whether the hypothesis was supported or disproved. From the results, a conclusion can be formed. Over the years, scientists who used microscopes to examine organisms found that cells are always present.

D **Publishing results** Results of an investigation are useful only if they are made available to other scientists for a peer review. Many scientists published their observations of cells in the scientific literature. Scientists will analyze the procedure, examine the evidence, identify faulty reasoning, point out statements that go beyond the evidence, and suggest alternative explanations for the same observations.

E **Forming a theory** A theory is a hypothesis that is supported by a large body of scientific evidence. By 1839, many scientific observations supported the hypothesis that cells are fundamental to life. The hypothesis became a theory.

F **Developing new hypotheses** A new theory may prompt scientists to ask new questions or form additional hypotheses. In 1833, Robert Brown hypothesized that the nucleus is an important control center of the cell.

G **Revising the theory** Theories are revised as new information is gathered. The cell theory gave biologists a start for exploring the basic structure and function of all life. Important discoveries, including the discovery of DNA, have resulted.

Purpose
Students will review methods used in scientific investigations.

Teaching Strategies
■ Point out that not every scientific investigation uses every method, nor do all investigations lead to a published theory.
■ Provide students with biological journals, such as *Science* and *Nature*. Ask them to look at the articles and identify the methods of science used. See parenthetical comment in Quick Demo, p. 15.

Visual Learning
■ Have students look at cork cells through a microscope and compare them with the photo on this page, then ask them to compare the capabilities of their microscopes with the one used by Robert Hooke.
■ For more help with using microscopes, refer to the **Skill Handbook.**

Critical Thinking
Other scientists repeat the same experiment to validate original results. Scientists extend understanding by performing experiments to answer related questions.

Inquiry
Activity Have students work in groups on a biological problem they perceive in your area. At the conclusion of the project, students should be able to explain the methods of science they used. **L2**
COOP LEARN

🎯 **CHALLENGE ACTIVITY**

Quantitative Data: *Linguistic* Have students review articles on biological research in *Scientific American, Science News, Newsweek,* or local newspapers. Ask students to write a short essay identifying the methods of science that were used. **L3**

3 Assess

Figure 1.15
Investigations have shown that male elephants communicate with other males using threat postures and low-frequency vibrations that warn rival males away.

For example, biologists studying the behavior of elephants in Africa published their observations. Other scientists, who were studying elephant communication, used that data to help determine which of the elephants' behaviors are related to communication. Further investigations showed that female elephants emit certain sounds in order to attract mates, and that some of the sounds produced by bull elephants warn other males away from receptive females, as described in *Figure 1.15*.

Theories and laws

People use the word *theory* in everyday life very differently from the way scientists use this word in their work. You may have heard someone say that he or she has a theory that a particular football team will win the Super Bowl this year. What the person really means is that he or she believes one team will play better for some reason. Much more evidence is needed to support a scientific theory.

In science, a hypothesis that is supported by many separate observations and investigations, usually over a long period of time, becomes a theory. A **theory** is an explanation of a natural phenomenon that is supported by a large body of scientific evidence obtained from many different investigations and observations. A theory results from continual verification and refinement of a hypothesis.

In addition to theories, scientists also recognize certain natural laws that are generally known to be true. The fact that a dropped apple falls to Earth is an illustration of the law of gravity.

Section Assessment

Understanding Main Ideas

1. Suppose you observed that bees prefer a yellow flower that produces more nectar over a purple flower that produces less nectar. List two separate hypotheses that you might make about bees and flowers.

2. Describe a controlled experiment you could perform to determine whether ants are more attracted to butter or to honey.

3. What is the difference between a theory and a hypothesis?

4. Why do some investigations require a control?

Thinking Critically

5. Describe a way that a baker might conduct a controlled experiment with a cookie recipe.

SKILL REVIEW

6. **Interpret Scientific Illustrations** Review *Figure 1.14*. What happens when a hypothesis is not supported? How does the strength of a scientific theory compare to the strength of a hypothesis? For more help, refer to *Interpret Scientific Illustrations* in the **Skill Handbook**.

 in.bdol.glencoe.com/self_check_quiz

Section Assessment

1. Students might hypothesize that bees prefer yellow flowers to purple flowers or that bees prefer flowers with more abundant nectar.

2. Set up an experimental chamber. Within a specific amount of time, count and record how many ants move to butter placed a specific distance from the ants. Repeat several times. Repeat using honey in place of the butter.

3. A hypothesis is a testable explanation for a question. A theory is a refined explanation supported by extensive experimentation.

4. A control provides greater certainty that observed results are not due to chance or other variables.

5. Prepare one batch of cookies using a known recipe and another batch, the experimental group, by varying a single item such as amount of sugar.

6. A new, revised hypothesis is tested, or the experiment may be changed. Theories are supported by the results of extensive experiments and observations.

e Nature of Biology

SEC

Obje

Compare and contrast quantitative and qualitative information.

Explain why science and technology cannot solve all problems.

Review Vocabulary
experiment: procedure that tests a hypothesis by collecting information (p. 13)

New Vocabulary
ethics
technology

Jo Ways to Describe Things

Jsing Prior Knowledge How would you describe your homeroom class? Would you mention how many classmates you have? Or would you describe them as good students? Would you tell someone how many boys or how many girls comprise the class? Perhaps you would narrate how your classmates carried out an experiment. Most information you could give would be either quantitative or qualitative. Quantitative information uses numbers or measurements, while qualitative information expresses qualities and behavior.

Organize Information *Make a list of ways you could describe your class. Divide the list into two categories: Quantitative and Qualitative.*

This group of students can be described with quantitative or qualitative information.

Bellringer
Section Focus Transparency 3

Transparency **3** Systems of Measurement

SECTION FOCUS
Use with Chapter 1, Section 1.3

① The person in the picture is measuring in cubits—an ancient Egyptian measurement that equals the distance from a person's elbow to the tip of the middle finger. What problems might occur if everyone used this unit?

② What characteristics should a measurement system have to make it accurate and easily understood by everyone?

BIOLOGY: The Dynamics of Life   SECTION FOCUS TRANSPARENCIES

Kinds of Information

You have learned that scientists use a variety of methods to test their hypotheses about the natural world. Scientific information can usually be classified into one of two main types, quantitative or qualitative.

Quantitative information

Biologists sometimes conduct controlled experiments that result in counts or measurements—that is, numerical data. These kinds of experiments occur in quantitative research. The data are analyzed by comparing numerical values.

Quantitative data may be used to make a graph or table. Graphs and tables communicate large amounts of data in a form that is easy to understand. Suppose, for example, that a biologist is studying the effects of climate on freshwater life. He or she may count the number of microscopic organisms, called *Paramecium*, that survive at a given temperature. This study is an example of quantitative research.

The data obtained from the *Paramecium* study is presented as a graph in *Figure 1.16*. You can practice using graphs by carrying out the *Problem-Solving Lab* on the next page.

Using Prior Knowledge

Organize Information Quantitative methods for describing the class include numbers, such as heights of students, number of minutes in the class, and number of students absent. Qualitative methods might use behavioral differences between students, colors of clothing, or type of footwear worn to class.

RESOURCE MANAGER

Unit 1 *FAST FILE* Resources
MiniLab Worksheet, p. 7
Reinforcement and Study Guide in English, p.16
Reinforcement and Study Guide in Spanish, p. 20
Transparency Worksheet, p. 23

Reading Essentials for Biology, Section 1.3
Section Focus Transparency 3

Purpose

Students will analyze a graph and determine that the amount of information obtained from a graph is limited.

Process Skills

acquire information, interpret data, think critically

Teaching Strategies

Review the terminology associated with graphs or refer students to the **Skill Handbook.**

Thinking Critically

1. no; No bar extends to the 100% line.
2. The number of students enrolled in physical education declines as students progress from 9th grade to 12th grade.
3. Data needed to answer the question are not supplied.
4. no; The graph does not provide this information.

Assessment

Skill Have students design a graph to illustrate why fewer seniors take physical education. Students can make up the questions to be surveyed and estimate the number of "yes" responses. Use the Performance Task Assessment List for Conducting a Survey and Graphing the Results in **PASC,** p. 107. **L2**

Caption Question Answer

Figure 1.16 Quantitative information is represented by the graph.

Problem-Solving Lab 1.2

Make and Use Graphs

What can be learned from a graph? One way to express information is to present it in the form of a graph. The amount of information available from a graph depends on the nature of the graph itself.

U.S. Students Enrolled in Physical Education

Solve the Problem

Study the graph at right. Answer the questions that follow and note the type of information that can and cannot be answered from the graph itself.

Thinking Critically

1. **Observe** Is there ever a year in high school when all students are enrolled in physical education? Explain your answer.
2. **Infer** Is there a relationship between the number of students enrolled in physical education and their year of high school? Explain your answer.
3. **Observe** Can you tell which states in the country have the largest number of students enrolled in physical education?
4. **Infer** Based on the graph, can you explain why so few students take physical education in their senior year?

Figure 1.16
This graph shows how many paramecia—microscopic organisms—survive as the temperature increases. **Infer** *What type of information is represented by the graph?*

Paramecium
LM Magnification: 65×

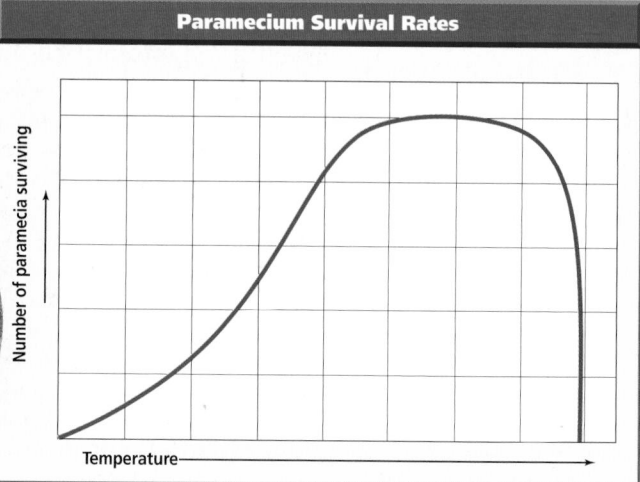

Paramecium Survival Rates

20 BIOLOGY: THE STUDY OF LIFE

Measuring in the International System

It is important that scientific research be understandable to scientists around the world. For example, what if scientists in the United States reported quantitative data in inches, feet, yards, ounces, pounds, pints, quarts, and gallons? People in many other countries would have trouble understanding these data because they are unfamiliar with the English system of measurement. Instead, scientists always report measurements in a form of the metric system called the International System of Measurement, commonly known as SI.

One advantage of SI is that there are only a few basic units, and nearly all measurements can be expressed in these units or combinations of them. The greatest advantage is that SI, like the metric system, is a decimal system. Measurements can be expressed in multiples of tens or tenths of a basic unit by applying a standard set of prefixes to the unit. In biology, the metric units you will encounter most often are meter (length), gram (mass),

CULTURAL DIVERSITY

Units and Standards The SI system is used in 95% of the countries in the world. It provides a standardized system of measurement for scientific communication. The ancient Egyptians used a unit called the cubit, which was based on the length of the arm from elbow to tip of the longest finger. Because sizes of individuals varied, the size of the unit varied. In England, a foot was the length of the foot of the king. When a new king came to power, the length became the size of his foot. Have students research measuring systems used around the world. **L3**

A Penguins cannot fly. They use their wings for swimming in the oceans of the southern hemisphere.

Figure 1.17
What kinds of information are gained by observing these animals?

B Toucans live in the rain forests of South America.

liter (volume), second (time), and Celsius degree (temperature). For a thorough review of measurement in SI, see *Math and Problem-Solving Skills* in the **Skill Handbook.**

✓Reading Check **Explain** why scientists use the SI system.

Qualitative information

Do you think the behavior of the animals shown in *Figure 1.17* would be easier to explain with numbers or with written descriptions of what the animals did? Observational data —that is, written descriptions of what scientists observe—are often just as important in the solution of a scientific problem as numerical data.

When biologists use purely observational data, they are using qualitative information. Qualitative information is useful because some phenomena aren't easily expressed as quantitative information. For example, the albatross example on page 13 cannot easily be illustrated with numbers. Practice your investigative skills in the *MiniLab* on the next page.

Science and Society

The road to scientific discovery includes making observations, formulating hypotheses, performing investigations, collecting and analyzing data, drawing conclusions, and reporting results in scientific journals. No matter what methods scientists choose, their research often provides society with important information that can be put to practical use.

Maybe you have heard people blame scientists for the existence of nuclear bombs or controversial drugs. To comprehend the nature of science in general, and biology in particular, people must understand that knowledge gained through scientific research is never inherently good or bad. Notions of good and bad arise out of human social, ethical, and moral concerns. **Ethics** refers to the moral principles and values held by humans. Scientists might not consider all the possible applications for the products of their research when planning their investigations. Society as a whole must take responsibility for the ethical use of scientific discoveries.

Can science answer all questions?

Some questions are simply not in the realm of science. Such questions may involve decisions regarding good versus evil, ugly versus beautiful, or similar judgments. There are also scientific questions that cannot be

Word Origin

technology from the Greek words *techne,* meaning an "art or skill," and *logos,* meaning "study"; Technology is the application of science in our daily lives.

Purpose

Students make observations and inferences and design an experiment that tests a hypothesis.

Process Skills

observe and infer, hypothesize, collect data, design an experiment

Safety Precautions

Pour the boiling water for the students. Do not have students pour it.

Teaching Strategies

■ Provide each group of students with two "dinosaur eggs" from specially marked packages of oatmeal. Each serving packet contains about 14 eggs.

■ Ask students to explain why this experiment would not be possible with real eggs.

Expected Results

The outer candy layer of a "dinosaur egg" dissolves in boiling water in less than a minute, leaving a dinosaur-shaped candy.

Analysis

1. Answers will vary.
2. To test heat, students might put eggs under a heat lamp. To test moisture, students might place eggs in various temperatures of water. Variable is heat or moisture. Control is the basis of comparison for the tested condition. Students could measure "hatching" time. Use as many eggs and trials as time permits.

Assessment

Performance Have students conduct the experiment they design. Use the Performance Task Assessment List for Carrying Out a Strategy and Collecting Data in **PASC,** p. 97. **L2**

Indiana Academic Standards

Pages 22–23: B.1.41

MiniLab 1.3

Observe and Infer

Hatching Dinosaurs Candy "dinosaur eggs" can be found in specially marked packages of oatmeal. You will conduct an investigation to determine what causes these pretend eggs to hatch.

Procedure 🖐️ 👕 👓

Data Table			
	Before Treatment	**Hot Water Treatment**	**Cold Water Treatment**
Appearance after one minute			

1 Copy the data table above.
2 Observe the dinosaur eggs provided, and record their characteristics in your table.
3 Place an egg in each of two containers.
4 Form a hypothesis about the water temperature that will cause the eggs to hatch.
5 Pour hot water into one container and cold water in the other. **CAUTION: *Be careful with hot water.*** Stir for one minute. Record your observations.

Analysis

1. **Analyze Data** Was your hypothesis supported? How would you revise it using the new information?
2. **Experiment** Design an experiment that would test either heat or moisture as the variable. What kind of quantitative data will you gather? What will be your control? How many trials will you run and how many eggs will you test? If time permits, conduct your experiment.

Figure 1.18 Technology allows doctors to develop and use better tools to diagnose medical problems.

INCLUSION STRATEGIES

Learning Disabled Create three displays of objects on a table in front of the classroom. Have the students write one qualitative term and one quantitative term to describe each display. **L1**

---

tested using scientific methods. However, this does not mean that these questions are unimportant.

Consider a particular question that is not testable. Some people assert that if a black cat crosses your path, you will have bad luck. On the surface, that hypothesis appears to be one that you could test. But what is bad luck, and how long would you have to wait for the bad luck to occur? How would you distinguish between bad luck caused by the black cat and bad luck that occurs at random? Once you examine the question, you can see there is no way to test it scientifically because you cannot devise a controlled experiment that would yield valid data.

Can technology solve all problems?

Science attempts to explain how and why things happen. Scientific study that is carried out mainly for the sake of knowledge—with no immediate interest in applying the results to daily living—is called pure science.

However, much of pure science eventually does have an impact on people's lives. Have you ever thought about what it was like to live in the world before the development of water treatment plants, vaccinations, antibiotics, or high-yielding crops? These and other life-saving developments, such as the brain scan shown in ***Figure 1.18,*** are indirect results of research done by scientists in many different fields over hundreds of years.

Other scientists work in research that has obvious and immediate applications. **Technology** (tek NAH luh jee) is the application of scientific research to society's needs and problems. It is concerned with making improvements in human life and the world around us. Technology has helped increase the production of food, reduced the amount of manual labor needed to make products and raise crops, and aided in the reduction of wastes and environmental pollution.

The advance of technology has benefited humans in numerous ways, but it has also resulted in some serious problems. For example, fertilizer is often used to boost the production of food crops, such as the corn shown in *Figure 1.19*. If more fertilizer is applied than the plants are able to use, the excess fertilizer can flow into streams or even oceans. Excess nitrogen has been shown to cause problems with some coral reefs by promoting the growth of algae.

Science and technology will never answer all of the questions we ask, nor will they solve all of our problems. However, during your study of biology you will have many of your questions answered, and you will explore many new concepts. As you learn more about living things, remember that you are a part of the living world, and you can use the processes of science to ask and answer questions about that world.

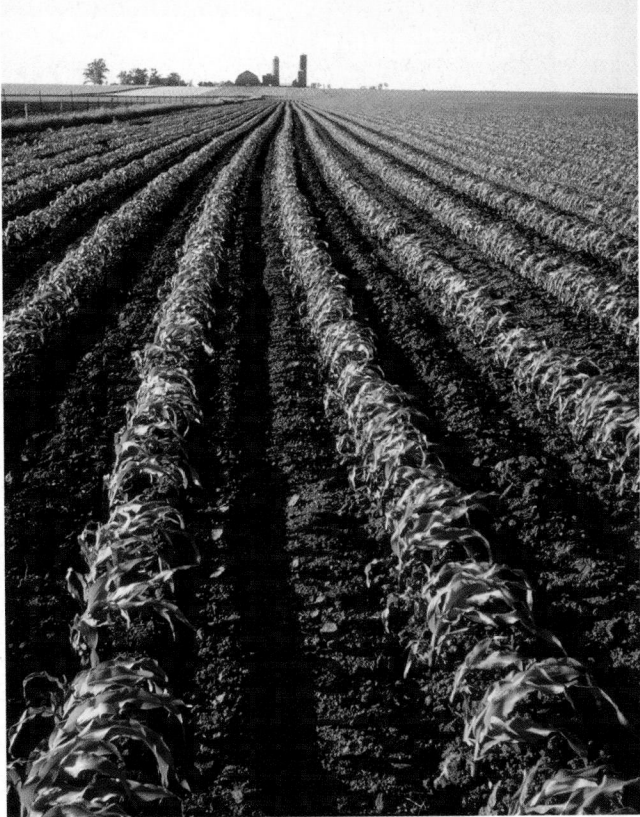

Figure 1.19
Technology allows farmers to use fertilizers that increase their crop production in order to meet the world's food needs. Crop yields from this field of corn are maximized with the use of improved plant breeds and fertilizer in order to feed the world's growing population.

Section Assessment

Understanding Main Ideas
1. Why is it important that scientific investigations be repeated? What happens when other scientists achieve different results when repeating an investigation?

2. Compare and contrast quantitative and qualitative. Explain how both types of information are important to biological studies.

3. Why is science considered to be a combination of information and process?

4. Why is technology not the solution to all scientific problems?

Thinking Critically
5. Biomedical research has led to the development of technology that can keep ill or incapacitated patients alive. How does this technology address the question of when such measures should be used on patients?

SKILL REVIEW

6. **Make and Use Graphs** Look at the graph in *Figure 1.16*. Why do you think that the high-temperature side of the graph drops off more sharply than the low-temperature side? For more help, refer to *Make and Use Graphs* in the **Skill Handbook.**

 in.bdol.glencoe.com/self_check_quiz

1.3 THE NATURE OF BIOLOGY **23**

DAILY INTERVENTION

Check for Understanding
Have students provide an example of: quantitative information, qualitative information, a contribution of technology, and an ethical issue in science. **L2**

Reteach
Ask students to prepare an outline of the major concepts of this section. **L2**

Resources
For more practice, use *Reading Essentials for Biology*, Section 1.3.

Extension

Logical-Mathematical Have students research the idea of "being able to beat cancer with a strong positive mental attitude." Have them explain why it may be difficult to evaluate scientifically how a positive mental attitude contributes to recovery from disease. **L3**

Assessment

Skill Have students measure their arm spans and palm widths in centimeters. Convert these measurements to millimeters and meters. **L3**

Section Assessment

1. to see if the results are repeatable, thus confirming their authenticity; original hypothesis may need to be revised

2. Quantitative information reports data in numerical values based on measuring. Qualitative information reports data in descriptions based on observations.

3. The processes of science are used to answer questions about or raised by scientific facts or information.

4. Some problems do not have a scientific basis. Some technological solutions may pose more problems than they solve.

5. The biomedical researchers sought to increase knowledge. The application of the resulting technology is a question society must answer.

6. Paramecia die above a certain temperature. This results in a rapid drop in numbers once this temperature is reached. They are better able to survive as low temperatures rise, thus the graph reflects this increased survival.

INTERNET BioLab

Time Allotment
one class period

Process Skills
collect data, define operationally, experiment, observe and infer, acquire information, think critically, communicate

Safety Precautions
Remind students to treat live animals gently and follow directions carefully. Have students wear goggles, lab aprons, and disposable gloves. Following the lab, students should wash hands thoroughly with soap and water.

PREPARATION

Pill bugs—also called sow bugs, wood lice, or isopods—may be collected locally or purchased from a biological supply house. *Armadillidium vulgare* is the only species that will roll tightly into a "pill," so it is preferred for this activity.

PROCEDURE

Troubleshooting
■ Students may have difficulty assessing whether pill bugs show an orderly structure. Advise them to make a "best guess" to answer this question.
■ Review the technique for preparing a histogram before you begin.

INTERNET BioLab

Before You Begin
Seeing different life forms, and even interacting with them, is pretty much part of a typical day. Petting a dog, swatting at a fly, cutting the grass, and talking to your friends are common examples. But, have you ever asked yourself the question, "What do all of these different life forms have in common?"

Data Table

Organization and Growth and Development	
Orderly structure?	yes
Pill bug length in mm	1.5 mm

Response to Environment	
☐Trial	Time in Seconds
1	3
2	3
3	7
4	5
5	5
Total	23
Average time	4

Collecting Biological Data

PREPARATION

Problem
What life characteristics can be observed in a pill bug?

Objectives
In this BioLab, you will:
■ **Observe** whether life characteristics are present in a pill bug.
■ **Measure** the length of a pill bug.
■ **Experiment** to determine if a pill bug responds to changes in its environment.
■ **Use the Internet** to collect and compare data from other students.

Materials
pill bugs, *Armadillidium* ruler
watch or classroom clock internet connection
container, glass or plastic pencil with dull point

Safety Precautions
CAUTION: *Always wear goggles in the lab.*

Skill Handbook
If you need help with this lab, refer to the **Skill Handbook**.

PROCEDURE

1. Make copies of the data table and graph outlines.
2. Obtain a pill bug from your teacher and place it in a small container.
3. Observe your pill bug to determine if it has an orderly structure. Record your observations in the data table.
4. Using millimeters, measure and record the length of your pill bug in the data table.
5. Using your data and data from your classmates, complete the graph "Pill Bug Length: Classroom Data."

Teaching Strategies
■ Allow students to work in small groups of two or three.
■ Make sure that students have already covered the section dealing with life characteristics before attempting this activity.

■ Review the procedure for determining an average. Have students round off their average data on the length of time in seconds the pill bug remains rolled up.

6. Go to in.bdol.glencoe.com/internet_lab to **post your data.**

7. *Gently* touch the underside of the pill bug with a *dull* pencil point. **CAUTION:** *Use care to avoid injuring the pill bug.*

8. Note its response and time, in seconds, how long the animal remains curled up. Record the time in the data table as Trial 1.

9. Repeat steps 7–8 four more times, recording each trial in the data table.

10. Calculate the average length of time your pill bug remains curled up.

11. **Post your data** at in.bdol.glencoe.com/internet_lab .

12. **CLEANUP AND DISPOSAL** Wash your hands after working with pill bugs. Return the pill bug to your teacher and suggest ways to release or reuse the bugs wisely.

Pill Bug Length: Classroom Data
Number of pill bugs / Length in millimeters

Pill Bug Length: Internet Data
Number of pill bugs / Length in millimeters

Average Pill Bug Response Time: Internet Data
Number of pill bugs / Response time in minutes

ANALYZE AND CONCLUDE

1. **Think Critically** Define the term "orderly structure." Explain how this trait also pertains to nonliving things.

2. **Use the Internet** Explain how data from the classroom and Internet graphs support the idea that pill bugs grow and develop.

3. **Interpret Data** What was the most common length of time pill bugs remained curled in response to being touched?

4. **Draw a Conclusion** Explain how the response to being touched is an adaptation.

5. **Experiment** How might you design an experiment to determine whether or not pill bugs reproduce?

6. **ERROR ANALYSIS** How might you collect or analyze data to better define a living organism?

Share Your Data

Find this BioLab using the link below, and post your data in the data table provided for this activity. Using the additional data from other students on the Internet, analyze the combined data, and complete your graphs.

 in.bdol.glencoe.com/internet_lab

1. Student answers will vary and may include the following: shows organization; has specific parts for certain jobs; all pill bugs look alike. Yes, orderly structure also applies to nonliving things. Many nonliving things are organized, including buildings, books, computers.

2. The graph shows that pill bugs vary in length, but most reach a maximum size of about 10 mm.

3. Pill bugs remain curled for an average of approximately 20 seconds.

4. The pill bugs' outer shell is rather tough; rolling into a ball could prevent predators from attacking its soft underside and fragile appendages.

5. Student answers will vary. Place several pill bugs in a sealed container and add food and moisture as needed. Observe pill bugs weekly and compare numbers present to those originally placed in container. Or, look for immature forms that may appear in the container.

6. **ERROR ANALYSIS** Students may suggest other types of information that would show that pill bugs are living things.

Share Your Data

To navigate the Internet BioLab, go to in.bdol.glencoe.com/internet_lab. Students should post their data in the data table provided. To expand this activity, have your students randomly choose data supplied by other students to determine how the average times differ.

Data and Observations

Students should conclude that pill bugs show organization, undergo growth and development, and adjust to their environment. Pill bugs will remain rolled in a ball for approximately 20 seconds. Typical length of a mature pill bug is 10 mm.

Assessment

Skill Ask students to prepare a graph of data that would be representative of the experimental results from "Share Your Data." Refer students to *Make and Use Graphs* in the **Skill Handbook.** Use the Performance Task Assessment List for Graph from Data in **PASC,** p. 111. **L2**

Biology and Society

Purpose

This feature allows students to analyze claims made about organically grown produce. Students are encouraged to formulate and present their own views.

Teaching Strategies

■ Provide recent newspaper and magazine articles regarding claims about organically grown produce.

■ Ask students to discuss the advantages and disadvantages of using herbicides, pesticides, and fertilizers on crops.

■ Have students interview produce managers in several supermarkets to obtain their views concerning organically grown produce. **L3**

■ Have students investigate the methods used for displaying produce in supermarkets. Ask them to write a summary of their findings. **L2**

Forming Your Opinion

Standards will differ. Look for recent research findings on types and amounts of pesticides, as well as analysis of products labelled as organic. Students should take positions based on their research and use this information in a debate. As part of the debate, students should present various forms of promotional claims about organic foods and evaluate those claims.

Going Further

Bring samples of organic and conventional produce to class. Ask students to compare the cost, appearance, and (with parent or guardian permission) taste of the samples and discuss how price, appearance, and taste might affect consumer purchase decisions. **L1**

26

Organic Food: Is it healthier?

The produce section of the supermarket has two bins of leafy lettuce that look very much alike. One is labeled "organic" and has a higher price. More and more consumers are willing to pay extra for organically grown fruits, vegetables, meats, and dairy products. What are they paying that extra money for?

The term "organic" usually refers to foods that are produced without the use of chemical pesticides, herbicides, or fertilizers. Organic farmers use nonchemical methods to control pests and encourage crop growth. Beneficial insects, such as ladybugs and *Trichogramma* wasps, are brought in to feed on aphids, caterpillars, and other damaging insects. Instead of applying herbicides, organic farmers pull weeds by hand or by machine. In place of fertilizers, they use composting and crop rotation to enrich the soil. Organic farming is very labor intensive, so organic foods are usually more expensive than those produced by conventional methods.

Perspectives People usually buy organic products because they want to be sure they're getting nutritious food with no chemical residues. But there are differences of opinion about how much better organic food actually is, and even which foods should be called organic.

Is organic food healthier? Agricultural chemicals can leave residues on food and contaminate drinking water supplies. Since exposure to some chemicals is known to cause health problems, including cancer, many consumers think that organic foods are healthier. Chemical pest controls kill beneficial organisms as well as unwanted pests, and can adversely affect the health of other animals, especially those that feed on insects. Organic pest control methods usually target specific pests and have little effect on beneficial organisms.

Produce from an organic farm

Conventionally grown food: Low cost, higher yield? Chemical fertilizers and pesticides make it possible to grow larger crops at lower cost, which makes more food available to more people. Making sure everyone can afford an adequate supply of fruits and vegetables may be more important than the risk of disease posed by agricultural chemicals.

Not everyone agrees about what is organic and what isn't. Should genetically engineered plant or animal foods be considered organic? What about herbs or meats preserved by irradiation, or lettuce and tomatoes fertilized with sewage sludge?

Forming Your Opinion

Analyze the Issue Use resources to investigate your state's standards for labeling food products as "organic." Look for research that shows that organically grown food is safer than conventionally grown food. Describe your findings in your science journal.

 To find out more about organic food, visit in.bdol.glencoe.com/biology_society

Chapter 1 Assessment

STUDY GUIDE

Section 1.1

What is biology?

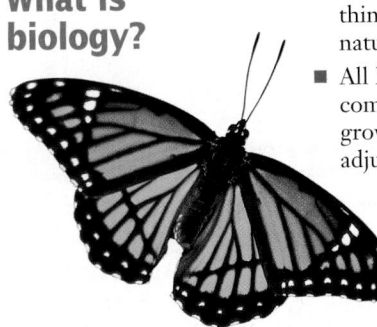

Key Concepts
- Biology is the organized study of living things and their interactions with their natural and physical environments.
- All living things have four characteristics in common: organization, reproduction, growth and development, and the ability to adjust to the environment.

Vocabulary
adaptation (p. 9)
biology (p. 3)
development (p. 8)
energy (p. 9)
environment (p. 8)
evolution (p. 10)
growth (p. 8)
homeostasis (p. 9)
organism (p. 6)
organization (p. 7)
reproduction (p. 7)
response (p. 9)
species (p. 7)
stimulus (p. 9)

Section 1.2

The Methods of Biology

Key Concepts
- Biologists use controlled experiments to obtain data that either do or do not support a hypothesis. By publishing the results and conclusions of an experiment, a scientist allows others to try to verify the results. Repeated verification over time leads to the development of a theory.
- Scientific methods are used by scientists to answer questions or solve problems. Scientific methods include observing, making a hypothesis, collecting data, publishing results, forming a theory, developing new hypotheses, and revising the theory.

Vocabulary
control (p. 13)
data (p. 15)
dependent variable (p. 13)
experiment (p. 13)
hypothesis (p. 12)
independent variable (p. 13)
safety symbol (p. 15)
scientific methods (p. 11)
theory (p. 18)

Section 1.3

The Nature of Biology

Key Concepts
- Biologists do their work in laboratories and in the field. They collect both quantitative and qualitative data from their experiments and investigations.
- Scientists conduct investigations to increase knowledge about the natural world. Scientific results may help solve some problems, but not all.

Vocabulary
ethics (p. 21)
technology (p. 22)

FOLDABLES™
Study Organizer To help you review the characteristics of living things, use the Organizational Study Fold on page 3.

 in.bdol.glencoe.com/vocabulary_puzzlemaker

CHAPTER 1 ASSESSMENT **27**

Key Concepts
Summary statements can be used by students to review the major concepts of the chapter.

 Biology Online

Visit in.bdol.glencoe.com
/self_check_quiz
/vocabulary_puzzlemaker
/chapter_test
/standardized_test

VOCABULARY PUZZLEMAKER

 For additional help with vocabulary, have students access the Vocabulary PuzzleMaker online at in.bdol.glencoe.com/vocabulary_puzzlemaker

FOLDABLES™
Have students use their Foldables to review content in Section 1.1. On the back of the paper, write a hypothesis about how each of the three organisms would survive in a habitat different from the one it usually lives in. In what way would they each have to adapt?

Use the ExamView®Pro Test Bank CD-ROM to:
- Create **multiple versions** of tests
- Create **modified** tests with one mouse click for **inclusion** students
- **Edit** existing questions and **add** your own questions
- Build tests aligned with state standards using built-in **State Curriculum Tags**
- Change **English** tests to **Spanish** with one mouse click and vice versa

 Indiana Academic Standards
Pages 26–27: B.1.41

Questions and answers have been aligned and verified by The Princeton Review.

Vocabulary Review

1. technology
2. adaptation
3. organism
4. species
5. hypothesis

Understanding Key Concepts

6. B		**8.** B	
7. D		**9.** D	

Constructed Response

10. It is composed of cells, which are organized into tissues and organs, which are organized into body systems.
11. Biometrics is used as an analysis tool, but recently biometrics has been used as an instrument for identification as well.
12. Evolution is the result of species adapting to environmental change.

Thinking Critically

13. open flame alert
14. Students may agree or disagree with Congressional views, but their opinions should be supported. Example: a student may be of the opinion that human cloning should not be allowed based on a belief that additional technology may only pose additional or more troublesome problems.

Vocabulary Review

Review the Chapter 1 vocabulary words listed in the Study Guide on page 27. Match the words with the definitions below.

1. the application of scientific research to society's needs and problems
2. any structure, behavior, or internal process that enables an organism to respond to environmental factors and live to produce offspring
3. anything that possesses all the characteristics of life
4. a group of organisms that can interbreed and produce fertile offspring in nature
5. an explanation for a question or problem that can be tested

Understanding Key Concepts

6. Which of the following is not an appropriate question for science to consider?
   A. How many seals can a killer whale consume in a day?
   B. Which type of orchid flower is most beautiful?
   C. What birds prefer seeds as a food source?
   D. When do hoofed mammals in Africa migrate northward?
7. Similar-looking organisms, such as the dogs shown below, that can interbreed and produce fertile offspring are called _____.
   A. a living system   C. organization
   B. an adaptation   D. a species

8. If data from repeated experiments do not support the hypothesis, what is the scientist's next step?
   A. Declare the experiment unsuccessful.
   B. Revise the hypothesis.
   C. Repeat the experiment.
   D. Overturn the theory.

---

9. The single factor that is altered in an experiment is the _____.
   A. control
   B. dependent variable
   C. hypothesis
   D. independent variable

Constructed Response

10. **Open Ended** Describe how the human body shows the life characteristic of organization.
11. **Open Ended** Scientists use quantitative data to derive mathematical models, termed biometrics. Research two definitions and uses of biometrics in today's society.
12. **Describe** Explain the relationships among an organism's environment, adaptations, and evolution.

Thinking Critically

Table 1.1 Safety Symbols

 Sharp Object Safety This symbol appears when a danger of cuts or punctures caused by the use of sharp objects exists.

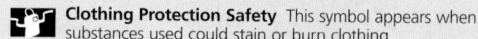 **Clothing Protection Safety** This symbol appears when substances used could stain or burn clothing.

Eye Safety This symbol appears when a danger to the eyes exists. Safety goggles should be worn when this symbol appears.

Chemical Safety This symbol appears when chemicals used can cause burns or are poisonous if absorbed through the skin.

13. **Interpret** An experiment involves heating chemicals in a test tube over a flame. Which of the safety symbols shown above should be used in the experiment? Which symbol from the **Skill Handbook** is needed above, but missing from this table?

14. **REAL WORLD BIOCHALLENGE** Recently members of Congress have debated the issue of human cloning. Visit **in.bdol.glencoe.com** to investigate this debate. Write an essay expressing your opinion. Use reasoning based on your understanding of the debate to support your opinion. Present your opinion in a debate with members of your class.

 in.bdol.glencoe.com/chapter_test

RUBRIC

Evaluating Open-Ended Questions
Open-ended assessment questions are graded by using a multilevel rubric that guides you in assessing a student's knowledge of a particular concept. The following rubric is a sample scoring device.

End-of-Course Assessment Practice

All questions aligned and verified by *The Princeton Review*

Part 1 ▸ Multiple Choice

The Effect of Temperature on Germination

A team of students measured the number of seeds that germinated over ten days in a control group at 18°C and in an experimental group at 25°C. They graphed their data as shown above. Study the graph and answer questions 15–18.

15. Which of the following best represents the hypothesis tested?
  A. Black seeds are best.
  B. Seeds germinate faster at warmer temperatures.
  C. Fertilization of seeds requires heat.
  D. Seeds germinate when freezing.

16. When did the experiment end?
  A. day 3   **C.** day 7
  B. day 6   **D.** day 10

17. Which of the following was the independent variable?
  A. kind of seeds
  B. number germinating
  C. temperature
  D. time

18. Which of the following was the dependent variable?
  A. kind of seeds
  B. number germinating
  C. temperature
  D. time

Use the drawing below to answer question 19.

19. In scientific investigations it is important to collect data and make measurements with precision. A graduated cylinder is often used to measure volumes of liquids accurately and precisely. The surface of many liquids in a graduated cylinder forms a curved surface called a meniscus. What is the volume of fluid in the graduated cylinder shown on the right?
  A. 79 mL   **C.** 81 mL
  B. 80 mL   **D.** 75 mL

20. Which of the following statements is true of a theory?
  A. A theory is considered true and never changes.
  B. A theory makes predictions about unknown phenomena.
  C. A theory is the same thing as a hypothesis.
  D. A theory is the usual outcome of an experiment.

Part 2 ▸ Constructed Response/Grid In

Record your answers on your answer document.

21. Open Ended Why does a panel of doctors, lawyers, clergy, and others sometimes convene to determine if an experimental operation should be allowed on human patients?

22. Open Ended Consider the following items: a flame, bubbles blown from a bubble wand, and a balloon released into the air. Describe characteristics of each that might indicate life and those that indicate they are not alive.

 in.bdol.glencoe.com/standardized_test

End-of-Course Assessment Practice

15. B   **18.** B
16. D   **19.** A
17. C   **20.** B

21. Ethics, the principles and values held by humans, often determine whether certain experiments are performed. The benefits of a procedure are weighed against possible harm to the individual and to society. This is one way that science is limited.

22. A flame uses energy, can move, and grow large. Bubbles and balloons move. However, none of these has all of the characteristics of living things.

FAST FILE

Answer Sheet A practice answer sheet can be found on p. 33 of *Unit 1 FAST FILE Resources.*

RUBRIC

SCORE	CRITERIA
4	A correct solution that is supported by well-developed, accurate explanations.
3	A generally correct solution, but may contain minor flaws in reasoning.

SCORE	CRITERIA
2	A partially correct interpretation and/or solution to the problem.
1	A correct solution with no supporting evidence or explanation.
0	An incorrect solution or no solution is given.

Indiana Academic Standards

Pages 28–29: B.1.31, B.1.43

29

Prepare

Short on Time?

This BioDigest can be used as a brief overview of the nature of science and the characteristics of life. If time is limited, you may wish to use this unit summary to teach these concepts in place of Chapter 1.

Key Concepts

Students are introduced to the characteristics of life and the methods of science. They learn about the nature and limitations of science and technology.

Bellringer

Show students a candle flame and a caged mouse. Ask students to explain the similarities and differences of the two to elicit the characteristics of life. **L1**

Microscope Activity

Visual-Spatial Have students examine slides of protists. Ask what characteristics of life the organisms share. **L1**

DAILY INTERVENTION

Check for Understanding
Have students explain why science and technology cannot answer all questions. **L2**

Reteach
Visual-Spatial Ask students to observe a seed and make a hypothesis about whether it is alive. Have them plant the seed and record the characteristics of life they note over the period of a week or two.

Indiana Academic Standards

Pages 30–31: B.1.11, B.1.16, B.1.18

What is biology?

Living things abound almost everywhere on Earth—in deep ocean trenches, atop the highest mountains, in dry deserts, and in wet tropical forests. Biology is the study of living organisms and the interactions among them. Biologists use a variety of scientific methods to study the details of life.

Characteristics of Life

Biologists have formulated a list of characteristics by which we can recognize living things.

Organization

All living things are organized into cells. Organisms may be composed of one cell or many cells. Cells are like rooms in a building. You can think of a many-celled organism as a building containing many rooms. Groups of rooms in different areas of the building are used for different purposes. These areas are analogous to the tissues, organs, and body systems of plants and animals.

Homeostasis

A stable internal environment is necessary for life. Organisms maintain this stability through homeostasis, which is a process that requires the controlled use of energy in cells. Plants obtain energy by converting light, water, and carbon dioxide into food. Other organisms obtain their energy indirectly from plants.

Response to a Stimulus

Living things respond to changes in their external environment. Any change, such as a rise in temperature or the presence of food, is a stimulus.

Growth and Development

When living things grow, their cells enlarge and divide. As organisms age, other changes also take place. Development consists of the changes in an organism that take place over time.

Reproduction

Living things reproduce by transmitting their hereditary information from one generation to the next.

Scientific Methods

Scientists employ a variety of scientific methods to investigate questions and solve problems. Not all investigations will use all methods, and the order in which they are used will vary.

Observation

Curiosity leads scientists to make observations that raise questions about natural phenomena.

Hypothesis

A statement that can be tested and presents a possible solution to a question is a hypothesis.

Experiment

After making a hypothesis, the next step is to test it. An experiment is a formal method of testing a hypothesis. In a controlled experiment, two groups are tested and all conditions except one are kept the same for both groups. The single condition that changes is the independent variable. The condition caused by the change in the independent variable is called the dependent variable.

Theory

When a hypothesis has been confirmed by many experiments, it may become a theory. Theories explain natural phenomena.

✔ Assessment

Skill Provide students with an example of a biological question or problem. Have the class discuss how they would use scientific methods to provide an answer.

RESOURCE MANAGER

Unit 1 *FAST FILE* Resources
Reinforcement and Study Guide in English, pp. 35–36
Reinforcement and Study Guide in Spanish, pp. 37–38
Student Recording Sheet, p. 39

End-of-Course Assessment Practice

TEST-TAKING TIP

Maximize Your Score

Ask how your test will be scored. In order to do your best, you need to know if there is a penalty for guessing, and if so, how much of a penalty. If there is no random-guessing penalty at all, you should always fill in an answer.

Part 1 Multiple Choice

1. The basic unit of organization of living things is a(n) _____.
A. atom   C. cell
B. organism   D. organ

2. Storing and periodically releasing energy obtained from food is an example of _____.
A. evolution   C. response
B. homeostasis   D. growth

3. A hypothesis that is supported many times may become a(n) _____.
A. experiment   C. theory
B. conclusion   D. observation

4. All of the procedures scientists use to answer questions are _____.
A. life characteristics   C. research
B. scientific methods   D. hypotheses

5. The environment includes _____.
A. air, water, and weather
B. response to a stimulus
C. adaptations
D. evolution

6. Which of the following is NOT a testable hypothesis?
A. Fertilizer A will make the KW variety of green bean produce more beans.
B. Smart people like the same music.
C. Vitamin C relieves cold symptoms.
D. There is more than one species of African elephant.

Use the lab procedure below to answer questions 7 and 8.

> A group of scientists wishes to see if using a new, environmentally friendly pesticide is effective in preventing insect damage to soybeans. Three different soybean plots are planted. The first plot contains soybeans treated with the traditional pesticide. The second plot is treated with the new environmentally friendly pesticide. The third plot is left untreated.

7. Which plot is the control group?
A. the first plot with traditional pesticide
B. the second plot with the new pesticide
C. the third plot with no pesticide
D. there is no control group

8. What could be concluded if the plot treated with the new pesticide has damage similar to the control plot?
A. The experiment is a failure.
B. The new pesticide may not be effective.
C. The control plot was problematic.
D. The new pesticide should be used.

Part 2 Constructed Response/Grid In

Record your answers on your answer document.

9. Open Ended List the characteristics you would check to see if a pine tree is a living thing. Give an example that shows how the tree exhibits each characteristic.

10. Open Ended Compare the characteristics of life with the flames of a fire. How are they similar and different?

11. Open Ended Why do most experiments have a control? Describe an experiment that does not have a control.

12. Open Ended Evaluate the impact that scientific research has on society.

---

 in.bdol.glencoe.com/standardized_test

UNIT 1 STANDARDIZED TEST PRACTICE **31**

This page contains practice questions in the various formats that can be found on the most frequently given standardized tests.

1. C   5. A
2. B   6. B
3. C   7. C
4. B   8. B

9. Cells would show cellular structure; homeostasis is shown by making and using energy from sunlight; growing toward the light is a response to stimulus; growth and development would be shown in the changes since the plant was a seed; reproduction occurs when it produces new seeds.

10. Fires can grow, use energy, and reproduce. Fires are not composed of cells.

11. A control is a basis for comparison. A behavior experiment may not have a control.

12. Answers will vary.

Answer Sheet A practice answer sheet can be found on p. 39 of *Unit 1 FAST FILE Resources.*

RUBRIC

For more help evaluating open-ended assessment questions, see the rubric on p. 9T.

Unit 2

Ecology

Unit Overview

Unit 2 focuses on the interactions that exist between organisms and between organisms and environments.

Chapter 2 introduces ecology and the biotic and abiotic factors that exist in an ecosystem.

Chapter 3 centers on succession, the development of communities, and describes major world biomes.

Chapter 4 presents characteristics of population growth and factors that limit population growth. Students study demographics.

Chapter 5 discusses people's impact on the environment, threats to biodiversity, and conservation biology strategies.

Introducing the Unit

Ask students to look at the scene in Glacier Bay National Park and Preserve in Alaska. Describe how the flowers are dependent on both living and nonliving things in their environment.

WebQuest

A WebQuest is an inquiry-based online project in which all information used by students is obtained from the Web. Students evaluate the information to complete the activity. Access the Unit 2 WebQuest at **in.bdol.glencoe.com/webquest**

Unit 2

History & Biology

1830 ● The lawn mower is invented.

1851 ● One hundred house sparrows are introduced in the United States.

1800　　　　　*1850*

16 000 B.C. ● The glaciers of the last ice age reach their greatest extent.

1859 ● The first oil well in the U.S. is drilled in Titusville, PA.

Ecology

What You'll Learn

Chapter 2
Principles of Ecology

Chapter 3
Communities and Biomes

Chapter 4
Population Biology

Chapter 5
Biological Diversity and Conservation

Unit 2 Review
BioDigest & Standardized Test Practice

Why It's Important

Everything on Earth—air, land, water, plants, and animals—is connected. Understanding these connections helps us keep our environment clean, healthy, and safe.

Indiana Standards

The following standards are covered in Unit 2:
B.1.18, B.1.32, B.1.37, B.1.38, B.1.39, B.1.40, B.1.41, B1.42, B.1.43, B.1.44, B.1.45, B.1.46, B.1.47

Understanding the Photo ▶

At the foot of the Elias Mountains in Glacier Bay National Park and Preserve in Alaska, a cold, clear stream moves silently past brilliant purple dwarf fireweed and red and yellow Indian paintbrush plants growing out of a rocky beach. The clouds are so low, it looks as if they could touch the stream. Ecology is the study of the interactions of plants and animals, where they live, how they survive, and sometimes, what causes their demise.

32 in.bdol.glencoe.com/webquest

Time Line

Discussion Have students look at the time span for the ecology time line. Have students think about entries on the time line, such as the growth of an introduced species (the house sparrow), the development of the use of various fuels, and the interest in conservation. Major environmental laws have also been enacted in the past 20 years. Have students research one of these actions. Then, as a class, discuss the strengths and weaknesses of each. **L2**

1872
Yellowstone becomes the world's first national park.

1916
The National Park Service is formed.

1957
American Bandstand airs nationally.

2000
One hundred fifty million house sparrows live in the United States

1900

1950

2000

1901
The modern oil industry begins in Spindletop, TX, with the Lucas Gusher.

1934
Federal Duck Stamp sales begin. The funds raised conserve wetlands.

1967
The first list of endangered species is issued.

1999
The world population reaches 6 billion.

1888
The first use of a large windmill to generate electricity takes place in Cleveland, OH.

Unit 2

Advance Materials Planning

The following materials may need to be ordered a few weeks in advance of the planned activity.

Chapter 2

- ■ **MiniLab** (p. 36) seeds
- ■ **Additional Lab** (p. 38) corn or pinto bean seeds
- ■ **Quick Demo** (p. 49) clear drinking glass
- ■ **Quick Demo** (p. 53) small terrarium
- ■ **MiniLab** (p. 54) test tubes, bromothymol blue, antacids
- ■ **BioLab** (p. 58) live *Paramecium* and *Didinium*

Chapter 3

- ■ **Quick Demo** (p. 66) cactus and houseplants
- ■ **MiniLab** (p. 67) lichen samples
- ■ **MiniLab** (p. 73) plankton
- ■ **Additional Lab** (p. 76) sand, clay, potting soil
- ■ **BioLab** (p. 84) sterilized pond water, pond plants, cooked rice

Chapter 4

- ■ **MiniLab** (p. 92) bananas
- ■ **Additional Lab** (p. 96) radish seeds
- ■ **Quick Demo** (p. 97) checkers
- ■ **BioLab** (p. 104) beans

Chapter 5

- ■ **MiniLab** (p. 112) activity site
- ■ **MiniLab** (p. 122) soil
- ■ **Quick Demo** (p. 124) gingko leaves

33

Unit Projects

Interview
Linguistic Students can interview an aquarium shop owner to find out how to maintain an aquarium. Students can describe how to maintain a healthy environment for the fish. **L1**

Make a Model
Kinesthetic Students can create a working aquatic ecosystem that contains both biotic and abiotic elements in a healthy balance. **L1** **ELL**

Use the Library
Intrapersonal Have students use the library to find out why space exploration may be dependent on the quest for artificial, closed ecosystems. **L2**

Chapter 2 Organizer

Section Objectives	National Science Standards	State/Local Standards	Advanced Lab and Demo Planning
Section 2.1 2 sessions, 1 block 1. **Distinguish** between the biotic and abiotic factors in the environment. 2. **Compare** the different levels of biological organization and living relationships important in ecology. 3. **Explain** the difference between a niche and a habitat.	UCP.1–3; A.1, A.2; C.4, C.5, C.6; F.3, F.5; G.1–4	**Indiana Standards** B.1.32, B.1.37, B.1.41, B.1.43, B.1.45, B.1.47	**Student Labs:** MiniLab 2.1, p. 36: 40 seeds of one species of plant, water, 10% saltwater solution, paper towels, plastic bags Problem-Solving Lab 2.1, p. 37 Additional Lab, p. 38: 120 seeds (corn, pinto beans), six paper cups, six plastic sandwich bags, water, paper toweling, graduated cylinder, labels
Section 2.2 3 sessions, 2 1/2 blocks 4. **Compare** how organisms satisfy their nutritional needs. 5. **Trace** the path of energy and matter in an ecosystem. 6. **Analyze** how matter is cycled in the abiotic and biotic parts of the biosphere.	UCP.1–3; A.1, A.2; B.3, B.6; C.4, C.5, C.6; D.1, D.2; F.3–5; G.1–3	**Indiana Standards** B.1.19, B.1.37, B.1.40, B.1.41, B.1.42, B.1.43, B.1.44, B.1.45, B.1.47	**Student Labs:** Problem-Solving Lab 2.2, p. 50 MiniLab 2.2, p. 54: two test tubes, bromothymol blue solution, antacid tablet, drinking straws Design Your Own BioLab, p. 58: See below materials. **Teacher Demonstrations:** Quick Demo, p. 49: water, pencil Quick Demo, p. 53: terrarium, soil, plants, plastic wrap
End of Chapter Assessment Student Edition Study Guide, p. 61 Content Assessment, pp. 62–63		**Indiana Standards** B.1.37, B.1.40, B.1.41, B.1.43, B.1.44, B.1.45, B.1.47	**Student Lab:** Design Your Own BioLab, p. 58: microscope, microscope slides, coverslips, live culture of *Didinium*, live culture of *Paramecium*, beakers or jars, eyedroppers, sterile pond water

Key to Teaching Strategies

L1 Level 1 activities should be appropriate for students with learning difficulties.

L2 Level 2 activities should be within the ability range of all students.

L3 Level 3 activities are designed for above-average students.

ELL ELL activities should be within the ability range of English Language Learners.

COOP LEARN Cooperative Learning activities are designed for small group work.

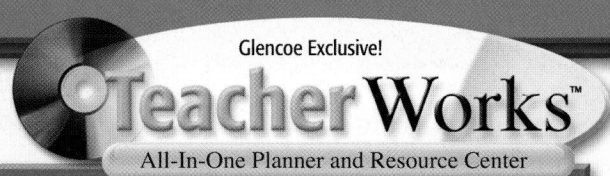

Glencoe Exclusive!

TeacherWorks™

All-In-One Planner and Resource Center

Reproducible Masters and Transparencies	Technology

Unit 2 FAST FILE Resources
- MiniLab Worksheet, p. 3
- Real World BioApplications, pp. 7–8
- Reinforcement and Study Guide in English, pp. 9–10
- Reinforcement and Study Guide in Spanish, pp. 13–14
- Critical Thinking/Problem Solving, p. 18
- Transparency Worksheet, p. 19

Reading Essentials for Biology, Section 2.1

Laboratory Manual, pp. 9–10

🖐 **Section Focus Transparency 4**

💿 **Interactive Chalkboard CD-ROM: Section 2.1 Presentation**
💿 **TeacherWorks™ CD-ROM**
🎵 **Guided Reading Audio Summaries MP3**
💿 **Virtual Labs CD-ROM**
    Virtual Lab: A Mini Biosphere

Unit 2 FAST FILE Resources
- MiniLab Worksheet, p. 4
- BioLab Worksheet, pp. 5–6
- Reinforcement and Study Guide in English, pp. 11–12
- Reinforcement and Study Guide in Spanish, pp. 15–16
- Concept Mapping, p. 17
- Transparency Worksheets, pp. 20–30

Reading Essentials for Biology, Section 2.2

Probeware Labs, pp. 1–4

Inside Story Poster

🖐 **Section Focus Transparency 5**

🖐 **Basic Concepts Transparencies 1, 2**

🖐 **Reteaching Skills Transparencies 1–3**

💿 **Interactive Chalkboard CD-ROM: Section 2.2 Presentation**
💿 **TeacherWorks™ CD-ROM**
🎵 **Guided Reading Audio Summaries MP3**

Unit 2 FAST FILE Resources
- Chapter Assessment, pp. 31–36
- Student Recording Sheet, p. 37

The Princeton Review **Reviewing Biology,** pp. 3–4

💿 **Interactive Chalkboard:**
Chapter 2 Assessment
💿 **MindJogger Videoquizzes DVD/VHS**
💿 **ExamView® Pro Test Bank CD-ROM**
💿 **TeacherWorks™ CD-ROM**
💿 **Succeeding on National Standards CD-ROM**

🖥 in.bdol.glencoe.com
/self_check_quiz
/vocabulary_puzzlemaker
/chapter_test
/standardized_test

 Indicates materials created specifically for Indiana.

Short on Time?

BIODIGEST The BioDigest at the end of this unit can be used as a(n):

- preview to introduce important unit concepts.
- overview if time does not permit teaching the entire chapter.
- review of key unit concepts.

Understanding the Photo

Provide students with the opportunity to discuss what the bird is doing. Cedar waxwings like the high sugar content of ripening fruit (in this case, Mountain ash berries). Ask students what clues this fact might give them about when the bird will be most visible. summer into early fall when fruit is ripe As you develop the concepts of biotic and abiotic factors, use this photo to make these concepts more real. The bird and the ripening fruit are biotic factors. The time of year, controlled by light and climate, is an abiotic factor that affects the time food is available to the bird. Later in the chapter, have students write or discuss how the photograph sums up the big picture of ecology.

INTERACTIVE CHALKBOARD with Image Bank

PowerPoint® Presentations

This CD-ROM is an editable Microsoft® PowerPoint® presentation that includes:

- Section presentations
- Section checks
- Image bank
- Hot links to Biology Online
- All transparencies

Chapter 2

Principles of Ecology

What You'll Learn

- You will describe ecology and the work of ecologists.
- You will identify important aspects of an organism's environment.
- You will trace the flow of energy and nutrients in the living and nonliving worlds.

Why It's Important

Organisms get what they need to survive from their immediate environment. There they find food and shelter, reproduce and interact with other organisms. It is important to understand how living things depend on their environments.

Understanding ▶ the Photo

If you have a sweet tooth and lots of friends, you have a lot in common with the cedar waxwing *(Bombycilla cedrorum)* shown here. These handsome birds are known for traveling in flocks and for their fruit-eating habits. They can be found wherever fruit is ripening and so their range is extensive throughout the year. In winter, flocks of up to 100 birds can be found from southern Canada to Central America.

Biology Online

Visit in.bdol.glencoe.com to
- study the entire chapter online
- access Web Links for more information and activities on ecology
- review content with the Interactive Tutor and self-check quizzes

34

Two-Minute Chapter Launcher

Demo Place a goldfish in one small bowl and a *Betta splendens* (Siamese fighting fish) in another. Goldfish are a cold-water species that eat large amounts of plant food, and bettas are a tropical species that are completely carnivorous. Have students observe the two fishes and discuss their different behaviors. If the bowls are close together, students may see the betta become agitated at the sight of the more docile goldfish. **CAUTION:** *Wash hands if in contact with the fishes or water.*

Organisms and Their Environment

Indiana Standards Standard B.1.43 Understand that and describe how organisms are influenced by a particular combination of living and nonliving components of the environment.

SECTION PREVIEW

Objectives
Distinguish between the biotic and abiotic factors in the environment.

Compare the different levels of biological organization and living relationships important in ecology.

Explain the difference between a niche and a habitat.

Review Vocabulary
species: a group of organisms that can interbreed and produce fertile offspring in nature (p. 7)

New Vocabulary
ecology
biosphere
abiotic factor
biotic factor
population
biological community
ecosystem
habitat
niche
symbiosis
commensalism
mutualism
parasitism

Where in the world am I?

Finding the Main Idea When you start to study a new topic in depth, it is sometimes difficult to see the big ideas and make the connections that you need to make. Learning about ecology is more than memorizing the vocabulary. Of all the subjects that you might study in biology, ecology makes you stand back to get the big picture—of how individual organisms interact with each other and with their environment, because it is your environment, too.

Organize Information *As you study this chapter, use the red and blue titles throughout the chapter to organize information or outline the main ideas of ecology.*

Transparency **4** Interactions Within Ecosystems — SECTION FOCUS — *Use with Chapter 2, Section 2.1*

① How do these organisms interact with one another and with the nonliving parts of the environment?

② What might happen if the zebras were removed?

BIOLOGY: The Dynamics of Life — SECTION FOCUS TRANSPARENCIES

Sharing the World

How much do you know about the environment and the organisms that share your life? As cities and suburbs expand, and humans move into territories previously occupied by fields and wildlife, animals such as raccoons and deer are tipping over garbage cans and meandering through backyards. Every day, you also interact with houseflies, mosquitoes, billions of dust mites, and other organisms that you cannot even see. What affects their environment also affects you. Understanding what affects the environment is important because it is where you live.

Studying nature

People have always shown an interest in their natural surroundings. You may know someone who can identify every animal, plant, and rock they see. Other people keep records of rainfall and temperature. The study of plants and animals, including where they grow and live, what they eat, or what eats them, is called natural history. Collecting data like these is similar to taking the pulse of an individual. These data reflect the status or health of the world in which you live.

Finding the Main Idea

Organize Information Students can use the red and blue titles and subtopics discussed to make an outline of the section (or chapter). An example of how the outline can begin is shown here:

I. Organisms and Their Environment
   A. Sharing the World
      1. Studying Nature
   B. What is ecology?
      1. Definition of ecology
      2. Ecological research
   C. The Biosphere
      1. Structure of the biosphere
      2. The nonliving environment
      3. The living environment
II. Levels of Organization and so on . . .

Unit 2 *FAST FILE* Resources
MiniLab Worksheet, p. 3
Real World BioApplications, pp. 7–8
Reinforcement and Study Guide in English, pp. 9–10
Reinforcement and Study Guide in Spanish, pp. 13–14
Critical Thinking/Problem Solving, p. 18
Transparency Worksheet, p. 19

Reading Essentials for Biology, Section 2.1
Laboratory Manual, pp. 9–10
Section Focus Transparency 4

Indiana Academic Standards

Pages 34–35: B.1.41, B.1.47

2 Teach

Purpose

Students will experiment with the abiotic factor of salinity to determine if seed germination is affected.

Process Skills

collect data, experiment, interpret data

Safety Precautions

Seeds can develop bacterial or fungal contamination. Caution students to wear protective, disposable gloves and to wash hands with soap before, to reduce contamination, and after completing cleanup.

Troubleshooting

Try using fewer seeds (as few as 5) if the roots tangle.

Teaching Strategies

■ Prepare the 10% sodium chloride (table salt) solution by dissolving 100 g of table salt in 900 mL of tap water.

■ Have students form a hypothesis prior to the experiment.

■ Ask students to identify the control and the independent and dependent variables in the experiment.

Expected Results

Seeds in freshwater will show germination. Seeds in salt water will show little or no germination.

Analysis

1. Yes. Seeds soaked in freshwater germinated. Seeds soaked in salt water did not.
2. salinity; germination
3. Probably not. Some seeds, such as those that grow in a salt marsh, are already adapted to germinate in salty environments. Experimentation is needed.

36

MiniLab 2.1

Experiment

Salt Tolerance of Seeds Salinity, the amount of salt dissolved in water, is a nonliving factor. Might salt water affect how certain seeds sprout or germinate? Experiment to find out.

Salt marsh

Freshwater pond

Procedure 🕶️ 👕 ☣️ 🚯

1. Obtain 40 seeds of one species of plant. Soak 20 of them in a freshwater solution and soak 20 seeds in a 10 percent saltwater solution overnight.
2. The next day, wrap the seeds in two different paper towels moistened with their soaking solutions. Slide each towel into its own self-sealing plastic bag.
3. Label the bags *Fresh* and *Salt*.
4. Examine all seeds two days later. Count the number of seeds in each treatment that show signs of root growth or sprouting, which is called germination. Record your data. **CAUTION:** *Be sure to wash your hands after handling seeds and seedlings. Make wise choices about disposal.*

Analysis

1. **Observe and Infer** Did the germination rates differ between the two treatments? If yes, how?
2. **Conclude** What nonliving factor was tested in this experiment? What living factor was affected?
3. **Infer** Would all seeds respond to the presence or absence of salt in a similar manner? How could you find out?

36 PRINCIPLES OF ECOLOGY

Assessment

Performance Have students design an experiment that determines the maximum percentage of salinity that will allow germination. Use the Performance Task Assessment List for Assessing a Whole Experiment and Planning the Next Experiment in **PASC,** p. 105. **L2**

What is ecology?

The branch of biology that developed from natural history is called ecology. **Ecology** is the study of interactions that take place between organisms and their environment.

Ecological research

Scientific research includes using descriptive and quantitative methods. Ecological research combines information and techniques from many scientific fields, including mathematics, chemistry, physics, geology, and other branches of biology. Most ecologists use both descriptive and quantitative research. They obtain descriptive information by observing organisms. They obtain quantitative data by making measurements and carrying out experiments in the field and in the laboratory. Ecologists may ask what a coyote eats, how day length influences plants or migrating birds, or why tiny shrimp help rid ocean fishes of parasites.

The Biosphere

On Earth, living things are found in the air, on land, and in both fresh- and salt water. The **biosphere** (BI uh sfihr) is the portion of Earth that supports living things. It extends from high in the atmosphere to the bottom of the oceans. This may seem extensive, but if you could shrink Earth to the size of an apple, the biosphere would be thinner than the apple's peel.

Although it is thin, the biosphere supports a diverse group of organisms in a wide range of climates. The climate, soils, plants, and animals in one part of the world can be very different from those same factors in other parts of the world. Living things are affected by both the physical or nonliving environment and by other living things.

Ecologists study how organisms survive and reproduce under different physical and biological conditions in Earth's biosphere.

The nonliving environment: Abiotic factors

The nonliving parts of an organism's environment are the **abiotic** (ay bi AH tihk) **factors**. Examples of abiotic factors include air currents, temperature, moisture, light, and soil. Ecology includes the study of features of the environment that are not living because these features are part of an organism's life. For example, a complete study of the ecology of moles would include an examination of the types of soil in which these animals dig their tunnels. Similarly, a thorough investigation of the life cycle of trout would need to include whether they need to lay their eggs on rocky or sandy stream bottoms.

Abiotic factors have obvious effects on living things and often determine which species survive in a particular environment. For example, extended lack of rainfall in the grassland shown in *Figure 2.1* can cause drought. What changes in a grassland might result from a drought? Grasses would grow more slowly. They might produce fewer seeds, and the animals that depend on seeds for food would find it harder to survive. Examine other ways that abiotic factors affect living things in the *MiniLab* and *Problem-Solving Lab* shown on these pages.

Problem-Solving Lab 2.1

Interpret Data

How does an abiotic factor affect food production? Green plants carry out the process of photosynthesis. Glucose, a sugar, is the food product made during this process. Glucose production can be used as a means for measuring the rate at which the process of photosynthesis is occurring.

Solve the Problem

Examine the following graph of a plant called saltbush (*Atriplex*). The graph shows how the plant's glucose (food) production is affected by temperature.

Food Production in Saltbush

Thinking Critically

1. **Observe and Infer** What is the abiotic factor influencing photosynthesis? How does this factor affect photosynthesis?
2. **Analyze** How much glucose is being produced at 20°C?
3. **Analyze** Based on the graph, at what temperature is glucose production greatest?
4. **Make and Use Graphs** Does the graph tell you how the rate of photosynthesis might vary for plants other than saltbush? Explain your answer.
5. **Analyze** What happens to the formation of glucose after the temperature reaches 30°C?

Figure 2.1
Drought is an abiotic condition common in grasslands that is the result of lack of moisture. As the grasses dry out, they turn yellow and appear to be dead, but new shoots grow from the bases of the plants soon after it rains. Some species, such as these grasses and prairie dogs, thrive in grasslands even though they experience periodic drought.

37

Problem-Solving Lab 2.1

Purpose
Students will determine how temperature influences the rate at which photosynthesis occurs for a specific plant.

Process Skills
analyze information, draw a conclusion, interpret data

Teaching Strategies
You may wish to introduce the process of photosynthesis by describing the raw materials needed and the role the process plays in providing food for all life forms.

Thinking Critically
1. Temperature; as temperature increases, the photosynthesis rate also increases until a maximum of 30°C (optimum temperature) is reached. Above 30°, the photosynthesis rate decreases.
2. 10 mg/h
3. 30°
4. The graph is specific for saltbush. The responses of other plants to temperature would have to be determined experimentally.
5. Glucose production declines.

Assessment
Skill Have students write a lab report summarizing the results of the lab. Use the Performance Task Assessment List for Lab Report in **PASC,** p. 119. **L2**

CHALLENGE ACTIVITY

Biotic and Abiotic Factors Have students observe and take notes on the biotic and abiotic factors in a local park, field, pond, or forest. They can use their notes to write a paper explaining the importance of each factor. **L3**

 Indiana Academic Standards

Pages 36–37: B.1.37, B.1.43, B.1.45, B.1.47

The living environment: Biotic factors

In addition to abiotic factors, a key consideration of ecology is that living organisms affect other living organisms. All the living organisms that inhabit an environment are called **biotic** (by AH tihk) **factors.**

Think about a goldfish in a bowl. Now consider its relationships with other organisms. Does the fish live alone or with other fishes? Are there live plants in the bowl? The fish may depend on other living things for food, or it may be food for other life. The goldfish needs members of the same species to reproduce. To meet its needs, the goldfish may compete with organisms of the same or different species that share the bowl.

✓ **Reading Check** **Compare** biotic and abiotic factors.

CAREERS IN BIOLOGY

Science Reporter

Does science fascinate you? Can you explain complex ideas and issues in a clear and interesting way? If so, you might consider a career as a science reporter.

Skills for the Job
As a science reporter, you are a writer first and a scientist second. A degree in journalism and/or a scientific field is usually necessary, but curiosity and good writing skills are also essential. You might work for newspapers, national magazines, medical or scientific publications, television networks, or internet news services. You could work as a full-time employee or a freelance writer. You must read daily to stay up-to-date. Many science reporters attend scientific conventions and events to find news of interest to the public. Then they relate what's new in science so that nonscientists can understand it.

 For more careers in related fields, visit in.bdol.glencoe.com/careers

All organisms depend on others directly or indirectly for food, shelter, reproduction, or protection. If you study an individual organism, such as a male white-tailed deer, you might find out what food it prefers, how often it eats, and how far it roams to search for food. However, studying a single individual won't tell you all there is to know about white-tailed deer. In fact, white tails are social animals. They live in small groups or a herd in which there is a strong social structure built around visual and vocal communications that keep the herd safe.

So you can see that the study of a single individual provides only part of the story of its life.

Levels of Organization

Ecologists study individual organisms, interactions among organisms of the same species, and interactions among organisms of different species, as well as the effects of abiotic factors on interacting species.

To help them understand the interactions of the biotic and abiotic parts of the world, ecologists have organized the living world into levels—the organism by itself, populations, communities, and ecosystems.

Interactions within populations

A **population** is a group of organisms, all of the same species, which interbreed and live in the same area at the same time.

How the organisms in a population share the resources of their environment may determine how far apart the organisms live and how large the populations become. Members of the same population may compete with each other for food, water, mates, or other resources. Competition increases when resources are in short supply.

Figure 2.2
Some adult insects and their young have different food requirements. These differences limit competition for food resources between members of the same species.

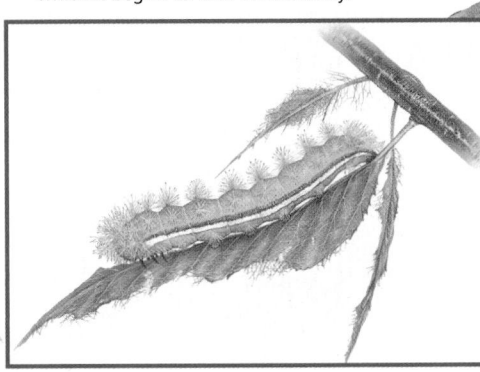

A The Io moth larva hatches on leaves on which it begins to feed immediately.

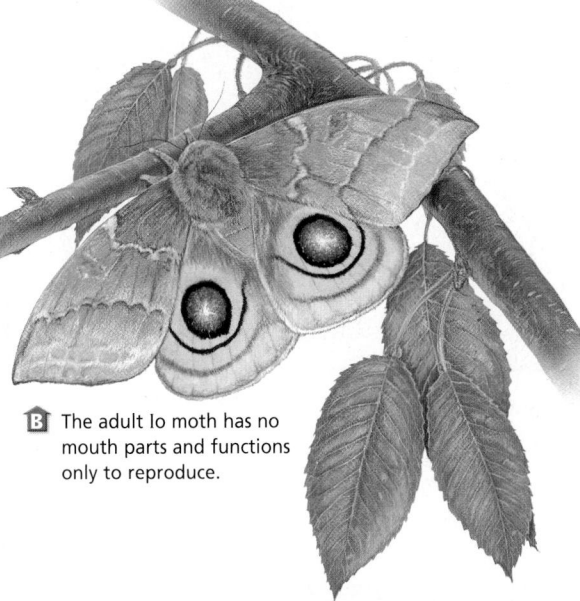

B The adult Io moth has no mouth parts and functions only to reproduce.

Some species have adaptations that reduce competition within a population. An example is the life cycle of a frog. The juvenile stage of the frog, called the tadpole, looks very different from the adult and has different food requirements. As you can see in *Figure 2.2*, many species of insects, including butterflies and moths, also produce juveniles that differ from the adult in body form and food requirements.

Interactions within communities

No species lives independently. Just as a population is made up of individuals, several different populations make up a biological community. A **biological community** is made up of interacting populations in a certain area at a certain time. An example of a community is shown in *Figure 2.3*.

A change in one population in a community may cause changes in the other populations. Some of these changes can be minor, such as when a small increase in the number of individuals of one population causes a small decrease in the size of another population. For example, if the population of mouse-eating hawks increases slightly, the population of mice will, as a result, decrease slightly. Other changes might be more extreme, as when the size of one population grows so large it begins affecting the food supply for another species in the community. *Figure 2.4* on the next page is a visual summary of the ecological levels of organization.

Figure 2.3
This community of flowers is made up of populations of different species of flowers.

CAUTION: *Remind students to wash their hands with soap before and after handling seeds.*

5. Starting the next day and continuing for five days, observe each group of seeds. Look for signs of germination (small roots growing from a seed), and record the number of seeds from each container that are germinating each day.

Analysis

1. What abiotic factor is being investigated? effect of water on seed germination
2. Which seems to be the optimum (best) time for seed germination? The time will depend on the seed type used.
3. Did the seeds all germinate at the same time? Explain. No, each seed has its own optimum soaking time.

Figure 2.4 Have students write a statement summarizing Figure 2.4. Possible answers might include that the photos show the levels of organization used in ecology to distinguish a species in all its possible groupings. Have them conclude their statement with a question that they may want to ask about the groupings.

Students may think that an environmentalist is the same as an ecologist.

Uncover the Misconception

Ask students to describe their idea of the work of an ecologist and their idea of the work of an environmentalist. They will probably think that both are the same.

Demonstrate the Concept

Point out that an ecologist is a scientist who investigates ecosystems including relationships between biotic and abiotic factors. The environmentalist, who may or may not be a scientist, is a person who works to get people to protect the environment.

Assess New Knowledge

Supply newspaper clippings about local environmental issues (a polluted local stream, pigeons in the city, or a local farm's blackbird problems). Have students discuss the type of scientists who might work on these problems.

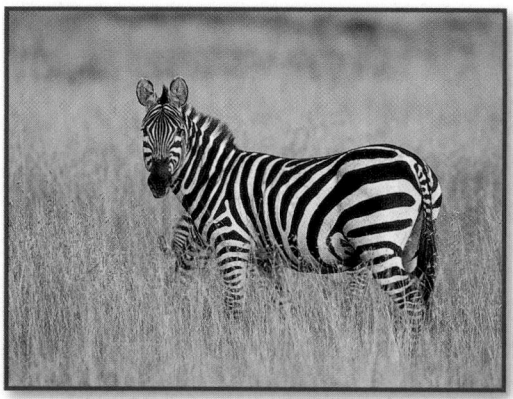

A Organism
An individual living thing that is made of cells, uses energy, reproduces, responds, grows, and develops

B Population
A group of organisms, all of one species, which interbreed and live in the same place at the same time

Figure 2.4
Levels of Organization
Ecology is the study of relationships on several levels of biological organization, including individual organisms, populations, communities, ecosystems, biomes, and the biosphere.

C Biological Community
All the populations of different species that live in the same place at the same time

D Ecosystem
Populations of plants and animals that interact with each other in a given area and with the abiotic components of that area

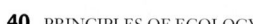

E Biosphere
The portion of Earth that supports life

Virtual Lab

CD-ROM Students will set up a closed terrarium ecosystem in *A Mini Biosphere.*

Biotic and abiotic factors form ecosystems

In a healthy forest community, interacting populations might include birds eating insects, squirrels eating nuts from trees, mushrooms growing from decaying leaves or bark, and raccoons fishing in a stream. In addition to how individuals in a population interact with each other, ecologists also study interactions between separate populations and their physical surroundings. An **ecosystem** is made up of interacting populations in a biological community and the community's abiotic factors. Because animals and plants in an area can change, and because abiotic factors can change, ecosystems are subject to change.

There are two major kinds of ecosystems—terrestrial ecosystems and aquatic ecosystems. Terrestrial ecosystems are those located on land. Examples include forests, meadows, and rotting logs. Aquatic ecosystems occur in both fresh- and saltwater

forms. Freshwater ecosystems include ponds, lakes, and streams. Saltwater ecosystems, also called marine ecosystems, make up approximately 70 percent of Earth's surface. *Figure 2.5* shows a freshwater and a marine ecosystem. Examples of ecosystems are given in *Table 2.1*.

Table 2.1 Examples of Ecosystems		
Terrestrial Ecosystems	**Aquatic Ecosystems**	**Other Sites for Ecosystems**
• Forest	Freshwater	Human body
• Old farm field	• Pond	• Skin
• Meadow	• Lake	• Intestine
• Yard	• Stream	• Mouth
• Garden plot	• Estuary	Buildings
• Empty lot	Salt water (marine)	• Mold in walls, floors, or basement
• Compost heap	• Ocean	• Ventilation systems
• Volcano site	• Estuary	• Bathrooms
• Rotting log	• Aquarium	Food
		• Any moldy food
		• Refrigerator

Figure 2.5
There may be hundreds of populations interacting in a pond or in areas where tides move in and out.
Infer *What abiotic factors in these environments affect the biotic factors?*

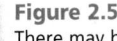 Ponds are made up of many populations of plants and animals. Water in a pond is usually calm or stationary.

B Daily, organisms living in tidal areas must survive measurable changes in abiotic factors. When the tide is high, ocean waves replenish the water containing dissolved nutrients and food sources. When the tide is low, water moves out and what remains evaporates, raising the concentration of nutrients.

41

Caption Question Answer
Figure 2.5 Abiotic factors affecting ponds and tidal areas include salinity, temperature, water quality, and water depth.

Inquiry

Guided Questions Ask students to use Figure 2.5 to describe adaptations that help animals living in tide pools survive when the tide is low for several hours. Responses may include shells that help the animal retain moisture or the ability to burrow into moist sand. Then ask students how they think the abiotic factors in these environments affect the biotic factors. Responses may include that sunlight affects water temperature and whether photosynthesis will occur. Air dissolved in the water affects the respiratory and photosynthetic processes of the pond organisms, which, in turn, affect the flow of energy.
L1

PROJECT

Ecosystems Have students select an ecosystem from the lists in Table 2.1 or describe, from personal experience, an ecosystem with which they are familiar. Have them explain why their selection fits the term *ecosystem*.

Students should describe the size of the site. They should list all the biotic and abiotic factors in their ecosystem. Photos, maps, and illustrations should be included and should have captions.

Indiana Academic Standards

Pages 40–41: B.1.32, B.1.43, B.1.47

Organisms in Ecosystems

A prairie dog living in a grassland makes its home in burrows that it digs underground. Some species of birds make their homes in the trees of a beech-maple forest. In these areas, they find food, avoid enemies, and reproduce. A **habitat** (HA buh tat) is the place where an organism lives out its life. A lawn, the bottom of a stream, and beech-maple forests are examples of habitats. Other habitats could be a wetland, a specific species of tree, a city lot or park, a pond, or a specific area in the ocean. Habitats can change, and even disappear. Habitats can change due to both natural and human causes. Examples of habitat changes are presented in *Biology and Society* at the end of this chapter.

✓ **Reading Check** **Compare** habitats and ecosystems.

Figure 2.6
This series of photographs shows how a habitat can be seen as a collection of several niches. As you can see, each species uses the available resources in a different way.

A A centipede is a predator that captures and eats beetles and other animals.

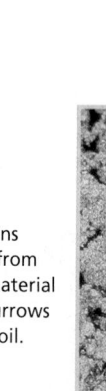

B A worm obtains nourishment from the organic material it eats as it burrows through the soil.

Niche

Although several species may share a habitat, the food, shelter, and other essential resources of that habitat are often used in different ways. For example, if you turn over a log like the one shown in *Figure 2.6*, you will find a community of millipedes, centipedes, insects, slugs, and earthworms. In addition, there are billions of fungi and bacteria at work breaking down the log, the leaves, and wastes produced by these animals. At first, it looks like members of this community are competing for the same food because they all live in the same habitat. But close inspection reveals that each population feeds in different ways, on different materials, and at different times. These differences lead to reduced competition. Each species is unique in satisfying all its needs. Each species occupies a niche (neesh).

42 PRINCIPLES OF ECOLOGY

A **niche** is all strategies and adaptations a species uses in its environment—how it meets its specific needs for food and shelter, how and where it survives, and where it reproduces. A species' niche, therefore, includes all its interactions with the biotic and abiotic parts of its habitat.

It is an advantage for a species to occupy a niche different from those of other species in the same habitat, although a species' niche may change during its life cycle. It is thought that two species can't exist for long in the same community if their niches are the same. In time, one of the species will gain control of the resources both need. The other will become extinct in that area, move elsewhere, or, over time, become adapted in the way its species uses that particular habitat's resources.

Organisms of different species use a variety of strategies to live and reproduce in their habitats. Life may be harsh in the polar regions, but the polar bear, with its thick coat, flourishes there. Nectar may be deep in the flower, inaccessible to most species, but the hummingbird, with its long beak and long tongue is adapted to retrieve it. Unique adaptations and structures are important to a species' niche and important because they reduce competition with other species in the same habitat.

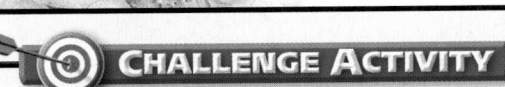
D These ants eat dead insects.

C A millipede eats decaying leaves near the log.

2.1 ORGANISMS AND THEIR ENVIRONMENT **43**

Using Science Terms
The term *niche* is sometimes described as an activity that a person is good at but that others find difficult. Ask how this is similar to the biological definition. Biologically, no two organisms can fill the same niche at the same time in the same habitat, and so, each organism's niche is unique. An organism in a niche has adaptations that give it an advantage over other organisms that may be competing for the same niche in the same environment.

Content Background
Discussion The term *competition* refers to the way species interact when there is a limited supply of resources. Competition can happen between members of the same species and members of different species. This term is important in a discussion of relationships within habitats.

Have students discuss the terms *niche* and *competition* to elicit misunderstandings that they might have about the two terms.

Guide students in their use of the terms, especially with regard to competition. Competition in nature is not a conscious act that organisms plan and execute. It is the result of shortages of needed resources. This also will prepare them for the discussion on symbiotic relationships on the next page. **L2**

CHALLENGE ACTIVITY

Life Under a Log Either bring in a decaying log or take students to a place on school grounds where there is a lot of leaf litter. They should not move objects or organisms with bare hands. Students should work in groups to identify organisms they find, making careful note of where the organisms were first noticed. Are there any holes or galleries in the wood? What would this mean? If the observations are made outside, students need to describe the whole area before they disturb it. **L2** **COOP LEARN**

Indiana Academic Standards
Pages 42–43: B.1.43, B.1.47

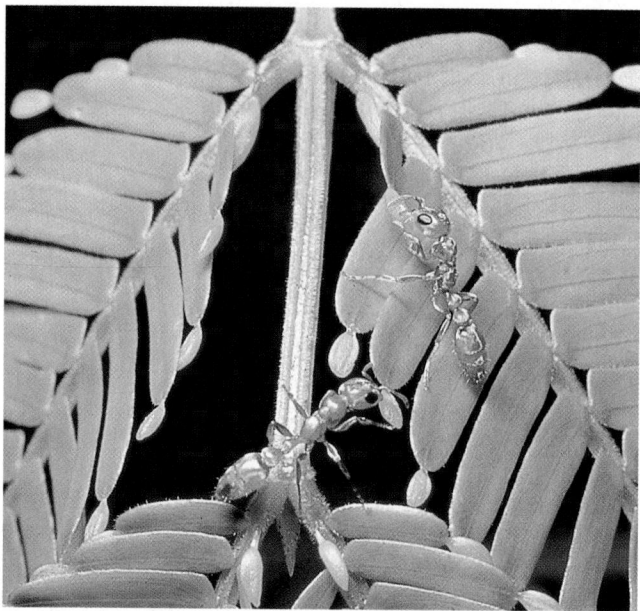

Figure 2.7
These ants and acacia trees both benefit from living in close association. This mutualistic relationship is so strong that in nature, the trees and ants are never found apart.

Survival Relationships

A predator is a type of consumer. Predators seek out and eat other organisms. Predation is found in all ecosystems and includes organisms that eat plants and animals. Predators may be animals such as lions and insect-eating birds. The animals that predators eat are called prey. Predator-prey relationships such as the one between cats and mice involve a fight for survival. Use the *BioLab* at the end of this chapter to examine a predator-prey relationship.

Not all organisms living in the same environment are in a continuous battle for survival. However, studies have shown that most species survive because of the relationships they have with other species.

These relationships help maintain survival in many species. The relationship in which there is a close and permanent association between organisms of different species is called **symbiosis** (sihm bee OH sus). Symbiosis means living together.

Three kinds of symbiosis are recognized: mutualism, commensalism, and parasitism.

Mutualism

Sometimes, two species of organisms benefit from living in close association. A symbiotic relationship in which both species benefit is called **mutualism** (MYEW chuh wuh lih zum). Ants and acacia trees living in the subtropical regions of the world illustrate mutualism, as shown in *Figure 2.7*. The ants protect the acacia tree by attacking any animal that tries to feed on the tree. The tree provides nectar and a home for the ants. In an experiment, ecologists removed the ants from some acacia trees. Results showed that the trees with ants grew faster and survived longer than trees without ants.

Commensalism

Commensalism (kuh MEN suh lih zum) is a symbiotic relationship in which one species benefits and the other species is neither harmed nor benefited.

Commensal relationships occur among animals and in plant species, too. Spanish moss is a kind of flowering plant that drapes itself on the branches of trees, as shown in *Figure 2.8*. Orchids, ferns, mosses, and other plants sometimes grow on the branches of larger plants. The larger plants are not harmed, but the smaller plants benefit from the habitat.

Parasitism

Some interactions are harmful to one species, yet beneficial to another. Have you ever owned a dog or cat that was attacked by ticks or fleas? Ticks, like the one shown in *Figure 2.9*, are examples of parasites. A symbiotic

Figure 2.8
Spanish moss grows on and hangs from the limbs of trees but does not obtain any nutrients or cause any harm to the trees.

relationship in which a member of one species derives benefit at the expense of another species (the host) is called **parasitism** (PER uh suh tih zum). Parasites have evolved in such a way that they harm, but usually do not kill the host species. If the host were to die, the parasite also would die unless it can quickly find another host. Some parasites, such as certain bacteria, tapeworms, and roundworms, live in or on other organisms.

Brown-headed cowbirds, in a behavior called brood parasitism, lay their eggs in the nests of songbirds, often at the expense of the host bird's eggs. The cowbird is about the size of an American Robin. It is not uncommon to see a much smaller bird species, such as a chipping sparrow, in the act of feeding a much larger, but younger, cowbird. Brown-headed cowbirds are known to parasitize about 200 other species of birds in North America.

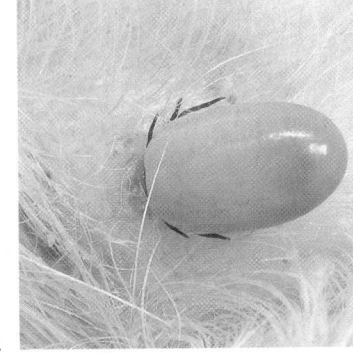

Figure 2.9
Ticks are blood-sucking parasites. Some transmit disease as they obtain nutrients from their host.

3 Assess

DAILY INTERVENTION

Check for Understanding
Have students explain the relationship between the words in each of the following pairs. **L1** **ELL**
a. biology—ecology
b. population—ecosystem
c. habitat—niche
d. symbiosis—mutualism

Reteach
Interpersonal Ask students to work in groups to provide examples of biotic and abiotic factors within the classroom or school. **L2**
COOP LEARN

Resources
For more practice, use *Reading Essentials for Biology,* Section 2.1.

Extension

Linguistic Ask students to research how abiotic factors limit life in the Arctic tundra or in a desert environment. Have them include a written summary of the information they gather in their portfolios. **L3**

✔ Assessment

Knowledge Ask students to consider the school grounds an ecosystem. Have them explain and give examples of populations and communities that live in this "ecosystem." **L2**

Section Assessment

Understanding Main Ideas

1. Compare and give several examples of biotic and abiotic factors in a forest ecosystem.

2. Compare and contrast the characteristics of populations and communities. Provide examples of populations in a community.

3. Give examples that would demonstrate the differences between the terms *niche* and *habitat.*

4. Interpret the interaction between a cowbird and a chipping sparrow as the sparrow raises the young of a brown-headed cowbird.

Thinking Critically

5. Clownfish are small, tropical marine fish often found swimming among the stinging tentacles of sea anemones without being harmed. Interpret and describe this type of relationship.

SKILL REVIEW

6. **Get the Big Picture** Analyze and interpret the effect of an increasing population of brown-headed cowbirds on the forest community it inhabits. For more help, refer to *Get the Big Picture* in the **Skill Handbook**.

 in.bdol.glencoe.com/self_check_quiz

2.1 ORGANISMS AND THEIR ENVIRONMENT **45**

Section Assessment

1. biotic—tree, grass, human, dog, ant; abiotic—daylight hours, amount of rainfall, humidity, air, soil

2. A population: members of a single species that are present in the same place at the same time. A community: made up of different interacting populations. Examples will vary, but may reflect Figures 2.5, 6, or 7.

3. Responses may be: Squirrel—habitat: forest; niche: gathers, eats, and stores nuts. Mushroom—habitat: moist forest soil; niche: decomposes organic matter. Bat—habitat: cave; niche: pollinates flowers, eats insects.

4. The relationship is a type of parasitism. The cowbird gets the sparrow to do the work of rearing.

5. Mutualism; the clownfish is not stung and may bring food to the anemone.

6. As brown-headed cowbirds increase, songbird populations decrease. Organisms that depend on songbirds or interact with them may be affected.

Section 2.2

Nutrition and Energy Flow

Indiana Standards Standard B.1.44 Describe the flow of matter, nutrients, and energy within ecosystems.

SECTION PREVIEW

Objectives

Compare how organisms satisfy their nutritional needs.

Trace the path of energy and matter in an ecosystem.

Analyze how matter is cycled in the abiotic and biotic parts of the biosphere.

Review Vocabulary
energy: the ability to cause change (p. 9)

New Vocabulary
autotroph
heterotroph
decomposer
food chain
trophic level
food web
biomass

Cycles of Matter Make the following Foldable to help you understand the cycles of water, carbon, nitrogen, and phosphorus.

STEP 1 **Fold** a sheet of paper in half lengthwise. Make the back edge about 2.5 cm longer than the front edge.

STEP 2 **Fold** in half, then fold in half again to make three folds.

STEP 3 **Unfold and cut** only the top layer along the three folds to make four tabs.

STEP 4 **Label** the Foldable as shown.

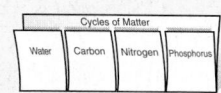

Use Models As you read Section 2.2, draw the cycle of each type of matter and describe the process of the cycle below it.

How Organisms Obtain Energy

The mosquito in *Figure 2.10* takes in a blood meal. This is one means by which the female mosquito obtains nutrients. Mosquitoes also feed on nectar as a source of energy. An important characteristic of a species' niche is how it obtains energy. Ecologists trace the flow of energy through communities to discover nutritional relationships between organisms.

Figure 2.10
Female mosquitoes obtain protein for egg development from blood.

The producers: Autotrophs

The ultimate source of the energy for life is the sun. Plants use the sun's energy to manufacture food in a process called photosynthesis. An organism that uses light energy or energy stored in chemical compounds to make energy-rich compounds is a producer, or **autotroph** (AW tuh trohf). Grass and trees in *Figure 2.11* are autotrophs. Although plants are the most familiar autotrophs, some unicellular organisms such as green algae, also make their own nutrients. Other organisms in the biosphere depend on autotrophs for nutrients and energy. These dependent organisms are called consumers.

46 PRINCIPLES OF ECOLOGY

RESOURCE MANAGER

2 Teach

Caption Question Answer
Figure 2.11 The trees and grasses are autotrophs; all of the animals are heterotrophs.

Using Science Terms
Call students' attention to the derivations of the terms *herbivore, carnivore,* and *omnivore,* presented in the margins of these pages. Ask students to explain the appropriateness of each term to the feeding habits of the organisms it describes. Herbivores are organisms that feed upon grasses and plants; carnivores feed on the flesh of animals; omnivores feed on both plant and animal products. **L2** **ELL**

Reinforcement
Naturalist Have students list common pets. Ask them to identify the foods that are typically provided for each pet on their list. Have students classify each pet as an omnivore, carnivore, or herbivore based upon the foods it eats. Have students check the ingredients on pet food labels. **L1**

Struggling Learners
Linguistic Pair students who understand the concept of producer and consumer with students who are having difficulty. Make two groups of terms: *producer, plant, autotroph* and *consumer, heterotroph, animal.* Have the pairs of students analyze the meanings of the groups. **L1** **ELL** **COOP LEARN**

The consumers: Heterotrophs

A deer nibbles the leaves of a clover plant; a bison eats grass; an owl swallows a mouse. The deer, bison, and owl are consumers, incapable of producing their own food. They obtain nutrients by eating other organisms. An organism that cannot make its own food and feeds on other organisms is called a **heterotroph** (HE tuh ruh trohf). Heterotrophs include organisms that feed only on autotrophs, organisms that feed only on other heterotrophs, and organisms that feed on both autotrophs and heterotrophs.

Some heterotrophs, such as grazing, seed-eating, and algae-eating animals, feed directly on autotrophs. Heterotrophs display a variety of feeding relationships.

1. A heterotroph that feeds only on plants is an herbivore. Herbivores include rabbits, grasshoppers, beavers, squirrels, bees, elephants, fruit-eating bats, and some humans.
2. Some heterotrophs eat other heterotrophs. Animals such as lions that kill and eat only other animals are carnivores.
3. Some heterotrophs, called scavengers, do not kill for food. Instead,

scavengers eat animals that have already died. Scavengers, such as black vultures, feed on dead animals and garbage and play a beneficial role in the ecosystem. Imagine for a moment what the environment would be like if there were no vultures to devour animals killed on the African plains, no buzzards to clean up dead animals along roads, and no ants and beetles to remove dead insects and small animals from sidewalks and basements.

Humans are an example of a third type of heterotroph. Most people eat a variety of foods that include both animal and plant materials. They are omnivores. Raccoons, opossums, and bears are other examples of omnivores.

Some organisms, such as bacteria and fungi, are decomposers. They break down and release nutrients from dead organisms. **Decomposers** break down the complex compounds of dead and decaying plants and animals into simpler molecules that can be more easily absorbed. Some protozoans, many bacteria, and most fungi carry out this essential process of nutrient recycling.

Word Origin

herbivore from the Latin words *herba,* meaning "grass," and *vorare,* meaning "to devour"; Herbivores feed on grass and other plants.

carnivore from the Latin word *caro,* meaning "flesh"; Carnivores eat animals.

omnivore from the Latin word *omnis,* meaning "all"; Omnivores eat both plants and animals.

2.2 NUTRITION AND ENERGY FLOW **47**

Visual Learning

Figure 2.12 Have students carefully relate the bold terms and concepts in each caption within individual organisms in Figure 2.12. Ask students to identify the herbivores shown. deer, mouse, turtle, butterflies, cardinal Ask them to identify the carnivores. owl, robins, white-breasted nuthatch Finally, ask them to identify the omnivores. bear, fish

Struggling Learners

Have students work in pairs to list some of the foods they have consumed in the past 24 hours. Then have each pair determine if they were a first-order, second-order, or third-order consumer for each food. **L1 COOP LEARN**

Inquiry

Discussion Have students identify some other organisms that might live in a temperate forest environment. Suggestions might be: rabbits, raccoons, oak trees, birch trees, foxes. Discuss what these organisms use for food. Answers will reflect the organisms named. Ask students why they wouldn't expect to find polar bears, seals, or penguins here. These organisms are adapted to other environments. **L1**

Figure 2.12
In order for a temperate forest ecosystem to function, its organisms depend on each other for a supply of energy.

Autotrophs The first level in all food chains is made up of producers. In this forest community, grasses, shrubs, trees, and some aquatic, photosynthetic plants are autotrophs.

First-order heterotrophs Herbivores, such as the deer, cardinal, turtle, and fish, make up the second level in a food chain. They obtain food from photosynthetic organisms.

Third-order heterotrophs Carnivores are animals that feed on second-order heterotrophs. Some bears may attack other animals, such as the deer. Bears also rely on a large diet of berries and so are termed omnivores.

48

Flow of Matter and Energy in Ecosystems

When you eat food, such as an apple, you consume matter. Matter, in the form of carbon, nitrogen, and other elements, flows through the levels of an ecosystem from producers to consumers. In doing so, the matter is cycled. The apple also contains energy from sunlight that was trapped in the plant during the process of photosynthesis. As you cycle the matter of the apple, some trapped energy is transferred from one level to the next. At each level, a certain amount of energy is also transferred to the environment as heat.

🎯 CHALLENGE ACTIVITY

School Grounds' Food Chains On the school grounds or nearby, have students survey organisms that would form a local food chain. This can include birds, ants and other insects, and whatever plants live in the area. Results should be illustrated using whatever materials are available to students. **L2 COOP LEARN**

Indiana Academic Standards

Pages 48–49: B.1.43, B.1.44, B.1.47

How do matter and energy flow through ecosystems? You have already learned that feeding relationships and symbiotic relationships describe the ways in which organisms interact. Ecologists study these interactions and make models to trace how matter and energy flow through ecosystems. The simplest models are called food chains.

Food chains: Pathways for matter and energy

A **food chain** is a simple model that scientists use to show how matter and energy move through an ecosystem. In a food chain, nutrients and energy move from autotrophs to heterotrophs and, eventually, to decomposers.

The forest community pictured in *Figure 2.12* illustrates examples of food chains. A food chain is drawn using arrows to indicate the direction in which energy is transferred from one organism to the next. One simple food chain on this page would be shown as:

berries $\rightarrow$ mice $\rightarrow$ black bear

Most food chains consist of two, three, or four transfers. The amount of energy remaining in the final transfer is only a portion of what was available at the first transfer. A portion of the energy is given off as heat at each transfer.

Second-order heterotrophs Some carnivores feed on first-order heterotrophs. Owls feed on fishes or mice, robins feed on worms or grubs, and nuthatches feed on small insects in tree bark.

Decomposers At every level in a food chain, bacteria and fungi break down living matter and help release nutrients.

49

Purpose
Students use their knowledge of trophic levels to organize and summarize information.

Process Skills
think critically, classify, sequence

Teaching Strategies
■ You may wish to provide the outline diagrams to students.
■ Review and/or define all terms: autotroph, heterotroph, producer, carnivore, herbivore. Explain the use of 1st-, 2nd-, 3rd-order heterotrophs. Organisms that feed on producers (or autotrophs) are 1st-order heterotrophs; those feeding on consumers that eat producers are 2nd-order heterotrophs, and so on.
■ Have students work in small groups. Remind them that there is only one correct placement for each label.

Thinking Critically
1. Small arrows show direction of energy from one trophic level to the next.
2. Less energy is available at each level. Small arrows show direction of energy from one trophic level to the next. The size of the box is analogous to matter and energy available at each level.

Modified Assessment
Skill Ask students to prepare a concept map of the ideas covered in this lab. Their maps must include all terms used on the diagram. Use the Performance Task Assessment List for Concept Map in **PASC**, p. 161. **L1** **ELL**

Trophic levels represent links in the chain

Each organism in a food chain represents a feeding step, or **trophic** (TROH fihk) **level,** in the passage of energy and materials. A first order heterotroph is an organism that feeds on plants, such as a grasshopper. A second order heterotroph is an organism that feeds on a first order heterotroph. An example of this would be a bird that feeds on a grasshopper. Examine how energy flows through trophic levels in the *Problem-Solving Lab* shown here.

A food chain represents only one possible route for the transfer of matter and energy through an ecosystem. Many other routes may exist. As *Figure 2.12* showed, many different species can occupy each trophic level in a forest ecosystem. In addition, many different kinds of organisms eat a variety of foods, so a single species may feed at several trophic levels. For example, the North American black bear may eat the mouse, but it also eats berries. The hawk may feed on the fish, or a mouse.

Food webs
A simple food chain such as

$$grass \longrightarrow mouse \longrightarrow hawk$$

is easy to study, but it does not indicate the complex relationships that exist for organisms that feed on more than one species. Ecologists interested in energy flow in an ecosystem may set up experiments with as many organisms in the community as they can. The model they create, called a **food web,** shows all the possible feeding relationships at each trophic level in a community. A food web is a more realistic model than a food chain because most organisms depend on more than one other species for food. The food web of the desert ecosystem shown in *Figure 2.13* represents a network of interconnected food chains formed by herbivores and carnivores.

✔**Reading Check** **Compare** food chains and food webs.

Apply Concepts

How can you organize trophic level information?
Diagrams help to summarize information or concepts in a logical and simple manner. This is the case with information that shows relationships among trophic levels.

Solve the Problem
Copy the diagram above. Use it to investigate the various relationships in a food chain.

Each box represents a trophic level. Write the name for each trophic level in the proper box. Use these choices: 1st-order heterotroph; autotroph; 2nd-order heterotroph; 3rd-order heterotroph.

Each bracket identifies one or more traits of the trophic levels. Use the following labels to identify them in their proper order: herbivore, carnivore, producer.

Thinking Critically
Infer What is represented by the small arrows connecting trophic levels? What does the decreasing width of each box mean in terms of available matter and energy at each level?

 CHALLENGE ACTIVITY

Food Web Model Have students work in groups to design three-dimensional models of food webs. Each group should select a different ecosystem to work on. Put ecosystem names on separate pieces of paper and put them in a hat. Each group can then make a selection. The organisms used in the web should be representative of an ecosystem that occurs in your area and students can be creative in materials used. **L3**

Energy and trophic levels: Ecological pyramids

Ecologists use food chains and food webs to model the distribution of matter and energy within an ecosystem. They also use another kind of model called an ecological pyramid. An ecological pyramid can show how energy flows through an ecosystem.

The base of the ecological pyramid on the next page represents the autotrophs, or first trophic level. Higher trophic levels are layered on top of one another. Examine each of the three types of ecological pyramids on the following pages.

Figure 2.13
A desert community food web includes many organisms at each trophic level. Arrows indicate the flow of materials and energy.

Chihuahuan raven

Honey mesquite (pods eaten by beetles)

Pronghorn antelope

Gambel quail

Jackrabbit

Long-tail weasel

Coyote (top carnivore)

Prickly pear cactus

Desert tortoise

Roadrunner

Kangaroo rat (seed eater)

Mojave rattlesnake

Ants

Mexican whiptail lizard

Texas horned lizard

Red spotted toad

Food chains are simple models that indicate direct feeding relationships between individuals. Food webs are more complex models that show multiple feeding relationships.

Reinforcement

Write the word *human* at the top of the chalkboard. Ask students to complete a food web that includes the two trophic levels below humans, using as many different organisms for each level as possible. Examples of first-order consumers may include chickens, cows, sheep, and pigs; examples of producers may include grass, shrubs, lettuce, pears, and corn. Ask students to explain why this represents a food web rather than a food chain. A food chain involves only one organism for each trophic level.

Tying to Prior Knowledge

Have students review the meanings of the terms *scavenger* and *decomposer*. Have students name some scavengers crows, jackels, vultures and decomposers. bacteria and fungi Ask them to describe the role of each type of organism in a food chain or food web. These organisms recycle nutrients. **L1** **ELL**

Visual Learning

Figure 2.13 Ask students to use Figure 2.13 to identify other animals that might occupy the third trophic level. Responses may include birds of prey, such as owls or eagles, or land animals, such as mountain lions, coyotes, or snakes. Accept all supported responses.

USING MODELS

Desert Food Chains Have students use the illustration of a desert ecosystem in Figure 2.13 and make concept maps of at least two food chains. **L2**

Indiana Academic Standards

Pages 50–51: B.1.43, B.1.44, B.1.47

Discussion Have students analyze the error in logic for the following scenario. *Humans are not at the mercy of producers for their food because most of them usually eat animals as a food source. Thus, not all people would suffer the loss of food if all autotrophs were suddenly to die out.* Students should recognize that the animals humans eat are themselves dependent on producers for their food. Some students may also bring up the fact that without autotrophs, photosynthesis would not take place and oxygen would not be made, so animals are dependent on autotrophs for more than just a source of energy. **L3**

Physical Science Connection

Remind students that energy conservation applies when energy is either converted or transferred. Although energy that is transferred might seem to be lost from a system, none is actually destroyed. Ask students for examples of energy transfer. Answers may include heat being transferred from the inside a refrigerator to the surrounding air during the process of refrigeration; and how an organism converts chemical energy in food to energy of motion (kinetic energy) and heat.

Indiana Academic Standards

Pages 52–53: B.1.37, B.1.40, B.1.43, B.1.44, B.1.47

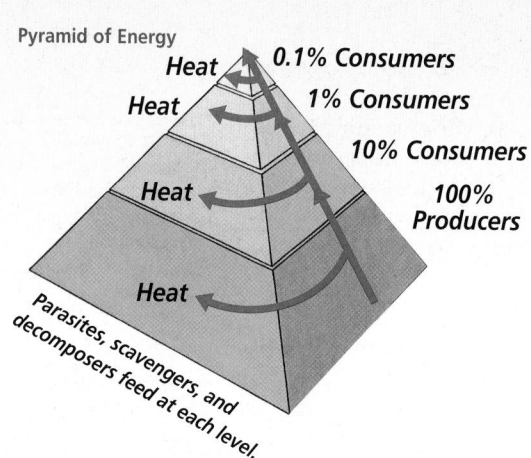

Figure 2.14
Each level in an energy pyramid represents the energy that is available within that trophic level. With each step up, only 10 percent of the energy is available for the next trophic level.

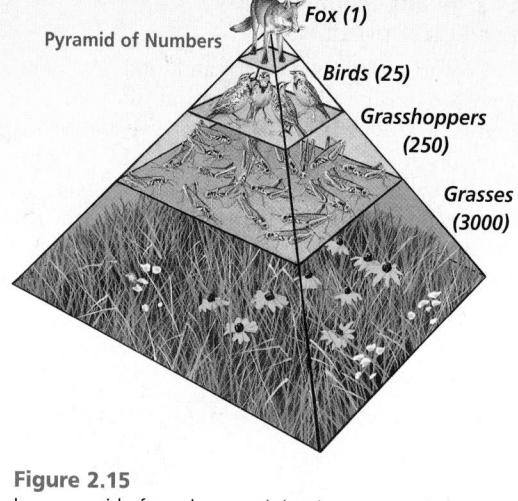

Figure 2.15
In a pyramid of numbers, each level represents the number of organisms consumed by the level above it.

Physical Science Connection

Conservation of energy The energy contained in food is in the form of chemical energy. When an organism consumes food, chemical energy in the food is converted into other forms of energy, such as heat and energy of motion. The law of conservation of energy—energy cannot be created or destroyed—always applies to all processes.

Each type of pyramid shown in *Figures 2.14, 2.15,* and *2.16* gives different information about an ecosystem.

The pyramid of energy illustrates that the amount of available energy decreases at each succeeding trophic level. The total energy transfer from one trophic level to the next is only about ten percent because organisms fail to capture and eat all the food energy available at the trophic level below them. When an organism consumes food, it uses some of the energy in the food for its metabolism—some for building body tissues, and some is given off as heat. When that organism is eaten, the energy that was used to build body tissue is again available as energy to be used by the organism that consumed it. According to the law of conservation of energy, energy is neither lost nor gained. Some of the energy transferred at each successive trophic level enters the environment as heat, but the total amount of energy remains the same.

A pyramid of numbers shows that population sizes decrease at each higher trophic level. This is not always true. For example, one tree can be food for thousands of insects. In this case, the pyramid would be inverted.

Biomass is the total weight of living matter at each trophic level. A pyramid of biomass represents the total dry weight of living material available at each trophic level.

Cycles in Nature

Food chains, food webs, and ecological pyramids are all models that show how energy moves in only one direction through the trophic levels of an ecosystem. Some of the energy also is transferred to the environment as heat generated by the body processes of organisms. Sunlight is the primary source of all this energy, and is always being replenished by the sun.

Matter, in the form of nutrients, also moves through, or is part of, all organisms at each trophic level. But matter is cycled and is not replenished like the energy from sunlight. There is a finite amount of matter. The atoms of

---

CHALLENGE ACTIVITY

Estimating Biomass Have students count the grass plants, ants, earthworms, or beetles in a ten-centimeter-square area on the school grounds. Students should use this to estimate the biomass for a ten-square meter area. **L3** **COOP LEARN**

yramid of Biomass

1 kilogram of human tissue

10 kilograms of beef

100 kilograms of grain

Figure 2.16
Each level in a pyramid of biomass represents the amount that the level above needs to consume to meet its needs.

carbon, nitrogen, and other elements that make up the bodies of organisms alive today are the same atoms that have been on Earth since life began. Matter is constantly recycled. It is never lost.

The water cycle

Life on Earth depends on water. Even before there was life on Earth, water cycled through stages. Have you ever left a glass of water out and a few days later observed there was less water in the glass? This is the result of evaporation. Just as the water evaporated from the glass, water evaporates from lakes and oceans and becomes water vapor in the air, as shown in *Figure 2.17*.

Physical Science Connection

Conservation of mass A number of physical and chemical reactions occur in natural cycles, such as the water cycle and carbon cycle. These reactions alter the physical and chemical properties of the substances involved. However, in all of these reactions, mass is neither created nor destroyed. This is the law of conservation of mass.

Figure 2.17
In the water cycle, water is constantly moving between the atmosphere and Earth.

Condensation

Evaporation

Transpiration

Precipitation

Evaporation

Runoff

Oceans

Groundwater

53

Quick Demo

Model the Water Cycle A terrarium, such as a large glass bowl containing soil and plants and capped with plastic wrap, can be used to show the water cycle. Have students identify the parts of the water cycle. Through evaporation and transpiration, water leaves the soil. The water vapor condenses on the plastic wrap and drops accumulate, simulating cloud formation. When the drops are large enough, they fall back to the soil, simulating precipitation.

Reinforcement

Visual-Spatial Have students diagram the water cycle as it occurs in their town or city for inclusion in their portfolios. Encourage them to label the major sources and processes involved in the water cycle, such as evaporation from streams, condensation, precipitation, respiration, transpiration, excretion, and decomposition. Students may use library reference materials if necessary. L2 ELL

Physical Science Connection

The following equation describes the chemical reaction that produces electrical energy in a car battery:
$$Pb + PbO_2 + 2H_2SO_4 \rightarrow 2PbSO_4 + 2H_2O$$
Have students compare the number of each type of atom on both sides of the equation. The number of each type of atom is the same on both sides of the equation. As a result, the mass of the reactants is the same as the mass of the products and mass is conserved.

CHALLENGE ACTIVITY

Follow the Light Energy Have students assume they have a "packet" of light energy from the sun with a value of 100 energy units. Have them trace a path through a simple food chain and indicate an energy value for each level. Have them assume that only ten percent of the energy is passed from one level to the next. See *BioChallenges and Enrichment* for additional projects and activities. L3

MiniLab 2.2

Purpose

Students will test for the presence of carbon dioxide gas.

Process Skills

acquire information, draw a conclusion, observe and infer, recognize cause and effect

Safety Precautions

Caution students NOT to inhale or drink the bromothymol solution. Have them wear goggles and a lab apron. Wash hands with soap after completing the activity.

Teaching Strategies

■ Prepare bromothymol blue solution as follows: Stock solution—add 0.5 g bromothymol blue powder to 500 mL distilled water. Dilute 10 mL stock solution with 500 mL of distilled water. (If solution is green, add one or more drops of NH_4OH until a blue color appears. If solution is deep blue, add one or more drops of HCl until it is light blue.)

■ Use an effervescent antacid. Ingredients must include a carbonate or bicarbonate and weak acid such as citric acid.

■ Bromothymol blue changes color in the presence of any acid in solution, such as the carbonic acid, which is formed by carbon dioxide and water.

Expected Results

Bromothymol blue changes to green or yellow when an antacid tablet is added or when sufficient CO_2 in exhaled air stimulates the formation of carbonic acid bubbled through the indicator.

Analysis

1. Bromothymol blue changes to green or yellow when carbon dioxide gas is added.
2. carbon dioxide
3. Yes, the color change in the bromothymol blue indicated the presence of CO_2.

MiniLab 2.2

Observe and Infer

Detecting Carbon Dioxide
Cellular respiration is the chemical process whereby food is broken down, energy is released, and carbon dioxide is given off. When carbon dioxide dissolves in water, an acid forms. Certain chemicals called indicators can be used to detect acids. One indicator, called bromothymol blue, will change from its normal blue color to green or yellow if an acid is present.

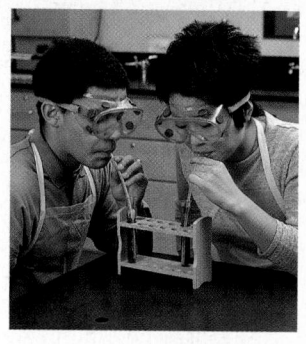

Procedure

1. Half fill a test tube with bromothymol blue solution.
2. Add a quarter of an effervescent antacid tablet to the tube and note any color change.
3. Half fill a second test tube with bromothymol blue solution. Using a straw, exhale into the bromothymol blue at least 30 times. Record any color change that occurs in the test tube. **CAUTION: DO NOT inhale the bromothymol blue.**

Analysis

1. **Observe** Describe the color change that occurs when sufficient carbon dioxide is added to bromothymol blue.
2. **Infer** What was the chemical composition of the bubbles seen in the tube with the antacid tablet?
3. **Conclude** Does exhaled air contain carbon dioxide? Explain how you can determine this.

Where do the drops of water that form on a cold can of soda come from? The water vapor in the air condenses on the surface of the can because the can is colder than the surrounding air. What takes place in the glass of water and on the cold soda can is similar to the global water cycle on the previous page. Water vapor also condenses on dust in the air and forms clouds. Further condensation makes small drops that build in size until they fall from the clouds as precipitation

in the form of rain, ice, or snow. The water falls to Earth and accumulates in oceans and lakes where evaporation continues. Plants and animals need water to live. Natural processes constantly recycle water throughout the environment. Plants pull water from the ground and lose water from their leaves through the process of transpiration. This activity puts water vapor into the air. Animals breathe out water vapor in every breath. When they perspire or urinate, water also is returned to the environment.

The carbon cycle

All life on Earth is based on carbon molecules. Atoms of carbon form the framework for proteins, carbohydrates, fats, and other important molecules. More than any other element, carbon is the molecule of life. It is an important part of all living organisms.

The carbon cycle described in *Figure 2.18* on the next page starts with an autotroph. During photosynthesis, energy from the sun is used by autotrophic organisms to convert carbon dioxide gas into energy-rich carbon molecules that many organisms use for food and a source of energy. Autotrophs use these molecules for growth and energy. Heterotrophs, which feed either directly or indirectly on the autotrophs, use these carbon molecules for growth and energy. When the autotrophs and heterotrophs use the carbon-containing molecules and release energy, carbon dioxide is released and returned to the atmosphere. As the term implies, carbon *cycles* again and again through this system. How rapidly it cycles depends upon whether it is in soil, leaves, roots, tied up in a forest, in oil or coal, in animal fossils, or in the world's vast calcium carbonate reserves. Learn how to detect the presence of carbon dioxide in the *MiniLab* shown here.

54 PRINCIPLES OF ECOLOGY

CLEANUP AND DISPOSAL

🗑 Recover unused bromothymol blue for reuse or follow district guidelines for disposal. See MSDS available online through **in.bdol.glencoe.com**

Assessment

Skill Have students make a hypothesis for an experiment using bromothymol blue and a decomposer. Use the Performance Task Assessment List for Formulating a Hypothesis in **PASC**, p. 93. **L2**

The Carbon Cycle

Figure 2.18

From proteins to sugars, carbon is the building block of the molecules of life. Linked carbon atoms form the frame for molecules produced by plants and other living things. Organisms use these carbon molecules for growth and energy. **Critical Thinking** *How is carbon released from the bodies of organisms?*

Forests use carbon dioxide.

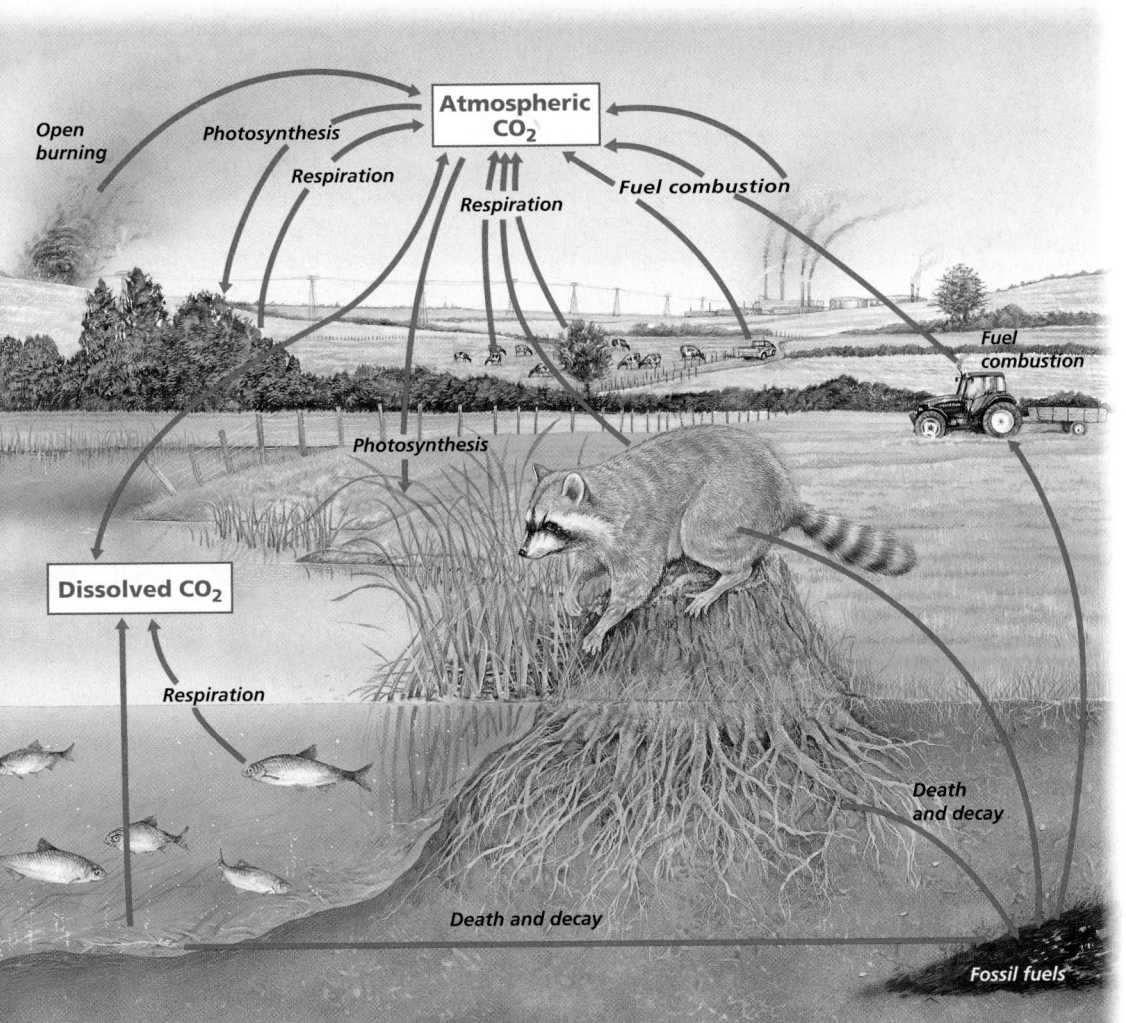

Open burning

Photosynthesis

Respiration

Atmospheric CO_2

Respiration

Fuel combustion

Respiration

Photosynthesis

Fuel combustion

Dissolved CO_2

Respiration

Death and decay

Death and decay

Fossil fuels

55

Purpose

Students study the cycling of carbon in the environment.

Teaching Strategies

■ Help students understand that the carbon dioxide that plants remove from the atmosphere becomes biomass. When plants and animals use the nutrients and release energy, carbon dioxide is returned to the atmosphere.

■ Using the figure, help students understand other ways carbon dioxide enters the atmosphere.

Visual Learning

Using Figure 2.18, have students trace a carbon from the atmosphere, through two trophic levels, and back to the atmosphere. **L1**

Critical Thinking

Carbon from biomass is released in the form of carbon dioxide through respiration, decay, or burning.

DESIGN YOUR OWN BioLab The BioLab at the end of the chapter can be used at this point in the lesson.

Resources

For additional high-interest activities, see the *Forensics and Biotechnology Lab Manual.*

Local Carbon Cycle Have students use maps, illustrations, and/or photographs to construct an image of the carbon cycle in their locale. Label all structures, plants, and animals involved. **L3**

Indiana Academic Standards

Pages 54–55: B.1.19, B.1.37, B.1.41, B.1.42, B.1.43, B.1.44, B.1.47

Reinforcement

Ask students to identify the roles of the producers, consumers, and decomposers in the cycling of nitrogen. **Producers take in nitrogen compounds in soil and pass these compounds to consumers that consume the producers. Decomposers break down the nitrogen compounds and release nitrogen gas to the air or usable nitrogen compounds to the soil.** **L2**

Enrichment

Show students plant fertilizer labels. These fertilizers add nitrogen and phosphorus to the soil because these substances frequently have been washed away from plants. Explain that these substances do not disappear, but often end up in streams. Explain the numbers on the label. For example, a plant fertilizer that is labeled 20-20-10 contains 20 percent nitrogen, 20 percent phosphorus, and 10 percent potassium compounds.

Caption Question Answer

Figure 2.20 (page 57) The mountains contain phosphorus that was bound up in sediments when the matter was still below sea level. Eventually this matter was uplifted and mountains formed.

The nitrogen cycle

If you add nitrogen fertilizer to a lawn, houseplants, or garden, you may see that they become greener, bushier, and taller. Even though the air is 78 percent nitrogen, plants seem to do better when they receive nitrogen fertilizer. This is because most plants cannot use the nitrogen in the air. They use nitrogen in the soil that has been converted into more usable forms.

As *Figure 2.19* shows, certain bacteria convert the nitrogen from air into these more usable forms. Chemical fertilizers also give plants nitrogen in a form they can use.

Plants use the nitrogen to make important molecules such as proteins. Herbivores eat plants and convert nitrogen-containing plant proteins into nitrogen-containing animal proteins. After you eat your food, you convert the protein components in food into human proteins in the form of muscle cells, blood cells, enzymes, and urine. Urine, an animal waste, contains nitrogen compounds. When an animal urinates, nitrogen returns to the water or soil. When organisms die and decay, nitrogen returns to the soil and eventually to the atmosphere. Plants reuse this nitrogen. Soil bacteria also act on these molecules and put nitrogen back into the air.

The phosphorus cycle

Materials other than water, carbon, and nitrogen cycle through ecosystems. Substances such as sulfur, calcium, and phosphorus, as well as others, must also cycle through an ecosystem. One essential element, phosphorus, cycles in two ways.

All organisms require phosphorus for growth and development. Plants

Figure 2.19
In the nitrogen cycle, nitrogen is converted from a gas to compounds important for life and back to a gas.

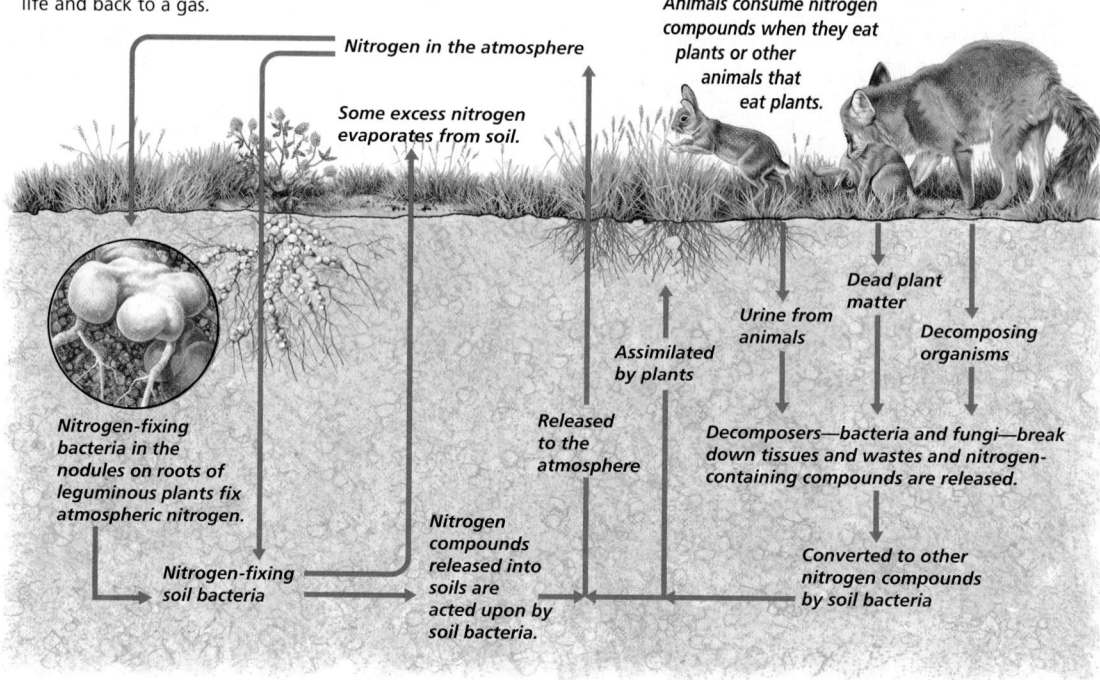

Nitrogen in the atmosphere

Animals consume nitrogen compounds when they eat plants or other animals that eat plants.

Some excess nitrogen evaporates from soil.

Nitrogen-fixing bacteria in the nodules on roots of leguminous plants fix atmospheric nitrogen.

Nitrogen-fixing soil bacteria

Nitrogen compounds released into soils are acted upon by soil bacteria.

Assimilated by plants

Released to the atmosphere

Urine from animals

Dead plant matter

Decomposing organisms

Decomposers—bacteria and fungi—break down tissues and wastes and nitrogen-containing compounds are released.

Converted to other nitrogen compounds by soil bacteria

56 PRINCIPLES OF ECOLOGY

CHALLENGE ACTIVITY

Living With a Legume A mutualistic symbiotic relationship exists between certain roots and bacteria. This relationship is commonly found in leguminous plants. Prepared slides are available of root nodules that show this relationship. Have students observe these slides under a microscope and make diagrams of their observations. Ask them to research the name of the bacterium that lives in the nodules. Students should write a report of their observations and explain how the relationship benefits the atmosphere. **L3**

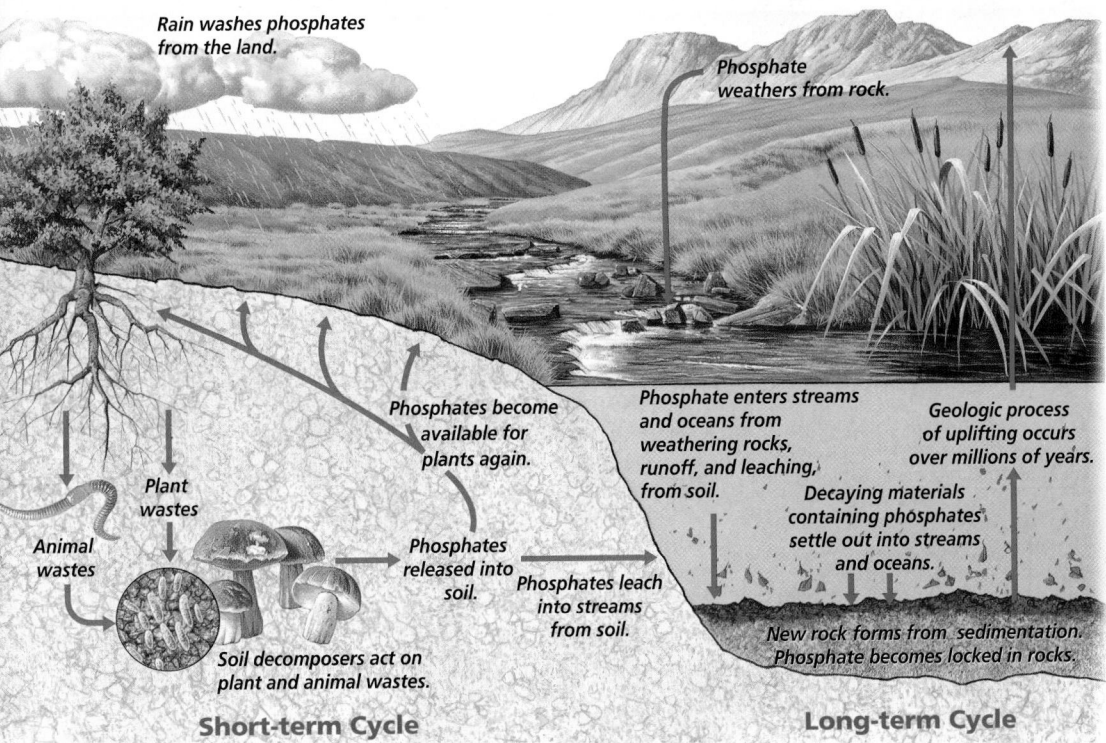

Rain washes phosphates from the land.

Phosphate weathers from rock.

Phosphates become available for plants again.

Plant wastes

Animal wastes

Phosphates released into soil.

Phosphates leach into streams from soil.

Soil decomposers act on plant and animal wastes.

Phosphate enters streams and oceans from weathering rocks, runoff, and leaching, from soil.

Geologic process of uplifting occurs over millions of years.

Decaying materials containing phosphates settle out into streams and oceans.

New rock forms from sedimentation. Phosphate becomes locked in rocks.

Short-term Cycle

Long-term Cycle

3 Assess

DAILY INTERVENTION

Check for Understanding
Have students explain the relationship between the words in each of the following pairs.
a. autotroph—producer
b. heterotroph—consumer
c. recycling—carbon
d. bacteria—nitrogen cycle
L1 **ELL**

Reteach
Have students identify the trophic level of each organism in a food chain and indicate the direction of energy flow. **L1**

Resources
For more practice, use *Reading Essentials for Biology*, Section 2.2.

obtain phosphorus from the soil. Animals obtain phosphorus by eating plants. When these animals die, they decompose and the phosphorus is returned to the soil to be used again. This is the short-term phosphorus cycle in *Figure 2.20.* Phosphorus also has a long-term cycle, where

phosphates washed into water become incorporated into rock as insoluble compounds. Millions of years later, as the environment changes, the rock containing phosphorus is exposed. As the rock erodes, the phosphorus again becomes part of the local ecological system.

Figure 2.20
In the phosphorus cycle, phosphorus moves between the living and nonliving parts of the environment.
Explain *What is the function of mountains in the phosphorus cycle?*

Extension

Naturalist Have students speculate about the consequences to a food web if an organism at the second trophic level were to be eliminated. This would eliminate a food source for some organisms at the third trophic level. **L2**

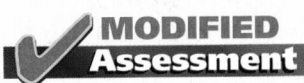 **MODIFIED Assessment**

Performance Have students diagram, label, and explain one of the following: a food web, water cycle, energy or biomass pyramid, or carbon cycle. **L1**

Section Assessment

Understanding Main Ideas
1. What is the difference between an autotroph and a heterotroph?
2. Why do autotrophs always occupy the lowest level of ecological pyramids?
3. Give two examples of how nitrogen cycles from the abiotic portion of the environment into living things and back.
4. Explain the interactions among organisms in pyramids of energy, numbers, and biomass.

Thinking Critically
5. Evaluate the adequacy of the pyramid model to explain energy and matter transfer in an ecosystem.

SKILL REVIEW

6. **Design an Experiment** Suppose there is a fertilizer called GrowFast. It contains extra nitrogen and phosphorus. Design an experiment to see if GrowFast increases the growth rate of plants. For more help, refer to *Design an Experiment* in the **Skill Handbook**.

 in.bdol.glencoe.com/self_check_quiz

Section Assessment

1. An autotroph makes its own food. A heterotroph must consume another organism to meet its nutritional needs.
2. Autotrophs capture light energy and create nutrients. When eaten, they provide nutrients for all other organisms.
3. (1) Nitrogen in the air passes to bacteria, which form compounds used by plants. Decay of dead plants returns nitrogen to air. (2) As in (1), but plants can be eaten by consumers. Decay of dead consumers returns nitrogen to air.
4. In pyramids of energy, numbers, and biomass, the numbers at each trophic level decrease. Pyramids of numbers usually decrease at each trophic level. An exception is when a large producer is consumed by many small herbivores.
5. Even "simple" ecosystems are extremely complex, and pyramid models do not completely explain energy and matter transfers in ecosystems.
6. Designs should include control and experimental groups. Sample size should be greater than one plant. Students should define *growth* as the increase in plant height.

Time Allotment

initial preparation: one class session; ten-minute sessions for one to two weeks every other day

Process Skills

observe, record and analyze data, design an experiment, separate and control variables

Safety Precautions

Use oven mitts when handling hot, sterile pond water. Have students wear goggles and aprons and wash their hands with soap after the lab and cleanup.

PREPARATION

Alternative Materials

To prepare sterile pond water, filter the water and place it in flat pans. Boil for 15 minutes. Allow to cool before using.

Possible Hypotheses

In general, if a predator population is added to a prey population, the size of the predator population will increase while the prey population decreases.

However, if a small predator population is added to a large prey population, no observable difference will occur in the sizes of the populations.

DESIGN YOUR OWN
BioLab

 Before You Begin

Why don't prey populations disappear when predators are present? Prey species have evolved a variety of defenses to avoid being eaten. Just as prey have evolved defenses to avoid predators, predators have evolved mechanisms to overcome those defenses.

Didinium is a unicellular protist that attacks and devours *Paramecium* larger than itself. Do populations of *Paramecium* change when a population of *Didinium* is present?

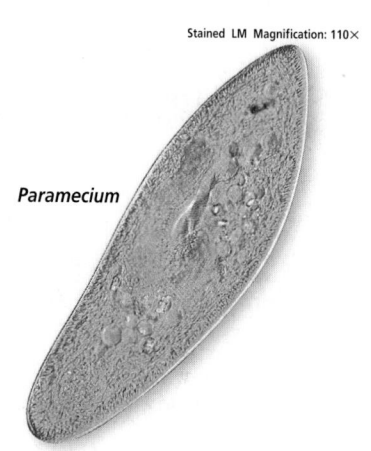

Stained LM Magnification: 110×

Paramecium

How can one population affect another?

Stained LM Magnification: 160×

PREPARATION

Problem

How does a population of *Paramecium* react to a population of *Didinium*?

Hypotheses

Have your group agree on an hypothesis to be tested. Record your hypothesis.

Objectives

In this BioLab, you will:
- **Design** an experiment to establish the relationships between *Paramecium* and *Didinium*.
- **Use** appropriate variables, constants, and controls in experimental design.

Possible Materials

microscope	culture of *Paramecium*
microscope slides	beakers or jars
coverslips	eyedroppers
culture of *Didinium*	sterile pond water

Safety Precautions

CAUTION: *Take care when using electrical equipment. Always use goggles in the lab. Handle slides and coverslips carefully. Dispose of broken glass in a container provided by your teacher.*

Skill Handbook

If you need help, with this lab, refer to the **Skill Handbook**.

PLAN THE EXPERIMENT

1. Review the discussion of feeding relationships in this chapter.
2. Select the materials you will use in your investigation. Record your list.
3. Be sure that your experimental plan contains a control, tests a single variable such as population size, and allows for the collection of quantitative data.
4. Prepare a list of numbered directions. Explain how you will use each of your materials.

Didi

PROCEDURE

Teaching Strategies

- A lower magnification provides a wider field of view, making counting easier.
- Methyl cellulose, available from supply houses, may be used to slow the protozoans.

Troubleshooting

- Cover or stack culture dishes to prevent drying out.
- Have students examine unmixed cultures first so they can later distinguish between *Paramecium* and *Didinium*.
- Suggest that several low-power field

counts be made and an average of these counts be used in the data tables.

CLEANUP AND DISPOSAL

Encourage students to make wise choices about disposal of live materials in the laboratory.

Check the Plan

Discuss the following points with other group members to decide final procedures. Make any needed changes to your plan.

1. What will you measure to determine the effect of the *Didinium* on *Paramecium?* If you count *Paramecia*, will you count all you can see in the field of vision of the microscope at a certain power? Will you have multiple trials? If so, how many?

2. What single factor will you vary? For example, will you put no *Didinium* in one culture of *Paramecium* and 5 mL of *Didinium* culture in another culture of *Paramecium?*

3. How long will you observe the populations?

4. How will you estimate the changes in the populations of *Paramecium* and *Didinium* during the experiment?

5. *Make sure your teacher has approved your experimental plan before you proceed further.*

6. Carry out your experiment.

7. Make a data table that has Date, Number of *Paramecium,* and Number of *Didinium* across the top. Place the data obtained for each culture in rows. Design and complete a graph of your data.

8. **CLEANUP AND DISPOSAL** Make wise choices as to how the organisms will be reused or disposed of at the end of your experiment. Always wash your hands with soap or detergent after handling these organisms.

Color-enhanced SEM Magnification: 1400×
A *Didinium* captures a *Paramecium.*

ANALYZE AND CONCLUDE

1. **Analyze Data** What differences did you observe among the experimental groups? Were these differences due to the presence of *Didinium?* Explain.

2. **Draw Conclusions** Did the *Paramecium* die out in any culture? Why or why not?

3. **Check Your Hypothesis** Was your hypothesis supported by your data? If not, suggest a new hypothesis.

4. **ERROR ANALYSIS** List several ways that your methods may have affected the outcome of the experiment and describe how you would change the experiment.

Apply Your Skill

Project Based on this lab experience, design another experiment that would help you answer any questions that arose from your work. What factors might you allow to vary if you kept the number of *Didinium* constant?

Web Links To find out more about population biology, visit in.bdol.glencoe.com/population_biology

ANALYZE AND CONCLUDE

1. Only cultures containing both *Didinium* and *Paramecium* will show a decline in numbers after a period of time. This difference is due to the presence of *Didinium* because they prey upon the *Paramecium.*

2. *Paramecium* die out in the mixed culture. They will be preyed upon by *Didinium.*

3. In most cases, hypotheses will be supported by data.

4. **ERROR ANALYSIS** The list may include counting errors, too few samples, or cultures becoming contaminated or being affected by temperatures. The amount of initial culture of the two species should be equal and can be quantified by pre-measuring the volume in the pipettes.

Assessment

Skill Ask students to prepare a summary of this experiment in their journals. Use the Performance Task Assessment List for Writing in Science in **PASC,** p. 159. **L2**

Apply Your Skill

Supply students with another type of protozoan or change the initial volume of predator culture. **L2**

Possible Procedures

Controls will consist of *Paramecium* cultures with no predators added. Food will have to be added to these cultures. Use one alfalfa tablet (available from pharmacies) per liter of water. (Note: If one culture receives food, all cultures must receive the same food to maintain control conditions.)

Data and Observations

Data and observations will vary. Typically, when the populations are mixed together, both will initially increase in number. A decrease in prey will then be detected as the predator population feeds upon them, with a final drop in the population of predators as their food supply runs out.

Indiana Academic Standards

Pages 58–59: B.1.43, B.1.44, B.1.47

Purpose

Students gain an understanding of the complexity of ecosystems and learn some ways in which human activities can affect the environment.

Teaching Strategies

After students have completed the reading, invite them to discuss issues involved in balancing the needs of both human and wildlife populations. The Everglades are economically important. Tourism, agriculture, and the sugar cane industries are very strong in Florida. Many Florida residents work in the tourism industry, and the Everglades brings large numbers of tourists, and therefore income, to the state. **L2**

Background

Everglades water that flows all the way to the Gulf coast carries with it nutrients that support the growth of mangrove swamps and sea grass beds. These two estuarine communities feed and shelter young fish, shellfish, and other important links in the marine food chain.

Changes in the water flow of the area sometimes result in the discharge of large amounts of freshwater into Florida Bay, changing the salinity of the water and endangering the health of mangroves.

Pollutants and excessive amounts of fresh water may also be endangering the coral reefs off the Florida coast.

Forming Your Opinion

The park was cut off from its water source. Even though land and wildlife inside the park were protected from development, not enough clean water reaches the park to keep it healthy.

The Everglades—Restoring an Ecosystem

The Florida Everglades ecosystem covers the southern portion of the Florida peninsula. As with any wetlands, water is the critical factor.

Each year, during the rainy season from May to October, the subtropical region of southern Florida receives between 100 and 165 cm (40–65 inches) of rain. Before extensive development took place, the heavy rainfall caused shallow Lake Okeechobee to overflow and a wide, thin sheet of water spread out from the lake, creating an extensive marshy area.

Early in the twentieth century, while Florida was still mostly wilderness, the seasonal slow-moving river that flowed slowly out of Lake Okeechobee was about 80 km (50 miles) wide in some places, and only 15–90 cm (six inches to three feet) deep. This wetland teemed with fishes, amphibians, and other animals that fed millions of wading birds. Healthy populations of crocodiles, alligators, and other large animals also lived here. During the dry season, from December to April, water levels in the marshes gradually dropped. Fishes and other water dwellers moved into deeper pools that held water all year long.

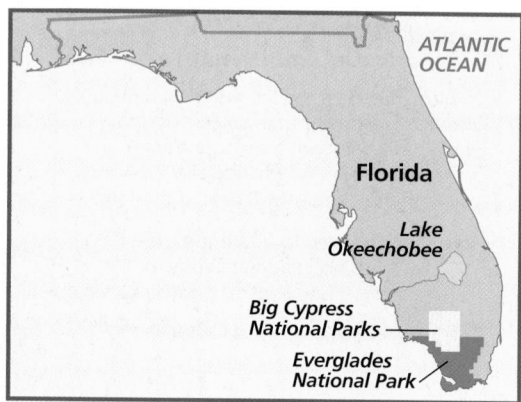

The map shows the location of the Everglades.

The Changing Everglades Water from Lake Okeechobee no longer floods the countryside, however. Because of its beauty and resources, people and industries were attracted to Florida beginning in the late 1880s and early 1900s. Over time, the area changed. As much as 70 percent of Lake Okeechobee's water was diverted to create dry land. The area around the lake became surrounded by farms and towns and is now unable to adequately renew the Everglades. As a result, the ecology of the area has been measurably affected. Since 1950, the wading bird population alone has declined more than 90 percent. Almost 70 percent of other native wildlife is now listed as threatened or endangered. As for the water supply, nearly 1.7 billion gallons of freshwater, which would normally flow slowly through the Everglades from Lake Okeechobee and other streams, now flows directly into the ocean instead.

Perspectives Agriculture and industry are important to the area's economy. However, over the years, runoff containing large amounts of toxins and excess nutrients (particularly phosphorus) has made its way into the water that eventually reaches the Everglades.

In 1993, a plan was put forth for restoring the deteriorating Everglades. The goals of the plan being worked out by federal, state, and industry are:
1. to reduce the levels of phosphorus and mercury runoff from industry to safe levels,
2. to restore the natural flow of unpolluted water into the Everglades,
3. to recover native habitats and species, and to create a sustainable ecosystem.

Forming Your Opinion

Point of View When Everglades National Park was established, scientists and government officials intended that a portion of the Everglades ecosystem would be preserved from development. Research the current history of attempts to restore the Everglades ecosystems.

 To find out more about the Everglades, visit in.bdol.glencoe.com/biology_society

---

Going Further

Naturalist Everglades habitats include sea grass beds, coastal prairies, mangrove swamps, freshwater sloughs, marl prairies, hammocks, and pinelands. Have students research one or more of these habitats and its organisms. **L3**

STUDY GUIDE

Section 2.1

Organisms and Their Environment

Key Concepts

- Natural history, the observation of how organisms live out their lives in nature, led to the development of the science of ecology—the study of the interactions of organisms with one another and with their environments.

- Ecologists classify and study the biological levels of organization from the individual to ecosystem. Ecologists study the abiotic and biotic factors that are a part of an organism's habitat. They investigate the strategies an organism is adapted with to exist in its niche.

Vocabulary

abiotic factor (p. 37)
biological community (p. 39)
biosphere (p. 36)
biotic factor (p. 38)
commensalism (p. 44)
ecology (p. 36)
ecosystem (p. 41)
habitat (p. 42)
mutualism (p. 44)
niche (p. 43)
parasitism (p. 44)
population (p. 38)
symbiosis (p. 44)

Section 2.2

Nutrition and Energy Flow

Key Concepts

- Autotrophs, such as plants, make nutrients that can be used by the plants and by heterotrophs. Heterotrophs include herbivores, carnivores, omnivores, and decomposers.

- Food chains are simple models that show how energy and materials move from autotrophs to heterotrophs and eventually to decomposers.

- Food webs represent many interconnected food chains and illustrate pathways in which energy and materials are transferred within an ecosystem. Energy is transferred through food webs. The materials of life, such as carbon and nitrogen, are used and reused as they cycle through the ecosystem.

Vocabulary

autotroph (p. 46)
biomass (p. 52)
decomposer (p. 47)
food chain (p. 49)
food web (p. 50)
heterotroph (p. 47)
trophic level (p. 50)

FOLDABLES Study Organizer To help you review the principles of ecology, use the Organizational Study Fold on page 46.

 in.bdol.glencoe.com/vocabulary_puzzlemaker

CHAPTER 2 ASSESSMENT **61**

Key Concepts

Summary statements can be used by students to review the major concepts of the chapter.

Biology Online

Visit in.bdol.glencoe.com
/self_check_quiz
/vocabulary_puzzlemaker
/chapter_test
/standardized_test

VOCABULARY PUZZLEMAKER

 For additional help with vocabulary, have students access the Vocabulary PuzzleMaker online at in.bdol.glencoe.com/vocabulary_puzzlemaker

FOLDABLES™

Have students use their Foldables to review the content of Section 2.2. In a paragraph on the back of the paper, students can discuss why these cycles are sometimes called biogeochemical cycles.

Use the ExamView®Pro Test Bank CD-ROM to:
- Create **multiple versions** of tests
- Create **modified** tests with one mouse click for **inclusion** students
- **Edit** existing questions and **add** your own questions
- Build tests aligned with state standards using built-in **State Curriculum Tags**
- Change **English** tests to **Spanish** with one mouse click and vice versa

 Indiana Academic Standards

Pages 60–61: B.1.37, B.1.41, B.1.43, B.1.44, B.1.47

Chapter 2 Assessment

 The Princeton Review **Questions and answers have been aligned and verified by The Princeton Review.**

Vocabulary Review

1. symbiosis   4. autotroph
2. food chain 5. niche
3. ecosystem

Understanding Key Concepts

6. A   8. A
7. D   9. B

Constructed Response

10. Decomposers can release nutrients for recycling through an ecosystem, maintaining its balance such as in tropical forests. In instances where decomposers work too slowly, the forest may die back or grow more slowly for lack of nutrients.

11. Answers will vary, but include several populations and the interactions of these with the environment.

12. Matter, in the form of carbon in the ecosystem, recycles and is changed from one form to another. However, the carbon atoms themselves are neither created nor destroyed.

Thinking Critically

13. The arrows indicate the direction of matter and energy flow; toward the consumer.

14. The base of the pyramid should contain grass, the producers. The middle level contains deer, the herbivores. The top of the pyramid contains the second order consumers, the cougar.

15. The algae are in a mutualistic relationship and moths are in a commensalistic relationship with the sloth.

16. Changes in abiotic factors within the community

Vocabulary Review

Review the Chapter 2 vocabulary words listed in the Study Guide on page 61. Match the words with the definitions below.

1. any close and permanent association among organisms of different species

2. a simple model used to show how matter and energy move through an ecosystem

3. interactions among the populations in a community and the community's abiotic factors

4. organisms that use energy from the sun or energy stored in chemical compounds to manufacture their own nutrients

5. strategies and adaptations a species uses in its environment

Understanding Key Concepts

6. Which of the following would be abiotic factors for a polar bear?
   A. extreme cold, floating ice
   B. eating only live prey
   C. large body size
   D. paws with thick hair

7. In the food web below, which of the organisms—X, Y, or Z—is an herbivore?

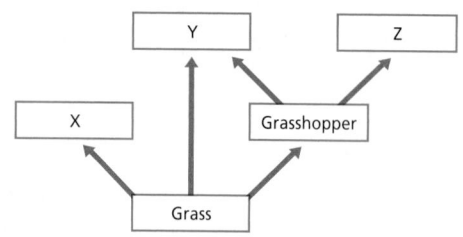

   A. Z   C. Both X and Y
   B. Y   D. X

8. Which of the following would most decrease the amount of carbon dioxide in the air?
   A. a growing maple tree
   B. a running dog
   C. a person driving a car
   D. a burning forest

---

9. Which of the following describes energy and matter in ecosystems?
   A. Both energy and matter are completely recycled.
   B. Matter recycles, but some energy is transferred.
   C. Energy is recycled, but most matter is lost.
   D. Both matter and energy are completely lost.

Constructed Response

10. **Open Ended** Decomposers are all microorganisms. Review the role of decomposers in food chains and explain how they can both maintain and disrupt the equilibrium or balance of an ecosystem. Use a specific example in your explanation.

11. **Open Ended** Identify and describe an ecosystem in or around your home. List all the biotic and abiotic factors interacting there and explain how you think they affect each other.

12. **Open Ended** According to the law of conservation of matter, matter can neither be created nor destroyed. Make a relationship between this statement and the recycling of carbon in an ecosystem.

Thinking Critically

13. **Explain** In a food chain, explain what the arrows mean.

14. **Interpret Scientific Illustrations** Draw and label a pyramid of numbers that includes the components: deer, cougar, grass.

15. **Analyze** The three-toed sloth often is camouflaged by algae. Which type of symbiosis does this represent and why?

16. **REAL WORLD BioCHALLENGE** Populations of amphibians are declining in areas worldwide. Visit **in.bdol.glencoe.com** to investigate the reasons for the decline. What are some reasons amphibian populations may be decreasing? Suggest ways to reverse the decline to your class.

 in.bdol.glencoe.com/chapter_test

(water quality, acid rain); viruses spread from one population to another are suggested reasons. Humans should avoid spreading pathogens. Humans also have a role in preserving habitat in critically sensitive areas such as tropical rain forests and other areas where amphibians are in decline.

RUBRIC

Evaluating Open-Ended Questions
Open-ended assessment questions are graded by using a multilevel rubric that guides you in assessing a student's knowledge of a particular concept. The following rubric is a sample scoring device.

End-of-Course Assessment Practice

The assessed Indiana standard appears next to the question.

All questions aligned and verified by The Princeton Review

Part 1 Multiple Choice

Use the picture of the food web shown here to answer questions 17 and 18.

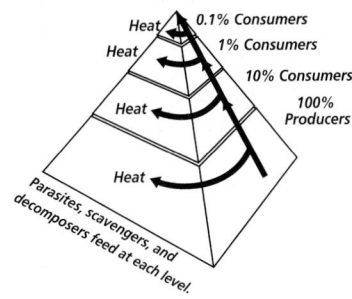

Heat — 0.1% Consumers
Heat — 1% Consumers
Heat — 10% Consumers
Heat — 100% Producers
Heat

Parasites, scavengers, and decomposers feed at each level.

17. In the pyramid of energy above, less energy
B.1.44 is available in the second level because
_____.
- **A.** there is more food than at the first level
- **B.** energy from the first level was given off as heat
- **C.** the organism at the top doesn't need very much
- **D.** producers don't use as much energy as consumers

18. The amount of energy at each level is about
B.1.44 _____ of what it was on the level before.
- **A.** 50 percent
- **B.** 25 percent
- **C.** 20 percent
- **D.** 10 percent

19. All the abiotic and biotic factors in a small
B.1.43 forest form a(n) _____.
- **A.** population
- **B.** community
- **C.** ecosystem
- **D.** biosphere

20. Because most humans consume both plant and animal products, they are described as _____.
- **A.** omnivores
- **B.** carnivores
- **C.** herbivores
- **D.** predators

21. The relationship of algae living in the fur
B.1.45 of 3-toed sloths and helping camouflage the sloths, is called _____.
- **A.** parasitism
- **B.** commensalism
- **C.** mutualism
- **D.** symbiosis

22. Why is a jar of pond water an ecosystem?
B.1.45 **A.** Depending on nonliving factors, many populations live in the jar.
- **B.** Only one population lives in the jar.
- **C.** Only the abiotic factors determine if algae can survive.
- **D.** Many different populations of microorganisms eat the algae.

Part 2 Constructed Response/Grid In

Use the flowchart of the phosphorus cycle below to answer question 23. Record your answers on your answer document.

23. Open Ended Phosphorus enters the cycle from sediments. Using evidence from the diagram, explain why and explain how the mountains in the diagram are related to the cycle.

24. Open Ended Using information from the nitrogen cycle, explain the niche of nitrogen-fixing soil bacteria. Why are they important for life?

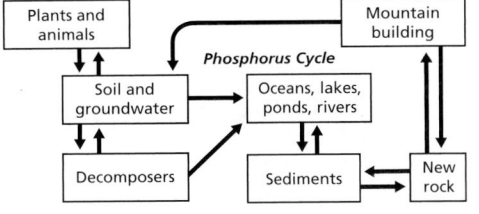

Phosphorus Cycle

Plants and animals → Soil and groundwater ↔ Mountain building
Soil and groundwater → Oceans, lakes, ponds, rivers
Decomposers → Sediments → New rock

 in.bdol.glencoe.com/standardized_test

CHAPTER 2 ASSESSMENT **63**

End-of-Course Assessment Practice

 FAST FILE

Answer Sheet A practice answer sheet can be found on p. 37 of *Unit 2 FAST FILE Resources.*

RUBRIC

SCORE	CRITERIA
4	A correct solution that is supported by well-developed, accurate explanations.
3	A generally correct solution, but may contain minor flaws in reasoning.

SCORE	CRITERIA
2	A partially correct interpretation and/or solution to the problem.
1	A correct solution with no supporting evidence or explanation.
0	An incorrect solution or no solution is given.

Indiana Academic Standards

Pages 62–63: B.1.37, B.1.40, B.1.41, B.1.43, B.1.44, B.1.45, B.1.47

Section Objectives	National Science Standards	State/Local Standards	Advanced Lab and Demo Planning
Section 3.1 2 sessions, 1 block 1. **Identify** some common limiting factors. 2. **Explain** how limiting factors and ranges of tolerance affect distribution of organisms. 3. **Sequence** the stages of ecological succession. 4. **Describe** the conditions under which primary and secondary succession takes place.	UCP.1, UCP.3, UCP.4; A.1, A.2; C.4, C.5; D.3; F.5; G.3	**Indiana Standards** B.1.18, B.1.39, B.1.40, B.1.43, B.1.45	**Student Labs:** MiniLab 3.1, p. 67: lichen samples, microscope, stained section of a lichen slide Problem-Solving Lab 3.1, p. 68 **Teacher Demonstration:** Quick Demo, p. 66: cactus, broad-leafed houseplant
Section 3.2 3 sessions, 1 1/2 blocks 5. **Compare and contrast** the photic and aphotic zones of marine biomes. 6. **Identify** the major limiting factors affecting distribution of terrestrial biomes. 7. **Distinguish** among biomes.	UCP.1–3; A.1, A.2; C.4, C.5, C.6; F.4; G.1, G.2, G.3	**Indiana Standards** B.1.18, B.1.31, B.1.37, B.1.39, B.1.40, B.1.41, B.1.43, B.1.44, B.1.45	**Student Labs:** Problem-Solving Lab 3.2, p. 72 MiniLab 3.2, p. 73: dropper, marine plankton, water, coverslip, microscope Additional Lab, p. 76: 3 cloth squares, large beaker, water, sand, clay, potting soil, balance, twist ties **Teacher Demonstrations:** Quick Demo, p. 75: atlas Quick Demo, p. 78: 2 paper towels, wax paper Quick Demo, p. 81: white sheet of paper
End of Chapter Assessment Student Edition **Study Guide,** p. 87 **Content Assessment,** pp. 88–89		**Indiana Standards** B.1.37, B.1.39, B.1.40, B.1.43, B.1.45, B.1.46	**Student Lab:** Investigate BioLab, p. 84: 3 small glass jars, labels, sterilized spring water, pond water containing plant material, glass slides, cover glasses, droppers, plastic wrap, cooked white rice, plastic teaspoon, microscope

Key to Teaching Strategies

L1 Level 1 activities should be appropriate for students with learning difficulties.

L2 Level 2 activities should be within the ability range of all students.

L3 Level 3 activities are designed for above-average students.

ELL ELL activities should be within the ability range of English Language Learners.

COOP LEARN Cooperative Learning activities are designed for small group work.

Legend

 Transparency   CD-ROM   MP3   Videocassette   DVD

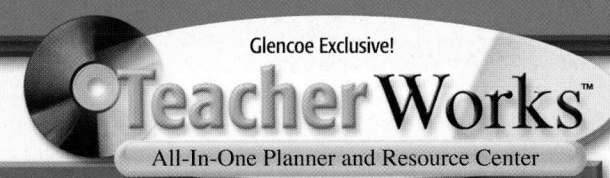

Glencoe Exclusive!

Teacher Works™

All-In-One Planner and Resource Center

Reproducible Masters and Transparencies	Technology

Reproducible Masters and Transparencies

Unit 2 FAST FILE Resources
  MiniLab Worksheet, p. 41
  BioLab Worksheet, pp. 43–44
  Reinforcement and Study Guide in English,
    pp. 45–46
  Reinforcement and Study Guide in Spanish,
    pp. 49–50
  Concept Mapping, p. 53
  Transparency Worksheets, pp. 55, 57–58, 59–60
Laboratory Manual, pp. 11–14
Probeware Labs, pp. 5–8
Section Focus Transparency 6
Basic Concepts Transparency 3
Reteaching Skills Transparency 4

Technology

- Interactive Chalkboard CD-ROM: Section 3.1 Presentation
- TeacherWorks™ CD-ROM
- Guided Reading Audio Summaries MP3

Unit 2 FAST FILE Resources
  MiniLab Worksheet, p. 42
  Reinforcement and Study Guide in English,
    pp. 47–48
  Reinforcement and Study Guide in Spanish,
    pp. 51–52
  Critical Thinking/Problem Solving, p. 54
  Transparency Worksheets, pp. 56, 61–62
Inside Story Poster
Section Focus Transparency 7
Reteaching Skills Transparency 5

- Interactive Chalkboard CD-ROM: Section 3.2 Presentation
- TeacherWorks™ CD-ROM
- Guided Reading Audio Summaries MP3

Unit 2 FAST FILE Resources
  Chapter Assessment, pp. 63–68
  Student Recording Sheet, p. 69

The Princeton Review **Reviewing Biology,** pp. 5–6

- Interactive Chalkboard: Chapter 3 Assessment
- MindJogger Videoquizzes DVD/VHS
- ExamView® Pro Test Bank CD-ROM
- TeacherWorks™ CD-ROM
- Succeeding on National Standards CD-ROM

in.bdol.glencoe.com
/self_check_quiz
/vocabulary_puzzlemaker
/chapter_test
/standardized_test

Indicates materials created specifically for Indiana.

Chapter 3

Communities and Biomes

Short on Time?

BIODIGEST The BioDigest at the end of this unit can be used as a(n):

- preview to introduce important unit concepts.
- overview if time does not permit teaching the entire chapter.
- review of key unit concepts.

Understanding the Photo

Most of the plants and animals found in a biome have adaptations that enable them to survive the extremes (the tolerance limits) of that biome. The marsh grasses in this photo don't have the choice of moving to warmer conditions if winter is severe. They are adapted to die back in winter and rebound in warmer weather. The birds, however, will more than likely move to warmer climates as temperatures and limited food supplies make this temperate biome temporarily intolerable.

PowerPoint® Presentations

This CD-ROM is an editable Microsoft® PowerPoint® presentation that includes:
- Section presentations
- Section checks
- Image bank
- Hot links to Biology Online
- All transparencies

What You'll Learn

- You will identify factors that limit the existence of species to certain areas.
- You will describe how and why different communities form.
- You will compare and contrast biomes of Earth.

Why It's Important

Life on Earth is found in communities made up of different species. To understand life on Earth, it is important to know about the variations, tolerances, and adaptations of plants and animals in these communities.

Understanding ▶ the Photo

Marsh grasses, birds, a supply of water rich in food resources, and a clear blue sky. This community in the Chesapeake Bay is a small example of the elements that make up larger ecosystems, called biomes, that make up the living world. Not every biome has these particular organisms or conditions. Organisms that make up communities in other biomes will reflect the climate and latitude of that part of the world.

 Biology Online

Visit in.bdol.glencoe.com **to**
- study the entire chapter online
- access Web Links for more information and activities on communities and biomes
- review content with the Interactive Tutor and self-check quizzes

64

Two-Minute Chapter Launcher

Activity Ask students to imagine what the land on which the school is built looked like 50 or 100 years ago. Responses should include that some changes have taken place in the land and that it may have had trees or been a farm field at that time. Have students make drawings that predict what the school's football field might look like in 100 years if left unused after this year's season. Discuss the drawings with the class.

Section 3.1

Communities

Indiana Standards Standard B.1.40 Understand and explain that like many complex systems, ecosystems tend to have cyclic fluctuations around a state of rough equilibrium…

Wonder Weeds

Using Prior Knowledge In most parts of the world, with regular rainfall, living organisms such as grasses and weeds stay alive and produce more of themselves. But, if no rain falls and it is very warm, the grasses turn brown. Soil cracks open. It seems that everything dies except the weeds.

Observe and Infer *Look at your neighborhood. List the types of changes that occur there in a year. Include changes that you have observed in plants, temperatures, or rainfall. Use this information to explain how your neighborhood is an ecological community.*

Dandelions in a lawn

Life in a Community

Look closely at a square meter of healthy, green lawn and you will discover that, hidden in the grass population, there are also populations of weeds, beetles and other insects, earthworms, and grubs. There may also be twigs, seeds, and maybe a bird feather, along with soil and moisture. Not so visible are the populations of bacteria and fungi that outnumber all the other organisms. This community is alive, and each population or factor in it contributes something important to the life of the lawn.

How do plants and animals survive where they live? What is there about a climate where green lawns live and die that is different from a climate where polar bears thrive? Various combinations of abiotic and biotic factors interact in different places around the world. The result is that conditions in one part of the world are suitable for supporting certain forms of life, but not others.

Limiting factors

Factors that affect an organism's ability to survive in its environment, such as the availability of water and food, predators, and temperature, are called limiting factors. A **limiting factor** is any biotic or abiotic factor that restricts the existence, numbers, reproduction, or distribution of organisms. The timberline in *Figure 3.1* on the next page shows that limiting factors affect the plant life of an ecosystem. High elevations, low temperatures, strong winds, and soil that is too thin to support the growth of anything more than small, shallow-rooted plants, mosses, ferns, and lichens are all limiting factors. Other common limiting factors are listed in *Table 3.1.*

3.1 COMMUNITIES **65**

SECTION PREVIEW

Objectives

Identify some common limiting factors.

Explain how limiting factors and ranges of tolerance affect distribution of organisms.

Sequence the stages of ecological succession.

Describe the conditions under which primary and secondary succession take place.

Review Vocabulary
community: a collection of interacting populations that inhabit a common environment (p. 39)

New Vocabulary
limiting factor
tolerance
succession
primary succession
climax community
secondary succession

---

2 Teach

Caption Question Answer
Figure 3.1 Depending on where students live, their answers will vary. Some parts of the country are dependent on water being directed from distant sources. Some students may live in an agricultural area and will depend on rainfall. Others may live in crowded cities where smog or emissions can be limiting factors.

Visual Learning
Figure 3.2 Lead students through this diagram. The main concept is that there is a range of conditions in which life processes work best. Beyond this range, life processes may become restricted in some way. Make certain that students understand that this concept is applicable to all organisms, not merely to fish. Have them suggest some other organisms in other situations. humans, pets, or trees in polluted air; plants with insufficient sunlight or water

Reading Check A limiting factor may restrict the ability of a population to exist and reproduce.

![Indiana] **Indiana Academic Standards**

Pages 66–67: B.1.18, B.1.40, B.1.43

Table 3.1 Common Limiting Factors
Sunlight
Climate
Temperature
Water
Nutrients/Food
Fire
Soil chemistry
Space
Other organisms

Figure 3.1
The timberline is the upper limit of tree growth on this mountainside. **Analyze** *How do the limiting factors in Table 3.1 affect your community?*

Factors that limit one population in a community may also have an indirect effect on another population. For example, a lack of water could restrict the growth of grass in a grassland, reducing the number of seeds produced. The population of mice dependent on the seeds for food will also be reduced. What about hawks that feed on mice? Their numbers also may be reduced as a result of a decrease in their food supply.

Reading Check **Describe** why a limiting factor is important.

Figure 3.2
The limits of an organism's tolerance are reached when the organism receives too much or too little of some environmental factor. Populations respond by becoming smaller as conditions move toward either extreme of the availability of resources.

Ranges of tolerance
Corn plants need two to three months of warm, sunny weather and a regular supply of water to produce a good yield. Corn grown in the shade or during a long dry period may survive, but probably won't produce a marketable crop. The ability of an organism to withstand fluctuations in biotic and abiotic environmental factors is known as **tolerance.** *Figure 3.2* illustrates that a population will survive according to its tolerance for environmental extremes.

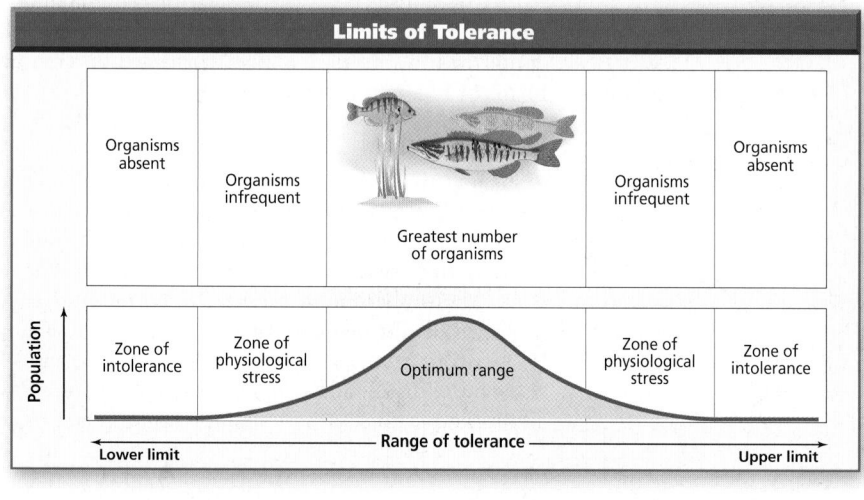

Limits of Tolerance

Organisms absent	Organisms infrequent	Greatest number of organisms	Organisms infrequent	Organisms absent
Zone of intolerance	Zone of physiological stress	Optimum range	Zone of physiological stress	Zone of intolerance

Population

Lower limit — Range of tolerance — Upper limit

66

Succession: Changes over Time

If grass were no longer cut on a lawn, what would it look like in one year? Five years? In 90 years? From experience, ecologists can predict the changes that will take place.

1. The grass gets taller; weeds start to grow. The area resembles a meadow.
2. Later, bushes grow, trees appear and different animals enter the area to live.
3. The bushes and trees change the environment; less light reaches the ground. The grass slowly disappears.
4. Thirty years later, the area is a forest.

Ecologists refer to the orderly, natural changes and species replacements that take place in the communities of an ecosystem as **succession** (suk SE shun).

Succession occurs in stages. At each stage, different species of plants and animals may be present. The conditions at each stage are suitable for some organisms but not for others. As succession progresses, new organisms move in. Others may die out or move out. Succession often is difficult to observe because it can take decades or even centuries for one community to succeed another. There are two types of succession—primary and secondary.

Primary succession

The colonization of barren land by communities of organisms is called **primary succession.** Primary succession takes place on land where there are no living organisms. For example, lava flowing from a volcano destroys everything in its path. When it cools, new, but barren, land has formed. The first species to take hold in an area like this are called pioneer species. An example of a pioneer species is a lichen, which is a combination of small organisms. Examine lichens in the *MiniLab* on this page.

Pioneer species eventually die. Decaying lichens, along with bits of sediment in cracks and crevices of rock, make up the first stage of soil development. In time, new soil makes it possible for small weedy plants, small ferns, fungi, and insects to become established. As these organisms die, more soil builds. Seeds, carried by water, wind or animals, move into these expanding patches of soil and begin to grow.

MiniLab 3.1

Observe

Looking at Lichens Lichens are known for being a pioneer species when it comes to primary succession. They colonize rocky areas and start the process of soil formation. How can lichens grow on a rock?

Color-enhanced SEM Magnification: 342×

Note the alga between the threadlike fungus in the close-up at left.

Procedure 🥽 🧤 ☣ ✋

1. Examine the lichen samples provided by your teacher. Note their color, shape, and texture.
2. Use a microscope to examine a prepared slide of a stained section of a lichen. Use low-power magnification and then change to high power as needed.
3. Observe the dark bodies that are cells containing chloroplasts. Notice that lichens are composed of an alga and a fungus. Diagram what you see. **CAUTION: *Use safe practices. Wash hands with soap at the end of the lab.***

Analysis

1. **Observe** Describe the general appearance of a whole lichen and of the lichen under a microscope.
2. **Interpret Interactions** Interpret the relationship between organisms in a lichen as mutualism.
3. **Make Inferences** How does mutualism explain why lichens are able to survive on rocks?

Purpose

Students will observe the gross and microscopic appearance of a lichen.

Process Skills

observe, apply concepts, define operationally, draw a conclusion

Safety Precautions

Remind students to wear goggles and aprons and to wash their hands after handling lichens.

Teaching Strategies

■ Have students review the definition and examples of the term *symbiosis* in Chapter 2 before starting this lab.
■ Prepared slides and whole lichens are available from biological supply houses. If available, gather whole lichens locally.
■ Teasing apart small sections of a whole lichen for microscopic observation is an alternative.

Expected Results

Students will be able to observe the algae and the fungi in a lichen.

Analysis

1. Color may be dull green, red, orange, or yellow; shape may be crusty or flat. The fungus portion may be long, clear strands; alga portion, small green cells.
2. The fungus receives food from the alga, and the alga receives moisture from the fungus.
3. Rocks offer harsh living conditions. The algae and fungi in lichens overcome this by making their own food and retaining moisture.

Assessment

Portfolio Have students design an experiment to determine if each component of a lichen could survive without the other. Use the Performance Task Assessment List for Designing an Experiment in **PASC**, p. 95. L2

INCLUSION STRATEGIES

English Language Learners: *Linguistic* Have students use a dictionary to explain why the term *pioneer organism* is well suited to the role such organisms perform. Pioneers are the first to colonize or settle an area. In succession, pioneer organisms are the first to inhabit a region. L1 ELL

Problem-Solving Lab 3.1

Purpose

Students will use a graphic representation to determine characteristics of primary and secondary succession.

Process Skills

think critically, apply concepts, compare and contrast, draw a conclusion, interpret scientific illustrations

Teaching Strategies

- Review the meanings of *primary* and *secondary*.
- Have students work in small groups to complete this activity.

Thinking Critically

1. Line 2-primary succession begins with no species. Line 1-secondary has some existing species.
2. C; Climax communities exist prior to a disturbance. D; Pioneer organisms have low species diversity.
3. a sudden, disruptive event, such as a fire followed by community recovery

Modified Assessment

Skill Have students copy each part of the graph on separate pages and write a statement that describes what is happening in each graph. Use the Performance Task Assessment List for Graph from Data in **PASC**, p. 111. **L1**

Visual Learning

Figure 3.3 Have students work in small groups to draw up a statement about what is taking place in the art from left to right. Answers should reflect that beginning with the weathering of rocks, soil can be built that eventually supports a community. **L2**

COOP LEARN

INVESTIGATE BioLab The BioLab at the end of the chapter can be used at this point in the lesson.

Problem-Solving Lab 3.1

Interpret Scientific Illustrations

How do you distinguish between primary and secondary succession? Succession is the series of gradual changes that occur in an ecosystem. Ecologists recognize two types of succession—primary and secondary. The events occurring during these two processes can be represented by a graph.

Solve the Problem

Examine the graph. The two lines marked 1 and 2 represent primary and secondary succession. Note, however, that neither line is identified as such for you.

Primary and Secondary Succession

Thinking Critically

1. **Analyze Trends from Data** Which line, 1 or 2, represents primary succession? Secondary succession? Explain.
2. **Make Inferences from Data** Which label, C or D, might best represent a climax community? Pioneer organisms? Explain.
3. **Predict Trends from Data** What does the sudden drop at point C represent? What happens between D and E?

After some time, primary succession slows down and the community becomes fairly stable, or reaches equilibrium. A stable, mature community that undergoes little or no change in species is a **climax community.** A climax community may last for hundreds of years.

Stability or equilibrium does not mean that change stops. Change is dynamic as the numbers of species may rise and fall in an area. Over time, however, the changes are balanced, so long as nothing drastic—such as fire—happens to the area. Succession from bare rock to a climax community is illustrated in *Figure 3.3*. Observe the characteristics of succession in the *BioLab* at the end of this chapter.

Secondary succession

What happens when a natural disaster such as a forest fire destroys a community? What happens when a field isn't replanted or when a building is demolished in a city and nothing is built on the site? Then secondary succession begins. **Secondary succession** is the sequence of changes that takes place after an existing community is severely disrupted in some way.

During secondary succession, as in primary succession, the community of organisms inhabiting an area gradually changes.

Figure 3.3
Over time, rocks weather and soil forms. Soil is a combination of minerals, decayed organisms, water, and air. From start to climax community may be hundreds of years.

Exposed rock — Moss Lichen **Pioneer species** *Primary succession* — *Secondary succession →* — → *Climax community*

TECH PREP

Highway Succession: *Visual-Spatial*
Many transportation departments let grassy areas near highways revert to their natural condition. Have students contact the local highway department to find out about state highway mowing regulations. **L3**

Secondary succession, however, occurs in areas that previously contained life, and on land that still contains soil. Therefore, the species involved in secondary succession are different from those in primary succession. Because soil already exists, secondary succession may take less time than primary succession to reach a climax community. Learn more about the differences between primary and secondary succession in the *Problem-Solving Lab.*

✓ Reading Check **Compare** primary and secondary succession.

An example of secondary succession

In 1988, forest fires burned from June to September in Yellowstone National Park. Hundreds of thousands of hectares of trees, shrubs, and grasses were burned. The fire has given biologists an opportunity to study secondary succession in a community. Ecologically, the fire represented change, not total destruction. Annual wildflowers, like

those in *Figure 3.4,* were among the first plants to grow back. Previously, the shade of the trees was a limiting factor for wildflower growth. Within three years of the fire, perennial wildflowers, grasses, ferns, and thousands of lodgepole-pine seedlings began to replace the annuals. Once the pine seedlings grow above the shade cast by the grasses and perennials, the trees will grow more quickly.

Figure 3.4
The spring after Yellowstone National Park's forest fire of 1988, wildflowers were already blooming in places where the fire had been most hot.

Section Assessment

Understanding Main Ideas

1. Explain how temperature is a limiting factor for a cactus in the desert.

2. Plan an investigation by writing two questions that would test temperature as a limiting factor for an organism in an ecosystem.

3. Give an example of secondary succession. Include plants and animals in your example.

4. A field has been left uncut for a year. Describe what it looks like at the end of one year and predict how it will be in five years. In ten years.

5. Compare primary succession and climax community. In your discussion, identify how long-term survival of species is dependent on resources that may be limited.

Thinking Critically

6. Explain how the growth of one population can bring about the disappearance of another population during the process of succession.

SKILL REVIEW

7. **Make and Use Graphs** Using the following data, graph the limits of tolerance for temperature for carp. Carp is a large freshwater fish found in many places throughout the world. In the following data, the first number in each pair is temperature in degrees Celsius; the second number is the number of carp surviving at that temperature: 0, 0; 10, 5; 20, 25; 30, 34; 40, 27; 50, 2; 60, 0. For more help, refer to *Make and Use Graphs* in the **Skill Handbook.**

in.bdol.glencoe.com/self_check_quiz

3.1 COMMUNITIES **69**

Section Assessment

1. Most cacti cannot tolerate freezing temperatures for long. Therefore, low temperatures for long periods limit the distribution of some species of cacti.
2. Examples: What is the maximum temperature at which fish feed? How do changing temperatures affect the movement of fish?
3. Forest fire; wildflowers return, then shrubs, then trees. Insects arrive followed by small, then larger mammals.
4. End of first year: grasses, low, scrubby plants; at 5 years: shrubs, saplings, grasses; 10 years: larger saplings, larger, patchy grass, larger but fewer shrubs
5. Primary succession: bare ground, no plant life; climax: maximum plant community and interacting animal life; Climax community will last so long as resources are there for biotic factors.
6. One species can crowd, block the sun, eat the available food, or absorb the nutrients and water needed by the other species.
7. Check graphs for logic and accuracy.

69

---

3 Assess

DAILY INTERVENTION

Check for Understanding
Have students explain how the terms in the following pairs are related. **L1** **ELL**
a. limiting factors—range of tolerance
b. primary succession—secondary succession
c. pioneer community—climax community

Reteach
Visual-Spatial Have students prepare a table showing similarities and differences between primary and secondary succession. **L2**

Resources
For more practice, use *Reading Essentials for Biology,* Section 3.1.

Extension

Visual-Spatial Have students use library references to prepare a flowchart showing the sequence of changes that occur during succession of a pond into a hardwood forest. **L2**

✓ Reading Check Unlike primary succession, secondary succession occurs in areas that contained life and on land that contains soil.

Indiana Academic Standards

Pages 68–69: B.1.39, B.1.40, B.1.43, B.1.45

1 Focus

Bellringer
Section Focus Transparency 7

Using Prior Knowledge

Have students review and define the terms *habitat* and *ecosystem*. In preparation for the larger concept of biome, have students brainstorm what they know about differences in climate and types of plants and animals around the world. Then introduce the term *biome* and lead students to make a relationship between biome and ecosystem. Ask: Compare biomes to ecosystems. Ecosystems are made up of groups of habitats. Biomes are the largest ecological units, made up of groups of ecosystems with similar features or characteristics.

FOLDABLES™
For an additional Foldables activity idea, see the Chapter 3 Foldables page in *Unit 2 FAST FILE Resources.*

Indiana Academic Standards
Pages 70–71: B.1.18, B.1.43

Section 3.2

Biomes

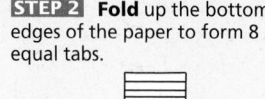

Indiana Standards Standard B.1.43 Understand that and describe how organisms are influenced by a particular combination of living and nonliving components of the environment.

SECTION PREVIEW

Objectives
Compare and contrast the photic and aphotic zones of marine biomes.
Identify the major limiting factors affecting distribution of terrestrial biomes.
Distinguish among biomes.

Review Vocabulary
biosphere: the portion of Earth that supports life (p. 36)

New Vocabulary
biome
photic zone
aphotic zone
estuary
intertidal zone
plankton
tundra
taiga
desert
grassland
temperate/deciduous forest
tropical rain forest

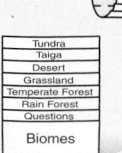
FOLDABLES™
Study Organizer

Biomes Make the following Foldable to help you understand the nature of terrestrial biomes.

STEP 1 **Collect** 4 sheets of paper and layer them about 1.5 cm apart vertically. Keep the edges level.

STEP 2 **Fold** up the bottom edges of the paper to form 8 equal tabs.

STEP 3 **Fold** the papers and crease well to hold the tabs in place. Staple along the fold. **Label** each tab as shown.

Identify and Describe Before you read Section 3.2, label each tab with the name of a terrestrial biome. Label the final tab "Questions" and list questions you would like to have answered. As you read, describe the biomes on your Foldable and answer your questions.

What is a biome?

Ecosystems that reach similar climax communities can be grouped into a broader category called a biome. A **biome** is a large group of ecosystems that share the same type of climax community. There are terrestrial biomes and aquatic biomes, each with organisms adapted to the conditions characteristic of the biome. Biomes located on land are called terrestrial biomes. Organisms such as the cardon cactus shown here, populate terrestrial desert biomes. Oceans, lakes, streams, ponds, or other bodies of water are aquatic biomes.

Aquatic Biomes

As a human who lives on land, you may think of Earth as a terrestrial planet. But one look at a globe, a world map, or a photograph of Earth taken from space tells you there is an aquatic world, too. Approximately 75 percent of Earth's surface is covered with water. Most of that water is salty. Oceans, seas, and even some inland lakes contain salt water. Freshwater is confined to rivers, streams, ponds, and most lakes. Saltwater and freshwater environments have important differences. As a result, aquatic biomes are separated into marine biomes and freshwater biomes.

Cardon cactus

RESOURCE MANAGER

Unit 2 *FAST FILE* Resources
MiniLab Worksheet, p. 42
Reinforcement and Study Guide in English, pp. 47–48
Reinforcement and Study Guide in Spanish, pp. 51–52
Critical Thinking/Problem Solving, p. 54

Transparency Worksheets, pp. 56, 61–62

Inside Story Poster
Section Focus Transparency 7
Reteaching Skills Transparency 5

2 Teach

Marine biomes

Different parts of the ocean differ in abiotic factors (salinity, depth, availability of light, and temperature) and biotic factors found there. The oceans contain a large amount of biomass, or living material. Most of this biomass is made up of extremely small, often microscopic, organisms that humans usually don't see but that large marine animals, such as baleen whales, depend upon.

One of the ways ecologists study marine biomes is to make separate observations in shallow, sunlit zones (photic zones) and deeper, unlighted zones (aphotic zones). The portion of the marine biome that is shallow enough for sunlight to penetrate is called the **photic zone.** Shallow marine environments exist along the coastlines of most landmasses on Earth. These coastal ecosystems include bays, rocky shores, sandy beaches, mudflats, and estuaries. Coral reefs also are located in shallow water in warmer parts of the ocean. All are part of the photic zone. Deeper water that never receives sunlight makes up the **aphotic zone.** The aphotic zone includes the deepest, least explored areas of the ocean.

Estuaries—Mixed waters

If you were to follow the course of a river, you would, in most cases, reach a sea or ocean. Wherever rivers join oceans, freshwater mixes with salt water. In many such places, an estuary forms. An **estuary** (ES chuh wer ee) is a coastal body of water, partially surrounded by land, in which freshwater and salt water mix.

The salinity, or amount of salt, in an estuary ranges between that of seawater and that of freshwater, and depends on how much freshwater the river brings into the estuary. Salinity in the estuary also changes with the tide and so a wide range of organisms can live in estuaries. Estuaries, as illustrated in *Figure 3.5,* may contain salt marsh ecosystems, which are dominated by salt-tolerant smooth cordgrass, salt marsh hay, or eelgrasses. These grasses can grow so thick that their stems and roots form a tangled mat that traps food material and provides a "nursery" habitat for small developing snails, crabs, and shrimp. These organisms feed on decaying, suspended materials. In turn, these small organisms attract a wide range of predators, including birds.

Physical Science Connection

Salinity and density of a solution Water that contains dissolved salts is denser than pure water. As the concentration of dissolved salts increases, the density of the solution increases. Because seawater is denser than freshwater, seawater tends to enter an estuary along the bottom.

3.2 BIOMES **71**

Purpose

Students will read a graph and analyze the extent and limitations of the information in it.

Process Skills

analyze information, draw a conclusion, hypothesize, interpret data, make and use graphs, predict, think critically

Teaching Strategies

■ To do this activity with the entire class, ask for their input on each question.
■ This activity is suitable for cooperative group analysis.
■ Review the concept of tide pools if necessary.

Thinking Critically

1. Answers may include that oxygen levels were measured in ppm, the experiment was conducted for 18 hours, the dependent variable (oxygen levels) is plotted on the y-axis, and the independent variable (time of day) is plotted on the x-axis.

2. Green algae are producers and provide oxygen.

3. The amount of dissolved oxygen in the tide pool rose sharply during the early afternoon and then fell sharply. The amount in the ocean rose and fell only slightly during the same periods.

Assessment

Knowledge Ask students to explain the scientists' findings. Have them correlate increases or decreases in oxygen levels with the fact that there is a photosynthetic organism present. Use the Performance Task Assessment List for Analyzing the Data in **PASC,** p. 99. **L3**

Indiana Academic Standards

Pages 72–73: B.1.37, B.1.43, B.1.44

Problem-Solving Lab 3.2

Analyze Information

How does oxygen vary in a tide pool?
Tide pools are depressions along rocky coasts that are covered by ocean water during high tide. During low tide, these tide pools become temporarily cut off from ocean water.

Oxygen Levels

(graph: Dissolved oxygen (ppm) vs. Time of day, showing "Tide pool" and "Ocean" curves; y-axis 4.0–6.5; x-axis Noon, 6:00 P.M., Midnight, 6:00 A.M.)

Solve the Problem

The graph shows results from tests of water samples taken in a tide pool and in the surrounding ocean. A scientist measured oxygen levels in ppm (parts per million). Both the ocean and tide pool have the same producer present, a green algae called *Cladophora*.

Thinking Critically

1. **Analyze Trends from Data** What can you tell about how the experiment was done using only the *x*- and *y*-axis information?

2. **Conclude** What is the importance of the green algae?

3. **Make Inferences from Data** What specific information was learned as a result of the experiment?

With the help of bacteria, decay of dead organisms proceeds quickly in an estuary and nutrients are released. Nutrients are recycled through the food web and as a result, microorganisms help maintain equilibrium.

The effects of tides

Daily, the gravitational pull of the sun and moon causes the rise and fall of ocean tides. The portion of the shoreline that lies between the high and low tide lines is called the **intertidal zone.** The size of this zone depends upon the slope of the land and the difference between the high and low tides. Intertidal ecosystems have high levels of sunlight, nutrients, and oxygen.

Tide pools, pools of water left when the water is at low tide, can isolate the organisms that live in the intertidal zone until the next high tide. Therefore, these areas can vary in nutrient and oxygen levels from one time of day to another. Compare and contrast oxygen content between tide pools and the ocean in the *Problem-Solving Lab* on this page.

Intertidal zones differ in rockiness and wave action. *Figure 3.6* shows a rocky intertidal zone. If the shore is rocky, waves constantly threaten to wash organisms into deeper water. Many intertidal animals, such as snails and sea stars, have adaptations that act by suction to hold onto wave-beaten rocks. Other animals, such as barnacles, secrete a strong glue that helps them remain anchored. If the shore is sandy, wave action keeps the bottom in constant motion.

Figure 3.6
Waves crashing against a rocky shore are a limiting factor for organisms in the intertidal zone.

PROJECT

Measuring Oxygen Purchase kits from a biological supply house that measure the dissolved oxygen in water. Have students use these kits to test water samples from different local bodies of water. Students need to set up data charts to record results. **L2** **ELL**

Clams, worms, snails, crabs, and other organisms that live along sandy shores survive by burrowing into the sand.

In the light

As you move into deeper water, the ocean bottom is less affected by waves or tides. Thousands of organisms live in this shallow-water region. Nutrients washed from the land by rainfall and runoff contribute to the abundant life and high productivity of this region of the photic zone.

The photic zone of the marine biome also includes the vast expanse of open ocean that covers most of Earth's surface. Most of the organisms that live in the marine biome are plankton. **Plankton** are small organisms that drift and float in the waters of the photic zone. They include autotrophs, diatoms, eggs, and the juvenile stages of many marine animals. Plankton are important because they form the base of all aquatic food chains. Not all organisms that eat plankton are small. Baleen whales and whale sharks, some of the largest organisms that have ever lived, consume vast amounts of plankton. Examine plankton in the *MiniLab* shown here.

In the dark

Imagine a darkness blacker than night and pressure so intense it exerts hundreds of pounds of weight on every square centimeter of your body's surface. These are the conditions deep in the ocean where light does not penetrate. Much of the ocean is more than a kilometer deep. The animals living there are far below the photic zone where plankton abound. Many of them still depend on plankton for food, either directly, or indirectly, by eating organisms that feed on plankton.

MiniLab 3.2

Compare and Contrast

Marine Plankton Plankton is the term used to define the floating protists, animal eggs and larvae present in an aquatic environment.

Procedure

Color-enhanced LM Magnification: 100×

1. Use a dropper to obtain a small sample of marine plankton.
2. Prepare a wet mount of the material. **CAUTION:** *Handle microscope slides and cover-slips carefully.*
3. Observe under low-power magnification of the microscope.
4. Look for a variety of organisms and diagram several different types. **CAUTION:** *Wash hands with soap at the end of the lab.*

Marine plankton

Analysis

1. **Observe** Describe and draw two specific planktonic organisms. Identify some common characteristics.
2. **Distinguish** Are both autotrophs and heterotrophs present? How can you distinguish them?
3. **Explain Interactions in a Food Chain** Why are plankton important in food chains?

Freshwater biomes

Have you ever gone swimming or boating in a lake or pond? If so, you may have noticed different kinds of plants, such as cattails, growing around the shoreline and into the water. The shallow water in which these plants grow serves as home for tadpoles, aquatic insects, turtles that bask on rocks and fallen tree trunks, and worms and crayfishes that burrow into the muddy bottom. Insect larvae, whirligig beetles, dragonflies, and fishes such as minnows, bluegill, and carp also live here and are each part of the local food chain.

MiniLab 3.2

Purpose

Students will study the diverse nature of ocean plankton.

Process Skills

observe and infer, classify, compare and contrast

Safety Precautions

Have students wash their hands after the MiniLab.

Teaching Strategies

■ Marine plankton samples are available from biological supply houses. Freeze-dried plankton can be purchased at pet shops.

■ Make students aware that because of the preservative used, many producer organisms may have lost their green color in the plankton samples.

■ You may wish to collect your own pond plankton samples. Small clusters of plants or algae from a pond system will provide examples of both producers and consumers. **CAUTION:** *Wear gloves and goggles when collecting.*

Expected Results

Students will observe a variety of young or larval stages of consumer organisms in plankton.

Analysis

1. Plankton can be diatoms, shrimplike, wormlike, or insectlike organisms.
2. Answers may vary. Producers are green, but consumers are not. The quality of students' microscopes may affect what they see.
3. Plankton are the basis of many marine food chains.

Modified Assessment

Knowledge Have students use references to identify some of the organisms. Use the Performance Task Assessment List for Making Observations and Inferences in **PASC**, p. 89. **L1**

CHALLENGE ACTIVITY

Plankton Have students research plankton and report on the differences between phytoplankton suspended aquatic microscopic plants such as green algae and zooplankton small, generally microscopic animals and fat-rich eggs of animals that float with currents. Reports should describe the importance of plankton and its place in food chains, and be illustrated with food chains or webs that show its importance. **L3**

Visual Learning

Figure 3.7 Ask students to compare the tolerances plants might have in the warmer and cooler layers of a lake. Photosynthesis takes place in the upper, warmer areas of the lake where light penetrates. Therefore, green plants are found there. Light does not penetrate to the deeper areas, so few to no plants are there.

Content Background

Explain to students that productivity is the rate at which biomass is added to the ecosystem (through photosynthesis). Biomass contains trapped carbon. This carbon is released from biomass through several processes. One is through respiration which returns CO_2 to the atmosphere. A second path is through the action of decomposers. Decomposers break down non-living biomass. Decomposers are located almost everywhere.

Inquiry

Discussion Review the term *scavenger*: an organism that obtains its energy by feeding on dead organic matter; Some common scavengers are crows and vultures. Detritivores, such as ants and beetles, feed on dead organic matter from plants, animals, or the excrement of animals. Decomposers, such as bacteria and fungi, break down and release any organic matter that remains. What purpose do these types of organisms serve? They help the cycling of matter. In doing so, they obtain the nutrients and energy they need for life.

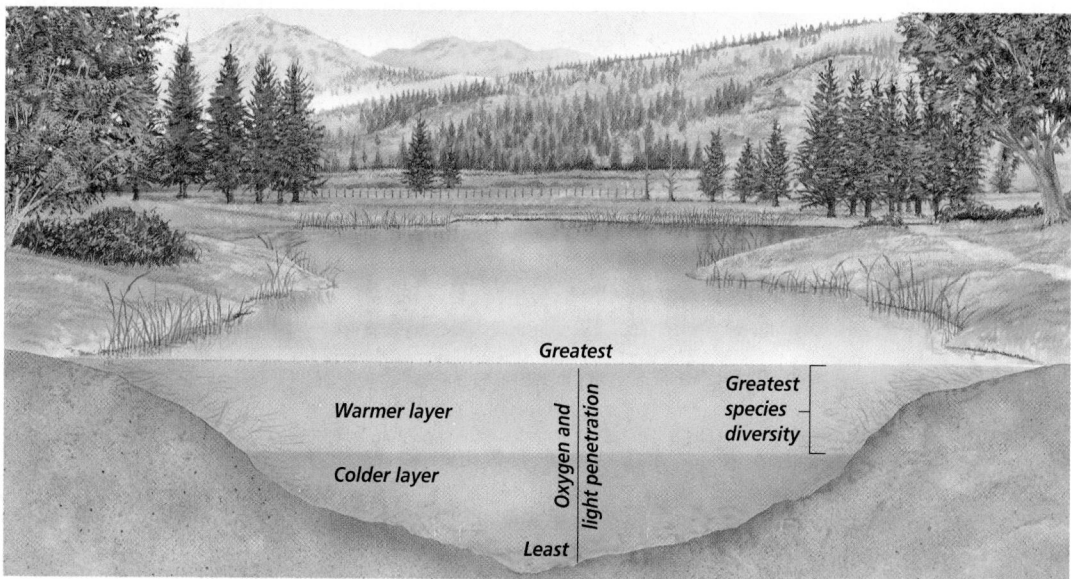

Figure 3.7
The shallow waters in this lake are exposed to sunlight. They are warmer and contain more oxygen, which can make these areas more productive than deeper, colder, more oxygen-poor layers.

Although the spring and summer sun heats the surface of a lake like the one in *Figure 3*.7, the water a few feet below the surface remains cold. Cold water is more dense than warm water. If you were to dive all the way to the bottom of the lake, you would discover layers of increasingly colder water as you descended. These temperature variations within a lake are an abiotic factor that limits the kinds of organisms that can survive in deep lakes.

Another abiotic factor that limits life in deep lakes is light. Not enough sunlight penetrates to the bottom to support photosynthesis, so few aquatic plants or algae grow. As a result, population density is lower in deeper waters. As dead organisms drift to the bottom, bacteria break them down and recycle the nutrients. Decay takes place more slowly at the bottom of a deep lake.

Other aquatic biomes

Other places where land and water meet are called wetlands, but there are several different kinds of wetlands. Swamps have trees. Marshes do not, but both usually have water flowing through them. Marshes are found inland and in coastal regions. Both are highly productive and are the source of food for many migratory birds and other animals. Other wetland areas, called bogs, get their water supply from rain. Water does not flow through bogs.

Terrestrial Biomes

If you are setting off on an expedition beginning at the north pole and traveling south to the equator, what kinds of environmental changes do you expect to experience and why? The weather gets warmer, and you see a change in the sizes, numbers, and kinds of plants that cover the ground. At the polar cap, temperatures are always freezing and no plants exist. A little farther south, where temperatures sometimes rise above freezing but the soil never thaws completely, you would be attacked by hordes of mosquitoes and black flies. You'd see soggy ground with lichens and low-growing cushion plants.

USING MODELS

Food Chain Roles Have students research and diagram a food chain that illustrates the relationships among photic zone organisms. Ask them to identify each organism in their food chain as a producer, first-order consumer, second-order consumer, or third-order consumer. **L2**

As you continue on your journey, temperatures rise a little and you enter forests of coniferous trees. Then there are deciduous forests, with moderate rainfall and temperatures. Farther on are grasslands and deserts, with high summertime temperatures and very little rain. Finally, as you approach the equator, you find yourself surrounded by the lush growth of a tropical forest, where it rains almost every day.

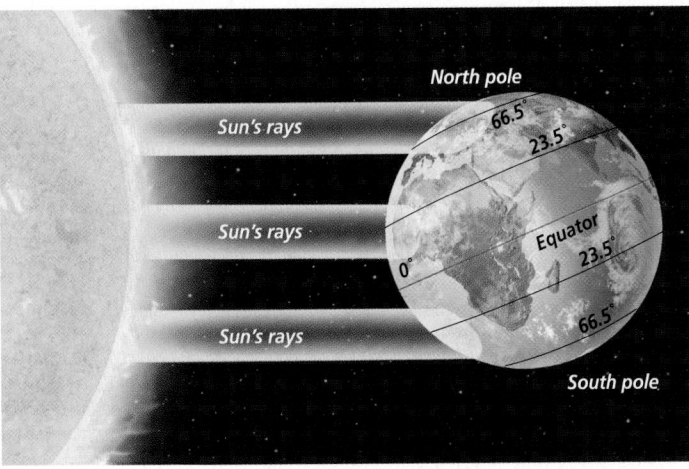

Figure 3.8
Because of Earth's curved surface, the sun's rays strike the equator more directly than areas toward the north or south poles.

Latitude and climate

What caused the changes that you experienced as you moved south from the north pole to the equator? As you traveled, you were changing latitude. Latitude describes your position in degrees north and south of the equator. Look at *Figure 3.8*. At different latitudes, the sun strikes Earth differently. As a result, the climate—wind, cloud cover, temperature, humidity and precipitation in that area—is different. Latitude and climate are abiotic factors that affect what plants and animals will survive in a given area. The graph in *Figure 3.9* shows how two abiotic factors—temperature and precipitation—influence the kind of climax community that develops. Small differences in temperature or precipitation can create different biomes. Look at the distribution of the six most common terrestrial biomes on pages 1062 and 1063 in the *Focus On*.

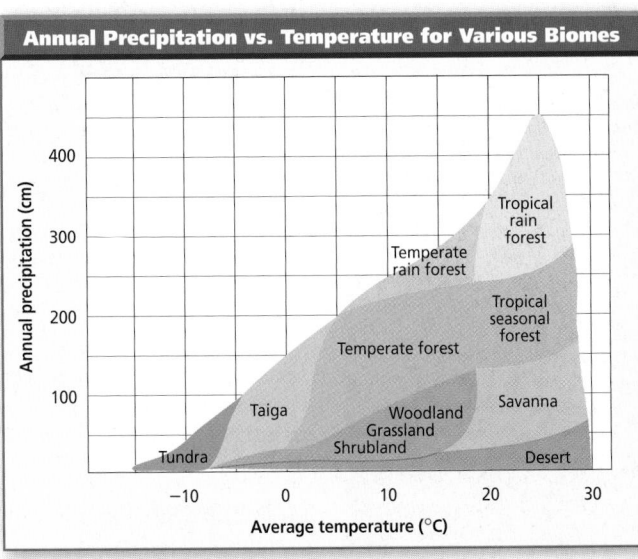

Annual Precipitation vs. Temperature for Various Biomes

Annual precipitation (cm) — vertical axis: 100, 200, 300, 400
Average temperature (°C) — horizontal axis: −10, 0, 10, 20, 30

Labels: Tundra, Taiga, Temperate forest, Temperate rain forest, Tropical rain forest, Tropical seasonal forest, Woodland Grassland Shrubland, Savanna, Desert

Figure 3.9
If you know the average annual temperature and rate of precipitation of a particular area, you should be able to determine the climax community that will develop. **Interpret Scientific Illustrations** *In what biome does annual rainfall exceed 400 cm?*

Quick Demo

Latitude and Longitude
Using an atlas, show students where they can find the latitude and longitude readings for where they live. Assign other parts of the world for interested students to research. Latitude is the distance in degrees north or south of the equator. Longitude is the distance in degrees east or west of the prime meridian.

Discussion
Discuss what effect increased altitude has on temperature. Ask students to use this information to explain why mountaintops in tropical areas may be covered by snow. **L2**

Portfolio
Recognizing Biome Characteristics Have students research the average annual temperature and precipitation for the area in which they live. Have them determine if the values correlate with those given in the text for the biome in which they live. Have students suggest reasons for discrepancies. **L2**

Caption Question Answer
Figure 3.9 tropical rain forest

🎯 **CHALLENGE ACTIVITY**

Rain Shadow: *Visual-Spatial* Topography, the way the surface of Earth is configured with mountains, valleys, and plains, affects the rain that falls in an area. Have interested students research the rain shadow effect (the dry conditions on the downward side of a mountain) that produces desert conditions in some areas. Ask students to prepare a diagram for their portfolios that explains this process. **L3**

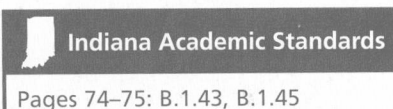

Indiana Academic Standards
Pages 74–75: B.1.43, B.1.45

A popularly held misconception is that large groups of lemmings, a small arctic mammal, periodically march into the ocean in mass suicides, thus reducing their large population.

Uncover the Misconception

Point out the lemming shown on this page. Ask students to discuss the phrase "to follow without thinking." Connect the phrase with the misconception about lemming behavior.

Demonstrate the Concept

Explain that lemmings are actually solitary animals, but migrate in large numbers to new areas after severely depleting an area of food. It is true that they sometimes stumble into the ocean during these mass migrations. According to a Canadian biologist who has studied lemming behavior for 60 years, their populations rise and fall in cycles every 4 to 10 years. However, he has been unable to discern why there is a large periodic die-off. The number of lemmings found in arctic ice differs little from other organisms (voles, rabbits, etc.) found dead in arctic ice.

Assess New Knowledge

Ask students to compare migration of lemmings with migrations of other animals they know about (caribou, bison, and similar animals) that migrate for the same reason.

Figure 3.10
Grasses, grasslike sedges, small annuals, and reindeer moss, a type of lichen on which reindeer feed, are the most numerous producers of the tundra. The growing season may last fewer than 60 days.

Key
■ Monthly temperature range (°C)
■ Monthly precipitation (cm)

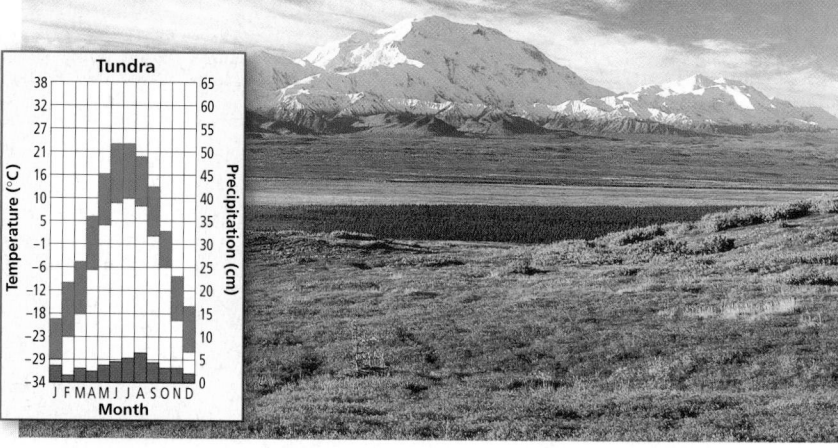

Figure 3.11
Snowy owls (A) are predators of the lemming (B) in the tundra. Populations of lemmings rise to exceedingly high numbers periodically and then plummet for unknown reasons.

Life on the tundra

As you begin traveling south from the north pole, you reach the first of two biomes that circle the north pole. This first area is the **tundra** (TUN druh), a treeless land with long summer days and short periods of winter sunlight.

Because of its latitude, temperatures in the tundra never rise above freezing for long, and only the topmost layer of soil thaws during the summer. Underneath this top layer is a layer of permanently frozen ground called permafrost.

In most areas of the tundra, the topsoil is so thin that it can support only shallow-rooted grasses and other small plants. The soil is lacking in nutrients. The process of decay is slow due to the cold temperatures and, as a result, nutrients are not recycled quickly. Lack of nutrients limits the types of organisms the tundra can support.

Summer days on the tundra may be long, but the growing season is short. Because all food chains depend on the producers of the community, the short growing season limits the type of plants found in this biome shown in **Figure 3.10,** to grasses, dwarf shrubs, and cushion plants. These organisms live a long time and are resistant to drought and cold.

Hordes of mosquitoes and blackflies are some of the most common tundra insects during the short summer. The tundra also is home to a variety of small mammals, including ratlike lemmings, weasels, arctic foxes, snowshoe hares, and even birds such as snowy owls and hawks. Musk oxen, caribou, and reindeer are among the few large animals that migrate into the area and graze during the summer months. **Figure 3.11** shows two common tundra animals.

✓**Reading Check** **Explain** why the tundra is treeless.

Additional Lab

Water-Holding Capacity of Soils

Purpose
Students are introduced to an abiotic factor.

Safety Precautions
Remind students to wash their hands after the lab and to make wise choices about disposal.

Materials 🚫 🥽 👕 🧤
3 cloth squares (30 cm per side), large beaker, water, sand, clay, potting soil, balance, twist ties

Procedure
Give students the following directions.
1. Put a sample of sand in a cloth square. Pull up the corners to form a bag and secure it with a twist tie.
2. Determine and record the mass of the bag.
3. Soak the sand bag in water for 5 minutes.

Life on the taiga

Just south of the tundra lies another biome that circles the north pole. The **taiga** (TI guh) also is called the boreal or northern coniferous forest. The taiga, shown in *Figure 3.12*, forms an almost continuous belt of coniferous trees worldwide. Common trees are larch, fir, hemlock, and spruce trees.

How can you tell when you leave the tundra and enter the taiga? The line between these two biomes can be indistinct, and one can blend into the other. For example, if the soil in the taiga is waterlogged, a peat swamp habitat develops that looks much like tundra. Because of their latitude, taiga communities usually are somewhat warmer and wetter than tundra. However, the prevailing climatic conditions are still harsh, with long, severe winters and short, mild summers.

In the taiga, which stretches across much of Canada, Northern Europe, and Asia, permafrost is usually absent. The topsoil, which develops slowly from decaying coniferous needles, is acidic and poor in minerals. When fire or logging disrupt the taiga

community, the first trees to recolonize the land may be birch, aspen, or other deciduous species because the new soil conditions are within their ranges of tolerance. The abundance of trees in the taiga provides more food and shelter for animals than the tundra. More large species of animals are found in the taiga as compared with the tundra. *Figure 3.13* shows some animals of the taiga. Others include weasels, red squirrels, voles, elk, red deer, and moose, along with a variety of migratory birds.

Figure 3.12
The dominant climax plants of the taiga in North America are primarily fir and spruce trees. **Evaluate Data** *What is the range of temperature in the taiga?*

Content Development

Visual-Spatial For each terrestrial biome beginning on page 76, review how to read the temperature and precipitation graphs that accompany the photograph of each biome.

Enrichment

Visual-Spatial Have students prepare a time line that shows the progression of plant types in the taiga after a fire or logging has occurred. Have students indicate if the succession is primary or secondary. Succession will progress as follows: grasses and other small plants ⇒ shrubs ⇒ birch, aspen, fir, or spruce trees. The succession is secondary. **L2**

✓**Reading Check** (p. 76) Only the topmost layer of soil thaws during the summer. Permafrost does not permit the growth of tree roots.

Biology Journal

Worldwide Taiga Have students research and briefly compare taiga plants and animals in different parts of the world—such as in Russia and in Canada.

Indiana Academic Standards

Pages 76–77: B.1.39, B.1.40, B.1.43, B.1.44

Figure 3.13
Taiga animals are adapted for cold temperatures.

A The lynx is a predator that depends on the snowshoe hare as a primary source of food.

C Caribou are large, herbivorous, migrating mammals. Herds of them spend spring and summer on the tundra and the rest of the year in the taiga.

B During the winter, the snowshoe hare grows a thick, white coat with extra hair on its feet.

---

4. Remove the bag from the water and allow it to drain for 1 minute. Determine and record the mass of the sand bag. Calculate the gain in mass of the sand.
5. Calculate and record the water-holding capacity (WHC) of sand using this formula: WHC = mass gain × 100/dry mass
6. Repeat steps 1–5 using the same amounts of clay and soil.

Analysis
1. Which samples held the highest and the lowest percentage of water? Highest was potting soil; lowest was sand.
2. How do your data support the fact that cacti evolved a water storage system to survive in an arid sandy desert? Sand does not hold on to much water for plant use.

Assessment
Knowledge Ask students to explain how they would improve the experiment. Students may suggest deducting the mass of wet and dry cloth from soil mass data. Use the Performance Task Assessment List for Assessing a Whole Experiment and Planning the Next Experiment in **PASC**, p. 105. **L2**

Plant Adaptations Tell students that the waxy material that coats creosote leaves is called cutin. Compare the action of cutin to a sheet of wax paper by doing the following: moisten two paper towels and flatten them on a table, cover one towel with wax paper on both sides, and note the time needed for the uncovered towel and the covered towel to dry out. Ask students to interpret the analogy and the results. **L2**

Biology Journal

Desert Life Have students select one plant and one animal that live in the desert and one plant and an animal from a temperate forest biome. (They may look at the illustrations in Figures 2.12 and 2.13 and select organisms from there.) Ask them to research the organisms, include a photograph or illustration of each organism, and write a summary of characteristics. Compare the way(s) in which the organisms are adapted for desert life or temperate forest life.

Inquiry

Activity Have students work in groups and select one of the four large North American deserts: the Mohave, the Great Basin, the Sonoran, or the Chihuahuan. Students should research the geographic position of their desert, the states it is located in, monthly temperature and precipitation records, and the plants and animals found there. Reports can be in the form of a written report with illustrations or in the form of a Foldable.

Figure 3.14
Creosote bushes cover many square kilometers of desert in the southwestern United States. These plants are adapted with small leaves containing a substance that deters herbivores from feeding on them.

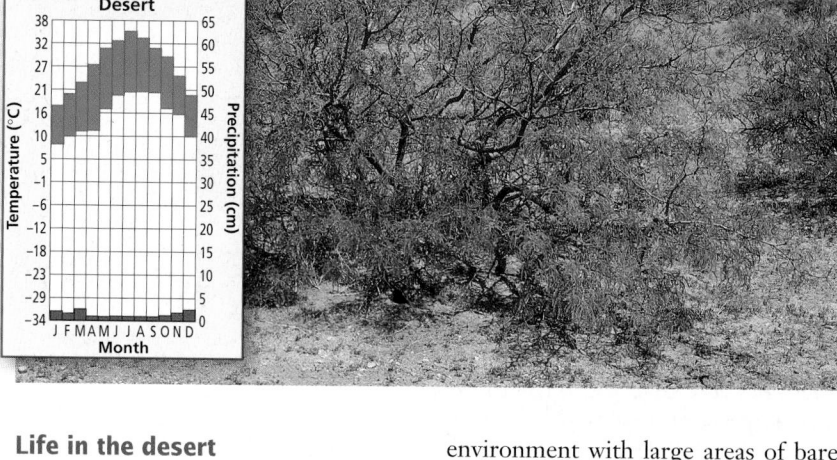

Key
■ Monthly temperature range (°C)
■ Monthly precipitation (cm)

Life in the desert

The driest biome is the desert biome. A **desert** is an arid region with sparse to almost nonexistent plant life. Deserts usually get less than 25 cm of precipitation annually. One desert, the Atacama Desert in Chile, is the world's driest place. This desert receives an annual rainfall of less than 0.004 inches due to competing winds at this latitude.

With rainfall as the major limiting factor, vegetation in deserts varies greatly. Areas that receive more rainfall produce a shrub community that may include drought-resistant trees such as mesquite. Less rainfall results in scattered plant life and produces an environment with large areas of bare ground. The driest deserts are drifting sand dunes. Plants such as the creosote (KREE uh soht) bush shown in *Figure 3.14* have various adaptations for living in arid areas. Many desert plants are annuals that germinate from seed and grow to maturity quickly after sporadic rainfall. Cacti have leaves reduced to spines, photosynthetic stems, and thick waxy coatings—all adaptations that conserve water. The leaves of some desert plants curl up, or even drop off altogether, thus reducing water loss during extremely dry spells. Spines, thorns, or poisons also are adaptations thought to discourage herbivores.

Many desert mammals are small herbivores that remain under cover during the heat of the day, emerging at night to forage on plants. The kangaroo rat is a desert herbivore that does not have to drink water. These rodents obtain the water they need from the water content in their food. Coyotes, hawks, owls, and roadrunners are carnivores that feed on the snakes, lizards, and small mammals of the desert. Scorpions are an example of a desert carnivore that uses venom to capture prey. Two of the many reptiles that make the desert their home are shown in *Figure 3.15*.

Figure 3.15
Desert tortoises **(A)** feed on insects and plants. Venomous snakes such as the diamondback rattlesnake **(B)** are major predators of small rodents.

78 COMMUNITIES AND BIOMES

Testing pH Have students test the pH of a variety of soil samples. Instruct them on the use of and significance of the test. Have them familiarize themselves with pH paper by testing samples of vinegar (an acid) and wet hand soap (a base). Make sure that soil samples are moist and include a sample collected from under a coniferous tree. Have students present their results in a written report. **L3** **ELL**

Life in the grassland

If an area receives between 25 and 75 cm of precipitation annually, a grassland usually forms. **Grasslands** are large communities covered with rich soil, grasses, and similar plants. Grasslands, such as the ones shown in *Figure 3.16,* occur principally in climates that experience a dry season, where insufficient water exists to support forests.

Grasslands contain few trees per hectare, though larger numbers of trees usually are found near streams and other water sources. This biome has a higher biological diversity than deserts, often having more than 50 species per hectare.

The soils of grasslands have considerable humus content because many grasses die off each winter, leaving byproducts to decay and build up in the soil. Grass roots survive through the winter, enlarging every year to form a continuous underground mat called sod.

Some grasslands are ideal for growing cereal grains such as oats, rye, and wheat. Each of these is a different species of grass; therefore, grasslands are known as the breadbaskets of the world. Many other plant species live in this environment, including drought-resistant and late-summer flowering species of wildflowers, such as blazing stars and sunflowers.

At certain times of the year, many grasslands are populated by herds of grazing animals. Bison, a species of mammal shown in *Figure 3.16A,* once ranged over the American prairie, but are now found only in small pockets of rangeland. Other important prairie animals include jack rabbits, deer, elk, and prairie dogs. Prairie dogs are seed-eating rodents that build underground "towns" that are known to stretch mile after mile under the grassland. Foxes and ferrets prey on prairie dogs. Many species of insects, birds, and reptiles, also make their homes in grasslands.

The term *prairie* is used in Australia, Canada, and the United States. Similar communities are called *steppes* in Russia, *savannas* in Africa, and *pampas* in Argentina. Grasslands in the United States can be found in the central and southwestern states.

Figure 3.16
The prairies of America support bison as well as many species of large mammals, birds, and insects **(A)**. Summers are hot, winters are cold, and rainfall is often uncertain in a temperate grassland **(B)**.

Figure 3.17
There are many types of temperate forests, each characterized by two or three dominant species of trees. Typical trees of the temperate forest include birch, hickory, oak, beech, and maple.

Figure 3.18
Black bears are residents of temperate forests in the United States. Other abundant animals in temperate forests are squirrels and salamanders.

Life in the temperate forest

When precipitation ranges from about 70 to 150 cm annually in the temperate zone, temperate deciduous forests, like the one in *Figure 3.17,* develop. **Temperate** or **deciduous forests** are dominated by broad-leaved hardwood trees that lose their foliage annually. Examples of these trees include maple, oak, birch, elm, and ash.

European settlers cleared vast tracts of temperate forest for farmland and lumber. Since then, secondary succession has restored much of the original forest, especially in the eastern United States.

The soil of temperate forests usually consists of a top layer that is rich in humus and a deeper layer of clay. If mineral nutrients released by the decay of the humus are not immediately absorbed by the roots of the living trees, they may be washed into the clay and lost from the food web for many years.

The animals that live in the temperate deciduous forest, as shown in *Figure 3.18,* include squirrels, mice, rabbits, deer, and bears. Many birds, such as bluejays, live in the forest all year long, whereas other birds migrate seasonally.

80

Life in rain forests

Rain forests are home to more species of organisms than any other biome on Earth. There are two types of rain forests in the world—the temperate rain forest and the more widely known tropical rain forest shown in *Figure 3.19*. Both are identified by extensive amounts of moisture supplied by rainfall or by coastal clouds and fog. Temperate rain forests are found on the Olympic Peninsula in Washington state and in other places throughout the world, such as South America, New Zealand, and Australia. The huge number of species in rain forests has made their protection an important objective.

As their name implies, **tropical rain forests** have warm temperatures, wet weather, and lush plant growth. These forests are warm because they are near the equator. The average temperature is about 25°C. They are moist because wind patterns drop a lot of precipitation on them. Rain forests receive at least 200 cm of rain annually; some rain forests receive 600 cm.

Why do tropical rain forests contain so many species? The following hypotheses have been proposed by ecologists:

1. Due to their location near the equator, tropical rain forests were not covered with ice during the last ice age. Thus, the communities of species had more time to evolve and greater biodiversity exists.
2. Unlike the temperate forests—where deciduous trees drop their leaves in autumn—the warm weather near the equator gives tropical rain forest plants year-round growing conditions. This creates a greater food supply in tropical rain forests, which can support larger numbers of organisms.
3. Tropical rain forests provide a multitude of habitats and niches for diverse organisms.

One reason for the large number of niches in rain forests is vertical layering. How are these layers, or stories, arranged? Find out by studying *Figure 3.20* on the next page. From top to bottom, the three major stories are the *canopy*, *understory*, and *ground* layers. The layers often blend together, but their differences allow many organisms to find a niche.

Most of the nutrients in a tropical rain forest are tied up in the living material. There are very few nutrients held in the soil and most are quickly recycled through complex food webs. The hot humid climate enables ants, termites, fungi, bacteria, and other decomposers to break down dead plants and animals rapidly. Plants must quickly absorb these nutrients before they are carried away from the soil by rain.

Tropical rain forest habitats support a wide variety of plants and animals. This makes them the most species-rich places on Earth.

Figure 3.19
Warm temperatures, high humidity, and abundant rainfall allow the growth and great species diversity found in rain forests.

Tropical Rain Forest

81

Quick Demo

Comparing Rainfall A tropical rain forest may receive as much as 400 inches (10 m) of rain in one year. Make this more visual by making a 400-inch strip of paper. Then cut another strip reflecting the average rainfall in your area. For example, average rainfall in a North Carolina city is 58 inches (1.5 m) per year. Ask students why rain forest soil is poor in spite of the large amount of available water. Heavy rain washes away nutrients. Also, little of the rain falls directly all the way to the ground. Much of it is caught up in plants growing in the trees. From here, it evaporates and provides intense humidity.

Reinforcement

Visual-Spatial Provide students with an outline map of North, South, and Central America. Ask them to color in regions that have tropical rain forests. **L1 ELL**

Inquiry

Discussion Nutrients are tied up in different ways in different types of forests. In tropical rain forests, which are very wet, about 90 percent of all nutrients are in the living organisms. There is also a huge array of organisms. In contrast, temperate/deciduous forests are drier, and the majority of nutrients are in the soil. These areas also have fewer insects and fungi than a wet forest. Ask students: Which of these forests is better for agriculture and why? temperate forest; The nutrients needed are in the soil in which the plants grow.

Indiana Academic Standards

Pages 78–79: B.1.37, B.1.41, B.1.43, B.1.44

PROJECT

Rain Forest Acreage Have students select one area in the world where rain forests are common (Central or parts of South America, Africa, India, Southeast Asia, or Indonesia.) Have students research the changes that have occurred in that country's rain forests. If possible, they should include the original acreage that was rain forest, the current acreage, and any economic advantage that the rain forest has given the people.

Purpose

Students study the layers of rain forests and how they act to increase biodiversity.

Teaching Strategies

■ Have students create their own mural of the rain forest layers. **L1** **ELL**

■ Have students make a table for each layer that shows the abiotic factors and organisms in that layer. **L2**

Visual Learning

■ Have students describe how conditions above the canopy differ from those below it. **L2**

■ Have students explain why rain forests support greater biodiversity than grasslands.

Using Science Terms

Epiphytes The prefix "epi-" means *on*. The suffix "-phyte" means *like a plant*. Epiphytes are plants that often grow on other plants. Epiphytes obtain their moisture from rain and their nutrients from dust and leaf litter. Examples of epiphytes are certain mosses and bromeliads found in tropical areas. They are commensals.

Lianas are woody vines that root themselves in the ground, attach to a young sapling and grow upward as the tree grows.

Critical Thinking

Life in the canopy is exposed to the sun, wind, and temperature extremes. Below the canopy, there are fewer wind, humidity, and temperature extremes. Organisms with different niches live in different layers.

Indiana Academic Standards

Pages 82–83: B.1.40, B.1.43, B.1.45

A Tropical Rain Forest

Figure 3.20

In the layers of a tropical rain forest are niches for thousands of species of plants and animals. Ecologists generally consider rain forests to have a storied structure. The illustration shows organisms in a Central American tropical rain forest. **Critical Thinking** *Research plants and animals in the tropical rain forest. Analyze relationships among organisms. Analyze the interactions that might occur between organisms in the different stories.*

Ⓐ Canopy The canopy layer, 25–45 meters high, is a living roof. The tree tops are exposed to rain, sunlight, and strong winds. A few giant trees called emergents poke through the canopy. Monkeys frequently pass through. Birds, such as scarlet macaws, live on the fruits and nuts of the trees.

Ⓑ Understory In the understory, the air is still, humid, and dark. Vines grow from the soil to the canopy. Leaf cutter ants harvest leaves and bring them to the ground. Plants include ferns, broad-leaved shrubs, and dwarf palms. Insects are common in the understory. The limbs of the trees are hung with a thick layer of epiphytes, plants that get most of their moisture from the air. Birds and bats prey upon the insects. Tree frogs are common understory amphibians. Reptiles include chameleons and snakes.

Ⓒ Ground The ground layer is a moist forest floor. Leaves and other organic materials decay quickly. Roots spread throughout the top 18 inches of soil. There is great competition for nutrients. Mammals living on the ground include rodents and cats, such as the jaguar. Ants, termites, earthworms, bacteria, and fungi live in the soil and quickly decompose organic materials.

82 COMMUNITIES AND BIOMES

CHALLENGE ACTIVITY

Life in a Tree: *Visual-Spatial* Have students research and prepare an illustrated chart that describes the major interactions of the canopy, understory, and forest floor. Students should include information about epiphytes and lianas in their charts. **L3**

Figure 3.21
Tropical rain forests are rich ecosystems. Sloths **(A)** and other mammals, as well as a multitude of bird species like this black-headed caique **(B)**, live in the rain forest canopy. Insects, such as this Hercules beetle **(C)**, are numerous in the understory.

Biomass, the total weight of organisms living in the area, is high. This is because sunlight, moisture, and nutrients are available in abundance for plants to convert light energy to chemical energy. This energy is used by the plants and passed to consumers, such as those pictured in *Figure 3.21.*

Some rain forest plants are important sources of medicinal products and hardwood trees and have provided a source of income for people. Agricultural land is not common in rain forests. The soil there does not convert to cropland easily. In temperate deciduous forests, topsoil has taken

hundreds or thousands of years to develop as leaves decayed and their nutrients became part of the soil. In contrast, soils in rain forests do not have substantial amounts of organic matter because leaf matter, which contains nutrients, disappears so quickly. Without organic matter, once rain forest soil is exposed and farmed, it becomes hard, almost brick-like, and nutrient-poor in a matter of a few years. Research is underway to find out how people can manage these lands so that they will be able to obtain the food and products they need.

Section Assessment

Understanding Main Ideas
1. Explain how organisms in the photic and aphotic zones are interdependent.
2. Describe the role of bacteria in maintaining healthy ecosystems. Give examples of where bacteria act in ecosystems.
3. Explain the interactions that take place in a tropical rain forest by describing two or more food chains that you would find there. Then show how these food chains might be part of a larger food web.
4. Describe three variations you would observe as you travel south from a taiga into a temperate forest.
5. Compare the biodiversity of the temperate forest biome with the tropical forest biome.

Thinking Critically
6. In reading before a family trip, George found that the area they were traveling to was cold in winter, hot in summer, and most of the land was planted in fields of wheat. Infer which biome George's family would visit. Explain your choice.

SKILL REVIEW
7. **Get the Big Picture** Make a table to show the climate, plant types, plant adaptations, animal types, and animal adaptations for the terrestrial biomes. For more help, refer to *Get the Big Picture* in the **Skill Handbook**.

in.bdol.glencoe.com/self_check_quiz

3.2 BIOMES **83**

3 Assess

DAILY INTERVENTION

Check for Understanding
Have students explain the following word relationships.
L1 **ELL**
a. photic zone—aphotic zone
b. intertidal zone—estuary
c. river—estuary—ocean
d. food chain—plankton
e. biome—limiting factor

Reteach
Naturalist Ask students to pick a biome and describe its location, climatic characteristics, typical animals and plants, and special or unusual traits. **L2**

Resources
For more practice, use *Reading Essentials for Biology,* Section 3.2.

Extension
Naturalist Have students explain the relationship among the following: greenhouse effect, rain forest destruction, and the carbon cycle. **L2**

✔ Assessment

Portfolio Have students describe how the destruction of a biome such as the ocean would affect them directly. Have them suggest one or two ways that they personally can make a difference in saving the biome they are a part of. **L2**

Section Assessment

1. The photic zone provides food for the scavengers and decomposers in the aphotic zone. Decomposers return nutrients to water that can be used by plants in the photic zone.
2. Bacteria are decomposers, parasites, and commensals. They are found everywhere.
3. Student answers will vary. Answers should reflect accurate food chains and food webs.
4. Answers may vary. It gets warmer, forests turn from coniferous to deciduous, summers are longer, and winters are less harsh.
5. Biodiversity is greater in tropical rain forests than in temperate forests.
6. Answers will vary, but should include grasslands. Most of the grassland biome has been replaced with grass-like crop plants such as wheat.
7. Students' tables should reflect information shown on pages 76–82.

Time Allotment

first day—one class period; every third day for the next three to four weeks—15 minutes

Process Skills

apply concepts, classify, experiment, compare and contrast, draw a conclusion, interpret data, observe and infer, predict

Safety Precautions

Have students wash their hands well each time they examine the jars.

PREPARATION

Alternative Materials

- Jar C can be "seeded" by adding protist cultures from a biological supply house.
- Cooked wheat or pea seeds may be used in place of rice. Do not use instant rice.
- Boiled and cooled tap water may be used in place of sterilized spring water (available from supply houses).
- Instructions for the preparation of sterile pond water are found on p. 18T.

FIELD Investigation **Before You Begin**

Succession describes the changes that take place in ecosystems over a period of time. Succession is a process that is going on all the time. It can be observed in a micro-ecosystem, such as in a jar of pond water. The type and number of organisms in the container will change over time.

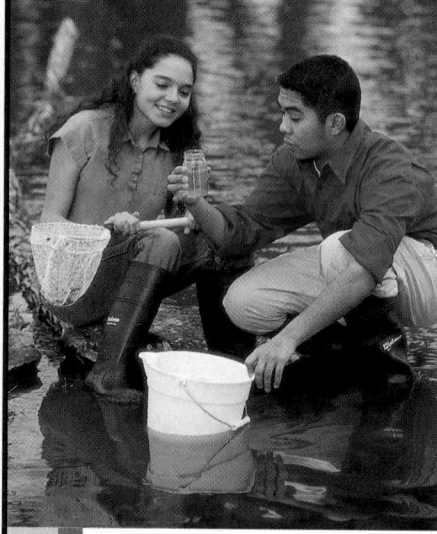

Succession in a Jar

PREPARATION

Problem

Can you observe succession in a pond water ecosystem?

Objectives

In this BioLab, you will:

- **Observe** changes in three pond water environments.
- **Count** the number of each type of organism seen.
- **Determine** if the changes observed illustrate succession.

Materials

small glass jars (3)	droppers
labels	plastic wrap
sterilized spring water	cooked white rice
pond water containing plant material	teaspoon, plastic microscope
glass slides and cover glasses	

Safety Precautions

CAUTION: *Use safe practices. Always wear goggles during this lab.*

Skill Handbook

If you need help with this lab, refer to the **Skill Handbook**.

PROCEDURE

1. Examine the pond water sample provided.
2. Label the jars *A*, *B*, and *C*. Add your name and the date. Fill the jars with equal amounts of sterilized spring water.
3. Add the following to the appropriate jar:
   to **Jar *A*:** Nothing else
   to **Jar *B*:** 3 grains of cooked white rice
   to **Jar *C*:** 3 grains of cooked white rice, one teaspoon of pond sediment, and a small amount of any plant material present in the pond water
4. Gently swirl the contents of each jar. Record the cloudiness of each jar in your data table. Score cloudiness on a scale of 1 to 10—1 meaning very clear; 10 meaning very cloudy.

PROCEDURE

Teaching Strategies

- A reference for identifying organisms is *Guide to Microlife*, available through Connecticut Valley Biological.
- Examine jars once a week if time is short.
- Continue the experiment for at least three weeks.

- Show overhead diagrams of common organisms to help students identify them.
- Hold each jar against newspaper print. Inability to read the print through the jar indicates turbidity (cloudiness).

- Have students add new sterilized spring water to replace any lost through evaporation.

Troubleshooting

To slow organisms down, drops of methylcellulose (available from supply houses) may be used.

5. Label glass slides *A*, *B*, or *C*. Using a different, clean dropper for each jar, prepare a wet mount of the liquid from each jar. **CAUTION:** *Handle glass slides, coverslips, and glassware carefully.*

6. Observe each sample under low power. Identify autotrophic and heterotrophic organisms by name, and either describe their appearance or make a sketch of each one.

7. Record the number of each type of organism.

8. Complete the data table for your first observations.

9. Cover each jar and place them in a lighted area.

10. Observe the jars every three days for several weeks. Repeat steps 4–9 each time an observation is made and collect data precisely.

11. **CLEANUP AND DISPOSAL** Determine ahead of time wise choices for disposing of these materials at the end of the investigation. **CAUTION:** *Wash hands with soap at the end of the lab.*

Data Table

Date	Jar	Cloudiness	Name, Description, or Diagram of Organism Seen	Autotroph or Heterotroph?	Number Seen Per Low-Power Field
	A				
	B				
	C				
	A				
	B				

ANALYZE AND CONCLUDE

1. **Apply Concepts** Which jar was a control? Explain.

2. **Observe and Infer** What is the role of the cooked rice?

3. **Recognize Cause and Effect** Why was there little, if any, cloudiness in jar *A?*

4. **Analyze Information** Describe the changes over time in the number and type of heterotrophs. Was this succession? Was it primary or secondary succession? Explain.

5. **Observe and Infer** Why would you say you had NOT observed a climax ecosystem during this experiment?

6. **ERROR ANALYSIS** Describe variables that could have affected the outcome and how these could be controlled.

Apply Your Skill

Field Investigation Plan and implement a field investigation that tests the effect of temperature on the rate at which succession occurs in pond water. Demonstrate safe practices during the field investigation.

 Web Links To find out more more about succession, visit in.bdol.glencoe.com/succession

ANALYZE AND CONCLUDE

1. A; only pasteurized water was added.

2. food for bacteria

3. There was little cloudiness because there were few or no living organisms.

4. See Data and Observations. Yes, any change in population is a key element of succession. This was secondary succession because living things had previously been present.

5. The community would have to continue to change for some time after the investigation to reach climax community status.

6. **ERROR ANALYSIS** Temperature, chemical composition of the water, food added, and starting populations are all variables that could affect the outcome.

Apply Your Skill

Field Investigation Experiments should focus on the changing populations in the pond, the amount of sediment coming into the pond, or similar factors that affect speed of succession. These investigations may take the entire school year to complete, or you may wish to carry them over from one year to the next. This would allow students to understand that some experiments are very long term.

Data and Observations

■ Jar A should remain clear, showing no turbidity or life forms. Jar B may show turbidity caused by bacteria but should show no autotrophs or protozoa.

■ Jar C will show increasing and then decreasing cloudiness. Autotrophic organisms will appear and increase in number. Heterotrophs will increase and decrease as follows: steady decrease in bacteria; sharp rise and then decline in *Colpidium* within first 20 days; sharp rise and then decline in *Euplotes* from days 40–60; slow and steady rise in *Paramecium* from days 10–0.

CLEANUP AND DISPOSAL

All glass slides and glassware need to be sterilized. Cultures themselves should be sterilized. Discuss why contaminated cultures can't be poured into a nearby pond.

Purpose

Students learn how a writer can influence public opinion and government policy towards the conservation of natural resources.

Teaching Strategies

- Ask students what they can do to protect the environment. Responses may include recycling, using public transportation, and eating organically grown foods.

- Have students debate whether public use of national parks should be restricted in order to protect the land from damage caused by overuse.

Further Reading

Encourage interested students to explore other science-themed literature. Examples of John Muir's writings are:

- Muir, John. The John Muir Library *Our National Parks*. Berkeley: University of California Press, 1991.

- Muir, John. The John Muir Library *Story of My Boyhood and Youth*. London: Trafalgar Press, 1988.

Other authors might include Rachel Carson, E.O. Wilson, and Annie Dillard.

---

connection to literature

Our National Parks

by John Muir

"Many of these pots and caldrons have been boiling thousands of years. Pots of sulphurous mush, stringy and lumpy, and pots of broth as black as ink, are tossed and stirred with constant care, and thin transparent essences, too pure and fine to be called water, are kept simmering gently in beautiful sinter cups and bowls that grow ever more beautiful the longer they are used."

—John Muir

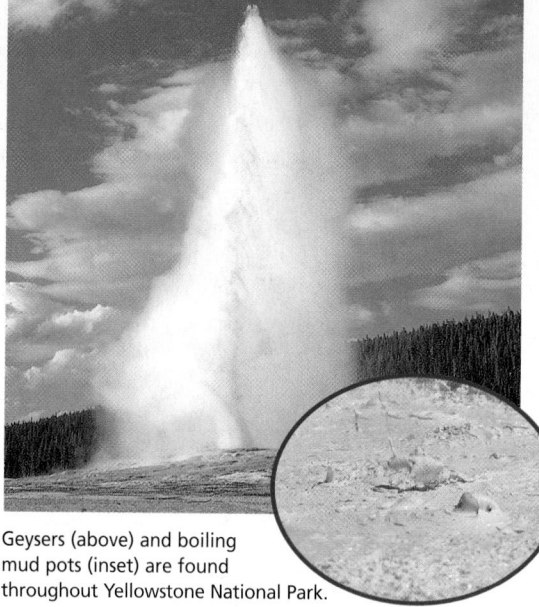

Geysers (above) and boiling mud pots (inset) are found throughout Yellowstone National Park.

The first, and largest, national park in the world was commissioned by an act of the United States Congress in 1872 as Yellowstone National Park. Because of the writing and influence of a man named John Muir, Congress also created the National Parks System, which includes Yellowstone, to preserve the lands that we enjoy today. In recognition of his contributions, Muir is often called "The Father of our National Park System."

Although it includes waterfalls, a high-elevation lake with one hundred and ten miles of shoreline, and one of the world's largest volcanic craters, Yellowstone National Park is probably most famous for its hot springs and geysers. In fact, more boiling caldrons and spouting plumes of hot water and mud are found in Yellowstone than in all of the rest of the world.

Muir's dream As a young man Muir had a vision of a "wildlands set aside by the government." The purpose of these lands would be simply to preserve the scenery and to educate people about the natural wonders of the land. As an adult, he was an avid explorer and prolific writer whose goals were to educate the public about the value of nature and the destructive effects man had on the natural environment.

Muir felt that the beauty of nature was as essential to the well-being of man as was food.

Muir the author In his book, *Our National Parks*, Muir provided his readers with the description of the boiling basins and geysers at Yellowstone that you read above. Over his lifetime, Muir wrote ten books and three hundred articles bringing the idea of wilderness to people. His writings so clearly depicted nature that Muir has been called the United States' most famous and influential naturalist and conservationist.

Writing About Biology

Research Contributions of Scientists In an essay, describe the contributions that Muir made toward expanding people's appreciation of nature.

To find out more about John Muir, Yellowstone National Park, and national parks worldwide, visit in.bdol.glencoe.com/literature

86 COMMUNITIES AND BIOMES

Writing About Biology

Essays might reflect that Muir was an excellent writer who was able to bring nature to life for people. His boyhood experiences in Scotland and in America prepared him for his later work as a naturalist and founder of the Sierra Club.

STUDY GUIDE

Section 3.1

Communities

Key Concepts

- Communities, populations, and individual organisms interact in areas where biotic or abiotic factors fall within their range of tolerance. Abiotic or biotic factors that define whether or not an organism can survive are limiting factors.

- The sequential development of living communities from bare rock is an example of primary succession. Secondary succession occurs when communities are disrupted. Left undisturbed, both primary succession and secondary succession will eventually result in a climax community which can last for hundreds of years.

Vocabulary

climax community (p. 68)
limiting factor (p. 65)
primary succession (p. 67)
secondary succession (p. 68)
succession (p. 67)
tolerance (p. 66)

Section 3.2

Biomes

Key Concepts

- Biomes are large areas that have characteristic climax communities. Aquatic biomes may be marine or freshwater. Estuaries occur at the boundaries of marine and freshwater biomes. Approximately three-quarters of Earth's surface is covered by aquatic biomes, and the vast majority of these are marine communities.

- Terrestrial biomes include tundra, taiga, desert, grassland, deciduous forest, and temperate and tropical rain forests. Latitude influences the angle at which the sun reaches Earth and is a strong factor in determining what a particular biome is like. Two climatic factors, temperature and precipitation, are major limiting factors for the formation of terrestrial biomes.

Vocabulary

aphotic zone (p. 71)
biome (p. 70)
desert (p. 78)
estuary (p. 71)
grassland (p. 79)
intertidal zone (p. 72)
photic zone (p. 71)
plankton (p. 73)
taiga (p. 77)
temperate/deciduous forest (p. 80)
tropical rain forest (p. 81)
tundra (p. 76)

FOLDABLES™
Study Organizer To help you review biomes, use the Organizational Study Fold on page 70.

in.bdol.glencoe.com/vocabulary_puzzlemaker   CHAPTER 3 ASSESSMENT **87**

Chapter 3 Assessment

Key Concepts
Summary statements can be used by students to review the major concepts of the chapter.

Biology Online

Visit in.bdol.glencoe.com
/self_check_quiz
/vocabulary_puzzlemaker
/chapter_test
/standardized_test

VOCABULARY PUZZLEMAKER

For additional help with vocabulary, have students access the Vocabulary PuzzleMaker online at in.bdol.glencoe.com/vocabulary_puzzlemaker

FOLDABLES™
Have students use their Foldables to review the content of Section 3.2. On the back of the Foldables, have them compare the climate and organisms found in the biome they live in to one that they have studied in this section.

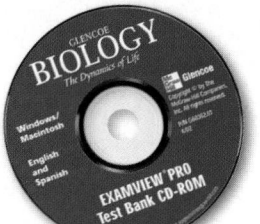

Use the ExamView®Pro Test Bank CD-ROM to:
- Create **multiple versions** of tests
- Create **modified** tests with one mouse click for **inclusion** students
- **Edit** existing questions and **add** your own questions
- Build tests aligned with state standards using built-in **State Curriculum Tags**
- Change **English** tests to **Spanish** with one mouse click and vice versa

Indiana Academic Standards
Pages 86–87: B.1.37, B.1.39, B.1.43

Questions and answers have been aligned and verified by The Princeton Review.

Vocabulary Review

1. photic zone—light is present; aphotic—no light
2. Primary—from bare rock; secondary—had life forms
3. Tundra is so cold that trees do not grow.
4. A biome is a large area defined by temperature and precipitation, whereas a climax community is one that becomes stable if left undisturbed.
5. The intertidal zone is the area between low and high tide. An estuary is an area where freshwater and salt water mix.

Understanding Key Concepts

6. D	8. B
7. C	9. C

Constructed Response

10. Student answers will vary. All discussions should include ecological factors.
11. The catfish is within its zone of tolerance for life, but outside its limits for reproduction.
12. Low precipitation and high temperatures are the two major limiting factors that combine to produce desert biomes such as the Chihuahuan Desert.

Thinking Critically

13. Answers will vary, but students should have supporting reasons for their opinion. Some may state that all fires should be allowed to burn because this is a natural event in grasslands and forests. Others may say that it is important to limit the fires near human communities, or fires caused by humans.

Vocabulary Review

Review the Chapter 3 vocabulary words listed in the Study Guide on page 87. Distinguish between the vocabulary words in each pair.

1. photic zone—aphotic zone
2. primary succession—secondary succession
3. taiga—tundra
4. biome—climax community
5. estuary—intertidal zone

Understanding Key Concepts

6. The removal of which of the following would have the biggest impact on a marine ecosystem?
   A. fishes   C. shrimp
   B. whales   D. plankton
7. An undersea volcano erupts, creating a new island in the Gulf of Mexico. Life slowly starts to appear on the island. What would probably be the first species to take hold and survive?
   A. ferns   C. lichens
   B. finches   D. grasses
8. The changes in communities that take place on the new island described in question 7 would best be described as _____.
   A. intertidal succession
   B. primary succession
   C. secondary succession
   D. tropical succession
9. The photograph shows a forest in Washington state. The annual rainfall is 300 cm and the average temperature is 15°C. What type of forest is shown?
   A. tropical rain forest
   B. coniferous forest
   C. temperate rain forest
   D. temperate forest

Constructed Response

10. **Open Ended** Select a biome and evaluate the effect of flood on that environment. Use ecological terms in your discussion.
11. **Open Ended** A population of catfish survives in a pond, but does not reproduce there. Discuss what might be happening here in terms of tolerance.

Study the map below to answer question 12.

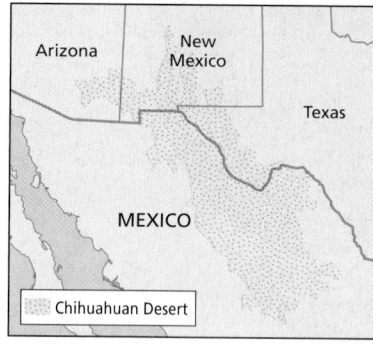

12. **Open Ended** Describe two limiting factors responsible for the desert biome on the map. How do they affect the biome? What would happen to the biome if one of these factors were to change?

Thinking Critically

13. **REAL WORLD BIOCHALLENGE** Each year, fires occur naturally or are set in forests throughout the United States. Fire ecology is the science that researches the effects of fires on the environment and deals with the management of fire in maintaining healthy forests. Visit in.bdol.glencoe.com to research various hypotheses about fire management. In class, analyze the strengths and weaknesses of these hypotheses.
14. **Explain** Explain why you travel through several biomes when climbing a tall mountain even though it is located near the equator. Compare the variations in plants from biome to biome.

 in.bdol.glencoe.com/chapter_test

14. As altitude increases, the temperature drops and one biome is replaced by another kind of biome. Increasing altitude is similar to increasing latitude. Plant variations should reflect those described on pages 74–83.
15. It is a climax community because the mature forest hasn't changed for a long time.

16. The shallow parts of the lake have greater biodiversity because sunlight penetrates there allowing plants to make nutrients and release oxygen. Deeper parts of the lake receive no sunlight and fewer species survive there.

15. Writing About Biology Beech trees and maple trees dominate a forest that has stayed the same for 100 years. What is the ecological term for this stable community? Explain your choice.

16. Explain Explain why the shallow parts of a lake have more sunlight, produce more oxygen, and have greater species diversity than the deepest part of the lake.

End-of-Course Assessment Practice

All questions aligned and verified by *The Princeton Review*

Part 1 Multiple Choice

Use the table below to answer questions 17 and 18.

Annual Precipitation Versus Temperature

17. According to the graph, which biome would be expected when rainfall ranges between 150 cm/year and 200 cm/year?
A. tropical rain forest
B. grassland
C. tropical seasonal forest
D. savanna

18. Which biome extends across the largest temperature variation?
A. temperate forest
B. taiga
C. grassland
D. desert

Productivity is the amount of biomass generated by producers per unit area in a given period. Use the information below to answer questions 19 and 20 about biome productivity.

Biome Productivity		
Biome	Percent of Earth's Surface	Estimated Productivity (grams per meter^2 per year)
Open ocean	65.0	125
Desert	3.5	90
Tropical rain forest	3.3	2000
Taiga	2.4	800
Tundra	1.6	140
Temperate/ deciduous forest	1.3	1250
Swamp/marsh	0.4	2000
Lake/stream	0.4	250
Estuary	0.3	1500

19. Which biomes have the least productivity per square meter per year?
A. desert and tundra
B. open ocean and tundra
C. lake/stream and desert
D. desert and open ocean

20. Which biome occupies the smallest percent of Earth's surface?
A. temperate deciduous forest
B. estuary
C. tundra
D. tropical rain forest

Part 2 Constructed Response/Grid In

Record your answers on your answer document.

21. Open Ended Describe how secondary succession in a forest differs from primary succession after a volcano.

22. Open Ended Explain how a swamp or marsh differs from other aquatic biomes.

in.bdol.glencoe.com/standardized_test

End-of-Course Assessment Practice

17. C	19. D
18. D	20. B

21. Soil, roots, and living organisms are present in a forest, and secondary succession begins. After a volcano, primary succession has to begin by developing soil first.

22. Wetland biomes are immersed in water for only part of the year. Aquatic biomes are always wet.

 FAST FILE

Answer Sheet A practice answer sheet can be found on p. 69 of *Unit 2 FAST FILE Resources.*

RUBRIC

SCORE	CRITERIA
4	A correct solution that is supported by well-developed, accurate explanations.
3	A generally correct solution, but may contain minor flaws in reasoning.

SCORE	CRITERIA
2	A partially correct interpretation and/or solution to the problem.
1	A correct solution with no supporting evidence or explanation.
0	An incorrect solution or no solution is given.

 Indiana Academic Standards

Pages 88–89: B.1.37, B.1.39, B.1.40, B.1.43, B.1.45, B.1.46

Chapter 4 Organizer

Section Objectives	National Science Standards	State/Local Standards	Advanced Lab and Demo Planning
Section 4.1 3 sessions, 1 block 1. **Compare and contrast** exponential and linear population growth. 2. **Relate** the reproductive patterns of different populations of organisms to models of population growth. 3. **Predict** effects of environmental factors on population growth.	UCP.1–3; A.1, A.2; C.4, C.5; F.2, F.4, F.5, F.6; G.1, G.2	**Indiana Standards** B.1.37, B.1.38, B.1.40, B.1.43, B.1.45	**Student Labs:** MiniLab 4.1, p. 92: banana, jar, cloth, rubber band Problem-Solving Lab 4.1, p. 95 Additional Lab, p. 96: 2 petri dishes, radish seeds, napkins, pipette Investigate BioLab, p. 104: See materials below. **Teacher Demonstration:** Quick Demo, p. 97: cardboard, 3 checkers
Section 4.2 2 sessions, 1 block 4. **Identify** how the birthrate and death rate affect the rate at which a population changes. 5. **Compare** the age structure of rapidly growing, slow-growing, and no-growth countries. 6. **Explain** the relationship between a population and the environment.	UCP.1–3; A.1, A.2; C.4, C.5, C.6; F.4, F.5; G.1, G.3	**Indiana Standards** B.1.37, B.1.41, B.1.43	**Student Labs:** Problem-Solving Lab 4.2, p. 101 MiniLab 4.2, p. 102
End of Chapter Assessment Student Edition **Study Guide,** p. 107 **Content Assessment,** pp. 108–109		**Indiana Standards** B.1.37, B.1.40, B.1.43	**Student Lab:** Investigate BioLab, p. 104: paper bag, beans, calculator (optional), permanent marker (dark color)

Key to Teaching Strategies

L1 Level 1 activities should be appropriate for students with learning difficulties.

L2 Level 2 activities should be within the ability range of all students.

L3 Level 3 activities are designed for above-average students.

ELL ELL activities should be within the ability range of English Language Learners.

COOP LEARN Cooperative Learning activities are designed for small group work.

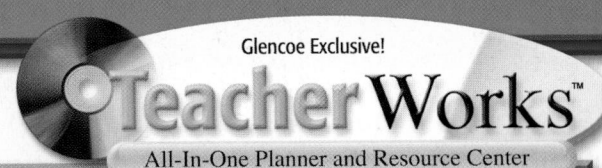
Glencoe Exclusive!
Teacher Works™
All-In-One Planner and Resource Center

Reproducible Masters and Transparencies	Technology

Reproducible Masters and Transparencies

Unit 2 *FAST FILE* **Resources**
MiniLab Worksheet, p. 73
BioLab Worksheet, pp. 75–76
Reinforcement and Study Guide in English, pp. 77–78
Reinforcement and Study Guide in Spanish, pp. 81–82
Concept Mapping, p. 85
Critical Thinking/Problem Solving, p. 86
Laboratory Manual, pp. 15–18, 19–22
Transparency Worksheets, pp. 87, 89–90
Section Focus Transparency 8
Reteaching Skills Transparency 6

Technology

⊙ **Interactive Chalkboard CD-ROM: Section 4.1 Presentation** ▮
⊙ TeacherWorks™ **CD-ROM** ▮
🎵 **Guided Reading Audio Summaries MP3**
⊙ **Virtual Labs CD-ROM**
Virtual Lab: Population Biology

Unit 2 *FAST FILE* **Resources**
MiniLab Worksheet, p. 74
Reinforcement and Study Guide in English, pp. 79–80
Reinforcement and Study Guide in Spanish, pp. 83–84
Transparency Worksheet, p. 88
Section Focus Transparency 9

⊙ **Interactive Chalkboard CD-ROM: Section 4.2 Presentation** ▮
⊙ TeacherWorks™ **CD-ROM** ▮
🎵 **Guided Reading Audio Summaries MP3**

Unit 2 *FAST FILE* **Resources**
Chapter Assessment, pp. 91–96
Student Recording Sheet, p. 97

The Princeton Review **Reviewing Biology,** pp. 7–8

⊙ **Interactive Chalkboard: Chapter 4 Assessment** ▮
⊙ **MindJogger Videoquizzes DVD/VHS**
⊙ **Exam***View*® **Pro Test Bank CD-ROM**
⊙ TeacherWorks™ **CD-ROM** ▮
⊙ **Succeeding on National Standards CD-ROM**

🖥 in.bdol.glencoe.com
/self_check_quiz
/vocabulary_puzzlemaker
/chapter_test
/standardized_test

▮ Indicates materials created specifically for Indiana.

Chapter 4

Population Biology

Short on Time?
BIODIGEST The BioDigest at the end of this unit can be used as a(n):

- preview to introduce important unit concepts.
- overview if time does not permit teaching the entire chapter.
- review of key unit concepts.

Understanding the Photo

King penguins (*Aptenodytes patagonicus*) are the second largest penguins on Earth. They are social animals and disagreements among them are rare. King penguins "fly" through the water in search of squid and fish in an area of the South Atlantic which few humans would find hospitable. Once hunted for their skins and oil, king penguin populations are on the rise again.

What You'll Learn

- You will explain how populations grow.
- You will identify factors that inhibit the growth of populations.
- You will summarize issues in human population growth.

Why It's Important

How a population of organisms grows is critical to the survival of its species. A population that grows rapidly may run out of food or space. A population that grows too slowly may become extinct.

Understanding ▶ the Photo

King penguins are highly social animals that live and breed in large colonies called rookeries in some of the most isolated islands in the subantarctic. Even though few people will ever encounter these animals, maintaining their populations is important for keeping the ecosystems in that portion of the world healthy.

Biology Online

Visit **in.bdol.glencoe.com** to
- study the entire chapter online
- access Web Links for more information and activities on population biology
- review content with the Interactive Tutor and self-check quizzes

Indiana Academic Standards

Pages 90–91: B.1.37, B.1.43

90

Two-Minute Chapter Launcher

Demo To elicit students' understanding of population growth, write the following on the chalkboard: Some bacteria can reproduce every twenty minutes. Calculate the growth of a population of 10 bacteria for 24 hours. Students should calculate 10 bacteria at time 0, and then 20, 40, 80, 160, 320, 640, 1280, 2560, 5120, 10 240, 20 480, 40 960. . . . . Visualize growth by using sunflower seeds (or dry beans) for the first five two-hour periods. Ask students: Could bacteria cover the world? They might, but they might run out of food, space, or other needs. Discuss the penguins shown in the photograph, and ask why their population doesn't grow as quickly as do bacteria. They have fewer offspring and reproduce less frequently.

Section 4.1

Population Dynamics

SECTION PREVIEW

Objectives

Compare and contrast exponential and linear population growth.

Relate the reproductive patterns of different populations of organisms to models of population growth.

Predict effects of environmental factors on population growth.

Review Vocabulary

population: a group of organisms of the same species that live in a specific area (p. 38)

New Vocabulary

exponential growth
carrying capacity
life-history pattern
density-dependent factor
density-independent factor

FOLDABLES™
Study Organizer

Populations Make the following Foldable to help you identify the main factors that affect populations.

STEP 1 **Fold** a sheet of paper in half lengthwise.

STEP 2 **Fold** in half, then fold in half again to make three folds.

STEP 3 **Unfold and cut** only the top layer along the three folds to make four tabs.

STEP 4 **Label** the tabs.

| Population Increase |
| Carrying Capacity |
| The Environment |
| Other Organisms |

Compare and Contrast As you read Chapter 4, compare the effects these factors have on population size. List some of the effects under the appropriate tab.

Figure 4.1
Ecologists can study bacterial population growth in the laboratory.

Principles of Population Growth

A population is a group of organisms, all of the same species, that live in a specific area. There are populations of spruce trees, populations of maple trees, of bluebirds, dandelions, fruit flies, and house cats. Every organism you can think of is a member of a population. A healthy population will grow and die at a relatively steady rate unless it runs out of water, food, or space, or is attacked in some way by disease or predators.

Scientists study changes in populations in a variety of ways. One method involves introducing organisms into a controlled environment with abundant resources; then watching how the organisms react. That is what is happening in *Figure 4.1.* Bacterial cells are placed in a dish of sterile, nutrient-rich solution and population growth is observed over a period of time. Through studies such as these, scientists have been able to identify some trends in the growth of bacterial cells.

4.1 POPULATION DYNAMICS **91**

1 Focus

INTERACTIVE CHALKBOARD
PowerPoint® Presentations

Bellringer
Section Focus Transparency 8

Transparency **8** **Predator-Prey Relationships**   **SECTION FOCUS**   *Use with Chapter 4, Section 4.1*

① How is the number of sea urchins in this community affected by the number of sea otters?

② How is the number of sea otters affected by the number of sea urchins?

BIOLOGY: The Dynamics of Life   SECTION FOCUS TRANSPARENCIES

INTERACTIVE CHALKBOARD
with Image Bank

PowerPoint® Presentations

This CD-ROM is an editable Microsoft® PowerPoint® presentation that includes:
• Section presentations
• Section checks
• Image bank
• Hot links to Biology Online
• All transparencies

FOLDABLES™
For an additional Foldables activity idea, see the Chapter 4 Foldables page in *Unit 2 FAST FILE Resources.*

RESOURCE MANAGER

Unit 2 *FAST FILE* Resources
MiniLab Worksheet, p. 73
BioLab Worksheet, pp. 75–76
Reinforcement and Study Guide in English, pp. 77–78
Reinforcement and Study Guide in Spanish, pp. 81–82
Concept Mapping, p. 85
Critical Thinking/Problem Solving, p. 86

Laboratory Manual, pp. 15–18, 19–22
Transparency Worksheets, pp. 87, 89–90
Section Focus Transparency 8
Reteaching Skills Transparency 6

2 Teach

Purpose

Students will learn that food is a factor in population growth.

Process Skills

observe and infer, interpret data

Safety Precautions

Have students wash their hands after each observation.

Teaching Strategies

- If temperatures are warm enough, fruit flies should be attracted quickly to the bananas.
- You can order vestigial fruit flies from a biological supply company.
- Have students record their data and observations in a table.

Expected Results

Fruit flies will arrive and quickly reproduce. Larvae will be evident on the jar and the banana. In a few weeks, the jar will be full of flies. Soon the population will decline because the food supply is limited.

Analysis

1. Answers will vary.
2. Answers will vary. Students may mention that the quality or amount of useful food decreased. Some may mention the presence of wastes.
3. clean jar; fresh food source

Assessment

Skill Have students describe how they could determine whether food type affects the type of animal attracted. Use the Performance Task Assessment List for Designing an Experiment in **PASC**, p. 95. **L2**

Indiana Academic Standards

Pages 92–93: B.1.37, B.1.43

MiniLab 4.1

Make and Use Tables

Fruit Fly Population Growth Fruit flies *(Drosophila melanogaster)* are used in biological research because they reproduce quickly and are easy to keep and count. In this activity you will observe the growth of a fruit fly population as it exploits a food supply.

Procedure

1. Place half of a banana in an uncovered jar and allow it to sit outside in a warm shaded area, or put it in a warm area in your classroom.
2. Leave the jar for one day or until you have at least three fruit flies in it. Put a cloth on top of the jar and fasten with the rubber band.
3. Each day for at least three weeks, record how many adult fruit flies are alive in the jar. Put data into table form. Graph your data. **CAUTION:** *Make wise choices. Do not eat the fruit. Return the flies and fruit to your teacher for disposal.*

Fruit flies feeding on a banana

Analysis

1. **Observe and Infer** How many fruit flies did you start with? On what day were there the most fruit flies? How many were there?
2. **Analyze Trends from Data** Why do you think the number of fruit flies decreased?
3. **Predict Trends from Data** What might help the population to begin growing again after a decrease?

Information on bacterial cell growth might be helpful in fighting disease. Studies of populations of larger organisms, such as an elk population in a national park, require methods such as the use of radio monitors. Use the *MiniLab* on this page to learn one method of measuring growth in a fruit fly population.

How fast do populations grow?

The growth of populations is unlike the growth of pay you get from a job. Suppose your job pays $5 per hour. You know if you work for two hours, you will be paid $10; if you work for four hours, you will be paid $20; if you work for eight hours, you will be paid $40; and so on. If you were to plot money earned against your time in hours, the graph would show a steady, straight-line (linear) increase.

Populations of organisms, however, do not experience linear growth. Rather, the graph of a growing population starts out slowly, then begins to resemble a J-shaped curve, as illustrated in a population of houseflies in *Figure 4.2*. The initial increase in the number of organisms is slow because the number of reproducing individuals is small. Soon, however, the rate of population growth increases because the total number of individuals that are able to reproduce has increased.

Figure 4.2
Because they grow exponentially, populations of houseflies have the potential for unchecked growth. Notice that the shape of the curve is like the letter *J*.

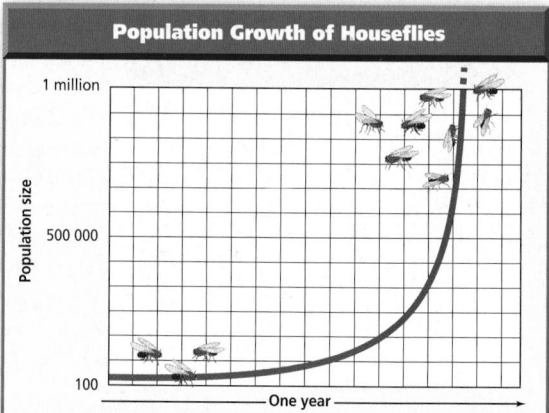

Exterminator Training Have students research the types of organisms most frequently encountered by exterminators. Cockroaches, houseflies, silverfish, bees, and ants are some that might be mentioned. Have students choose one of these organisms and investigate the life cycle, finding out at which point in the life cycle extermination might be most effective. Students should also see if they can determine the economic impact an infestation by one of these organisms can have on a business or home.

Is growth unlimited?

A J-shaped growth curve illustrates exponential population growth. **Exponential growth** means that as a population gets larger, it also grows at a faster rate. Exponential growth results in unchecked growth.

What can limit growth?

Can a population of organisms grow indefinitely? Through observation and population experiments, scientists have found that population growth does have limits. Eventually, limiting factors, such as availability of food, disease, predators, or lack of space, will cause population growth to slow. Under these pressures, the population may stabilize in an S-shaped growth curve, which you can see in *Figure 4.3*.

Carrying capacity

The number of organisms of one species that an environment can support indefinitely is its **carrying capacity.** When a population is developing in an environment with resources, there are more births than deaths and the population increases until the carrying capacity is reached or passed. When a population overshoots the carrying capacity, then limiting factors may come into effect. Deaths begin to exceed births and the population falls below carrying capacity. Thus, the number of organisms in a population is sometimes more than the environment can support and sometimes less than the environment can support. *Figure 4.4* on the next page shows a population growth line that moves above and below the carrying capacity. Many different types of organisms can show such growth patterns in nature.

Characteristics of Population Growth

Figure 4.3
The graph above compares exponential growth and growth that is influenced by limiting factors such as disease, space, predators, or food. Over time, one or more of these limiting factors can keep a population at or below the carrying capacity of the environment.

Reproduction Patterns

In nature, animal and plant populations change in size. For example, mosquitoes are more numerous at certain times of the year than others. Why don't populations reach carrying capacity and remain stable? To answer this question, population biologists study the factor that determines population growth—an organism's reproductive pattern, also called its **life-history pattern.**

A variety of population growth patterns are possible in nature. Two extremes of these patterns are demonstrated by the population growth rates of mosquitoes and elephants. Mosquitoes exhibit a rapid life-history pattern. Elephants, like many other large organisms, exhibit characteristics of the slow life-history pattern. Mosquitoes reproduce very rapidly and produce many offspring in a short period of time, whereas elephants have a slow rate of reproduction and produce relatively few young over their lifetime.

4.1 POPULATION DYNAMICS **93**

Purpose

Students learn about the general pattern of population growth in stable environments.

Teaching Strategies

■ Have students write a one-paragraph summary of how a population grows, including why a population growth curve might level off. **L1**

■ Give each group of students a die. For time period 1, they roll the die and record the number that shows up as a population size. Do the same for time period 2, 3, all the way to 10. On the *x*-axis, plot the time periods 1 to 10. On the *y*-axis, plot the population size. Have them find the average population size for the 10 time periods and draw a straight line to reflect this average. Relate this line to carrying capacity.

Critical Thinking

The population begins exponential growth. This resembles the letter **J**. Eventually growth slows down and the population levels off. After it levels off, it fluctuates above and below the carrying capacity as the population is affected by one or more limiting factors.

Modified Assessment

Ask students to draw an S-shaped population curve. Have them identify the following: slow growth phase, exponential growth phase, plateau, point where carrying capacity is reached. Ask how this graph might change with a sudden increase or decrease in food supply. **L1**

Indiana Academic Standards

Pages 94–95: B.1.37, B.1.45

INSIDE STORY

Population Growth

Figure 4.4
When a population is in an environment unaffected by factors such as predators, fire, or drought, and there are sufficient resources, the population increases. Ecologists have discovered that these population increases show a pattern. Whether it is a plant or animal, whether on land or in the ocean, populations grow in predictable manners.
Critical Thinking *Why can a population fluctuate once it reaches carrying capacity?*

Humpback whales have a slow life-history pattern.

D Carrying capacity The environment can support this many organisms. If population size rises above the carrying capacity, more organisms die than are born. The population drops below the carrying capacity.

E Fluctuations The number of organisms tends to rise above and fall below the carrying capacity due to limiting factors.

Carrying capacity

C Leveling off As the population grows, more organisms are using the existing resources. Growth slows. Overall, the graph begins to resemble the letter *S*.

B Rapid growth There are many organisms, each reproducing, resulting in a faster increase in the number of individuals. Growth is exponential.

Number of organisms of one species

A Beginning growth The population increase begins slowly, as the few starting members have offspring.

Time

PROJECT

Population Growth in Pictures Have students create flipbooks that show population growth. Draw scenes on the right sides of index cards. On the first cards, show a few organisms, then exponential growth. Show competition for resources. Then show a relatively constant population size. A line on a graph can advance in each scene. **L1 ELL**

Rapid life-history patterns

Rapid life-history patterns are common among organisms from changeable or unpredictable environments. Rapid life-history organisms have a small body size, mature rapidly, reproduce early, and have a short life span. Populations of rapid life-history organisms increase rapidly, then decline when environmental conditions such as temperature suddenly change and become unsuitable for life. The small population that survives will reproduce exponentially when conditions are again favorable. The *Problem-Solving Lab* on this page explores growth in bacteria, an organism with a rapid life-history pattern.

Slow life-history patterns

Large species that live in more stable environments usually have slow life-history patterns. Elephants, bears, whales, humans, and plants, such as trees, are long lived. The pronghorn antelope shown in *Figure 4.5*, are slow life-history organisms.

Ⓐ

Ⓑ

Problem-Solving Lab 4.1

Predict

How rapidly can bacteria reproduce? Bacteria are examples of rapidly reproducing organisms. They are often used in experiments about population studies or trends.

Reproduction Rate of Bacteria

Number of organisms

1 072 431 104

32 728

0

Time in hours
0   5   10

Solve the Problem

Here are some facts regarding unchecked bacterial reproduction:

1. A single bacterium can reproduce to yield two bacteria under ideal conditions every 20 minutes.
2. Ideal conditions for bacterial reproduction include proper temperature, unlimited food, space to grow, and dispersion of waste materials.

Thinking Critically

1. **Calculate** Suppose you start with one bacterium under ideal conditions. If no bacteria die, compute the number of bacteria present after 1 hour, 5 hours, and 10 hours.
2. **Predict Trends** What environmental factors might affect a bacterial population's reproduction?
3. **Error Analysis** The above graph is an example of one group's data.
   a. What error did they make in the *y*-axis of the graph?
   b. Redraw the graph correctly.
4. **Infer** An elephant reproduces once every four to six years. Why are elephants not likely to be used in laboratory population studies?

Figure 4.5
Wild mustard plants taking over an abandoned field represent a species with a rapid life-history pattern **(A)**. Organisms that have a slow life-history pattern, such as these pronghorn antelope, provide much parental care for their young **(B)**. **Predict Trends** *Which of these organisms would be more successful in a rapidly changing environment? Explain.*

4.1   POPULATION DYNAMICS   **95**

🎯 **CHALLENGE ACTIVITY**

Life as a Mosquito Have students hypothesize the conditions that make a mosquito's environment subject to rapid change. Students will have to research life stages and breeding habits and habitats of mosquitoes. **L3**

Revealing Misconceptions

Exponential growth may be misunderstood. Students may think that the growth rate in all things must be very fast. In fact, the growth rate can be small and the rate itself is predictable, as in the growth of money in a savings account.

Uncover the Misconception

Ask students to explain how putting their money each payday into a bank might be better than saving it at home in a jar. Point out that although the balance will increase slowly beyond what they continue to put in a bank, there is no chance for an increase in a jar.

Demonstrate the Concept

Use this analogy to help students understand the concept. You put $100 in the bank and get 2% interest per year. How much will you have after the first five years? $102, $104.04, $106.12, $108.24, $110.41

Assess New Knowledge

Ask students whether they'd rather have $100 in a week, or a penny today that doubles its worth every twelve hours. They'd have $163.84 instead of $100 if they opted for the slow, but exponential, growth of the penny.

Figure 4.6
Organisms disperse in a variety of ways: random (**A**), clumped (**B**), and uniform (**C**). Clumping may be the most common. Uniform dispersal may be the least common although it is visible with birds on a wire and among creosote bushes in a desert. The orderly planting of crops, such as rows of corn, is not a natural dispersal.

Random **A**

Clumped **B**

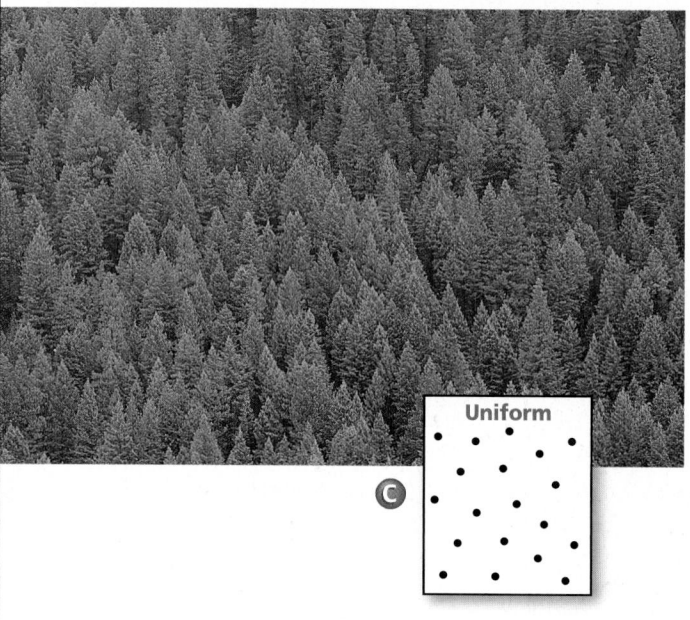
Uniform **C**

Slow life-history organisms reproduce and mature slowly, and are long-lived. They maintain population sizes at or near carrying capacity.

Density factors and population growth

Recall that limiting factors are biotic or abiotic factors that determine whether or not an organism can live in a particular environment. Limited food supply, space, chemicals produced by plants themselves, extreme temperatures, and even storms affect populations.

How organisms are dispersed can also be important. *Figure 4.6* shows three patterns of dispersal: random, clumped, and uniform.

Ecologists have identified two kinds of limiting factors that are related to dispersal: density-dependent and density-independent factors. Population density describes the number of individuals in a given area.

Additional Lab

Germinating Radishes

Purpose

Students will plan an investigation to test a hypothesis and calculate the percent of germination of radish seeds.

Safety Precautions

Have students wash their hands after handling the seeds.

Materials per Group

two petri dishes, radish seeds, napkins

Procedure

Cut a napkin into two circles that will fit into a petri dish. Place one circle into the dish, put some seeds on top, and place the other circle on top of the seeds. Add a small amount of water. Cover the dish. Then give students these instructions

1. With your group, choose one variable to change, such as the amount or type of solution used for watering. You could also investigate the effects of heat, light, or music.

Density-dependent factors include disease, competition, predators, parasites, and food. These factors have an increasing effect as the population increases. Disease, for example, can spread more quickly in a population with members that live close together. In crops such as corn or soybeans in which large numbers of the same plant are grown together, a disease can spread rapidly throughout the whole crop. In less dense populations, fewer individuals may be affected. Disease is also a factor in human populations. The presence of HIV/AIDS in many of the world's populations is considered by some scientists to be a limiting factor in the growth of those populations.

Density-independent factors can affect populations, regardless of their density. Most density-independent factors are abiotic factors, such as volcanic eruptions, temperature, storms, floods, drought, chemical pesticides, and major habitat disruption, such as that shown in *Figure 4.7*. Although all populations can be affected by these factors, the most vulnerable appear to be small organisms with large populations, such as insects. No matter how many earthworms live in a field, they will drown if it floods. It doesn't matter if there are many or few mosquitoes—a severe winter will kill the adults of most species.

Organism Interactions Limit Population Size

Population sizes are limited not only by abiotic factors, but also are controlled by various interactions among organisms that share a community.

Predation affects population size

A barn owl kills and eats a mouse. A swarm of locusts eats and destroys acres of lettuce on a farm. When the brown tree snake was introduced in Guam, an

island in the North Pacific, there were no native predators for the snake. Consequently, it freely preyed on the native birds of the island. These examples demonstrate how predation can affect population sizes in both minor and major ways. When a predator consumes prey on a large enough scale (as in the case of the brown tree snake), it can have a drastic effect on the size of the prey population. For this reason, predation can be a limiting factor on population size.

Populations of predators and their prey are known to experience cycles or changes in their numbers over periods of time. Under controlled conditions, such as in a laboratory, predator-prey relationships often show a predictable cycle of population increases and decreases over time. In nature, these cycles have also been observed. One classic example of this has been demonstrated in *Figure 4.8* on the next page, which shows a graph of 90 years of data about the populations of the Canadian lynx and the snowshoe hare. A member of the cat family, the lynx stalks, attacks, and eats the snowshoe hare as a primary source of food.

Figure 4.7
A flood of catastrophic proportions, such as this flood in San Antonio, Texas in the summer of 2002, can be a limiting factor, especially for human populations. Among other things, flooding affects drinking water and sewage systems. These are limiting factors for modern urban life. **Infer** *What else in this photograph might be affected by flooding?*

2. Complete this problem statement: What is the effect of _____ on the germination of a radish seed? Write a hypothesis to answer this question.
3. Write out procedures before starting. Plan control and experimental groups.
4. Set up your experiments and wait 48 hours. Then report your results. Was your hypothesis supported?

Analysis
1. What percent of the seeds germinated? Answers will vary with age of seed and treatment.
2. Was your variable a biotic or abiotic factor? Most will be abiotic factors.
3. What was your conclusion for your experiment? Answers will vary.

Assessment
Performance Have students write a lab report describing the procedure they followed and their conclusions. Use the Performance Task Assessment List for Lab Report in **PASC**, p. 119. **L1**

Tying to Prior Knowledge

Explain how the decrease in available energy at the top trophic level of a food chain serves as a limiting factor on predator population size.

Visual Learning

Figure 4.8 Have students answer these questions: In what approximate year were there the most hares? 1865 In what year were there the most lynxes? 1935 After the hare population spikes, how many years pass until it crashes? approximately 5 years Use the graph to point out the cyclic nature of these events. Elicit from students why cycles might occur between predators and prey.

Inquiry

Activity Have students graph the following data about the effect of different population densities on house mice (*Mus musculus*) reproduction rates. Average number/m³ means the number of mice in one cubic meter of space.

Population Densities in Mice			
Densities →	Low	Medium	High
Av. No./m³	34	118	975
Av. % pregnant	58	49	47
Av. No. per litter	6.2	5.7	5.4

Discuss the response of the mice to the different densities. It appears that as the population increases, the percentage of pregnancies declines, the average number of mice per litter decreases.

Indiana Academic Standards

Pages 98–99: B.1.37, B.1.40, B.1.43

98

The data in *Figure 4.8* show the lynx and hare populations appear to rise and fall fairly closely in a 10-year cycle. When the hare population increases, there is more food for the lynx population, and the lynx population increases. When the lynx population rises, predation increases, and the hare population then declines. With fewer hares available for food, the lynx population then declines. Then, with fewer predators, the hare population increases, and the cycle continues. This example shows how predator populations can affect the size of the prey populations. At the same time, prey populations affect the size of the predator populations. As the snowshoe hare's food supply of grasses and herbs dwindles during the fall and winter months, the hare population decreases. Because there are now fewer hares to hunt, the lynx population also decreases. With the return of spring, the hare's food supply and its population recover. This leads to more hares, allowing the lynx population to increase as well.

Usually, in prey populations, the young, old, or injured members are caught. Predation increases the chance that resources will be available for the remaining individuals in a prey population.

Competition within a population

The hare and the lynx belong to different populations. What happens when organisms within the same population compete for resources? When population numbers are low, resources can build up and become plentiful. Then, as these resources are used, the population increases in size and competition for resources such as food, water, and territory again increases significantly. Competition is a density-dependent factor. When only a few individuals compete for resources, no problem arises. When a population increases to the point at which demand for resources exceeds the supply, the population size decreases.

Figure 4.8
The data in this graph reflect the number of hare and lynx pelts sold to the Hudson's Bay Company in northern Canada from 1845 through 1935. Notice that as the number of hares increased, so did the number of lynx.

* Data from 1844 through 1904 reflects actual pelts counted. Data from 1905 through 1935 is based on answers to a questionnaire.

98 POPULATION BIOLOGY

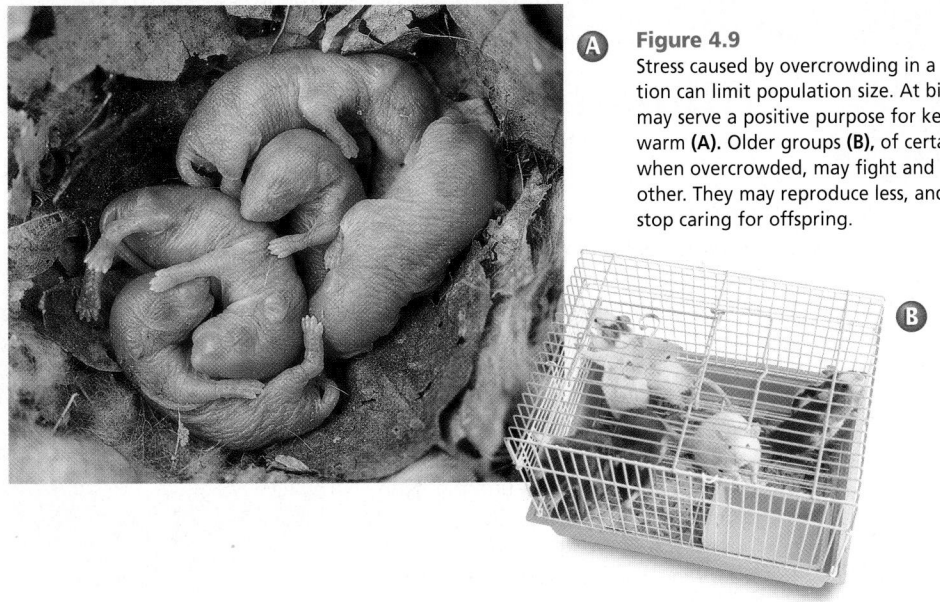

(A) **Figure 4.9**
Stress caused by overcrowding in a rat population can limit population size. At birth, crowding may serve a positive purpose for keeping young warm **(A)**. Older groups **(B)**, of certain organisms when overcrowded, may fight and kill each other. They may reproduce less, and they may stop caring for offspring.

(B)

The effects of crowding and stress

When populations of certain organisms become crowded, individuals may exhibit symptoms of stress. The factors that create stress are not well understood, but the effects have been documented from experiments and observations of populations of several organisms including fish, deer, rabbits, and rats as shown in *Figure 4.9*.

As populations increase in size in environments that cannot support increased numbers, individual animals can exhibit a variety of stress symptoms. These include aggression, decrease in parental care, decreased fertility, and decreased resistance to disease. All of these symptoms can have negative effects on a population. They become limiting factors for growth and keep populations below carrying capacity.

Section Assessment

Understanding Main Ideas
1. Explain and illustrate how the long-term survival of a species depends on resources that may be limited from time to time.
2. Compare short and long life-history patterns.
3. Describe how density-dependent and density-independent factors regulate population growth.
4. Describe the population growth curve of houseflies.

Thinking Critically
5. How can a density-dependent factor, such as a food supply, affect the carrying capacity of a habitat?

 in.bdol.glencoe.com/self_check_quiz

SKILL REVIEW

6. **Get the Big Picture** Graph the following seasonal population data for an organism shown in the table below and analyze whether the organism has a population growth pattern closer to a rapid or slow life-history pattern. For more help, refer to *Get the Big Picture* in the **Skill Handbook**.

Seasonal Population Data				
Year	Spring	Summer	Autumn	Winter
1995	564	14 598	25 762	127
1996	750	16 422	42 511	102
1997	365	14 106	36 562	136

4.1 POPULATION DYNAMICS **99**

3 Assess

DAILY INTERVENTION

Check for Understanding
Ask students to explain the difference between the words in each of the following pairs. **L1** **ELL**
a. linear growth—exponential growth
b. carrying capacity—population size
c. density-dependent factors—density-independent factors
d. predation—competition

Reteach
Have students provide an example that shows an understanding of the meaning of each vocabulary word in this section. **L1** **ELL**

Resources
For more practice, use *Reading Essentials for Biology,* Section 4.1.

Extension
Ask students to count the potential offspring (the number of seeds) in one green pepper. **CAUTION:** *Have them wash their hands after handling seeds.* Ask why the world is not covered with green pepper plants. **L2**

 Assessment

Knowledge Provide students with an unlabeled copy of the graph in Figure 4.3. Have them label the parts of the graph. Students should answer the following question. How is a population showing a J curve different from a population showing an S curve? Use the Performance Assessment List for Written Summary of a Graph in PASC, p. 113 **L2**

Section Assessment

1. When limiting factors are variable, species must have strategies to survive over time.
2. short life-history organisms: rapid increase and decline caused by unpredictable environments; long life-history organisms: slow population change within stable environments

and usually maintain sizes near carrying capacity
3. Density-dependent factors have an increasing effect as population size increases. Density-independent factors affect a population no matter its size.
4. Growth curve will be exponential—a J-shaped curve.

5. Decreased food supply can decrease carrying capacity.
6. The graphs should show a rapid life-history pattern. The organism reproduces rapidly and declines rapidly.

1 Focus

INTERACTIVE CHALKBOARD
PowerPoint® Presentations

Bellringer
Section Focus Transparency 9

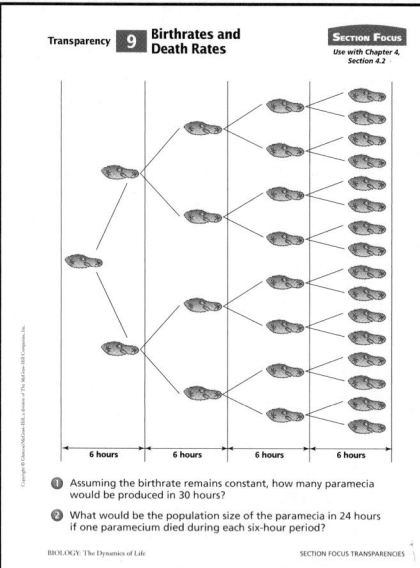

Transparency **9** Birthrates and Death Rates

SECTION FOCUS
Use with Chapter 4, Section 4.2

6 hours 6 hours 6 hours 6 hours

❶ Assuming the birthrate remains constant, how many paramecia would be produced in 30 hours?

❷ What would be the population size of the paramecia in 24 hours if one paramecium died during each six-hour period?

BIOLOGY: The Dynamics of Life   SECTION FOCUS TRANSPARENCIES

Finding the Main Idea

Summarize Students' sentences will vary, but should reflect the main idea of each paragraph. If bold terms occur in the paragraph, they should be used in the summary.

Inquiry

Activity Have students pretend they are demographers. They can work in groups to research changes in population of local communities. Have students use the most recent census data to find out what the population was ten years ago and what it is today. What changes in the community (new industry or the decline of an industry) have affected growth or decline of the populations? Has housing increased or decreased? If so, by how much? **L2**
COOP LEARN

Indiana Academic Standards

Pages 100–101: B.1.37, B.1.41, B.1.43

Section 4.2

Human Population

Indiana Standards Standard B.1.41 Recognize that and describe how human beings are part of Earth's ecosystems. Note that human activities can, deliberately or inadvertently, alter the equilibrium in ecosystems.

SECTION PREVIEW

Objectives
Identify how the birthrate and death rate affect the rate at which a population changes.
Compare the age structure of rapidly growing, slow-growing, and no-growth countries.
Explain the relationship between a population and the environment.

Review Vocabulary
limiting factor: factors that affect an organism's ability to survive in its environment (p. 65)

New Vocabulary
demography
birthrate
death rate
doubling time
age structure

Keeping Track

Finding the Main Idea Can you imagine having the responsibility of keeping track of how many people there are in the world? Why is it important to know how many people there are and where they are located? These are topics discussed in this section. To help you keep track of the information, it might be a good idea to find the main idea discussed in each paragraph.

Summarize As you study, look at each bold head. Then read the information under it carefully. After each paragraph, write one sentence that summarizes the main idea of the paragraph.

World Population

In the United States, a census is taken every ten years. Among other things, this information provides a picture of how many people there are in the United States, their economic condition, and where they live. Worldwide, the United Nations Population Division tracks similar information on all the countries of the world. One of the most useful pieces of data is the rate at which each country's population is growing or declining. These figures are the basis for **demography** (de MAH gra fee), the study of human population size, density and distribution, movement, and its birth and death rates.

What is the history of population growth for humans? *Figure 4.10* summarizes how world human population has grown since 1800. The graph indicates that until the 1800s, human population growth remained fairly slow. Since the 1930s, world population has grown rapidly, reaching 6 billion in 1999. In 2002, the human population was growing at a rate of more than 80 million people per year.

Figure 4.10
It is estimated that it took from the dawn of human history to 1800 for the world's population to reach 1 billion people. Today, there are more than 6 billion people in the world, and scientists estimate that by the year 2050, there will be more than 9 billion people on Earth.

1st billion   2nd billion   3rd billion   4th billion   5th billion   6th billion

1800   1930   1960   1975 1987 1999

100 POPULATION BIOLOGY

RESOURCE MANAGER

Unit 2 FAST FILE Resources
MiniLab Worksheet, p. 74
Reinforcement and Study Guide in English, pp. 79–80
Reinforcement and Study Guide in Spanish, pp. 83–84

Transparency Worksheet, p. 88
Section Focus Transparency 9

Human population growth

What factors affect growth of human population? In Section 1 of this chapter, bacteria and housefly populations were shown to continue to grow so long as they had sufficient resources. Human population growth is different because humans can consciously change their environment. During the past century, humans have eradicated diseases such as smallpox. They have developed methods for producing more food. Infant mortality rate has decreased and technological developments have improved the delivery of clean water. When these factors are accounted for, people live longer and are able to produce offspring that live long enough to produce offspring, hence, a population grows.

Calculating growth rate

There are a number of factors that determine population growth rate. These are births, deaths, immigration and emigration. **Birthrate** is the number of live births per 1000 population in a given year. **Death rate** is the number of deaths per 1000 population in a given year. Movement of individuals into a population is immigration. Movement out of a population is emigration. You can calculate a country's population growth rate with a formula that takes these four factors into account:

(Birthrate + Immigration rate) −
(Death rate + Emigration rate) =
Population Growth Rate (PGR)

For convenience, and because immigration and emigration rates are not always accurate, this formula is often stated as:

Birthrate − Death rate =
Population Growth Rate (PGR)

If the birthrate of a population equals its death rate, then the population growth rate is zero. If the rate is zero, that doesn't mean that the population

isn't changing. Rather, it means that new individuals enter the population (by birth and immigration) at the same rate that individuals are leaving (by death and emigration) the population. The population is changing, but it is stable. If the PGR is above zero, more new individuals are entering the population than are leaving, so the population is growing.

Problem-Solving Lab 4.2

Make and Use Graphs

How is world population changing? Total world population and the rate at which it is growing are predicted to change in the next 50 years. Plotting this information on a graph can provide a visual that tells you how it is predicted to change.

Total Midyear Population for the World 1950–2050			
Year	Population	Year	Population
1950	2 555 360 972	2010	6 812 009 338
1960	3 039 669 330	2015	7 171 736 193
1970	3 708 067 105	2020	7 515 218 898
1980	4 454 607 332	2025	7 834 028 430
1985	4 850 118 838	2030	8 127 277 506
1990	5 275 407 789	2035	8 397 941 844
1995	5 685 286 921	2040	8 646 671 023
2000	6 078 684 329	2045	8 874 116 015
2005	6 448 684 573	2050	9 078 850 714

The table above contains figures from the U.S. Census Bureau and the United Nations Population Bureau that predict world population change through 2050. Graph the data and answer the questions that follow.

Thinking Critically

1. **Analyze Trends from Data** Study your graph and choose the term that best describes the trend that the graph illustrates: Rising, leveling off, or declining. Explain your choice.
2. **Infer** Based on the data in the table, what can you infer happened to the population growth rate after 1985?
3. **Predict Trends from Data** Based on the data predicted for 2010 through 2050, how would you describe world population? Growing? Declining? Stable? Explain your choice.

Problem-Solving Lab 4.2

Purpose
Students will analyze trends in human population changes.

Process Skills
think critically, apply concepts, analyze information, use numbers, draw a conclusion, make and use graphs

Teaching Strategies
■ Review the meanings of density-dependent factors, density-independent factors, and carrying capacity from Chapter 2.
■ Allow students to use calculators.

Thinking Critically
1. Most students will choose *leveling off.* Explanations should include that the growth rate appears to be slowing down.
2. It began to decrease.
3. Growing. The graph keeps climbing. Some may say that it is becoming more stable because the rate of growth is slowing.

Modified Assessment
Knowledge Have students write three questions about this lab and quiz each other. Use the Performance Assessment List for Asking Questions in **PASC**, p. 91. **L1**

 CHALLENGE ACTIVITY

Demographics Students who need an additional challenge can write a computer program that demonstrates demographic trends. Students might interview a computer teacher to discuss variables. **L3**

Purpose

Students will learn the concept of "doubling time" and use a formula to calculate this value.

Process Skills

use numbers, acquire information, analyze information, compare and contrast, predict, recognize cause and effect

Teaching Strategies

■ Organize the class into small groups. Place students with poorer math skills with those who are more skilled.
■ Allow students to use calculators.
■ The value of "70" used in the formula is a constant.

Expected Results

Region A = 29.2 years
       B = 41.2 years
       C = 50.0 years
       D = 140.0 years
Region E's population is presently decreasing and may never double.

Analysis

1. A; D
2. Students may list the high potential for disease, problem with waste disposal, and lack of space and lack of water.

Assessment

Portfolio Have students prepare a bar graph using their calculated values for doubling time. Use the Performance Assessment List for Graph from Data in **PASC**, p. 111. **L2**

Indiana Academic Standards

Pages 102–103: B.1.37, B.1.41, B.1.43

102

Use Numbers

Doubling Time The time needed for any population to double its size is known as its "doubling time." For example, if a population grows slowly, its doubling time will be long. If it is growing rapidly, its doubling time will be short.

Procedure

1 The following formula is used to calculate a population's doubling time:

$$\text{Doubling time (in years)} = \frac{70}{\text{annual percent growth rate}}$$

2 Copy the data table below.

3 Complete the table by calculating the doubling time of human populations for the listed geographic regions.

Data Table		
Geographic Region	Annual Percent Growth Rate	Doubling Time
A	2.4	
B	1.7	
C	1.4	
D	0.5	
E	−0.1	

Analysis

1. **Analyze Trends from Data** Which region has the fastest doubling time? Slowest doubling time?
2. **Predict Trends from Data** What are some ecological implications for an area with a fast doubling time?

A PGR can also be less than zero. In 2002, the population growth rate for Europe was negative (−0.1 percent) as fewer individuals are entering the population than are leaving.

The effect of a positive growth rate

If the world population growth rate in the year 1995 were 1.7 percent and had dropped to 1.3 percent in 2001, the population growth rate would have become lower, but world population would have continued to

---

grow, just at a slower rate. In other words, unless the growth rate becomes negative, the population continues to grow, but just not as rapidly as it did before.

Doubling time

Another quantitative factor that demographers look at is the doubling time of a population. **Doubling time** is the time needed for a population to double in size. The time it takes for a population to double varies depending on the current population and growth rate. A slow or negative growth rate means that it will take a country's population a long time to double in size, if ever. A rapid growth rate indicates that a country's population will double in a shorter time. A country that has a slow doubling time is sometimes categorized as a developed country. One with a rapid doubling time may be referred to as a developing country. Doubling time can be calculated for the world, a country, or even a smaller region, such as a city. Learn how to calculate doubling time in the *MiniLab* on this page.

Age structure

Have you ever filled out a survey? Often, one of the questions is about age. Are you between the ages of 10 and 14? 15 and 19? 20 and 24? The survey is trying to pinpoint where you are in the age structure of the population. **Age structure** refers to the proportions of the population that are in different age levels. Based on information from population counts, an age structure graph has been constructed for every country in the world. Look at the age structure graphs in *Figure 4.11*. An age structure graph can tell you approximately how many males and females there are in a population, and how many people there are at each age level. Rapidly growing countries have age structures with a wide base because a large

---

USING MODELS

Age Structure Charts Have students study the age structure charts in Figure 4.11. Tell students that the shape of the models will change as time passes because the populations at the bottom age groups are always moving up into the next age levels. If the population growth rate in a rapidly growing country remains the same, what will the shape of the age structure chart be when people in the 15–19 year level reach the 45–49 year level? **L2**

102

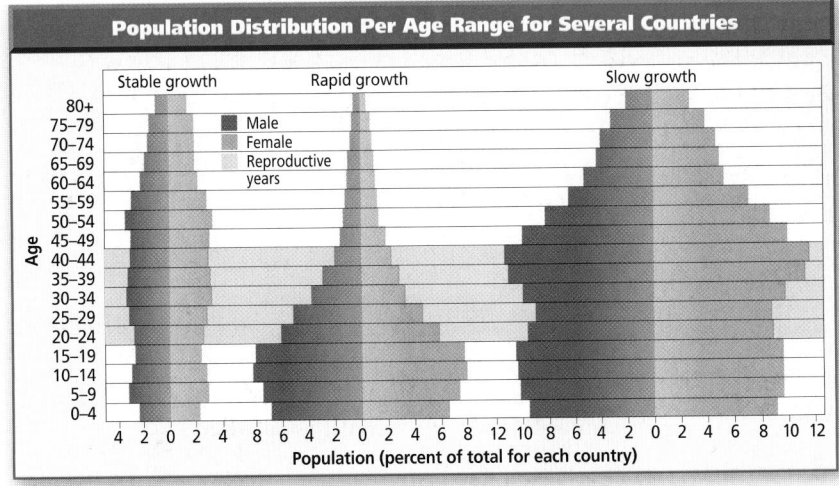

Population Distribution Per Age Range for Several Countries

Stable growth   Rapid growth   Slow growth

Male
Female
Reproductive
years

Age

80+
75–79
70–74
65–69
60–64
55–59
50–54
45–49
40–44
35–39
30–34
25–29
20–24
15–19
10–14
5–9
0–4

Population (percent of total for each country)

Figure 4.11
Notice that in a rapid growth country the large number of individuals in the "Under 5 Through 14 years" will add significantly to the population when they reach age 15. Populations that are not growing or are stable have an almost even distribution of ages among the population.

Check for Understanding
Have students explain the relationship between the words in each of the following pairs. **L1** **ELL**
a. population growth—birth and death rate
b. age of population—population growth

Reteach
Ask students to explain how a high fertility rate with low death rate will influence a population's size. Population will increase. **L2**

Resources
For more practice, use *Reading Essentials for Biology*, Section 4.2.

Extension
Have students research and contrast the immigration patterns of two countries. How have these countries' populations been affected by immigration? **L3**

 Assessment

Performance Currently, the human population shows a J-shaped growth pattern. Have students write a paragraph that expresses their opinion as to whether the human population will ever become S-shaped and what will cause it to become so. **L2**

percentage of the population is made up of children and teenagers. If the percentage of people in each age category is fairly equal, the population is stable.

Ecology and growth

The needs of populations differ greatly throughout the world. Some countries are concerned about providing the most basic needs for their growing population. Other, more stable growth populations are concerned about maintaining the healthy conditions that they already have.

What do populations need? Think about the resources that humans depend upon every day. Some of these resources might be uncontaminated water for drinking and agriculture, adequate sewage facilities, and the ability to provide food for a growing population.

Sometimes, a population grows more rapidly than the available resources can handle. Resources that are needed for life, such as food and water, become scarce or contaminated. The amount of waste produced by a population becomes difficult to dispose of properly. These conditions can lead to stress on current resources and contribute to the spread of diseases that affect the stability of human populations both now and to come.

Section Assessment

Understanding Main Ideas
1. What characteristics of populations do demographers study? Why?

2. How do birthrate and death rate each affect the growth of a population?

3. What clues can an age structure graph provide about the future of a country's population growth?

4. Explain the relationship between a growing population and the environment.

Thinking Critically
5. Suggest reasons why the lack of available clean water could be a limiting factor for a country's population.

SKILL REVIEW
6. **Make and Use Graphs** Construct a bar graph showing the age structure of Kenya using the following data: pre-reproductive years (0–14)—42 percent; reproductive years (15–44)—39 percent; post-reproductive years (45–85+)—19 percent. For more help, refer to *Make and Use Graphs* in the **Skill Handbook.**

in.bdol.glencoe.com/self_check_quiz

4.2 HUMAN POPULATION **103**

Section Assessment

1. Demographers study growth rate, age structure, and geographic distribution to predict changes in human populations.
2. Both rates must be taken into account; birthrates are usually lower in developed countries.
3. It can determine if a population is growing rapidly, slowly, or not at all.
4. Growing populations will eventually stress the environment and encounter limiting factors.
5. Clean water is necessary for health. Without it, the death rate increases.
6. Evaluate students' graphs for logic and accuracy.

INVESTIGATE BioLab

Time Allotment
one class period

Process Skills
apply concepts, collect data, experiment, formulate models, interpret data, predict, use numbers, write about biology

Safety Precautions
Have students wash their hands after handling the bean seeds.

PREPARATION

- Prepare bags in advance. Place 150–175 beans in each bag.
- Shortcut to counting beans—count out 165 beans. Then determine the volume of this number of beans by placing them into a graduated cylinder. Read the volume and use this as a guide in preparing the other bags. All bags do not have to have the same number of beans.
- Remove all marked beans from the bag at the end of each class and replace with unmarked beans.

INVESTIGATE BioLab

Before You Begin
In the field, scientists determine the number of animals in a large population by sampling. They trap and mark a few animals in a specified area. The animals are released and the traps are reset. Scientists wait a period of time before they retrap. This time allows organisms to mix randomly into the population again. Among the animals caught the second time, some will already be marked and some will be unmarked. Scientists then calculate the total population based on the ratio of marked animals to unmarked animals.

How can you determine the size of an animal population?

PREPARATION

Problem
How can you model a field-measuring technique to determine the size of an animal population?

Objectives
In this BioLab, you will:
- **Model,** using a simulation, a procedure used to measure an animal population.
- **Collect** data on a modeled animal population.
- **Calculate** the size of a modeled animal population.

Materials
paper bag containing beans
calculator (optional)
permanent marker (dark color)

Safety Precautions
CAUTION: *Always wear goggles in the lab. Wash hands with soap and water after working with plant material and after clean up.*

Skill Handbook
If you need help with this lab, refer to the **Skill Handbook.**

PROCEDURE

1. Copy the data table.
2. Reach into your bag and remove 20 beans.
3. Use the marker to color these beans. They represent *caught* and *marked* animals.
4. When the ink has dried, return the beans to the bag.
5. Shake the bag. Without looking into the bag, reach in and remove 30 beans.
6. Record the number of marked beans (recaught and marked) and the number of unmarked beans (caught and unmarked) in your data table as trial 1.
7. Return all the beans to the bag.

PROCEDURE

Teaching Strategies
- Do not tell students the total number of beans in each bag.
- Any type of marker is suitable. Make sure the color contrasts with the bean color. Make sure all sides of the bean are colored.

- The number of beans removed in step 5 does not have to be exactly 30 but should be close.
- Review the technique for calculating an average.

Data and Observations
Sample data may appear as shown on page 105.

8. Repeat steps 5 to 7 four more times for trials 2 to 5.

9. Calculate averages for each of the columns.

10. Using average values, calculate the original size of the bean population in the bag by using the following formula:
M = number initially marked
CwM = average number caught with marks
Cw/oM = average number caught without marks

$$\frac{\text{Calculated}}{\text{Population Size}} = \frac{M \times (CwM + Cw/oM)}{CwM}$$

11. Record the *calculated population size* in the data table.

12. To verify the *actual population size*, count all the beans in the bag and record this value in the data table.

13. CLEANUP AND DISPOSAL   Make wise choices as to how you will dispose of the beans. Can some be recycled?

Data Table

Trial	Total Caught	Number Caught With Marks	Number Caught Without Marks
1	30		
2	30		
3	30		
4	30		
5	30		
Averages	30		

Calculated population size = _____

Actual population size = _____

ANALYZE AND CONCLUDE

1. Think Critically Explain why this type of activity is best done as a simulation.

2. ERROR ANALYSIS Compare the calculated to the actual population size. Explain why they may not agree exactly. What changes to the procedure would improve the accuracy of the activity?

3. Make Inferences Explain why this technique is used more often with animals than with plants when calculating population size.

4. Make Predictions Assume you were doing this experiment with living animals. What would you be doing in step 2? Step 3? Step 5?

Apply Your Skill

Field Investigation Assume that you are a field biologist on an island. Plan investigative procedures, including selecting equipment, to determine the deer population on the island.

 Web Links To find out more about ecology field research, visit in.bdol.glencoe.com/ecology

ANALYZE AND CONCLUDE

1. It would take more time and be more difficult if done in the field.

2. ERROR ANALYSIS   The calculated value is based on counting a representation of the population. To increase the accuracy of the activity, one could increase the number of trials, the number of animals re-caught, or the number of animals caught and marked.

3. Plants do not move about and so are easier to count.

4. Step 2, capture animals in cages, step 3, tag or mark the animals in some manner, step 5, reset traps and capture more animals.

Assessment

Skill Provide students with raw data and have them calculate the size of a population. Use the Performance Task Assessment List for Using Math in Science in **PASC**, p. 101. **L3**

Apply Your Skill

Field Investigation Check to be sure that students have an adequate plan and that they have taken into account proper statistical techniques to determine the deer population.

Data Table

Trial	Total caught	Number caught with marks	Number caught without marks
1	30	3	27
2	30	2	28
3	30	5	25
4	30	4	26
5	30	6	24
Totals	150	20	130
Average	30	4	26

Calculated population size = __150__

Actual population size = __160__

(This number will vary per bag.)

Purpose

Students will find out some advantages and disadvantages of a commonly used plastic called polystyrene.

Teaching Strategies

■ Use a dozen colored, plastic-coated paper clips to demonstrate how monomers link to form polymers. Make a chain with two alternating colors. Have a volunteer identify the monomers. If time allows, have students consult basic chemistry books to make models of complex plastic polymers.

■ Have students survey plastic containers at home or at stores to determine some of the many uses of polystyrene. Inform them that plastics labeled with the number "6" are polystyrene. Compile a master list of uses, which might include yogurt, cottage cheese, and sour cream containers; audiocassette boxes; frozen dinner trays; toy parts; picnic tableware; and others. **L1 ELL**

■ Have students suggest several situations in which disposable tableware would benefit those using it. Answers might include hospitals, where the transmission of pathogens can be a problem to patients (especially those with immunodeficiency diseases), or in school cafeterias, where cleaning reusable dishes, glasses, and cutlery might be cost prohibitive. **L2**

Connection to Biology

Environmentalists are concerned about widespread use of plastics and dependence on single-use items. An advantage of polystyrene is that it helps keep diseases from spreading. A disadvantage is that it does not break down in a short time.

106

Polymers for People

Polymerization is the process in which single molecules of a substance are joined chemically to form long chains called polymers. One polymer that has had a great affect on modern life is polystyrene. Because of polystyrene, we have numerous disposable plastic items in our lives, from plastic grocery bags to jewel cases for CDs.

Polystyrene, in the form of foamed plastic, is about 98 percent air. It is made by blowing tiny air-containing holes, called cells, into a polymer. In the beginning, chlorofluorocarbons, or CFCs, were used to make the cells. In the 1980s, CFCs were outlawed for this and other processes. Since then, most foamed polystyrene has been made using pentane as the blowing agent.

Polystyrene products Foam beverage cups and plates, plastic utensils, some packaging "peanuts," insulation, and many disposable pieces of medical equipment are made from polystyrene. In the food service industry, polystyrene products keep hot foods hot and cold foods cold. These products are popular for their health safety because they are used once and thrown away. This feature reduces the chance of contamination and transmission of disease.

Because of all of its positive characteristics, polystyrene is used extensively. However, the edges of highways and our landfills reflect its widespread use by a growing population. Foamed plastic, as it currently exists, is not biodegradable within a reasonable amount of time. How can the problems created by mass disposal of items made from polystyrene be avoided? Is there a way to make a biodegradable plastic bag, a CD case, toy, or toothbrush?

Biodegradable products For something to be biodegradable, it has to be able to be broken down into simpler components by decomposers. Polystyrene can be broken down, but it takes a long time for that to happen. Is there anything that can be broken down more quickly?

Corn into plastic Have you ever worn a shirt made out of corn resin? Research for more environmentally-friendly substances is an on-going project. Since the 1980s, manufacturing processes for turning corn starch and corn fibers into useful products have become a reality. Corn-based packing "peanuts" have been developed. Molded bottles are being manufactured for use in short-term shelf products such as milk. The hope is that these products and others will conserve fossil fuels, be quickly biodegradable, and therefore, more environmentally friendly. Markets for corn-based polymers are similar to those for petroleum-based polystyrene products—leaf and lawn bags, food packaging, and textiles for clothing. Research is ongoing with regard to how well microorganisms break down the materials.

Writing About Biology

Research Find out about alternative biodegradable materials being developed for the purpose of conserving fossil fuels and for making landfills more useful. Evaluate the impact of polymers by surveying your own home for them. Compare your findings with those of your classmates.

 To find out more about plastics and biodegradable products and their role in the environment, visit in.bdol.glencoe.com/chemistry

---

Writing About Biology

Student findings will vary, but should include a variety of alternate materials. Students are likely to identify many polymers in their homes.

Chapter 4 Assessment

Chapter 4 Assessment

STUDY GUIDE

Section 4.1

Population Dynamics

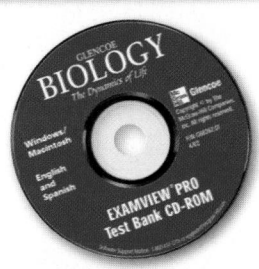

Key Concepts

- Populations of some organisms do not exhibit linear growth. If there is nothing to stop or slow growth, a population's growth appears as a J-shaped curve on a graph.

- Populations grow slowly at first, then more rapidly as more and more individuals begin to reproduce.

- Under normal conditions, with limiting factors, populations show an S-shaped curve as they approach the carrying capacity of the environment where they live.

- If a population overshoots the environment's carrying capacity, deaths exceed births and the total population falls below the environment's carrying capacity. The number of individuals will fluctuate above and below the carrying capacity.

- Density-dependent factors and density-independent factors affect population growth. Density-dependent factors include disease, competition for space, water, and food supply. Density-independent factors are volcanic eruptions and changes in climate that result in catastrophic incidents such as floods, drought, hurricanes, or tornadoes.

Vocabulary

carrying capacity (p. 93)
density-dependent factor (p. 97)
density-independent factor (p. 97)
exponential growth (p. 93)
life-history pattern (p. 93)

Section 4.2

Human Population

Key Concepts

- Demography is the study of population characteristics such as growth rate, age structure, and movement of individuals.

- Birthrate, death rate, immigration, emigration, doubling time, and age structures differ considerably among different countries. There are uneven population growth patterns throughout the world.

Vocabulary

age structure (p. 102)
birthrate (p. 101)
death rate (p. 101)
demography (p. 100)
doubling time (p. 102)

FOLDABLES
Study Organizer To help you review population biology, use the Organizational Study Fold on page 91.

 in.bdol.glencoe.com/vocabulary_puzzlemaker

CHAPTER 4 ASSESSMENT **107**

Key Concepts

Summary statements can be used by students to review the major concepts of the chapter.

 Biology Online

Visit in.bdol.glencoe.com
/self_check_quiz
/vocabulary_puzzlemaker
/chapter_test
/standardized_test

VOCABULARY PUZZLEMAKER

 For additional help with vocabulary, have students access the Vocabulary PuzzleMaker online at in.bdol.glencoe.com/vocabulary_puzzlemaker

FOLDABLES™

Have students use their Foldables to review the content of Section 4.1. On the back of the Foldables, decide whether you think there are limits to the human population on Earth. Students should defend their responses.

Use the Exam*View*®Pro Test Bank CD-ROM to:

- Create **multiple versions** of tests
- Create **modified** tests for **inclusion** students with one mouse click
- **Edit** existing questions and **add** your own questions
- Build tests aligned with state standards using built-in **State Curriculum Tags**
- Change **English** tests to **Spanish** with one mouse click and vice versa

 Indiana Academic Standards

Pages 106–107: B.1.37, B.1.41, B.1.43

The Princeton Review *Questions and answers have been aligned and verified by The Princeton Review.*

Vocabulary Review

1. Birthrate is live births per 1000 per year; death rate is the number of deaths per 1000 per year.
2. Density-dependent factors depend on the size of a population within a particular area. Density-independent factors do not.
3. Life-history pattern is the reproductive pattern of a population. Age structure is the percentage of individuals at various ages.
4. Population is the number of individuals of a species in a given area at a given time. Demography is the study of population trends.
5. limiting factor: any factor in the environment that limits a population's size; carrying capacity: the upper limit of a population's size that an environment can maintain

Understanding Key Concepts

6. C   7. D   8. C
9. C

Constructed Response

10. The population may have experienced an outbreak of disease and recovered. If the population has a rapid growth pattern, the food may have declined in one area, forcing a decline in population until a new food source emerged.
11. Doubling time would give information about time needed for new roads, sewers, etc.
12. Age structure gives information about how many stu-

Vocabulary Review

Review the Chapter 4 vocabulary words listed in the Study Guide on page 107. Distinguish between the vocabulary words in each pair.

1. birthrate—death rate
2. density-dependent factor—density-independent factor
3. life-history pattern—age structure
4. population—demography
5. limiting factor—carrying capacity

Understanding Key Concepts

6. Describe what is happening to the growth of the population shown at interval **3** in the diagram below.
   A. slow growth
   B. exponential or rapid growth
   C. slowing growth reaching carrying capacity
   D. population reaching equilibrium near carrying capacity

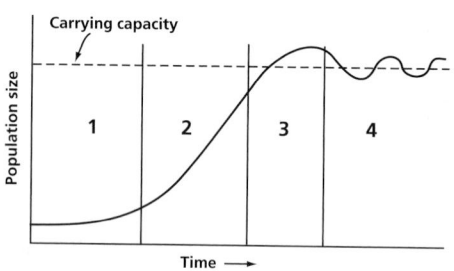

7. Which organisms would be most affected by density-independent factors?
   A. cats
   B. humans
   C. houseflies
   D. deer

8. When plotted on a graph, a population of field mice over time shows a J-shaped curve. This indicates that _____.
   A. the population is decreasing
   B. predators of the mice are increasing
   C. there may be no predators
   D. food supply is low

9. When populations increase, resource depletion may bring about _____.
   A. exponential growth
   B. straight-line growth
   C. increased competition
   D. decreased competition

Constructed Response

10. **Open Ended** A population of animals shows a sudden decline and then recovers. Using ecological principles, discuss two specific reasons why this might occur.
11. **Open Ended** Give at least two reasons why it would be important for the planning board of a city to know the city's doubling time.
12. **Open Ended** For what reasons would a school board need to refer to an age structure chart of the local community when planning a five year budget?

Thinking Critically

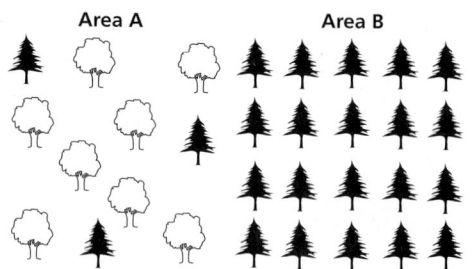

13. **Analyze** Using the diagram above, identify the factor that would cause more trees in Area B to be affected by an invasion of disease-carrying insects than in Area A. Explain your choice.
14. **Infer** Are predators a density-dependent or density-independent limiting factor for the population growth of their prey? Explain.
15. **Infer** Why are short life-history species, such as mosquitoes and some weeds, successful, even though they often experience massive population declines?

 in.bdol.glencoe.com/chapter_test

dents to expect and what supplies and facilities will be needed.

Thinking Critically

13. The large, densely packed population of the same species would cause the insects to spread more quickly and cause greater damage in Area B.

14. Predators are a density-dependent factor because the density of prey limits the population size of the predators.
15. Because their populations can quickly take advantage of favorable environments, they tend to move from place to place having large population fluctuations.

16. **REAL WORLD BIOCHALLENGE** Every 10 years the United States is required by law to complete a census. Visit **in.bdol.glencoe.com** to find out about the most recent census. Pretend that you are a demographer for your state. What change, if any, occurred in the population of your state from 1990 to 2000? Display these changes on a map. Determine if your state's population is growing, declining, or has reached stability. Research and explain your choice.

End-of-Course Assessment Practice

The assessed Indiana standard appears next to the question.

All questions aligned and verified by *The Princeton Review*

Part 1 Multiple Choice

Use the graph below to answer questions 17 and 18.

Number of Colonies of a Bacterium Grown at Different Temperatures

17. A bacterial species was grown at different
B.1.43 temperatures represented in the graph above by cultures 1 through 4. From the graph, identify the culture for which temperature was the greatest limiting factor.
   A. 1
   B. 2
   C. 3
   D. 4

18. Which culture showed the greatest growth rate?
   A. 1   C. 3
   B. 2   D. 4

Use the following diagram to answer questions 19 and 20.

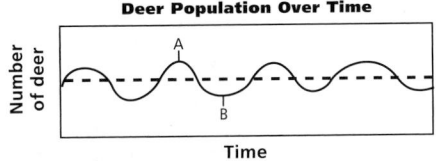

Deer Population Over Time

19. The dotted line in the graph above represents
B.1.40 the _____ for the deer population.
   A. death rate   C. carrying capacity
   B. birthrate   D. age structure

20. The solid curve in the graph from point A
B.1.40 to point B indicates that _____.
   A. more deer are dying than being born
   B. more deer are being born than are dying
   C. there are not enough predators
   D. no limiting factors are at work

Part 2 Constructed Response/Grid In

Record your answers on your answer document.

21. **Open Ended** A small group of mice invaded a new habitat with unlimited resources and their
B.1.40 population grew rapidly. A flood then swept through the habitat and three quarters of the mice were lost. Two months later, the population was increasing again. What role did the flood play for the mouse population? Draw a graph depicting the population history of this group.

22. **Open Ended** What is the relationship between a population and a species?

23. **Open Ended** Water hyacinth populations double in 6 to 18 days. Introduced in the 1880s, populations of this plant have clogged major waterways in several states. No predators for it exist in the United States. Does this species have a J-shaped or an S-shaped growth pattern? Explain your choice.

 in.bdol.glencoe.com/standardized_test

16. Students will create a map that shows increase and decrease in the population for different areas of the state. Reasons for the shifts may be job availability, price of housing, and availability of medical care among many others.

RUBRIC

For more help evaluating open-ended assessment questions, see the rubric on p. 9T.

End-of-Course Assessment Practice

17. D   19. C
18. C   20. A

21. The flood is a limiting factor. Many mice may have drowned. Graphs should initially show a steep increase beginning from a zero point, then a vertical drop with the flood reducing the population by 75 percent, then a slow increase followed by a steep increase.

22. A population refers to the number of organisms of a single species in a particular area. There may be many populations of the same species.

23. With no natural enemies in the area, growth will be unchecked and will have a J-shaped curve.

 FAST FILE

Answer Sheet A practice answer sheet can be found on p. 97 of *Unit 2 FAST FILE Resources.*

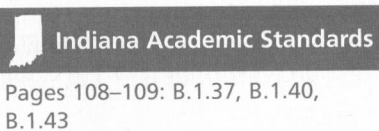

Indiana Academic Standards

Pages 108–109: B.1.37, B.1.40, B.1.43

Chapter 5 Organizer

Section Objectives	National Science Standards	State/Local Standards	Advanced Lab and Demo Planning
Section 5.1 2 sessions, 1 block 1. **Explain** biodiversity and its importance. 2. **Relate** various threats to the loss of biodiversity.	UCP.1–3; A.1, A.2; C.4, C.5, C.6; E.1, E.2; F.1–6; G.1–3	**Indiana Standards** B.1.37, B.1.38, B.1.41, B.1.43, B.1.45, B.1.46	**Student Labs:** MiniLab 5.1, p. 112 Problem-Solving Lab 5.1, p. 115 Additional Lab, p. 118: self-sealing plastic bags, paper toweling, small cups, labels, water, vinegar, small seeds **Teacher Demonstration:** Quick Demo, p. 117: cardboard, masking tape
Section 5.2 2 sessions, 1 block 3. **Describe** strategies used in conservation biology. 4. **Relate** success in protecting an endangered species to the methods used to protect it	UCP.1–3; A.1, A.2; C.4, C.5, C.6; E.1, E.2; F.2–6; G.1–3	**Indiana Standards** B.1.38, B.1.41, B.1.43, B.1.45, B.1.46, B.1.47	**Student Labs:** MiniLab 5.2, p. 122: 200 mL water, beaker, tray, soil, dish, graduated cylinder Problem-Solving Lab 5.2, p. 124 Internet BioLab, p. 126: See materials below. **Teacher Demonstration:** Quick Demo, p. 124: gingko leaves
End of Chapter Assessment **Student Edition** **Study Guide**, p. 129 **Content Assessment**, pp. 130–131		**Indiana Standards** B.1.37, B.1.41, B.1.43, B.1.45	**Student Lab:** Internet BioLab, p. 126: access to the Internet

Key to Teaching Strategies

L1 Level 1 activities should be appropriate for students with learning difficulties.

L2 Level 2 activities should be within the ability range of all students.

L3 Level 3 activities are designed for above-average students.

ELL ELL activities should be within the ability range of English Language Learners.

COOP LEARN Cooperative Learning activities are designed for small group work.

Legend

 Transparency   CD-ROM   MP3   ▦ Videocassette   ⊙ DVD

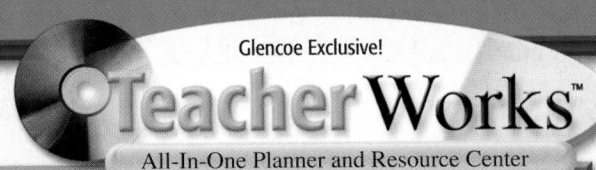
Glencoe Exclusive!
Teacher Works™
All-In-One Planner and Resource Center

Reproducible Masters and Transparencies

Unit 2 FAST FILE Resources
MiniLab Worksheet, pp. 101–102
BioLab Worksheet, pp. 105–106
Real World BioApplications, pp. 107–108
Reinforcement and Study Guide in English, pp. 111–113
Reinforcement and Study Guide in Spanish, pp. 115–117
Concept Mapping, p. 119
Critical Thinking/Problem Solving, p. 120
Transparency Worksheets, pp. 121, 123–128
Reading Essentials for Biology, Section 5.1
Laboratory Manual, pp. 23–24
Probeware Labs, pp. 9–12
Section Focus Transparency 10
Reteaching Skills Transparencies 7a, 7b, 7c

Unit 2 FAST FILE Resources
MiniLab Worksheet, p. 103
Real World BioApplications, pp. 109–110
Reinforcement and Study Guide in English, p. 114
Reinforcement and Study Guide in Spanish, p. 118
Transparency Worksheet, p. 122
Reading Essentials for Biology, Section 5.2
Section Focus Transparency 11

Unit 2 FAST FILE Resources
Chapter Assessment, p. 129
Student Recording Sheet, p. 135

The Princeton Review **Reviewing Biology,** pp. 9–10

Technology

⊙ **Interactive Chalkboard CD-ROM: Section 5.1 Presentation**
⊙ **Teacher Works™ CD-ROM**
♪ **Guided Reading Audio Summaries MP3**
⊙ **Virtual Labs CD-ROM**
    Virtual Lab: Assessing Water Quality

⊙ **Interactive Chalkboard CD-ROM: Section 5.2 Presentation**
⊙ **Teacher Works™ CD-ROM**
♪ **Guided Reading Audio Summaries MP3**

⊙ **Interactive Chalkboard: Chapter 5 Assessment**
⊙ **MindJogger Videoquizzes DVD/VHS**
⊙ **ExamView® Pro Test Bank CD-ROM**
⊙ **Teacher Works™ CD-ROM**
⊙ **Succeeding on National Standards CD-ROM**

🖥 in.bdol.glencoe.com
/self_check_quiz
/vocabulary_puzzlemaker
/chapter_test
/standardized_test

▮ Indicates materials created specifically for Indiana.

Biological Diversity and Conservation

Short on Time?

BIODIGEST The BioDigest at the end of this unit can be used as a(n):

- preview to introduce important unit concepts.
- overview if time does not permit teaching the entire chapter.
- review of key unit concepts.

Understanding the Photo

Use this photo to emphasize that even in places where environmental conditions don't seem to foster or protect life, a variety of living things thrive. The tundra may not have as many species as some other biomes, but the ones that are there are well adapted to the conditions. The lichens and the low-growing plants (not more than about 20 cm in height) like those shown, summers with plenty of moisture from snowmelt, large grazing animals, migratory birds, and an abundant supply of insects for the birds to feed upon, add up to a substantial representation of organism biodiversity.

Using Prior Knowledge

To help students relate to biodiversity, have them review the six major biomes in Chapter 3. In a chart, they can list each biome and summarize the nature of the plants and animals found there. Are there many or few? Have students give each biome a numeric rank of 1 through 6, with 1 for the biome containing the greatest biodiversity.

What You'll Learn

- You will explain the importance of biological diversity.
- You will distinguish environmental changes that may result in the loss of species.
- You will describe the work of conservation biologists.

Why It's Important

When all the members of a species die, that species is gone forever. Knowledge of biological diversity leads to strategies to protect the permanent loss of species from Earth.

Understanding the Photo ▶

In the tundra in the fall, carpets of brilliant red bearberry plants stretch for miles in all directions. These plants, along with dwarf blueberries, crowberry, and bog rosemary, are some of the producers on which tundra animals depend. The tundra ecosystem would change significantly if this selection of plants were to disappear. The other plantlike organisms shown are varieties of reindeer lichen.

Biology Online

Visit in.bdol.glencoe.com **to**
- study the entire chapter online
- access Web Links for more information and activities on biological diversity and conservation
- review content with the Interactive Tutor and self-check quizzes

Two-Minute Chapter Launcher

Demo Hold up a photograph of a nature scene. Ask students to identify common organisms in the photograph. Have them estimate the number of species in the photograph. Explain that this chapter is about species, how and why different species live in different areas of Earth, and how species can be protected from extinction.

Section 5.1

Vanishing Species

Indiana Standards Standard **B.1.41** Recognize that and describe how human beings are part of Earth's ecosystems. **Note that human activities can, deliberately or inadvertently, alter the equilibrium in ecosystems.**

SECTION PREVIEW

Objectives

Explain biodiversity and its importance.

Relate various threats to the loss of biodiversity.

Review Vocabulary

habitat: the place where an organism lives out its life (p. 42)

New Vocabulary

biodiversity
extinction
endangered species
threatened species
habitat fragmentation
edge effect
habitat degradation
acid precipitation
ozone layer
exotic species

FOLDABLES™
Study Organizer

Biodiversity Make the following Foldable to help you identify main ideas about biodiversity.

STEP 1 **Fold** the top of a vertical piece of paper down and the bottom up to divide the paper into thirds.

STEP 2 **Turn** the paper horizontally. **Unfold and label** the three columns as shown.

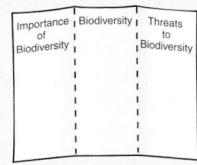

| Importance of Biodiversity | Biodiversity | Threats to Biodiversity |

Read for Main Ideas Write a definition of biodiversity in the center column. Then, as you read Chapter 5, list factors that make biodiversity important in the left column, and list threats to biodiversity in the right column.

Biological Diversity

A rain forest has a greater amount of biological diversity, or biodiversity, than a cornfield. **Biodiversity** refers to the variety of species in a specific area. The simplest and most common measure of biodiversity is the number of different species that live in a certain area. For example, a hectare of farmland, like the one in *Figure 5.1B*, is dominated by one species of plant—corn. In contrast, one hectare of a rain forest may contain 400 species of plants. The cornfield also may contain hundreds of species of insects and several species of birds, but the rain forest may have thousands of species of insects and hundreds of species of birds.

Figure 5.1
A temperate rain forest in Washington state **(A)** and a cornfield **(B)** have different biodiversities.

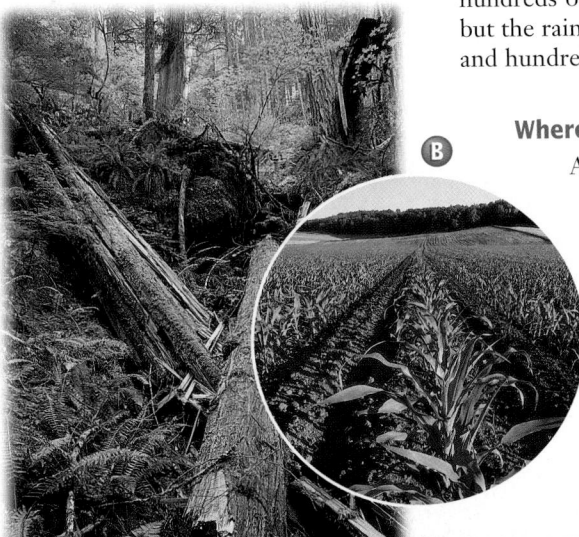

Where is biodiversity found?

Areas around the world differ in biodiversity. A hectare of tropical rain forest in Amazonian Peru may have 300 tree species, while one hectare of temperate deciduous forest in the United States is more likely to have only 30 tree species. Therefore, the tropical rain forest has more biodiversity. Biodiversity increases as you move toward the equator. Tropical regions contain two-thirds of all land species on Earth.

5.1   VANISHING SPECIES   **111**

1 Focus

INTERACTIVE CHALKBOARD
PowerPoint® Presentations

Bellringer
Section Focus Transparency 10

Transparency **10** Protecting Wildlife — SECTION FOCUS — Use with Chapter 5, Section 5.1

① Why are animals kept in zoos?

② What are some problems of keeping animals in zoos?

BIOLOGY: The Dynamics of Life — SECTION FOCUS TRANSPARENCIES

INTERACTIVE CHALKBOARD
with Image Bank

PowerPoint® Presentations

This CD-ROM is an editable Microsoft® PowerPoint® presentation that includes:
- Section presentations
- Section checks
- Image bank
- Hot links to Biology Online
- All transparencies

FOLDABLES™

For an additional Foldables activity idea, see the Chapter 5 Foldables page in *Unit 2 FAST FILE Resources.*

RESOURCE MANAGER

Unit 2 *FAST FILE* Resources
MiniLab Worksheet, pp. 101–102
BioLab Worksheet, pp. 105–106
Real World BioApplications, pp. 107–108
Reinforcement and Study Guide in English, pp. 111–113
Reinforcement and Study Guide in Spanish, pp. 115–117
Concept Mapping, p. 119

Critical Thinking/Problem Solving, p. 120
Transparency Worksheets, pp. 121, 123–128
Laboratory Manual, pp. 23–24
Probeware Labs, pp. 9–12
Section Focus Transparency 10
Reteaching Skills Transparencies 7a, 7b, 7c

Indiana Academic Standards

Pages 110–111: B.1.43, B.1.45

111

MiniLab 5.1

Purpose

Students will survey an area near school and calculate an index of diversity (I.D.).

Process Skills

apply concepts, collect data, compare and contrast, interpret data, observe and infer, organize data, predict, use numbers

Safety Precautions

Check site ahead of time for any hazards (poison ivy, etc.). Students need to be within eyesight of teacher.

Teaching Strategies

■ The study can be conducted as a field trip.

■ If possible, locate and mark off an area that contains about 10 trees of different species. The trees do not have to be in a straight line but will have to be marked so they can be numbered in order of observation.

■ If a field trip is not possible, provide students with a map of trees labeled by species.

Expected Results

An index below one (decimals) indicates a low index of diversity. An index over 1 shows greater diversity. A typical city street may yield an I.D. of slightly over 1.

Analysis

1. A vacant lot might have a higher I.D. because many different species might be present in a small area. A grass lawn with only one species would have a much lower I.D.

2. A higher I.D. would indicate greater species diversity. Communities with a low I.D. are more vulnerable if environmental conditions change.

MiniLab 5.1

Measure Species Diversity

Field Investigation
Index of diversity (I.D.) is a mathematical way of expressing the biodiversity and species distribution in a community. As you collect data, take care not to disturb the environment.

A tree-lined street

Procedure

1. Copy the data table below.

2. Survey a city block or an area designated by your teacher and in your data table, record the number of different species of trees present.

3. Survey the area again. This time, make a list of the trees by assigning each a number as you walk by it. Place an X under Tree 1 on your list. If Tree 2 is the same species as Tree 1, mark an X below it. Continue to mark an X under the trees as long as the species is the same as the previous one. When a different species is encountered, mark an O under that tree on your list. Continue to mark an O if the next tree is the same species as the previous. If the next tree is different, mark an X.

4. Record in your data table:

   a. the number of "runs." Runs are represented by a group of similar symbols in a row. Example: XXOOOXO would be 4 runs (XX = first run, OOO = second run, X = third run, O = fourth run).

   b. the total number of trees counted.

5. Calculate the I.D. using the formula in the data table.

Index of Diversity	
Number of species =	
Number of runs =	
Number of trees =	
Index of diversity =	$\dfrac{\text{Number of species} \times \text{number of runs}}{\text{Number of trees}}$

Analysis

1. **Analyze Trends from Data** Compare how your tree I.D. might compare with that of a vacant lot and with that of a grass lawn. Explain.

2. **Make Inferences from Data** Would it be best to have a relatively low I.D. or high I.D. for an environment? Explain your answer.

112 BIOLOGICAL DIVERSITY AND CONSERVATION

The richest environments for biodiversity all seem to be warm places: tropical rain forests, coral reefs, and large tropical lakes. Learn one way to measure species diversity in the *MiniLab* on this page.

Studying biodiversity

How do ecologists perform experiments related to biodiversity? The study of islands has led to an understanding of factors that influence biodiversity. In the 1960s, an investigation was devised for testing the development of biodiversity on islands. The scientists thought that using a miniaturized situation such as very small islands would help them see clearly what changes take place when organisms move into or out of a defined area. To do this, the scientists selected some small islands of mangrove trees off the coast of Florida like those in *Figure 5.2*. They counted the number of insect and spider species that were on each island, and then removed all the existing species from the islands except for the trees. Then they observed the following as organisms moved back onto the islands.

1. Insects and spiders returned first.

2. The farther away the island was from the source of the new species (the mainland), the longer it took for the island to be recolonized.

3. Eventually, the islands had about the same number of species that they had originally, but the makeup of the community was now different from the original community.

The scientists also saw that the larger the island, the more habitats and species it seemed to have, implying that the number of species depends on the number of habitats.

Research like this is not simple to do. Today you can read about projects in rain forests that require

---

Assessment

Knowledge Ask students why a city with one major industry may suffer in a downturn in that industry, whereas a city with a diverse industrial base can withstand a downturn. Compare this to biodiversity and loss of species in an area with only one type of tree. Use the Performance Task Assessment List for Making Observations and Inferences in **PASC**, p. 89. **L2**

Figure 5.2
Size may be an important factor in the level of biodiversity that an island can support. Research on red mangrove islets off the coast of Florida showed that the larger the island, the greater its biodiversity.

Enrichment

The biodiversity experiment on red mangrove (*Rhizophora mangle*) islands (shown in Figure 5.2) is described as *biogeography*—the science of the distribution of plants and animals. Have students relate biogeography with biomes that they studied in Chapter 3. The experiment described on the previous page is the work of Edward O. Wilson, a renowned ecologist. The experiment is recounted in his autobiography, *Naturalist*, Warner Books, 1995.

scientists to work more than 30 meters up in the canopy while they collect species that live only at that level. Other researchers catalogue the organisms that live in coral reefs, and others attach radio collars to deer. Still others work in laboratories comparing the DNA of members of isolated populations to see how or if these populations might be changing.

Importance of Biodiversity

Compare a parking lot covered with asphalt to your favorite place in nature, perhaps your backyard, a wooded area, or a local lake. You might go to an area like this to relax or to think. Artists get inspiration from these areas for songs, paintings, photographs, and literature. Looking at one of Art Wolfe's photographs in the *Connection to Art* on page 128 can help you appreciate the beauty biodiversity gives our world. Beyond beauty, why is biodiversity important?

Importance to nature

Living things are interdependent. Animals could not exist without green plants. Many flowering plants could not exist without animals to pollinate them. Plants are dependent on decomposers that break down dead or decaying material into nutrients they can absorb. In a rain forest, a tree grows from nutrients released by decomposers. A sloth eats the leaves of the tree. Moss grows on the back of the sloth. Thus, living things can be niches for other living things.

Populations are adapted to live together in communities. Although ecologists have studied many complex relationships among organisms, many relationships are yet to be discovered. Scientists do know that if a species is lost from an ecosystem, the loss may have consequences for other living things in the area. An organism suffers when a plant or animal it feeds upon is removed permanently from a food chain or food web. A population may soon exceed the area's carrying capacity if its predators are removed. If the symbiotic relationships among organisms are broken due to the loss of one species, then the remaining species will also be affected.

Inquiry

Guided Questioning Ask students to recall the biomes they studied in Chapter 3. Which had the highest biological diversity? tropical rain forest Write the terms *number of species* and *number of organisms* on the board. Ask students to explain the difference. Which is a better indicator of biological diversity? number of species

PROJECT

Comparing Diversity Have students rope off (or use string) two different areas (grass area and treed or shrubbed area) of the school grounds, each about 1 m square. Ask them to count all the species of plants and insects in each area. Students should NOT include in their tallies any plant or animal that lies across the edge of the boundary rope. Then have them compare the numbers and suggest reasons for any differences in diversity between the two areas. **L2** **ELL**

 Indiana Academic Standards

Pages 112–113: B.1.37, B.1.43, B.1.45

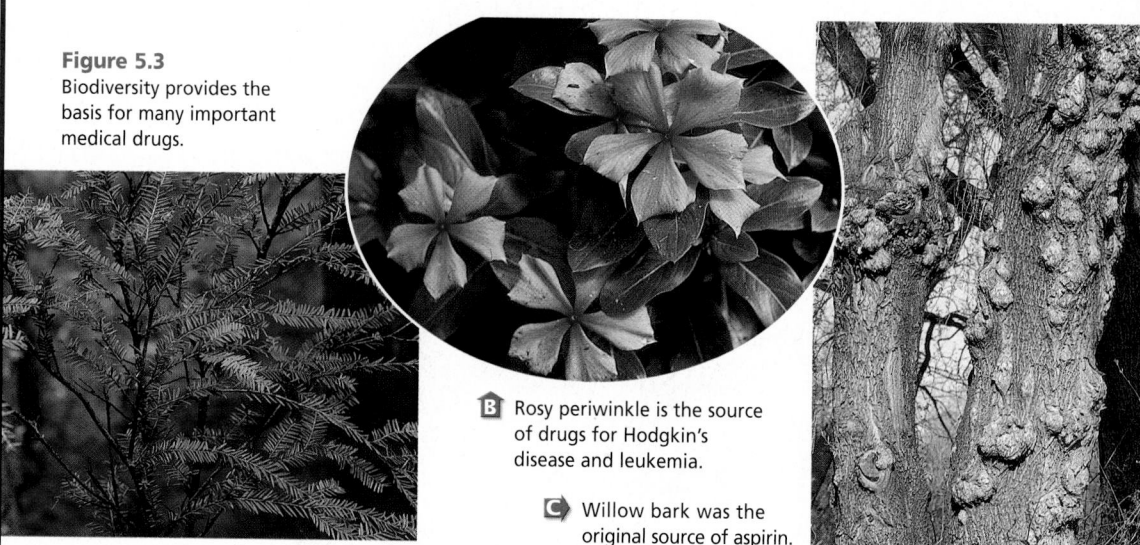

Figure 5.3
Biodiversity provides the basis for many important medical drugs.

B Rosy periwinkle is the source of drugs for Hodgkin's disease and leukemia.

C Willow bark was the original source of aspirin.

A Taxol, a strong anti-cancer drug, was first discovered in the Pacific yew.

Biodiversity brings stability

Biodiversity can bring stability to an ecosystem. A pest could easily destroy all the corn in a farmer's field, but it would be far more difficult for a single type of insect or disease to destroy all individuals of a plant species in a rain forest. There, instead of being clumped together, the plants exist scattered in many parts of the rain forest, making it more difficult for the disease organism to spread. In summary, ecosystems are stable if their biodiversity is maintained. A change in species can destabilize them.

Importance to people

Humans depend on other organisms for their needs. Oxygen, on which animals depend, is supplied, and carbon dioxide is removed from the air by diverse species of plants and algae living in a variety of ecosystems throughout the world. Beef, chicken, tuna, shrimp, and pork are a few of the meats and seafood humans eat. Think of all the plant products that people eat, from almonds to zucchini. Yet only a few species of plants and animals supply the major portion of the food eaten by the human population. Biodiversity could help breeders produce additional food crops. For example, through crossbreeding with a wild plant, a food crop might be made pest-resistant or drought-tolerant. People also rely on the living world for raw materials used in clothes, furniture, and buildings.

Another important reason for maintaining biodiversity is that it can be used to improve people's health. Living things supply the world pharmacy. Although drug companies manufacture synthetic drugs, active compounds in these drugs are usually first isolated from living things, such as those in *Figure 5.3*. The antibiotic penicillin came from the mold *Penicillium*. The antimalarial drug quinine came from the bark of the cinchona tree. Even the importance of soil microorganisms should not be overlooked. The drug cyclosporine, which prevents rejection of transplanted organs, was discovered in a soil fungus in 1971. Preserving biodiversity ensures there will be a supply of living things, some of which may provide future drugs. Will a cure for cancer or HIV be found in the leaves of an obscure rain forest plant?

114 BIOLOGICAL DIVERSITY AND CONSERVATION

Loss of Biodiversity

Have you ever seen a flock of passenger pigeons? How about a blue pike, or a dusky seaside sparrow? Unless you have seen a photograph or a specimen in a museum, your answer will be "No" to each of these questions. These animals are extinct. **Extinction** (ek STINGK shun) is the disappearance of a species when the last of its members dies. Extinction is a natural process and Earth has experienced several mass extinctions during its history. There is also a certain level of natural extinction, called background extinction, that goes on. Scientists estimate that background extinction accounts for the loss of one species per year per million species. However, the current rate of extinction exceeds that by many times. Scientists hypothesize that this rise is due in part to the needs of the expanding human population, habitat loss, and land exploitation. Is there evidence of a link between land use and species extinction? Look at one scientist's analysis in the *Problem-Solving Lab* on this page.

A species is considered to be an **endangered species** when its numbers become so low that extinction is possible. *Figure 5.4* shows species listed as endangered in the United States.

Problem-Solving Lab 5.1

Interpret Data

Does species extinction correlate to land area? Species are at risk of extinction when their habitats are destroyed. Is there a better chance for survival when land area is large?

Solve the Problem

A study of land mammals was conducted by a scientist to determine the effect of land area on species extinction. His research was confined to a group of South Pacific islands of Indonesia. The scientist's basis for determining the initial number of species present was based on research conducted by earlier scientists and from fossil evidence.

Relationship of Land Area to Extinctions				
Island	Area in km²	Initial Number of Species	Extinctions	Percent of Loss
Borneo	751 709	153	30	20
Java	126 806	113	39	35
Bali	5443	66	47	71

Thinking Critically

1. **Evaluate Trends from Data** From the data, what is the relationship between island size and the initial number of species?
2. **Analyze Trends from Data** From the data, how does land area seem to correlate with loss of species?
3. **Analyze Scientific Explanations** Hypothesize why the study was conducted on only land mammals. What might be some strengths and weaknesses of this research?

Figure 5.4
In the United States, scientists have developed programs designed to save some endangered species.

 The Endangered Species list includes several species of sea turtles.

A In 1982, the California condor (*Gymnogyps californianus*) was nearly extinct in the wild. The 22 remaining condors were captured and placed in reserves. As of 2002, more than 70 birds were released to the wild. They remain endangered.

Problem-Solving Lab 5.1

Purpose
Students will determine that reduced land area contributes to the extinction of species.

Process Skills
think critically, analyze information, compare and contrast, draw a conclusion, interpret data, predict, recognize cause and effect, use numbers

Teaching Strategies
- Have students locate these island areas on a map.
- Review the procedure for calculating percent. Allow students to use calculators.

Thinking Critically
1. The larger the island, the more initial species it has.
2. There is a higher percent of species loss for smaller areas.
3. Answers will vary, but students may mention that it's easier to trap and observe land mammals, and the initial data on species numbers may be more reliable.

Assessment
Portfolio Have students work together in pairs to write an article describing ways to reduce the number of extinctions of land mammal species on an island. What are the strengths and weaknesses of their suggestions? Use the Performance Task Assessment List for Newspaper Article in **PASC**, p. 141. **L2** **COOP LEARN**

CHALLENGE ACTIVITY

Finding Answers Have students choose an extinct organism from anywhere in the world and research reasons for its extinction. Create a classroom bulletin board on extinction. Suggestions from the Extinct Species list are eastern elk, Florida black wolf, Texas red wolf, Dodo bird, passenger pigeon, blue pike, and bigleaf scurfpea. **L3**

Indiana Academic Standards

Pages 114–115: B.1.41, B.1.43, B.1.46

Discussion Ask students to explain ways that people alter habitats. Have students identify whether the changes affect the biotic or abiotic factors of that habitat. For example, cutting trees can have biotic effects, such as reducing the food supply for certain animals in the forest. The same activity can also have abiotic effects, such as increasing the amount of sunlight that reaches an area.

Reading Check Biodiversity is important because life depends upon life. A lost habitat may not be recoverable. Many organisms are sources of food. If a species is lost from an ecosystem, the loss may have consequences for other species. Loss of certain plants may mean the loss of a source of medicine for a particular disease.

Content Development

Green Space Have students research what practical measures their community might be taking or what measures are required by law to retain open green spaces. Building codes in some communities require that builders set aside a certain percentage of land as green space in developments.

Caption Question Answer
Figure 5.6 Coral provides habitats for a wide variety of species.

Figure 5.5
Through the Fish and Wildlife Service, information is available to the public on all species threatened or endangered. *T,* under *Listing Status,* refers to *threatened.* An *E* would indicate *endangered.*

Results of Species Search*				
Scientific Name	**Common Name**	**Group**	**Listing Status**	**Current Range**
Loxodonta africana	African elephant	Mammals	T	Africa

*U.S. Fish & Wildlife Service Threatened and Endangered Species System (TESS)

When the population of a species is likely to become endangered, it is said to be a **threatened species.** African elephants, for example, are listed as a threatened species. In 1979, the estimated wild elephant population was about 1.3 million. Twenty years later, the population was estimated to be 700 000. In 1998, a survey published by the African Elephant Database estimated a minimum number of elephants at about 300 000. The United States Fish and Wildlife Service maintains a listing of threatened and endangered species for the United States and the world. *Figure 5.5* shows the type of information available from the Fish and Wildlife Service on its Threatened and Endangered Species System database.

Reading Check **Explain** why biodiversity is important.

Figure 5.6
Coral reefs are rich in biodiversity. **Conclude** *How does removal of coral result in a loss of habitat for reef organisms?*

116

Threats to Biodiversity

Complex interactions among species make each ecosystem unique. The species there are usually well adapted to their habitats. Changes to habitats can therefore threaten organisms with extinction. What are some of the activities that can bring this about?

Habitat loss

One of the biggest reasons for decline in biodiversity is habitat loss. In the 1970s and 1980s, in the Amazonian rain forest, thousands of hectares of land were cleared in an effort to create farmland and to supply firewood. Much of this land lost its usefulness for agriculture after only a few years because rain forest soil by itself has little or no useful nutrient supply. Clearing the land erased habitats that will not be reestablished easily. Without these habitats, certain plants and animals become vulnerable to extinction.

Other areas affected by habitat loss are coral reefs. Coral reefs, like the one in *Figure 5.6,* are thought to be similar to tropical rain forests in biodiversity richness. The structure of coral provides habitats for varieties of fish, anemones, sponges, and other marine organisms. Disease and changes in water temperature can damage or kill coral. As a result, habitats are lost and the organisms that depend on the coral also are affected.

Indiana Academic Standards

Pages 116–117: B.1.41, B.1.45, B.1.46

CHALLENGE ACTIVITY

Finding Species Each year, previously unidentified species or organisms are found somewhere in the world. Have students research the finding of a wild camel (Tibet), giant squid (Tasmania), tree rat (Peruvian Andes), muntjak deer (Vietnam), a pheasant (Vietnam), and the golden Vietnamese cypress. **L3**

Figure 5.7
Wildlife areas that are broken up or surrounded by development result in habitat fragmentation. The areas remaining may be too small to support reproducing populations. The pathway from one habitat to another may be cut off or greatly reduced in size.

Habitat fragmentation

Habitat fragmentation is the separation of wilderness areas from other wilderness areas. Habitat fragmentation has been found to contribute to:
- increased extinction of local species.
- disruption of ecological processes.
- new opportunities for invasions by introduced or exotic species.
- increased risk of fire.
- changes in local climate.

Fragmented areas are similar to islands. The smaller the fragment, the less biodiversity the area can support. This is because, as species migrate from an area that has become unsuitable for some reason, other species that depend on the migrating individuals lose their life support. As a result, overall species diversity declines.

Geographic isolation can lead to genetic isolation. When an individual organism's habitat becomes too small, its population becomes isolated from other populations of its species. The organism doesn't have the chance to breed with members of its species in other populations.

Habitat fragmentation, as shown in *Figure 5.7*, presents problems for organisms that need large areas to gather food or find mates. Large predators may not be able to obtain enough food if restricted to too small an area. Habitat fragmentation also

makes it difficult for species to reestablish themselves in an area. Imagine a small fragment of forest where a species of salamander lives. A fast-burning fire started by lightning destroys trees and the salamanders living there. In a nonfragmented forest, as the area recovers, new salamanders would eventually move into the area. However, if the burned forest was isolated from another forest where other salamanders live, no route would exist for these salamanders to reestablish populations in the burned area. In the next section of this chapter, read about corridors that connect one piece of fragmented land to another.

Edge Effect

The edge of a habitat or ecosystem is where one habitat or ecosystem meets another. This can be where a forest meets a field, where water meets land, or where a road cuts through a field or wooded area. The different conditions along the boundaries of an ecosystem are called **edge effects.** An edge may have two different sets of abiotic factors. Edges tend to have greater biodiversity because different habitats with different species are brought together. When an edge changes, animals from one area might migrate from the area or move to the new edge, thereby

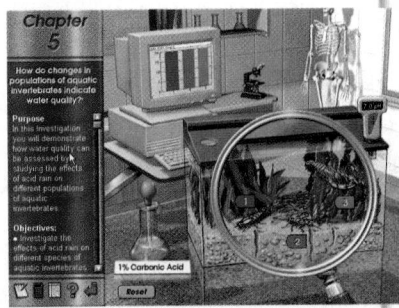

Students usually identify water as having no pH or a pH of 7 (neutral). Pure water is pH 7 at 25°C and 1 atmosphere (atm) pressure. Generally, tapwater has a pH less than 7 and is acidic.

Uncover the Misconception

Students may have the idea that everything associated with the word *acidic* is dangerous, when in fact, many everyday food items are acidic and harmless.

Demonstrate the Concept

Gather some familiar solutions such as orange juice, grapefruit juice, and lemon juice. Use litmus paper or pH paper to show students these juices they may have consumed are acidic.

Assess New Knowledge

Have students test the pH of tap water at school. If available, have them test rainwater that has been collected during a recent storm.

Figure 5.8
Acid precipitation and acid fog may be major contributors of damage to these trees.

Physical Science Connection

Environmental impact of generating electricity More than 50% of the electrical energy produced in the United States comes from burning coal. Compared to other fossil fuels, coal contains more impurities, such as sulfur. As a result, more pollutants, such as sulfur dioxide, are produced when coal is burned than when oil or natural gas is burned.

bringing species from different ecosystems in contact with one another. If a piece of land is cleared or divided by a road, new edges are created. This action may expose animals attracted to the edge to more predators than they were previously.

What happens at the edge of a habitat may affect what goes on in the interior of the area. In a developed area, there may be more housecats, and therefore, birds that nested undisturbed in the area before may be preyed upon.

Habitat degradation

Another threat to biodiversity is **habitat degradation,** the damage to a habitat by pollution. Three types of pollution are air, water, and land pollution. Air pollution can cause breathing problems and irritate membranes in the eyes and nose. Pollutants enter the atmosphere in many ways—including volcanic eruptions and forest fires. Burning fossil fuels is also a major source of air pollutants such as sulfur dioxide.

Acid precipitation—rain, snow, sleet, and fog with low pH values—has been linked to the deterioration

of some forests and lakes. Sulfur dioxide from coal-burning factories and nitrogen oxides from automobile exhaust combine with water vapor in the air to form acidic droplets of water vapor. When these droplets fall from the sky, the moisture leaches calcium, potassium, and other nutrients from the soil. This loss of nutrients can lead to the death of trees. Acid precipitation also damages plant tissues and interferes with plant growth. Worldwide, many trees such as those shown in *Figure 5.8* are dying and acid rain and fog are thought to be the cause. Acid precipitation also is linked to degrading lake ecosystems. When acid rain falls into a lake, or enters as runoff from streams, the pH of the lake water falls.

Ultraviolet waves emitted by the Sun also can cause damage to living organisms. Ozone, a compound consisting of three oxygen atoms, is found mainly in a region of Earth's atmosphere between about 15 km and 35 km altitude. The ozone in this region—known as the **ozone layer**—absorbs some of the ultraviolet waves striking the atmosphere, reducing the ultraviolet radiation reaching Earth's surface. Over some parts of Antarctica, the amount of ozone overhead is reduced by as much as 60 percent during the Antarctic spring. Ozone amounts then increase during the summer. This seasonal ozone reduction is known as the Antarctic ozone hole, and is caused by the presence in the atmosphere of human-produced chemicals such as chlorofluorocarbons (CFCs). Smaller seasonal reductions also have been observed over the Arctic and there is a small downward trend in global ozone concentrations. However, the causes of this ozone loss and its biological consequences are still uncertain.

Additional Lab

Acids and Seed Germination

Purpose

Students will observe the effect of acid precipitation on seed germination.

Materials 🥽 🧤 🚫
self-sealing plastic bags, paper toweling, small cups, water, vinegar, small seeds

Procedure

Give the following directions to students.

1. Place 20 seeds in a small, labeled cup of water and 20 seeds in a small, labeled cup of vinegar. **CAUTION:** *Wear goggles while handling and pouring vinegar.*

Wash your hands after working with any seeds.

2. Allow seeds to soak overnight.

3. The next day, remove seeds from the water. Wrap the seeds in a paper towel. Moisten the towel with water and slide it into a self-sealing plastic bag. Label the bag with your name, date, and the word *water*.

Water pollution

Water pollution degrades aquatic habitats in streams, rivers, lakes, and oceans. A variety of pollutants can affect aquatic life. Excess fertilizers and animal wastes, as shown in *Figure 5.9*, are often carried by rain into streams and lakes. The sudden availability of nutrients causes algal blooms, the excessive growth of algae. As the algae die, they sink and decay, removing needed oxygen from the water. Silt from eroded soils can also enter water and clog the gills of fishes. Detergents, heavy metals, and industrial chemicals in runoff can cause death in aquatic organisms. Abandoned drift nets in oceans have been known to entangle and kill dolphins, whales, and other sea life.

Land pollution

How much garbage does your family produce every day? Trash, or solid waste, is made up of the cans, bottles, paper, plastic, metals, dirt, and spoiled food that people throw away every day. The average American produces about 1.8 kg of solid waste daily. That's a total of about 657 kg of waste per person per year. At what rate does it decompose? Although some of it might decompose quickly, most trash becomes part of the billions of tons of solid waste that are buried in landfills. Strict controls on the design, construction, and placement of landfills are meant to reduce contamination of groundwater supplies.

The use of pesticides and other chemicals can also lead to habitat degradation. For many years, DDT was used liberally to control insects and to kill mosquito larvae. Birds that fed on DDT-treated crops, or insects, fish, and other small animals exposed to DDT, were observed to have high levels of DDT in their bodies. The DDT was passed on in food chains to the predators that ate these animals.

Figure 5.9
Runoff from large feedlots and agricultural operations can contain large amounts of nitrogen and phosphorus.

A The cattle on this feedlot produce nitrogen-rich liquid and solid wastes. Because of the volume of these wastes, research is ongoing as to how to make good use of them.

 B Large amounts of phosphorus in runoff from fertilized fields can stimulate the rapid growth of algae in waterways downstream. This lush growth consumes all or most of the oxygen in the water, making it impossible for insects, fishes, and other animals to live.

5.1 VANISHING SPECIES **119**

119

3 Assess

B Zebra mussels were introduced unintentionally into the Great Lakes from the ballast of ships. These fast-growing mussels clear the water, but block many food chains.

Figure 5.10
Exotic species can cause many problems when introduced into new ecosystems either intentionally or unintentionally.

A Kudzu was introduced intentionally into the U.S. as an ornamental and to reduce soil erosion. However, it grows rapidly, smothering areas of native plants.

Because of the DDT in their bodies, some species of predators, such as the bald eagle and the peregrine falcon, were found to lay eggs with very thin shells that cracked easily, killing the chicks and leading to sharp population declines. These observations contributed to the ban on DDT in the United States in 1972.

Exotic species

People sometimes introduce a new species into an ecosystem, either intentionally or unintentionally. These species can cause problems for the native species. When people brought goats to Santa Catalina Island, located off the coast of California, 48 native species of plants soon disappeared from the local environment. Building the Erie canal in the nineteenth century made it possible for the sea lamprey to swim into the Great Lakes. The sea lamprey, which resembles an eel, clamps onto a fish's body and, using its sharp teeth and tongue, sucks fluids out of the fish. The lamprey has totally eliminated certain fish species from some of the Great Lakes. **Exotic species,** such as the goat and the lamprey, are not native to a particular area. Some other examples of exotic species are shown in *Figure 5.10*. When exotic species are introduced, these species can grow at an exponential rate due to the fact that they are not immediately as vulnerable to local competitors or predators as are the established native species.

Section Assessment

Understanding Main Ideas
1. What are two reasons for a species to become threatened or endangered?
2. Explain how land that gets broken up can contribute to loss of species diversity.
3. What is an edge effect? Explain how change in an ecosystem's edges can affect organisms.
4. How can exotic species affect populations of native species?

Thinking Critically
5. Explain the interactions in a tropical ecosystem that enable it to have great biodiversity.

SKILL REVIEW

6. **Recognize Cause and Effect** Explain why water is not subject to loss, but is subject to degradation. How does water degradation affect biodiversity? For more help, refer to *Recognize Cause and Effect* in the **Skill Handbook.**

 in.bdol.glencoe.com/self_check_quiz

Section Assessment

1. Answers may include habitat loss, degradation, or fragmentation; introduction of exotic species; or excessive hunting or collecting.
2. Some species require large, unbroken plots to maintain their population. When plots are fragmented, diversity may decrease.
3. Edge effect is the result of changed conditions along the community's edge. The changes might affect the area's diversity either positively or negatively.
4. The exotics can out-compete the native species for food or shelter, or the exotic species may eat a native species.
5. Vertical layers of the forests provide different habitats and niches for more organisms. With rain and sunlight, plants produce nutrients to support more life.
6. Water continuously recycles. However, it may be degraded by pollution, resulting in decreased biodiversity.

1 Focus

INTERACTIVE CHALKBOARD
PowerPoint® Presentations

Bellringer
Section Focus Transparency 11

Transparency **11** Insecticides: Helpful or Harmful?

SECTION FOCUS
Use with Chapter 5, Section 5.2

① How is the gardener's activity helpful?
② How might the activity be harmful?

BIOLOGY: The Dynamics of Life   SECTION FOCUS TRANSPARENCIES

Section 5.2

SECTION PREVIEW

Objectives

Describe strategies used in conservation biology.

Relate success in protecting an endangered species to the methods used to protect it.

Review Vocabulary
biodiversity: the variety and abundance of life in an area (p. 111)

New Vocabulary
conservation biology
natural resources
habitat corridors
sustainable use
reintroduction programs
captivity

Conservation of Biodiversity

Indiana Standards Standard B.1.41 Recognize that and describe how human beings are part of Earth's ecosystems. **Note that human activities can, deliberately or inadvertently, alter the equilibrium in ecosystems.**

Back from the Brink

Using Prior Knowledge

Whoops! Have you ever stood at the sink and watched as a ring slid off your soapy finger and slipped down the drain before you could grab it? Could you retrieve it? The loss of a species is thought by many to be a significant occurrence. Once that species is gone, the unique role that it played and the unique genetic message that it contained are gone forever. Scientists, like the ones shown here reintroducing a gray wolf to the wild, are making efforts to keep species from becoming extinct.

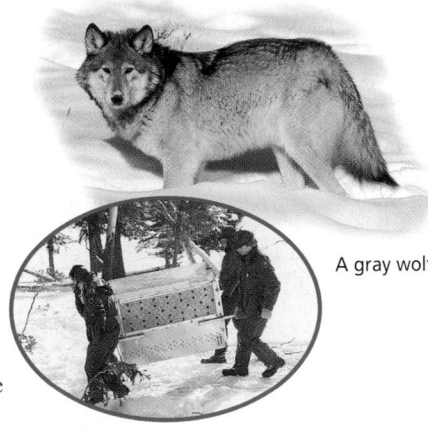

A gray wolf

Research *Research some organisms that have been brought back from the brink of extinction. Describe the steps taken for one such organism. What are the strengths and weaknesses of such programs?*

Conservation Biology

Conservation biology is the study and implementation of methods to protect biodiversity. Effective conservation strategies are based on principles of ecology. These strategies include natural resource conservation and species conservation. Even soil has to be conserved. Learn about what can happen to soil in the *MiniLab* on the next page.

Natural resources are those parts of the environment that are useful or necessary for living organisms. Natural resources include sunlight, water, air, and plant and animal resources. Because species are dependent upon sufficient supplies of natural resources, they must be considered during the planning of any conservation activity.

Legal protections of species

In response to concern about species extinction, the U.S. Endangered Species Act became law in 1973. This law made it illegal to harm any species on the endangered or threatened species lists. Further, the law made it illegal for federal agencies to fund any project that would harm organisms on these lists. Harm includes changing an ecosystem where endangered or threatened species live.

5.2 CONSERVATION OF BIODIVERSITY **121**

Using Prior Knowledge

Research Students may check **bdol.glencoe.com** for links to sites with lists of threatened or endangered species, such as the American bald eagle, the American alligator, the brown pelican, or the gray wolf.

RESOURCE MANAGER

Unit 2 *Fast File* Resources
  MiniLab Worksheet, p. 103
  Real World BioApplications, pp. 109–110
  Reinforcement and Study Guide in
    English, p. 114
  Reinforcement and Study Guide in
    Spanish, p. 118
  Transparency Worksheet, p. 122

Reading Essentials for Biology, Section 5.2
 Section Focus Transparency 11

Indiana Academic Standards

Pages 120–121: B.1.38, B.1.41, B.1.43, B.1.45

2 Teach

Purpose

Students will determine that soil erosion is reduced on land areas with vegetation.

Process Skills

compare and contrast, draw a conclusion, interpret data, measure in SI, recognize cause and effect, formulate a model

Safety Precautions

Have students wear a lab apron and safety goggles. Have students wash hands thoroughly with soap after the activity and cleanup.

Teaching Strategies

■ Obtain soil with grass growing in it from a lawn area (with permission) or purchase sod from a garden store.

■ Try to keep the volume of soil equal in both trays. Water should be poured slowly.

■ Review the use of a graduated cylinder for reading volumes. Remind students to allow the soil to settle after they pour it into the cylinder.

Expected Results

There will be less measured soil erosion when vegetation is present than when soil is bare.

Analysis

1. water washing soil down the incline
2. Roots from the plants reduce soil erosion.

Modfied Assessment

Knowledge Pull a small plant from the ground and have students examine the root system and the soil clinging to it. Have students explain how roots reduce soil erosion. Use the Performance Task Assessment List for Making Observations and Inferences in **PASC,** p. 89. **L1**

122

MiniLab 5.2

Investigate

Conservation of Soil Soil is as important a natural resource as plant and animal species and should be conserved. How does one conserve soil? What factors speed up the unnecessary loss or erosion of soil?

Procedure

1 Copy the data table below.

Soil Erosion			
Source of Sample	Volume of Original Water	Volume of Collected Water	Volume of Eroded Soil
Bare soil			
Soil with grass			

2 Measure 200 mL of water in a beaker.

3 Fill a tray with soil as shown in the photograph.

4 Pour the water onto the soil, tilting the tray over a dish as indicated in the photograph.

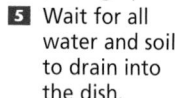

5 Wait for all water and soil to drain into the dish.

6 Pour the soil and water from the dish into a graduated cylinder. Wait several minutes for the soil to settle. Measure the volume of soil and water that washed or eroded into the dish. Record these values in your data table.

7 Repeat steps 2–6. This time use a section of soil in which grass is growing. **CAUTION:** *Always wash your hands with soap and water after working with soil.*

8 Make wise choices about disposal of the materials.

Analysis

1. **Analyze Trends from Data** What part of the experiment simulated soil erosion?
2. **Make Inferences from Data** Based on this experiment, explain why farmers usually plant unused fields with some type of crop cover.

Worldwide, the Convention on International Trade in Endangered Species (CITES) has established lists of species for which international trade is prohibited or controlled. This agreement has been endorsed by more than 120 countries.

Preserving habitats

The importance of preserving habitats has been recognized in the United States and many other countries. A habitat is the physical location where an organism lives and interacts with its environment. One way that habitats have been protected is through the creation of natural preserves and parks. The United States established its first national park—Yellowstone National Park—in 1872. Initially Yellowstone was created to protect the region's unique geology. However, its ecological importance is recognized as being equally significant. Species of bear, bison, moose, and elk roam the park in much the same way that they roamed the area hundreds of years ago. Other national parks in the United States include Big Cypress National Preserve, Crater Lake National Park, Big Bend National Park, and Sequoia National Park. Each park protects a unique natural environment and provides habitats for many organisms.

Establishing parks and other protected regions has been an effective way to preserve ecosystems and the communities of species that live in them. Although natural preserves make up a relatively small amount of land in some countries, these areas contain a large amount of biodiversity. For example, 3.9 percent of the land in the Democratic Republic of Congo in Africa has been protected. However, this small amount of land is home to almost 90 percent of the nation's bird species.

TECH PREP

Parks and Recreation Maintenance Have students find out how natural areas in their communities are maintained. What skills, training, and equipment are required to maintain these areas? **L2**

Habitat corridors

Is it better to protect one large piece of land or several smaller, disconnected pieces of land? Recall the research describing the number of insect and spider species on islands of different sizes. In general, larger islands had more species than smaller islands had. Therefore, a general strategy for protecting the biodiversity of an area probably is to protect the largest area possible. However, research is showing that keeping wildlife populations completely separate from one another may be resulting in inbreeding within populations. Therefore, another strategy for preserving biodiversity is to connect protected areas with habitat corridors.

Corridors such as the one in *Figure 5.11* are being built in Florida to protect the Florida panther. **Habitat corridors** are protected strips of land that allow the migration of organisms from one wilderness area to another. Research has shown that corridors can help overcome some of the effects of habitat destruction and are beneficial for both plants and animals.

Working with people

Saying an area is protected does not automatically make all the species there safe. Parks and protected areas usually hire people, such as rangers, to manage the parks and ensure the protection of organisms. In some areas, access by people is restricted. In other lands, people can harvest food or obtain materials but this sort of activity is managed. The philosophy of **sustainable use** strives to enable people to use natural resources in ways that will benefit them and maintain the ecosystem. For example, in *Figure 5.12,* people harvest Brazil nuts to eat and to sell. This provides the opportunity to earn a living and the ecology of the area is maintained.

Figure 5.11
In Florida, the Florida panther can move from one habitat to another by crossing under a highway. Construction of these habitat corridors has resulted in a decrease of panthers being struck by cars.

Figure 5.12
Sustainable use of wildlife areas enables people to protect these areas. The sale of Brazil nuts, sustainably harvested from rain forests in the Amazon, provides income for people living there.

5.2 CONSERVATION OF BIODIVERSITY **123**

Concept Development
Point out that sustainable use often leads to conflicts. Some people want access to more of a resource, while others want to conserve resources. Ask students if they think hunting can be a conservation measure. Hunting can conserve a species. Reducing a population in a managed way can ensure that the remaining populations have enough food to remain healthy.

✓ MODIFIED Assessment

Portfolio Have students discuss how setting up a park in a community might protect the habitat of local animals. Ask them how a new park might threaten an existing habitat. Use the Performance Task Assessment List for Science Portfolio in **PASC**, p. 177. **L1**

Inquiry
Guided Questioning Are reintroduction programs always the correct choice? Answers will be for and against. Students may have the misconception that all reintroductions are easy and successful. Point out that reintroductions are only successful when the problems affecting a species have been corrected. Bison were almost extinct because of overhunting and destruction of habitat. They have begun to recover because they are protected and were placed in areas of rehabilitated habitat. What other factors affect reintroduction programs? cost of followup, disease potential

---

🎯 CHALLENGE ACTIVITY

National Parks Students who need an extra challenge can research the early history and planning of a specific national park. Ask them to write a newspaper article that talks about the positives and negatives of setting aside land for use as a national park. Write-ups may include how large an area will be, how it will be acquired, costs involved, and potential uses. Students should remember that they are writing at the time of the park's founding. **L3**

Indiana Academic Standards

Pages 122–123: B.1.41, B.1.43, B.1.45

Purpose

Students will explore opinions regarding the preservation of certain endangered species.

Process Skills

think critically, analyze information, communicate, draw a conclusion, recognize cause and effect

Teaching Strategies

■ Have teams of volunteers debate the strengths and weaknesses of reintroduction programs.

■ Remind students to show respect for others' opinions.

Thinking Critically

1. Ranchers may think that any wolf they see is threatening their livestock.

2. The wolves were native and had been eliminated by humans.

3. Scientists would offer scientific reasons for introducing wolves.

Assessment

Performance Have volunteers give persuasive speeches to convince "decision-makers" to continue reintroducing wolves or to end the program. Use the Performance Assessment List for Investigating an Issue Controversy in **PASC**, p. 137. **L2**

Quick Demo

Saving a Species Gingko leaves are distinctive. Bring in a few leaves so students can identify the tree.

Indiana Academic Standards

Pages 124–125: B.1.41, B.1.45, B.1.47

124

Problem-Solving Lab 5.2

Think Critically

Why are conservation efforts sometimes controversial? There have been many attempts to breed wild animals or move them from one area to another. The goal is to preserve wildlife species. However, reintroduction programs of some species can have unintended consequences.

A gray wolf

Solve the Problem

Case 1: In March 1998, the U.S. Fish and Wildlife Service reintroduced 11 captive-bred Mexican gray wolves (*Canis lupus baileyi*) into parts of Arizona. They had been extinct from the area for 20 years. By law, ranchers are not allowed to kill native wolves. However, reintroduced wolves received special legal status under the Endangered Species Act and can be killed by ranchers if the wolves threaten livestock.

Case 2: In 1995, a group of gray wolves (*Canis lupus*) was captured in Canada and introduced into Yellowstone National Park, where gray wolves once had been abundant. Because the wolves killed some cattle in the region, legal pressure was mounted to have the wolves removed from the park. In December 1997, a United States district court ruled that the wolves should be removed from the park. However, some groups have appealed the decision and the future home of the wolves is undecided.

Thinking Critically

1. **Evaluate the Impact of Research on Society** Imagine that you are a rancher described in Case 1. What complaints might you have about the 1998 reintroduction program?

2. **Evaluate the Impact of Research on Society** In Case 1, describe the arguments that might be offered in favor of the reintroduction program.

3. **Evaluate the Impact of Research on Society** In Case 2, describe the role that scientists might have in deciding whether the wolves should be removed.

Figure 5.13
A black-footed ferret is reintroduced into its native habitat in Wyoming. The caregiver wears a mask to reduce the chances she will transmit a human disease to the ferret.

Reintroduction and species preservation programs

The year is 1991. A wildlife manager carries a cage containing a captive-bred black-footed ferret, like the one in *Figure 5.13*. She opens the cage door, and the ferret steps out onto the ground. In the 1970s, the black-footed ferret was almost lost from the wild and was listed as an endangered species. The ferret depends upon prairie dogs for food, and prairie dog habitat had been reduced by rural land use. In 1981, a small population of black-footed ferrets was found by a rancher. Biologists studied the ferrets and established a captive-breeding program at the National Black-footed Ferret Conservation Center in Wyoming. The captive-breeding program has become a success, and black-footed ferrets have been released into the wild in a number of western states. **Reintroduction programs,** such as this one, release organisms into an area where the species once lived. Today, about 350 black-footed ferrets live in the wild. To learn about the controversy surrounding the reintroduction of some species to the wild, read the *Problem-Solving Lab.*

INCLUSION STRATEGIES

Success Stories Have student groups select an organism that has been saved from extinction, research the process, and share with the class. Reports could be in the form of a Foldable or bulletin board. Each report could be made up of five points: the name of the organism, where it was originally located, what caused it to become almost extinct, steps taken to help it survive, and where it was reintroduced. Suggested organisms are: bald eagle, golden lion tamarin, the gray wolf, and the Arabian oryx. **L1 COOP LEARN**

The most successful reintroductions occur when organisms are taken from an area in the wild and transported to a new suitable habitat. The brown pelican was once common along the shores of the Gulf of Mexico. DDT caused this bird's eggs to break, and the brown pelican completely disappeared from these areas. After DDT was banned in the United States in 1972, 50 brown pelicans were taken from Florida and put on Grand Terre Island in Louisiana. The population grew and spread, and today more than 7000 brown pelicans live in the area.

Captivity

Some species no longer exist in the wild, but a small number of individual organisms is maintained by humans. An organism that is held by people is said to be in **captivity**. The ginkgo tree, as shown in *Figure 5.14*, is an example of a species surviving extinction because it was kept by people. The ginkgo is an ancient tree; all similar species became extinct long ago. However, Chinese monks planted the ginkgo tree around their temples, thereby preventing the tree from becoming extinct.

Protecting plant species

The ideal way to protect a plant species is to allow it to exist in a natural ecosystem. But seeds can be cooled and stored for long periods of time. By establishing seed banks for threatened and endangered plants, the species can be reintroduced if they become extinct.

Reintroductions of captive animals are more difficult than for plants. Keeping animals in captivity, with enough space, adequate care, and proper food, is expensive. Animals kept in captivity may lose the necessary behaviors to survive and reproduce in the wild. Despite the difficulties involved, some species held in captivity, such as the Arabian oryx and the California condor, have been reintroduced to their native habitats after becoming nearly extinct in the wild.

Figure 5.14
The ginkgo tree would probably be extinct if not for the care given to specimens that had been planted on monastery grounds. *Ginkgo biloba* survives pollution well, making it useful for urban landscapes.

3 Assess

DAILY INTERVENTION

Check for Understanding
Have students explain which conservation biology strategy they feel is the most important and why.

Reteach
Have students list the three conservation biology strategies in this section. For each strategy, they should describe one organism that was helped. **L2**

Resources
For more practice, use *Reading Essentials for Biology,* Section 5.2.

Extension

Visual-Spatial Have students create endangered species posters. Each poster should have a picture, a description of the organism's niche, and what could be done to help the organism. **L2** **ELL**

 Assessment

Discussion Hold a class discussion about ways that individuals can help conserve biodiversity. Discuss projects that might meet a local need. What would be the pluses and minuses of conserving a local wetland area? **L2**

Section Assessment

Understanding Main Ideas
1. Contrast the fields of conservation biology and ecology.
2. Describe the U.S. Endangered Species Act. When did it become law, and how does it help protect or preserve endangered species?
3. Evaluate the difficulties with reintroduction programs using captive-born animals.
4. Choose one species that you have read about, either here or in your library, and explain how conservation strategies lead to its recovery.

Thinking Critically
5. How can habitat degradation cause changes in an area's biodiversity?

SKILL REVIEW

6. **Get the Big Picture** How might habitat corridors help overcome problems with habitat fragmentation? Research some actual situations concerning the Florida panther, including the costs involved. For more help, refer to *Get the Big Picture* in the **Skill Handbook**.

in.bdol.glencoe.com/self_check_quiz

5.2 CONSERVATION OF BIODIVERSITY **125**

Section Assessment

1. Conservation biology focuses on protecting biodiversity. Ecology is the study of interactions in nature.
2. This 1973 law made it illegal to harm organisms on the threatened or endangered species lists.
3. Captive-born animals are expensive to raise and may lose their wild behaviors.
4. Students might describe the California condor as being helped by reintroduction or elephants being helped by a ban on the sale of ivory.
5. Habitat degradation reduces the quality and size of niches and can result in decreased biodiversity.
6. Habitat corridors can effectively increase the size of useable habitats, and can reduce losses as a result of auto accidents.

INTERNET
BioLab

Time Allotment
If conducted at home, the activity will require a 15-minute orientation in class. If computers with Internet access are used in class, the activity will take one to two periods.

Process Skills
acquire information, collect data, compare and contrast, draw a conclusion, think critically, define operationally

---

PREPARATION

Alternative Materials
■ Use current magazines if Internet access is not available.
■ Arrange for a guest lecturer, such as a veterinarian or zoo keeper. Ask the speaker to discuss the issue and provide specific information for students to record in their data tables.

INTERNET
BioLab

Before You Begin
What would it be like to own a pet like a snake or a black-footed ferret? Use **in.bdol.glencoe.com/ internet_lab** as a research tool to locate information on exotic pets. Consider any animal as exotic if it is not commonly domesticated and is not native to your area.

Scarlet macaw

A hedgehog

Researching Information on Exotic Pets

PREPARATION

Problem
How can you use the **in.bdol.glencoe.com/ internet_lab** to gather information on keeping an exotic animal as a pet?

Objectives
In this BioLab, you will:
■ **Select** one animal that is considered an exotic pet.
■ **Use the Internet** to collect and compare information from other students.
■ **Conclude** whether the animal you have chosen would or would not make a good pet.

Materials
access to the Internet

A rhesus monkey

PROCEDURE

1. Copy the data table and use it as a guide for the information to be researched.
2. Pick an exotic pet from the following list of choices: hedgehog, large cat such as tiger or panther, monkey, ape, and iguana.
3. Go to **in.bdol.glencoe.com/internet_lab** to find links that will provide you with information for this BioLab.
4. Post your findings in the data table at **in.bdol.glencoe.com/internet_lab**

PROCEDURE

Teaching Strategies
■ Students with home computers and access to the Internet should be encouraged to complete this activity at home. Students lacking access to computers can gain the information needed through articles in current periodicals.

■ If necessary, review how to research a topic.

Troubleshooting
Students may need to be directed to narrow their searches or ignore certain Web sites.

Data and Conclusions
Student data and conclusions will differ, depending on the animals they researched, the Web sites they visited, and other references they used.

Data Table

Category	Response
Exotic pet choice	
Scientific name	
Natural habitat (where found in nature)	
Adult size	Data will vary
Dietary needs	with choice
Special health problems	of organism.
Source of medical care, if needed	
Safety issues for humans	
Size of cage area needed	
Special environmental needs	
Social needs	
Cost of purchase	
Cost of maintaining (monthly estimate)	
Care issues (high/low maintenance)	
Additional information	
Additional sources	

A ferret

Iguanas

ANALYZE AND CONCLUDE

1. **Define Operationally** What is meant by the term *domesticated?*

2. **Interpret Data** Does your data make it clear as to why the organism you selected is considered exotic or not? Explain.

3. **Analyze Data** Look at the findings posted by other students. Which of the animals researched would make a pet? Which would not be a wise choice? Why?

4. **Think Critically** What positive contribution might be made to the cause of conservation when keeping an exotic pet? Explain.

5. **Think Critically** How can keeping exotic pets be a negative influence on conservation biology efforts?

6. **Analyze Data** What are some reasons why zoos rather than individuals are better able to handle exotic animals?

Share Your Data

Use the link below to post your findings in the data table provided for this activity. Use additional data from other students to answer the questions for this BioLab.

 in.bdol.glencoe.com/internet_lab

ANALYZE AND CONCLUDE

1. *Domesticated* means "bred for an extended period of time in captivity."

2. Answers may include that exotic pets are interesting, have a good market for resale, attract attention, and are challenging to raise. Answers may include that these animals are expensive and difficult to feed and care for, including finding veterinarian services.

3. Answers will depend on the information students located.

4. Answers may include that keeping these pets allows for possible breeding, thus helping to expand the population and save an endangered species.

5. Students may note that buying these pets endangers species even more by encouraging illegal trade.

6. Zoos can meet the animals' needs for food, shelter, and medical care better than an individual.

Share Your Data

To navigate the Internet BioLab, go to **in.bdol.glencoe. com/internet_lab**. Have students determine whether capture, breeding, and release programs have been successful for certain species of endangered animals. **L2**

Assessment

Performance Ask volunteers to debate this issue. One group should support the keeping of exotic pets, and the other group should be opposed to the idea. Use the Performance Task Assessment List for Investigating an Issue Controversy in **PASC**, p. 137. **L2**

Indiana Academic Standards

Pages 126–127: B.1.41, B.1.43

connection to Earth Science

Purpose
Students will learn about global warming and the greenhouse effect.

Teaching Strategies
■ Review the carbon cycle with students.

■ Explain to students that about 25 percent of the sunlight that strikes Earth's surface reflects back into space. Most of the remaining solar energy is absorbed by greenhouse gases and Earth.

■ Differentiate for students that greenhouse effect is a natural process, whereas global warming may partly be caused by humans.

■ Tell students that despite the emphasis on carbon dioxide in the atmosphere, water is the most abundant greenhouse gas.

■ The causes of global warming are controversial. Reinforce with students that many scientific ideas are not completely understood. Nor do scientists always agree. Hypotheses are refined as new information becomes available.

connection to Earth Science

Global Warming

The World Meteorological Organization, NASA, and the U.S. National Oceanic and Atmospheric Administration compile data from a network of ships, buoys, and land-based weather stations to measure Earth's temperature. Since the late 1800s, the average global surface temperature has risen about 0.6°C. This rise in Earth's average temperature is called global warming.

Comparisons of recent concentrations of carbon dioxide (CO_2) in the atmosphere to concentrations of CO_2 trapped in air bubbles in glacial or polar ice reveal that atmospheric concentrations of CO_2 are now higher than any in the last 450,000 years. Does CO_2 concentration in the atmosphere affect global climate?

The carbon cycle All matter recycles throughout the environment. In the carbon cycle, green plants, algae, and some bacteria cycle carbon by removing CO_2 from the atmosphere during photosynthesis. This process forms energy-rich, carbon-based molecules used by many organisms for nutrients. Plants and animals release CO_2 back into the atmosphere as a waste product of respiration. Carbon dioxide also enters the atmosphere by other natural processes, such as weathering of limestone and decomposition of plants and animals. In addition, CO_2 is released due to burning.

Affecting the carbon cycle Most CO_2 in the environment occurs naturally. However, the concentration of CO_2 in the atmosphere has increased nearly 30 percent since the late 1800s. Deforestation has removed significant amounts of vegetation that would normally absorb CO_2 during photosynthesis. The release of huge quantities of CO_2 by human activities, such as the burning of coal, oil, and gas, also has increased the CO_2 in Earth's atmosphere.

The greenhouse effect Earth would not be a habitable planet without the natural process called the greenhouse effect. The greenhouse effect is the warming of Earth's surface that occurs when gases in Earth's atmosphere, referred to as greenhouse gases, absorb solar energy that has been reflected or converted to heat and radiated from Earth's surface. Greenhouse gases—carbon dioxide, water, and other gases—prevent some heat from traveling back into space. Without the greenhouse effect, Earth would be too cold to sustain life as we know it. On the other hand, an increase in greenhouse gases in the atmosphere leads to an increase in the greenhouse effect, and possibly a greater overall average global temperature.

The cause of global warming is a controversial issue. Many scientists believe there is a strong correlation between global warming and increasing CO_2 in Earth's atmosphere. Some scientists think that it is a result of natural change, whereas others think that it is a result of human activities.

Writing About Biology

Research Efforts to reduce the amount of CO_2 released into the atmosphere require lifestyle changes and place heavy demands on the world economy. Research the expected changes to global climate as a result of global warming and the efforts to find alternative energy sources. Debate with your classmates whether you think these efforts are necessary.

 To find out more about global warming, visit in.bdol.glencoe.com/earth_science

128   BIOLOGICAL DIVERSITY AND CONSERVATION

Writing About Biology

Potential impacts of global warming and a changing climate include more frequent and severe heat waves, more frequent extreme events such as floods and droughts, glacial melting, the rise of ocean levels, and more intense storms.

 Indiana Academic Standards

Pages 128–129: B.1.38, B.1.41, B.1.46

STUDY GUIDE

Section 5.1

Vanishing Species

Key Concepts

- Biodiversity refers to the variety of life in an area.
- The most common measure of biodiversity is the number of species in an area.
- Maintaining biodiversity is important because if a species is lost from an ecosystem, the loss may have consequences for other species in the same area, including humans.
- Extinctions occur when the last members of species die.
- Habitat loss, fragmentation, and degradation have accelerated the rate of extinctions.
- Exotic species, introduced on purpose or by accident, upset the normal ecological balance in a given area because there are no natural competitors or predators in that area to keep their growth in check.

Vocabulary

acid precipitation (p. 118)
biodiversity (p. 111)
edge effect (p. 117)
endangered species (p. 115)
exotic species (p. 120)
extinction (p. 115)
habitat degradation (p. 118)
habitat fragmentation (p. 117)
ozone layer (p. 118)
threatened species (p. 116)

Section 5.2

Conservation of Biodiversity

Key Concepts

- Conservation biology is the study and implementation of methods to preserve Earth's biodiversity.
- In 1973, the Endangered Species Act was signed into law in response to concerns about species extinction. The law protects species on the endangered and threatened species lists in an effort to prevent their extinction.
- Larger protected areas generally have greater biodiversity than smaller protected areas.
- Animal reintroduction programs have been more successful when the reintroduced organisms come from the wild rather than from captivity.

Vocabulary

captivity (p. 125)
conservation biology (p. 121)
habitat corridors (p. 123)
natural resources (p. 121)
reintroduction programs (p. 124)
sustainable use (p. 123)

FOLDABLES
Study Organizer To help you review biological diversity and conservation, use the Organizational Study Foldables on page 111.

 in.bdol.glencoe.com/vocabulary_puzzlemaker

CHAPTER 5 ASSESSMENT **129**

Chapter 5 Assessment

Key Concepts
Summary statements can be used by students to review the major concepts of the chapter.

 Biology Online

Visit in.bdol.glencoe.com
/self_check_quiz
/vocabulary_puzzlemaker
/chapter_test
/standardized_test

VOCABULARY PUZZLEMAKER

For additional help with vocabulary, have students access the Vocabulary PuzzleMaker online at in.bdol.glencoe.com/vocabulary_puzzlemaker

FOLDABLES™
Have students use their Foldables to review the content of Section 5.1. On the back of their Foldables, have students list steps that could be taken to reduce threats to biodiversity. Follow this with a class discussion about the strengths and weaknesses of some of these steps.

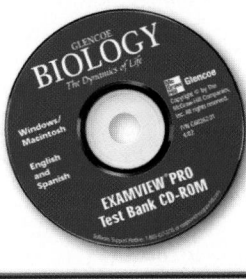

Use the Exam*View*®Pro Test Bank CD-ROM to:
- Create **multiple versions** of tests
- Create **modified** tests with one mouse click for **inclusion** students
- **Edit** existing questions and **add** your own questions
- Build tests aligned with state standards using built-in **State Curriculum Tags**
- Change **English** tests to **Spanish** with one mouse click and vice versa

Chapter 5 Assessment

 Questions and answers have been aligned and verified by The Princeton Review.

Vocabulary Review

1. extinction
2. biodiversity
3. sustainable use
4. habitat fragmentation
5. reintroduction program

Understanding Key Concepts

6. C   8. C
7. C   9. A

Constructed Response

10. Although DDT initially may have been an effective insecticide, the insects quickly develop a resistance. In addition, DDT residues buildup in the fatty tissues of many organisms. Such a build up of insecticide residues can cause problems such as egg thinning and an increase in cancer rates. DDT however, does remain effective against the mosquito that carries malaria, and limited use of it will continue to be allowed for fighting this disease because without it, many people would die.

11. Answers may vary but can include evidence that research about island size informs decision makers that parks or preserves must be of a size large enough to support the ecosystems being protected.

12. Answers will vary. Habitat loss threatens biodiversity by reducing the number and quality of niches.

Thinking Critically

13. Choice B would produce the least impact because all other choices increase habitat fragmentation more than choice B.

130

Vocabulary Review

Review the Chapter 5 vocabulary words listed in the Study Guide on page 129. Match the words with the definitions below.

1. when the last member of a species dies
2. number of species that live in an area
3. use of resources of wilderness areas in ways that do no damage
4. separation of wilderness into smaller parts
5. release of captive organisms into areas where they once lived

Understanding Key Concepts

6. In a study of major bodies of water in the world, aquatic ecologists sampled equal volumes of water and counted the number of species in each sample. Where would you expect to find the smallest number of species?
   A. Lake Victoria, a very large tropical lake in East Africa
   B. the Great Barrier Reef, a coral reef off the coast of Australia
   C. Lake Champlain, a large lake between New York and Vermont
   D. coral reefs in the Red Sea, between Israel and Egypt

7. A protected wildlife area allows local hunters to shoot deer when the deer population rises above a certain level. This is an effort to prevent _____.
   A. habitat loss
   B. habitat fragmentation
   C. habitat degradation
   D. habitat conservation

8. The variety of species in an ecosystem is referred to as its _____.
   A. endangered species
   B. edge effect
   C. biodiversity
   D. threatened species

---

9. The few remaining California condors, nearly extinct in the wild, were taken and bred in captivity. Offspring were successfully released. The success might be due to the fact that _____.
   A. the birds were released in an area away from the factors that caused them to die out
   B. corridors were built to allow the birds to fly unrestricted in the wild
   C. the bird is an exotic species and when released survived because there were no predators
   D. the birds were reintroduced to an area similar to their original territory but in another state.

Constructed Response

10. **Open Ended** Each year, more than a million people die from malaria, which is carried by mosquitoes. These mosquitoes could be controlled by the application of DDT. Research and analyze the strengths and weaknesses of explanations about DDT use.

11. **Open Ended** Research how island size may help in planning national parks and preserves. Use scientific evidence to discuss the strengths and weaknesses of this hypothesis.

12. **Open Ended** Why is habitat loss a threat to biodiversity? Describe a situation in which a specific animal or plant might be at risk.

Thinking Critically

13. **Analyze** A national park has four choices for how roads will cross through the park. Which method would produce the least habitat fragmentation? Give reasons for your choice.

A.   B.   C.   D.

 in.bdol.glencoe.com/chapter_test

---

14. Chances increase unless habitat corridors are created.

15. Studies should be made to determine the numbers of fishes that can be caught without decreasing the overall abundance of fishes or adversely affecting other populations. Limits should be placed to reduce the possibility of catching fishes above these limits. Plans may include limiting the number of fishes taken, size of the fishes taken, or taking fishes only in certain seasons.

16. The Web site should contain information and links to the California condor, bald eagle, peregrine falcon, timber wolf, red wolf, and black-footed ferret. In each case the reintroduction was expensive, there was at least some public resistance, and continued protection is in place.

14. Refer to the illustration below. An adult male Florida panther requires an average of 10.52 km² of territory to survive and reproduce. Development has changed a particular panther's territory from 21 km² in diagram A to the territory configuration in diagram B which is broken up by roadways. What can be done to improve the panther's habitat in situation B?

Habitat fragmentation

A.   **B.**

15. Using the idea of carrying capacity, design a plan for sustainable use of trout in a mid-western lake.

16. **REAL WORLD BIOCHALLENGE** In recent years there have been some important successes with reintroduction programs. Visit **in.bdol.glencoe.com** to investigate some of the success stories. What are the similarities between each of the successful reintroductions? Make a map to show the range of at least two species before and after their reintroduction and relate your findings to the class.

The assessed Indiana standard appears next to the question.

 End-of-Course Assessment Practice

All questions aligned and verified by **The Princeton Review**

Part 1 Multiple Choice

Use the graph below to answer questions 17 and 18 about wetland-dependent species in a northeastern state.

State Wetland Data

Total number of endangered species	Percent wetland dependent
157 plants	65
510 vertebrates	58

17. Calculate the number of endangered plants B.1.43 that are wetland dependent.
- **A.** 157
- **B.** 296
- **C.** 102
- **D.** 123

18. What is the total number of endangered B.1.43 species that are wetland dependent?
- **A.** 102
- **B.** 157
- **C.** 296
- **D.** 398

19. A federally funded project was halted when an B.1.41 endangered species was found on the land. This probably occurred because _____.
- **A.** the U.S. Endangered Species Act forbids the development
- **B.** a reintroduction program was under way
- **C.** the endangered species was an animal and not a plant
- **D.** the Endangered Species list needed to be updated

20. Which of the following is an abiotic factor B.1.43 associated with loss of biodiversity?
- **A.** An exotic species is introduced to the area.
- **B.** A predator disappears.
- **C.** A population doubles.
- **D.** Habitat corridors open new territories.

Part 2 Constructed Response/Grid In

Record your answers on your answer document.

21. Open Ended Large carnivores have a greater chance of becoming extinct than smaller organisms. What factors make this statement true? Provide examples.

22. Open Ended Why is it important for people to know something about the social and economic as well as the scientific aspects of an area when planning a national park?

in.bdol.glencoe.com/standardized_test   CHAPTER 5 ASSESSMENT **131**

End-of-Course Assessment Practice

17. C   **19.** A
18. D   **20.** A

21. Large carnivores generally require greater areas to feed, to defend, and to find a mate. Incursion, generally by humans reduces the available habitat and therefore, cuts back on available areas for the carnivore.

22. Discussions should include strengths and weaknesses. Many factors affect decisions about setting aside areas that will no longer be available for commercial development. Jobs may be affected negatively although new ones may be created. There is also the cost of the development to be factored.

Answer Sheet A practice answer sheet can be found on p. 135 of *Unit 2 FAST FILE Resources.*

RUBRIC

For more help evaluating open-ended assessment questions, see the rubric on p. 9T.

 Indiana Academic Standards

Pages 130–131: B.1.37, B.1.41, B.1.43, B.1.45

Prepare

Short on Time?

This BioDigest can be used as an introduction to or as an overview of ecology, biomes, population ecology, succession, and biodiversity. If time is limited, you may wish to use this unit summary to teach about ecology in place of the chapters in the ecology unit.

Key Concepts

Students learn about the interdependence of organisms and the abiotic and biotic factors in ecosystems. They are introduced to nutrient cycles, trophic levels, population growth, succession, and biodiversity.

1 Focus

Bellringer

Before presenting the lesson, write the term *food chain* on the chalkboard. Then write these terms with connecting arrows: *rose* ⇒ *aphid* ⇒ *ladybug*. Ask students what they think the arrows show. how one organism consumes or depends on another; the movement of matter and energy

Display the transparency for Chapter 2, Section 2.1. Based on the food chain discussion, have students point out the interactions that are shown in the transparency.

Ecology

An organism's environment is the source of all its needs and all its threats. Living things depend on their environments for food, water, and shelter. Yet, environments may contain things that can injure or kill organisms, such as storms, diseases, or predators. Ecology is the study of the interactions between organisms and their environments.

Ecosystems

The relationships among living things and how the nonliving environment affects life are the key aspects of ecology. An ecosystem is made up of all the interactions among organisms and their environment that occur within a defined space.

Abiotic Factors

Around the world there are many types of biomes, such as rain forests and grasslands. The nonliving parts of the environment, called abiotic factors, influence life. For example, latitude, temperature, and precipitation influence the type of life in a terrestrial biome.

▼ This coral reef's survival strategies include methods of obtaining needs and avoiding dangers.

▲ Hot temperatures and little precipitation are abiotic factors in this desert biome.

FOCUS ON ADAPTATIONS

Symbiosis

Bees pollinate flowers, and in return, bees obtain nectar.

Clingfish hide in the spines of a sea urchin.

Relationships formed between organisms are important biotic factors in an environment. Adaptations, which can be physiological, structural, or behavioral, enable organisms to profit from relationships. In symbiosis, the close relationship between two species, at least one species profits. There are three categories of symbiosis that depend on whether the other species profits, suffers, or is unaffected by the relationship.

Mutualism In mutualism, both species benefit from their relationship. For example, bees have a mutualistic relationship with flowers. As the bee eats nectar from the flower, pollen becomes attached to the bee. The bee moves to another flower, and some of the pollen from the first flower may pollinate the second flower. The bee gets food, and the plant is able to reproduce.

132

RESOURCE MANAGER

Unit 2 *FAST FILE* Resources
Reinforcement and Study Guide in
English, pp. 137–138
Reinforcement and Study Guide in
Spanish, pp. 139–140
Student Recording Sheet, p. 141

In photosynthesis, plants use nonliving (abiotic) materials, including water, carbon dioxide, and light energy, to produce energy-rich nutrients. For this reason, photosynthetic organisms are called producers.

The water cycle, featuring evaporation from lakes and oceans, condensation to produce clouds, and precipitation, provides an understanding of how water cycles through an ecosystem. Nitrogen and carbon also cycle through ecosystems. In the carbon cycle, plants produce nutrients from carbon dioxide in the atmosphere. When these nutrients are broken down, energy is released. Carbon dioxide is also released and returns to the atmosphere.

Biotic Factors

Living organisms and the effects they have on each other are biotic factors. A population consists of one species. Within a community, different populations compete for needs, predators kill prey, and diseases spread.

Autotrophs and Heterotrophs

Organisms that make their own food, such as plants and algae, are called autotrophs. Organisms that cannot make their food must consume other organisms. These organisms are called heterotrophs or consumers. Heterotrophs that consume only plants are called herbivores. Heterotrophs that consume only animals are called carnivores. Omnivores are heterotrophs that consume plants and animals.

Nutrient and Energy Flow

Life on Earth depends on energy from the sun. Plants use this light energy to make food. Animals eat plants or other animals for food.

The path the nutrients and energy take can be shown in a food chain such as:

rose → aphid → ladybug

This shows that the aphid eats the rose and obtains its nutrients and energy. The ladybug eats the aphid and obtains its nutrients and energy. This food chain is simple. More complex feeding relationships are represented by a food web.

In summary, nutrients cycle through ecosystems. Today, there is as much nitrogen and carbon or phosphorus and water as there was millions of years ago. Energy is transferred from one organism to another, but at each transfer, some energy is given off to the environment as heat.

Commensalism In commensalism, one species benefits, while another species is neither helped nor hurt. A clingfish hiding in the stinging spines of a sea urchin is an example of commensalism. The clingfish hides from predators because the sea urchin's sting deters many predatory organisms. The clingfish benefits from the relationship, but the sea urchin is not harmed.

Parasitism Another form of symbiosis is parasitism, which exists when a smaller parasite obtains its nutrition from a larger host. The relationship benefits the parasite, and is harmful to the host. An example of parasitism includes a tapeworm in the intestines of a human.

A tree parasitized by mistletoe

133

2 Teach

Using Science Terms

Abiotic and Biotic Factors On the chalkboard, list ten or more miscellaneous biotic and abiotic items. Have students identify each term as either abiotic or biotic and defend their choice. Suggested terms are: animals (live), soil, air, water, temperature, mold, bacteria, light, and plants. Some more challenging items might be leaves on trees, leaves that have fallen to the ground, acorns, seeds in a package.

Content Background

Symbiotic Relationships Discuss the various types of symbiotic relationships described on these pages. Every organism is involved in some way in an interaction with one or more organisms in its lifetime. How an individual species behaves in these relationships may be the result of adaptations that have helped the species survive and evolve.

Certain adaptations may help reduce competition with other organisms, and thus increase the chances of survival. One organism, the spittlebug, feeds on plant juices. While doing so, it covers itself with foam. The ability to do this (an adaptation) apparently deters other organisms from feeding on the spittlebug.

Quick Demo

Mutualism Bring in and display a lichen. Explain that this is an example of the symbiotic relationship called mutualism. A species of fungus and alga work together to form the lichen and allow it to survive on dry, barren rocks. Ask students why this is an example of mutualism.

133

Revealing Misconceptions

All predators are large, meat-eating animals.

Uncover the Misconception

Have students review the definition of a predator. Then have them brainstorm organisms that they think are predators. The list will probably include lions, tigers, bears, and snakes.

Demonstrate the Concept

Show illustrations (photos or art) of smaller predatory organisms. Examples include spiders (all), cats (lynx), dogs (coyotes), birds (robins, insect-eating species, eagles), foxes. There are also plants that are classified as parasites or predators, some of animals (pitcher plants and Venus's-flytrap) and others of plants (dodder, strangler fig, mistletoe). Plants that are predators of animals obtain their supply of nitrogen from animal tissues.

Assess New Knowledge

Have students research a predator, its habitat, where it is found geographically, its usual prey, and what threats there may be to its existence as a species.

Trophic Levels

Nutrients and energy move from autotroph to herbivore to carnivore. Each of these steps is called a trophic level. If a forest area were roped off and three piles created—autotrophs, herbivores, and carnivores, the autotroph pile would be larger than the herbivore pile, which would be larger than the carnivore pile. The mass of the piles indicates the biological mass, or biomass, of the three trophic levels. The mass of autotrophs is usually about ten times the mass of the herbivores, and the mass of the herbivores is about ten times the mass of the carnivores.

VITAL STATISTICS

Vital Statistics

Energy in a 100 m × 100 m section of forest:
Producers—24 055 000 kilocalories
Herbivores—2 515 000 kilocalories
Carnivores—235 000 kilocalories

Population Size

A population is defined as all the members of one species living in an area. The size of a population is influenced by the environment. For example, a lack of food could limit the number of organisms. Other limiting factors in population growth are water, shelter, and space. As population size increases, competition for some needed items intensifies.

Populations may be kept below their carrying capacity due to predation.

Carrying Capacity

The maximum population size an environment can support is called its carrying capacity. When population size rises above the carrying capacity, some organisms die because they cannot meet all their needs. The population falls back to below the carrying capacity until it reaches equilibrium with the environment.

Exponential Growth

If a population has no predators, and the organisms are in a resource-rich environment, population size would grow quickly. This fast growth is called exponential growth. Exponential growth cannot continue forever; at some point, some need will become a limiting factor in the population's growth.

FOCUS ON ADAPTATIONS

Pioneer Species

As lichens grow, they break down rocks and produce soil.

The first organisms to colonize new areas are pioneer species. Rocky areas, such as land recently covered by a lava flow, have pioneer species different from areas that already have soil. Rocky areas are usually first colonized by lichens.

On rock Lichens are made up of two organisms, a species of fungus and a species of photosynthetic algae or bacteria. The fungus holds its photosynthetic partner between thick fiber layers, allowing just enough light to penetrate to allow photosynthesis (food production) without drying out the lichen. The fungus provides a tough case and the photosynthetic partner supplies nutrition. Through this mutualistic relationship, lichens are able to survive in the harshest of climates such as high on mountains, in cold arctic regions, and in hot deserts.

134

INCLUSION STRATEGIES

Learning Disabled Cut three segments of 2 × 4 inch (5 × 10 cm) lumber, 10 inches (25 cm), 8 inches (20 cm), and 6 inches (15 cm) long. The first plank represents producers, the second herbivores, and the third, carnivores. Have students use the pieces to explain a biomass pyramid. **L1 ELL**

TECH PREP

Encouraging Pioneers: *Visual-Spatial* In the schoolyard or a nearby vacant lot, remove all plants from a patch of ground that is about 1 meter square. Have students draw and identify the first plants that begin to grow in the empty space. **L2 ELL**

Succession

What happens when a building is torn down and not replaced? Usually the land begins to change almost immediately. New plants sprout. No doubt, one of the first things to grow are weeds. Blown in or carried by animals into an area that already has soil, plants act as pioneer species, the first organisms to thrive in a new environment.

After the plants take hold in an area, others appear, including annual flowers, grasses and then bushes. These provide shade. Now tree seeds germinate. Once the tree saplings are large enough, they shade the ground, blocking the sun from plants underneath. New conditions are forming to make the environment suitable for other organisms. If left to themselves long enough, abandoned areas become new forests. Succession is the process by which these and other types of areas change.

Biodiversity

During succession, the species living in an ecosystem change, usually by moving in or dying out of an area, over time. Consequently, the ecosystem changes too. Earth's biosphere, the part of the planet that supports life, changes over time as well. The measure of change that takes place in a small habitat or a large ecosystem is the number of species of organisms—plants, animals, bacteria, fungi, and other microorganisms that are found in the area. This number of species in an area is the area's biodiversity.

The variety of species in coral reefs is important in maintaining Earth's biodiversity.

Populations

There are many pressures that act as controls on the growth of all populations. Predators and disease help control populations. In addition, Earth's organisms compete with each other for food, shelter, and space. Some of these pressures bring about the extinction or threat of extinction of species. How to use and find enough of the resources needed by all living organisms, especially land, food, air, and water, is of immediate concern for maintaining Earth's biodiversity. As land is converted for other uses, organisms lose their habitats. When organisms die out of a habitat that has been destroyed, organisms that depend on those habitats are also affected.

In soil After existing land is disturbed, such as after a forest fire, secondary succession begins as pioneer species appear. Most pioneer plants produce many small seeds that are dispersed easily over wide areas, so that when land is disturbed, the seeds are there, ready to grow. Another characteristic of pioneer species is they tend to grow and reproduce quickly. When a fresh patch of soil is disturbed, pioneer species sprout quickly and produce many new seeds to colonize other areas.

Dandelions are an effective pioneer species for secondary succession because they grow fast and disperse many seeds.

135

CHALLENGE ACTIVITY

Preserving Pioneers Encourage students to create a leaf press of common weeds in your area. Have them explain why the weeds are good pioneer soil species, and make this part of their portfolios. **L3**

 Indiana Academic Standards

Pages 134–135: B.1.39, B.1.40, B.1.43, B.1.44, B.1.45

This page contains practice questions in the various formats that can be found on the most frequently given standardized tests.

 Part 1 Multiple Choice

1. B	4. C	7. D
2. A	5. A	8. B
3. B	6. A	9. C

FAST FILE

Answer Sheet A practice answer sheet can be found on p. 141 of *Unit 2 FAST FILE Resources.*

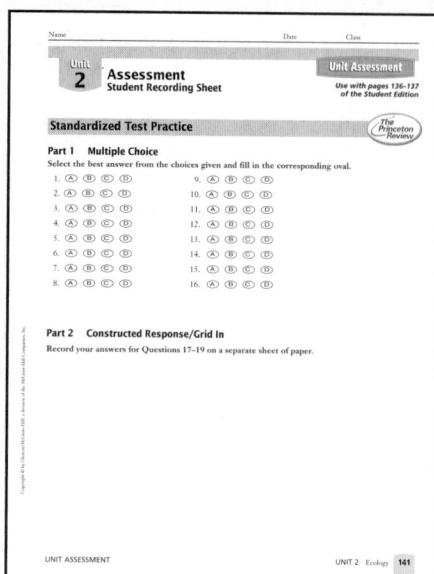

End-of-Course Assessment Practice

The assessed Indiana standard appears next to the question.

The Princeton Review **TEST-TAKING TIP**

Stumbling Is Not Falling

From time to time you find a question that completely throws you. You read the question over and over, and it still doesn't make sense. If it is a multiple choice question, focus on something in the question that you do know something about. Eliminate as many of the choices as you can. Take a best guess, and move on.

Part 1 Multiple Choice

Use the graph below to answer questions 1–3. The graph compares the growth rates of two organisms when grown together and when grown separately.

Growth Rates of Two Organisms

1. When grown separately, how would you best **B.1.43** describe what happened to organism 2 during week 3?
  A. It reached carrying capacity.
  B. The population died out.
  C. It became threatened.
  D. It began to grow exponentially.

2. When the organisms were grown together, what was the approximate rate of growth between weeks 2 and 6?
  A. 75 per week
  B. 100 per month
  C. 50 per week
  D. 25 per day

3. From the data, the association between the **B.1.40** organisms is _____.
  A. commensalism
  B. parasitism
  C. mutualism
  D. socialism

---

4. The number of species in an area is known as _____.
  A. population
  B. competition
  C. biodiversity
  D. carrying capacity

5. Which of the following is a biotic factor in an ecosystem? **B.1.43**
  A. number of predators
  B. amount of light received
  C. average precipitation
  D. average temperature

Study the graph and answer questions 6–9.

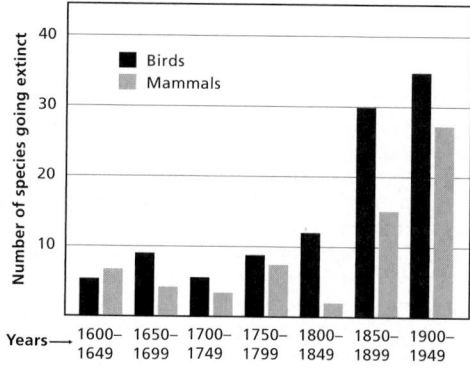

Extinctions of Birds and Mammals

6. In which interval were there more extinctions for mammals than for birds?
  A. 1600–1649
  B. 1650–1699
  C. 1750–1799
  D. 1850–1859

7. In which interval were there the most mammal extinctions?
  A. 1600–1649
  B. 1650–1699
  C. 1850–1859
  D. 1900–1949

8. Approximately how many bird species became extinct in the interval 1650–1699?
  A. 5
  B. 10
  C. 15
  D. 20

9. Approximately how many bird species became extinct in the interval 1600–1949?
  A. 37
  B. 70
  C. 110
  D. 300

Indiana Academic Standards

Pages 136–137: B.1.40, B.1.43

Use the information below and your knowledge of science to answer questions 10–13.

The Texas Horned Lizard

The Texas "horny toad," *Phrynosoma cornutum,* is known by many names, but it is a lizard—a true reptile—and not a toad. Despite its spiny appearance, this lizard was collected extensively as a pet for many years. However, horned lizards do not do well as pets, and once in captivity, most starve to death even if food is available.

In the wild, horned lizards will eat some grasshoppers and beetles, but harvester ants make up about 66 percent of their diet. Where harvester ant habitats have been damaged, horned lizard populations have also declined. When fire ants established themselves in Texas, harvester ant populations decreased. The horned lizard will not feed on fire ants.

Desert Food Web

Hawks

Coyotes

Diamondback rattlesnake

Other lizards

Harvester ants

Prickly pear catus

Texas horned lizard

Decomposers

10. According to the food web shown, all organisms except the cactus are _____.
B.1.44
   A. decomposers
   B. consumers
   C. producers
   D. scavengers

11. Texas horned lizards may have declined in number because they are _____.
B.1.44
   A. preyed upon by harvester ants
   B. protected by law
   C. a threatened species
   D. losing their supply of food

12. The Texas horned lizard primarily competes with _____ for its food.
B.1.43
   A. snakes
   B. cactus plants
   C. other lizards
   D. fire ants

13. Horned lizards are ectotherms. Energy they absorb by lying on hot rocks is transferred by _____.
B.1.44
   A. convection
   B. radiation
   C. conduction
   D. evaporation

Part 2 Constructed Response

Record your answers on your answer document.

14. Open Ended What eventually happens to a population that is currently experiencing exponential growth? Explain.

15. Open Ended Describe how a specific abiotic factor and a specific biotic factor could affect the life of a deer.
B.1.43

10. B	**12.** C
11. D	**13.** C

Part 2 Constructed Response/Grid In

14. With unlimited supplies of resources (food and space), the population could grow unchecked (in a J-shape) even as members of the population die off. Resources may become scarce and limit population growth. Perhaps if dead members are not removed from the population, the population growth rate will slow because the quality of the resources will have changed.

15. A biotic factor that could affect the life of the deer is food supply. Lack of food could bring about starvation and disease to a population. An abiotic factor could be space. If the area that the deer live in is inadequate for a growing population, then usually the food supply becomes insufficient and members become ill or die off.

RUBRIC

For more help evaluating open-ended assessment questions, see the rubric on p. 9T.

Unit Overview

Unit 3 introduces students to basic chemistry, cell structure and function, and cell energetics.
Chapter 6 presents basic concepts of chemistry important in biology.
Chapter 7 introduces cell structure and function.
Chapter 8 expands upon the discussion in Chapter 7 through an in-depth view of cellular transport and the cell cycle.
Chapter 9 acquaints students with the details of energy flow in photosynthesis and respiration.

Introducing the Unit

Ask students to describe some of the things they see in the photographs of cells within the unit. Lead a discussion on what knowledge and questions the students have about cells. Take notes and revisit them after the unit is complete to reassess their knowledge.

WebQuest A WebQuest is an inquiry-based online project in which all information used by students is obtained from the Web. Students evaluate the information to complete the activity. Access the Unit 3 WebQuest at **in.bdol.glencoe.com/webquest**

Indiana Academic Standards

Pages 138–139: B.1.3

138

Unit 3

History & Biology

1620 Pilgrims aboard the *Mayflower* land at Plymouth, Massachusetts.

1600 — 1700

1665 Robert Hooke first describes and names cells when he observes a slice of cork using a hand-crafted microscope that magnifies 30 times.

1674 The first living cells—single-celled organisms—are observed. They are called *animalcules* meaning "little animals."

The Life of a Cell

What You'll Learn

Chapter 6
The Chemistry of Life

Chapter 7
A View of the Cell

Chapter 8
Cellular Transport and the Cell Cycle

Chapter 9
Energy in a Cell

Unit 3 Review
BioDigest & Standardized Test Practice

Why It's Important

A cell is the most basic unit of living organisms. No matter how complex an organism is, at its core it is a collection of cells. In many organisms, cells work together, forming more complex structures.

Indiana Standards
The following standards are covered in Unit 3:
B.1.1, B.1.2, B.1.3, B.1.4, B.1.5, B.1.6, B.1.7, B.1.8, B.1.9, B.1.12, B.1.16, B.1.43, B.1.44

Understanding the Photo ▶

This is a color-enhanced image of a plant cell taken with a transmission electron microscope. Note the many compartments within the cell. These compartments keep the cell's functions separated.

Color-enhanced TEM Magnification: 4200×

138 in.bdol.glencoe.com/webquest

Time Line

Discussion As students read the unit, have them refer to the time line above. Ask students to consider the reasons that many cell discoveries came in short bursts (such as 1665–1674, 1831–1839, and 1950–1991), followed by longer periods of non-discovery (such as 1674–1831, and 1855–1950). Students should realize that discovery and knowledge of cells was dependent on technology, especially advances and developments in microscopes. **L2**

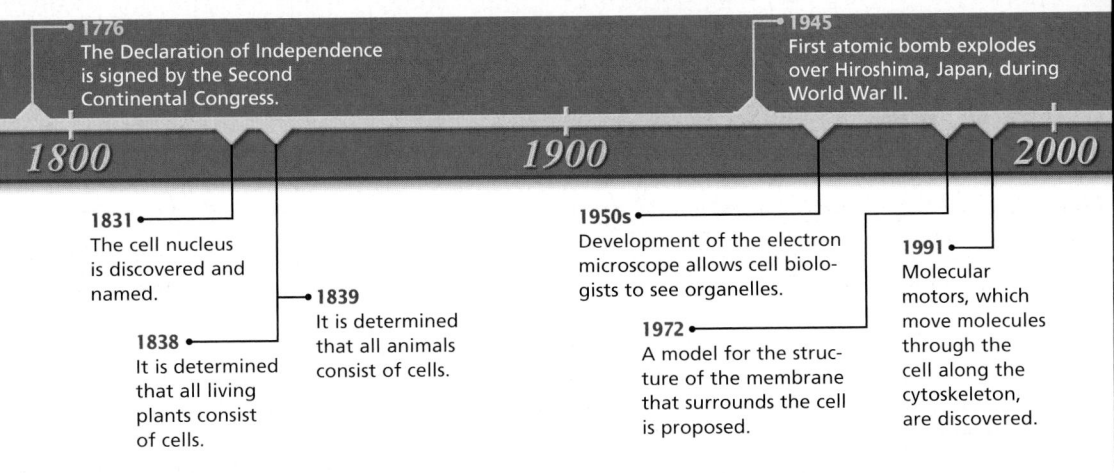

1776
The Declaration of Independence is signed by the Second Continental Congress.

1945
First atomic bomb explodes over Hiroshima, Japan, during World War II.

1800   *1900*   *2000*

1831
The cell nucleus is discovered and named.

1838
It is determined that all living plants consist of cells.

1839
It is determined that all animals consist of cells.

1950s
Development of the electron microscope allows cell biologists to see organelles.

1972
A model for the structure of the membrane that surrounds the cell is proposed.

1991
Molecular motors, which move molecules through the cell along the cytoskeleton, are discovered.

139

Unit 3

Advance Materials Planning

The following materials may need to be ordered a few weeks in advance of the planned activity.

Chapter 6
- ■ **Quick Demo** (p. 146) 9-volt battery, wire
- ■ **Quick Demo** (p. 159) ball-and-stick models

Chapter 7
- ■ **Additional Lab** (p. 182) *Elodea* plant, prepared slide of human cheek cells
- ■ **BioLab** (p. 188) prepared slides of *Bacillus subtilis*, frog blood, *Elodea* leaf

Chapter 8
- ■ **MiniLab** (p. 198) iodine solution
- ■ **MiniLab** (p. 209) fish mitosis slides
- ■ **BioLab** (p. 214) prepared onion root tip slides

Chapter 9
- ■ **MiniLab** (p. 226) filter paper
- ■ **MiniLab** (p. 236) plastic pipettes
- ■ **BioDigest** (p. 246) molecular model of a lipid, dialysis bags

Unit Projects

Building a Model
Kinesthetic Ask students to build a three-dimensional model of an atom. Students should use objects to represent protons, electrons, and neutrons. Suspend these in the appropriate place. Wire loops can represent energy levels. **L2**

Using the Library
Intrapersonal Encourage students to find out how a cell grows and divides. Have them design a poster showing the steps of this process. **L2**

Cells Alive
Visual-Spatial Have students view slides of different types of cells at in.bdol.glencoe.com/microscopy . They can draw diagrams of each and postulate why each has its unique shape. **L1** **ELL**

139

Section Objectives	National Science Standards	State/Local Standards	Advanced Lab and Demo Planning
Section 6.1 1 session, 1/2 block 1. **Relate** the particle structure of an atom to the identity of elements. 2. **Relate** the formation of covalent and ionic chemical bonds to the stability of atoms. 3. **Distinguish** mixtures and solutions. 4. **Define** acids and bases and relate their importance to biological systems.	UCP.1, UCP.2, UCP.3; A.1, A.2; B.1–3; C.5; E.1, E.2; F.1; G.1, G.2	**Indiana Standards** B.1.5, B.1.9	**Student Labs:** Problem-Solving Lab 6.1, p. 145 MiniLab 6.1, p. 151: beakers or small glass containers, lemon juice, prepared household ammonia solution, liquid detergent, shampoo, vinegar, pH paper **Teacher Demonstration:** Quick Demo, p. 146: beaker, salted water, wire, 9-volt battery
Section 6.2 1 session, 1/2 block 5. **Relate** water's unique features to polarity. 6. **Explain** how the process of diffusion occurs and why it is important to cells.	UCP.1, UCP.2, UCP.3; A.1, A.2; B.1–4, B.6; C.5; G.1–3	**Indiana Standards** B.1.2, B.1.5, B.1.9	**Student Labs:** Problem-Solving Lab 6.2, p. 154 MiniLab 6.2, p. 155: single-edge razor blade, raw peeled potato, forceps, cup or beaker, purple dye **Teacher Demonstration:** Quick Demo, p. 153: paper towel, water
Section 6.3 3 sessions, 1 block 7. **Classify** the variety of organic compounds. 8. **Describe** how polymers are formed and broken down in organisms. 9. **Compare** the chemical structures of carbohydrates, lipids, proteins, and nucleic acids, and relate their importance to living things. 10. **Identify** the effects of enzymes.	UCP.1, UCP.2, UCP.3; A.1, A.2; B.1–3, B.6; C.5; E.1, E.2; F.1, F.5; G.1–3	**Indiana Standards** B.1.3, B.1.4, B.1.5, B.1.6, B.1.9, B.1.10	**Student Labs:** Additional Lab, pp. 160–161: 4 paper cups with gelatin, fresh pineapple, knife, waxed paper, canned chunk pineapple, grapes or orange sections, refrigerator Investigate BioLab, p. 164: See materials below. **Teacher Demonstration:** Quick Demo, p. 159: ball-and-stick model of a methane molecule
End of Chapter Assessment Student Edition **Study Guide,** p. 167 **Content Assessment,** pp. 168–169		**Indiana Standards** B.1.2, B.1.5, B.1.6, B.1.9	**Student Lab:** Investigate BioLab, p. 164: clock or timer, 400-mL beaker, kitchen knife, tongs or large forceps, 5-mm thick potato slices, ice, hot plate, waxed paper, non-mercury thermometer, 3% hydrogen peroxide

Key to Teaching Strategies

L1 Level 1 activities should be appropriate for students with learning difficulties.

L2 Level 2 activities should be within the ability range of all students.

L3 Level 3 activities are designed for above-average students.

ELL ELL activities should be within the ability range of English Language Learners.

COOP LEARN Cooperative Learning activities are designed for small group work.

Legend

- 🖐 Transparency
- 💿 CD-ROM
- 🎵 MP3
- ▭ Videocassette
- 💿 DVD

Glencoe Exclusive!

TeacherWorks™
All-In-One Planner and Resource Center

Reproducible Masters and Transparencies

Unit 3 *FAST FILE* **Resources**
MiniLab Worksheet, p. 3
BioLab Worksheet, pp. 5–6
Reinforcement and Study Guide in English, pp. 9–10
Reinforcement and Study Guide in Spanish, pp. 13–14
Transparency Worksheets, pp. 19, 23–28
Reading Essentials for Biology, Section 6.1
🖐 **Section Focus Transparency 12**
🖐 **Basic Concepts Transparencies 4, 5a, 5b**

Unit 3 *FAST FILE* **Resources**
MiniLab Worksheet, p. 4
Reinforcement and Study Guide in English, p. 11
Reinforcement and Study Guide in Spanish, p. 15
Concept Mapping, p. 17
Transparency Worksheet, p. 20
Reading Essentials for Biology, Section 6.2
🖐 **Section Focus Transparency 13**

Unit 3 *FAST FILE* **Resources**
Real World BioApplications, pp. 7–8
Reinforcement and Study Guide in English, p. 12
Reinforcement and Study Guide in Spanish, p. 16
Critical Thinking/Problem Solving, p. 18
Transparency Worksheets, pp. 21, 29–30
Reading Essentials for Biology, Section 6.3
Laboratory Manual, pp. 27–34
🖐 **Section Focus Transparency 14**
🖐 **Reteaching Skills Transparency 8**

Unit 3 *FAST FILE* **Resources**
Chapter Assessment, pp. 31–36
Student Recording Sheet, p. 37
The Princeton Review **Reviewing Biology,** pp. 11–12

Technology

💿 **Interactive Chalkboard CD-ROM: Section 6.1 Presentation**
💿 **TeacherWorks™ CD-ROM**
🎵 **Guided Reading Audio Summaries MP3**

💿 **Interactive Chalkboard CD-ROM: Section 6.2 Presentation**
💿 **TeacherWorks™ CD-ROM**
🎵 **Guided Reading Audio Summaries MP3**

💿 **Interactive Chalkboard CD-ROM: Section 6.3 Presentation**
💿 **TeacherWorks™ CD-ROM**
🎵 **Guided Reading Audio Summaries MP3**
💿 **Virtual Labs CD-ROM**
Virtual Lab: Enzyme-Controlled Reactions

💿 **Interactive Chalkboard: Chapter 6 Assessment**
💿 **MindJogger Videoquizzes DVD/VHS**
💿 **ExamView® Pro Test Bank CD-ROM**
💿 **TeacherWorks™ CD-ROM**
💿

🖥 in.bdol.glencoe.com
/self_check_quiz
/vocabulary_puzzlemaker
/chapter_test
/standardized_test

🖐 Indicates materials created specifically for Indiana.

Short on Time?

BIODIGEST The BioDigest at the end of this unit can be used as a(n):

- preview to introduce important unit concepts.
- overview if time does not permit teaching the entire chapter.
- review of key unit concepts.

Understanding the Photo

Ask students to list the features of living things and compile a list on the board. Brainstorm to see what students know about how living things are chemically different and similar to nonliving materials. Ask them to speculate about why early scientists thought a mysterious force controlled chemical changes in organisms.

INTERACTIVE CHALKBOARD with Image Bank

PowerPoint® Presentations

This CD-ROM is an editable Microsoft® PowerPoint® presentation that includes:
- Section presentations
- Section checks
- Image bank
- Hot links to Biology Online
- All transparencies

The Chemistry of Life

What You'll Learn

- You will relate an atom's interactions with other atoms to its structure.
- You will explain why water is important to life.
- You will compare the role of biomolecules in organisms.

Why It's Important

Living organisms are made of simple elements as well as complex carbon compounds. With an understanding of these elements and compounds, you will be able to relate them to how living organisms function.

Understanding the Photo ▶

This butterfly, as well as the colorful flower, is made of atoms. Atoms also make up the breakfast you ate this morning, the air you breathe, and the pages of this book. Why, then, are all these things different?

Biology Online

Visit in.bdol.glencoe.com to
- study the entire chapter online
- access Web Links for more information and activities on the chemistry of life
- review content with the Interactive Tutor and self-check quizzes

140

Two-Minute Chapter Launcher

Demo Using a piece of carbon (such as coal), a bottle of water, and sugar cubes, tell students that the combination of carbon and water contains the same elements as sugar. Mix a small amount of water in a beaker containing some powdered pieces of coal. Sugar does not result. Ask students why you don't get sugar when you mix water with the coal. Help them understand that the elements (carbon in coal; hydrogen and oxygen in water) only combine as sugar when chemical bonds form. Unlike the coal and water mixture, sugar cannot be easily separated into its components.

Section 6.1

Atoms and Their Interactions

Indiana Standards Standard B.1.9 Recognize and describe that both living and nonliving things are composed of compounds, which are themselves made up of elements joined by energy-containing bonds, such as those in ATP.

Atoms: The Building Blocks of Rocks— and You!

Using Prior Knowledge The difference between living and nonliving things may be readily apparent to you. For example, these corals are responding to their surroundings, something you would not expect a rock to do. We know, however, that living things have a great deal in common with rocks, CDs, computer chips, and other nonliving objects. Both living and nonliving things are composed of the basic building blocks called atoms.

Cup corals eat a juvenile octopus.

Compare and Contrast *What makes a living thing different from a nonliving thing? How are the particles that make up a rock similar to those of a coral?*

Elements

Everything—whether it is a rock, frog, or flower—is made of substances called **elements.** Suppose you find a nugget of pure gold. You could grind it into a billion bits of powder and every particle would still be gold. You could treat the gold with every known chemical, but you could never break it down into simpler substances. That's because gold is an element. An element is a substance that can't be broken down into simpler chemical substances.

Natural elements in living things

Of the naturally occurring elements on Earth, only about 25 are essential to living organisms. *Table 6.1* on the next page lists some elements found in the human body. Notice that four of the elements—carbon, hydrogen, oxygen, and nitrogen—together make up more than 96 percent of the mass of a human body. Each element is identified by a one- or two-letter abbreviation called a symbol. For example, the symbol C represents the element carbon, Ca represents the element calcium, and Cl represents the element chlorine.

6.1 ATOMS AND THEIR INTERACTIONS **141**

1 Focus

INTERACTIVE CHALKBOARD
PowerPoint® Presentations

Bellringer
Section Focus Transparency 12

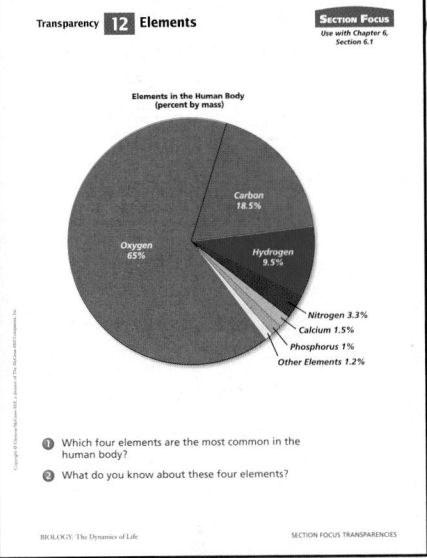

Transparency **12** Elements

SECTION FOCUS
Use with Chapter 6, Section 6.1

Elements in the Human Body
(percent by mass)

Carbon 18.5%
Oxygen 65%
Hydrogen 9.5%
Nitrogen 3.3%
Calcium 1.5%
Phosphorus 1%
Other Elements 1.2%

❶ Which four elements are the most common in the human body?
❷ What do you know about these four elements?

BIOLOGY: The Dynamics of Life
SECTION FOCUS TRANSPARENCIES

Using Prior Knowledge

Compare and Contrast Living things and nonliving things are all made of atoms. It is the way the atoms combine into different elements that affects their physical and chemical properties and whether they are living or nonliving. The particles that form a rock and the hard outer covering of a coral are made of similar substances that are combined differently.

2 Teach

Visual Learning

Visual-Spatial Discuss possible dietary sources of each element listed in Table 6.1. Have students redesign the table to include pictures that show two sources of each element listed. Have students conduct additional research if necessary. **L2** **ELL**

Concept Development

Stress that the elements carbon, hydrogen, nitrogen, oxygen, phosphorus, and sulfur are the main components of living matter. All of these elements form molecules through covalent bonding. Refer to this during the discussion of covalent bonds on pages 145–146.

Display

Make a bulletin board display that models the structure of an atom. Label the nucleus, protons, neutrons, and electrons of the model. Refer to the display when discussing atomic structure.

Table 6.1 Some Elements That Make Up the Human Body					
Element	Symbol	Percent By Mass in Human Body	Element	Symbol	Percent By Mass in Human Body
Oxygen	O	65.0	Iron	Fe	trace
Carbon	C	18.5	Zinc	Zn	trace
Hydrogen	H	9.5	Copper	Cu	trace
Nitrogen	N	3.3	Iodine	I	trace
Calcium	Ca	1.5	Manganese	Mn	trace
Phosphorus	P	1.0	Boron	B	trace
Potassium	K	0.4	Chromium	Cr	trace
Sulfur	S	0.3	Molybdenum	Mo	trace
Sodium	Na	0.2	Cobalt	Co	trace
Chlorine	Cl	0.2	Selenium	Se	trace
Magnesium	Mg	0.1	Fluorine	F	trace

Trace elements

Some of the elements listed in ***Table 6.1,*** such as iron and copper, are present in living things in very small amounts. Such elements are known as trace elements. They play a vital role in maintaining healthy cells in all organisms, as shown by the examples in ***Figure 6.1.*** Plants obtain trace elements by absorbing them through their roots; animals get them from the foods they eat.

Atoms: The Building Blocks of Elements

Whether elements are found in living things, like cup corals, mammals, or plants, or in nonliving things, like rocks, they are made of atoms. An **atom** is the smallest particle of an element that has the characteristics of that element. Atoms are the basic building blocks of all matter. The way they are structured affects their properties and their chemical behavior.

Figure 6.1
Some elements that are needed in small amounts are involved in cell metabolism.

A Mammals use iodine (I) to produce hormones, substances that affect chemical activities in the body.

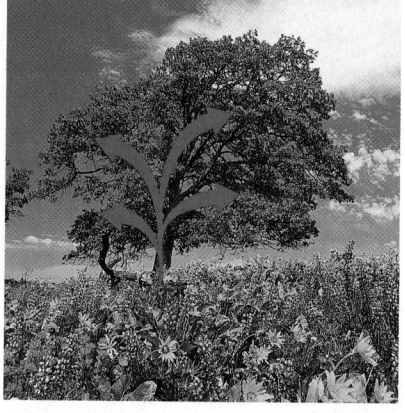

B Plants use magnesium (Mg) to form chlorophyll, which captures light energy for sugar production.

PROJECT

Table of Elements To help students better understand elements, create a Periodic Table of Everyday Things. Have students bring in objects to represent as many elements as possible on the Periodic Table of Elements (coal for carbon, an aluminum can for aluminum). Display these in the same order as the Periodic Table. Use photos to represent hard-to-find or unsafe elements. Refer to this Periodic Table throughout the year as elements are discussed. **L2** **ELL**

Figure 6.2
Electrons move rapidly around nuclei composed of protons and neutrons.

Nucleus
1 proton (p^+)
0 neutrons (n^0)

Hydrogen atom

B Hydrogen, the simplest atom, has just one electron in its first energy level and one proton in its nucleus.

Nucleus
8 protons (p^+)
8 neutrons (n^0)

Nucleus

Electron energy levels

A An atom has a nucleus and electrons in energy levels.

Oxygen atom

C Oxygen has two electrons in its first energy level and six electrons in the second level.

The structure of an atom

All atoms have the same general structure. The center of an atom is called the **nucleus** (NEW klee us) (plural, nuclei). All nuclei contain positively charged particles called protons (p^+). Most contain particles that have no charge, called neutrons (n^0). All nuclei are positively charged because of the presence of protons. Each element has distinct characteristics that result from the number of protons in the nuclei of the atoms that compose the element. For example, the element iron differs from the element aluminum because iron atoms have a different number of protons than aluminum atoms.

The region of space surrounding the nucleus contains extremely small, negatively charged particles called electrons (e^-). The electrons are held in this region by their attraction to the positively charged nucleus. You can visualize this region as an electron cloud. Although it is impossible to pinpoint the exact location of an electron, the electron cloud is the area where it is most likely to be found.

Electron energy levels

Electrons exist around the nucleus in regions known as energy levels, as indicated in *Figure 6.2A*. The first energy level can hold only two electrons. The second level can hold a maximum of eight electrons. The third level can hold up to 18 electrons. The oxygen atom in *Figure 6.2C* has a total of eight electrons. Two electrons fill the first energy level. The remaining six electrons occupy the second energy level.

Atoms contain equal numbers of electrons and protons; therefore, they have no net charge. The hydrogen (H) atom in *Figure 6.2B* has just one electron and one proton. Oxygen (O) has eight electrons and eight protons.

Intrapersonal The scanning tunneling microscope (STM) provides a three-dimensional map of a molecule's surface by measuring the flow of electrons across a small vacuum gap. A tungsten tip similar to a phonograph needle is positioned a few angstroms from the substance being studied. When a small voltage is applied, some electrons jump across the gap between the tip and the surface. As the tip moves across the surface, the current varies according to the contours of the atoms present. Have capable students research these microscopes and give a presentation to the class. **L3**

✓ **Reading Check** An oxygen atom has a total of 8 electrons, 8 protons, and 8 neutrons. The protons and neutrons form the nucleus, two electrons are in the first energy level, and 6 electrons occupy the second level.

Discussion

Radiation can penetrate and disrupt the functions of living cells. However, certain radioisotopes have practical uses in medicine as diagnostic tools. For example, radioactive iodine is used to identify problems with the thyroid gland. Lead a discussion on how the benefits of such radiation compare with the risks of exposure.

Sulfur

Carbon

Gold

Figure 6.3
The properties of an element are determined by its atoms. As you can see, carbon, gold, and sulfur have very different properties.

Figure 6.3 shows three other elements whose properties differ because of the number of protons in their nuclei.

✓ **Reading Check** **Describe** the structure of an oxygen atom.

Isotopes of an Element

Atoms of the same element always have the same number of protons but may contain different numbers of neutrons. Atoms of the same element that have different numbers of neutrons are called **isotopes** (I suh tohps)

Figure 6.4
Radioactive isotopes are used in medicine to diagnose and/or treat some diseases. Radiation given off when radioactive isotopes break apart is deadly to many rapidly growing cancer cells. This patient is being treated with radiation from a radioactive isotope of cobalt (Co).

of that element. For example, most carbon nuclei contain six neutrons. However, some have seven or eight neutrons. Each of these atoms is an isotope of the element carbon. Scientists refer to isotopes by stating the combined total of protons and neutrons in the nucleus. Thus, the most common carbon atom is referred to as carbon-12 because it has six protons and six neutrons. Other isotopes of carbon include carbon-13 and carbon-14.

Isotopes are often useful to scientists. The nuclei of some isotopes, such as carbon-14, are unstable and tend to break apart. As nuclei break, they give off radiation. These isotopes are said to be radioactive. Because radiation is detectable and can damage or kill cells, scientists have developed some useful applications for radioactive isotopes, as described in *Figure 6.4*.

Atomic models like those discussed in the *Problem-Solving Lab* on the next page help scientists and students visualize the structure of atoms and understand complex intermolecular interactions.

⊙ **CHALLENGE ACTIVITY**

Stable Isotopes Not all isotopes are unstable and radioactive. There are some isotopes—stable isotopes—that do not decay. Like radioisotopes, stable isotopes can be useful in biological research. Challenge advanced students to research how stable isotopes can be used to map the location where a migrating bird was feeding as it grew new feathers. Ask students to research other uses for stable isotopes in scientific studies. **L3**

Compounds and Bonding

Table salt is a substance that is familiar to everyone; however, table salt is not an element. Rather, salt is a type of substance called a compound. A **compound** is a substance that is composed of atoms of two or more different elements that are chemically combined. Table salt (NaCl) is a compound composed of the elements sodium and chlorine. If an electric current is passed through molten salt in an industrial process, the salt breaks down into these elements. You can see in *Figure 6.5* that the properties of a compound are different from those of its individual elements.

How covalent bonds form

Most elements in nature are found combined in the form of compounds. But how and why do atoms combine, and what is it that holds the atoms together in a compound? Atoms combine with other

atoms only when the resulting compound is more stable than the individual atoms.

For many elements, an atom becomes stable when its outermost energy level is full, as when eight electrons are in the second level. An exception is hydrogen, which becomes stable when its first energy level is full (two electrons). How do elements fill the energy levels and become stable? One way is to share electrons with other atoms.

Figure 6.5
Table salt is made from the elements sodium (Na) and chlorine (Cl). The flask contains the poisonous, yellow-green chlorine gas. The lump of silver-white metal is the element sodium. The white crystals of table salt no longer resemble either sodium or chlorine.

Problem-Solving Lab 6.1

Interpret Scientific Illustrations

What can be learned by studying the nucleus of an atom? Looking at a model of the particles in an atom's nucleus can reveal certain information about that particular atom. Models may help predict electron number, the distribution of electrons in energy levels, and how isotopes of an element differ from each other.

Solve the Problem

Examine diagrams A and B. Both are models of an atom of beryllium. Only the nucleus of each atom is shown.

Beryllium nucleus   *Beryllium nucleus*

Thinking Critically

1. **Infer** What is the neutron number for A? For B?
2. **Evaluate** Which diagram represents an isotope of beryllium? Explain how you were able to tell.
3. **Predict** How many electrons are present in atoms A and B? Explain how you were able to tell.
4. **Predict** How many energy levels would be present in atoms of A and B? How might the electrons in A and B be distributed in these levels?

Problem-Solving Lab 6.1

Purpose
Students will use models of the particles in nuclei of beryllium to predict electron number, position of electrons in energy levels, and how differences in the number of neutrons affect the element.

Process Skills
think critically, apply concepts, compare and contrast, define operationally, interpret data

Teaching Strategies
■ Review the concept of isotopes with students. Provide other examples for them to analyze.
■ Explain or emphasize the concept that all atoms of the same element have the same electron and proton number. They may differ only in the number of neutrons.
■ Review the charges associated with each atomic particle.

Thinking Critically
1. 5, 4
2. Both A and B have four protons, so they are both isotopes of beryllium.
3. 4; Electron and proton numbers are always the same.
4. 2; two electrons in each level

Assessment
Knowledge Provide students with two diagrams of the nucleus for the element fluorine. Have one nucleus with 9 neutrons and one with 10 neutrons. Advise them of the most common form (with 9 neutrons). Ask them to provide the same information as they did for beryllium. Use the Performance Task Assessment List for Making Observations and Inferences in **PASC**, p. 89. **L2**

Kenichi Fukui and Chemical Reactions
In the 1950s, Japanese chemist Kenichi Fukui (1918–1998) developed the idea that chemical reactions occur as a result of interactions of the outer-level electrons of one atom or molecule with the outer-level electrons of another atom

or molecule. In 1981, Fukui received the Nobel Prize for Chemistry for his investigations of the mechanisms of chemical reactions. Discuss with students the work of Kenichi Fukui toward understanding chemical interactions. **L2**

 Indiana Academic Standards
Pages 144–145: B.1.9

Figure 6.6
Sometimes atoms combine by sharing electrons to form covalent bonds.

A Hydrogen gas (H_2) exists as two hydrogen atoms sharing electrons with each other. The electrons move around the nuclei of both atoms.

Hydrogen molecule

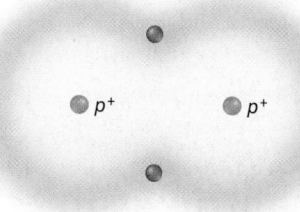

B When two hydrogens share electrons with oxygen, they form covalent bonds to produce a molecule of water (H_2O).

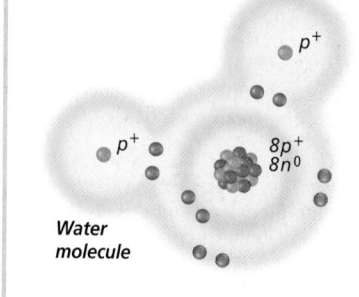

Water molecule

Look at *Figure 6.6A.* You will see that two hydrogen atoms can combine with each other by sharing their electrons. As you know, hydrogen atoms contain only one electron. Each atom becomes stable by sharing its electron with the other atom. The two shared electrons move about the nuclei of both atoms. The attraction of the positively charged nuclei for the shared, negatively charged electrons holds the atoms together. When two atoms share electrons, such as two hydrogen atoms sharing electrons, the force that holds them together is called a **covalent** (koh VAY lunt) **bond.** Most compounds in organisms have covalent bonds. Examples include sugars, fats, proteins, and water.

A **molecule** is a group of atoms held together by covalent bonds. It has no overall charge. In a molecule of water, *Figure 6.6B,* two hydrogen atoms and one oxygen atom share eight electrons. Each of the hydrogen atoms contributes one electron, and the oxygen atom contributes six electrons. Thus, all three atoms are stable.

146 THE CHEMISTRY OF LIFE

A molecule of water is represented by the chemical formula H_2O. The subscript 2 represents two atoms of hydrogen (H) combined with one atom of oxygen (O). As you will see, many compounds in living things have more complex formulas.

How ionic bonds form

Not all atoms bond with each other by sharing electrons. Sometimes atoms combine with each other by first gaining or losing electrons in their outer energy levels. An atom (or group of atoms) that gains or loses electrons has an electrical charge and is called an ion. An **ion** is a charged particle made of atoms.

A different type of chemical bond holds ions together. The bond formed between a sodium atom (Na) and chlorine atom (Cl) in table salt is a good example of this. A sodium atom contains 11 electrons, including one in the third energy level. A chlorine atom has 17 electrons, with the outer level holding seven electrons. The sodium atom loses one electron to the chlorine atom, and the chlorine atom gains one electron from the sodium atom. With eight electrons in its outer level, the chloride ion formed is stable and has a negative charge. The sodium ion has eight electrons in

its outer energy level. The sodium ion is stable and has a positive charge. The attractive force between two ions of opposite charge is known as an **ionic bond.** The bond between sodium and chlorine when they combine is an ionic bond, as shown in *Figure 6.7.*

Ionic compounds are less abundant in living things than are covalent molecules, but ions are important in biological processes. For example, sodium and potassium ions are required for transmission of nerve impulses. Calcium ions are necessary for muscles to contract. Plant roots absorb essential minerals in the form of ions.

Chemical Reactions

Chemical reactions occur when bonds are formed or broken, causing substances to recombine into different substances. In organisms, chemical reactions occur inside cells. All of the chemical reactions that occur within an organism are referred to as that organism's **metabolism.** These reactions break down and build molecules that are important for the functioning of organisms. Scientists represent chemical reactions by writing chemical equations.

Word Origin

metabolism from the Greek word *metabole,* meaning "change"; Metabolism involves many chemical changes.

Figure 6.7
The positive charge of a sodium ion attracts the negative charge of a chloride ion. This attraction is called an ionic bond. **Use Models** *How many electrons does sodium lose in bond formation?*

Ionic bond

Na atom: $11p^+$ $11e^-$		Cl atom: $17p^+$ $17e^-$		Na$^+$ ion: $11p^+$ $10e^-$		Cl$^-$ ion: $17p^+$ $18e^-$
Sodium atom	+	**Chlorine atom**	⟹	**Sodium$^+$ ion**	+	**Chloride$^-$ ion**

Reinforcement

Logical-Mathematical Give students several chemical formulas related to living things, such as CO_2 (carbon dioxide) and $C_6H_{12}O_6$ (sugar). Have them practice identifying the elements in the compounds and the numbers of atoms of each type of element shown in each formula. **L2**

Chalkboard Example

Logical-Mathematical Write a few chemical equations on the chalkboard and work with students to balance the equations. Once the equations are balanced, have students confirm the balance by counting the number of atoms of each kind on each side of the equation. Reinforce the idea that atoms are neither created nor destroyed in ordinary reactions. Some possible equations are: **L1**

$Mg + 2HCl \Rightarrow MgCl_2 + H_2$
$2C_2H_2 + 5O_2 \Rightarrow 2H_2O + 4CO_2$
$2H_2S + 3O_2 \Rightarrow 2H_2O + 2SO_2$

Caption Question Answer

Figure 6.7 Sodium loses one electron in bond formation.

PROJECT

Modeling Have students build models of water molecules. Students may use toothpicks and gumdrops or colored marshmallows to represent the atoms in the molecule. **L1 ELL**

CHALLENGE ACTIVITY

Metabolism Have students research different kinds of metabolism, such as anabolism and catabolism. Challenge them to present the results in creative ways. **L3**

Indiana Academic Standards
Pages 146–147: B.1.9

Portfolio

Mixtures and Compounds Have students construct a table to compare and contrast mixtures and compounds. Encourage students to reread the section entitled "Mixtures and Solutions" to find the information needed to complete their tables. L2

Physical Science Connection

Have students review rules for balancing chemical equations, and then balance the following reaction:
$Cl_2 + NaBr \rightarrow NaCl + Br_2$
Because there are two bromine atoms on the right side of the equation, a coefficient of 2 is placed before NaBr; likewise, there are two chlorine atoms on the left side of the equation so a coefficient of 2 is placed before NaCl. The balanced equation is:
$Cl_2 + 2NaBr \rightarrow 2NaCl + Br_2$

Figure 6.8
This balanced equation shows two molecules of hydrogen gas reacting with one molecule of oxygen gas to produce two molecules of water.
Interpret Scientific Illustrations *Which of the molecules shown here are reactants? Which are products?*

    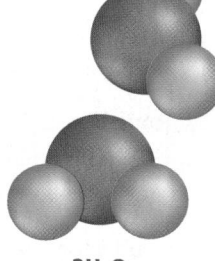

$2H_2$ + O_2 $\longrightarrow$ $2H_2O$

Physical Science Connection

Conservation of mass in chemical reactions In a chemical reaction, atoms are neither created nor destroyed. As a result, mass is conserved as a chemical reaction. This means that the mass of the reactants equals the mass of the products.

Figure 6.9
In this illustration of a mixture, both the sand and sugar retain their original properties.

Writing chemical equations

The reaction that takes place when hydrogen gas combines with oxygen gas is shown in *Figure 6.8*. In a chemical reaction, substances that undergo chemical reactions, such as hydrogen and oxygen, are called reactants. Substances formed by chemical reactions, such as water, are called products.

It's easy to tell how many molecules are involved in a reaction. In a chemical equation the number before each chemical formula indicates the number of molecules of each substance. The subscript numbers in a formula indicate the number of atoms of each element in a molecule of the substance.

A molecule of table sugar can be represented by the formula $C_{12}H_{22}O_{11}$. The lack of a number before a formula or under a symbol indicates that only one molecule or atom is present.

Looking at *Figure 6.8,* you can see that each molecule of hydrogen gas is composed of two atoms of hydrogen. Likewise, a molecule of oxygen gas is made of two oxygen atoms. Perhaps the easiest way to understand chemical equations is to know that atoms are neither created nor destroyed in chemical reactions. They are simply rearranged. An equation is written so that the same numbers of atoms of each element appear on both sides of the arrow. In other words, equations must always be written so that they balance.

Mixtures and Solutions

When elements combine chemically to form a compound, the elements no longer have their original properties. What happens if substances are just mixed together and do not combine chemically? A **mixture** is a combination of substances in which the individual components retain their own properties. *Figure 6.9* shows a mixture of sand and sugar crystals.

PROJECT

Concept Mapping Have students create a concept map poster showing the relationships among elements, mixtures, compounds, and solutions. The following terms should be included: atoms, elements, molecules, compounds, mixtures, solutions, solvent. Students may add other terms and should supply their own connecting words. Posters can be presented or displayed as part of a concept review. L2

When you stir sand and sugar together, you can still tell the sand from the sugar. Neither component of the mixture changes; that is, the components would not combine chemically. You can easily separate them by adding water to dissolve the sugar and then filtering the mixture to collect the sand.

A **solution** is a mixture in which one or more substances (solutes) are distributed evenly in another substance (solvent). In other words, one substance is dissolved in another and will not settle out of solution. You may remember using powdered drink mix when you were younger. The sugar molecules in the powdered drink mix dissolve easily in water to form a solution, as shown in *Figure 6.10.*

Solutions are important in living things. In organisms, many vital substances, such as sugars and mineral ions, are dissolved in water. The more solute that is dissolved in a given amount of solvent, the greater is the solution's concentration. The concentration of a solute is important to organisms. Organisms can't live unless the concentration of dissolved substances stays within a specific, narrow range. Organisms have many mechanisms to keep the concentrations of molecules and ions within this range. For example, the pancreas and other organs in your body produce substances such as insulin and glucagon that keep the amount of sugar dissolved in your bloodstream within a critical range.

Acids and bases

Chemical reactions can occur only when conditions are right. A reaction may depend on available energy, temperature, or a certain concentration of a substance dissolved in solution.

Figure 6.10
The sugar molecules in the powdered drink mix dissolve in the water, making a solution. Here, sugar is the solute and water is the solvent.

Water molecules

Sugar molecules

Sugar crystal

MiniLab 6.1

Purpose

Students will determine the pH of common solutions.

Process Skills

observe and infer, interpret data

Safety Precautions

Have students wear aprons and safety goggles. **CAUTION:** *Both high and low pH solutions can injure the skin and eyes.* Have students wash hands after this activity.

Teaching Strategies

- Prepare the ammonia solution ahead of time. Dilute household ammonia with water at a 1:10 ratio. **CAUTION:** *Ammonia is a skin and eye irritant and is harmful if inhaled.*
- Use a pH paper that measures from pH 0 to 14.

Expected Results

The approximate pH of the solutions are: lemon juice, pH 3; household ammonia, pH 11; liquid detergent, pH 10; shampoo, pH 7; and vinegar, pH 3.

Analysis

1. lemon juice and vinegar
2. household ammonia and liquid detergent
3. H^+ ions and OH^- ions; Household ammonia contains the most OH^- ions; it had the highest pH.

Modified Assessment

Portfolio Have students make a pH scale in their portfolios and show where each solution falls on the scale. Use the Performance Task Assessment List for Scientific Drawing in **PASC,** p. 127. **L1 ELL**

Indiana Academic Standards

Pages 150–151: B.1.5, B.1.9

Figure 6.11
Substances commonly found in the household are acids and bases. Lemon and tomato are acidic (pH < 7). Pure water is neutral (pH 7). Ammonia (pH 11) is basic.

Milk pH 6

Tomato pH 4

Lemon pH 2

Antacid pH 10

Egg pH 8

0   1   2   3   4   5   6   7   8   9   10

Neutral

More acidic

CAREERS IN BIOLOGY

Weed/Pest Control Technician

A career working with chemicals does not always require a Ph.D. Weed and pest control technicians use chemicals to get rid of unwanted weeds, insects, and other pests.

Skills for the Job

After high school, most technicians receive on-the-job training in pest control or take correspondence courses to earn a degree in this field. In many states, you must pass a test to become licensed.

As a technician, you may visit homes, office buildings, restaurants, hotels, and other places where insects, animals, or weeds have become a problem. You will choose the correct chemical and form, such as a spray or gas, to get rid of or prevent infestations of flies, roaches, termites, or other creatures. You will select different chemicals to deal with weeds. You might also set traps to catch rats, mice, moles, or other animals.

 For more careers in related fields, visit
in.bdol.glencoe.com/careers

Chemical reactions in organisms also depend on the pH of the environment within the organism. The **pH** is a measure of how acidic or basic a solution is. A scale with values ranging from below 0 to above 14 is used to measure pH. *Figure 6.11* shows the pH of some common substances.

Substances with a pH below 7 are acidic. An **acid** is any substance that forms hydrogen ions (H^+) in water. When hydrogen chloride (HCl) is added to water, hydrogen ions (H^+) and chloride ions (Cl^-) are formed. Thus, hydrogen chloride in solution with water as a solvent is called hydrochloric acid. This acidic solution contains an abundance of H^+ ions and has a pH below 7. A solution is neutral if its pH equals 7.

Substances with a pH above 7 are basic. A **base** is any substance that forms hydroxide ions (OH^-) in water. For example, if sodium hydroxide (NaOH) is dissolved in water, it forms sodium ions (Na^+) and hydroxide ions (OH^-). This basic solution contains an abundance of OH^- ions and has a pH above 7.

CAREERS IN BIOLOGY

Career Path

Courses in high school: chemistry, mathematics, biology, and carpentry

College: a degree in biology for managers or supervisors

Other education sources: on-the-job training and correspondence courses

Career Issue

Ask students whether weed and pest control technicians should tell their customers about non-chemical ways to control weeds and insects. Why or why not?

For More Information

For more about pest control, write to:

National Pest Management Association
8100 Oak Street
Dunn Loring, VA 22027

Household ammonia pH 11

Drain cleaner pH 13

11　12　13　14

More basic

Many of the foods you eat, such as oranges and grapefruits, are acidic. Some plants grow well only in acidic soil, whereas others require soil that is basic. Acids and bases are important to living systems, but strong acids and bases can be dangerous. The *MiniLab* describes how you can investigate several household solutions to determine if they are acids or bases.

✓**Reading Check** **Describe** the behavior of an acid in water.

MiniLab 6.1

Experiment

Determine pH The pH of a solution is a measurement of how acidic or basic that solution is. An easy way to measure the pH of a solution is to use pH paper.

Procedure

1 Pour a small amount (about 5 mL) of each of the following into separate clean, labeled beakers or other small glass containers: lemon juice, prepared household ammonia solution, liquid detergent, shampoo, and vinegar.

2 Dip a fresh strip of pH paper briefly into each solution and remove.

3 Compare the color of the wet paper with the pH color chart; record the pH of each material. **CAUTION:** *Wash your hands with soap after handling lab materials.*

Household solutions

Analysis

1. **Evaluate Data** Which solutions are acids?
2. **Evaluate Data** Which solutions are bases?
3. **Draw Conclusions** What ions in the solution caused the pH paper to change color? Which solution contained the highest concentration of hydroxide ions? How do you know?

Section Assessment

Understanding Main Ideas
1. Describe where the electrons are located in an atom.
2. A nitrogen atom contains seven protons, seven neutrons, and seven electrons. Make a labeled drawing of the structure of a nitrogen atom. How can this atom become stable?
3. How does the formation of an ionic bond differ from the formation of a covalent bond?
4. What can you say about the amount of hydrogen ions relative to the amount of hydroxide ions in a solution that has a pH of 2?

Thinking Critically
5. Are all mixtures solutions? Are all solutions mixtures? Give an example.

SKILL REVIEW
6. **Interpret Scientific Illustrations** *Figure 6.10* shows the process of a compound dissolving in water. Describe what is happening to the molecules. Describe the nature of the mixture after the sugar completely dissolves. For more help, refer to *Interpret Scientific Illustrations* in the **Skill Handbook.**

in.bdol.glencoe.com/self_check_quiz

6.1 ATOMS AND THEIR INTERACTIONS **151**

in.bdol.glencoe.com/self_check_quiz

Section Assessment

1. Electrons move around the nucleus in regions known as energy levels.
2. In their drawings, the nucleus contains seven protons and seven neutrons. The first energy level contains two electrons. The next energy level contains five electrons and could become stable by sharing these other electrons in a covalent bond.
3. Ionic bonds form between ions as one atom gains electrons and another gives up electrons. Covalent bonds involve the sharing of electrons between atoms.
4. There are more hydrogen than hydroxide ions in an acidic solution of pH 2.
5. A solution is one type of mixture where the solutes are evenly distributed in the solvent, but a mixture does not have to be a solution. For example, sand and marbles together are a mixture, but not a solution.
6. Sugar molecules separate from the sugar crystal. Sugar molecules (solute) are evenly distributed in the water (solvent), creating a solution.

151

1 Focus

INTERACTIVE CHALKBOARD
PowerPoint® Presentations

Bellringer
Section Focus Transparency 13

Finding Main Ideas

Organize Information

Properties of Water

1. polar
2. resists temperature change
3. expands when it freezes

Importance in Homeostasis

1. allows tops of plants to get water from soil
2. helps prevent large temperature changes in organisms
3. bottoms of lakes and ponds won't freeze

Physical Science Connection

Have students research examples of polar and nonpolar molecules. Then, ask them to sketch the molecules in their science notebooks, illustrating the overall geometries and charge distributions of the molecules. Examples include ammonia (polar), sulfur dioxide (polar), carbon dioxide (nonpolar), and methane (nonpolar).

Section 6.2

Water and Diffusion

Indiana Standards Standard B.1.2 Explain that every cell is covered by a membrane that controls what can enter and leave the cell…

SECTION PREVIEW

Objectives

Relate water's unique features to polarity.

Identify how the process of diffusion occurs and why it is important to cells.

Review Vocabulary

homeostasis: regulation of the internal environment of a cell or organism to maintain conditions suitable for life (p. 9)

New Vocabulary

polar molecule
hydrogen bond
diffusion
dynamic equilibrium

Physical Science Connection

The structure of water molecules Water is sometimes called the universal solvent because of its ability to dissolve a wide range of materials. This ability is related to the polarity of the water molecule, which is due to its "V" shape as well as the polarity of the hydrogen-oxygen bonds. Water molecules would not be polar if they were linear, with hydrogen atoms on opposite sides of the oxygen atom.

Water—It's One of a Kind!

Finding Main Ideas Most of us take water for granted. We turn on the kitchen faucet at home to get a drink and expect water to come out of the faucet. We don't think about how important water's properties are to life.

Organize Information As you read this section, make a list of the properties of water. Next to each property, write how it is important in maintaining homeostasis in living organisms.

Water is vital to the living world.

Water and Its Importance

Water is perhaps the most important compound in living organisms. Most life processes can occur only when molecules and ions are free to move and collide with one another. This condition exists when they are dissolved in water. Water also serves to transport materials in organisms. For example, blood and plant sap, which are mostly water, transport materials in animals and plants. In fact, water makes up 70 to 95 percent of most organisms.

Water is polar

Sometimes, when atoms form covalent bonds, they do not share the electrons equally. The water molecule pictured in *Figure 6.12A* shows that the shared electrons are attracted by the oxygen nucleus more strongly than by the hydrogen nuclei. As a result, the electrons spend more time near the oxygen nucleus than they do near the hydrogen nuclei.

When atoms in a covalent bond do not share the electrons equally, they form a polar bond. A **polar molecule** is a molecule with an unequal distribution of charge; that is, each molecule has a positive end and a negative end. As illustrated in *Figure 6.12B*, water is an example of a polar molecule. Polar water molecules attract ions as well as other polar molecules. Because of this attraction, water can dissolve many ionic compounds, such as salt, and many other polar molecules, such as sugar.

152 THE CHEMISTRY OF LIFE

RESOURCE MANAGER

Unit 3 *Fast File* Resources
MiniLab Worksheet, p. 4
Reinforcement and Study Guide in English, p. 11
Reinforcement and Study Guide in Spanish, p. 15
Concept Mapping, p. 17
Transparency Worksheet, p. 20

Reading Essentials for Biology, Section 6.2
Section Focus Transparency 13

Figure 6.12
Electrons are not shared equally in a water molecule.

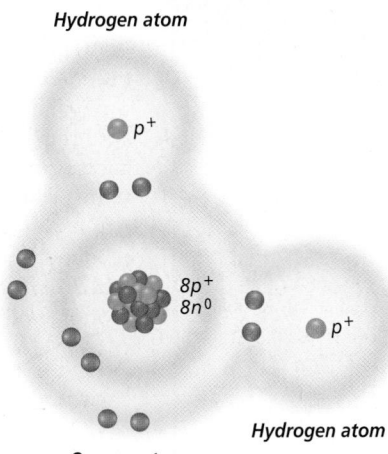

Hydrogen atom

Positively
+ charged end

+

−

Negatively
charged end

Hydrogen atom

Oxygen atom

A In a covalent bond between hydrogen and oxygen, the electrons spend more time near the oxygen nucleus than near the hydrogen nucleus.

B Because oxygen tends to attract the shared electrons more strongly than hydrogen does, the protruding oxygen end of a water molecule has a slight negative charge, and the ends with protruding hydrogen atoms have a slight positive charge.

Water molecules also attract other water molecules. The positively charged hydrogen atoms of one water molecule attract the negatively charged oxygen atoms of another water molecule. This attraction of opposite charges between hydrogen and oxygen forms a weak bond called a **hydrogen bond.** Hydrogen bonds are important to organisms because they help hold many biomolecules, such as proteins, together.

Also because of its polarity, water has the unique property of being able to creep up thin tubes. Plants in particular take advantage of this property, called capillary action, to get water from the ground. Capillary action and the tension on the water's surface, which is also a result of polarity, play major roles in getting water from the soil to the tops of even the tallest trees.

**Water resists
temperature changes**

Water resists changes in temperature. Therefore, water requires more heat to increase its temperature than do most other common liquids. Likewise, water loses a lot of heat

when it cools. In fact, water is like an insulator that helps maintain a steady environment when conditions fluctuate. Because cells exist in an aqueous environment, this property of water is extremely important to cellular functions as it helps cells maintain homeostasis.

Water expands when it freezes

Water is one of the few substances that expands when it freezes. Because of this property, ice is less dense than liquid water so it floats as it forms in a body of water. Use the *Problem-Solving Lab* on the next page to investigate this property. Water expands as it freezes inside the cracks of rocks. As it expands, it often breaks apart the rocks. Over long time periods, this process helps form soil.

The properties of water make it an excellent vehicle for carrying substances in living systems. One way to move substances is by diffusion.

☑ Reading Check **Infer** why coastal communities usually experience milder temperatures than cities that are not located near large bodies of water.

Physical Science Connection

Density of liquids Water is most dense at about 4°C. When the surface of a lake cools to 4°C, the surface water sinks and warmer water takes its place. This process continues until all the water has cooled to 4°C. Only then can the surface start freezing if it is cooled further. Even if the surface is frozen and air temperatures are well below freezing, the water near the bottom of the lake is at 4°C—warm enough for aquatic life to survive.

☑ Reading Check Because water resists changes in temperature, areas around large bodies of water usually will also have milder temperatures when compared to towns that are farther away from the water.

Purpose

Students will calculate the densities for water and ice and will correlate this information with the fact that water expands as it freezes.

Process Skills

compare and contrast, draw a conclusion, measure in SI, think critically, use numbers, recognize cause and effect

Teaching Strategies

- Review the equation for calculating density. Provide some examples for students to use as practice.
- Review the use of units such as cm^3 and mL if necessary.
- Remind students that cm^3 is the same as cubic centimeters or cc.
- Review the procedure for arriving at the proper units to express density.

Thinking Critically

1. The density of water is 1 g/cm^3; density of ice is 0.9 g/cm^3. Ice is less compact; mass in example is the same, but volume for ice is greater. A lower density indicates a greater volume with the same mass as water.
2. farther apart; This pattern accounts for increased volume.
3. Water expands as it freezes and eventually breaks glass.
4. Formation of ice crystals and the expansion within delicate cells and tissues could damage a living organism.

Modified Assessment

Knowledge Have students make a list of materials that they think will float in water (are less dense than water). Students can test these materials to see if their predictions are accurate. Use the Performance Task Assessment List for Designing an Experiment in **PASC**, p. 95. **L1**

Problem-Solving Lab 6.2

Use Numbers

Why does ice float? Most liquids contract when frozen. Water is different; it expands. The density of water changes when ice forms, allowing ice to float. Density refers to compactness and is often described as the mass of a substance per unit of volume. A mathematical expression of density would read as follows:

$$\text{Density} = \frac{\text{Mass}}{\text{Volume}}$$

Solve the Problem

Examine the following table. It shows the volume and mass for a sample of water and ice.

Data Table		
Source of Sample	Volume (cm^3)	Mass (g)
Water	126	126
Ice	140	126

Thinking Critically

1. **Compare** How does the density of ice compare with the density of water? Use specific values and proper units expressing density in your answer. Which of the two, ice or water, is less compact? Explain your answer.
2. **Think Critically** Are the molecules of water moving closer together or farther apart as water freezes? Explain.
3. **Infer** Explain why a glass bottle filled with water might shatter if placed in a freezer.
4. **Recognize Cause and Effect** Explain why ice forming within a living organism may result in its death.

Figure 6.13
Like these table tennis balls, atoms and molecules have kinetic energy, the energy of motion. **Describe** *What happens when two balls collide?*

Caption Question Answer
Figure 6.13 When two balls collide, they bounce back from each other in different directions.

Diffusion

All objects in motion have energy of motion called kinetic energy. A moving particle of matter moves in a straight line until it collides with another particle, much like the table tennis balls shown in *Figure 6.13*. After the collision, both particles rebound. Particles of matter, like the table tennis balls, are in constant motion, colliding with each other.

Early observations: Brownian motion

In 1827, Scottish scientist Robert Brown used a microscope to observe pollen grains suspended in water. He noticed that the grains moved constantly in little jerks, as if being struck by invisible objects. This motion, he thought, was the result of a life force hidden within the pollen grains. However, when he repeated his experiment using dye particles, which are nonliving, he saw the same motion. This motion is now called Brownian motion. Brown had no explanation for the motion, but today we know that Brown was observing evidence of the random motion of atoms and molecules. The random movement that Brown observed is characteristic of gases, liquids, and some solids.

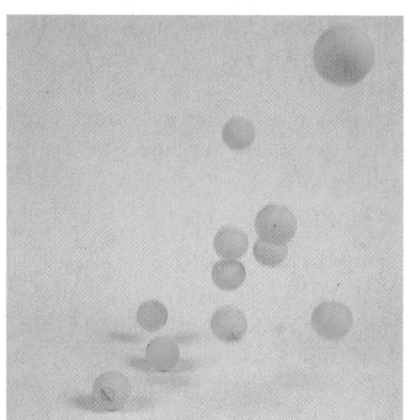

Inquiry

Activity Have students mix a variety of liquids with a polar liquid like water and observe what happens. Allow students to choose the liquids for their explorations. Have them make predictions before testing the liquids. (Food coloring can help distinguish clear liquids.) What do students observe? What questions do they have about polarity and liquids? **L1**

The process of diffusion

Particles of different substances that are in constant motion have an effect on each other. For example, if you layer pure corn syrup on top of corn syrup colored with food coloring in a beaker as illustrated in *Figure 6.14,* over time you will observe that the colored corn syrup has mixed with the pure corn syrup. This mixture is the result of the random movement of corn syrup and water molecules. **Diffusion** is the net movement of particles from an area of higher concentration to an area of lower concentration. Diffusion results because of the random movement of particles (Brownian motion).

Diffusion is a slow process because it relies on the random motion of atoms and molecules. You will see evidence that the corn syrup in *Figure 6.14* has begun to diffuse within hours but it will take months to mix completely if undisturbed.

Three key factors—concentration, temperature, and pressure—affect the rate of diffusion. The concentration of the substances involved is the primary controlling factor. The more concentrated the substances, the more rapidly diffusion occurs because there are more collisions between the particles of the substances. Two external factors—temperature and pressure—can change the rate of diffusion. An increase in temperature increases energy and will cause more rapid particle motion. This will increase the rate of diffusion. Similarly, increasing pressure will accelerate particle motion and, therefore, diffusion. With common materials, you can use the *MiniLab* shown here to learn more about diffusion in a cell.

✓ Reading Check **Explain** why diffusion is a slow process.

Figure 6.14
The random movement of molecules of corn syrup and water will cause the uncolored sample to diffuse into the colored sample.

MiniLab 6.2

Apply Concepts

Investigate the Rate of Diffusion In this lab, you will place a small potato cube in a solution of purple dye and observe how far the dark purple color diffuses into the potato after a given length of time.

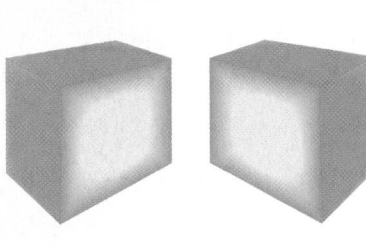

Procedure

1. Using a single-edge razor blade, cut a cube 1 cm on each side from a raw, peeled potato. **CAUTION:** *Be careful with sharp objects. Do not cut objects while holding them in your hand.*
2. Use forceps to carefully place the cube in a cup or beaker containing the purple solution. The solution should cover the cube. Note and record the time. Let the cube stand in the solution for between 10 and 30 minutes.
3. Using forceps, remove the cube from the solution and note the time. Cut the cube in half.
4. Measure, in millimeters, how far the purple solution has diffused, and divide this number by the number of minutes you allowed your potato to remain in the solution. This is the diffusion rate.

Analysis

1. **Measure** How far did the purple solution diffuse?
2. **Calculate** What was the diffusion rate per minute?

MiniLab 6.2

Purpose

Students will determine the rate of diffusion of a solution.

Process Skills

measure in SI, collect and organize data, interpret data, experiment, and analyze

Teaching Strategies

■ Prepare a dark purple dye solution by using food coloring, dye tablets, or highly-concentrated powdered drink mix.
■ Caution students that the solution can stain. To keep the solution off their hands, students should set the cube on waxed paper or foil when they remove it from the solution and hold the cube with the forceps as it is cut. Also remind students to cut away from their bodies.

Expected Results

The color will diffuse only a few millimeters into the cube, the exact distance depending upon the amount of time it is in the solution.

Analysis

1. Answers will depend on the amount of time the cube is in the solution.
2. The rate will be in tenths to hundredths of millimeters per minute.

Assessment

Portfolio Have students write a report of the MiniLab for their portfolios. Use the Performance Task Assessment List for Lab Report in **PASC**, p. 119. **L2**

🎯 CHALLENGE ACTIVITY

Research Bacteria: *Intrapersonal*
Some bacteria can live on snow. Ask students to research how these bacteria keep from freezing. **L3**

✓ Reading Check Diffusion is a slow process because it relies on the random movement of atoms and molecules.

Indiana Academic Standards

Pages 154–155: B.1.2

3 Assess

Material moving out of cell equals material moving into cell

Figure 6.15
When a cell is in dynamic equilibrium with its environment, materials move into and out of the cell at equal rates. As a result, there is no net change in concentration inside or outside the cell.

The results of diffusion

As the pure corn syrup continues to diffuse into the colored corn syrup, the two will become evenly distributed eventually. After this point, the molecules continue to move randomly and collide with one another; however, no further change in concentration will occur. This condition, in which there is continuous movement but no overall concentration change, is called **dynamic equilibrium.** *Figure 6.15* illustrates dynamic equilibrium in a cell.

Diffusion in living systems

Most substances in and around a cell are in water solutions where the ions and molecules of solute are distributed evenly among water molecules, as in the powdered drink mix and water example. The difference in concentration of a substance across space is called a concentration gradient. Because ions and molecules diffuse from an area of higher concentration to an area of lower concentration, they are said to move with the gradient. If no other processes interfere, diffusion will continue until there is no longer a concentration gradient. At this point, dynamic equilibrium occurs. Diffusion is one of the methods by which cells move substances in and out of the cell.

Diffusion in biological systems is also evident outside of the cell and can involve substances other than molecules in an aqueous environment. For example, oxygen (a gas) diffuses into the capillaries of the lungs because there is a greater concentration of oxygen in the air sacs of the lungs than in the capillaries.

Section Assessment

Understanding Main Ideas
1. Explain why water is a polar molecule.
2. How does a hydrogen bond compare to a covalent bond?
3. What property of water explains why it can travel to the tops of trees?
4. What is the eventual result of the cellular process of diffusion? Describe concentration prior to and at this point.

Thinking Critically
5. If a substance is known to enter a cell by diffusion, what effect would raising the temperature have on the cell? Why does it have this effect?

SKILL REVIEW

6. **Get the Big Picture** Explain why water dissolves so many different substances. For more help, refer to *Get the Big Picture* in the **Skill Handbook.**

 in.bdol.glencoe.com/self_check_quiz

Section Assessment

1. The oxygen and two hydrogens do not share the electrons equally (electrons are more strongly attracted to the oxygen). As a result, the oxygen is negatively charged and the hydrogens are positively charged.
2. Hydrogen bonds are very weak compared with covalent bonds.
3. capillary action
4. The particles will move from areas of high concentration to low concentration until they reach dynamic equilibrium. After this point, there is no further concentration change.
5. An increase in temperature causes an increase in kinetic energy which, in turn, increases the rate of diffusion of the substance into the cell.
6. Because water molecules are polar and attract other charged particles, water easily dissolves many substances.

Section 6.3

Section 6.3

Life Substances

Indiana Standards Standard B.1.4 Understand and describe that the work of the cell is carried out by the many different types of molecules it assembles, such as proteins, lipids, carbohydrates, and nucleic acids.

SECTION PREVIEW

Objectives

Classify the variety of organic compounds.

Describe how polymers are formed and broken down in organisms.

Compare the chemical structures of carbohydrates, lipids, proteins, and nucleic acids, and relate their importance to living things.

Identify the effects of enzymes.

Review Vocabulary

organism: anything that possesses all the characteristics of life (p. 6)

New Vocabulary

isomer
polymer
carbohydrate
lipid
protein
amino acid
peptide bond
enzyme
nucleic acid
nucleotide

 FOLDABLES™ Study Organizer

Biomolecules Make the following Foldable to help you compare the structures and functions of four types of organic compounds called biomolecules.

STEP 1 **Draw** a mark at the midpoint of a sheet of paper along the side edge. Then **fold** the top and bottom edges in to touch the midpoint.

STEP 2 **Fold** in half from side to side.

 STEP 3 **Open and cut** along the inside fold lines to form four tabs.

 STEP 4 **Label** each tab.

| Carbohydrates | Lipids |
| Proteins | Nucleic Acids |

Classify As you read Section 6.3, draw the structure and list the characteristics of carbohydrates, lipids, proteins, and nucleic acids under the appropriate tab.

The Role of Carbon in Organisms

A carbon atom has four electrons available for bonding in its outer energy level. In order to become stable, a carbon atom forms four covalent bonds that fill its outer energy level. Look at the model showing carbon atoms and bond types in *Figure 6.16*. Carbon can bond with other carbon atoms, as well as with many other elements. When each atom shares two electrons, a double bond is formed. A double bond is represented by two bars between carbon atoms. When each atom shares three electrons, a triple bond is formed. Triple bonds are represented by three bars between carbon atoms.

Figure 6.16
When two carbon atoms form a covalent bond, they can share one, two, or three electrons each.

Single Bond

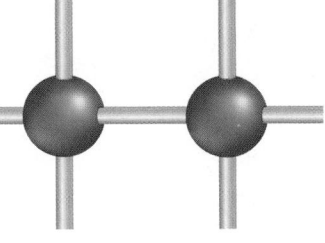

Double Bond

Triple Bond

1 Focus

 INTERACTIVE CHALKBOARD
PowerPoint® Presentations

Bellringer
Section Focus Transparency 14

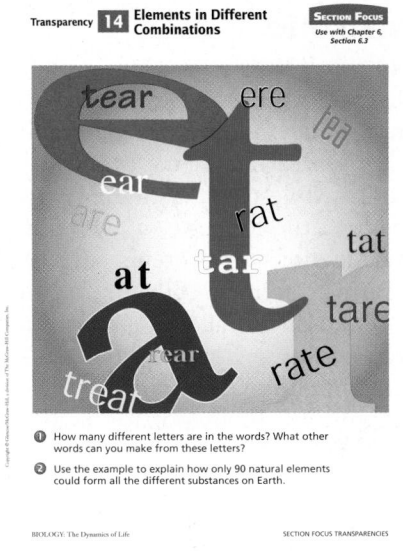

Transparency **14** Elements in Different Combinations — SECTION FOCUS — *Use with Chapter 6, Section 6.3*

① How many different letters are in the words? What other words can you make from these letters?

② Use the example to explain how only 90 natural elements could form all the different substances on Earth.

BIOLOGY: The Dynamics of Life — SECTION FOCUS TRANSPARENCIES

FOLDABLES™
For an additional Foldables activity idea, see the Chapter 6 Foldables page in *Unit 3 FAST FILE Resources.*

RESOURCE MANAGER

Unit 3 *FAST FILE* Resources
Real World BioApplications, pp. 7–8
Reinforcement and Study Guide in English, p. 12
Reinforcement and Study Guide in Spanish, p. 16
Critical Thinking/Problem Solving, p. 18
Transparency Worksheets, pp. 21, 29–30

Reading Essentials for Biology, Section 6.3
Laboratory Manual, pp. 27–34
🔖 **Section Focus Transparency 14**
🔖 **Reteaching Skills Transparency 8**

Indiana Academic Standards
Pages 156–157: B.1.2, B.1.6, B.1.9

When carbon atoms bond to each other, they can form straight chains, branched chains, or rings. These chains and rings can have almost any number of carbon atoms and can include atoms of other elements as well. This ability to bond in so many ways makes a huge number of carbon structures possible. In addition, compounds with the same chemical formula often differ in structure. Compounds that have the same chemical formula but different three-dimensional structures are called **isomers** (I suh murz). The glucose and fructose molecules shown in *Figure 6.17* have the same formula, $C_6H_{12}O_6$, but different structures.

Molecular chains

Carbon compounds vary greatly in size. Some compounds contain just one or two carbon atoms, whereas others contain tens, hundreds, or even thousands of carbon atoms. These large organic compounds are called biomolecules. Proteins are examples of biomolecules that are found in organisms. Cells build biomolecules by bonding small molecules together to form chains called polymers. A **polymer** is a large molecule formed when many smaller molecules bond together.

Many polymers are formed by a chemical reaction known as condensation. In condensation, the small molecules that are bonded together to make a polymer have an –H and an –OH group that can be removed to form H–O–H, a water molecule. The subunits become bonded by a covalent bond, as shown in *Figure 6.18*. These polymers can be broken apart by hydrolysis. Hydrogen and hydroxyl groups from water attach to the bonds between the subunits that make up the polymer, thus breaking the polymer as shown in *Figure 6.18*.

The structure of carbohydrates

You may have heard of runners eating large quantities of spaghetti or bread the day before a race. This practice is called "carbohydrate loading." It works because carbohydrates are used by cells to provide energy. A **carbohydrate** is a biomolecule composed of carbon, hydrogen, and oxygen with a ratio of about two hydrogen atoms and one oxygen atom for every carbon atom.

Figure 6.17
The different arrangement of hydrogen (–H) and hydroxide (–OH) groups around each carbon atom gives glucose and fructose molecules different chemical properties. When glucose and fructose combine, they form the disaccharide sucrose, also known as table sugar. **Use Models** *What other product is formed in this reaction?*

Figure 6.18
Many polymers are formed by condensation and can be broken by hydrolysis, the reactions that occur when water is added to or removed from a polymer.

The simplest type of carbohydrate is a simple sugar called a monosaccharide (mah noh SA kuh ride). Common examples are the isomers glucose and fructose. Two monosaccharide molecules can combine to form a disaccharide, a two-sugar carbohydrate. When glucose and fructose link together by a condensation reaction, a molecule of sucrose, known as table sugar, is formed.

The largest carbohydrate molecules are polysaccharides, polymers composed of many monosaccharide subunits. The starch, glycogen, and cellulose pictured in *Figure 6.19* are examples of polysaccharides. Starch consists of branched chains of glucose units and is used as energy storage by plant cells and as food reservoirs in seeds and bulbs. Mammals store energy in the liver in the form of glycogen, a highly branched glucose polymer. Cellulose is another glucose polymer that forms the cell walls of plants and gives plants structural support. Cellulose is made of long chains of glucose units linked together in arrangements somewhat like a chain-link fence.

Figure 6.19
Look at the structural differences among the polysaccharides starch, glycogen, and cellulose. Notice that all three are polymers of glucose. **Compare and Contrast** *What are some similarities and differences between these polysaccharides?*

Starch

Potato

Glycogen

Liver

Cellulose

Cotton

6.3 LIFE SUBSTANCES **159**

Carbon Bonds Use a ball-and-stick model of a methane molecule (CH_4) to show students the regular tetrahedron arrangement formed by the bonds of carbon atoms. Contrast the arrangement of the atoms in the methane molecule to those in a molecule of water.

Caption Question Answer
Figure 6.19 starch—made of branched chains of glucose, used by plants for energy storage; glycogen—highly branched chains of glucose, used by animals for energy storage; cellulose—long chains of glucose linked together like a chain-link fence, used for structural support in plants

Enrichment
Intrapersonal Have students research the differences in the structures of starch, glycogen, and cellulose to determine how there can be more than one polymer of glucose. **L3**

CHALLENGE ACTIVITY

Planning a Healthy Menu: *Logical-Mathematical* Have students make a weekly meal plan that contains low levels of lipids. Challenge them to calculate totals of saturated and unsaturated fats by carefully reading the nutritional labels provided on packaged foods. A healthy diet should get no more than 30% of calories from fat. No more than 10% of those fat calories should be from saturated fats. See *BioChallenges and Enrichment* for additional activities. **L3 ELL**

 Indiana Academic Standards

Pages 158–159: B.1.6

The structure of lipids

Lipids are large biomolecules that are made mostly of carbon and hydrogen with a small amount of oxygen. Fats, oils, waxes, and steroids are all lipids. They are insoluble in water because their molecules are nonpolar and are not attracted by water molecules.

A common type of lipid, shown in *Figure 6.20,* consists of three fatty acids linked with a molecule of glycerol. A fatty acid is a long chain of carbon and hydrogen. If each carbon in the chain is bonded to other carbons by single bonds, the fatty acid is said to be saturated. If a double bond is present in the chain, the fatty acid is unsaturated.

Fatty acids with more than one double bond are polyunsaturated.

Lipids are very important for the proper functioning of organisms. Cells use lipids for energy storage, insulation, and protective coverings. In fact, lipids are the major components of the membranes that surround all living cells. To learn more about lipids in your body, read the *Biotechnology* feature at the end of this chapter.

The structure of proteins

Proteins are essential to all life. They provide structure for tissues and organs and carry out cell metabolism. A **protein** is a large, complex polymer composed of carbon, hydrogen, oxygen, nitrogen, and sometimes sulfur.

Figure 6.20
Glycerol is a three-carbon molecule that serves as a backbone for a lipid molecule. Attached to the glycerol are three fatty acid groups.

Butter

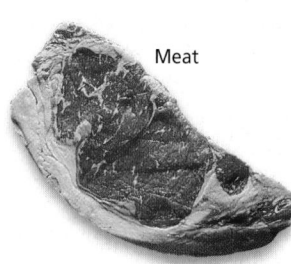
Meat

A The carbon atoms in saturated fatty acid groups, like those found in some meat and dairy products, cannot bond with any more hydrogen atoms.

Glycerol

B The carbon atoms in unsaturated and polyunsaturated fatty acid groups can bond with more hydrogen atoms when the double bonds are broken. These types of lipids can be found in some vegetable oils.

Peanut butter

160 THE CHEMISTRY OF LIFE

Figure 6.21
(A) Each amino acid contains a central carbon atom to which are attached a carboxyl group (–COOH), a hydrogen atom, an amino group (–NH₂), and a variable group (–R) that makes each amino acid different. **(B)** Amino acids are linked together by peptide bonds.

The basic building blocks of proteins are called **amino acids,** shown in *Figure 6.21A.* There are about 20 common amino acids. These building blocks, in various combinations, make literally thousands of proteins.

Amino acids are linked together when an –H from the amino group of one amino acid and an –OH group from the carboxyl group of another amino acid are removed to form a water molecule. The covalent bond formed between the amino acids, like the bond labeled in *Figure 6.21B,* is called a **peptide bond.**

Proteins come in a large variety of shapes and sizes. The number and sequence of amino acids that make up a protein are important in determining its shape. Certain amino acids are acidic, some are basic, and some are not charged. These properties cause the amino acids to attract or repel each other in different ways. The amino acid chain that makes up the protein twists and turns as the amino acids interact. Many proteins consist of two or more amino acid chains that are held together by hydrogen bonds. The ultimate three-dimensional shape that the protein folds into is extremely important to the functioning of the protein. If the sequence of amino acids in the protein were to change, the protein might fold differently and not be able to carry out its function in the cell.

Proteins are the building blocks of many structural components of organisms, as illustrated in *Figure 6.22.* Proteins are also important in the contracting of muscle tissue, transporting oxygen in the bloodstream, providing immunity, regulating other proteins, and carrying out chemical reactions.

Enzymes are important proteins found in living things. An **enzyme** is a protein that changes the rate of a chemical reaction. In some cases, enzymes increase the speed of reactions that would otherwise occur slowly.

Enzymes are involved in nearly all metabolic processes. They speed the reactions in digestion of food. The activities of enzymes depend on the temperature, ionic conditions, and the pH of the surroundings.

Figure 6.22
Proteins, such as those found in hair, fingernails, horns, and hoofs, make up much of the structure of organisms.

Using an Analogy

To increase understanding of how fewer than 25 amino acids can create such a variety of proteins, relate the naturally occurring amino acids to the letters of the alphabet. Elicit from students why the letters of the alphabet can be used to create such a large number of words. Relate this phenomenon to how a similar number of amino acids can create so many different proteins.

The BioLab at the end of the chapter can be used at this point in the lesson.

Visual Learning

Figure 6.20 Ask students to use Figure 6.20 to answer the following questions. (a) What compound serves as the backbone for lipid molecules? glycerol (b) How do the bonds in saturated fats differ from those in unsaturated fats? Saturated fats have single bonds; unsaturated fats have double bonds.

Enrichment

Amino Acids There is evidence that there are additional amino acids, like pyrrolysine and selenocysteine, that help build proteins. Have students research the discovery of these amino acids and how they work. **L3**

---

3 grapes in half, or choose three orange slices. Set these aside on waxed paper.

3. Add the following to each cup. Make sure the fruits are submerged.
   Cup 1—nothing
   Cup 2—canned pineapple chunks
   Cup 3—fresh pineapple chunks
   Cup 4—grape halves or orange slices
4. Set cups in the refrigerator. Check the cups at the end of the period.

Expected Results
Students should observe that the gelatin with fresh pineapple remained liquefied.

Analysis
1. What was the purpose of cup 1? control
2. Gelatin is a protein. Bromelin is a protein-digesting enzyme. What happened to the bromelin in the canned pineapple? It was destroyed by heat during the canning process.

Assessment
Knowledge Ask students this question: "Based on this activity, what can you conclude about which fruits have enzymes that act on protein?" Use the Performance Task Assessment List for Analyzing the Data in **PASC,** p. 99. **L2**

Purpose

Students will study the way enzymes function in a reaction.

Teaching Strategy

Ask students to make an analogy of a lock and key to show how enzymes function. Students should also describe where the analogy fails. Even though the lock and key fit together specifically, the lock does not change shape when the key fits in the keyhole. **L2**

Visual Learning

Reinforce the idea that an enzyme can be used repeatedly without being changed. Use clay for the enzyme and plastic building blocks that can snap together as the substrate. Demonstrate each step of Figure 6.23 using these materials. If materials allow, have students work with you. At the end of the reaction, the clay can be returned to its original shape, like an enzyme would.

Critical Thinking

Encourage students to describe enzyme activity in their own words. Discuss the strengths and weaknesses of the model as illustrated in the text. Challenge students to formulate their own enzyme action model to share with the class.

Indiana Academic Standards

Pages 162–163: B.1.3, B.1.4, B.1.9, B.1.10

162

INSIDE STORY

Action of Enzymes

Figure 6.23
An enzyme enables molecules, called substrates, to undergo a chemical change to form new substances, called products. The enzyme has an area called an active site on its surface that fits the shape of the substrate. When the substrate binds to the active site, the enzyme alters its shape slightly as shown below. Enzymes change the rate of a reaction but they do not change the amount of end product. **Critical Thinking** *Carefully evaluate this model. What is another way that enzyme activity could be represented?*

Lysozyme action

A **Enzymes** act on specific substrates, such as sucrose, a disaccharide made up of glucose and fructose bonded together.

Substrate (sucrose)

Active sites

Enzyme

B **Each substrate** fits into the active site. This fitting together is often compared to a lock-and-key mechanism. However, the enzyme changes shape a little to fit with the substrate. The enzyme-substrate complex puts stress on the substrate due to the binding of the substrate to the enzyme.

$+H_2O$

Products

Glucose   Fructose

Active sites

Enzyme

C **The products** are released; in this case the sucrose bonds are hydrolyzed, releasing glucose and fructose.

D **After the reaction,** the enzyme released is in its original shape and can go on to carry out the same reaction again and again. In doing so, enzymes change the speed at which chemical reactions occur without being altered themselves by the reaction.

162 THE CHEMISTRY OF LIFE

✓ **Reading Check** The shape of a protein is determined by the number and sequence of amino acids and whether the protein is made of one or more chains of amino acids. The interactions between the amino acids fold the protein into its final three-dimensional shape.

How do enzymes act like a lock and key to facilitate chemical reactions within a cell? Examine *Figure 6.23* to find out. The *BioLab* at the end of this chapter also experiments with enzymes.

> ✓ **Reading Check** **Identify** what determines the shape of a protein.

The structure of nucleic acids

Nucleic acids are another important type of organic compound that is necessary for life. A **nucleic** (noo KLAY ihk) **acid** is a complex biomolecule that stores cellular information in the form of a code. Nucleic acids are polymers made of smaller subunits called **nucleotides.**

Nucleotides consist of carbon, hydrogen, oxygen, nitrogen, and phosphorus atoms arranged in three groups—a nitrogenous base, a simple sugar, and a phosphate group—as shown in *Figure 6.24*. You have probably heard of the nucleic acid DNA, which stands for deoxyribonucleic acid. DNA is the master copy of an organism's information code. The information coded in DNA contains the instructions used

to form all of an organism's enzymes and structural proteins. Thus, DNA forms the genetic code that determines how an organism looks and acts. DNA's instructions are passed on every time a cell divides and from one generation of an organism to the next.

Another important nucleic acid is RNA, which stands for ribonucleic acid. RNA is a nucleic acid that forms a copy of DNA for use in making proteins. The chemical differences between RNA and DNA are minor but important. A later chapter discusses how DNA and RNA work together to produce proteins.

Phosphate   **Sugar**   **Nitrogenous base**

Figure 6.24
Each nucleic acid is built of subunits called nucleotides that are formed from a sugar molecule bonded to a phosphate group and a nitrogenous base.

Section Assessment

Understanding Main Ideas

1. List three important functions of lipids in living organisms.

2. Describe the process by which many polymers in living things are formed from smaller molecules.

3. How does a monosaccharide differ from a disaccharide?

4. Describe the basic components of DNA (deoxyribonucleic acid).

5. Complete the concept map by using the following vocabulary terms: nucleotides, protein, enzymes, nucleic acids.

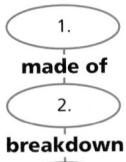

1.
made of
2.
breakdown
3.
to form
4.

Thinking Critically

6. Enzymes are proteins that facilitate chemical reactions. Based on your knowledge of enzymes, what might the result be if one particular enzyme malfunctioned or was not present?

SKILL REVIEW

7. **Make and Use Tables** Make a table comparing polysaccharides, lipids, proteins, and nucleic acids. List these four types of biomolecules in the first column. In the second column, list the subunits that make up each substance. In the third column, describe the functions of each of these organic compounds in living organisms. In the last column, provide some examples of each from the chapter. For more help, refer to *Make and Use Tables* in the **Skill Handbook**.

in.bdol.glencoe.com/self_check_quiz   6.3 LIFE SUBSTANCES **163**

---

3 Assess

DAILY INTERVENTION

Check for Understanding

Visual-Spatial Prepare a handout showing structural formulas for lipids, proteins, carbohydrates, and nucleic acids. Ask students to identify the type of biomolecule shown in each diagram. **L2**

Reteach

The concept of large polymers being composed of repeating units of monomers can be reinforced by having students list items that are composed of smaller units, such as beads making up a necklace, chain links, jigsaw puzzle pieces, or letters making up words. **L1 ELL**

Resources

For more practice, use *Reading Essentials for Biology,* Section 6.3.

Extension

Linguistic Encourage above-level students to read *The Double Helix* by James Watson (Atheneum, 1968), which tells the story of the discovery of the DNA structure. **L3**

✓ **MODIFIED Assessment**

Knowledge Use flash cards containing the names of monomers on one side and the corresponding polymer on the other side. First, show students the polymer name (e.g., protein) and then have them respond with the appropriate monomer name (amino acid), and vice versa. **L1 ELL**

Section Assessment

1. long-term energy storage, insulation, protective coatings
2. In condensation, one monomer loses an H^+ ion and another loses an OH^- to form water. A covalent bond forms between the monomers.
3. A disaccharide is made of two simple sugars called monosaccharides.
4. Like other nucleic acids, DNA is composed of smaller nucleotides consisting of a phosphate group, a simple sugar, and a nitrogenous base.
5. 1. Enzymes; 2. protein; 3. nucleic acids; 4. nucleotides
6. The chemical reaction would not proceed at the same rate.

7.

Carbohydrates Monosaccharides	Energy storage Structural components	Starch, glycogen, cellulose
Lipids Glycerol Fatty acids	Energy storage	Animal fats, vegetable oils
Proteins Amino acids	Structure Enzymes	Muscle proteins, immunity, and enzymes
Nucleic acids Nucleotides	Store information in cells	DNA & RNA

163

Time Allotment
one class period

Process Skills
form a hypothesis, design an experiment, interpret data, recognize cause and effect

Safety Precautions
Students should wear aprons and safety goggles. Remind students to use caution with heat sources and handle glassware with tongs. Use hot plates with even surfaces so hot liquids cannot easily tip over.

PREPARATION
Obtain potatoes, knives, hydrogen peroxide, and waxed paper.

Alternative Materials
Pieces of raw liver can be used instead of potato.

Possible Hypotheses
- If temperatures are very high or very low, the enzymes will be deactivated.
- If the temperature is raised, the speed at which the enzyme will work will increase.

Indiana Academic Standards
Pages 164–165: B.1.5

DESIGN YOUR OWN
BioLab

INQUIRY

Before You Begin
The compound hydrogen peroxide, H_2O_2, is a by-product of metabolic reactions in most living things. However, hydrogen peroxide is damaging to delicate molecules inside cells. As a result, nearly all organisms, such as potatoes, contain the enzyme peroxidase, which speeds up the breakdown of H_2O_2 into water and gaseous oxygen. You will detect this reaction by observing the oxygen bubbles generated.

Does temperature affect an enzyme reaction?

PREPARATION

Problem
Does the enzyme peroxidase work in cold temperatures? Does peroxidase work better at higher temperatures? Does peroxidase work after being frozen or boiled?

Hypotheses
Make a hypothesis regarding how you think temperature will affect the rate at which the enzyme peroxidase breaks down hydrogen peroxide. Consider both low and high temperatures.

Objectives
In this BioLab, you will:
- **Investigate** the activity of an enzyme.
- **Compare** the activity of the enzyme at various temperatures.

Possible Materials

clock or timer	ice
400-mL beaker	hot plate
kitchen knife	non-mercury thermometer
tongs or large forceps	or temperature probe
5-mm thick potato slices	3% hydrogen peroxide

Safety Precautions
CAUTION: *Be sure to wash your hands with soap before and after handling the lab materials. Always wear goggles in the lab. Use only GFCI protected circuits for electrical devices.*

Skill Handbook
If you need help with this lab, refer to the **Skill Handbook.**

PLAN THE EXPERIMENT

1. Decide on a way to test your group's hypothesis. Choose your materials from those available.
2. When testing the activity of the enzyme at a certain temperature, consider the length of time it will take for the potato to reach that temperature, and how the temperature will be measured.

PROCEDURE

Teaching Strategies
- Discuss the factors that might affect the rate of a reaction controlled by an enzyme.
- Students who cool the potato to low temperatures should be sure to run the test while the potato is still cool.
- Allow groups to discuss how their results differed when different experimental procedures were used.

Possible Procedures
- Students may place a piece of potato on ice for 5 minutes, boil a second piece for 5 minutes, and allow a third piece of potato to sit at room temperature for 5 minutes. Each potato will then be tested for enzyme activity.

3. To test for peroxidase activity, add 1 drop of hydrogen peroxide to the potato slice and observe what happens. **CAUTION:** *Hydrogen peroxide is a skin and eye irritant.*

4. When heating a thin potato slice, first place it in a small amount of water in a beaker. Then heat the beaker slowly so that the temperature of the water and the temperature of the slice are always the same. Try to make observations at several temperatures between 10°C and 100°C.

Check the Plan

Discuss the following points with other groups to decide on the final procedure for your experiment.

1. What data will you collect? How will you record them?

2. What factors should be controlled?

3. What temperatures will you test?

4. How will you achieve those temperatures?

5. *Make sure your teacher approves your experimental plan before you proceed further.*

6. Carry out your experiment. **CAUTION:** *Be careful with chemicals and heat. Do not heat hydrogen peroxide.*

7. **CLEANUP AND DISPOSAL** Clean all equipment as instructed by your teacher and return everything to its proper place. Wash your hands thoroughly.

ANALYZE AND CONCLUDE

1. Identify Effects Describe your observations of the effects of peroxidase on hydrogen peroxide.

2. Check Your Hypothesis Do your data support or reject your hypothesis? Explain.

3. Analyze Data At what temperature did peroxidase work best?

4. Recognize Cause and Effect If you've ever used hydrogen peroxide as an antiseptic to treat a cut or scrape, you know that it foams as soon as it touches an open wound. How can you account for this observation?

5. **ERROR ANALYSIS** What factors did you need to control in your tests? What might have caused errors in your results?

Apply Your Skill

Change Variables To carry this experiment further, you may wish to use hydrogen peroxide to test for the presence of peroxidase in other materials, such as cut pieces of different vegetables. Also, test raw beef and diced bits of raw liver.

Web Links To find out more about enzymes, visit in.bdol.glencoe.com/enzymes

ANALYZE AND CONCLUDE

1. Students should describe the number of bubbles produced and their approximate duration.

2. Students should explain whether their data support or reject their hypotheses.

3. between 20°C–50°C

4. Human tissue contains peroxidase, so the hydrogen peroxide is broken down and releases oxygen.

5. **ERROR ANALYSIS** Factors to control may include the amount of time that each potato was exposed to the temperature, the sizes of the potato slices, and the amount of peroxide added. Answers for errors in results may include incomplete heating of the potato before testing.

Assessment

Portfolio In their portfolios, have students summarize the results, especially the cold treatment. Discuss how results differed between cool pieces tested immediately and those allowed to warm to room temperature. Use the Performance Task Assessment List for Evaluating a Hypothesis in **PASC**, p. 103. **L2**

Apply Your Skill

Change Variables Ask students why vegetables are boiled for a short time before freezing. One reason is that boiling inactivates enzymes that begin to break down the other molecules in the vegetables.

Data and Observations

Cooling will not deactivate the enzymes but can slow the overall reaction. Potato slices heated over 70°C will not generate oxygen bubbles.

CLEANUP AND DISPOSAL

 Students should carefully clean and put away all equipment. Make sure students wash their hands thoroughly with soap or detergent after handling hydrogen peroxide and cleaning up. Peroxide of 3% concentration or less can be poured down the drain.

BIO TECHNOLOGY

Purpose

Students learn about two classes of lipoproteins and how they are measured.

Background

Cholesterol is transported through the body by large molecules called lipoproteins. Technology used to separate lipoprotein classes is based on specific physical properties of matter. Centrifugation is based on density, while electrophoresis is based on electrical charge.

Teaching Strategies

- Help students understand that blood is a mixture. It serves as the body's transport mechanism, and a variety of substances needed or discarded by the body must be dissolved in it. Have students brainstorm a list of substances that are carried by blood.

- Explain that technology is used to separate substances based on specific physical and chemical properties. Give examples of mixtures that must be separated by scientists and engineers, and have students hypothesize possible methods used to separate them. (Examples: petroleum products spilled into water, gasoline from underground storage tanks dissolved into soil.)

Applying Biotechnology

A small amount of material is placed in a test tube, then inserted into a centrifuge. The centrifuge spins the test tube rapidly, forcing the parts of the mixture to separate by density, like the parts of an oil and vinegar salad dressing when left unshaken. Electrophoresis is also used to separate components. However, rather than being separated by density, materials are separated based on electrical charge.

The "Good" News and the "Bad" News About Cholesterol

An electrophoresis system is used to separate lipoproteins.

About 10 percent of people ages 12 to 19 have blood cholesterol levels which put them at risk later in life for developing heart disease—the leading cause of death in the United States. Biotechnology can help scientists understand the link between cholesterol and heart disease.

Cholesterol is critical to certain body functions, including the formation of cell membranes and some hormones. Cholesterol is a lipid; it will not dissolve in a watery liquid like blood. However, blood must absorb it so that it can be transported. Molecules called lipoproteins are the water-soluble "packages" that transport cholesterol and other lipids to the tissues where they are needed.

Are all lipoproteins created equal? Lipoproteins vary in density and function. High-density lipoproteins (HDL) and low-density lipoproteins (LDL) have both been studied extensively. HDL carries excess cholesterol from tissues and blood vessels to the liver where the cholesterol is discarded from the body. HDL is often called "good cholesterol" because higher levels of this substance appear to provide some protection against coronary artery disease. LDL ("bad cholesterol") deposits cholesterol in body tissues and on blood vessel walls. While body tissues need some cholesterol, excess buildup on arterial walls can lead to blockages and heart disease.

Using technology To measure the amount of HDL and LDL in the blood, the lipoproteins must be separated. A blood sample is spun at high speed in a centrifuge for a long period of time. This process of centrifugation causes the densest lipoproteins to settle to the bottom.

Each type of lipoprotein is then measured with an electrophoresis system. Electrophoresis is based on the principle that lipoproteins, like all proteins, have an electric charge. The blood sample is placed in a gel and an electric current is applied. The lipoproteins migrate through the gel and each quantity is measured.

Changes in thinking Scientists once thought a person with a total cholesterol level below 200 milligrams per deciliter (mg/dL) was less likely to develop heart disease. Research has shown that the ratio of LDL to HDL, not the total amount of cholesterol, is a more accurate measure of the risk of heart disease. Based on this research, a person with a total cholesterol level below 200 mg/dL still may be at risk for heart disease.

Proactive measures Elevated cholesterol levels can begin in childhood so it is vital to form healthy habits early in life. A diet low in fat and cholesterol—including a variety of fruits, vegetables, and whole grains—can help keep LDL levels low. To keep HDL levels high, maintain a healthy weight, exercise regularly, and refrain from smoking. A healthy lifestyle in the teenage years can help reduce the risk of developing heart disease later on.

Applying Biotechnology

Think Critically Explain how a centrifuge works. How do electrophoresis and centrifugation differ?

in.bdol.glencoe.com/biotechnology

Going Further

The technologies described in this article are used by biologists to examine substances other than lipoproteins. Research centrifugation and electrophoresis to determine other uses of these technologies by biologists.

STUDY GUIDE

Section 6.1

Atoms and Their Interactions

Key Concepts

- Atoms are the basic building blocks of all matter.
- Atoms consist of a nucleus containing protons and usually neutrons. The positively charged nucleus is surrounded by rapidly moving, negatively charged electrons.
- Atoms become stable by bonding to other atoms through covalent or ionic bonds.
- Components of mixtures retain their properties.
- Solutions are mixtures in which the components are evenly distributed.
- Acids are substances that form hydrogen ions in water. Bases are substances that form hydroxide ions in water.

Vocabulary

acid (p. 150)
atom (p. 142)
base (p. 150)
compound (p. 145)
covalent bond (p. 146)
element (p. 141)
ion (p. 147)
ionic bond (p. 147)
isotope (p. 144)
metabolism (p. 147)
mixture (p. 148)
molecule (p. 146)
nucleus (p. 143)
pH (p. 150)
solution (p. 149)

Section 6.2

Water and Diffusion

Key Concepts

- Water is the most abundant compound in living things.
- Water is an excellent solvent due to the polar property of its molecules.
- Particles of matter are in constant motion.
- Diffusion occurs from areas of higher concentration to areas of lower concentration.

Vocabulary

diffusion (p. 155)
dynamic equilibrium (p. 156)
hydrogen bond (p. 153)
polar molecule (p. 152)

Section 6.3

Life Substances

Key Concepts

- All organic compounds contain carbon atoms.
- There are four principal types of organic compounds, or biomolecules, that make up living things: carbohydrates, lipids, proteins, and nucleic acids.
- The structure of a biomolecule will help determine its properties and functions.

Vocabulary

amino acid (p. 161)
carbohydrate (p. 158)
enzyme (p. 161)
isomer (p. 158)
lipid (p. 160)
nucleic acid (p. 163)
nucleotide (p. 163)
peptide bond (p. 161)
polymer (p. 158)
protein (p. 160)

FOLDABLES™
Study Organizer To help you review biomolecules, use the Organizational Study Fold on page 157.

 in.bdol.glencoe.com/vocabulary_puzzlemaker

Key Concepts
Summary statements can be used by students to review the major concepts of the chapter.

Biology Online

Visit in.bdol.glencoe.com
/self_check_quiz
/vocabulary_puzzlemaker
/chapter_test
/standardized_test

VOCABULARY PUZZLEMAKER

For additional help with vocabulary, have students access the Vocabulary PuzzleMaker online at in.bdol.glencoe.com/vocabulary_puzzlemaker

FOLDABLES™
Have students use their Foldables to review the content of Section 6.3.

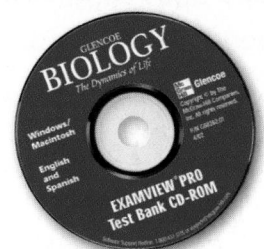

Use the ExamView®Pro Test Bank CD-ROM to:
- Create **multiple versions** of tests
- Create **modified** tests with one mouse click for **inclusion** students
- **Edit** existing questions and **add** your own questions
- Build tests aligned with state standards using built-in **State Curriculum Tags**
- Change **English** tests to **Spanish** with one mouse click and vice versa

 Indiana Academic Standards

Pages 166–167: B.1.4, B.1.6, B.1.9, B.1.10

167

Chapter 6 Assessment

 The Princeton Review **Questions and answers have been aligned and verified by The Princeton Review.**

Vocabulary Review

1. atom		**3.** diffusion
2. metabolism		**4.** enzyme

Understanding Key Concepts

5. C	**8.** C	**11.** B
6. D	**9.** D	**12.** B
7. D	**10.** D	**13.** B

Constructed Response

14. Enzymes have an area on their surface called the active site that fits the shape of the substrate. When the substrate fits into the active site, the enzyme alters its shape slightly, putting stress on the substrate, causing the reaction to proceed more rapidly.

15. In a water molecule, the oxygen atom attracts the electrons more strongly than the hydrogen atoms. The electrons spend more time near the oxygen atom, giving that end a slightly negative charge and the hydrogen atoms a slightly positive charge, making water polar. Because it is a polar molecule, water dissolves ionic compounds and other polar molecules, moves through capillary action, and has a high surface tension.

16. Because diffusion depends on random particle motion, an increase in temperature increases the random movement of the particles. Diffusion occurs more rapidly.

Thinking Critically

17. No. The liquids in the beaker are oil and water. Oil is insoluble in water so they cannot form a solution.

168

Vocabulary Review

Review the Chapter 6 vocabulary words listed in the Study Guide on page 167. Match the words with the definitions below.

1. the smallest particle of an element that has the properties of that element

2. all of the chemical reactions within an organism

3. the net movement of particles from an area of higher concentration to an area of lower concentration

4. a protein that changes the rate of a chemical reaction

Understanding Key Concepts

5. Which feature of water explains why water has high surface tension?
   A. water diffuses into cells
   B. water's resistance to temperature changes
   C. water is a polar molecule
   D. water expands when it freezes

6. Which of the following carbohydrates is a polysaccharide?
   A. glucose   **C.** sucrose
   B. fructose   **D.** starch

7. Which of the following pairs is unrelated?
   A. sugar—carbohydrate
   B. fat—lipid
   C. amino acid—protein
   D. starch—nucleic acid

8. An acid is any substance that forms _____ in water.
   A. hydroxide ions   **C.** hydrogen ions
   B. oxygen ions   **D.** sodium ions

9. Which of these is NOT made up of proteins?
   A. hair   **C.** fingernails
   B. enzymes   **D.** cellulose

10. Which of the following is NOT a smaller subunit of a nucleotide?
   A. phosphate   **C.** sugar
   B. nitrogenous base   **D.** glycerol

18. In sickle-cell anemia, the hemoglobin error causes red blood cells to become sickle-shaped. This clogs blood vessels and prevents oxygen delivery to tissues.

---

11. The calcium atom shown here has 20 protons. How many electrons does it have?
   A. 10   **C.** 40
   B. 20   **D.** 80

12. A(n) _____ bond involves sharing of electrons.
   A. ionic   **C.** hydrogen
   B. covalent   **D.** molecular

13. The first energy level of an atom holds a maximum of _____ electrons.
   A. 8   **C.** 16
   B. 2   **D.** 32

Constructed Response

14. Open Ended Explain how substrates and enzymes fit together.

15. Open Ended Discuss how the structure of a water molecule affects its properties.

16. Open Ended Explain why an increase in temperature would increase the rate of diffusion of substances into or out of cells.

Thinking Critically

17. Interpret Scientific Illustrations Is the liquid in the beaker classified as a solution? Explain your answer.

— Oil
— Water

18. REAL WORLD BIOCHALLENGE Many genetic disorders are caused by proteins that are made incorrectly in the body. Visit **in.bdol.glencoe.com** to investigate the protein error in hemoglobin that causes sickle cell anemia. How does the error in the hemoglobin affect the capacity of red blood cells to deliver oxygen to the tissues? Communicate your conclusions to the class.

 in.bdol.glencoe.com/chapter_test

RUBRIC

Evaluating Open-Ended Questions
Open-ended assessment questions are graded by using a multilevel rubric that guides you in assessing a student's knowledge of a particular concept. The following rubric is a sample scoring device.

End-of-Course Assessment Practice

The assessed Indiana standard appears next to the question.

All questions aligned and verified by The Princeton Review

Part 1 Multiple Choice

Two students were studying the effect of temperature on two naturally occurring enzymes. Study the graph of their data to answer questions 19–21.

Effects of Temperature on Two Naturally Occuring Enzymes

19. At what temperature does the maximum
B.1.4 activity of enzyme B occur?
   A. 0°
   B. 35°
   C. 60°
   D. 75°

20. At what temperature do both enzymes have
B.1.4 an equal rate of reaction?
   A. 10°
   B. 20°
   C. 50°
   D. 60°

21. Which description best explains the patterns
B.1.4 of temperature effects shown?
   A. Each enzyme has its own optimal temperature range.
   B. Both enzymes have the same optimal temperature ranges.
   C. Each enzyme will function at room temperature.
   D. Both enzymes are inactivated by freezing temperatures.

Use the table to answer questions 22 and 23.

Element	Number of Protons	Number of Neutrons
A	6	6
B	7	7
C	20	40
D	20	41

22. Which element listed above would have four
B.1.6 electrons in its outer energy level?
   A. A   **C.** C
   B. B   **D.** D

23. Which two items listed above are isotopes of
B.1.6 the same element?
   A. A and B
   B. C and D
   C. B and C
   D. A and D

Part 2 Constructed Response/Grid In

The graph at the right compares the abundance of four elements in living things to their abundance in Earth's crust, oceans, and atmosphere. Use it to answer questions 24 and 25. Record your answers on your answer document.

24. Open Ended Compare the general composition of living things to nonliving matter near Earth's surface.

25. Open Ended Explain why carbon is the most
B.1.6 critical element to living things even though it is not the most abundant.

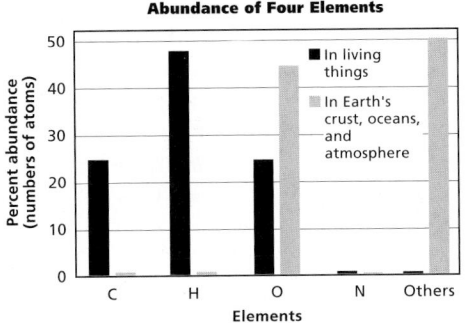

Abundance of Four Elements

Legend: In living things; In Earth's crust, oceans, and atmosphere

Elements: C, H, O, N, Others

 in.bdol.glencoe.com/standardized_test

End-of-Course Assessment Practice

19. D   **22.** A
20. C   **23.** B
21. A

24. Living things are composed primarily of hydrogen, carbon, and oxygen. Nonliving things are made of a greater variety of elements.

25. Carbon is the building block element of the four basic substances (carbohydrates, lipids, proteins, and nucleic acids) found in all known living organisms.

 FAST FILE

Answer Sheet A practice answer sheet can be found on p. 37 of *Unit 3 FAST FILE Resources.*

Indiana Academic Standards

Pages 168–169: B.1.2, B.1.5, B.1.6, B.1.9

169

 RUBRIC

SCORE	CRITERIA
4	A correct solution that is supported by well-developed, accurate explanations.
3	A generally correct solution, but may contain minor flaws in reasoning.

SCORE	CRITERIA
2	A partially correct interpretation and/or solution to the problem.
1	A correct solution with no supporting evidence or explanation.
0	An incorrect solution or no solution is given.

Chapter 7 Organizer

Section Objectives	National Science Standards	State/Local Standards	Advanced Lab and Demo Planning
Section 7.1 1 session, 1/2 block 1. **Relate** advances in microscope technology to discoveries about cells and cell structure. 2. **Compare** the operation of a compound light microscope with that of an electron microscope. 3. **Identify** the main ideas of the cell theory.	UCP.1, UCP.5; A.1, A.2; C.1; E.1, E.2; G.1–3	**Indiana Standards** B.1.3, B.1.8, B.1.12	**Student Lab:** MiniLab 7.1, p. 173: water, microscope, glass slide **Teacher Demonstration:** Quick Demo, p. 172: cork
Section 7.2 2 sessions, 1 block 4. **Describe** how a cell's plasma membrane functions. 5. **Relate** the function of the plasma membrane to the fluid mosaic model.	UCP.1–3, UCP.5; A.1, A.2; B.2; C.1, C.5	**Indiana Standards** B.1.2, B.1.4, B.1.6, B.1.9	**Student Lab:** Problem-Solving Lab 7.1, p. 176 **Teacher Demonstration:** Quick Demo, p. 177: colored water, alcohol, salad oil
Section 7.3 3 sessions, 1 1/2 blocks 6. **Identify** the structure and function of the parts of a typical eukaryotic cell. 7. **Explain** the advantages of highly folded membranes in cells. 8. **Compare and contrast** the structures of plant and animal cells.	UCP.1–3, UCP.5; A.1, A.2; C.1, C.5; G.1–3	**Indiana Standards** B.1.2, B.1.3, B.1.12	**Student Labs:** Problem-Solving Lab 7.2, p. 180 MiniLab 7.2, p. 182: water, glass slide, onion skin, microscope, iodine stain Investigate BioLab, p. 188: See materials below. Additional Lab, p. 182: microscope, glass slides, coverslips, droppers, forceps, *Elodea* plant, prepared slide of human cheek cells **Teacher Demonstration:** Quick Demo, p. 185: gelatin, grapes, various fruits
End of Chapter Assessment Student Edition Study Guide, p. 191 **Content Assessment**, pp. 192–193		**Indiana Standards** B.1.2, B.1.3, B.1.12	**Student Lab:** Investigate BioLab, p. 188: microscope, coverslip, *Bacillus subtilis* slide, frog blood slide, dropper, forceps, glass slide, *Elodea* leaf

Key to Teaching Strategies

L1 Level 1 activities should be appropriate for students with learning difficulties.

L2 Level 2 activities should be within the ability range of all students.

L3 Level 3 activities are designed for above-average students.

ELL ELL activities should be within the ability range of English Language Learners.

COOP LEARN
Cooperative Learning activities are designed for small group work.

Glencoe Exclusive!
Teacher Works™
All-In-One Planner and Resource Center

Reproducible Masters and Transparencies

Technology

Unit 3 FAST FILE Resources
MiniLab Worksheet, p. 41
Reinforcement and Study Guide in English, p. 47
Reinforcement and Study Guide in Spanish, p. 51
Transparency Worksheets, pp. 57, 65–66
Laboratory Manual, pp. 35–38, 39–42
🔥 **Section Focus Transparency 15**
🔥 **Reteaching Skills Transparency 9**

💿 **Interactive Chalkboard CD-ROM: Section 7.1 Presentation** ▮
💿 **TeacherWorks™ CD-ROM** ▮
🎵 **Guided Reading Audio Summaries MP3**

Unit 3 FAST FILE Resources
Real World BioApplications, pp. 45–46
Reinforcement and Study Guide in English, p. 48
Reinforcement and Study Guide in Spanish, p. 52
Transparency Worksheets, pp. 58, 61–62
🔥 **Section Focus Transparency 16**
🔥 **Basic Concepts Transparency 6**

💿 **Interactive Chalkboard CD-ROM: Section 7.2 Presentation** ▮
💿 **TeacherWorks™ CD-ROM** ▮
🎵 **Guided Reading Audio Summaries MP3**

Unit 3 FAST FILE Resources
MiniLab Worksheet, p. 42
BioLab Worksheet, pp. 43–44
Reinforcement and Study Guide in English, pp. 49–50
Reinforcement and Study Guide in Spanish, pp. 53–54
Concept Mapping, p. 55
Critical Thinking/Problem Solving, p. 56
Transparency Worksheets, pp. 59, 63–64, 67–68
Inside Story Poster
🔥 **Section Focus Transparency 17**
🔥 **Basic Concepts Transparency 7**
🔥 **Reteaching Skills Transparency 10**

💿 **Interactive Chalkboard CD-ROM: Section 7.3 Presentation** ▮
💿 **TeacherWorks™ CD-ROM** ▮
🎵 **Guided Reading Audio Summaries MP3**
💿 **Virtual Labs CD-ROM**
Virtual Lab: Cellular Pursuit

Unit 3 FAST FILE Resources
Chapter Assessment, pp. 69–74
Student Recording Sheet, p. 75
The Princeton Review **Reviewing Biology,** pp. 13–14

💿 **Interactive Chalkboard: Chapter 7 Assessment** ▮
💿 **MindJogger Videoquizzes DVD/VHS**
💿 **ExamView® Pro Test Bank CD-ROM**
💿 **TeacherWorks™ CD-ROM** ▮
💿

🖱 **in.bdol.glencoe.com**
/self_check_quiz
/vocabulary_puzzlemaker
/chapter_test
/standardized_test

▮ Indicates materials created specifically for Indiana.

A View of the Cell

Short on Time?

BIODIGEST The BioDigest at the end of this unit can be used as a(n):

- preview to introduce important unit concepts.
- overview if time does not permit teaching the entire chapter.
- review of key unit concepts.

Understanding the Photo

The image of this nerve cell was taken with a scanning electron microscope (SEM). The mitochondria have been colored blue using a computer. Students can learn more about different microscope technologies in the Focus On feature on pages 1064–1065.

PowerPoint® Presentations

This CD-ROM is an editable Microsoft® PowerPoint® presentation that includes:
- Section presentations
- Section checks
- Image bank
- Hot links to Biology Online
- All transparencies

Indiana Academic Standards

Pages 170–171: B.1.3, B.1.8

What You'll Learn

- You will identify the parts of prokaryotic and eukaryotic cells.
- You will identify the structure and function of the plasma membrane.
- You will relate the structure of cell parts to their functions.

Why It's Important

Cells are the foundation for all life forms. Birth, growth, development, death, and all life functions begin as cellular processes.

Understanding ▶ the Photo

You and all other organisms are made of cells. A human cell appears in this color-enhanced photograph. Scientists use color enhancement with assistance from computer software to distinguish various cell parts.

Color-enhanced TEM Magnification: 4700×

Biology Online

Visit in.bdol.glencoe.com to
- study the entire chapter online
- access Web Links for more information and activities on cells
- review content with the Interactive Tutor and self-check quizzes

170

Two-Minute Chapter Launcher

Demo To elicit students' preconceptions about cell size, write on the chalkboard:
- Bird egg yolks are the largest known cells.
- Ostrich egg yolks have a diameter of 450 mm; chickens' are 45 mm.

Have students discuss the question: What makes you bigger than a bird, given that both humans and birds are made of cells? Most human cells are not larger than birds' cells; humans just have more of them.

As they study the chapter, students will make direct observations about the relationship between the size of an organism and the size of cells; ask them to make inferences during the activities and challenge them to justify their conclusions.

Section 7.1

The Discovery of Cells

Indiana Standards Standard B.1.12 Compare and contrast the form and function of prokaryotic and eukaryotic cells.

SECTION PREVIEW

Objectives

Relate advances in microscope technology to discoveries about cells and cell structure.

Compare the operation of a compound light microscope with that of an electron microscope.

Identify the main ideas of the cell theory.

Review Vocabulary
organization: the orderly structure of cells in an organism (p. 7)

New Vocabulary
cell
compound light microscope
cell theory
electron microscope
organelle
prokaryote
eukaryote
nucleus

FOLDABLES™ Study Organizer

The Cell Theory Make the following Foldable to help you organize the ideas of the cell theory.

STEP 1 **Collect** 2 sheets of paper and layer them about 1.5 cm apart vertically. Keep the edges level.

STEP 2 **Fold** up the bottom edges of the paper to form 4 equal tabs.

STEP 3 **Fold** the papers and crease well to hold the tabs in place. Staple along the fold. **Label** each tab with one of the main ideas of the cell theory.

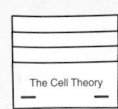

The Cell Theory

Summarize After you read Section 7.1, summarize the three main ideas of the cell theory in your own words. Review the theory using the information provided and note its strengths and weaknesses.

The History of the Cell Theory

Before microscopes were invented, people believed that diseases were caused by curses and supernatural spirits. They had no idea that organisms such as bacteria existed. As scientists began using microscopes, they quickly realized they were entering a new world—one of microorganisms (my kroh OR guh nih zumz). Microscopes enabled scientists to view and study **cells,** the basic units of living organisms.

Light microscopes

The microscope Anton van Leeuwenhoek (LAY vun hook) used in the 1600s is considered a simple light microscope because it contained one lens and used light to view objects. Over the next 200 years, scientists greatly improved microscopes by grinding higher quality lenses and developing the compound light microscope. **Compound light microscopes** use a series of lenses to magnify objects in steps. These microscopes can magnify objects up to about 1500 times. As the observations of organisms viewed under a microscope expanded, scientists began to draw conclusions about the organization of living matter. With the microscope established as a valid scientific tool, scientists had to learn the size relationship of magnified objects to their true size. See what specimens look like at different magnifications on pages 1064–1065 in the *Focus On.*

7.1 THE DISCOVERY OF CELLS **171**

---

1 Focus

INTERACTIVE CHALKBOARD
PowerPoint® Presentations

Bellringer
Section Focus Transparency 15

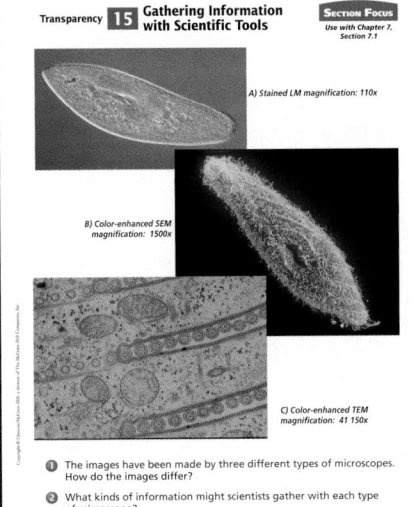

Transparency **15** Gathering Information with Scientific Tools

SECTION FOCUS Use with Chapter 7, Section 7.1

A) Stained LM magnification: 110x

B) Color-enhanced SEM magnification: 1500x

C) Color-enhanced TEM magnification: 41 150x

❶ The images have been made by three different types of microscopes. How do the images differ?

❷ What kinds of information might scientists gather with each type of microscope?

BIOLOGY: The Dynamics of Life   SECTION FOCUS TRANSPARENCIES

FOLDABLES™
For an additional Foldables activity idea, see the Chapter 7 Foldables page in *Unit 3 FAST FILE Resources.*

Physical Science Connection

The human brain interprets light waves that enter the eye as having traveled in straight lines. Ask students to explain why objects underwater seem to be in a different location than they really are.

Light waves that travel from water to air change direction at the air-water interface. As a result of this refraction, the brain interprets the light rays from an underwater object as having come from a different location.

RESOURCE MANAGER

Unit 3 FAST FILE Resources
MiniLab Worksheet, p. 41
Reinforcement and Study Guide in English, p. 47
Reinforcement and Study Guide in Spanish, p. 51
Transparency Worksheets, pp. 57, 65–66

Reading Essentials for Biology, Section 7.1
Laboratory Manual, pp. 35–38, 39–42
Section Focus Transparency 15
Reteaching Skills Transparency 9

2 Teach

Enrichment

Research Microscopes Have students research how various electron microscopes work. Students can write a report or make an oral presentation to the class. **L3**

Caption Question Answer

Figure 7.1 Hooke thought the shapes looked similar to the rooms, or "cells," in which monks lived at a monastery.

✓**Reading Check** The main ideas of the cell theory are: 1) all organisms are composed of one or more cells; 2) the cell is the basic unit of organization within an organism; 3) all cells come from preexisting cells.

Inquiry

Microscope Activity What do ordinary things look like under a microscope? Let students choose their own materials and allow them observation time with a microscope. If time allows, bring them outside to collect specimens like leaves, flowers, seeds, etc. or have a variety of materials on hand. Suggestions: different kinds of cloth, coins, newspaper, color pictures, foam, rocks, and shells. **L1** **ELL**

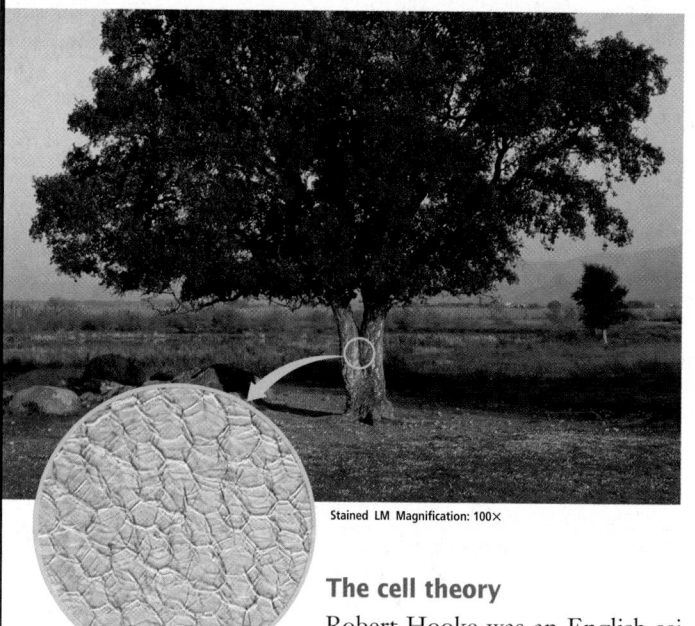

Stained LM Magnification: 100×

Figure 7.1
Cork cells (above) from the dead bark of an oak tree (top) were observed by Robert Hooke using a crude compound light microscope that magnified structures only 30 times. **Infer** *Why did Hooke name them "cells"?*

The cell theory

Robert Hooke was an English scientist who lived at the same time as van Leeuwenhoek. Hooke used a compound light microscope to study cork, the dead cells of oak bark. In cork, Hooke observed small geometric shapes, like those shown in *Figure 7.1.* Hooke gave these box-shaped structures the name *cells* because they reminded him of the small rooms monks lived in at a monastery. Cells are the basic units of all living things.

Several scientists extended Hooke's observations and drew some important conclusions. In the 1830s, the German scientist Matthias Schleiden observed a variety of plants and concluded that all plants are composed of cells. Another German scientist, Theodor Schwann, made similar observations on animals. The observations and conclusions of these scientists are summarized as the cell theory, one of the fundamental ideas of modern biology.

The **cell theory** is made up of three main ideas:

1. *All organisms are composed of one or more cells.* An organism may be a single cell, such as the organisms van Leeuwenhoek saw in water. Others, like the plants and animals with which you are most familiar, are multicellular, or made up of many cells.

2. *The cell is the basic unit of structure and organization of organisms.* Although organisms such as humans, dogs, and trees can become very large and complex, the cell remains the simplest, most basic component of any organism.

3. *All cells come from preexisting cells.* Before the cell theory, no one knew how cells were formed, where they came from, or what determined the type of cell they became. The cell theory states that a cell divides to form two identical cells.

✓**Reading Check** **Summarize** the main ideas of the cell theory.

Electron microscopes

The microscopes we have discussed so far use a beam of light and can magnify an object up to about 1500 times its actual size. Although light microscopes continue to be valuable tools, scientists knew that another world, which they could not yet see, existed within a cell. In the 1930s and 1940s, a new type of microscope, the **electron microscope,** was developed. This microscope uses a beam of electrons instead of light to magnify structures up to 500 000 times their actual size, allowing scientists to see structures within a cell. Because the electrons can collide with air particles and scatter, specimens must be examined in a vacuum.

There are two basic types of electron microscopes. Scientists commonly use the scanning electron microscope (SEM) to scan the surfaces of cells to learn their three-dimensional shape. The transmission electron microscope

Indiana Academic Standards

Pages 172–173: B.1.3, B.1.12

CHALLENGE ACTIVITY

Cell Magnification Have students study a cell under the microscope at increasing magnifications (or use photographs). Have them describe the cells in detail and draw diagrams based on their descriptions. **L3** **ELL**

Quick Demo

Compare Models Show students a piece of cork and have them examine the cellular structure. Emphasize that cork was a living part of an organism. It is the dead cells of oak bark.

(TEM) allows scientists to study the structures contained within a cell.

New types of microscopes and new techniques are continually being designed. For example, the scanning tunneling microscope (STM) uses the flow of electrons to create computer images of atoms on the surface of a molecule. New techniques using the light microscope have increased the information scientists can gain with this basic tool. Most of these new techniques seek to add contrast to structures within the cells, such as adding dyes that stain some parts of a cell, but not others. Try *MiniLab 7.1* to practice the basic technique of measuring objects under a microscope.

Two Basic Cell Types

With the development of better microscopes, scientists observed that all cells contain small, specialized structures called **organelles.** Many, but not all, organelles are surrounded by membranes. Each organelle has a specific function in the cell.

Cells can be divided into two broad groups: those that contain membrane-bound organelles and those that do not. Cells that do not contain any membrane-bound organelles are called prokaryotic (pro kar ee AW tik) cells. Most unicellular organisms, such as bacteria, do not have membrane-bound organelles and are therefore called **prokaryotes.**

Cells of the other type, those containing membrane-bound organelles, are called eukaryotic (yew kar ee AW tik) cells. Most of the multicellular organisms we know are made up of eukaryotic cells and are therefore called **eukaryotes.** It is important to note, however, that some eukaryotes, such as amoebas, or some algae and yeast, are unicellular organisms.

MiniLab 7.1

Measure in SI

Measuring Objects Under a Microscope Knowing the diameter of the circle of light you see when looking through a microscope allows you to measure the size of objects being viewed. For most microscopes, the diameter of the circle of light is 1.5 mm, or 1500 μm (micrometers), under low power and 0.375 mm, or 375 μm, under high power.

Stained LM Magnification: 75×

Human hair

Procedure

1. Look at diagram A that shows an object viewed under low power. Knowing the circle diameter to be 1500 μm, the estimated length of object (a) is 400 μm. What is the estimated length of object (b)?
2. Look at diagram B that shows an object viewed under high power. Knowing the circle diameter to be 375 μm, the estimated length of object (c) is 100 μm. What is the estimated length of object (d)?
3. With help from your teacher, prepare a wet mount of a strand of your hair. **CAUTION:** *Use caution when handling microscopes and glass slides.* Measure the diameter of your hair strand while viewing it under low and then high power.

Analysis

1. **Observe and Infer** An object can be magnified 100, 200, or 1000 times when viewed under a microscope. Does the object's actual size change with each magnification? Explain.
2. **Estimate** Do your observations of the diameter of your hair strand under low and high power support the answer to question 1? If not, offer a possible explanation why.

MiniLab 7.1

Purpose

Students will learn how to estimate an object's size under the microscope.

Process Skills

measure in SI, observe and infer, use numbers, estimate

Safety Precautions

Remind students to handle slides carefully and dispose of broken glass properly.

Teaching Strategies

- Review the procedure for making a wet mount.
- Give students some sample problems to practice estimating size and converting from mm to μm
- Provide other objects, such as diatoms and yeast cells, for viewing and measuring.

Expected Results

Object (b) is about 700 μm and object (d) is 25 μm. Hair width may be within the range of 60–100μm and will be the same (or very close) under low- and high-power magnification.

Analysis

1. No. An object's size does not change, only its magnification changes.
2. Observations under low and high power should be close. Error in estimating may be the cause of differing measurements.

Assessment

Knowledge Ask students to measure the length of a small object, such as a grain of rice. Place the grain of rice under a microscope at low power. Ask students if the actual size of the grain of rice has changed. Ask students to estimate the diameter of the viewing field. **L2**

3 Assess

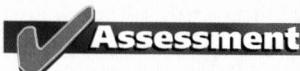
Figure 7.2
Some parts of prokaryotic and eukaryotic cells are shown here.

Size Comparison
Prokaryote
Eukaryote

Eukaryotic cells are generally one to one hundred times bigger than prokaryotic cells.

Average size ranges
Eukaryotic cells: 0.01mm to 0.1mm
Prokaryotic cells: 0.001 mm to 0.01mm

Ribosomes   DNA   Plasma membrane   Cell wall

A A prokaryotic cell does not have internal organelles surrounded by a membrane. Most of a prokaryote's metabolism takes place in the cytoplasm.

Nucleus
Nucleolus
Chromosomes
Plasma membrane
Organelles

B This eukaryotic cell from an animal has distinct membrane-bound organelles that allow different parts of the cell to perform different functions.

Compare the prokaryotic and eukaryotic cells in ***Figure 7.2.*** Separation of cell functions into distinct compartments—the organelles—benefits the eukaryotic cell. One benefit is that chemical reactions that would normally not occur in the same area of the cell can now be carried out at the same time.

Robert Brown, a Scottish scientist, observed that eukaryotic cells contain a prominent structure, which Rudolf Virchow later concluded was the structure responsible for cell division. We now know this structure as the **nucleus,** the central membrane-bound organelle that manages or controls cellular functions.

Section Assessment

Understanding Main Ideas
1. Describe the history of microscopes, and evaluate their impact in the study of cells.
2. How does the cell theory describe the levels of organization of living organisms?
3. Compare the sources of the beam in light microscopes and electron microscopes.
4. Describe the differences between a prokaryotic and a eukaryotic cell, and identify their parts.
5. Explain the difference between a scanning electron microscope and a transmission electron microscope and their uses.

Thinking Critically
6. Suppose you discovered a new type of plant. Applying the cell theory, what can you say for certain about this organism?

SKILL REVIEW
7. **Care and Use of a Microscope** Most compound light microscopes have four objective lenses with magnifications of 4×, 10×, 40×, and 100×. What magnifications are available if the eyepiece magnifies 15 times? For more help, refer to *Care and Use of a Microscope* in the **Skill Handbook.**

174 A VIEW OF THE CELL

 in.bdol.glencoe.com/self_check_quiz

Section Assessment

1. Compound light microscopes were built with multiple lenses, better resolution, and higher magnification. Electron microscopes increased resolution and magnification further. Microscopes provide the visual understanding for the structure of cells.

2. Cells are the basic unit of organization of all living organisms.
3. light microscopes—natural light; electron microscopes—electron beam
4. Eukaryotic cells have membrane-bound organelles, including a nucleus. A prokaryotic cell has no membrane-bound organelles. Most of its metabolism takes place in its cytoplasm.

5. SEMs have lower magnification than TEMs; SEMs can get 3-dimensional views.
6. The plant is made of cells—its basic units of organization—which came from preexisting cells.
7. 60×, 150×, 600×, 1500×

The Plasma Membrane

Indiana Standards Standard B.1.2 Explain that every cell is covered by a membrane that controls what can enter and leave the cell...

Controlling the Flow

Using Prior Knowledge In this section, you will learn about the plasma membrane which surrounds the cell and serves as a gateway through which materials enter and exit the cell. The plasma membrane is composed of two layers of lipids. You have read that lipids are organic compounds that are insoluble in water, which is why the oil and vinegar in this salad dressing form two separate layers that do not dissolve in each other.

Infer *Considering that a cell's environment is extremely watery, why might lipids be important to the composition of the plasma membrane?*

Maintaining a Balance

You are comfortable in your house largely because the thermostat maintains the temperature within a limited range regardless of what's happening outside. Similarly, all living cells must maintain a balance regardless of internal and external conditions. Survival depends on the cell's ability to maintain the proper conditions within itself.

Why cells must control materials

Your cells need nutrients such as glucose, amino acids, and lipids to function. It is the job of the **plasma membrane,** the flexible boundary between the cell and its environment, to allow a steady supply of these nutrients to come into the cell no matter what the external conditions are. However, too much of any of these nutrients or other substances, especially ions, can be harmful to the cell. If levels become too high, the excess is removed through the plasma membrane. Waste and other products also leave the cell through the plasma membrane. Recall that this process of maintaining balance in the cell's environment is called homeostasis.

How does the plasma membrane maintain homeostasis? One mechanism is **selective permeability,** a process in which a membrane allows some molecules to pass through while keeping others out. In your home, a screen in a window can perform selective permeability in a similar way. When you open the window, the screen lets fresh air in and keeps most insects out.

7.2   THE PLASMA MEMBRANE   **175**

SECTION PREVIEW

Objectives
Describe how a cell's plasma membrane functions.
Relate the function of the plasma membrane to the fluid mosaic model.

Review Vocabulary
ion: an atom or group of atoms with a positive or negative electrical charge (p. 147)

New Vocabulary
plasma membrane
selective permeability
phospholipid
fluid mosaic model
transport protein

Word Origin

permeable from the Latin words *per,* meaning "through," and *meare,* meaning "to glide"; Materials move easily (glide) through permeable membranes.

Bellringer
Section Focus Transparency 16

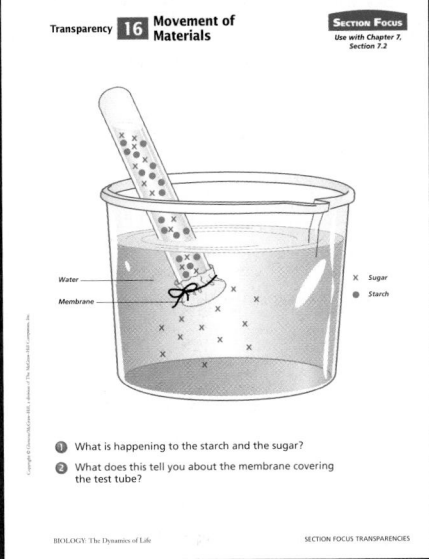

Transparency **16** Movement of Materials

SECTION FOCUS
Use with Chapter 7, Section 7.2

Water
Membrane

× Sugar
● Starch

❶ What is happening to the starch and the sugar?
❷ What does this tell you about the membrane covering the test tube?

BIOLOGY: The Dynamics of Life

SECTION FOCUS TRANSPARENCIES

Using Prior Knowledge

Infer Having lipids in the plasma membrane means that at least a portion of the membrane repels the water that constantly surrounds it. Allowing too much water inside the cell could cause the cell to burst.

Struggling Learners

Group students and have them build models of a plasma membrane using materials such as polystyrene "peanuts," yarn, pipe cleaners, and popsicle sticks. Encourage students to be creative.

L2 **ELL** **COOP LEARN**

RESOURCE MANAGER

Unit 3 *FAST FILE* Resources
Real World BioApplications, pp. 45–46
Reinforcement and Study Guide in English, p. 48
Reinforcement and Study Guide in Spanish, p. 52
Transparency Worksheets, pp. 58, 61–62

Reading Essentials for Biology, Section 7.2
Section Focus Transparency 16
Basic Concepts Transparency 6

Indiana Academic Standards

Pages 174–175: B.1.2, B.1.3, B.1.4, B.1.8, B.1.12

2 Teach

Purpose

Students will determine how the plasma membrane of living cells is a selective barrier to certain molecules.

Process Skills

compare and contrast, interpret scientific illustrations, recognize cause and effect, think critically

Teaching Strategies

■ Remind students that yeast cells are living organisms. Elicit the composition of the blue stain (molecules of a chemical compound).

■ Have students describe some of the organelles that should be present in yeast and verify that the plasma membrane is included in the discussion. **L2**

Thinking Critically

1. Boiling killed the cells; it disrupted the intact plasma membrane.

2. Possible answers include: If yeast cells are boiled and killed, then their membrane can no longer serve as a barrier to the blue stain.

3. Yes. While alive, yeast cell membranes prevent the blue stain from entering the interior. Once cells are dead, the membranes can no longer keep the blue stain out.

Assessment

Knowledge Have students make diagrams depicting the before and after appearance of the yeast cell membranes. Have them show the blue stain in both diagrams. Students are to assume that no carrier molecules were involved. Use the Performance Task Assessment List for Scientific Drawing in **PASC**, p. 127. **L2 ELL**

176

Problem-Solving Lab 7.1

Recognize Cause and Effect

Is the plasma membrane a selective barrier? Yeast cells are living organisms and are surrounded by a plasma membrane. Below are the results of an experiment which shows that living yeast plasma membranes can limit what enters the cell.

Solve the Problem

Diagram A shows yeast cells in a solution of blue stain. Note their color as well as the color of the surrounding stain.

Diagram B also shows yeast cells in a solution of blue stain. These cells, however, were boiled for 10 minutes before being placed in the stain. Again, note the color of the yeast cells as well as the color of the surrounding stain.

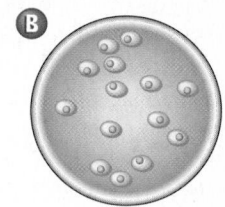

Thinking Critically

1. **Explain** How does boiling affect the yeast cells?
2. **Hypothesize** Why is the color of the cells different under different conditions? Be sure that your hypothesis takes the role of the plasma membrane into consideration.
3. **Infer** Are plasma membranes selective barriers? Explain.

Figure 7.3
The selectively permeable plasma membrane controls substances entering and leaving a cell.

A A window screen is selectively permeable because it allows air but not most insects to pass through it.

176 A VIEW OF THE CELL

Some molecules, such as water, freely enter the cell through the plasma membrane, as shown in *Figure 7.3*. Other particles, such as sodium and calcium ions, must be allowed into the cell only at certain times, in certain amounts, and through certain channels. The plasma membrane must be selective in allowing these ions to enter. Use the *Problem-Solving Lab* here to analyze the plasma membrane of a yeast cell.

Structure of the Plasma Membrane

Now that you understand the basic function of the plasma membrane, you can study its structure. Recall from Chapter 6 that lipids are large molecules that are composed of glycerol and three fatty acids. If a phosphate group replaces a fatty acid, a phospholipid is formed. Thus, a **phospholipid** (fahs foh LIH pid) has a glycerol backbone, two fatty acid chains, and a phosphate group. The plasma membrane is composed of a phospholipid bilayer, which has two layers of phospholipids back-to-back.

B The plasma membrane is also selectively permeable. Substances, such as glucose, must enter and stay in a cell. Other substances must leave a cell, and some substances must be prevented from entering a cell.

CULTURAL DIVERSITY

Ernest Everett Just Discuss the history of the study of the plasma membrane and the important contributions of African American embryologist Ernest Everett Just (1883–1941). Just is best known for his experimental studies on fertilization in marine invertebrates.

Figure 7.4
The plasma membrane has proteins on its surface or embedded in it. The phospholipid and protein molecules are free to move sideways within the membrane. *Infer Why do the polar heads of the phospholipids face the outsides of the membrane?*

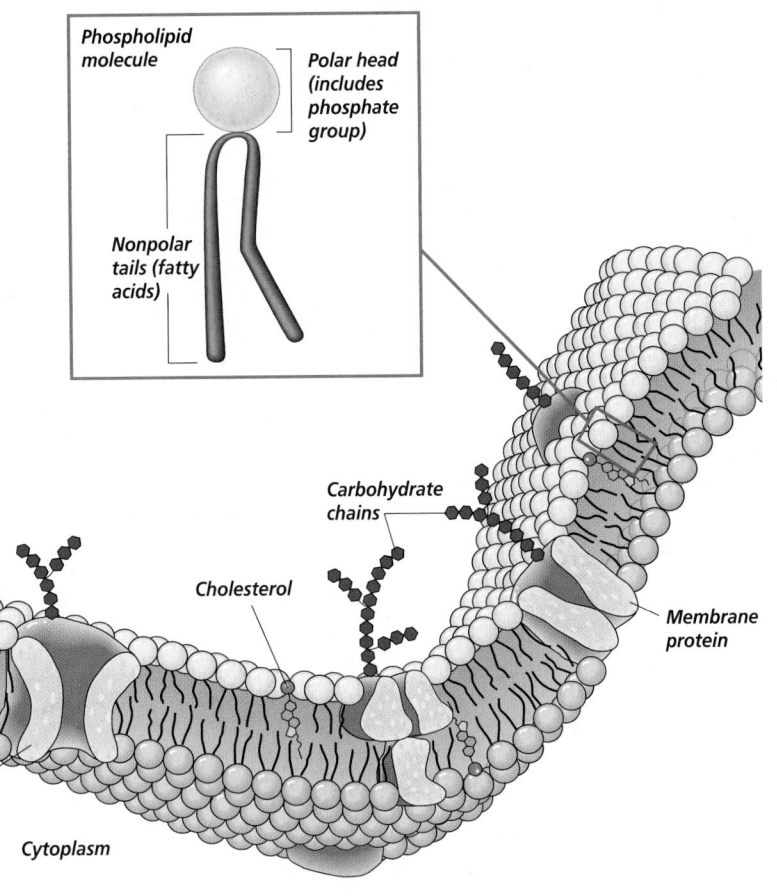

Phospholipid molecule

Polar head (includes phosphate group)

Nonpolar tails (fatty acids)

Carbohydrate chains

Cholesterol

Membrane protein

Membrane protein

Cytoplasm

Caption Question Answer
Figure 7.4 The polar heads face toward the outside where they interact with the watery exterior of the cell.

Quick Demo

Like Dissolves Like Mix polar substances such as colored water and alcohol to show that the substances dissolve in each other. Then add a small amount of salad oil to the colored water. Point out that the oil is nonpolar. Stir the mixture vigorously. Explain that the oil forms spheres because the oil molecules have an affinity for each other but not for the water molecules.

✓**Reading Check** The phospholipid bilayer consists of two layers of phospholipid molecules aligned so that their non-polar fatty acid tails are toward the interior and the polar phosphate heads are toward the watery exterior.

The phospholipid bilayer

The phosphate group is critical for the formation and function of the plasma membrane. The two fatty acid tails of the phospholipids are nonpolar, whereas the head of the phospholipid molecule containing the phosphate group is polar.

Water is a key component of living organisms, both inside and outside the cell. The polar phosphate group allows the cell membrane to interact with its watery environment because, as you recall, water is also polar. The fatty acid tails, on the other hand, avoid water. The two layers of phospholipid molecules make a sandwich with the fatty acid tails forming the interior of the membrane and the phospholipid heads facing the watery environments found inside and outside the cell. *Figure 7.4* illustrates phospholipids and their place within the structure of the plasma membrane. When many phospholipid molecules come together in this manner, a barrier is created that is water-soluble at its outer surfaces and water-insoluble in the middle. Water-soluble molecules will not easily move through the membrane because they are stopped by this water-insoluble layer.

✓**Reading Check** **Describe** the structure of the phospholipid bilayer.

Physical Science Connection

Solubility and the nature of solute and solvent
Solvents made of polar molecules usually dissolve polar and ionic solutes. Solvents made of nonpolar molecules, such as oil or fat, usually dissolve nonpolar solutes.

Physical Science Connection

Explain to students that ascorbic acid, known as vitamin C, is a polar molecule. Have them predict whether vitamin C is a water- or fat-soluble vitamin. They can check their answers in Table 35.2 on page 926. Vitamin C is water soluble. Excess vitamin C is expelled from the body in urine.

PROJECT

Learning About Scientists Have students make a table that lists the name and contributions of each scientist discussed in this chapter. Students can also research other cell scientists. Encourage students to keep their tables in their portfolios and to add information about other scientists throughout the remainder of the course. **L2**

 Indiana Academic Standards

Pages 176–177: B.1.2, B.1.4, B.1.6, B.1.9

3 Assess

Figure 7.5
Eukaryotic plasma membranes can contain large amounts of cholesterol—as many as one molecule for every phospholipid molecule.

The model of the plasma membrane is called the **fluid mosaic model.** It is fluid because the phospholipids move within the membrane just as water molecules move with the currents in a lake. At the same time, proteins in the membrane also move among the phospholipids like boats with their decks above water and hulls below water. These proteins create a "mosaic," or pattern, on the membrane surface.

Other components of the plasma membrane

Cholesterol, shown in *Figure 7.5,* is also found in the plasma membrane where it helps to stabilize the phospholipids by preventing their fatty acid tails from sticking together.

Cholesterol is a common topic in health issues today because high levels are associated with reduced blood flow in blood vessels. Yet, for all the emphasis on cholesterol-free foods, it is important to recognize that cholesterol plays a critical role in the stability of the plasma membrane and is therefore a necessary part of your diet.

You've learned that proteins are found within the lipid membrane. Proteins that span the entire membrane help form the selectively permeable membrane that regulates which molecules enter and which molecules leave a cell. These proteins are called transport proteins. **Transport proteins** move needed substances or waste materials through the plasma membrane. Other proteins and carbohydrates that stick out from the cell surface help cells to identify chemical signals and each other. As you will discover later, these characteristics are important in protecting your cells from infection. Proteins at the inner surface of a plasma membrane play an important role in attaching the plasma membrane to the cell's internal support structure, giving the cell its flexibility.

✓ Reading Check **Explain** how a water-soluble substance can pass through the plasma membrane.

Section Assessment

Understanding Main Ideas
1. Describe the plasma membrane, and explain why it is called a bilayer structure.
2. Describe the structure of a phospholipid. Use the terms *polar* and *nonpolar* in your answer.
3. What are the specialized parts of the phospholipid bilayer, and how do their structures relate to the structure of the plasma membrane?
4. Why is the structure of the plasma membrane referred to as a fluid mosaic?

Thinking Critically
5. Suggest what might happen if cells grow and reproduce in an environment where no cholesterol is available.

SKILL REVIEW
6. **Get the Big Picture** Plasma membranes allow certain materials to pass through them. Investigate how this property contributes to homeostasis. For more help, refer to *Get the Big Picture* in the **Skill Handbook.**

178 A VIEW OF THE CELL

 in.bdol.glencoe.com/self_check_quiz

Section Assessment

1. Phospholipids that form the membrane consist of a double layer.
2. A phospholipid has a glycerol backbone, 2 fatty acid chains, and a phosphate group. The polar head includes the phosphate group, while the 2 fatty acid tails are nonpolar.
3. Two lipid layers consisting of a glycerol backbone, two fatty acid tails, and a phosphate group are positioned with heads facing out and tails facing in.
4. The lipids and proteins in the membrane are free to move, making a pattern like a mosaic.
5. The membranes would be very fragile and would not hold together.
6. Selective permeability allows materials that are needed for metabolism and survival to enter the cell.

Eukaryotic Cell Structure

Indiana Standards Standard B.1.3 Know and describe that within the cell are specialized parts for the transport of materials, energy capture and release, protein building, waste disposal, information feedback, and movement...

SECTION PREVIEW

Objectives

Identify the structure and function of the parts of a typical eukaryotic cell.

Explain the advantages of highly folded membranes in cells.

Compare and contrast the structures of plant and animal cells.

Review Vocabulary
enzyme: a protein that speeds up the rate of a chemical reaction (p. 161)

New Vocabulary
cell wall
chromatin
nucleolus
ribosome
cytoplasm
endoplasmic reticulum
Golgi apparatus
vacuole
lysosome
chloroplast
plastid
chlorophyll
mitochondria
cytoskeleton
microtubule
microfilament
cilia
flagella

Working Together for a Common Goal

Using an Analogy When you work on a group project, each person has his or her own skills and talents that add a particular value to the group's work. In the same way, each component of a eukaryotic cell has a specific job, and all of the parts of the cell work together to help the cell survive.

Organize Information *As you read the section, make a list of the cell parts. Next to each one, identify something from everyday life that functions in the same way. Then, explain what they both do.*

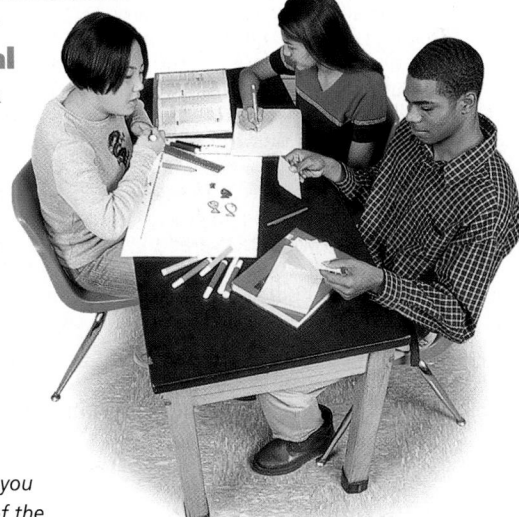

Cell structures, like this team of students, work together.

Cellular Boundaries

When a group works together, someone on the team decides what resources are necessary for the project and provides these resources. In the cell, the plasma membrane, shown in *Figure 7.6,* performs this task by acting as a selectively permeable membrane. The fluid mosaic model describes the plasma membrane as a flexible boundary of a cell. However, plant cells, fungi, bacteria, and some protists have an additional boundary, the cell wall. The **cell wall** is a fairly rigid structure located outside the plasma membrane that provides additional support and protection.

Figure 7.6
The plasma membrane is made up of two layers, which are diagrammed in the center image. You can see the layers in the photomicrograph.

Outside of cell

Inside of cell

Plasma membrane

Plasma membrane

Color-enhanced TEM Magnification: 250 000×

Section 7.3

1 Focus

INTERACTIVE CHALKBOARD
PowerPoint® Presentations

Bellringer
Section Focus Transparency 17

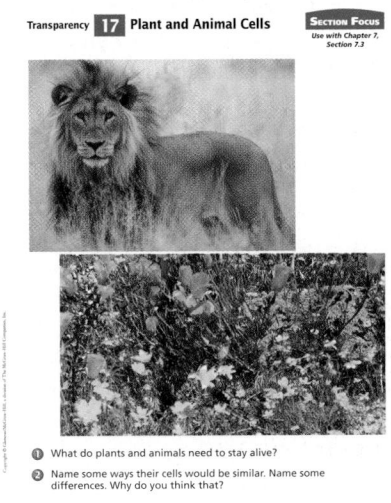

Transparency **17** Plant and Animal Cells

SECTION FOCUS
Use with Chapter 7, Section 7.3

❶ What do plants and animals need to stay alive?
❷ Name some ways their cells would be similar. Name some differences. Why do you think that?

BIOLOGY: The Dynamics of Life   SECTION FOCUS TRANSPARENCIES

Using an Analogy

Organize Information Encourage students to be creative and use analogies from their everyday lives. For example, they might picture the school cafeteria in the role of a chloroplast, manufacturing food for later use by the school.

Virtual Lab
CD-ROM Students will take a spin on the wheel of cells in *Cellular Pursuit.*

RESOURCE MANAGER

Unit 3 *FAST FILE* Resources
MiniLab Worksheet, p. 42
BioLab Worksheet, pp. 43–44
Reinforcement and Study Guide in English, pp. 49–50
Reinforcement and Study Guide in Spanish, pp. 53–54
Concept Mapping, p. 55
Critical Thinking/Problem Solving, p. 56

Transparency Worksheets, pp. 59, 63–64, 67–68
Reading Essentials for Biology, Section 7.3
Inside Story Poster
Section Focus Transparency 17
Basic Concepts Transparency 7
Reteaching Skills Transparency 10

Indiana Academic Standards
Pages 178–179: B.1.2, B.1.4, B.1.6, B.1.9

2 Teach

Purpose

Students will become familiar with the role of the nucleus in directing cell activities.

Process Skills

relate cause and effect, interpret data

Background

Two species of *Acetabularia* both have nuclei in their "feet" but produce different caps. Cutting and replacing the caps allows one to determine the role the nucleus plays in directing production of cellular proteins.

Teaching Strategies

You may wish to draw diagrams of the *Acetabularia* species used in this study on the chalkboard or show a transparency and review the results as a class. Lead a discussion about why the final cap ended as it did.

Thinking Critically

The nucleus produces substances that control the type of cap the cell has. The first cap was of intermediate form because the cytoplasm contained substances from both the previous nucleus and the present nucleus. The cytoplasm of the second cap had only substances from the present nucleus.

Modified Assessment

Portfolio Ask students to draw each step of this experiment and to describe what happened in their own words. **L1**

180

Problem-Solving Lab 7.2

Interpret the Data

What organelle directs cell activity? *Acetabularia*, a type of marine alga, grows as single, large cells 2 to 5 cm in height. The nuclei of these cells are in the "feet." Different species of these algae have different kinds of caps, some petal-like and others that look like umbrellas. If a cap is removed, it quickly grows back. If both cap and foot are removed from the cell of one species and a foot from another species is attached, a new cap will grow. This new cap will have a structure with characteristics of both species. If this new cap is removed, the cap that grows back will be like the cell that donated the nucleus.

The scientist who discovered these properties was Joachim Hämmerling. He wondered why the first cap that grew had characteristics of both species, yet the second cap was clearly like that of the cell that donated the nucleus.

Solve the Problem

Look at the diagram below and identify how the final cell develops.

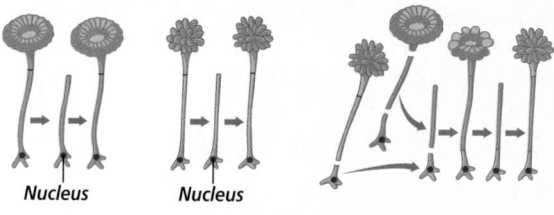

Nucleus   Nucleus

Thinking Critically

Interpret Data Why is the final cap like that of the cell from which the nucleus was taken?

The cell wall

The cell wall forms an inflexible barrier that protects the cell and gives it support. *Figure* 7.7 shows a plant cell wall composed of a carbohydrate called cellulose. The cellulose forms a thick, tough mesh of fibers. This fibrous cell wall is very porous and allows molecules to enter. Unlike the plasma membrane, it does not select which molecules can enter into the cell.

The Nucleus and Cell Control

Just as every team needs a leader to direct activity, so the cell needs a leader to give directions. The nucleus is the leader of the eukaryotic cell because it contains the directions to make proteins. Every part of the cell depends on proteins, so by containing the blueprint to make proteins, the nucleus controls the activity of the organelles. Read the *Problem-Solving Lab* on this page and consider how the *Acetabularia* (a suh tab yew LAIR ee uh) nucleus controls the cell.

The master set of directions for making proteins is contained in **chromatin,** which are strands of the genetic material, DNA. When a cell

---

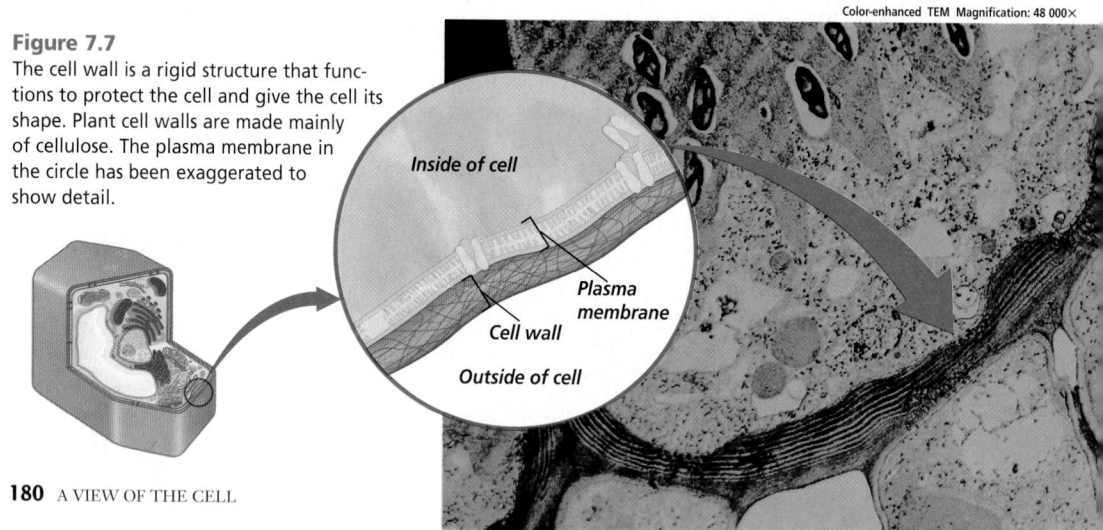

Color-enhanced TEM Magnification: 48 000×

Figure 7.7
The cell wall is a rigid structure that functions to protect the cell and give the cell its shape. Plant cell walls are made mainly of cellulose. The plasma membrane in the circle has been exaggerated to show detail.

Inside of cell
Plasma membrane
Cell wall
Outside of cell

180 A VIEW OF THE CELL

CHALLENGE ACTIVITY

Write a Play Students who need an additional challenge can write a play chronicling the creation and process of a protein in a cell. The protein could begin with planning in the nucleus, continue with transport through the cell organelles, and end with destruction within a lysosome. Make sure that each cell organelle plays a part. The story may be told creatively, as if the protein were aware of its surroundings. **L3**
COOP LEARN

divides, the chromatin condenses to form chromosomes. Within the nucleus is a prominent organelle called the **nucleolus,** which makes ribosomes. **Ribosomes** are the sites where the cell produces proteins according to the directions of DNA. Unlike other organelles, ribosomes are not bound by a membrane. They are simple structures made of RNA and protein. Look at the onion cells as described in the *MiniLab* on the next page and try to identify the nucleus.

For proteins to be made, ribosomes must leave the nucleus and enter the cytoplasm, and the blueprints contained in DNA must be translated into RNA and sent to the cytoplasm. **Cytoplasm** is the clear, gelatinous fluid inside a cell. Ribosomes and translated RNA are transported to the cytoplasm through the nuclear envelope—a structure that separates the nucleus from the cytoplasm, as shown in *Figure 7.8.* The nuclear envelope is a double membrane made up of two phospholipid bilayers containing small nuclear pores for substances to pass through. Ribosomes and translated RNA pass into the cytoplasm through these pores in the nuclear envelope.

Assembly, Transport, and Storage

You have begun to follow the trail of protein production as directed by the cell manager—the nucleus. But what happens to the copy of the blueprints for proteins once it passes from the nucleus into the cytoplasm?

Organelles for assembly and transport of proteins

The cytoplasm suspends the cell's organelles. One particular organelle in a eukaryotic cell, the **endoplasmic reticulum** (ER), is the site of cellular chemical reactions. Shown in *Figure 7.9,* the ER is arranged in a series of highly folded membranes in the cytoplasm. Its folds are like the folds of an accordion. If you spread the accordion out, it would take up tremendous space. By pleating and folding, the accordion fits into a compact unit. Similarly, a large amount of folded ER is available to do work in a small space.

Ribosomes in the cytoplasm are attached to the surface of the endoplasmic reticulum, called rough endoplasmic reticulum, where they carry out the function of protein synthesis.

Figure 7.8
The transmission electron photomicrograph shows the nucleus of a eukaryotic cell. The large holes in the nuclear envelope are pores.

Color-enhanced TEM Magnification: 14 000×

Cytoplasm
Nucleus
Nucleolus
Chromatin
Nuclear pores
Nuclear envelope of two membranes

Purpose

Students will learn the technique and value of using stains for doing microscope observations.

Process Skills

compare and contrast, experiment, observe and infer

Teaching Strategies

- Review the procedure for making a wet mount.
- Emphasize that reducing the microscope's light may be critical for viewing onion tissue.
- Demonstrate how to peel an onion epidermis from the bulb.
- Iodine stain may be placed in dark dropper bottles—add 1.5 g potassium iodide and 0.3 g iodine to 1 L water.
- **CAUTION:** *Iodine is a skin, eye, and respiratory tract irritant. Handle with care and wash hands after use.*

Expected Results

Students will observe more organelles when cells are stained than when cells are unstained.

Analysis

1. cell wall, cytoplasm; cell wall, cytoplasm, nucleus
2. Stains allow certain organelles to be more easily observed.

Modified Assessment

Skill Ask students to diagram and label organelles of two onion cells, one with and one without stain. Use the Performance Task Assessment List for Scientific Drawing in **PASC**, p. 127. **L1** **ELL**

MiniLab 7.2

Experiment

Cell Organelles Adding stains to cellular material helps you distinguish cell organelles.

Procedure

CAUTION: *Iodine stain is hazardous. Handle it with care. Be sure to wash hands with soap or detergent before and after this lab.*

1 Prepare a water wet mount of onion skin. Do this by using your fingernail to peel off the inside of a layer of onion bulb. The layer must be almost transparent. Use the following diagram as a guide.

2 Make sure that the onion layer is lying flat on the glass slide and is not folded.

3 Observe the onion cells under low- and high-power magnification. Identify as many organelles as possible.

4 Repeat steps 1 through 3, only this time use an iodine stain instead of water.

Analysis

1. **Observe and Infer** What organelles were easily seen in the unstained onion cells? In cells stained with iodine?
2. **Experiment** How are stains useful for viewing cells?

The ribosome's job is to make proteins. Each protein made in the rough ER has a particular function; it may become a protein that forms a part of the plasma membrane, a protein that is released from the cell, or a protein transported to other organelles. Ribosomes can also be found floating freely in the cytoplasm. They make proteins that perform tasks within the cytoplasm itself.

Areas of the ER that are not studded with ribosomes are known as smooth endoplasmic reticulum. The smooth ER is involved in numerous biochemical activities, including the production and storage of lipids.

After proteins are made, they are transferred to another organelle called the **Golgi** (GAWL jee) **apparatus.** The Golgi apparatus, as shown in *Figure 7.10,* is a flattened stack of tubular membranes that modifies the proteins. The Golgi apparatus sorts proteins into packages and packs them into membrane-bound structures, called vesicles, to be sent to the appropriate destination, like mail being sorted at the post office.

✓ **Reading Check** **Compare and contrast** the two types of ER.

Figure 7.9
The endoplasmic reticulum is a complex system of membranes in the cytoplasm of eukaryotic cells. **Infer** *What substances are produced and stored in the ER?*

Endoplasmic reticulum

Ribosomes

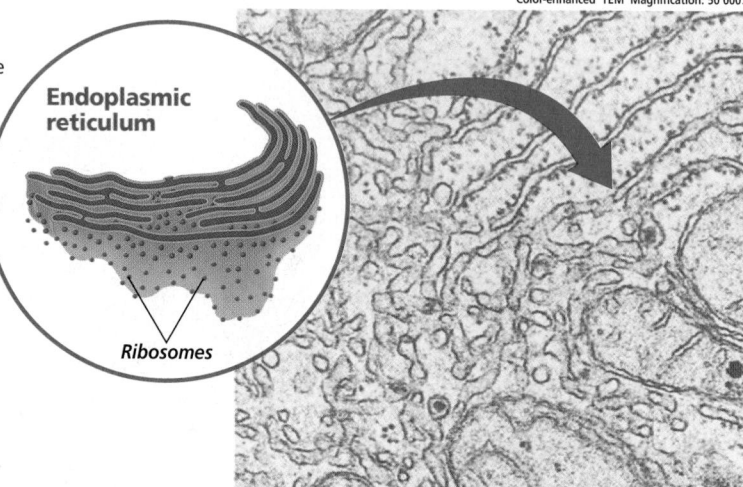

Color-enhanced TEM Magnification: 50 000×

Additional Lab

Differences Between Plant and Animal Cells

Purpose

This lab will allow students to compare plant and animal cells.

Safety Precautions

Students should wear aprons and goggles. Remind students to handle glass slides carefully and dispose of them properly. Students should wash their hands thoroughly.

Materials

microscope, glass slides and coverslips, droppers, forceps, *Elodea* plant, prepared slide of human cheek cells

Procedure

Give students the following directions.

1. Use a dropper to place a drop of water in the center of a slide. Use the forceps to remove a leaf from the tip of an *Elodea* sprig and place it in the water on your slide. Add a coverslip.

2. Under low power, look for a thin area of the leaf where you can see the cells most clearly. Change to high power and locate a single cell. Observe carefully for a minute.

Figure 7.10

The Golgi apparatus, as viewed with a TEM, looks like a side view of a stack of pancakes. Also visible are many spherical vesicles that are involved in protein transport.

Vesicles   **Golgi apparatus**

Color-enhanced TEM Magnification: 45 000×

Vacuoles and storage

Now let's look at some of the other members of the cell team important for the cell's functioning. Cells have membrane-bound compartments, called **vacuoles,** for temporary storage of materials. A vacuole, like that in *Figure 7.11A,* is a sac used to store food, enzymes, and other materials needed by a cell. Some vacuoles store waste products. Animal cells usually do not contain vacuoles. If they do, the vacuoles are much smaller, as shown in *Figure 7.11B.*

Lysosomes and recycling

Did anyone ever ask you to take out the trash? Is that action part of a team effort? In a cell, it is. **Lysosomes** are organelles that contain digestive enzymes. They digest excess or worn out organelles, food particles, and engulfed viruses or bacteria. The membrane surrounding a lysosome prevents the digestive enzymes inside from destroying the cell. Lysosomes can fuse with vacuoles and dispense their enzymes into the vacuole, digesting its contents.

Figure 7.11
Plant cells usually have one large vacuole (A); some animal cells contain many smaller vacuoles (B).

Color-enhanced TEM Magnification: 1850×

A

Color-enhanced TEM Magnification: 13 000×

B

Caption Question Answer

Figure 7.9 Lipids are produced and stored in the smooth ER. Ribosomes may be found on the rough ER.

Reading Check The rough ER is rough because of the ribosomes attached to it. The ribosomes actively construct proteins. The smooth ER has no ribosomes, and carries out other functions, such as lipid production and storage.

Visual Learning

Figure 7.10 Discuss how showing cell organelles both in photographs and in art is useful. Point out that illustrations can often accentuate structures to make them clearer than they appear in photographs.

Display

Use models of plant cells and animal cells (available from biological supply houses) to review and reinforce knowledge of cell parts.

Chalkboard Activity

Have students list body systems they need to live. Write their responses on the chalkboard. Use this list to introduce cell organelles as the structures that perform or help to perform the life functions of cells. **L1**

Indiana Academic Standards

Pages 182–183: B.1.3

---

3. Draw the cell and label the structures you see.
4. Place the prepared slide of human cheek cells on the microscope stage and view under low power, moving the slide to center a single cell. Change to high power and observe the cell. Draw the cell and label the structures.

Analysis

1. What structures did you see in each cell? What are their functions? Responses may include cell walls, cell membranes, vacuoles, and nuclei. Accept all logical descriptions of the functions of each cell part named.
2. Methylene blue is one stain used when observing cells. What is its function? Stain makes it possible to see some parts of the cell that might not otherwise be visible.

Assessment

Performance Have students prepare a lab report describing what they have seen. They should include drawings of both the *Elodea* and cheek cell and the answers to the analysis questions. Use the Performance Task Assessment List for Lab Report in **PASC**, p. 119. **L2**

Students often believe that because plants carry on photosynthesis, they do not also respire.

Uncover the Misconception

Write the words *respiration, photosynthesis, plants,* and *animals* on the board in front of the class. Have students copy the terms and connect the related terms. (*respiration* connects to *plants* and *animals; photosynthesis* connects to *plants*) Have the class share which terms they connected.

Demonstrate the Concept

Students may connect only *plant* with *photosynthesis* and only *animal* with *respiration.* Show students the art in Figure 7.14 of plant and animal cells. Point out that mitochondria, which carry out respiration, are present in both plant and animal cells.

Assess New Knowledge

Have students summarize the processes plants and animals have in common. Although plants carry on photosynthesis and respiration as part of life processes, animal cells can only respire, and require food from plant cells.

✓ **Reading Check** The inner membranes are arranged in stacks, called grana. The fluid surrounding the grana is called stroma.

Word Origin
chloroplast from the Greek words *chloros,* meaning "green," and *platos,* meaning "formed object"; Chloroplasts capture light energy and produce food for plant cells. Plants are green because they contain the green pigment chlorophyll.

For example, when an amoeba engulfs food and encloses it in a vacuole, a lysosome fuses with the vacuole and releases its enzymes, which digest the food. Sometimes, lysosomes digest the cells that contain them. When a tadpole develops into a frog, lysosomes within the cells of the tadpole's tail cause its digestion. The molecules released are used to build different cells, perhaps in the legs of the adult frog.

Energy Transformers

After learning about cell parts and what they do, it's easy to imagine that each of these cell team members requires a lot of energy. Protein production, modification, transportation, digestion—all require energy. Two other organelles, chloroplasts and mitochondria, provide that energy.

Chloroplasts and energy

When you walk through a field or pick a vegetable from the garden, you may not think of the plants as energy generators. In fact, that is exactly what you see. Located in the cells of green plants and some protists, chloroplasts are the heart of the generator. **Chloroplasts** are cell organelles that capture light energy and convert it to chemical energy.

A chloroplast, like a nucleus, has a double membrane. The diagram and TEM photomicrograph of a chloroplast in *Figure 7.12* shows an outer membrane and a folded inner membrane system. It is within these inner thylakoid membranes that the energy from sunlight is trapped. These inner membranes are arranged in stacks of membranous sacs called grana, which resemble stacks of coins. The fluid that surrounds the stacks of grana is called stroma.

The chloroplast belongs to a group of plant organelles called **plastids,** which are used for storage. Some plastids store starches or lipids, whereas others contain pigments, molecules that give color. Plastids are named according to their color or the pigment they contain. Chloroplasts contain the green pigment chlorophyll. **Chlorophyll** traps light energy and gives leaves and stems their green color.

✓ **Reading Check Describe** the internal structure of a chloroplast.

Figure 7.12
Chloroplasts are usually disc-shaped but have the ability to change shape and position in the cell as light intensity changes. The pigment chlorophyll is embedded in the inner series of thylakoid membranes.

Color-enhanced TEM Magnification: 6300×

Chloroplast
Stroma
Granum
Thylakoid
Two membranes

USING MODELS

Build a Giant Cell: *Kinesthetic* Turn part of your classroom into a giant animal cell. From the ceiling, hang four strings to make a "square" cell. Have students calculate the magnification factor by dividing the length of a side (in µm) by 20 µm (the length of a liver cell). Have students research the sizes of organelles and calculate how large they need to make each organelle using the magnification factor (cell organelle size × magnification factor). Have students use paper and other materials to build cell organelles to scale, and then hang them inside the classroom cell. **L2** **ELL**

Figure 7.13
Mitochondria are granular and rod-shaped, with an inner membrane that forms long, narrow folds. This TEM shows a cross section of a mitochondrion.
Explain *Why is the inner membrane folded?*

Color-enhanced TEM Magnification: 9000×

Inner membrane
Outer membrane
Mitochondrion

Caption Question Answer
Figure 7.13 Folding the membrane allows much more material to be compressed into the small space. This maximizes the amount of energy production that can take place within this space.

Word Origin

Have the students research to find and define other words using "cyte" as part of the root, such as *cytology* and *cytogenetics*.

Mitochondria and energy

The chemical energy generated by chloroplasts is stored in the bonds of sugar molecules until they are broken down by mitochondria, shown in *Figure 7.13*. **Mitochondria** are membrane-bound organelles in plant and animal cells that transform energy for the cell. This energy is then stored in the bonds of other molecules that cell organelles can access easily and quickly when energy is needed.

A mitochondrion has an outer membrane and a highly folded inner membrane. As with the endoplasmic reticulum and chloroplasts, the folds of the inner membrane provide a large surface area that fits in a small space. Energy-storing molecules are produced on the inner folds. Mitochondria occur in varying numbers depending on the function of the cell. For example, liver cells may have up to 2000 mitochondria.

Although the process by which energy is transformed and used in the cells is a technical concept that you will learn in a later chapter, the *Connection to Literature* at the end of this chapter explains how cellular processes can also be inspiring.

Organelles for Support and Locomotion

Scientists once thought that cell organelles just floated in a sea of cytoplasm. More recently, cell biologists have discovered that cells have a support structure called the **cytoskeleton** within the cytoplasm.

The cytoskeleton

The cytoskeleton forms a framework for the cell, like the skeleton that forms the framework for your body. However, unlike your bones, the cytoskeleton is a constantly changing structure. It can be dismantled in one place and reassembled somewhere else in the cell, changing the cell's shape.

The cytoskeleton is a network of tiny rods and filaments. **Microtubules** are thin, hollow cylinders made of protein. **Microfilaments** are smaller, solid protein fibers. Together, they act as a sort of scaffold to maintain the shape of the cell in the same way that poles maintain the shape of a tent. They also anchor and support many organelles and provide a sort of highway system through which materials move within the cell.

Word Origin

cytoskeleton from the Greek word *cyte*, meaning "cell"; The cytoskeleton provides support and structure for the cell.

Physical Science Connection

Conservation of energy Energy can exist in different forms, such as thermal, electrical, chemical, and light energy. However, even though energy can change from one form to another, energy cannot be created or destroyed—it is always conserved.

Quick Demo

Gelatin Models To aid students in understanding the orientation of organelles in a cell, create a cell model from gelatin containing whole grapes and chunks of different fruits. Have students compare cell parts suspended in cytoplasm to the fruit suspended in the gelatin. Have students speculate how the angle on which the cell is cut relates to the shapes organelles may take in an electron micrograph.
L2 **ELL**

Physical Science Connection

Have students brainstorm examples of energy conversion that they have encountered or used in everyday life. Remind them that energy is transformed, not lost, as it changes form. Examples include burning coal (chemical energy) to produce electrical energy, and mechanical energy transforming into thermal energy.

INCLUSION STRATEGIES

Visually Impaired Ask sighted students to describe what they see in microscope labs. You can also prepare slides for a projection microscope or provide 3-dimensional replicas to help visually impaired students. **L2**

Indiana Academic Standards

Pages 184–185: B.1.2, B.1.3

Purpose

Students will compare plant and animal cells and discover the similarities.

Teaching Strategies

Review cell organelles with your class, then use Figure 7.14 to compare plant and animal cells with regard to organelles. Be sure to point out the number and type of organelles these cells have in common. Also emphasize the organelles and structures that are unique to plant and animal cells.

Visual Learning

Make a table with the headings: nucleus, ribosomes, centrioles, endoplasmic reticulum, vacuoles, mitochondria, plasma membrane, and cell wall. Underneath the headings list animal cell and plant cell. Have the class complete the table using Figure 7.14. **L1**

Critical Thinking

Most cells, whether they belong to a plant or an animal, must perform the same critical functions to survive, grow, and reproduce. Therefore, plant and animal cells have many of the same organelles to meet these needs.

The BioLab at the end of the chapter can be used at this point in the lesson.

INSIDE STORY

Comparing Animal and Plant Cells

Figure 7.14

You can easily recognize that a person does not look like a flower and a moose does not resemble a tree. But at the cellular level under a microscope, the cells that make up all of the different animals and plants of the world are very much alike. **Critical Thinking** *Why are animal and plant cells similar?*

Animal Cells A
Notice that animal cells have centrioles, whereas plant cells do not. Animal cells typically have small lysosomes.

Lysosome
Cytoskeleton
Plasma membrane
Golgi apparatus
Cytoplasm
Centriole
Free ribosomes
Nucleus
Nucleolus
Mitochondrion
Endoplasmic reticulum
Ribosomes

Mitochondrion
Cytoplasm
Endoplasmic reticulum
Chloroplast
Free ribosomes
Ribosomes
Golgi apparatus
Cytoskeleton
Cell wall
Nucleus
Nucleolus
Vacuole
Plasma membrane

B Plant Cells Plant cells are characterized by a cell wall and chloroplasts. Plant cells usually have one large vacuole.

186 A VIEW OF THE CELL

Table 7.1 Comparison of Prokaryotic and Eukaryotic Cells

Cell Part	Function	Prokaryotic Cell	Eukaryotic Cell
Plasma membrane	Maintains homeostasis	Present	Present
Cell wall	Supports and protects cell	Present	Present in plants
Ribosome	Makes proteins	Present	Present
Chloroplast	Produces food	Absent	Present in plants
Cytoskeleton	Provides internal structure	Absent	Present
Endoplasmic reticulum	Chemical reactions	Absent	Present
Golgi apparatus	Sorts and transports	Absent	Present
Lysosome	Digests material	Absent	Present in some
Mitochondrion	Transforms energy	Absent	Present
Nucleus	Cell control center	Absent	Present
Vacuole	Storage	Absent	Present

Centrioles

Centrioles are organelles found in the cells of animals and most protists. They occur in pairs and are made up of microtubules. Centrioles play an important role in cell division.

Cilia and flagella

Some cell surfaces have cilia and flagella, which are organelles made of microtubules that aid the cell in locomotion or feeding. Cilia and flagella can be distinguished by their structure and by the nature of their action. **Cilia** are short, numerous projections that look like hairs.

Their motion is similar to that of oars in a rowboat. **Flagella** are longer projections that move with a whip-like motion. A cell usually has only one or two flagella. In unicellular organisms, cilia and flagella are the major means of locomotion.

Remember that prokaryotic cells lack the membrane-bound organelles that are found in eukaryotic cells. *Table 7.1* shows a side-by-side comparison of eukaryotic and prokaryotic cells, their cell parts, and what those parts do. *Figure 7.14* summarizes the structure of eukaryotic plant and animal cells.

Section Assessment

Understanding Main Ideas

1. How are highly folded membranes an advantage for the functions of cellular parts? Name an organelle that has highly folded membranes.

2. If a cell synthesizes large quantities of protein molecules, which organelles might be numerous in that cell?

3. A cell's digestive enzymes are enclosed in a membrane-bound organelle. How can these molecules function in the cell?

4. Compare and contrast the functions of a cell wall to the functions of a plasma membrane.

5. Compare the number of vacuoles in plant cells and animal cells.

Thinking Critically

6. Compare mitochondria and chloroplasts. Why are they referred to as energy transformers?

SKILL REVIEW

7. **Student Presentation Builder** Create a class presentation that follows a protein molecule from its formation to its final destination, using the *Student Presentation Builder*.

3 Assess

DAILY INTERVENTION

Check for Understanding Ask students what would happen if a cell had a decreased number of mitochondria. The cell would probably not have enough energy to carry out all life functions. **L2**

Reteach
Interpersonal Ask students working in groups to role-play the organelles of a typical animal cell. Students should show how organelles work together to keep the entire cell functioning. **L1** **ELL** **COOP LEARN**

Resources
For more practice, use *Reading Essentials for Biology,* Section 7.3.

Extension

Interpersonal Have students play vocabulary football with cell terms. Divide the class into two teams. Ask a question of one team. If they answer correctly, advance the ball 10 yards on a football field drawn on the chalkboard. If they miss the question, ask the other team. The team scoring the most touchdowns wins. **L2**

MODIFIED Assessment

Portfolio Divide students into groups of three or four. Assign each group a cell part and have students develop a commercial to "sell" their cell part. **L1** **ELL** **COOP LEARN**

Section Assessment

1. The folding increases the surface area where chemical reactions occur. Examples: endoplasmic reticulum and mitochondria.

2. rough endoplasmic reticulum and Golgi apparatus

3. The lysosome joins with what is to be digested so the cell isn't damaged.

4. Cell walls provide support and protection for plant cells. Plasma membranes maintain homeostasis.

5. Plant cells usually have one large vacuole. Animal cells have smaller vacuoles, if they have them at all.

6. Both mitochondria and chloroplasts are composed of two membranes, with the inner membrane being highly folded. Chloroplasts contain chlorophyll and other pigments used to capture light energy. Mitochondria and chloroplasts transform energy from one form to another.

7. Have the students take turns giving their presentations to the class. All should correctly demonstrate the formation of a protein and follow the protein to its destination.

187

Time Allotment
one class period

Process Skills
observe and infer, measure in SI, hypothesize, compare and contrast, use numbers

Safety Precautions
Students must handle prepared slides, glass slides, and especially coverslips with care. Students should wash their hands thoroughly.

Gather the materials for the lab and review microscopy procedures prior to performing the lab.

Alternative Materials
- *Elodea* is available in pet shops. Prepared slides may be substituted.
- Epithelium slides are available as prepared frog skin or human cheek cells in place of frog blood. Do not substitute human blood.
- Any prepared slide of stained bacteria may be used.

Indiana Academic Standards
Pages 188–189: B.1.12

Teaching Strategies
- Review the technique used for preparing a wet mount.
- Review the technique used for measuring objects under the microscope (see MiniLab 7.1). Review the conversion of millimeters to micrometers.

- Do not reveal the cell type in advance. That is, do not tell students that *Bacillus subtilis* is a bacterium.

Troubleshooting
- Individual *Elodea* cells are best observed along the leaf edge.

- If students cannot see organelles, have them practice changing their depth of view by rapidly moving the fine adjustment back and forth while viewing a cell under high-power magnification.

Before You Begin
Are all cells alike in appearance, shape, and size? Do all cells have some of the same organelles present within their cell boundaries? One way to answer these questions is to observe a variety of cells using a light microscope. In this lab, you will make observations of a bacterial cell (*Bacillus subtilis*), frog blood cells, and a plant cell (from *Elodea*).

Observing and Comparing Different Cell Types

Problem
Are all cells alike in appearance and size?

Objectives
In this BioLab, you will:
- **Observe, diagram,** and **measure** cells and their organelles.
- **Infer** whether cells are prokaryotic or eukaryotic and whether they are from unicellular organisms or multicellular organisms.
- **List** the traits of plant and animal cells.

Materials
microscope   dropper   glass slide
coverslip   forceps   *Elodea* leaf
prepared slides of *Bacillus subtilis* and frog blood

Safety Precautions
CAUTION: *Use care when handling slides. Dispose of any broken glass in a container provided by your teacher. Always wear goggles in the lab.*

Skill Handbook
If you need help with this lab, refer to the **Skill Handbook.**

1. Copy the data table.
2. Examine a prepared slide of *Bacillus subtilis* using both low- and high-power magnification. (Note: This slide has been stained. Bacterial cells have no natural color.)

Data Table

	Bacillus subtilis	*Elodea*	Frog Blood
Organelles observed	none	vacuole, cell wall, chloroplasts	nucleus
Prokaryote or eukaryote	prokaryote	eukaryote	eukaryote
From a multicellular or unicellular organism	unicellular	multicellular	multicellular
Diagram (with size in micrometers, μm)	8μm	Check students' diagrams; 30μm	15μm

3. Identify and record the names of any observed organelles. Infer whether these cells are prokaryotic or eukaryotic. Infer whether these cells are from a unicellular or multicellular organism. Record your findings in the table.

4. Diagram one cell as seen under high-power magnification.

5. While using high power, determine the length and width in micrometers of this cell. Refer to *Thinking Critically* in the **Skill Handbook** for help with determining magnification. Record your measurements on the diagram.

6. Prepare a wet mount of a single leaf from *Elodea* using the diagram as a guide.

7. Observe the *Elodea* cells under low- and high-power magnification.

8. Repeat steps 3 through 5 for *Elodea*.

9. Examine a prepared slide of frog blood. (Note: This slide has been stained. Its natural color is pink.)

10. Observe cells under low- and high-power magnification.

11. Repeat steps 3 through 5 for frog blood cells.

12. **CLEANUP AND DISPOSAL** Clean all equipment as instructed by your teacher, and return everything to its proper place for reuse. Wash your hands thoroughly.

Leopard frog

ANALYZE AND CONCLUDE

1. **Observe and Infer** Which cells were prokaryotic and which were eukaryotic? How were you able to tell?

2. **Predict** Which cell was from a plant and which was from an animal? Explain your answer.

3. **Measure** Are prokaryotic or eukaryotic cells larger? Give specific measurements to support your answer.

4. **Define Operationally** Compare the structure and function of the plant and animal cells you saw.

5. **ERROR ANALYSIS** Suppose you estimate that eight *Elodea* cells will fit across the high-power field of view of your microscope. You calculate that the diameter of an *Elodea* cell is approximately 50 mm. Is this a reasonable value? If not, what was the error in your analysis?

Apply Your Skill

Lab Techniques Prepare a wet mount of very thin slices of bamboo (saxophone reed). Observe under low and high power. What structures are you looking at? Explain the absence of all other organelles from this material.

Web Links To find out more about microscopy and cell types, visit in.bdol.glencoe.com/microscopy

7.3 EUKARYOTIC CELL STRUCTURE **189**

ANALYZE AND CONCLUDE

1. *Bacillus subtilis* is prokaryotic—no internal organelles are visible. *Elodea* and blood cells are eukaryotic—internal organelles are observed.

2. *Elodea* is from a plant—cell wall and chloroplasts are visible. Blood cells are from an animal—no cell wall or chloroplasts are visible.

3. Eukaryotic cells are larger—the prokaryotic cell is less than 5 μm while both eukaryotic cells are in the range of 10–100 μm.

4. Students can draw or describe the parts of the cells they observed. A review of Section 7.3 may help with their descriptions of the functions of the organelles.

5. **ERROR ANALYSIS** You may have used millimeters (mm) as your measurement standard instead of micrometers.

Assessment

Portfolio Have students draw *Bacillus subtilis* as they think it would look through a TEM. Use the Performance Task Assessment List for Scientific Drawing in **PASC,** p. 127. **L2**

Apply Your Skill

Lab Techniques Ask students to observe the following under the microscope and determine if cells are prokaryotes or eukaryotes: *Gloeocapsa, Euglena, Spirogyra,* liver tissue, frog blood cells. *Gloeocapsa* is the only prokaryote. **L2**

Data and Observations

Bacterial cells are prokaryotic with no visible internal organelles; size ranges between 0.5 and 3 μm. *Elodea* cells are eukaryotic with visible organelles such as chloroplasts and a nucleus; size ranges between 10 and 100 μm. Blood cells are from a multicellular, eukaryotic organism and are approximately 10–20 μm.

CLEANUP AND DISPOSAL

Make sure microscopes are stored with the low-power objective in place. Encourage students to make wise choices concerning disposal and recycling of lab materials.

Purpose

Students will be introduced to the thoughts and scientific writings of Lewis Thomas.

Teaching Strategies

■ Lewis Thomas said that his writings are "Notes of a Biology Watcher." Have students discuss what this phrase means and explain how all people are "Biology Watchers."

■ Students should realize that just by observing themselves and the world around them, they are "Biology Watchers."

■ Have students read all of Lewis Thomas's *Lives of a Cell* or his book *Medusa and the Snail*. Ask students to prepare a written report on the book they read. **L3**

Further Reading

Encourage interested students to explore other science-themed literature. Some prime examples are:

• *Walden, or, Life in the Woods*, by Henry David Thoreau

• *Silent Spring*, by Rachel Carson

• *The Sacred Beetle*, by Jean-Henri Fabre

---

connection to literature

The Lives of a Cell

by Lewis Thomas

"I have been trying to think of the earth as a kind of organism, but it is no go. I cannot think of it this way. It is too big, too complex, with too many working parts lacking visible connections. . . . I wondered about this. If not like an organism, what is it like, what is it most like? Then, satisfactorily for that moment, it came to me: it is most like a single cell."

—Lewis Thomas

Color-enhanced TEM Magnification: 10 000×

Earth "is most like a single cell."

You may think of yourself as a body made up of parts. Arms, legs, skin, stomach, eyes, brain, heart, lungs. In actual fact, you are a community of living structures that work together for growth and survival.

Your body is made up of eukaryotic cells containing organelles that work together for each cell's survival. Organelles such as the Golgi apparatus and vesicles may work closely together. Other organelles, such as the mitochondria that serve as the cell's power plants, may perform a unique function within the cell.

On a much more complex level, an organism is similar to a cell in that many parts work together for the good of the whole. Groups of cells work together as tissues. Several tissues form an organ, and many organs form an organ system. For example, in an organ system such as the digestive system, cells and tissues form an organ such as the stomach, but several related organs—including the intestines, the pancreas, and the liver—are needed to completely digest and absorb the food you eat. In a similar manner, the organisms within a community are all connected to and dependent upon each other. You could extend this view to the entire Earth, which consists of a collection of interconnected ecosystems.

Words are like organelles Now that you have formed an image in your mind of a cell and its working parts, imagine a paragraph composed of words. Just as a cell contains a group of organelles working together, the words in a paragraph interact to convey thoughts and ideas. Despite all his technical knowledge, Dr. Thomas —a physician and medical researcher—writes simply and engagingly about everything from the tiny universe inside a single cell to the possibility of visitors from a distant planet.

Medicine, a young science Dr. Thomas grew up with the practice of medicine. As a boy, he accompanied his father, a family physician, on house calls to patients. Years later, Lewis Thomas described those days in his autobiography, *The Youngest Science*. The title reflects his belief that the practice of medicine is "still very early on" and that some basic problems of disease are just now yielding to exploration.

Writing About Biology

Critique Evaluate Dr. Thomas's comparison of Earth to a cell. How do you think Earth is like a cell? How would you disagree with this model?

To find out more about the works of Dr. Lewis Thomas, visit in.bdol.glencoe.com/literature

Writing About Biology

Students may write that Earth is like a cell in its use of energy and resources, or that it relies on a complex, integral structure. To assess students' critiques of the model, use the Performance Task Assessment List for Writer's Guide to Nonfiction in **PASC**, p. 157.

STUDY GUIDE

Section 7.1
The Discovery of Cells

Key Concepts
- Microscopes enabled biologists to see cells and develop the cell theory.
- The cell theory states that the cell is the basic unit of organization, all organisms are made up of one or more cells, and all cells come from preexisting cells.
- Using electron microscopes, scientists can study cell structure in detail.
- Cells are classified as prokaryotic or eukaryotic based on whether or not they have membrane-bound organelles.

Vocabulary
cell (p. 171)
cell theory (p. 172)
compound light microscope (p. 171)
electron microscope (p. 172)
eukaryote (p. 173)
nucleus (p. 174)
organelle (p. 173)
prokaryote (p. 173)

Section 7.2
The Plasma Membrane

Key Concepts
- Through selective permeability, the plasma membrane controls what enters and leaves a cell.
- The fluid mosaic model describes the plasma membrane as a phospholipid bilayer with embedded proteins.

Vocabulary
fluid mosaic model (p. 178)
phospholipid (p. 176)
plasma membrane (p. 175)
selective permeability (p. 175)
transport proteins (p. 178)

Section 7.3
Eukaryotic Cell Structure

Key Concepts
- Eukaryotic cells have a nucleus and other organelles and are enclosed by a plasma membrane. Some cells have a cell wall that provides support and protection.
- Cells make proteins on ribosomes that are often attached to the highly folded endoplasmic reticulum. Cells store materials in the Golgi apparatus and vacuoles.
- Mitochondria break down sugar molecules to release energy. Chloroplasts convert light energy into chemical energy.
- The cytoskeleton helps maintain cell shape and is involved in the movement of organelles and materials.

Vocabulary
cell wall (p. 179)
chlorophyll (p. 184)
chloroplast (p. 184)
chromatin (p. 180)
cilia (p. 187)
cytoplasm (p. 181)
cytoskeleton (p. 185)
endoplasmic reticulum (p. 181)
flagella (p. 187)
Golgi apparatus (p. 182)
lysosome (p. 183)
microfilament (p. 185)
microtubule (p. 185)
mitochondria (p. 185)
nucleolus (p. 181)
plastid (p. 184)
ribosome (p. 181)
vacuole (p. 183)

FOLDABLES™ Study Organizer To help you review the cell theory, use the Organizational Study Fold on page 171.

Key Concepts
Summary statements can be used by students to review the major concepts of the chapter.

 Biology Online

Visit in.bdol.glencoe.com
/self_check_quiz
/vocabulary_puzzlemaker
/chapter_test
/standardized_test

VOCABULARY PUZZLEMAKER

 For additional help with vocabulary, have students access the Vocabulary PuzzleMaker online at in.bdol.glencoe.com/vocabulary_puzzlemaker

FOLDABLES™
Have students use their Foldables to review the content of Section 7.1. On the back of the paper, analyze how the development of various microscopes helped scientists in their understanding of cells.

Use the Exam*View*®Pro Test Bank CD-ROM to:
- Create **multiple versions** of tests
- Create **modified** tests with one mouse click for **inclusion** students
- **Edit** existing questions and **add** your own questions
- Build tests aligned with state standards using built-in **State Curriculum Tags**
- Change **English** tests to **Spanish** with one mouse click and vice versa

 Indiana Academic Standards
Pages 190–191: B.1.3

The Princeton Review **Questions and answers have been aligned and verified by The Princeton Review.**

Vocabulary Review

1. plasma membrane
2. mitochondria
4. ribosomes
5. cell

Understanding Key Concepts

6. C	9. B	12. A
7. C	10. C	13. C
8. D	11. C	

Constructed Response

14. The packets contain proteins from the rough ER. Lysosomes will use these to degrade waste products.

15. The phospholipid bilayer allows some materials to pass through and keeps others out. Transport proteins in the plasma membrane facilitate movement of some materials.

16. Specimens for electron microscopes need to be examined in a vacuum so electrons will not collide with air particles and scatter. Live specimens will not survive in a vacuum.

Thinking Critically

17. Muscle cells contain more mitochondria because they require a great deal of energy to do cellular work.

18. Only very large cells are visible to the unaided eye. Most cells are microscopic. Visual displays will vary depending on the cells chosen for illustration.

19. Because the cells are moving water against a gradient, they require energy produced by mitochondria.

20. Van Leeuwenhoek ground single lenses to make simple microscopes. Hooke used a compound microscope to discover cells. Schleiden and Schwann made observations that contributed to the cell theory. The work of all of the early scientists contributed to what we know today.

Vocabulary Review

Review the Chapter 7 vocabulary words listed in the Study Guide on page 191. Match the words with the definitions below.

1. organelle that is the boundary between the cell and its environment
2. membrane-bound organelles that transform energy in all eukaryotic cells
3. highly organized structures within cells
4. organelles that are the sites of protein synthesis
5. basic unit of organization of both unicellular and multicellular organisms

Understanding Key Concepts

6. In what type of cell would you find a chloroplast?
   A. prokaryote   C. plant
   B. animal   D. fungus

7. In which of the following pairs are the terms NOT related?
   A. nucleus—DNA
   B. chloroplasts—chlorophyll
   C. flagella—chromatin
   D. cell wall—cellulose

8. Magnifications greater than 10 000× can be obtained when using _____.
   A. light microscopes
   B. metric rulers
   C. hand lenses
   D. electron microscopes

9. A bacterium is classified as a prokaryote because it _____.
   A. has cilia
   B. has no membrane-bound nucleus
   C. is a single cell
   D. has no DNA

10. What is the difference between a prokaryote and a eukaryote?
    A. the need for nutrients
    B. plasma membranes
    C. membrane-bound organelles
    D. cell walls

---

11. Which of these structures captures the sun's energy when synthesizing carbohydrates?

    A.   C.

    B.   D.

12. Which of the following structures is NOT found in both plant and animal cells?
    A. chloroplast   C. ribosomes
    B. cytoskeleton   D. mitochondria

13. Which biomolecule is NOT stored in plastids?
    A. a lipid   C. an amino acid
    B. a pigment   D. a starch

Constructed Response

14. **Open Ended** Suggest a reason why packets of proteins collected by the Golgi apparatus might merge with lysosomes.

15. **Open Ended** How does the structure of the plasma membrane allow materials to move across it in both directions?

16. **Open Ended** Can live specimens be examined with an electron microscope? Explain.

Thinking Critically

17. **Writing in Biology** Predict whether you would expect muscle cells or fat cells to contain more mitochondria and explain why.

18. **REAL WORLD BIOCHALLENGE** Organelles, cells, and organisms have a wide range of sizes. Visit **in.bdol.glencoe.com** to find out about these size comparisons. Can any cell be seen with the naked eye? Make a visual display, such as a poster or model, that shows the range of sizes. Present this information to your class.

 in.bdol.glencoe.com/chapter_test

RUBRIC

Evaluating Open-Ended Questions
Open-ended assessment questions are graded by using a multilevel rubric that guides you in assessing a student's knowledge of a particular concept. The following rubric is a sample scoring device.

19. Infer In plants, cells that transport water against the force of gravity are found to contain many more mitochondria than do some other plant cells. What is the reason for this?

20. Writing About Biology Describe the contributions of the early cell scientists. Evaluate the impact of their research on scientific thought.

End-of-Course Assessment Practice

The assessed Indiana standard appears next to the question.

All questions aligned and verified by *The Princeton Review*

Part 1 Multiple Choice

Use the photo to answer questions 21–23.

TEM Magnification: 50 000×

21. The small dots are composed of _____.
B.1.3 **A.** DNA and lipids
B. DNA and proteins
C. RNA and lipids
D. RNA and proteins

22. The small dots are made in the _____.
B.1.3 **A.** nucleolus
B. endoplasmic reticulum
C. Golgi apparatus
D. lysosome

23. The function of the small dots is to
B.1.3 _____.
A. synthesize lipids
B. transport materials throughout the cell
C. synthesize proteins
D. harness energy for the cell

Use the diagram to answer questions 24–27.

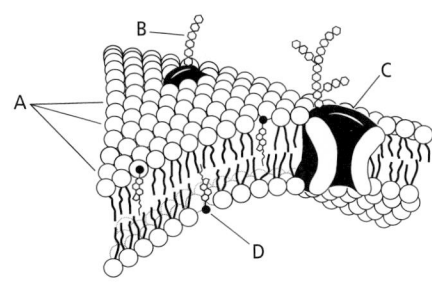

24. Which component stabilizes the
B.1.2 phospholipids?
A. A   **C.** C
B. B   **D.** D

25. Which component helps polar molecules
B.1.2 and ions to enter the cell?
A. A   **C.** C
B. B   **D.** D

26. Which component helps cells identify each
B.1.2 other?
A. A   **C.** C
B. B   **D.** D

27. Which component prevents the cell's watery
B.1.2 environment from entering the cell?
A. A   **C.** C
B. B   **D.** D

Part 2 Constructed Response/Grid In

Record your answers on your answer document.

28. Open Ended Identify and describe a cellular process that maintains homeostasis within a cell.

29. Open Ended Explain the differences between van Leeuwenhoek's microscope and a modern compound light microscope.

 in.bdol.glencoe.com/standardized_test

CHAPTER 7 ASSESSMENT **193**

End-of-Course Assessment Practice

21. D   **24.** D   **26.** B
22. A   **25.** C   **27.** A
23. C
28. The plasma membrane is selectively permeable, letting needed substances in via transport proteins—allowing wastes to leave—maintaining homeostasis within the cell.
29. Anton van Leeuwenhoek invented a simple microscope, meaning it has a single lens. A modern compound microscope has multiple lenses and much better optics. The magnification possible from both is about the same.

 FAST FILE

Answer Sheet A practice answer sheet can be found on p. 75 of *Unit 3 FAST FILE Resources.*

RUBRIC

SCORE	CRITERIA
4	A correct solution that is supported by well-developed, accurate explanations.
3	A generally correct solution, but may contain minor flaws in reasoning.

SCORE	CRITERIA
2	A partially correct interpretation and/or solution to the problem.
1	A correct solution with no supporting evidence or explanation.
0	An incorrect solution or no solution is given.

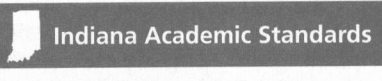 **Indiana Academic Standards**

Pages 192–193: B.1.2, B.1.3, B.1.12

Section Objectives	National Science Standards	State/Local Standards	Advanced Lab and Demo Planning
Section 8.1 2 sessions, 1 block 1. **Explain** how the processes of diffusion, passive transport, and active transport occur and why they are important to cells. 2. **Predict** the effect of a hypotonic, hypertonic, or isotonic solution on a cell.	UCP.1–3, UCP.5; A.1, A.2; B.6; C.1, C.5	**Indiana Standards** B.1.2, B.1.8	**Student Labs:** MiniLab 8.1, p. 198: plastic bag, starch, twist tie, beaker, 50 mL iodine solution Additional Lab, p. 196: potato, 2 100-mL beakers or paper cups, measuring spoon, salt, graduated cylinder, label, pen, stirring rod, balance, plastic wrap or aluminum foil **Teacher Demonstration:** Quick Demo, p. 196: microprojector, dilute solution of India ink, microscope slide, water, lightbulb
Section 8.2 2 sessions, 2 blocks 3. **Sequence** the events of the cell cycle. 4. **Relate** the function of a cell to its organization into tissues, organs, and organ systems.	UCP.1–3, UCP.5; A.1, A.2; B.2, B.3; C.1, C.5; G.1–3	**Indiana Standards** B.1.2, B.1.7, B.1.8	**Student Labs:** Problem-Solving Lab 8.1, p. 203 Problem-Solving Lab 8.2, p. 204 MiniLab 8.2, p. 209: fish mitosis slide, microscope **Teacher Demonstration:** Quick Demo, p. 202: insulated electrical cord, string, rubber band
Section 8.3 2 sessions, 1/2 block 5. **Describe** the role of enzymes in the regulation of the cell cycle. 6. **Distinguish** between the events of a normal cell cycle and the abnormal events that result in cancer. 7. **Identify** ways to potentially reduce the risk of cancer.	UCP.1, UCP.2; A.1, A.2; C.1, C.6; E.1, E.2; F.1, F.4, F.5, F.6; G.1, G.2	**Indiana Standards** B.1.1, B.1.4, B.1.7, B.1.8	**Student Lab:** Problem-Solving Lab 8.3, p. 212 Investigate BioLab, p. 214: See materials below.
End of Chapter Assessment **Student Edition** **Study Guide,** p. 217 **Content Assessment,** pp. 218–219		**Indiana Standards** B.1.2, B.1.3, B.1.7, B.1.8	**Student Lab:** Investigate BioLab, p. 214: prepared slide of onion root tip, microscope

Key to Teaching Strategies

L1 Level 1 activities should be appropriate for students with learning difficulties.

L2 Level 2 activities should be within the ability range of all students.

L3 Level 3 activities are designed for above-average students.

ELL ELL activities should be within the ability range of English Language Learners.

COOP LEARN Cooperative Learning activities are designed for small group work.

Legend

 Transparency   CD-ROM   MP3   Videocassette   DVD

Glencoe Exclusive!
TeacherWorks™
All-In-One Planner and Resource Center

Reproducible Masters and Transparencies

Technology

Unit 3 FAST FILE Resources
    MiniLab Worksheet, p. 79
    Reinforcement and Study Guide in English, p. 85
    Reinforcement and Study Guide in Spanish, p. 89
    Concept Mapping, p. 93
    Transparency Worksheets, pp. 95, 99–102, 105–108
Laboratory Manual, pp. 43–44
Section Focus Transparency 18
Basic Concepts Transparencies 8, 9
Reteaching Skills Transparencies 11, 12

- Interactive Chalkboard CD-ROM: Section 8.1 Presentation
- TeacherWorks™ CD-ROM
- Guided Reading Audio Summaries MP3

Unit 3 FAST FILE Resources
    MiniLab Worksheet, p. 80
    BioLab Worksheet, pp. 81–82
    Reinforcement and Study Guide in English, pp. 86–87
    Reinforcement and Study Guide in Spanish, pp. 90–91
    Transparency Worksheets, pp. 96, 103–104, 109–110
Laboratory Manual, pp. 45–48
Section Focus Transparency 19
Basic Concepts Transparency 10
Reteaching Skills Transparency 13

- Interactive Chalkboard CD-ROM: Section 8.2 Presentation
- TeacherWorks™ CD-ROM
- Guided Reading Audio Summaries MP3
- Virtual Labs CD-ROM
    Virtual Lab: Cell Reproduction

Unit 3 FAST FILE Resources
    Reinforcement and Study Guide in English, p. 88
    Reinforcement and Study Guide in Spanish, p. 92
    Critical Thinking/Problem Solving, p. 94
    Transparency Worksheets, p. 97
Section Focus Transparency 20

- Interactive Chalkboard CD-ROM: Section 8.3 Presentation
- TeacherWorks™ CD-ROM
- Guided Reading Audio Summaries MP3

Unit 3 FAST FILE Resources
    Chapter Assessment, pp. 111–116
    Student Recording Sheet, p. 117

The Princeton Review **Reviewing Biology,** pp. 15–16

- Interactive Chalkboard: Chapter 8 Assessment
- MindJogger Videoquizzes DVD/VHS
- ExamView® Pro Test Bank CD-ROM
- TeacherWorks™ CD-ROM
- Succeeding on National Standards CD-ROM

     in.bdol.glencoe.com
     /self_check_quiz
     /vocabulary_puzzlemaker
     /chapter_test
     /standardized_test

Indicates materials created specifically for Indiana.

Short on Time?

BIODIGEST The BioDigest at the end of this unit can be used as a(n):

- preview to introduce important unit concepts.
- overview if time does not permit teaching the entire chapter.
- review of key unit concepts.

Understanding the Photo

The image of this plant cell in anaphase was taken using a light microscope that diffracts the light. The chromosomes, colored yellow in this photo, become most visible during the middle and later stages of the cell cycle. Students can learn more about the stages of the cell cycle beginning on page 204. Refer to the accompanying illustration to help locate the features of the photo.

Cellular Transport and the Cell Cycle

Color-enhanced TEM Magnification: 1600×

What You'll Learn

- You will discover how molecules are transported across the plasma membrane.
- You will sequence the stages of cell division.
- You will identify the relationship between the cell cycle and cancer.

Why It's Important

Transportation of molecules and particles through the plasma membrane and cell reproduction are two important functions that help cells maintain homeostasis and keep you healthy.

Understanding ▶ the Photo

This photo shows a cell in a plant's root tip in one stage of the cell cycle. Color enhancement helps distinguish the chromosomes, which appear yellow in this photo.

Biology Online

Visit in.bdol.glencoe.com to
- study the entire chapter online
- access Web Links for more information and activities on the cell cycle
- review content with the Interactive Tutor and self-check quizzes

194

Chromosomes

Spindle fibers

Cell wall

Two-Minute Chapter Launcher

Activity Have students observe osmosis by placing a few raisins in warm water for several minutes. After removing the raisins from the water, ask students about their observations. How does the appearance of the raisins change after several minutes in the water? The raisins will swell somewhat because water has entered the cells by osmosis, thus making them larger. **L1**

194

SECTION PREVIEW

Objectives

Explain how the processes of diffusion, passive transport, and active transport occur and why they are important to cells.

Predict the effect of a hypotonic, hypertonic, or isotonic solution on a cell.

Review Vocabulary
plasma membrane: the boundary between the cell and its environment (p. 175)

New Vocabulary
osmosis
isotonic solution
hypotonic solution
hypertonic solution
passive transport
facilitated diffusion
active transport
endocytosis
exocytosis

Cellular Transport

Indiana Standards **Standard B.1.2 Explain that every cell is covered by a membrane that controls what can enter and leave the cell.** Recognize that in all but quite primitive cells, a complex network of proteins provides organization and shape. In addition, understand that flagella and/or cilia may allow some Protista, some Monera, and some animal cells to move.

FOLDABLES
Study Organizer

Osmosis Make the following Foldable to help identify what you already know about osmosis, and what you learned about how osmosis affects cells.

STEP 1 **Fold** a vertical sheet of paper from side to side. Make the back edge about 2 cm longer than the front edge.

STEP 2 **Turn** lengthwise and **fold** into thirds.

STEP 3 **Unfold and cut** only the top layer along both folds to make three tabs.

STEP 4 **Label** each tab.

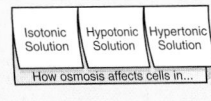

| Isotonic Solution | Hypotonic Solution | Hypertonic Solution |

How osmosis affects cells in...

Answer Questions Before you read Chapter 8, write under each tab what you already know about how osmosis affects cells. After you read the chapter, list what you learned about how osmosis affects cells in each type of solution listed on your Foldable.

Osmosis: Diffusion of Water

Although the plasma membrane of a cell can act as a dam or pump for water-soluble molecules that cannot pass freely through the membrane, it does not limit the diffusion of water. Recall that diffusion is the movement of particles from an area of higher concentration to an area of lower concentration. In a cell, water always moves to reach an equal concentration on both sides of the membrane. The diffusion of water across a selectively permeable membrane is called **osmosis** (ahs MOH sus). Regulating the water flow through the plasma membrane is an important factor in maintaining homeostasis within the cell.

Word Origin

osmosis from the Greek word *osmos*, meaning "pushing"; Osmosis can push out a cell's plasma membrane.

What controls osmosis?

If you add sugar to water, the water becomes sweeter as you add more sugar. If a strong sugar solution and a weak sugar solution are placed in direct contact, water molecules diffuse in one direction and sugar molecules diffuse in the other direction until all molecules are evenly distributed throughout.

8.1 CELLULAR TRANSPORT **195**

---

1 Focus

INTERACTIVE
CHALKBOARD
PowerPoint® Presentations

Bellringer
Section Focus Transparency 18

Transparency **18** Water in the Cell

Figure A   Figure B

① How do the plant cells in figures A and B differ?
② What is the effect of this difference on the plants?

BIOLOGY: The Dynamics of Life   SECTION FOCUS TRANSPARENCIES

INTERACTIVE
CHALKBOARD
with Image Bank

PowerPoint® Presentations
This CD-ROM is an editable Microsoft® PowerPoint® presentation that includes:
• Section presentations
• Section checks
• Image bank
• Hot links to Biology Online
• All transparencies

FOLDABLES™
For an additional Foldables activity idea, see the Chapter 8 Foldables page in *Unit 3 FAST FILE Resources.*

RESOURCE MANAGER

Unit 3 *FAST FILE* Resources
MiniLab Worksheet, p. 79
Reinforcement and Study Guide in English, p. 85
Reinforcement and Study Guide in Spanish, p. 89
Concept Mapping, p. 93
Transparency Worksheets, pp. 95, 99–102, 105–108

Reading Essentials for Biology, Section 8.1
Laboratory Manual, pp. 43–44
📔 **Section Focus Transparency 18**
📔 **Basic Concepts Transparencies 8, 9**
📔 **Reteaching Skills Transparencies 11, 12**

Indiana Academic Standards
Pages 194–195: B.1.2, B.1.8

195

2 Teach

Enrichment
The kinetic theory of matter explains the transport of molecules from one place to another. Elicit what the major differences, at the molecular level, are among a solid, a liquid, and a gas. Students should recognize that the freedom of random particle movement is the only difference.

Figure 8.1
During osmosis, water diffuses across a selectively permeable membrane. Notice that the number of sugar molecules did not change on each side of the membrane, but the number of water molecules on either side of the membrane did change.

Before osmosis **After osmosis**

Selectively permeable membrane

- Water molecule
- Sugar molecule

If the two solutions are separated by a selectively permeable membrane that allows only water to diffuse across it, water flows to the side of the membrane where the water concentration is lower. The water continues to diffuse until it is in equal concentration on both sides of the membrane, as shown in *Figure 8.1*. Therefore, we know that unequal distribution of particles, called a concentration gradient, is one factor that controls osmosis.

Word Origin
iso-, hypo-, hyper- from the Greek words *isos*, meaning "equal," *hypo*, meaning "under," and *hyper*, meaning "over," respectively.

Cells in an isotonic solution
It is important to understand how osmosis affects cells. Most cells, whether in multicellular or unicellular organisms, are subject to osmosis because they are surrounded by water solutions. In an **isotonic solution**, the concentration of dissolved substances in the solution is the same as the concentration of dissolved substances inside the cell. Likewise, the concentration of water in the solution is the same as the concentration of water inside the cell.

Cells in an isotonic solution do experience osmosis, but because water diffuses into and out of the cells at the same rate, the cells retain their normal shape, as shown in *Figure 8.2*.

Cells in a hypotonic solution
In the **hypotonic solution** in *Figure 8.3A*, the concentration of dissolved substances is lower in the solution outside the cell than the concentration inside the cell. Therefore, there is more water outside the cell than inside. Cells in a hypotonic solution experience osmosis. Water moves through the plasma membrane into the cell. The cell swells and its internal pressure increases.

As the pressure increases inside animal cells, the plasma membrane swells, like the red blood cells shown in *Figure 8.3B*. If the solution is extremely hypotonic, the plasma membrane may be unable to withstand this pressure and may burst.

Because plant cells contain a rigid cell wall that supports the cell, they do not burst when in a hypotonic solution. As the pressure increases inside the cell, the plasma membrane is pressed against the cell wall, as shown in *Figure 8.3C*. Instead of bursting, the plant cell becomes more firm. Grocers keep produce looking fresh by misting the fruits and vegetables with water.

Cells in a hypertonic solution
In a **hypertonic solution**, the concentration of dissolved substances outside the cell is higher than the concentration inside the cell. Cells in a hypertonic solution experience osmosis that causes water to flow out.

Animal cells in a hypertonic solution shrivel because of decreased pressure in the cells.

196 CELLULAR TRANSPORT AND THE CELL CYCLE

Additional Lab

Observing Osmosis
Purpose
Students will observe and measure the effect of osmosis on a potato.

Safety Precautions
Students should wear goggles and an apron.

196

Materials
2-cm potato cubes, two 100-mL beakers or paper cups, measuring spoon, salt, graduated cylinder, label, pen, stirring rod, balance, plastic wrap or aluminum foil

Procedure
Give the following directions to students.
1. Label one beaker *Water* and the other *Salt*. Place 100 mL of water into each.

2. Place 3 tablespoons of salt into the salt beaker and stir until the salt is dissolved.
3. Measure and record the mass of each potato piece. Then place one piece in the water beaker and the other in the salt beaker. Record the texture of the potato cubes before soaking.
4. Cover the beakers with plastic wrap or aluminum foil and allow them to sit undisturbed for two days.

Figure 8.2
In an isotonic solution, water molecules move into and out of the cell at the same rate, and cells retain their normal shape (A). Notice the concave disc shape of a red blood cell (B). A plant cell has its normal shape and pressure in an isotonic solution (C).

H_2O
H_2O

○ Water molecule
● Dissolved molecule

Magnification: unavailable

Figure 8.3
In a hypotonic solution, water enters a cell by osmosis, causing the cell to swell (A). Animal cells, like these red blood cells, may continue to swell until they burst (B). Plant cells swell beyond their normal size as pressure increases (C).

H_2O
H_2O

○ Water molecule
● Dissolved molecule

Magnification: unavailable

Figure 8.4
In a hypertonic solution, water leaves a cell by osmosis, causing the cell to shrink (A). Animal cells like these red blood cells shrivel up as they lose water (B). Plant cells lose pressure as the plasma membrane shrinks away from the cell wall (C).

H_2O
H_2O

○ Water molecule
● Dissolved molecule

Magnification: unavailable

Concept Development
Explain to students that net movement is the overall movement of a material and not the specific movement of each particle.

Word Origin

Have students research to find and define other words using "hyper" as part of the root such as *hyperactive* and *hypersensitive.*

Inquiry
Activity Have students investigate how much a gummy candy increases in size when placed in water because of concentration gradient. Students should find the length, width, and mass of a gummy candy before and after being placed in water for various lengths of time. **L1**

5. On the second day, carefully remove the potato cubes one at a time and blot them dry on the outside. Weigh the pieces and record their masses.

Analysis
1. Describe what happened to the mass of each cube after soaking. The mass of the potato placed in salt water decreased, while the one in plain water increased.

2. Describe what happened to the texture of each cube after soaking. The potato in the salt water became softer than that in the plain water.

3. Explain the changes you observed in terms of osmosis. Water in the potato placed in salt water left the potato by osmosis because of the high salt content of the water outside the potato.

Assessment
Portfolio Have students prepare a written laboratory report containing a data table and the answers to the analysis questions. Use the Performance Task Assessment List for Lab Report in **PASC**, p. 119. **L2**

Purpose

Students will determine if a plastic membrane is selectively permeable.

Process Skills

formulate models, draw conclusions, observe and infer, recognize cause and effect

Safety Precautions

Have students wear gloves, aprons, and goggles. Remind students to rinse immediately if iodine gets on skin or clothing. If iodine gets in eyes, rinse thoroughly at the eyewash station.

Teaching Strategies

■ Allow students to work in teams of two or three.
■ See p. 18T of the Teacher Guide for preparation of starch and iodine solutions. Lightweight, inexpensive bags work best for this lab.

Expected Results

The inside of the bag will be purple, indicating passage of iodine into the bag. The outside of the bag will be a rust color, indicating starch did not pass out of the bag.

Analysis

1. start—starch was clear, iodine was rust; end—starch was purple, iodine was rust
2. iodine; The liquid inside the bag changes color.
3. Students may suggest that the plastic bag is an adequate model because it allows iodine to cross, but not the starch. Others may suggest that real membranes are more complex in their response. Both observations are correct.

Assessment

Skill Ask students to make a diagram depicting pore size of the plastic membrane in relation to molecule size of iodine and starch. Use the Performance Task Assessment List for Scientific Drawing in **PASC**, p. 127. **L2**

MiniLab 8.1

Formulate Models

Cell Membrane Simulation In this experiment, a plastic bag is used to model a selectively permeable membrane. Starch is placed inside of the bag. When iodine and starch molecules come in contact with one another, a dark purple color results.

Procedure

1. Fill a plastic bag with 50 mL of starch. Seal the bag with a twist tie.
2. Fill a beaker with 50 mL of iodine solution. **CAUTION:** *Rinse with water if iodine gets on skin. Iodine is toxic.*
3. Note and record the color of the starch and iodine.
4. Place the bag into the beaker. **CAUTION:** *Wash your hands with soap after handling lab materials.*
5. Note and record the color of the starch and iodine 24 hours later.

Analysis

1. **Describe** Compare the color of the iodine and starch at the start and at the conclusion of the experiment.
2. **Observe** Which molecules crossed the membrane? What is your evidence?
3. **Think Critically** Evaluate whether or not a plastic bag is an adequate model of a selectively permeable membrane.

Plant cells in a hypertonic environment lose water, mainly from the central vacuole. The plasma membrane and cytoplasm shrink away from the cell wall, as shown in *Figure 8.4C*. Loss of water in a plant cell results in a drop in pressure and explains why plants wilt.

Passive Transport

Some molecules, like water, can pass through the plasma membrane by simple diffusion, as shown in *Figure 8.5A*. The cell uses no energy to move these particles; therefore, this movement of particles across the membrane is classified as **passive transport.** You can investigate passive transport by performing the *MiniLab* on this page.

Passive transport by proteins

Recall that transport proteins help substances move through the plasma membrane. Passive transport of materials across the membrane using transport proteins is called **facilitated diffusion.**

Some transport proteins, called channel proteins, form channels that allow specific molecules to flow through, as illustrated in *Figure 8.5B.*

Figure 8.5
Passive transport can occur by **(A)** simple diffusion, **(B)** facilitated diffusion by channel proteins, and **(C)** facilitated diffusion by carrier proteins.

198 CELLULAR TRANSPORT AND THE CELL CYCLE

Table 8.1 Transport Through the Cell Membrane				
Type of Transport	Transport Protein Used?	Direction of Movement	Requires Energy Input from Cell?	Classification of Transport
Simple Diffusion	No	With concentration gradient	No	Passive
Facilitated Diffusion	Yes—channel proteins or carrier proteins	With concentration gradient	No	Passive
Active Transport	Yes—carrier proteins	Against concentration gradient	Yes	Active

The movement is with the concentration gradient, and requires no energy input from the cell.

Carrier proteins are another type of transport protein. Carrier proteins change shape to allow a substance to pass through the plasma membrane, as shown in *Figure 8.5C*. In facilitated diffusion by carrier protein, the movement is with the concentration gradient and requires no energy input from the cell.

Active Transport

A cell can move particles from a region of lower concentration to a region of higher concentration, but it must expend energy to counteract the force of diffusion that is moving the particles in the opposite direction. Movement of materials through a membrane against a concentration gradient is called **active transport** and requires energy from the cell.

How active transport occurs

In active transport, a transport protein called a carrier protein first binds with a particle of the substance to be transported. In general, each type of carrier protein has a shape that fits a specific molecule or ion. When the proper molecule binds with the protein, chemical energy

allows the cell to change the shape of the carrier protein so that the particle to be moved is released on the other side of the membrane, something like the opening of a door. Once the particle is released, the protein's original shape is restored, as illustrated in *Figure 8.6*. Active transport allows particle movement into or out of a cell against a concentration gradient.

Transport of substances across the cell membrane is required for cells to maintain homeostasis. The types of transport are summarized in *Table 8.1*.

✓ **Reading Check** **Compare and contrast** active and passive transport across the cell membrane.

Figure 8.6
Carrier proteins are used in active transport to pick up ions or molecules from near the cell membrane, carry them across the membrane, and release them on the other side. **Think Critically** *Why does active transport require energy?*

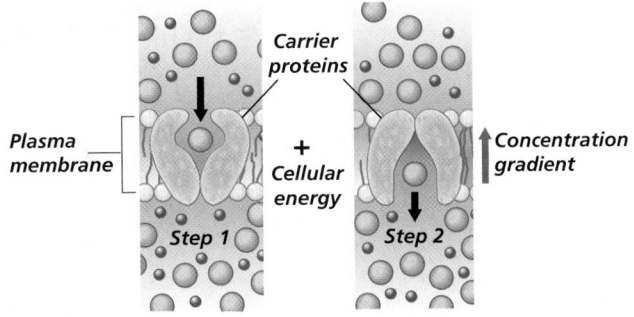

Carrier proteins

Plasma membrane

+ Cellular energy

Concentration gradient

Step 1   Step 2

CHALLENGE ACTIVITY

Channel Proteins Students who need an additional challenge can research the channel proteins in cystic fibrosis. Have them create a model that explains normal chloride ion transport through channel proteins and abnormal transport in the disease. **L3**

3 Assess

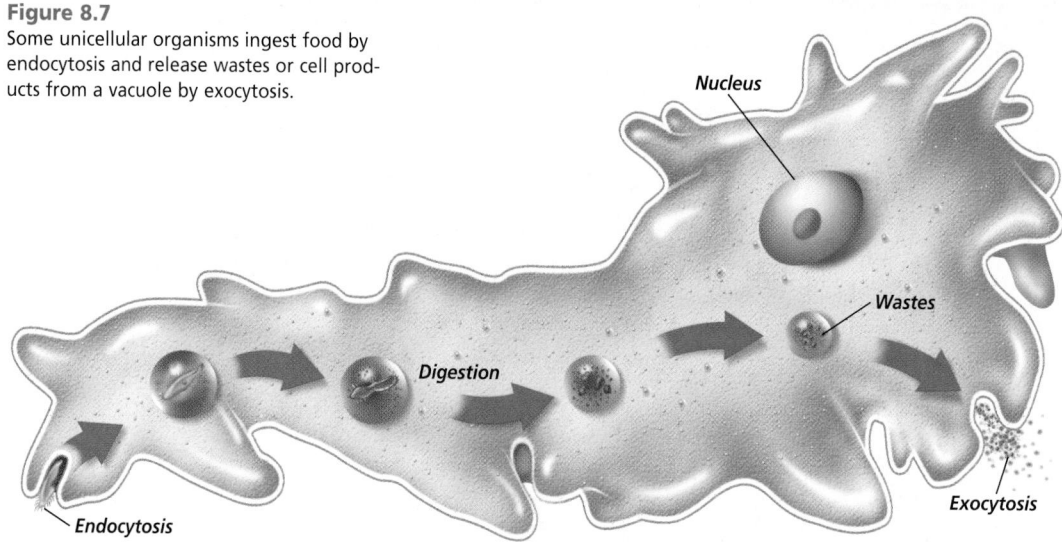

Figure 8.7
Some unicellular organisms ingest food by endocytosis and release wastes or cell products from a vacuole by exocytosis.

Nucleus

Wastes

Digestion

Exocytosis

Endocytosis

Transport of Large Particles

Word Origin

endo-, exo- from the Greek words *endon,* meaning "within," and *exo,* meaning "out"; Endocytosis moves materials into the cell; exocytosis moves materials out of the cell.

Some cells can take in large molecules, groups of molecules, or even whole cells. **Endocytosis** is a process by which a cell surrounds and takes in material from its environment as shown in *Figure 8.7*. This material does not pass directly through the membrane. Instead, it is engulfed and enclosed by a portion of the cell's plasma membrane. That portion of the membrane then breaks away, and the resulting vacuole with its contents moves to the inside of the cell.

Figure 8.7 also shows the reverse process of endocytosis, called exocytosis. **Exocytosis** is the expulsion or secretion of materials from a cell. Cells use exocytosis to expel wastes. They also use this method to secrete substances, such as hormones produced by the cell. Because endocytosis and exocytosis both move masses of material, they both require energy.

With the various mechanisms the cell uses to transport materials in and out, cells must also have mechanisms to regulate size and growth.

Section Assessment

Understanding Main Ideas

1. What factors affect the diffusion of water through a membrane by osmosis?

2. How do animal cells and plant cells react differently in a hypotonic solution?

3. Compare and contrast active transport and facilitated diffusion.

4. How do carrier proteins facilitate passive transport of molecules across a membrane?

Thinking Critically

5. A paramecium expels water when it is in freshwater. What can you conclude about the concentration gradient in the organism's environment?

SKILL REVIEW

6. **Observe and Infer** What effect do you think a temperature increase has on osmosis? For more help, refer to *Observe and Infer* in the **Skill Handbook**.

200 CELLULAR TRANSPORT AND THE CELL CYCLE

 in.bdol.glencoe.com/self_check_quiz

Section Assessment

1. The concentration of water on either side of the membrane and the permeability of the membrane.

2. In an animal cell, the extra water may cause the plasma membrane to burst. In a plant cell, the plasma membrane pushes against the cell wall, providing added support.

3. Facilitated diffusion and active transport use carrier proteins. Facilitated diffusion does not require energy; active transport does.

4. Carrier proteins move substances that cannot diffuse through the plasma membrane from an area of higher to lower concentration.

5. The organism is in a hypotonic environment and the concentration gradient is from outside to inside.

6. Increasing temperature will increase the rate of osmosis, but it will not change the final outcome because it cannot change the membrane permeability to other solutes.

Section 8.2

Cell Growth and Reproduction

Indiana Standards Standard B.1.8 Understand and describe that all growth and development is a consequence of an increase in cell number, cell size, and/or cell products. Explain that cellular differentiation results from gene expression and/or environmental influence. **Differentiate between mitosis and meiosis.**

What makes up your body?

Using an Analogy Where do you live? This question sounds simple enough, but it has many answers. You live at a certain address, which is a part of a city. Many cities and towns form the state in which you live. The states form a country. Some tasks are performed by the country as a whole, while others are performed by states, cities, or individuals. In the same way, your body cells are parts of tissues, organs, organ systems, and the body as a whole.

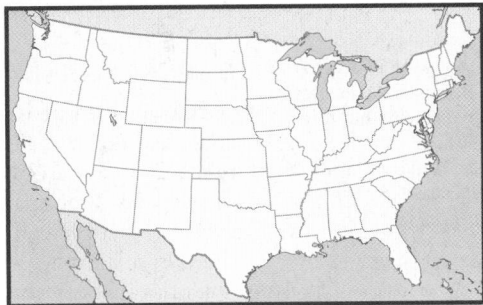

Compare and Contrast *Cells in multicellular and unicellular organisms undergo cell division. Which type of cells do you think is more specialized?*

SECTION PREVIEW

Objectives

Sequence the events of the cell cycle.

Relate the function of a cell to its organization in tissues, organs, and organ systems.

Review Vocabulary
organelle: the membrane-bound structures within eukaryotic cells (p. 173)

New Vocabulary
chromosome
chromatin
cell cycle
interphase
mitosis
prophase
sister chromatid
centromere
centriole
spindle
metaphase
anaphase
telophase
cytokinesis
tissue
organ
organ system

Cell Size Limitations

The cells that make up a multicellular organism come in a wide variety of sizes and shapes. Some cells, such as red blood cells, measure only 8 μm (micrometers) in diameter. Other cells, such as nerve cells in large animals, can reach lengths of up to 1 m but have small diameters. The cell with the largest diameter is the yolk of an ostrich egg measuring 8 cm. Most living cells, however, are between 2 and 200 μm in diameter. Considering this wide range of cell sizes, why then can't most organisms be just one giant cell?

Diffusion limits cell size

You know that the plasma membrane allows nutrients to enter the cell and wastes to leave. Within the cell, nutrients and wastes move by diffusion.

Although diffusion is a fast and efficient process over short distances, it becomes slow and inefficient as the distances become larger. Imagine a mitochondrion at the center of a cell with a diameter of 20 cm. It would have to wait months before receiving molecules entering the cell. Because of the slow rate of diffusion, organisms can't be just one giant-sized cell.

1 Focus

INTERACTIVE CHALKBOARD
PowerPoint® Presentations

Bellringer
Section Focus Transparency 19

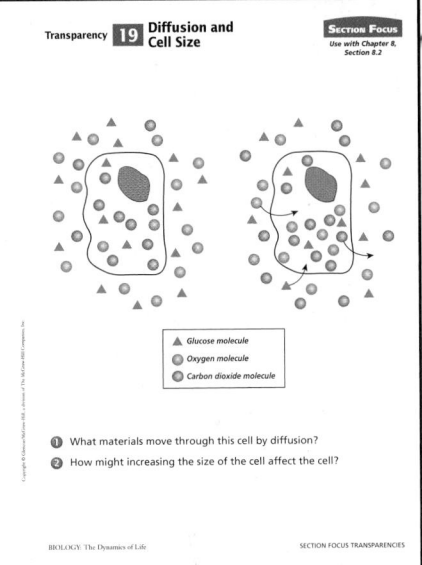

Using an Analogy

Compare and Contrast Cells in multicellular organisms are more specialized.

Biology Journal

Limits to Cell Size Using what they know about the relationship of surface area to the volume of an object, ask students to write a paragraph explaining why the existence of a single-celled giant creature, such as the one in the movie *The Blob*, would be impossible. **L2**

Indiana Academic Standards

Pages 200–201: B.1.2, B.1.8

Quick Demo

Chromatid Separation
Show how chromatids separate during anaphase. Slightly separate the middle portion between the two covered wires of an old piece of insulated electrical cord. Tie a piece of string to each piece of the separated cord. Slip a rubber band around the cord and through the strings. Pull the strings slowly apart until the wire splits in two, similar to the way chromatids are pulled along the spindle in a dividing cell.

Caption Question Answer
Figure 8.8 Having many nuclei allows cell activities to be carried out quickly and efficiently.

✓ **Reading Check** (p. 203) Cells divide to maintain a proper surface-to-volume ratio during growth and to replace cells that die.

LM Magnification: 100×

Figure 8.8
This giant amoeba is only several millimeters in diameter, but it can have up to 1000 nuclei. **Explain** *How does this benefit the organism?*

DNA limits cell size

You have learned that the nucleus contains blueprints for the cell's proteins. Proteins are used throughout the cell by almost all organelles to perform critical cell functions. But there is a limit to how quickly the blueprints for these proteins can be copied in the nucleus and made into proteins in the cytoplasm. The cell cannot survive unless there is enough DNA to support the protein needs of the cell.

What happens in larger cells where an increased amount of cytoplasm requires increased supplies of enzymes? In many large cells, such as the giant amoeba *Pelomyxa* shown in *Figure 8.8*, more than one nucleus is present. Large amounts of DNA in many nuclei ensure that cell activities are carried out quickly and efficiently.

Surface area-to-volume ratio

Another size-limiting factor is the cell's surface area-to-volume ratio. As a cell's size increases, its volume increases much faster than its surface area. Picture a cube-shaped cell like those shown in *Figure 8.9*. The smallest cell has 1 mm sides, a surface area of 6 mm², and a volume of 1 mm³. If the side of the cell is doubled to 2 mm, the surface area will increase fourfold to $6 \times 2 \times 2 = 24$ mm². Observe what happens to the volume; it increases eightfold to 8 mm³.

What does this mean for cells? How does the surface area-to-volume ratio affect cell function? If cell size doubled, the cell would require eight times more nutrients and would have eight times more waste to excrete.

Figure 8.9
Surface area-to-volume ratio is one of the factors that limits cell size. Note how the surface area and the volume change as the sides of a cell double in length from 1 mm to 2 mm.

1 mm   1 mm
1 mm
Surface area = 6 mm²
Volume = 1 mm³

2 mm   2 mm
2 mm
Surface area = 24 mm²
Volume = 8 mm³

4 mm   4 mm
4 mm
4 mm

INCLUSION STRATEGIES

Visually Impaired: *Kinesthetic* To demonstrate chromosome coiling and thickening to students who are visually impaired, remove a short, coiled telephone cord from a telephone. Have students stretch out the cord. Explain that the stretched cord represents an interphase chromosome. Have students allow the cord to return to its normal shape. Explain that this coiling is what happens to chromosomes during prophase, when the chromatin condenses. **L1** **ELL**

🔶 **Indiana Academic Standards**

Pages 202–203: B.1.7, B.1.8

The surface area, however, would increase by a factor of only four. Thus, the plasma membrane would not have enough surface area through which oxygen, nutrients, and wastes could diffuse. The cell would either starve to death or be poisoned from the buildup of waste products. You can investigate surface area-to-volume ratios yourself in the *Problem-Solving Lab* shown here.

Because cell size can have dramatic and negative effects on a cell, cells must have some method of maintaining optimum size. In fact, cells divide before they become too large to function properly. Cell division accomplishes other purposes, too, as you will read next.

Cell Reproduction

Recall that the cell theory states that all cells come from preexisting cells. Cell division is the process by which new cells are produced from one cell. Cell division results in two cells that are identical to the original, parent cell. Right now, as you are reading this page, many of the cells in your body are growing, dividing, and dying. Old cells on the soles of your feet and on the palms of your hands are being shed and replaced, cuts and bruises are healing, and your intestines are producing millions of new cells each second. New cells are produced as tadpoles become frogs, and as an ivy vine grows and wraps around a garden trellis. All organisms grow and change; worn-out tissues are repaired or are replaced by newly produced cells.

✓ **Reading Check** **Explain** two reasons why cell division is a required cell process.

Problem-Solving Lab 8.1

Draw Conclusions

What happens to the surface area of a cell as its volume increases? One reason cells are small is that they need a large surface area as compared to volume so nutrients can diffuse in and wastes can diffuse out.

Solve the Problem
Look at the cubes shown below. Note the size and magnitude of difference in surface area and volume.

1 mm 1 mm
1 mm
Surface area = 6 mm²
Volume = 1 mm³

2 mm 2 mm
2 mm
Surface area = 24 mm²
Volume = 8 mm³

4 mm 4 mm
4 mm
4 mm

Thinking Critically
1. **Estimate** How many small cubes (1 mm) do you think it would take to fill the largest cube (4 mm)?
2. **Use Models** Using the cubes as models, describe how a cell is affected by its size.
3. **Infer** Explain how a small change in cell size can have a huge impact on cellular processes.

The discovery of chromosomes

Early biologists observed that just before cell division, several short, stringy structures suddenly appeared in the nucleus. Scientists also noticed that these structures seemed to vanish soon after division of a cell. These structures, which contain DNA and become darkly colored when stained, are called **chromosomes** (KROH muh sohmz).

Eventually, scientists learned that chromosomes are the carriers of the genetic material that is copied and passed from generation to generation of cells. This genetic material is crucial to the identity of the cell. Accurate transmission of chromosomes during cell division is critical.

Word Origin

chromosome from the Greek words *chroma*, meaning "colored," and *soma*, meaning "body"; Chromosomes are dark-staining structures that contain genetic material.

Problem-Solving Lab 8.1

Purpose
Students will compare the increase in volume of an object with the increase in its surface area.

Background
Cell volume increases much faster than cell surface area. In cells, this fact contributes to cell size limitation because cells do not have sufficient surface area to accommodate the influx of nutrients to support the volume of a large size.

Process Skills
measure in SI, use numbers, recognize cause and effect, interpret data, analyze

Teaching Strategies
Ask students if they have ever wondered why cells can't continue to grow larger and larger to become giant cells. Then ask them to consider the fact that most cells, whether from an elephant or an earthworm, are microscopic in size.

Thinking Critically
1. 64
2. As the cell surface area grows, its volume increases dramatically. More resources are needed by organelles and more waste is produced.
3. As the cell grows, it reaches a point where the surface area is not large enough to transport resources and wastes to allow the cell to survive.

Assessment
Performance Students should write a summary of the MiniLab, including the Analysis questions, for their journals. Use the Performance Task Assessment List for Lab Report in **PASC**, p. 119. **L2**

USING MODELS

Surface Area Using a few small boxes, one large box (approximately the same size as the small boxes combined), and wrapping paper, ask the students to figure out which set will need more paper, the large box or the small boxes each wrapped separately. **L1**

Problem-Solving Lab 8.2

Purpose
Students will compare cell cycles of two different types of cells.

Background
Mitosis requires the same relative amount of time no matter what type of cell is dividing. The amount of time spent in interphase determines the length of the cell cycle.

Process Skills
compare and contrast, interpret data, analyze

Teaching Strategies
Relate this lab to the uncontrolled growth of cancer cells, which spend a very short time in interphase.

Thinking Critically
1. The first part of interphase, in which the cell is growing, is the most variable in length.
2. The cell with the longer period of growth would carry on more metabolic activities than the more rapidly dividing cell.
3. Students should justify their answers with statements such as that certain types of cells are always being damaged and need to be replaced.

Modified Assessment
Performance Have students write three questions related to this lab in their journals. Use the Performance Task Assessment List for Asking Questions in **PASC**, p. 91. **L1**

Indiana Academic Standards

Pages 204–205: B.1.7, B.1.8

The structure of eukaryotic chromosomes

For most of a cell's lifetime, chromosomes exist as **chromatin,** long strands of DNA wrapped around proteins called histones. Under an electron microscope, chromatin looks like beads on a string. Each bead is a group of histones called a nucleosome. Before a cell can divide, the long strands of chromatin must be reorganized, just as you would coil a long strand of rope before storing it. As the nucleus begins to divide, chromosomes take on a different structure in which the chromatin becomes tightly packed. Look at *Figure 8.10* for more information on chromosome structure.

Problem-Solving Lab 8.2

Observe and Infer

How does the length of the cell cycle vary? The cell cycle varies greatly in length from one kind of cell to another. Some kinds of cells divide rapidly, while others divide more slowly.

Solve the Problem
Examine the cell cycle diagrams of two different types of cells. Observe the total length of each cell cycle and the length of time each cell spends in each phase of the cell cycle.

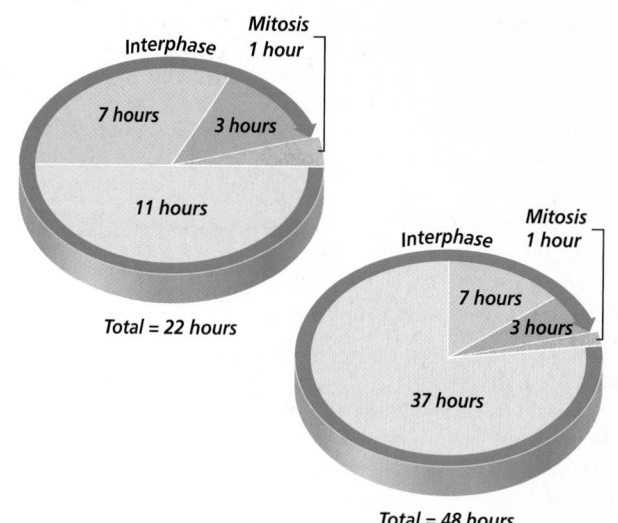

Thinking Critically
1. **Make and Use Graphs** Which part of the cell cycle is most variable in length?
2. **Infer** What can you infer about the functions of these two types of cells?
3. **Think Critically** Why do you think the cycle of some types of cells is faster than in others? Explain your answer.

The Cell Cycle

Fall follows summer, night follows day, and low tide follows high tide. Many events in nature follow a recurring, cyclical pattern. Living organisms are no exception. One cycle common to most living things is the cycle of the cell. The **cell cycle** is the sequence of growth and division of a cell.

As a cell proceeds through its cycle, it goes through two general periods: a period of growth and a period of division. The majority of a cell's life is spent in the growth period known as **interphase.** During interphase, a cell grows in size and carries on metabolism. Also during this period, chromosomes are duplicated in preparation for the period of division.

Following interphase, a cell enters its period of nuclear division called **mitosis** (mi TOH sus). Mitosis is the process by which two daughter cells are formed, each containing a complete set of chromosomes. Interphase and mitosis make up the bulk of the cell cycle. Following mitosis, the cytoplasm divides, separating the two daughter cells. You can use the *Problem-Solving Lab* on this page and the *BioLab* at the end of this chapter to investigate the rate of mitosis.

Chromosome Structure

Figure 8.10
The chromosomes of a eukaryotic cell undergo changes in shape and structure during the different phases of the cell cycle. A metaphase chromosome is a compact arrangement of DNA and proteins. During interphase, the chromosomes are long and tangled, resembling a plate of spaghetti. **Critical Thinking** *Why is it important for the chromosomes to be compact and untangled during mitosis?*

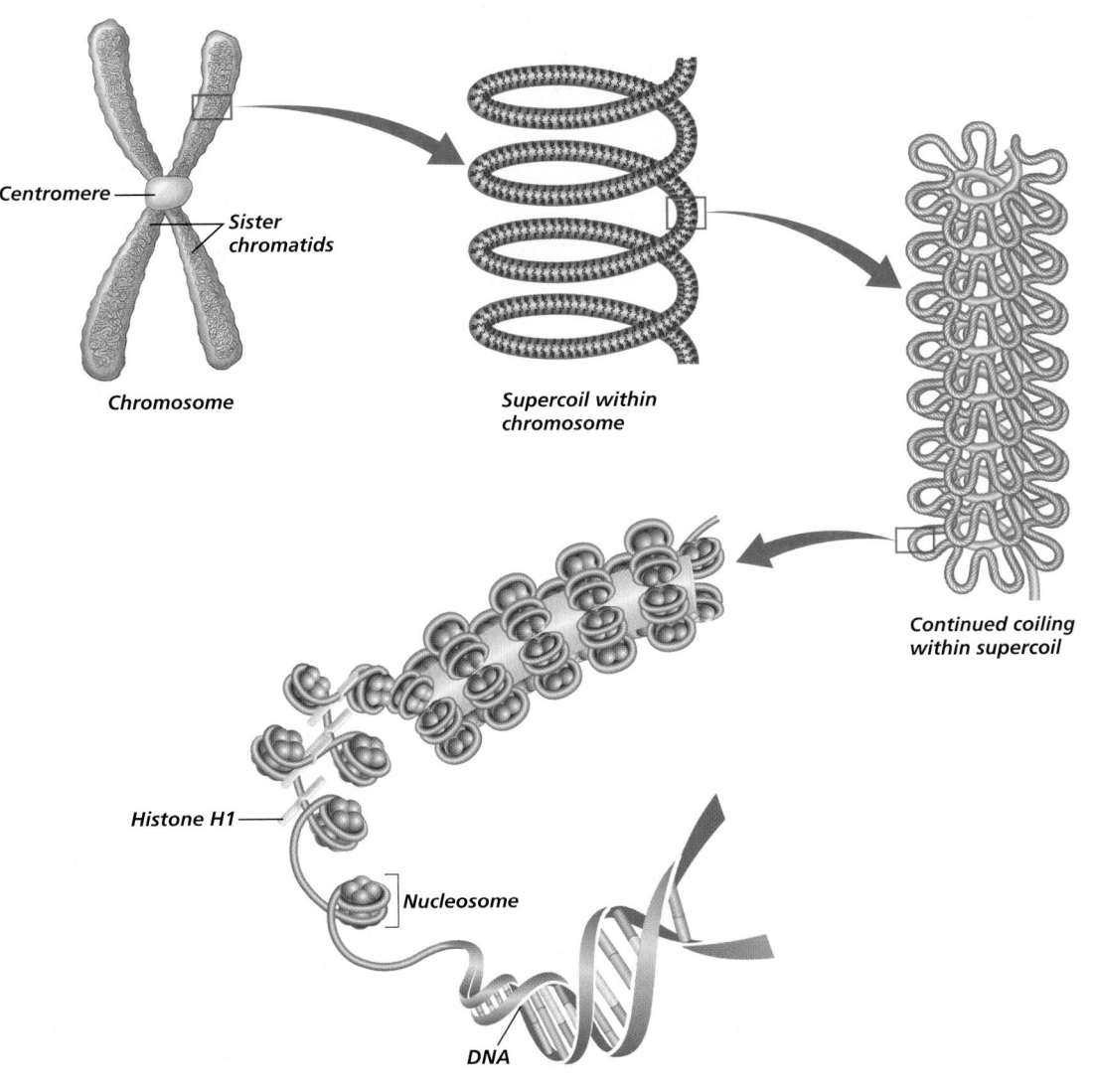

Centromere

Sister chromatids

Chromosome

Supercoil within chromosome

Continued coiling within supercoil

Histone H1

Nucleosome

DNA

Purpose
Students will visualize the microscopic structure of a chromosome during mitosis.

Background
Most of a cell's life is spent in interphase while the chromosomes are elongated and tangled. During mitosis, the chromosomes are packed for division.

Teaching Strategy
Ask students to make an analogy that explains the change in the structure of the chromosome from interphase to mitosis.

Visual Learning
■ Have students draw a cell showing the levels of DNA packaging in a metaphase chromosome.
■ Ask how nucleosomes resemble pearls on the strand of a necklace.

Critical Thinking
Compact chromosomes are not as easily broken during mitosis as tangled and elongated chromosomes would be.

Extension
Intrapersonal Have students hypothesize as to what might be happening to the nuclear envelope during mitosis. Have students design an experiment that could test their hypothesis. **L3**

CHALLENGE ACTIVITY

Mitosis: *Intrapersonal* Have students research the newest findings on what triggers the onset of mitosis and how microtubules are assembled and disassembled during spindle formation. Students could also research the formation of cell walls after cell division in plants. **L3**

205

Enrichment

Kinesthetic Have students work in groups to design models of the four stages of mitosis. Students might use colored macaroni or licorice for chromosomes. Have students include their completed models in their portfolios. **L1**
ELL COOP LEARN

The BioLab at the end of the chapter can be used at this point in the lesson.

Portfolio

Cell Cycle The average human cell that is capable of dividing has a cell cycle of 20 hours. Have students calculate how many cells there would be in one week if they start with one cell at time zero. Students should show their work and place the pages in their portfolios. There are 168 hours in one week. If a cell divides every 20 hours, there would be 256 cells at the end of one week. At 20 hours, there would be 2 cells; 40 hours, 4 cells; 60 hours, 8 cells and so on, until 160 hours when there would be 256 cells. **L2**

Figure 8.11
In preparation for mitosis, most of the time spent in the cell cycle is in interphase. The process of mitosis, represented here by the yellow wedge, is shown in detail in **Figure 8.13.**

Interphase: A Busy Time

Interphase, the busiest phase of the cell cycle, is divided into three parts as shown in **Figure 8.11.** During the first part, the cell grows and protein production is high. In the next part of interphase, the cell copies its chromosomes. DNA synthesis does not occur all through interphase but is confined to this specific time. After the chromosomes have been

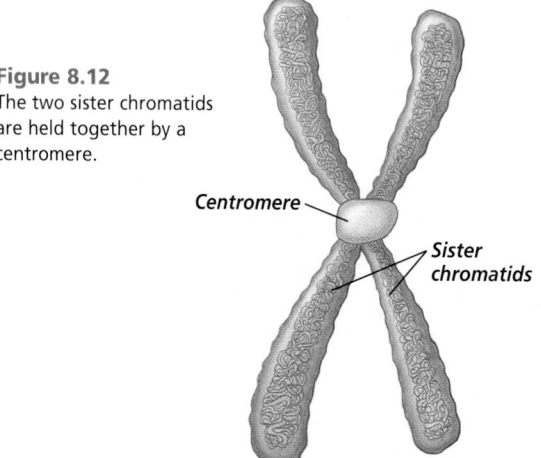

Figure 8.12
The two sister chromatids are held together by a centromere.

duplicated, the cell enters another shorter growth period in which mitochondria and other organelles are manufactured and cell parts needed for cell division are assembled. Following this activity, interphase ends and mitosis begins.

The Phases of Mitosis

Cells undergo mitosis as they approach the maximum cell size at which the nucleus can provide blueprints for proteins, and the plasma membrane can efficiently transport nutrients and wastes into and out of the cell.

Although cell division is a continuous process, biologists recognize four distinct phases of mitosis—each phase merging into the next. The four phases of mitosis are prophase, metaphase, anaphase, and telophase. Refer to **Figure 8.13** to help you understand the process as you read about mitosis.

Prophase: The first phase of mitosis

During **prophase,** the first and longest phase of mitosis, the long, stringy chromatin coils up into visible chromosomes. As you can see in **Figure 8.12,** each duplicated chromosome is made up of two halves. The two halves of the doubled structure are called **sister chromatids.** Sister chromatids and the DNA they contain are exact copies of each other and are formed when DNA is copied during interphase. Sister chromatids are held together by a structure called a **centromere,** which plays a role in chromosome movement during mitosis. By their characteristic location, centromeres also help scientists identify and study chromosomes.

As prophase continues, the nucleus begins to disappear as the nuclear envelope and the nucleolus disintegrate.

206 CELLULAR TRANSPORT AND THE CELL CYCLE

USING MODELS

Mitosis Use models of plant or animal cell mitosis (available from biological supply houses) to visualize and reinforce the discussion of mitosis. **L1**

Indiana Academic Standards
Pages 206–207: B.1.7, B.1.8

Figure 8.13
Mitosis begins after interphase. Follow the stages of mitosis as you read the text. The diagrams and the photos show mitosis in plant cells.

Spindle fibers

Disappearing nuclear envelope

Doubled chromosome

Centromere

Sister chromatids

Nuclear envelope reappears

Two daughter cells are formed

Stained LM Magnification: 500×

A Prophase
The chromatin coils to form visible chromosomes.

Stained LM Magnification: 360×

B Metaphase
The chromosomes move to the equator of the spindle.

Stained LM Magnification: 400×

C Anaphase
The centromeres split and the sister chromatids are pulled apart to opposite poles of the cell.

Stained LM Magnification: 640×

D Telophase
Two distinct daughter cells are formed. The cells separate as the cell cycle proceeds into the next interphase.

Discussion

Linguistic Discuss the details of the timing mechanism of the cell cycle with the class.

The DNA synthesis and replication phase of interphase and mitosis may be triggered by an enzyme called "cdc2 kinase." Another protein called "cyclin" is also involved in cell division control. In a new cell, cyclin is synthesized continuously and once it builds up to a critical level, it links up with cdc2 kinase protein to form a complex.

Several other biochemical steps then serve to activate the cdc2–cyclin complex, transforming it into maturation-promoting factor (MPF). Mitosis then takes place.

Now ask the students to write about another process (biological or otherwise) and the timing mechanism that governs the steps or phases of the process. Students should include a discussion of what happens if one portion of the process breaks down. **L3**

Virtual Lab

CD-ROM Students will explore the phases of a cell cycle in *Cell Reproduction.*

TECH PREP

Biology in Practice: *Interpersonal* Ask a cell biologist to talk to the class about how basic cell biology is critical to advanced research. Ask the speaker to describe how his or her investigations revolve intricately around what the class is learning in this unit. Have the class prepare some questions in advance to ask the guest. **L2**

Students often think that mitosis occurs in all cells of an organism throughout life. However, some cells rarely undergo mitosis once they have matured.

Uncover the Misconception

Ask students if all cells regularly divide by mitosis. Have them describe how often they think cells divide.

Demonstrate the Concept

Show students a plant that has had the soil washed away from the roots. Point to the leaves, stem, and mature roots. Explain that the cells in these parts of a plant rarely divide by mitosis. Show students meristem tissues where new cells are produced near the tips of branches or roots.

Assess New Knowledge

Ask students to suggest some other cells that do not undergo mitosis. Examples may include nerve cells and bone cells in adults.

Reinforcement

Kinesthetic Have groups of students make models of cells at various stages of cell division. Pipe cleaners or yarn pieces can represent chromosomes. **L1** **ELL** **COOP LEARN**

Indiana Academic Standards

Pages 208–209: B.1.7, B.1.8

By late prophase, these structures are completely absent. In animal cells, two important pairs of structures, the centrioles, begin to migrate to opposite ends of the cell. **Centrioles** are small, dark, cylindrical structures that are made of microtubules and are located just outside the nucleus, as shown in *Figure 8.14.* Centrioles play a role in chromatid separation.

As the pairs of centrioles move to opposite ends of the cell, another important structure, called the spindle, begins to form between them. The **spindle** is a football-shaped, cagelike structure consisting of thin fibers made of microtubules. In plant cells, the spindle forms without centrioles. The spindle fibers play a vital role in the separation of sister chromatids during mitosis.

Metaphase: The second stage of mitosis

During **metaphase,** the short second phase of mitosis, the doubled chromosomes become attached to the spindle fibers by their centromeres. The chromosomes are pulled by the spindle fibers and begin to line up on the midline, or equator, of the spindle. Each sister chromatid is attached to its own spindle fiber. One sister chromatid's spindle fiber extends to one pole, and the other extends to the opposite pole. This arrangement is important because it ensures that each new cell receives an identical and complete set of chromosomes.

Anaphase: The third phase of mitosis

The separation of sister chromatids marks the beginning of **anaphase,** the third phase of mitosis. During anaphase, the centromeres split apart and chromatid pairs from each chromosome separate from each other. The chromatids are pulled apart by the shortening of the microtubules in the spindle fibers.

Figure 8.14
Centrioles duplicate during interphase. In the photomicrograph, one centriole is cut crosswise and the other longitudinally.

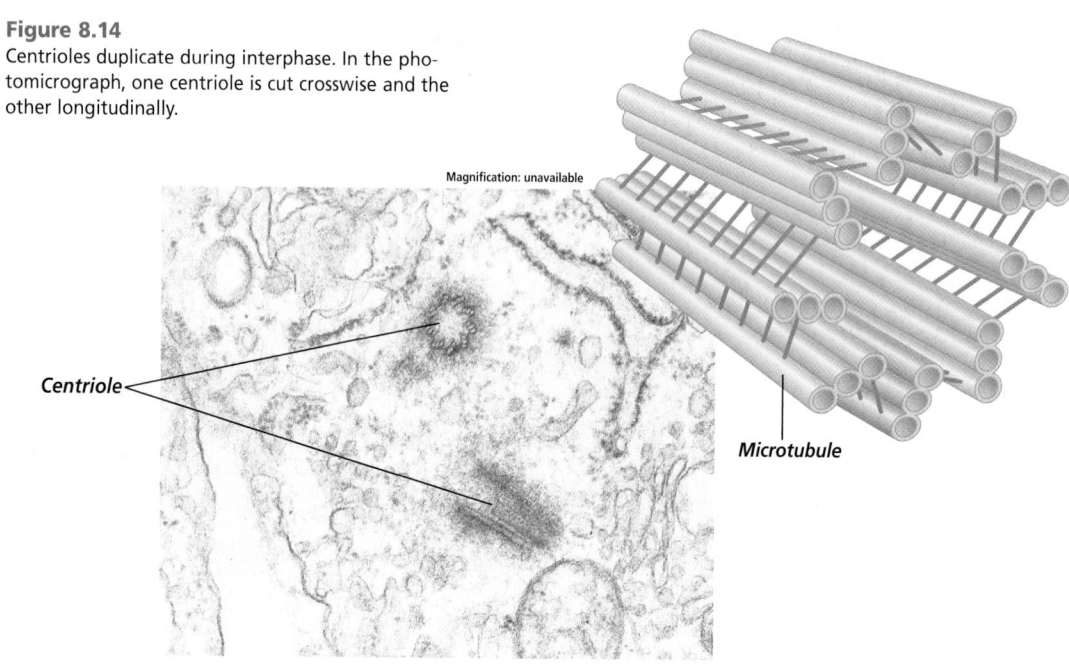

Magnification: unavailable

Centriole

Microtubule

208 CELLULAR TRANSPORT AND THE CELL CYCLE

Spindle Fibers Have students research discoveries on the structure of spindle fibers and on how movement occurs along these fibers. Have students present their findings to the class. **L3**

Telophase: The fourth phase of mitosis

The final phase of mitosis is **telophase.** Telophase begins as the chromatids reach the opposite poles of the cell. During telophase, many of the changes that occurred during prophase are reversed as the new cells prepare for their own independent existence. The chromosomes, which had been tightly coiled since the end of prophase, now unwind so they can begin to direct the metabolic activities of the new cells. The spindle begins to break down, the nucleolus reappears, and a new nuclear envelope forms around each set of chromosomes. Finally, a new double membrane begins to form between the two new nuclei.

Cytokinesis

Following telophase, the cell's cytoplasm divides in a process called **cytokinesis** (si toh kih NEE sus). Cytokinesis differs between plants and animals. Toward the end of telophase in animal cells, the plasma membrane pinches in along the equator as shown in *Figure 8.15.* As the cell cycle proceeds, the two new cells are separated. Find out more about mitosis in animal cells in the *MiniLab.*

Plant cells have a rigid cell wall, so the plasma membrane does not pinch in. Rather, a structure known as the cell plate is laid down across the cell's equator. A cell membrane forms around each cell, and new cell walls form on each side of the cell plate until separation is complete.

Figure 8.15
The furrow, created when proteins positioned under the plasma membrane at the equator of this frog cell contracted and slid past each other, will deepen until the cell is pinched in two.

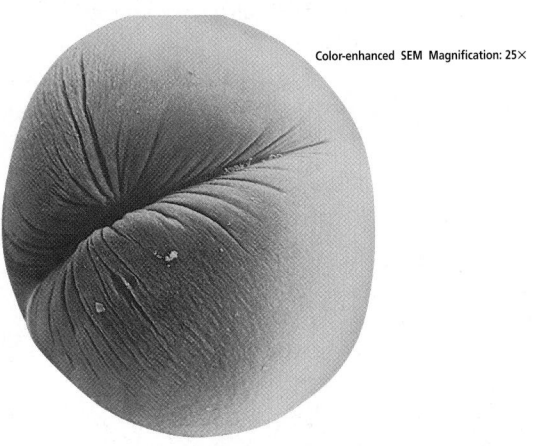

Color-enhanced SEM Magnification: 25×

MiniLab 8.2

Compare and Contrast

Seeing Asters The result of the process of mitosis is similar in plant and animal cells. However, animal cells develop structures called asters that are thought to serve as a brace for the spindle fibers, while plant cells do not develop asters.

Stained LM Magnification: 250×

Asters

Procedure

1. Examine a slide showing fish mitosis under low- and high-power magnification. **CAUTION:** *Use care when handling prepared slides.*
2. Find cells that are undergoing mitosis. You will be able to see dark-stained rodlike structures within certain cells. These structures are chromosomes.
3. Note the appearance and location of asters. They will appear as ray or starlike structures at opposite ends of cells that are in metaphase.
4. Asters may also be observed in cells that are in other phases of the cell cycle.

Analysis

1. **Describe** What is the location of asters in cells that are in prophase?
2. **Infer** How do you know that asters are not critical to mitosis?
3. **Use Models** Sketch and label a plant cell and an animal cell in prophase.

MiniLab 8.2

Purpose

Students will observe animal cells that are undergoing mitosis and will note the location and appearance of the aster.

Process Skills

compare and contrast, observe and infer, critical thinking

Teaching Strategies

- Advise students that the slide material is taken from fish blastulas. Ask students why this material is ideal for the study of cells undergoing mitosis.
- To reduce cost of purchasing a class set of prepared slides, purchase one slide and use a microvideo camera or a microprojector if available. Alternatively, purchase 35 mm slides and project them onto the screen with a slide projector.
- If necessary, review the stages of mitosis with students.

Analysis

1. Asters are starlike projections of microtubules associated with centrioles. Asters are found at the cell poles in prophase.
2. Asters are not critical because plant cells undergo mitosis without the structures.
3. Sketches should show the chromatin coils forming visible chromosomes. Asters can be included for the animal cell.

Assessment

Portfolio Have students research the role and function of the aster and summarize the scientific opinion in their portfolios. Use the Performance Task Assessment List for Writing in Science in **PASC,** p. 159. **L3**

INCLUSION STRATEGIES

Learning Disabled To help students better understand the phases of mitosis, have them research the prefixes *inter, pro, meta, ana,* and *telo.* Have them relate the meanings of the prefixes to the phases of mitosis. **L1**

DAILY INTERVENTION

Check for Understanding
Test the students' ability to recognize the various phases of mitosis. Place photomicrographs on an overhead projector and ask the class to identify each stage. **L2**

Reteach
Visual-Spatial Review the phases of mitosis, emphasizing that the process is continuous and that one phase blends into the next. Use photomicrographs and diagrams to help students identify the phases and learn the terms associated with structures in mitosis. **L2** **ELL**

Resources
For more practice, use *Reading Essentials for Biology*, Section 8.2.

Extension
Encourage students to research the stages of the cell cycle. They may find information on how long each stage lasts for various species and what events occur at each stage. **L3**

✔ Assessment

Performance Call out various stages of mitosis and have students find and show that stage to their lab partners using onion root slides under the microscope. Walk around the room to check their results. **L1**

Caption Question Answer
Figure 8.16 A blood cell is a part of every level.

Figure 8.16
Cells of complex multicellular organisms are organized into tissues, organs, and organ systems. **Sequence** *What levels of organization is a human blood cell a part of?*

| Cell (muscle cell) | Tissue (muscle tissue) | Organ (stomach) | Organ system (digestive system) | Organism (Florida panther) |

Results of Mitosis

Mitosis is a process that guarantees genetic continuity, resulting in the production of two new cells with chromosome sets that are identical to those of the parent cell. These new daughter cells will carry out the same cellular processes and functions as those of the parent cell and will grow and divide just as the parent cell did.

When mitosis is complete, unicellular organisms remain as single cells—the organism simply multiplied. In multicellular organisms, cell growth and reproduction result in groups of cells that work together as **tissue** to perform a specific function. Tissues organize in various combinations to form **organs** that perform more complex roles within the organism. For example, cells make up muscle tissue, then muscle tissue works with other tissues in the organ called the stomach to mix up food. Multiple organs that work together form an **organ system.** The stomach is one organ in the digestive system, which functions to break up and digest food.

All organ systems work together for the survival of the organism, whether the organism is a fly or a human. *Figure 8.16* shows an example of cell specialization and organization for a complex organism. In addition to its digestive system, the panther has a number of other organ systems that have developed through cell specialization. It is important to remember that no matter how complex the organ system or organism becomes, the cell is still the most basic unit of that organization.

Section Assessment

Understanding Main Ideas
1. Describe how a cell's surface area-to-volume ratio limits its size.
2. Why is it necessary for a cell's chromosomes to be distributed to its daughter cells in such a precise manner?
3. Relate cells to each level of organization in a multicellular organism.
4. In multicellular organisms, describe two cellular specializations that result from mitosis.

Thinking Critically
5. At one time, interphase was referred to as the resting phase of the cell cycle. Why do you think this description is no longer used?

SKILL REVIEW
6. **Get the Big Picture** Make a table sequencing the phases of the cell cycle. Mention one important event that occurs at each phase. For more help, refer to *Get the Big Picture* in the **Skill Handbook.**

210 CELLULAR TRANSPORT AND THE CELL CYCLE

 in.bdol.glencoe.com/self_check_quiz

Section Assessment

1. As volume increases, surface area does not increase sufficiently to support large cells.
2. Each daughter cell must get an identical copy of the set of chromosomes.
3. Cells are the basic level of organization. Similar cells that perform the same function make up tissues. Organs are made up of tissues. Several organs make up an organ system.
4. Possible answers include tissues, organs, organ systems.
5. The cell is not resting, but growing, producing proteins, and replicating its chromosomes in preparation for division.
6. Interphase: chromosomes are copied; prophase: nuclear envelope disappears; metaphase: chromosomes line up; anaphase: chromatids separate; telophase: chromosomes move to the poles

Control of the Cell Cycle

Indiana Standards Standard B.1.7 Explain that complex interactions among the different kinds of molecules in the cell cause distinct cycles of activities, such as growth and division. Note that cell behavior can also be affected by molecules from other parts of the organism, such as hormones.

SECTION PREVIEW

Objectives

Describe the role of enzymes in the regulation of the cell cycle.

Distinguish between the events of a normal cell cycle and the abnormal events that result in cancer.

Identify ways to potentially reduce the risk of cancer.

Review Vocabulary

protein: a large complex polymer composed of carbon, hydrogen, oxygen, nitrogen, and sometimes sulfur (p. 160)

New Vocabulary

cancer
gene

Getting Control

Finding Main Ideas As you read through the section on control of the cell cycle, answer the following questions.

Study Organizer

1. Enzymes control the cell cycle. What controls enzyme production?

2. What are two environmental factors that contribute to the development of cancer? List any possible ways you can influence these factors.

3. How does a person's diet relate to the chances of getting cancer?

Color-enhanced SEM Magnification: 7500×

This tumor is developing due to a mistake in the cell cycle.

Normal Control of the Cell Cycle

Why do some types of cells divide rapidly, while others divide slowly? What tells a cell when it is time to leave one part of the cell cycle and begin the next?

Proteins and enzymes control the cell cycle

The cell cycle is controlled by proteins called cyclins and a set of enzymes that attach to the cyclin and become activated. The interaction of these molecules, based on conditions both in the cell's environment and inside the cell, controls the cell cycle. Occasionally, cells lose control of the cell cycle. This uncontrolled dividing of cells can result from the failure to produce certain enzymes, the overproduction of enzymes, or the production of other enzymes at the wrong time. **Cancer** is a malignant growth resulting from uncontrolled cell division. This loss of control may be caused by environmental factors or by changes in enzyme production.

Enzyme production is directed by genes located on the chromosomes. A **gene** is a segment of DNA that controls the production of a protein.

Many studies point to the portion of interphase just before DNA replication as being a key control period in the cell cycle. Scientists have identified several enzymes that trigger DNA replication.

8.3 CONTROL OF THE CELL CYCLE **211**

1 Focus

INTERACTIVE CHALKBOARD
PowerPoint® Presentations

Bellringer
Section Focus Transparency 20

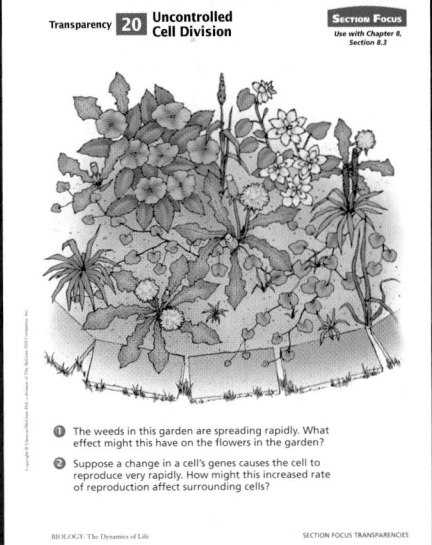

Transparency **20** Uncontrolled Cell Division — SECTION FOCUS — Use with Chapter 8, Section 8.3

❶ The weeds in this garden are spreading rapidly. What effect might this have on the flowers in the garden?

❷ Suppose a change in a cell's genes causes the cell to reproduce very rapidly. How might this increased rate of reproduction affect surrounding cells?

BIOLOGY: The Dynamics of Life — SECTION FOCUS TRANSPARENCIES

Finding Main Ideas
Study Organizer

1. Enzyme production is controlled by feedback from the cellular environment and the DNA in the nucleus.

2. UV radiation and cancer causing chemicals are possible answers. Avoid exposure to UV radiation from suntan booths and sunlight. Do not smoke.

3. Many dietary experts agree that a diet low in fat and high in fiber can reduce the risk of certain kinds of cancer. Foods that contain certain vitamins and minerals also can reduce the risk of getting cancer.

RESOURCE MANAGER

Unit 3 *Fast File* Resources
Reinforcement and Study Guide in English, p. 88
Reinforcement and Study Guide in Spanish, p. 92
Critical Thinking/Problem Solving, p. 94
Transparency Worksheets, p. 97

Section Focus Transparency 20
Reading Essentials for Biology, Section 8.3

Indiana Academic Standards

Pages 210–211: B.1.1, B.1.4, B.1.7, B.1.8

Purpose

Students will analyze a graph showing incidence of certain body organ cancers.

Process Skills

interpret data, think critically, analyze information, sequence, make and use graphs

Teaching Strategies

■ Allow students to work in small groups.

■ Explain the difference between skin melanoma and basal cell or squamous skin cancers.

■ Help student to determine percent survival if they are having difficulty.

Thinking Critically

1. basal cell and squamous; skin melanoma
2. lung; basal cell and squamous
3. calculation: new cases − deaths = survivors; so (survivors ÷ new cases) × 100 = % survival. 180 000 − 40 000 = 140 000. Then (140 000 ÷ 180 000) × 100 = 78%
4. approximately nine percent

Assessment

Portfolio Have students gather information on a specific type of cancer and prepare a brief oral report. Use the Performance Task Assessment List for Oral Presentation in **PASC**, p. 143. **L2**

✓Reading Check The cancer may have spread to vital organs and damaged them beyond repair.

Indiana Academic Standards

Pages 212–213: B.1.4, B.1.7, B.1.8

Problem-Solving Lab 8.3

Interpret Data

How does the incidence of cancer vary? Cancer affects many different body organs. In addition, the same body organ, such as our skin, can be affected by several different types of cancer. Some types of cancer are more treatable than others. Use the following graph to analyze the incidence of cancer.

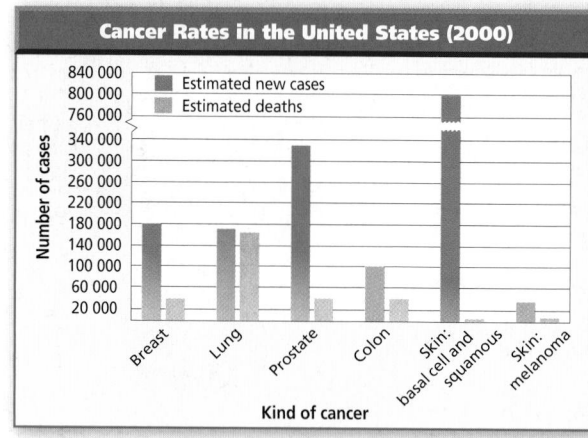

Cancer Rates in the United States (2000)

Thinking Critically

1. **Make and Use Graphs** Which cancer type is most common? Least common?
2. **Interpret Data** Which cancer type seems to be least treatable? Most treatable?
3. **Interpret Data** Using breast cancer as an example, calculate the percent of survival for this cancer type.
4. **Use Numbers** Approximately what percentage of new cancer cases in the United States in 2000 were lung cancer?

Cancer: A Mistake in the Cell Cycle

Currently, scientists consider cancer to be a result of changes in one or more of the genes that produce substances that are involved in controlling the cell cycle. These changes are expressed as cancer when something prompts the damaged genes into action. Cancerous cells form masses

---

of tissue called tumors that deprive normal cells of nutrients. In later stages, cancer cells enter the circulatory system and spread throughout the body, a process called metastasis, forming new tumors that disrupt the function of organs, organ systems, and ultimately, the organism.

Cancer is the second leading cause of death in the United States, exceeded only by heart disease. Cancer can affect any tissue in the body. In the United States, lung, colon, breast, and prostate cancers are the most prevalent types. Use the *Problem-Solving Lab* on this page to estimate the number of people in the United States who will develop these kinds of cancers in this decade, and how many people are expected to die from cancers. The *Connection to Health* feature at the end of this chapter further discusses skin cancer.

✓Reading Check **Infer** why cancer is difficult to treat in later stages.

The causes of cancer

The causes of cancer are difficult to pinpoint because both genetic and environmental factors are involved. The environmental influences of cancer become obvious when you consider that people in different countries develop different types of cancers at different rates. For example, the rate of breast cancer is relatively high in the United States, but relatively low in Japan. Similarly, stomach cancer is common in Japan, but rare in the United States.

Other environmental factors, such as cigarette smoke, air and water pollution, and exposure to ultraviolet radiation from the sun, are all known to damage the genes that control the cell cycle. Cancer may also be caused by viral infections that damage the genes.

🎯 CHALLENGE ACTIVITY

Cancer Have students interview the school nurse or other healthcare official to find out the warning signs of cancer. Have students compile their results on a poster to hang in the classroom. **L2**

Cancer prevention

From recent and ongoing investigations, scientists have established a clear link between a healthy lifestyle and the incidence of cancer.

Physicians and dietary experts agree that diets low in fat and high in fiber content can reduce the risk of many kinds of cancer. For example, diets high in fat have been linked to increased risk for colon, breast, and prostate cancers, among others. People who consume only a minimal amount of fat reduce the potential risk for these and other cancers and may also maintain a healthy body weight more easily. In addition, recent studies suggest that diets high in fiber are associated with reduced risk for cancer, especially colon cancer. Fruits, vegetables, and grain products are excellent dietary options because of their fiber content and because they are naturally low in fat. The foods displayed in *Figure 8.17* illustrate some of the choices that are associated with cancer prevention.

Vitamins and minerals may also help prevent cancer. Key in this category are carotenoids, vitamins A, C, and E, and calcium. Carotenoids are found in foods such as yellow and orange vegetables and green leafy vegetables. Citrus fruits are a great source of vitamin C, and many dairy products are rich in calcium.

In addition to diet, other healthy choices such as daily exercise and not using tobacco also are known to reduce the risk of cancer.

Figure 8.17
A healthy diet may reduce your risk of cancer. **Classify** *What types of food make up a diet that reduces the risk of cancer?*

---

in.bdol.glencoe.com/self_check_quiz

Section Assessment

Understanding Main Ideas
1. Do all cells complete the cell cycle in the same amount of time?
2. Describe how enzymes control the cell cycle.
3. How can disruption of the cell cycle result in cancer?
4. How does cancer affect normal cell functioning?

Thinking Critically
5. What evidence shows that the environment influences the occurrence of cancer?

SKILL REVIEW
6. **Recognize Cause and Effect** Although not all cancers are preventable, some lifestyle choices, such as a healthy diet and regular exercise, can decrease your cancer risk. Give a summary of how these two lifestyle choices could be implemented by teens. For more help, refer to *Recognize Cause and Effect* in the **Skill Handbook**.

8.3 CONTROL OF THE CELL CYCLE **213**

---

3 Assess

DAILY INTERVENTION

Check for Understanding
Have students compare a normal and a cancer cell cycle. L2

Reteach
Write the following cell reproduction times (in minutes) on the board. Normal chicken stomach cells: interphase 120, prophase 60, metaphase 10, anaphase 3, telophase 12. Cancerous chicken stomach cells: interphase 16, prophase 15, metaphase 2, anaphase 1, telophase 3. Ask students to suggest possible reasons why they are different.

Resources
For more practice, use *Reading Essentials for Biology*, Section 8.3.

Extension

Intrapersonal Ask students to find out how chemotherapy drugs work. Ask them to find out why hair follicles and the lining of the digestive system are affected by these drugs, resulting in hair loss and nausea. L3

MODIFIED Assessment

Skill Ask students to make a poster that sequences the events that regulate the cell cycle. L1

Caption Question Answer
Figure 8.17 fruits, vegetables, and grain as well as any foods low in fat or high in fiber content

---

Section Assessment

1. No, the rate of completion varies widely depending on the cell and its function.
2. Under the proper environmental conditions inside a cell, enzymes activate by attaching to cyclins.
3. Uncontrolled cell division could cause tumor formation and cancer.
4. Cancer cells form masses of tissue that deprive normal cells of nutrients.
5. People in different countries get cancer at different rates.
6. Many cancers are a result of environmental factors. Teens who protect their skin and do not smoke can prevent the majority of skin and lung cancers.

INVESTIGATE BioLab

Time Allotment

one class period

Process Skills

collect data, compare and contrast, apply concepts, think critically, interpret data, observe and infer

Safety Precautions

Students must handle prepared slides, glass slides, and coverslips with care.

PREPARATION

Obtain prepared slides of Allium (onion) root tip from a biological supply house.

Data Table

Phase	Area X	Area Y
Interphase	95	36
Prophase	15	0
Metaphase	5	0
Anaphase	2	0
Telophase	4	0

Indiana Academic Standards

Pages 214–215: B.1.8

INVESTIGATE BioLab

Before You Begin

Mitosis and the resulting multiplication of cells are responsible for the growth of an organism. Does mitosis occur in all areas of an organism at the same rate, or are there certain areas within an organism where mitosis occurs more often? You will answer this question in this BioLab. Your organism will be an onion, and the areas you are going to investigate will be different locations in its root.

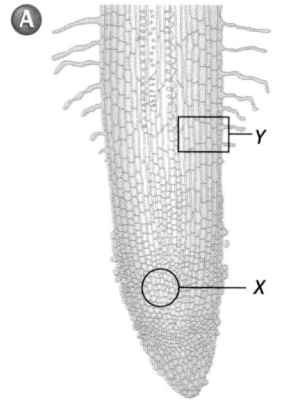

Where is mitosis most common?

PREPARATION

Problem

Does mitosis occur at the same rate in all of the parts of an onion root?

Objectives

In this BioLab, you will:
- **Observe** cells in two different root areas.
- **Identify** the stages of mitosis in each area.

Materials

prepared slide of onion root tip
microscope

Skill Handbook

If you need help with this lab, refer to the **Skill Handbook.**

Safety Precautions

CAUTION: *Report any glass breakage to your teacher.*

PROCEDURE

1. Using diagram **A** as a guide, locate area X on a prepared slide of onion root tip.
2. Place the prepared slide under your microscope and use low power to locate area X. **CAUTION:** *Use care when handling prepared slides.*
3. Switch to high power.
4. Using diagram **B** as a guide:
   a. Identify those cells that are in mitosis and those cells that are in interphase.
   b. Create a data table. Record the number of cells observed in each phase of mitosis and interphase for area X. Note: It will be easier to count and keep track of cells by following rows. See diagram **C** as a guide to counting.
5. Using diagram **A** again, locate area Y on the same prepared slide.

PROCEDURE

Teaching Strategies

- Review the phases of mitosis with students.
- Allow students to look at the onion root tip slide macroscopically or through a dissecting microscope first to locate areas X and Y.

- You may wish to verify that students are looking at the correct areas before they begin their counts.
- If materials are in short supply, consider doing the lab using a microprojector or with a video camera setup.
- Advise students that the cells on the prepared slide are not alive.

Troubleshooting

Remind students that when slides are placed on the microscope stage, everything is reversed. The tip end of the root should be facing away from the student, and when moving from area X to Y, the slide must be moved away from the student.

Ⓑ Interphase

Prophase

Telophase

Metaphase

Anaphase

Ⓒ End counting here

Start counting here

High-power view

6. Place the prepared slide under your microscope and use low power to locate area Y.

7. Switch to high power.

8. Using diagram **B** as a guide:

   a. Identify those cells that are in mitosis and those that are in interphase.

   b. Record in the data table the number of cells observed in each phase of mitosis and interphase for area Y.

9. CLEANUP AND DISPOSAL Clean all equipment as instructed by your teacher, and return everything to its proper place.

ANALYZE AND CONCLUDE

1. **Observe** Which area of the onion root tip (X or Y) had the greatest percentage of cells undergoing mitosis? The lowest? Use specific totals from your data table to support your answer.

2. **Predict** If mitosis is associated with rapid growth, where do you believe is the location of most rapid root growth, area X or Y? Explain your answer.

3. **Apply** Where might you look for cells in the human body that are undergoing mitosis?

4. **Think Critically** Assume that you were not able to observe cells in every phase of mitosis. Explain why this might be, considering the length of each phase.

5. ERROR ANALYSIS What factors might cause misleading results? How could you avoid these problems?

Apply Your Skill

Make and Use Graphs Prepare a circle graph that shows the total number of cells counted in area X and the percentage of cells in each phase of mitosis.

 Web Links To find out more about mitosis, visit in.bdol.glencoe.com/mitosis

ANALYZE AND CONCLUDE

1. X, Y; Student totals will vary to support the conclusions.

2. X; This was the area showing cells undergoing mitosis at the highest rate.

3. an area of rapid growth such as skin, hair follicles, intestine lining

4. Answers may vary: the phase has already occurred, the phase has not yet occurred, area of view is not rapidly growing, incorrect observation or recording stage

5. ERROR ANALYSIS Errors might result from counting cells out of the area of greatest growth, or by not counting enough cells.

Assessment

Knowledge Ask students to explain the steps that could be taken to make the gathering of data more accurate. Use the Performance Task Assessment List for Designing an Experiment in **PASC,** p. 95. L2

Apply Your Skill

Make and Use Graphs Have students prepare their own slides of onion mitosis. Kits that provide the onion tips, stain, and directions are available through biological supply houses. L2

■ Remind students that all cells will not be viewed from the side, and they may not be able to classify the stage of mitosis for each cell.

Data and Observations

Student data will vary but the sample data on page 214 can be used as a guide: Mitosis should be observed in cells in area X but not in area Y.

CLEANUP AND DISPOSAL

Make sure microscopes are handled properly and that they are stored with the low-power objective lens in place.

connection to Health

Purpose

Students will examine the types and causes of skin cancer.

Teaching Strategies

Some schools in Australia are making sunscreen mandatory for all students while they are on the playground. Discuss with students the dangers of exposure to the sun and whether or not sunscreen should be made mandatory for students in the United States.

Extension

Intrapersonal Have students research other types of skin cancer. If available, have them provide photos as well as research the warning signs of cancer. As a class, have students make an informational brochure about the different kinds of skin cancer. **L3**

connection to Health

Skin Cancer

Skin cancer accounts for one-third of all malignancies diagnosed in the United States, and the incidence of skin cancer is increasing. Most cases are caused by exposure to harmful ultraviolet rays emitted by the sun, so skin cancer most often develops on the exposed face or neck. The people most at risk are those whose fair skin contains smaller amounts of a protective pigment called melanin.

Skin is composed of two layers of tissue, the epidermis and the dermis. The epidermis is the part that we see on the surface of our bodies and is composed of multiple layers of closely packed cells. As the cells reach the surface, they die and become flattened. Eventually they flake away. To replace the loss, cells on the innermost layer of the epidermis are constantly dividing.

Your body has a natural protection system to shield skin cells from potentially harmful rays of the sun. A pigment called melanin is produced by cells called melanocytes and absorbs the UV rays before they reach basal cells.

Types of skin cancers Uncontrolled division of epidermal cells leads to skin cancer. Squamous cell carcinoma is a common type of skin cancer that affects cells throughout the epidermis. Squamous cell cancer takes the form of red or pink tumors that can grow rapidly and spread. Precancerous growths produced by sun-damaged basal cells can become basal cell carcinoma, another common type of skin cancer. In basal cell carcinoma, the cancerous cells are from the layer of the epidermis that replenishes the shed epithelial cells. Both squamous cell carcinoma and basal cell carcinoma are usually discovered when they are small and can be easily removed in a doctor's office. Both types also respond to treatment such as surgery, chemotherapy, and radiation therapy.

Melanoma

Epidermis

Dermis

Melanocytes

Melanin granules

Structure of the skin

The most lethal skin cancer is malignant melanoma. Melanomas are cancerous growths of the melanocytes that normally protect other cells in the epithelium from the harmful rays of the sun. An important indication of a melanoma can be a change in color of an area of skin to a variety of colors including black, brown, red, dark blue, or gray. A single melanoma can have several colors within the tumor. Melanomas can also form at the site of moles. Melanomas can be dangerous because cancerous cells from the tumor can travel to other areas of the body before the melanoma is detected. Early detection is essential, and melanomas can be surgically removed.

Writing About Biology

Describe Scientists know that the UV rays of sunlight can contribute to skin cancer. Write a paragraph describing how you can minimize the risk.

 To find out more about skin cancer, visit in.bdol.glencoe.com/health

Writing About Biology

Paragraphs will vary but should include the idea that as people learn the facts about the role of the sun in causing skin cancer, their perceptions may change.

 Indiana Academic Standards

Pages 216–217: B.1.2, B.1.4, B.1.7, B.1.8

STUDY GUIDE

Section 8.1

Cellular Transport

Key Concepts

- Osmosis is the diffusion of water through a selectively permeable membrane.
- Passive transport moves a substance with the concentration gradient and requires no energy from the cell.
- Active transport moves materials against the concentration gradient and requires energy to overcome the flow of materials opposite the concentration gradient.
- Large particles may enter a cell by endocytosis and leave by exocytosis.

Vocabulary

active transport (p. 199)
endocytosis (p. 200)
exocytosis (p. 200)
facilitated diffusion (p. 198)
hypertonic solution (p. 196)
hypotonic solution (p. 196)
isotonic solution (p. 196)
osmosis (p. 195)
passive transport (p. 198)

Section 8.2

Cell Growth and Reproduction

Key Concepts

- Cell size is limited largely by the diffusion rate of materials into and out of the cell, the amount of DNA available to program the cell's metabolism, and the cell's surface area-to-volume ratio.
- The life cycle of a cell is divided into two general periods: a period of active growth and metabolism known as interphase, and a period that leads to cell division known as mitosis.
- Mitosis is divided into four phases: prophase, metaphase, anaphase, and telophase.
- The cells of most multicellular organisms are organized into tissues, organs, and organ systems.

Vocabulary

anaphase (p. 208)
cell cycle (p. 204)
centriole (p. 208)
centromere (p. 206)
chromatin (p. 204)
chromosome (p. 203)
cytokinesis (p. 209)
interphase (p. 204)
metaphase (p. 208)
mitosis (p. 204)
organ (p. 210)
organ system (p. 210)
prophase (p. 206)
sister chromatid (p. 206)
spindle (p. 208)
telophase (p. 209)
tissue (p. 210)

Section 8.3

Control of the Cell Cycle

Color-enhanced SEM
Magnification: 7500×

Key Concepts

- The cell cycle is controlled by key enzymes that are produced at specific points in the cell cycle.
- Cancer is caused by genetic and environmental factors that change the genes that control the cell cycle.

Vocabulary

cancer (p. 211)
gene (p. 211)

FOLDABLES
Study Organizer   To help you review osmosis, use the Organizational Study Fold on page 195.

in.bdol.glencoe.com/vocabulary_puzzlemaker

CHAPTER 8 ASSESSMENT **217**

Key Concepts

Summary statements can be used by students to review the major concepts of the chapter.

Biology Online

Visit in.bdol.glencoe.com
/self_check_quiz
/vocabulary_puzzlemaker
/chapter_test
/standardized_test

VOCABULARY PUZZLEMAKER

For additional help with vocabulary, have students access the Vocabulary PuzzleMaker online at in.bdol.glencoe.com/vocabulary_puzzlemaker

FOLDABLES™

Have students use their Foldables to review the content of Section 8.1. On the back of the paper, analyze what would happen to a cell that has lost its ability to transport ions against a concentration gradient.

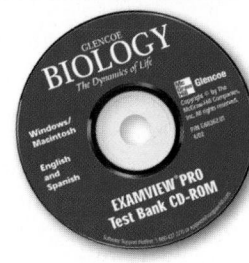

Use the ExamView®Pro Test Bank CD-ROM to:

- Create **multiple versions** of tests
- Create **modified** tests with one mouse click for **inclusion** students
- **Edit** existing questions and **add** your own questions
- Build tests aligned with state standards using built-in **State Curriculum Tags**
- Change **English** tests to **Spanish** with one mouse click and vice versa

The Princeton Review **Questions and answers have been aligned and verified by The Princeton Review.**

Vocabulary Review

1. cancer   **4.** true
2. centrioles   **5.** mitosis
3. osmosis

Understanding Key Concepts

6. B   **10.** D
7. B   **11.** D
8. C   **12.** B
9. D   **13.** D

Constructed Response

14. Cells that carry on a great deal of active transport would have more mitochondria.
15. By being able to control the enzymes, scientists may be able to modify the rapid cell division in cancer cells.
16. The solution outside the bag will turn blue-black.

Thinking Critically

17. The paramecium, being in a hypertonic solution, would probably die because water diffuses out.
18. Student essays may indicate the incidence of the disorder, that it is caused by a recessive allele, the therapy to treat the disorder, as well as other information.

Vocabulary Review

Review the Chapter 8 vocabulary words listed in the Study Guide on page 217. Determine if each statement is true or false. If false, replace the underlined word with the correct vocabulary word.

1. <u>Mitosis</u> is the result of uncontrolled division of cells.
2. Small, dark cylindrical structures that are made of microtubules and located just outside the nucleus are called <u>genes</u>.
3. Diffusion of water across a selectively permeable membrane is called <u>cytokinesis</u>.
4. In a <u>hypotonic solution</u>, the concentration of dissolved substances inside cells is higher than the concentration outside the cell.
5. <u>Cancer</u> is a period of nuclear division in a cell.

Understanding Key Concepts

6. What kind of environment is described when the concentration of dissolved substances is greater outside the cell than inside?
   - **A.** hypotonic   **C.** isotonic
   - **B.** hypertonic   **D.** saline
7. How is osmosis defined?
   - **A.** as active transport
   - **B.** as diffusion of water through a selectively permeable membrane
   - **C.** as an example of facilitated diffusion
   - **D.** as requiring a transport protein
8. An amoeba ingests large food particles by what process?
   - **A.** osmosis   **C.** endocytosis
   - **B.** diffusion   **D.** exocytosis
9. Of what are chromosomes composed?
   - **A.** cytoplasm   **C.** RNA and proteins
   - **B.** centrioles   **D.** DNA and proteins
10. Which of the following does NOT occur during interphase?
    - **A.** excretion of wastes
    - **B.** cell repair
    - **C.** protein synthesis
    - **D.** nuclear division

Stained LM Magnification: 250×

11. During metaphase, the chromosomes move to the equator of what structure (shown here)?
    - **A.** poles
    - **B.** cell plate
    - **C.** centriole
    - **D.** spindle
12. All but which of the following factors limit cell size?
    - **A.** time required for diffusion
    - **B.** elasticity of the plasma membrane
    - **C.** presence of only one nucleus
    - **D.** surface area-to-volume ratio
13. Which of the following is NOT a known cause of cancer?
    - **A.** environmental influences
    - **B.** certain viruses
    - **C.** cigarette smoke
    - **D.** bacterial infections

Constructed Response

14. **Open Ended** How would you expect the number of mitochondria in a cell to be related to the amount of active transport it carries out?
15. **Open Ended** Suppose that all of the enzymes that control the normal cell cycle were identified. Suggest some ways that this information might be used to fight cancer.
16. **Open Ended** Substance A's molecules are small. Substance B's molecules, which react with substance A to produce a blue-black color, are larger in comparison. If a solution of substance A is placed inside a selectively permeable bag, and the bag is placed in a solution of substance B, what will happen?

Thinking Critically

17. **Predict** What do you think will happen when a freshwater paramecium is placed in salt water?

 in.bdol.glencoe.com/chapter_test

RUBRIC

Evaluating Open-Ended Questions
Open-ended assessment questions are graded by using a multilevel rubric that guides you in assessing a student's knowledge of a particular concept. The following rubric is a sample scoring device.

18. **REAL WORLD BIOCHALLENGE** Cystic fibrosis is a genetic disorder that results from the inability of cells to properly transport some materials. Visit in.bdol.glencoe.com to investigate cystic fibrosis. Write an essay that explains what you have learned about cystic fibrosis and present it to your class.

End-of-Course Assessment Practice

The assessed Indiana standard appears next to the question.

All questions aligned and verified by The Princeton Review

Part 1 Multiple Choice

Use the following illustration to answer questions 19–23.

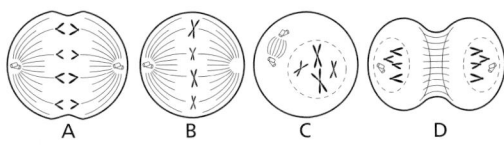

A   B   C   D

19. Which drawing indicates a cell in metaphase
B.1.8 of mitosis?
  - **A.** A
  - **B.** B
  - **C.** C
  - **D.** D

20. During which stage do the chromatids of
B.1.8 chromosomes separate?
  - **A.** A
  - **B.** B
  - **C.** C
  - **D.** D

21. Which drawing indicates a cell whose
B.1.8 nuclear membrane is dissolving?
  - **A.** A
  - **B.** B
  - **C.** C
  - **D.** D

22. Which of the following indicates the correct
B.1.8 order of mitosis in animal cells?
  - **A.** A-B-C-D
  - **B.** B-C-A-D
  - **C.** C-A-D-B
  - **D.** C-B-A-D

23. Which drawing shows a cell in anaphase?
B.1.8
  - **A.** A
  - **B.** B
  - **C.** C
  - **D.** D

24. A biologist notes that some cells are growing
B.1.7 faster than others in a tissue culture. A week later, the fast-growing cells have tripled in number. This observation is a clue that the fast-growing cells _____.
  - **A.** have killed the slow-growing cells
  - **B.** might be unable to control mitosis
  - **C.** were exposed to radiation or chemicals
  - **D.** contain an unknown enzyme

 Nucleosome

25. Which parts of the nucleosome are made of DNA?
  - **A.** 1 and 2
  - **B.** 1 and 3
  - **C.** 2 and 3
  - **D.** 2 and 4

26. Which parts of the nucleosome are made of protein?
  - **A.** 1 and 2
  - **B.** 1 and 3
  - **C.** 2 and 3
  - **D.** 2 and 4

Part 2 Constructed Response/Grid In

Record your answers on your answer document.

27. **Open Ended** The cell cycle can be affected by internal and external factors. Injury to a tissue
B.1.7 can prompt changes in the cell cycle of the cells near the injury site. Formulate a testable hypothesis concerning a specific type of cell's response to injury. State your hypothesis, plan an investigative procedure to test your hypothesis, and list the steps.

28. **Open Ended** Explain why drinking quantities of ocean water is dangerous to humans.

End-of-Course Assessment Practice

- **19.** B   **23.** A
- **20.** A   **24.** B
- **21.** C   **25.** D
- **22.** D   **26.** B
- **27.** Student responses will vary but should contain a testable hypothesis and reasonable steps to test the hypothesis.
- **28.** Ocean water contains high concentrations of salts. In order to excrete the excess salt, the body excretes more water than it takes in and you dehydrate.

FAST FILE

Answer Sheet A practice answer sheet can be found on p. 117 of *Unit 3 FAST FILE Resources.*

RUBRIC

SCORE	CRITERIA
4	A correct solution that is supported by well-developed, accurate explanations.
3	A generally correct solution, but may contain minor flaws in reasoning.

SCORE	CRITERIA
2	A partially correct interpretation and/or solution to the problem.
1	A correct solution with no supporting evidence or explanation.
0	An incorrect solution or no solution is given.

Indiana Academic Standards

Pages 218–219: B.1.2, B.1.3, B.1.7, B.1.8

219

Chapter 9 Organizer

Section Objectives	National Science Standards	State/Local Standards	Advanced Lab and Demo Planning
Section 9.1 1 session, 1/2 block 1. **Explain** why organisms need a supply of energy. 2. **Describe** how energy is stored and released by ATP.	UCP.1–3; A.1, A.2; B.3, B.6; C.5; G.1, G.3	**Indiana Standards** B.1.3, B.1.4, B.1.6, B.1.7, B.1.9, B.1.16, B.1.44	**Student Lab:** Problem-Solving Lab 9.1, p. 222 **Teacher Demonstration:** Quick Demo, p. 223: potato, boiling water or microwave oven
Section 9.2 2 sessions, 1 block 3. **Relate** the structure of chloroplasts to the events in photosynthesis. 4. **Describe** light-dependent reactions. 5. **Explain** the reactions and products of the light-independent Calvin cycle.	UCP.1–3, UPC.5; A.1, A.2; B.3, B.6; C.5; G.1, G.3	**Indiana Standards** B.1.3, B.1.4, B.1.6, B.1.7, B.1.9	**Student Labs:** MiniLab 9.1, p. 226: plant solution, 5 cm × 14 cm strip of filter paper, rubbing alcohol, 100-mL beaker MiniLab 9.2, p. 228 Internet BioLab, p. 238: See materials below. **Teacher Demonstration:** Quick Demo, p. 227: prism
Section 9.3 3 sessions, 1/2 block 6. **Compare and contrast** cellular respiration and fermentation. 7. **Explain** how cells obtain energy from cellular respiration.	UCP.1–3, UCP.5; A.1, A.2; B.3, B.6; C.5; G.1	**Indiana Standards** B.1.3, B.1.4, B.1.7, B.1.9, B.1.43	**Student Labs:** Additional Lab, p. 234: black paper, labels, iodine solution, *Coleus* plants, paper clip, hot plate, beaker, 95% alcohol, small bowl Problem-Solving Lab 9.2, p. 235 MiniLab 9.3, p. 236: test tube, water, plastic pipette, metal washers, yeast, apple juice **Teacher Demonstration:** Quick Demo, p. 232: tablespoon of sugar, cup of warm water, deep jar or flask, baker's yeast
End of Chapter Assessment **Student Edition** **Study Guide,** p. 241 **Content Assessment,** pp. 242–243		**Indiana Standards** B.1.3, B.1.4, B.1.7, B.1.9, B.1.43	**Student Lab:** Internet BioLab, p. 238: 1000-mL beaker, 3 *Elodea* plants, string, washers, colored cellophane (assorted colors), lamp with reflector and 150-watt bulb, 0.25% sodium hydrogen carbonate (baking soda) solution, watch with second hand

Key to Teaching Strategies

L1 Level 1 activities should be appropriate for students with learning difficulties.

L2 Level 2 activities should be within the ability range of all students.

L3 Level 3 activities are designed for above-average students.

ELL ELL activities should be within the ability range of English Language Learners.

COOP LEARN Cooperative Learning activities are designed for small group work.

Glencoe Exclusive!

Teacher Works™
All-In-One Planner and Resource Center

Reproducible Masters and Transparencies	Technology

Reproducible Masters and Transparencies

Unit 3 FAST FILE Resources
MiniLab Worksheet, p. 121
Real World BioApplications, pp. 125–126
Reinforcement and Study Guide in English, p. 127
Reinforcement and Study Guide in Spanish, p. 131
Transparency Worksheets, pp. 137, 141–142
⚑ **Section Focus Transparency 21**
⚑ **Basic Concepts Transparency 11**

Technology

💿 Interactive Chalkboard CD-ROM: Section 9.1 Presentation ⚑
💿 TeacherWorks™ CD-ROM ⚑
🎵 Guided Reading Audio Summaries MP3

Unit 3 FAST FILE Resources
MiniLab Worksheet, p. 122
BioLab Worksheet, pp. 123–124
Reinforcement and Study Guide in English,
   pp. 128–129
Reinforcement and Study Guide in Spanish,
   pp. 132–133
Concept Mapping, p. 135
Critical Thinking/Problem Solving, p. 136
Transparency Worksheets, pp. 138, 143–144
⚑ **Section Focus Transparency 22**
⚑ **Basic Concepts Transparency 12**

💿 Interactive Chalkboard CD-ROM: Section 9.2 Presentation ⚑
💿 TeacherWorks™ CD-ROM ⚑
🎵 Guided Reading Audio Summaries MP3

Unit 3 FAST FILE Resources
Reinforcement and Study Guide in English, p. 130
Reinforcement and Study Guide in Spanish, p. 134
Transparency Worksheets, pp. 139, 145–146,
   147–152
Laboratory Manual, pp. 49–52
Probeware Labs, pp. 13–16
⚑ **Section Focus Transparency 23**
⚑ **Basic Concepts Transparency 13**
⚑ **Reteaching Skills Transparencies 14, 15**

💿 Interactive Chalkboard CD-ROM: Section 9.3 Presentation ⚑
💿 TeacherWorks™ CD-ROM ⚑
🎵 Guided Reading Audio Summaries MP3

Unit 3 FAST FILE Resources
Chapter Assessment, pp. 151–156
Student Recording Sheet, p. 157

The Princeton Review **Reviewing Biology,** pp. 17–18

💿 **Interactive Chalkboard:** ⚑
   Chapter 9 Assessment
📀 **MindJogger Videoquizzes DVD/VHS**
💿 **ExamView® Pro Test Bank CD-ROM**
💿 TeacherWorks™ CD-ROM ⚑
💿 **Succeeding on National Standards CD-ROM**

🖥 in.bdol.glencoe.com
/self_check_quiz
/vocabulary_puzzlemaker
/chapter_test
/standardized_test

⚑ Indicates materials created specifically for Indiana.

Energy in a Cell

Short on Time?

BIODIGEST The BioDigest at the end of this unit can be used as a(n):

- preview to introduce important unit concepts.
- overview if time does not permit teaching the entire chapter.
- review of key unit concepts.

Understanding the Photo

This gray squirrel cannot make its own food. It must consume other organisms, in this case a pinecone, to get the energy it needs to perform life functions. In this chapter, students will learn how cells use certain molecules to supply energy for life processes. As students read Section 9.1, have them keep a log of activities that they do each day that require energy.

What You'll Learn

- You will recognize why organisms need a constant supply of energy and where that energy comes from.
- You will identify how cells store and release energy as ATP.
- You will describe the pathways by which cells obtain energy.
- You will compare ATP production in mitochondria and in chloroplasts.

Why It's Important

Every cell in your body needs energy in order to function. The energy your cells store is the fuel for basic body functions such as walking and breathing.

Understanding ▶ the Photo

This squirrel is eating seeds produced by the conifer. The conifer traps light energy and stores it in the bonds of certain molecules for later use. How do the squirrel's cells, which cannot trap light energy, use the molecules in the seeds to supply energy for the squirrel?

Biology Online

Visit **in.bdol.glencoe.com** to
- study the entire chapter online
- access Web Links for more information and activities on cell energy
- review content with the Interactive Tutor and self-check quizzes

Indiana Academic Standards

Pages 220–221: B.1.4, B.1.16, B.1.44

Two-Minute Chapter Launcher

Discussion Not all cellular activities require all of the energy available in food molecules. Some activities may require less energy to perform than others. To demonstrate this concept, ask students to determine how they would purchase a soda from a vending machine if all they had was a **$100 bill.** Students should indicate that they would have to get change for the $100 bill to purchase a soda.

Explain to students that sometimes a large amount of energy must be broken down into smaller amounts, just as a $100 bill must be broken down into smaller bills to purchase a soda from a vending machine.

As students read the chapter, have them make a list of cellular activities that they think require less energy than others. **L2**

Section 9.1

The Need for Energy

Indiana Standards Standard B.1.9 Recognize and describe that both living and nonliving things are composed of compounds, ... joined by energy-containing bonds, such as those in ATP.

SECTION PREVIEW

Objectives

Explain why organisms need a supply of energy.

Describe how energy is stored and released by ATP.

Review Vocabulary

active transport: movement of materials through a membrane against a concentration gradient; requires energy from the cell (p. 199)

New Vocabulary

ATP (adenosine triphosphate)
ADP (adenosine diphosphate)

Why ATP?

Using an Analogy A spring stores energy when it is compressed. When the compressed spring is released, energy also is released, energy that sends this smiley-faced toy flying into the air. Like this coiled spring, chemical bonds store energy that can be released when the bond is broken. Just as some springs are tighter than others, some chemical bonds store more energy than others.

Summarize *Scan this section and make a list of general ways in which cells use energy.*

Stored energy

Figure 9.1
Because this panda cannot trap the sun's energy for use in its body, it eats bamboo. Molecules in bamboo leaves contain energy in their chemical bonds. Some of those molecules supply energy for the panda.

Cell Energy

Energy is essential to life. All living organisms must be able to obtain energy from the environment in which they live. Plants and other green organisms are able to trap the light energy in sunlight and store it in the bonds of certain molecules for later use. Other organisms, such as the panda shown in *Figure 9.1,* cannot use sunlight directly. Instead, they eat green plants. In that way, they obtain the energy stored in plants.

Work and the need for energy

You've learned about several cell processes that require energy. Active transport, cell division, movement of flagella or cilia, and the production, transport, and storage of proteins are some examples. You can probably come up with other examples of biological work, such as muscles contracting during exercise, your

9.1   THE NEED FOR ENERGY   **221**

1 Focus

Bellringer
Section Focus Transparency 21

PowerPoint® Presentations
This CD-ROM is an editable Microsoft® PowerPoint® presentation that includes:
• Section presentations
• Section checks
• Image bank
• Hot links to Biology Online
• All transparencies

Using an Analogy

Summarize Bring in a variety of materials that store energy, such as a battery or something with a spring that can be "cocked." Some of these things might be borrowed from a physics teacher. Discuss with students the concept of stored energy. Review how cells and organisms store energy and what types of activities they can use this energy for.

2 Teach

Problem-Solving Lab 9.1

Purpose

Students will determine that fat, rather than carbohydrates, is the preferred compound for energy storage in humans.

Background

Fats yield more ATPs than carbohydrates because they have more C–H bonds. A six-carbon fat fragment has a molecular weight of about 100, while the same carbohydrate size has a molecular weight of 180. Fats are hydrophobic while carbohydrates are hydrophilic.

Process Skills

acquire information, compare and contrast, think critically, draw a conclusion

Teaching Strategies

Emphasize that this lab discusses the storage of excess energy and reiterate that carbohydrates are also important compounds.

Thinking Critically

1. Because the metabolism of water yields no ATP, water is "excess baggage." Fat, with no water, carries less "excess baggage," helping to make it more efficient.
2. Because we store excess energy as fat, we do not carry the weight of water that is associated with carbohydrates.

Assessment

Performance Have students research where fat is stored within the human body, including any differences between male and female. Use the Performance Task Assessment List for Asking Questions in **PASC**, p. 91. **L3**

Problem-Solving Lab 9.1

Recognize Cause and Effect

Why is fat the choice?
Humans store their excess energy as fat rather than as carbohydrates. Why is this? From an evolutionary and efficiency point of view, fats are better for storage than carbohydrates. Find out why.

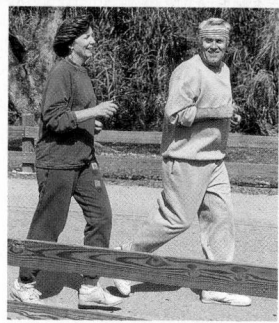

Solve the Problem

The following facts compare certain characteristics of fats and carbohydrates:

A. When broken down by the body, each six-carbon molecule of fat yields 51 ATP molecules. Each six-carbon carbohydrate molecule yields 36 ATP molecules.

B. Carbohydrates bind and store water. The metabolism of water yields no ATP. Fat has no water bound to it.

C. An adult who weighs 70 kg can survive on the energy derived from stored fat for 30 days without eating. The same person would have to weigh nearly 140 kg to survive 30 days on stored carbohydrates.

Thinking Critically

1. **Analyze** From an ATP production viewpoint, use fact B to make a statement regarding the efficiency of fats vs. carbohydrates.

2. **Define Operationally** Explain why the average weight for humans is close to 70 kg and not 140 kg.

Word Origin

mono-, di-, tri- from the Greek words *mono* and *di*, and the Latin word *tri*, meaning "one," "two," and "three," respectively; Adenosine triphosphate contains three phosphate groups.

---

heart pumping and your brain controlling your entire body. This work cannot be done without energy.

When you finish strenuous physical exercise, such as running cross country, your body needs a quick source of energy, so you may eat a granola bar. On a cellular level, there is a molecule in your cells that is a quick source of energy for any organelle in the cell that needs it.

This energy is stored in the chemical bonds of the molecule and can be used quickly and easily by the cell.

The name of this energy molecule is **adenosine triphosphate** (uh DEH nuh seen • tri FAHS fayt), or **ATP** for short. ATP is composed of an adenosine molecule with three phosphate groups attached. Recall that phosphate groups are charged particles, and remember that particles with the same charge do not like being too close to each other.

Forming and Breaking Down ATP

The charged phosphate groups act like the positive poles of two magnets. If like poles of a magnet are placed next to each other, it is difficult to force the magnets together. Likewise, bonding three phosphate groups to form adenosine triphosphate requires considerable energy. When only one phosphate group bonds, a small amount of energy is required and the chemical bond does not store much energy. This molecule is called adenosine monophosphate (AMP). When a second phosphate group is added, more energy is required to force the two groups together. This molecule is called **adenosine diphosphate**, or **ADP**. An even greater amount of energy is required to force a third charged phosphate group close enough to the other two to form a bond. When this bond is broken, energy is released.

The energy of ATP becomes available to a cell when the molecule is broken down. In other words, when the chemical bond between the second and third phosphate groups in ATP is broken, energy is released and the resulting molecule is ADP. At this

---

USING MODELS

Modeling Chemical Compounds Provide students with toothpicks and gumdrops of different sizes and colors. Have them use the materials to make models of adenosine triphosphate (ATP) and adenosine diphosphate (ADP). Have students include in their portfolios a description of how the molecules differ from each other and how these differences relate to energy. **L2**

point, ADP can form ATP again by bonding with another phosphate group. This process creates a renewable cycle of ATP formation and breakdown. *Figure 9.2A* illustrates the chemical reactions that are involved in the cycle.

The formation/breakdown recycling activity is important because it relieves the cell of having to store all of the ATP it needs. As long as phosphate groups are available, the cell can make more ATP. Another benefit of the formation/breakdown cycle is that ADP also can be used as an energy source. Although most cell functions require the amount of energy in ATP, some cell functions do not require as much energy and can use the energy stored in ADP. Read the *Problem-Solving Lab* on the opposite page and think about how the human body stores energy.

How cells tap into the energy stored in ATP

When ATP is broken down and the energy is released, as shown in *Figure 9.2B*, the energy must be captured and used efficiently by cells. Otherwise, it is wasted. ATP is a small molecule. Many proteins have a specific site where ATP can bind. Then, when the phosphate bond is broken and the energy released, the cell can use the energy for activities such as making a protein or transporting molecules through the plasma membrane. This cellular process is similar to the way energy in batteries is used by a radio. Batteries sitting on a table are of little use if the energy stored within the batteries cannot be accessed. When the batteries are snapped into the holder in the radio, the radio then has access to the stored energy and can use it. When the energy in the

Quick Demo

Model Energy Transfer To demonstrate that energy can be transferred, heat a potato in boiling water or in a microwave oven in the school cafeteria. When it is cool enough to handle safely, have students pass the heated potato to one another. Ask students who first handle the potato to describe its temperature as hot, warm, cool, or cold. Have a student near the end make the same observation. Ask students what happened to the energy as the potato cooled.

Biology Journal
Surviving Without Bread or Water Have students research how long a person can survive without food and without water. Have students report their findings and evaluate why people perish without water before they perish without food. **L2**

Figure 9.2
The formation and breakdown of ATP is cyclic.

Adenosine

P   P   P

Adenosine triphosphate (ATP)

P

P

Adenosine

P   P

Adenosine diphosphate (ADP)

ATP

Protein

P + Energy

ADP

ADP

A The addition and release of a phosphate group on adenosine diphosphate creates a cycle of ATP formation and breakdown.

B To access the energy stored in ATP, proteins bind ATP and uncouple the phosphate group. The ADP that is formed is released, and the protein binding site can once again bind ATP.

9.1   THE NEED FOR ENERGY   **223**

INCLUSION STRATEGIES

Learning Disabled: *Intrapersonal* Give students a photograph of an organism from a magazine or similar source and ask them to list the activities of the organism that require energy from ATP. **L1**

 Indiana Academic Standards

Pages 222–223: B.1.4, B.1.6, B.1.9, B.1.16

3 Assess

Check for Understanding
Ask students why energy must be stored in small amounts and relate the answer to paying for a small purchase with a $1 bill rather than with a $50 bill.

Reteach
Kinesthetic Have students join like poles of three small magnets to simulate the storage of energy in ATP. Explain how energy is released when the magnets are pulled apart. **L1** **ELL**

Resources
For more practice, use *Reading Essentials for Biology*, Section 9.1.

Extension
Linguistic Have interested students write a report about the energy needs of a bioluminescent organism. **L2**

MODIFIED Assessment

Knowledge Ask students to make a list of organisms they are familiar with and how each uses energy. **L1**

Reading Check Answers may include synthesis of molecules, maintain homeostasis, movement of ions and molecules, nerve transmission, producing light in bioluminescence, and cellular movement.

Caption Question Answer
Figure 9.3 cilia or flagella

Figure 9.3
ATP fuels the cellular activity that drives the organism. **Define Operationally** *What organelles do these cells or organisms use for movement?*

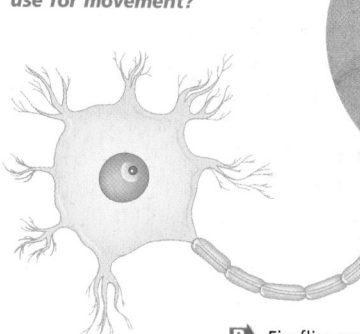

Stained TEM Magnification: 18 000×

C Some organisms (left) use energy from ATP to move.

A Nerve cells transmit impulses by using ATP to power the active transport of certain ions.

B Fireflies and many marine organisms, such as the jellyfish shown here, produce light by a process called bioluminescence. The light results from a chemical reaction that is powered by the breakdown of ATP.

batteries has been used, the batteries can be taken out, recharged, and replaced in the holder. In a similar fashion in a cell, when ATP has been broken down to ADP, the ADP is released from the binding site in the protein and the binding site may then be filled by another ATP molecule.

Uses of Cell Energy

You can probably think of hundreds of physical activities that require energy, but energy is equally important at the cellular level.

Making new molecules is one way that cells use energy. Some of these molecules are enzymes. Other molecules build membranes and cell organelles. Cells use energy to maintain homeostasis. Kidneys use energy to move molecules and ions in order to eliminate waste substances while keeping needed substances in the bloodstream. *Figure 9.3* shows several ways that cells use energy.

Reading Check **List** three cellular activities that require energy.

Section Assessment

Understanding Main Ideas
1. Identify cellular processes that need energy from ATP.
2. How does ATP store energy?
3. How can ADP be "recycled" to form ATP again?
4. How do proteins in your cells access the energy stored in ATP?
5. List three biological activities that require energy.

Thinking Critically
6. Phosphate groups in ATP repel each other because they have negative charges. What charge might be present in the ATP binding site of a protein to attract ATP?

SKILL REVIEW
7. **Get the Big Picture** How does an animal access the energy in sunlight? For more help, refer to *Get the Big Picture* in the **Skill Handbook**.

224 ENERGY IN A CELL

 in.bdol.glencoe.com/self_check_quiz

Section Assessment

1. active transport, movement, and protein synthesis are examples
2. ATP stores energy in its phosphate–phosphate bonds.
3. A phosphate group can be added to ADP, reforming ATP.
4. They may have a pocket that ATP will fit into so that when ATP releases energy, the protein can use it.
5. muscles contracting, heart pumping, brain functions
6. Opposite charges attract, so an ATP binding site might have a positive charge.
7. Animals access the energy in sunlight by eating plant materials containing sugars and starch synthesized by plants using the sun's energy.

<table>
<tr><td>

Section 9.2

SECTION PREVIEW

Objectives
Relate the structure of chloroplasts to the events in photosynthesis.

Describe light-dependent reactions.

Explain the reactions and products of the light-independent Calvin cycle.

Review Vocabulary
chloroplast: cell organelle that captures light energy and produces food to store for later use (p. 184)

New Vocabulary
photosynthesis
light-dependent reactions
light-independent reactions
pigment
chlorophyll
electron transport chain
$NADP^+$
photolysis
Calvin cycle

</td><td>

Photosynthesis: Trapping the Sun's Energy

Indiana Standards Standard B.1.3 Know and describe that within the cell are specialized parts for the transport of materials, energy capture and release, protein building, waste disposal, information feedback, and movement…

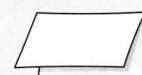
Study Organizer

Photosynthesis Make the following Foldable to help you illustrate what happens during each phase of photosynthesis.

STEP 1 **Fold** a vertical sheet of paper in half from top to bottom.

STEP 2 **Fold** in half from side to side with the fold at the top.

STEP 3 **Unfold** the paper once. **Cut** only the fold of the top flap to make two tabs.

STEP 4 **Turn** the paper vertically and **label** on the front tabs as shown.

| 1st Phase Light-Dependent |
| 2nd Phase Light-Independent |

Compare and Contrast As you read Section 9.2, compare and contrast the two phases of photosynthesis under the appropriate tab.

</td></tr>
</table>

Word Origin

photosynthesis from the Greek words *photo,* meaning "light," and *syntithenai,* meaning "to put together"; Photosynthesis puts together sugar molecules using water, carbon dioxide, and energy from light.

Trapping Energy from Sunlight

To use the energy in sunlight, the cells of green organisms must trap light energy and store it in a manner that is readily usable by cell organelles—in the chemical bonds of ATP. However, light energy is not available 24 hours a day, so the cell must also store some of the energy for use during the dark hours. The process that uses the sun's energy to make simple sugars is called **photosynthesis.** These simple sugars are then converted into complex carbohydrates, such as starches, which store energy.

Photosynthesis happens in two phases. The **light-dependent reactions** convert light energy into chemical energy. The molecules of ATP produced in the light-dependent reactions are then used to fuel the **light-independent reactions** that produce simple sugars. The general equation for photosynthesis is written as follows:

$$6CO_2 + 6H_2O \rightarrow C_6H_{12}O_6 + 6O_2$$

The *BioLab* at the end of this chapter can be performed to study what factors influence the rate of photosynthesis.

9.2 PHOTOSYNTHESIS: TRAPPING THE SUN'S ENERGY **225**

2 Teach

MiniLab 9.1

Purpose

Students will examine the different types of pigments found in common plants by separating the pigments from the leaves.

Process Skills

interpret data, analyze data, infer, hypothesize, draw conclusions

Teaching Strategies

If pigment colors are not showing up as well as expected, use 1 butanol as the solvent if some is available. It shows more dramatic separation of pigments.

Expected Results

As the solvent (rubbing alcohol) moves up the filter paper, slight differences in color will begin to appear, starting with green and progressing to yellow and perhaps orange.

Analysis

1. Students may indicate that the solvent moved up the filter paper about 5 cm and then stopped. As the solvent progressed, varying shades of green and yellow appeared.
2. Different components of the plant solution have varying attraction for the filter paper. Therefore the colors will be deposited at different distances up the filter paper.

Assessment

Performance Have students repeat the experiment using a black permanent marker. Have them write a summary of both experiments in which they compare and contrast the results. Use the Performance Task Assessment List for Analyzing the Data in **PASC**, p. 99. L2

MiniLab 9.1

Experiment

Separating Pigments
Chromatography is an important diagnostic tool. In this experiment, you will use paper chromatography to separate different pigments from plant leaves.

Procedure

1. Obtain a pre-made plant solution from your teacher.
2. Place a few drops 2 cm high on a 5-cm × 14-cm strip of filter paper. Let it dry. Make sure a small colored spot is visible.
3. Pour rubbing alcohol in a 100-mL beaker to a depth of 1 cm.
4. Place the filter paper into the beaker. The filter paper should touch the alcohol, but the dot should not. Hold it in place 15 minutes and observe what happens.

Analysis

1. **Explain** What did you observe as the solvent moved up the filter paper?
2. **Infer** Why did you see different colors at different locations on the filter paper?

Figure 9.4
The red, yellow, and purple pigments are visible in the autumn.
Recognize Cause and Effect *Why can't you see these colors during the summer?*

The chloroplast and pigments

Recall that the chloroplast is the cell organelle where photosynthesis occurs. It is in the membranes of the thylakoid discs in chloroplasts that the light-dependent reactions take place.

To trap the energy in the sun's light, the thylakoid membranes contain **pigments,** molecules that absorb specific wavelengths of sunlight. Pigments are arranged within the thylakoid membranes in clusters known as photosystems. Although a photosystem contains several kinds of pigments, the most common is **chlorophyll.** Chlorophyll absorbs most wavelengths of light except green. Because chlorophyll cannot absorb this wavelength, it is reflected, giving leaves a green appearance. In the fall, trees stop producing chlorophyll in their leaves. Other pigments become visible, giving leaves like those in *Figure 9.4* a wide variety of colors. The *MiniLab* on this page will allow you to separate the pigments in a leaf. Read the *Connection to Chemistry* at the end of this chapter to find out more about biological pigments.

Light-Dependent Reactions

The first phase of photosynthesis requires sunlight. As sunlight strikes the chlorophyll molecules in a photosystem of the thylakoid membrane, the energy in the light is transferred to electrons. These highly energized, or excited, electrons are passed from chlorophyll to an **electron transport chain,** a series of proteins embedded in the thylakoid membrane. *Figure 9.5* summarizes this process.

Each protein in the chain passes energized electrons along to the next protein, similar to a bucket brigade in which a line of people pass a bucket of

---

INCLUSION STRATEGIES

Physically Challenged For students who have difficulty traveling outdoors, bring in samples of different-colored leaves for them to observe. Have them use the leaves in a class presentation on how chlorophyll affects the color of leaves. L2

water from person to person to fight a fire. At each step along the transport chain, the electrons lose energy, just as some of the water might be spilled from buckets in the fire-fighting chain. This "lost" energy can be used to form ATP from ADP, or to pump hydrogen ions into the center of the thylakoid disc.

After the electrons have traveled down the electron transport chain, they are re-energized in a second photosystem and passed down a second electron transport chain. At the bottom of this chain, the electrons are still very energized. So that this energy is not wasted, the electrons are transferred to the stroma of the chloroplast. To do this, an electron carrier molecule called **NADP⁺** (nicotinamide adenine dinucleotide phosphate) is used. $NADP^+$ can combine with two excited electrons and a hydrogen ion (H^+) to become NADPH. NADPH does not use the energy present in the energized electrons; it simply stores the energy until it can transfer it to the stroma. There, NADPH will play an important role in the light-independent reactions.

✓ **Reading Check** **Explain** how energy from electrons is released.

Restoring electrons

Recall that at the beginning of photosynthesis, electrons are lost from chlorophyll molecules when light is absorbed. If these electrons are not replaced, the chlorophyll will be unable to absorb additional light and the light-dependent reactions will stop, as will the production of ATP. To replace the lost electrons, molecules of water are split in the first photosystem. This reaction is called **photolysis** (fo TAH luh sis). For every water molecule that is

Figure 9.5
Chlorophyll molecules absorb light energy and energize electrons for producing ATP and NADPH.

Light-Dependent Reactions

Sun

Light energy transfers to chlorophyll.

Chlorophyll passes energy down through the electron transport chain.

Energized electrons provide energy that

splits H₂O

bonds (P) to ADP

forming ATP

H⁺

NADP⁺

oxygen released

NADPH

for use in the light-independent reactions.

PROJECT

Growing Plants in Colored Light Have students place a plant in each of several closed boxes containing a colored light-bulb. Using caution, tape the opening through which the electric cord passes so no outside light can enter. Provide the plants in each box with equal amounts of water. Have students write a summary about how the plants in each box grew compared with a control plant. **L2**

MiniLab 9.2

Purpose

Students will build a model to trace the fate of molecules involved in photosynthesis.

Process Skills

analyze information, define operationally, formulate models, think critically, predict

Teaching Strategies

- Models may be constructed from colored beads, building toys, or colored clay. Make sure that students provide a key (probably by color) to show the molecules being referenced. **L1** **ELL**
- If materials for modeling are not available, students can trace molecules from the left to right side of the equation by using lines and arrows.

Expected Results

Student models will show that all carbon from carbon dioxide ends up in CH_2O; all oxygen from carbon dioxide ends up in CH_2O and water; all hydrogen from water (on the left side) ends up in CH_2O and water.

Analysis

1. If an isotope is radioactive, it can be traced by identifying the radioactive product of the reaction.
2. a. incorporated into CH_2O or water
   b. incorporated into CH_2O
   c. incorporated into CH_2O and water

Assessment

Knowledge Have students model the equation for the van Niel experiment starting with an isotope of hydrogen in the water molecule to the left of the arrow. Use the Performance Task Assessment List for Model in **PASC,** p. 123. **L2**

MiniLab 9.2

Formulate Models

Use Isotopes to Understand Photosynthesis C. B. van Niel demonstrated that photosynthesis is a light-dependent reaction in which the O_2 comes from water. Other scientists confirmed his findings by using radioactive isotopes of oxygen as tracers. Radioactive tracers are used to follow a particular molecule through a chemical reaction.

van Niel

Procedure 👓

1. Study the following general equation that resulted from the van Niel experiment:

$$CO_2 + 2H_2O^* \rightarrow CH_2O + H_2O + O_2^*$$

2. Radioactive water, water tagged with an isotope of oxygen as a tracer (shown by the *), was used. Note where the tagged oxygen ends up on the right side of the equation.
3. Assume that the experiment was repeated, but this time a radioactive tag was put on the oxygen in CO_2.
4. Using materials provided by your teacher, model what you predict the appearance of the results would be. Your model must include a "tag" to indicate the oxygen isotope on the left side of the arrow as well as where it ends up on the right side of the arrow.
5. You also must use labels or different colors in your model to indicate what happens to the carbon and hydrogen.

Analysis

1. **Explain** How can an isotope be used as a tag?
2. **Use Models** Using your model, predict what happens to:
   a. all oxygen molecules that originated from carbon dioxide.
   b. all carbon molecules that originated from carbon dioxide.
   c. all hydrogen molecules that originated from water.

228 ENERGY IN A CELL

🎯 CHALLENGE ACTIVITY

Oxygen Journey After the class has performed MiniLab 9.2, have the students write a story describing the pathway taken by the radioactively labeled oxygen in the van Niel experiment. Encourage creativity while at the same time conveying biological accuracy. **L2**

---

split, one half molecule of oxygen, two electrons, and two hydrogen ions are formed, as shown in *Figure 9.6.* The oxygen produced by photolysis is released into the air and supplies the oxygen we breathe. The electrons are returned to chlorophyll. The hydrogen ions are pumped into the thylakoid, where they accumulate in high concentration. Because this difference in concentration forms a concentration gradient across the membrane, H^+ ions diffuse out of the thylakoid and provide energy for the production of ATP. This coupling of the movement of H^+ ions to ATP production is called chemiosmosis (keh mee oz MOH sis). The *MiniLab* on this page shows how the steps of photosynthesis were traced.

Light-Independent Reactions

The second phase of photosynthesis does not require light. It is called the **Calvin cycle,** which is a series of reactions that use carbon dioxide to form sugars. The Calvin cycle takes place in the stroma of the chloroplast, as shown in *Figure 9.*7.

Figure 9.6
In photolysis, a molecule of water is split to replace electrons lost from chlorophyll, H^+ for chemiosmosis, and oxygen. **Infer** *How many molecules of water must be split to make a molecule of oxygen gas?*

Sun

Chlorophyll

$H_2O \longrightarrow 2H^+ + \frac{1}{2}O_2 + 2e^-$

$\frac{1}{2}O_2 + 2H^+$

$2e^-$

H_2O

Caption Question Answer
Figure 9.6 two

The Calvin Cycle

Figure 9.7
The Calvin cycle takes the carbon in CO_2, adds it to one molecule of RuBP, and forms sugars through a series of reactions in the stroma of chloroplasts. The NADPH and ATP produced during the earlier light-dependent reactions are important molecules for this series of reactions. **Critical Thinking** *Why is the Calvin cycle in plants directly and indirectly important to animals?*

Color-enhanced TEM
Magnification: 6300×

The stroma in chloroplasts hosts the Calvin cycle.

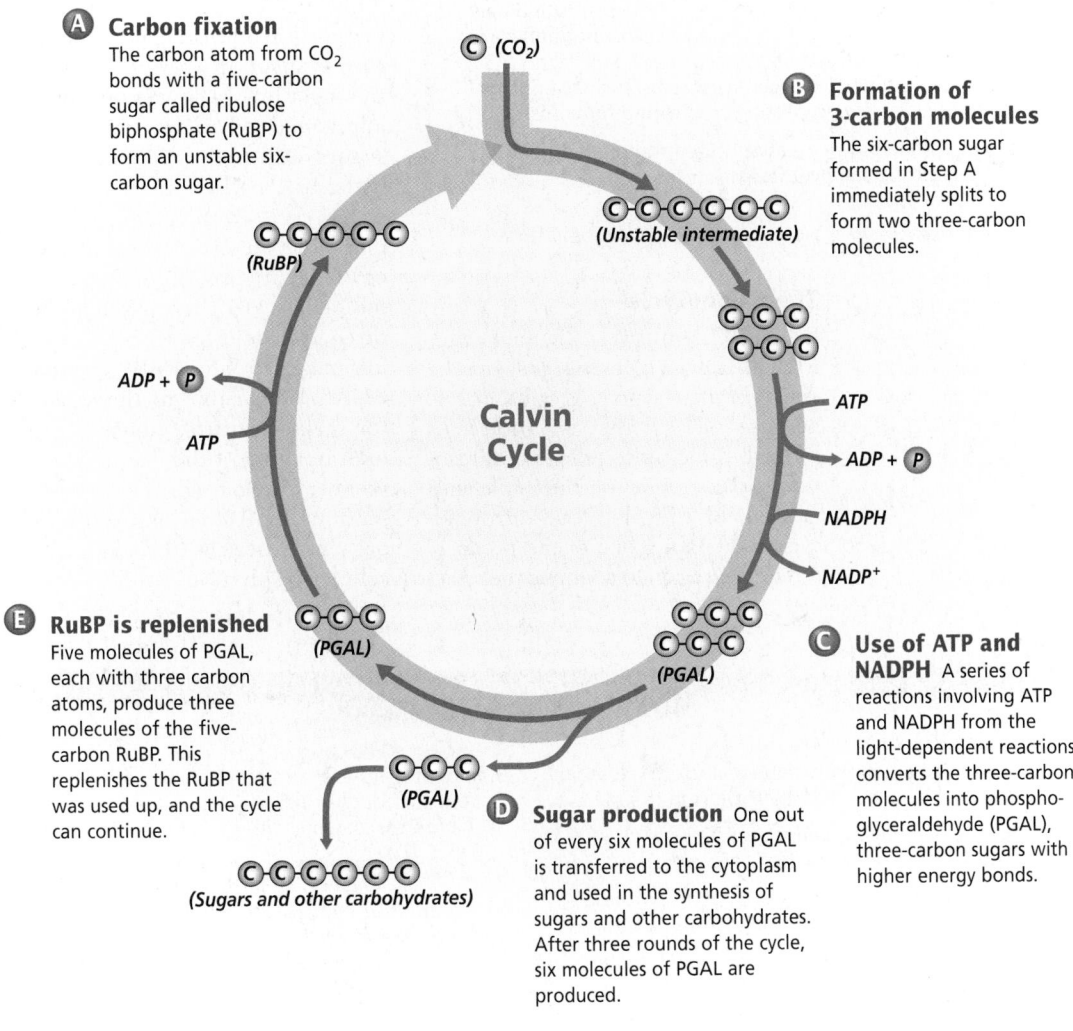

A Carbon fixation
The carbon atom from CO_2 bonds with a five-carbon sugar called ribulose biphosphate (RuBP) to form an unstable six-carbon sugar.

B Formation of 3-carbon molecules
The six-carbon sugar formed in Step A immediately splits to form two three-carbon molecules.

C Use of ATP and NADPH A series of reactions involving ATP and NADPH from the light-dependent reactions converts the three-carbon molecules into phosphoglyceraldehyde (PGAL), three-carbon sugars with higher energy bonds.

D Sugar production One out of every six molecules of PGAL is transferred to the cytoplasm and used in the synthesis of sugars and other carbohydrates. After three rounds of the cycle, six molecules of PGAL are produced.

E RuBP is replenished
Five molecules of PGAL, each with three carbon atoms, produce three molecules of the five-carbon RuBP. This replenishes the RuBP that was used up, and the cycle can continue.

9.2 PHOTOSYNTHESIS: TRAPPING THE SUN'S ENERGY **229**

Purpose
Students will learn the steps of the Calvin cycle and how CO_2 is used to make glucose.

Background
Energy from the light reactions is used to make sugar molecules that will serve as a long-term storage for energy.

Teaching Strategies
Have students identify the main steps of the Calvin cycle.

Visual Learning
Have students make a chart of everything required for one round of the Calvin cycle, including the number of molecules. **L2**

Critical Thinking
The energy in the bonds of sugars synthesized by plants is the source of energy for animals. Indirectly, plants also provide shelter and a home to many animals.

CHALLENGE ACTIVITY

Changing Variables Students who need an additional challenge can repeat the BioLab at the end of the chapter using different variables, such as using one color of light, and changing the distance of the lamp from the plants. Moving the lamp farther from the plants will decrease the light intensity. It will take longer for bubbles to appear. Other results will depend on the color of light selected. **L3**

 Indiana Academic Standards

Pages 228–229: B.1.3, B.1.4, B.1.7, B.1.9

229

3 Assess

BIOTECHNOLOGY CAREERS

Career Path
Courses in high school: chemistry, mathematics, biology, other science
College: bachelor's and master's degree in biochemistry, chemistry; doctorate required for advanced research or management
Career Issue
Debate whether biochemists should clone animals.
For More Information
Write to the
American Society for Biochemistry and Molecular Biology 9650 Rockville Pike Bethesda, MD 20814.

BIOTECHNOLOGY CAREERS

Biochemist

If you are curious about what makes plants and animals grow and develop, consider a career as a biochemist. The basic research of biochemists seeks to understand how processes in an organism work to ensure the organism's survival.

Skills for the Job

A bachelor's degree in chemistry or biochemistry will qualify you to be a lab assistant. For a more involved position, you will need a master's degree; advanced research requires a Ph.D. Some biochemists work with genes to create new plants and new chemicals from plants. Others research the causes and cures of diseases or the effects of poor nutrition. Still others investigate solutions for urgent problems, such as finding better ways of growing, storing, and caring for crops.

 To find out more about careers in related fields, visit in.bdol.glencoe.com/careers

The Calvin cycle

The Calvin cycle, named after Melvin Calvin, who worked out the details of the reactions, is called a cycle because one of the last molecules formed in the series of chemical reactions is also one of the molecules needed for the first reaction of the cycle. Therefore, one of the products can be used again to continue the cycle.

You have learned that in the electron transport chain, an energized electron is passed from protein to protein, and the energy is released slowly. You can imagine that making a complex carbohydrate from a molecule of CO_2 would be a large task for a cell, so the light-independent reactions in the stroma of the chloroplast break down the complicated process into small steps.

At the beginning of the Calvin cycle, one molecule of carbon dioxide is added to one molecule of RuBP to form a six-carbon sugar. This step is called carbon fixation because carbon is "fixed" into a six-carbon sugar. In a series of reactions, the sugar breaks down and is eventually converted to two three-carbon sugars called phosphoglyceraldehyde, or PGAL. After three rounds of the cycle, with each round fixing one molecule of CO_2, six molecules of PGAL are produced. Five of these molecules are rearranged to form three molecules of RuBP, the starting material. The sixth molecule of PGAL is available to the organism for making sugars, complex carbohydrates, and other organic compounds. As you will see in the next section, PGAL is important to all organisms because it plays a role in cellular respiration.

Section Assessment

Understanding Main Ideas
1. Why do you see green when you look at a leaf on a tree? Why do you see other colors in the fall?

2. How do the light-dependent reactions of photosynthesis relate to the Calvin cycle?

3. What is the function of water in photosynthesis? Explain the reaction that achieves this function.

4. How does the electron transport chain transfer light energy in photosynthesis?

Thinking Critically
5. In photosynthesis, is chlorophyll considered a reactant, a product, or neither? How does the role of chlorophyll compare with the roles of CO_2 and H_2O?

SKILL REVIEW

6. **Get the Big Picture** Identify the parts of the chloroplast in which the various steps of photosynthesis take place. For more help, refer to *Get the Big Picture* in the **Skill Handbook.**

 in.bdol.glencoe.com/self_check_quiz

Section Assessment

1. The chlorophyll in the leaf reflects green and yellow while absorbing other colors. In the fall, chlorophyll is absorbed, revealing other leaf pigments.
2. ATP and NADPH from the light reactions are used in the Calvin cycle.
3. Photolysis splits water to provide hydrogen ions for the Calvin cycle and restore electrons to chlorophyll.
4. Proteins convey energized electrons through the chloroplast.
5. Chlorophyll is neither a reactant nor a product. It contributes electrons to photosynthesis but is not changed during the reaction. CO_2 and H_2O are reactants.
6. Light-dependent reactions take place in the thylakoid membranes of the chloroplast, and light-independent reactions take place in the stroma of the chloroplast.

Getting Energy to Make ATP

Indiana Standards Standard B.1.3 Know and describe that within the cell are specialized parts for the transport of materials, energy capture and release, protein building, waste disposal, information feedback, and movement...

What happens to sugars?

Using Prior Knowledge You know that the chlorophyll in green plants is the key to photosynthesis and that sugars are produced. You also know that your body needs energy to survive. Sugars can be broken down in cells to yield large amounts of energy. But, your cells can't convert light energy to sugars. What will you do? Fortunately, the cells of all organisms can use the sugars made by plants during the Calvin cycle. By eating plant material, animals, too, can access the sun's energy.

Identify *In which organelle are sugars converted to ATP?*

Cellular Respiration

The process by which mitochondria break down food molecules to produce ATP is called **cellular respiration.** There are three stages of cellular respiration: glycolysis, the citric acid cycle, and the electron transport chain. The first stage, glycolysis, is **anaerobic**—no oxygen is required. The last two stages are **aerobic** and require oxygen to be completed.

Glycolysis

Glycolysis (gli KAH lih sis) is a series of chemical reactions in the cytoplasm of a cell that break down glucose, a six-carbon compound, into two molecules of pyruvic (pie RUE vik) acid, a three-carbon compound. Because two molecules of ATP are used to start glycolysis, and only four ATP molecules are produced, glycolysis is not very effective, producing only two ATP molecules for each glucose molecule broken down.

In the electron transport chain of photosynthesis, an electron carrier called $NADP^+$ was described as carrying energized electrons to another location in the cell for further chemical reactions. Glycolysis also uses an electron carrier, called NAD^+ (nicotinamide adenine dinucleotide). NAD^+ forms NADH when it accepts two electrons.

9.3   GETTING ENERGY TO MAKE ATP   **231**

1 Focus

INTERACTIVE CHALKBOARD
PowerPoint® Presentations

Bellringer
Section Focus Transparency 23

Transparency **23** Cellular Respiration   SECTION FOCUS
Use with Chapter 9, Section 9.3

① Which of these organisms require energy?
② How does the manner in which these organisms get energy differ?

BIOLOGY: The Dynamics of Life   SECTION FOCUS TRANSPARENCIES

Using Prior Knowledge

Identify Glucose is converted to ATP in the mitochondria.

 Indiana Academic Standards

Pages 230–231: B.1.3, B.1.4

2 Teach

Concept Development

Read a recipe for making bread. Explain to students that the yeasts used in the recipe are microorganisms classified as fungi. Discuss how, unlike most organisms, yeast carry out processes that release energy in the absence of oxygen. Explain that bakers use yeast in their recipes for almost all breads, because as yeast function anaerobically, they release CO_2, which causes the bread to rise.

Reinforcement

Make sure students understand that pyruvic acid is the intermediate product for both types of fermentation. Challenge students to explain how pyruvic acid changes in each type of fermentation.

Caption Question Answer
Figure 9.9 acetyl-CoA, NADH, and H^+

Indiana Academic Standards

Pages 232–233: B.1.3, B.1.4, B.1.7, B.1.9

232

Figure 9.8
Glycolysis breaks down a molecule of glucose into two molecules of pyruvic acid. In the process, it forms a net of two molecules of ATP, two molecules of NADH , and two hydrogen ions.

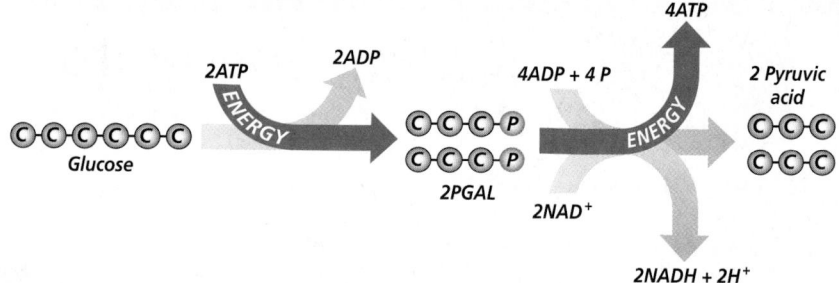

Notice in *Figure 9.8* that two molecules of PGAL are formed during glycolysis. Recall that PGAL also forms in the Calvin cycle. The PGAL made during photosynthesis can enter the glycolysis pathway and lead to the formation of ATP and organic molecules.

Following glycolysis, the pyruvic acid molecules move into the mitochondria, the organelles that transform energy for the cell. In the presence of oxygen, two more stages complete cellular respiration: the citric acid cycle and the electron transport chain of the mitochondrion. Before these two stages can begin, however, pyruvic acid undergoes a series of reactions in which it gives off a molecule of CO_2 and combines with a molecule called coenzyme A to form acetyl-CoA. The reaction with coenzyme A produces a molecule of NADH and H^+. These reactions are shown in *Figure 9.9*.

The citric acid cycle

The **citric acid cycle**, also called the Krebs cycle, is a series of chemical reactions similar to the Calvin cycle in that the molecule used in the first reaction is also one of the end products. Read *Figure 9.10* to study the citric acid cycle.

For every turn of the cycle, one molecule of ATP and two molecules of carbon dioxide are produced. Two electron carriers are used, NAD^+ and FAD (flavin adenine dinucleotide). A total of three NADH, three H^+ ions, and one $FADH_2$ are formed. The electron carriers each pass two energized electrons along to the electron transport chain in the inner membrane of the mitochondrion.

Figure 9.9
Before the citric acid cycle and electron transport chain begin, pyruvic acid undergoes a series of reactions. **Infer** *What products are formed as a result of the reactions within the mitochondrion?*

232 ENERGY IN A CELL

The Citric Acid Cycle

Figure 9.10
The citric acid cycle breaks down a molecule of acetyl-CoA and forms ATP and CO_2. The electron carriers NAD^+ and FAD pick up energized electrons and pass them to the electron transport chain in the inner mitochondrial membrane. **Critical Thinking** *How many CO_2 molecules are produced for every glucose molecule that entered the cellular respiration pathways?*

Magnification: unavailable

The mitochondria host the citric acid cycle.

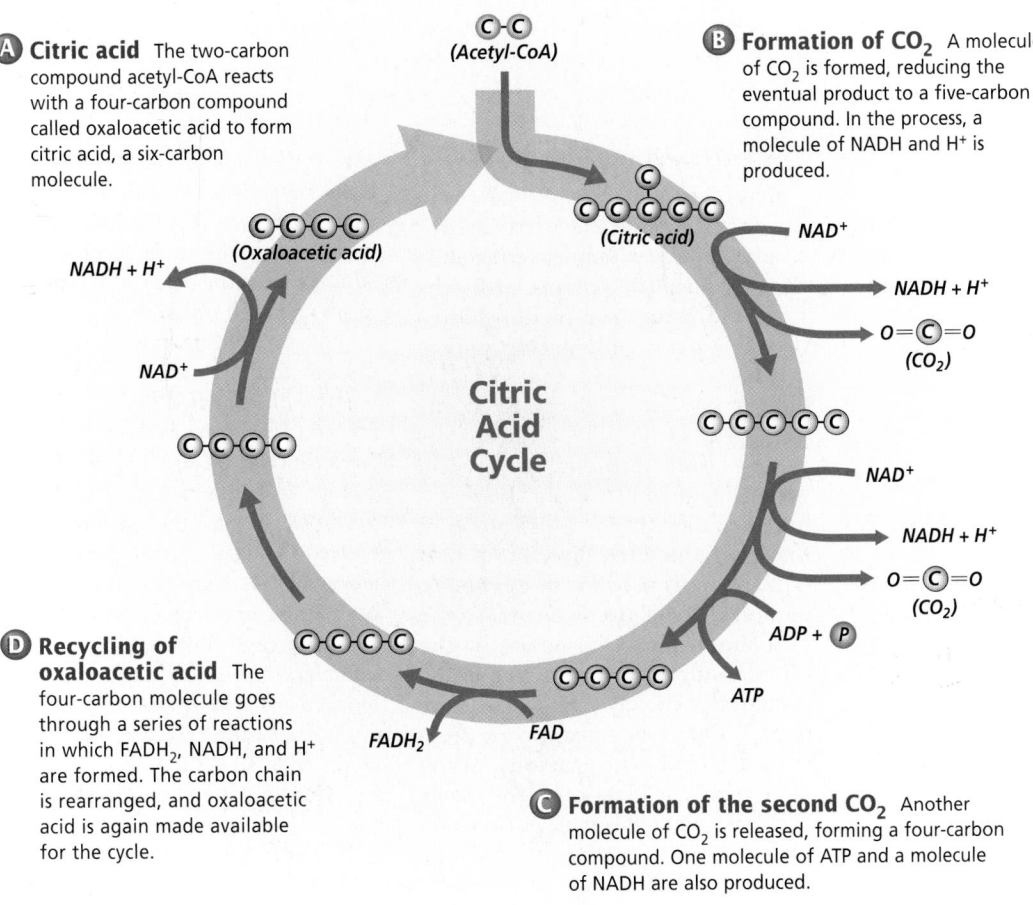

A **Citric acid** The two-carbon compound acetyl-CoA reacts with a four-carbon compound called oxaloacetic acid to form citric acid, a six-carbon molecule.

C–C
(Acetyl-CoA)

C–C–C–C–C–C
(Citric acid)

NADH + H⁺
(Oxaloacetic acid)
C–C–C–C

NAD⁺

Citric Acid Cycle

C–C–C–C

NAD⁺

B **Formation of CO_2** A molecule of CO_2 is formed, reducing the eventual product to a five-carbon compound. In the process, a molecule of NADH and H⁺ is produced.

NAD⁺

NADH + H⁺

O=C=O
(CO₂)

C–C–C–C–C

NAD⁺

NADH + H⁺

O=C=O
(CO₂)

ADP + P

ATP

C–C–C–C

FADH₂   FAD

D **Recycling of oxaloacetic acid** The four-carbon molecule goes through a series of reactions in which FADH₂, NADH, and H⁺ are formed. The carbon chain is rearranged, and oxaloacetic acid is again made available for the cycle.

C **Formation of the second CO_2** Another molecule of CO_2 is released, forming a four-carbon compound. One molecule of ATP and a molecule of NADH are also produced.

Purpose

to teach students the main events of the citric acid cycle that break down acetyl-CoA to form ATP, NADH, FADH₂, hydrogen ions, and carbon dioxide

Background

Glycolysis initiates the breakdown of glucose. Pyruvate, the end product of glycolysis, undergoes a series of reactions to form acetyl-CoA, which enters the citric acid cycle. The citric acid cycle is important for its large energy yield.

Teaching Strategies

Ask students to describe the four stages of the citric acid cycle. Include the products for each stage. **L2**

Visual Learning

Make a table with the following headings: ATP, NADH, and FADH₂. Under the headings list one round of the citric acid cycle. Have the students fill in the number of each molecule produced during one round.

Critical Thinking

six

CULTURAL DIVERSITY

Severo Ochoa Have students research the efforts of Spanish-American biochemist Severo Ochoa (1905–1993) toward the modern understanding of the citric acid cycle and photosynthesis. Ochoa showed how the oxidation of one glucose molecule could yield 38 ATP molecules. He also elucidated the mechanisms of the citric acid cycle and photosynthesis by identifying the function of key enzymes.

Ochoa's research in cellular respiration in the 1930s and 1940s resulted ultimately in the discovery of the mechanisms of RNA and DNA synthesis, for which Ochoa and colleague Arthur Kornberg received a Nobel prize in 1959. **L3**

233

Reading Check (p. 235) The human body carries out lactic acid fermentation in muscle cells when there isn't enough oxygen to carry out the citric acid cycle.

Figure 9.11
In the electron transport chain, the carrier molecules NADH and $FADH_2$ give up electrons that pass through a series of reactions. Oxygen is the final electron acceptor.

The electron transport chain

The electron transport chain in the inner membrane of the mitochondrion is very similar to the electron transport chains of the thylakoid membrane in the chloroplasts of plant cells during photosynthesis. NADH and $FADH_2$ deliver energized electrons at the top of the chain. The electrons are passed from protein to protein within the membrane, slowly releasing their energy in steps. Some of that energy is used directly to form ATP; some is used by an enzyme to pump H^+ ions into the center of the mitochondrion. Consequently, the mitochondrion inner membrane becomes positively charged because of the high concentration of positively charged hydrogen ions. At the same time, the exterior of the membrane is negatively charged, which further attracts hydrogen ions. The gradient of H^+ ions that results across the inner membrane of the mitochondrion provides the energy for ATP production, just as it does in the chemiosmotic process that takes place at the thylakoid membranes in the chloroplasts. *Figure 9.11* summarizes the electron transport chain and the formation of ATP.

The final electron acceptor at the bottom of the chain is oxygen, which reacts with four hydrogen ions ($4H^+$) and four electrons to form two molecules of water (H_2O). This is why oxygen is so important to our bodies. Without oxygen, the proteins in the electron transport chain cannot pass along the electrons. If a protein cannot pass along an electron to oxygen, it cannot accept another electron. Very quickly, the entire chain becomes blocked and ATP production stops.

Overall, the electron transport chain adds 32 ATP molecules to the four already produced. Obviously, the aerobic process of ATP production is very effective. In the absence of oxygen, however, an anaerobic process can produce small amounts of ATP to keep the cell from dying.

Additional Lab

Carbon Fixation

Purpose
Students will demonstrate that without light, carbon fixation slows or stops.

Materials
black paper, labels, iodine solution, *Coleus* plants, paper clip, hot plate, beaker, 95% alcohol, small bowl

Procedure
1. Cut out two identical pieces of black paper in the shape of a small square.
2. Stick a label on one piece and write your initials and the date on it.
3. Use a paper clip to fasten the black shapes to the top and bottom surfaces of a *Coleus* leaf so that they match up exactly.
4. Leave the plant in sunlight for 7 days. Then remove the leaf that was partially covered and take off the paper clip and papers.

Fermentation

There are times, such as during heavy exercise, when your cells are without oxygen for a short period of time. When this happens, an anaerobic process called fermentation follows glycolysis and provides a means to continue producing ATP until oxygen is available again. There are two major types of fermentation: lactic acid fermentation and alcoholic fermentation. The table in *Figure 9.12* compares the two processes with respiration. Perform the *Problem-Solving Lab* shown here to further compare and contrast cellular respiration and fermentation.

Reading Check **Infer** when your body might perform fermentation reactions.

Lactic acid fermentation

You know that under anaerobic conditions, the electron transport chain backs up because oxygen is not present

Figure 9.12
Lactic acid and alcoholic fermentations are comparable in the production of ATP, but compared to cellular respiration, it is obvious that fermentation is far less efficient in ATP production. This runner's muscles have been depleted of oxygen and fermentation is taking place.

Problem-Solving Lab 9.2

Acquire Information

Cellular respiration or fermentation? The methods by which organisms derive ATP may differ; however, the result, the production of ATP molecules, is similar.

Solve the Problem

Study the table in *Figure 9.12* and evaluate cellular respiration, lactic acid fermentation, and alcoholic fermentation.

Thinking Critically

1. **Describe** Why does cellular respiration produce so much more ATP than does fermentation?
2. **Use Scientific Explanations** Describe a situation when a human would need to use more than one of the processes listed above.
3. **Analyze** Think of an organism that might generate ATP only by fermentation and consider why fermentation is the best process for the organism.

Comparison of Fermentation to Cellular Respiration		
Lactic Acid	**Alcoholic**	**Cellular respiration**
glucose	glucose	glucose
↓	↓	↓
glycolysis (pyruvic acid)	glycolysis (pyruvic acid)	glycolysis (pyruvic acid)
↓	↓	↓
	carbon dioxide	carbon dioxide
	+	+
lactic acid	alcohol	water
+	+	+
2 ATP	2 ATP	36 ATP

Problem-Solving Lab 9.2

Purpose

Students will compare and contrast the process of aerobic respiration, lactic acid fermentation, and alcoholic fermentation.

Process Skills

think critically, compare and contrast, acquire information, analyze information, sequence, define operationally

Teaching Strategies

It will be necessary for students to review the sections dealing with aerobic respiration, lactic acid fermentation, and alcoholic fermentation before they attempt to complete this lab.

Thinking Critically

1. The chemical reactions of the citric acid cycle provide more ATP than does fermentation. Cellular respiration better meets the energy requirements of complex organisms.
2. During a time of intense exercise, we revert to lactic acid fermentation.
3. For an organism that lives in anaerobic conditions and uses small amounts of energy, cellular respiration may not be economical if fermentation consistently provides sufficient energy.

Modified Assessment

Skill Provide an incomplete table similar to the table in Figure 9.12 and have the students complete it. Use the Performance Task Assessment List for Data Table in **PASC**, p. 109. **L1**

---

5. Place the leaf into a beaker of boiling 95% alcohol enclosed in a fume hood and boil it until it turns white. **CAUTION: *Do not use a heat source that has an open flame or a hot plate with an unsealed element.***
6. Remove the leaf and place it in a small bowl. Pour iodine solution on the leaf and let it absorb the iodine for a few minutes. **CAUTION: *Iodine is an irritant.***

Rinse thoroughly if iodine gets on skin or clothing. Wear goggles during activity and cleanup.
7. Rinse the leaf with tap water and observe.

Analysis

1. What happens when the leaf is boiled in alcohol? Its chlorophyll dissolves.
2. In what part of the leaf did carbon fixation slow or stop? The covered part received no light, and therefore could not carry on photosynthesis, which is a carbon-fixation process.

Assessment

Performance Have students write a summary of the lab. Use the Performance Task Assessment List for Lab Report in **PASC**, p. 119. **L2**

MiniLab 9.3

Purpose

Students will observe the production of CO_2 resulting from yeast fermenting sugar.

Process Skills

observe and infer, interpret data, experiment, analyze data

Safety Precautions

Have students wear aprons and safety goggles.

Teaching Strategies

Ask students to brainstorm and list the uses of industrial alcoholic fermentation. Ask them which products (alcohol or CO_2) of the process are important. **L2**

Expected Results

Students will see gas bubbles coming from the yeast/apple juice mixture.

Analysis

1. CO_2
2. The rate would increase.
3. Warm water increases the metabolic rate of the yeast.
4. anaerobic because no oxygen is available in the bulb of the pipette covered with water

Assessment

Performance Have students prepare a summary of the MiniLab in their journals. Use the Performance Task Assessment List for Lab Report in **PASC**, p. 119. **L2**

Caption Question Answer

Figure 9.13 Once the dough is baked, the CO_2 dissipates and the bubble pockets are left behind.

Indiana Academic Standards

Pages 236–237: B.1.4, B.1.9

MiniLab 9.3

Predict

Determine if Apple Juice Ferments Some organisms, such as yeast, can break down food molecules and synthesize ATP when no oxygen is available. When food is available, yeast carry out alcoholic fermentation, producing CO_2. Thus, the production of CO_2 in the absence of oxygen can be used to judge whether alcoholic fermentation is taking place.

Procedure 👓 🧤

1. Carefully study the diagram and set up the experiment as shown.
2. Hold the test tube in a beaker of warm (not hot) water and observe.

Test tube

Water

Plastic pipette

Metal washers

Yeast and apple juice

Analysis

1. **Interpret Data** What were the gas bubbles that came from the plastic pipette?
2. **Hypothesize** What would happen to the rate of bubbles given off if more yeast were present in the mixture?
3. **Analyze** Why was the test tube placed in warm water?
4. **Draw Conclusions** Was the process you demonstrated aerobic or anaerobic? Explain.

---

as the final electron acceptor. As NADH and $FADH_2$ arrive at the chain from the citric acid cycle and glycolysis, they cannot release their energized electrons. The citric acid cycle and glycolysis cannot continue without a steady supply of NAD^+ and FAD.

The cell does not have a method to replace FAD during anaerobic conditions; however, NAD^+ can be replaced through lactic acid fermentation. **Lactic acid fermentation** is one of the processes that supplies energy when oxygen is scarce. Two molecules of pyruvic acid produced in glycolysis use NADH to form two molecules of lactic acid. This releases NAD^+ to be used in glycolysis, allowing two ATP molecules to be formed for each glucose molecule. The lactic acid is transferred from muscle cells, where it is produced during strenuous exercise, to the liver that converts it back to pyruvic acid. The lactic acid that builds up in muscle cells results in muscle fatigue.

Alcoholic fermentation

Another type of fermentation, **alcoholic fermentation,** is used by yeast cells and some bacteria to produce CO_2 and ethyl alcohol. When making bread, like that shown in *Figure 9.13*, yeast cells produce CO_2 that forms bubbles in the dough. Eventually the heat of the oven kills the yeast and the bubble pockets are left to lighten the bread. You can do the *MiniLab* on this page to study alcoholic fermentation in apple juice.

Figure 9.13
Alcoholic fermentation by the yeast in bread dough produces CO_2 bubbles that raise the dough. **Think Critically** *What happens to the CO_2?*

🔹 **TECH PREP** 🔹

Forestry Management Scientists are considering how the clearance of forested lands will affect the balance between photosynthesis and respiration in the biosphere. Have students investigate scientific models of forestry management and develop a plan to ease any imbalance. **L2**

Comparing Photosynthesis and Cellular Respiration

The production and breakdown of food molecules are accomplished by distinct processes that bear certain similarities. Both photosynthesis and cellular respiration use electron carriers and a cycle of chemical reactions to form ATP. Both use electron transport chains to form ATP and to create a chemical and a concentration gradient of H^+ within a cell. This hydrogen ion gradient can be used to form ATP by chemiosmosis.

However, despite using such similar tools, the two cellular processes accomplish quite different tasks. Photosynthesis produces high-energy carbohydrates and oxygen from the sun's energy, whereas cellular respiration uses oxygen to break down carbohydrates to form ATP and compounds that provide less energy. Also, one of the end products of cellular respiration is CO_2, which is one of the beginning products for photosynthesis. The oxygen produced during photosynthesis is a critical molecule necessary for cellular respiration. *Table 9.1* compares these complementary processes.

Table 9.1 Comparison of Photosynthesis and Cellular Respiration	
Photosynthesis	**Cellular Respiration**
Food synthesized	Food broken down
Energy from sun stored in glucose	Energy of glucose released
Carbon dioxide taken in	Carbon dioxide given off
Oxygen given off	Oxygen taken in
Produces sugars from PGAL	Produces CO_2 and H_2O
Requires light	Does not require light
Occurs only in presence of chlorophyll	Occurs in all living cells

Section Assessment

Understanding Main Ideas

1. Compare the ATP yields of glycolysis, the citric acid cycle, and the electron transport chain.
2. How do alcoholic fermentation and lactic acid fermentation differ?
3. How is most of the ATP from aerobic respiration produced?
4. Why is lactic acid fermentation important to the cell when oxygen is scarce?
5. How many ATP molecules are produced after the electrons go down the electron transport chain?

Thinking Critically

6. Compare the energy-producing processes in a jogger's leg muscles with those of a sprinter's leg muscles. Which is likely to build up more lactic acid? Explain.

SKILL REVIEW

7. **Get the Big Picture** How are the chemical reactions of photosynthesis and cellular respiration connected? What is the significance of this connection? For more help, refer to *Get the Big Picture* in the **Skill Handbook**.

in.bdol.glencoe.com/self_check_quiz

9.3   GETTING ENERGY TO MAKE ATP   **237**

Section Assessment

1. Glycolysis produces 2 ATP molecules; the citric acid cycle produces one ATP molecule; the electron transport chain produces 32 ATP molecules.
2. Alcoholic fermentation produces alcohol and carbon dioxide. Lactic acid fermentation produces lactic acid.
3. Most of the ATP is produced by the reactions of the electron transport chain.
4. It supplies energy when oxygen is unavailable.
5. 32
6. Aerobic respiration occurs in the muscles of both runners. The sprinter may build up more lactic acid because of an oxygen debt associated with the quick burst of energy.
7. Photosynthesis is basically the reverse of cellular respiration. Photosynthesis takes the sun's energy and synthesizes glucose from carbon dioxide and water. Cellular respiration breaks down glucose into carbon dioxide, water, and usable units of bond energy (ATP).

237

INTERNET BioLab

INTERNET BioLab

What factors influence photosynthesis?

Time Allotment
one class period

Process Skills
use variables and controls, think critically, observe and infer, collect data, interpret data

Safety Precautions
Students should always wear goggles in the lab. Be sure hands and work areas are dry when handling electrical equipment and have students wash hands at the end of the lab. Caution students not to get water on the lighted bulbs.

Before You Begin

Oxygen is one of the products of photosynthesis. Because oxygen is only slightly soluble in water, aquatic plants such as *Elodea* give off visible bubbles of oxygen as they carry out photosynthesis. By measuring the rate at which bubbles form, you can measure the rate of photosynthesis.

PREPARATION

Problem
How do different wavelengths of light that a plant receives affect its rate of photosynthesis?

Objectives
In this BioLab, you will:
- **Observe** photosynthesis in an aquatic organism.
- **Measure** the rate of photosynthesis.
- **Research** the wavelengths of various colors of light.
- **Observe** how various wavelengths of light influence the rate of photosynthesis.
- **Use the Internet** to collect and compare data from other students.

Materials
1000-mL beaker	lamp with reflector and
three *Elodea* plants	150-watt bulb
string	0.25% sodium hydrogen
washers	carbonate (baking soda)
colored cellophane,	solution
assorted colors	watch with second hand

Safety Precautions
CAUTION: *Always wear goggles in the lab.*

Skill Handbook
If you need help with this lab, refer to the **Skill Handbook.**

PREPARATION

Prepare sodium hydrogen carbonate solution by mixing 2.5 g sodium hydrogen carbonate with 1000 mL of water.

Alternative Materials
- If *Elodea* is unavailable, you can use any other green aquatic plant.
- Students can use the classroom clock if the second hand is visible.

PROCEDURE

1. Construct a basic setup like the one shown here.
2. Create a data table to record your measurements. Be sure to include a column for each color of light you will investigate and a column for the control.
3. Place the *Elodea* plants in the beaker, then completely cover them with water. Add some of the baking soda solution. The solution provides CO_2 for the aquarium plants. **Be sure to use the same amount of water and solution for each trial.**

PROCEDURE

Teaching Strategies
Place the *Elodea* sprigs in a large bowl and place them under a lamp for about 10 minutes before students begin the lab. This reduces the time the students will wait to begin seeing evidence of photosynthesis.

Troubleshooting
- You may wish to circulate through the room during this activity to ensure that the setups are constructed properly and that the students are seeing evidence of photosynthesis.

- Make sure that students do not stir the *Elodea* while they are conducting their experiment. Stirring the plant will make it difficult to obtain accurate data.

4. Conduct a control by directing the lamp (without colored cellophane) on the plant and noticing when you see the bubbles.

5. Observe and record the number of oxygen bubbles that *Elodea* generates in five minutes.

6. Cover the lamp with a piece of colored cellophane and repeat steps 4 and 5.

7. Repeat steps 4 and 5 with a different color of cellophane.

8. Go to in.bdol.glencoe.com/internet_lab to **post your data.**

9. **CLEANUP AND DISPOSAL** Return plant material to an aquarium to prevent it from drying out.

Data Table

	Control	Color 1	Color 2
Bubbles observed in five minutes	Answers will vary.	Answers will vary.	Answers will vary.

ANALYZE AND CONCLUDE

1. **Interpret Observations** From where did the bubbles of oxygen emerge?

2. **Make Inferences** Explain how counting bubbles measures the rate of photosynthesis.

3. **Use the Internet** Look up the wavelengths of the colors of light you used. Make a graph of your data and data posted by other students with the rate of photosynthesis per minute plotted against the wavelengths of light you tested for both the control and experimental setups. Write a sentence or two explaining the graph.

4. **ERROR ANALYSIS** Why was it important to use the same amount of sodium hydrogen carbonate in each trial?

Share Your Data

Find this BioLab using the link below and post your data in the data table provided for this activity. Using the additional data from other students on the Internet, analyze the combined data and expand your graph.

 in.bdol.glencoe.com/internet_lab

ANALYZE AND CONCLUDE

1. The bubbles emerged from the end of the stem of the *Elodea* plant.

2. Oxygen is an end product of photosynthesis. As the rate of photosynthesis changes, so will the rate at which oxygen is produced.

3. The rate for the control setup should be the greatest and therefore the highest line. The rates corresponding to colored, filtered light will be lower than the control. Results will vary depending on the color of cellophane the students use.

4. **ERROR ANALYSIS** Sodium hydrogen carbonate is a source of carbon dioxide. If you change the amount of sodium hydrogen carbonate, it will change the amount of carbon dioxide available to the aquatic plants. This variable change may affect the rate of photosynthesis.

Assessment

Portfolio Have students write an evaluation of the lab. Their evaluations should include an overview of the experiment, data analysis, and conclusion statements. Have them also write hypotheses about how photosynthesis might be affected if another condition, such as temperature, were changed. Use the Performance Task Assessment List for Formulating a Hypothesis in **PASC**, p. 93. **L2**

Share Your Data

To navigate the Internet BioLabs, go to in.bdol.glencoe.com/internet_lab. The advantage of using the Internet for an experiment is that students can collect considerably more and varied data than they could collect on their own in the allotted time.

Data and Observations

Students should record data under control conditions and then under experimental conditions for the same amount of time—at least 5 minutes.

CLEANUP AND DISPOSAL

 The sodium hydrogen carbonate solution can be rinsed down the sink with water.

connection to Chemistry

Purpose

Students should recognize the role that pigments, such as chlorophyll, play in the process of photosynthesis.

Background

There are far more chlorophyll molecules in a green leaf than carotenoids, and for most of the growing season, chlorophyll masks the presence of those accessory pigments. In the autumn, however, chlorophyll breaks down and the other pigments in leaves are visible as "fall colors." The cause of this chlorophyll breakdown is not completely understood, but it seems to be tied to the gradual reduction in daylight that takes place as summer ends.

Teaching Strategies

■ Have students examine live (or preserved) specimens of green, brown, and red algae to observe the difference in pigments. Make sure students wash their hands after handling live specimens. **L2** **ELL**

■ Melanin is a pigment in animals that absorbs ultraviolet radiation and protects skin and other tissues from sun damage. Have students research melanin along with a plant pigment and create posters that compare the two. **L3**

Plant Pigments

In photosynthesis, light energy is converted into chemical energy. To begin the process, light is absorbed by colorful pigment molecules contained in chloroplasts.

A pigment is a substance that can absorb specific wavelengths of visible light. You can observe the colors of the various wavelengths of light by letting sunlight pass through a prism to create a "rainbow," or spectrum, that has red light on one end, violet on the other, and orange, yellow, green, blue, and indigo light in between.

Every photosynthetic pigment is distinctive in that it absorbs specific wavelengths in the visible light spectrum.

LM Magnification: 450×

Pigments color cyanobacteria (above) and red algae (inset).

Chlorophylls *a* and *b* The principal pigment of photosynthesis is chlorophyll. Chlorophyll exists in two forms, designated as *a* and *b*. Chlorophyll *a* and *b* both absorb light in the violet to blue and the red to red-orange parts of the spectrum, although at somewhat different wavelengths. These pigments also reflect green light, which is why plant leaves appear green.

When chlorophyll *b* absorbs light, it transfers the energy it acquires to chlorophyll *a*, which then feeds that energy into the chemical reactions that lead to the production of ATP and NADPH. In this way, chlorophyll *b* acts as an "accessory" pigment by making it possible for photosynthesis to occur over a broader spectrum of light than would be possible with chlorophyll *a* alone.

Carotenoids and phycobilins Carotenoids and phycobilins are other kinds of accessory pigments that absorb wavelengths of light different from those absorbed by chlorophyll *a* and *b*, and so extend the range of light that can be used for photosynthesis.

Carotenoids are yellow-orange pigments. They are found in all green plants, but their color is usually masked by chlorophyll.

Carotenoids are also found in cyanobacteria and in brown algae. A particular carotenoid called fucoxanthin gives brown algae their characteristic dark brown or olive green color.

Phycobilins are blue and red. Red algae get their distinctive blood-red coloration from phycobilins. Some phycobilins can absorb wavelengths of green, violet, and blue light, which penetrate deep water. One species of red algae that contains these pigments is able to live at ocean depths of 269 meters (882.5 feet). The algae's pigments absorb enough of the incredibly faint light that penetrates to this depth—only a tiny percent of what is available at the water's surface—to power photosynthesis.

Writing About Biology

Think Critically How do you think accessory pigments may have influenced the spread of photosynthetic organisms into diverse habitats such as the deep sea?

 To find out more about pigments, visit in.bdol.glencoe.com/chemistry

Writing About Biology

Accessory pigments have made it possible for photosynthetic organisms to use a broader range of the visible light spectrum, and in so doing, survive in places where the amount or quality of visible light is minimal.

STUDY GUIDE

Section 9.1

The Need for Energy

Key Concepts
- ATP is the molecule that stores energy for easy use within the cell.
- ATP is formed when a phosphate group is added to ADP. When ATP is broken down, ADP and phosphate are formed and energy is released.
- Green organisms trap the energy in sunlight and store it in the bonds of certain molecules for later use.
- Organisms that cannot use sunlight directly obtain energy by consuming plants or other organisms that have consumed plants.

Vocabulary
(ADP) adenosine diphosphate (p. 222)
(ATP) adenosine triphosphate (p. 222)

Section 9.2

Photosynthesis: Trapping the Sun's Energy

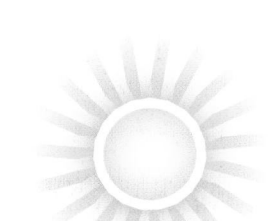

Key Concepts
- Photosynthesis is the process by which cells use light energy to make simple sugars.
- Chlorophyll in the chloroplasts of plant cells traps light energy needed for photosynthesis.
- The light reactions of photosynthesis produce ATP and result in the splitting of water molecules.
- The reactions of the Calvin cycle make carbohydrates using CO_2 along with ATP and NADPH from the light reactions.

Vocabulary
Calvin cycle (p. 228)
chlorophyll (p. 226)
electron transport chain (p. 226)
light-dependent reactions (p. 225)
light-independent reactions (p. 225)
$NADP^+$ (p. 227)
photolysis (p. 227)
photosynthesis (p. 225)
pigment (p. 226)

Section 9.3

Getting Energy to Make ATP

Key Concepts
- In cellular respiration, cells break down carbohydrates to release energy.
- The first stage of cellular respiration, glycolysis, takes place in the cytoplasm and does not require oxygen.
- The citric acid cycle takes place in mitochondria and requires oxygen.

Vocabulary
aerobic (p. 231)
alcoholic fermentation (p. 236)
anaerobic (p. 231)
cellular respiration (p. 231)
citric acid cycle (p. 232)
glycolysis (p. 231)
lactic acid fermentation (p. 236)

FOLDABLES™
Study Organizer To help you review photosynthesis and cellular respiration, use the Organizational Study Fold on page 225.

Key Concepts
Summary statements can be used by students to review the major concepts of the chapter.

Biology Online

Visit in.bdol.glencoe.com
/self_check_quiz
/vocabulary_puzzlemaker
/chapter_test
/standardized_test

VOCABULARY PUZZLEMAKER

For additional help with vocabulary, have students access the Vocabulary PuzzleMaker online at in.bdol.glencoe.com/vocabulary_puzzlemaker

FOLDABLES™
Have students use their Foldables to review the content of Section 9.2.

Use the ExamView®Pro Test Bank CD-ROM to:
- Create **multiple versions** of tests
- Create **modified** tests with one mouse click for **inclusion** students
- **Edit** existing questions and **add** your own questions
- Build tests aligned with state standards using built-in **State Curriculum Tags**
- Change **English** tests to **Spanish** with one mouse click and vice versa

 Indiana Academic Standards

Pages 240–241: B.1.3, B.1.4, B.1.7, B.1.9

Chapter 9 Assessment

 The Princeton Review *Questions and answers have been aligned and verified by The Princeton Review.*

Vocabulary Review

1. Calvin cycle; Calvin cycle is part of light-independent photosynthesis; the other terms are associated with light-dependent photosynthesis.
2. aerobic; Aerobic is associated with oxygen but the other terms are not.
3. $NADP^+$; Chlorophyll is a type of pigment; $NADP^+$ is a high-energy molecule.
4. Calvin cycle; See explanation in #1.
5. photosynthesis; Citric acid cycle is part of cellular respiration but photosynthesis is not.

Understanding Key Concepts

6.	B	10.	D
7.	B	11.	B
8.	A	12.	D
9.	D	13.	A

Constructed Response

14. During physical activity, muscle cells must release energy at a higher rate than skin cells.
15. Photosynthesis stores energy, whereas respiration releases energy, and the products of one process are the reactants of the other process.
16. Other pigments in the plant absorb some of the light of other wavelengths and pass the energy to chlorophyll for use in photosynthesis. The remaining light that is not trapped is reflected or absorbed as heat.

Thinking Critically

17. Electrons pass from protein to protein until they are

Vocabulary Review

Review the Chapter 9 vocabulary words listed in the Study Guide on page 241. For each set of vocabulary words, choose the one that does not belong. Explain why it does not belong.

1. light-dependent reactions—Calvin cycle—chlorophyll
2. glycolysis—alcoholic fermentation—aerobic
3. $NADP^+$—chlorophyll—pigment
4. photolysis—Calvin cycle—light-dependent reactions
5. cellular respiration—citric acid cycle—photosynthesis

Understanding Key Concepts

6. Which of the following is a product of the Calvin cycle?
   A. carbon dioxide
   B. $NADP^+$
   C. oxygen
   D. $FADH_2$

7. _____ processes require oxygen, whereas _____ processes do not.
   A. Anaerobic—aerobic
   B. Aerobic—anaerobic
   C. Photolysis—aerobic
   D. Aerobic—respiration

8. Four molecules of glucose would give a net yield of _____ ATP following glycolysis.
   A. 8   C. 4
   B. 16   D. 12

9. In which of the following structures do the light-independent reactions of photosynthesis take place?

   A.   C.

   B.   D.

---

10. What is the first process in an animal cell to be affected by anaerobic conditions?
    A. citric acid cycle
    B. fermentation
    C. glycolysis
    D. electron transport chain

11. In which stage of cellular respiration is glucose broken down into two molecules of pyruvic acid?
    A. Calvin cycle
    B. glycolysis
    C. citric acid cycle
    D. electron transport chain

12. Which of the following is a similarity between the citric acid cycle and the Calvin cycle?
    A. Both cycles utilize oxygen.
    B. Both cycles produce carbon dioxide.
    C. Both cycles utilize ATP to break down carbon bonds.
    D. Both cycles recycle the molecule needed for the first reaction.

13. When yeast ferments the sugar in a bread mixture, what is produced that causes the bread dough to rise?
    A. carbon dioxide   C. ethyl alcohol
    B. water   D. oxygen

Constructed Response

14. **Open Ended** Why would human muscle cells contain many more mitochondria than skin cells?

15. **Open Ended** How are cellular respiration and photosynthesis complementary processes?

16. **Open Ended** What happens to sunlight that strikes a leaf but is not trapped by chlorophyll?

Thinking Critically

17. **Sequence** Describe the pathway of electrons from the time they enter the intermembrane space of the mitochondrion to the time they are returned to the inside of the mitochondrion.

 in.bdol.glencoe.com/chapter_test

---

transferred to the enzymes used to synthesize ATP. Here they flow across the membrane and return to the inside of the mitochondrion and ATP is formed.

18. 1. glycolysis; 2. citric acid cycle; 3. electron transport chain; 4. cellular respiration

19. Slow-twitch fibers, which have a well-developed blood supply and many mitochondria, split ATP slowly. Fast twitch fibers split ATP rapidly. Activities that use rapid energy use mainly fast twitch fibers, and activities that are sustained use more slow twitch fibers.

18. Concept Map Make a concept map using the following vocabulary terms: cellular respiration, glycolysis, citric acid cycle, electron transport chain.

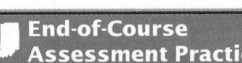

19. **REAL WORLD BIOCHALLENGE** Muscle tissue is made of different types of fibers—fast-twitch and slow-twitch. These fibers vary in metabolic activities. Visit **in.bdol.glencoe.com** to find out about the various types of muscle fibers. How do the metabolic activities of these fibers vary? What types of fibers are used for different movements and why?

End-of-Course Assessment Practice

20. D   **22.** C
21. A   **23.** D

24. In photosynthesis, the sun's energy is stored in sugar bonds. In cellular respiration, the sugar bond energy is transferred to small, usable units of bond energy in the form of ATP.

25. In lactic acid fermentation, pyruvic acid is converted to lactic acid and two ATPs are formed. In alcoholic fermentation, pyruvic acid is converted to alcohol and two ATPs.

Answer Sheet A practice answer sheet can be found on p. 157 of *Unit 3 FAST FILE Resources.*

End-of-Course Assessment Practice

The assessed Indiana standard appears next to the question.

All questions aligned and verified by The Princeton Review

Part 1 **Multiple Choice**

Study the table and answer questions 20–23.

The following experimental data was collected by placing equal amounts of various plant parts in sealed containers and exposing them to various light colors. After eight hours in the container, the increase in oxygen was measured in the container.

Rate of Photosynthesis

Container	Plant	Plant Part	Light Color	Temperature (°C)	Increase in O$_2$ (mL)
1	Geranium	Leaf	Red	22	120
2	Geranium	Leaf	Green	22	15
3	Geranium	Root	Red	22	0
4	Violet	Leaf	Red	22	80
5	Violet	Leaf	Green	22	10

20. One could compare the amount of oxygen produced in eight hours at two different light colors by comparing _____.
  A. 1 and 3   **C.** 1 and 5
  B. 2 and 4   **D.** 1 and 2

21. In which container was photosynthesis taking place at the fastest rate?
  A. 1   **C.** 3
  B. 2   **D.** 4

22. In which container was photosynthesis not occurring?
  A. 1   **C.** 3
  B. 2   **D.** 4

23. According to the data, which variable determined whether or not photosynthesis occurred?
  A. plant   **C.** temperature
  B. light color **D.** plant part

Part 2 **Constructed Response/Grid In**

Record your answers on your answer document.

24. Open Ended Compare the energy storage in photosynthesis to the energy storage in cellular respiration.
B.1.9

25. Open Ended Compare alcoholic fermentation and lactic acid fermentation in terms of starting and ending material and ATP production.
B.1.9

 in.bdol.glencoe.com/standardized_test

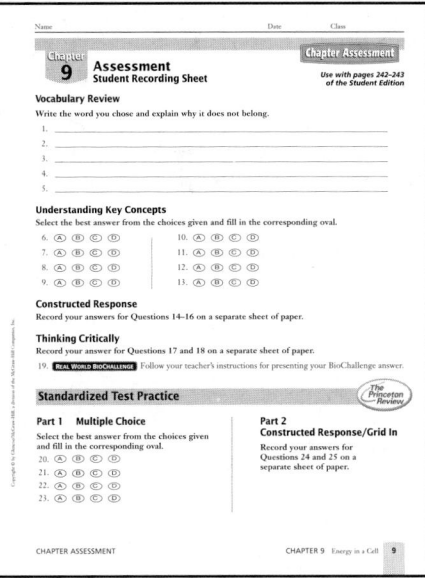

RUBRIC

For more help evaluating open-ended assessment questions, see the rubric on p. 9T.

 Indiana Academic Standards

Pages 242–243: B.1.3, B.1.4, B.1.7, B.1.9, B.1.43

Prepare

Short on Time?

This BioDigest can be used as an introduction to or as an overview of the structure and function of the cell. If time is limited, you may wish to use this unit summary to teach about the cell in place of the chapters in the cell unit.

Key Concepts

Students will learn that chemistry is an integral component of biology and living organisms. According to the cell theory, the cell is the basic unit of organization of all living matter. This means that all organisms, as simple as bacteria or as complex as a tree or an elephant, are made up of cells. Students will learn that the structures and functions of cells are similar, even for cells that serve different purposes. The concepts of how a cell transforms energy from the sun and food sources, as well as how a cell reproduces, will be described.

1 Focus

Bellringer

Display an overhead transparency of a eukaryotic cell. Point out each of the organelles and ask students to identify the functions of each organelle. **L1** **ELL**

The Life of a Cell

All organisms are made of cells, and each cell is like a complex, self-contained machine that can perform life functions. Yet as small as they are, all of the mechanisms and processes of these little machines are not fully known, and scientists continue to unravel the marvelous mysteries of the living cell.

The Chemistry of Life

Although you are studying biology, chemistry is fundamental to all biological functions. Understanding some of the basic concepts of chemistry will enhance your understanding of the biological world.

Elements and Atoms

Every substance in and on Earth is composed of one or more kinds of elements. An atom, the smallest component of an element, is made of even smaller particles called electrons, protons, and neutrons. Atoms react to form compounds.

Cells are microscopic machines.

VITAL STATISTICS

Carbon Isotopes
Isotopes of carbon contain different numbers of neutrons.
Carbon-12: six protons and six neutrons
Carbon-13: six protons and seven neutrons
Carbon-14: six protons and eight neutrons

FOCUS ON HISTORY
The Cell Theory

LM Magnification: 100×

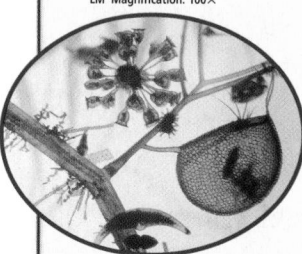

Van Leeuwenhoek might have viewed microorganisms like these found in a droplet of pond water.

In the 1600s, Anton van Leeuwenhoek was the first person to view living organisms through a microscope. Another scientist, Robert Hooke, named the structures *cells*. Two hundred years later, several scientists, including Matthias Schleiden, Theodor Schwann, and Rudolf Virchow continued to study animal and plant tissues under the microscope. Conclusions from many scientists were combined to form the cell theory:

1. All organisms are composed of one or more cells.
2. The cell is the basic unit of organization of organisms.
3. All cells come from preexisting cells.

244

RESOURCE MANAGER

Unit 3 *FAST FILE* **Resources**
Reinforcement and Study Guide in English, pp. 159–160
Reinforcement and Study Guide in Spanish, pp. 161–162
Student Recording Sheet, p. 163

Organic Compounds

Carbohydrates are chemical compounds made of carbon, hydrogen, and oxygen. Common carbohydrates include sugars, starches, and cellulose. Lipids, known as fats and oils, contain a glycerol backbone and three fatty acid chains. Proteins are large molecules made of amino acids connected by peptide bonds. Enzymes are proteins that change the rates of chemical reactions. Nucleic acids such as DNA and RNA are complex biomolecules that store cellular information in the form of a code.

Active site

Substrate

▲ An enzyme has an area called an active site in which a specific substrate undergoes a chemical reaction.

sphate

bonds between us bases

Nucleic acids are made ▶ of subunits called nucleotides. Each one consists of a sugar, a phosphate group, and a nitrogenous base.

Eukaryotes and Prokaryotes

All cells are surrounded by a plasma membrane. Eukaryotic cells contain membrane-bound organelles within the cell. Cells without internal membrane-bound organelles are called prokaryotic cells.

Color-enhanced TEM Magnification: 41 150×

▲ A prokaryotic cell does not contain membrane-bound organelles.

Color-enhanced TEM
Magnification: 4800×

Organelles

▲ A eukaryotic cell contains membrane-bound organelles.

2 Teach

Quick Demo

Organic Compounds in Food Bring in food items to demonstrate organic compounds. A potato or bread can demonstrate carbohydrates, meat can demonstrate proteins, and vegetable oil or shortening can demonstrate lipids. Combine this experience with a molecular model of a lipid. Relate the model to the lipid food item and to the overall structure of the plasma membrane.

Discussion

Direct students to look at the photographs throughout the textbook. Ask students to list the features of living and nonliving things. Discuss these features as a class. Ask students to speculate why early scientists thought a mysterious force controlled chemical changes in organisms. **L2**

CHALLENGE ACTIVITY

Vitamins Many people take vitamin supplements as part of their diets. Have students research what kinds of compounds vitamins are and how they compare to compounds they've studied like carbohydrates, lipids, and proteins. **L3**

Inquiry

Activity Have students explore osmosis in hypotonic, isotonic, and hypertonic solutions. Using dialysis tubing with a 15% sucrose solution dyed red, students should determine what kinds of solutions would be hypotonic (distilled water, for example), isotonic (15% clear sucrose solution), and hypertonic (30% sucrose solution).

Conduct the activity at the students' direction or have them work in small groups to complete this exploration. One way to use the dialysis equipment is to tie the top of each dialysis bag around a hollow piece of glass tubing. Clamp each bag to a ring stand and place them in the solutions identified by the students.

Use student observations to discuss osmosis within the solutions. What questions do they have about osmosis after this exploration? If possible, choose one of their questions to explore as a group. Also discuss any problems that you may have encountered in your setup and how those could be addressed. **L2**

Indiana Academic Standards

Pages 246–247: B.1.2, B.1.3, B.1.8

Cell Organelles

The organelles of a cell work together to carry out the functions necessary for cell survival.

Gateway to the Cell

According to the fluid mosaic model, the plasma membrane is formed by two layers of phospholipids with the fatty acid chains facing each other; the phosphate groups face the cell's internal and external environments, and proteins are embedded in the membrane.

▲ The plasma membrane is composed of a lipid bilayer with embedded proteins.

Control of Cell Functions

The nucleus contains the master plans for proteins, which are then produced by organelles called ribosomes. The nucleus also controls cellular functions.

Assembly, Transport, and Storage

The cytoplasm suspends the cell's organelles, including endoplasmic reticulum, Golgi apparatus, vacuoles, and lysosomes. The endoplasmic reticulum and Golgi apparatus transport and modify proteins.

Energy Transformers

Chloroplasts are found in plant cells. They capture the sun's light energy so it can be transformed into useable chemical energy. Mitochondria are found in both animal and plant cells. They transform the food you eat into a useable energy form.

Support and Locomotion

A network of microfilaments and microtubules attach to the plasma membrane to give the cell structure. Cilia are short, numerous projections that move like the oars of a boat. Flagella are longer projections that move in a whiplike fashion to propel a cell.

Plant cell

Animal cell

Plasma membrane
Mitochondrion
Nucleus
Chloroplast
Cell wall
Vacuole
Golgi apparatus
Ribosomes
Rough endoplasmic reticulum

Color-enhanced TEM Magnification: unavailable

Color-enhanced TEM Magnification: 1250×

USING MODELS

The Plasma Membrane: *Visual-Spatial*
In their portfolios, have students draw a plasma membrane. They should include phospholipids showing the polar head and fatty acid tails forming a bilayer with the heads and tails properly oriented. Have them include several transmembrane proteins. **L1** **ELL**

Diffusion and Osmosis

The selectively permeable plasma membrane allows only certain substances to cross. Diffusion is the movement of a substance from an area of higher concentration to an area of lower concentration. Diffusion of water across a selectively permeable membrane is called osmosis.

Simple diffusion occurs by random movement of molecules or ions. In facilitated diffusion, proteins bind to and move molecules across a membrane. Active transport uses energy to move molecules against a concentration gradient.

Active transport

Energy in a Cell

Adenosine triphosphate (ATP) is the most common energy source in a cell. Two organelles help form ATP from other sources of energy.

Chloroplasts in plant cells convert energy from the sun's rays into ATP using light-dependent reactions and store that energy in sugars via light-independent reactions and the Calvin cycle.

Mitochondria in both plant and animal cells convert food energy into ATP through a series of chemical reactions including glycolysis, the citric acid cycle, and the electron transport chain.

Mitosis

As cells grow, they reach a size where the plasma membrane cannot transport enough nutrients and wastes to maintain cell growth. At this point, the cell undergoes mitosis and divides.

The period prior to mitosis, called interphase, is one of intense metabolic activity. The first stage of mitosis is prophase, when the duplicated chromosomes condense and the mitotic spindle forms. The chromosomes line up in the center of the cell during metaphase and slowly separate during anaphase. In telophase the nucleus divides followed by cytokinesis, which separates the daughter cells.

During the stages of mitosis, chromosomes are separated into two daughter cells.

VITAL STATISTICS

ATP production for each molecule of glucose
Glycolysis: produces a net gain of two ATP, two NADH, and two H^+
Citric acid cycle (Krebs cycle): produces two ATP, six NADH, and two $FADH_2$
Electron transport chain: produces 32 ATP from NADH and $FADH_2$
Lactic acid fermentation: produces two ATP and lactic acid

THE LIFE OF A CELL **247**

3 Assess

DAILY INTERVENTION

Check for Understanding
Linguistic Ask students to name as many organelles as they can and identify the function of each. **L1**

Reteach
Display an overhead of the stages of mitosis and have students identify the stages and describe the events. **L2**

Extension

Linguistic Have students research melanoma and prepare a presentation illustrating its occurrence and treatment. Have them also develop a prevention plan. **L3**

✓ Assessment

Skill Ask students to describe what will happen to a cell's volume if it is placed in a hypotonic, isotonic, or hypertonic environment. **L2**

INCLUSION STRATEGIES

Visually Impaired: *Kinesthetic* Tie pairs of socks together in the middle to simulate chromosomes undergoing mitosis. Create a series of cells and place the pairs of socks in the appropriate places to mimic the stages of mitosis. Have visually impaired students manipulate the sock chromosomes. **L1 ELL**

Unit 3 Review
Standardized Test Practice

This page contains practice questions in the various formats that can be found on the most frequently given standardized tests.

Part 1 Multiple Choice

1. B	7. C	13. C
2. D	8. A	14. C
3. C	9. D	15. C
4. C	10. C	16. B
5. A	11. A	17. B
6. C	12. A	

 FAST FILE

Answer Sheet A practice answer sheet can be found on p. 163 of *Unit 3 FAST FILE Resources.*

TEST-TAKING TIP

When Eliminating, Cross It Out

List the answer choice letters on scratch paper and, with your pencil, cross out choices you've eliminated. You'll stop yourself from choosing an answer you've mentally eliminated.

Part 1 Multiple Choice

Use the table below to answer questions 1–3.

Chromosome Comparison of Four Organisms				
Organism	Human	Rye	Potato	Guinea pig
Number of chromosomes in body cells	46	14	48	64
Number of chromatids during metaphase	92	A	96	128
Number of chromosomes in daughter cells	46	14	48	64

1. What number belongs in the space labeled *A* under "Rye" in the table?
   - **A.** 14
   - **B.** 28
   - **C.** 7
   - **D.** 21

2. If one pair of chromatids failed to separate during mitosis in rye cells, how many chromosomes would end up in the two daughter cells?
   - **A.** 28 and 28
   - **B.** 14 and 14
   - **C.** 7 and 8
   - **D.** 13 and 15

3. What is the relationship between the number of chromosomes in body cells and the complexity of an organism?
   - **A.** The more complex the organism, the more chromosomes it has.
   - **B.** The more complex the organism, the fewer chromosomes it has.
   - **C.** There is no relationship.
   - **D.** The number of chromosomes is determined by the sex of the organism.

4. The isotopes of the element magnesium differ in their number of _____.
   - **A.** proteins
   - **B.** electrons
   - **C.** neutrons
   - **D.** protons

5. Which of the following organelles are found in all cells?
   - **A.** plasma membrane and ribosomes
   - **B.** mitochondria and chloroplasts
   - **C.** microtubules and lysosomes
   - **D.** Golgi apparatus and endoplasmic reticulum

6. During late interphase, the chromosomes double to form chromatids that are attached to each other. During which phase of mitosis do the chromatids separate?
   - **A.** prophase
   - **B.** metaphase
   - **C.** anaphase
   - **D.** telophase

7. Plants must have a constant supply of _____ for photosynthesis, but they provide _____ for cellular respiration.
   - **A.** water—carbon dioxide
   - **B.** carbon dioxide—water
   - **C.** carbon dioxide—oxygen
   - **D.** oxygen—water

8. Which type of bond involves the sharing of electrons?
   - **A.** covalent
   - **B.** ionic
   - **C.** hydrogen
   - **D.** electrostatic

9. The primary organelle used for storing information in a cell is the _____.
   - **A.** cell wall
   - **B.** endoplasmic reticulum
   - **C.** mitochondria
   - **D.** nucleus

10. A biologist studies cells under a microscope that have been drawn from an unknown solution. The cells appear shriveled. What can the biologist conclude about the solution?
 A. It is hypotonic.
 B. It is isotonic.
 C. It is hypertonic.
 D. It is polar.

11. Which helps capture the sun's energy?
 A. light-dependent reactions
 B. citric acid cycle
 C. Calvin cycle
 D. light-independent reactions

Use the word equation below to answer questions 12–14.

 sucrose + water → glucose + fructose

12. The reaction above illustrates the _____.
 A. hydrolysis of sucrose
 B. condensation of sucrose
 C. hydrolysis of glucose
 D. condensation of fructose

13. The product(s) of this reaction is/are _____.
 A. sucrose
 B. water
 C. glucose and fructose
 D. sucrose and water

14. Glucose and fructose are _____.
 A. disaccharides
 B. polysaccharides
 C. monosaccharides
 D. starches

Part 2 ▶ Constructed Response/Grid In

Record your answers on your answer document.

18. Open Ended How is an ionic bond different from a covalent bond?

19. Open Ended Describe the role of transport proteins in plasma membranes.

20. Open Ended Compare the functions of mitochondria and chloroplasts in cells. Be sure to include ATP in your answer.

21. Open Ended Describe the cellular process of mitosis.

 in.bdol.glencoe.com/standardized_test

Use the figure below to answer questions 15–17.

A.   **B.**

C.   **D.**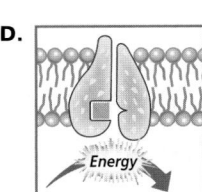
Energy

15. The illustrations above demonstrate the transport of an ion across the plasma membrane, but they are out of sequence. In what order do they belong?
B.1.2
 A. D-C-B-A   **C.** C-B-D-A
 B. A-B-D-C   **D.** A-D-B-C

16. What statement is true about diagram D?
B.1.2
 A. The ion movement is random.
 B. Energy is required.
 C. The fatty acids in the plasma membrane could also move apart to allow the ion through.
 D. The concentration of ions is higher at the top of diagram D than at the bottom.

17. Which process is best represented by these diagrams?
B.1.2
 A. diffusion   **C.** endocytosis
 B. active transport   **D.** passive transport

Part 2 ▶ Constructed Response/Grid In

18. An ionic bond is formed by the attractive force of two ions of opposite charge, like Na^+ and Cl^-. A covalent bond is formed when atoms share electrons. Hydrogen and oxygen are examples of elements that share electrons to form a covalent bond.

19. Transport proteins span the entire plasma membrane. They allow needed substances or waste materials to move through the plasma membrane, giving the plasma membrane its characteristic selective permeability.

20. Chloroplasts, found only in plant cells, capture light energy and convert it to ATP for the cell. Mitochondria in both plant and animal cells convert food energy into ATP for the cell.

21. Prior to mitosis (cell division), in interphase, there is intense metabolic activity in the cell. In prophase, the first stage, the duplicated chromosomes condense and the mitotic spindle forms. During metaphase, the chromosomes line up in the center of the cell and slowly separate during anaphase. In telophase, the nucleus divides.

RUBRIC

For more help evaluating open-ended assessment questions, see the rubric on p. 9T.

Genetics

Unit Overview

Unit 4 presents genetics and its role in determining traits of organisms.

Chapter 10 introduces genetics through a historical presentation of Gregor Mendel's work. Meiosis is then introduced.

Chapter 11 presents the structure of DNA and replication is explained. Transcription and translation are explained. Various mutations are described.

Chapter 12 examines non-Mendelian heredity and the principles of human genetics.

Chapter 13 discusses selective breeding, DNA technology, and the Human Genome Project.

Introducing the Unit

Have students look at the picture of the tiger cubs and describe the traits they see. The white tiger is not an albino, or a separate species. It is a tiger with recessive color genes. Unit 4 will discuss how genes determine an organism's physical traits, as well as how those traits are inherited.

WebQuest   A WebQuest is an inquiry-based online project in which all information used by students is obtained from the Web. Students evaluate the information to complete the activity. Access the Unit 4 WebQuest at **in.bdol.glencoe.com/webquest**

Indiana Academic Standards
Pages 250–251: B.1.21

250

History & Biology

1800   *1850*

1863 ●
Lincoln writes the Emancipation Proclamation.

1865 ●
Mendel discovers the rules of inheritance.

Genetics

What You'll Learn

Chapter 10
Mendel and Meiosis

Chapter 11
DNA and Genes

Chapter 12
Patterns of Heredity and Human Genetics

Chapter 13
Genetic Technology

Unit 4 Review
BioDigest & Standardized Test Practice

Why It's Important

Physical traits, such as the stripes of these tigers, are encoded in small segments of a chromosome called genes, which are passed from one generation to the next. By studying the inheritance pattern of a trait through several generations, the probability that future offspring will express that trait can be predicted.

Indiana Standards
The following standards are covered in Unit 4:
B.1.8, B.1.21, B.1.22, B.1.23, B.1.24, B.1.25, B.1.26, B.1.27, B.1.28, B.1.29, B.1.30, B.2.4

Understanding the Photo ▶

White tigers differ from orange tigers by having ice-blue eyes, a pink nose, and creamy white fur with brown or black stripes. They are not albinos. The only time a white tiger is born is when its parents each carry the white-coloring gene. White tigers are very rare, and today, they are only seen in zoos.

250 in.bdol.glencoe.com/webquest

Time Line

Discussion As students read Unit 4, have them refer to the above time line. Ask students to infer how Mendel's discovery of the rules of inheritance (1865) led to the conclusion that DNA is the genetic material (1952) and how both events led to the Human Genome Project (1990s). Have student groups research and discuss future uses of the human genome map.

250

Timeline

1950 • The Korean War begins when North Korea invades South Korea.

1964 • The Beatles make their first appearance on American TV.

1900   1950   2000

1910 Scientists determine that genes reside on chromosomes.

1944 • Scientists suggest genetic material is DNA, not protein. The results are not accepted.

1952 Alfred Hershey and Martha Chase show conclusively that DNA is the genetic material.

1953 Watson, Crick, Wilkins, and Franklin determine the structure of DNA.

1961 The genetic code is cracked.

2000 • Most of the human DNA sequence is completed.

1990 • The Human Genome Project begins to map and sequence the entire human genome.

Advance Materials Planning

The following materials may need to be ordered a few weeks in advance of the planned activity.

Chapter 10
- **MiniLab** (p. 254) microscope slide and coverslip, microscope
- **Project** (p. 257) *Brassica rapa* seeds
- **MiniLab** (p. 268) clay
- **BioLab** (p. 274) small flower-pots or seedling flats

Chapter 11
- **Additional Lab** (p. 282) 3-ply yarn
- **Quick Demo** (p. 285) zipper
- **Quick Demo** (p. 298) coiled telephone cord

Chapter 12
- **Additional Lab** (p. 316) het-erozygous tobacco seeds
- **Project** (p. 321) mustard seeds
- **Additional Lab** (p. 324) pre-pared slides of male and female cheek cells
- **BioLab** (p. 330) *Brassica rapa* seeds—normal and variegated

Chapter 13
- **MiniLab** (p. 350) Random page from a novel
- **Additional Lab** (p. 350) pre-pared slide of cheek cells, human hair (blond and dark)
- **Quick Demo** (p. 351) human chromosome map

251

Unit Projects

Using the Library
Intrapersonal Research one disease in which gene therapy is an experi-mental therapeutic approach such as cancer, hemophilia, Alzheimer's disease, and sickle cell anemia. **L2**

Interview
Linguistic Interview someone with a family pedigree that demon-strates an inherited disease such as Huntington's disease, hemophilia, and Tay-Sachs disease. **L1**

Final Report
Have student groups present their findings about genetics in reports that could be presented to stu-dents at your local middle school. **L3** **COOP LEARN**

Chapter 10 Organizer

Section Objectives	National Science Standards	State/Local Standards	Advanced Lab and Demo Planning
Section 10.1 2 sessions, 2 blocks 1. **Relate** Mendel's two laws to the results he obtained in his experiments with garden peas. 2. **Predict** the possible offspring of a genetic cross by using a Punnett square.	UCP.1–3, UCP.5; A.1, A.2; G.1–3	**Indiana Standards** B.1.21, B.1.22, B.1.29, B.2.4	**Student Labs:** MiniLab 10.1, p. 254: flower, water, glass slide, coverslip, pencil with eraser, microscope Problem-Solving Lab 10.1, p. 262 **Teacher Demonstration:** Quick Demo, p. 259: 300 black beans, 100 white beans, small cup or bag
Section 10.2 3 sessions, 2 blocks 3. **Analyze** how meiosis maintains a constant number of chromosomes within a species. 4. **Infer** how meiosis leads to variation in a species. 5. **Relate** Mendel's laws of heredity to the events of meiosis.	UCP.1–3; A.1, A.2; C.1, C.2; E.1, E.2; F.6; G.1–3	**Indiana Standards** B.1.8, B.1.21, B.1.22, B.1.28, B.1.29, B.2.4	**Student Labs:** Problem-Solving Lab 10.2, p. 264 Additional Lab, p. 266: long length of yarn, paper clips, long length of string, toothpicks, tape or glue, scissors MiniLab 10.2, p. 268: clay Internet BioLab, p. 274: See materials below. **Teacher Demonstration:** Quick Demo, p. 266
End of Chapter Assessment Student Edition **Study Guide,** p. 277 **Content Assessment,** pp. 278–279		**Indiana Standards** B.1.8, B.1.21, B.1.22, B.1.28, B.1.29	**Student Lab:** Internet BioLab, p. 274: potting soil, small flowerpots or seedling flats, two groups of tobacco seeds, hand lens, light source, thermometer, plant-watering bottle

Key to Teaching Strategies

L1 Level 1 activities should be appropriate for students with learning difficulties.

L2 Level 2 activities should be within the ability range of all students.

L3 Level 3 activities are designed for above-average students.

ELL ELL activities should be within the ability range of English Language Learners.

COOP LEARN
Cooperative Learning activities are designed for small group work.

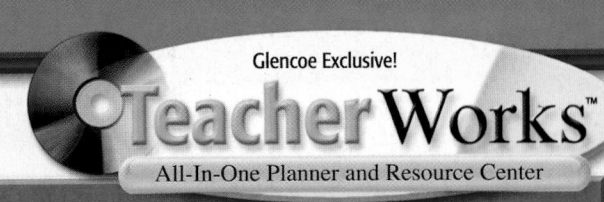

Glencoe Exclusive!

TeacherWorks™
All-In-One Planner and Resource Center

Reproducible Masters and Transparencies

Technology

Unit 4 FAST FILE Resources
   MiniLab Worksheet, p. 3
   BioLab Worksheet, pp. 5–6
   Real World BioApplications, pp. 7–8
   Reinforcement and Study Guide in English,
     pp. 9–10
   Reinforcement and Study Guide in Spanish,
     pp. 13–14
   Critical Thinking/Problem Solving, p. 18
   Transparency Worksheets, pp. 19, 21–22, 25–26
Reading Essentials for Biology,
   Section 10.1
👆 **Section Focus Transparency 24**
👆 **Basic Concepts Transparency 14**
👆 **Reteaching Skills Transparency 16**

💿 **Interactive Chalkboard CD-ROM: Section 10.1 Presentation** 📍
💿 **TeacherWorks™ CD-ROM** 📍
🎵 **Guided Reading Audio Summaries MP3**
💿 **Virtual Labs CD-ROM**
   Virtual Lab: Punnett Squares

Unit 4 FAST FILE Resources
   MiniLab Worksheet, p. 4
   Reinforcement and Study Guide in English,
     pp. 11–12
   Reinforcement and Study Guide in Spanish,
     pp. 15–16
   Concept Mapping, p. 17
   Transparency Worksheets, pp. 20, 23–24, 27–28
Reading Essentials for Biology,
   Section 10.2
👆 **Laboratory Manual,** pp. 53–54, 55–58
👆 **Section Focus Transparency 25**
👆 **Basic Concepts Transparency 15**
👆 **Reteaching Skills Transparency 17**

💿 **Interactive Chalkboard CD-ROM: Section 10.2 Presentation** 📍
💿 **TeacherWorks™ CD-ROM** 📍
🎵 **Guided Reading Audio Summaries MP3**

Unit 4 FAST FILE Resources
   Chapter Assessment, pp. 29–34
   Student Recording Sheet, p. 35

| The Princeton Review | **Reviewing Biology,** pp. 19–20 |

💿 **Interactive Chalkboard:**
   Chapter 10 Assessment 📍
💿 **MindJogger Videoquizzes**
   DVD/VHS
💿 **ExamView® Pro Test Bank**
   CD-ROM
💿 **TeacherWorks™ CD-ROM** 📍
💿 **Succeeding on National Standards CD-ROM**

🖱 **in.bdol.glencoe.com**
   /self_check_quiz
   /vocabulary_puzzlemaker
   /chapter_test
   /standardized_test

📍 Indicates materials created specifically for Indiana.

Short on Time?

BIODIGEST The BioDigest at the end of this unit can be used as a(n):

- preview to introduce important unit concepts.
- overview if time does not permit teaching the entire chapter.
- review of key unit concepts.

Understanding the Photo

A zebra's stripes are thought to be an adaptation that helps them avoid predators. Zebras recognize each other by their stripes. Their stripes are like fingerprints—they are passed on genetically, and every zebra's stripe pattern is different.

Mendel and Meiosis

What You'll Learn

- You will identify the basic concepts of genetics.
- You will examine the process of meiosis.

Why It's Important

Genetics explains why you have inherited certain traits from your parents. If you understand how meiosis occurs, you can see how these traits were passed on to you.

Understanding the Photo

Zebras usually travel in large groups, and each zebra's stripes blend in with the stripes of the zebras around it. This confuses predators. Rather than seeing individual zebras, predators see a large, striped mass. Zebra stripe patterns are like human fingerprints—they are genetically determined, and every zebra's stripe pattern is unique.

Biology Online

Visit **in.bdol.glencoe.com** to
- study the entire chapter online
- access Web Links for more information and activities on genetics and meiosis
- review content with the Interactive Tutor and self-check quizzes

Two-Minute Chapter Launcher

Demo Show students wrinkled and smooth pea seeds. Have them compare and contrast the physical traits of the pea seeds. Encourage them to speculate about less obvious traits such as biochemical or physiological characteristics. The wrinkled nature of the seeds is due to a lack of well-formed starch grains and lower water retention. **L2**

Section 10.1

Mendel's Laws of Heredity

Indiana Standards Standard B.1.22 Understand and explain the genetic basis for Mendel's laws of segregation and independent assortment.

SECTION PREVIEW

Objectives

Relate Mendel's two laws to the results he obtained in his experiments with garden peas.

Predict the possible offspring of a genetic cross by using a Punnett square.

Review Vocabulary
experiment: a procedure that tests a hypothesis by the process of collecting data under controlled conditions (p. 13)

New Vocabulary
heredity
trait
genetics
gamete
fertilization
zygote
pollination
hybrid
allele
dominant
recessive
law of segregation
phenotype
genotype
homozygous
heterozygous
law of independent assortment

FOLDABLES™
Study Organizer

Heredity Make the following Foldable to help you organize information about Mendel's laws of heredity.

STEP 1 **Fold** one piece of paper lengthwise into thirds.

STEP 2 **Fold** the paper widthwise into fifths.

STEP 3 **Unfold,** lay the paper lengthwise, and draw lines along the folds.

STEP 4 **Label** your table as shown.

Mendel	Describe in Your Words	Give an Example
Rule of unit factors		
Rule of dominance		
Law of segregation		
Law of independent assortment		

Make a Table As you read Chapter 10, complete the table describing Mendel's rules and laws of heredity.

Why Mendel Succeeded

People have noticed for thousands of years that family resemblances are inherited from generation to generation. However, it was not until the mid-nineteenth century that Gregor Mendel, an Austrian monk, carried out important studies of **heredity**—the passing on of characteristics from parents to offspring. Characteristics that are inherited are called **traits.** Mendel was the first person to succeed in predicting how traits are transferred from one generation to the next. A complete explanation requires the careful study of **genetics**—the branch of biology that studies heredity.

Mendel chose his subject carefully

Mendel chose to use the garden pea in his experiments for several reasons. Garden pea plants reproduce sexually, which means that they produce male and female sex cells, called **gametes.** The male gamete forms in the pollen grain, which is produced in the male reproductive organ. The female gamete forms in the female reproductive organ. In a process called **fertilization,** the male gamete unites with the female gamete. The resulting fertilized cell, called a **zygote** (ZI goht), then develops into a seed.

Word Origin
heredity from the Latin word *hered-,* meaning "heir"; Heredity describes the way the genetic qualities you receive from your ancestors are passed on.

10.1 MENDEL'S LAWS OF HEREDITY **253**

Bellringer
Section Focus Transparency 24

Transparency **24** Predicting Combinations

SECTION FOCUS
Use with Chapter 10, Section 10.1

Group 1

Group 2

① What possible combinations can result from combining one coin from each group?

② What is the ratio of the possible combinations?

BIOLOGY: The Dynamics of Life   SECTION FOCUS TRANSPARENCIES

INTERACTIVE
CHALKBOARD
with Image Bank

PowerPoint® Presentations

This CD-ROM is an editable Microsoft® PowerPoint® presentation that includes:
- Section presentations
- Section checks
- Image bank
- Hot links to Biology Online
- All transparencies

FOLDABLES™
For an additional Foldables activity idea, see the Chapter 10 Foldables page in *Unit 4 FAST FILE Resources.*

RESOURCE MANAGER

Unit 4 *FAST FILE* Resources
  MiniLab Worksheet, p. 3
  BioLab Worksheet, pp. 5–6
  Real World BioApplications, pp. 7–8
  Reinforcement and Study Guide in English, pp. 9–10
  Reinforcement and Study Guide in Spanish, pp. 13–14
  Critical Thinking/Problem Solving, p. 18

Transparency Worksheets, pp. 19, 21–22, 25–26
  Section Focus Transparency 24
  Basic Concepts Transparency 14
  Reteaching Skills Transparency 16
  Reading Essentials for Biology, Section 10.1

Indiana Academic Standards

Pages 252–253: B.1.21, B.2.4

2 Teach

MiniLab 10.1

Purpose
Students will observe pollen grains in plants.

Process Skills
observe and infer

Safety Precautions
Caution students when handling slides and coverslips. Have students wash their hands after handling flowers and flower parts.

Teaching Strategies
■ Preserved flower material is available from biological supply houses.
■ Forceps may be used to remove stamens from the flower.
■ If coverslips or slides break during the squashing process, have students place them in a container for broken glass and start over with new material.

Expected Results
Students will observe that each anther contains thousands of small pollen grains.

Analysis
1. Numbers should be in the several thousands.
2. Student answers will vary depending on species used. Pollen grains are microscopic cells, often round in shape.
3. Pollen grains contain male reproductive cells needed for fertilization. They provide chromosomes and genes of the male parent.

Assessment
Performance Have students diagram several pollen cells under high power and have them include pollen size, in micrometers. If students have not done any previous measuring, refer them to MiniLab 7.1. Use the Performance Task Assessment List for Using Math in Science in **PASC**, p. 101. **L2**

254

MiniLab 10.1

Observe and Infer

Looking at Pollen Pollen grains are formed within the male anthers of flowers. What is their role? Pollen contains the male gametes, or sperm cells, needed for fertilization. This means that pollen grains carry the hereditary units from male parent plants to female parent plants. The pollen grains that Mendel transferred from the anther of one pea plant to the female pistil of another plant carried the hereditary traits that he so carefully observed in the next generation.

Anther
Pistil
Stamens

Procedure

1. Examine a flower. Using the diagram as a guide, locate the stamens of your flower. There are usually several stamens in each flower.
2. Remove one stamen and locate the enlarged end—the anther.
3. Add a drop of water to a microscope glass slide. Place the anther in the water. Add a coverslip. Using the eraser end of a pencil, tap the coverslip several times to squash the anther.
4. Observe under low power. Look for numerous small round structures. These are pollen grains.

Analysis

1. **Estimate** Provide an estimate of the number of pollen grains present in an anther.
2. **Describe** What does a single pollen grain look like?
3. **Explain** What is the role of pollen grains in plant reproduction?

Figure 10.1
In his experiments, Mendel often had to transfer pollen from one plant to another plant with different traits. This is called making a cross.
Describe *How did Mendel make a cross?*

Remove male parts

Female part

Transfer pollen

Male parts

Pollen grains

Cross-pollination

254 MENDEL AND MEIOSIS

The transfer of pollen grains from a male reproductive organ to a female reproductive organ in a plant is called **pollination.** In peas, both organs are located in the same flower and are tightly enclosed by petals. This prevents pollen from other flowers from entering the pea flower. As a result, peas normally reproduce by self-pollination; that is, the male and female gametes come from the same plant. In many of Mendel's experiments, this is exactly what he wanted. When he wanted to breed, or cross, one plant with another, Mendel opened the petals of a flower and removed the male organs, as shown in *Figure 10.1A*. He then dusted the female organ with pollen from the plant he wished to cross it with, as shown in *Figure 10.1B*. This process is called cross-pollination. By using this technique, Mendel could be sure of the parents in his cross.

Mendel was a careful researcher

Mendel carefully controlled his experiments and the peas he used. He studied only one trait at a time to control variables, and he analyzed his data mathematically. The tall pea plants he worked with were from populations of plants that had been tall for many generations and had always produced tall offspring. Such plants are said to be true breeding for tallness. Likewise, the short plants he worked with were true breeding for shortness.

Caption Question Answer
Figure 10.1 Mendel removed pollen from the anther of one flower and placed it on the stigma of another.

Mendel's Monohybrid Crosses

What did Mendel do with the tall and short pea plants he selected? He crossed them to produce new plants. Mendel referred to the offspring of this cross as hybrids. A **hybrid** is the offspring of parents that have different forms of a trait, such as tall and short height. Mendel's first experiments are called monohybrid crosses because *mono* means "one" and the two parent plants differed from each other by a single trait—height.

The first generation

Mendel selected a six-foot-tall pea plant that came from a population of pea plants, all of which were over six feet tall. He cross-pollinated this tall pea plant with pollen from a short pea plant that was less than two feet tall and which came from a population of pea plants that were all short. When he planted the seeds from this cross, he found that all of the offspring grew to be as tall as the taller parent. In this first generation, it was as if the shorter parent had never existed.

The second generation

Next, Mendel allowed the tall plants in this first generation to self-pollinate. After the seeds formed, he planted them and counted more than 1000 plants in this second generation. Mendel found that three-fourths of the plants were as tall as the tall plants in the parent and first generations. He also found that one-fourth of the offspring were as short as the short plants in the parent generation. In other words, in the second generation, tall and short plants occurred in a ratio of about three tall plants to one short plant, as shown in *Figure 10.2*. The short trait had reappeared as if from nowhere.

The original parents, the true-breeding plants, are known as the P_1 generation. The P stands for "parent." The offspring of the parent plants are known as the F_1 generation. The F stands for "filial"—son or daughter. When you cross two F_1 plants with each other, their offspring are the F_2 generation—the second filial generation. You might find it easier to understand these terms if you

Figure 10.2
When Mendel crossed true-breeding tall pea plants with true-breeding short pea plants, all the offspring were tall. When he allowed first-generation tall plants to self-pollinate, three-fourths of the offspring were tall and one-fourth were short.

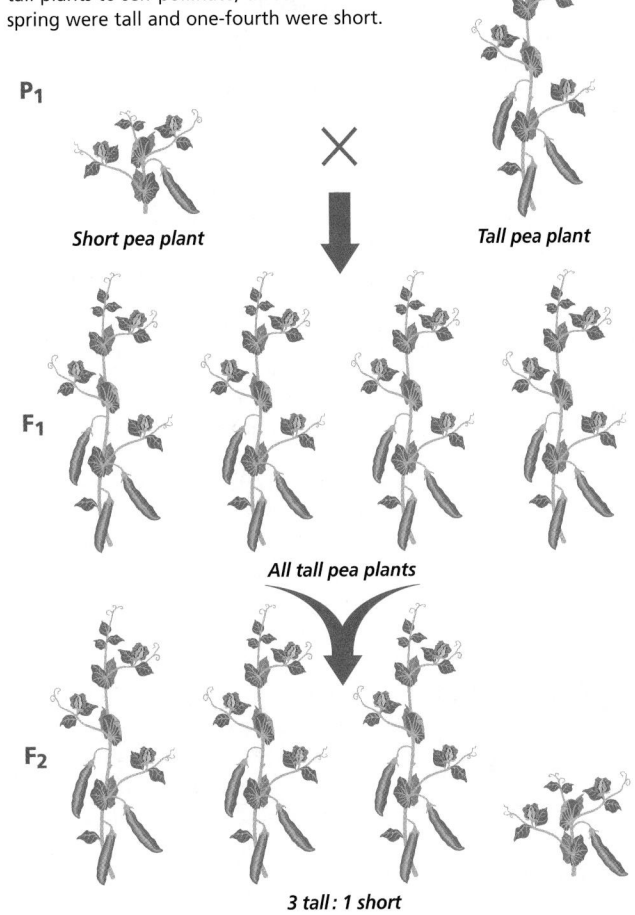

P_1

Short pea plant   Tall pea plant

F_1

All tall pea plants

F_2

3 tall : 1 short

Figure 10.3 Mendel studied variations in seed shape and color, flower color and position, pod color and shape, and plant height. Many other variations also exist.

Revealing Misconceptions

Almost all students think that the dominant trait must be most common or desirable. However, the dominant trait is merely one that masks an alternate allele that may be present in the heterozygous condition.

Uncover the Misconception

Ask students to give examples of dominant traits. When a student names a recessive trait that is really dominant, point out the error.

Demonstrate the Concept

Explain that Huntington's disease, polydactyly, and hypercholesterolemia (having dangerously high levels of blood cholesterol) are three dominant traits inherited in humans, although all three traits are very rare.

Assess New Knowledge

Have students state the definition of dominance. Ask them to state how it is possible for a dominant trait to rarely appear. The number of recessive alleles in the gene pool for a particular trait may be far greater than the number of dominant alleles in the pool.

	Seed shape	Seed color	Flower color	Flower position	Pod color	Pod shape	Plant height
Dominant trait	round	yellow	purple	axial (side)	green	inflated	tall
Recessive trait	wrinkled	green	white	terminal (tips)	yellow	constricted	short

Figure 10.3
Mendel chose seven traits of peas for his experiments. Each trait had two clearly different forms; no intermediate forms were observed. **Compare** *What genetic variations are observed in plants?*

Word Origin

allele from the Greek word *allelon*, meaning "of each other"; Genes exist in alternative forms called alleles.

look at your own family. Your parents are the P_1 generation. You are the F_1 generation, and any children you might have in the future would be the F_2 generation.

Mendel did similar monohybrid crosses with a total of seven pairs of traits, studying one pair of traits at a time. These pairs of traits are shown in *Figure 10.3*. In every case, he found that one trait of a pair seemed to disappear in the F_1 generation, only to reappear unchanged in one-fourth of the F_2 plants.

The rule of unit factors

Mendel concluded that each organism has two factors that control each of its traits. We now know that these factors are genes and that they are located on chromosomes. Genes exist in alternative forms. We call these different gene forms **alleles** (uh LEELZ). For example, each

of Mendel's pea plants had two alleles of the gene that determined its height. A plant could have two alleles for tallness, two alleles for shortness, or one allele for tallness and one for shortness. An organism's two alleles are located on different copies of a chromosome—one inherited from the female parent and one from the male parent.

The rule of dominance

Remember what happened when Mendel crossed a tall P_1 plant with a short P_1 plant? The F_1 offspring were all tall. In other words, only one trait was observed. In such crosses, Mendel called the observed trait **dominant** and the trait that disappeared **recessive.** Mendel concluded that the allele for tall plants is dominant to the allele for short plants. Thus, plants that had one allele for tallness and one for shortness were tall.

CHALLENGE ACTIVITY

Rules of Heredity For students needing an additional challenge, have them work in groups and imagine that they are Gregor Mendel and that they have just formulated the principles of dominance and segregation. Have them work together to write an illustrated article describing their findings for a local newspaper. They should remember that the year is 1863. See *BioChallenges and Enrichment* for additional projects and activities. **L3**

Expressed another way, the allele for short plants is recessive to the allele for tall plants. Pea plants with two alleles for tallness were tall, and those with two alleles for shortness were short. You can see in *Figure 10.4* how the rule of dominance explained the resulting F₁ generation.

When recording the results of crosses, it is customary to use the same letter for different alleles of the same gene. An uppercase letter is used for the dominant allele and a lowercase letter for the recessive allele. The dominant allele is always written first. Thus, the allele for tallness is written as *T* and the allele for shortness as *t*, as it is in *Figure 10.4.*

✓ Reading Check **Describe** Mendel's two rules of heredity.

The law of segregation

Now recall the results of Mendel's cross between F₁ tall plants, when the trait of shortness reappeared. To explain this result, Mendel formulated the first of his two laws of heredity. He concluded that each tall plant in the F₁ generation carried one dominant allele for tallness and one unexpressed recessive allele for shortness. Each plant received the allele for tallness from its tall parent and the allele for shortness from its short parent in the P₁ generation. Because each F₁ plant has two different alleles, it can produce two types of gametes—"tall" gametes and "short" gametes. This conclusion, illustrated in *Figure 10.5* on the next page, is called the **law of segregation.** The law of segregation states that every individual has two alleles of each gene and when gametes are produced, each gamete receives one of these alleles. During fertilization, these gametes randomly pair to produce four combinations of alleles.

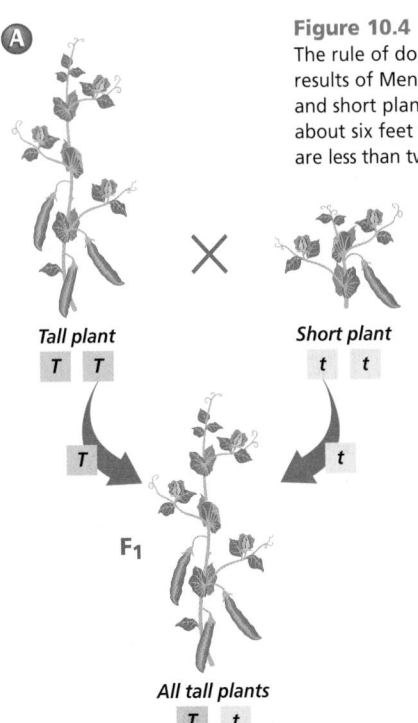

Figure 10.4
The rule of dominance explains the results of Mendel's cross between P₁ tall and short plants **(A)**. Tall pea plants are about six feet tall, whereas short plants are less than two feet tall **(B)**.

Ⓐ

Tall plant
| T | T |

Short plant
| t | t |

| T |

| t |

F₁

All tall plants
| T | t |

Ⓑ

257

PROJECT

Experimental Crosses Rapid-cycling *Brassica rapa* plants complete their life cycle in 30 to 40 days. They are ideal for use in the classroom because within this short time, the plants flower and form seeds for the next generation. Genetic studies can be carried out using different traits, such as petal-less flowers or hairy stems. Students will find it easy to carry out the pollinating between plants. These plants are an ideal experimental organism for genetic studies. **L2**

Indiana Academic Standards
Pages 256–257: B.1.21, B.1.22, B.1.29, B.2.4

258

Figure 10.5
Mendel's law of segregation explains the results of his cross between F_1 tall plants. He concluded that the two alleles for each trait must separate when gametes are formed. A parent, therefore, passes on at random only one allele for each trait to each offspring.

Law of segregation   ***Tt* × *Tt* cross**

F_1

Tall plant   T t   Tall plant   T t

F_2

Tall   T T   Tall   T t   Tall   T t   Short   t t

3   1

Word Origin

phenotype from the Greek words *phainein*, meaning "to show," and *typos*, meaning "model"; The visible characteristics of an organism make up its phenotype.

genotype from the Greek words *gen* or *geno*, meaning "race," and *typos*, meaning "model"; The allele combination of an organism makes up its genotype.

Phenotypes and Genotypes

Mendel showed that tall plants are not all the same. Some tall plants, when crossed with each other, yielded only tall offspring. These were Mendel's original P_1 true-breeding tall plants. Other tall plants, when crossed with each other, yielded both tall and short offspring. These were the F_1 tall plants in *Figure 10.5* that came from a cross between a tall plant and a short plant.

Two organisms, therefore, can look alike but have different underlying allele combinations. The way an organism looks and behaves is called its **phenotype** (FEE noh tipe). The phenotype of a tall plant is tall, whether it is *TT* or *Tt*. The allele combination an organism contains is known as its **genotype** (JEE noh tipe). The genotype of a tall plant that has two alleles for tallness is *TT*. The genotype of a tall plant that has one allele for tallness and one allele for shortness is *Tt*. You can see that an organism's genotype can't always be known by its phenotype.

An organism is **homozygous** (hoh moh ZI gus) for a trait if its two alleles for the trait are the same. The true-breeding tall plant that had two alleles for tallness (*TT*) would be homozygous for the trait of height. Because tallness is dominant, a *TT* individual is homozygous dominant for that trait. A short plant would always have two alleles for shortness (*tt*). It would, therefore, always be homozygous recessive for the trait of height.

An organism is **heterozygous** (heh tuh roh ZI gus) for a trait if its two alleles for the trait differ from each other. Therefore, the tall plant that had one allele for tallness and one allele for shortness (*Tt*) is heterozygous for the trait of height.

Now look at *Figure 10.5* again. Can you identify the phenotype and genotype of each plant? Is each plant homozygous or heterozygous? You can practice determining genotypes and phenotypes in the *BioLab* at the end of this chapter.

Mendel's Dihybrid Crosses

Mendel performed another set of crosses in which he used peas that differed from each other in two traits rather than only one. Such a cross involving two different traits is called a dihybrid cross because *di* means "two." In a dihybrid cross, will the two traits stay together in the next generation or will they be inherited independently of each other?

The first generation

Mendel took true-breeding pea plants that had round yellow seeds (*RRYY*) and crossed them with true-breeding pea plants that had wrinkled green seeds (*rryy*). He already knew that when he crossed plants that produced round seeds with plants that produced wrinkled seeds, all the plants in the F$_1$ generation produced seeds that were round. In other words, just as tall plants were dominant to short plants, the round-seeded trait was dominant to the wrinkled-seeded trait. Similarly, when he crossed plants that produced yellow seeds with plants that produced green seeds, all the plants in the F$_1$ generation produced yellow seeds—yellow was dominant. Therefore,

Mendel was not surprised when he found that the F$_1$ plants of his dihybrid cross all had the two dominant traits of round and yellow seeds, as *Figure 10.6* shows.

The second generation

Mendel then let the F$_1$ plants pollinate themselves. As you might expect, he found some plants that produced round yellow seeds and others that produced wrinkled green seeds. But that's not all. He also found some plants with round green seeds and others with wrinkled yellow seeds. When Mendel sorted and counted the plants of the F$_2$ generation, he found they appeared in a definite ratio of phenotypes—9 round yellow: 3 round green: 3 wrinkled yellow: 1 wrinkled green. To explain the results of this dihybrid cross, Mendel formulated his second law.

Dihybrid cross   round yellow × wrinkled green

P$_1$ Round yellow   ×   Wrinkled green

F$_1$ All round yellow

F$_2$

| 9 Round yellow | 3 Round green | 3 Wrinkled yellow | 1 Wrinkled green |

Figure 10.6
When Mendel crossed true-breeding plants that produced round yellow seeds with true-breeding plants that produced wrinkled green seeds, the seeds of all the offspring were round and yellow. When the F$_1$ plants were allowed to self-pollinate, they produced four different kinds of plants in the F$_2$ generation.

Resources

For additional high-interest activities, see the *Forensics and Biotechnology Lab Manual*.

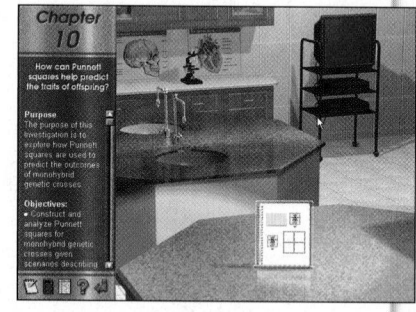
The law of independent assortment

Mendel's second law states that genes for different traits—for example, seed shape and seed color—are inherited independently of each other. This conclusion is known as the **law of independent assortment.** When a pea plant with the genotype *RrYy* produces gametes, the alleles *R* and *r* will separate from each other (the law of segregation) as well as from the alleles *Y* and *y* (the law of independent assortment), and vice versa. These alleles can then recombine in four different ways. If the alleles for seed shape and color were inherited together, only two kinds of pea seeds would have been produced: round yellow and wrinkled green.

Punnett Squares

In 1905, Reginald Punnett, an English biologist, devised a shorthand way of finding the expected proportions of possible genotypes in the offspring of a cross. This method is called a Punnett square. It takes account of the fact that fertilization occurs at random, as Mendel's law of segregation states. If you know the genotypes of the parents, you can use a Punnett square to predict the possible genotypes of their offspring.

Monohybrid crosses

Consider the cross between two F_1 tall pea plants, each of which has the genotype *Tt*. Half the gametes of each parent would contain the *T* allele, and the other half would contain the *t* allele. A Punnett square for this cross is two boxes tall and two boxes wide because each parent can produce two kinds of gametes for this trait. The two kinds of gametes from one parent are listed on top of the square, and the two kinds of gametes from the other parent are listed on the left side, as *Figure 10.7A* shows. It doesn't matter which set of gametes is on top and which is on the side, that is, which parent contributes the *T* allele and which contributes the *t* allele. Refer to the Punnett square in *Figure 10.7B* to determine the possible genotypes of the offspring. Each box is filled in with the gametes above and to the left side of that box. You can see that each box then contains two alleles—one possible genotype.

Figure 10.7
This Punnett square predicts the results of a monohybrid cross between two heterozygous pea plants.

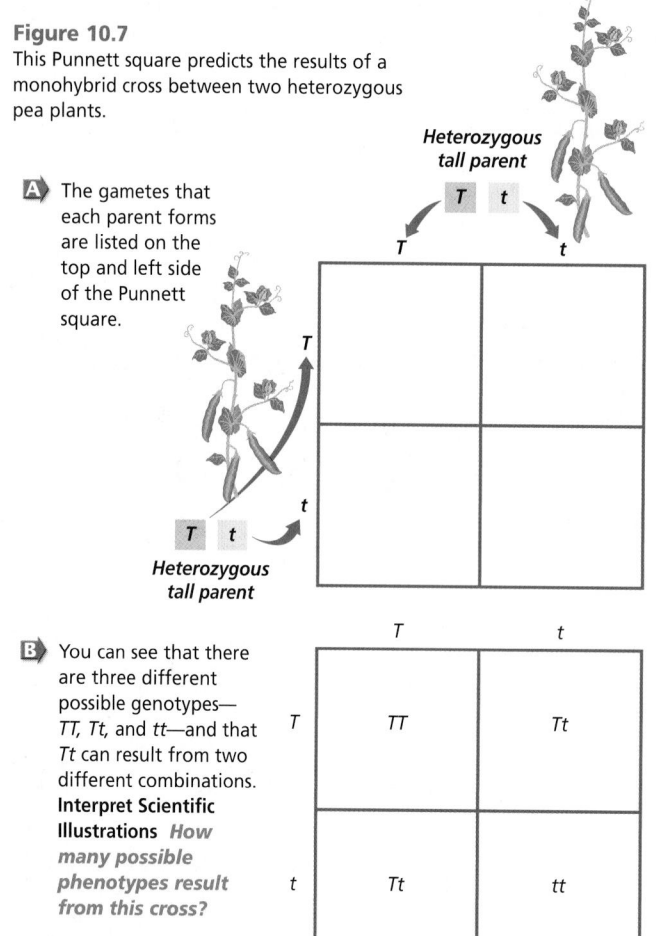

A The gametes that each parent forms are listed on the top and left side of the Punnett square.

Heterozygous tall parent

B You can see that there are three different possible genotypes—*TT*, *Tt*, and *tt*—and that *Tt* can result from two different combinations. **Interpret Scientific Illustrations** *How many possible phenotypes result from this cross?*

	T	t
T	TT	Tt
t	Tt	tt

After the genotypes have been determined, you can determine the phenotypes. Looking again at the Punnett square in *Figure 10.7B*, you can see that three-fourths of the off-spring are expected to be tall because they have at least one dominant allele. One-fourth are expected to be short because they lack a dominant allele. Of the tall offspring, one-third will be homozygous dominant *(TT)* and two-thirds will be heterozygous *(Tt)*. Note that whereas the genotype ratio is 1*TT*: 2*Tt*: 1*tt*, the phenotype ratio is 3 tall: 1 short. You can practice doing calculations such as Mendel did in the *Connection to Math* at the end of this chapter.

Dihybrid crosses

What happens in a Punnett square when two traits are considered? Think again about Mendel's cross between pea plants producing round yellow seeds and plants producing wrinkled green seeds. All the F_1 plants produced seeds that were round and yellow and were heterozygous for each trait *(RrYy)*. What kind of gametes will these F_1 plants form?

Mendel explained that the traits for seed shape and seed color would be inherited independently of each other. This means that each F_1 plant will produce gametes containing the following combinations of genes with equal frequency: round yellow *(RY)*, round green *(Ry)*, wrinkled yellow *(rY)*, and wrinkled green *(ry)*. A Punnett square for a dihybrid cross will then need to be four boxes on each side for a total of 16 boxes, as *Figure 10.8* shows.

Probability

Punnett squares are good for showing all the possible combinations of gametes and the likelihood that each

Punnett Square of Dihybrid Cross
Gametes from RrYy parent

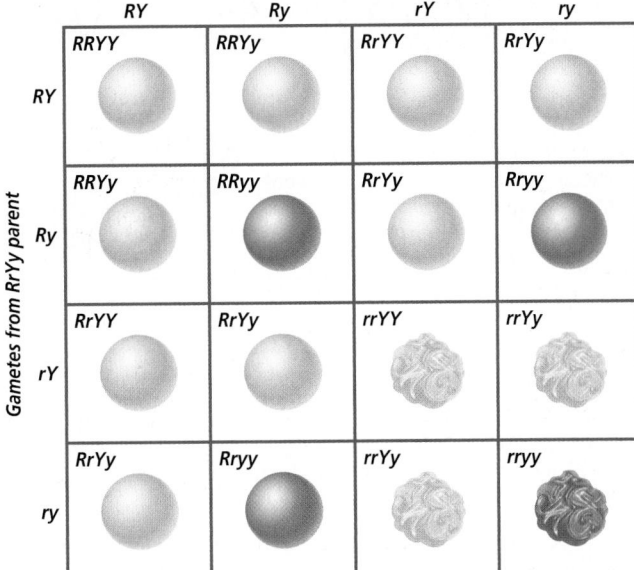

Figure 10.8
A Punnett square for a dihybrid cross between heterozygous pea plants producing round yellow seeds shows clearly that the offspring fulfill Mendel's observed ratio of 9 round yellow: 3 round green: 3 wrinkled yellow: 1 wrinkled green.

F_1 cross: *RrYy* × *RrYy*
○ round yellow
● round green
◆ wrinkled yellow
◆ wrinkled green

will occur. In reality, however, you don't get the exact ratio of results shown in the square. That's because, in some ways, genetics is like flipping a coin—it follows the rules of chance.

When you toss a coin, it lands either heads up or tails up. The probability or chance that an event will occur can be determined by dividing the number of desired outcomes by the total number of possible outcomes. Therefore, the probability of getting heads when you toss a coin would be one in two chances, written as 1:2 or ½. A Punnett square can be used to determine the probability of getting a pea plant that produces round seeds when two plants that are heterozygous *(Rr)* are crossed.

10.1 MENDEL'S LAWS OF HEREDITY **261**

3 Assess

DAILY INTERVENTION

Check for Understanding
Have students describe the relationship between or among the following terms. **L1** **ELL**
a. pollination—fertilization
b. allele—dominant—recessive
c. genotype—phenotype
d. homozygous—heterozygous
e. monohybrid—dihybrid

Reteach
Have students provide an example of each relationship provided in Check for Understanding. **L1**

Resources
For more practice, use *Reading Essentials for Biology*, Section 10.1.

Extension

Have students list the genotypes and phenotypes resulting from (a) an *RrYy* plant cross-pollinated by an *RRyy* plant; (b) an *rrYy* plant cross-pollinated by a *RrYy* plant. (a) genotypes: *RrYy, RRyy, RRYy, Rryy*; phenotypes: ½ round yellow, ½ round green; (b) genotypes: *RrYY; RrYy, Rryy, rrYY, rrYy, rryy*; phenotypes: 3 round yellow; 3 wrinkled yellow; 1 round green; 1 wrinkled green **L2**

✓ MODIFIED Assessment

Knowledge Have students explain what each of the following represents in a Punnett square: (a) the letters written at the top and side of the square; (b) the letters written within each box; (c) the boxes. (a) gametes; (b) genotype of an offspring; (c) possible offspring **L1**

Purpose

Students will convert and express two sets of related numbers as a ratio.

Background

The round seeds contain an abundance of well-formed starch grains and have higher water retention than the wrinkled seeds. A lack of well-formed starch grains and lower water retention account for the wrinkled appearance.

Process Skills

use and interpret data, calculate

Teaching Strategies

- Have students work in groups. Place students with poor math skills with students working at grade level. **COOP LEARN**
- Provide students with an example if they are having difficulty in determining a ratio.

Thinking Critically

1. The observed ratio is slightly lower than expected.
2. The observed and expected ratios may differ slightly due to chance.

Assessment

Skill Provide students with other examples of traits and data. Have them calculate ratios. Use the Performance Task Assessment List for Using Math in Science in **PASC**, p. 101. **L2**

Problem-Solving Lab 10.1

Analyze Information

Data Analysis In addition to crossing tall and short pea plants, Mendel crossed plants that formed round seeds with plants that formed wrinkled seeds. He found a 3:1 ratio of round-seeded plants to wrinkled-seeded plants in the F_2 generation.

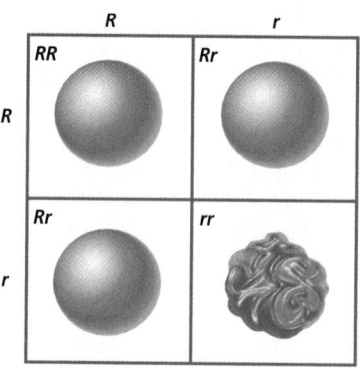

Solve the Problem

Mendel's F_2 results are shown to the right.

Mendel's Results	
Kind of Plant	Number of Plants
Round-seeded	5474
Wrinkled-seeded	1850

1. Calculate the actual ratio of round-seeded plants to wrinkled-seeded plants by dividing the number of round-seeded plants by the number of wrinkled-seeded plants. Your answer tells you how many more times round-seeded plants resulted than wrinkled-seeded plants.
2. To express your answer as a ratio, write the number from step 1 followed by a colon and the numeral *1*.

Thinking Critically

1. **Compare** How does Mendel's observed ratio compare with the expected 3:1 ratio?
2. **Analyze** Why did the actual and expected ratios differ?

The Punnett square in *Figure 10.9* shows three plants with round seeds out of four total plants, so the probability is ¾. Yet, if you calculate the probability of round-seeded plants from Mendel's actual data in the *Problem-Solving Lab* on this page, you will see that slightly less than three-fourths of the plants were round-seeded. It is important to remember that the results predicted by probability are more likely to be seen when there is a large number of offspring.

Figure 10.9
The probability that the offspring from a mating of two heterozygotes will show a dominant phenotype is 3 out of 4, or 3/4.

	R	r
R	RR	Rr
r	Rr	rr

Section Assessment

Understanding Main Ideas

1. What structural features of pea plant flowers made them suitable for Mendel's genetic studies?
2. What are the genotypes of a homozygous and a heterozygous tall pea plant?
3. One parent is homozygous tall and the other is heterozygous. Make a Punnett square to show how many offspring will be heterozygous.
4. How many different gametes can an *RRYy* parent form? What are they?

Thinking Critically

5. In garden peas, the allele for yellow peas is dominant to the allele for green peas. Suppose you have a plant that produces yellow peas, but you don't know whether it is homozygous dominant or heterozygous. What experiment could you do to find out? Draw Punnett squares to help you.

SKILL REVIEW

6. **Observe and Infer** The offspring of a cross between a plant with purple flowers and a plant with white flowers are 23 plants with purple flowers and 26 plants with white flowers. Use the letter *P* for purple and *p* for white. What are the genotypes of the parent plants? Explain your reasoning. For more help, refer to *Observe and Infer* in the **Skill Handbook**.

262 MENDEL AND MEIOSIS

 in.bdol.glencoe.com/self_check_quiz

Section Assessment

1. They are self-pollinating, and male flower parts can be easily removed to allow for cross-pollination.
2. homozygous tall = *TT*, heterozygous = *Tt*
3. One-half of all offspring will be heterozygous. (Note: It will not matter if the homozygous parent is homozygous dominant or recessive.)
4. two; *RY* and *Ry*
5. Cross the unknown yellow plant with a recessive green parent. If the offspring are all yellow, the unknown genotype is homozygous yellow. If half the offspring are yellow and half green, the unknown genotype is heterozygous.
6. Genotypes of parents are *Pp* for the purple-flowered plant and *pp* for the white-flowered plant. Purple is dominant.

Meiosis

Indiana Standards Standard B.1.28 Illustrate that the sorting and recombination of genes in sexual reproduction results in a great variety of possible gene combinations from the offspring of any two parents. Recognize that genetic variation can occur from such processes as crossing over, jumping genes, and deletion and duplication of genes.

Solving the Puzzle

Using an Analogy Mendel's study of inheritance was based on careful observations of pea plants, but pieces of the hereditary puzzle were still missing. Modern technologies such as high-power microscopes allow us a glimpse of things that Mendel could only imagine. Chromosomes, such as those shown here, were the missing pieces of the puzzle because they carry the traits that Mendel described. The key to solving the puzzle was discovering the process by which these traits are transmitted to the next generation.

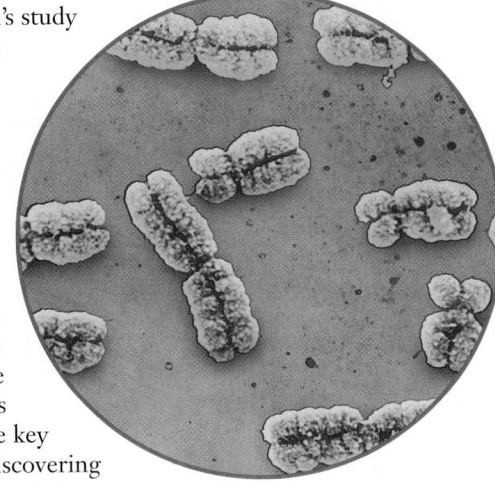

Color-enhanced SEM Magnification: 650×

Metaphase chromosomes

Organize Information As you read this section, make a list of the ways in which meiosis explains Mendel's results.

Genes, Chromosomes, and Numbers

Organisms have tens of thousands of genes that determine individual traits. Genes do not exist free in the nucleus of a cell; they are lined up on chromosomes. Typically, a chromosome can contain a thousand or more genes along its length.

Diploid and haploid cells

If you examined the nucleus in a cell of one of Mendel's pea plants, you would find it had 14 chromosomes—seven pairs. In the body cells of animals and most plants, chromosomes occur in pairs. One chromosome in each pair came from the male parent, and the other came from the female parent. A cell with two of each kind of chromosome is called a **diploid** cell and is said to contain a diploid, or *2n*, number of chromosomes. This pairing supports Mendel's conclusion that organisms have two factors—alleles—for each trait. One allele is located on each of the paired chromosomes.

Organisms produce gametes that contain one of each kind of chromosome. A cell containing one of each kind of chromosome is called a **haploid** cell and is said to contain a haploid, or *n*, number of chromosomes.

10.2 MEIOSIS **263**

Purpose

Students will compare alleles on homologous chromosomes.

Process Skills

interpret scientific diagrams, apply concepts, compare and contrast, think critically

Teaching Strategies

Review the meaning of alleles and homologous chromosomes.

Thinking Critically

1. 2 is homologous with 1. Alleles may or may not be identical, as long as they are positioned at the same location on matching chromosomes.
2. 3 is not homologous with 1. Genes must be identical. Gene K is not the same as gene J.
3. 4 is not homologous with 1. Chromosomes must match in physical size and location of genes in order to be homologous. (Sex chromosomes are an exception to the rule of matching physical size.)
4. 5 is homologous with 1 for the same reasons as in question 1.

Assessment

Performance Ask students to make a diagram of a chromosome with three marked gene locations. Have them diagram all the homologous chromosomes that are possible for this chromosome. Use the Performance Task Assessment List for Scientific Drawing in **PASC,** p. 127. L2

264

This fact supports Mendel's conclusion that parent organisms give one factor, or allele, for each trait to each of their offspring.

Each species of organism contains a characteristic number of chromosomes. *Table 10.1* shows the diploid and haploid numbers of chromosomes of some species. Note the large range of chromosome numbers. Note also that the chromosome number of a species is not related to the complexity of the organism.

Homologous chromosomes

The two chromosomes of each pair in a diploid cell are called **homologous** (hoh MAH luh gus) **chromosomes**. Each of a pair of homologous chromosomes has genes for the same traits, such as plant height. On homologous chromosomes, these genes are arranged in the same order, but because there are different possible alleles for the same gene, the two chromosomes in a homologous pair are not always identical to each other. Identify the homologous chromosomes in the *Problem-Solving Lab*.

Let's look at the seven pairs of homologous chromosomes in the cells of Mendel's peas. These chromosome pairs are numbered 1 through 7. Each pair contains certain genes located at specific places on the chromosome. Chromosome 4 contains the genes for three of the traits that Mendel studied. Many other genes can be found on this chromosome as well.

Every pea plant has two copies of chromosome 4. It received one from each of its parents and will give one at random to each of its offspring. Remember, however, that the two copies of chromosome 4 in a pea plant may not necessarily have identical alleles. Each chromosome can have one of the different alleles possible for each gene. The homologous chromosomes diagrammed in *Figure 10.10* show both alleles for each of three traits. Thus, the plant represented by these chromosomes is heterozygous for each of the traits.

✓ Reading Check **Explain** what homologous chromosomes are.

Problem-Solving Lab 10.2

Interpret Scientific Illustrations

Can you identify homologous chromosomes? Homologous chromosomes are paired chromosomes having genes for the same trait located at the same place on the chromosome. The gene itself, however, may have different alleles, producing different forms of the trait.

Solve the Problem

The diagram below shows chromosome 1 with four different genes present. These genes are represented by the letters *F, g, h,* and *J*. Possible homologous chromosomes of chromosome 1 are labeled 2–5. Examine the five chromosomes and the genes they contain to determine which of chromosomes 2–5 are homologous with chromosome 1.

Thinking Critically

1. **Classify** Could chromosome 2 be homologous with chromosome 1? Explain.
2. **Classify** Could chromosome 3 be homologous with chromosome 1? Explain.
3. **Classify** Could chromosome 4 be homologous with chromosome 1? Explain.
4. **Classify** Could chromosome 5 be homologous with chromosome 1? Explain.

CULTURAL DIVERSITY

Everett Anderson Introduce students to the contribution of African American cell biologist Everett Anderson to the modern understanding of the meiotic process. Anderson (1928), who received his Ph.D. in 1955, has been one of the leading researchers in developing electron microscopic techniques to study meiosis. Obtain a copy of Anderson's 1972 publication, *The Meiotic Process: Pairing, Recombination, and Chromosome Movements,* and discuss with students the methodologies used in studying the process of meiosis.

Adder's
tongue fern

Table 10.1 Chromosome Numbers of Common Organisms

Organism	Body Cell (2n)	Gamete (n)
Fruit fly	8	4
Garden pea	14	7
Corn	20	10
Tomato	24	12
Leopard frog	26	13
Apple	34	17
Human	46	23
Chimpanzee	48	24
Dog	78	39
Adder's tongue fern	1260	630

Corn

Leopard
frog

Why meiosis?

When cells divide by mitosis, the new cells have exactly the same number and kind of chromosomes as the original cells. Imagine if mitosis were the only means of cell division. Each pea plant parent, which has 14 chromosomes, would produce gametes that contained a complete set of 14 chromosomes. That means· that each offspring formed by fertilization of gametes would have twice the number of chromosomes as each of its parents. The F_1 pea plants would have cell nuclei with 28 chromosomes, and the F_2 plants would have cell nuclei with 56 chromosomes.

Clearly, there must be another form of cell division that allows offspring to have the same number of chromosomes as their parents. This kind of cell division, which produces gametes containing half the number of chromosomes as a parent's body cell, is called **meiosis** (mi OH sus). Meiosis occurs in the specialized body cells of each parent that produce gametes.

Meiosis consists of two separate divisions, known as meiosis I and meiosis II. Meiosis I begins with one diploid ($2n$) cell. By the end of meiosis II, there are four haploid (n) cells. These haploid cells are called sex cells—gametes. Male gametes are called **sperm.** Female gametes are called **eggs.** When a sperm fertilizes an egg, the resulting zygote once again has the diploid number of chromosomes.

Figure 10.10

Each chromosome 4 in garden peas contains genes for flower position, pod shape, and height, among others. Flower position can be either axial (flowers located along the stems) or terminal (flowers clustered at the top of the plant). Pod shape can be either inflated or constricted. Plant height can be either tall or short.

Homologous Chromosome 4

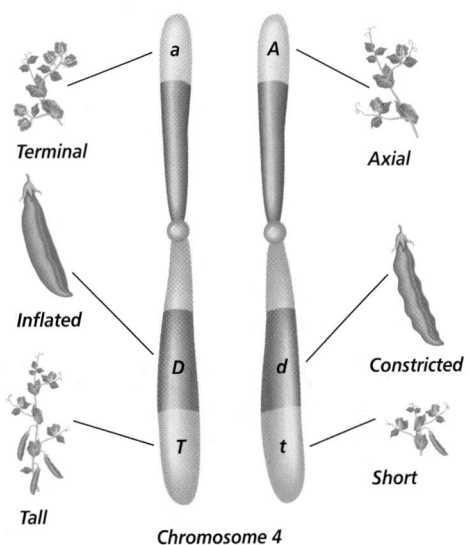

Terminal

a   A

Axial

Inflated

Constricted

D   d

Short

T   t

Tall

Chromosome 4

10.2 MEIOSIS **265**

Visual Learning

Table 10.1 Ask students whether there is any evidence to support the idea that plants have fewer chromosomes than animals. Tell students to use examples from the table to support their answers. No; apples have 34 chromosomes, which is more than fruit flies or frogs have. Ask for the chromosome numbers in skin cells of a leopard frog and a dog, 26 and 78 and in root cells of tomatoes and garden peas. 24 and 14

Inquiry

Discussion Show students an egg and explain that it is a gamete. Based on previous information, students should be able to tell how many alleles are present for each trait. one Ask why an organism cannot produce gametes by mitosis. Mitosis produces a cell with two alleles for each trait.

INCLUSION STRATEGIES

Learning Disabled: *Kinesthetic* Have students use pipe cleaners or jelly beans to show why meiosis is necessary to prevent the number of chromosomes from doubling in each generation. Students should start with a cell containing two pipe cleaners or jelly beans, *2n.* After meiosis, gametes should each contain one, *n.* After fertilization, the zygote has two. Students can repeat the process for several generations, assuming gametes are formed by mitosis. Students will see that the number of chromosomes doubles in each generation. **L1** **ELL** **COOP LEARN**

Indiana Academic Standards

Pages 264–265: B.1.8, B.1.21, B.1.22, B.1.28, B.1.29

Visual Learning

Figure 10.12 Ask students how the processes of mitosis and meiosis are different. Events that occur in meiosis but not in mitosis include (1) in prophase I, pairs of homologous chromosomes form tetrads and crossing over can occur; (2) in metaphase I, homologous chromosomes line up in pairs rather than independently; (3) in anaphase I, homologous chromosomes, not chromatids, separate; (4) in telophase I, each cell has only one chromosome from each pair; and (5) at the end of meiosis II, each new cell has the haploid number of chromosomes. **L2**

Reading Check Meiosis is necessary to provide variation and maintain the diploid number of chromosomes after reproduction.

The zygote then develops by mitosis into a multicellular organism. This pattern of reproduction, involving the production and subsequent fusion of haploid sex cells, is called **sexual reproduction.** It is illustrated in *Figure 10.11.*

Reading Check **Explain** why meiosis is necessary in organisms.

The Phases of Meiosis

During meiosis, a spindle forms and the cytoplasm divides in the same ways they do during mitosis. However, what happens to the chromosomes in meiosis is very different. *Figure 10.12* illustrates interphase and the phases of meiosis. Examine the diagram and photo of each phase as you read about it.

Interphase

Recall from Chapter 8 that, during interphase, the cell replicates its chromosomes. The chromosomes are replicated during interphase that precedes meiosis I, also. After replication, each chromosome consists of two identical sister chromatids, held together by a centromere.

Prophase I

A cell entering prophase I behaves in a similar way to one entering prophase of mitosis. The DNA of the chromosomes coils up and a spindle forms. As the DNA coils, homologous chromosomes line up with each other, gene by gene along their length, to form a four-part structure called a tetrad. A tetrad consists of two homologous chromosomes, each made up of two sister chromatids. The chromatids in a tetrad pair tightly. In fact, they pair so tightly that non-sister chromatids from homologous chromosomes can actually break and exchange genetic material in a process known as **crossing over.** Crossing over can occur at any location on a chromosome, and it can occur at several locations at the same time.

Figure 10.11
In sexual reproduction, the doubling of the chromosome number that results from fertilization is balanced by the halving of the chromosome number that results from meiosis.

Haploid gametes (n = 23)
Sperm cell
Meiosis
Meiosis
Egg cell
Fertilization
Diploid zygote (2n = 46)
Mitosis and Development
Multicellular diploid adults (2n = 46)

Figure 10.12

Compare these diagrams of meiosis with those of mitosis in Chapter 8. After telophase II, meiosis is finished and gametes form. **Compare and Contrast** *In what other ways are mitosis and meiosis different?*

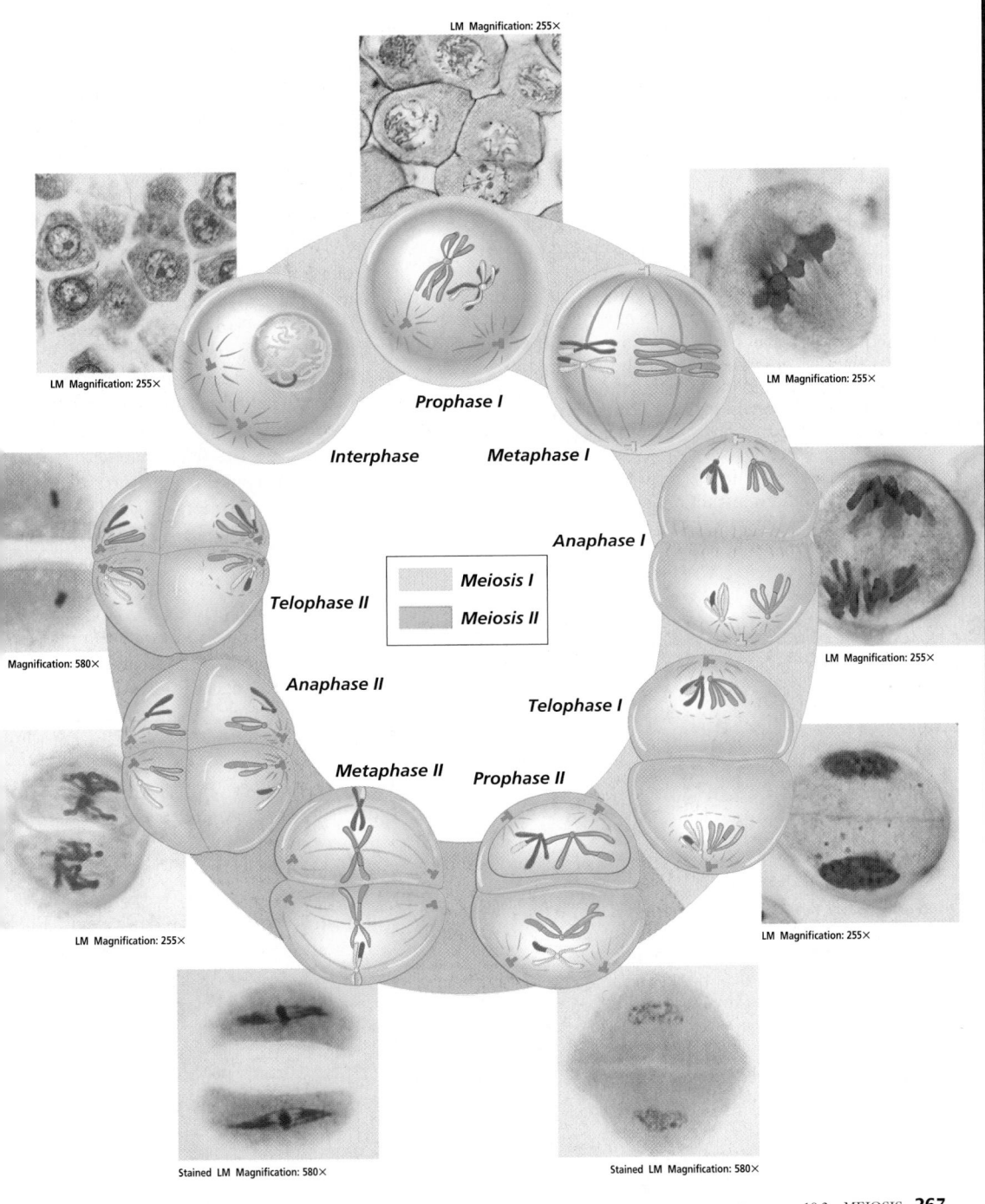

LM Magnification: 255×

LM Magnification: 255×

Prophase I

Interphase   *Metaphase I*

LM Magnification: 255×

Anaphase I

Meiosis I
Meiosis II

Telophase II

Magnification: 580×

LM Magnification: 255×

Anaphase II   *Telophase I*

Metaphase II   *Prophase II*

LM Magnification: 255×

LM Magnification: 255×

Stained LM Magnification: 580×   Stained LM Magnification: 580×

Using an Analogy

To reinforce the concept of homologous chromosomes, sister chromatids, tetrad formation, crossing over, and anaphase I, try the following analogy: A magic pair of shoes (left and right) is found on a shelf (homologous chromosomes in a cell). These shoes, being magic, can and do replicate (interphase replication).

Each copy is tied to its original with its shoelaces (centromere; both lefts are tied together and both rights are tied together). Both rights are now called right sister shoes (sister chromatids). Both lefts are now called left sister shoes (sister chromatids). All four shoes line up next to one another (tetrad formation).

While next to one another, part of one nonsister shoe (a left shoe) exchanges its innersole with another nonsister shoe (a right shoe) (crossing over). Right shoes move away from left shoes to different shelves (anaphase I, with homologous chromosomes separating and going to two different cells. Both rights are still tied together and both lefts are still tied together).

To improve the analogy, locate two identical pairs of shoes to demonstrate the events as they are described.

Caption Question Answer

Figure 10.12 There are two divisions in meiosis and only one in mitosis. Meiosis produces haploid cells and mitosis produces diploid cells.

---

4. Only one pair of chromosomes is to be followed through all models. Glue or tape all parts in place.

5. Model interphase, prophase I, metaphase I, anaphase I, and telophase I, prophase II, metaphase II, anaphase II, and telophase II.

Expected Results

Students will gain an understanding of meiosis when visualizing each phase.

Analysis

1. What happens to the chromosome number during meiosis? reduced by 1/2

2. How many cells are formed during meiosis? 4

3. What is the fate of the cells formed during meiosis? They form either egg or sperm cells.

Assessment

Knowledge Ask students to write a paragraph explaining the value of making models such as the ones in this lab. Use the Performance Task Assessment List for Writing in Science in **PASC**, p. 159. **L2**

Purpose

Students will model the process of crossing over.

Process Skills

apply concepts, compare and contrast, formulate models, recognize cause and effect, think critically, define operationally

Teaching Strategies

- Plasticene or clay is available from biological supply houses or craft stores.
- String or twine may be used as a substitute for twist ties.
- Review the concept that gametes contain only one chromosome from each pair.
- Make sure students wash their hands after the lab.

Expected Results

All gametes will show the same combination of genes if no crossing over occurs and different combinations of genes if crossing over does occur.

Analysis

1. Only two chromosomes should be drawn. The sequence of genes would be C B A on one chromosome and c B a on the other.
2. Yes, crossing over is the exchange of genetic material between nonsister chromatids during prophase I of meiosis.
3. Student answers will vary. There is a mixing of the gene traits from their original order as would occur in shuffling cards.
4. There would be no mixing of gene traits when compared with the original chromosomes because sister chromatids are identical.
5. Student answers will vary. For the purposes of explaining crossing over, the model is simplistic but accurate.

Formulate Models

Modeling Crossing Over
Crossing over occurs during meiosis and involves only the nonsister chromatids that are present during tetrad formation. The process is responsible for the appearance of new combinations of alleles in gamete cells.

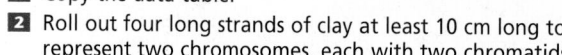

2 chromosomes with chromatids

— Twist tie

— Mark genes with a pencil point.

Nonsister chromatids

Procedure

1. Copy the data table.
2. Roll out four long strands of clay at least 10 cm long to represent two chromosomes, each with two chromatids.
3. Use the figure above as a guide to joining and labeling these model chromatids. Although there are four chromatids, assume that they started out as a single pair of homologous chromosomes prior to replication. The figure shows tetrad formation during prophase I of meiosis.
4. First, assume that no crossing over takes place. Model the appearance of the chromosomes in the four gamete cells that will result at the end of meiosis. Record your model's appearance by drawing the gametes' chromosomes and their genes in your data table.
5. Next, repeat steps 2–4. This time, however, assume that crossing over occurs between genes B and C.

Data Table	
No Crossing Over	**Crossing Over**
Appearance of chromosomes	Appearance of chromosomes

Analysis

1. **Predict** What will be the appearance of the chromosomes prior to replication?
2. **Compare** Are there any differences in the combinations of alleles on chromosomes in gamete cells when crossing over occurs and when it does not occur?
3. **Analogy** Crossing over has been compared to "shuffling the deck" in cards. Explain what this means.
4. **Think Critically** What would be accomplished if crossing over occurred between sister chromatids? Explain.
5. **Evaluate** Does your model adequately represent crossing over in a cell?

268 MENDEL AND MEIOSIS

It is estimated that during prophase I of meiosis in humans, there is an average of two to three crossovers for each pair of homologous chromosomes.

This exchange of genetic material is diagrammed in *Figure 10.13B*. Crossing over results in new combinations of alleles on a chromosome, as you can see in *Figure 10.13C*. You can practice modeling crossing over in the *MiniLab* at the left.

Metaphase I

During metaphase I, the centromere of each chromosome becomes attached to a spindle fiber. The spindle fibers pull the tetrads into the middle, or equator, of the spindle. This is an important step unique to meiosis. Note that homologous chromosomes are lined up side by side as tetrads. In mitosis, on the other hand, they line up on the spindle's equator independently of each other.

Anaphase I

Anaphase I begins as homologous chromosomes, each with its two chromatids, separate and move to opposite ends of the cell. This separation occurs because the centromeres holding the sister chromatids together do not split as they do during anaphase in mitosis. This critical step ensures that each new cell will receive only one chromosome from each homologous pair.

Telophase I

Events occur in the reverse order from the events of prophase I. The spindle is broken down, the chromosomes uncoil, and the cytoplasm divides to yield two new cells. Each cell has half the genetic information of the original cell because it has only one chromosome from each homologous pair. However, another cell division is needed because each chromosome is still doubled.

Modified Assessment

Performance Ask students to model the appearance of gamete cells if crossing over occurred between sister chromatids. This should confirm their answer to question 5. Use the Performance Task Assessment List for Model in **PASC**, p. 123. **L1** **ELL**

The phases of meiosis II

The newly formed cells in some organisms undergo a short resting stage. In other organisms, however, the cells go from late anaphase of meiosis I directly to metaphase of meiosis II.

The second division in meiosis is simply a mitotic division of the products of meiosis I. Meiosis II consists of prophase II, metaphase II, anaphase II, and telophase II. During prophase II, a spindle forms in each of the two new cells and the spindle fibers attach to the chromosomes. The chromosomes, still made up of sister chromatids, are pulled to the center of the cell and line up randomly at the equator during metaphase II. Anaphase II begins as the centromere of each chromosome splits, allowing the sister chromatids to separate and move to opposite poles. Finally, nuclei re-form, the spindles break down, and the cytoplasm divides during telophase II. The events of meiosis II are identical to those you studied for mitosis except that the chromosomes do not replicate before they divide at the centromeres.

At the end of meiosis II, four haploid cells have been formed from one diploid cell. Each haploid cell contains one chromosome from each homologous pair. These haploid cells will become gametes, transmitting the genes they contain to offspring.

Meiosis Provides for Genetic Variation

Cells that are formed by mitosis are identical to each other and to the parent cell. Crossing over during meiosis, however, provides a way to rearrange allele combinations. Rather than the alleles from each parent staying together, new combinations of alleles can form. Thus, variability is increased.

Genetic recombination

How many different kinds of sperm can a pea plant produce? Each cell undergoing meiosis has seven pairs of chromosomes. Because each of the seven pairs of chromosomes can line up at the cell's equator in two different ways, 128 different kinds of sperm are possible ($2^n = 2^7 = 128$).

Word Origin

pro- from the Greek word *pro*, meaning "before"

meta- from the Greek word *meta*, meaning "after"

ana- from the Greek word *ana*, meaning "up, back, again"

telo- from the Greek *telos*, meaning "end"

The four phases of cell division are prophase, metaphase, anaphase, and telophase.

Figure 10.13
Late in prophase I, the homologous chromosomes come together to form tetrads **(A)**. Arms of nonsister chromatids wind around each other **(B)**, and genetic material may be exchanged **(C)**.

Sister chromatids
Nonsister chromatids
Tetrad
Homologous chromosomes
Crossing over in tetrad
Gametes

Using an Analogy

Continue the shoe analogy or demonstration of meiosis to illustrate telophase I, metaphase II, and telophase II events.

Start with two right shoes tied together. Both sets are separate from each other on different closet shelves (two new cells formed after telophase I). The shoes untie (centromere splits after metaphase II). They move to different shelves in the closet (two new cells formed in telophase II).

Ask students: (a) How many shoes are now on separate shelves (separate cells)? 4 (b) How many shoes were present at the start of this analogy? 2 (c) Is the chromosome number in a cell diploid or haploid before a cell undergoes meiosis? diploid (d) How many shoes are present on each shelf at the end of the process? 1 (e) How many shoes were on the original shelf? 2 (f) Is the chromosome number in each of the four new cells formed in meiosis reduced by half? yes **L2**

Concept Development

The chances of two humans being born exactly alike is almost an impossibility (except for identical twins). Explain why children in the same family can nevertheless resemble one another rather closely.

USING MODELS

Meiosis Use models of plant or animal cell meiosis (available from biological supply houses) to help students visualize the process.

 Indiana Academic Standards

Pages 268–269: B.1.8, B.1.21, B.1.28, B.1.29

Portfolio

Comparing Mitosis and Meiosis
Provide students with two sets of simple line drawings, one showing interphase and the phases of mitosis and the other showing interphase and meiosis. Place comparable phases next to each other when possible (prophase of mitosis next to prophase I of meiosis, and so on). Ask students to describe in their portfolios the similarities and differences between processes. Also have them indicate the type of cell formed at the end of the process—body or gamete—and whether its chromosome number would be diploid or haploid. **L2**

In the same way, any pea plant can form 128 different eggs. Because any egg can be fertilized by any sperm, the number of different possible offspring is 16 384 (128 × 128). A simple example of how genetic recombination occurs is shown in *Figure 10.14A*. You can see that the gene combinations in the gametes vary depending on how each pair of homologous chromosomes lines up during metaphase I, a random process.

These numbers increase greatly as the number of chromosomes in the species increases. In humans, $n = 23$, so the number of different kinds of eggs or sperm a person can produce is more than 8 million (2^{23}). When fertilization occurs, $2^{23} \times 2^{23}$, or 70 trillion, different zygotes are possible! It's no wonder that each individual is unique.

In addition, crossing over can occur almost anywhere at random on a chromosome. This means that an almost endless number of different possible chromosomes can be produced by crossing over, providing additional variation to the variation already produced by the random assortment of chromosomes. This reassortment of chromosomes and the genetic information they carry, either by crossing over or by independent segregation of homologous chromosomes, is called **genetic recombination.** It is a major source of variation among organisms. Variation is important to a species because it is the raw material that forms the basis for evolution.

Reading Check **Explain** how crossing over increases genetic variability.

Meiosis explains Mendel's results

The behavior of the chromosomes in meiosis provides the physical basis for explaining Mendel's results. The segregation of chromosomes in anaphase I of meiosis explains Mendel's observation that each parent gives one allele for each trait at random to each offspring, regardless of whether the allele is expressed. The segregation of chromosomes at random during anaphase I also explains how factors, or genes, for different traits are inherited independently of each other. Today, Mendel's laws and the events of meiosis together form the foundation of the chromosome theory of heredity.

Figure 10.14
If a cell has two pairs of chromosomes—A and a, B and b ($n = 2$)—four kinds of gametes (2^2) are possible, depending on how the homologous chromosomes line up at the equator during meiosis I **(A)**. This event is a matter of chance. When zygotes are formed by the union of these gametes, $2^2 \times 2^2$ or 16 possible combinations may occur **(B)**.

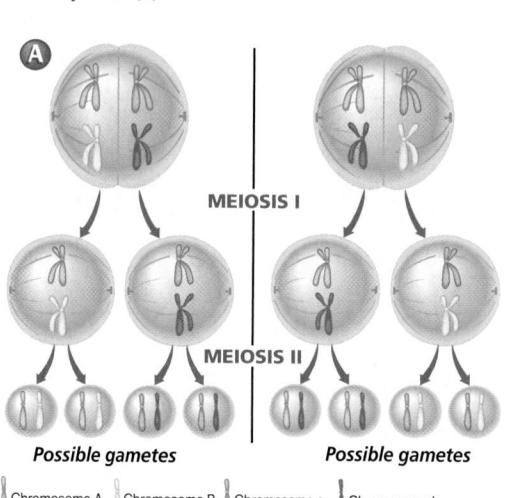

MEIOSIS I

MEIOSIS II

Possible gametes   *Possible gametes*

Chromosome A   Chromosome B   Chromosome a   Chromosome b

B Possible combination of chromosomes in sperm

	AB	Ab	aB	ab
AB	AABB	AABb	AaBB	AaBb
Ab	AABb	AAbb	AaBb	Aabb
aB	AaBB	AaBb	aaBB	aaBb
ab	AaBb	Aabb	aaBb	aabb

Possible combination of chromosomes in eggs

Possible combinations of chromosomes in zygotes (in boxes)

USING MODELS

Modeling the Membrane Have student groups invent a mechanism for demonstrating how the plasma membrane of an animal cell pinches together during telophase I and II of meiosis. Students can use a variety of common objects as models, such as balloons, string, and wire. **L2** **ELL** **COOP LEARN**

Nondisjunction

Although the events of meiosis usually proceed accurately, sometimes chromosomes fail to separate correctly. The failure of homologous chromosomes to separate properly during meiosis is called **nondisjunction.** Recall that during meiosis I, one chromosome from each homologous pair moves to each pole of the cell. In nondisjunction, both chromosomes of a homologous pair move to the same pole of the cell.

In one form of nondisjunction, two kinds of gametes result. One has an extra chromosome, and the other is missing a chromosome. The effects of nondisjunction are often seen after gametes fuse. For example, when a gamete with an extra chromosome is fertilized by a normal gamete, the zygote will have an extra chromosome. This condition is called trisomy (TRI soh mee). In humans, if a gamete with an extra chromosome number 21 is fertilized by a normal gamete, the resulting zygote has 47 chromosomes instead of 46. This zygote will develop into a baby with Down syndrome.

Although organisms with extra chromosomes often survive, organisms lacking one or more chromosomes usually do not. When a gamete with a missing chromosome fuses with a normal gamete during fertilization, the resulting zygote lacks a chromosome. This condition is called monosomy. In humans, most zygotes with monosomy do not survive. If a zygote with monosomy does survive, the resulting organism usually does not. An example of monosomy that is not lethal is Turner syndrome, in which human females have only a single X chromosome instead of two.

Another form of nondisjunction involves a total lack of separation of homologous chromosomes. When this happens, a gamete inherits a complete diploid set of chromosomes, like those shown in *Figure 10.15*. When a gamete with an extra set of chromosomes is fertilized by a normal haploid gamete, the offspring has three sets of chromosomes and is triploid. The fusion of two gametes, each with an extra set of chromosomes, produces offspring with four sets of chromosomes—a tetraploid.

Figure 10.15
Follow the steps to see how a tetraploid plant, such as this chrysanthemum, is produced.

Male parent (2n) — Meiosis Nondisjunction — Abnormal gamete (2n) — Zygote (4n)

Female parent (2n) — Meiosis Nondisjunction — Abnormal gamete (2n)

Purpose

Students study the process of crossing over and its importance in genetic recombination.

Teaching Strategies

Ask students to describe the process of crossing over. **L2**

Visual Learning

■ Have students examine the photograph and count the chiasmata—regions where chromosomes appear to be physically linked.

■ *Visual-Spatial* Have students draw chromosomes before and after crossing over. The use of colored pencils will help students visualize how this process leads to genetic recombination. **L2** **ELL**

Critical Thinking

The farther apart two alleles are from each other on a chromosome, the greater the chance that the chromosome will be tangled, broken, and rearranged between them.

Caption Question Answer

Figure 10.17 There are no seeds in the fruits.

Indiana Academic Standards

Pages 272–273: B.1.8, B.1.21, B.1.22, B.1.28, B.1.29

INSIDE STORY

Chromosome Mapping

Figure 10.16

Crossing over, the exchange of genetic material by nonsister chromatids, provides information that can be used to make chromosome maps. Crossing over occurs more frequently between genes that are far apart on a chromosome than between genes that are closer together. **Critical Thinking** *Why is the frequency of crossing over related to the distance between genes on a chromosome?*

Stained TEM Magnification: 1905×

A **Crossing over** In prophase I of meiosis, nonsister chromatids cross over, as shown in the photo above. Each X-shaped region is a crossover.

B **Mapping** Crossing over produces new allele combinations. Geneticists use the frequency of crossing over to map the relative positions of genes on a chromosome. Genes that are farther apart on a chromosome are more likely to have crossing over occur between them than are genes that are closer together.

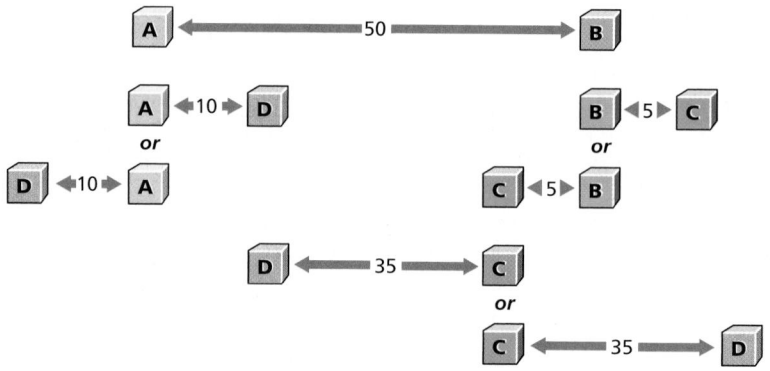

C **Frequencies and distance** Suppose there are four genes—A, B, C, and D—on a chromosome. Geneticists determine that the frequencies of recombination among them are as follows: between A and B—50%; between A and D—10%; between B and C—5%; between C and D—35%. The recombination frequencies can be converted to map units: A–B = 50; A–D = 10; B–C = 5; C–D = 35. These map units are not actual distances on the chromosome, but they give relative distances between genes. Geneticists line up the genes as shown above.

D **Making the map** The genes can be arranged in the sequence that reflects the recombination data. This sequence is a chromosome map

272 MENDEL AND MEIOSIS

Chromosome Mapping Have interested students map the four genes on a chromosome given that the frequencies of recombination between the genes are as follows: A and D—60%, A and B—15%, C and D—10%, and B and C—35%. Have them predict where on the chromosome crossing over is most likely to occur. **L3**

Polyploidy

Organisms with more than the usual number of chromosome sets are called polyploids. Polyploidy is rare in animals and almost always causes death of the zygote. However, polyploidy frequently occurs in plants. Often, the flowers and fruits of these plants are larger than normal, and the plants are healthier. Many polyploid plants, such as the sterile banana plant shown in *Figure 10.17*, are of great commercial value.

Meiosis is a complex process, and the results of an error occurring are sometimes unfortunate. However, the resulting changes can be beneficial, such as those that have occurred in agriculture. Hexaploid (6*n*) wheat, triploid (3*n*) apples, and polyploid chrysanthemums all are available commercially. You can see that a thorough understanding of meiosis and genetics would be very helpful to plant breeders. In fact, plant breeders have learned to produce polyploid plants artificially by using chemicals that cause nondisjunction.

Gene Linkage and Maps

Genes sometimes appear to be inherited together instead of independently. If genes are close together on the same chromosome, they usually

Figure 10.17
The banana plant is an example of a triploid plant. **Think Critically**
Why do you think the banana plant is sterile?

are inherited together. These genes are said to be linked. In fact, all the genes on a chromosome usually are linked and inherited together. It is the chromosomes, rather than the individual genes, that follow Mendel's law of independent assortment.

Linked genes may become separated on different homologous chromosomes as a result of crossing over. When crossing over produces new gene combinations, geneticists can use the frequencies of these new gene combinations to make a chromosome map showing the relative locations of the genes. *Figure 10.16* illustrates this process.

Section Assessment

Understanding Main Ideas

1. How are the cells at the end of meiosis different from the cells at the beginning of meiosis? Use the terms *chromosome number, haploid,* and *diploid* in your answer.
2. What is the significance of meiosis to sexual reproduction?
3. Why are there so many varied phenotypes within a species such as humans?
4. If the diploid number of a plant is 10, how many chromosomes would you expect to find in its triploid offspring?

Thinking Critically

5. How do the events that take place during meiosis explain Mendel's law of independent assortment?

SKILL REVIEW

6. **Get the Big Picture** Compare *Figures 10.12* and *8.13* of meiosis and mitosis. Explain why crossing over between nonsister chromatids of homologous chromosomes cannot occur during mitosis. For more help, refer to *Get the Big Picture* in the **Skill Handbook**.

in.bdol.glencoe.com/self_check_quiz

10.2 MEIOSIS **273**

3 Assess

DAILY INTERVENTION

Check for Understanding
Ask students to explain how the words in the following combinations are related.
L1 **ELL**
a. diploid—haploid
b. homologous chromosomes —allele
c. sperm—egg—zygote
d. meiosis—gamete
e. crossing over—genetic recombination

Reteach
Ask students to prepare a list of important characteristics of each step in meiosis. Then have them prepare a second list of the reasons meiosis is important to organisms that reproduce sexually. **L2**

Resources
For more practice, use *Reading Essentials for Biology*, Section 10.2.

Extension

Oogenesis and spermatogenesis are terms used to describe egg and sperm cell formation in humans through meiosis. Have students research how these processes differ and how they are alike. **L3**

MODIFIED Assessment

Skill Provide students with simple line diagrams of various phases of meiosis. The diagrams should not be in sequence. Have students place the diagrams in proper sequence, name each phase, and describe what is occurring. **L1**

Section Assessment

1. The chromosome number in a cell at the end is half the chromosome number in a parent cell. The original cell has a diploid number of chromosomes and each of the new cells has a haploid number.
2. Meiosis reduces the chromosome number in gametes. When sexual reproduction occurs, the zygote recombines the chromosomes and maintains the 2n condition.
3. Crossing over as well as the reassortment of the 46 chromosomes both contribute to the large number of phenotypes that are possible.
4. 15
5. After meiosis, only one member of each homologous chromosome pair can be found in a gamete. Thus, no gamete will end up with two homologues. Alleles on different chromosomes will sort independently from one another.
6. Tetrad formation does not occur during mitosis. This prevents crossing over from taking place.

273

Time Allotment

initial session: one class period; follow-up session: 5 minutes each day for watering, 20 minutes on last day for counting

Process Skills

hypothesize, observe and infer, collect data

Safety Precautions

Some seed materials are poisonous. Do not allow students to eat the seeds. Have students wash their hands after the lab.

PREPARATION

Alternative Materials

Seeds can be germinated and observed in petri dishes. This will eliminate the need for soil, flats, or pots. Place seeds on moistened paper towels in the bottom of the dish and keep the dish covered.

Teaching Strategies

■ When supplying seeds to students, make sure that the two types are kept separate from each other. Stick seeds onto a piece of tape for dispensing.
■ An ideal quantity of seeds to use is 20–30 per type.
■ Cotyledons (seed leaves) will appear after about 10 days.

Possible Hypotheses

■ If the parent plants were true breeding for green color, then all offspring will be green.
■ If the parent plants were heterozygous for green color, then offspring will show an approximate ratio of 3 green to 1 white.

Indiana Academic Standards

Pages 274–275: B.1.21, B.1.28, B.1.29

274

INTERNET
BioLab

Before You Begin

It's difficult to predict the traits of plants if all that you see is their seeds. But if these seeds are planted and allowed to grow, certain traits will appear. By observing these traits, you might be able to determine the possible phenotypes and genotypes of the parent plants that produced these seeds. In this lab, you will determine the genotypes of plants that grow from two groups of tobacco seeds. Each group of seeds came from different parents. Plants will be either green or albino (white) in color. Use the following genotypes for this cross. *CC* = green, *Cc* = green, and *cc* = albino

274 MENDEL AND MEIOSIS

How can phenotypes and genotypes of plants be determined?

PREPARATION

Problem

Can the phenotypes and genotypes of the parent plants that produced two groups of seeds be determined from the phenotypes of the plants grown from the seeds?

Hypotheses

Have your group agree on a hypothesis to be tested that will answer the problem question. Record your hypothesis.

Objectives

In this BioLab, you will:
■ **Analyze** the results of growing two groups of seeds.
■ **Draw conclusions** about phenotypes and genotypes based on those results.
■ **Use the Internet** to collect and compare data from other students.

Possible Materials

potting soil	light source
small flowerpots or seedling flats	thermometer or temperature probe
two groups of tobacco seeds	plant-watering bottle
hand lens	

Safety Precautions

CAUTION: *Always wash your hands after handling plant materials. Always wear goggles in the lab.*

Skill Handbook

If you need help with this lab, refer to the **Skill Handbook.**

PLAN THE EXPERIMENT

1. Examine the materials provided by your teacher. As a group, make a list of the possible ways you might test your hypothesis.
2. Agree on one way that your group could investigate your hypothesis.

PROCEDURE

Troubleshooting

■ Students should keep growing conditions for the two seed groups as constant as possible. Soil should be kept moist at all times. Natural window light should be sufficient. Temperature should be kept above 20°C.

■ Seeds should be planted about 1 cm below the soil. Planting is easier if the soil is moist.
■ Be sure students mark the seed type planted in the flat or pot. Craft sticks can serve as markers.

3. Design an experiment that will allow you to collect quantitative data. For example, how many plants do you think you will need to examine?

4. Prepare a numbered list of directions. Include a list of materials and the quantities you will need.

5. Make a data table for recording your observations.

Check the Plan

1. Carefully determine what data you are going to collect. How many seeds will you need? How long will you carry out the experiment?

2. What variables, if any, will have to be controlled? (Hint: Think about the growing conditions for the plants.)

3. *Make sure your teacher has approved your experimental plan before you proceed further.*

4. Carry out your experiment. Make any needed observations, such as the numbers of green and albino plants in each group, and complete your data table.

5. Visit in.bdol.glencoe.com/internet_lab to post your data.

6. CLEANUP AND DISPOSAL Make wise choices in the disposal of materials.

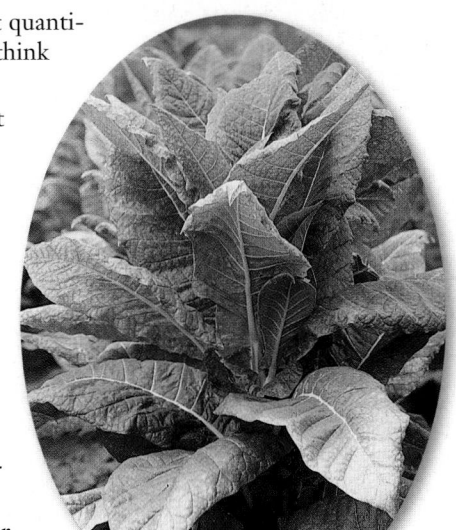

ANALYZE AND CONCLUDE

1. **Think Critically** Why was it necessary to grow plants from the seeds in order to determine the phenotypes of the plants that formed the seeds?

2. **Draw Conclusions** Using the information in the introduction, describe how the gene for green color (C) is inherited.

3. **Make Inferences** For the group of seeds that yielded all green plants, are you able to determine exactly the genotypes of the parents that formed these seeds? Can you determine the genotype of each plant observed? Explain.

4. **Make Inferences** For the group of seeds that yielded some green and some albino plants, are you able to determine exactly the genotypes of the plants that formed these seeds? Can you determine the genotype of each plant observed? Explain.

5. ERROR ANALYSIS Use the data posted on in.bdol.glencoe.com/internet_lab to compare your experimental design with that of other students. Were your results similar? What might account for the differences?

Share Your Data

Find this BioLab using the link below and post your results in the table provided. Briefly describe your experimental design.

 in.bdol.glencoe.com/internet_lab

ANALYZE AND CONCLUDE

1. Leaf color cannot be observed in the seed but appears only after the plant has emerged from the seed.

2. The gene for green color is a dominant trait.

3. No, one parent may have been true breeding for green (CC), the other may have been heterozygous (Cc). This would have yielded all green offspring. Offspring may be CC or Cc but still appear green.

4. Yes, both parents must be heterozygous to yield a ratio of 3 green to 1 albino. For the offspring genotypes, you can conclude only that the albino offspring are cc. Green are either CC or Cc.

5. Answers may vary. Genetic ratios are governed by the laws of probability. The larger the population size, the closer the calculated value will be to the theoretical.

Assessment

Portfolio Ask students to make diagrams that show the parental and offspring genotypes and phenotypes for both groups of seeds used in this experiment. Use the Performance Task Assessment List for Scientific Drawing in **PASC**, p. 127. L2

Share Your Data

To navigate the Internet BioLabs, go to in.bdol.glencoe. com/internet_lab. Students should visit this site only after they have done the experiment and collected their data to post their experimental design and compare it with that of other students. Students should be careful that only data from identical crosses are pooled.

Data and Observations

Seeds that came from true breeding plants will produce plants that are all green. Seeds from heterozygous parents will produce both green and albino seedlings in the ratio of about 3 green to 1 albino. Have students review Problem-Solving Lab 10.1 for help in calculating the ratio of green to albino plants.

connection to Math

connection to Math

Purpose

Students will gain insight into the importance of mathematics to the study of biology. They will learn how mathematics aided Mendel in understanding the laws of heredity.

Teaching Strategies

■ Students may be surprised to learn that a biologist of Charles Darwin's stature missed a great opportunity in his brilliant career. Had he interpreted his data about snapdragon flower shapes correctly, the whole world might have understood the laws of heredity 40 years earlier.

■ Discuss how ratios helped Mendel see that definite factors were being passed on from parents to offspring. He didn't know what these factors were, nor how they operated. He knew nothing about chromosomes and meiosis, yet was able to show how traits were transmitted because of his mathematical analysis.

A Solution from Ratios

In 1866, Gregor Mendel, an Austrian monk, published the results of eight years of experiments with garden peas. His work was ignored until 1900, when it was rediscovered.

Mendel had three qualities that led to his discovery of the laws of heredity. First, he was curious, impelled to find out why things happened. Second, he was a keen observer. Third, he was a skilled mathematician. Mendel was the first biologist who relied heavily on statistics for solutions to how traits are inherited.

Darwin missed his chance About the same time that Mendel was carrying out his experiments with pea plants, Charles Darwin was gathering data on snapdragon flowers. When Darwin crossed plants that had normal-shaped flowers with plants that had odd-shaped flowers, all the offspring had normal-shaped flowers. He thought the two traits had blended. When he allowed the F_1 plants to self-pollinate, his results were 88 plants with normal-shaped flowers and 37 plants with odd-shaped flowers. Darwin was puzzled by the results and did not continue his studies with these plants. Lacking Mendel's statistical skills, Darwin failed to see the significance of the ratio of normal-shaped flowers to odd-shaped flowers in the F_2 generation. What was this ratio? Was it similar to Mendel's ratio of dominant to recessive traits in pea plants?

Finding the ratios for four other traits *Figure 10.3* on page 256 shows seven traits that Mendel studied in pea plants. You have already looked at Mendel's data for plant height and seed shape. Now use the data for seed color, flower position, pod color, and pod shape to find the ratios of dominant to recessive for these traits in the F_2 generation.

Draw Table B in your notebook or journal. Calculate the ratios for the data in Table A and complete Table B by following these steps:
- Step 1 Divide the larger number by the smaller number.
- Step 2 Round to the nearest hundredth.
- Step 3 To express your answer as a ratio, write the number from step 2 followed by a colon and the number *1*.

Table A Mendel's Results			
Seed Color	**Flower Position**	**Pod Color**	**Pod Shape**
Yellow 6022	Axial 651	Green 428	Inflated 882
Green 2001	Terminal 207	Yellow 152	Constricted 299

Table B Calculating Ratios for Mendel's Results				
	Seed Color	**Flower Position**	**Pod Color**	**Pod Shape**
Calculation	$\frac{6022}{2001} = 3.00$	$\frac{651}{207} = 3.14$	$\frac{428}{152} = 2.82$	$\frac{882}{299} = 2.95$
Ratio	3:1 yellow: green			

Math in Biology

Think Critically Why are ratios so important in understanding how dominant and recessive traits are inherited?

 To find out more about Mendel's work, visit in.bdol.glencoe.com/math

Math in Biology

Students may say that the ratios revealed that a dominant trait showed up three times more often because it was always able to overcome the effect of a recessive trait that accompanied it.

 Indiana Academic Standards

Pages 276–277: B.1.8, B.1.21, B.1.22, B.1.28, B.1.29, B.2.4

STUDY GUIDE

Section 10.1

Mendel's Laws of Heredity

Key Concepts

- Genes are located on chromosomes and exist in alternative forms called alleles. A dominant allele can mask the expression of a recessive allele.

- When Mendel crossed pea plants differing in one trait, one form of the trait disappeared until the second generation of offspring. To explain his results, Mendel formulated the law of segregation.

- Mendel formulated the law of independent assortment to explain that two traits are inherited independently.

- Events in genetics are governed by the laws of probability.

Vocabulary

allele (p. 256)
dominant (p. 256)
fertilization (p. 253)
gamete (p. 253)
genetics (p. 253)
genotype (p. 258)
heredity (p. 253)
heterozygous (p. 259)
homozygous (p. 258)
hybrid (p. 255)
law of independent assortment (p. 260)
law of segregation (p. 257)
phenotype (p. 258)
pollination (p. 254)
recessive (p. 256)
trait (p. 253)
zygote (p. 253)

Section 10.2

Meiosis

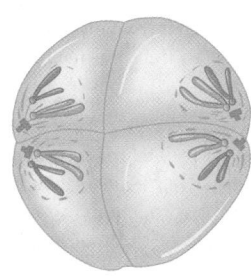

Key Concepts

- In meiosis, one diploid (*2n*) cell produces four haploid (*n*) cells, providing a way for offspring to have the same number of chromosomes as their parents.

- In prophase I of meiosis, homologous chromosomes come together and pair tightly. Exchange of genetic material, called crossing over, takes place.

- Mendel's results can be explained by the distribution of chromosomes during meiosis.

- Random assortment and crossing over during meiosis provide for genetic variation among the members of a species.

- The outcome of meiosis may vary due to nondisjunction, the failure of chromosomes to separate properly during cell division.

- All the genes on a chromosome are linked and are inherited together. It is the chromosomes rather than the individual genes that are assorted independently.

Vocabulary

crossing over (p. 266)
diploid (p. 263)
egg (p. 265)
genetic recombination (p. 270)
haploid (p. 263)
homologous chromosome (p. 264)
meiosis (p. 265)
nondisjunction (p. 271)
sexual reproduction (p. 266)
sperm (p. 265)

FOLDABLES™
Study Organizer To help you review Mendel's work, use the Organizational Study Fold on page 253.

Key Concepts

Summary statements can be used by students to review the major concepts of the chapter.

Biology Online

Visit in.bdol.glencoe.com
  /self_check_quiz
  /vocabulary_puzzlemaker
  /chapter_test
  /standardized_test

VOCABULARY PUZZLEMAKER

For additional help with vocabulary, have students access the Vocabulary PuzzleMaker online at in.bdol.glencoe.com/vocabulary_puzzlemaker

FOLDABLES™

Have students use their Foldables to review the content of Section 10.1. On the back of the paper, use Mendel's laws of heredity to determine the offspring from the following cross: *AaBbCc* × *AaBbCc*.

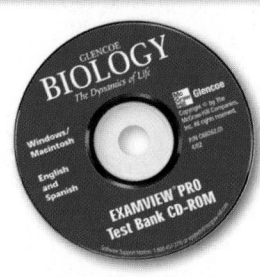

Use the Exam*View*®Pro Test Bank CD-ROM to:

- Create **multiple versions** of tests
- Create **modified** tests with one mouse click for **inclusion** students
- **Edit** existing questions and **add** your own questions
- Build tests aligned with state standards using built-in **State Curriculum Tags**
- Change **English** tests to **Spanish** with one mouse click and vice versa

Chapter 10 Assessment

The Princeton Review **Questions and answers have been aligned and verified by The Princeton Review.**

Vocabulary Review

1. A zygote results from the union of egg and sperm.
2. Homozygous contains two identical alleles.
3. Alleles are the factors that produce genotypes and phenotypes
4. Nondisjunction is a failure of crossing over and its resulting genetic recombination.
5. Gametes are haploid.

Understanding Key Concepts

6. D   9. C
7. B   10. A
8. D   11. C

Constructed Response

12. The likelihood that close relatives share the same recessive genes is greater than in the general population, thus raising the risk of a child being homozygous for those traits.
13. The order of lining up at the equator during metaphase I of meiosis will vary, thus providing additional variation when the chromosomes separate during anaphase I.
14. Controlled experiments, such as Mendel's, require that no more than one variable be manipulated at a time. By doing many experiments, Mendel was able to determine the principles that govern genetics. These principles would not have been easily observable without controlled experiments.
15. Sexual reproduction provides for variations, some of which will be able to survive and reproduce during changing conditions.

278

Vocabulary Review

Review the Chapter 10 vocabulary words listed in the Study Guide on page 277. For each set of vocabulary words, choose the one that does not belong. Explain why it does not belong.

1. egg—sperm—zygote
2. homozygous—hybrid—heterozygous
3. phenotype—genotype—allele
4. nondisjunction—genetic recombination—crossing over
5. zygote—diploid—gamete

Understanding Key Concepts

6. At the end of meiosis, how many haploid cells have been formed from the original cell?
   A. one   C. three
   B. two   D. four
7. When Mendel transferred pollen from one pea plant to another, he was _____ the plants.
   A. self-pollinating   C. self-fertilizing
   B. cross-pollinating   D. cross-fertilizing
8. Which of these does NOT show a recessive trait in garden peas?

A.   B.   C.   D.

9. During what phase of meiosis do sister chromatids separate?
   A. prophase I   C. anaphase II
   B. telophase I   D. telophase II
10. During what phase of meiosis do nonsister chromatids cross over?
   A. prophase I   C. telophase I
   B. anaphase I   D. telophase II
11. A dihybrid cross between two heterozygotes produces a phenotypic ratio of _____.
   A. 3:1   C. 9:3:3:1
   B. 1:2:1   D. 1:6:9

Constructed Response

12. **Open Ended** On the average, each human has about six recessive alleles that would be lethal if expressed. Why do you think that human cultures have laws against marriage between close relatives?
13. **Open Ended** How does separation of homologous chromosomes during anaphase I of meiosis increase variation among offspring?
14. **Open Ended** Relating to the methods of science, why do you think it was important for Mendel to study only one trait at a time during his experiments?
15. **Open Ended** Explain why sexual reproduction is an advantage to a population that lives in a rapidly changing environment.

Thinking Critically

16. **Observe and Infer** Why is it possible to have a family of six girls and no boys, but extremely unlikely that there will be a public school with 500 girls and no boys?
17. **Recognize Cause and Effect** Why is it sometimes impossible to determine the genotype of an organism that has a dominant phenotype?
18. **Observe and Infer** While examining a cell in prophase I of meiosis, you observe a pair of homologous chromosomes pairing tightly. What is the significance of the places at which the chromosomes are joined?
19. **REAL WORLD BIOCHALLENGE** Several human genetic disorders result from nondisjunction in meiosis, including Down syndrome, Kleinfelter's syndrome, and Turner syndrome. Visit **in.bdol.glencoe.com** to investigate these disorders. What characteristic is common to each? Choose one of these disorders, or another human disorder caused by nondisjunction, and prepare a visual display that explains the disorder. Explain the disorder to your class.

 in.bdol.glencoe.com/chapter_test

Thinking Critically

16. The probability of a family with six girls is $(1/2)^6$, but the probability of an entire school of girls would be $(1/2)^{500}$.
17. If the dominant allele completely masks the recessive allele, you cannot tell if an organism with the dominant trait is homozygous or heterozygous for the dominant trait.
18. These are places where crossing over takes place and genetic material is exchanged.
19. All three disorders result from nondisjunction. Students may make displays that show karyotypes or examples of people with the disorders.

Chapter 10 Assessment

End-of-Course Assessment Practice

The assessed Indiana standard appears next to the question.

All questions aligned and verified by The Princeton Review

Part 1 Multiple Choice

Use the diagram to answer questions 20–23.

	T	t
T	1	2
t	3	4

20. Which of the following is true?
B.1.28
  A. Individual 1 is heterozygous.
  B. Individuals 2 and 3 are homozygous.
  C. Individual 4 is recessive.
  D. All individuals will be male.

21. Which of the following has the *Tt* genotype?
B.1.29
  A. 1   **C.** 3
  B. 2   **D.** 2 and 3

22. If *T* is the allele for purple flowers and *t* is
B.1.29 the allele for white flowers, the results
  would be _____.
  A. 3 out of 4 are purple
  B. 3 out of 4 are white
  C. equal numbers of white and purple
  D. all of the same color

23. Which of Mendel's observations would
B.1.22 describe the results of the experimental
  cross in question 22?
  A. rule of dominance
  B. law of segregation
  C. law of independent assortment
  D. rule of unit factors

24. Recessive traits appear only when an
B.1.29 organism is _____.
  A. mature
  B. different from its parents
  C. heterozygous
  D. homozygous

25. The stage of meiosis shown
B.1.8 here is _____.
  A. anaphase I
  B. metaphase II
  C. telophase I
  D. telophase II

Study the diagram and answer questions 26–28.

26. What name is given to the process shown
  above?
  A. fertilization   **C.** meiosis
  B. zygote   **D.** gametes

27. What name is given to the cells shown in
  the diagram above?
  A. fertilization   **C.** meiosis
  B. zygotes   **D.** gametes

28. If each of the cells shown in the diagram has
B.1.8 16 chromosomes, how many chromosomes
  would you expect to find in a skin cell of the
  resulting organism?
  A. 16   **C.** 32
  B. 64   **D.** 8

Part 2 Constructed Response/Grid In

Record your answers on your answer document.

29. Open Ended Explain the difference between trisomy and triploidy. Describe a way that each
B.1.29 condition could occur. Use diagrams to clarify your answer.

30. Open Ended Compare metaphase of mitosis with metaphase I of meiosis. Explain the significance of
B.1.8 the differences between the two stages in terms of sexual reproduction and genetic variation.

 in.bdol.glencoe.com/standardized_test

CHAPTER 10 ASSESSMENT **279**

End-of-Course Assessment Practice

20. C   **23.** B   **26.** A
21. D   **24.** D   **27.** D
22. A   **25.** C   **28.** C

29. Trisomy—three chromosomes of the same type. Triploidy—three sets of chromosomes in a cell.

30. In mitosis, metaphase is the stage where duplicated chromosomes line up on the equator. Each sister chromatid is attached to a spindle fiber, which extends to opposite poles. The sister chromatids will separate into two new cells. There is no genetic variation in these new cells. In meiosis, metaphase I is the point where alleles on homologous chromosomes pair up on the equator, and spindle fibers are attached to each chromosome on opposing poles. The new cells formed are haploid. If the alleles are different, then half of the daughter cells will carry a genetic variation different from the other.

Indiana Academic Standards

Pages 278–279: B.1.8, B.1.21, B.1.22, B.1.28, B.1.29

RUBRIC

For more help evaluating open-ended assessment questions, see the rubric on p. 9T.

Chapter 11 Organizer

Section Objectives	National Science Standards	State/Local Standards	Advanced Lab and Demo Planning
Section 11.1 2 sessions, 1 block 1. **Analyze** the structure of DNA. 2. **Determine** how the structure of DNA enables it to reproduce itself accurately.	UCP.1–3; A.1, A.2; B.2, B.3; C.2, C.3; G.1–3	**Indiana Standards** B.1.21, B.1.26, B.1.27	**Student Labs:** Additional Lab, p. 282: 2 skeins of 3-ply yarn, scissors, box about 100 cm × 50 cm Problem-Solving Lab 11.1, p. 283 **Teacher Demonstration:** Quick Demo, p. 285: zipper
Section 11.2 2 sessions, 2 blocks 3. **Relate** the concept of the gene to the sequences of nucleotides in DNA. 4. **Sequence** the steps involved in protein synthesis.	UCP.1, UCP.2; A.1, A.2; B.2; C.2; G.1	**Indiana Standards** B.1.21, B.1.26, B.1.27, B.1.30	**Student Labs:** Problem-Solving Lab 11.2, p. 291 MiniLab 11.1, p. 293 **Teacher Demonstration:** Quick Demo, p. 289
Section 11.3 2 sessions, 1 block 5. **Categorize** the different kinds of mutations that can occur in DNA. 6. **Compare** the effects of different kinds of mutations on cells and organisms.	UCP.1–4; A.1, A.2; B.2; C.2, C.3, C.4; E.1, E.2; F.1, F.4, F.5; G.1, G.2	**Indiana Standards** B.1.21, B.1.23, B.1.24, B.1.25, B.1.26, B.1.28	**Student Labs:** Problem-Solving Lab 11.3, p. 299 MiniLab 11.2, p. 300 Investigate BioLab, p. 302: See materials below. **Teacher Demonstration:** Quick Demo, p. 298: coiled telephone cord, twist ties
End of Chapter Assessment **Student Edition** **Study Guide,** p. 305 **Content Assessment,** pp. 306–307		**Indiana Standards** B.1.21, B.1.23, B.1.24, B.1.25, B.1.26, B.1.27, B.1.30	**Student Lab:** Investigate BioLab, p. 302: 5 colors of construction paper, scissors, clear tape

Key to Teaching Strategies

L1 Level 1 activities should be appropriate for students with learning difficulties.

L2 Level 2 activities should be within the ability range of all students.

L3 Level 3 activities are designed for above-average students.

ELL ELL activities should be within the ability range of English Language Learners.

COOP LEARN Cooperative Learning activities are designed for small group work.

Legend

♦ Transparency ◐ CD-ROM 🎵 MP3 ▭ Videocassette ◐ DVD

Glencoe Exclusive!

TeacherWorks™
All-In-One Planner and Resource Center

Reproducible Masters and Transparencies

Technology

Unit 4 *FAST FILE* Resources
Reinforcement and Study Guide in English, p. 47
Reinforcement and Study Guide in Spanish, p. 51
Concept Mapping, p. 55
Transparency Worksheets, pp. 57, 61–62
Laboratory Manual, pp. 59–62
♦ **Section Focus Transparency 26**
♦ **Basic Concepts Transparency 16**

◐ Interactive Chalkboard CD-ROM: Section 11.1 Presentation
◐ TeacherWorks™ CD-ROM
🎵 Guided Reading Audio Summaries MP3

Unit 4 *FAST FILE* Resources
MiniLab Worksheets, pp. 39–40
BioLab Worksheets, pp. 43–46
Reinforcement and Study Guide in English, pp. 48–49
Reinforcement and Study Guide in Spanish, pp. 52–53
Critical Thinking/Problem Solving, p. 56
Transparency Worksheets, pp. 58, 63–68
♦ **Section Focus Transparency 27**
♦ **Basic Concepts Transparencies 17, 18**
♦ **Reteaching Skills Transparencies 18**

◐ Interactive Chalkboard CD-ROM: Section 11.2 Presentation
◐ TeacherWorks™ CD-ROM
🎵 Guided Reading Audio Summaries MP3

Unit 4 *FAST FILE* Resources
MiniLab Worksheet, p. 41
Reinforcement and Study Guide in English, p. 50
Reinforcement and Study Guide in Spanish, p. 54
Transparency Worksheets, pp. 59, 69–72
Laboratory Manual, pp. 63–66
♦ **Section Focus Transparency 28**
♦ **Reteaching Skills Transparencies 19a, 19b**

◐ Interactive Chalkboard CD-ROM: Section 11.3 Presentation
◐ TeacherWorks™ CD-ROM
🎵 Guided Reading Audio Summaries MP3

Unit 4 *FAST FILE* Resources
Chapter Assessment, pp. 73–78
Student Recording Sheet, p. 79

The Princeton Review **Reviewing Biology,** pp. 21–22

◐ Interactive Chalkboard: Chapter 11 Assessment
◐ MindJogger Videoquizzes DVD/VHS
◐ *ExamView*® Pro Test Bank CD-ROM
◐ TeacherWorks™ CD-ROM
◐ Succeeding on National Standards CD-ROM

🖥 in.bdol.glencoe.com
/self_check_quiz
/vocabulary_puzzlemaker
/chapter_test
/standardized_test

Indicates materials created specifically for Indiana.

DNA and Genes

Short on Time?

BIODIGEST The BioDigest at the end of this unit can be used as a(n):

- preview to introduce important unit concepts.
- overview if time does not permit teaching the entire chapter.
- review of key unit concepts.

Understanding the Photo

A horse's genetics are determined by 64 chromosomes. These chromosomes contain all of the genetic material that determines the traits of a horse. A horse's genome contains between 60 000 to 80 000 genes. Each gene is a segment of DNA on a chromosome, which codes for proteins and enzymes. Ninety-five percent of DNA does not code for proteins. Two things, genetics and the environment, affect all traits in horses.

What You'll Learn

- You will relate the structure of DNA to its function.
- You will explain the role of DNA in protein production.
- You will distinguish among different types of mutations.

Why It's Important

An understanding of genetic disorders, viral diseases, cancer, aging, genetic engineering, and even criminal investigations depends upon knowing about DNA, how it holds information, and how it plays a role in protein production.

Understanding ▶ the Photo

Shetland ponies originated in Shetland—a group of islands off the coast of Scotland. The islands are mostly barren and have extremely cold winters. Due to the isolation of these islands in the past, the characteristics of the pony—small stature, thick hair (coat, mane, and tail), strength, and hardiness—are firmly imprinted in its DNA.

Biology Online

Visit in.bdol.glencoe.com to
- study the entire chapter online
- access Web Links for more information and activities on DNA and genes
- review content with the Interactive Tutor and self-check quizzes

 Two-Minute Chapter Launcher

Discussion Show students photographs of fruit fly mutations such as various eye colors and wing shapes. Ask students to share ways that the flies could have developed the mutations. Explain that various environmental factors can cause mutations while others can be a result of genetics. Some mutations are passed to offspring and some are not. Guide the discussion to the concept of the DNA molecule, which serves as the blueprint for life.

DNA: The Molecule of Heredity

Indiana Standards Standard B.1.21 Understand and explain that the information passed from parents to offspring is transmitted by means of genes which are coded in DNA molecules.

Life's Instructions

Using an Analogy Can you imagine all of the information that could be contained in 1000 textbooks? Remarkably, that much information—and more—is carried by the genes of a single organism. Scientists have found that the DNA contained in genes holds this information. Because of the unique structure of DNA, new copies of the information can be easily reproduced.

List *Make a list of current events issues concerning DNA that you may have read about in a newspaper. As you read this section, refer to your list and add explanations from the text.*

Model of a DNA molecule

What is DNA?

Although the environment influences how an organism develops, the genetic information that is held in the molecules of DNA ultimately determines an organism's traits. DNA achieves its control by determining the structure of proteins. Living things contain proteins. Your skin contains protein, your muscles contain protein, and your bones contain protein mixed with minerals. All actions, such as eating, running, and even thinking, depend on proteins called enzymes. Enzymes are critical for an organism's function because they control the chemical reactions needed for life. Within the structure of DNA is the information for life—the complete instructions for manufacturing all the proteins for an organism.

DNA as the genetic material

In the early 1950s, many scientists believed that protein was the genetic material, mainly because the structure of these large molecules was so varied. In 1952, however, Alfred Hershey and Martha Chase performed experiments using radioactively labeled viruses that infect bacteria.

11.1   DNA: THE MOLECULE OF HEREDITY   **281**

1 Focus

INTERACTIVE CHALKBOARD
PowerPoint® Presentations

Bellringer
Section Focus Transparency 26

Transparency **26** DNA Structure

SECTION FOCUS
Use with Chapter 11, Section 11.1

Nitrogen base

Phosphate

Deoxyribose sugar

DNA nucleotide

❶ What are the three components of this DNA nucleotide?
❷ What is the function of DNA in the cell?

BIOLOGY: The Dynamics of Life   SECTION FOCUS TRANSPARENCIES

INTERACTIVE CHALKBOARD
with Image Bank

PowerPoint® Presentations
This CD-ROM is an editable Microsoft® PowerPoint® presentation that includes:
• Section presentations
• Section checks
• Image bank
• Hot links to Biology Online
• All transparencies

Using an Analogy

List The day before you begin Section 11.1, ask students to count the number of words on a randomly chosen page in their biology textbook. As you introduce this section, have the class calculate the average number of words on a page. Then calculate the number of words in the textbook by multiplying the average by the number of pages in the book. Multiply this number by 6 000 to get an idea of how many bases are found in our DNA. There are about 3 000 000 000.

2 Teach

Discussion

Ask students whether they know why each of them is a unique individual. Students may suggest that hereditary factors determine their uniqueness. Why has there been no other human on Earth exactly like any of them? Each individual, unless he or she is an identical twin, has different DNA and thus different traits. Even identical twins can be different because of different environmental influences.

Enrichment

Intrapersonal Have students research one of the people involved in the discovery of the structure and function of DNA: Fred Griffith, O.T. Avery, Alfred Hershey, Linus Pauling, Martha Chase, Erwin Chargaff, Rosalind Franklin, or Maurice Wilkins. Have students prepare short oral reports on what these scientists contributed. **L3**

Indiana Academic Standards

Pages 282–283: B.1.21

Figure 11.1
Double-ringed nitrogenous bases—adenine and guanine—are called purines **(A)**. Single-ringed nitrogenous bases—thymine and cytosine—are called pyrimidines **(B)**. Each of the four nucleotides that make up DNA contains a phosphate group, the sugar deoxyribose, and one of four different nitrogenous bases **(C)**.

These viruses were made of only protein and DNA. Hershey and Chase created two different types of viruses. One type had radioactive DNA and the other type had radioactive protein. Each type of virus infected a separate bacteria culture. Only the DNA entered the bacteria and produced new viruses. These results were convincing evidence that DNA is the genetic material.

The structure of nucleotides

DNA is capable of holding all its information because it is a very long molecule. Recall that DNA is a polymer made of repeating subunits called nucleotides. Nucleotides have three parts: a simple sugar, a phosphate group, and a nitrogenous base. The simple sugar in DNA, called deoxyribose (dee ahk sih RI bos), gives DNA its name—deoxyribonucleic acid. The phosphate group is composed of one

atom of phosphorus surrounded by four oxygen atoms. A **nitrogenous base** is a carbon ring structure that contains one or more atoms of nitrogen. In DNA, there are four possible nitrogenous bases: adenine (A), guanine (G), cytosine (C), and thymine (T). Thus, in DNA there are four possible nucleotides, each containing one of these four bases, as shown in *Figure 11.1*.

Nucleotides join together to form long chains, with the phosphate group of one nucleotide bonding to the deoxyribose sugar of an adjacent nucleotide. The phosphate groups and deoxyribose molecules form the backbone of the chain, and the nitrogenous bases stick out like the teeth of a zipper. In DNA, the amount of adenine is always equal to the amount of thymine, and the amount of guanine is always equal to the amount of cytosine. You can see this in the *Problem-Solving Lab* on the next page.

Additional Lab

Gene and Chromosome Size

Purpose

Students will conceptualize the size of a gene and a bacterial chromosome by constructing yarn models that are scaled up a million times in size.

Materials 📋 🥽

4–8 oz. skeins of yarn for a class of 20–30, scissors, box about 100 cm × 50 cm

Procedure

Give students the following directions.

1. One nucleotide in a molecule of DNA occupies a length of 3.4×10^{-10} m. If an average gene coding for an average-sized protein contains 1200 base pairs,

how long is an average gene? 3.4×10^{-10} m × 1200 = 4.08×10^{-7} m How many amino acids would these nucleotides code for? 1200 bases ÷ 3 bases per codon = 400 codons = 400 amino acids

2. Carefully cut a piece of yarn 40 cm long to represent the average gene. This length is 1 000 000 times that of a gene.

The structure of DNA

In 1953, James Watson and Francis Crick published a letter in a journal that was only one page in length, yet monumental in importance. Watson and Crick proposed that DNA is made of two chains of nucleotides held together by nitrogenous bases. Just as the teeth of a zipper hold the two sides of the zipper together, the nitrogenous bases of the nucleotides hold the two strands of DNA together with weak hydrogen bonds. Hydrogen bonds can form only between certain bases, so the bases on one strand determine the bases on the other strand. Specifically, adenine on one strand pairs only with thymine on the other strand, and guanine on one strand pairs only with cytosine on the other strand. These paired bases, called complementary base pairs, explain why adenine and thymine are always present in equal amounts. Likewise, the guanine-cytosine base pairs result in equal amounts of these nucleotides in DNA. Watson and Crick also proposed that DNA is shaped like a long zipper that is twisted into a coil like a spring. When something is twisted like a spring, the shape is called a helix. Because DNA is composed of two strands twisted together, its shape is called a **double helix.** This shape is shown in *Figure 11.2.*

The importance of nucleotide sequences

A cattail, a cat, and a catfish are all different organisms composed of different proteins. If you compare the chromosomes of these organisms, you will find that they all contain DNA made up of the same four nucleotides with adenine, thymine, guanine, and cytosine as their nitrogenous bases. How can organisms be so different from each other if their genetic material is made of the same four nucleotides?

Problem-Solving Lab 11.1

Interpret the Data

What does chemical analysis reveal about DNA? Much of the early research on the structure and composition of DNA was done by carrying out chemical analyses. The data from experiments by Erwin Chargaff provided evidence of a relationship among the nitrogenous bases of DNA.

Solve the Problem

Examine the table below. Compare the amounts of adenine, guanine, cytosine, and thymine found in the DNA of each of the cells studied.

Percent of Each Base in DNA Samples				
Source of Sample	A	G	C	T
Human liver	30.3	19.5	19.9	30.3
Human thymus	30.9	19.9	19.8	29.4
Herring sperm	27.8	22.2	22.6	27.5
Yeast	31.7	18.2	17.4	32.6

Thinking Critically

1. **Compare and Contrast** Compare the amounts of A, T, G, and C in each kind of DNA. Why do you think the relative amounts are so similar in human liver and thymus cells?
2. **Compare and Contrast** How do the relative amounts of each base in herring sperm compare with the relative amounts of each base in yeast?
3. **Summarize** What fact can you state about the overall composition of DNA, regardless of its source?

Figure 11.2
DNA normally exists in the shape of a double helix. This shape is similar to that of a twisted zipper.

Purpose
Students will analyze a table showing the percentages of four bases in DNA samples.

Process Skills
compare and contrast, observe and infer, interpret data

Background
In 1950, American biochemist Erwin Chargaff first showed that there is a 1:1 ratio between adenine and thymine and between guanine and cytosine in all DNA.

Teaching Strategies
Guide students to compare the numbers within each sample before comparing different samples.

Thinking Critically
1. The ratio of A:T and of C:G is approximately 1:1. The relative amounts of each base are so similar in human liver and thymus cells because they come from the same species.
2. The relative amounts of each base are different in herring and in yeast because they are different species.
3. The ratio of A:T and G:C is 1:1 for all sources.

Assessment
Knowledge Have students summarize their analysis of the data and write a paragraph explaining why the ratio of bases was important in determining the structure of DNA. Use the Performance Task Assessment List for Writing in Science in **PASC**, p. 159. **L2**

---

3. Carefully cut a piece of yarn that would represent 150 genes. 150 × 40 cm = 60 m Tie the end of your 60-m piece of yarn to another until all yarn strands in the class are connected.

Expected Results
The total length of all yarn pieces, 1500 m, represents the length of DNA in a bacterium if the cell were scaled up to the size of the box.

Analysis
1. Compare the length of DNA with the size of the "cell" (box). How does all the DNA fit inside the cell? The DNA is coiled and twisted.
2. A human cell contains about 80 000 genes. How long would the yarn be that represents all the DNA in a human cell? 80 000 × 40 cm = 32 000 m

Assessment
Skill Ask students to write a lab report and calculate the answers to the analysis questions. Use the Performance Task Assessment List for Using Math in Science in **PASC**, p. 101.

Their differences result from the sequence of the four different nucleotides along the DNA strands, as shown in *Figure 11.3*.

The sequence of nucleotides forms the unique genetic information of an organism. For example, a nucleotide sequence of A-T-T-G-A-C carries different information from a sequence of T-C-C-A-A-A. In a similar way, two six-letter words made of the same letters but arranged in different order have different meanings. The closer the relationship is between two organisms, the more similar their DNA nucleotide sequences will be.

The DNA sequences of a chimpanzee are similar to those of a gorilla, but different from those of a rosebush. Scientists use nucleotide sequences to determine evolutionary relationships among organisms, to determine whether two people are related, and to identify bodies of crime victims.

Replication of DNA

A sperm cell and an egg cell of two fruit flies, both produced through meiosis, unite to form a fertilized egg. From one fertilized egg, a fruit fly with millions of cells is produced by the process of mitosis. Each cell has a copy of the DNA that was in the original fertilized egg. As you have learned, before a cell can divide by mitosis or meiosis, it must first make a copy of its chromosomes. The DNA in the chromosomes is copied in a process called **DNA replication.** Without DNA replication, new cells would have only half the DNA of their parents. Species could not survive, and

Figure 11.3
The structure of DNA is shown here.

Chromosome

A In each chain of nucleotides, the sugar of one nucleotide is joined to the phosphate group of the next nucleotide by a covalent bond.

Sugar-phosphate backbone

Hydrogen bonds between nitrogenous bases

B The two chains of nucleotides in a DNA molecule are held together by hydrogen bonds between the bases. In DNA, cytosine forms three hydrogen bonds with guanine, and thymine forms two hydrogen bonds with adenine.

C Complementary base pairing produces a long, two-stranded molecule that is often compared to a zipper. As you can see, the sides of the zipper are formed by the sugar and phosphate units, while the teeth of the zipper are the pairs of bases.

284 DNA AND GENES

Figure 11.4
DNA replication produces two molecules from one. **Compare** *How do the new molecules compare with the original?*

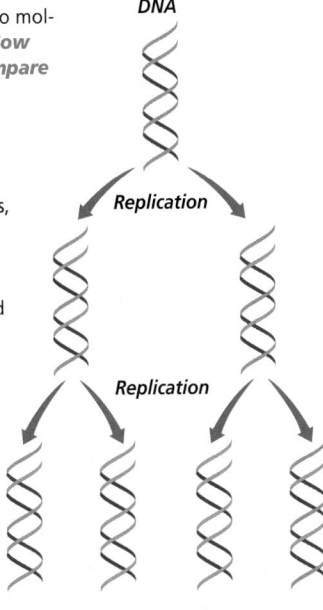

DNA

A When a DNA molecule replicates, two molecules are formed. Each molecule has one original strand and one new strand. Newly synthesized strands are shown in red.

Replication

Replication

B This DNA is replicating. Replication is taking place at the points where the DNA has unzipped to create a "bubble."

Color-enhanced TEM Magnification: 75 000×

individuals could not grow or reproduce successfully. All organisms undergo DNA replication. *Figure 11.4B* shows bacterial DNA replicating.

How DNA replicates

You have learned that a DNA molecule is composed of two strands, each containing a sequence of nucleotides. As you know, an adenine on one strand pairs with a thymine on the other strand. Similarly, guanine pairs with cytosine. Therefore, if you know the order of bases on one strand, you can predict the sequence of bases on the other, complementary strand. In fact, part of the process of DNA replication is done in just the same way. During replication, each strand serves as a pattern, or template, to make a new DNA molecule. How can a molecule serve as a template? Examine *Figure 11.5* on the next page to find out.

Replication begins as an enzyme breaks the hydrogen bonds between bases that hold the two strands

together, thus unzipping the DNA. As the DNA continues to unzip, nucleotides that are floating free in the surrounding medium are attached to their base pair by hydrogen bonding. Another enzyme bonds these nucleotides into a chain.

This process continues until the entire molecule has been unzipped and replicated. Each new strand formed is a complement of one of the original, or parent, strands. The result is the formation of two DNA molecules, each of which is identical to the original DNA molecule.

When all the DNA in all the chromosomes of the cell has been copied by replication, there are two copies of the organism's genetic information. In this way, the genetic makeup of an organism can be passed on to new cells during mitosis or to new generations through meiosis followed by sexual reproduction.

Reading Check **Explain** why DNA must unzip before it can be copied.

11.1 DNA: THE MOLECULE OF HEREDITY **285**

Quick Demo

Explain Hold up a zipped zipper, and relate the zipper teeth to the nucleotides and the cloth band to the deoxyribosephosphate backbone of DNA. Explain that hydrogen bonds hold the two strands together. Help students realize that to make a copy, the DNA must unzip. The nucleotides separate along the hydrogen bonds. Unzip the zipper to show this. Then have two students each carry over a zipper half and show how they would align the halves to the exposed teeth of the original "DNA molecule." They will not be able to zip the zipper halves together, so the students should hold them in place. **L1**

Reading Check DNA must unzip for replication because each half of the DNA is used as a template for the enzyme to build a new half of DNA.

Caption Question Answer
Figure 11.4 New molecules of DNA consist of one of the old strands and a new strand synthesized as a complement to the old strand. They are identical in sequence to each other.

Inquiry

Discussion Have students research how the discoveries of the structure and function of DNA have been applied to other fields, such as agriculture and industry, and then divide them into groups and have them discuss their findings. **L2**

Purpose

Students study the steps involved in the replication of DNA.

Teaching Strategies

■ Have students write a one-paragraph summary of the events in replication. **L2**

■ Have students write a single strand sequence and exchange it with a partner. The partner should write the complementary strand and return it to the first student to be checked. **L1**
COOP LEARN

Visual Learning

Have students draw the steps of replication as separate diagrams. **L1** **ELL**

Critical Thinking

The most likely occurrence is that both daughter cells would be missing some of their chromosomes and would not be able to live. Another possibility is that one cell would receive the complete set of chromosomes and could live and function. The other cell would receive no chromosomes and would die.

Copying DNA

Figure 11.5

DNA is copied during interphase prior to mitosis and meiosis. It is important that the new copies are exactly like the original molecules. The structure of DNA provides a mechanism for accurate copying of the molecule. The process of making copies of DNA is called DNA replication. **Critical Thinking** *What might be the outcome if mitosis occurred before replication took place?*

A **Separation of strands** When a cell begins to copy its DNA, the two nucleotide strands of a DNA molecule separate when the hydrogen bonds connecting the base pairs are broken. As the DNA molecule unzips, the bases are exposed.

Original DNA strand

New DNA strand

C **Bonding of bases** The sugar and phosphate parts of adjacent nucleotides bond together with covalent bonds to form the backbone of the new strand. Each original strand is now hydrogen-bonded to a new strand.

B **Base pairing** The bases in free nucleotides pair with exposed bases in the DNA strand. If one nucleotide on a strand has thymine as a base, the free nucleotide that pairs with it would be adenine. If the strand contains cytosine, a free guanine nucleotide will pair with it. Thus, each strand builds its complement by base pairing—forming hydrogen bonds—with free nucleotides.

Original DNA

286 DNA AND GENES

Indiana Academic Standards

Pages 286–287: B.1.21, B.1.26, B.1.27

286

PROJECT

Flip Books: *Visual-Spatial* Have students create animated flip books showing replication by drawing scenes near the edges of a stack of index cards. They should show DNA unzipping, individual nucleotides bonding to the exposed strands, and the formation of two DNA molecules. The stack can be held together with a rubber band. Have students share their "films" with classmates. **L1** **ELL**

New DNA
molecule

Color-enhanced TEM Magnification: 75 000×

Two molecules of DNA from one

New DNA
molecule

Free nucleotides

Original DNA strand

D **Results of replication** The process of replication produces two molecules of DNA. Each new molecule has one strand from the original molecule and one strand that has been newly synthesized from free nucleotides in the cell.

3 Assess

DAILY INTERVENTION

Check for Understanding
Have students each write two questions about the process of DNA replication. Collect the questions and use them to quiz the class. **L1**

Reteach
Kinesthetic Divide the class into four equal groups. Give each group a letter name—A, T, G, or C. Give each student a card with his or her letter. Write a base sequence for one strand of a DNA molecule on the chalkboard. Be sure to write as many bases as there are students. Give students two minutes to line up next to the appropriate complementary letter on the chalkboard. Tell them they have just replicated a DNA molecule. **L1** **ELL**

Resources
For more practice, use *Reading Essentials for Biology,* Section 11.1.

Extension
Have students research the semi-conservative nature of DNA replication.

 Assessment

Knowledge Prepare a sheet showing a short section of two-stranded DNA. Ask students to diagram the steps this short section would go through in order to replicate. **L2**

Section Assessment

Understanding Main Ideas
1. Describe the structure of a nucleotide.

2. How do the nucleotides in DNA bond with each other within a strand? How do they bond with each other across strands?

3. Explain why the structure of a DNA molecule is often described as a zipper.

4. How does DNA hold information?

Thinking Critically
5. The sequence of nitrogenous bases on one strand of a DNA molecule is GGCAGTTCATGC. What would be the sequence of bases on the complementary strand?

SKILL REVIEW

6. **Get the Big Picture** Sequence the steps that occur during DNA replication. For more help, refer to *Get the Big Picture* in the **Skill Handbook.**

 in.bdol.glencoe.com/self_check_quiz

11.1 DNA: THE MOLECULE OF HEREDITY **287**

Section Assessment

1. A nucleotide consists of a sugar, a phosphate group, and a nitrogen base.
2. The phosphate of one nucleotide bonds to the sugar of an adjacent nucleotide. Across the strands cytosine forms hydrogen bonds with guanine; thymine bonds with adenine.

3. The molecule is shaped like a twisted zipper with the sides formed by the sugar and phosphate molecules. The teeth of the zipper are the pairs of bases.
4. The information is held in the sequence of nucleotides.

5. CCGTCAAGTACG
6. The two strands separate at the base pairs. Free complementary nucleotides are attracted to those on the strands. Enzymes join the new nucleotides to form strands complementary to the original strands. Two DNA molecules are the final product.

1 Focus

Bellringer
Section Focus Transparency 27

Reading Check DNA controls the production of proteins. Proteins are key cell structures and regulators of cell functions.

FOLDABLES™
For an additional Foldables activity idea, see the Chapter 11 Foldables page in *Unit 4 FAST FILE Resources.*

Section 11.2

From DNA to Protein

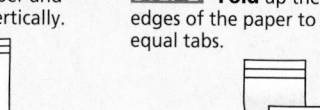

Indiana Standards Standard B.1.26 Demonstrate how the genetic information in DNA molecules provides instructions for assembling protein molecules and that this is virtually the same mechanism for all life forms.

SECTION PREVIEW

Objectives

Relate the concept of the gene to the sequence of nucleotides in DNA.

Sequence the steps involved in protein synthesis.

Review Vocabulary
polymer: a large molecule formed from smaller subunits that are bonded together (p. 158)

New Vocabulary
messenger RNA
ribosomal RNA
transfer RNA
transcription
codon
translation

FOLDABLES™ Study Organizer

Protein Synthesis Make the following Foldable to help you understand the process of protein formation.

STEP 1 **Collect** 3 sheets of paper and layer them about 1.5 cm apart vertically. Keep the edges level.

STEP 2 **Fold** up the bottom edges of the paper to form 6 equal tabs.

STEP 3 **Fold** the papers and crease well to hold the tabs in place. Staple along the fold. **Label** each tab.

Sequence After you read Section 11.2, begin at the top tab and sequence the five steps of translation.

Genes and Proteins

The sequence of nucleotides in DNA contain information. This information is put to work through the production of proteins. Proteins fold into complex, three-dimensional shapes to become key structures and regulators of cell functions. Some proteins become important structures, such as the filaments in muscle tissue. Other proteins, such as enzymes, control chemical reactions that perform key life functions—breaking down glucose molecules in cellular respiration, digesting food, or making spindle fibers during mitosis. In fact, enzymes control all the chemical reactions of an organism. Thus, by encoding the instructions for making proteins, DNA controls cells.

You learned earlier that proteins are polymers of amino acids. The sequence of nucleotides in each gene contains information for assembling the string of amino acids that make up a single protein.

Reading Check **Explain** how DNA controls the activities of cells.

RNA

RNA, like DNA, is a nucleic acid. However, RNA structure differs from DNA structure in three ways, shown in *Figure 11.6.* First, RNA is single stranded—it looks like one-half of a zipper—whereas DNA is double stranded. The sugar in RNA is ribose; DNA's sugar is deoxyribose.

RESOURCE MANAGER

Unit 4 FAST FILE Resources
MiniLab Worksheets, pp. 39–40
BioLab Worksheets, pp. 43–46
Reinforcement and Study Guide in English, pp. 48–49
Reinforcement and Study Guide in Spanish, pp. 52–53
Critical Thinking/Problem Solving, p. 56

Transparency Worksheets, pp. 58, 63–68
Reading Essentials for Biology, Section 11.2
Section Focus Transparency 27
Basic Concepts Transparencies 17, 18
Reteaching Skills Transparencies 18

Figure 11.6
The three chemical differences between DNA and RNA are shown here. **Interpret Scientific Illustrations** *What is the three-dimensional shape of RNA?*

A An RNA molecule usually consists of a single strand of nucleotides, not a double strand. This single-stranded structure is closely related to its function.

Phosphate

Ribose

B Ribose is the sugar in RNA, rather than the deoxyribose sugar in DNA.

Uracil

Hydrogen bonds

Adenine

C The nitrogenous base uracil (U) replaces thymine (T) in RNA. In RNA, uracil forms base pairs with adenine just as thymine does in DNA.

Finally, both DNA and RNA contain four nitrogenous bases, but rather than thymine, RNA contains a similar base called uracil (U). Uracil forms a base pair with adenine in RNA, just as thymine does in DNA.

What is the role of RNA in a cell? Perhaps you have seen a car being built on an automobile assembly line. Complex automobiles are built in many simple steps. Engineers tell workers how to make the cars, and workers follow directions to build the cars on the assembly line. Suppliers bring parts to the assembly line so they can be installed in the car. Protein production is similar to car production. DNA provides workers with the instructions for making the proteins, and workers

build the proteins. Other workers bring parts, the amino acids, over to the assembly line. The workers for protein synthesis are RNA molecules. They take from DNA the instructions on how the protein should be assembled, then—amino acid by amino acid—they assemble the protein.

There are three types of RNA that help build proteins. Extending the car-making analogy, you can consider all three of these RNA molecules to be workers in the protein assembly line. One type of RNA, **messenger RNA** (mRNA), brings instructions from DNA in the nucleus to the cell's factory floor, the cytoplasm. On the factory floor, mRNA moves to the assembly line, a ribosome.

Quick Demo

Assembly Have a few students simulate the assembly line manufacture of "widgets." Some students bring design plans to the assembly line, others bring supplies to the line, and still others do the assembly on the line. Relate this to the manufacture of proteins. **L2**

Tying to Prior Knowledge

Have students recall the structure of proteins, amino acids, polypeptides, and peptide bond formation from Chapter 6. Make sure students understand that most proteins require the synthesis of two or more polypeptide chains.

Caption Question Answer
Figure 11.6 RNA is a single-stranded helix or coiled strand (similar to a spring toy).

USING MODELS

RNA Use the DNA model you made for "Using Models" on page 285 to build models of mRNA and tRNA. Use these models to demonstrate protein synthesis as you teach this section. **L2**

Enrichment

Intrapersonal Scientists have developed a technique that uses fluorescence microscopes to film DNA. The biotechnology technique involves attaching a fluorescent dye to DNA to make it glow. Then, just as you can watch a firefly travel across the yard, researchers can follow the DNA and its movements. Scientists are using this method to investigate how chromosomal DNA is tightly bound to histones and other proteins and how they fold into their functional forms. Have interested students investigate this technique and propose other possible uses for it. **L3**

The BioLab at the end of the chapter can be used at this point in the lesson.

The ribosome, made of **ribosomal RNA** (rRNA), binds to the mRNA and uses the instructions to assemble the amino acids in the correct order. The third type of RNA, **transfer RNA** (tRNA) is the supplier. Transfer RNA delivers amino acids to the ribosome to be assembled into a protein.

Figure 11.7
Messenger RNA is made during the process of transcription.

A The process of transcription begins as enzymes unzip the molecule of DNA in the region of the gene to be transcribed.

B Free RNA nucleotides form base pairs with their complementary nucleotides on the DNA strand. The mRNA strand is complete when the RNA nucleotides bond together.

C The mRNA strand breaks away, and the DNA strands rejoin. The mRNA strand leaves the nucleus and enters the cytoplasm.

DNA strand

RNA strand

RNA strand

DNA strand

G

C

U

G

A

RNA strand

Transcription

How does the information in DNA, which is found in the nucleus, move to the ribosomes in the cytoplasm? Messenger RNA carries this information through the nuclear envelope to the ribosomes for manufacturing proteins, just as a worker carries information from the engineers to the assembly line for manufacturing a car. In the nucleus, enzymes make an RNA copy of a portion of a DNA strand in a process called **transcription** (trans KRIHP shun). Follow the steps in *Figure 11.7* as you read about transcription.

The main difference between transcription and DNA replication is that transcription results in the formation of one single-stranded RNA molecule rather than a double-stranded DNA molecule.

290 DNA AND GENES

INCLUSION STRATEGIES

Learning Disabled Help students differentiate between DNA and RNA by using the statement "You are single." Explain that "You" stands for "U"; RNA has uracil. "Are" stands for "R"; RNA has ribose sugar. "Single" refers to RNA being single stranded.

Indiana Academic Standards

Pages 290–291: B.1.21, B.1.26, B.1.27, B.1.30

290

Modeling transcription in the *BioLab* on pages 302–303 will help you to understand this process. You can find out how scientists use new microscopes to "watch" transcription take place by reading the *Biotechnology* at the end of the chapter.

RNA Processing

Not all the nucleotides in the DNA of eukaryotic cells carry instructions—or code—for making proteins. Genes usually contain many long noncoding nucleotide sequences, called introns (for *in*tervening regions), that are scattered among the coding sequences. Regions that contain information are called exons because they are *ex*pressed. When mRNA is transcribed from DNA, both introns and exons are copied. The introns must be removed from the mRNA before it can function to make a protein. Enzymes in the nucleus cut out the intron segments and paste the mRNA back together. The mRNA then leaves the nucleus and travels to the ribosome.

The Genetic Code

The nucleotide sequence transcribed from DNA to a strand of messenger RNA acts as a genetic message, the complete information for the building of a protein. Think of this message as being written in a language that uses nitrogenous bases as its alphabet. As you know, proteins contain chains of amino acids. You could say that the language of proteins uses an alphabet of amino acids. A code is needed to convert the language of mRNA into the language of proteins. There are 20 common amino acids, but mRNA contains only four types of bases. How can four bases form a code for all possible proteins? The *Problem-Solving Lab* shows you how.

Formulate Models

How many nitrogenous bases determine an amino acid? After the structure of DNA had been discovered, scientists tried to predict the number of nucleotides that code for a single amino acid. It was already known that there were 20 amino acids, so at least 20 groups were needed. If one nucleotide coded for an amino acid, then only four amino acids could be represented. How many nucleotides are needed?

Solve the Problem

Examine the three safes. Letters representing nitrogenous bases have replaced numbers on the dials. Copy the data table. Calculate the possible number of combinations that will open the safe in each diagram using the formula provided in the table. The *4* corresponds to the number of letters on each dial; the superscript refers to the number of available dials.

Safe 1   Safe 2   Safe 3

Data Table				
	Number of Dials	Number of Letters per Dial	Total Possible Combinations	Formula
Safe 1				4^1
Safe 2				4^2
Safe 3				4^3

Thinking Critically

1. **Use Models** Using Safe 1, write down several examples of dial settings that might open the safe. Do the total possible combinations seen in Safe 1 equal or surpass the total number of common amino acids?
2. **Analyze** Could a nitrogenous base (A, T, C, or G) taken one at a time code for 20 different amino acids? Explain.
3. **Use Numbers** Using Safe 2, write down several examples of dial combinations that might open the safe. Do the total possible combinations seen in Safe 2 equal or surpass the total number of common amino acids?
4. **Analyze** Could nitrogenous bases taken two at a time code for 20 different amino acids? Explain.
5. **Analyze** Could nitrogenous bases taken three at a time code for 20 different amino acids? Explain.
6. **Draw Conclusions** Does the analogy prove that three bases code for an amino acid? Explain.

Purpose

Students will use an analogy to see that at least three nitrogenous bases are required to code for a single amino acid.

Process Skills

analyze information, apply concepts, collect data, compare and contrast, draw a conclusion, interpret data, predict, think critically, use numbers

Background

The coding for amino acids using three nitrogenous bases is said to be redundant. That is, there can be several different codons that code for the same amino acid. Thus, the number of combinations is as high as 61 (64 if stops are considered). The number 64 agrees perfectly when three of any four nitrogenous bases combine in any order to code for an amino acid.

Teaching Strategies

- Remind students that there are 20 amino acids.
- You may wish to have students determine the number of two-letter combinations without the use of the formula. It may not be practical, however, to have them actually determine the number of combinations for a three-dial safe.

Thinking Critically

1. A or T or C or G; no
2. No, there are 20 amino acids and only 4 different codes.
3. AA, AT, CT, CG, etc; no
4. No, there are 20 amino acids and only 16 different codes.
5. ATT, ATC, ATG, ATA, etc; yes there are 20 amino acids and 64 possible combinations.
6. No, it shows only that at least 3 bases are needed.

Assessment

Knowledge Ask students to determine which letter in the sequence of three has the most influence in coding for a specific amino acid. Have them give specific examples while referring to Table 11.1 on page 292. Use the Performance Task Assessment List for Analyzing the Data in **PASC**, p. 99. **L2**

291

Biochemists began to crack the genetic code when they discovered that a group of three nitrogenous bases in mRNA code for one amino acid. Each group is known as a **codon.** For example, the codon UUU results in the amino acid phenylalanine being placed in a protein.

Sixty-four combinations are possible when a sequence of three bases is used; thus, 64 different mRNA codons are in the genetic code, shown in *Table 11.1.* Some codons do not code for amino acids; they provide instructions for making the protein. For example, UAA is a *stop* codon indicating that the protein chain ends at that point. AUG is a *start* codon as well as the codon for the amino acid methionine. As you can see, more than one codon can code for the same amino acid. However, for any one codon, there can be only one amino acid.

All organisms use the same genetic code. For this reason, it is said to be universal, and this provides evidence that all life on Earth evolved from a common origin. From the chlorophyll of a birch tree to the digestive enzymes of a bison, a large number of proteins are produced from DNA. It may be hard to imagine that only four nucleotides can produce so many diverse proteins; yet, think about computer programming. You may have seen computer code, such as 00010101110000110. Through a binary language with only two options—zeros and ones—many types of software are created. From computer games to World Wide Web browsers, complex software is built by stringing together the zeros and ones of computer code into long chains. Likewise, complex proteins are built from the long chains of DNA carrying the genetic code.

Table 11.1 The Messenger RNA Genetic Code

First Letter	Second Letter				Third Letter
	U	C	A	G	
U	Phenylalanine (UUU)	Serine (UCU)	Tyrosine (UAU)	Cysteine (UGU)	U
	Phenylalanine (UUC)	Serine (UCC)	Tyrosine (UAC)	Cysteine (UGC)	C
	Leucine (UUA)	Serine (UCA)	Stop (UAA)	Stop (UGA)	A
	Leucine (UUG)	Serine (UCG)	Stop (UAG)	Tryptophan (UGG)	G
C	Leucine (CUU)	Proline (CCU)	Histidine (CAU)	Arginine (CGU)	U
	Leucine (CUC)	Proline (CCC)	Histidine (CAC)	Arginine (CGC)	C
	Leucine (CUA)	Proline (CCA)	Glutamine (CAA)	Arginine (CGA)	A
	Leucine (CUG)	Proline (CCG)	Glutamine (CAG)	Arginine (CGG)	G
A	Isoleucine (AUU)	Threonine (ACU)	Asparagine (AAU)	Serine (AGU)	U
	Isoleucine (AUC)	Threonine (ACC)	Asparagine (AAC)	Serine (AGC)	C
	Isoleucine (AUA)	Threonine (ACA)	Lysine (AAA)	Arginine (AGA)	A
	Methionine; Start (AUG)	Threonine (ACG)	Lysine (AAG)	Arginine (AGG)	G
G	Valine (GUU)	Alanine (GCU)	Aspartate (GAU)	Glycine (GGU)	U
	Valine (GUC)	Alanine (GCC)	Aspartate (GAC)	Glycine (GGC)	C
	Valine (GUA)	Alanine (GCA)	Glutamate (GAA)	Glycine (GGA)	A
	Valine (GUG)	Alanine (GCG)	Glutamate (GAG)	Glycine (GGG)	G

292 DNA AND GENES

CHALLENGE ACTIVITY

Translation: From mRNA to Protein

How is the language of the nucleic acid mRNA translated into the language of proteins? The process of converting the information in a sequence of nitrogenous bases in mRNA into a sequence of amino acids in protein is known as **translation.** You can summarize transcription and translation by completing the *MiniLab.*

Translation takes place at the ribosomes in the cytoplasm. In prokaryotic cells, which have no nucleus, the mRNA is made in the cytoplasm. In eukaryotic cells, mRNA is made in the nucleus and travels to the cytoplasm. In the cytoplasm, a ribosome attaches to the strand of mRNA like a clothespin clamped onto a clothesline.

The role of transfer RNA

For proteins to be built, the 20 different amino acids dissolved in the cytoplasm must be brought to the ribosomes. This is the role of transfer RNA (tRNA), modeled in *Figure 11.8.* Each tRNA molecule attaches to only one type of amino acid.

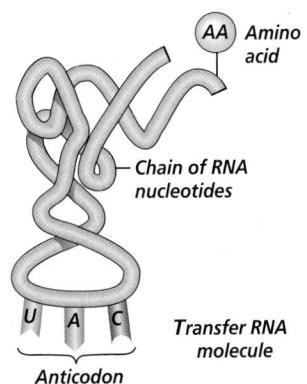

Figure 11.8
A tRNA molecule is composed of about 80 nucleotides. Each tRNA recognizes only one amino acid. The amino acid becomes bonded to one side of the tRNA molecule. Located on the other side of the tRNA molecule are three nitrogenous bases, called an anticodon, that pair up with an mRNA codon during translation.

MiniLab 11.1

Predict

Transcribe and Translate Molecules of DNA carry the genetic instructions for protein formation. Converting these DNA instructions into proteins requires a series of coordinated steps in transcription and translation.

Procedure

1. Copy the data table.
2. Complete column B by writing the correct mRNA codon for each sequence of DNA bases listed in the column marked *DNA Base Sequence.* Use the letters A, U, C, or G.
3. Identify the process responsible by writing its name on the arrow in column A.
4. Complete column D by writing the correct anticodon that binds to each codon from column B.
5. Identify the process responsible by writing its name on the arrow in column C.
6. Complete column E by writing the name of the correct amino acid that is coded by each base sequence. Use *Table 11.1* on page 292 to translate the mRNA base sequences to amino acids.

Data Table

DNA Base Sequence	A Process	B mRNA Codon	C Process	D tRNA Anticodon	E Amino Acid
AAT	→		→		
GGG	→		→		
ATA	→		→		
AAA	→		→		
GTT	→		→		

Analysis

1. **Recognize Spatial Relationships** Where within the cell:
   a. are the DNA instructions located?
   b. does transcription occur?
   c. does translation occur?
2. **Formulate Models** Describe the structure of a tRNA molecule.
3. **Use Scientific Explanations** Explain why specific base pairing is essential to the processes of transcription and translation.

293

MiniLab 11.1

Purpose
Students will follow a series of DNA base codes through transcription and translation.

Process Skills
apply concepts, analyze information, compare and contrast, draw a conclusion

Teaching Strategies
■ Make sure that students have read and reviewed the section in the text dealing with transcription and translation before attempting this activity.
■ If you feel it is necessary, you may want to walk students through the first example.

Expected Results
See the table below.

Analysis
1. a. on chromosomes in the nucleus
   b. in the nucleus
   c. on the ribosomes
2. tRNA is a small molecule that has a three-base anticodon at one end and an amino-acid attachment site at the opposite end.
3. Precise base pairing is essential to transcription and translation so that the correct genetic information in DNA is transferred to the forming protein.

Assessment
Skill Provide students with a series of amino acids and have them make a poster, working backward from these amino acids to a possible tRNA anticodon to the mRNA codon to DNA. Use the Performance Task Assessment List for Poster in **PASC**, p. 145.

Data Table

DNA Base Sequence	A Process	B mRNA Codon	C Process	D tRNA Anticodon	E Amino Acid
AAT	Transcription	UUA	Translation	AAU	Leucine
GGG	Transcription	CCC	Translation	GGG	Proline
ATA	Transcription	UAU	Translation	AUA	Tyrosine
AAA	Transcription	UUU	Translation	AAA	Phenylalanine
GTT	Transcription	CAA	Translation	GUU	Glutamine

Portfolio

Translation Have students write a summary of the events that are being shown in Figure 11.9. Have them include the events that led up to and that will follow translation. **L2**

3 Assess

Check for Understanding
Review the processes of transcription and translation orally. Ask students to define important terms, including DNA, complementary codons, mRNA, tRNA, ribosomal RNA, transcription, translation, and anticodons. Discuss the definitions. **L1**

Reteach
Visual-Spatial On the chalkboard, illustrate the processes of transcription and translation of a particular portion of a DNA strand. Have students copy the diagram and label each process. Then have them check each other's papers. **L1**

Resources
For more practice, use *Reading Essentials for Biology,* Section 11.2.

Indiana Academic Standards

Pages 294–295: B.1.21, B.1.26, B.1.27

294

Figure 11.9
A protein is formed by the process of translation.

A As translation begins, a ribosome attaches to the mRNA strand. Molecules of tRNA, each carrying a specific amino acid, approach the ribosome.

B The codon AUG, which codes for the amino acid methionine, signals the start of protein synthesis. The tRNA molecule carrying methionine attaches to the ribosome and mRNA strand.

C A new tRNA molecule carrying an amino acid attaches to the ribosome and mRNA strand next to the previous tRNA molecule. The amino acids on the tRNA molecules join by peptide bonds.

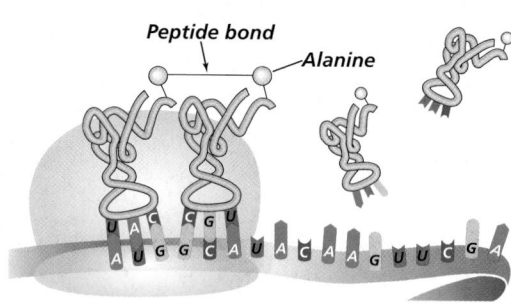

D After the peptide bond is formed, the ribosome slides along the mRNA to the next codon. The tRNA molecule no longer carrying an amino acid is released. A new tRNA molecule carrying an amino acid can attach to the ribosome and mRNA strand.

E A chain of amino acids is formed until a stop codon is reached on the mRNA strand.

294 DNA AND GENES

CHALLENGE ACTIVITY

Protein Synthesis Have interested students write a short paragraph about protein synthesis. Have them predict what would happen to a protein if one base were changed. What would changing one amino acid do to protein structure? **L3**

Correct translation of the mRNA message depends upon the joining of each mRNA codon with the correct tRNA molecule. How does a tRNA molecule carrying its amino acid recognize which codon to attach to? The answer involves base pairing. There is a sequence of three nucleotides on the opposite side of the transfer-RNA molecule from the amino-acid attachment site, that is the complement of the nucleotides in the codon. These three nucleotides are called an anticodon because they bind to the codon of the mRNA. The tRNA carries only the amino acid that the anticodon specifies. For example, one tRNA molecule for the amino acid cysteine has an anticodon of ACA. This anticodon binds to the mRNA codon UGU.

Translating the mRNA code

Follow the steps in *Figure 11.9* as you read how translation occurs. As translation begins, a tRNA molecule brings the first amino acid to the mRNA strand that is attached to the ribosome, *Figure 11.9A*. The anticodon forms a base pair with the codon of the mRNA strand, *Figure 11.9B*. This places the amino acid in the correct position for forming a peptide bond with the next amino acid. The ribosome slides down the mRNA chain to the next codon, and a new tRNA molecule brings another amino acid, *Figure 11.9C*. The amino acids bond; the first tRNA releases its amino acid and detaches from the mRNA, *Figure 11.9D*. The tRNA molecule is now free to pick up and deliver another molecule of its specific amino acid to a ribosome. Again, the ribosome slides down to the next codon; a new tRNA molecule arrives, and its amino acid bonds to the previous one. A chain of amino acids begins to form. When a *stop* codon is reached, translation ends, and the amino acid strand is released from the ribosome, *Figure 11.9E*.

Amino acid chains become proteins when they are freed from the ribosome and twist and curl into complex three-dimensional shapes. Each protein chain forms the same shape every time it is produced. These proteins become enzymes and cell structures.

Now that you have followed the process of protein synthesis, you have seen that the pathway of information flows from DNA to mRNA to protein. This scheme is called the central dogma of biology and is found in all organisms from the simplest bacterium to the most complex plant and animal. The formation of protein, originating from the DNA code, produces the diverse and magnificent living world.

Word Origin

codon from the Latin word *codex,* meaning "a tablet for writing"; A codon is the three-nucleotide sequence that codes for an amino acid.

Extension

Kinesthetic Have students research the structure and function of histone molecules. They could build a model of the eukaryotic chromosome. "Simulating the Eukaryotic Chromosome" by Leo E. Spencer, *Journal of College Science Teaching*, May 1985, may be helpful. **L3**

Assessment

Knowledge On the chalkboard, write the sequence for one strand of DNA. Have students copy the sequence and write the corresponding sequences for mRNA, the tRNA anticodons, and the coded protein. Students should follow the changes in logical steps from the original DNA through transcription and translation. Afterward, go through the correct answer on the board. **L2**

Section Assessment

Understanding Main Ideas
1. How does the DNA nucleotide sequence determine the amino acid sequence in a protein?
2. What is a codon, and what does it represent?
3. What is the role of tRNA in protein synthesis?
4. Compare DNA replication and transcription.

Thinking Critically
5. You have learned that there are *stop* codons that signal the end of an amino acid chain. Why is it

important that a signal to stop translation be part of protein synthesis?

SKILL REVIEW

6. **Get the Big Picture** Sequence the steps involved in protein synthesis from the production of mRNA to the final translation of the DNA code. For more help, refer to *Get the Big Picture* in the **Skill Handbook**.

 in.bdol.glencoe.com/self_check_quiz

Section Assessment

1. A sequence of three nucleotides in DNA codes for an amino acid. The amino acid sequence determines the protein structure.
2. A codon is a 3-base sequence of mRNA that codes for a single amino acid.
3. Transfer RNA brings a specific amino acid to a ribosome by matching a codon on the messenger RNA strand.
4. Replication produces 2 molecules of double-stranded DNA. Transcription results in the production of 1 molecule of single-stranded RNA.
5. Because a protein's 3-dimensional structure depends on its length as well as its amino acid sequence, translation must start and stop at precise positions.
6. The DNA strands separate and free RNA

nucleotides pair with complementary DNA bases on one of the DNA strands, forming mRNA. mRNA leaves the nucleus and attaches to a ribosome. tRNA molecules, carrying specific amino acids, pair with the appropriate mRNA codons. When 2 amino acids are in place, an enzyme joins them together.

1 Focus

INTERACTIVE CHALKBOARD
PowerPoint® Presentations

Bellringer

Section Focus Transparency 28

Transparency **28** Nitrogen Base Sequence

SECTION FOCUS
Use with Chapter 11, Section 11.3

tRNA

mRNA

Stop codon

❶ What would be the resulting sequence of amino acids in this growing protein chain, based on the sequence of bases in the illustrated messenger RNA?

❷ Why is this exact base sequence important?

BIOLOGY: The Dynamics of Life   SECTION FOCUS TRANSPARENCIES

Word Origin

Using the word *mutation,* which comes from the Latin word *matare,* which means "change," have students list the types of changes that occur in DNA.

Using Prior Knowledge

Recognize Cause and Effect A mutation in a body cell may only affect that cell. If the mutation kills the single body cell, there may be no effect. Because there are multiple codons for a single amino acid, a mutation may also have no effect if the change still codes for the same amino acid.

Indiana Academic Standards

Pages 296–297: B.1.21, B.1.23, B.1.24, B.1.25

296

Section 11.3

SECTION PREVIEW

Objectives

Categorize the different kinds of mutations that can occur in DNA.

Compare the effects of different kinds of mutations on cells and organisms.

Review Vocabulary

cancer: diseases believed to be caused by changes in the genes that control the cell cycle (p. 211)

New Vocabulary

mutation
point mutation
frameshift mutation
chromosomal mutation
mutagen

Physical Science Connection

Gamma radiation as a wave
Gamma radiation, or gamma rays, are electromagnetic waves. Gamma radiation is emitted by processes that occur in the nuclei of atoms. They have the shortest wavelengths and highest frequencies of any waves in the electromagnetic spectrum.

Genetic Changes

Indiana Standards Standard B.1.23 Understand that and describe how inserting, deleting, or substituting DNA segments can alter a gene. Recognize that an altered gene may be passed on to every cell that develops from it, and that the resulting features may help, harm, or have little or no effect on the offspring's success in its environment.

When Things Go Wrong

Using Prior Knowledge You know that DNA controls the structures and functions of a cell. What happens when the sequence of DNA nucleotides in a gene is changed? Sometimes it may have little or no harmful effect—like the thick, tightly crimped fur on this American Wirehair cat—and the DNA changes are passed on to offspring of the organism. At other times, however, the change can cause the cell to behave differently. For example, in skin cancer, UV rays from the sun damage the DNA and cause the cells to grow and divide rapidly.

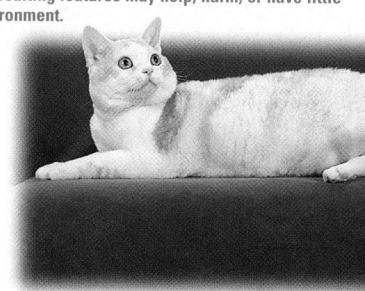

American Wirehair cat

Recognize Cause and Effect *Why might a mutation have little or no harmful effect on an organism?*

Mutations

If the DNA in all the cells of an adult human body were lined up end to end, it would stretch nearly 100 billion kilometers—60 times the distance from Earth to Jupiter. This DNA is the end result of thousands of replications, beginning with the DNA in a fertilized egg. Organisms have evolved many ways to protect their DNA from changes. In spite of these mechanisms, however, changes in the DNA occasionally do occur. Any change in the DNA sequence is called a **mutation.** Mutations can be caused by errors in replication, transcription, cell division, or by external agents. One such cause is discussed in *Figure 11.10.*

Mutations in reproductive cells

Mutations can affect the reproductive cells of an organism by changing the sequence of nucleotides within a gene in a sperm or an egg cell. If this cell takes part in fertilization, the altered gene would become part of the genetic makeup of the offspring. The mutation may produce a new trait or it may result in a protein that does not work correctly, resulting in structural or functional problems in cells and in the organism. Sometimes, the mutation results in a protein that is nonfunctional, and the embryo may not survive.

In some rare cases, a gene mutation may have positive effects. An organism may receive a mutation that makes it faster or stronger; such a mutation may help an organism—and its offspring—better survive in its environment.

RESOURCE MANAGER

Unit 4 *FAST FILE* Resources
MiniLab Worksheet, p. 41
Reinforcement and Study Guide in English, p. 50
Reinforcement and Study Guide in Spanish, p. 54
Transparency Worksheets, pp. 59, 69–72

Reading Essentials for Biology, Section 11.3
Laboratory Manual, pp. 63–66
Section Focus Transparency 28
Reteaching Skills Transparencies 19a, 19b

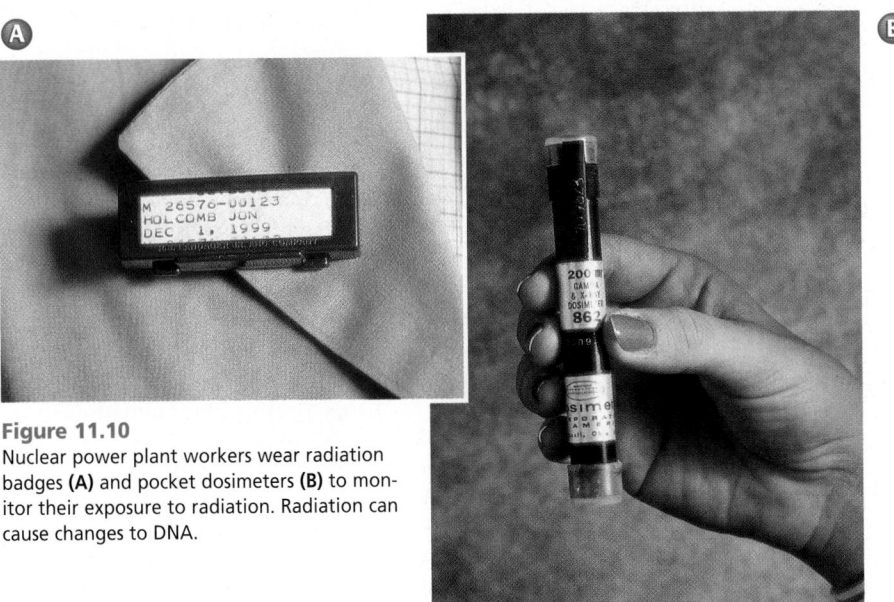

(A)

(B)

Figure 11.10
Nuclear power plant workers wear radiation badges **(A)** and pocket dosimeters **(B)** to monitor their exposure to radiation. Radiation can cause changes to DNA.

You will learn later that mutations that benefit a species play an important role in the evolution of that species.

Mutations in body cells

What happens if powerful radiation, such as gamma radiation, hits the DNA of a nonreproductive cell, a cell of the body such as in skin, muscle, or bone? If the cell's DNA is changed, this mutation would not be passed on to offspring. However, the mutation may cause problems for the individual. Damage to a gene may impair the function of the cell; for example, it may cause a cell in the stomach to lose its ability to make acid needed for digestion, or a skin cell may lose its elasticity. When that cell divides, the new cells also will have the same mutation. Many scientists suggest that the buildup of cells with less than optimal functioning is an important cause of aging.

Some mutations of DNA in body cells affect genes that control cell division. This can result in the cells growing and dividing rapidly, producing cancer. As you learned earlier, cancer is the uncontrolled dividing of cells.

CAREERS IN BIOLOGY

Genetic Counselor

Are you fascinated by how you inherit traits from your parents? If so, you could become a genetic counselor and help people assess their risk of inheriting or passing on genetic disorders.

Skills for the Job

Genetic counselors are medical professionals who work on a health care team. They analyze families' medical histories to determine the parents' risk of having children with genetic disorders, such as hemophilia or cystic fibrosis. Counselors also educate the public and help families with genetic disorders find support and treatment. These counselors may work in a medical center, a private practice, research, or a commercial laboratory. To become a counselor, you must earn a two-year master's degree in medical genetics and pass a test to become certified. The most important requirement is the ability to listen and to help families make difficult decisions.

 For more careers in related fields, visit
in.bdol.glencoe.com/careers

---

2 Teach

Enrichment

Logical-Mathematical Ask students which scenario is worse as a result of DNA damage by radiation to a body cell: (a) the function of the cell is altered but the cell survives, or (b) the cell dies. Probably (a) is a worse outcome. When the cell dies, others can take its place. When it has DNA damage, all new cells that come from this cell will contain the same defects. **L3**

CAREERS IN BIOLOGY

Career Path
TECH PREP **Courses in high school:** biology, psychology, and communication
College: bachelor's degree in biology, genetics, nursing, public health, social work, or psychology; master's degree in medical genetics

Career Issue
Ask students whether genetic counselors should only give families information about their genetic background, or should they try to influence the families' decisions about having children. Have them give reasons for their answer. **L2**

For More Information
For more information about becoming a genetic counselor, write to:

National Society of Genetic Counselors
233 Canterbury Drive
Wallingford, PA 19086-6617

Physical Science Connection

(p. 296) Have students research gamma-ray detectors, including how they are used and the information they yield. Types of gamma-ray detectors include gas-filled detectors, scintillation counters, and semiconductor detectors. Gamma-ray detectors have been used to obtain information about the structure of nuclei as well as the chemical properties and behavior of chemical compounds. Gamma-ray detectors on satellites above Earth's atmosphere also have detected gamma-ray bursts whose cause and identity are still a mystery.

Use Models Use a coiled telephone cord and twist ties to show students how the three-dimensional shape of a protein can change when a single amino acid is changed in a point mutation. The twist ties can represent cross linkages between certain amino acids such as cystine.

Reinforcement

Logical-Mathematical Have students write a sequence of twelve mRNA nucleotides. The sequence should be exchanged with a classmate, who will write the protein strand produced and return the sequence to the first student to check. Now the first student changes one nucleotide to simulate a point mutation. Students should repeat the exchanges. **L1**
COOP LEARN

✓ **Reading Check** Mutations in body cells may impair their function by causing a loss in the ability to make a protein that is important to the cell's function. When that cell divides, it passes on the mutation. The buildup of mutated cells may play a role in aging.

Caption Question Answer
Figure 11.11 a frameshift mutation

Cancer results from gene mutations. For example, ultraviolet radiation in sunlight can change the DNA in skin cells. The cells reproduce rapidly, causing skin cancer.

✓ **Reading Check** **Explain** how mutations in body cells cause damage.

The effects of point mutations

Consider what might happen if an incorrect amino acid were inserted into a growing protein chain during the process of translation. The mistake might affect the structure of the entire molecule. Such a problem can occur if a point mutation arises. A **point mutation** is a change in a single base pair in DNA.

A simple analogy can illustrate point mutations. Read the following two sentences. Notice what happens when a single letter in the first sentence is changed.

> THE DOG BIT THE CAT.
> THE DOG BIT THE CAR.

As you can see, changing a single letter changes the meaning of the above sentence. Similarly, a change in a single nitrogenous base can change the entire structure of a protein because a change in a single amino acid can affect the shape of the protein. *Figure 11.11A* shows what can happen with a point mutation.

Frameshift mutations

When the ribosome moves along the mRNA strand, a new amino acid is added to the protein for every codon on the mRNA strand. What would happen if a single base were lost from a DNA strand?

Figure 11.11
The results of a point mutation and a frameshift mutation are different. The diagrams show the mRNA and protein that would be formed from each corresponding DNA. **Infer** *Which type of mutation is likely to cause greater genetic damage?*

Ⓐ In this point mutation, the mRNA produced by the mutated DNA had the base guanine changed to adenine. This change in the codon caused the insertion of serine rather than glycine into the growing amino acid chain. The error may or may not interfere with protein function.

Ⓑ Proteins that are produced as a result of frameshift mutations seldom function properly because such mutations usually change many amino acids. Adding or deleting one base of a DNA molecule will change nearly every amino acid in the protein after the addition or deletion.

298 DNA AND GENES

This new sequence with the deleted base would be transcribed into mRNA. But then, the mRNA would be out of position by one base. As a result, every codon after the deleted base would be different, as shown in *Figure 11.11B.* This mutation would cause nearly every amino acid in the protein after the deletion to be changed. In the sentence THE DOG BIT THE CAT, deleting a G would produce the sentence THE DOB ITT HEC AT. The same effect would result from the addition of a single base. A mutation in which a single base is added to or deleted from DNA is called a **frameshift mutation** because it shifts the reading of codons by one base. In general, point mutations are less harmful to an organism because they disrupt only a single codon. The *MiniLab* on the next page will help you distinguish point mutations from frameshift mutations, and the *Problem-Solving Lab* on this page will show you an example of a common mutation in humans.

✓ **Reading Check** **Compare and contrast** the cause and effect of a point mutation and a frameshift mutation.

Chromosomal Alterations

Changes may occur in chromosomes as well as in genes. Alterations to chromosomes may occur in a variety of ways. For example, sometimes parts of chromosomes are broken off and lost during mitosis or meiosis. Often, chromosomes break and then rejoin incorrectly. Sometimes, the parts join backwards or even join to the wrong chromosome. These structural changes in chromosomes are called **chromosomal mutations.**

Chromosomal mutations occur in all living organisms, but they are especially common in plants. Such mutations affect the distribution of genes to the gametes during meiosis. Homologous chromosomes do not pair correctly when one chromosome has extra or missing parts, so separation of the homologous chromosomes does not occur normally. Gametes that should have a complete set of genes may end up with extra copies or a complete lack of some genes.

✓ **Reading Check** Point mutations occur when an incorrect base is inserted into the sequence and may or may not affect the protein function. Frameshift mutations occur when a base is either inserted to or deleted from the sequence and will affect nearly every amino acid in the protein after the insertion or deletion.

Problem-Solving Lab 11.3

Make and Use Tables

What type of mutation results in sickle-cell anemia?
A disorder called sickle-cell anemia results from a genetic change in the base sequence of DNA. Red blood cells in patients with sickle-cell anemia have molecules of hemoglobin that are mis-shapen. As a result of this change in protein shape, sickled blood cells clog capillaries and prevent normal flow of blood to body tissues, causing severe pain.

Solve the Problem
The table below shows the sequence of bases in a short seg-ment of the DNA that controls the order of amino acids in the protein hemoglobin.

DNA Base Sequences	
Normal hemoglobin	GGG CTT CTT TTT
Sickled hemoglobin	GGG CAT CTT TTT

Thinking Critically
1. **Interpret Data** Use *Table 11.1* on page 292 to transcribe and translate the DNA base sequence for normal hemo-globin and for sickled hemoglobin into amino acids. Remember that the table lists mRNA codons, not DNA base sequences.
2. **Define Operationally** Does this genetic change illustrate a point mutation or frameshift mutation? Explain your answer.
3. **Explain** Why is the correct sequence of DNA bases impor-tant to the production of proteins?
4. **Analyze** Assume that the base sequence reads GGG CTT CTT AAA instead of the normal sequence for hemoglobin. Would this result in sickled hemoglobin? Explain.

Problem-Solving Lab 11.3

Purpose
Students will compare the base sequence of a segment of normal DNA with the base sequence of DNA that codes for sickled human hemoglobin.

Process Skills
analyze information, apply con-cepts, compare and contrast, rec-ognize cause and effect

Teaching Strategies
- Make sure that students are familiar with Table 11.1 on page 292 and understand how it is to be used.
- Discuss sickle-cell anemia briefly and point out its greater occurrence among African Americans.

Thinking Critically
1. normal: proline, glutamate, glutamate, lysine; sickled: proline, valine, glutamate, lysine
2. point mutation; One codon has been altered and one amino acid is different.
3. In this example, the correct sequence of amino acids is needed to form a molecule of normal hemoglobin. With a change of only one amino acid, the protein molecule no longer functions in a normal manner.
4. Student answers may vary. Probably not; protein forma-tion is very specific and the substitution of a different amino acid could result in a totally different form of hemoglobin.

Assessment
Performance Ask students to write an informative newspaper article in which they describe sickle-cell anemia and explain its cause to the public. Use the Performance Task Assessment List for Newspaper Article in **PASC**, p. 141. **L2**

MiniLab 11.2

Purpose
Students will examine the effect of gene mutations on proteins.

Process Skills
recognize cause and effect, analyze

Teaching Strategies
Individual students can do this MiniLab at their desks.

Expected Results
Base sequence of mRNA: UUACGGUCACCAAGCGUG; amino acids: leucine-arginine-serine-proline-serine-valine; Changing the fourth base in the DNA from G to C would change the second amino acid from arginine to glycine. Adding G at the fourth position of the DNA would result in the mRNA base sequence UUACCGGUCAC-CAAGCGUG and the amino acid sequence leucine-proline-valine-threonine-lysine-arginine.

Analysis
1. Changing G to C was a point mutation; adding G was a frameshift mutation.
2. The point mutation changed only one amino acid.
3. The frameshift mutation changed every amino acid following the addition of G.

Modified Assessment
Performance Ask students to give an oral presentation explaining the effect of substituting C for a T in the third position of the DNA strand above. The amino acid sequence will be the same because both sequences code for leucine. Use the Performance Task Assessment List for Oral Presentation in **PASC**, p. 143. L1

Indiana Academic Standards

Pages 300–301: B.1.21, B.1.23, B.1.24, B.1.25

300

MiniLab 11.2

Make and Use Tables

Gene Mutations and Proteins
Gene mutations often have serious effects on proteins. In this activity, you will demonstrate how such mutations affect protein synthesis.

DNA segment

Procedure
1. Copy the following base sequence of one strand of an imaginary DNA molecule: AATGCCAGTGGTTCGCAC.
2. Then, write the base sequence for an mRNA strand that would be transcribed from the given DNA sequence.
3. Use *Table 11.1* to determine the sequence of amino acids in the resulting protein fragment.
4. If the fourth base in the original DNA strand were changed from G to C, how would this affect the resulting protein fragment?
5. If a G were added to the original DNA strand after the third base, what would the resulting mRNA look like? How would this addition affect the protein?

Analysis
1. **Define Operationally** Which change in DNA was a point mutation? Which was a frameshift mutation?
2. **Infer** How did the point mutation affect the protein?
3. **Analyze** How did the frameshift mutation affect the protein?

300 DNA AND GENES

Few chromosomal mutations are passed on to the next generation because the zygote usually dies. In cases where the zygote lives and develops, the mature organism is often sterile and thus incapable of producing offspring. The most important of these mutations—deletions, insertions, inversions, and translocations—are illustrated in *Figure 11.12*.

Causes of Mutations
Some mutations seem to just happen, perhaps as a mistake in base pairing during DNA replication. These mutations are said to be spontaneous. However, many mutations are caused by factors in the environment. Any agent that can cause a change in DNA is called a **mutagen** (MYEW tuh jun). Mutagens include radiation, chemicals, and even high temperatures.

Forms of radiation, such as X rays, cosmic rays, ultraviolet light, and

Figure 11.12
Study the four kinds of chromosomal mutations.

A When a part of a chromosome is left out, a deletion occurs.
Deletion

B When part of a chromatid breaks off and attaches to its sister chromatid, an insertion occurs. The result is a duplication of genes on the same chromosome.
Insertion

C When part of a chromosome breaks off and reattaches backwards, an inversion occurs.
Inversion

D When part of one chromosome breaks off and is added to a different chromosome, a translocation occurs.
Translocation

CHALLENGE ACTIVITY

Protein Building Have students write an essay comparing the building of proteins to the building of a house and what will occur if there are problems with or changes made to the blueprint guiding the builders. L3

nuclear radiation, are dangerous mutagens because the energy they contain can damage or break apart DNA. The breaking and reforming of a double-stranded DNA molecule can result in deletions. Some kinds of radiation can convert a base into a different, incorrect base or fuse two bases together.

Chemical mutagens include dioxins, asbestos, benzene, and formaldehyde, substances that are commonly found in buildings and in the environment, *Figure 11.13*. These mutagens are highly reactive substances that interact with the DNA molecule and cause changes. Chemical mutagens usually cause substitution mutations.

Repairing DNA

The cell processes that copy genetic material and pass it from one generation to the next are usually accurate. This accuracy is important to ensure the genetic continuity of both new cells and offspring. Yet, mistakes sometimes do occur. There are many sources of mutagens in an organism's environment. Although many of these are due to human activities, others—such as cosmic rays from outer space—have affected living things since the beginning of life. Repair mechanisms that fix mutations in cells have evolved.

Much like a book editor, enzymes proofread the DNA and replace incorrect nucleotides with correct nucleotides. These repair mechanisms work extremely well, but they are not perfect. The greater the exposure to a mutagen such as UV light, the more likely is the chance that a mistake will not be corrected. Thus, it is wise for people to limit their exposure to mutagens.

Figure 11.13
Asbestos was formerly used to insulate buildings. It is now known to cause lung cancer and other lung diseases and must be removed from buildings, as these workers are doing.

Section Assessment

Understanding Main Ideas
1. What is a mutation?
2. Describe how point mutations and frameshift mutations affect the synthesis of proteins.
3. Explain why a mutation in a sperm or egg cell has different consequences than one in a heart cell.
4. How are mutations and cancer related?

Thinking Critically
5. The chemicals in cigarette smoke are known to cause cancer. Propose a series of steps that could lead to development of lung cancer in a smoker.

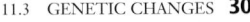
SKILL REVIEW

6. **Recognize Cause and Effect** In an experiment with rats, the treatment group is exposed to radiation while the control group is not. Months later, the treatment group has a greater percentage of rats with cancer and more newborn rats with birth defects than the control group. Explain how the exposure to radiation may have affected the treatment group's DNA. Infer how these effects could have caused cancer and birth defects. For more help, refer to *Recognize Cause and Effect* in the **Skill Handbook.**

in.bdol.glencoe.com/self_check_quiz

Section Assessment

1. A mutation is any mistake or change in the DNA sequence.
2. A point mutation may change a single amino acid in a protein. A frameshift mutation may alter every amino acid after the mutation because the shift in bases occurs all along the strand.
3. A mutation of a reproductive cell affects the individual's offspring.

A mutation of a heart cell affects only the individual.
4. Mutations of a body cell may cause cancer by altering the cell processes that control cell division. This makes the cells divide rapidly.
5. Chemicals in cigarette smoke can change the DNA of cells, which may result in the cells' excessive multiplying,

straying to other areas, and harming their environment.
6. Greater incidence of cancer can be explained by the radiation causing mutations in the processes that control cell division in body cells. More birth defects can be explained by mutations in the reproductive cells.

Time Allotment
one class period

Process Skills
sequence, observe and infer, recognize cause and effect

Safety Precautions
Remind students to use care when cutting with scissors and to cut away from their bodies.

Instead of having students copy models onto construction paper, you may use the masters provided in *Unit 4 FAST FILE Resources* booklet. Copy these onto white paper and have students color the models with pencils or crayons.

Before You Begin
Although DNA remains in the nucleus of a cell, it passes its information into the cytoplasm by way of another nucleic acid, messenger RNA. The base sequence of this mRNA is complementary to the sequence in the strand of DNA. It is produced by base pairing during transcription. In this activity, you will demonstrate the process of transcription through the use of paper DNA and mRNA models.

RNA Transcription

Problem
How does the order of bases in DNA determine the order of bases in mRNA?

Objectives
In this BioLab, you will:
- **Formulate a model** to show how the order of bases in DNA determines the order of bases in mRNA.
- **Infer** why the structure of DNA enables it to be easily transcribed.

Materials
construction paper, 5 colors
scissors
clear tape

Safety Precautions
CAUTION: *Be careful when using scissors. Always use goggles in the lab.*

Skill Handbook
If you need help with this lab, refer to the **Skill Handbook.**

Parts for DNA Nucleotides   **Extra Parts for RNA Nucleotides**

Teaching Strategies
- You may give each student two envelopes to hold the nucleotide pieces. One can be used for the DNA nucleotides and the other for the RNA nucleotides.

- To make larger, more varied models, the lab groups could pool their models.

Data and Observations
Students should construct a DNA molecule and a complementary mRNA molecule.

PROCEDURE

1. Copy the parts for the four different DNA nucleotides onto your construction paper, making sure that each different nucleotide is on a different color paper. Make ten copies of each nucleotide.

2. Using scissors, carefully cut out the shapes of each nucleotide.

3. Using any order of nucleotides that you wish, construct a double-stranded DNA molecule. If you need more nucleotides, copy them as in step 1.

4. Fasten your molecule together using clear tape. Do not tape across base pairs.

5. As in step 1, copy the parts for A, G, and C RNA nucleotides. Use the same colors of construction paper as in step 1. Use the fifth color of construction paper to make copies of uracil nucleotides.

6. With scissors, carefully cut out the RNA nucleotide shapes.

7. With your DNA molecule in front of you, demonstrate the process of transcription by first pulling the DNA molecule apart between the base pairs.

8. Using only one of the strands of DNA, begin matching complementary RNA nucleotides with the exposed bases on the DNA model to make mRNA.

9. When you are finished, tape your new mRNA molecule together.

ANALYZE AND CONCLUDE

1. **Observe and Infer** Does the mRNA model more closely resemble the DNA strand from which it was transcribed or the complementary strand that wasn't used? Explain your answer.

2. **Recognize Cause and Effect** Explain how the structure of DNA enables the molecule to be easily transcribed. Why is this important for genetic information?

3. **Relate Concepts** Why is RNA important to the cell? How does an mRNA molecule carry information from DNA? Where does the mRNA molecule take the information?

Apply Your Skill

Research Do research to find out more about how the bases in DNA were identified and how the base pairing pattern was determined.

 Web Links To find out more about DNA, visit in.bdol.glencoe.com/DNA

ANALYZE AND CONCLUDE

1. mRNA more closely resembles the complementary DNA. They have the same base sequence except that mRNA has uracil in place of thymine.

2. Because DNA is double-stranded, sections can be unzipped to allow complementary bases to hydrogen bond while the remaining DNA stays zipped. Thus, only the information needed at one time is being transcribed. Complementary pairing allows accurate DNA copying.

3. The mRNA is formed as a complementary copy of the genetic information. The RNA copy can leave the nucleus while the "master copy" stays protected within the nucleus. The mRNA carries information to ribosomes within the cytoplasm.

Assessment

Portfolio Have students write a lab report summarizing the lab and including answers to Analyze and Conclude. Use the Performance Task Assessment List for Lab Report in **PASC,** p. 119. **L2**

Apply Your Skill

Research Have students use Table 11.1 on page 292 to determine which amino acids they "produced" in the BioLab. **L1**

INCLUSION STRATEGIES

Visually Impaired Cut copies of the five different nucleotides (A, T, C, G, and U) out of cardboard, textured paper or sandpaper so visually impaired students can participate in the lab.

Purpose

Students learn about the operation and the capabilities of scanning probe microscopy.

Background

If the current is increased slightly above the levels required to produce an image, a scanning probe microscope can pick up atoms and move them around. Before the 1990s, water molecules had to be removed from the cell for observation.

Teaching Strategies

■ Explain that this is the first type of microscopy able to produce images at the scale of the nanometer—10^{-9} meters, the scale at which molecular bonding occurs. They can also produce images at somewhat larger scales, including 10^{-8}, the scale of the DNA molecule, 10^{-7}, the scale of the nucleus and other organelles, and 10^{-6}, the scale of intact cells.

■ Point out that biology is not the only field that benefits from scanning probe microscopes. For example, physicists look at the structure of metals and other materials. Chemists observe molecules during chemical reactions. Materials scientists explore methods of fabricating ever-tinier computer chips.

Applying Biotechnology

Scanning probe microscopes can show the arrangements of atoms on the surface of the molecule. Because specimens can be examined in liquid or air, biological molecules can be observed functioning as they would inside the cell. Answers to future applications may vary, but might involve increasing the understanding of cell functioning and improper functioning in cells due to disease or disorders.

![BIO TECHNOLOGY]

Scanning Probe Microscopes

Have you ever heard of someone dissecting a chromosome to get a closer look at DNA? Imagine an instrument small enough to allow you to grab hold of one of the nucleotides in a strand of DNA, yet powerful enough to provide a detailed image.

Scanning probe microscopes can show the arrangement of atoms on the surface of a molecule. They make it possible for scientists to pick up molecules, and even atoms, and move them around. They can also be used to observe how biological molecules interact. There are many types of scanning probe microscopes. All of them use a very sharp probe that may be only a single atom wide at its tip. The probe sits very close to the specimen but does not actually touch it. As the probe moves across, or scans, the specimen, it measures some property of the specimen.

Magnification: unavailable

STM image of DNA

The scanning tunneling microscope (STM)
The STM uses a probe through which a tiny amount of electric current flows. As the probe scans a molecule, it encounters ridges and valleys formed by the different kinds of atoms on the molecule's surface. The probe moves up and down as needed to keep the current constant. The movements of the probe are recorded by a computer, which produces an image of the molecule.

The atomic force microscope (AFM)
The AFM can measure many different properties, including electricity, magnetism, and heat. As the probe moves across the specimen, changes in the property being measured move the probe. These changes are used to create the image.

What can they do?
One of the primary advantages of scanning probe microscopy, besides its atomic-level resolution, is the ability to observe

304 DNA AND GENES

molecules in air or liquid. This means that biologists can "watch" molecules interact as they would inside a cell.

Scanning probe microscopes are being used to study patterns in liquid crystals, wave convection, molecular surfaces of materials and molecular events such as the function of bacterial toxins and ion channels, actin and myosin interactions in muscle cells, and protein folding.

Imaging transcription Biologists currently are imaging factors that are involved in the transcription of DNA. These factors include enzymes that cut DNA and those that repair DNA errors. By using the AFM, biologists are beginning to identify the DNA binding sites for these enzymes, which will be used in mapping studies of DNA. This will allow further understanding of the process of transcription.

Applying Biotechnology

Think Critically What advantages do scanning probe microscopes have over other types of microscopes? Predict some future applications that would make use of these advantages.

 To find out more about microscopes, visit in.bdol.glencoe.com/biotechnology

Going Further

Intrapersonal Improvements to this microscope technology continue to be made. Invite students to research recent images produced by scanning probe microscopes. **L2**

STUDY GUIDE

Section 11.1

DNA: The Molecule of Heredity

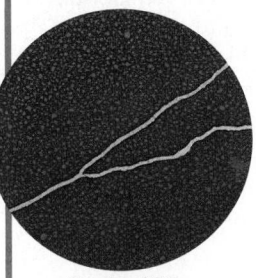

Color-enhanced TEM
Magnification: 75 000×

Key Concepts

- Alfred Hershey and Martha Chase demonstrated that DNA is the genetic material.
- DNA, the genetic material of organisms, is composed of four kinds of nucleotides. A DNA molecule consists of two strands of nucleotides with sugars and phosphates on the outside and bases paired by hydrogen bonding on the inside. The paired strands form a twisted-zipper shape called a double helix.
- Because adenine can pair only with thymine, and guanine can pair only with cytosine, DNA can replicate itself with great accuracy.

Vocabulary

DNA replication (p. 284)
double helix (p. 283)
nitrogenous base (p. 282)

Section 11.2

From DNA to Protein

Key Concepts

- Genes are small sections of DNA. Most sequences of three bases in the DNA of a gene code for a single amino acid in a protein.
- Messenger RNA is made in a process called transcription. The order of nucleotides in DNA determines the order of nucleotides in messenger RNA.
- Translation is a process through which the order of bases in messenger RNA codes for the order of amino acids in a protein.

Vocabulary

codon (p. 292)
messenger RNA (p. 289)
ribosomal RNA (p. 290)
transcription (p. 290)
transfer RNA (p. 290)
translation (p. 293)

Section 11.3

Genetic Changes

Key Concepts

- A mutation is a change in the base sequence of DNA. Mutations may affect only one gene, or they may affect whole chromosomes.
- Mutations in eggs or sperm affect future generations by producing offspring with new characteristics. Mutations in body cells affect only the individual and may result in cancer.

Vocabulary

chromosomal mutation (p. 299)
frameshift mutation (p. 299)
mutagen (p. 300)
mutation (p. 296)
point mutation (p. 298)

FOLDABLES™
Study Organizer To help you review DNA, use the Organizational Study Fold on page 288.

 in.bdol.glencoe.com/vocabulary_puzzlemaker CHAPTER 11 ASSESSMENT **305**

Key Concepts

Summary statements can be used by students to review the major concepts of the chapter.

Biology Online

Visit in.bdol.glencoe.com
/self_check_quiz
/vocabulary_puzzlemaker
/chapter_test
/standardized_test

VOCABULARY PUZZLEMAKER

For additional help with vocabulary, have students access the Vocabulary PuzzleMaker online at in.bdol.glencoe.com/ vocabulary_puzzlemaker

FOLDABLES™

Have students use their Foldables to review the content of Section 11.2.

Use the Exam*View*®Pro Test Bank CD-ROM to:

- Create **multiple versions** of tests
- Create **modified** tests with one mouse click for **inclusion** students
- **Edit** existing questions and **add** your own questions
- Build tests aligned with state standards using built-in **State Curriculum Tags**
- Change **English** tests to **Spanish** with one mouse click and vice versa

 Indiana Academic Standards

Pages 304–305: B.1.21, B.1.23, B.1.24, B.1.25, B.1.26

Questions and answers have been aligned and verified by The Princeton Review.

Vocabulary Review

1. Transcription is the process of making an mRNA copy from a portion of a DNA strand. Translation is the process of converting the mRNA sequence into a sequence of amino acids in a protein.

2. A point mutation is a change in a single base pair in DNA, whereas a frameshift mutation is when a single base is added or deleted from DNA, which shifts the reading of codons by one base.

3. Messenger RNA brings the instructions from the DNA to the ribosome, and transfer RNA delivers amino acids to the ribosome to be assembled into a protein.

4. Any change in DNA sequence is a mutation. An agent that can cause the change in DNA is called a mutagen.

5. A nitrogenous base is a nitrogen-containing carbon ring structure that makes up part of a nucleotide. A codon is a set of three nitrogenous bases that codes for a particular amino acid.

Understanding Key Concepts

6. C	9. D	12. A
7. B	10. C	13. A
8. A	11. D	

Constructed Response

14. The lung cell mutation does not affect the reproductive cells. Thus, this mutation would not be passed on to offspring.

15. Sequences will likely vary because more than one codon can code for the

Vocabulary Review

Review the Chapter 11 vocabulary words listed in the Study Guide on page 305. Distinguish between the vocabulary words in each pair below.

1. transcription—translation
2. point mutation—frameshift mutation
3. transfer RNA—messenger RNA
4. mutation—mutagen
5. nitrogenous base—codon

Understanding Key Concepts

6. Which of the following processes requires prior DNA replication?
   A. transcription   C. mitosis
   B. translation   D. protein synthesis

7. In which of the following processes does the DNA unzip?
   A. transcription and translation
   B. transcription and replication
   C. replication and translation
   D. mutation

8. Which DNA strand can base pair with the DNA strand shown at the right?

   A. T-A-C-G-A-T   C. U-A-C-G-A-U
   B. A-T-G-C-T-A   D. A-U-G-C-U-A

9. Which of the following nucleotide chains could be part of a molecule of RNA?
   A. A-T-G-C-C-A   C. G-C-C-T-T-G
   B. A-A-T-A-A-A   D. A-U-G-C-C-A

10. Which of the following mRNA codons would cause synthesis of a protein to terminate? Refer to *Table 11.1*.
    A. GGG   C. UAG
    B. UAC   D. AAG

11. The genetic code for an oak tree is _____.
    A. more similar to an ash tree than to a squirrel
    B. more similar to a chipmunk than to a maple tree
    C. more similar to a mosquito than to an elm tree
    D. exactly the same as for an octopus

12. A deer is born normal, but UV rays cause a mutation in its retina. Which of the following statements is *least* likely to be true?
    A. The mutation may be passed on to the offspring of the deer.
    B. The mutation may cause retinal cancer.
    C. The mutation may interfere with the function of the retinal cell.
    D. The mutation may interfere with the structure of the retinal cell.

13. Chemical Q causes the change in the sequence of nucleotides shown below. This change is an example of a(n) _____.
    A. point mutation
    B. frameshift mutation
    C. translocation
    D. inversion

Constructed Response

14. **Open Ended** Explain why a mutation in a lung cell would not be passed on to offspring.

15. **Open Ended** Write the sequence for a segment of DNA that codes for the following chain of amino acids: valine-serine-proline-glycine-leucine. Compare your DNA sequence with another student's sequence. Why are they likely to be different?

16. **Open Ended** Would the amount of cytosine and guanine be equal to each other in an RNA molecule? Explain your answer.

Thinking Critically

17. **Make Inferences** Explain how the universality of the genetic code is evidence that all organisms alive today may have evolved from a common ancestor in the past.

in.bdol.glencoe.com/chapter_test

same amino acid. Example sequence: CAA — AGG — GGT — CCG — GAA

16. No, RNA is a single strand, not a double, pairing strand, so the amount of cytosine does not have to equal the amount of guanine.

Thinking Critically

17. The genetic code of all organisms is based on the same four nucleotides and the same sequences, suggesting a link to a common ancestor.

18. The blue DNA unzips and new red strands are made to complement each blue strand, so the new DNA is ½ new red strands and ½ old blue strands.

18. Summarize Using the diagram to the right, describe the way DNA replicates. Refer to the red and blue strands in your answer.

19. **REAL WORLD BIOCHALLENGE** Cystic fibrosis is an inherited genetic disorder that affects about 1 in 3900 live births of all Americans. Visit **in.bdol.glencoe.com** to find out what type of changes in DNA cause this disorder. How are these changes reflected in the symptoms of the disorder?

The assessed Indiana standard appears next to the question.

End-of-Course Assessment Practice

All questions aligned and verified by *The Princeton Review*

Part 1 Multiple Choice

Use the diagram to answer questions 20–22.

20. What process is shown in diagrams A–C?
  A. transcription **C.** translocation
  B. translation **D.** replication

21. What occurred between diagrams A and B?
  A. DNA was copied.
  B. DNA was translated.
  C. DNA was unzipped.
  D. DNA mutated.

22. What structure is represented by the circle marked "X"?
  A. nitrogenous base **C.** nucleotide
  B. deoxyribose **D.** phosphate group

The following graph records the amount of DNA in liver cells that have been grown in a culture so that all the cells are at the same phase in the cell cycle. Study the graph and answer questions 23 and 24.

Change in DNA Content Per Cell

23. What process are the cells undergoing at part A of the graph to cause the observed change in DNA content?
  A. transcription
  B. translation
  C. DNA replication
  D. meiosis

24. During what part of the graph is translation most likely to occur?
  A. at part A
  B. at part B
  C. at part C
  D. at both part A and part C

Part 2 Constructed Response/Grid In

Record your answers on your answer document.

25. Open Ended A point mutation that doesn't change the amino acid sequence of a protein is known
1.23 as a silent mutation. Explain why a silent mutation might not affect the protein for which it codes.

 in.bdol.glencoe.com/standardized_test

CHAPTER 11 ASSESSMENT **307**

End-of-Course Assessment Practice

20. D **22.** A **24.** C
21. C **23.** C
25. Since silent mutations do not change the sequence of amino acids, the protein structure remains the same; therefore, there is no change in cell structure or function.

 FAST FILE

Answer Sheet A practice answer sheet can be found on p. 79 of *Unit 4 FAST FILE Resources.*

19. Around 70% of mutations in Cystic Fibrosis (CF) patients involve a deletion of 3 base pairs, which results in a loss of an amino acid from the CF protein. The mutant proteins cause problems with body chloride levels, which affects the thickness of body secretions. Symptoms include thick mucus in the lungs, respiratory infections, and digestive problems.

RUBRIC

For more help evaluating open-ended assessment questions, see the rubric on p. 9T.

Indiana Academic Standards

Pages 306–307: B.1.21, B.1.23, B.1.24, B.1.27, B.1.30

Section Objectives	National Science Standards	State/Local Standards	Advanced Lab and Demo Planning
Section 12.1 1 session, 1/2 block 1. **Interpret** a pedigree. 2. **Identify** human genetic disorders caused by inherited recessive alleles. 3. **Predict** how a human trait can be determined by a simple dominant allele.	UCP.1–3, UCP.5; A.1, A.2; C.2; F.1, F.5; G.1, G.2, G.3	**Indiana Standards** B.1.21, B.1.29	**Student Labs:** MiniLab 12.1, p. 310 Problem-Solving Lab 12.1, p. 311 **Teacher Demonstration:** Quick Demo, p. 312
Section 12.2 2 sessions, 2 1/2 blocks 4. **Distinguish** between alleles for incomplete dominance and codominance. 5. **Explain** the patterns of multiple allelic and polygenic inheritance. 6. **Analyze** the pattern of sex-linked inheritance. 7. **Summarize** how internal and external environments affect gene expression.	UCP.1–3, UCP.5; A.1, A.2; C.2; F.1, F.5; G.3	**Indiana Standards** B.1.21, B.1.23, B.1.24, B.1.28, B.1.29	**Student Labs:** Additional Lab, p. 316: petri dish, paper toweling, heterozygous tobacco seeds Problem-Solving Lab 12.2, p. 318 **Teacher Demonstration:** Quick Demo, p. 317: colored chalk
Section 12.3 2 sessions, 1 1/2 blocks 8. **Identify** codominance, multiple allelic, sex-linked, and polygenic patterns of inheritance in humans. 9. **Distinguish** among conditions that result from extra autosomal or sex chromosomes.	UCP.1–3, UCP.5; A.1, A.2; C.2; E.1; F.1, F.5; G.3	**Indiana Standards** B.1.21, B1.26, B.1.28, B.1.29	**Student Labs:** Problem-Solving Lab 12.3, p. 326 Additional Lab, p. 324: prepared slides of male and female cheek cells, microscope MiniLab 12.2, p. 327: magnifying glass, colored pencils. Design Your Own BioLab, p. 330: See materials below. **Teacher Demonstration:** Quick Demo, p. 328
End of Chapter Assessment Student Edition **Study Guide**, p. 333 **Content Assessment**, pp. 334–335		**Indiana Standards** B.1.21, B1.26, B.1.28, B.1.29	**Student Lab:** Design Your Own BioLab, p. 330: *Brassica rapa* seeds, normal and variegated, potting soil and trays, paintbrushes, forceps, single-edge razor blade, light source, labels

Key to Teaching Strategies

L1 Level 1 activities should be appropriate for students with learning difficulties.

L2 Level 2 activities should be within the ability range of all students.

L3 Level 3 activities are designed for above-average students.

ELL ELL activities should be within the ability range of English Language Learners.

COOP LEARN Cooperative Learning activities are designed for small group work.

Legend

⚑ Transparency   ⊙ CD-ROM   🎵 MP3   📼 Videocassette   ⊙ DVD

Reproducible Masters and Transparencies	Technology
Unit 4 FAST FILE Resources MiniLab Worksheet, p. 83 Real World BioApplications, pp. 87–88 Reinforcement and Study Guide in English, p. 89 Reinforcement and Study Guide in Spanish, p. 93 Critical Thinking/Problem Solving, p. 98 Transparency Worksheets, pp. 99, 103–104 ⚑ **Section Focus Transparency 29** ⚑ **Reteaching Skills Transparency 20**	⊙ **Interactive Chalkboard CD-ROM: Section 12.1 Presentation** ⊙ TeacherWorks™ **CD-ROM** 🎵 **Guided Reading Audio Summaries MP3**

Unit 4 FAST FILE Resources
MiniLab Worksheet, p. 84
BioLab Worksheets, pp. 85–86
Reinforcement and Study Guide in English,
  pp. 90–91
Reinforcement and Study Guide in Spanish,
  pp. 94–95
Concept Mapping, p. 97
Transparency Worksheets, pp. 100, 105–106
⚑ **Section Focus Transparency 30**
⚑ **Reteaching Skills Transparency 21**
	⊙ **Interactive Chalkboard CD-ROM: Section 12.2 Presentation**
	⊙ TeacherWorks™ **CD-ROM**
	🎵 **Guided Reading Audio Summaries MP3**
	⊙ **Virtual Labs CD-ROM**
	Virtual Lab: Sex-Linked Traits

Unit 4 FAST FILE Resources Reinforcement and Study Guide in English, p. 92 Reinforcement and Study Guide in Spanish, p. 96 Transparency Worksheet, p. 101 **Laboratory Manual,** pp. 71–74 ⚑ **Section Focus Transparency 31**	⊙ **Interactive Chalkboard CD-ROM: Section 12.3 Presentation** ⊙ TeacherWorks™ **CD-ROM** 🎵 **Guided Reading Audio Summaries MP3**
Unit 4 FAST FILE Resources Chapter Assessment, pp. 107–112 Student Recording Sheet, p. 113 _The Princeton Review_ **Reviewing Biology,** pp. 23–24	⊙ **Interactive Chalkboard: Chapter 12 Assessment** ⊙ **MindJogger Videoquizzes DVD/VHS** ⊙ **ExamView® Pro Test Bank CD-ROM** ⊙ TeacherWorks™ **CD-ROM** ⊙ **Succeeding on National Standards CD-ROM** 🖥 in.bdol.glencoe.com /self_check_quiz /vocabulary_puzzlemaker /chapter_test /standardized_test

🚩 Indicates materials created specifically for Indiana.

Patterns of Heredity and Human Genetics

Short on Time?

BIODIGEST The BioDigest at the end of this unit can be used as a(n):

- preview to introduce important unit concepts.
- overview if time does not permit teaching the entire chapter.
- review of key unit concepts.

Understanding the Photo

Having identical twins is not hereditary. Age is a contributing factor—the older the mother, the greater her chances of having identical twins. Identical twins occur when one fertilized egg divides into two fetuses. If the egg divides one day after fertilization, twins are the most identical, yet they may have separate placentas and be mistaken for fraternal twins. Most eggs divide during days four or five. If the egg divides during days nine or ten, the twins share an inner sac, which can be dangerous because their umbilical cords can get tangled or wrapped around their necks. During this time, "mirror-image" twins may result. "Mirror-image" twins appear to be a reflection of each other. Conjoined twins occur when the egg divides during days 13 through 15.

What You'll Learn

- You will compare the inheritance of recessive and dominant traits in humans.
- You will analyze the inheritance patterns of traits with incomplete dominance and codominance.
- You will determine the inheritance of sex-linked traits.

Why It's Important

The transmission of traits from generation to generation affects your appearance, your behavior, and your health. Understanding how these traits are inherited is important in understanding traits you may pass on to a future generation.

Understanding the Photo ▶

Inherited traits are the expressions of DNA codes found on chromosomes. The grandmother, father, and mother have DNA that is unique to each of them. However, the identical twin daughters have identical DNA and, therefore, inherited the same traits.

💻 Biology Online

Visit in.bdol.glencoe.com to
- study the entire chapter online
- access Web Links for more information and activities on genetics
- review content with the Interactive Tutor and self-check quizzes

 Two-Minute Chapter Launcher

Discussion Provide or project on a screen pictures of various families, some where children look like one parent, some where children look somewhat like both parents, and some where the children look like neither parent. Use the pictures to discuss why this might happen, weaving the concept of genes and inheritance into the discussion. **L2**

Mendelian Inheritance of Human Traits

Indiana Standards Standard B.1.29 Understand that and explain how the actions of genes, patterns of inheritance, and the reproduction of cells and organisms account for the continuity of life, and give examples of how inherited characteristics can be observed at molecular and whole-organism levels – in structure, chemistry, or behavior.

SECTION PREVIEW

Objectives

Interpret a pedigree.

Identify human genetic disorders caused by inherited recessive alleles.

Predict how a human trait can be determined by a simple dominant allele.

Review Vocabulary
trait: any characteristic that is inherited (p. 253)

New Vocabulary
pedigree
carrier
fetus

FOLDABLES™
Study Organizer

Pedigrees Make the following Foldable to help you understand the symbols used in a pedigree.

STEP 1 **Fold** a vertical sheet of notebook paper from side to side.

STEP 2 **Cut** along every fifth line of only the top layer to form tabs.

STEP 3 **Label** each tab.

Use Models As you read Chapter 12, list the symbols that are used in a pedigree on the tabs. As you learn what each symbol means, write the meaning under the tab for each symbol.

 Male

 Parents

 Female

Siblings

 Affected male

 Known heterozygotes for recessive allele

 Affected female

 Mating

 Death

Figure 12.1
Geneticists use these symbols to make and analyze a pedigree.

Making a Pedigree

At some point, you have probably seen a family tree, either for your family or for someone else's. A family tree traces a family name and various family members through successive generations. Through a family tree, you can identify the relationships among your cousins, aunts, uncles, grandparents, and great-grandparents.

Pedigrees illustrate inheritance

Geneticists often need to map the inheritance of genetic traits from generation to generation. A **pedigree** is a graphic representation of genetic inheritance. It is a diagram made up of a set of symbols that identify males and females, individuals affected by the trait being studied, and family relationships. At a glance, it looks very similar to any family tree. Some commonly used pedigree symbols are shown in *Figure 12.1*.

1 Focus

Bellringer
Section Focus Transparency 29

① Which of these traits do you have?

② For each trait, how would knowing your parents' phenotypes help you determine your genotype?

PowerPoint® Presentations

This CD-ROM is an editable Microsoft® PowerPoint® presentation that includes:
- Section presentations
- Section checks
- Image bank
- Hot links to Biology Online
- All transparencies

FOLDABLES™

For an additional Foldables activity idea, see the Chapter 12 Foldables page in *Unit 4 FAST FILE Resources.*

RESOURCE MANAGER

Unit 4 *FAST FILE* Resources
MiniLab Worksheet, p. 83
Real World BioApplications, pp. 87–88
Reinforcement and Study Guide in English, p. 89
Reinforcement and Study Guide in Spanish, p. 93
Critical Thinking/Problem Solving, p. 98

Transparency Worksheets, pp. 99, 103–104
Reading Essentials for Biology, Section 12.1
Section Focus Transparency 29
Reteaching Skills Transparency 20

 Indiana Academic Standards

Pages 308–309: B.1.21, B.1.29

309

2 Teach

Purpose

Students will observe a specific human trait and prepare a pedigree.

Process Skills

observe and infer, interpret scientific illustrations

Teaching Strategies

■ If a student is adopted, be sure he or she is paired with a student who is not adopted and can contribute family information to the pair's pedigree.

■ Provide students with information about various human traits that are inherited in a simple Mendelian pattern.

Expected Results

Students will construct pedigrees of a human trait.

Analysis

1. Answers may include earlobe shape, widow's peak, tongue rolling, or ability to taste PTC paper.
2. The number of individuals may be too small to determine the inheritance pattern.

Modified Assessment

Knowledge Provide a pedigree that consists of only a few individuals and has enough information so that students can determine genotypes for the given phenotypes. Use the Performance Task Assessment List for Analyzing the Data in **PASC**, p. 99. **L1**

MiniLab 12.1

Analyze Information

Illustrating a Pedigree The pedigree method of studying a trait in a family uses records of phenotypes extending for two or more generations. Studies of pedigrees yield a great deal of genetic information about a family.

Sample pedigree

Procedure

1 Working with a partner at home, choose one human trait, such as earlobe types or tongue rolling, that interests both of you. Looking through this chapter might give you some other ideas.

2 Using either your or your partner's family, collect information about your chosen trait. Include whether each person is male or female, does or does not have the trait, and the relationship of the individual to others in the family.

3 Use your information to draw a pedigree for the trait.

4 Try to determine the inheritance pattern of the trait you studied.

Analysis

1. **Classify** What trait did you study? Can you determine from your pedigree what the apparent inheritance pattern of the trait is?

2. **Critique** How is the study of inheritance patterns limited in pedigree analysis?

Figure 12.2 This pedigree shows how a rare, recessive allele is transmitted from generation to generation.

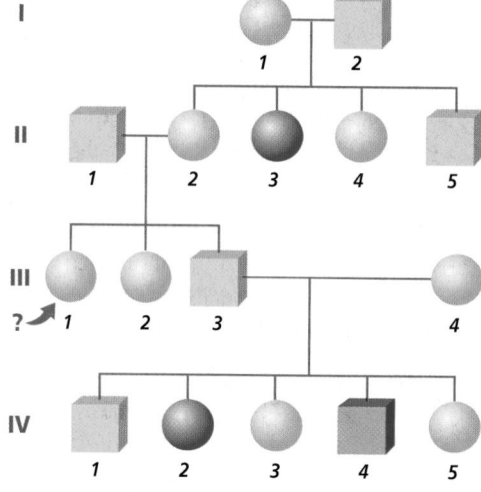

310 PATTERNS OF HEREDITY AND HUMAN GENETICS

In a pedigree, a circle represents a female; a square represents a male. Shaded circles and squares represent individuals showing the trait being studied. Unshaded circles and squares designate individuals that do not show the trait. A half-shaded circle or square represents a **carrier,** a heterozygous individual. A horizontal line connecting a circle and a square indicates that the individuals are parents, and a vertical line connects parents with their offspring. Each horizontal row of circles and squares in a pedigree designates a generation, with the most recent generation shown at the bottom. The generations are identified in sequence by Roman numerals, and each individual is given an Arabic number. Practice using these symbols to make a pedigree in *MiniLab 12.1*.

Analyzing a pedigree

An example of a pedigree for a fictitious rare, recessive disorder in humans is shown in *Figure 12.2*. This genetic disorder could be any of several recessive disorders which shows up only if the affected person carries two recessive alleles for the trait. Follow this pedigree as you read how to analyze a pedigree.

Suppose individual III-1 in the pedigree wants to know the likelihood of passing on this allele to her children. By studying the pedigree, the individual will be able to determine the likelihood that she carries the allele. Notice that information can also be gained about other members of the family by studying the pedigree. For example, you know that I-1 and I-2 are both carriers of the recessive allele for the trait because they have produced II-3, who shows the recessive phenotype. If you drew a Punnett square for the mating of individuals I-1 and I-2, you would find, according to Mendelian segregation,

---

310

that the ratio of homozygous dominant to heterozygous to homozygous recessive genotypes among their children would be 1:2:1. Of those genotypes possible for the members of generation II, only the homozygous recessive genotype will express the trait, which is the case for II-3.

You can't tell the genotypes of II-4 and II-5, but they have a normal phenotype. If you look at the Punnett square you made, you can see that the probability that II-4 and II-5 are carriers is two in three for each because they can have only two possible genotypes—homozygous normal and heterozygous. The homozygous recessive genotype is not a possibility in these individuals because neither of them shows the affected phenotype.

Because none of the children in generation III are affected and because the recessive allele is rare in the general population, it is reasonably safe to assume that II-1 is not a carrier. You know that II-2 must be a carrier like her parents because she has passed on the recessive allele to subsequent generation IV. Because III-1 has one parent who is heterozygous and the other parent who is assumed to be homozygous normal, III-1 most likely has a one-in-two chance of being a carrier. If her parent II-1 had been heterozygous instead of homozygous normal, III-1's chances of being a carrier are increased to two in three.

Simple Recessive Heredity

Most genetic disorders are caused by recessive alleles. You can practice calculating the chance that offspring will be born with some of these genetic traits in the *Problem-Solving Lab* on this page.

Problem-Solving Lab 12.1

Apply Concepts

What are the chances? Using a Punnett square allows you to calculate the chance that offspring will be born with certain traits. In order to do this, however, you must first know the genotype of the parents and whether the trait that is being described is dominant or recessive.

Polydactyly—having six fingers

Solve the Problem
Use the following traits and their alleles to answer the questions below.

Human Traits		
Trait	Dominant Allele	Recessive Allele
Number of fingers	D = six	d = five
Cleft chin	C = cleft chin	c = no cleft chin
Earlobes	F = hanging	f = attached

Thinking Critically
1. **Use Numbers** What are the chances that a child will be born with six fingers if
   a. both parents are heterozygous?
   b. one parent has five fingers, the other is heterozygous?
   c. both parents have five fingers?
2. **Use Numbers** Predict how many children in a family of four will have cleft chins if
   a. one parent has a cleft chin and the other is homozygous for cleft chin.
   b. both parents have cleft chins and both are homozygous.
   c. both parents have cleft chins and each of them has a parent who has a cleft chin.
3. **Infer** A child is born with attached earlobes, but both parents have hanging earlobes.
   a. What are the genotypes and phenotypes for the parents?
   b. What is the genotype and phenotype for the child?

Problem-Solving Lab 12.1

Purpose
Students will use Punnett squares to determine the chance of offspring receiving certain traits.

Process Skills
apply concepts, draw a conclusion, predict, think critically

Teaching Strategies
■ Review the technique for setting up, using, and completing Punnett squares.
■ Review the terminology used in describing traits: homozygous, heterozygous, dominant, recessive, genotype, phenotype.
■ Review the meaning of the phrase "chance that" when referring to the outcome of a Punnett square.

Thinking Critically
1. a. three out of four
   b. two out of four
   c. no chance of child having six fingers
2. a. all will have cleft chins
   b. all children will have cleft chins
   c. three out of four will have cleft chins
3. a. Both parents are *Aa* and have hanging earlobes.
   b. The child is *aa* and has attached earlobes.

Modified Assessment
Performance Take a class survey for earlobe type. Ask students to predict their genotypes. Only those who have attached earlobes can predict correctly. All others are either homozygous dominant or heterozygous. Use the Performance Task Assessment List for Conducting a Survey and Graphing the Results in **PASC**, p. 107. **L1**

TECH PREP

Human Genetic Disorders Have students research several human genetic disorders. Ask them to write a paragraph or two about the sensitivity of these articles. **L2**

Indiana Academic Standards

Pages 310–311: B.1.21, B.1.29

Caption Question Answer
Figure 12.3 The genotype of individual II-3 is male, heterozygous for Tay-Sachs (*Aa*).

Cystic fibrosis

Cystic fibrosis (CF) is a fairly common genetic disorder among white Americans. Approximately one in 28 white Americans carries the recessive allele, and one in 2500 children born to white Americans inherits the disorder. Due to a defective protein in the plasma membrane, cystic fibrosis results in the formation and accumulation of thick mucus in the lungs and digestive tract. Physical therapy, special diets, and new drugs have continued to raise the average life expectancy of people that have CF.

Tay-Sachs disease

Tay-Sachs (tay saks) disease is a recessive disorder of the central nervous system. In this disorder, a recessive allele results in the absence of an enzyme that normally breaks down a lipid produced and stored in tissues of the central nervous system. Because this lipid fails to break down properly, it accumulates in the cells. The allele for Tay-Sachs is especially common in the United States among Ashkenazic Jews, whose ancestors came from eastern Europe. *Figure 12.3* shows a typical pedigree for Tay-Sachs disease.

Phenylketonuria

Phenylketonuria (fen ul kee tun YOO ree uh), also called PKU, is a recessive disorder that results from the absence of an enzyme that converts one amino acid, phenylalanine, to a different amino acid, tyrosine. Because phenylalanine cannot be broken down, it and its by-products accumulate in the body and result in severe damage to the central nervous system. The PKU allele is most common in the United States among people whose ancestors came from Norway, Sweden, or Ireland.

A homozygous PKU newborn appears healthy at first because its mother's normal enzyme level prevented phenylalanine accumulation during development. However, once the infant begins drinking milk, which is rich in phenylalanine, the amino acid accumulates and mental retardation occurs. Today, a PKU test is normally performed on all infants a few days after birth. Infants affected by PKU are given a diet that is low in phenylalanine until their brains are fully developed. With this special diet, the toxic effects of the disorder can be avoided.

Ironically, the success of treating phenylketonuria infants has resulted in a new problem. If a female who is homozygous recessive for PKU becomes pregnant, the high phenylalanine levels in her blood can damage her **fetus**—the developing baby. This problem occurs even if the fetus is heterozygous and would be phenotypically normal.

Figure 12.3
A study of families who have children with Tay-Sachs disease shows typical pedigrees for traits inherited as simple recessives. Note that the trait appears to skip generations, a characteristic of a recessive trait.
Analyze *What is the genotype of individual II-3?*

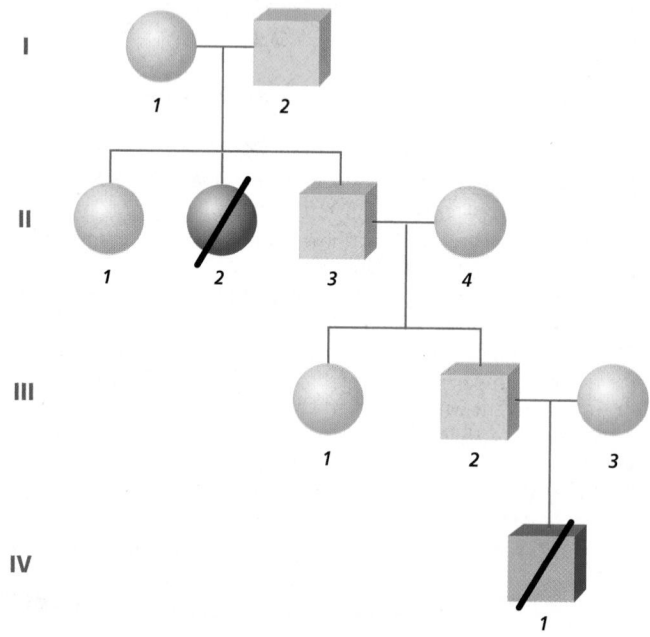

312 PATTERNS OF HEREDITY AND HUMAN GENETICS

Indiana Academic Standards

Pages 312–313: B.1.21, B.1.29

Figure 12.4
The allele *F* for freely hanging earlobes **(A)** is dominant to the allele *f* for attached earlobes **(B)**. Having a pointed frontal hairline called a widow's peak **(C)**, indicates that one or two dominant alleles for the trait have been inherited.

You may have noticed PKU warnings on cans of diet soft drinks. Because most diet foods are sweetened with an artificial sweetener that contains phenylalanine, a pregnant woman who is homozygous recessive must limit her intake of diet foods.

Simple Dominant Heredity

Unlike the inheritance of recessive traits in which a recessive allele must be inherited from both parents for a person to show the recessive phenotype, many traits are inherited just as the rule of dominance predicts. Remember that in Mendelian inheritance, a single dominant allele inherited from one parent is all that is needed for a person to show the dominant trait.

Simple dominant traits

A cleft chin is one example of a simple dominant trait. If you have a cleft chin, you've inherited the dominant allele from at least one of your parents. A widow's peak hairline and earlobe types, shown in *Figure 12.4,* are other dominant traits that are determined by simple Mendelian inheritance. Having earlobes that are attached to the head is a recessive trait *(ff)*, whereas heterozygous *(Ff)* and homozygous dominant *(FF)* individuals have earlobes that hang freely.

There are many other human traits that are inherited by simple dominant inheritance. *Figure 12.5* shows one of these traits—hitchhiker's thumb, the

Figure 12.5
Hitchhiker's thumb is a dominant trait.

INCLUSION STRATEGIES

English Language Learners Have students think of two questions about simple recessive heredity and two questions about simple dominant heredity. Divide students into pairs and have them quiz each other. **L1** **ELL**

3 Assess

Extension

Ask student groups to contact the local March of Dimes organization to gather information on the help it gives individuals with genetic disorders. Students can give a report on their findings. **L1** **COOP LEARN**

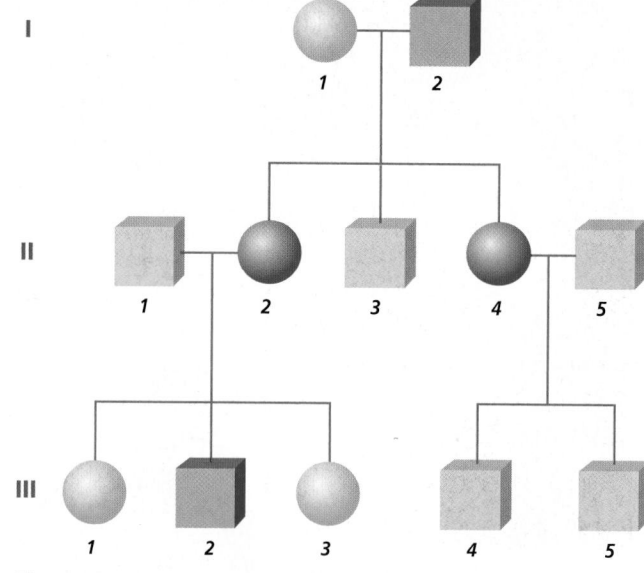

Figure 12.6
This is a typical pedigree for a simple, dominant inheritance of Huntington's disease. This particular chart shows the disorder in each generation and equally distributed among males and females.

ability to bend your thumb tip backward more than 30 degrees. A straight thumb is recessive. Other dominant traits in humans include almond-shaped eyes (round eyes are recessive), thick lips (thin lips are recessive), and the presence of hair on the middle section of your fingers.

Huntington's disease

Huntington's disease is a lethal genetic disorder caused by a rare dominant allele. It results in a breakdown of certain areas of the brain. No effective treatment exists.

Ordinarily, a dominant allele with such severe effects would result in death before the affected individual could have children and pass the allele on to the next generation. But because the onset of Huntington's disease usually occurs between the ages of 30 and 50, an individual may already have had children before knowing whether he or she is affected. A genetic test has been developed that detects the presence of this allele. Although this test allows individuals with the allele to decide whether they want to have children and risk passing the trait on to future generations, it also means that they know they will develop the disease. For this reason, some people may choose not to be tested. The pedigree in *Figure 12.6* shows a typical pattern for the occurrence of Huntington's disease in a family.

✔ Reading Check **Predict** the chance of an individual with Huntington's disease having an affected child if the other parent is unaffected.

Section Assessment

Understanding Main Ideas

1. In your own words, define the following symbols used in a pedigree: a square, a circle, an unshaded circle, a shaded square, a horizontal line, and a vertical line.
2. Describe one genetic disorder that is inherited as a recessive trait.
3. How are the cause and onset of symptoms of Huntington's disease different from those of PKU and Tay-Sachs disease?
4. Describe one trait that is inherited as a dominant allele. If you carried that trait, would you necessarily pass it on to your children?

Thinking Critically

5. Suppose that a child with free-hanging earlobes has a mother with attached earlobes. Can a man with attached earlobes be the child's father?

SKILL REVIEW

6. **Interpret Scientific Illustrations** Make and interpret a pedigree for three generations of a family that shows at least one member of each generation who demonstrates a particular trait. Would this trait be dominant or recessive? For more help, refer to *Interpret Scientific Illustrations* in the **Skill Handbook**.

314 PATTERNS OF HEREDITY AND HUMAN GENETICS

 in.bdol.glencoe.com/self_check_quiz

Section Assessment

1. A square represents a male, a circle a female. An unshaded circle is an unaffected female. A shaded square is an affected male. A horizontal line indicates two parents. A vertical line indicates offspring (children).
2. Students could describe cystic fibrosis, Tay-Sachs, or phenylketonuria.

3. Huntington's disease is an autosomal dominant disorder with onset between the ages of 30 and 50, whereas PKU and Tay-Sachs disease are autosomal recessive disorders with onset at birth.
4. Huntington's disease, tongue rolling, and widow's peak are all examples of dominant traits. If your children inherit

even one dominant allele from you, they will express a dominant trait.
5. The man cannot be the father because the child had to receive an allele for free-hanging earlobes from one parent; the father would have to have at least one dominant allele for this trait.
6. This trait would be dominant. See Figure 12.6 for a sample pedigree.

When Heredity Follows Different Rules

Indiana Standards Standard B.1.29 Understand that and explain how the actions of genes, patterns of inheritance, and the reproduction of cells and organisms account for the continuity of life, and give examples of how inherited characteristics can be observed at molecular and whole-organism levels – in structure, chemistry, or behavior.

SECTION PREVIEW

Objectives

Distinguish between alleles for incomplete dominance and codominance.

Explain the patterns of multiple allelic and polygenic inheritance.

Analyze the pattern of sex-linked inheritance.

Summarize how internal and external environments affect gene expression.

Review Vocabulary
allele: an alternative form of a gene (p. 256)

New Vocabulary
incomplete dominance
codominant allele
multiple allele
autosome
sex chromosome
sex-linked trait
polygenic inheritance

Breaking the Rules

Using Prior Knowledge
Exceptions to the pattern of inheritance explained by Mendel became known soon after his work was rediscovered. Kernel color in corn is one of those exceptions. Today, geneticists know that most traits do not follow Mendel's simple rules of inheritance. Examine the photo of Indian corn to the right, and think about why the inheritance of kernel color in corn breaks Mendel's rules.

Analyze *What clue in the photo made you think that the inheritance of kernel color in corn is not simple Mendelian?*

Indian corn

Complex Patterns of Inheritance

Patterns of inheritance that are explained by Mendel's experiments are often referred to as simple Mendelian inheritance—inheritance controlled by dominant and recessive paired alleles. However, many inheritance patterns are more complex than those studied by Mendel. As you will learn, most traits are not simply dominant or recessive. The *BioLab* at the end of this chapter investigates a type of inheritance that doesn't even involve chromosomes.

Incomplete dominance: Appearance of a third phenotype

When inheritance follows a pattern of dominance, heterozygous and homozygous dominant individuals both have the same phenotype. When traits are inherited in an **incomplete dominance** pattern, however, the phenotype of heterozygous individuals is intermediate between those of the two homozygotes. For example, if a homozygous red-flowered snapdragon plant (*RR*) is crossed with a homozygous white-flowered snapdragon plant (*R′R′*), all of the F₁ offspring will have pink flowers.

12.2 WHEN HEREDITY FOLLOWS DIFFERENT RULES **315**

INTERACTIVE CHALKBOARD
PowerPoint® Presentations

Bellringer
Section Focus Transparency 30

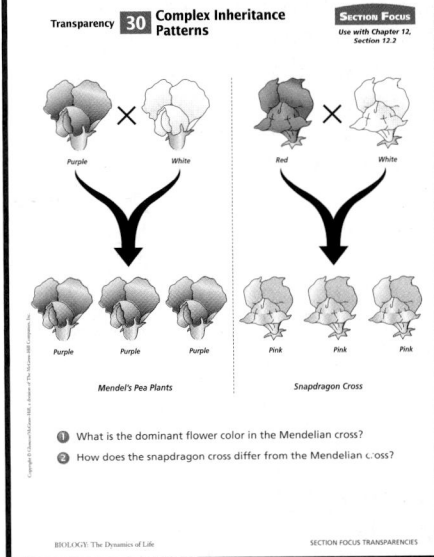

Transparency **30** Complex Inheritance Patterns

SECTION FOCUS
Use with Chapter 12, Section 12.2

Purple × White   Red × White

Purple Purple Purple   Pink Pink Pink

Mendel's Pea Plants   *Snapdragon Cross*

❶ What is the dominant flower color in the Mendelian cross?
❷ How does the snapdragon cross differ from the Mendelian cross?

BIOLOGY: The Dynamics of Life   SECTION FOCUS TRANSPARENCIES

Using Prior Knowledge

Analyze Students need to know that each kernel of corn is like an individual, as each is pollinated separately. The kernels on the Indian corn have many different colors and patterns. With simple Mendelian inheritance, there would only be two possible phenotypes of kernels.

Biology Journal

Codominance Provide students with practice working with codominance by having them determine the phenotypes of offspring resulting from the following crosses. (a) a checkered rooster mated to a checkered hen; (b) a checkered rooster mated to a white hen; (c) a checkered rooster mated to a black hen. **L2**

RESOURCE MANAGER

Unit 4 *FAST FILE* Resources
MiniLab Worksheet, p. 84
BioLab Worksheets, pp. 85–86
Reinforcement and Study Guide in English, pp. 90–91
Reinforcement and Study Guide in Spanish, pp. 94–95

Concept Mapping, p. 97
Transparency Worksheets, pp. 100, 105–106
Reading Essentials for Biology, Section 12.2
Section Focus Transparency 30
Reteaching Skills Transparency 21

Indiana Academic Standards

Pages 314–315: B.1.21, B.1.28, B.1.29

2 Teach

Discussion

Exhibit photos of a red shorthorn bull, a white shorthorn cow, and a roan shorthorn cow. Tell students that the roan cow, offspring of the red bull and the white cow, has both red and white hairs. Ask students whether Mendel's law of dominance applies to the inheritance of coat color in cattle. Why or why not? No, because a third phenotype appears when the red and white cattle are crossed, and traits that Mendel studied had only two phenotypes. Ask students what type of inheritance pattern explains how roan cattle express their coat color. codominance

The BioLab at the end of the chapter can be used at this point in the lesson.

Reading Check The heterozygous phenotype results because the *R* allele codes for a red pigment and its flowers produce only half the amount of red pigment, producing an offspring that appears pink.

Indiana Academic Standards

Pages 316–317: B.1.21, B.1.29

Figure 12.7
A Punnett square of snapdragon color shows that the red-flowered snapdragon is homozygous for the allele *R*, and the white-flowered snapdragon is homozygous for the allele *R'*. All of the pink-flowered snapdragons are heterozygous, or *RR'*.

Figure 12.7 shows that the intermediate pink form of the trait occurs because neither allele of the pair is completely dominant. Note that the letters *R* and *R'*, rather than *R* and *r*, are used to show incomplete dominance.

The new phenotype occurs because the flowers contain enzymes that control pigment production. The *R* allele codes for an enzyme that produces a red pigment. The *R'* allele codes for a defective enzyme that makes no pigment. Because the heterozygote has only one copy of the *R* allele, its flowers appear pink because they produce only half the amount of red pigment that red homozygote flowers produce. The *R'R'* homozygote has no normal enzyme, produces no red pigment, and appears white.

Note that the segregation of alleles is the same as in simple Mendelian inheritance. However, because neither allele is dominant, the plants of the F_1 generation all have pink flowers. When pink-flowered F_1 plants are crossed with each other, the offspring in the F_2 generation appear in a 1:2:1 phenotypic ratio of red to pink to white flowers. This result supports Mendel's law of segregation.

Reading Check **Explain** why snapdragon heterozygotes have flowers with an intermediate color.

Codominance: Expression of both alleles

In chickens, black-feathered and white-feathered birds are homozygotes for the *B* and *W* alleles, respectively. Two different uppercase letters are used to represent the alleles in codominant inheritance.

One of the resulting heterozygous offspring in a breeding experiment between a black rooster and a white hen is shown in *Figure 12.8*. You might expect that heterozygous chickens, *BW*, would be black if the pattern of inheritance followed Mendel's law of dominance, or gray if the trait were incompletely dominant. Notice, however, that the heterozygote is neither

316 PATTERNS OF HEREDITY AND HUMAN GENETICS

Incomplete Dominance

Purpose
Students will observe the phenotypic ratio that appears with incomplete dominance.

Safety Precautions

Materials
petri dish, paper toweling, heterozygous tobacco seeds

Procedure
Give the following directions to students.

1. Label the top of a petri dish with your name and the date. Place several layers of paper toweling inside the dish.
2. Moisten the toweling with water and place 20 tobacco seeds on it.

3. Cover the dish and place it where it will receive light.
4. Check the seeds for the next 10 days. Keep the toweling moist but not soaked. After 8–10 days, count the number of plants with green, yellow-green, and yellow leaves.
5. Design a data table to record your results and class totals.
6. Wash your hands after handling seeds.

black nor gray. Instead, all of the off-spring are checkered; some feathers are black and other feathers are white. In such situations, the inheritance pattern is said to be codominant. **Codominant alleles** cause the phenotypes of both homozygotes to be produced in heterozygous individuals. In codominance, both alleles are expressed equally.

Multiple phenotypes from multiple alleles

Although each trait has only two alleles in the patterns of heredity you have studied thus far, it is common for more than two alleles to control a trait in a population. This is understandable when you recall that a new allele can be formed any time a mutation occurs in a nitrogenous base somewhere within a gene. Although only two alleles of a gene can exist within an individual diploid cell, multiple alleles for a single gene can be studied in a population of organisms.

Traits controlled by more than two alleles have **multiple alleles.**

Figure 12.8
When a certain variety of black chicken is crossed with a white chicken, all of the offspring are checkered. Both feather colors are produced by codominant alleles. **Think Critically** *What color would the chicken be if feather color were inherited by incomplete dominance?*

The pigeons pictured in *Figure 12.9* show the effects of multiple alleles for feather color. Three alleles of one gene govern their feather color, although each pigeon can have only two of these alleles. The number of alleles for any particular trait is not limited to three, and there are instances in which more than 100 alleles are known to exist for a single trait! You can learn about another example of multiple alleles in the *Problem-Solving Lab* on the next page.

Figure 12.9
In pigeons, one gene that controls feather color has three alleles. An enzyme that activates the production of a pigment is controlled by the *B* allele. This enzyme is lacking in *bb* pigeons.

A The dominant *B^A* allele produces ash-red colored feathers.

B The *B* allele produces wild-type blue feathers. *B* is dominant to *b* but recessive to *B^A*.

C The allele *b* produces a chocolate-colored feather and is recessive to both other alleles.

Purpose

Students will work with problems that deal with multiple alleles.

Process Skills

acquire information, apply concepts, predict, think critically

Teaching Strategies

■ Have students sequence the genotypes in order from dominant to recessive. **L2**

■ Emphasize again that only two alleles at a time govern coat color. However, there are 10 different combinations that are possible when dealing with four different alleles in a multiple allele situation.

■ Have students define in their own words *multiple allele*.

Thinking Critically

1. a. CC, Cc^{ch}, Cc^h, Cc
   b. $c^{ch}c^{ch}$, $c^{ch}c^h$, $c^{ch}c$
   c. c^hc^h, c^hc
   d. cc

2. chinchilla; The c^{ch} allele for chinchilla is dominant to the c^h allele for Himalayan.
   dark gray; The C allele is dominant to all other alleles.

3. Yes, if the chinchilla rabbit is $c^{ch}c$.

4. No; Himalayan and white rabbits have no alleles for chinchilla.

Assessment

Portfolio Ask students to plan a breeding program that would produce all Himalayan rabbit offspring when starting with one white parent and one dark gray parent known to be Cc^{ch}. Punnett squares should be included where appropriate. All work should be placed in student portfolios. Use the Performance Task Assessment List for Designing an Experiment in **PASC**, p. 95. **L3**

Caption Question Answer
Figure 12.10 male parent

Problem-Solving Lab 12.2

Predict

How is coat color in rabbits inherited? Coat color in rabbits is inherited as a series of multiple alleles. This means that there can be more than just two alleles for a gene. In the case of coat color in rabbits, there are four alleles, and each one is expressed with a different phenotype.

Solve the Problem

Examine the table below. Use this information to answer the questions. Remember, each rabbit can have only two alleles for coat color.

Coat Color in Rabbits		
Phenotype	Allele	Pattern of Inheritance
Dark gray coat	C	Dominant to all other alleles
Chinchilla	c^{ch}	Dominant to Himalayan and to white
Himalayan	c^h	Dominant to white
White	c	Recessive

Thinking Critically

1. **Classify** List all possible genotypes for a
   a. dark gray-coated rabbit (there are 4).
   b. chinchilla rabbit (there are 3).
   c. Himalayan rabbit (there are 2).
   d. white rabbit (there is 1).
2. **Predict** What is the phenotype for a rabbit with a c^hc^{ch} and a rabbit with a Cc^{ch} genotype? Explain.
3. **Explain** Would it be possible to obtain white rabbits if one parent is white and the other is chinchilla? Explain.
4. **Analyze** Is it possible to obtain chinchilla rabbits if one parent is Himalayan and the other is white? Explain.

Sex determination

Recall that in humans the diploid number of chromosomes is 46, or 23 pairs. There are 22 pairs of homologous chromosomes called **autosomes.** Homologous autosomes look alike. The 23rd pair of chromosomes differs in males and females. These two chromosomes, which determine the sex of an individual, are called **sex chromosomes** and are indicated by the letters X and Y. If you are female, your 23rd pair of chromosomes are homologous, XX, as in *Figure 12.10A*. However, if you are male, your 23rd pair of chromosomes, XY, look different. Males usually have one X and one Y chromosome and produce two kinds of gametes, X and Y. Females usually have two X chromosomes and produce only X gametes. It is the male gamete that determines the sex of the offspring. *Figure 12.10B* shows that after fertilization, a 1:1 ratio of males to females is expected. Because fertilization is governed by the laws of probability, the ratio usually is not exactly 1:1 in a small population.

Sex-linked inheritance

Drosophila (droh SAH fuh luh), commonly known as fruit flies, inherit sex chromosomes in the same way as humans. Traits controlled by genes

Figure 12.10
The sex chromosomes in humans are called X and Y. **Analyze** *Which parent determines the sex of the offspring?*

A The sex chromosomes are named for the letters they resemble.

X   X
Female

X   Y
Male

B The offspring of any mating between humans will have a 50-50 chance of having two X chromosomes, XX, which is female, or of having one X and one Y chromosome, XY, which is male.

XY *Male*
X   Y
XX *Female*
X   X

	X	Y
X	XX *Female*	XY *Male*
X	XX *Female*	XY *Male*

318 PATTERNS OF HEREDITY AND HUMAN GENETICS

INCLUSION STRATEGIES

Learning Disabled/Visually Impaired:
Kinesthetic Make large cardboard X and Y chromosomes. Have students manipulate them to see how each parent donates one of his/her sex chromosomes to each gamete and how they come together during fertilization to produce offspring of each sex. **L1** **ELL**

Visual Learning

Figure 12.10 Ask students why the X and Y chromosomes are not homologous? They do not have the same size, shape, or similar genes. However, they are able to pair during meiosis because they have a small homologous region at one end of each of the chromosomes.

Make it clear to students that there is a 50% chance that each offspring will receive XX chromosomes, which is female, and a 50% chance that each offspring will receive XY chromosomes, which is male.

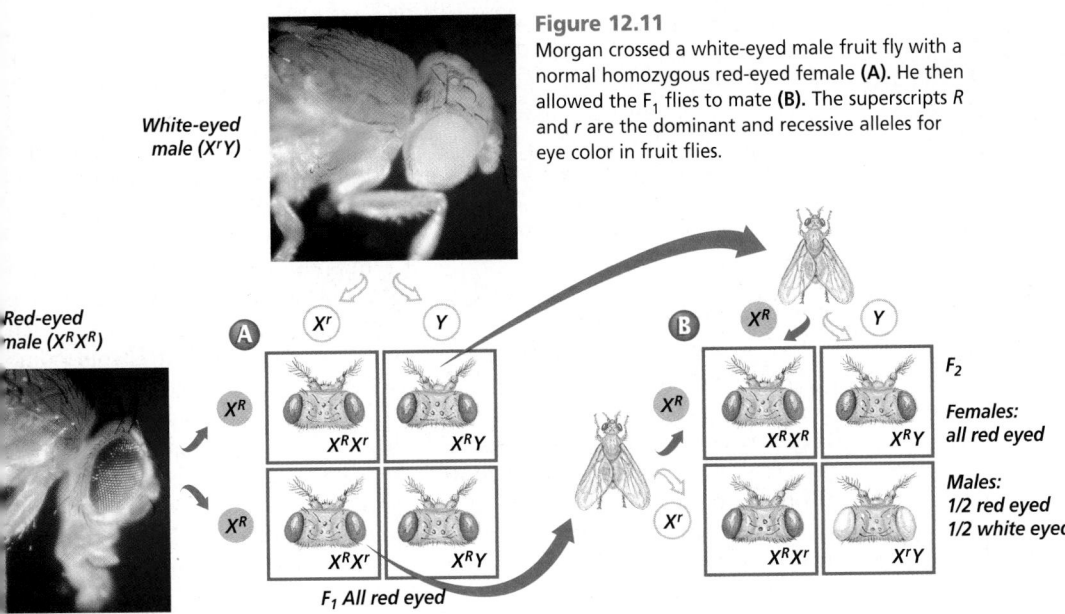

White-eyed male (X^rY)

Figure 12.11
Morgan crossed a white-eyed male fruit fly with a normal homozygous red-eyed female (**A**). He then allowed the F_1 flies to mate (**B**). The superscripts R and r are the dominant and recessive alleles for eye color in fruit flies.

Red-eyed male (X^RX^R)

F_1 All red eyed

F_2
Females: all red eyed
Males: 1/2 red eyed 1/2 white eyed

located on sex chromosomes are called **sex-linked traits.** The alleles for sex-linked traits are written as superscripts of the X or Y chromosome. Because the X and Y chromosomes are not homologous, the Y chromosome has no corresponding allele to one on the X chromosome and no superscript is used. Also remember that any recessive allele on the X chromosome of a male will not be masked by a corresponding dominant allele on the Y chromosome.

In 1910, Thomas Hunt Morgan discovered traits linked to sex chromosomes. Morgan noticed one day that one male fly had white eyes rather than the usual red eyes. He crossed the white-eyed male with a homozygous red-eyed female. All of the F_1 offspring had red eyes, indicating that the white-eyed trait is recessive. Then Morgan allowed the F_1 flies to mate among themselves. According to simple Mendelian inheritance, if the trait were recessive, the offspring in the F_2 generation

would show a 3:1 ratio of red-eyed to white-eyed flies. As you can see in **Figure 12.11,** this is what Morgan observed. However, he also noticed that the trait of white eyes appeared only in male flies.

Morgan hypothesized that the red-eye allele was dominant and the white-eye allele was recessive. He also reasoned that the gene for eye color was located on the X chromosome and was not present on the Y chromosome. In heterozygous females, the dominant allele for red eyes masks the recessive allele for white eyes. In males, however, a single recessive allele is expressed as a white-eyed phenotype. When Morgan crossed a heterozygous red-eyed female with a white-eyed male, half of all the males and half of all the females inherited white eyes. The only explanation of these results is Morgan's hypothesis: The allele for eye color is carried on the X chromosome and the Y chromosome has no corresponding allele for eye color.

Reinforcement

Draw a Punnett square. Place sex chromosomes X and X along the left side, and X and Y along the top to represent gametes. Ask students why each gamete has only one sex chromosome. The sex chromosomes are separated during meiosis.

12.2 WHEN HEREDITY FOLLOWS DIFFERENT RULES **319**

USING MODELS

Sex-Linked Traits: *Visual-Spatial* Provide students with a pedigree outline from Queen Victoria's family for hemophilia. Queen Victoria was a carrier for hemophilia. One of her four sons (Leopold) had the disease, and two of her five daughters (Beatrice and Alice) were also carriers. Leopold had one daughter who was a carrier. Two of Beatrice's three sons had hemophilia, and her daughter had two sons with hemophilia. One of Alice's two sons died from hemophilia as a child, and one of her four daughters had five children—one of whom was a hemophiliac. Above each symbol, have students record the sex chromosomes and alleles that each individual possesses for the trait. **L2**

Indiana Academic Standards
Pages 318–319: B.1.21, B.1.29

Word Origin

polygenic from the Greek words *polys,* meaning "many," and *genos,* meaning "kind"; Polygenic inheritance involves many genes.

Figure 12.12
In this example of polygenic inheritance, three genes each have two alleles that contribute to the trait. When the distribution of plant heights is graphed, a bell-shaped curve is formed. Intermediate heights occur most often.

The genes that govern sex-linked traits follow the inheritance pattern of the sex chromosome on which they are found. Eye color in fruit flies is an example of an X-linked trait. Y-linked traits are passed only from a male to male offspring because the genes for these traits are on the Y chromosome.

Polygenic inheritance

Some traits, such as skin color and height in humans, and cob length in corn, vary over a wide range. Such ranges occur because these traits are governed by many genes. **Polygenic inheritance** is the inheritance pattern of a trait that is controlled by two or more genes. The genes may be on the same chromosome or on different chromosomes, and each gene may have two or more alleles. For simplicity, uppercase and lowercase letters are used to represent the alleles, as they are in Mendelian inheritance. Keep in mind, however, that the allele represented by an uppercase letter is not dominant. All heterozygotes are intermediate in phenotype.

In polygenic inheritance, each allele represented by an uppercase letter contributes a small, but equal, portion to the trait being expressed. The result is that the phenotypes usually show a continuous range of variability from the minimum value of the trait to the maximum value.

Suppose, for example, that stem length in a plant is controlled by three different genes: *A, B,* and *C.* Each gene is on a different chromosome and has two alleles, which can be represented by uppercase or lowercase letters. Thus, each diploid plant has a total of six alleles for stem length. A plant that is homozygous for short alleles at all three gene locations (*aabbcc*) might grow to be only 4 cm tall, the base height. A plant that is homozygous for tall alleles at all three gene locations (*AABBCC*) might be 16 cm tall. The difference between the tallest possible plant and the shortest possible plant is 12 cm, or 2 cm per each tall allele.

Suppose a 16-cm-tall plant were crossed with a 4-cm-tall plant. In the F_1 generation, all offspring would be *AaBbCc.* If each tall gene *A, B,* and *C* contributed 2 cm of height to the base height of 4 cm, the expected height of these plants would be 10 cm (4 cm + 6 cm)—an intermediate height. If they are allowed to interbreed, the F_2 offspring will show a range of heights. A Punnett square of this trihybrid cross would show that 10-cm-tall plants are most often expected, and the tallest and shortest plants are seldom expected. Notice in *Figure 12.12* that when these results are graphed, the shape of the graph confirms the prediction of the Punnett square.

Stem Length Variation in a Plant Polygenic for the Trait

y-axis: Expected number of F_2 plants
x-axis: Stem length (cm)

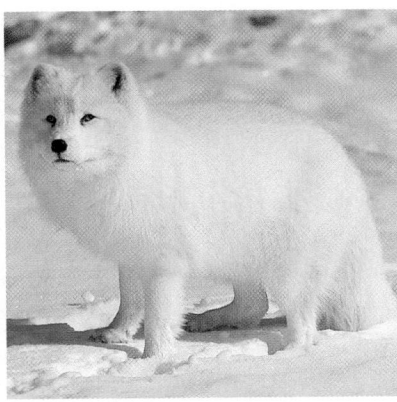

Figure 12.13
The arctic fox has gray-brown fur in warm temperatures. When temperatures fall, however, the fur becomes white. **Think Critically** *Why is white fur an adaptive advantage in winter?*

Caption Question Answer
Figure 12.13 White fur in the winter months would act as camouflage for the fox against the snow, where its gray-brown fur would stand out.

Virtual Lab

CD-ROM Students will use Punnett squares to perform genetic crosses in *Sex-Linked Traits*.

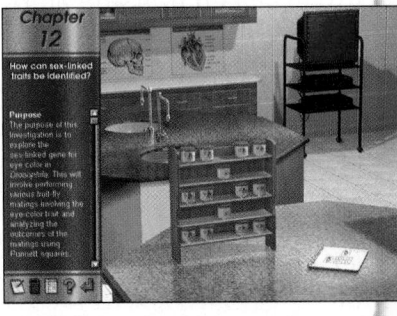

Word Origin

Have students research to find and define other words using "poly" as a part of the root, such as *polygon* and *polygraph*.

Environmental Influences

Even when you understand dominance and recessiveness, and you have solved the puzzles of the other patterns of heredity, the inheritance picture is not complete. The genetic makeup of an organism at fertilization determines only the organism's potential to develop and function. As the organism develops, many factors can influence how the gene is expressed, or even whether the gene is expressed at all. Two such influences are the organism's external and internal environments.

Influence of external environment

Sometimes, individuals known to have a particular gene fail to express the phenotype specified by that gene. Temperature, nutrition, light, chemicals, and infectious agents all can influence gene expression. In Siamese cats and arctic foxes, as shown in *Figure 12.13*, temperature has an effect on the expression of coat color. External influences can also be seen in leaves. Leaves can have different sizes, thicknesses, and shapes depending on the amount of light they receive.

Influence of internal environment

The internal environments of males and females are different because of hormones and structural differences. For example, horn size in mountain sheep is expressed differently in males and females, as shown in *Figure 12.14*.

Figure 12.14
The horns of a ram (male) are much heavier and more coiled than those of a ewe (female) although their genotypes for horn size are identical.

PROJECT

Genes and the Environment Have student groups germinate mustard seeds (available from the condiment section of a grocery store) in petri dishes that have been lined with paper toweling. They should moisten the toweling with water and add 20 seeds. Cover the dish and place it in the dark. Examine the seedlings after about 7 days. All seedlings will be white. Remove the dishes from the dark, place them in bright light for 24 hours, and then note their color. Have students write a report in which they explain how this project illustrates the role of the environment in influencing gene expression. **L2** **COOP LEARN**

Indiana Academic Standards

Pages 320–321: B.1.21, B.1.23, B.1.24, B.1.29

3 Assess

DAILY INTERVENTION

Check for Understanding
Have students explain how the following differ from one another. (a) incomplete dominance and codominance; (b) multiple alleles and polygenic inheritance; (c) autosomes and sex chromosomes; (d) sex-linked trait and autosomal trait **L1**

Reteach
Ask students to provide an example of each of the following patterns or types of inheritance: (a) incomplete dominance; (b) codominance; (c) multiple allelic trait; (d) polygenic trait; (e) sex-linked trait. **L1**

Resources
For more practice, use *Reading Essentials for Biology,* Section 12.2.

Extension

Intrapersonal Have students describe and record some of the changes associated with human aging that alter gene expression. To get students started, provide them with a hint, such as a change in hair color from black or blond to gray. **L2**

 Assessment

Performance Ask students to illustrate through the use of Punnett squares how sex-linked inheritance differs from autosomal inheritance. They should use the same allele letters and parental genotypes. **L2**

Figure 12.15
Some traits are expressed differently in the sexes.

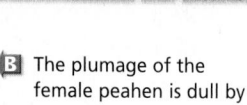
A The plumage of the male peacock is highly decorated and colored.

B The plumage of the female peahen is dull by comparison.

C Human male-pattern baldness, premature balding that occurs in a characteristic pattern, is dominant in males but recessive in females.

Male-pattern baldness in humans, and feather color in peacocks also are expressed differently in the sexes, as shown in *Figure 12.15*. These differences are controlled by different hormones, which are determined by different sets of genes.

An organism's age can also affect gene function. The nature of such a pattern is not well understood, but it is known that the internal environment of an organism changes with age.

Understanding how genes interact with each other and with the environment gives a more complete picture of inheritance. Mendel's idea that heredity is a composite of many individual traits still holds. Later researchers have filled in more details of Mendel's great contributions.

Section Assessment

Understanding Main Ideas

1. A cross between a purebred animal with red hairs and a purebred animal with white hairs produces an animal that has both red hairs and white hairs. What type of inheritance pattern is involved?

2. If a white-eyed male fruit fly were crossed with a heterozygous red-eyed female fruit fly, what ratio of genotypes would be expected in the offspring?

3. A red-flowered plant is crossed with a white-flowered plant. All of the offspring are pink. What inheritance pattern is expressed?

4. The color of wheat grains shows variability between red and white with multiple phenotypes. What is the inheritance pattern?

Thinking Critically

5. Armadillos always have four offspring that have identical genetic makeups. Suppose that, within a litter, each young armadillo is found to have a different phenotype for a particular trait. How could you explain this?

SKILL REVIEW

6. **Hypothesize** A population of a plant species in a meadow consists of plants that produce red, yellow, white, pink, or purple flowers. Hypothesize what the inheritance pattern is. For more help, refer to *Hypothesize* in the **Skill Handbook.**

 in.bdol.glencoe.com/self_check_quiz

Section Assessment

1. Alleles for both red and white hairs are expressed, which is typical of a pattern of codominance.

2. One-half the females would be $X^R X^r$, 1/2 the females would be $X^r X^r$, 1/2 the males would be $X^R Y$, and 1/2 the males would be $X^r Y$.

3. Incomplete dominance is being expressed because the heterozygous plant is an intermediate form between red and white.

4. polygenic inheritance

5. The environment in the mother's uterus before birth may have been different for each of the offspring. The external temperature can affect gene expression;

6. This is probably a case of multiple allelic or polygenic inheritance.

Complex Inheritance of Human Traits

Indiana Standards
Standard B.1.29
Understand that and explain how the actions of genes, patterns of inheritance, and the reproduction of cells and organisms account for the continuity of life, and give examples of how inherited characteristics can be observed at molecular and whole-organism levels — in structure, chemistry, or behavior.

SECTION PREVIEW

Objectives

Identify codominance, multiple allelic, sex-linked, and polygenic patterns of inheritance in humans.

Distinguish among conditions that result from extra autosomal or sex chromosomes.

Review Vocabulary
homozygous: having two identical alleles for a particular gene (p. 258)

New Vocabulary
karyotype

It's Not So Simple

Finding Main Ideas Have you ever thought about which of your traits came from your father or mother? Perhaps you can see one of your traits in a grandparent or another relative. As scientists study traits such as height and eye color, they are discovering that the inheritance of these traits can be very complex.

Organize Information *As you read this section, make a list of some physical characteristics that appear in your family members or friends. Try to determine how each trait is inherited by examining its inheritance pattern.*

The inheritance of eye color and height is complex.

Codominance in Humans

Remember that in codominance, the phenotypes of both homozygotes are produced in the heterozygote. One example of this in humans is a group of inherited red blood cell disorders called sickle-cell anemia.

Sickle-cell anemia

Sickle-cell anemia is a major health problem in the United States and in Africa. In the United States, it is most common in black Americans whose families originated in Africa and in white Americans whose families originated in the countries surrounding the Mediterranean Sea. About one in 12 African Americans, a much larger proportion than in most populations, is heterozygous for the disorder.

In an individual who is homozygous for the sickle-cell allele, the oxygen-carrying protein hemoglobin differs by one amino acid from normal hemoglobin. This defective hemoglobin forms crystal-like structures that change the shape of the red blood cells. Normal red blood cells are disc-shaped, but abnormal red blood cells are shaped like a sickle, or half-moon.

12.3 COMPLEX INHERITANCE OF HUMAN TRAITS **323**

Bellringer
Section Focus Transparency 31

Section Focus
Use with Chapter 12,
Section 12.3

Transparency **31** A Complex Inheritance Trait

How many different hair colors are shown?
Is this trait inherited as a simple Mendelian trait? How do you know?

BIOLOGY: The Dynamics of Life

SECTION FOCUS TRANSPARENCIES

Finding Main Ideas

Organize Information Have students line up in order from tallest to shortest. Use this as an example to discuss the differences in height, having many phenotypes as a result of complex inheritance.

Indiana Academic Standards

Pages 322–323: B.1.21, B.1.26, B.1.28, B.1.29

323

2 Teach

Microscope Activity

Visual-Spatial Have students view a prepared slide of sickled blood cells and compare it with a slide of normal blood cells. **L1** **ELL**

✓**Reading Check** Possible types are $I^A I^A$, $I^B I^B$, and $I^A I^B$.

Portfolio

Blue People Have students research blue people of Troublesome Creek and construct a pedigree from their research. These people have an autosomal recessive gene that causes their skin to appear dark blue. Have students explain this disorder. **L2**

🏴 **Indiana Academic Standards**

Pages 324–325: B.1.21, B.1.28, B.1.29

The change in shape occurs in the body's narrow capillaries after the hemoglobin delivers oxygen to the cells. Abnormally shaped blood cells, like the one shown in *Figure 12.16A,* slow blood flow, block small vessels, and result in tissue damage and pain. Because sickled cells block blood flow and have a shorter life span than normal red blood cells, the person can have several related disorders.

Individuals who are heterozygous for the allele produce both normal and sickled hemoglobin, an example of codominance. They produce enough normal hemoglobin that they do not have the serious health problems of those homozygous for the allele and can lead relatively normal lives. Individuals who are heterozygous are said to have the sickle-cell trait because they can show some signs of sickle-cell-related disorders if the availability of oxygen is reduced.

Multiple Alleles Govern Blood Type

You have learned that more than two alleles of a gene are possible for certain traits. Mendel's laws of heredity also can be applied to traits that have more than two alleles. The ABO blood group is a classic example of a single gene that has multiple alleles in humans.

Human blood types, listed in the table in *Figure 12.17,* are determined by the presence or absence of certain molecules on the surfaces of red blood cells. As the determinant of blood types A, B, AB, and O, the gene *I* has three alleles: I^A, I^B, and *i*. Study the table to see the genotypes of the different blood types.

The importance of blood typing

Determining blood type is necessary before a person can receive a blood transfusion because the red blood cells of incompatible blood types could clump together, causing death. Blood typing also can be helpful in solving cases of disputed parentage. For example, if a child has type AB blood and his or her mother has type A, a man with type O blood could not possibly be the father. But blood tests cannot prove that a certain man definitely is the father; they indicate only that he could be. DNA tests are necessary to determine actual parenthood.

Figure 12.16
In sickle-cell anemia, the gene for hemoglobin produces a protein that is different by one amino acid. This hemoglobin crystallizes when oxygen levels are low, changing the red blood cells into a sickle shape **(A)**. A normal red blood cell is disc-shaped **(B)**.

Ⓐ Color-enhanced SEM Magnification: 18 000×

Ⓑ Color-enhanced SEM Magnification: 18 000×

✓**Reading Check** **Determine** the possible blood types of the children of parents that both have type AB.

324 PATTERNS OF HEREDITY AND HUMAN GENETICS

Additional Lab

Barr Bodies

Purpose
Students will locate Barr bodies in cells.

Safety Precautions 🥽👕🧹

Materials
prepared slides of male and female cheek cells, microscope

Background
Females have two X chromosomes, but early in development of a female embryo, one of the X chromosomes in each cell becomes inactive. The inactive chromosome becomes condensed and can be seen as a Barr body. Cells of males do not contain Barr bodies.

Procedure
Give students the following directions.
1. Place the slide of female cheek cell on the microscope.
2. Examine cells under high power. A Barr body will be seen in each cell as a darkly stained mass just inside the nuclear membrane.

The ABO Blood Group

Figure 12.17
The gene for blood type, gene *I*, codes for a molecule that attaches to a membrane protein found on the surface of red blood cells. The *I^A* and *I^B* alleles each code for a different molecule. Your immune system recognizes the red blood cells as belonging to you. If cells with a different surface molecule enter your body, your immune system will attack them. **Critical Thinking** *If your blood is type O and your mother's blood is type A, what blood types could your father have?*

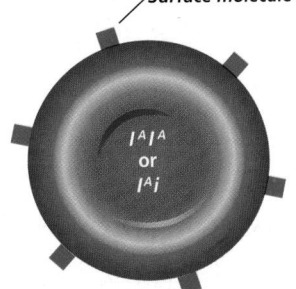
Surface molecule A

I^A I^A or *I^A i*

A Phenotype A The *I^A* allele is dominant to *i*, so inheriting either the *I^A i* alleles or the *I^A I^A* alleles from both parents will give you type A blood. Surface molecule A is produced.

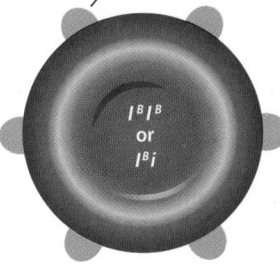
Surface molecule B

I^B I^B or *I^B i*

B Phenotype B The *I^B* allele is also dominant to *i*. To have type B blood, you must inherit the *I^B* allele from one parent and either another *I^B* allele or the *i* allele from the other. Surface molecule B is produced.

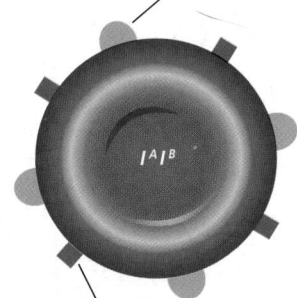
Surface molecule B

I^A I^B

Surface molecule A

C Phenotype AB The *I^A* and *I^B* alleles are codominant. This means that if you inherit the *I^A* allele from one parent and the *I^B* allele from the other, your red blood cells will produce both surface molecules and you will have type AB blood.

Color-enhanced SEM Magnification: 973×
Red blood cells

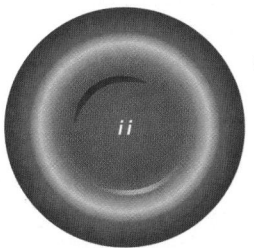
ii

D Phenotype O The *i* allele is recessive and produces no surface molecules. Therefore, if you are homozygous *ii*, your blood cells have no surface molecules and you have blood type O.

Human Blood Types		
Genotypes	**Surface Molecules**	**Phenotypes**
I^A I^A or *I^A i*	A	A
I^B I^B or *I^B i*	B	B
I^A I^B	A and B	AB
ii	None	O

Purpose
Students will learn the genetic basis of ABO blood types.

Teaching Strategies
Give students a genotype and ask them to identify the phenotype on red blood cells.

Visual Learning
- Have students create a table with genotypes as the headings. Under each genotype, have them correctly place the resulting phenotype. **L1**
- Ask students to draw red blood cells with cell surface proteins in their journals. Have them draw red blood cells for all four blood types and write possible genotypes underneath the cells. **L1**

Critical Thinking
Father could be *I^A i*, *I^B i*, or *ii*.

---

3. Examine the slide of male cheek cells for the presence of Barr bodies.
4. Draw a cell with a Barr body and one without a Barr body.
5. Wash your hands when you have finished your observations.

Expected Results
Students will see Barr bodies in cells from females but not in those from males.

Analysis
1. Do all your body cells have Barr bodies? yes for females; no for males
2. What percentage of a female's cells have visible Barr bodies? 100%
3. How many Barr bodies would you find in a cell of an XXX female? 2

Assessment
Performance Students should include a summary of the lab, their drawings, and the answers to the Analysis questions in their journals. Use the Performance Task Assessment List for Lab Report in **PASC**, p. 119. **L3**

Purpose

Students will determine the pattern of inheritance for Duchenne's muscular dystrophy.

Process Skills

observe and infer, recognize cause and effect

Background

Because various forms of muscular dystrophy can be inherited as autosomal dominant, autosomal recessive, or sex-linked disorders, a family pedigree must be analyzed to determine the pattern of inheritance. From the pedigree, the mode of inheritance of Duchenne's muscular dystrophy can be inferred to be X-linked.

Teaching Strategies

Ask students which individuals in the pedigree were key to determine the type of inheritance involved.

Thinking Critically

There is a 100% probability that the daughter will be a carrier because the only X chromosome she can inherit from her father would have the defective gene. The son would not inherit the disorder because his X chromosome would come from his mother, who presumably is not a carrier.

Assessment

Knowledge Ask students what mating would have to occur to produce a female child with Duchenne's muscular dystrophy. mating a female carrier or an affected female with an affected male Use the Performance Task Assessment List for Formulating a Hypothesis in **PASC,** p. 93. **L2**

Figure 12.18
If a trait is X-linked, males pass the X-linked allele to all of their daughters but not to their sons **(A).** Heterozygous females have a 50 percent chance of passing a recessive X-linked allele to each child **(B).**

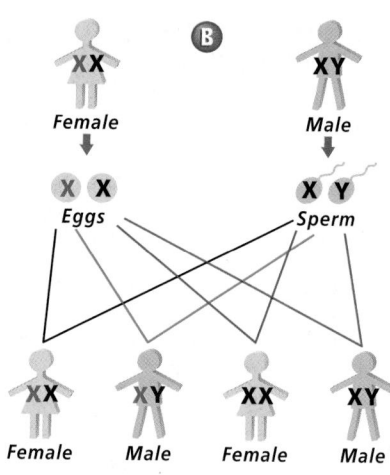

Draw a Conclusion

How is Duchenne's muscular dystrophy inherited? Muscular dystrophy is a group of genetic disorders that produce muscular weakness, progressive deterioration of muscular tissue, and loss of coordination. Different forms of muscular dystrophy can be inherited as an autosomal dominant, an autosomal recessive, or a sex-linked disorder. These three patterns of inheritance appear different from one another when a pedigree is made. One form of muscular dystrophy, called Duchenne's muscular dystrophy, affects three in 10 000 American males.

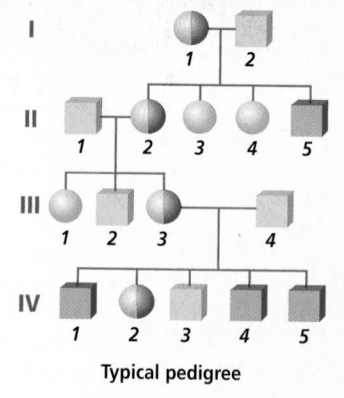

Typical pedigree

Solve the Problem

The pedigree shown here represents the typical inheritance pattern for Duchenne's muscular dystrophy. Refer to *Figure 12.1* if you need help interpreting the symbols. Analyze the pedigree above to determine the pattern of inheritance. Is this an autosomal or a sex-linked disorder?

Thinking Critically

Draw Conclusions If individual IV-1 had a daughter and a son, what would be the probability that the daughter is a carrier? That the son inherited the disorder?

Sex-Linked Traits in Humans

Many human traits are determined by genes that are carried on the sex chromosomes; most of these genes are located on the X chromosome. The pattern of sex-linked inheritance is explained by the fact that males, who are XY, pass an X chromosome to each daughter and a Y chromosome to each son. Females, who are XX, pass one of their X chromosomes to each child, as illustrated in *Figure 12.18*. If a son receives an X chromosome with a recessive allele, the recessive phenotype will be expressed because he does not inherit on the Y chromosome from his father a dominant allele that would mask the expression of the recessive allele.

Two traits that are governed by X-linked recessive inheritance in humans are red-green color blindness and hemophilia. X-linked dominant and Y-linked human disorders are rare. Determine whether Duchenne's muscular dystrophy is sex-linked by completing the *Problem-Solving Lab* on this page.

INCLUSION STRATEGIES

Learning Disabled/Visually Impaired Help students understand the need to type blood before it is used for a transfusion by using cardboard circles with different surface molecules attached, similar to those in Figure 12.17, on the previous page. These circles represent blood cell types A, B, AB, and O. Also, use cardboard pieces that will fit the surface molecules like puzzle pieces, as antibodies. Those that fit type A should be around type B blood cells. Those that fit type B should be around type A blood cells. Type AB should have no antibodies around, since type AB blood cells have both surface molecules. Type O should have both antibodies around, because they have neither surface molecules. **L1**

Red-green color blindness

People who have red-green color blindness can't differentiate these two colors. Color blindness is caused by the inheritance of a recessive allele at either of two gene sites on the X chromosome. Both genes affect red and green receptors in the cells of the eyes. A serious problem for people with this disorder is the inability to identify red and green traffic lights by color.

Hemophilia: An X-linked disorder

Did you ever notice that most cuts stop bleeding quickly? This human adaptation is essential. If your blood didn't have the ability to clot, any cut could take a long time to stop bleeding. Of greater concern would be internal bleeding resulting from a bruise, which a person may not immediately notice.

Hemophilia A is an X-linked disorder that causes such a problem with blood clotting. About one male in every 10 000 has hemophilia, but only about one in 100 million females inherits the same disorder. Why? Males inherit the allele for hemophilia on the X chromosome from their carrier mothers. One recessive allele for hemophilia will cause the disorder in males. Females would need two recessive alleles to inherit hemophilia. The family of Queen Victoria, pictured in the *Connection to Social Studies* at the end of this chapter, is the best-known study of hemophilia A, also called royal hemophilia.

Hemophilia A can be treated with blood transfusions and injections of Factor VIII, the blood-clotting enzyme that is absent in people affected by the condition. However, both treatments are expensive. New methods of DNA technology are being used to develop a cheaper source of the clotting factor.

MiniLab 12.2

Observe and Infer

Detecting Colors and Patterns in Eyes Human eye color, like skin color, is determined by polygenic inheritance. You can detect several shades of eye color, especially if you look closely at the iris with a magnifying glass. Often, the pigment is deposited so that light reflects from the eye, causing the iris to appear blue, green, gray, or hazel (brown-green). In actuality, the pigment may be yellowish or brown, but not blue.

Hazel eye color

Procedure

CAUTION: *Do not touch the eye with the magnifying glass or any other object.*

1. Use a magnifying glass to observe the patterns and colors of pigment in the eyes of five classmates.
2. Use colored pencils to make drawings of the five irises.
3. Describe your observations in your journal.

Analysis

1. **Observe** How many different pigments were you able to detect in each eye?
2. **Critique** From your data, do you suspect that eye color might not be inherited by simple Mendelian rules? Explain.
3. **Analyze** Suppose that two people have brown eyes. They have two children with brown eyes, one with blue eyes, and one with green eyes. What pattern might this suggest?

Polygenic Inheritance in Humans

Think of all the traits you inherited from your parents. Although many of your traits were inherited through simple Mendelian patterns or through multiple alleles, many other human traits are determined by polygenic inheritance. These kinds of traits usually represent a range of variation that is measurable. The *MiniLab* on this page examines one of these traits—the color variations in human eyes.

MiniLab 12.2

Purpose

Students will observe the colors and patterns in the eyes of several classmates in order to hypothesize how eye color is inherited.

Process Skills

observe and infer, recognize cause and effect

Teaching Strategies

Provide students with five cards, each with a circle and a line under the circle. Students should write the name of the person on the line and then draw the iris within the circle. Provide colored pencils. **L1 ELL**

Expected Results

Students will detect many different pigments, suggesting polygenic inheritance.

Analysis

1. Students may detect brown, blue, yellow, gray, green, and black pigments in each eye.
2. Eye color is probably not inherited by simple Mendelian rules because there are so many phenotypes.
3. The pattern suggests polygenic inheritance.

Assessment

Knowledge Ask students to write a paragraph telling how they could determine the number of genes involved in the inheritance of eye color. Use the Performance Task Assessment List for Writing in Science in **PASC**, p. 159. **L2**

CHALLENGE ACTIVITY

Genetic Connection: *Linguistic*
Have students who need an additional challenge research the connection between chromosome 14, 19, and 21 and Alzheimer's disease. Ask them to include a copy of their findings in their portfolios. **L3**

 Indiana Academic Standards

Pages 326–327: B.1.21, B.1.28, B.1.29

327

Many different types of color-blindness are possible. Make color-blindness testing charts available to students. Color-blindness testing kits are also available. Have pairs of students use the kits.

Polygenic Inheritance
Have students re-examine the section opener photograph of students whose heights form a bell-shaped curve. Which figure in this chapter does the inheritance pattern of height most closely resemble? The pattern of inheritance exhibited by the students' heights most closely resembles that of Figures 12.12 and 12.19 demonstrating polygenic inheritance.

Visual Learning

Figure 12.19 The graph of what number of genes most closely matches the observed distribution of skin color? The actual data match the 4-gene graph best.

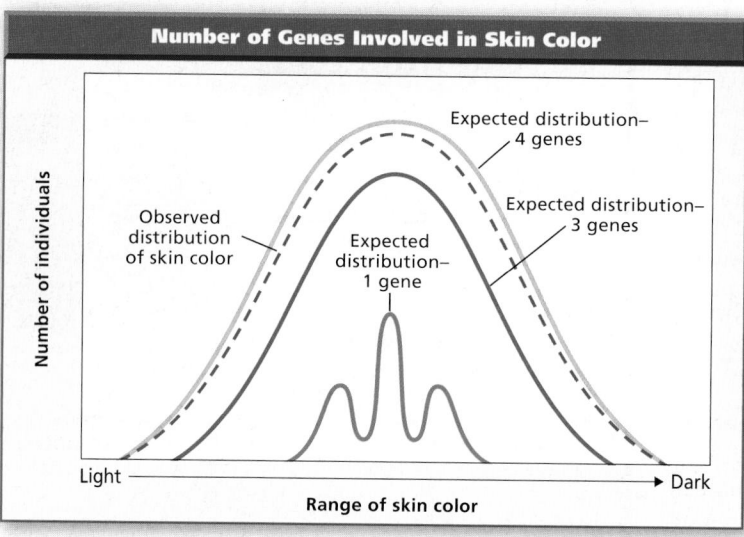

Number of Genes Involved in Skin Color

Expected distribution—4 genes

Expected distribution—3 genes

Observed distribution of skin color

Expected distribution—1 gene

Number of individuals

Light — Dark

Range of skin color

Figure 12.19
This graph **(A)** shows the expected distribution of human skin color if controlled by one, three, or four genes. The observed distribution of skin color **(B)** closely matches the distribution shown by four genes.

Skin color: A polygenic trait

In the early 1900s, the idea that polygenic inheritance occurs in humans was first tested using data collected on skin color. Scientists found that when light-skinned people mate with dark-skinned people, their offspring have intermediate skin colors. When these children produce the F_2 generation, the resulting skin colors range from the light-skin color to the dark-skin color of the grandparents (the P_1 generation), with most children having an intermediate skin color. As shown in *Figure 12.19*, the variation in skin color indicates that between three and four genes are involved.

Changes in Chromosome Numbers

You have been reading about traits that are caused by one or several genes on chromosomes. What would happen if an entire chromosome or part of a chromosome were missing from the complete set? What if a cell's nucleus contained an extra chromosome? As you have learned, abnormal numbers of chromosomes in offspring usually, but not always, result from accidents of meiosis. Many abnormal phenotypic effects result from such mistakes.

Abnormal numbers of autosomes

You know that a human usually has 23 pairs of chromosomes, or 46 chromosomes altogether. Of these 23 pairs of chromosomes, 22 pairs are autosomes. Humans who have an extra whole or partial autosome are trisomic—that is, they have three of a particular autosomal chromosome instead of just two. In other words, they have 47 chromosomes. Recall that trisomy usually results from nondisjunction, which occurs when paired homologous chromosomes fail to separate properly during meiosis.

CULTURAL DIVERSITY

Mary Styles Harris In your discussion of sickle-cell anemia, point out contributions of contemporary African American scientists in the treatment and etiology of this disorder. One of the more prominent workers in this field has been geneticist Mary Styles Harris (born 1949). From 1977 to 1979, Harris was the executive director of the Sickle Cell Foundation of Georgia. She wrote and produced a series for Georgia TV and audio-visual materials about health issues. She is the president and genetic counselor for her own company in Atlanta, Georgia.

To identify an abnormal number of chromosomes, a sample of cells is obtained from an individual or from a fetus. Metaphase chromosomes are photographed; the chromosome pictures are then enlarged and arranged in pairs by a computer according to length and location of the centromere, as shown in *Figure 12.20*. This chart of chromosome pairs is called a **karyotype,** and it is valuable in identifying unusual chromosome numbers in cells.

Down syndrome: Trisomy 21

Most human abnormal chromosome numbers result in embryo death often before a woman even realizes she is pregnant. Fortunately, these rarely occur. Down syndrome is the only autosomal trisomy in which affected individuals survive to adulthood. It occurs in about one in 700 live births.

Down syndrome is a group of symptoms that results from trisomy of chromosome 21. Individuals who have Down syndrome have at least some degree of mental retardation. The incidence of Down syndrome births is higher in older mothers, especially those over 40.

Abnormal numbers of sex chromosomes

Many abnormalities in the number of sex chromosomes are known to exist. An X chromosome may be missing (designated as XO) or there may be an extra one (XXX or XXY). There may also be an extra Y chromosome (XYY), as you can see by examining *Figure 12.20.* Any individual with at least one Y chromosome is a male, and any individual without a Y chromosome is a female. Most of these individuals lead normal lives, but they cannot have children and some have varying degrees of mental retardation.

Figure 12.20
This karyotype demonstrates XYY syndrome, where two Y chromosomes are inherited from the father instead of just one Y chromosome. **Infer** *What sex is an XYY individual?*

Section Assessment

Understanding Main Ideas

1. Describe how a zygote with trisomy 21 is likely to occur during fertilization.
2. In addition to revealing chromosome abnormalities, what other information about an individual would a karyotype show?
3. What would the genotypes of parents have to be for them to have a color-blind daughter? Explain.
4. Describe a genetic trait in humans that is inherited as codominance. Describe the phenotypes of the two homozygotes and that of the heterozygote. Why is this trait an example of codominance?

Thinking Critically

5. A man is accused of fathering two children, one with type O blood and another with type A blood. The mother of the children has type B blood. The man has type AB blood. Could he be the father of both children? Explain your answer.

SKILL REVIEW

6. **Get the Big Picture** Construct a table of the traits discussed in this section. For column heads, use Trait, Pattern of inheritance, and Characteristics. For more help, refer to *Get the Big Picture* in the **Skill Handbook.**

 in.bdol.glencoe.com/self_check_quiz

12.3 COMPLEX INHERITANCE OF HUMAN TRAITS **329**

---

3 Assess
DAILY INTERVENTION

Check for Understanding
Linguistic Ask students to summarize the patterns shown by multiple allelic, polygenic, and sex-linked inheritance. **L1**

Reteach
Visual-Spatial Have students draw the phases of meiosis to demonstrate how various changes in chromosome numbers occur. **L1** **ELL**

Resources
For more practice, use *Reading Essentials for Biology,* Section 12.3.

Extension

Ask students to research the rare sex-linked disorder severe combined immune deficiency (SCID). The "boy in the bubble" had this disorder. What experimental treatments are currently being used to treat or cure this disorder? **L3**

✔ MODIFIED Assessment

Skill Provide students with filled-in Punnett squares showing genotypes and phenotypes of offspring. Have students determine the pattern of inheritance from the information given. **L1**

Caption Question Answer
Figure 12.20 male

Section Assessment

1. One parent's gamete (most likely the female parent) was produced by nondisjunction of the 21 chromosome, resulting in a gamete with two 21 chromosomes.
2. the sex of the child
3. The father must be color-blind (have recessive allele on his X chromosome). The mother must have at least one X chromosome with a color-blind allele.
4. In sickle-cell anemia, an individual homozygous for normal hemoglobin will produce only normal hemoglobin. An individual homozygous for sickle-cell anemia will produce only abnormal hemoglobin. A heterozygote will produce both types of hemoglobin.
5. The mother could be I^Bi or I^BI^B and the father is I^AI^B. If a child received I^A from the father and i from the mother, it would be type A so the man could have fathered the type A child. This man could not father a type O child because he has no i allele.
6. Material for the table can be found on pages 323–329 of the text.

Time Allotment

initial session: one class period for planting of P_1 generation, then 5 minutes daily for watering; one class period for cross-pollination; 10 days later, one class period for collecting and planting of F_1 seeds; 10 days later: one class period for examination of F_2 plants

Process Skills

form a hypothesis, observe and infer, collect data

Safety Precautions

Have students use caution when handling light fixtures or light banks. Students should use caution when using a razor blade.

PREPARATION

- Seeds of normal and variegated *Brassica rapa* can be ordered from biological supply houses.
- Provide light in fluorescent banks (cool-white, 40 watts/bulb) continuously to complete the life cycle in such a short time. Light banks should be adjustable to remain about 5–8 cm above the plants' growing tips.
- Soil must be kept moist.

Possible Hypotheses

If the trait is inherited through the cytoplasm, then the female parent contributes the trait.

If the trait is inherited through the nucleus, then the male parent contributes the trait.

 INQUIRY **Before You Begin**

The mitochondria of all eukaryotes and the chloroplasts of plants and algae contain DNA. This DNA is not in chromosomes, but it still carries genes. Many of the mitochondrial genes control steps in the respiration process.

The genes in chloroplasts control traits such as chlorophyll production. Lack of chlorophyll in some cells causes the appearance of white patches in a leaf. This trait is known as variegated leaf. In this BioLab, you will carry out an experiment to determine the pattern of inheritance of the variegated leaf trait in *Brassica rapa*.

What is the pattern of cytoplasmic inheritance?

PREPARATION

Problem

What inheritance pattern does the variegated leaf trait in *Brassica rapa* show?

Hypotheses

Consider the possible evidence you could collect that would answer the problem question. Form a hypothesis with your group that you can test to answer the question, and write the hypothesis in your journal.

Objectives

In this BioLab, you will:

- **Determine** which crosses of *Brassica rapa* will reveal the pattern of cytoplasmic inheritance.
- **Analyze** data from *Brassica rapa* crosses.

Possible Materials

Brassica rapa seeds, normal and variegated
potting soil and trays
paintbrushes

forceps
single-edge razor blade
light source
labels

Safety Precautions

CAUTION: *Always wear goggles in the lab. Handle the razor blade with extreme caution. Always cut away from you. Wash your hands with soap and water after working with plant material.*

Skill Handbook

If you need help with this lab, refer to the **Skill Handbook.**

PLAN THE EXPERIMENT

1. Decide which crosses will be needed to test your hypothesis.
2. Keep the available materials in mind as you plan your procedure. How many seeds will you need?
3. Record your procedure, and list the materials and quantities you will need.

PLAN THE EXPERIMENT

Teaching Strategies

- Students should work in groups.
- Review fertilization and make sure students realize that the egg contributes most of the cytoplasm and organelles to the zygote. The sperm is almost all nucleus.

- Variegated plants grow a little slower than nonvariegated plants. Therefore, they should be started about 4 days earlier.
- *Brassica* will not self-pollinate. Keep the two plant types separate from each other to avoid random cross-pollination.

Possible Procedures

Both variegated and nonvariegated seed types should be planted and grown. After 13–15 days students will perform the following cross-pollinations depending on their hypotheses: variegated female with nonvariegated male and nonvariegated

4. Assign a task to each member of the group. One person should write data in a journal, another can pollinate the flowers, while a third can set up the plant trays. Determine who will set up and clean up materials.

5. Design and construct a data table.

Check the Plan

Discuss the following points with other group members to decide the final procedure for your experiment.

1. What data will you collect, and how will it be recorded?

2. When will you pollinate the flowers? How many flowers will you pollinate?

3. How will you transfer pollen from one flower to another?

4. How and when will you collect the seeds that result from your crosses?

5. What variables will have to be controlled? What controls will be used?

6. When will you end the experiment?

7. *Make sure your teacher has approved your experimental plan before you proceed further.*

8. Carry out your experiment.

9. CLEANUP AND DISPOSAL Make wise choices in the disposal of materials.

ANALYZE AND CONCLUDE

1. Student answers will vary depending on their hypotheses.

2. Variegation is inherited as a cytoplasmic trait from the female parent.

3. Sperm cells contain little to no cytoplasm. Cytoplasm containing chloroplasts is contributed only by the egg.

4. female

5. Diagrams should show the trait being transmitted in an egg cell of the female but not in pollen of the male.

6. ERROR ANALYSIS Sufficient light must be supplied to the plants to maximize the contrast between green and white leaves.

Assessment

Skill Have students draw Punnett squares to explain the inheritance pattern in offspring if this trait were inherited as a simple dominant allele. Have them show how cytoplasmic inheritance deviates from this pattern. Use the Performance Task Assessment List for Scientific Drawing in **PASC**, p. 127. L2

ANALYZE AND CONCLUDE

1. Check Your Hypothesis Did your data support your hypothesis? Why or why not?

2. Interpret Observations What is the inheritance pattern of variegated leaves in *Brassica rapa?*

3. Make Inferences Explain why genes in the chloroplast are inherited in this pattern.

4. Draw Conclusions Which parent passes the variegated trait to its offspring?

5. Make Scientific Illustrations Draw a diagram tracing the inheritance of this trait through cell division.

6. ERROR ANALYSIS What, besides genetics, might cause white leaves to form?

Apply Your Skill

Project Make crosses between normal *Brassica rapa* and genetically dwarfed, mutant *Brassica rapa* to determine the inheritance pattern of the dwarf mutation.

 Web Links To find out more about inheritance of traits, visit in.bdol.glencoe.com/traits

Apply Your Skill

Project Have students carry out crosses between nonvariegated male and female parents as well as variegated male and female parents. L3 ELL

12.3 COMPLEX INHERITANCE OF HUMAN TRAITS **331**

female with variegated male. Pods of seeds will mature between days 28 and 30. These seeds will then be planted, and new offspring will be observed for the presence of the variegated trait.

Data and Observations

Variegated F$_1$ plants will appear in crosses where the female parent was variegated.

CLEANUP AND DISPOSAL

 Used razor blades should be placed in a "sharp" container and disposed of by the teacher. Soil, plants, and other containers can be disposed of in the trash. Have students wash their hands when the activity and cleanup are complete.

Indiana Academic Standards

Pages 330–331: B.1.21, B.1.26

connection to Social Studies

Purpose

Students will learn why hemophilia has been called the royal disease.

Teaching Strategies

■ Inform students that about 1 in 10 000 males has hemophilia, whereas about 1 in 100 000 000 females inherits this disorder. Make sure students realize that the reason for this is the fact that hemophilia is an X-linked disorder.

■ Have students hypothesize how Queen Victoria became a carrier of the disease when neither of her parents had the disorder. Students should be able to deduce that one of Victoria's parents developed a spontaneous mutation in his or her X chromosome, which was then passed to her. The mutation could not have occurred during the production of one of Victoria's egg cells because so many of her children were affected. **L2**

connection to Social Studies

Queen Victoria surrounded by her family

Queen Victoria and Royal Hemophilia

One of the most famous examples of a pedigree demonstrating inheritance of a sex-linked trait is the family of Queen Victoria of England and hemophilia.

Queen Victoria had four sons and five daughters. Her son Leopold had hemophilia and died as a result of a minor fall. Two of her daughters, Alice and Beatrice, were carriers for the trait. The disorder was passed to royal families in Spain, Prussia (formerly a kingdom in Germany), and Russia over four generations.

The Spanish royal family Victoria's daughter Beatrice, a carrier for the trait, married Prince Henry of Battenberg, a descendent of Prussian royalty. Two of their sons inherited the trait, both dying before the age of 35. Her daughter, Victoria, was a carrier and married King Alfonso XIII of Spain, thus transmitting the allele to the Spanish royal family. Two of their sons died from hemophilia in their early thirties.

The Prussian royal family Alice, another of Victoria's daughters, married Louis IV of Hesse, a member of the Prussian royal family and related to Prince Henry of Battenberg. One of Alice's sons, Frederick, died at the age of three from hemophilia. One of her daughters, Irene, passed the trait to the next generation of Prussian royalty—two of her sons.

The Russian royal family Irene's sister and Queen Victoria's granddaughter, Alexandra, married Czar Nicholas II of Russia. Four healthy daughters were born, but the only male heir, Alexis, showed signs of bleeding and

bruising at only six weeks of age. Having a brother, an uncle, and two cousins who had suffered from the disorder and died at early ages, you can imagine the despair Alexandra felt for her son and the future heir. In desperation, the family turned to Rasputin, a man who claimed to have healing abilities and used Alexis' illness for his own political power. The series of events surrounding Alexis and his hemophilia played a role in the downfall of the Russian monarchy.

The British throne today Queen Elizabeth II, the current British monarch, is descended from Queen Victoria's eldest son, Edward VII. Because he did not inherit the trait, he could not pass it on to his children. Therefore, the British monarchy today does not carry the recessive allele for hemophilia, at least not inherited from Queen Victoria.

Math in Biology

Use Numbers If you were the child of a female carrier for a sex-linked trait such as hemophilia, what would be your chances of carrying the trait?

 To find out more about hemophilia, visit in.bdol.glencoe.com/social_studies

Math in Biology

50%, or one out of two, chance

 Indiana Academic Standards

Pages 332–333: B.1.21, B.1.26, B.1.28, B.1.29

STUDY GUIDE

Section 12.1

Mendelian Inheritance of Human Traits

Key Concepts
- A pedigree is a family tree of inheritance.
- Most human genetic disorders are inherited as rare recessive alleles, but a few are inherited as dominant alleles.

Vocabulary
carrier (p. 310)
fetus (p. 312)
pedigree (p. 309)

Section 12.2

When Heredity Follows Different Rules

Key Concepts
- Some alleles can be expressed as incomplete dominance or codominance.
- There may be many alleles for one trait or many genes that interact to produce a trait.
- Cells have matching pairs of homologous chromosomes called autosomes.
- Sex chromosomes contain genes that determine the sex of an individual.
- Inheritance patterns of genes located on sex chromosomes are due to differences in the number and kind of sex chromosomes in males and in females.
- The expression of some traits is affected by the internal and external environments of the organism.

Vocabulary
autosome (p. 318)
codominant allele (p. 317)
incomplete dominance (p. 315)
multiple allele (p. 317)
polygenic inheritance (p. 320)
sex chromosome (p. 318)
sex-linked trait (p. 319)

Section 12.3

Complex Inheritance of Human Traits

Color-enhanced SEM Magnification: 18 000×

Key Concepts
- The majority of human traits are controlled by multiple alleles or by polygenic inheritance. The inheritance patterns of these traits are highly variable.
- Sex-linked traits are determined by inheritance of sex chromosomes. X-linked traits are usually passed from carrier females to their male offspring. Y-linked traits are passed only from male to male.
- Nondisjunction may result in an abnormal number of chromosomes. Abnormal numbers of autosomes usually are lethal.
- A karyotype can identify unusual numbers of chromosomes in an individual.

Vocabulary
karyotype (p. 329)

FOLDABLES™
Study Organizer To help you review patterns of heredity, use the Organizational Study Fold on page 309.

Key Concepts
Summary statements can be used by students to review the major concepts of the chapter.

Biology Online

Visit in.bdol.glencoe.com
/self_check_quiz
/vocabulary_puzzlemaker
/chapter_test
/standardized_test

VOCABULARY PUZZLEMAKER

For additional help with vocabulary, have students access the Vocabulary PuzzleMaker online at in.bdol.glencoe.com/vocabulary_puzzlemaker

FOLDABLES™
Have students use their Foldables to review the content of Section 12.1. On the back of the paper have them practice making a pedigree chart for a trait present in their families. Have them begin with their grandparents and go through the present generation.

Use the ExamView®Pro Test Bank CD-ROM to:
- Create **multiple versions** of tests
- Create **modified** tests with one mouse click for **inclusion** students
- **Edit** existing questions and **add** your own questions
- Build tests aligned with state standards using built-in **State Curriculum Tags**
- Change **English** tests to **Spanish** with one mouse click and vice versa

Chapter 12 Assessment

The Princeton Review *Questions and answers have been aligned and verified by The Princeton Review.*

Vocabulary Review

1. true
2. false—karyotype
3. true
4. true
5. false—sex chromosomes

Understanding Key Concepts

6. A 9. C 12. B
7. B 10. B
8. D 11. D

Constructed Response

13. If the woman's father had the allele on his X chromosome, he would have had hemophilia, but he did not. Thus, the X chromosome she received from him is free of the allele. It is possible, but unlikely, that she received an X chromosome that carries the allele from her mother. In that case, she could pass it to her son.
14. The man could be $I^B i$ and be the father. A blood test can show only that he could possibly be the father, but not that he is the father.
15. People tend to marry within their own ethnic groups, allowing recessive alleles to show up more frequently in the populations.
16. The protein may be one that is transported or used in many systems. Malfunctions of one body system usually affect others.

Thinking Critically

17. Males have only one X chromosome and females have two X chromosomes. A deletion in the X chromosome will affect males because they have only one X chromosome.

334

Vocabulary Review

Review the Chapter 12 vocabulary words listed in the Study Guide on page 333. Determine if each statement is true or false. If false, replace the underlined word with the correct vocabulary word.

1. A <u>carrier</u> is always a heterozygous individual.
2. A <u>pedigree</u> is a chart showing the chromosome pairs of an individual.
3. In <u>polygenic inheritance</u>, there is a wide range of expression of a trait.
4. The phenotype of the heterozygote is intermediate for <u>incomplete dominance</u>.
5. Genes located on <u>autosomes</u> determine the sex of an individual.

Understanding Key Concepts

6. If a trait is X-linked, males pass the X-linked allele to _____ of their daughters.
   A. all C. none
   B. half D. ¼
7. Two parents with normal phenotypes have a daughter who has a genetically inherited disorder. This is an example of a(n) _____ trait in humans.
   A. autosomal dominant
   B. autosomal recessive
   C. sex-linked
   D. polygenic
8. Which of the following disorders would be inherited according to the pedigree shown here?
   A. Tay-Sachs disease
   B. sickle-cell anemia
   C. cystic fibrosis
   D. Huntington's disease
9. Which of the following disorders is likely to be inherited by more males than females?
   A. Huntington's disease
   B. Down syndrome
   C. hemophilia
   D. cystic fibrosis

---

10. A karyotype reveals _____.
    A. an abnormal number of genes
    B. an abnormal number of chromosomes
    C. polygenic traits
    D. multiple alleles for a trait
11. A mother with blood type $I^B i$ and a father with blood type $I^A I^B$ have children. Which of the following genotypes would be possible for their children?
    A. AB C. B
    B. O D. A and C are correct
12. The genotype of the individual represented by this pedigree symbol is _____. Use the letters Y and y to represent alleles.
    A. YY
    B. Yy
    C. yy
    D. YYy

Constructed Response

13. **Open Ended** The brother of a woman's father has hemophilia. Her father was unaffected, but she worries that she may have an affected son. Should she worry? Explain.
14. **Open Ended** If a child has blood type O and its mother has type A, could a man with type B be the father? Why couldn't a blood test be used to prove that he is the father?
15. **Open Ended** Why do certain human genetic disorders, such as sickle-cell anemia, occur more frequently among one ethnic group than another?
16. **Open Ended** How can one gene mutation in a protein such as hemoglobin affect several body systems?

Thinking Critically

17. **Recognize Cause and Effect** Deletion of part of a chromosome may be lethal in a male but only cause a few problems in a female. Explain how that could be possible.

 in.bdol.glencoe.com/chapter_test

---

18. Infant Z's parents' blood types are mother AB, father O or A.
    Infant X's parents' blood types are mother B, father A or O.
19. Students should be able to find information about the necessity of a male heir to carry on the Czar lineage in Russia and the influence of Rasputin on the Czar.

RUBRIC

Evaluating Open-Ended Questions Open-ended assessment questions are graded by using a multilevel rubric that guides you in assessing a student's knowledge of a particular concept. The following rubric is a sample scoring device.

18. Analyze Infant X has blood type O, and infant Z has blood type A. Match the following parents with their child.

Father—blood type O;
Mother—blood type AB.
Father—blood type A;
Mother—blood type B.

19. **REAL WORLD BIOCHALLENGE** Visit in.bdol.glencoe.com to find out more about the role hemophilia played in Russian history during the reign of Czar Nicholas II, especially in regards to Rasputin. Summarize your results in a multimedia presentation for your class.

End-of-Course Assessment Practice

20. A	22. B	24. A
21. B	23. D	25. A

26. Male-pattern baldness inheritance is also influenced by the internal environment (hormones).

27. A female offspring inherits a second X chromosome from her mother. In order for a female to inherit a recessive trait, she must receive a recessive trait from both her father and her mother.

 FAST FILE

Answer Sheet A practice answer sheet can be found on p. 113 of *Unit 4 FAST FILE Resources.*

End-of-Course Assessment Practice

The assessed Indiana standard appears next to the question.

All questions aligned and verified by **The Princeton Review**

Part 1 **Multiple Choice**

Use the diagram to answer questions 20–22

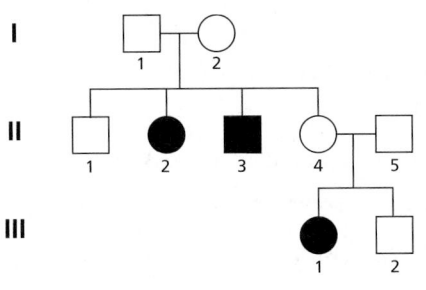

20. Which type of inheritance pattern is shown
1.29 in the above pedigree?
   A. simple recessive
   B. simple dominant
   C. sex-linked inheritance
   D. codominance

21. What is individual II-4's genotype?
1.29 **A.** *AA*   **C.** *aa*
   B. *Aa*   **D.** cannot be determined

22. How many different genotypes are possible
1.29 for individual III-2?
   A. one   **C.** three
   B. two   **D.** cannot be determined

Study the karyotype and answer questions 23–25.

23. What is not normal about the above human karyotype?
   A. There are too many chromosome pairs.
   B. There are too few chromosome pairs.
   C. The sex chromosomes are not paired correctly.
   D. There are three number 21 chromosomes.

24. What is the name of the disorder displayed in the karyotype?
   A. Down syndrome **C.** hemophilia
   B. Turner syndrome **D.** sickle-cell anemia

25. What is the sex of this individual?
   A. male   **C.** cannot be determined
   B. female   **D.** abnormal

Part 2 **Constructed Response/Grid In**

Record your answers on your answer document.

26. Open Ended How does the inheritance of male-pattern baldness differ from other types of
1.29 Mendelian inheritance?

27. Open Ended Explain why a male with a recessive X-linked trait usually produces no female
1.29 offspring with the trait.

 in.bdol.glencoe.com/standardized_test   12.3 COMPLEX INHERITANCE OF HUMAN TRAITS **335**

RUBRIC

SCORE	CRITERIA	SCORE	CRITERIA
4	A correct solution that is supported by well-developed, accurate explanations.	2	A partially correct interpretation and/or solution to the problem.
3	A generally correct solution, but may contain minor flaws in reasoning.	1	A correct solution with no supporting evidence or explanation.
		0	An incorrect solution or no solution is given.

 Indiana Academic Standards

Pages 334–335: B.1.21, B.1.26, B.1.28, B.1.29

Section Objectives	National Science Standards	State/Local Standards	Advanced Lab and Demo Planning
Section 13.1 1 session 1. **Predict** the outcome of a test cross. 2. **Evaluate** the importance of plant and animal breeding to humans.	UCP.2, UCP.3; A.1, A.2; C.2; G.1, G.3	**Indiana Standards** B.1.21, B.1.22, B.1.27	**Student Lab:** Problem-Solving Lab 13.1, p. 339 **Teacher Demonstration:** Quick Demo, p. 338: pictures of pets and pets' parents and offspring, poster board
Section 13.2 1 session 3. **Summarize** the steps used to engineer transgenic organisms. 4. **Give examples** of applications and benefits of genetic engineering.	UCP.2, UCP.3; A.1, A.2; C.2; E.1, E.2; F.1, F.5, F.6; G.1, G.2	**Indiana Standards** B.1.23	**Student Labs:** MiniLab 13.1, p. 343 Problem-Solving Lab 13.2, p. 347 Investigate BioLab, p. 354: See materials below. **Teacher Demonstration:** Quick Demo, p. 342: several vegetables and fruits (corn, strawberries)
Section 13.3 2 sessions 5. **Analyze** how the effort to completely map and sequence the human genome will advance human knowledge. 6. **Predict** future applications of the Human Genome Project.	UCP.2, UCP.3; A.1, A.2; C.2; E.1, E.2; F.1, F.5, F.6; G.1, G.3	**Indiana Standards** B.1.23, B.1.27	**Student Labs:** MiniLab 13.2, p. 350: novel Additional Lab, p. 350: glass slide, red juice, 5 bar codes (2 that match), 2 strands of human hair, T-shirt with spot of red ink, stained slide of female cheek cells, microscope Problem-Solving Lab 13.3, p. 353 **Teacher Demonstration:** Quick Demo, p. 351: human chromosome map
End of Chapter Assessment Student Edition **Study Guide,** p. 357 **Content Assessment,** pp. 358–359		**Indiana Standards** B.1.21, B.1.23, B.1.27	**Student Lab:** Investigate BioLab, p. 354: white paper, colored pencils (red and green), tape, scissors

Key to Teaching Strategies

L1 Level 1 activities should be appropriate for students with learning difficulties.

L2 Level 2 activities should be within the ability range of all students.

L3 Level 3 activities are designed for above-average students.

ELL ELL activities should be within the ability range of English Language Learners.

COOP LEARN
Cooperative Learning activities are designed for small group work.

Legend

Reproducible Masters and Transparencies	Technology
Unit 4 *FAST FILE* Resources Reinforcement and Study Guide in English, p. 125 Reinforcement and Study Guide in Spanish, p. 129 Transparency Worksheets, pp. 135, 139–140 **Reading Essentials for Biology, Section 13.1** **Laboratory Manual,** pp. 75–78 **Section Focus Transparency 32** **Basic Concepts Transparency 19**	**Interactive Chalkboard CD-ROM: Section 13.1 Presentation** **TeacherWorks™ CD-ROM** **Guided Reading Audio Summaries MP3**
Unit 4 *FAST FILE* Resources MiniLab Worksheet, pp. 117–118 BioLab Worksheet, pp. 121–122 Real World BioApplications, pp. 123–124 Reinforcement and Study Guide in English, pp. 126–127 Reinforcement and Study Guide in Spanish, pp. 130–131 Transparency Worksheets, pp. 136, 141–142 **Reading Essentials for Biology, Section 13.2** **Laboratory Manual,** pp. 79–82 **Section Focus Transparency 33** **Reteaching Skills Transparency 22**	**Interactive Chalkboard CD-ROM: Section 13.2 Presentation** **TeacherWorks™ CD-ROM** **Guided Reading Audio Summaries MP3** **Virtual Labs CD-ROM** Virtual Lab: Tracking Grizzlies
Unit 4 *FAST FILE* Resources MiniLab Worksheet, pp. 119–120 Reinforcement and Study Guide in English, p. 128 Reinforcement and Study Guide in Spanish, p. 132 Concept Mapping, p. 133 Critical Thinking/Problem Solving, p. 134 Transparency Worksheet, p. 137 **Reading Essentials for Biology, Section 13.3** **Section Focus Transparency 34**	**Interactive Chalkboard CD-ROM: Section 13.3 Presentation** **TeacherWorks™ CD-ROM** **Guided Reading Audio Summaries MP3**
Unit 4 *FAST FILE* Resources Chapter Assessment, pp. 143–148 Student Recording Sheet, p. 149 **The Princeton Review** Reviewing Biology, pp. 25–26	**Interactive Chalkboard: Chapter 13 Assessment** **MindJogger Videoquizzes DVD/VHS** **Exam*View*® Pro Test Bank CD-ROM** **TeacherWorks™ CD-ROM** **Succeeding on National Standards CD-ROM** in.bdol.glencoe.com /self_check_quiz /vocabulary_puzzlemaker /chapter_test /standardized_test

Indicates materials created specifically for Indiana.

Short on Time?

BIODIGEST The BioDigest at the end of this unit can be used as a(n):

- preview to introduce important unit concepts.
- overview if time does not permit teaching the entire chapter.
- review of key unit concepts.

Understanding the Photo

Using DNA technology, researchers can identify the species and sex of individual bears. Hair is collected from places where bears rub and from hair traps. A hair trap is a single-strand barbed wire corral that contains a scented lure. The barbed wire is placed 50 cm above the ground and hairs are left on the barbs as the bears crawl underneath to reach the lure.

Genetic Technology

What You'll Learn

- You will evaluate the importance of plant and animal breeding to humans.
- You will summarize the steps used to engineer transgenic organisms.
- You will analyze how mapping the human genome is benefitting human life.

Why It's Important

Genetic technology will continue to impact every aspect of your life, from producing improved foods to treating diseases.

Understanding the Photo

DNA technology makes it possible to monitor wildlife populations without handling the animals. Researchers with The Greater Glacier Area Bear DNA Project are identifying and tracking grizzlies, as well as black bears, by analyzing the DNA in hair and bear feces.

Biology Online

Visit in.bdol.glencoe.com **to**
- study the entire chapter online
- access Web Links for more information and activities on genetic technology
- review content with the Interactive Tutor and self-check quizzes

 Two-Minute Chapter Launcher

Activity Have students make a list of dominant, recessive, and sex-linked genetic disorders that they learned about in Chapter 12. All of these disorders may one day be repaired or treated using genetic technology. Review with students the problem with each of the genetic disorders. One example is hemophilia, a disorder where an affected individual produces a defective hemoglobin molecule. This disorder is inherited in a sex-linked pattern. **L2**

 Indiana Academic Standards

Pages 336–337: B.1.21, B.1.27

Section 13.1

Applied Genetics

Indiana Standards Standard B.1.21 Understand and explain that the information passed from parents to offspring is transmitted by means of genes which are coded in DNA molecules.

SECTION PREVIEW

Objectives

Predict the outcome of a test cross.

Evaluate the importance of plant and animal breeding to humans.

Review Vocabulary

hybrid: an organism whose parents have different forms of a trait (p. 255)

New Vocabulary

inbreeding
test cross

FOLDABLES™
Study Organizer

Selective Breeding Make the following Foldable to help you illustrate the pros and cons of selective breeding.

STEP 1 **Fold** a vertical sheet of paper in half from top to bottom.

STEP 2 **Fold** in half from side to side with the fold at the top.

STEP 3 **Unfold** the paper once. **Cut** only the fold of the top flap to make two tabs.

STEP 4 **Turn** the paper vertically and **label** the front tabs as shown.

Selective Breeding Pros
Selective Breeding Cons

Illustrate and Label As you read Chapter 13, list the pros and cons of selective breeding under the appropriate tab.

Selective Breeding

For thousands of years, humans have selected plants and animals with certain qualities, and selectively bred them so that the qualities were common and of more use to humans. The same principle of selective breeding is still used today, in the food we eat and the animals we raise.

From ancient times, breeders have chosen plants and animals with the most desired traits to serve as parents of the next generation. Farmers select seeds from the largest heads of grain, the juiciest berries, and the most disease-resistant clover. They raise the calves of the best milk producer and save the eggs of the best egg-laying hen for hatching. Breeders of plants and animals want to be sure that their populations breed consistently so that each member shows the desired trait. You can read about the selective breeding of domesticated cats on pages 1066–1067 in the *Focus On.*

The process of selective breeding requires time, patience, and several generations of offspring before the desired trait becomes common in a population. Although our ancestors did not realize it, their efforts at selective breeding increased the frequency of a desired allele within a population. Increasing the frequency of desired alleles in a population is the essence of genetic technology.

✓**Reading Check** **Explain** selective breeding in terms of alleles.

13.1   APPLIED GENETICS   **337**

1 Focus

INTERACTIVE CHALKBOARD
PowerPoint® Presentations

Bellringer
Section Focus Transparency 32

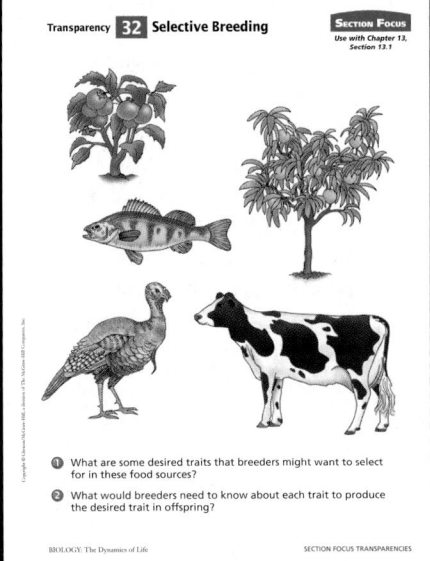

Transparency **32** Selective Breeding

SECTION FOCUS
Use with Chapter 13, Section 13.1

❶ What are some desired traits that breeders might want to select for in these food sources?

❷ What would breeders need to know about each trait to produce the desired trait in offspring?

BIOLOGY: The Dynamics of Life   SECTION FOCUS TRANSPARENCIES

INTERACTIVE CHALKBOARD
with Image Bank

PowerPoint® Presentations

This CD-ROM is an editable Microsoft® PowerPoint® presentation that includes:
• Section presentations
• Section checks
• Image bank
• Hot links to Biology Online
• All transparencies

FOLDABLES™

For an additional Foldables activity idea, see the Chapter 13 Foldables page in *Unit 4 FAST FILE Resources.*

✓**Reading Check** By choosing the parents and knowing their alleles, the breeder uses selective breeding to choose the desired traits that will result in their offspring.

337

RESOURCE MANAGER

Unit 4 FAST FILE Resources
Reinforcement and Study Guide in English, p. 125
Reinforcement and Study Guide in Spanish, p. 129
Transparency Worksheets, pp. 135, 139–140

Reading Essentials for Biology, Section 13.1
Laboratory Manual, pp. 75–78
Section Focus Transparency 32
Basic Concepts Transparency 19

2 Teach

Quick Demo

Identifying Pet Families

Have volunteers bring in pictures of their pets and pets' parents, offspring, and/or siblings. If students don't have access to pictures from several generations of their pets' families, contact a local breeder or pet store for pictures. At least some of the animals should be mixed breeds. Arrange the pictures on poster board and have students attempt to match the animals with their relatives. Discuss the characteristics used to identify the pet families. **L1** **ELL**

Caption Question Answer

Figure 13.1 Answers might include the coloration of the fur, the size and shape of the dog, and personality traits.

Figure 13.1
A pure breed, such as this German shepherd dog, is homozygous for the particular characteristics for which it has been bred. **Infer** *What characteristics might have been bred into this German shepherd dog?*

One example of the effectiveness of selective breeding is seen in a comparison of milk production in cattle in 1947 and 1997. In 1947, an average milk cow produced 4997 pounds of milk per year. In 1997, 50 years later, an average milk cow produced 16 915 pounds of milk in a year, more than three times more milk per cow. Fewer than half the number of cows are now needed to produce the same amount of milk, resulting in savings for dairy farmers.

Figure 13.2
These different cultivars of roses have been hybridized to combine traits such as color, scent, and flower shape.

Inbreeding develops pure lines

To make sure that breeds consistently exhibit a trait and to eliminate any undesired traits from their breeding lines, breeders often use the method of inbreeding. **Inbreeding** is mating between closely related individuals. It results in offspring that are homozygous for most traits. However, inbreeding can bring out harmful, recessive traits because there is a greater chance that two closely related individuals both may carry a harmful recessive allele for the trait.

Horses and dogs are two examples of animals that breeders have developed as pure breeds. A breed (called a cultivar in plants) is a selected group of organisms within a species that has been bred for particular characteristics. For example, the pure breed German shepherd dog in *Figure 13.1* has long hair, is black with a buff-colored base, has a black muzzle, and resembles a wolf.

Hybrids are usually bigger and better

Selective breeding of plants can increase productivity of food for humans. For example, plants that are disease resistant can be crossed with others that produce larger and more numerous fruit. The result is a plant that will produce a lot of fruit and be more disease resistant. Recall that a hybrid is the offspring of parents that have different forms of a trait. When two cultivars or closely related species are crossed, their offspring will be hybrids. Hybrids produced by crossing two purebred plants are often larger and stronger than their parents. Many crop plants such as wheat, corn, and rice, and garden flowers such as roses and dahlias have been developed by hybridization. *Figure 13.2* shows some examples.

 Indiana Academic Standards

Pages 338–339: B.1.21

CHALLENGE ACTIVITY

Test Crosses: *Linguistic* Ask students to write a paragraph explaining why it would not be helpful when conducting a test cross to mate the animal being tested with either homozygous-dominant or heterozygous individuals. Have students use Punnett squares to help with technical explanations. Mating with a homozygous-dominant individual would result in offspring showing the dominant trait. If the animal being tested were heterozygous, mating with a heterozygous animal reduces the chances of an offspring showing the recessive trait from 50% to 25%. **L3**

Determining Genotypes

A good breeder must be careful to determine which plants or animals will have the greatest chances of transmitting a desired trait to the next generation. Choosing the best parents may be difficult. The genotype of an organism that is homozygous recessive for a trait is obvious to an observer because the recessive trait is expressed. However, organisms that are either homozygous dominant or heterozygous for a trait controlled by Mendelian inheritance have the same phenotype. How can a breeder learn which genotype should be used for breeding?

Test crosses can determine genotypes

One way to determine the genotype of an organism is to perform a test cross. A **test cross** is a cross of an individual of unknown genotype with an individual of known genotype. The pattern of observed phenotypes in the offspring can help determine the unknown genotype of the parent. Usually, the parent with the known genotype is homozygous recessive for the trait in question.

Many traits, such as disease vulnerability in roses and progressive blindness in German shepherd dogs, are inherited as recessive alleles. These traits are maintained in a population by carriers of the trait. A carrier, or heterozygous individual, has the same phenotype as an individual that is homozygous dominant.

What are the possible results of a test cross? If a known parent is homozygous recessive and an unknown parent is homozygous dominant for a trait, all of the offspring will be heterozygous and show the dominant trait (be phenotypically dominant), as shown in *Figure 13.3B* on the next page. However, if the organism being

tested is heterozygous, the expected 1:1 phenotypic ratio will be observed, *Figure 13.3C*. If any of the offspring have the undesired trait, the parent in question must be heterozygous. Doing the *Problem-Solving Lab* will show you how to set up and analyze a test cross.

Design an Experiment

When is a test cross practical? How can you tell the genotype of an organism that has a dominant phenotype? There are two ways. The first is through the use of pedigree studies. This technique works well as long as a family is fairly large and records are accurate. The second technique is a test cross. Test crosses help determine whether an organism is homozygous or heterozygous for a dominant trait.

Solve the Problem

Your pet guinea pig has black hair. This trait is dominant and can be represented by a *B* allele. Your neighbor has a white guinea pig. This trait is recessive and can be represented by a *b* allele. You want to breed the two guinea pigs but want all offspring from the mating to be black. You are not sure, however, of the genotype of your black guinea pig and want to find out before starting the breeding program.

Thinking Critically

1. **Infer** What may be the possible genotypes of your black guinea pig? Explain.
2. **Infer** What is the genotype of the white guinea pig? Explain how you are able to tell.
3. **Outline** Outline a procedure that will determine the coat color genotype for your black guinea pig. Include Punnett squares to illustrate the conclusions that you will reach. (Hint: You will be doing a test cross.)
4. **Analyze** What options do you have for breeding all black offspring if you determine that your guinea pig is heterozygous for black color?
5. **Think Critically** Explain why a test cross is not practical when trying to determine human genotypes.

Purpose

Students will describe a procedure for determining a genotype.

Process Skills

think critically, apply concepts, draw a conclusion

Teaching Strategies

Pedigree studies will work in determining genotypes only when there are many offspring and when certain individuals are homozygous recessive. Illustrate this point with a pedigree that shows a small family of two parents (both with a dominant phenotype) and one offspring (with a dominant phenotype). There is no way to predict whether any individuals are heterozygous.

Thinking Critically

1. *BB* or *Bb;* both genotypes show a black phenotype.
2. *bb;* the trait is recessive and the white phenotype can show only when both alleles are recessive.
3. Mate an unknown black guinea pig with a white guinea pig. If all offspring are black, you may conclude that the black guinea pig is *BB*. If any white offspring are born, however, the black guinea pig must be heterozygous.
4. Continue to breed your guinea pig with a white guinea pig but understand that half of all offspring will be white, or breed your black guinea pig with a homozygous black guinea pig. In the last case, all offspring will be black but half will be heterozygous.
5. Because humans usually have only one offspring per birth, it would require too much time for determining genotype. The person would have to mate with a homozygous recessive individual for the trait in question.

Modified Assessment

Skill Show students prepared Punnett squares that illustrate the results of a cross between two heterozygous black guinea pigs and between one heterozygous and one homozygous black. Which mating would be preferred if only black offspring were desired? Use the Performance Task Assessment List for Scientific Drawing in **PASC**, p. 127. **L1**

3 Assess

Figure 13.3
In this test cross of Alaskan malamutes, the known test dog is homozygous recessive for a dwarf allele *(dd)*, and the other dog's genotype is unknown.

? × dd

A The unknown dog can be either homozygous dominant *(DD)* or heterozygous *(Dd)* for the trait.

B If the unknown dog's genotype is homozygous dominant, all of the offspring will be phenotypically dominant.

Homozygous × Homozygous

	DD	dd
	d	d
D	Dd	Dd
D	Dd	Dd

Offspring: all dominant

Dd   Dd

C If the unknown dog's genotype is heterozygous, half the offspring will express the recessive trait and appear dwarf. The other half will express the dominant trait and be of normal size.

Heterozygous × Homozygous

	Dd	dd
	d	d
D	Dd	Dd
d	dd	dd

Offspring: 1/2 dominant 1/2 recessive

Dd   dd

Section Assessment

Understanding Main Ideas

1. A test cross made with a cat that may be heterozygous for a recessive trait produces ten kittens, none of which has the trait. What is the presumed genotype of the cat? Explain.

2. Suppose you want to produce a plant cultivar that has red flowers and speckled leaves. You have two cultivars, each having one of the desired traits. How would you proceed?

3. Why is inbreeding rarely a problem among animals in the wild?

4. Hybrid corn is produced that is resistant to bacterial infection and is highly productive. What might have been the phenotypes of the two parents?

Thinking Critically

5. What effect might selective breeding of plants and animals have on the size of Earth's human population? Why?

SKILL REVIEW

6. **Make and Use Tables** A bull is suspected of carrying a rare, recessive allele. Following a test cross with a homozygous recessive cow, four calves are born, two that express the recessive trait and two that do not. Draw a Punnett square that shows the test cross, and determine the genotype of the bull. For more help, refer to *Make and Use Tables* in the **Skill Handbook**.

340 GENETIC TECHNOLOGY

 in.bdol.glencoe.com/self_check_quiz

Section Assessment

1. The cat is probably homozygous dominant. If it were heterozygous, there would probably have been some offspring with the recessive trait.

2. First, breed the red flower plants among themselves to ensure that they are breeding true. Do the same for the plants with speckled leaves. Then, hybridize the two cultivars by breeding them together.

3. In nature, mate selection is random and the chance that a mate will be closely related is greatly reduced.

4. One parent was highly productive. The other was resistant to bacterial infection.

5. Selective breeding can increase crop size and provide for more nutritious and more disease-resistant crops, and this might increase the human population.

6. Students' Punnett squares should show a cross between homozygous-recessive and heterozygous individuals. Half the offspring will be normal and half will express the recessive trait. Therefore, the bull was heterozygous.

Section 13.2

Recombinant DNA Technology

Cut 'n Paste

Indiana Standards Standard B.1.23 Understand that and describe how inserting, deleting, or substituting DNA segments can alter a gene...

Using an Analogy You have learned that DNA can function like a zipper, opening up to allow replication and transcription. Scientists have found a series of enzymes, from bacteria, that can cut DNA at specific locations, sometimes unzipping the strands as they cut. These enzymes allow scientists to insert genes from other sources into DNA. The glowing plant shown here was created by inserting a firefly gene into the DNA of a tobacco plant.

Think Critically *Predict why a gene from a firefly can function in a tobacco plant.*

Tobacco plant that contains a gene from a firefly

SECTION PREVIEW

Objectives

Summarize the steps used to engineer transgenic organisms.

Give examples of applications and benefits of genetic engineering.

Review Vocabulary
nitrogenous base: a carbon ring structure found in DNA and RNA that is part of the genetic code (p. 282)

New Vocabulary
genetic engineering
recombinant DNA
transgenic organism
restriction enzyme
vector
plasmid
clone

Genetic Engineering

You learned that selective breeding increases the frequency of an allele in a population. You also learned that it may take many generations of breeding for a trait to become homozygous and consistently expressed in the population. **Genetic engineering** is a faster and more reliable method for increasing the frequency of a specific allele in a population. This method involves cutting—or cleaving—DNA from one organism into small fragments and inserting the fragments into a host organism of the same or a different species. You also may hear genetic engineering referred to as recombinant (ree KAHM buh nunt) DNA technology. **Recombinant DNA** is made by connecting, or recombining, fragments of DNA from different sources.

Transgenic organisms contain recombinant DNA

Recombinant DNA can be inserted into a host organism's chromosomes and that organism will use this foreign DNA as if it were its own. Plants and animals that contain functional recombinant DNA from an organism of a different genus are known as **transgenic organisms** because they contain foreign DNA. The glowing tobacco plant shown above contains foreign DNA and is the result of a three-step process that produces a transgenic organism.

Word Origin

transgenic from the Latin word *trans*, meaning "across," and the Greek word *genos*, meaning "race"; A transgenic organism contains genes from another species.

---

1 Focus

INTERACTIVE CHALKBOARD
PowerPoint® Presentations

Bellringer
Section Focus Transparency 33

Transparency **33** Making a New Food

SECTION FOCUS
Use with Chapter 13, Section 13.2

❶ Suppose you could make a better food by combining the traits of these different fruits and vegetables. What traits would you combine?

❷ Describe the new food. Why is it better?

BIOLOGY: The Dynamics of Life · SECTION FOCUS TRANSPARENCIES

Using An Analogy

Think Critically The way genes function is the same in all organisms. When a gene of a firefly is inserted into a tobacco plant, the tobacco plant will produce proteins from the firefly gene just like it would from one of its native genes.

Word Origin

Have students name some examples of transgenic organisms. Some examples include the liger (a combined tiger and lion) and a bacteria with a human gene inserted in its genome.

Indiana Academic Standards

Pages 340–341: B.1.21, B.1.22, B.1.23

RESOURCE MANAGER

Unit 4 *FAST FILE* Resources
MiniLab Worksheet, pp. 117–118
BioLab Worksheet, pp. 121–122
Real World BioApplications, pp. 123–124
Reinforcement and Study Guide in English, pp. 126–127
Reinforcement and Study Guide in Spanish, pp. 130–131

Transparency Worksheets, pp. 136, 141–142
Reading Essentials for Biology, Section 13.2
Laboratory Manual, pp. 79–82
 Section Focus Transparency 33
Reteaching Skills Transparency 22

2 Teach

Discussion

Ask students what genetic changes people might want to engineer into their pets. Students might suggest stamina, intelligence, hair retention, and disease resistance.

Concept Development

To help students remember EcoR1, explain that this enzyme was discovered in the bacterium *Escherichia coli*. "E" comes from *Escherichia*, "co" from *coli*, "R" from restriction enzyme, and "1" indicates that this enzyme was the first restriction enzyme found in this bacterium.

Caption Question Answer
Figure 13.4 The two sticky ends are AATT and TTAA.

Figure 13.4
In the presence of the restriction enzyme *Eco*RI, a double strand of DNA containing the sequence—GAATTC— is cleaved between the G and the A on each strand. **Interpret Scientific Illustrations** *What is the sequence of each sticky end?*

The first step of the process is to isolate the foreign DNA fragment that will be inserted. The second step is to attach the DNA fragment to a carrier. The third step is the transfer into the host organism. Each of these three steps now will be discussed in greater detail.

Restriction enzymes cleave DNA

To isolate a DNA fragment, small pieces of DNA must be cut from a chromosome. In the example of the glowing tobacco plant, the fragment is a section of firefly DNA that codes for a light-producing enzyme. The discovery in the early 1970s of DNA-cleaving enzymes called restriction enzymes made it possible to cut DNA.

Restriction enzymes are bacterial proteins that have the ability to cut both strands of the DNA molecule at a specific nucleotide sequence. There are hundreds of restriction enzymes; each can cut DNA at a specific point in a specific nucleotide sequence. The resulting DNA fragments are different lengths. Cutting DNA with restriction enzymes is similar to cutting a zipper into pieces by cutting only between certain teeth of the zipper. Note in *Figure 13.4* that the same sequence of bases is found on both DNA strands, but in opposite orders. This arrangement is called a palindrome (PA luhn drohm). Palindromes are words or sentences that read the same forward and backward. The words *mom* and *dad* are two examples of palindromes.

Some enzymes produce fragments in which the DNA is cut straight across both strands. These are called blunt ends. Other enzymes, such as the enzyme called *Eco*RI, cut palindromic sequences of DNA by unzipping them for a few nucleotides, as shown in *Figure 13.4*. When this DNA is cut, double-stranded fragments with single-stranded ends are formed. The single-stranded ends have a tendency to join with other single-stranded ends to become double stranded, so they attract DNA they can join with. For this reason, these ends are called sticky ends. This is the key to recombinant DNA because if the same enzyme is used to cleave DNA from two organisms, such as firefly DNA and bacterial DNA, the two pieces of DNA will have matching sticky ends and will join together at these ends. When the firefly DNA joins with bacterial DNA, recombinant DNA is formed. The *MiniLab* on the opposite page models the way restriction enzymes work.

Vectors transfer DNA

Loose fragments of DNA do not readily become part of a host organism's chromosomes, so the fragments are first attached to a carrier that will transport them into the host organism's cells. A **vector** is the means by which DNA from another species can be carried into the host cell. In the case of the transgenic tobacco plant, the light-producing firefly DNA had to be inserted into bacterial DNA before it could be placed inside the plant. The bacterial DNA is the vector.

Vectors may be biological or mechanical. Biological vectors include viruses and plasmids. A **plasmid,** shown in *Figure 13.5*, is a small ring of DNA found in a bacterial cell. The genes it carries are different from those on the larger bacterial chromosome.

Two mechanical vectors carry foreign DNA into a cell's nucleus. One, a micropipette, is inserted into a cell; the other is a microscopic metal bullet coated with DNA that is shot into the cell from a gene gun.

Figure 13.5
Plasmids are small rings of DNA. The large ring is the bacterium's chromosome.

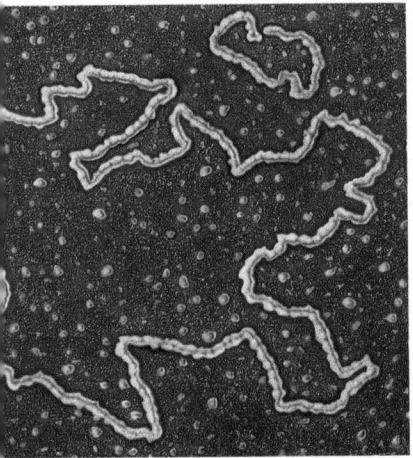

Magnification: unavailable

MiniLab 13.1

Apply Concepts

Matching Restriction Enzymes to Cleavage Sites Many restriction enzymes cut palindromic sequences of DNA that result in single-stranded, dangling sequences of DNA. These sticky ends can pair with complementary bases in a plasmid or a piece of viral DNA.

DNA fragment

Procedure

1 Copy the data table and DNA sequences below.

Data Table

Restriction Enzyme	Cutting Pattern of Enzyme	Cleaved Fragments of DNA	DNA Sequence this Enzyme Will Cut
EcoRI	-G A A T T C- -C T T A A G-	-G A A T T C- -C T T A A G-	
BamHI	-G G A T C C- -C C T A G G-		
HindIII	-A A G C T T- -T T C G A A-		
KpnI	-G G T A C C- -C C A T G G-		

DNA Sequences

A. -C A G G A T C C C A T G -
   | | | | | | | | | | | | |
  -C T C C T A G G G T A C-

B. -G A C T A G G T A C C A A-
   | | | | | | | | | | | | |
  -C T G A T C C A T G G T T-

C. -G C A G A A T T C G A T C-
   | | | | | | | | | | | | |
  -C G T C T T A A G C T A G-

D. -A A G C T T G A C T A
   | | | | | | | | | | |
  -T T C G A A C T G A T

2 Fill in the third column. *Eco*RI is done for you. Then, fill in the letter of the DNA sequence that each restriction enzyme will cut.

Analysis

1. **Use Models** Construct a DNA sequence that would be cut twice by *Hind*III.
2. **Analyze** Record the DNA sequence of a piece of viral DNA if its ends would "stick to" a piece of DNA that was cut with *Bam*HI.
3. **Draw Conclusions** Are restriction enzymes specific as to where they cleave DNA? Explain and give an example.

343

Data Table

Restriction Enzyme	Cutting Pattern of Enzyme	Cleaved Fragments of DNA	Sequence Enzyme Will Cut
EcoRI	-G A A T T C- -C T T A A G-	-G A A T T C- -C T T A A G-	C
BamHI	-G G A T C C- -C C T A G G-	-G G A T C C- -C C T A G G-	A
HindIII	-A A G C T T- -T T C G A A-	-A A G C T T- -T T C G A A-	D
KpnI	-G G T A C C- -C C A T G G-	-G G T A C C- -C C A T G G-	B

INVESTIGATE BioLab The BioLab at the end of the chapter can be used at this point in the lesson.

Reading Check Gene clones are genetically identical copies of DNA molecules.

Virtual Lab

CD-ROM Students will use biotechnology to determine the whereabouts of a bear missing from a zoo in *Tracking Grizzlies*.

Figure 13.6
Foreign DNA is inserted into a plasmid vector. The recombined plasmid then carries the foreign DNA into the bacterial cell, where it replicates independently of the bacterial chromosome. If the foreign DNA contained a gene for human growth hormone, each cell will make the hormone, which can be used to treat patients with dwarfism.

Insertion into a vector

As you have learned, if a plasmid and foreign DNA have been cleaved with the same restriction enzyme, the ends of each will match and they will join together, reconnecting the plasmid ring. The foreign DNA is recombined into a plasmid or viral DNA with the help of a second enzyme. You can model this process in the *BioLab* at the end of this chapter.

Gene cloning

After the foreign DNA has been inserted into the plasmid, the recombined DNA is transferred into a bacterial cell. The plasmid is capable of replicating separately from the bacterial host and can produce up to 500 copies per bacterial cell. An advantage to using bacterial cells to clone DNA is that they reproduce quickly; therefore, millions of bacteria are produced and each bacterium contains hundreds of recombinant DNA molecules. **Clones** are genetically identical copies. Each identical recombinant DNA molecule is called a gene clone.

Plasmids also can be used to deliver genes to animal or plant cells, which incorporate the recombinant DNA. Each time the host cell divides it copies the recombinant DNA along with its own. The host cell can produce the protein encoded on the recombinant DNA. Scientists can study the function of this protein in cells that don't normally produce such proteins. Scientists also can produce mutant forms of a protein and determine how that mutation alters the protein's function within the cell.

Using other vectors, recombinant DNA can be inserted into yeast, plant, and animal cells. *Figure 13.6* summarizes the formation and cloning of recombinant DNA in a bacterial host cell.

Reading Check **Explain** what is meant by a gene clone.

Cloning of animals

So far, you have read about cloning one gene. For decades, scientists attempted to expand the technique from a gene to an entire animal. The most famous cloned animal is Dolly, the sheep, first cloned in 1997. Since then, various mammals including goats, mice, cattle, and pigs have been cloned. Although their techniques are inefficient, scientists are coming closer to perfecting the process of cloning animals. One of the benefits for humans in cloning animals is that ranchers and dairy farmers could clone particularly productive, healthy animals to increase yields.

344 GENETIC TECHNOLOGY

CHALLENGE ACTIVITY

Knockout Mice Mice with mutant genes are particularly valuable to scientists studying human diseases. Using a grant, scientists have developed what they call "knockout mice." Have students who need an additional challenge find out how these mice are produced and how scientists study the effect of missing genes on genetic disorders in the mice. **L3**

Indiana Academic Standards

Pages 344–345: B.1.23

Polymerase chain reaction

In order to replicate DNA outside living organisms, a method called polymerase chain reaction (PCR) has been developed. This method uses heat to separate DNA strands from each other. An enzyme isolated from a heat-loving bacterium is used to replicate the DNA when the appropriate nucleotides are added in a PCR machine. The machine repeatedly replicates the DNA, making millions of copies in less than a day. Because the machine uses heat to separate the DNA strands and cycles over and over to replicate the DNA, it is called a thermocycler.

PCR has become one of the most powerful tools for molecular biologists. The technique is essential to the analysis of bacterial, plant, and animal DNA, including human DNA. PCR has helped bring molecular genetics into crime investigations and the diagnosis of infectious diseases such as AIDS. PCR can help doctors identify extremely small amounts of HIV in blood or the lymphatic system.

Sequencing DNA

Another application of genetic engineering is to provide pure DNA for use in determining the sequence or correct order of the DNA bases. This information can allow scientists to identify mutations.

In DNA sequencing, millions of copies of a double-stranded DNA fragment are cloned using PCR. Then, the strands are separated from each other. The single-stranded fragments are placed in four different test tubes, one for each DNA base. Each tube contains four normal nucleotides (A,C,G,T) and an enzyme that can catalyze the synthesis of a complementary strand. One nucleotide in each tube is tagged with a different fluorescent color. The reactions produce complementary strands of varying lengths. These strands are separated according to size by gel electrophoresis (ih lek troh fuh REE sus), producing a pattern of fluorescent bands in the gel. The bands are visualized using a laser scanner or UV light. How do the DNA fragments separate from each other in the gel? See *Figure 13.8* on the next page to find out.

Applications of DNA Technology

Once it became possible to transfer genes from one organism to another, large quantities of hormones and other products could be produced. How is this technology of use to humans? The main areas proposed for recombinant bacteria are in industry, medicine, and agriculture.

Recombinant DNA in industry

Many species of bacteria have been engineered to produce chemical compounds used by humans. Scientists have modified the bacterium *E. coli* to produce the expensive indigo dye that is used to color denim blue jeans, like those shown in *Figure 13.*7.

Figure 13.7
Genetically modified bacteria produce the blue dye that colors denim blue jeans.

Purpose

Students will learn how gel electrophoresis separates DNA fragments of different sizes.

Background

Gel electrophoresis is a basic technique used in the preparation of DNA samples for other techniques such as DNA sequencing.

Teaching Strategies

■ Give students several paper "DNA fragments" of different sizes. Have them draw what a gel electrophoresis of these fragments would look like. Make sure they indicate at which end of the gel the fragments were added. **L1**

■ Have students describe orally the steps necessary to run a gel.

Visual Learning

Use colored chalk to demonstrate different-sized DNA fragments that have been run in a gel.

Critical Thinking

DNA sequencing can be done only on small pieces of DNA. Gel electrophoresis separates the small pieces of DNA from large pieces before sequencing takes place.

Indiana Academic Standards

Pages 346–347: B.1.23

346

![INSIDE STORY]

Gel Electrophoresis

Figure 13.8

Restriction enzymes are the perfect tools for cutting DNA. However, once the DNA is cut, a scientist needs to determine exactly what fragments have been formed. After DNA fragments have been separated on a gel, many other techniques, such as DNA sequencing, can be used to specifically identify a DNA fragment.

Critical Thinking *Why might gel electrophoresis be an important step before DNA sequencing can be done?*

The gel that contains separated DNA fragments is treated with a dye that glows under ultraviolet light, allowing the bands to be studied.

A **Restriction enzymes** Either one or several restriction enzymes is added to a sample of DNA. The enzymes cut the DNA into fragments.

DNA fragments

Gel

B **The gel** With a consistency that is firmer than dessert gelatin, the gel is molded so that small wells form at one end. Small amounts of the fragmented DNA are placed into these wells.

D **The fragments move** The negatively charged DNA fragments travel toward the positive end. The smaller the fragment, the faster it moves through the gel. The smallest fragments move the farthest from the well.

Power source

Negative end

Positive end

Completed gel

Shorter fragments

Longer fragments

C **An electric field** The gel is placed in a solution and an electric field is applied making one end of the gel positive and the other end negative.

346 GENETIC TECHNOLOGY

![PROJECT]

Enzyme Model Have students build a model demonstrating the use of restriction enzymes on DNA. They could use various materials to represent the DNA nucleotides, such as colored pushpins or colored paper clips.

L2 **ELL** **COOP LEARN**

The production of cheese, laundry detergents, pulp and paper production, and sewage treatment have all been enhanced by the use of recombinant DNA techniques that increase enzyme activity, stability, and specificity. Research is currently going on to develop high-protein corn with protein levels comparable to beef and to develop a process for making automobile fuel from discarded cornstalks.

Recombinant DNA in medicine

Pharmaceutical companies already are producing molecules made by recombinant DNA to treat human diseases. Recombinant bacteria are used in the production of human growth hormone to treat pituitary dwarfism. Also, the human gene for insulin is inserted into a bacterial plasmid by genetic engineering techniques. Recombinant bacteria produce large quantities of insulin. Human antibodies, hormones, vaccines, enzymes, and various compounds needed for diagnosis and treatment have been made using recombinant DNA. Read about engineered vaccines in *Biotechnology* at the end of this chapter.

Transgenic animals

Scientists can study diseases and the role specific genes play in an organism by using transgenic animals. Because mice reproduce quickly, they often are used for transgenic studies. Mouse chromosomes also are similar to human chromosomes. In addition, scientists know the locations of many genes on mouse chromosomes. The roundworm *Caenorhabditis elegans* is another organism with well-understood genetics that is used for transgenic studies. A third animal commonly used for transgenic studies is the fruit fly, *Drosophila melanogaster.*

Problem-Solving Lab 13.2

Think Critically

How might gene transfer be verified? When you spray weeds with a chemical herbicide, they die. The problem with herbicides, however, is that they often get sprayed accidentally onto crops, and they also die. Glyphosate is the active ingredient in some herbicides. A certain gene will confer resistance to glyphosate. If this gene can be genetically engineered into crop plants, they will survive when sprayed with this herbicide.

Solve the Problem

In the diagram below, plants A and D are sensitive to glyphosate and plants B and E are naturally resistant. Plants C and F have been treated with recombinant DNA, but it isn't known if the treatment worked. Plants A, B, and C are sprayed with water. Plants D, E, and F are sprayed with a herbicide containing glyphosate.

Sprayed with water

No resistance to herbicide | Resistance to herbicide | Received gene for resistance

Sprayed with herbicide

Thinking Critically

1. **Predict** Assume that the transfer of glyphosate resistance was successful in plant F. Predict whether each of plants D, E, and F will remain healthy after being sprayed with glyphosate. Explain your prediction.
2. **Infer** Will plant F remain healthy if the transfer of glyphosate resistance was not successful?
3. **Define Operationally** Which plants are transgenic organisms? Explain your answer.
4. **Use Variables, Constants, and Controls** Why were plants A, B, and C sprayed with water?

Purpose

Students will analyze the results of an experiment designed to illustrate genetic transfer.

Process Skills

think critically, analyze information, apply concepts, draw a conclusion, interpret data, predict

Background

Glyphosate blocks the synthesis of amino acids phenylalanine, tyrosine, and tryptophan. Cells unable to form these amino acids die. Glyphosate inhibits the enzyme EPSP synthase from synthesizing these amino acids.

Teaching Strategies

- You may wish to discuss the technique that is used to transfer the resistant gene to its host plant. The organism or vector is *Agrobacterium tumefaciens*, a bacterium that infects plants.
- Make sure that students understand that plants sprayed with glyphosate will die if they do not contain genes making them resistant to the chemical.
- Students may work in small cooperative groups to complete this activity.

Thinking Critically

1. Plants E and F will remain healthy because they have the gene that imparts resistance. Plant D will die because it is not resistant to glyphosate.
2. If resistance is not transferred, plant F will die because it is not resistant to glyphosate.
3. Plants C and F are transgenic organisms. They contain foreign DNA.
4. Plants A, B, and C were controls. They were sprayed with water to show that spraying does not transfer resistance to the chemical.

Assessment

Performance Have students design and carry out an experiment to test whether glyphosate affects seeds of plants. Use the Performance Task Assessment List for Designing an Experiment in **PASC**, p. 95. **L3**

3 Assess

Extension
Interested students can look into the applications of protein engineering and computer modeling to produce modified natural proteins or to create entirely new proteins. **L3**

Assessment

Knowledge Have students summarize the formation of recombinant DNA. **L2**

Reading Check In developing countries, high-nutrient crops would help treat the malnutrition that is present.

On the same farm in Scotland that produced the cloned sheep Dolly, a transgenic sheep was produced that contained the corrected human gene for hemophilia A. Recall from Chapter 12 that people with hemophilia are missing a protein-clotting factor in their blood. This human gene inserted into the sheep chromosomes allows the production of the clotting protein in the sheep's milk. The protein then can be separated for use by patients with hemophilia. This farm also has produced transgenic sheep which produce a protein that helps lungs inflate and function properly. The protein is given to people with emphysema, a lung disease associated mainly with cigarette smoking.

Figure 13.9
Soybeans, corn, cotton, and canola were the most frequently grown, genetically modified (GM) crops in 2000, covering 16 percent of the 271 million hectares devoted to those four crops.

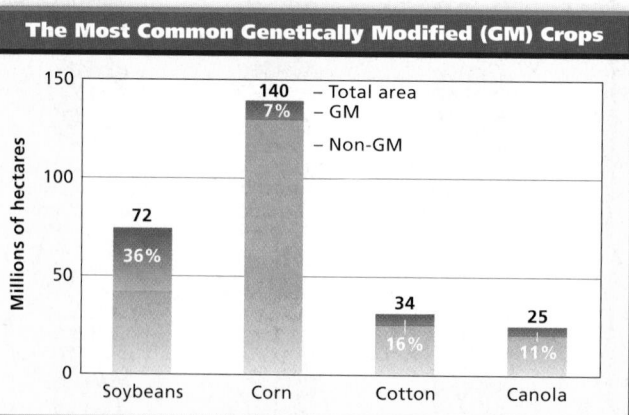

The Most Common Genetically Modified (GM) Crops

Recombinant DNA in agriculture
Recombinant DNA technology has been highly utilized in the agricultural and food industries. Crops have been developed that are better tasting, stay fresh longer, and are protected from disease and insect infestations. Corn, broccoli, cotton, and potatoes have been developed to produce *Bt* toxin from a bacterial gene, which makes them resistant to certain insect pests. Various plants have been made resistant to a herbicide used to rid the fields of unwanted weeds. You can learn more about this herbicide in the *Problem-Solving Lab* on the previous page. Canola plants have been modified so they make a higher yield of oil. Currently, research is increasing the amounts of various vitamins in certain crops. These plants could be grown and used in developing countries to supplement local diets that are vitamin deficient. Other research includes the development of peanuts and soybeans that do not cause allergic reactions, a problem for a significant number of people. *Figure 13.9* shows a graph of production acreage for the most common genetically modified crops.

Reading Check **Explain** why high-nutrient crops are important to humans.

Section Assessment

Understanding Main Ideas
1. How are transgenic organisms different from natural organisms of the same species?
2. How are sticky ends important in making recombinant DNA?
3. How does gel electrophoresis separate fragments of DNA?
4. Explain two ways in which recombinant bacteria are used for human applications.

Thinking Critically
5. Many scientists consider genetic engineering to be simply an efficient method of selective breeding. Explain.

SKILL REVIEW
6. **Get the Big Picture** Order the steps in producing recombinant DNA in a bacterial plasmid. For more help, refer to *Get the Big Picture* in the **Skill Handbook**.

348 GENETIC TECHNOLOGY

 in.bdol.glencoe.com/self_check_quiz

Section Assessment

1. Transgenic organisms contain DNA from other sources.
2. Sticky ends allow the cleaved DNA to join to complementary single strands on DNA molecules from another organism.
3. Gel electrophoresis separates the DNA fragments based on size and charge.

Smaller fragments travel farther in the gel.
4. Recombinant bacteria produce human growth hormone, insulin, and phenylalanine. They are also used for better crop production such as frost-resistant strawberries.
5. Answers may include that both genetic

engineering and selective breeding involve increasing the frequency of a desired gene in a population by human intervention.
6. Cleave the plasmid and foreign DNA with the same restriction enzyme, and the sticky ends will join, reconnecting the plasmid ring.

Section 13.3

The Human Genome

Indiana Standards Standard B.1.27 Explain that the similarity of human DNA sequences and the resulting similarity in cell chemistry and anatomy identify human beings as a unique species, different from all others. Likewise, understand that every other species has its own characteristic DNA sequence.

On the Cutting Edge

Using Prior Knowledge You have already learned about several genetic disorders that affect humans— Huntington's disease, cystic fibrosis, Tay Sach's disease, and sickle-cell anemia. In the last section, you learned that transgenic bacteria are being designed to treat disorders such as hemophilia and dwarfism. Scientists hope someday to be able to treat more disorders. To accomplish this, they are sequencing the entire human genome.

Research As a class, build a reference file of the latest discoveries by the Human Genome Project. Use library resources or visit in.bdol.glencoe.com to collect information. Update the file throughout the school year.

Color-enhanced LM Magnification: 410×

Sickled red blood cells

SECTION PREVIEW

Objectives

Analyze how the effort to completely map and sequence the human genome will advance human knowledge.

Predict future applications of the Human Genome Project.

Review Vocabulary
mutation: a change in the DNA sequence of an individual (p. 296)

New Vocabulary
human genome
linkage map
gene therapy

Word Origin

genome from the Greek word *genos,* meaning "race"; A genome is the total number of genes in an individual.

Mapping and Sequencing the Human Genome

In 1990, scientists in the United States organized the Human Genome Project (HGP). It is an international effort to completely map and sequence the **human genome,** the approximately 35 000–40 000 genes on the 46 human chromosomes. In February of 2001, the HGP published its working draft of the 3 billion base pairs of DNA in most human cells. The sequence of chromosomes 21 and 22 was finished by May 2000. The *MiniLab* on the next page gives you an idea of the size of the human genome.

Linkage maps

The locations of thousands of the total number of genes have been mapped to particular chromosomes, and half of the genome has been completely sequenced. However, scientists still don't know the exact locations of all the genes on the chromosomes.

The genetic map that shows the relative locations of genes on a chromosome is called a **linkage map.** The historical method used to assign genes to a particular human chromosome was to study linkage data from human pedigrees. Recall from your study of meiosis that crossing over occurs during prophase I. As a result of crossing over, gametes and, thus, offspring can have a combination of alleles not found in either parent.

13.3 THE HUMAN GENOME **349**

1 Focus

INTERACTIVE CHALKBOARD
PowerPoint® Presentations

Bellringer
Section Focus Transparency 34

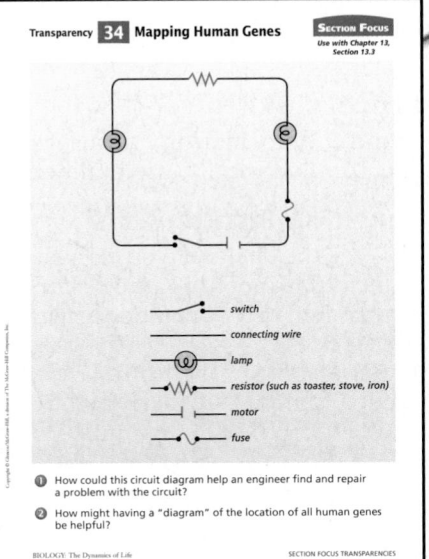

Transparency **34** Mapping Human Genes   SECTION FOCUS
Use with Chapter 13, Section 13.3

- switch
- connecting wire
- lamp
- resistor (such as toaster, stove, iron)
- motor
- fuse

❶ How could this circuit diagram help an engineer find and repair a problem with the circuit?

❷ How might having a "diagram" of the location of all human genes be helpful?

BIOLOGY: The Dynamics of Life   SECTION FOCUS TRANSPARENCIES

Using Prior Knowledge

Research Scientists are using technology described in this section to sequence the individual nucleotide sequence of the human genome in order to gain the sequence of both normal genes and those in genetic disorders. Knowing the sequences may help treat or cure genetic disorders.

RESOURCE MANAGER

Unit 4 *FAST FILE* Resources
MiniLab Worksheet, pp. 119–120
Reinforcement and Study Guide in English, p. 128
Reinforcement and Study Guide in Spanish, p. 132
Concept Mapping, p. 133

Critical Thinking/Problem Solving, p. 134
Transparency Worksheet, p. 137
Reading Essentials for Biology, Section 13.3
 Section Focus Transparency 34

Indiana Academic Standards

Pages 348–349: B.1.23, B.1.27

2 Teach

Purpose
Students will estimate the size of the human genome using an analogy.

Process Skills
acquire information, interpret data, think critically, use numbers

Teaching Strategies
- Place the data table on an overhead projector and work through each calculation with students.
- Photocopy a page from a novel for students to use. Advise them of the total number of pages in the book.

Expected Results
Sample data: A = 80; B = 45; C = 3600; D = 1800; E = 400; F = 720 000; G = 4167

Analysis
1. Average several pages to arrive at the total characters per page.
2. The human genome is made up of 3 billion bases.
3. DNA bases are paired. Thus, the genome is expressed in pairs so the number of characters must be expressed in pairs.
4. using sample data: a. 4167 books, b. 4.17 books

Modified Assessment
Portfolio Have students calculate the number of base pairs on each chromosome, assuming that all chromosomes are the same length. Use the Performance Task Assessment List for Using Math in Science in **PASC**, p. 101. **L1**

MiniLab 13.2

Use Numbers

Storing the Human Genome It has been estimated that the human genome consists of three billion nitrogenous base pairs. How much room would all of the genetic information in one cell take up if it were printed in a 400-page novel?

Procedure
1. Copy the right column of the data table marked "Letters and Numbers."
2. Select a random page from a novel.
3. Follow the directions in the table. Record your calculations in your data table.

Data Table

Directions	Letters and Numbers
A. Count the number of characters (letters, punctuation marks, and spaces) across one entire line of your selected page.	
B. Count the number of lines on the page.	
C. Calculate the number of characters on the page. (Multiply A × B.)	
D. Let one nitrogenous base equal one character. Knowing that DNA is made of nitrogenous base pairs, divide C by 2.	
E. Record the number of pages in your novel.	
F. Calculate the number of base pairs in your novel. (Multiply E × D.)	
G. Calculate the number of books the size of your novel needed to hold the human genome. (Divide 3 billion by F.)	

Analysis
1. **Critique** What changes could be taken to improve the accuracy of this activity at steps A–C?
2. **Think Critically** What assumption is being made at step G?
3. **Analyze** Explain the logic for step D.
4. a. **Use Numbers** How many books the size of your novel would be needed to store the human genome?
   b. **Use Numbers** How many books the size of your novel would be needed to store a typical bacterial genome? Assume there are three million base pairs in the genome of a bacterium.

The frequency with which these alleles occur together is a measure of the distance between the genes. Genes that cross over frequently must be farther apart than genes that rarely cross over. Recall from Chapter 10 that the percentage of crossed-over traits appearing in offspring can be used to determine the relative position of genes on the chromosome, and thus, to create a linkage map.

Because humans have only a few offspring compared with the larger numbers of offspring in some other species, and because a human generation time is so long, mapping by linkage data is extremely inefficient. Biotechnology now has provided scientists with new methods of mapping genes. Using polymerase chain reaction (PCR), millions of copies of DNA fragments are cloned in a matter of a few hours. These fragments contain genetic markers that are spread throughout the genome. A genetic marker is a segment of DNA with an identifiable physical location on a chromosome and whose inheritance can be followed. A marker can be a gene, or it can be some section of DNA with no known function. Because DNA segments that are near each other on a chromosome tend to be inherited together, markers are often used as indirect ways of tracking the inheritance pattern of a gene that has not yet been identified, but whose approximate location is known.

Sequencing the human genome
The difficult job of sequencing the human genome is begun by cleaving samples of DNA into fragments using restriction enzymes, as described earlier in this chapter. Then, each individual fragment is cloned and sequenced. The cloned fragments are aligned in the proper

---

Additional Lab

Crime Analysis

Purpose
Students will solve a crime using human genetics and DNA technology.

Materials 🔬 ✋ 📷 🧤

glass slide, red juice, 5 bar codes (2 that match), 2 strands of human hair (blond and dark), T-shirt with spot of red ink, stained slide of female cheek cells, microscope

Preparation
Table 1: hair from the scene; Table 2: shirt with a blood stain (red ink) and a slide with two drops of juice to represent blood typing (no clotting with the addition of anti-A and anti-B sera); Table 3: slide of stained cheek cells with microscope pointer on a Barr body; Table 4: bar code representing the DNA fingerprint of blood from the crime scene (one of two that match). Place a bar code in each of four envelopes marked: blond female, type O blood (matching bar code); blond male, type B blood; dark-haired male, type O blood; and dark-haired male, type B blood.

order by overlapping matching sequences, thus determining the sequence of a longer fragment. Automated machines can perform this work, greatly increasing the speed of map development.

Applications of the Human Genome Project

As chromosome maps are made, how can they be used? Improved techniques for prenatal diagnosis of human disorders, use of gene therapy, and development of new methods of crime detection are areas currently being researched.

Diagnosis of genetic disorders

One of the most important benefits of the HGP has been the diagnosis of genetic disorders. The DNA of people with and without a genetic disorder is compared to find differences that are associated with the disorder. Once it is clearly understood where a gene is located (see *Figure 13.10*) and that a mutation in the gene causes the disorder, a diagnosis can be made for an individual, even before birth. Cells are obtained from the fluid surrounding the fetus. DNA is isolated and PCR is used to analyze the area where the mutation is found. If the gene is normal, the PCR product will be a standard size—a deviation means a mutation is present. For some diagnostic tests, the DNA must be analyzed using gel electrophoresis only. This is usually when the disease-causing mutation alters a restriction enzyme-cutting site, producing DNA fragments of different sizes than normal. Thus, when DNA from fetal cells is examined and found to have the mutation associated with the disorder, the fetus will develop the disorder.

Stained LM Magnification: 500×

Figure 13.10
Fluorescently labeled complementary DNA for the gene to be mapped is made and added to metaphase chromosomes. The labeled DNA binds to the gene and its location is shown as a glowing spot. In this photo, six genes are mapped simultaneously. A karyotype can be made for clarity.

BIOTECHNOLOGY CAREERS

Forensic Analyst

Would you like to work in a crime laboratory, helping police and investigators figure out "who done it?" Then consider a career as a forensic analyst.

Skills for the Job

Forensic analysts include identification technicians (who work with fingerprints), crime lab technologists (who use microscopes, lasers, and other tools to analyze tissue samples and other evidence), and medical examiners (who perform autopsies to determine the cause of death). Most forensic analysts work in labs operated by the federal, state, or local government. Requirements include on-the-job training for technicians, one or more college degrees that include crime lab work for technologists, and a medical degree for medical examiners. Analysts hired by the FBI complete an additional 14-week training program.

 For more careers in related fields, visit
in.bdol.glencoe.com/careers

Purpose

Students will analyze DNA fingerprints to determine the identity of an unidentified soldier.

Process Skills

think critically, analyze information, apply concepts, compare and contrast, interpret data, interpret scientific illustrations

Teaching Strategies

■ Advise students that photos of DNA fingerprints are X rays of electrophoresis results. The DNA is treated with radioactive dyes that expose X-ray film.

■ Remind students that each person has unique DNA (except for identical twins). Each contains DNA from both parental DNA. Ask them to recall the number of chromosomes contributed at fertilization by each parent to future offspring.

■ Photocopy the diagram for student use so that they do not write in the book.

■ Suggest that a ruler be placed along the bottom edge of each band for ease in matching.

Thinking Critically

1. Parents C and D; half of the soldier's DNA matched parent C and the other half matched parent D.
2. 50% from each parent; each parent contributes half of his or her DNA to an offspring.
3. Yes, half of the soldier's DNA would match the living parent's half.

Caption Question Answer

Figure 13.11 The virus has been genetically engineered and therefore it is a variant without the ability to cause disease in humans.

Gene therapy

Individuals who inherit a serious genetic disorder may now have hope—gene therapy. **Gene therapy** is the insertion of normal genes into human cells to correct genetic disorders. This technology is still experimental, but ongoing trials involving over 3000 patients are attempts to treat genetic and acquired diseases. Trials that treat SCID (severe combined immunodeficiency syndrome) have been the most successful. In this disorder, a person's immune system is shut down and even slight colds can be life-threatening. In gene therapy for this disorder, the cells of the immune system are removed from the patient's bone marrow, and the functional gene is added to them. The modified cells are then injected back into the patient. *Figure 13.11* shows this process.

Other trials involve gene therapy for cystic fibrosis, sickle-cell anemia, hemophilia, and other genetic disorders. Research is also going on to use gene therapy to treat cancer, heart disease, and AIDS. It is hoped that in the next decade DNA technology that uses gene therapy will be developed to treat many different disorders.

DNA fingerprinting

Law-enforcement workers use unique fingerprint patterns to determine whether suspects have been at a crime scene. In the past ten years, biotechnologists have developed a method that determines DNA fingerprints. DNA fingerprinting can be used to convict or acquit individuals of criminal offenses because every person is genetically unique.

Chromosomes consist of genes that are separated by segments of noncoding DNA, DNA that doesn't code for proteins. The genes follow fairly standard patterns from person to person, but the noncoding segments produce distinct combinations of patterns unique to each individual. In fact, DNA patterns can be used like fingerprints to identify the person (or other organism) from whom they came. DNA fingerprinting works because no

Figure 13.11
In SCID gene therapy, bone marrow cells are removed from a patient's hipbone and grown in a flask. Genetically engineered viruses containing a normal SCID gene are added. The bone marrow cells insert the normal gene into their DNA. When the modified cells are returned to the patient's bone marrow, the gene begins to function. **Think Critically** *Why doesn't the virus cause disease in the patient?*

Cell culture flask
Bone marrow cells
Add virus with functioning SCID gene
Gene
Hip bone
Bone marrow cell with integrated gene

Assessment

Knowledge Ask students: Could the unidentified soldier be identified if he were adopted? not unless his birth parents are known Can the unknown soldier from WW I be identified through DNA technology? Not likely; his parents must be deceased. Use the Performance Task Assessment List for Writing in Science in **PASC**, p. 159. **L1**

two individuals (except identical twins) have the same DNA sequences, and because all cells (except gametes) of an individual have the same DNA. You can read about a real example of DNA fingerprinting in the *Problem-Solving Lab.*

In a forensic application of DNA fingerprinting, a small DNA sample is obtained from a suspect and from blood, hair, skin, or semen found at the crime scene. The DNA, which includes the unique noncoding segments, is cut into fragments with restriction enzymes. The fragments are separated by gel electrophoresis, then further analyzed. If the samples match, the suspect most likely is guilty.

DNA technology has been used to clone DNA from many sources. Geneticists are using PCR to clone DNA from mummies and analyze it in order to better understand ancient life. Abraham Lincoln's DNA has been taken from the tips of a lock of his hair and studied for evidence of a possible genetic disorder. The DNA from fossils has been analyzed and used to compare extinct species with living species, or even two extinct species with each other. The uses of DNA technology are unlimited.

☑ **Reading Check** **Explain** why an individual's DNA fingerprint is so unique if humans all have similar genes.

Problem-Solving Lab 13.3

Apply Concepts

How is identification made from a DNA fingerprint? DNA fingerprint analysis requires a sample of DNA from a person, living or dead. First the DNA is cut into smaller segments with enzymes. Then the segments are separated according to size using gel electrophoresis. When stained, the DNA segments appear as colored bands that form a DNA fingerprint.

Solve the Problem

A U.S. soldier from the Vietnam War who had been placed in the Tomb of the Unknowns at Arlington National Cemetery was identified through DNA fingerprinting. The soldier could have been one of four individuals. A DNA sample from his body was analyzed. The DNA from the parents of the four possible soldiers was analyzed. The diagram

shows a DNA fingerprint pattern analysis similar to the one that was actually done. Find the match between the soldier's DNA fingerprint pattern and those of his parents.

Thinking Critically

1. **Draw Conclusions** Which parental DNA matched the soldier's DNA? Explain.
2. **Use Numbers** What percent of the soldier's DNA matched his father's DNA? His mother's? Explain.
3. **Think Critically** Could an exact identification have been made with only one parent's DNA? Explain.

Section Assessment

Understanding Main Ideas
1. What is the Human Genome Project?
2. Compare a linkage map and a sequencing map.
3. What is the goal of gene therapy?
4. Explain why DNA fingerprinting can be used as evidence in law enforcement.

Thinking Critically
5. Describe some possible benefits of the Human Genome Project.

SKILL REVIEW

6. **Get the Big Picture** Suppose a SCID patient has been treated with gene therapy. The therapy has involved the insertion of a normal allele into the patient's bone marrow cells using a virus vector. If successful, does this person still run the risk of passing the disorder to his or her offspring? Explain. For more help, refer to *Get the Big Picture* in the **Skill Handbook.**

 in.bdol.glencoe.com/self_check_quiz

13.3 THE HUMAN GENOME **353**

Section Assessment

1. an international effort to completely map and sequence the human genome
2. A sequencing map shows the sequence of DNA bases; a linkage map shows the position of genes on a chromosome.
3. the insertion of normal alleles into human cells to correct genetic disorders
4. The DNA of every individual, except identical twins, is unique. It can be used to identify individuals with great accuracy.
5. If the location of genes is known, then gene therapy can be used to replace defective genes and cure a disorder.
6. Because only the bone marrow cells had the allele replaced, the sex cells would still contain the SCID allele and the disorder would be passed on to the offspring.

Time Allotment

one class period

Process Skills

compare and contrast, observe and infer, recognize cause and effect

Safety Precautions

Be careful with sharp edges of scissors. Always cut away from the body.

PREPARATION

■ Review the chemical structure of DNA from Chapter 11 before students begin the BioLab.

■ Additional background material on modeling recombinant DNA can be found. You may wish to read some articles before you teach the BioLab.

Before You Begin

Experimental procedures have been developed that allow recombinant DNA molecules to be engineered in a test tube. From a wide variety of restriction enzymes available, scientists choose one or two that recognize particular sequences of DNA within a longer DNA sequence of a chromosome. The enzymes are added to the DNA, which is cleaved at the recognition sites. Because the cleaved fragments have ends that are available for attachment to complementary strands, the fragments can be added to plasmids or to viral DNA that has been similarly cut. When the DNA fragment has been incorporated into the plasmid or virus, it is called recombinant DNA.

Modeling Recombinant DNA

PREPARATION

Problem

How can you model recombinant DNA technology?

Objectives

In this BioLab, you will:

■ **Model** the process of preparing recombinant DNA.

■ **Analyze** a model for preparation of recombinant DNA.

Materials

white paper   tape
colored pencils (red and green)   scissors

Safety Precautions

CAUTION: *Always wear goggles in the lab. Be careful with sharp objects.*

Skill Handbook

If you need help with this lab, refer to the **Skill Handbook.**

PROCEDURE

1. Cut a 3-cm × 28-cm strip from a sheet of white paper. This strip of paper represents a long sequence of DNA containing a particular gene that you wish to combine with a plasmid.

2. Cut a 3-cm × 10-cm strip of paper. When taped into a ring in step 5, this piece of paper will represent a bacterial plasmid.

3. Use your colored pencils to color the longer strip red and the shorter strip green.

4. Write the following DNA sequence once on the shorter strip of paper, and write it two times about 5 cm apart on the longer strip of paper.

-G-G-A-T-C-C-
　|　|　|　|　|　|
-C-C-T-A-G-G-

5. After coloring the shorter strip of paper and writing the sequence on it, tape the ends together.

PROCEDURE

Teaching Strategies

■ Students can do this lab alone or with partners.

■ If red and green colored paper is available, then colored pencils will not be necessary.

■ If you make cardboard models of DNA bases for the Inclusion Strategies on page 342, use them in this BioLab.

```
-G-G-A-T-C-C-          -G-G-A-T-C-C-
 | | | | | |            | | | | | |
-C-C-T-A-G-G-          -C-C-T-A-G-G-
```

6. Assume that a particular restriction enzyme is able to cleave DNA in a staggered way as illustrated here.

```
-G              G-A-T-C-C-
  |
-C-C-T-A-G              G-
```

Cut the longer strand of DNA in both places as shown above. You now have a cleaved foreign DNA fragment containing a gene that can be inserted into the plasmid.

7. Once the sequence containing the foreign gene has been cleaved, cut the plasmid in the same way.

8. Insert the foreign gene into the plasmid by taping the paper together where the sticky ends pair properly. The new plasmid represents recombinant DNA.

9. Copy the data table. Relate the steps of producing recombinant DNA to the activities of the modeling procedure by explaining how the terms relate to the model.

Data Table

Term	BioLab Model
Gene insertion	
Plasmid	
Restriction enzyme	
Sticky ends	
Recombinant DNA	

ANALYZE AND CONCLUDE

1. **Compare and Contrast** How does the paper model of a plasmid resemble a bacterial plasmid?

2. **Compare and Contrast** How is cutting with the scissors different from cleaving with a restriction enzyme?

3. **Think Critically** Enzymes that modify DNA, such as restriction enzymes, have been discovered and isolated from living cells. What functions do you think they have in living cells?

4. **Critique** Does the model accurately represent the process of producing recombinant DNA?

Apply Your Skill

Project Design and construct a three-dimensional model that illustrates the process of preparing recombinant DNA. Consider using clay or other materials in your model. Label the model and explain it to your classmates.

 Web Links To find out more about recombinant DNA, visit in.bdol.glencoe.com/ genetic_engineering

13.3 THE HUMAN GENOME **355**

ANALYZE AND CONCLUDE

1. It is a small circular piece of DNA.

2. The scissors can cut the DNA anywhere, but the restriction enzyme recognizes a particular sequence.

3. These enzymes may function in a cell by cutting up and destroying invading viral DNA.

4. Even though the model is a simplified example of the real procedure, it accurately represents what is happening in recombinant DNA.

Assessment

Performance Have students write a paragraph summarizing what they have learned about the use of restriction enzymes. Have students explain how the BioLab model is like the terms listed in the data table. Use the Performance Task Assessment List for Writing in Science in **PASC**, p. 159.

Apply Your Skill

Project Students could use different colors of clay, or use food coloring to dye plaster of Paris to show recombinant DNA in their models. **L1** **ELL**

Data and Observations

Data for completing the table should be as follows: Gene insertion—process of taping green and red paper together; Plasmid—green strip; Restriction enzyme—scissors; Sticky ends—cut ends on paper; Recombinant DNA—red and green strips taped together.

Purpose

Students will learn about techniques used to make new vaccines that may help fight against the world's most deadly diseases.

Background

In 1796, Edward Jenner pioneered the field when he developed a smallpox vaccine. About 150 years later, work of Albert Sabin and Jonas Salk led to a vaccine against polio. Since the early 1980s, 14 new or improved vaccines have been developed, including vaccines using genetic material. Researchers today are challenged by diseases such as AIDS, malaria, influenza, and cancer, among others.

Teaching Strategies

Discuss with students the vaccination schedule established by the American Academy of Pediatrics (AAP), the Advisory Committee on Immunization Practices (ACIP), the Centers for Disease Control and Prevention (CDC), and the American Academy of Family Physicians. At birth, children receive the first Hepatitis B vaccination; at 2 months: the first DTaP (diphtheria, tetanus, and pertussis), Polio, Hib (*Haemophilus influenzae* type b), Pneumococcus, and the second Hepatitis B vaccinations; at 4 months: the second DTaP, Polio, Hib, and Pneumococcus vaccinations; at 6 months: the third DTaP, Hib, and Pneumococcus vaccinations; at 12 months: the first MMR (measles, mumps and rubella) and the Varicella (chicken pox) vaccinations; at 15 months: the third Hepatitis B, the fourth Hib, and Pneumococcus vaccinations; at 18 months: the third Polio and the fourth DTaP vaccinations; between 4 and 6 years: the second MMR, the fourth Polio, and the fifth DTaP vaccinations; between 11 and 13 years: a Td (tetanus/diphtheria) booster

356

New Vaccines

Greater understanding of how the immune system works and rapid advances in gene technology have paved the way for the development of new types of vaccines that offer hope in the fight against some of the world's most deadly and widespread diseases.

Traditionally, most vaccines have been made from weakened or killed forms of a disease-causing virus or bacterium, or from some of its cellular components or toxins. Although these types of vaccines have helped to prevent disease, they sometimes cause severe side effects. Furthermore, it hasn't been possible to create vaccines for diseases such as malaria and AIDS using traditional methods. With the help of genetic engineering technology, researchers can now manipulate microbial genes to create entirely new kinds of vaccines.

Recombinant vaccines One revolutionary approach to developing vaccines uses recombinant DNA technology, a process in which genes from one organism are inserted into another organism. The hepatitis B virus vaccine was the first genetically engineered vaccine to be produced in this way. Researchers isolated the gene in the hepatitis virus that codes for the production of an antigen, a protein that stimulates an immune response. Then they inserted that gene into yeast cells. Like tiny microbial machines, the genetically engineered yeast cells produce great quantities of pure hepatitis B antigen, which is then used to make a vaccine.

Live vector vaccines An antigen-coding gene from a disease-causing virus such as HIV can be inserted into a harmless "carrier" virus such as cowpox virus. When a vaccine made from the carrier virus is injected into a host, the virus replicates and in the process produces the antigen protein, which causes an immune response. This type of vaccine, called a live vector vaccine, shows promise against AIDS.

Researchers who work with viruses must wear protective clothing.

DNA vaccines DNA vaccines differ from other vaccines in that only the cloned segment of DNA that codes for a disease-causing antigen is injected into a host—the DNA itself is the vaccine. The DNA can be injected through a hypodermic needle into muscle tissue, or microscopic DNA-coated metal beads can be fired into muscle cells using a "gene gun." Once in the cells, the foreign DNA is expressed as antigen protein that induces an immune response. Researchers currently are working on DNA vaccines for cancer and tuberculosis.

Applying Biotechnology

Think Critically It is possible to insert antigen-coding genes for several different diseases into one virus carrier that can be used to make a vaccine. What would be an advantage of such a vaccine?

 To find out more about vaccines, visit in.bdol.glencoe.com/biotechnology

---

Applying Biotechnology

Encourage students to research the latest developments in genetic vaccines. Have them discuss or write a report about their discoveries. They should include the diseases that are being focused on by researchers. Also, advantages and disadvantages of using one carrier to make a vaccine for several different diseases should be included.

STUDY GUIDE

Section 13.1

Applied Genetics

Key Concepts

■ Test crosses determine the genotypes of individuals and the probability that offspring will have a particular allele.

■ Plant and animal breeders selectively breed organisms with a desirable trait which increases the frequency of a desired allele in a population.

Vocabulary

inbreeding (p. 338)
test cross (p. 339)

Section 13.2

Recombinant DNA Technology

Key Concepts

■ Scientists have developed methods to move genes from one species into another. These processes use restriction enzymes to cleave DNA into fragments and other enzymes to insert a DNA fragment into a plasmid or viral DNA. Transgenic organisms can make genetic products foreign to themselves using recombinant DNA.

■ Bacteria, plants, and animals have been genetically engineered to be of use to humans.

■ Gene cloning can be done by inserting a gene into bacterial cells, which copy the gene when they reproduce, or by a technique called polymerase chain reaction.

■ Many species of animals have been cloned; the first cloned mammal was a sheep.

Vocabulary

clone (p. 344)
genetic engineering (p. 341)
plasmid (p. 343)
recombinant DNA (p. 341)
restriction enzyme (p. 342)
transgenic organism (p. 341)
vector (p. 343)

Section 13.3

The Human Genome

Color-enhanced SEM Magnification: unavailable

Key Concepts

■ The Human Genome Project, an international effort, has sequenced the chromosomal DNA of the human genome. Efforts are underway to determine the location for every gene.

■ DNA fingerprinting can be used to identify individuals.

■ Gene therapy technology can be used to treat genetic disorders.

Vocabulary

gene therapy (p. 352)
human genome (p. 349)
linkage map (p. 349)

 FOLDABLES **Study Organizer** To help you review selective breeding, use the Organizational Study Fold on page 337.

Key Concepts

Summary statements can be used by students to review the major concepts of the chapter.

 Biology Online

Visit in.bdol.glencoe.com
/self_check_quiz
/vocabulary_puzzlemaker
/chapter_test
/standardized_test

VOCABULARY PUZZLEMAKER

 For additional help with vocabulary, have students access the Vocabulary PuzzleMaker online at in.bdol.glencoe.com/vocabulary_puzzlemaker

FOLDABLES™

Have students use their Foldables to review the content of Section 13.1. On the back of the Foldable have students list possible uses of selective breeding.

Use the ExamView®Pro Test Bank CD-ROM to:

● Create **multiple versions** of tests
● Create **modified** tests with one mouse click for **inclusion** students
● **Edit** existing questions and **add** your own questions
● Build tests aligned with state standards using built-in **State Curriculum Tags**
● Change **English** tests to **Spanish** with one mouse click and vice versa

 Indiana Academic Standards

Pages 356–357: B.1.23, B.1.27

Questions and answers have been aligned and verified by The Princeton Review.

Vocabulary Review

1. inbreeding
2. restriction enzymes
3. plasmid
4. vector
5. genetic engineering

Understanding Key Concepts

6. C   9. A
7. B   10. B
8. D   11. D

Constructed Response

12. treating and curing human genetic disorders
13. This may upset the balance between the natural nitrogen-converting bacteria and the plants, possibly disrupting the soil ecosystem. Plant growth would increase because nitrogen is usually a limiting factor.
14. If many alleles were to be transferred into the normal population, their frequency would change. This would affect the genetic makeup of the population.

Thinking Critically

15. The order of the fragments from the well is 7, 4, 2, 1. The fragments travel toward the positive electrode with the smallest fragment traveling the farthest and the largest fragment traveling the least distance.
16. The students' arguments should logically address the side they choose and the concerns of the opposition.

358

Vocabulary Review

Review the Chapter 13 vocabulary words listed in the Study Guide on page 357. Match the words with the definitions below.

1. mating between closely related individuals

2. bacterial proteins that have the ability to cut both strands of a DNA molecule at specific nucleotide sequences

3. a small ring of DNA found in a bacterial cell

4. a vehicle for carrying DNA fragments into a host cell

5. the insertion of normal genes into human cells to correct genetic disorders

Understanding Key Concepts

6. Polymerase chain reaction is used to _____.

   A. cleave DNA   C. copy DNA
   B. insert DNA   D. protect DNA

7. What is the purpose of a test cross?
   A. produce offspring that consistently exhibit a specific trait
   B. check for carriers of a trait
   C. explain recessiveness
   D. show polygenic inheritance

8. The goal of gene therapy is to insert a _____ into cells to correct a genetic disorder.
   A. recessive allele   C. dominant allele
   B. growth hormone   D. normal allele

9. Restriction enzyme *Eco*RI cuts DNA strands, leaving _____ ends.
   A. sticky   C. blunt
   B. smooth   D. linked

10. _____ usually increases the appearance of genetic disorders.
    A. Cloning   C. PCR
    B. Inbreeding   D. Gene therapy

---

11. Cells in a cell culture all have the same genetic material because they are _____.
    A. vectors   C. hybrids
    B. plasmids   D. clones

Constructed Response

12. **Open Ended** What is the potential use of a map showing the sequence of DNA bases in a human chromosome?

13. **Open Ended** Assume that transgenic organisms can be developed to speed nitrogen fixation. How might use of these organisms affect an ecosystem?

14. **Open Ended** How might transgenic organisms alter the course of evolution for a species?

Thinking Critically

15. **Interpret Scientific Illustrations** A gel electrophoresis was run on DNA fragments 1 megabase (MB), 2 MB, 4 MB, and 7 MB in size. (MB=1 million nucleotide base pairs.) Identify the fragments and explain your answer.

16. **REAL WORLD BIOCHALLENGE** Through biotechnology, genetically modified food crops that are pesticide resistant, hardier, and higher yielding have been developed. However, the sale and use of genetically modified foods (GM foods) has become controversial. Research the pros and cons of genetically modified foods. Choose one side and make a class presentation that addresses the concerns of the opposite side.

 in.bdol.glencoe.com/chapter_test

RUBRIC

Evaluating Open-Ended Questions
Open-ended assessment questions are graded by using a multilevel rubric that guides you in assessing a student's knowledge of a particular concept. The following rubric is a sample scoring device.

Chapter 13 Assessment

Part 1 ▶ Multiple Choice

17. .1.29 A test cross was made between two Alaskan malamutes, a dominant phenotype for normal size and a homozygous recessive dwarf. Which of these results would indicate that the normal-sized dog is heterozygous?

  A. All puppies were phenotypically dominant.
  B. All puppies were phenotypically recessive.
  C. Some puppies were phenotypically dominant and some were recessive.
  D. none of the above

Use the diagram below to answer question 18.

1. Bacterium   2. Plasmid
Plasmid
3.   4. Plasmid
Cleavage site

18. B.1.23 What is the proper sequence of steps for cloning recombinant DNA using a plasmid?

  A. 1–2–3–4
  B. 2–3–4–1
  C. 2–4–1–3
  D. 4–2–1–3

Use the table below to answer question 19.

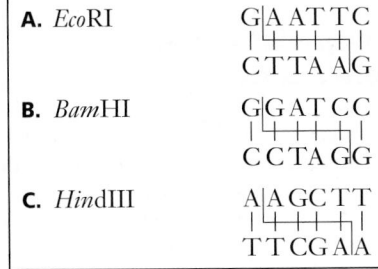

A. *Eco*RI	G A A T T C	C T T A A G
B. *Bam*HI	G G A T C C	C C T A G G
C. *Hin*dIII	A A G C T T	T T C G A A

19. Which restriction enzyme could be used to cut the following DNA strand?

-G G G G A T C C C G-
 | | | | | | | | | |
-C C C C T A G G G C-

  A. A   **C.** C
  B. B   **D.** both A and B

Part 2 ▶ Constructed Response/Grid In

Record your answers on your answer document.

20. Open Ended Why was the discovery of restriction enzymes important to recombinant DNA technology?

21. Open Ended A wildlife officer found deer blood in the forest after hunting season ended. He took a sample to the lab for DNA fingerprinting. DNA fingerprinting also was done on deer meat from a suspect's freezer. As controls, DNA tests were done on the blood and meat of another deer. Was the suspect innocent or guilty? Explain.

Control deer meat	Control deer blood	Freezer meat	Forest blood

17. C
18. D
19. B
20. Restriction enzymes allow DNA to be cut at specific sites for making recombinant DNA.
21. The suspect was guilty. DNA fingerprinting bands from the deer meat matched the blood bands perfectly, so they were from the same source.

 FAST FILE

Answer Sheet A practice answer sheet can be found on p. 149 of *Unit 4 FAST FILE Resources.*

RUBRIC

SCORE	CRITERIA
4	A correct solution that is supported by well-developed, accurate explanations.
3	A generally correct solution, but may contain minor flaws in reasoning.

SCORE	CRITERIA
2	A partially correct interpretation and/or solution to the problem.
1	A correct solution with no supporting evidence or explanation.
0	An incorrect solution or no solution is given.

Indiana Academic Standards

Pages 358–359: B.1.21, B.1.23, B.1.27

Prepare

Short on Time?

This BioDigest can be used as an introduction to or as an overview of genetics. If time is limited, you may wish to use this unit summary to teach genetics in place of the chapters in the genetics unit.

Key Concepts

Students will learn about Mendel and his insights into heredity. The process by which genetic information is copied and proteins are formed by the genetic code is described. Finally, the patterns of human heredity and DNA technology are discussed.

1 Focus

Bellringer

Visual-Spatial Have students closely examine the flower of a pea plant so they can become familiar with the materials with which Mendel worked. **L1** **ELL**

Color-enhanced TEM Magnification: 3500×

Chromosomes

Genetics

Genetics is the study of inheritance. The physical traits, or phenotype, of an individual are encoded in small segments of chromosomes called genes. Not all genes are expressed as a phenotype. Therefore, the genotype, the traits encoded in the genes, may be different from the expressed phenotype.

Simple Mendelian Inheritance

A trait is dominant if only one allele of a gene is needed for that trait to be expressed. If two alleles are needed for expression, the trait is said to be recessive. In pea plants, the allele for purple flowers is dominant, and the allele for white flowers is recessive. Any plant with *PP* or *Pp* alleles will have purple flowers. Any plant with *pp* alleles will have white flowers.

Purple (PP)   White (pp)

All purple flowers (Pp)

> When a *PP* purple pea plant is crossed with a *pp* white plant, all the offspring are purple, *Pp*. When two *Pp* plants are crossed, three-fourths of the plants in the next generation will be purple and one-fourth will be white.

PP   Pp   Pp   pp

3 purple : 1 white

FOCUS ON HISTORY

Mendel

Gregor Mendel

To investigate the genetic inheritance of pea plant traits, Austrian monk Gregor Mendel used critical thinking skills to design his experiments. When he collected data, he considered not only the qualitative characteristics, such as whether the plants were tall or short, but also the quantitative data by analyzing the ratios of tall to short plants in each generation. Mendel observed that there were two variations for each trait, such as tall and short plants. He formed the hypothesis that alleles transmitted these traits from one generation to the next. After studying several traits for many generations, Mendel formed two laws. The law of segregation states that the two alleles for each trait separate when gametes are formed. The law of independent assortment states that genes for different traits are inherited independently of each other.

360

RESOURCE MANAGER

Unit 4 *FAST FILE* **Resources**
Reinforcement and Study Guide in English, pp. 151–152
Reinforcement and Study Guide in Spanish, pp. 153–154
Student Recording Sheet, p. 155

Meiosis

Meiosis produces gametes that contain only one copy of each chromosome instead of two. Some stages of meiosis are similar to those of mitosis, but in meiosis, homologous chromosomes come together as tetrads to exchange genes during a process called crossing over. Meiosis also provides a mechanism for re-sorting the genetic information carried by cells. Both crossing over and the re-sorting of genes during meiosis produce genetic variability, which can give offspring a survival advantage if the environment changes.

Prophase I   Metaphase I   Meiosis I   Anaphase I   Telophase I
                                         Meiosis II

Prophase II   Metaphase II   Anaphase II   Telophase II

Meiosis consists of two divisions, meiosis I and meiosis II. During meiosis I, the replicated homologous chromosomes separate from each other. In meiosis II, the sister chromatids of each replicated chromosome separate from each other.

Producing Physical Traits

Deoxyribonucleic acid (DNA) is a double-stranded molecule made up of a sequence of paired nucleotides that encode each gene on a chromosome. There are four nitrogenous bases in DNA: A, T, C, and G. Because of their molecular shape, A can pair only with T, and C can pair only with G. This precise pairing allows the DNA molecule to copy itself in a process called DNA replication.

A DNA molecule is a double helix that resembles a zipper. The bases form the zipper's teeth.

DNA

---

2 Teach

Discussion

Have students discuss Mendelian inheritance. Begin by comparing and contrasting genotype and phenotype. What are the possible genotype(s) of a dominant trait? A recessive trait? A genotype is the alleles for a trait that an individual possesses. A phenotype is the physical appearance of that trait. The possible genotypes of a dominant trait are homozygous, *PP*, or heterozygous, *Pp*, for the purple flower color. A recessive trait must be homozygous, *pp*, for the recessive phenotype.

Activity

Visual-Spatial Have students draw a cell undergoing meiosis. Make sure they label homologous chromosomes and sister chromatids. **L2** **ELL**

Inquiry

Discussion Have students compare and contrast mitosis with meiosis. They should include the processes as well as the results. **L2**

CHALLENGE ACTIVITY

Mendel's Experiments Have students research and write a report about Mendel's experiments and his conclusions. What scientific methods did he include in his experiments? Students' reports should include his hypotheses, variables, and controls. What two laws did he derive from his studies? **L3**

Visual Learning 👆

Display a transparency of transcription and ask students questions about the process. Ask them to define a gene, transcription, and mRNA. Have them identify the bases of DNA. A gene is a segment of DNA containing the information for making a protein. Transcription is the process whereby a DNA sequence of bases is copied into a sequence of bases in mRNA. mRNA will carry the code for proteins into the cytoplasm. The bases of DNA are adenine, thymine, cytosine, and guanine.

Discussion

Discuss the idea that some traits, such as sickle-cell anemia, may confer an advantage for survival to a heterozygote. How might this idea have been used throughout evolution to define characteristics of living species? Traits that confer an advantage to individuals in a species increase the chances of that individual surviving to reproduce and pass on the traits.

Visual Learning 👆

Display a transparency of translation and have students differentiate between mRNA and tRNA. Give students a sequence of several mRNA codons and ask them to "translate" the RNA bases into an amino acid sequence. mRNA is a copy of a gene from DNA. tRNA carries amino acids to ribosomes.

362

Genetics

Transcription

To make a protein, the segment of DNA containing the gene for that protein must be transcribed. First, the bases in the DNA segment separate and the sequence is copied into a molecule of messenger ribonucleic acid (mRNA), which moves through the nuclear envelope into the cytoplasm. RNA is similar to DNA except that RNA is a single strand and contains the base U in place of T.

In transcription, the two strands of DNA separate and a molecule of mRNA is made according to the sequence of bases in the DNA.

Translation

A codon is a sequence of three mRNA nitrogenous bases that codes for an amino acid. Translation occurs at a ribosome as it moves along the mRNA strand. The "start" codon—AUG—begins a protein. A transfer RNA (tRNA) molecule with a specific amino acid attached to it, comes to the mRNA and "reads" the codon. Another tRNA with an amino acid attached reads the next codon and the two amino acids bond. This process is repeated over and over as the ribosome moves along the mRNA until it comes to the "stop" codon—UAA.

In translation, the sequence of nitrogenous bases in the mRNA is translated into a sequence of amino acids in a protein chain. Every three bases code for a specific amino acid.

Complex Inheritance Patterns

An incomplete dominance pattern of inheritance produces an intermediate phenotype in the heterozygote. In codominant inheritance, the heterozygote expresses both alleles. Some traits, such as human blood types, are governed by multiple alleles, although any individual can carry only two of those alleles.

The X chromosome, one of two sex chromosomes, carries many genes, including the genes for hemophilia and color blindness. Most X-linked disorders appear in males because they inherit only one X chromosome. In females, a normal allele on one X chromosome can mask the expression of a recessive allele on the other X chromosome. Finally, some traits, such as skin color, are polygenic—governed by several genes.

Father's chromosomes

	X	Y
X	**XX** Female	**XY** Male
X	**XX** Female	**XY** Male

Mother's chromosomes

In any mating between humans, half the offspring will have the XX genotype, which are females, and half the offspring will have the genotype XY, which are males.

Recombinant DNA Technology

To make recombinant DNA, a small segment of DNA containing a desired gene is inserted into a bacterial plasmid, a small ring of DNA. The plasmid acts as a vector to carry the DNA segment into a host bacterial cell. Every time the bacterium reproduces, the plasmid containing the inserted DNA is duplicated, producing copies of the recombinant DNA along with the host chromosome. Because these new DNA segments are identical to the original, they are called clones. The host cell produces large quantities of the protein encoded by the recombinant DNA it contains.

Cleavage sites

Foreign DNA (gene for insulin)

Recombined plasmid

Plasmid

Recombinant DNA

Bacterial chromosome

E. coli

Insulin

Recombinant DNA containing a desired gene can be produced in bacteria. The recombinant DNA is then cloned to make many copies of the desired gene. In this diagram, the gene for insulin production has been inserted into a bacterial plasmid. The recombinant bacteria can then produce insulin.

---

3 Assess

DAILY INTERVENTION

Check for Understanding
Ask students to define transcription and translation and to explain each process.

Reteach
Display a transparency of the stages of meiosis and ask students to identify the stages.

Extension

Intrapersonal Have students research some of the uses of genetic technology, such as the production of human insulin and human growth hormone. **L3**

✔ Assessment

Knowledge Put an example of incomplete dominance or codominance on the board and ask students to identify the pattern of inheritance. **L1**

Portfolio

Punnett Squares Have students make Punnett squares demonstrating various crosses between individuals with a dominant trait, a recessive trait, incomplete dominance, codominance, and a sex-linked trait. **L1** **ELL**

CHALLENGE ACTIVITY

Genetics Have students make a table with the following headings: *Dominant, Recessive, Incomplete Dominance, Codominance, Multiple Alleles, Polygenic Inheritance,* and *X-linked Traits.* Under each heading, they should list the following: genotype(s), whether the trait is more common in males or females, one specific example from the text, and how many phenotypes are possible. **L3**

Indiana Academic Standards
Pages 362–363: B.1.21, B.1.22, B.1.23, B.1.26, B.1.28

This page contains practice questions in the various formats that can be found on the most frequently given standardized tests.

Part 1 ▶ Multiple Choice

1. A	6. B	11. C
2. B	7. C	12. B
3. C	8. C	13. C
4. C	9. D	14. B
5. C	10. B	

FAST FILE

Answer Sheet A practice answer sheet can be found on p. 155 of *Unit 4 Fast File Resources.*

RUBRIC

For more help evaluating open-ended assessment questions, see the rubric on p. 9T.

Indiana Academic Standards

Pages 364–365: B.1.21, B.1.23, B.1.26

End-of-Course Assessment Practice

The assessed Indiana standard appears next to the question.

The Princeton Review

TEST-TAKING TIP
Use the Buddy System

Study in a group. A small study group works well because it allows you to draw from a broader base of skills and content knowledge. Keep it small, question each other, and keep on target.

Part 1 ▶ Multiple Choice

1. Two parents have cleft chins. Their first child does not have a cleft chin. What type of inheritance does this display? *B.1.29*
   A. Cleft chins are dominant.
   B. Cleft chins are recessive.
   C. Cleft chins are codominant.
   D. Cleft chins are incompletely dominant.

2. What carries the information from the DNA to the cytoplasm? *B.1.21*
   A. tRNA
   B. mRNA
   C. enzymes
   D. rRNA

3. What type of inheritance shows a pattern where the only phenotype of the heterozygote is intermediate between those of the two homozygotes? *B.1.29*
   A. polygenic inheritance
   B. sex-linked inheritance
   C. incomplete dominance
   D. codominance

4. During what phase of meiosis do replicated homologous chromosomes line up next to each other at the cell's equator? *B.1.8*
   A. anaphase I
   B. metaphase II
   C. metaphase I
   D. prophase I

5. What is the source of most of the plasmids used in genetic engineering?
   A. yeast cells
   B. animal cells
   C. bacterial cells
   D. plant cells

For an investigation of the ability of a bioengineered species of bacteria to break down oil, the following procedure was followed:

1. Add 40 mL of oil to a culture of the bioengineered bacteria and to a culture of naturally occurring bacteria of the same species.
2. Measure the volume of oil in each culture daily for four weeks.
3. Graph the resulting data.

Use the graph below to answer questions 6–8.

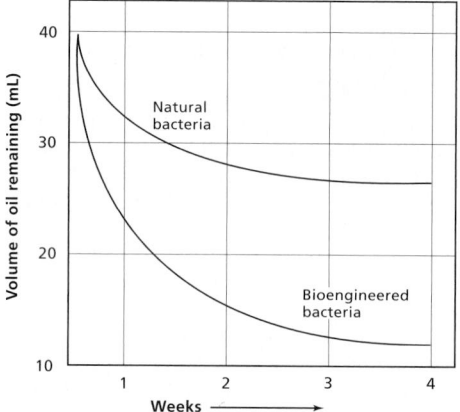

Breakdown of Oil by Bacteria

6. Approximately how much oil did the natural bacteria convert into harmless products after four weeks?
   A. 4 mL
   B. 14 mL
   C. 24 mL
   D. 40 mL

7. About how much oil did the bioengineered bacteria convert after four weeks?
   A. 4 mL
   B. 14 mL
   C. 28 mL
   D. 40 mL

8. About how much more efficient are the bioengineered bacteria than the natural bacteria?
   A. 1×
   B. 1.5×
   C. 2×
   D. 3×

Use the graph below to answer questions 9–11. The graph illustrates an inherited trait—the number of flowers produced per plant—in a certain plant population.

Number of Flowers Produced by Plants

Number of plants (y-axis): 100, 200, 300, 400, 500
Numbers of flowers per plant (x-axis): 4, 8, 12, 16, 20, 24, 28

9. Which bars represent the homozygous condition for this trait?
- **A.** 8—16
- **B.** 12—20
- **C.** 16—24
- **D.** 4—28

10. Which of these groups of bars represent the heterozygous condition for this trait?
- **A.** 4—12—20
- **B.** 8—16—24
- **C.** 12—20—28
- **D.** 4—16—28

11. What pattern of inheritance is suggested by B.1.29 the graph?
- **A.** multiple alleles
- **B.** incomplete dominance
- **C.** polygenic inheritance
- **D.** sex-linkage

12. A couple has four children who are all boys. B.1.29 What are the chances that their next child also will be a boy?
- **A.** 100%
- **B.** 50%
- **C.** 75%
- **D.** 0%

13. A female, nonpregnant lab rat is exposed to B.1.24 X rays. Its future offspring will be affected only if a mutation occurs in one of the rat's _____ cells.
- **A.** body
- **B.** liver
- **C.** sex
- **D.** nerve

14. A frameshift mutation is more damaging than B.1.23 a point mutation because _____.
- **A.** the genetic code is changed in a frameshift mutation
- **B.** more codons are affected in a frameshift mutation
- **C.** more bases are deleted from the DNA in a frameshift mutation
- **D.** more bases are deleted from the DNA in a point mutation

Part 2 Constructed Response/Grid In

Record your answers on your answer document.

15. Open Ended Explain the differences between the terms *monoploid*, *triploid*, and *tetraploid*. Would 1.8 meiosis be affected by each of these conditions? Would mitosis be affected? Explain.

16. Open Ended Explain how RNA differs from DNA. Can RNA be replicated by the process that is 1.21 described in Chapter 11? Explain.

17. Open Ended Draw a Punnett square for the following situation and summarize the results. A man 1.29 who is color-blind is married to a woman who carries an allele for color blindness. What phenotypes of children can this couple have?

18. Open Ended Explain how a foreign gene can be inserted into a plasmid. Use the term *restriction* 1.23 *enzyme* in your answer.

 in.bdol.glencoe.com/standardized_test

UNIT 4 STANDARDIZED TEST PRACTICE **365**

Part 2 Constructed Response/Grid In

15. As a result of nondisjunction when gametes are formed, abnormal chromosome numbers result in the zygote. When the zygote lacks a chromosome, it is monoploid. A zygote that has a set with three chromosomes is triploid. When a zygote has an extra set of chromosomes, it is tetraploid. Prophase I of meiosis would be affected by the monoploid and triploid conditions as an homologous chromosome would be unpaired for both. The tetraploid condition would not affect meiosis. Mitosis would not be affected by any of these conditions, since homologous chromosomes do not pair.

16. RNA is single stranded instead of double stranded, its sugar is ribose instead of deoxyribose, and it contains the nitrogenous base uracil instead of thymine. No, RNA is made during transcription not replication. During transcription, a copy of a portion of DNA is made, resulting in a single stranded RNA molecule.

17.

	X^r	Y
X^R	$X^R X^r$	$X^R Y$
X^r	$X^r X^r$	$X^r Y$

Their children can be color-blind or have normal color vision.

18. A piece of DNA is cut, using restriction enzymes, from the chromosome and inserted into a bacterial plasmid.

Change Through Time

Unit Overview

In this unit, students will study the concepts and principles of evolution and classification. **Chapter 14** deals with the history of life on Earth, and some hypotheses about how life began. **Chapter 15** discusses Darwin's theory of evolution by natural selection. The role of natural selection in the evolution of new species is presented. **Chapter 16** explores evidence of the ancestry of humans. **Chapter 17** introduces taxonomy and the diversity of organisms.

Introducing the Unit

Have students look at the elephants in the photo and describe their successful adaptations. Tell students that they also will learn in this unit why the ancestors of birds may be extinct dinosaurs. Explain to students that as the environment changes, populations may adapt, migrate, or become extinct.

Web Quest A WebQuest is an inquiry-based online project in which all information used by students is obtained from the Web. Students evaluate the information to complete the activity. Access the Unit 5 WebQuest at **in.bdol.glencoe.com/webquest**

Indiana Academic Standards

Pages 366–367: B.1.30

History & Biology

1593
The Roman city of Pompeii is discovered.

1500   1600   170

1500
Leonardo da Vinci recognizes that fossil shells represent ancient marine life.

◄ Fossil shell

Change Through Time

What You'll Learn

Chapter 14
The History of Life

Chapter 15
The Theory of Evolution

Chapter 16
Primate Evolution

Chapter 17
Organizing Life's Diversity

Unit 5 Review
BioDigest & Standardized Test Practice

Why It's Important

Life on Earth has a history of change that is called evolution. An enormous variety of fossils, such as those of early birds, provides evidence of evolution. Genetic studies of populations of bacteria, protists, plants, insects, and even humans provide further evidence of the history of change among organisms that live or have lived on Earth.

Indiana Standards
The following standards are covered in Unit 5:
B.1.13, B.1.24, B.1.28, B.1.30, B.1.31, B.1.32, B.1.33, B.1.34, B.1.35, B.1.36, B.1.47, B.2.1, B.2.2, B.2.3

Understanding the Photo ▶
These African elephants are well-adapted to their environment. Scientists study these and other organisms to learn about their adaptations and how the organisms have changed through time.

Time Line

Discussion As students read the chapters in Unit 5, have them refer to the time line shown above. Ask students to consider how each new hominid fossil discovery advances our knowledge of human history and human ancestry. Have students research one of the latest hominid fossils or other fossil groups, such as early bird or dinosaur discoveries, and present their findings to the class. **L2**

Advance Materials Planning

The following materials may need to be ordered a few weeks in advance of the planned activity.

Chapter 14

- **MiniLab 14.1** (p. 371) diatomaceous earth
- **Quick Demo** (p. 377) prepared slide of *Oscillatoria*
- **Additional Lab** (p. 382) 1% gelatin solution, 1% gum arabic solution, hydrochloric acid

Chapter 15

- **Additional Lab** (p. 408) culture of *Bacillus subtillis*, 3 tubes of nutrient agar, tube of streptomycin agar

Chapter 16

- **BioLab** (p. 436) casts of various hominid and age skulls

Chapter 17

- **MiniLab 17.1** (p. 446) dichotomous keys for local trees and shrubs
- **BioLab** (p. 460) identification guide for insects and other organisms

367

Unit Projects

Display

Visual-Spatial Students can use photographs or illustrations from magazines and science journals to make a collage showing different living things. **L1** **ELL**

Interview

Linguistic Students can interview nature professionals to find out how they care for the diverse life forms under their protection. Have students prepare their interview questions in advance. **L1**

Using the Library

Intrapersonal Students can read Chapter 17, which is "Galápagos Archipelago," of *Voyage of the Beagle* by Charles Darwin to find out about the diversity of birds and reptiles in the Galápagos. **L3**

Section Objectives	National Science Standards	State/Local Standards	Advanced Lab and Demo Planning
Section 14.1 2 sessions, 1 block 1. **Identify** the different types of fossils and how they are formed. 2. **Summarize** the major events of the geologic time scale.	UCP.1–4; A.1, A.2; C.3, C.6; D.3; G.1–3	**Indiana Standards** B.1.32, B.1.33	**Student Labs:** MiniLab 14.1, p. 371: microscope slide, water, diatomaceous earth, microscope Problem-Solving Lab 14.1, p. 372 MiniLab 14.2, p. 376: meterstick, 5-m strip of adding machine tape **Teacher Demonstration:** Quick Demo, p. 377: microscope, living culture or prepared slide of *Oscillatoria*
Section 14.2 2 sessions, 1 block 3. **Analyze** early experiments that support the concept of biogenesis. 4. **Review, analyze, and critique** modern theories of the origin of life. 5. **Relate** hypotheses about the origin of cells to the environmental conditions of early Earth.	UCP.2–5; A.1, A.2; B.2, B.3; C.1, C.3, C.6; D.2; E.1; F.3, F.4; G.1–3	**Indiana Standards** B.1.32, B.1.33, B.2.1	**Student Labs:** Problem-Solving Lab 14.2, p. 384 Additional Lab, p. 382: 1% gelatin solution, 3 droppers, 1% gum arabic solution, pH papers, microscopes, microscope slides, coverslips, 0.1M hydrochloric acid, test tubes, stirring rods Investigate BioLab, p. 386: See materials below. **Teacher Demonstration:** Quick Demo, p. 381: 2 bouillon cubes, 2 flasks, water, rubber stopper
End of Chapter Assessment Student Edition **Study Guide,** p. 389 **Content Assessment,** pp. 390–391		**Indiana Standards** B.1.32, B.1.33	**Student Lab:** Investigate BioLab, p. 386: shoe box with lid, 100 pennies, graph paper

Key to Teaching Strategies

L1 Level 1 activities should be appropriate for students with learning difficulties.

L2 Level 2 activities should be within the ability range of all students.

L3 Level 3 activities are designed for above-average students.

ELL ELL activities should be within the ability range of English Language Learners.

COOP LEARN Cooperative Learning activities are designed for small group work.

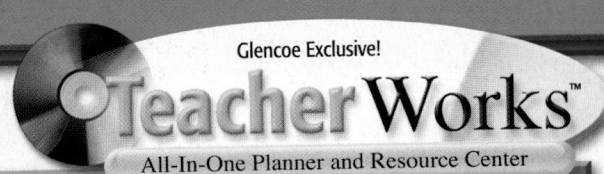

Glencoe Exclusive!
Teacher Works™
All-In-One Planner and Resource Center

Reproducible Masters and Transparencies	Technology
Unit 5 FAST FILE Resources MiniLab Worksheet, pp. 3, 4 BioLab Worksheet, pp. 5–6 Reinforcement and Study Guide in English, pp. 7–8 Reinforcement and Study Guide in Spanish, pp. 11–12 Concept Mapping, p. 15 Critical Thinking/Problem Solving, p. 16 Transparency Worksheets, pp. 17, 21–22 **Reading Essentials for Biology, Section 14.1** **Laboratory Manual,** pp. 83–84, 85–86 🖐 **Section Focus Transparency 35** 🖐 **Reteaching Skills Transparency 23**	💿 **Interactive Chalkboard CD-ROM: Section 14.1 Presentation** 💿 TeacherWorks™ **CD-ROM** 🎵 **Guided Reading Audio Summaries MP3**
Unit 5 FAST FILE Resources Reinforcement and Study Guide in English, pp. 9–10 Reinforcement and Study Guide in Spanish, pp. 13–14 Transparency Worksheets, pp. 18, 19–20 **Reading Essentials for Biology, Section 14.2** 🖐 **Section Focus Transparency 36** 🖐 **Basic Concepts Transparency 20**	💿 **Interactive Chalkboard CD-ROM: Section 14.2 Presentation** 💿 TeacherWorks™ **CD-ROM** 🎵 **Guided Reading Audio Summaries MP3**
Unit 5 FAST FILE Resources Chapter Assessment, pp. 23–28 Student Recording Sheet, p. 29 The Princeton Review **Reviewing Biology,** pp. 27–28	💿 **Interactive Chalkboard: Chapter 14 Assessment** 💿 **MindJogger Videoquizzes DVD/VHS** 💿 **ExamView® Pro Test Bank CD-ROM** 💿 TeacherWorks™ **CD-ROM** 💿 **Succeeding on National Standards CD-ROM** 🖱 in.bdol.glencoe.com /self_check_quiz /vocabulary_puzzlemaker /chapter_test /standardized_test

Indicates materials created specifically for Indiana.

Short on Time?

BIODIGEST The BioDigest at the end of this unit can be used as a(n):

- preview to introduce important unit concepts.
- overview if time does not permit teaching the entire chapter.
- review of key unit concepts.

Understanding the Photo

This photo shows lava flows that are called by the Hawaiian word *pahoehoe*, which refers to lava with a smooth, ropy surface. Spectacular lava fountains are found in the same area this photo was taken. Students can learn more about the conditions on early Earth on page 369.

PowerPoint® Presentations

This CD-ROM is an editable Microsoft® PowerPoint® presentation that includes:
- Section presentations
- Section checks
- Image bank
- Hot links to Biology Online
- All transparencies

The History of Life

What You'll Learn

- You will examine how rocks and fossils provide evidence of changes in Earth's organisms.
- You will correlate the geologic time scale with biological events.
- You will sequence the steps by which small molecules may have produced living cells.

Why It's Important

Knowing the geological history of Earth and understanding ideas about how life began provide background for an understanding of the theory of evolution.

Understanding the Photo

Erupting volcanoes and lava flows, such as this one in Hawaii, may provide a model for conditions on early Earth.

Biology Online

Visit in.bdol.glencoe.com to
- study the entire chapter online
- access Web Links for more information on the origin of life
- review content with the Interactive Tutor and self-check quizzes

Two-Minute Chapter Launcher

Demo To elicit students' preconceptions about lava, allow them to handle samples of aa and pahoehoe lava, pumice, and obsidian. Ask students why these igneous rocks are so different. The cooling rates are different for these four, due to differences in temperature and dissolved gas content. Pahoehoe flows are smooth and ropey, while aa flows are blocky and rough. Obsidian is formed when lava cools extremely quickly into a glass. Pumice forms when the lava contains a lot of dissolved gasses.

Section 14.1

The Record of Life

Indiana Standards Standard B.1.33 Describe how life on Earth is thought to have begun as simple, one-celled organisms about 4 billion years. Note that during the first 2 billion years, only single-cell microorganisms existed, but once cells with nuclei developed about a billion years ago, increasingly complex multicellular organisms evolved.

SECTION PREVIEW

Objectives
Identify the different types of fossils and how they are formed.

Summarize the major events of the geologic time scale.

Review Vocabulary
isotope: atoms of the same element that have different numbers of neutrons (p. 144)

New Vocabulary
fossil
plate tectonics

FOLDABLES™
Study Organizer

Geologic Time Make the following Foldable to help you organize events in Earth's history and the major life forms that appeared during each event.

STEP 1 **Fold** two vertical sheets of paper in half from top to bottom.

STEP 2 **Turn** both papers horizontally and **cut** the papers in half along the folds.

STEP 3 **Fold** the four vertical pieces in half from top to bottom.

STEP 4 **Turn** the papers horizontally. **Tape** the short ends of the pieces together (overlapping the edges slightly) to make an accordion time line.

STEP 5 **Label** each fold.

Tape

Sequence As you read Chapter 14, arrange the divisions of the geologic scale from oldest to youngest beginning at the far left of the Foldable. Then write the major life forms and events that appeared in each era.

Physical Science Connection

Movement of heat The movement of heat from Earth's interior out to space involves the processes of conduction, convection, and radiation. Earth's interior can behave like a fluid, so that heat is transferred to the outer crust by convection and conduction. Heat then moves through the solid crust by conduction and into space by radiation.

Early History of Earth

What was early Earth like? Some scientists suggest that it was probably very hot. The energy from colliding meteorites could have heated its surface, while both the compression of minerals and the decay of radioactive materials heated its interior. Volcanoes might have frequently spewed lava and gases, relieving some of the pressure in Earth's hot interior. These gases helped form Earth's early atmosphere. Although it probably contained no free oxygen, water vapor and other gases, such as carbon dioxide and nitrogen, most likely were present. If ancient Earth's atmosphere was like this, you would not have survived in it.

About 4.4 billion years ago, Earth might have cooled enough for the water in its atmosphere to condense. This might have led to millions of years of rainstorms with lightning—enough rain to fill depressions that became Earth's oceans. Some scientists propose that life originated in Earth's oceans between 3.9 and 3.4 billion years ago.

14.1 THE RECORD OF LIFE **369**

---

1 Focus

INTERACTIVE CHALKBOARD
PowerPoint® Presentations

Bellringer
Section Focus Transparency 35

Transparency **35** Inferring from Fossils

SECTION FOCUS
Use with Chapter 14, Section 14.1

1 The diagram shows a set of fossilized footprints. What observations can you make about the footprints?

2 What can you infer from the observations?

BIOLOGY: The Dynamics of Life
SECTION FOCUS TRANSPARENCIES

FOLDABLES™
For an additional Foldables activity idea, see the Chapter 14 Foldables page in *Unit 5 FAST FILE Resources.*

Physical Science Connection

Have students brainstorm other examples of heat movement, and classify them by type. radiant—heat moves from a fireplace into a surrounding room; conductive—metal spoon becomes hot when left in contact with a pan on the stove; convective—warm air masses rise and cooler air masses sink, forming convection cells in the atmosphere

---

RESOURCE MANAGER

Unit 5 FAST FILE Resources
MiniLab Worksheet, pp. 3, 4
BioLab Worksheet, pp. 5–6
Reinforcement and Study Guide in English, pp. 7–8
Reinforcement and Study Guide in Spanish, pp. 11–12
Concept Mapping, p. 15

Critical Thinking/Problem Solving, p. 16
Transparency Worksheets, pp. 17, 21–22
Reading Essentials for Biology, Section 14.1
Laboratory Manual, pp. 83–84, 85–86
Section Focus Transparency 35

Reteaching Skills Transparency 23

Students sometimes think that fossils are rare when, in fact, fossils can be found nearly anywhere sedimentary rocks are exposed.

Uncover the Misconception

Ask students to describe what they think of when they hear the word *fossil*. Describe the process of fossilization.

Demonstrate the Concept

Show students several examples of fossils. Point out that the fossil record is far from complete because most organisms decay before they can be fossilized. Explain that when environments are favorable for fossilization, fossils sometimes occur in millions. Fossils have been found nearly everywhere that sedimentary rock layers occur.

Assess New Knowledge

Challenge students to describe where fossils may be found in your area. Some students may point out that fossils occur in the limestone used in buildings. If time permits, you may have students bring in fossils that they have found in their area.

Indiana Academic Standards

Pages 370–371: B.1.32

History in Rocks

Can scientists be sure that Earth formed in this way? No, they cannot. There is no direct evidence of the earliest years of Earth's history. The physical processes of Earth constantly destroy and form rocks. The oldest rocks that have been found on Earth formed about 3.9 billion years ago. Although rocks cannot provide information about Earth's infancy, they are an important source of information about the diversity of life that has existed on the planet.

Fossils—Clues to the past

If you've ever visited a zoo or toured a botanical garden, you've seen evidence of the diversity of life. But the millions of species living today are probably only a small fraction of all the species that ever existed. About 95 percent of the species that have existed are extinct—they no longer live on Earth. Among other techniques, scientists study fossils to learn about ancient species. A **fossil** is evidence of an organism that lived long ago.

Because fossils can form in many different ways, there are many types of fossils, as you can see in *Table 14.1*. Use the *MiniLab* on the next page to observe some marine fossils under your microscope.

Paleontologists—Detectives to the past

The study of fossils is a lot like solving a mystery. Paleontologists (pay lee ahn TAHL uh justs), scientists who study ancient life, are like detectives who use fossils to understand events that happened long ago. They use fossils to determine the kinds of organisms that lived during the past and sometimes to learn about their behavior. For example, fossil bones and

Table 14.1 Some Types of Fossils		
Fossils Types	**Formation**	**Example**
Trace fossils	A trace fossil is any indirect evidence left by an animal and may include a footprint, a trail, or a burrow.	
Casts	When minerals in rocks fill a space left by a decayed organism, they make a replica, or cast, of the organism.	
Molds	A mold forms when an organism is buried in sediment and then decays, leaving an empty space.	
Petrified/ Permineralized fossils	Petrified—minerals sometimes penetrate and replace the hard parts of an organism. Permineralized—void spaces in original organism infilled by minerals.	
Amber- preserved or frozen fossils	At times, an entire organism was quickly trapped in ice or tree sap that hardened into amber.	

370

Motonori Matuyama and Paleomagnetism For unexplained reasons, Earth's magnetic polarity has changed many times so that Earth's north magnetic pole became Earth's south magnetic pole or vice versa. The Japanese geologist Motonori Matuyama (1884–1958) first discovered these reversals. Because these polarity changes have been dated in volcanic rocks, the magnetic polarity of some sedimentary successions can be used to estimate the ages of the rock layers.

teeth can indicate the size of animals, how they moved, and what they ate.

Paleontologists also study fossils to gain knowledge about ancient climate and geography. For example, when scientists find a fossil like the one in *Figure 14.1*, which resembles a present-day plant that lives in a mild climate, they may reason that the ancient environment was also mild.

By studying the condition, position, and location of rocks and fossils, geologists and paleontologists can make deductions about the geography of past environments. You can use the *Problem-Solving Lab* on the next page to try to solve a fossil mystery.

✓ **Reading Check** **Infer** how fossil teeth could be used to determine an animal's diet.

Fossil formation

For fossils to form, organisms usually have to be buried in mud, sand, or clay soon after they die. These particles are compressed over time and harden into a type of rock called sedimentary rock. Today, fossils still form at the bottoms of lakes, streams, and oceans.

Most fossils are found in sedimentary rocks. These rocks form at relatively low temperatures and pressures that may prevent damage to the organism. How do these fossils become visible millions of years later?

MiniLab 14.1

Observe and Infer

Marine Fossils Certain sedimentary rocks are formed almost totally from the fossils of once-living marine or ocean organisms called diatoms. These sedimentary rocks usually form in oceans, but can be lifted above sea level during periods of geological change.

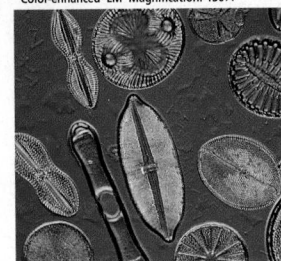
Color-enhanced LM Magnification: 130×
Present-day diatoms

Procedure

1. Prepare a wet mount of a small amount of diatomaceous earth. **CAUTION:** *Use care in handling microscope slides and coverslips. Do not breathe in dry diatomaceous earth.*
2. Examine the material under low-power magnification.
3. Draw several of the different shapes you see.
4. Compare the shapes of the fossils you observe to present-day diatoms shown in the photograph. Remember, however, that the fossils you observe are probably only pieces of the whole organism.

Analysis

1. **Describe** Describe the appearance of fossil diatoms.
2. **Compare and Contrast** How are fossil diatoms similar to and different from the diatoms in the photo? Can you use these similarities and differences to predict how diatoms have changed over time? Explain your answer.
3. **Infer** What part of the original diatom did you observe under the microscope? How did this part survive millions of years? Why were the fossils you observed broken?

Ⓐ **Figure 14.1**
This fossil leaf is from rocks about 200 million years old **(A)**. They are remarkably similar to the leaves of *Ginkgo biloba* **(B)**, trees that are planted as ornamentals throughout the United States.

Ⓑ

14.1 THE RECORD OF LIFE **371**

✓ **Reading Check** The type of fossil teeth can show whether an animal was an herbivore, carnivore, or omnivore.

Purpose

Students will analyze a situation and evaluate its explanations.

Background

It is assumed that the fossil ferns grew in similar temperate climates as the modern fern species.

Process Skills

analyze information, draw a conclusion, judge, think critically

Teaching Strategies

Review the appearance of Gondwanaland.

Thinking Critically

1. It's unlikely that ferns could grow in Antarctica's current cold temperatures. The presence of these fern fossils must mean that Antarctica was much warmer at one time.
2. not reasonable; It is unlikely that mutations could result in ferns adapted to extreme cold.
3. reasonable; Antarctica may have been closer to the equator and thus, its climate would have been warmer.

Modified Assessment

Skill Ask students to suggest other reasons why fern fossils are in Antarctica. Use the Performance Task Assessment List for Designing an Experiment in **PASC,** p. 95. **L1**

Caption Question Answer

Figure 14.2 There could have been faulting or folding to overturn the sequence.

Problem-Solving Lab 14.1

Think Critically

Could ferns have lived in Antarctica? Scientists have discovered fossil remains of ferns in the rocks of Antarctica. These fern fossils are related to ferns that grow in temperate climates on Earth today.

Fern fossil from Antarctica

Solve the Problem

Read each statement below and critique whether or not the statement is reasonable. Explain the reason for each of your critiques.

Thinking Critically

1. Fern fossils in Antarctica are of plants that could withstand freezing temperatures.
2. The ferns in Antarctica may have been mutated forms of ferns that grew in warm climates.
3. The temperature of Earth may have been much warmer millions of years ago than it is today.

Figure 14.2

Most sedimentary rocks form in primarily horizontal layers with the younger layers closer to the surface. Older rocks and fossils will be found deeper in the sequence, with the oldest at the bottom. **Infer** *What might have happened to a section with the oldest fossils at the top of the sequence?*

To answer the question, look at *Figure 14.3.* Fossils are not usually found in other types of rock because of the ways those rocks form. For example, metamorphic rocks form when heat, pressure, and chemical reactions change other rocks. The conditions under which metamorphic rocks form often destroy any fossils that were in the original sedimentary rock.

Relative dating

Scientists use a variety of methods to determine the age of fossils. One method is a technique called relative dating. To understand relative dating, imagine yourself stacking newspapers at home. As each day's newspaper is added to the stack, the stack becomes taller. If the stack is left undisturbed, the newspapers at the bottom are older than ones at the top.

The relative dating of rock layers uses the same principle. In *Figure 14.2,* you see fossils in different layers of rock. If the rock layers have not been disturbed, the layers at the surface must be younger than the deeper layers. The fossils in the top layer must also be younger than those in deeper layers. Using this principle, scientists can determine relative age and the order of appearance of the species that are preserved as fossils in the layers.

Radiometric dating

You cannot determine the actual age in years of a fossil or rock by using relative dating techniques. To find the specific ages of rocks, scientists use radiometric dating techniques utilizing the radioactive isotopes in rocks. Most fossils and sedimentary rocks cannot be directly radiometrically dated. Most dates are for volcanic or other igneous rocks, or metamorphic rocks that are closely associated with the sedimentary rocks.

The Fossilization Process

Figure 14.3
Few organisms become fossilized because, without burial, bacteria and fungi immediately decompose their dead bodies. Occasionally, however, organisms do become fossils in a process that usually takes many years. Most fossils are found in sedimentary rocks. **Critical Thinking** *Describe how the movements of Earth might expose a fossil.*

Protoceratops skull

A **A Protoceratops*** drinking at a river falls into the water and drowns. *An adult Protoceratops was about 2.4 meters long (8 feet).

B **Sediments from upstream** rapidly cover the body, slowing its decomposition. Minerals from the sediments seep into the body.

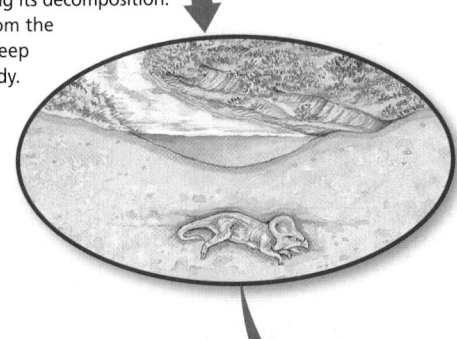

C **Over time,** additional layers of sediment compress the sediments around the body, forming rock. Minerals eventually replace all the body's bone material.

E **After discovery,** scientists carefully extract the fossil from the surrounding rock.

D **Earth movements** or erosion may expose the fossil millions of years after it formed.

14.1 THE RECORD OF LIFE **373**

Purpose
Students will study some of the geological and biological processes involved in fossil formation.

Teaching Strategies
■ Point out that an organism's remains are subjected to destructive environmental factors, such as bacterial decay, heat, cold, and pressure. Therefore, the number and quality of fossils is limited.
■ Have students make a flowchart of the events that lead to the formation of fossils. **L2**

Visual Learning
Visual-Spatial Sedimentation allows fossils to form. Model the process using objects and sediments of various sizes and weights placed in a 2-L plastic container three-quarters full of water. Shake the container. Have students observe what occurs. Explain that over time, pressure and other physical and chemical changes can result in the formation of fossils. **L2 ELL**

Critical Thinking
Earth's surface can rupture during earthquakes and some rock layers can fold over others. Uplift by faulting or folding may expose layers containing fossils to erosion. The slow erosion of rock may uncover fossils.

PROJECT

Fossil Preservation: *Kinesthetic* Student groups can carry out the following activity to learn more about the preservation of fossils.
1. Place fresh fruit, such as strawberries or orange slices, in an open plastic container. Cover the fruit with water and place the container in a freezer.

2. Put the same amount and types of fruit in a similar container. Leave the container undisturbed at room temperature.

3. After three days, observe all the fruit. Summarize your observations and draw a conclusion about any differences you observe between the containers. **L1 ELL COOP LEARN**

Explain to students that radioactive dating is an accurate technique for geological timekeeping because the decay rate of a radioactive element is constant.

Enrichment

Visual-Spatial If possible, schedule a visit to a local museum of natural history. Most have displays of the geological time scale and fossils. **L2** **ELL**

CAREERS IN BIOLOGY

Career Path
Courses in high school: biology, mathematics, and English
College: degree in biology or zoology for zoo/aquarium work
Other educational sources: on-the-job-training; two-year program in animal health

Career Issue
Ask students whether they think a person can love animals so much that he or she is unable to care for them effectively. Have them explain their answers.

For More Information
For more information, write to:
American Association of
  Zoo Keepers, Inc.
3601 SW 29th St., Ste. 133
Topeka, Kansas 66614-2054
  or
Animal Caretakers
  Information
Humane Society of the
  United States
Companion Animals Division
2100 L Street NW
Washington, DC 20037

374

CAREERS IN BIOLOGY

Animal Keeper

Would you like to make a career out of caring for animals? There are many opportunities if you love animals.

Skills for the Job

Animal keepers or caretakers give animals food and water, exercise them, clean their cages, groom them, monitor their health, and sometimes administer medicines. Keepers must finish high school. Many pet shops, kennels, shelters, and stables provide on-the-job training. Humane societies, veterinarians, and research laboratories hire graduates of two-year programs in animal health. Most zoos and aquariums employ keepers with four-year degrees in zoology or biology. Taking care of animals often means working weekends and holidays, so keepers must care about their work.

 For more careers in related fields, visit
in.bdol.glencoe.com/careers

Recall that radioactive isotopes are atoms with unstable nuclei that break down, or decay, over time, giving off radiation. A radioactive isotope forms a new isotope after it decays. The rate at which a radioactive isotope decays is related to the half-life of the isotope. The half-life is the length of time needed for half of the atoms of the isotope to decay.

Scientists try to determine the approximate ages of rocks by comparing the amount of a radioactive isotope and the new isotope into which it decays. For example, suppose that when a rock forms it contains a radioactive isotope that decays to half its original amount in one million years. Today, if the rock contains equal amounts of the original radioactive isotope and the new isotope into which it decays, then the rock must be about 1 million years old.

Scientists use potassium-40, a radioactive isotope that decays to argon-40, to date rocks containing potassium-bearing minerals. Based on chemical analysis, chemists have determined that potassium-40 decays to half its original amount in 1.3 billion years. Scientists use carbon-14 to date fossils

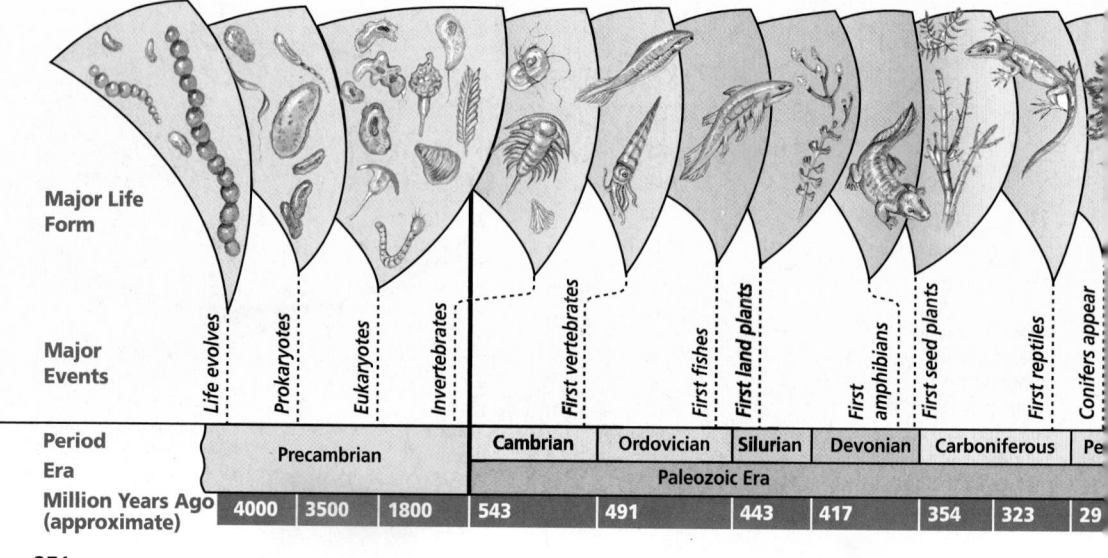

Major Life Form										
Major Events	Life evolves	Prokaryotes	Eukaryotes	Invertebrates	First vertebrates	First fishes	First land plants	First amphibians	First seed plants	First reptiles	Conifers appear
Period		Precambrian			Cambrian	Ordovician	Silurian	Devonian	Carboniferous	Pe
Era						Paleozoic Era				
Million Years Ago (approximate)	4000	3500	1800	543	491	443	417	354	323	29

CHALLENGE ACTIVITY

Graphing For those students who need an extra challenge, have them solve the following problems by drawing a bar graph.
■ A radioactive element has a half-life of 20 days. How much of a 16-g sample of the radioactive element will remain unchanged after 80 days? 1 g

■ A fossil contains a radioactive element with a half-life of 10 000 years. If the ratio of radioactive element to the decay element is 1:3, how old is the fossil? 2 half-lives or 20 000 years
See *BioChallenges and Enrichment* for additional projects and activities. **L3**

less than 50 000 years old. Again, based on chemical analysis, they know that carbon-14 decays to half its original amount in 5730 years.

Use the *BioLab* at the end of this chapter to simulate this dating technique. Scientists always analyze many samples of a rock using as many methods as possible to obtain consistent values for the rock's age. Errors can occur if the rock has been heated, causing some of the radioactive isotopes to be lost or gained. If this occurs, the age obtained will be inaccurate.

A Trip Through Geologic Time

By examining sequences containing sedimentary rock and fossils and dating some of the igneous or metamorphic rocks that are found in the sequences, scientists have put together a chronology, or calendar, of Earth's history. This chronology, called the geologic time scale, is based on evidence from Earth's rocks and fossils.

The geologic time scale

Rather than being based on months or even years, the geologic time scale is divided into four large sections that you see in *Figure 14.4*—the Precambrian (pree KAM bree un), the Paleozoic (pay lee uh ZOH ihk) Era, the Mesozoic (me zuh ZOH ihk) Era, and the Cenozoic (se nuh ZOH ihk) Era. An era is a large division in the scale and represents a very long period of time. Each era is subdivided into periods.

The divisions in the geologic time scale are distinguished by the organisms that lived during that time interval. The fossil record indicates that there were several episodes of mass extinction that fall between time divisions. A mass extinction is an event that occurs when many organisms disappear from the fossil record almost at once.

The geologic time scale begins with the formation of Earth about 4.6 billion years ago. To understand the large size of this number, try the *MiniLab* on the next page, and also try scaling down

Figure 14.4
The geologic time scale is a calendar of Earth's history based on evidence found in rocks. Life probably first appeared on Earth between 3.9 and 3.4 billion years ago.

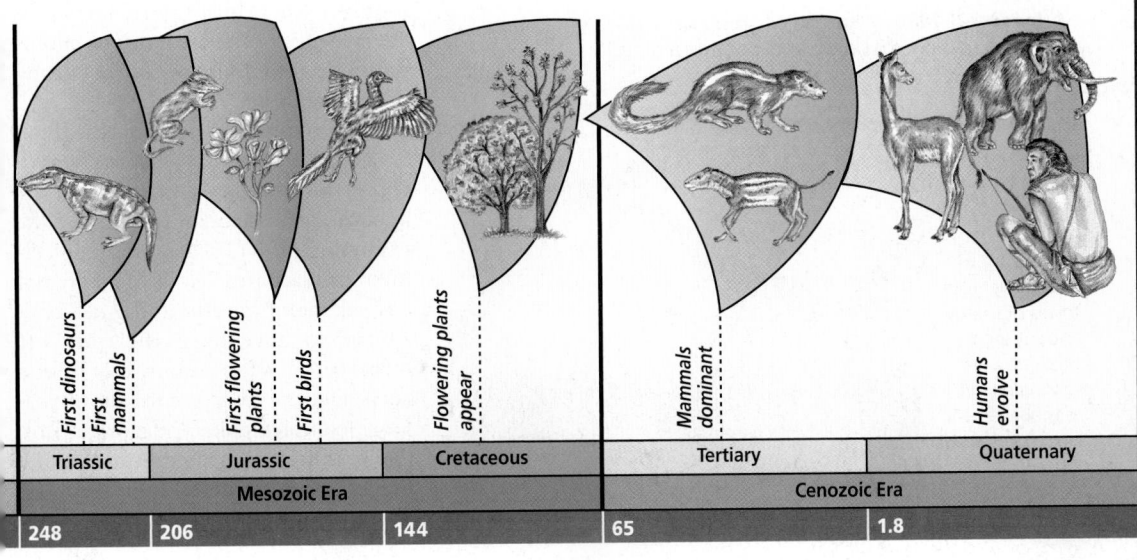

First dinosaurs / First mammals	First flowering plants	First birds	Flowering plants appear	Mammals dominant	Humans evolve
Triassic	Jurassic		Cretaceous	Tertiary	Quaternary
	Mesozoic Era			Cenozoic Era	
248	206		144	65	1.8

The BioLab at the end of the chapter can be used at this point in the lesson.

Resources

For additional high interest activities, see the *Forensics and Biotechnology Lab Manual.*

Chalkboard Example

To illustrate the concept of geological time, reproduce on the chalkboard or an overhead transparency a page from a monthly calendar. Remind students that the total area of the page represents a unit of time equal to one month. Divide the calendar into four (or five) horizontal strips. Ask students what amount of time each strip represents. one week Cut one of the strips into seven pieces and ask students what each square represents. one day Then, ask students how minutes and seconds could be shown. Elicit from students how geologic time, like calendars, is also divided into units.

USING MODELS

Summarizing Geological Time Have students draw a large box on a sheet of paper in their journals. Then have them divide the box into four smaller boxes. Have students label each box with the name of a major interval of geologic time: Precambrian time, Paleozoic Era, Mesozoic Era, Cenozoic Era. As students read about these time intervals, have them write descriptive terms or phrases inside the appropriate box. Students can use their sheets as study tools. **L1 ELL**

Indiana Academic Standards
Pages 374–375: B.1.32

MiniLab 14.2

Purpose
Students will model the geologic time scale.

Process Skills
use a table, sequence, measure in SI

Teaching Strategies
- Review how to make a scale model.
- Review the geologic time scale's major divisions.

Expected Results
Students perform the calculations that establish their scales. They plot major events on the scale.

Analysis
1. the longest era—Paleozoic; the shortest era—Cenozoic
2. Mesozoic Era
3. primates

Modified Assessment
Performance Have student groups collect pictures of 15–20 organisms. Ask them to illustrate the geologic time scale on poster board, and glue each picture where the organism first appeared in the fossil record. Use the Performance Task Assessment List for Poster in **PASC**, p. 145.
L1 **ELL** **COOP LEARN**

Organize Data

A Time Line In this activity, you will construct a time line that is a scale model of the geologic time scale. Use a scale in which 1 meter equals 1 billion years. Each millimeter then represents 1 million years.

Procedure
1. Use a meterstick to draw a continuous line down the middle of a 5-m strip of adding-machine tape.
2. At one end of the tape, draw a vertical line and label it "The Present."
3. Measure off the distance that represents 4.6 billion years ago. Draw a vertical line at that point and label it "Earth's Beginning."
4. Using the table at right, plot the location of each event on your time line. Label the event, and label when it occurred.

Geologic Time Scale	
Event	Estimated Years Ago
Earliest evidence of life	3.4 billion
Paleozoic Era begins	543 million
First land plants	443 million
Mesozoic Era begins	248 million
Triassic Period begins	248 million
Jurassic Period begins	206 million
First dinosaurs	225 million
First birds	150 million
Cretaceous Period begins	144 million
Dinosaurs become extinct	65 million
Cenozoic Era begins	65 million
Primates appear	65 million
Humans appear	200 000

Analysis
1. **Calculate** Which era is the longest? The shortest?
2. **Interpret Data** In which eras did dinosaurs and birds appear on Earth?
3. **Interpret Data** What major group first appeared around the same time that dinosaurs became extinct?

Figure 14.5
The filamentous fossils of these ancient organisms resemble some modern cyanobacteria.

376 THE HISTORY OF LIFE

Life during the Precambrian

the history of Earth into a familiar, but hypothetical, calendar year.

In your hypothetical calendar year, the first day of January becomes the date on which Earth formed. The oldest fossils are found in Precambrian rocks that are about 3.4 billion years old—near the end of March on the hypothetical calendar. Scientists found these fossils, which are shown in *Figure 14.5*, in rocks found in the deserts of western Australia. They have found more examples of similar types of fossils on other continents. The fossils resemble the forms of modern species of photosynthetic cyanobacteria (si a noh bak TIHR ee uh). You will read more about cyanobacteria in a later chapter.

Scientists have also found dome-shaped structures called stromatolites (stroh MAT ul ites) in Australia and on other continents. Stromatolites still form today in Australia from mats of cyanobacteria, *Figure 14.6*. Thus, the stromatolites are evidence of the existence of photosynthetic organisms on Earth during the Precambrian.

The Precambrian accounts for about 87 percent of Earth's history—until about the middle of October in the hypothetical calendar year. Near the beginning of the Precambrian, unicellular prokaryotes—cells that do not have a membrane-bound nucleus—appear to have been the only life forms on Earth. About 2.1 billion years ago, the fossil record shows that more complex eukaryotic organisms, living things with membrane-bound nuclei in their cells, appeared. By the end of the Precambrian, about

---

PROJECT

Extinct Animals Ask students to research an extinct animal, such as a woolly mammoth, brachiosaur, pterodactyl, or saber-toothed cat. Have them describe in their journals what foods, environments, enclosures, or other factors might be required to keep the animal alive in a zoo. **L2**

CHALLENGE ACTIVITY

Development of the Geologic Time Scale Have students prepare a newspaper article describing the argument between Adam Sedgwick and Roderick Murchison about the definition of the boundary between Cambrian rocks and Silurian rocks in Britain.

543 million years ago, multicellular eukaryotes, such as sponges and jellyfishes, diversified and filled the oceans.

Diversity during the Paleozoic

In the Paleozoic Era, which lasted until 248 million years ago, many more types of animals and plants were present on Earth, and some were preserved in the fossil record. The earliest part of the Paleozoic Era is called the Cambrian Period. Paleontologists often refer to a "Cambrian explosion" of life because the fossil record shows an enormous increase in the diversity of life forms during this time. During the Cambrian Period, the oceans teemed with many types of animals, including worms, sea stars, and unusual arthropods, similar to the one shown in *Figure 14.7*.

During the first half of the Paleozoic, fishes, the oldest animals with backbones, appeared in Earth's waters. There is also fossil evidence of ferns and early seed plants existing on land about 400 million years ago. Around the middle of the Paleozoic, four-legged animals such as amphibians appeared on Earth. During the last half of the era, the fossil record shows that reptiles appeared and began to flourish on land.

The largest mass extinction recorded in the fossil record marked the end of the Paleozoic. About 90 percent of Earth's marine species and 70 percent of the land species disappeared at this time.

Life in the Mesozoic

The Mesozoic Era began about 248 million years ago, which would be about December 10 on the hypothetical one-year calendar. Many changes, in both Earth's organisms and its geology, occurred over the span of this era.

Figure 14.6
Fossils of stromatolites, similar to the modern Australian examples shown here, provide evidence that photosynthetic cyanobacteria lived on Earth 3.4 billion years ago.

The Mesozoic Era is divided into three periods. Fossils from the Triassic Period, the oldest period, show that mammals appeared on Earth at this time. These fossils of mammals indicate that early mammals were small and mouselike. They probably scurried around in the shadows of huge fern forests, trying to avoid dinosaurs, reptiles that also appeared during this time.

The middle of the Mesozoic, called the Jurassic Period, began about 206 million years ago, or mid-December on the hypothetical calendar.

Recent fossil discoveries support the idea that modern birds evolved from one of the groups of dinosaurs toward the end of this period.

Figure 14.7
Arthropods, similar to this Devonian trilobite, were among the many groups of animals that first appeared during the Cambrian explosion.

377

Figure 14.8
Both fossil evidence like this *Archaeopteryx* (**A**) and some characteristics of present-day birds like this hoatzin (**B**) suggest that dinosaurs might have been the ancestors of today's birds.

Word Origin

tectonics from the Greek word *tecton,* meaning "builder"; Plate tectonics is a theory that explains mountain building.

For example, in ***Figure 14.8A,*** you see the fossil of *Archaeopteryx,* a small bird discovered in Germany. The fossil reveals that *Archaeopteryx* had feathers, a birdlike feature. You also see a present-day bird, the hoatzin, in ***Figure 14.8B.*** This bird has a reptilian feature, claws on its wings, for its first few weeks of life. It also flies poorly, as the earliest birds probably did. Scientists suggest that such evidence supports the idea that modern birds evolved from dinosaurs.

A mass extinction

The last period in the Mesozoic, the Cretaceous, began about 144 million years ago. During this period, many new types of mammals appeared and flowering plants flourished on Earth. The mass extinction of the dinosaurs marked the end of the Cretaceous Period about 65 million years ago. Scientists estimate that not only dinosaurs, but more than two-thirds of all living species at the time became extinct. Some scientists propose that a large meteorite collision caused this mass extinction. Such a collision could have filled the atmosphere with thick, possibly toxic dust that, in turn, changed the climate to one in which many species could no longer survive. Based on geological evidence of a large crater of Cretaceous age in the waters off eastern Mexico, scientists theorize that this was the impact site.

Changes during the Mesozoic

Geological events during the Mesozoic changed the places in which species lived and affected their distribution on Earth. The theory of continental drift, which is illustrated in ***Figure 14.9,*** suggests that Earth's continents have moved during Earth's history and are still moving today at a rate of about six centimeters per year. This is about the same rate at which your hair grows. Early in the Mesozoic, the continents were merged into one large landmass. During the era, this supercontinent broke up and the pieces drifted apart.

378 THE HISTORY OF LIFE

The theory that explains how the continents move is called **plate tectonics** (tek TAH nihks). According to this idea, Earth's surface consists of several rigid plates that drift on top of a plastic (capable of flow), partially molten layer of rock. These plates are continually moving—spreading apart, sliding by, or pushing against each other. The movements affect organisms. For example, after a long time, the descendants of organisms living on plates that are moving apart may be living in areas with very different climates.

The Cenozoic Era

The Cenozoic began about 65 million years ago—around December 26 on the hypothetical calendar of Earth's history. It is the era in which you now live. Mammals began to flourish during the early part of this era. Among the mammals that appeared was a group of animals to which you belong, the primates. Primates first appeared approximately more than 65 million years ago and have diversified greatly. The modern human species appeared perhaps as recently as 200 000 years ago. On the hypothetical calendar of Earth's history, 200 000 years ago is late in the evening of December 31.

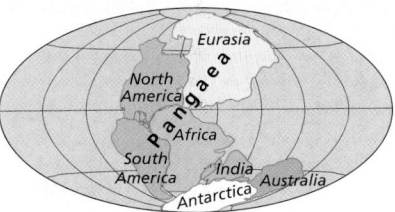

A About 245 million years ago, the continents were joined in a landmass known as Pangaea.

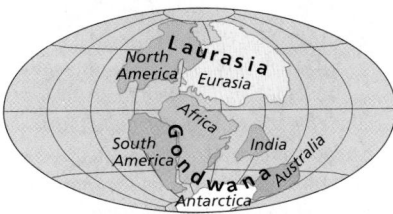

B By 135 million years ago, Pangaea broke apart resulting in two large landmasses.

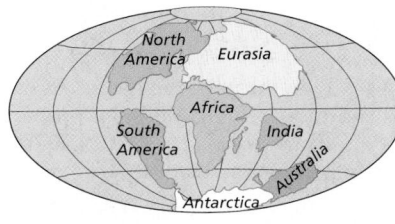

C By 65 million years ago, the end of the Mesozoic, most of the continents had taken on their modern shapes.

Figure 14.9
The theory of continental drift describes the movement of the landmasses over geological time. **Describe** *How has Africa moved over time?*

3 Assess

DAILY INTERVENTION

Check for Understanding
Interpersonal Prepare an in-class "game show" to check student understanding of the topics in this section. Prepare questions on index cards in a variety of categories, such as types of fossils, fossil formation, dating techniques, and the geologic time scale. Have students work in teams to answer the questions. **L2** **ELL** **COOP LEARN**

Reteach
Visual-Spatial Have students demonstrate the concept of radiometric dating using balls of clay or other materials to represent radioactive materials. **L1**

Resources
For more practice, use *Reading Essentials for Biology*, Section 14.1.

MODIFIED Assessment

Performance Ask groups of students to pick one division of the geologic time scale, and show on a bulletin board all the kinds of life that existed then. **L1** **ELL** **COOP LEARN**

Caption Question Answer
Figure 14.9 Africa has moved from high latitudes closer to the south pole toward the equator.

Section Assessment

Understanding Main Ideas
1. Describe what some scientists propose Earth was like before life arose.
2. Why are most fossils found in sedimentary rocks?
3. Using fossils, identify evidence showing that species have changed over geologic time.
4. Explain the difference between relative dating and radiometric dating.

Thinking Critically
5. Suppose you are examining layers of sedimentary rock. In one layer, you discover the remains of an extinct relative of the polar bear. In a deeper layer, you discover the fossil of an extinct alligator. What can you hypothesize about changes over time in this area's environment?

SKILL REVIEW

6. **Make and Use Tables** Make a table listing the four major divisions of the geologic time scale, their time spans, and the major life forms that appeared during each interval. Use the information to construct a time line based on a clock face. For more help, refer to *Make and Use Tables* in the **Skill Handbook**.

Section Assessment

1. Earth was hot, meteors bombarded its surface, and volcanoes erupted. As Earth cooled, it rained constantly.
2. They form at low temperatures and pressures, preventing damage to a fossil.
3. Precambrian fossils were simple prokaryotic organisms. Through time, organisms have become more complex. Through time, many organisms have become extinct, such as trilobites, dinosaurs, and mastodons. Fossil evidence from organisms, such as *Archaeopteryx*, shows both reptile-like and bird-like characteristics.
4. Relative dating relies on the position of rock layers and results in relative dates. Radiometric dating relies on half-lives of radioactive elements.
5. The climate of the region may have changed from a warmer one to a colder one.
6. Tables should be constructed from the information in Figure 14.4 and under the heading "A Trip Through Geologic Time" in the text. Check tables and time lines for accuracy.

1 Focus

INTERACTIVE CHALKBOARD
PowerPoint® Presentations

Bellringer
Section Focus Transparency 36

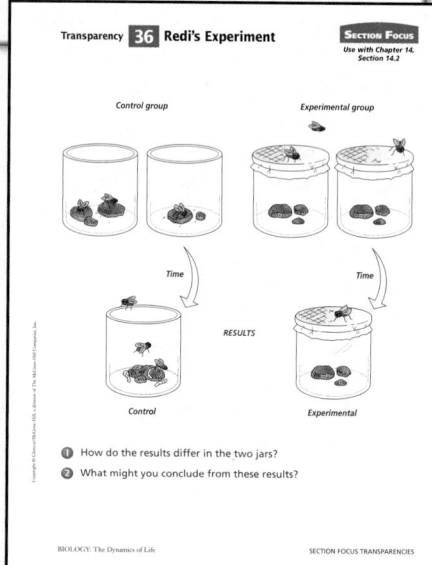

Transparency **36** Redi's Experiment

SECTION FOCUS
Use with Chapter 14, Section 14.2

Control group   Experimental group

Time   Time

RESULTS

Control   Experimental

① How do the results differ in the two jars?
② What might you conclude from these results?

BIOLOGY: The Dynamics of Life   SECTION FOCUS TRANSPARENCIES

Using Prior Knowledge

Experiment The cooked hot dog should change more slowly than the uncooked hot dog. The reason is that more bacteria were present in the uncooked meat and began to decompose the hot dog faster.

Section 14.2

The Origin of Life

Indiana Standards Standard B.1.33 Describe how life on Earth is thought to have begun as simple, one-celled organisms about 4 billion years. Note that during the first 2 billion years, only single-cell microorganisms existed, but once cells with nuclei developed about a billion years ago, increasingly complex multicellular organisms evolved.

SECTION PREVIEW

Objectives

Analyze early experiments that support the concept of biogenesis.

Review, analyze, and critique modern theories of the origin of life.

Relate hypotheses about the origin of cells to the environmental conditions of early Earth.

Review Vocabulary
prokaryotes: unicellular organisms that lack internal membrane-bound structures (p. 173)

New Vocabulary
spontaneous generation
biogenesis
protocell
archaebacteria

Figure 14.10
Francesco Redi's controlled experiment tested the spontaneous generation of maggots from decaying meat.

Mold and Mudskippers

Using Prior Knowledge You've probably opened your refrigerator and found some leftovers with an unpleasant surprise—mold. Where did the mold come from? Was it in the air or in the food originally? Did these mudskippers come from the mud or from the air?

Experiment *Cut a hot dog in half. Cook one half and place it in an airtight, sealable plastic bag. Place the uncooked half in another airtight, sealable plastic bag. Leave both bags out at room temperature until a change is observed. How did each hot dog sample change? Which sample changed faster? Hypothesize why the changes you observed occurred.*

Mudskippers

Origins: The Early Ideas

In the past, the ideas that decaying meat produced maggots, mud produced fishes, and grain produced mice were reasonable explanations for what people observed occurring in their environment. After all, they saw maggots appear on meat and young mice appear in sacks of grain. Such observations led people to believe in **spontaneous generation**—the idea that nonliving material can produce life.

Control group   Time

Ⓐ Redi placed decaying meat in several uncovered control jars and in covered experimental jars. The covers prevented flies from landing on the meat.

Experimental group   Time

Ⓑ In time, maggots and flies filled the open jars, but not the covered jars, showing that only flies produce flies.

RESOURCE MANAGER

Unit 5 *FAST FILE* Resources
Reinforcement and Study Guide in English, pp. 9–10
Reinforcement and Study Guide in Spanish, pp. 13–14
Transparency Worksheets, pp. 18, 19–20

Reading Essentials for Biology, Section 14.2
🔖 **Section Focus Transparency 36**
🔖 **Basic Concepts Transparency 20**

Figure 14.11
Some of Pasteur's flasks, still free of microorganisms, are at the Pasteur Institute in Paris.

A Each of Pasteur's broth-filled flasks was boiled to kill all microorganisms.

B The flask's S-shaped neck allowed air to enter, but prevented microorganisms from entering the flask.

C Pasteur tilted a flask, allowing the microorganisms to enter the broth.

D Microorganisms soon grew in the broth, showing that they come from other microorganisms.

Spontaneous generation is disproved

In 1668, an Italian physician, Francesco Redi, disproved a commonly held belief at the time—the idea that decaying meat produced maggots, which are immature flies. You can follow the steps of Redi's experiment in *Figure 14.10*. Redi's well-designed, controlled experiment successfully convinced many scientists that maggots, and probably most large organisms, did not arise by spontaneous generation.

However, during Redi's time, scientists began to use the latest tool in biology—the microscope. With the microscope, they saw that microorganisms live everywhere. Although Redi had disproved the spontaneous generation of large organisms, many scientists thought that microorganisms were so numerous and widespread that they must arise spontaneously—probably from a vital force in the air.

Pasteur's experiments

Disproving the existence of a vital force in air proved difficult. Finally, in the mid-1800s, Louis Pasteur designed an experiment that disproved the spontaneous generation of microorganisms. Pasteur set up an experiment in which air, but no microorganisms, was allowed to contact a broth that contained nutrients. You can see how Pasteur carried out his experiment in *Figure 14.11*.

Pasteur's experiment showed that microorganisms do not simply arise in broth, even in the presence of air. From that time on, **biogenesis** (bi oh JEN uh sus), the idea that living organisms come only from other living organisms, became a cornerstone of biology.

Origins: The Modern Ideas

Biologists have accepted the concept of biogenesis for more than 100 years. However, biogenesis does not answer the question: How did life begin on Earth? No one has yet proven scientifically how life on Earth began. However, scientists have developed theories about the origin of life

2 Teach

Quick Demo

Pasteur's Experiment
Explain that people once believed that life spontaneously arose from nonliving matter, such as broth. Dissolve two bouillon cubes in separate flasks of hot water. Boil the bouillon for several minutes. Seal one flask with a rubber stopper right away and label it *boiled* after it has cooled. Leave the second flask open. Set the flasks on a shelf in the classroom. Have students observe the flasks every day and record their observations in their portfolios. **L2 ELL**

Visual Learning

Figures 14.10 and 14.11 The experiments by Redi, Pasteur, and others to disprove spontaneous generation are examples of the application of scientific methods. Use the illustrations to reinforce students' understanding of scientific methods. Discuss the purpose of each step of the procedures with students.

Concept Development

Point out that the spontaneous generation of cells was harder to disprove than the spontaneous generation of whole organisms because microscopes were not powerful enough to show cells dividing until 1875.

INCLUSION STRATEGIES

Learning Disabled Have students use block diagrams on paper to model how the experiments of Redi or Pasteur demonstrate scientific methods. Have students record their procedures and observations. **L1 ELL**

USING MODELS

Disproving Spontaneous Generation Make a model of Redi's controlled experiment shown in Figure 14.10 using a *Drosophila* culture medium. Use this model to explain the idea of spontaneous generation and how Pasteur disproved the idea. **L2**

Tying to Prior Knowledge

Review the chemistry concepts that students studied previously, particularly the role of carbon in organic molecules. Review the general structure of proteins and nucleic acids. Relate this information to the hypotheses about the origin of life.

Word Origin

Have the students research to find other words using "primo" as part of the root, such as *primogenitor* and *primordial meristem*.

Tying to Prior Knowledge

Review the basic structure and function of cells. Emphasize the substances cells need to live and the different ways cells release energy. Relate this information to the evolution of cells.

Indiana Academic Standards

Pages 382–383: B.1.33

Figure 14.12
Miller and Urey's experiments showed that under the proposed conditions on early Earth, small organic molecules, such as amino acids, could form.

Entry for hydrogen, methane, and ammonia gases

Electrode

High voltage source

Condenser for cooling

Solution of organic compounds

Boiling water

Word Origin

primordial from the Latin word *primordium*, meaning "origin"; The origin of life may have been in the primordial soup.

on Earth from testing scientific hypotheses about conditions on early Earth. The *Biology and Society* at the end of this chapter summarizes some important viewpoints about the origin of life on Earth.

Simple organic molecules formed

Scientists hypothesize that two developments must have preceded the appearance of life on Earth. First, simple organic molecules, or molecules that contain carbon, must have formed. Then these molecules must have become organized into complex organic molecules such as proteins, carbohydrates, and nucleic acids that are essential to life.

Remember that Earth's early atmosphere probably contained no free oxygen. Instead, the atmosphere was probably composed of water vapor, carbon dioxide, nitrogen, and perhaps methane and ammonia. Many scientists have tried to explain how these substances could have joined together and formed the simple organic molecules that are found in all organisms today.

In the 1930s, a Russian scientist, Alexander Oparin, hypothesized that

life began in the oceans that formed on early Earth. He suggested that energy from the sun, lightning, and Earth's heat triggered chemical reactions to produce small organic molecules from the substances present in the atmosphere. Then, rain probably washed the molecules into the oceans to form what is often called a primordial soup.

In 1953, two American scientists, Stanley Miller and Harold Urey, tested Oparin's hypothesis by simulating the conditions of early Earth in the laboratory. In an experiment similar to the one shown in *Figure 14.12,* Miller and Urey mixed water vapor (steam) with ammonia, methane, and hydrogen gases. They then sent an electric current that simulated lightning through the mixture. Then, they cooled the mixture of gases, produced a liquid that simulated rain, and collected the liquid in a flask. After a week, they analyzed the chemicals in the flask and found several kinds of amino acids, sugars, and other small organic molecules, providing evidence that supported Oparin's hypothesis.

Additional Lab

Making Coacervates

Purpose
Students will investigate the conditions under which the first cells may have evolved.

Materials
1% gelatin solution, droppers (3), 1% gum arabic solution, pH papers, microscopes, microscope slides, coverslips, 0.1M hydrochloric acid (HCl), test tubes, stirring rods; For preparation instructions, see page 17T of the Teacher Guide.

Safety Precautions
Remind students to wear safety goggles, a lab apron, and disposable gloves. Remind

them to use care when working with a microscope and glass slides, and to wash hands thoroughly when finished.

Procedure
Give the following directions.
1. Measure 5 mL of 1% gelatin solution. Pour it into the test tube. Add 3 mL of 1% gum arabic solution. Mix gently.
2. Record the pH of the mixture.
3. Make a wet mount of the mixture. Observe under high power, and record

The formation of protocells

The next step in the origin of life, as proposed by some scientists, was the formation of complex organic compounds. In the 1950s, various experiments were performed and showed that if the amino acids are heated without oxygen, they link and form complex molecules called proteins. A similar process produces ATP and nucleic acids from small molecules. These experiments convinced many scientists that complex organic molecules might have originated in pools of water where small molecules had concentrated and been warmed.

How did these complex chemicals combine to form the first cells? The work of American biochemist Sidney Fox in 1992 showed how the first cells may have occurred. As you can see in *Figure 14.13*, Fox produced protocells by heating solutions of amino acids. A **protocell** is a large, ordered structure, enclosed by a membrane, that carries out some life activities, such as growth and division.

Reading Check **Summarize** the theories for how organic molecules were first formed on Earth.

The Evolution of Cells

Fossils indicate that by about 3.4 billion years ago, photosynthetic prokaryotic cells existed on Earth. But these were probably not the earliest cells. What were the earliest cells like, and how did they evolve?

The first true cells

The first forms of life may have been prokaryotic forms that evolved from a protocell. Because Earth's atmosphere lacked oxygen, scientists have proposed that these organisms were most likely anaerobic. For food, the first prokaryotes probably used some of the organic molecules that were abundant in Earth's early oceans. Because they obtained food rather than making it themselves, they would have been heterotrophs.

Over time, these heterotrophs would have used up the food supply. However, organisms that could make food had probably evolved by the time the food was gone. These first autotrophs were probably similar to present-day archaebacteria.

Visual Learning

Figure 14.13 Have students study the illustration of Fox's experiment. Discuss how Fox's experiment relates to Oparin's hypothesis and the Miller-Urey experiment.

Discussion

Ask students why studying modern archaebacteria and cyanobacteria is important for determining the origin of life. Such bacteria resemble the earliest known living things and indicate the conditions required to support life then.

Reading Check The first organic molecules were formed when energy from the sun or lightning combined with a mixture of water vapor, ammonia, methane, and hydrogen gas. Miller and Urey lent support to Oparin by showing that simple molecules could form complex organic compounds in a watery environment. Sidney Fox's experiments produced ordered structures called protocells from amino acids.

Color-enhanced TEM
Magnification: 7800×

Figure 14.13
Sidney Fox showed how short chains of amino acids could cluster to form protocells.

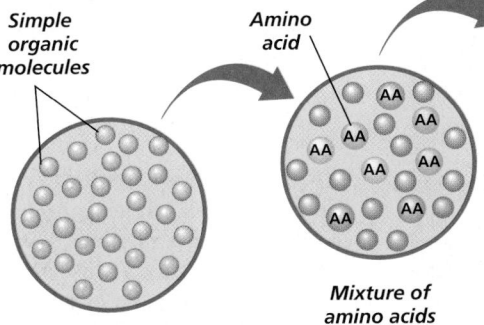

Simple organic molecules

Amino acid

Primordial soup

Mixture of amino acids

Short chains of amino acids that will form protocells

Protocells that simulate cell division

---

your observations.

4. Stir one drop of 0.1*M* HCl solution into the mixture. Record the mixture's pH.
5. Repeat step 3 for the HCl mixture.
6. Repeat steps 4 and 5 until you see coacervates, clumps that look like cells. Record the mixture's pH, and describe the appearance of the coacervates.
7. Repeat steps 4 and 5 until the coacervates disappear.

Analysis

1. What living things do coacervates resemble? cells
2. Around what pH did you observe coacervates? pH 5
3. What conditions of early Earth does the mixture of gelatin (a protein) and gum arabic (a carbohydrate) simulate? the amino acids and simple sugars in the "primordial soup"

Assessment

Knowledge Have students present an oral report of the investigation. Ask: "What was the role of hydrochloric acid? How does this investigation relate to hypotheses about the origin of life?" Use the Performance Task Assessment List for Oral Presentation in **PASC**, p. 143. **L2**

Purpose

Students will use a model to show events on the geologic time scale.

Process Skills

observe and infer, sequence, use an illustration

Teaching Strategies

■ Question students about the history of life to assess their knowledge before they start.
■ Students could also model the geologic time scale using a 24-hour clock.

Thinking Critically

Prokaryotes appeared around 4:00 to 4:30 A.M. and eukaryotes around 10:00 A.M.

Assessment

Knowledge Have students approximate the time of evolution of three other groups of organisms by finding out when they appear in the fossil record. **L2**

Caption Question Answer

Figure 14.14 In this environment, an organism would need to be able to survive high temperatures, possibly acidic conditions, and the presence of minerals, such as sulfur.

Inquiry

Discussion Ask students to evaluate the strengths and weaknesses of the endosymbiont theory. Be sure that students understand that Margulis's theory does not suggest how the original cells evolved. **L2**

Problem-Solving Lab 14.2

Interpret Data

Can a clock model Earth's history? As a result of studying fossils and analyzing geological events, scientists have been able to construct the geologic time scale, a timetable that shows the appearance of organisms during the history of Earth.

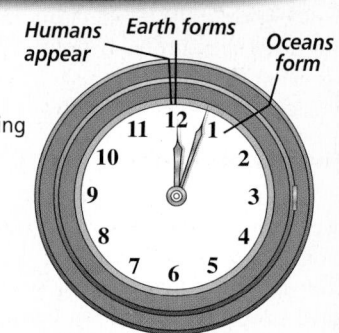

Humans appear · Earth forms · Oceans form

Solve the Problem

The diagram shown here compresses the history of Earth into a 12-hour clock face. On the clock, assume that the formation of Earth occurred at midnight. The oceans formed at 1:00 A.M. Use this information to help you answer the following questions.

Thinking Critically

Use Models Based on fossil evidence, at what time on the face of the clock did prokaryotes evolve? At what time did the first eukaryotes appear?

Figure 14.14
Present-day archaebacteria live in places like this hot spring in Yellowstone National Park. **Infer** *What adaptations would an organism need to survive in this environment?*

Archaebacteria (ar kee bac TEER ee uh) are prokaryotic and live in harsh environments, such as deep-sea vents and hot springs like the one shown in *Figure 14.14.* Some early autotrophs may have made glucose by chemosynthesis rather than by photosynthesis, which requires light-trapping pigments. These autotrophs released the energy of inorganic compounds, such as sulfur compounds, in their environment to make their food.

Photosynthesizing prokaryotes

Eventually, photosynthesizing prokaryotes capable of releasing oxygen from water evolve. Recall that the process of photosynthesis produces oxygen. As the first photosynthetic organisms increased in number, the concentration of oxygen in Earth's atmosphere began to increase. Organisms that could respire aerobically would have evolved and thrived. In fact, the fossil record indicates that there was a large increase in the diversity of prokaryotic life about 2.8 billion years ago.

The presence of oxygen in Earth's atmosphere probably affected life on Earth in another important way. The sun's rays would have converted much of the oxygen into ozone molecules that would then have formed a layer that contained more ozone than the rest of the atmosphere. The ozone layer, that now exists 10 to 15 miles (16–24 km) above Earth's surface, probably shielded organisms from the harmful effects of ultraviolet radiation and enabled the evolution of more complex organisms, the eukaryotes.

The endosymbiont theory

Complex eukaryotic cells probably evolved from prokaryotic cells. Use the *Problem-Solving Lab* on this page to determine how long the event might have taken. The endosymbiont theory,

---

Figure 14.15
The eukaryotic cells of plants and animals probably evolved by endosymbiosis.

A A prokaryote ingested some aerobic bacteria. The aerobes were protected and produced energy for the prokaryote.

B Over a long time, the aerobes become mitochondria, no longer able to live on their own.

C Some primitive prokaryotes also ingested cyanobacteria, which contain photosynthetic pigments.

D The cyanobacteria become chloroplasts, no longer able to live on their own.

Aerobic bacteria

Mitochondria

Cyanobacteria

Chloroplasts

Prokaryote

Animal cell

Plant cell

proposed by American biologist Lynn Margulis in the 1960s, explains how eukaryotic cells may have arisen.

The endosymbiont (en doh SIHM bee ont) theory as shown in *Figure 14.15*, proposes that eukaryotes evolved through a symbiotic relationship between ancient prokaryotes. Margulis based her hypothesis on observations and experimental evidence of present-day unicellular organisms. For example, some bacteria that are similar to cyanobacteria and chloroplasts resemble each other in size and in the ability to photosynthesize. Likewise, mitochondria and some bacteria look similar. Experimental evidence revealed that both chloroplasts

and mitochondria contain DNA that is similar to the DNA in prokaryotes and unlike the DNA in eukaryotic nuclei.

New evidence from scientific research supports this theory and has shown that chloroplasts and mitochondria have their own ribosomes that are similar to the ribosomes in prokaryotes. In addition, both chloroplasts and mitochondria reproduce independently of the cells that contain them. The fact that some modern prokaryotes live in close association with eukaryotes also supports the theory.

3 Assess

DAILY INTERVENTION

Check for Understanding
Have students list the three main conclusions of this section in their journals. Life comes from existing life; life probably originated on Earth through the reaction of chemicals in Earth's atmosphere and their further reaction on Earth's surface; and cells probably evolved as the chemicals on early Earth became more organized. Ask students to list the scientific evidence that supports each conclusion. **L2**

Reteach
Ask students to list the scientists who experimented about the origin of life and their conclusions. Have them use their lists to quiz each other. **L1** **COOP LEARN**

Resources
For more practice, use *Reading Essentials for Biology,* Section 14.2.

Extension

Intrapersonal Ask students who have mastered this section to find out how scientists think that nucleic acids may have developed from elements already present on Earth. **L3**

Section Assessment

Understanding Main Ideas

1. How did Pasteur's experiment finally disprove spontaneous generation?

2. Review Oparin's hypothesis and explain how it was tested experimentally.

3. Why do scientists think the first living cells to appear on Earth were probably anaerobic heterotrophs?

4. How would the increasing number of photosynthesizing organisms on Earth have affected both Earth and its other organisms?

Thinking Critically

5. Some scientists speculate that lightning was not present on early Earth. How could you modify the Miller-Urey experiment to reflect this new idea? What energy source would you use to replace lightning?

SKILL REVIEW

6. **Sequence** Make a flowchart sequencing the evolution of life from protocells to eukaryotes. For more help, refer to *Sequence* in the **Skill Handbook.**

in.bdol.glencoe.com/self_check_quiz

14.2 THE ORIGIN OF LIFE **385**

Section Assessment

1. Life did not appear in sterile broth. Life did appear in broth where there were previously existing organisms.

2. Life began in Earth's oceans after organic molecules formed from ocean substances. Miller and Urey tested the hypothesis.

3. There was no oxygen in the atmosphere, and there were food molecules in the "organic soup" of the ocean.

4. They eventually created an oxygen-rich atmosphere. Organisms evolved that could use the oxygen.

5. Possible answers include sunlight, radioactivity, or heat from volcanoes.

6. protocells ⇒ anaerobic prokaryotes ⇒ photosynthetic prokaryotes ⇒ eukaryotes

INVESTIGATE BioLab

Time Allotment

one class period

Process Skills

make and use graphs, collect data, define operationally, formulate models, interpret data, use numbers

PREPARATION

- Any box large enough to hold the 100 pennies may be used.
- Provide graph paper.

PROCEDURE

Teaching Strategies

- Have students work in groups to reduce the quantity of materials needed.
- Be sure that students understand the value of a simulation investigation such as this one. You may want to discuss with students why this particular lab would have to be run as a simulation.
- Remind students not to return the "tail" pennies to the box.
- Review the experimental need for several trials to collect data.
- Review how to determine an average.
- Review the meaning of a symbol, such as K-40, and how to determine the number of protons in an element.

INVESTIGATE BioLab

Before You Begin

To date a rock using a radioactive isotope, the half-life of the radioactive isotope and the isotope formed when the radioactive isotope decays must be known. Also, the amount of the radioactive isotope in the rock when it formed and the amount of radioactive isotope currently in the rock must be measured. For example, the half-life of K-40 to decay to Ar-40 is 1.3 billion years. When rocks form, they contain no Ar-40, so measuring the amounts of K-40 and Ar-40 currently in a rock gives the inital amount of K-40 in the rock. Then the age of the rock can be calculated.

Determining a Rock's Age

PREPARATION

Problem

How can you simulate radioactive half-life?

Objectives

In this BioLab you will:

- **Formulate Models** Simulate the radioactive decay of K-40 into Ar-40 with pennies.
- **Collect Data** Collect data to determine the amount of K-40 present after several half-lives.
- **Make and Use Graphs** Graph your data and use its values to determine the age of rocks.

Materials

shoe box with lid
100 pennies
graph paper

Skill Handbook

If you need help with this lab, refer to the **Skill Handbook.**

PROCEDURE

1. Copy the data table.
2. Place 100 pennies in a shoe box.
3. Arrange the pennies so that their "head" sides are facing up. Each "head" represent an atom of K-40, and each "tail" an atom of Ar-40.
4. Record the number of "heads" and "tails" present at the start of the experiment. Use the row marked "0" in the data table.
5. Cover the box. Then shake the box well. Let the shake represent one half-life of K-40, which is 1.3 billion years.
6. Remove the lid and record the number of "heads" you see facing up. Remove all the "tail" pennies.
7. To complete the first trial, repeat steps 5 and 6 four more times.
8. Run two more trials and determine an average for the number of "heads" present at each half-life.

CLEANUP AND DISPOSAL

 Make sure students wash their hands thoroughly after handling the coins. Encourage students to make wise choices concerning disposal and recycling of lab materials.

Data Table

Number of Shakes (half-lives)	Number of Heads (K-40 atoms left)				
	Trial 1	Trial 2	Trial 3	Totals	Average
0					
1					
2					
3					
4					
5					

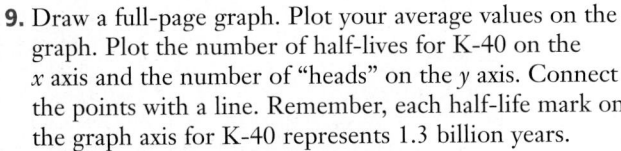

9. Draw a full-page graph. Plot your average values on the graph. Plot the number of half-lives for K-40 on the *x* axis and the number of "heads" on the *y* axis. Connect the points with a line. Remember, each half-life mark on the graph axis for K-40 represents 1.3 billion years.

10. **CLEANUP AND DISPOSAL** Return everything to its proper place for reuse. Wash hands thoroughly.

ANALYZE AND CONCLUDE

1. **Apply Concepts** What symbol represented an atom of K-40 in this experiment? What symbol represented an atom of Ar-40?

2. **Think Critically** Compare the numbers of protons and neutrons of K-40 and Ar-40. (Consult the Periodic Table on page 1112 for help.) Can Ar-40 change back to K-40? Explain your answer, pointing out what procedural part of the experiment supports your answer.

3. **Define Operationally** Define the term half-life. What procedural part of the simulation represented a half-life period of time in the experiment?

4. **Communicate** Explain how scientists use radioactive dating to approximate a rock's age.

5. **Make and Use Graphs** You are attempting to determine the age of a rock sample. Use your graph to read the rock's age if it has:
   a. 70% of its original K-40 amount.
   b. 35% of its original K-40 amount.
   c. 10% of its original K-40 amount.

6. **ERROR ANALYSIS** Could the size of the box and how vigorously the box was shaken introduce errors into the data? Explain.

Apply Your Skill

Graph Suppose you had calculated the same data for an element with a half-life of 5000 years rather than 1.3 billion years. Plot a graph for the hypothetical isotope. How do the graphs compare?

Web Links To find out more about radioactive dating, visit in.bdol.glencoe.com/radioactive_dating

Data and Observations

Half-life	Average number of K40
0	100
1	50
2	25
3	12
4	6
5	3

ANALYZE AND CONCLUDE

1. K-40—penny with "head" side up; Ar-40—penny with "tail" side up

2. Potassium has 19 protons and 21 neutrons, and Argon has 18 protons and 22 neutrons; no; K-40 decays or changes into Ar-40. Remove "tail" pennies.

3. A half-life is the time needed for half the number of atoms of a radioactive element to change into atoms of a different element. Shaking the box represented a half-life.

4. Because the original amount of radioactive element cannot be known, scientists analyze how much is present now and compare it to the amount of its daughter product now present. The ratio tells how many half-lives have passed.

5. a. 650 000 000
   b. 1 950 000 000
   c. 4 550 000 000

6. **ERROR ANALYSIS** A small box that constricts the flipping of the coins could alter the results. If the coins are not shaken vigorously enough to get them to flip, the results could also be altered.

Assessment

Portfolio Have students write a summary of this experiment in their portfolios that emphasizes the value of using the simulation to illustrate the concept of radioactive decay. Use the Performance Task Assessment List for Lab Report in **PASC**, p. 119. **L2**

Apply Your Skill

Graph The graphs will appear the same. Ask students to research how a radioactive element decays to form a different element. **L2**

Biology and Society

Biology and Society

The Origin of Life

How life originated on Earth is a fascinating and challenging question. Many have proposed answers, but the mystery remains unsolved. Because it is impossible to travel in time, the question of how life originated on Earth might never be answered. However, a number of beliefs and hypotheses exist. Some of these are described below.

Divine origins Common to human cultures throughout history is the belief that life on Earth did not arise spontaneously. Many of the world's major religions teach that life was created on Earth by a supreme being. The followers of these religions believe that life could only have arisen through the direct action of a divine force.

A variation of this belief is that organisms are too complex to have developed only by evolution. Instead, some people believe that the complex structures and processes of life could not have formed without some guiding intelligence.

Meteorites One scientific hypothesis about the origin of life on Earth is that the molecules necessary for life arrived here on meteorites, rocks from space that collide with Earth's surface. Many meteorites contain some organic matter. These organic molecules, which are necessary for the formation of cells, might have arrived on Earth and entered its oceans.

Primordial soup Another hypothesis was proposed by A. I. Oparin. It states that Earth's ancient atmosphere contained the gases nitrogen, methane, and ammonia, but no free oxygen. Energy from the sun, volcanoes, and lightning caused chemical reactions among these gases, which eventually combined into small organic molecules such as amino acids. Rain trapped and then carried these molecules into the oceans, making a primordial soup of organic molecules. In this soup, proteins, lipids, and the other complex organic molecules found in present-day cells formed. Harold Urey and Stanley Miller

Stanley Miller

provided the first experimental evidence to support this idea. They produced organic molecules in the laboratory by creating a spark in a gas mixture similar to Earth's early atmosphere.

An RNA world Some scientists hypothesize that the formation of self-replicating molecules preceded the formation of cells. Today's self-replicating molecules, DNA and RNA, provide clues about the earliest self-replicating molecules. Scientists hypothesize that RNA, which is central to the functioning of a cell, probably predated DNA on Earth. However, because RNA is a more complex molecule than protein, it is not easy to obtain data that supports the idea that RNA was formed on early Earth.

Forming Your Opinion

Review, analyze, and critique the different ideas about the origin of life presented here. Consider strengths and weaknesses during your review.

 To find out more about the origin of life, visit in.bdol.glencoe.com/biology_society

STUDY GUIDE

Section 14.1

The Record of Life

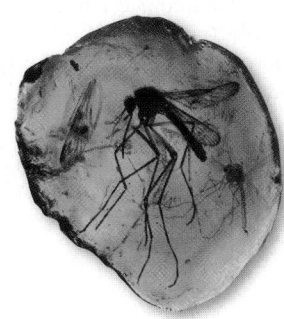

Key Concepts

■ Fossils provide a record of life on Earth. Fossils come in many forms, such as a leaf imprint, a worm burrow, or a bone.

■ By studying fossils, scientists learn about the diversity of life and about the behavior of ancient organisms.

■ Fossils can provide information on ancient environments. For example, fossils can help to predict whether an area had been a river environment, terrestrial environment, or a marine environment. In addition, fossils may provide information on ancient climates.

■ Earth's history is divided into the geologic time scale, based on evidence in rocks and fossils.

■ The four major divisions in the geologic time scale are the Precambrian, Paleozoic Era, Mesozoic Era, and Cenozoic Era. The eras are further divided into periods.

Vocabulary
fossil (p. 370)
plate tectonics (p. 379)

Section 14.2

The Origin of Life

Key Concepts

■ Francesco Redi and Louis Pasteur designed controlled experiments to disprove spontaneous generation. Their experiments and others like them convinced scientists to accept biogenesis.

■ Small organic molecules might have formed from substances present in Earth's early atmosphere and oceans. Small organic molecules can form complex organic molecules.

■ The earliest organisms were probably anaerobic, heterotrophic prokaryotes. Over time, chemosynthetic prokaryotes evolved and then photosynthetic prokaryotes that produced oxygen evolved, changing the atmosphere and triggering the evolution of aerobic cells and eukaryotes.

Vocabulary
archaebacteria (p. 384)
biogenesis (p. 381)
protocell (p. 383)
spontaneous
   generation (p. 380)

FOLDABLES
Study Organizer To help you review the geologic time scale, use the Organizational Study Fold on page 369.

Key Concepts

Summary statements can be used by students to review the major concepts of the chapter.

Biology Online

Visit in.bdol.glencoe.com
/self_check_quiz
/vocabulary_puzzlemaker
/chapter_test
/standardized_test

VOCABULARY PUZZLEMAKER

For additional help with vocabulary, have students access the Vocabulary PuzzleMaker online at in.bdol.glencoe.com/ vocabulary_puzzlemaker

FOLDABLES™

Have students use their Foldables to review the content of Section 14.1. On the back of the paper, write a paragraph to describe the major event that ended each era.

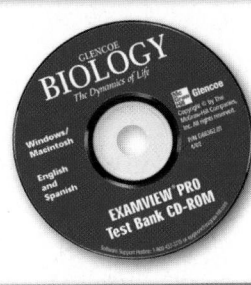

Use the ExamView®Pro Test Bank CD-ROM to:
● Create **multiple versions** of tests
● Create **modified** tests with one mouse click for **inclusion** students
● **Edit** existing questions and **add** your own questions
● Build tests aligned with state standards using built-in **State Curriculum Tags**
● Change **English** tests to **Spanish** with one mouse click and vice versa

Chapter 14 Assessment

 The Princeton Review *Questions and answers have been aligned and verified by The Princeton Review.*

Vocabulary Review

1. archaebacteria
2. spontaneous generation
3. fossil
4. biogenesis

Understanding Key Concepts

5. C 7. C 9. D
6. A 8. B

Constructed Response

10. The theory of plate tectonics explains that the two continents were once joined.
11. The earliest organisms were probably anaerobic heterotrophs, not autotrophs.
12. From fossils, scientists may be able to determine whether animals lived in large groups, what they ate, how they obtained their food, and what their home ranges were.

Thinking Critically

13. According to the endosymbiont hypothesis, primitive cells called phagocytes consumed early bacteria. These cells evolved into the ancestral eukaryotes when the bacteria evolved into cell parts.
14. Students should produce a visual that explains that new discoveries change our understanding of the timing of evolutionary events, and serve to refine evolutionary understanding.
15. The earliest organisms probably were heterotrophic, obtaining energy through anaerobic processes. Some later anaerobic organisms may have been autotrophic, increasing the amount of oxygen in the atmosphere.

Vocabulary Review

Review the Chapter 14 vocabulary words listed in the Study Guide on page 389. Match the words with the definitions below.

1. prokaryotes that live in harsh environments
2. the idea that nonliving material can produce life
3. evidence of an organism that lived long ago
4. the idea that living organisms come only from other living organisms

Understanding Key Concepts

5. About how many years ago do scientists suggest that Earth cooled enough for water vapor to condense?
   A. 20 million years   C. 4.4 billion years
   B. 4.6 billion years   D. 5.5 billion years
6. Most fossils occur in layers of _____ rocks.
   A. sedimentary   C. igneous
   B. metamorphic   D. volcanic
7. Who was the scientist who showed that microscopic life is not produced by spontaneous generation?
   A. Francesco Redi
   B. Stanley Miller
   C. Louis Pasteur
   D. Harold Urey
8. Scientists theorize that oxygen buildup in the atmosphere resulted from _____.
   A. respiration
   B. photosynthesis
   C. chemosynthesis
   D. rock weathering
9. An entire, intact organism may be preserved in _____ and _____.
   A. casts—trace fossils
   B. molds—casts
   C. trace fossils—petrified fossils
   D. amber—ice

Constructed Response

10. **Open Ended** Explain why there might be similar fossils on the east coast of South America and the west coast of Africa.

11. **Open Ended** Why do scientists propose that the 3.4 billion-year-old fossils of cyanobacteria-like prokaryotic cells found in Australia were not the first species to have evolved on Earth?

12. **Open Ended** Explain how fossils might help paleontologists to learn about the important behaviors of different types of animals. Which social behaviors might they provide information about?

Thinking Critically

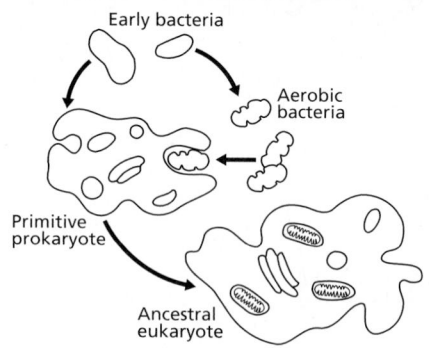

Early bacteria

Aerobic bacteria

Primitive prokaryote

Ancestral eukaryote

13. **Interpret Scientific Illustrations** Use the illustration above to explain the endosymbiont hypothesis.

14. **REAL WORLD BIOCHALLENGE** Recent scientific evidence from fossils indicates that feathered dinosaurs may have been a direct ancestor of birds. Visit **in.bdol.glencoe.com** to investigate these finds. How do such finds impact our understanding of evolution? Present your findings to the class in a poster or other visual format.

15. **Infer** How might the way organisms obtain energy have evolved over time?

16. **Writing About Biology** Why is knowledge of geology important to paleontologists?

17. **Writing About Biology** Explain why Francesco Redi's experiment with flies did not completely disprove spontaneous generation.

 in.bdol.glencoe.com/chapter_test

The presence of oxygen in the atmosphere and the evolution of cells with mitochondria allowed organisms to use oxygen in aerobic respiration.

16. Because fossils are found in sedimentary rock, paleontologists need to know how and where such rocks form.

17. Some people suggested that biogenesis must be true for large organisms like flies, but that bacteria could arise spontaneously.

End-of-Course Assessment Practice

The assessed Indiana standard appears next to the question.

All questions aligned and verified by The Princeton Review

Part 1 Multiple Choice

Use the graph to answer questions 18 and 19.

Ranges of Brachiopod (Lamp Shell) Orders

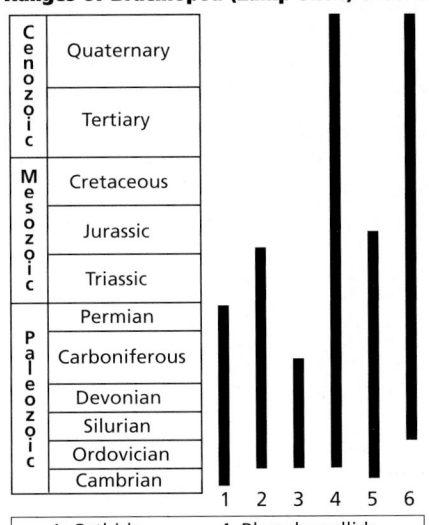

1. Orthida
2. Strophomena
3. Pentamerida
4. Rhynchonellida
5. Spiriferida
6. Terebratulida

18. Which group of organisms had the shortest history?
- **A.** Orthida
- **B.** Rhynchonellida
- **C.** Terebratulida
- **D.** Pentamerida

19. Which group of organisms evolved first?
- **A.** Orthida
- **B.** Rhynchonellida
- **C.** Terebratulida
- **D.** Pentamerida

Part 2 Constructed Response/Grid In

Record your answers on your answer document.

24. Open Ended The element in the graph above would best be used to date rocks from what era? Explain why.

25. Open Ended What kinds of clues can fossils provide about the past, including climate, what organisms ate, and the environment in which they lived?

.1.32

 in.bdol.glencoe.com/standardized_test

20. Which of the following rock types would most likely contain fossils?
- **A.** sedimentary rock composed of limestone
- **B.** igneous rock ejected from a volcano
- **C.** metamorphic rock
- **D.** hardened lava

Study the graph and answer questions 21–24.

Decay Rate of a Radioactive Element

21. How long does it take for half of the element to decay?
- **A.** 1 billion years
- **B.** 2 billion years
- **C.** 3 billion years
- **D.** 4 billion years

22. How much of the original material is left after 4 billion years?
- **A.** 50%
- **B.** 25%
- **C.** 12.5%
- **D.** less than 10%

23. This element would best be used to date fossils that are _____ years old.
- **A.** a few thousand
- **B.** less than a million
- **C.** a few million
- **D.** a billion

CHAPTER 14 ASSESSMENT **391**

End-of-Course Assessment Practice

18. D	**20.** A	**22.** D
19. A	**21.** A	**23.** D

24. Precambrian; because rocks that have ages over one billion years could be dated using this isotope, and the Precambrian ended roughly 543 million years ago.

25. Fossils sometimes indicate climate if a fossil of a particular plant or animal species is found that only occurs in particular climates. Fossil remains of animals, including teeth and structure of jaws, stomach contents, and even limbs can indicate what animals ate. Fossils indicate environmental conditions by the type of sedimentary rock in which the remains occur.

 FAST FILE

Answer Sheet A practice answer sheet can be found on p. 29 of *Unit 5 FAST FILE Resources.*

RUBRIC

For more help evaluating open-ended assessment questions, see the rubric on p. 9T.

Section Objectives	National Science Standards	State/Local Standards	Advanced Lab and Demo Planning
Section 15.1 2 sessions, 1 block 1. **Summarize** Darwin's theory of natural selection. 2. **Explain** how the structural and physiological adaptations of organisms relate to natural selection. 3. **Distinguish** among the types of evidence for evolution.	UCP.1–5; A.1, A.2; C.1–4, C.6; F.4; G.1–3	**Indiana Standards** B.1.31, B.1.32, B.1.34, B.1.36, B.1.47, B.2.2, B.2.3	**Student Labs:** Problem-Solving Lab 15.1, p. 397 MiniLab 15.1, p. 398: sheet of white paper, paper hole punch, 2 sheets of black paper **Teacher Demonstration:** Quick Demo, p. 394: "feeder" gold fish in a bowl, fancier variety gold fish in a bowl, or photos of both
Section 15.2 3 sessions, 2 blocks 4. **Summarize** the effects of the different types of natural selection on gene pools. 5. **Relate** changes in genetic equilibrium to mechanisms of speciation. 6. **Explain** the role of natural selection in convergent and divergent evolution.	UCP.1–5; A.1, A.2; C.1–4, C.6; F.4; G.1–3	**Indiana Standards** B.1.24, B.1.28, B.1.30, B.1.31, B.1.34, B.1.36	**Student Labs:** MiniLab 15.2, p. 407: millimeter ruler, peanut shells Additional Lab, p. 408: culture of *Bacillus subtilis*, 3 tubes of nutrient agar, tube of streptomycin agar, inoculation loop, 2 petri dishes, Bunsen burner, wax pencil, test tube Internet BioLab, p. 414: See materials below. **Teacher Demonstration:** Quick Demo, p. 410: picture of organisms in an environment
End of Chapter Assessment **Student Edition** **Study Guide**, p. 417 **Content Assessment**, pp. 418–419		**Indiana Standards** B.1.31, B.1.32, B.1.34, B.1.35, B.1.36, B.1.47	**Student Lab:** Internet BioLab, p. 414: colored pencils, graph paper, white navy beans, paper bag, pinto beans

Key to Teaching Strategies

L1 Level 1 activities should be appropriate for students with learning difficulties.

L2 Level 2 activities should be within the ability range of all students.

L3 Level 3 activities are designed for above-average students.

ELL ELL activities should be within the ability range of English Language Learners.

COOP LEARN Cooperative Learning activities are designed for small group work.

Glencoe Exclusive!

Teacher Works™
All-In-One Planner and Resource Center

Reproducible Masters and Transparencies

Technology

Unit 5 *FAST FILE* Resources
MiniLab Worksheet, p. 33
Reinforcement and Study Guide in English,
  pp. 37–38
Reinforcement and Study Guide in Spanish,
  pp. 41–42
Concept Mapping, p. 45
Critical Thinking/Problem Solving, p. 46
Transparency Worksheet, p. 47
Reading Essentials for Biology,
  Section 15.1
Laboratory Manual, pp. 87–88, 89–92
🔥 **Section Focus Transparency 37**

💿 **Interactive Chalkboard CD-ROM: Section 15.1 Presentation**
💿 TeacherWorks™ **CD-ROM**
🎵 **Guided Reading Audio Summaries MP3**
💿 **Virtual Labs CD-ROM**
  Virtual Lab: Natural Selection

Unit 5 *FAST FILE* Resources
MiniLab Worksheet, p. 34
BioLab Worksheet, pp. 35–36
Reinforcement and Study Guide in English,
  pp. 39–40
Reinforcement and Study Guide in Spanish,
  pp. 43–44
Transparency Worksheets, pp. 48, 49–54
Reading Essentials for Biology,
  Section 15.2
🔥 **Section Focus Transparency 38**
🔥 **Basic Concepts Transparencies 21, 22**
🔥 **Reteaching Skills Transparency 24**

💿 **Interactive Chalkboard CD-ROM: Section 15.2 Presentation**
💿 TeacherWorks™ **CD-ROM**
🎵 **Guided Reading Audio Summaries MP3**

Unit 5 *FAST FILE* Resources
Chapter Assessment, pp. 55–60
Student Recording Sheet, p. 61

The Princeton Review **Reviewing Biology,** pp. 29–30

💿 **Interactive Chalkboard:**
  Chapter 15 Assessment
💿 **MindJogger Videoquizzes**
  DVD/VHS
💿 **Exam***View*® **Pro Test Bank**
  CD-ROM
💿 TeacherWorks™ **CD-ROM**
💿 **Succeeding on National Standards CD-ROM**

🖱 in.bdol.glencoe.com
/self_check_quiz
/vocabulary_puzzlemaker
/chapter_test
/standardized_test

Indicates materials created specifically for Indiana.

Short on Time?

BIODIGEST The BioDigest at the end of this unit can be used as a(n):

• preview to introduce important unit concepts.

• overview if time does not permit teaching the entire chapter.

• review of key unit concepts.

Understanding the Photo

The crayfish illustrates some common features found in many cave species. Pigment is absent or greatly reduced in many cave species; some are blind, or even eyeless. Like this crayfish, many cave species have elongated antennae or other appendages.

The Theory of Evolution

What You'll Learn

■ You will analyze the theory of evolution.
■ You will compare and contrast the processes of evolution.

Why It's Important

Evolution is the key concept for understanding biology. Evolution explains the diversity of species and predicts changes.

Understanding ▶ the Photo

This crayfish lives in dark caves and is blind. It has sighted relatives that live where there is light. Both the cave-dwelling species and their relatives are adapted to different environments. As populations adapt to new or changing environments, individuals in the population that are best adapted survive long enough to reproduce.

Biology Online

Visit **in.bdol.glencoe.com** to
• study the entire chapter online
• access Web Links for more information and activities on evolution
• review content with the Interactive Tutor and self-check quizzes

392

Two-Minute Chapter Launcher

Demo To elicit students' understanding about use of senses, blindfold a student volunteer. Place a couple of small, familiar objects, such as a stapler and pen, on a desk. Ask the student to identify the objects.

Have the students discuss the question: How can a species that lives in a dark cave be successful? Many species do not depend on sight as their primary sense. Some use smell or hearing, while others use touch or taste. Point out that species that are successful in their environments are adapted to survive in those conditions.

Bellringer
Section Focus Transparency 37

Transparency **37** Camouflage

SECTION FOCUS
Use with Chapter 15, Section 15.1

Snowshoe hare in summer

Snowshoe hare in winter

❶ What is the advantage of this snowshoe hare's seasonal color change?

❷ The adaptation that allows an animal to blend in with its environment is called camouflage. What examples of camouflage are you familiar with?

BIOLOGY: The Dynamics of Life

SECTION FOCUS TRANSPARENCIES

Section 15.1

Natural Selection and the Evidence for Evolution

 Indiana Standards Standard B.1.32 Explain how natural selection leads to organisms that are well suited for survival in particular environments, and discuss how natural selection provides scientific explanation for the history of life on Earth as depicted in the fossil record and in the similarities evident within the diversity of existing organisms.

SECTION PREVIEW

Objectives

Summarize Darwin's theory of natural selection.

Explain how the structural and physiological adaptations of organisms relate to natural selection.

Distinguish among the types of evidence for evolution.

Review Vocabulary
evolution: the changes in populations over time (p. 10)

New Vocabulary
artificial selection
natural selection
mimicry
camouflage
homologous structure
analogous structure
vestigial structure
embryo

FOLDABLES™
Study Organizer

Evolution Make the following Foldable to help you analyze and critique evidence supporting the theory of evolution.

STEP 1 **Draw** a mark at the midpoint of a vertical sheet of paper along the side edge.

STEP 2 **Turn** the paper horizontally and **fold** the outside edges in to touch at the midpoint mark.

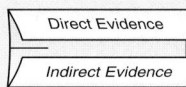
Direct Evidence
Indirect Evidence

STEP 3 **Label** the tabs as shown.

Analyze and Critique As you read Chapter 15, summarize, analyze, and critique the direct and indirect evidence used to support the theory of evolution.

Charles Darwin and Natural Selection

The modern theory of evolution is the fundamental concept in biology. Recall that evolution is the change in populations over time. Learning the principles of evolution makes it easier to understand modern biology. One place to start is by learning about the ideas of English scientist Charles Darwin (1809–1882)—ideas supported by fossil evidence.

Fossils shape ideas about evolution

Biologists have used fossils in their work since the eighteenth century. In fact, fossil evidence formed the basis of early evolutionary concepts. Scientists wondered how fossils formed, why many fossil species were extinct, and what kinds of relationships might exist between the extinct and the modern species.

Before geologists provided evidence indicating that Earth was much older than many people had originally thought, biologists suspected that species change over time, or evolve. Many explanations about how species evolve have been proposed, but the ideas first published by Charles Darwin are the basis of modern evolutionary theory.

15.1 NATURAL SELECTION AND THE EVIDENCE FOR EVOLUTION **393**

---

with Image Bank

PowerPoint® Presentations

This CD-ROM is an editable Microsoft® PowerPoint® presentation that includes:
• Section presentations
• Section checks
• Image bank
• Hot links to Biology Online
• All transparencies

FOLDABLES™
For an additional Foldables activity idea, see the Chapter 15 Foldables page in *Unit 5 FAST FILE Resources.*

Indiana Academic Standards

Pages 392–393: B.1.31, B.1.32, B.1.47, B.2.3

RESOURCE MANAGER

Unit 5 *FAST FILE* Resources
MiniLab Worksheet, p. 33
Reinforcement and Study Guide in English, pp. 37–38
Reinforcement and Study Guide in Spanish, pp. 41–42
Concept Mapping, p. 45

Critical Thinking/Problem Solving, p. 46
Transparency Worksheet, p. 47
Reading Essentials for Biology, Section 15.1
Laboratory Manual, pp. 87–88, 89–92
 Section Focus Transparency 37

2 Teach

Goldfish Traits Bring in a "feeder" goldfish and a fancier variety in separate fish bowls. Allow students to observe both types of goldfish for a few minutes. Point out that the "feeder" goldfish is more similar to the carp variety found in nature than the fancier goldfish. Ask students to speculate how the fancier variety of goldfish has evolved from the one found in nature. Ancestors of the fancier variety of goldfish were domesticated by selective breeding. Selective breeding is similar to natural selection as described on the next page, but is under the direction of humans.

Concept Development

A significant influence on Darwin's thinking was the book *The Principles of Geology* by Charles Lyell. This book proposed that Earth is very old and that the forces that have produced changes on Earth's surface in the past are the same ones that continue to operate today. Discuss how Darwin was influenced by other ideas of his day.

Visual Learning

Figure 15.1 Have the students examine the photos of the finch, tortoise, and iguana. Discuss each organism, asking students to identify its adaptations.

Darwin on HMS *Beagle*

It took Darwin years to develop his theory of evolution. He began in 1831 at age 22 when he took a job as a naturalist on the English ship HMS *Beagle*, which sailed around the world on a five-year scientific journey.

As the ship's naturalist, Darwin studied and collected biological and fossil specimens at every port along the route. As you might imagine, these specimens were quite diverse. Studying the specimens made Darwin curious about possible relationships among species. His studies provided the foundation for his theory of evolution by natural selection.

Darwin in the Galápagos

The Galápagos (guh LAH puh gus) Islands are a group of small islands near the equator, about 1000 km off the west coast of South America. The observations that Darwin made and the specimens that he collected there were especially important to him.

On the Galápagos Islands, Darwin studied many species of animals and plants, *Figure 15.1*, that are unique to the islands but similar to species elsewhere. These observations led Darwin to consider the possibility that species can change over time. However, after returning to England, he could not at first explain how such changes occur.

Figure 15.1
The five-year voyage of HMS *Beagle* took Darwin around the world. Animal species in the Galápagos Islands have unique adaptations.

A The beak of this Galápagos finch is adapted to feed on cacti.

B Galápagos tortoises are the largest on Earth, differing from other tortoises in body size and shape.

C Galápagos marine iguanas eat algae from the ocean, an unusual food source for reptiles. Large claws help them cling to slippery rocks.

394 THE THEORY OF EVOLUTION

Darwin continues his studies

For the next two decades, Darwin worked to refine his explanation for how species change over time. He read, studied, collected specimens, and conducted experiments.

English economist Thomas Malthus had proposed an idea that Darwin modified and used in his explanation. Malthus's idea was that the human population grows faster than Earth's food supply. How did this help Darwin? He knew that many species produce large numbers of offspring. He also knew that such species had not overrun Earth. He realized that individuals struggle to compete in changing environmental conditions. There are many kinds of competition, such as competing for food and space, escaping from predators, finding mates, and locating shelter. Only some individuals survive the competition and produce offspring. Which individuals survive?

Darwin gained insight into the mechanism that determined which organisms survive in nature from his pigeon-breeding experiments. Darwin observed that the traits of individuals vary in populations. Variations are then inherited. By breeding pigeons with desirable variations, Darwin produced offspring with these variations. Breeding organisms with specific traits in order to produce offspring with identical traits is called **artificial selection.** Darwin hypothesized that there was a force in nature that worked like artificial selection.

Darwin explains natural selection

Using his collections and observations, Darwin identified the process of natural selection, the steps of which you can see summarized in *Figure 15.2*. **Natural selection** is a mechanism for change in populations. It occurs when organisms with favorable variations

A In nature, organisms produce more offspring than can survive. Fishes, for example, can sometimes lay millions of eggs.

B In any population, individuals have variations. Fishes, for example, may differ in color, size, and speed.

C Individuals with certain useful variations, such as speed, survive in their environment, passing those variations to the next generation.

D Over time, offspring with certain variations make up most of the population and may look entirely different from their ancestors.

Figure 15.2
Darwin proposed the idea of natural selection to explain how species change over time.

Different Viewpoints in Biology

Provide students with a set of class data, such as the data they gathered in this chapter's Getting Started. Ask different students to interpret the data to show how the same information can be interpreted differently. **L2**

Visual Learning

Figure 15.3 illustrates the probable evolution of the common mole rat from a member of the rodent family Bathyergidae. After students have studied each step of the illustration, ask them to list the steps that may have occurred during the evolution of the sightless, cave-dwelling fish genus *Amblyopsis*, and the blind, burrowing snake genus *Typhlops*.

✓**Reading Check** (p. 397) Organisms produce more offspring than can survive. Variations occur in all populations. Individuals with useful variations are more likely to survive and reproduce. Over time, offspring with the most useful variations make up most of the population.

Indiana Academic Standards

Pages 396–397: B.1.32, B.1.36, B.1.47, B.2.2, B.2.3

396

survive, reproduce, and pass their variations to the next generation. Organisms without these variations are less likely to survive and reproduce. As a result, each generation consists largely of offspring from parents with these variations that aid survival.

Darwin was not the only one to recognize the significance of natural selection for populations. As a result of his studies on islands near Indonesia in the Pacific Ocean, Alfred Russel Wallace, another British naturalist, reached a similar conclusion. After Wallace wrote Darwin to share his ideas about natural selection, Darwin and Wallace had their similar ideas jointly presented to the scientific community. Soon thereafter,

Darwin published the first book about evolution called *On the Origin of Species by Means of Natural Selection* in 1859. The ideas detailed in Darwin's book are a basic unifying theme of biology today.

Interpreting evidence after Darwin

Volumes of scientific data have been gathered as evidence for evolution since Darwin's time. Much of this evidence is subject to interpretation by different scientists. One of the issues is that evolutionary processes are difficult for humans to observe directly. The short scale of human life spans makes it difficult to comprehend evolutionary processes.

Figure 15.3
Darwin's ideas about natural selection can explain some adaptations of mole-rats.

A The ancestors of today's common mole-rats probably resembled African rock rats.

B Some ancestral rats may have avoided predators better than others because of variations such as the size of teeth and claws.

C Ancestral rats that survived passed their variations to offspring. After many generations, most of the population's individuals would have these adaptations.

D Over time, natural selection produced modern mole-rats. Their blindness may have evolved because vision had no survival advantage for them.

396 THE THEORY OF EVOLUTION

PROJECT

Variation in Beans: *Logical-Mathematical*
Students can study the effects of individual variations by planting a pinto bean garden. Have them wash their hands after handling bean seeds. Obtain some pinto bean seeds and ask the students to measure and observe them, placing the seeds into categories, such as short, long, wide, thin, etc. Have them write hypotheses that predict how each category of bean seed will grow. Then plant 3 or 4 beans from each category. Students should observe the plants each day, recording their observations. Have them write a brief summary after 4–5 weeks of plant growth. **L1** **ELL**

that occur over millions of years. Despite this, much data about the biological world has been gathered from many sources. These data are best explained by evolution. Almost all of today's biologists accept the theory of evolution by natural selection. The advent of genetics has added yet more data to our understanding of evolution. This means that the change in the gene pool of a population over time can be added to our modern definition of evolution. Use *Problem-Solving Lab 15.1* to analyze data from a study of peppered moths.

✓ Reading Check **Summarize** the main ideas of natural selection.

Adaptations: Evidence for Evolution

Have you noticed that some plants have thorns and some plants don't? Have you noticed that some animals have distinctive coloring but others don't? Have you ever wondered how such variations arose? Recall that an adaptation is any variation that aids an organism's chances of survival in its environment. Thorns are an adaptation of some plants and distinctive colorings are an adaptation of some animals. Darwin's theory of evolution explains how adaptations may develop in species.

Structural adaptations arise over time

According to Darwin's theory, adaptations in species develop over many generations. Learning about adaptations in mole-rats can help you understand how natural selection has affected them. Mole-rats that live underground in darkness are blind. These blind mole-rats have many adaptations that enable them to live

Problem-Solving Lab 15.1

Interpret Data

How can natural selection be observed? In some organisms that have a short life cycle, biologists have observed the evolution of adaptations to rapid environmental changes. Scientists studied camouflage adaptations in a population of light- and dark-colored peppered moths, *Biston betularia*. The moths sometimes rested on trees that grew in both the

Biston betularia

country and the city. Moths are usually speckled gray-brown, and dark moths, which occur occasionally, are black. Some birds eat peppered moths. Urban industrial pollution had blackened the bark of city trees with soot. In the photo, you see a city tree with dark bark similar to the color of one of the moths.

Solve the Problem

Scientists raised more than 3000 caterpillars to provide adult moths. They marked the wings of the moths these caterpillars produced so they would recapture only their moths. In a series of trials in the country and the city, they released and recaptured the moths. The number of moths recaptured in a trial indicates how well the moths survived in the environment. Examine the table below.

Comparison of Country and City Moths

Location		Numbers of Light Moths	Numbers of Dark Moths
Country	Released	496	488
	Recaptured	62	34
City	Released	137	493
	Recaptured	18	136

Thinking Critically

Interpret Data Calculate the percentage of moths recaptured in each experiment, and explain any differences in survival rates in the country and the city moths in terms of natural selection.

successfully underground. Look at *Figure 15.3* to see how these modern mole-rat adaptations might have evolved over millions of years from characteristics of their ancestors.

Problem-Solving Lab 15.1

Purpose
Students will analyze data from a natural selection study.

Process Skills
use a table, form a hypothesis

Background
A dark variety of peppered moth was first observed in English cities in 1848. It was hard to see on the dark tree trunks near polluted areas. Over the next 100 years, near the cities, scientists observed greater numbers of dark moths relative to light moths. In the 1950s, English scientist H. B. Kettlewell tested the hypothesis that natural selection accounted for the difference.

Teaching Strategies
Remind students that these data are from an experiment used to support the theory of evolution by natural selection.

Thinking Critically
country/light moths = 12.5%; country/dark moths = 0.7%; city/light moths = 13.0%; city/dark moths = 27.6%
The differences in survival rates are due to camouflage. There was natural selection for the dark variation in the city where pollution darkened the tree trunks, and natural selection for the light variation in the country where the trees were not darkened.

Modified Assessment
Portfolio Discuss the Abert and Kaibab squirrels of the Grand Canyon area. Have students prepare short summaries of the discussion to put in their portfolios. Summaries should describe the environment that each squirrel lives in, the characteristics of each species, and possible hypotheses for how the differences evolved. **L1**

🎯 CHALLENGE ACTIVITY

Mimicry and Camouflage Students who need an additional challenge can make a small collection of insects that demonstrate mimicry and camouflage. If you make this assignment, it is suggested that students be warned about any biting or stinging insects to which they may be allergic, to collect only common and unprotected species, and to never collect more than one or two specimens of any given species. **L3**

Purpose

Students will model how a camouflage adaptation can aid an organism's survival.

Process Skills

observe and infer, form a hypothesis

Teaching Strategies

■ Have students do this activity after studying camouflage.

■ Explain that students will simulate how natural selection might operate on a population of insects that vary in color.

Expected Results

Most groups will have picked up more white dots than black dots.

Analysis

1. white dots
2. Light-colored insects may be seen and preyed on more easily than dark-colored insects. Therefore, dark-colored insects have a higher survival rate.
3. Over time, an insect population might become dark-colored because light-colored insects were eliminated from the population.

Assessment

Knowledge Have students research and write a summary about insect adaptations that aid survival in specific environments. Use the Performance Task Assessment List for Writing in Science in **PASC**, p. 159. **L2**

MiniLab 15.1

Formulate Models

Camouflage Provides an Adaptive Advantage Camouflage is a structural adaptation that allows organisms to blend with their surroundings. In this activity, you'll discover how natural selection can result in camouflage adaptations in organisms.

Procedure

1 Working with a partner, punch 100 dots from a sheet of white paper with a paper hole punch. Repeat with a sheet of black paper. These dots will represent black and white insects.

2 Scatter both white and black dots on a sheet of black paper.

3 Decide whether you or your partner will role-play a bird.

4 The "bird" looks away from the paper, then turns back, and immediately picks up the first dot he or she sees.

5 Repeat step 4 for one minute.

Analysis

1. **Observe** What color dots were most often collected?
2. **Infer** How does color affect the survival rate of insects?
3. **Hypothesize** What might happen over many generations to a similar population in nature?

Figure 15.4
Mimicry and camouflage are protective adaptations of organisms. The colors and body shape of a yellow jacket wasp **(A)** and a harmless syrphid fly **(B)** are similar. Predators avoid both insects. Camouflage enables organisms, such as this leaf frog **(C)**, to blend with their surroundings.

398

The structural adaptations of common mole-rats include large teeth and claws. These are body parts that help mole-rats survive in their environment by, for example, enabling them to dig better tunnels. Structural adaptations such as the teeth and claws of mole-rats are often used to defend against predators. Some adaptations of other organisms that keep predators from approaching include a rose's thorns or a porcupine's quills.

Some other structural adaptations are subtle. **Mimicry** is a structural adaptation that enables one species to resemble another species. In one form of mimicry, a harmless species has adaptations that result in a physical resemblance to a harmful species. Predators that avoid the harmful species also avoid the similar-looking, harmless species. See if you can tell the difference between a harmless fly and the wasp it mimics when you look at *Figures 15.4A* and *B*.

In another form of mimicry, two or more harmful species resemble each other. For example, yellow jacket hornets, honeybees, and many other

USING MODELS

Illustrating Evolution Using Figure 15.3 as a guide, have the students model possible evolutionary sequences by illustrating or describing one of the following: (1) the evolution of long necks in giraffes from short-necked ancestors, (2) the evolution of whales from terrestrial carnivores, (3) the evolution of flight in birds from bipedal dinosaurs, (4) the evolution of high-speed running in cheetahs from slower movements of their ancestors. **L2**

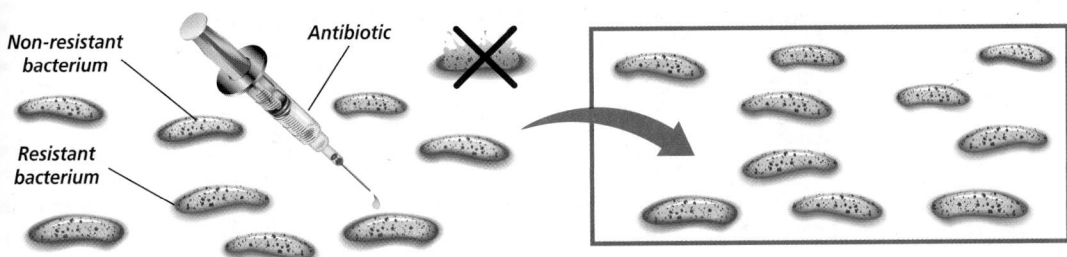

A The bacteria in a population vary in their ability to resist antibiotics.

B When the population is exposed to an antibiotic, only the resistant bacteria survive.

C The resistant bacteria live and produce more resistant bacteria.

Figure 15.5
The development of bacterial resistance to antibiotics is direct evidence for evolution.
Infer *What problems can antibiotic-resistant bacteria cause?*

species of wasps all have harmful stings and similar coloration and behavior. Predators may learn quickly to avoid any organism with their general appearance.

Another subtle adaptation is **camouflage** (KA muh flahj), an adaptation that enables species to blend with their surroundings, as shown in *Figure 15.4C.* Because well-camouflaged organisms are not easily found by predators, they survive to reproduce. Try *MiniLab 15.1* to experience how camouflage can help an organism survive and adapt to it's environment.

✓**Reading Check** **Explain and illustrate** how mimicry and camouflage can cause populations to change over time.

Physiological adaptations can develop rapidly

In general, most structural adaptations develop over millions of years. However, there are some adaptations that evolve much more rapidly. For example, do you know that some of the medicines developed during the twentieth century to fight bacterial diseases are no longer effective? When the antibiotic drug penicillin was discovered about 50 years ago, it was called a wonder drug because it killed many

types of disease-causing bacteria and saved many lives. Today, penicillin no longer affects as many species of bacteria because some species have evolved physiological (fih zee uh LAH jih kul) adaptations to prevent being killed by penicillin. Look at *Figure 15.5* to see how resistance develops in bacteria.

Physiological adaptations are changes in an organism's metabolic processes. In addition to species of bacteria, scientists have observed these adaptations in species of insects and weeds that are pests. After years of exposure to specific pesticides, many species of insects and weeds have become resistant to these chemicals that used to kill them.

Other Evidence for Evolution

The development of physiological resistance in species of bacteria, insects, and plants is direct evidence of evolution. However, most of the evidence for evolution is indirect, coming from sources such as fossils and studies of anatomy, embryology, and biochemistry.

Fossils

Fossils are an important source of evolutionary evidence because they

✓**Reading Check** Mimicry can change populations when one organism looks like another that is less likely to be preyed upon. Example: syrphid fly and yellow jacket wasp. Camouflage can change a population when an organism begins to look like an object that is not prey. Example: leaf frog and leaf

Caption Question Answer
Figure 15.5 Antibiotic-resistant bacteria make diseases more difficult to treat. They can cause doctors to have to use more expensive medicines.

Portfolio
Camouflage and Mimicry Have the students write about an organism that has camouflage or mimicry adaptations. The report should include the organism's name, details about its environment and predators, and a description of its camouflage or mimicry adaptations.

Research Students who need an additional challenge can do research on the development of a particular kind of antibiotic-resistant bacteria and write an essay that describes their findings. **L3**

 Indiana Academic Standards

Pages 398–399: B.1.32, B.1.34, B.1.36

Visual Learning

Use Table 15.1 to illustrate that, although the fossil record provides evidence for evolution, a relatively complete sequence of fossils, such as those that exist for camels and horses, is rare. Relate this fact to students' previous knowledge of problems in fossil preservation, dating, and interpretation.

Inquiry

Activity Have students prepare a short report about a dog breed of their choice, describing its characteristics, the reasons why it was originally bred, the details about its breeding, and the characteristics of closely related breeds. Students should include a picture of the breed in their report. **L1**

Activity

Identify Homologous Structures
Provide several skeletons of organisms such as a dog, bird, fish, human, or others that you may have. Have students identify homologous structures and compare their functions in the different organisms. **L2**

provide a record of early life and evolutionary history. For example, paleontologists conclude from fossils that the ancestors of whales were probably land-dwelling, doglike animals.

Although the fossil record provides evidence that evolution occurred, the record is incomplete. Working with an incomplete fossil record is something like trying to put together a jigsaw puzzle with missing pieces. But, after the puzzle is together, even with missing pieces, you will probably still understand the overall picture. It's the same with fossils. Although paleontologists do not have fossils for all the changes that have occurred, they can still understand the overall picture of how most groups evolved.

Fossils are found throughout the world. As the fossil record becomes more complete, the sequences of evolution become clearer. For example, in *Table 15.1* you can see how paleontologists have charted the evolutionary path that led to today's camel

after piecing together fossil skulls, teeth, and limb bones.

Anatomy

Look at the forelimb bones of the animals shown in *Figure 15.6.* Although the bones of each forelimb are modified for their function, the basic arrangement of the bones in each limb is similar. Evolutionary biologists view such structural similarities as evidence that organisms evolved from a common ancestor. It would be unlikely for so many animals to have similar structures if each species arose separately. Structural features with a common evolutionary origin are called **homologous structures.** Homologous structures can be similar in arrangement, in function, or in both.

The structural or functional similarity of a body feature doesn't always mean that two species are closely related. In *Figure 15.7,* you can compare the wing of a butterfly with the

Table 15.1
Fossils are used by scientists to understand how camels evolved.

Table 15.1 Camel Evolution					
Age	Paleocene 65 million years ago	Eocene 54 million years ago	Oligocene 33 million years ago	Miocene 23 million years ago	Present
Organism					
Skull and teeth					
Limb bones					

400 THE THEORY OF EVOLUTION

400

PROJECT

Evolving Bacteria: *Interpersonal* Have student groups research for a class presentation a bacterium that has evolved quickly to develop resistance to antibiotics. Possible bacteria include those that cause staph and strep infections, TB, and childhood ear infections. Students should identify the bacterium, the disease it causes, how it is transmitted, and the data that suggest the bacterium is resistant to antibiotic treatment. Students can make visuals—graphs, data tables, and time lines—to illustrate their presentations. **L2**
COOP LEARN

Figure 15.6
The forelimbs of crocodiles, whales, and birds are homologous structures. The bones of each are modified for their function.

Whale forelimb

Crocodile forelimb

Bird wing

wing of a bird. Bird and butterfly wings are not similar in structure, but they are similar in function. The wings of birds and insects evolved independently of each other in two distantly related groups of ancestors. The body parts of organisms that do not have a common evolutionary origin but are similar in function are called **analogous structures.**

Although analogous structures don't shed light on evolutionary relationships, they do provide evidence of evolution. For example, insect and bird wings probably evolved separately when their different ancestors adapted independently to similar ways of life.

Another type of body feature that suggests an evolutionary relationship is a **vestigial** (veh STIH jee ul) **structure**—a body structure in a present-day organism that no longer serves its original purpose, but was probably useful to an ancestor. A structure becomes vestigial when the species no longer needs the feature for its original function, yet it is still inherited as part of the body plan for the species.

Figure 15.7
Insect and bird wings are similar in function but not in structure. Bones are the framework of bird wings, whereas a tough material called chitin composes insect wings.

15.1 NATURAL SELECTION AND THE EVIDENCE FOR EVOLUTION **401**

402

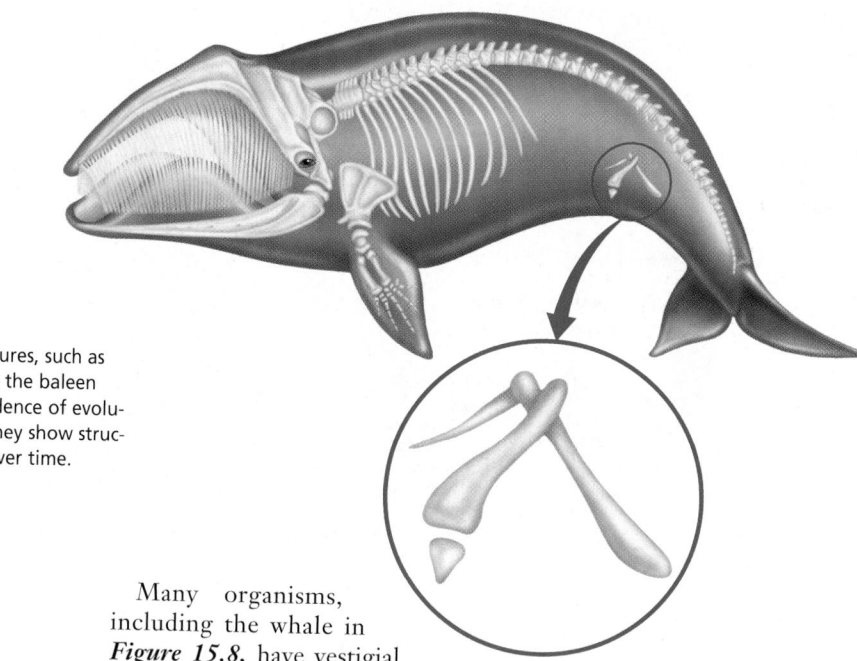

Figure 15.8
Vestigial structures, such as pelvic bones in the baleen whale, are evidence of evolution because they show structural change over time.

Many organisms, including the whale in *Figure 15.8,* have vestigial structures. The eyes of blind mole-rats and cave fish are vestigial structures because they are no longer used for sight. Two flightless birds—an extinct elephant bird and an African ostrich—have extremely reduced forelimbs. Their ancestors probably foraged on land for food and nested on the ground. As a result, over time, the ancestral birds became quite large and unable to fly, features evident in fossils of the elephant bird and present in the African ostrich.

Word Origin

vestigial from the Latin word *vestigium,* meaning "sign"; The forelimbs of ostriches are vestigial structures.

Embryology

It's very easy to see the difference between an adult bird and an adult mammal, but can you distinguish between them by looking at their embryos? An **embryo** is the earliest stage of growth and development of both plants and animals. The embryos of a fish, a reptile, a bird, and a mammal are shown in *Figure 15.9.* At this stage of development, all the embryos have a tail and pharyngeal pouches. In fish, these pouches develop into the supports for the gills, while in mammals, reptiles, and birds, they develop into parts of ears, jaws, and throat. It is the shared features in the young embryos that suggest evolution from a distant, common ancestor.

Biochemistry

Biochemistry also provides strong evidence for evolution. Nearly all

Figure 15.9
In other stages of embryonic development, these organisms look different. However, at some point they look similar. **Hypothesize** *the strengths and weaknesses of embryology as evidence for evolution.*

| Fish | Reptile | Bird | Mammal |

Dr. R. Kessel and Dr. G. Shih | N. Bromhall | Dr. J.D. Cunningham | Dr. F. Hossler

402 THE THEORY OF EVOLUTION

Table 15.2 Biochemical Similarities of Organisms	
Comparison of Organisms	Percent Substitutions of Amino Acids in Cytochrome c Residues
Two orders of mammals	5 and 10
Birds vs. mammals	8–12
Amphibians vs. birds	14–18
Fish vs. land vertebrates	18–22
Insects vs. vertebrates	27–34
Algae vs. animals	57

Figure 15.10
This drawing shows the evolutionary relationship of some of the groups in the table.

organisms share DNA, ATP, and many enzymes among their biochemical molecules. One enzyme, cytochrome c, occurs in organisms as diverse as bacteria and bison. Biologists compared the differences that exist among species in the amino acid sequence of cytochrome c. Data from these biochemical studies are shown in **Table 15.2.** The data show the number of amino acid substitutions in the amino acid sequences for the different organisms. Organisms that are biochemically similar have fewer differences in their amino acid sequences. Groups that share more similarities are interpreted as being more closely related or as sharing a closer ancestor. The evolutionary relationships of some of the groups in the table are shown in **Figure 15.10.**

Since Darwin's time, scientists have constructed evolutionary diagrams that show levels of relationships among species. In the 1970s, some biologists began to use RNA and DNA nucleotide sequences to construct evolutionary diagrams. Today, scientists combine data from fossils, comparative anatomy, embryology, and biochemistry in order to interpret the evolutionary relationships among species.

Section Assessment

Understanding Main Ideas

1. Briefly review, analyze, and critique Darwin's ideas about natural selection.
2. Some snakes have vestigial legs. Why is this considered evidence for evolution?
3. Explain how mimicry and camouflage help species survive.
4. How do homologous structures provide evidence for evolution?

Thinking Critically

5. A parasite that lives in red blood cells causes the disease called malaria. In recent years, new strains of the parasite have appeared that are resistant to the drugs used to treat the disease. Explain how this could be an example of natural selection occurring.

SKILL REVIEW

6. **Get the Big Picture** Fossils indicate that whales evolved from ancestors that had legs. Using your knowledge of natural selection, sequence the steps that may have occurred during the evolution of whales from their terrestrial, doglike ancestors. For more help, refer to *Get the Big Picture* in the **Skill Handbook.**

in.bdol.glencoe.com/self_check_quiz

403

Section Assessment

1. Organisms produce many offspring with variations, some of which enable offspring to reproduce and pass on their genes. Variations with a survival advantage are widespread among descendants. Darwin's ideas remain the cornerstone of evolutionary theory.
2. They suggest that snake ancestors had functional legs and today's snakes may have evolved from them.
3. They reduce a species' visibility to predators or mimic the appearance of an organism that predators avoid.
4. They suggest common ancestry.
5. Some parasites had a variation that made them resistant to drugs. They survived and passed this variation to their offspring.
6. Ancestral whales were forced to live in water. Individuals with variations that had survival advantages in water reproduced, passing on these variations. Over time the variations became common in the population.

403

3 Assess

DAILY INTERVENTION

Check for Understanding
Linguistic Have students describe how each of the following concepts relates to natural selection: overproduction, favorable variations, population change over time. **L1**

Reteach
Intrapersonal Have students identify five of an organism's traits, such as its hair color or size. Ask them to name five variations for each trait and state how each variation would affect the organism in its environment. **L1**

Resources
For more practice, use *Reading Essentials for Biology,* Section 15.1.

Extension

Have students solve this problem: Anteaters, toothless mammals that live in South American rain forests, feed on termites. If the termites they normally feed on are replaced by termites that are too large to swallow whole, how might the anteaters change over time?

MODIFIED Assessment

Knowledge Divide the class into groups and show photos of different organisms. Have groups brainstorm a list of the organisms' adaptations and three explanations for each adaptation. **L1**

1 Focus

Bellringer
Section Focus Transparency 38

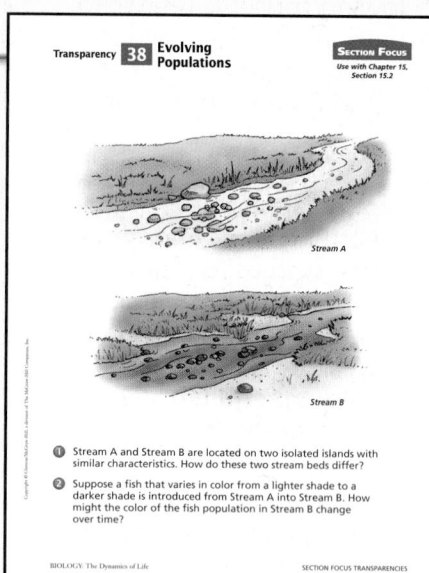

Using Prior Knowledge

Infer Foods, mating rituals, territory, etc. are all important in reducing competition between closely related species, such as meadowlarks.

Section 15.2

Mechanisms of Evolution

Indiana Standards Standard B.1.36 Trace the relationship between environmental changes and changes in the gene pool, such as genetic drift and isolation of sub-populations.

SECTION PREVIEW

Objectives

Summarize the effects of the different types of natural selection on gene pools.

Relate changes in genetic equilibrium to mechanisms of speciation.

Explain the role of natural selection in convergent and divergent evolution.

Review Vocabulary
gene: DNA segment that controls protein production and the cell cycle (p. 211)

New Vocabulary
gene pool
allelic frequency
genetic equilibrium
genetic drift
stabilizing selection
directional selection
disruptive selection
speciation
geographic isolation
reproductive isolation
polyploid
gradualism
punctuated equilibrium
adaptive radiation
divergent evolution
convergent evolution

Interspecies Competition

Using Prior Knowledge You may recognize the birds shown here as meadowlarks. These birds range throughout much of the United States. Meadowlarks look so similar that it's often difficult to tell them apart. Although they are closely related and occupy the same ranges in parts of the central United States, these different meadowlarks do not normally interbreed and are classified as distinct species.

Infer Using your knowledge of birds and animal behavior, infer what prevents competition between two meadowlark species that occupy the same area.

Western meadowlark—
Sturnella neglecta

Eastern meadowlark—
Sturnella magna

Population Genetics and Evolution

When Charles Darwin developed his theory of natural selection in the 1800s, he did so without knowing about genes. Since Darwin's time, scientists have learned a great deal about genes and modified Darwin's ideas accordingly. At first, genetic information was used to explain the variation among individuals of a population. Then, studies of the complex behavior of genes in populations of plants and animals developed into the field of study called population genetics. The principles of today's modern theory of evolution are rooted in population genetics and other related fields of study and are expressed in genetic terms.

Populations, not individuals, evolve

Can individuals evolve? That is, can an organism respond to natural selection by acquiring or losing characteristics? Recall that genes determine most of an individual's features, such as tooth shape or flower color. If an organism has a feature—called a phenotype in genetic terms—that is poorly adapted to its environment, the organism may be unable to survive and reproduce. However, within its lifetime, it cannot evolve a new phenotype by natural selection in response to its environment.

404 THE THEORY OF EVOLUTION

RESOURCE MANAGER

Unit 5 FAST FILE Resources
MiniLab Worksheet, p. 34
BioLab Worksheet, pp. 35–36
Reinforcement and Study Guide in English, pp. 39–40
Reinforcement and Study Guide in Spanish, pp. 43–44

Transparency Worksheets, pp. 48, 49–54
Reading Essentials for Biology, Section 15.2
Section Focus Transparency 38
Basic Concepts Transparencies 21, 22
Reteaching Skills Transparency 24

First generation					Phenotype frequency	Allele frequency
RR	RR	RR'	RR'	RR	White = 0 Pink = 0.5 Red = 0.5	R = 0.75 R' = 0.25
RR	RR'	RR	RR'			

Second generation					Phenotype frequency	Allele frequency
RR	RR'	RR	RR'	RR	White = 0.125 Pink = 0.25 Red = 0.625	R = 0.75 R' = 0.25
RR	R'R'	RR	RR			

Figure 15.11
Incomplete dominance produces three phenotypes: red flowers *(RR)*, white flowers *(R'R')*, and pink flowers *(RR')*. Although the phenotype frequencies of the generations vary, the allelic frequencies for the *R* and *R'* alleles do not vary.

Rather, natural selection acts on the range of phenotypes in a population. Recall that a population consists of all the members of a species that live in an area. Each member has the genes that characterize the traits of the species, and these genes exist as pairs of alleles. Just as all of the individuals make up the population, all of the genes of the population's individuals make up the population's genes. Evolution occurs as a population's genes and their frequencies change over time.

How can a population's genes change over time? Picture all of the alleles of the population's genes as being together in a large pool called a **gene pool.** The percentage of any specific allele in the gene pool is called the **allelic frequency.** Scientists calculate the allelic frequency of an allele in the same way that a baseball player calculates a batting average. They refer to a population in which the frequency of alleles remains the same over generations as being in **genetic equilibrium.** In the *Connection to Math* at the end of the chapter, you can read about the

mathematical description of genetic equilibrium. You can study the effect of natural selection on allelic frequencies in the *BioLab* at the end of the chapter.

Look at the population of snapdragons shown in *Figure 15.11*. A pattern of heredity called incomplete dominance, which you learned about earlier, governs flower color in snapdragons. If you know the flower-color genotypes of the snapdragons in a population, you can calculate the allelic frequency for the flower-color alleles. The population of snapdragons is in genetic equilibrium when the frequency of its alleles for flower color is the same in all its generations.

Changes in genetic equilibrium

A population that is in genetic equilibrium is not evolving. Because allelic frequencies remain the same, phenotypes remain the same, too. Any factor that affects the genes in the gene pool can change allelic frequencies, disrupting a population's genetic equilibrium, which results in the process of evolution.

Concept Development

Point out that in small populations that interbreed, such as certain religious groups and royal families, gene pools change quickly at first because the number of potential mates is limited.

Tying to Prior Knowledge

Review meiosis. Explain how random factors involved in some of the steps of meiosis can contribute to genetic drift.

Using An Analogy

Flip a coin to show how small populations can be affected by genetic drift. If you flip a coin 100 times, the chance of getting 100 heads and 0 tails—or even 80 heads and 20 tails—is unlikely. The result will probably be close to 50-50. But if you flip the coin 10 times, the chance of getting 8 heads and 2 tails—or even 10 heads and 0 tails—is more likely to occur. Similarly, the loss of alleles by chance is lower in large populations than in small ones.

Figure 15.12
Genetic drift can result in an increase of rare alleles in a small population. Notice the child has six fingers on each hand.

You have learned that one mechanism for genetic change is mutation. Environmental factors, such as radiation or chemicals, cause many mutations, but other mutations occur by chance. Of the mutations that affect organisms, many are lethal, and the organisms do not survive. Thus, lethal mutations are quickly eliminated. However, occasionally, a mutation results in a useful variation, and the new gene becomes part of the population's gene pool by the process of natural selection.

Another mechanism that disrupts a population's genetic equilibrium is **genetic drift**—the alteration of allelic frequencies by chance events.

Genetic drift can greatly affect small populations that include the descendants of a small number of organisms. This is because the genes of the original ancestors represent only a small fraction of the gene pool of the entire species and are the only genes available to pass on to offspring. The distinctive forms of life that Darwin found in the Galápagos Islands may have resulted from genetic drift.

Genetic drift has been observed in some small human populations that have become isolated due to reasons such as religious practices and belief systems. For example, in Lancaster County, Pennsylvania, there is an Amish population of about 12 000 people who have a unique lifestyle and marry other members of their community. By chance, at least one of the original 30 Amish settlers in this community carried a recessive allele that results in short arms and legs and extra fingers and toes in offspring, *Figure 15.12*. Because of the small gene pool, many individuals inherited the recessive allele over time. Today, the frequency of this allele among the Amish is high—1 in 14 rather than 1 in 1000 in the larger population of the United States.

Genetic equilibrium is also disrupted by the movement of individuals in and out of a population. The transport of genes by migrating individuals

Figure 15.13
These swallowtail butterflies live in different areas of North America. Despite their slight variations, they can interbreed to produce fertile offspring.

Papilio ajax ajax

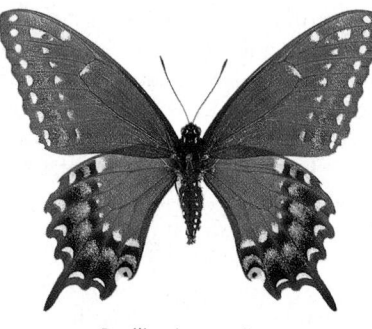

Papilio ajax ampliata

406 THE THEORY OF EVOLUTION

 Indiana Academic Standards

Pages 406–407: B.1.24, B.1.30, B.1.31, B.1.36

is called gene flow. When an individual leaves a population, its genes are lost from the gene pool. When individuals enter a population, their genes are added to the pool.

Mutation, genetic drift, and gene flow may significantly affect the evolution of small and isolated gene pools, such as those on islands. However, their effect is often insignificant in larger, less isolated gene pools. Natural selection is usually the most significant factor that causes changes in established gene pools—small or large.

Natural selection acts on variations

As you've learned, traits have variation, as shown in the butterflies pictured in *Figure 15.13*. Try measuring variations in *MiniLab 15.2*.

Recall that some variations increase or decrease an organism's chance of survival in an environment. These variations can be inherited and are controlled by alleles. Thus, the allelic frequencies in a population's gene pool will change over generations due to the natural selection of variations. There are three different types of natural selection that act on variation: stabilizing, directional, and disruptive.

✓ **Reading Check** **Explain** why populations that are in genetic equilibrium are not evolving.

MiniLab 15.2

Collect Data

Detecting a Variation Pick almost any trait—height, eye color, leaf width, or seed size—and you can observe how the trait varies in a population. Some variations are an advantage to an organism and some are not.

Procedure

1 Copy the data table shown here, but include the lengths in millimeters (numbers 25 through 45) that are missing from this table.

Data Table

Length in mm	20	21	22	23	24	—	46	47	48	49	50
Checks											
My Data—Number of Shells											
Class Data—Number of Shells											

2 Use a millimeter ruler to measure a peanut shell's length. In the Checks row, check the length you measured.

3 Repeat step 2 for 29 more shells.

4 Count the checks under each length and enter the total in the row marked My Data.

5 Use class totals to complete the row marked Class Data.

Analysis

1. **Collect and Organize Data** Was there variation among the lengths of peanut shells? Use class data to support your answer.

2. **Draw Conclusions** If larger peanut shells were a selective advantage, would this be stabilizing, directional, or disruptive selection? Explain your answer.

Papilio ajax curvifascia

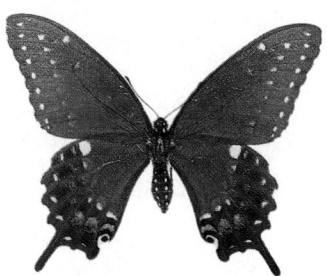

Papilio ajax ehrmann

MiniLab 15.2

Purpose

Students will measure and determine that peanut shells vary in length.

Process Skills

collect data, interpret data, make and use tables, make and use graphs, measure in SI

Safety Precautions

Some students may be allergic to peanuts. Sunflower seeds can be substituted for peanuts.

Teaching Strategies

- Have students wash their hands after handling peanuts.
- Unshelled peanuts are available in most large supermarkets.
- Have students pool their data on the chalkboard.
- Tell students that peanut shells contain seeds, and discuss briefly the role of seeds in plant reproduction.

Expected Results

Student data should indicate a wide range in shell length. There should be few shells at either extreme and the majority of shells should fall in the middle range of the measurements.

Analysis

1. yes; Student answers will vary.
2. directional selection; Larger shells may favor the survival of offspring because they may contain larger, more viable seeds.

Modified Assessment

Skill Have students prepare a histogram of the class data. Use the Performance Task Assessment List for Graph from Data in **PASC**, p. 111. **L1**

✓ **Reading Check** The composition of their gene pool is unchanging.

CULTURAL DIVERSITY

The Neutral Theory of Evolution
Explain to students the neutral theory of evolution developed by Japanese biologist Mootoo Kimura. This theory holds that most sequence changes that occur in DNA and proteins do not affect how the proteins do their job. In other words, most mutations have a neutral affect on organisms.

The neutral theory was heavily debated upon its presentation in 1968, but today it is viewed as an improvement of Darwinian theory because it provides testable predictions about molecular evolution. The strongest advocate of the neutral theory is Japanese geneticist Tomoko Ohta, head of Japan's National Institute of Genetics.

Visual Learning

Figure 15.14 illustrates the three main types of natural selection. Refer to each type and offer students several other examples of each.

Reinforcement

Logical-Mathematical Have students describe the type of natural selection in each of the following examples.

- Members of a population of Amazon tree frogs hop from tree to tree searching for food in the rain forest. They vary in leg length. Events result in massive destruction of the forest's trees. After several generations, only long-legged tree frogs remain alive. directional selection
- Different grass plants in a population range in length from 8 cm to 28 cm. The 8–10-cm grass blades receive little sunlight, and the 25–28-cm grass blades are eaten quickly by grazing animals. stabilizing selection
- The spines of a sea urchin population's members vary in length. The short-spined sea urchins are camouflaged easily on the seafloor. However, long-spined sea urchins are well defended against predators. disruptive selection

Have students illustrate each situation and predict what will happen to the members of each population if natural selection continues to operate. **L1**

Figure 15.14
Different types of natural selection act over the range of a trait's variation. The red, bell-shaped curve indicates a trait's variation in a population. The blue, bell-shaped curve indicates the effect of a natural selection.

A **Stabilizing selection** favors average individuals. This type of selection reduces variation in a population.

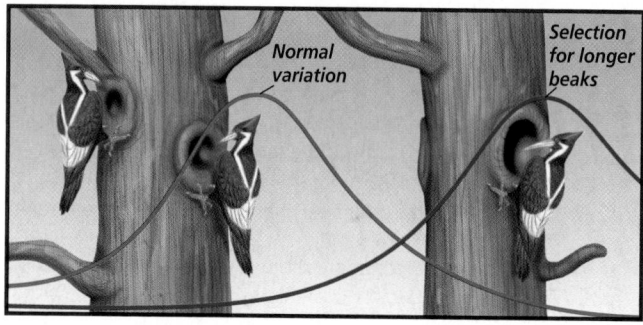

B **Directional selection** favors one of the extreme variations of a trait and can lead to the rapid evolution of a population.

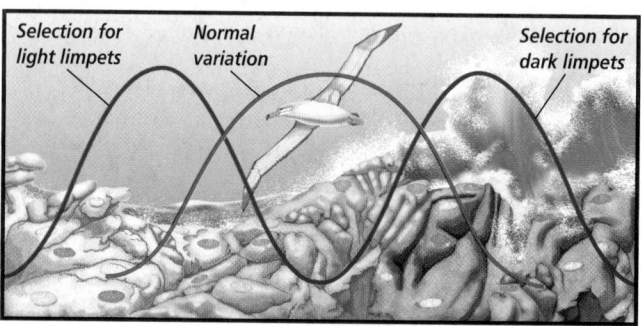

C **Disruptive selection** favors both extreme variations of a trait, resulting eventually in no intermediate forms of the trait and leading to the evolution of two new species.

408 THE THEORY OF EVOLUTION

Stabilizing selection is natural selection that favors average individuals in a population, as shown in *Figure 15.14.* Consider a population of spiders in which average size is a survival advantage. Predators in the area might easily see and capture spiders that are larger than average. However, small spiders may find it difficult to find food. Therefore, in this environment, average-sized spiders are more likely to survive—they have a selective advantage, or are "selected for."

Directional selection occurs when natural selection favors one of the extreme variations of a trait. For example, imagine a population of woodpeckers pecking holes in trees to feed on the insects living under the bark. Suppose that a species of insect that lives deep in tree tissues invades the trees in a woodpecker population's territory. Only woodpeckers with long beaks could feed on that insect. Therefore, the long-beaked woodpeckers in the population would have a selective advantage over woodpeckers with very short or average-sized beaks.

Finally, in **disruptive selection,** individuals with either extreme of a trait's variation are selected for. Consider, for example, a population of marine organisms called limpets. The shell color of limpets ranges from white, to tan, to dark brown. As adults, limpets live attached to rocks. On light-colored rocks, white-shelled limpets have an advantage because their bird predators cannot easily see them. On dark-colored rocks, dark-colored limpets have the advantage because they are camouflaged. On the other hand, birds easily see tan-colored limpets on either the light or dark backgrounds. Disruptive selection tends to eliminate the intermediate phenotypes.

Additional Lab

Bacterial Resistance

Purpose
Students will study variation in bacterial resistance to antibiotics. Dispose of used dishes after autoclaving or incinerating.

Safety Precautions
Wear goggles, aprons, and disposable gloves when working with bacteria.

Materials
culture of *Bacillus subtilis,* 3 tubes of nutrient agar, tube of streptomycin agar, inoculation loop, 2 petri dishes, Bunsen burner, wax pencil, test tube

Procedure
Give the following directions.
1. Write *A* and *B* on the halves of one petri dish and *C* and *D* on another.
2. Pour streptomycin agar into dish *A-B.* Cover the dish. Place the dish on a pencil so the liquid flows to one side to solidify. **CAUTION:** *Liquid agar is hot.*

Natural selection can significantly alter the genetic equilibrium of a population's gene pool over time. Significant changes in the gene pool could lead to the evolution of a new species over time.

The Evolution of Species

You've just read about how natural processes such as mutation, genetic drift, gene flow, and natural selection can change a population's gene pool over time. But how do the changes in the makeup of a gene pool result in the evolution of new species? Recall that a species is defined as a group of organisms that look alike and can interbreed to produce fertile offspring in nature. The evolution of new species, a process called **speciation** (spee shee AY shun), occurs when members of similar populations no longer interbreed to produce fertile offspring within their natural environment.

Physical barriers can prevent interbreeding

In nature, physical barriers can break large populations into smaller ones. Lava from volcanic eruptions can isolate populations. Sea-level changes along continental shelves can create islands. The water that surrounds an island isolates its populations. **Geographic isolation** occurs whenever a physical barrier divides a population.

A new species can evolve when a population has been geographically isolated. For example, imagine a population of tree frogs living in a rain forest, *Figure 15.15*. If small populations of tree frogs were geographically isolated, they would no longer be able to interbreed and exchange genes. Over time, each small population might adapt to its environment through natural selection and develop its own gene pool. Eventually, the gene pools of each population might become so different

Word Origin

speciation from the Latin word *species,* meaning "kind"; Speciation is a process that produces two species from one.

Figure 15.15
When geographic isolation divides a population of tree frogs, the individuals no longer mate across populations. **Explain and Illustrate** *How could geographic isolation result in natural selection and possibly new species?*

Discussion

Remind students that scientists used to classify organisms only on the basis of morphological comparisons. This type of classification is useful but limited. For example, using morphological classification, North American yellow-shafted flickers, red-shafted flickers, and their hybrid offspring could be considered three different species.

According to the biological species concept, organisms are classified by whether or not they can naturally interbreed with one another to produce fertile offspring, as the yellow-shafted flickers and red-shafted flickers can do. Elicit from students how many species of North American flickers exist based on this biological species definition. one

Caption Question Answer
Figure 15.15 Small populations cut off from the main population are likely to harbor variations that can be increased rapidly throughout the population. Over time, the environment can change enough that natural selection of these variations produces a new species.

Indiana Academic Standards
Pages 408–409: B.1.31, B.1.34

 Tree frogs are a single population.

 The formation of a river may divide the frogs into two populations. A new form may appear in one population.

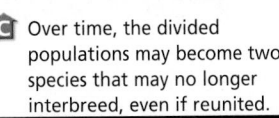 Over time, the divided populations may become two species that may no longer interbreed, even if reunited.

3. After the agar solidifies, pour a tube of hot nutrient agar into the dish and cover the dish.
4. Pour the other tubes of agar into the C-D dish. Cover the dish after it cools.
5. Sterilize the inoculation loop in the Bunsen burner's flame. Remove the stopper and quickly pass the entire lip of the bacterial culture through an open flame.
6. Dip the loop into the culture and remove it. Flame the lip of the container again and replace the stopper.
7. Streak the agar in dish A-B with the loop. Do not break the agar surface.
8. Repeat steps 5–7 on the C-D dish.
9. Recover the dishes, invert them, and place them in a dark drawer or closet. Do not open the dishes again after you have inoculated and recovered them. Observe

them after 24 hours. Dispose of used petri dishes as your teacher instructs.

Expected Results
There should be more bacterial growth in the C-D dish than in the A-B dish.

Assessment
Knowledge Explain your observations of the dishes. Streptomycin accounts for the different number of colonies. **L2**

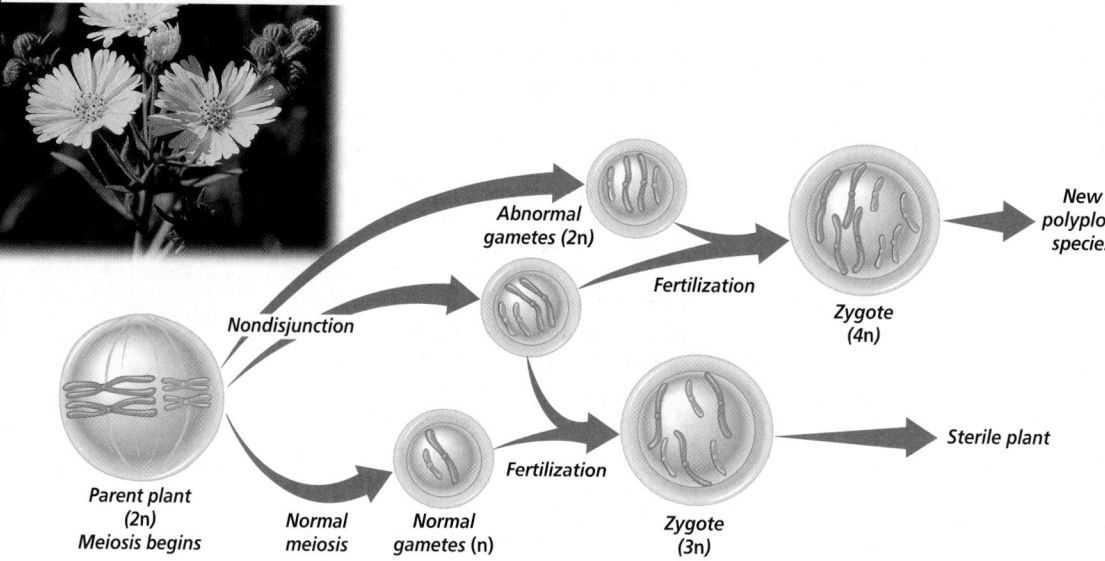

Figure 15.16
Many flowering plants, such as this California tarweed, are polyploids—individuals that result from mistakes made during meiosis.

Word Origin

polyploidy from the Greek word *polys*, meaning "many"; Polyploid plants contain multiple sets of chromosomes.

that they could no longer interbreed with the other populations. In this way, natural selection results in new species.

Reproductive isolation can result in speciation

As populations become increasingly distinct, reproductive isolation can arise. **Reproductive isolation** occurs when formerly interbreeding organisms can no longer mate and produce fertile offspring.

There are different types of reproductive isolation. Two examples are given here. One type occurs when the genetic material of the populations becomes so different that fertilization cannot occur. Some geographically separated populations of salamanders in California have this type of reproductive isolation. Another type of reproductive isolation is behavioral. For example, if one population of tree frogs mates in the fall, and another mates in the summer, these two populations will not mate with each other and are reproductively isolated.

A change in chromosome numbers and speciation

Chromosomes can also play a role in speciation. Many new species of plants and some species of animals have evolved in the same geographic area as a result of polyploidy (PAH lih ploy dee), illustrated in *Figure 15.16.* Any individual or species with a multiple of the normal set of chromosomes is known as a **polyploid.**

Mistakes during mitosis or meiosis can result in polyploid individuals. For example, if chromosomes do not separate properly during the first meiotic division, diploid (2*n*) gametes can be produced instead of the normal haploid (*n*) gametes. Polyploidy may result in immediate reproductive isolation. When a polyploid mates with an individual of the normal species, the resulting zygotes may not develop normally because of the difference in chromosome numbers. In other cases, the zygotes develop into adults that probably cannot reproduce. However, polyploids within a population may interbreed and form a separate species.

Polyploids can arise from within a species or from hybridization between species. Many flowering plant species and many important crop plants, such as wheat, cotton, and apples, originated by polyploidy.

Speciation rates

Although polyploid speciation takes only one generation, most other mechanisms of speciation do not occur as quickly. What is the usual rate of speciation?

Scientists once argued that evolution occurs at a slow, steady rate, with small, adaptive changes gradually accumulating over time in populations. **Gradualism** is the idea that species originate through a gradual change of adaptations. Some evidence from the fossil record supports gradualism. For example, fossil evidence shows that sea lilies evolved slowly and steadily over time.

In 1972, Niles Eldredge and Stephen J. Gould proposed a different hypothesis known as **punctuated equilibrium.** This hypothesis argues that speciation occurs relatively quickly, in rapid bursts, with long periods of genetic equilibrium in between. According to this hypothesis, environmental changes, such as higher temperatures or the introduction of a competitive species, lead to rapid changes in a small population's gene pool that is reproductively isolated from the main population. Speciation happens quickly—in about 10 000 years or less. Like gradualism, punctuated equilibrium is supported by fossil evidence as shown in *Figure 15.17.*

Biologists generally agree that both gradualism and punctuated equilibrium can result in speciation, depending on the circumstances. It shouldn't

Figure 15.17
The fossil record of elephant evolution supports the view of punctuated equilibrium. Several elephant species may have evolved from an ancestral population in a short time.

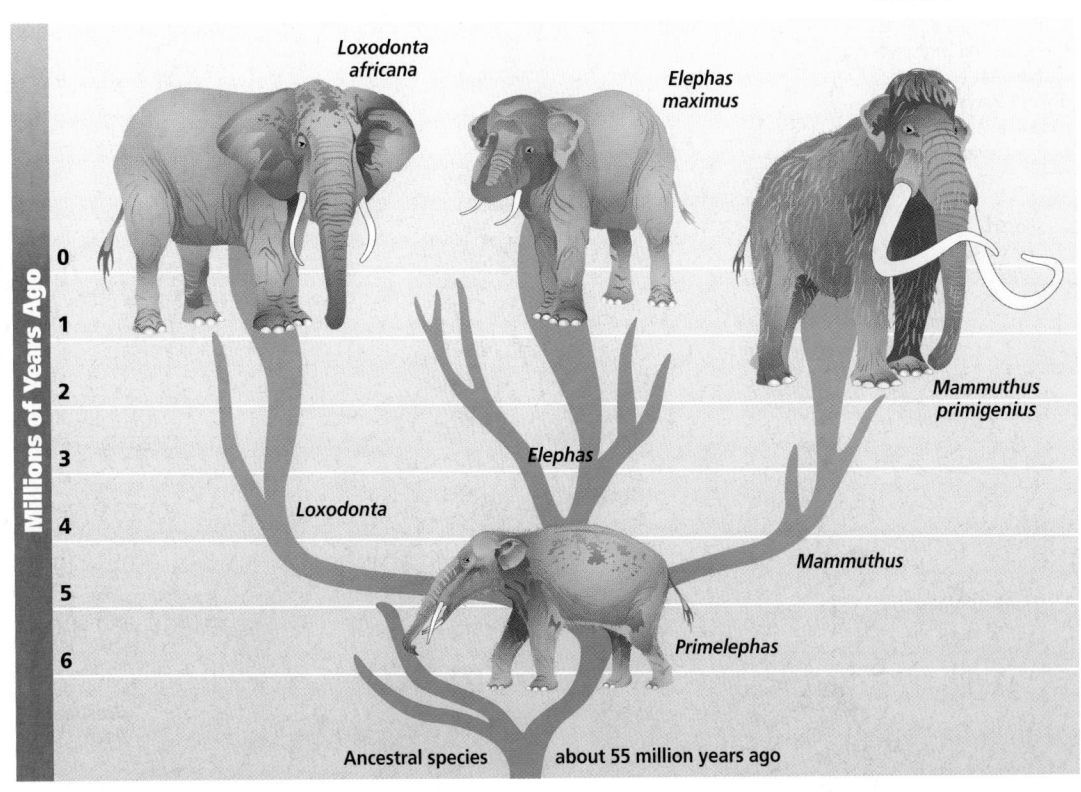

Loxodonta africana

Elephas maximus

Mammuthus primigenius

Elephas

Loxodonta

Mammuthus

Primelephas

Ancestral species   about 55 million years ago

Millions of Years Ago
0
1
2
3
4
5
6

Concept Development

Darwin believed that species evolve slowly over long periods of time. For example, fossils show that today's horseshoe crabs, genus *Limulus*, are nearly identical to ancestors that lived hundreds of millions of years ago. If possible, show a modern specimen of the horseshoe crab and a fossil counterpart to demonstrate their similarities. Remind students that gradualism and punctuated equilibrium are both supported and refuted in the fossil record. Point out an example that does support punctuated equilibrium, such as African mammals.

Enrichment

Research Have students research the Abert and Kaibab squirrels of the Grand Canyon area. Their reports should include the environment that each squirrel lives in, the characteristics of each species, and possible hypotheses for how the differences evolved.

CHALLENGE ACTIVITY

Speciation Rate: *Linguistic* Have the students research speciation rate. Divide the students into two groups. Have one group read Gould and Eldredge's 1972 article concerning punctuated equilibrium entitled "Punctuated Equilibria: An alternative to phyletic gradualism," found in *Models in Paleobiology,* T. J. M. Schopf (ed.), Freeman, Cooper, and Co. Have the other group research gradualism. Hold a debate between the two groups in front of the rest of the class. **L3**

Indiana Academic Standards
Pages 410–411: B.1.28, B.1.31, B.1.34, B.1.47

411

surprise you to see scientists offer alternative hypotheses to explain observations. The nature of science is such that new evidence or new ideas can modify theories.

Patterns of Evolution

Biologists have observed different patterns of evolution that occur throughout the world in different natural environments. These patterns support the idea that natural selection is an important agent for evolution.

Diversity in new environments

An extraordinary diversity of unique plants and animals live or have lived on the Hawaiian Islands, among them a group of birds called Hawaiian honeycreepers. This group of birds is interesting because, although similar in body size and shape, they differ sharply in color and beak shape.

Different species of honeycreepers evolved to occupy their own niches.

Despite their differences, scientists hypothesize that honeycreepers, as shown in *Figure 15.18*, evolved from a single ancestral species that lived on the Hawaiian Islands long ago. When an ancestral species evolves into an array of species to fit a number of diverse habitats, the result is called **adaptive radiation.**

Adaptive radiation in both plants and animals has occurred and continues to occur throughout the world and is common on islands. For example, the many species of finches that Darwin observed on the Galápagos Islands are a typical example of adaptive radiation.

Adaptive radiation is a type of **divergent evolution,** the pattern of evolution in which species that once were similar to an ancestral species diverge, or become increasingly

Figure 15.18
Evolutionary biologists have suggested that the ancestors of all Hawaiian Island honeycreepers migrated from North America about 5 million years ago. As this ancestral bird population settled in the diverse Hawaiian niches, adaptive radiation occurred.

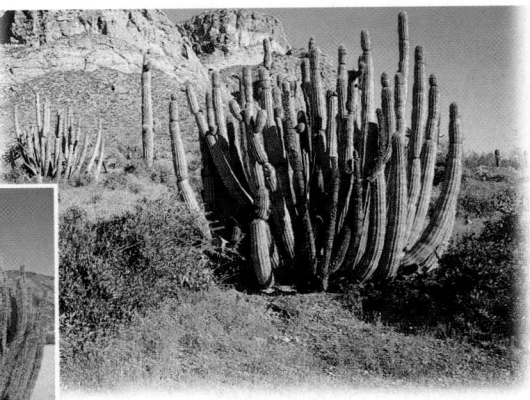

Figure 15.19
Unrelated species of plants such as the organ pipe cactus (**A**) and this *Euphorbia* (**B**) share a similar fleshy body type and no leaves.

distinct. Divergent evolution occurs when populations change as they adapt to different environmental conditions, eventually resulting in new species.

Different species can look alike

A pattern of evolution in which distantly related organisms evolve similar traits is called **convergent evolution.** Convergent evolution occurs when unrelated species occupy similar environments in different parts of the world. Because they share similar environmental pressures, they share similar pressures of natural selection.

For example, in *Figure 15.19* you see an organ pipe cactus (family Cactaceae) that grows in the deserts of North and South America and a plant of the family Euphorbiaceae that looks similar and lives in African deserts. Although these plants are unrelated species, their environments are similar. You can see that they both have fleshy bodies and no leaves. That convergent evolution has apparently occurred in unrelated species, is further evidence for natural selection.

Reading Check **Compare and contrast** convergent and divergent evolution.

DAILY INTERVENTION

Check for Understanding
Develop five questions about types of natural selection and patterns of evolution. Have students work in groups to answer the questions. **L1**
COOP LEARN

Reteach
Visual-Spatial Have students make a concept map to demonstrate how natural selection acts on the variation of a trait. **L1** **ELL**

Resources
For more practice, use *Reading Essentials for Biology,* Section 15.2.

Extension
Linguistic Have the students write a summary about how Darwin's finches illustrate adaptive radiation. **L2**

 Assessment

Skill Have students analyze the following data on rabbit population allele frequencies.

1st generation: $A = 0.5$, $a = 0.5$

2nd generation: $A = 0.6$, $a = 0.4$

3rd generation: $A = 0.7$, $a = 0.3$

4th generation: $A = 0.8$, $a = 0.2$

5th generation: $A = 0.9$, $a = 0.1$

Have students describe what is happening in the population if A represents an allele for white fur, and a represents an allele for brown fur. **L2**

Section Assessment

Understanding Main Ideas
1. Explain and illustrate why the evolution of resistance to antibiotics in bacteria is an example of directional natural selection.

2. How can geographic isolation change a population's gene pool?

3. Why is rapid evolutionary change more likely to occur in small populations?

4. How do gradualism and punctuated equilibrium differ? How are they similar? Include in your answer the patterns of extinction observed in both theories.

Thinking Critically
5. Hummingbird moths are night-flying insects whose behavior and appearance are similar to those of hummingbirds. Explain how these two organisms demonstrate convergent evolution.

SKILL REVIEW

6. **Experiment** Biologists discovered two squirrel species living on opposite sides of the Grand Canyon. They hypothesize that the species evolved from a common ancestor. What observations or experiments could provide evidence for this hypothesis? For more help, refer to *Experiment* in the **Skill Handbook.**

in.bdol.glencoe.com/self_check_quiz

Section Assessment

1. Only bacteria that are totally resistant to antibiotics survive.
2. It may result in different local environments for a separated population. Different adaptations are useful in different environments, and the gene pool will in time reflect the differences.
3. It occurs because of genetic drift and the limited number of mates.
4. Gradualism takes a much longer time than punctuated equilibrium, but they both result in evolution. Extinction occurs over a short period in punctuated equilibrium.
5. Although not closely related, they share similar environments and have evolved similar behaviors and appearances.
6. Analyze the DNA, structure, and behavior of each. Examine fossils.

Time Allotment
one class period

Process Skills
make and use tables, observe and infer, make and use graphs

PREPARATION

Alternative Materials
Beads or other small objects may be substituted for beans.

PROCEDURE

Teaching Strategies
■ Tell students that they will simulate natural selection on a population to see how allelic frequency changes.
■ You may wish to circulate during this activity to ensure that students are following the procedure correctly.
■ Have students wash their hands after handling the beans.

Data and Observations
Make sure students are correctly calculating allelic frequency after each "generation" and recording these data in their data tables. Students should observe changes in the allelic frequencies of the rabbit population. Student graphs should show an increase in the frequency of the *G* allele and a decrease in the *g* allele.

Assessment
Knowledge Ask students whether allele frequencies would change as fast if only 60% of the white rabbits were removed from the population each generation. Why or why not? No, because the gene pool would contain more *g* alleles that could produce more

INTERNET
BioLab

Before You Begin
Evolution can be described as the change in allelic frequencies of a gene pool over time. Natural selection can place pressure on specific phenotypes and cause a change in the frequency of the alleles that produce the phenotypes. In this activity, you will simulate the effects of eagle predation on a population of rabbits, where *GG* represents the homozygous condition for gray fur, *Gg* is the heterozygous condition for gray fur, and *gg* represents the homozygous condition for white fur.

white rabbits. Use the Performance Task Assessment List for Analyzing the Data in **PASC**, p. 99. **L2**

Natural Selection and Allelic Frequency

PREPARATION

Problem
How does natural selection affect allelic frequency?

Objectives
In this BioLab, you will:
■ **Simulate** natural selection by using beans of two different colors.
■ **Calculate** allelic frequencies over five generations.
■ **Demonstrate** how natural selection can affect allelic frequencies over time.
■ **Use the Internet** to collect and compare data from other students.

Materials
colored pencils (2)   paper bag
graph paper   pinto beans
white navy beans

Safety Precautions
CAUTION: *Clean up spilled beans immediately to prevent anyone from slipping.*

Skill Handbook
If you need help with this lab, refer to the **Skill Handbook.**

PROCEDURE

1. Copy the data table shown on the next page.
2. Place 50 pinto beans and 50 white navy beans into the paper bag.
3. Shake the bag. Remove two beans. These represent one rabbit's genotype. Set the pair aside, and continue to remove 49 more pairs.
4. Arrange the beans on a flat surface in two columns representing the two possible rabbit phenotypes, gray (genotypes *GG* or *Gg*) and white (genotype *gg*).
5. Examine your columns. Remove 25 percent of the gray rabbits and 100 percent of the white rabbits. These numbers represent a random selection pressure on your rabbit population. If the number you calculate is a fraction, remove a whole rabbit to make whole numbers.

CLEANUP AND DISPOSAL
Make sure students return their materials to the proper places and clean up any spilled beans.

414

6. Count the number of pinto and navy beans remaining. Record this number in your data table.

7. Calculate the allelic frequencies by dividing the number of beans of one type by 100. Record these data.

8. Begin the next generation by placing 100 beans into the bag. The proportions of pinto and navy beans should be the same as the percentages you calculated in step 7.

9. Repeat steps 3 through 8, collecting data for five generations.

10. Go to in.bdol.glencoe.com/internet_lab to **post your data.**

11. Graph the frequencies of each allele over five generations. Plot the frequency of the allele on the vertical axis and the number of the generation on the horizontal axis. Use a different colored pencil for each allele.

12. **CLEANUP AND DISPOSAL** Return all materials to their proper places for reuse.

Data Table

Sample Data

	Allele G			Allele g		
Generation	Number	Percentage	Frequency	Number	Percentage	Frequency
Start	50	50	0.50	50	50	0.50
1	38	68	0.68	18	32	0.32
2	49	79	0.79	13	21	0.21
3	58	81	0.81	14	19	0.19
4	63	89	0.89	8	11	0.11
5	66	89	0.89	8	11	0.11

ANALYZE AND CONCLUDE

1. **Analyze Data** Did either allele disappear? Why or why not?

2. **Think Critically** What does your graph show about allelic frequencies and natural selection?

3. **Infer** What would happen to the allelic frequencies if the number of eagles declined?

4. **ERROR ANALYSIS** Explain any differences in allelic frequencies you observed between your data and the data from the Internet. What advantage is there to having a large amount of data? What problems might there be in using data from the Internet?

Share Your Data

Graph Find this BioLab using the link below, and post your data in the data table provided for this activity. Using the additional data from other students, analyze the combined data, and complete your graph.

in.bdol.glencoe.com/internet_lab

ANALYZE AND CONCLUDE

1. Neither allele disappeared from the population because the g allele is also in the heterozygous (Gg) rabbits.

2. The graph shows an increase in the frequency of the G allele and a decrease in the frequency of the g allele due to natural selection against white rabbits.

3. There would be less selective pressure on white rabbits and, therefore, less decline in the frequency of the g allele.

4. **ERROR ANALYSIS** Students should notice little difference in the allelic frequencies posted on the Internet and the frequencies they calculated. By combining data students may get more accurate results.

Share Your Data

Graph To navigate the Internet BioLabs, go to in.bdol.glencoe.com/internet_lab. The data from many trials supports a student's data and the conclusions the student may draw from the data.

Indiana Academic Standards

Pages 414–415: B.1.31, B.1.34

connection to *Math*

connection to *Math*

Mathematics and Evolution

A population of penquins

In the early 1900s, G. H. Hardy, a British mathematician, and W. Weinberg, a German doctor, independently discovered how the frequency of a trait's alleles in a population could be described mathematically.

Suppose that in a population of pea plants, 36 plants are homozygous dominant for the tall trait *(TT)*, 48 plants are heterozygous tall *(Tt)*, and 16 plants are short plants *(tt)*. In the homozygous tall plants, there are (36) (2), or 72, *T* alleles and in the heterozygous plants there are 48 *T* alleles, for a total of 120 *T* alleles in the population. There are 48 *t* alleles in the heterozygous plants plus (16) (2), or 32, *t* alleles in the short plants, for a total of 80 *t* alleles in the population. The number of *T* and *t* alleles in the population is 200. The frequency of *T* alleles is 120/200 or 0.6, and the frequency of *t* alleles is 80/200, or 0.4.

The Hardy-Weinberg principle The Hardy-Weinberg principle states that the frequency of the alleles for a trait in a stable population will not vary. This statement is expressed as the equation $p + q = 1$, where p is the frequency of one allele for the trait, and q is the frequency of the other allele. The sum of the frequencies of the alleles always includes 100 percent of the alleles, and is therefore stated as 1.

Squaring both sides of the equation produces the equation $p^2 + 2pq + q^2 = 1$. You can use this equation to determine the frequency of genotypes in a population: homozygous dominant individuals (p^2), heterozygous individuals $(2pq)$, and recessive individuals (q^2). For example, in the pea plant population described above, the frequency of the genotypes would be

$$(0.6)(0.6) + 2(0.6)(0.4) + (0.4)(0.4) = 1$$

The frequency of the homozygous tall genotype is 0.36, the heterozygous genotype is 0.48, and the short genotype is 0.16.

In any sexually reproducing, large population, genotype frequencies will remain constant if no mutations occur, random mating occurs, no natural selection occurs, and no genes enter or leave the population.

Implications of the principle The Hardy-Weinberg principle is useful for several reasons. First, it explains that the genotypes in populations tend to remain the same. Second, because a recessive allele may be masked by its dominant allele, the equation is useful for determining the recessive allele's frequency in the population. Finally, the Hardy-Weinberg principle is useful in studying natural populations to determine how much natural selection may be occurring in the population.

Math in Biology

Draw Conclusions The general population of the United States is getting taller. Assuming that height is a genetic trait, does this observation violate the Hardy-Weinberg principle? Explain your answer.

 To find out more about the Hardy-Weinberg principle, visit in.bdol.glencoe.com/math

Math in Biology

No; The United States is not in genetic equilibrium because new genes enter the population, mating is probably not random, and natural selection affects the trait of human height.

STUDY GUIDE

Section 15.1

Natural Selection and the Evidence for Evolution

Key Concepts

■ After many years of experimentation and observation, Charles Darwin proposed the idea that species originated through the process of natural selection.

■ Natural selection is a mechanism of change in populations. In a specific environment, individuals with certain variations are likely to survive, reproduce, and pass these variations to future generations.

■ Evolution has been observed in the lab and field, but much of the evidence for evolution has come from studies of fossils, anatomy, and biochemistry.

Vocabulary

analogous structure (p. 401)
artificial selection (p. 395)
camouflage (p. 399)
embryo (p. 402)
homologous structure (p. 400)
mimicry (p. 398)
natural selection (p. 395)
vestigial structure (p. 401)

Section 15.2

Mechanisms of Evolution

Key Concepts

■ Evolution can occur only when a population's genetic equilibrium changes. Mutation, genetic drift, and gene flow can change a population's genetic equilibrium, especially in a small, isolated population. Natural selection is usually a factor that causes change in established gene pools—both large and small.

■ The separation of populations by physical barriers can lead to speciation.

■ There are many patterns of evolution in nature. These patterns support the idea that natural selection is an important mechanism of evolution.

■ Gradualism is the hypothesis that species originate through a gradual change in adaptations. The alternative hypothesis, punctuated equilibrium, argues that speciation occurs in relatively rapid bursts, followed by long periods of genetic equilibrium. Evidence for both evolutionary rates can be found in the fossil record.

Vocabulary

adaptive radiation (p. 412)
allelic frequency (p. 405)
convergent evolution (p. 413)
directional selection (p. 408)
disruptive selection (p. 408)
divergent evolution (p. 412)
gene pool (p. 405)
genetic drift (p. 406)
genetic equilibrium (p. 405)
geographic isolation (p. 409)
gradualism (p. 411)
polyploid (p. 410)
punctuated equilibrium (p. 411)
reproductive isolation (p. 410)
speciation (p. 409)
stabilizing selection (p. 408)

FOLDABLES
Study Organizer To help you review the evidence for evolution, use the Organizational Study Fold on page 393.

 in.bdol.glencoe.com/vocabulary_puzzlemaker

Key Concepts

Summary statements can be used by students to review the major concepts of the chapter.

 Biology Online

Visit in.bdol.glencoe.com
/self_check_quiz
/vocabulary_puzzlemaker
/chapter_test
/standardized_test

VOCABULARY PUZZLEMAKER

For additional help with vocabulary, have students access the Vocabulary PuzzleMaker online at in.bdol.glencoe.com/ vocabulary_puzzlemaker

FOLDABLES™

Have students use their Foldables to review the content of Section 15.1.

Use the Exam*View*®Pro Test Bank CD-ROM to:
- Create **multiple versions** of tests
- Create **modified** tests with one mouse click for **inclusion** students
- **Edit** existing questions and **add** your own questions
- Build tests aligned with state standards using built-in **State Curriculum Tags**
- Change **English** tests to **Spanish** with one mouse click and vice versa

Chapter 15 Assessment

The Princeton Review *Questions and answers have been aligned and verified by The Princeton Review.*

Vocabulary Review

1. camouflage
2. natural selection
3. speciation
4. punctuated equilibrium

Understanding Key Concepts

5. C	**7.** D	**9.** D
6. C	**8.** B	

Constructed Response

10. Many adaptations are related to escaping from predators. Poisons are a natural defense. If a predator eats a brightly colored insect and becomes ill, it may avoid such an organism the next time. Bright colors can indicate that organisms may be poisonous and deter predation.

11. Genetic drift occurs when alleles change in small populations that become separated. An example is the Galápagos finches. Geographic isolation may separate populations and result in speciation, such as in the cougars in Florida compared to those in the rest of the United States. Polyploidy can cause speciation such as in strawberries. Students may give other examples.

12. All mammals are related to each other and are theorized to have evolved from a common ancestor.

Thinking Critically

13. Finches in the Galápagos Islands have adapted to the various available foods, resulting in different-sized beaks among the 13 different species. Students may

Vocabulary Review

Review the Chapter 15 vocabulary words listed in the Study Guide on page 417. Match the words with the definitions below.

1. adaptation that enables an individual to blend with its surroundings
2. mechanism for change in a population
3. process of evolution of a new species
4. hypothesis that speciation occurs in rapid bursts

Understanding Key Concepts

5. Which of the structures shown below is NOT homologous with the others?

A.   **B.**   **C.**   **D.**

6. Which type of natural selection favors average individuals in a population?
- **A.** directional
- **B.** disruptive
- **C.** stabilizing
- **D.** divergent

7. Which of the following pairs of terms is NOT related?
- **A.** analogous structures—butterfly and bird wings
- **B.** evolution—natural selection
- **C.** vestigial structure—eyes in blind fish
- **D.** adaptive radiation—convergent evolution

8. The fish and whale shown here are not closely related. Their structural similarities appear to be the result of _____.

- **A.** adaptive radiation
- **B.** convergent evolution
- **C.** divergent evolution
- **D.** punctuated equilibrium

9. Which of the following is a true statement about evolution?
- **A.** Individuals evolve more slowly than populations.
- **B.** Individuals evolve; populations don't.
- **C.** Individuals evolve by changing the gene pool.
- **D.** Populations evolve; individuals don't.

Constructed Response

10. Open Ended How might the bright colors of poisonous species aid in their survival?

11. Open Ended Explain the different ways in which a new species can evolve as a result of natural selection. Give examples of species that illustrate and support your conclusions.

12. Open Ended Explain why the forelimbs of a cat, a bat, and a whale would be homologous structures.

Thinking Critically

13. REAL WORLD BIOCHALLENGE Examples of divergent evolution are especially evident in island archipelagoes. Visit **in.bdol.glencoe.com** to find out about some examples of divergent evolution. Chose an island group, such as the Galápagos Islands or the Hawaiian Islands. Make a map of the islands and drawings of a group of organisms that shows divergent evolution. Your drawings should show at least three species that are closely related. Explain you findings to the class.

14. Draw Conclusions What can be concluded from the observation that many organisms have the same chemical enzymes that work in exactly the same way?

15. Observe and Infer Describe adaptive radiation as a form of divergent evolution.

 in.bdol.glencoe.com/chapter_test

choose to study divergent evolution in the Galápagos Islands, Hawaii, or other island group. Their drawings should show at least three species that are closely related, but divergent from one another.

14. The organisms have had a common ancestor with the same chemical enzymes.

15. In adaptive radiation, a generalized ancestor encounters an area of many available niches and eventually diverges into many species. This is an example of divergent evolution, in which species similar to ancestral species adapt to different environmental conditions.

16. Explain In terms of natural selection, why do many municipalities no longer routinely spray insecticides to kill mosquitoes during the summer months?

17. Infer The structural characteristics of many species, such as sharks, have changed little over time. What evolutionary factors might be affecting their stability?

The assessed Indiana standard appears next to the question.

End-of-Course Assessment Practice

All questions aligned and verified by *The Princeton Review*

Part 1 Multiple Choice

Use the graph below to answer question 18.

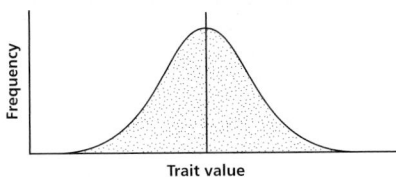

Distribution Before Selection

Frequency

Trait value

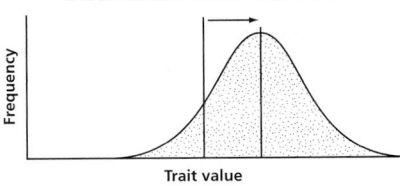

Distribution After Selection

Frequency

Trait value

18. Which pattern of natural selection is illustrated above?
A. disruptive selection
B. stabilizing selection
C. directional selection
D. random selection

19. Which of the following provides for instant reproductive isolation?
B.1.36
A. polyploidy
B. most geographic barriers such as rivers and mountain belts
C. climate changes
D. behavior changes in females of the species

20. Which type of adaptation develops quickly in bacteria that are antibiotic resistant?
A. structural adaptation
B. physical adaptation
C. physiological adaptation
D. phenotypic adaptation

Use the illustration below to answer questions 21 and 22.

Multiple-descendant species

Extinction

Time

Divergence

Ancestral species

21. The pattern of evolution shown above indicates _____.
B.1.34
A. convergent evolution
B. divergent evolution
C. stabilizing selection
D. geographic isolation

22. The pattern of evolution shown above most closely resembles that of _____.
B.1.34
A. Hawaiian honeycreepers and Galápagos finches
B. organ pipe cactus and *Euphorbia*
C. bat wings and butterfly wings
D. forelimbs of whales and crocodiles

Part 2 Constructed Response/Grid In

Record your answers on your answer document.

 23. Open Ended Give an example of two species that evolved due to geographic isolation.

24. Open Ended How is it possible for both Darwin's idea of gradualism and Eldredge and Gould's idea of punctuated equilibrium to be valid?

in.bdol.glencoe.com/standardized_test

---

16. Routine spraying of insecticides increases the potential for mosquito populations to become resistant.

17. Marine biomes are very stable and slow to change. Shark populations may be close to genetic equilibrium.

RUBRIC

For more help evaluating open-ended assessment questions, see the rubric on p. 9T.

End-of-Course Assessment Practice

18. C **20.** C **22.** A
19. A **21.** B
23. Hawaiian honeycreepers, Galápagos finches (students may list other examples)
24. Gradualism and punctuated equilibrium are not competing ideas. Both explain the pace of evolution as observed through geological time. For long periods of time, species appear to evolve slowly, just as gradualism predicts. After mass extinctions and other geological events, there appears to be a rapid burst of evolution when species radiate, just as punctuated equilibrium predicts.

FAST FILE

Answer Sheet A practice answer sheet can be found on p. 61 of *Unit 5 FAST FILE Resources.*

Indiana Academic Standards

Pages 418–419: B.1.31, B.1.32, B.1.34, B.1.35, B.1.36, B.1.47

Section Objectives	National Science Standards	State/Local Standards	Advanced Lab and Demo Planning
Section 16.1 1/2 session 1. **Recognize** the adaptations of primates. 2. **Compare and contrast** the diversity of living primates. 3. **Distinguish** the evolutionary relationships of primates.	UCP.1–5; A.1, A.2; C.3, C.4, C.6; G.1–3	**Indiana Standards** B.1.32, B.1.47	**Student Labs:** MiniLab 16.1, p. 425: tape, pen, tennis ball Problem-Solving Lab 16.1, p. 426 **Teacher Demonstration:** Quick Demo, p. 424: photos, illustrations, models, or actual skulls of strepsirrhines and haplorhines
Section 16.2 1 1/2 sessions 4. **Compare and contrast** the adaptations of australopithecines with those of apes and humans. 5. **Identify** the evidence of the major anatomical changes in hominids during human evolution.	UCP.2–5; A.1, A.2; C.3, C.6; E.1, E.2; G.1–3	**Indiana Standards** B.1.30, B.1.32, B.1.35	**Student Labs:** MiniLab 16.2, p. 429 Additional Lab, p. 432: metric ruler or tape measure Problem-Solving Lab 16.2, p. 433 Investigate BioLab, p. 436: See materials below. **Teacher Demonstration:** Quick Demo, p. 432: video
End of Chapter Assessment **Student Edition** **Study Guide,** p. 439 **Content Assessment,** pp. 440–441		**Indiana Standards** B.1.30, B.1.32	**Student Lab:** Investigate BioLab, p. 436: metric ruler, protractor, copy of skull diagrams

Key to Teaching Strategies

L1 Level 1 activities should be appropriate for students with learning difficulties.

L2 Level 2 activities should be within the ability range of all students.

L3 Level 3 activities are designed for above-average students.

ELL ELL activities should be within the ability range of English Language Learners.

COOP LEARN
Cooperative Learning activities are designed for small group work.

Legend

🖐 Transparency   💿 CD-ROM   🎵 MP3   📼 Videocassette   💿 DVD

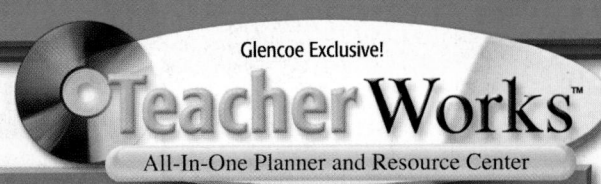

Glencoe Exclusive!

TeacherWorks™
All-In-One Planner and Resource Center

Reproducible Masters and Transparencies	Technology

Reproducible Masters and Transparencies

Unit 5 FAST FILE Resources
   MiniLab Worksheet, p. 65
   Reinforcement and Study Guide in English, pp. 73–74
   Reinforcement and Study Guide in Spanish, pp. 77–78
   Concept Mapping, p. 81
   Transparency Worksheet, p. 83
Reading Essentials for Biology, Section 16.1
Laboratory Manual, pp. 93–96
Inside Story Poster
🖐 **Section Focus Transparency 39**

Technology

💿 **Interactive Chalkboard CD-ROM: Section 16.1 Presentation**
💿 **TeacherWorks™ CD-ROM**
🎵 **Guided Reading Audio Summaries MP3**

Unit 5 FAST FILE Resources
   MiniLab Worksheet, p. 62
   BioLab Worksheet, pp. 67–69
   Real World BioApplications, pp. 71–72
   Reinforcement and Study Guide in English, pp. 75–76
   Reinforcement and Study Guide in Spanish, pp. 79–80
   Critical Thinking/Problem Solving, p. 82
   Transparency Worksheets, pp. 84, 85–86, 87–88
Reading Essentials for Biology, Section 16.2
Laboratory Manual, pp. 97–100
🖐 **Section Focus Transparency 40**
🖐 **Basic Concepts Transparency 23**
🖐 **Reteaching Skills Transparency 25**

💿 **Interactive Chalkboard CD-ROM: Section 16.2 Presentation**
💿 **TeacherWorks™ CD-ROM**
🎵 **Guided Reading Audio Summaries MP3**

Unit 5 FAST FILE Resources
   Chapter Assessment, pp. 89–94
   Student Recording Sheet, p. 95

The Princeton Review **Reviewing Biology,** pp. 31–32

💿 **Interactive Chalkboard: Chapter 16 Assessment**
💿 **MindJogger Videoquizzes DVD/VHS**
💿 **ExamView® Pro Test Bank CD-ROM**
💿 **TeacherWorks™ CD-ROM**
💿 **Succeeding on National Standards CD-ROM**

🖱 **in.bdol.glencoe.com**
/self_check_quiz
/vocabulary_puzzlemaker
/chapter_test
/standardized_test

🚩 Indicates materials created specifically for Indiana.

Short on Time?

BIODIGEST If time does not permit teaching the entire chapter, use the BioDigest at the end of the unit as an overview.

Understanding the Photo

Humans were once thought to be the only animals to use tools. However, Jane Goodall found that chimpanzees possess this ability, too. The use of tools is a rare phenomenon, but several species of birds and a few mammals also are known to make and use tools.

Biology Journal

Observing a Primate Have students find the scientific name of a primate they have seen and then write answers to the following questions: Where did you first see the primate? What was it doing? What about the primate interested you? What more about the primate would you like to learn? **L1**

Primate Evolution

What You'll Learn

■ You will compare and contrast primates and their adaptations.
■ You will analyze the evidence for the ancestry of humans.

Why It's Important

Humans are primates. A knowledge of primates and their evolution can provide an understanding of human origins.

Understanding ▶ the Photo

Humans are not the only animals that use tools. This chimpanzee is using a stone to crack a nutshell.

Biology Online

Visit **in.bdol.glencoe.com** to
• study the entire chapter online
• access Web Links for more information and activities on primate evolution
• review content with the Interactive Tutor and self-check quizzes

Two-Minute Chapter Launcher

Discussion To elicit students' preconceptions about the uniqueness of humans, have them brainstorm answers to the following question: What makes you different from other species? Students may offer many traits, however many will not be unique. For example, students may say that humans walk on two legs, humans can talk, or that humans can grasp objects. You may give examples that show that other animals share most of our traits. Be especially careful to introduce students to the common characteristics humans share with primates.

Bellringer
Section Focus Transparency 39

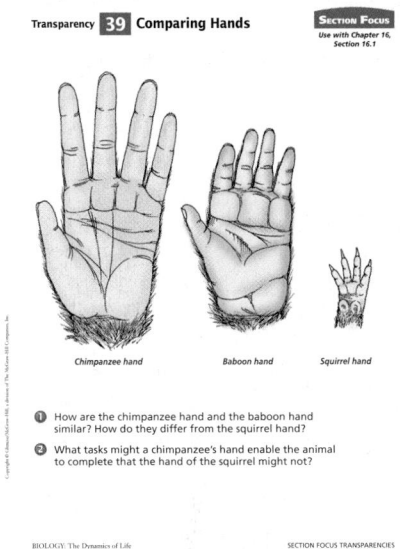

Transparency **39** Comparing Hands

SECTION FOCUS
Use with Chapter 16, Section 16.1

Chimpanzee hand   *Baboon hand*   *Squirrel hand*

❶ How are the chimpanzee hand and the baboon hand similar? How do they differ from the squirrel hand?

❷ What tasks might a chimpanzee's hand enable the animal to complete that the hand of the squirrel might not?

BIOLOGY: The Dynamics of Life   SECTION FOCUS TRANSPARENCIES

PowerPoint® Presentations

This CD-ROM is an editable Microsoft® PowerPoint® presentation that includes:
- Section presentations
- Section checks
- Image bank
- Hot links to Biology Online
- All transparencies

FOLDABLES™

For an additional Foldables activity idea, see the Chapter 16 Foldables page in *Unit 5 Fast File Resources.*

Primate Adaptation and Evolution

Indiana Standards Standard B.1.32 Explain how natural selection leads to organisms that are well suited for survival in particular environments, and discuss how natural selection provides scientific explanation for the history of life on Earth as depicted in the fossil record **and in the similarities evident within the diversity of existing organisms.**

SECTION PREVIEW

Objectives

Recognize the adaptations of primates.

Compare and contrast the diversity of living primates.

Distinguish the evolutionary relationships of primates.

Review Vocabulary

speciation: the process of evolution of a new species that occurs when members of similar populations no longer interbreed to produce fertile offspring (p. 409)

New Vocabulary

primate
opposable thumb
anthropoid
prehensile tail

FOLDABLES™
Study Organizer

Investigating Primates Make the following Foldable to help you organize information about the two groups of primates.

STEP 1 **Fold** a sheet of paper in half lengthwise. Make the back edge about 2 cm longer than the front edge.

STEP 2 **Turn** the paper so the fold is on the bottom. Then **fold** it in half.

STEP 3 **Unfold and cut** only the top layer along the fold to make two tabs.

STEP 4 **Label** the Foldable as shown.

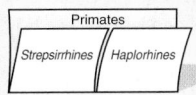

Primates
| Strepsirrhines | Haplorhines |

Illustrate and Label As you read Chapter 16, identify the characteristics of each group of primates under the appropriate tab.

What is a primate?

Have you ever gone to a zoo and seen monkeys, chimpanzees, gorillas, or baboons? If you have, then you've observed some different types of primates. The **primates** are a group of mammals that includes lemurs, monkeys, apes, and humans. Primates come in a variety of shapes and sizes, but, despite their diversity, they share common traits. Learn more about primates on pages 1068–1069 in the *Focus On.*

What characteristics account for the complex behaviors of primates? Find out by reading *Figure 16.1* on the next page. Primates have rounded heads with flattened faces, unlike most other mammals. Fitting snugly inside the rounded head is a brain that, relative to body size, is the largest brain of any terrestrial mammal. Primate brains are also more complex than those of other animals. The diverse behaviors and social interactions of primates reflect the complexity of their brains.

The majority of primates are arboreal, meaning they live in trees, and have several adaptations that help them survive there. All primates have relatively flexible shoulder and hip joints. These flexible joints are important to some primates for climbing and swinging among branches.

16.1 PRIMATE ADAPTATION AND EVOLUTION **421**

RESOURCE MANAGER

Unit 5 *Fast File* Resources
MiniLab Worksheet, p. 65
Reinforcement and Study Guide in English, pp. 73–74
Reinforcement and Study Guide in Spanish, pp. 77–78
Concept Mapping, p. 81
Transparency Worksheet, p. 83

Reading Essentials for Biology, Section 16.1
Laboratory Manual, pp. 93–96
Inside Story Poster
Section Focus Transparency 39

Indiana Academic Standards

Pages 420–421: B.1.32

Purpose

Students examine traits common to primates.

Teaching Strategies

■ Ask students why primates are popular zoo attractions and what makes primates unique. List responses on the chalkboard.

■ Remind students that humans are primates and, although not arboreal, share these adaptations.

■ Discuss each major primate characteristic, having students explain how each is an important human adaptation.

Visual Learning

■ Display pictures or specimens of primate (including human) and other mammalian skeletons and teeth to compare and contrast them.

■ Show how a human skeleton's hands, feet, and joints are similar to those of other primates.

Critical Thinking

Binocular vision allows primates to judge depth, a useful adaptation for arboreal species.

A Primate

Figure 16.1

Primates are a diverse group of mammals, but they share some common features. For example, you can see in the drawing of a gibbon that primates have rounded heads and flattened faces, unlike most other groups of mammals.

Critical Thinking *Why would binocular vision be an adaptive advantage for primates?*

Gibbon

Ⓐ Opposable thumbs The primate's opposable thumbs enable it to grasp and manipulate objects. The thumb is also flexible, which increases the primate's ability to manipulate objects.

Ⓑ Vision Vision is the dominant sense in a primate. In addition to good visual perception, a primate has binocular vision, which provides it with a stereoscopic view of its surroundings.

Ⓒ Brain volume A primate's brain volume is large relative to its body size. The complex behaviors of a primate reflect its large brain.

Ⓓ Arm movement The shoulders of a primate are adapted for arm movement in different directions. Flexible arm movement is an important advantage for arboreal primates.

Ⓔ Flexible joints The flexible joints in a primate's elbow and wrist allow the primate to turn its hand in many directions.

Ⓕ Feet A primate's feet can grasp objects. However, primates have different degrees of efficiency for grasping objects with their feet.

422 PRIMATE EVOLUTION

USING MODELS

Idea Map Have students create an idea map about the characteristics of primates, using Figure 16.1 as a guide. Have students start with the word *Primate.* Students should include characteristics of primates around the word *Primate.* **L2**

Indiana Academic Standards

Pages 422–423: B.1.32, B.1.47

422

Primate hands and feet are unique among mammals. Their digits, fingers and toes, have nails rather than claws and their joints are flexible. In addition, primates have an **opposable thumb**—a thumb that can cross the palm to meet the other fingertips. Opposable thumbs enable primates to grasp and cling to objects, such as the branches of trees. Primates can also hold and manipulate tools, as shown in *Figure 16.2*.

Primates have a highly developed type of vision, called binocular vision. Primate eyes face forward so that they see an object simultaneously from two viewpoints, or through both eyes. This positioning of the eyes enables primates to perceive depth and thus gauge distances. As you might imagine, this type of vision is helpful for an animal jumping from tree to tree. Primates also have color vision that aids depth perception, enhances their ability to detect predators, and helps them find ripe fruits.

✓ **Reading Check** **List** some common characteristics of primates.

Primate Origins

The similarities among the many primates is evidence that primates

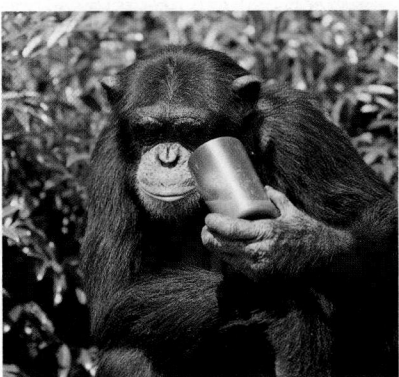

Figure 16.2
Chimpanzees have opposable thumbs to help them grasp and cling to objects and manipulate them.

share an evolutionary history. Scientists use fossil evidence and comparative anatomical, genetic, and biochemical studies of modern primates to propose ideas about how primates are related and how they evolved. Biologists classify primates into two major groups: strepsirrhines and haplorhines, as shown in *Figure 16.3*.

Primates

Present-day strepsirrhines are small primates that include, among others, the lemurs and aye-ayes. Most strepsirrhines have large eyes and are nocturnal. They live in the tropical forests of Africa and Southeast Asia. The earliest fossils of strepsirrhines are about 50 to 55 million years old.

Word Origin

anthropoid from the Greek words *anthropos,* meaning "man," and *eidos,* meaning "shape"; The anthropoid apes resemble humans in their general appearance.

Figure 16.3
Primates are divided into two groups: the strepsirrhines and the haplorhines, which are subdivided into Old World monkeys, New World monkeys, and hominoids.

Primate Ancestors

Haplorhines
Anthropoids
Hominoids
Hominids
Strepsirrhines

Old World monkeys
Gibbons
Orangutans
African apes
Humans
New World monkeys
Tarsiers
Lemurs
Lorises, Pottos, and Galagos

16.1 PRIMATE ADAPTATION AND EVOLUTION **423**

Tying to Prior Knowledge

Review environmental conditions and the types of organisms living in the early Cenozoic Era, when primates evolved. Remind students that many mammalian groups diversified at this time. Discuss how these factors may have influenced primate evolution.

Quick Demo

Comparing Primates Use photos, illustrations, models, or actual skulls to show the differences between strepsirrhines and haplorhines. For example, contrast the fused frontal bone of haplorhines to the unfused one of strepsirrhines.

Inquiry

Guided Questioning Many unanswered questions about primate evolution remain. Have students research and report on one of the following topics. **L3**

- What group gave rise to the primates?
- What is the phylogeny of tarsiers?
- How did New World monkeys reach South America?

Figure 16.4
Most basal primates are small, nocturnal animals that live in tropical environments.

B Tarsiers are primates that live in the Philippines, Borneo, and Sumatra.

A The aye-aye, a primate found in Madagascar, uses its long middle finger to dig for grubs.

Some scientists consider fossils of an organism called *Purgatorius* to be the earliest of primate fossils. *Purgatorius*, which probably resembled a squirrel, was a strepsirrhinelike animal that lived about 66 million years ago. Although there are no living species of *Purgatorius*, present-day strepsirrhines, **Figure 16.4**, are quite similar.

Humanlike primates evolve

The remaining living primates are members of a group called haplorhines. This group consists of tarsiers and the **anthropoids** (AN thruh poydz), the humanlike primates. Anthropoids include hominoids and Old and New World monkeys, as shown in **Figure 16.5**. In turn, hominoids include apes and humans.

Figure 16.5
Monkeys and hominoids are classified as anthropoids.

A Golden lion tamarins are arboreal New World monkeys that live in South America.

B This mandrill is an Old World monkey that lives in the forests of West Africa, and spends most of its time on the ground.

424 PRIMATE EVOLUTION

INCLUSION STRATEGIES

Learning Disabled: *Visual-Spatial* Give students photographs, illustrations, or videos of each group of primates. Have students write the names of each group and at least five of its characteristics in their journals. Then, have students review their lists to compare and contrast the characteristics. Have student volunteers write their lists on the chalkboard. Ask the class to compare and contrast the characteristics. **L1 ELL**

Many features characterize anthropoids. Anthropoids have more complex brains than strepsirrhines. Anthropoids are also larger and have different skeletal features, such as a more or less upright posture, than strepsirrhines.

What are commonly called "monkeys" are classified as either New World monkeys or Old World monkeys. New World monkeys, which live in the rain forests of South America and Central America, are all arboreal. A long, muscular **prehensile** (pree HEN sul) **tail** characterizes many of these primates. They use the tail as a fifth limb, grasping and wrapping it around branches as they move from tree to tree. Among the New World monkeys are tiny marmosets and larger spider monkeys.

Old World monkeys are generally larger than New World monkeys. They include the arboreal monkeys, such as the colobus monkeys and guenons, the terrestrial monkeys, such as baboons, and monkeys, such as macaques, which are equally at home in trees or on the ground. Old World monkeys do not have prehensile tails. They are adapted to many environments that range from the hot, dry savannas of Africa to the cold mountain forests of Japan.

Hominoids are classified as apes or humans. Apes include orangutans, gibbons, chimpanzees, bonobos, and gorillas. Apes lack tails and have different adaptations for arboreal life from those of the strepsirrhines and monkeys. For example, apes have long, muscled forelimbs for climbing in trees, swinging from branches, and knuckle walking, or walking on two legs with support from their hands. Try the *MiniLab* shown here to investigate an adaptation for tree climbing. Although many apes are arboreal, most also spend time on the ground. Gorillas, the largest of the apes, live

in social groups on the ground. Among the apes, social interactions indicate a large brain capacity.

Humans have an even larger brain capacity and walk upright. You will read more about human primates in the next section. Anthropologists have suggested that monkeys, apes, and humans share a common anthropoid ancestor based on their structural and social similarities. Use the *Problem-Solving Lab* on the next page to explore this idea. The oldest anthropoid fossils

MiniLab 16.1

Infer

How useful is an opposable thumb? Have you ever thought about what makes you different from other mammals as diverse as cows and dogs? One key difference between primates like you and the other mammals is that you have opposable thumbs. You may not live in trees like some other primates, but this adaptation is useful in a variety of additional ways. In this activity, you will explore the importance of your thumbs.

Procedure
1. Loosely wrap your dominant hand with tape so that your thumb points in the same direction as your fingers.
2. Try to pick up a pen and write a sentence.
3. Pick up your textbook and hand it to another student.
4. Pitch a tennis ball into an empty trash can two meters away.
5. Repeat steps 2–4 after unwrapping your hand.

Analysis
1. **Compare** Describe the results of your performance with the absence of an opposable thumb and with one.
2. **Infer** Why is an opposable thumb an important adaptation for primates?
3. **Use Models** Design models for completing three simple tasks without using your thumb, such as turning a doorknob or switching on a light.

MiniLab 16.1

Purpose
Students will compare and contrast completion of a task with and without the use of an opposable thumb.

Process Skills
compare and contrast, infer, use models

Analysis
1. Performance should be better with the use of an opposable thumb.
2. Primates with opposable thumbs can use tools and climb.
3. Student models will vary, but should complete the task without the use of an opposable thumb.

Assessment
Portfolio Have students formulate three hypotheses about the natural selection pressures that may have taken place during australopithecine evolution. Have them place their hypotheses in their portfolios. Use the Performance Task Assessment List for Formulating a Hypothesis in **PASC,** p. 93. **L2**

USING MODELS

Ape and Baboon Evolution Have students draw the probable events in baboon and ape evolution. Their illustrations should include the time period and the environmental factors that may have influenced ape and baboon evolution. **L3 ELL**

Purpose

Students will observe that the weights of several body regions of an infant and adult primate correlate with different percentages of their body weights.

Process Skills

analyze information, compare and contrast, draw a conclusion, make and use graphs, think critically, use numbers

Teaching Strategies

■ Explain to students that non-human infant primates typically go everywhere with their mother, clinging at first to her belly, and later to her back.

■ Remind students that, unlike a primate's other organs, the weight of its brain does not increase much after age three.

Thinking Critically

1. Major changes in brain size do not occur during growth.

2. The percentage decreases because the need for strong muscles to continually grasp their mother diminishes. no; Human infants do not cling to their mother.

Assessment

Portfolio Ask students to prepare a graph similar to the one they just used. The graph should compare the percent body weight for a human infant and an adult. Use the Performance Task Assessment List for Graph from Data in **PASC**, p. 111. **L2**

Caption Question Answer

Figure 16.6 Old World monkey; gorilla

Problem-Solving Lab 16.1

Use Numbers

How do primate infants and adults compare? Some infant primates, such as macaques, cling to their mothers for their first few months of life. Therefore, muscles associated with clinging may represent a higher percentage of total body weight in infant macaques than in adult macaques.

Solve the Problem

The graph shows the percentages of body weight for specific body parts of adult and infant macaques.

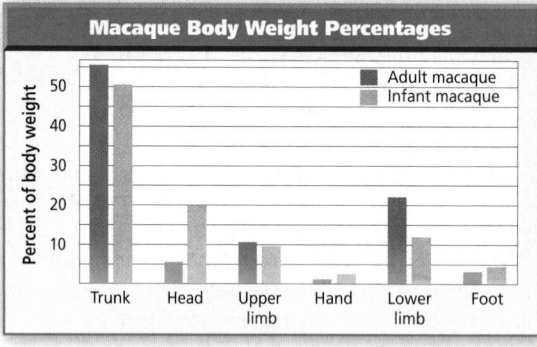

Macaque Body Weight Percentages

Thinking Critically

1. **Compare** Explain the difference between the percentage of body weight of infant heads and adult heads.

2. **Hypothesize** Explain why the percentage of body weight for hands and feet changes as macaques mature. Would you expect the same pattern in humans? Explain your answer.

are from Africa and Asia and date to about 37 to 40 million years ago.

Anthropoids evolved worldwide

The oldest monkey fossils are of New World monkeys and are 30 to 35 million years old. Although New World monkeys probably share a common anthropoidlike ancestor with the Old World monkeys, they evolved independently of the Old World monkeys because of geographic isolation. In *Figure 16.6,* you can see the worldwide geographic distribution of monkeys and apes.

Old World monkeys evolved more recently than New World monkeys. Scientists suspect this is true because the oldest fossils of Old World monkeys are only about 20 to 22 million years old. The fossils indicate that the earliest Old World monkeys were arboreal like today's New World monkeys.

Hominoids evolved in Asia and Africa

According to the fossil record, there was a global cooling when the hominoids evolved in Asia and Africa. Important changes in vegetation

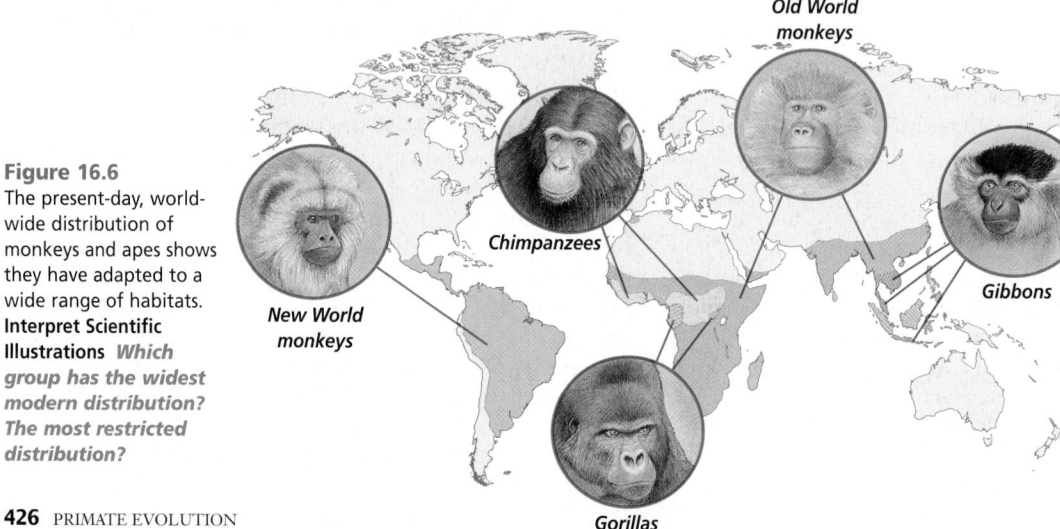

Figure 16.6
The present-day, world-wide distribution of monkeys and apes shows they have adapted to a wide range of habitats. **Interpret Scientific Illustrations** *Which group has the widest modern distribution? The most restricted distribution?*

Old World monkeys

Chimpanzees

Gibbons

New World monkeys

Gorillas

426 PRIMATE EVOLUTION

CHALLENGE ACTIVITY

Describe Have students research the probable events in baboon and ape evolution. They may write an illustrated newspaper article that includes the time period and environmental factors that may have influenced ape and baboon evolution. Students can also include illustrations to help illustrate their ideas. Have interested students share their articles with the class. **L3**

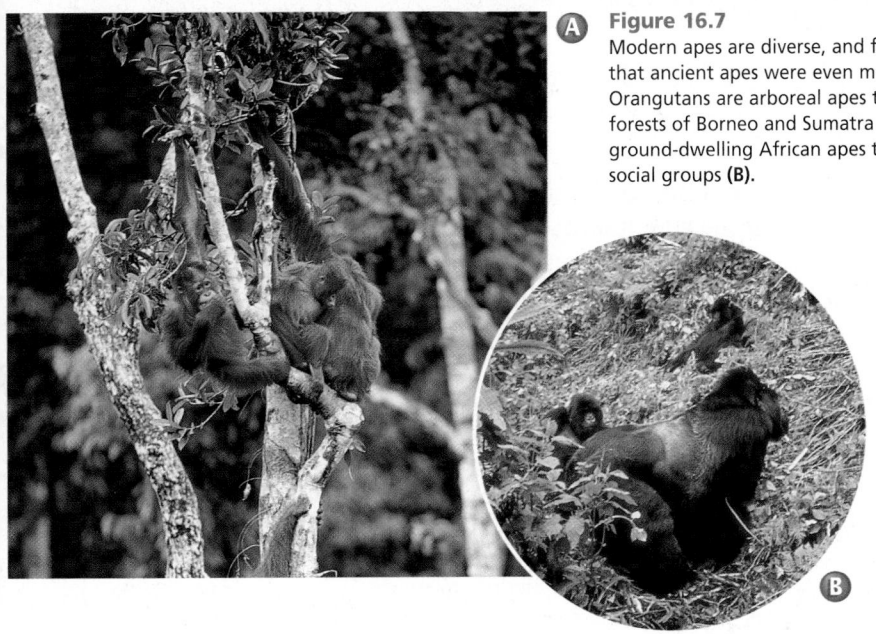

Figure 16.7
Modern apes are diverse, and fossils indicate that ancient apes were even more diverse. Orangutans are arboreal apes that live in the forests of Borneo and Sumatra (A). Gorillas are ground-dwelling African apes that live in small social groups (B).

such as the evolution of grass, also occurred. At about the same time, the Old World monkeys became adapted to this climatic cooling. Fossils indicate how the apes adapted and diversified. You can see two examples of the present-day diversity of apes in *Figure 16.7.*

Remember that hominoids include the apes and humans. By examining the DNA of each of the modern hominoids, scientists have evaluated the probable order in which the different apes and humans evolved. From this type of evaluation, it appears that gibbons were probably the first apes that evolved, followed by the orangutans that are found in southeast Asia. Finally, the African apes, gorillas and chimpanzees, evolved. Morphological and molecular data suggest that chimpanzees share the closest common ancestor with modern humans.

Section Assessment

Understanding Main Ideas
1. What adaptations help primates live in the trees?
2. What features distinguish anthropoids from strepsirrhines?
3. Draw a concept map to illustrate one possible pathway for the evolutionary history (phylogeny) of hominoids.

Thinking Critically
4. Imagine you are a world famous primatologist, a scientist who studies primates. An unidentified, complete fossil skeleton arrives at your lab. You suspect that it's a primate fossil. What observations would you make to determine if your suspicions are accurate?

SKILL REVIEW

5. **Get the Big Picture** Make a table listing the different types of primates, key facts about each group, and how the groups might be related. For more help, refer to *Get the Big Picture* in the **Skill Handbook.**

Section Assessment

1. Opposable thumbs, digits with nails, and flexible feet help primates grip branches. Flexible skeletons and binocular vision enable them to gauge depth and distance.
2. Anthropoids have larger brains, different skull and skeletal structures, and larger body sizes than strepsirrhines.
3. Concept maps will likely reflect the phylogeny shown in Figure 16.3.
4. Observations could include the presence of an opposable thumb, a larger brain size, nails rather than claws, binocular vision, and flexible joints.
5. Check student lists for accuracy and understanding of the main concepts.

Bellringer
Section Focus Transparency 40

Transparency **40** Skeletal Clues

SECTION FOCUS
Use with Chapter 16, Section 16.2

Gorilla

Australopithecine

❶ What do these skeletons suggest about the way each organism moved?

❷ How might the australopithecine be better suited than the gorilla for using tools?

BIOLOGY: The Dynamics of Life

SECTION FOCUS TRANSPARENCIES

Using Prior Knowledge

Infer Skulls provide information about diet, brain volume, bipedalism, binocular vision, face shape, and even height. Students may choose other skeletal parts, and their answers should be accepted if they provide plausible explanations.

Indiana Academic Standards

Pages 428–429: B.1.30, B.1.32

Section 16.2

Human Ancestry

Indiana Standards Standard B.1.35 Explain that the degree of kinship between organisms or species can be estimated from the similarity of their DNA sequences, which often closely matches their classification based on anatomical similarities. Know that amino acid similarities also provide clues to this kinship.

SECTION PREVIEW

Objectives

Compare and contrast the adaptations of australopithecines with those of apes and humans.

Identify the evidence of the major anatomical changes in hominids during human evolution.

Review Vocabulary
fossil: evidence of an organism that lived long ago that is preserved in Earth's rocks (p. 370)

New Vocabulary
hominoid
bipedal
hominid
australopithecine
Neandertal
Cro-Magnon

Solving a Puzzle

Using Prior Knowledge Have you ever tried to put together a jigsaw puzzle and found that some of the pieces were missing? If several pieces are lost, it is difficult to figure out what the puzzle is a picture of. Sometimes it depends on which part of the puzzle is missing. If the puzzle is a picture of a famous person and pieces of the face are missing, it's hard to tell who it is. But if the missing pieces are part of the background, you can still identify the person. Scientists who study human ancestry try to fit together a puzzle from scattered pieces of fossils—a puzzle with most of the pieces missing!

Homo habilis skull

Infer *What parts of a skeleton do you think would provide scientists with the most information? Explain your answer.*

Hominids

Some scientists propose that between 5 and 8 million years ago in Africa, a population that was ancestral to chimpanzees and humans diverged into two lines. According to this hypothesis, one line evolved into chimpanzees, and the other line eventually evolved into modern humans. These two lines are collectively called the **hominoids** (HAH mih noydz)—primates that can walk upright on two legs and include gorillas, chimpanzees, bonobos, and humans. There are relatively few fossils to support this hypothesis, but DNA studies of the modern hominoids provide data that support the idea. You can work with some of these data in *MiniLab 16.2* on the next page.

Some scientists suggest that the divergence of the population of ancestral hominoids might have occurred in response to environmental changes that forced some ancestral hominoids to leave their treetop environments and move onto the ground to find food. In order to move efficiently on the ground while avoiding predators, it was helpful for the hominoids to be **bipedal,** meaning able to walk on two legs. **Hominids** (HAH mih nudz) are bipedal primates that include modern humans and their direct ancestors. In addition to increased speed, walking on two legs leaves the arms and hands free for other activities, such as feeding, protecting young, and using tools. Therefore, hominoids with the ability to walk upright probably survived more successfully on the ground.

RESOURCE MANAGER

Unit 5 *FAST FILE* Resources
MiniLab Worksheet, p. 66
BioLab Worksheet, pp. 67–69
Real World BioApplications, pp. 71–72
Reinforcement and Study Guide in English, pp. 75–76
Reinforcement and Study Guide in Spanish, pp. 79–80
Critical Thinking/Problem Solving, p. 82

Transparency Worksheets, pp. 84, 85–86, 87–88
Reading Essentials for Biology, Section 16.2
Laboratory Manual, pp. 97–100
Section Focus Transparency 40
Basic Concepts Transparency 23
Reteaching Skills Transparency 25

These individuals then lived to reproduce and pass the characteristics to their offspring. According to this reasoning, the bipedal organisms that evolved might have been the earliest hominids.

Although the fossil record is incomplete, more hominid fossils are found every year. The many fossils that scientists have found reveal much about the anatomy and behavior of early hominids. Fossils of skulls provide scientists with information about the appearance and brain capacity of the early hominid types. Complete the *BioLab* at the end of the chapter to learn more about the kinds of information scientists gather from skulls of hominids.

Early hominids walked upright

In *Figure 16.8,* you see a South African anatomist, Raymond Dart, who, in 1924, discovered a skull of a young hominoid with a braincase and facial structure similar to those of an ape.

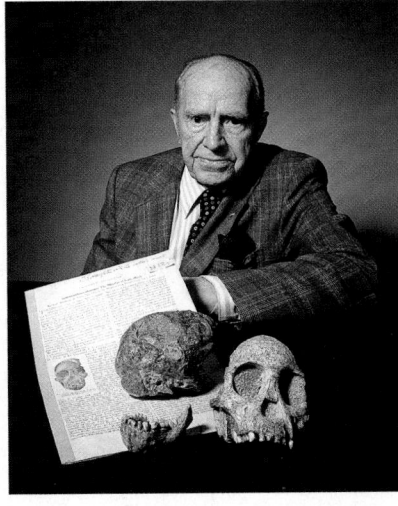

Figure 16.8
Raymond Dart discovered the first australopithecine fossil, the Taung child, *Australopithecus africanus.* The skull has features of both apes and humans.

MiniLab 16.2

Analyze Information

Compare Human Proteins with Those of Other Primates
Scientists use differences in amino acid sequences in proteins to determine the evolutionary relationships of living species. In this activity, you'll compare representative short sequences of the amino acids of a specific protein among groups of primates to determine their evolutionary history.

Amino Acid Sequences in Primates

Baboon	Chimp	Lemur	Gorilla	Human
ASN	SER	ALA	SER	SER
THR	THR	THR	THR	THR
THR	ALA	SER	ALA	ALA
GLY	GLY	GLY	GLY	GLY
ASP	ASP	GLU	ASP	ASP
GLU	GLU	LYS	GLU	GLU
VAL	VAL	VAL	VAL	VAL
ASP	GLU	GLU	GLU	GLU
ASP	ASP	ASP	ASP	ASP
SER	THR	SER	THR	THR
PRO	PRO	PRO	PRO	PRO
GLY	GLY	GLY	GLY	GLY
GLY	GLY	SER	GLY	GLY
ASN	ALA	HIS	ALA	ALA
ASN	ASN	ASN	ASN	ASN

Procedure
1. Prepare a data table.
2. For each primate listed in the table above, determine how many amino acids differ from the human sequence. Record these numbers in the data table.
3. Calculate the percentage differences by dividing the numbers by 15 and multiplying by 100. Record the numbers in your data table.

Analysis
1. **Interpret Data** Which primate is most closely related to humans? Least closely related?
2. **Formulate Models** Construct a diagram of primate evolutionary relationships that most closely fits your results.

2 Teach

INVESTIGATE BioLab The BioLab at the end of the chapter can be used at this point in the lesson.

MiniLab 16.2

Purpose
Students will learn how comparing amino acid sequences indicates phylogenetic relationships.

Process Skills
compare and contrast, make and use tables, interpret data

Teaching Strategies
Explain the molecular and biochemical methods used to determine phylogeny.

Expected Results
The human, chimpanzee, and gorilla sequences are identical. Baboons differ by 33 percent and lemurs by 47 percent.

Analysis
1. gorilla and chimpanzee; lemur
2. Baboons should branch off lemurs. Gorillas, chimpanzees, and humans should be close together.

Modified Assessment
Portfolio Ask students to summarize this activity. Have them predict the results of analyzing another protein. Use the Performance Task Assessment List for Lab Report in **PASC,** p. 119. **L1**

CULTURAL DIVERSITY

The Hominid Gang: *Linguistic* Finding human fossils is difficult and requires considerable expertise. Introduce the contributions of Kenyan fossil expert Kamoya Kimeu, the leader of a team of fossil hunters known as the Hominid Gang. Since the 1960s, Kimeu's work has led to the discovery of many important hominid fossils, including "Lucy" and the 12-year-old *Homo erectus* male, the "Strapping Youth."

Have students read sections from *Origins Reconsidered* by Richard Leakey and Roger Lewin or other similar books to learn more about Kimeu and the techniques involved in finding human fossils. **L3**

However, the skull also had an unusual feature for an ape skull—the position of the *foramen magnum,* the opening in the skull through which the spinal cord passes as it leaves the brain.

In the fossil, the opening was located on the bottom of the skull, as it is in humans but not in apes. Because of this feature, Dart proposed that the organism had walked upright. He classified the organism as a new primate species, *Australopithecus africanus* (aw stray loh PIH thuh kus • a frih KAH nus), which means "southern ape from Africa." The skull that Dart found has been dated at between 2.5 and 2.8 million years old.

Since Dart's discovery, paleoanthropologists, scientists who study human fossils, have recovered many more australopithecine specimens. They describe an **australopithecine** as an early hominid that lived in Africa and possessed both apelike and humanlike characteristics.

Early hominids: Apelike and humanlike

Later, in East Africa in 1974 an American paleoanthropologist Donald Johanson, discovered one of the most complete australopithecine skeletons that he called "Lucy." Radiometric dating shows that Lucy probably lived about 3.2 million years ago. Johanson proposed that the Lucy skeleton was a new species, *Australopithecus afarensis.* Other fossils of *A. afarensis* indicate that this species probably existed between 3 and 4 million years ago.

Although the fossils show that *A. afarensis* individuals had apelike shoulders and forelimbs, the structure of the pelvis, as shown in *Figure 16.9,* indicates that these individuals were bipedal, like humans. On the other hand, the size of the braincase suggests that their brains had a small, apelike volume and not a larger human volume.

Figure 16.9
Some skeletal features of an australopithecine are intermediate between those of modern apes and humans. Compare the skull and pelvic bone of *Australopithecus afarensis* **(B)** with those of the chimpanzee **(A)** and the human **(C).**

Chimpanzee *Pan Troglodytes* **(A)**

Ancient Hominid *Australopithecus afarensis* **(B)**

Human *Homo Sapiens* **(C)**

Ilium · Acetabulum · Ischial tuberosity

You may be wondering what life was like for hominids like Lucy. Because of the combination of apelike and humanlike features, one idea is that *A. afarensis* and other species of australopithecines might have lived in small family groups, sleeping and eating in trees. But, to travel, they walked upright on the ground. The fossil record indicates that an *A. afarensis* individual rarely survived longer than 25 years.

In addition to fossils of *A. afarensis* and *A. africanus*, fossils of three or perhaps four other species of australopithecines have been found. These other species, discovered in East Africa and South Africa, are dated from about 2.5 to 4.3 million years old. Three other species of hominids have been found that are similar to australopithecines. These earlier hominids are grouped into the genus *Paranthropus* because their fossils suggest that they had larger teeth and jaws and sturdier bodies than australopithecines.

The relationships among australopithecines are not entirely clear from the fossil record. However, the genus disappears from the record between 2.0 and 2.5 million years ago. Although australopithecines became extinct, some paleoanthropologists propose that an early population of these hominids might have been ancestral to modern humans.

✓ **Reading Check** **Identify** the differences in fossil hominid species using anatomical evidence.

The Emergence of Modern Humans

Any ideas about the evolution of modern hominids must include how bipedalism and a large brain evolved. Australopithecine fossils provide

Figure 16.10
Mary and Louis Leakey discovered many fossils in the Olduvai Gorge area of Tanzania, Africa. **Describe** *Why was the Leakeys' discovery of* Homo habilis *important?*

support for the idea that bipedalism evolved first. But when did a large brain evolve in a hominid species? When did hominids begin to use tools and develop culture?

Early members of the genus *Homo* made stone tools

In 1964, anthropologists Louis and Mary Leakey, *Figure 16.10,* described skull portions belonging to another type of hominid in Tanzania, Africa. This skull was more humanlike than those of australopithecines. In particular, the braincase was larger and the teeth and jaws were smaller, more like those of modern humans. Because of the skull's human similarities, the Leakeys classified the hominid with modern humans in the genus *Homo.* Because stone tools were found near the fossil skull, they named the species *Homo habilis,* which means "handy human."

Radiometric dating indicates that *H. habilis* lived between about 1.5 and 2.5 million years ago. It is the earliest known hominid to make and use stone tools. These tools suggest that *H. habilis* might have been a scavenger who used the stone tools to cut meat from carcasses of animals that had been killed by other animals. You can see a *H. habilis* skull in *Figure 16.11* on the next page.

Revealing Misconceptions

"If humans evolved from apes, why are there still apes alive today?" is a question often posed by students. The question represents a common misconception that students have about human evolution.

Uncover the Misconception

Explain that humans evolved from ancestors of apes, which were neither humans nor apes, and the common ancestor probably lived during the Miocene.

Demonstrate the Concept

Use an example from the previous chapter to explain the concept of common ancestry. You might use an example from the Galápagos Islands, or divergent evolution of the honeycreepers in Hawaii.

Assess New Knowledge

Ask students to suggest other examples of species that are closely related and what their common ancestor may have been. Have them suggest how they might explain this to a friend.

PROJECT

Interpreting Behavior Paleoanthropologists use a variety of methods to interpret primate behavior from fossil evidence. Have student groups report on one of the following methods:

■ Analyzing the wear on teeth to learn what extinct primates ate **L2** **ELL** **COOP LEARN**

■ Using cladistics to determine phylogeny **L2** **COOP LEARN**

■ Analyzing muscle function in living primates **L3** **COOP LEARN**

Student reports should include one or two examples of how the method answered a question about primate evolution.

Think Critically Ask students to imagine that they are studying evidence of *Homo erectus* in a cave. Have them make a list of evidence-gathering rules that include ways of protecting the site and assuring accurate measurements, map-making, and information recording in a database. **L2 ELL**

Indiana Academic Standards

Pages 432–433: B.1.32

Figure 16.11
The average brain volume of *Homo habilis* was 600 to 700 cm³, smaller than the average 1350 cm³ volume of modern humans, but larger than the 400 to 500 cm³ volume of australopithecines.

Hunting and using fire

Some anthropologists propose that a *H. habilis* population or another species, *Homo ergaster*, gave rise to a new species about 1.5–1.8 million years ago. This new hominid species was called *Homo erectus*, which means "upright human." *H. erectus* had a larger brain and a more humanlike face than *H. habilis*. However, it had prominent browridges and a lower jaw without a chin, as shown in *Figure 16.12*, which are apelike characteristics.

Some scientists interpret the stone tools called hand axes that they find at some *H. erectus* excavation sites as an indication that *H. erectus* hunted. In caves at these sites, they have also found hearths with charred bones. This evidence suggests that these hominids used fire and lived in caves.

The distribution of fossils indicates that *H. erectus* migrated from Africa about 1 million years ago. Then this hominid spread through Africa and Asia, and possibly migrated into Europe, before becoming extinct between 130 000 and 300 000 years ago. However, some scientists propose that more human-looking hominids might have arisen from *H. erectus* before it disappeared.

Ⓐ

Figure 16.12
A nearly complete *Homo erectus* skeleton of a young male was discovered in East Africa in 1985 **(A)**. *H. erectus* had a brain volume of about 1000 cm³ and long legs like modern humans **(B)**.

Ⓑ

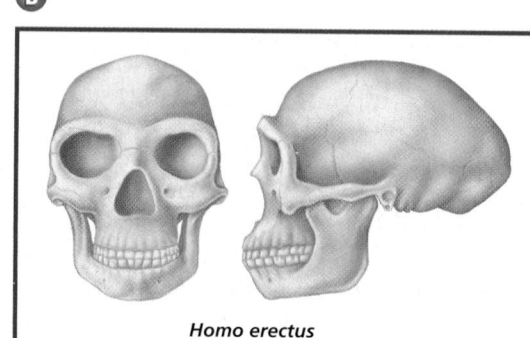

Homo erectus

Additional Lab

Measuring Human Variation

Purpose
Students will analyze variations in three human traits.

Materials
metric ruler or tape measure

Procedure
Give students the following directions.

1. Prepare a data table with the following headings: *Height (cm)*, *Length of Left Index Finger (cm)*, and *Length of Left Forearm (cm)*.

2. Working with a partner, measure in centimeters your height, the length of your left index finger, and length of your left forearm (elbow to wrist). Record the results in your data table and on a class data table. Calculate a class average for each measurement.

3. Divide the class measurements for each trait into five equal intervals. Count the number of students within each interval. Make bar graphs for each measurement.

Culture developed in modern humans

Many hypotheses have been suggested to explain how modern humans, *Homo sapiens*, might have emerged. These hypotheses were formed after studying evidence from fossil bones and teeth, and from studies of certain types of DNA. A description of the most popular hypothesis follows.

The fossil record indicates that the species *H. sapiens* appeared in Europe, Africa, the Middle East, and Asia about 100 000 to 500 000 years ago. The forms that are thought to precede *H. sapiens* are placed by most scientists into one of two groups—*H. antecessor* or *H. heidelbergensis* (hi duhl berg EN sus). It is not yet clear which of these species represents the direct ancestor to *Homo sapiens*. More fossil evidence and additional research into fossil DNA sequences still are needed. These early forms have skulls that resemble *H. erectus* or *H. ergaster* but have less prominent browridges, more bulging foreheads, and smaller teeth. Also, the braincases are larger than *H. erectus*, with brain volumes of 1000 to 1650 cm³, which is within the modern human range. A well-known *Homo* species was the Neandertals (nee AN dur tawlz), illustrated in *Figure 16.13*.

Problem-Solving Lab 16.2

Apply Concepts

How similar are Neandertals and humans? Fossil evidence can provide clues to similarities and differences between Neandertals and humans.

Solve the Problem

Examine the diagram of a human skull superimposed on a Neandertal skull. The cranial capacities (brain size) of the two skulls are provided.

1450 cm³

1600 cm³

Brow-ridge

— Neandertal
□ Modern human

Thinking Critically

1. **Measure** How much larger is a Neandertal brain than a human brain? Express the value as a percentage.
2. **Interpret Scientific Illustrations** Which skull has the more protruding jaw? A thicker browridge? Are a protruding jaw and thick browridges more apelike or humanlike characteristics? Explain your judgment.
3. **Identify** What clues do fossils such as spear points and hand axes, shelters made of animal skins, and flowers and animal horns at burial sites provide about the lifestyle of Neandertals?

Figure 16.13
Neandertals (*Homo neanderthalensis*) were skilled hunters. They had many tools, including spears, scrapers, and knives.

433

Activity For students who need an additional challenge, have them research evolutionary pathways proposed by humans. Have students complete a brochure describing human evolution, and include probable evolutionary pathways of humans that include time periods and characteristics of species that change. **L3**

Discussion

Infer Discuss what future paleoanthropologists might determine about present-day humans. Have students identify probable artifacts and their information.

Brainstorming

Social Behavior Have small groups of students develop a project for studying nonhuman primates to infer social behavior in early hominids.

Visual Learning

Figure 16.15 (p. 435) illustrates a possible phylogenetic tree of human evolution. Point out that some paleoanthropologists have suggested alternative phylogenies. Have students analyze, review, or critique this or other hypotheses.

Figure 16.14
The dwelling sites of Cro-Magnons, full of cave paintings, detailed stone and bone artifacts, and tools, have been excavated in Europe.

The **Neandertals** lived from about 35 000 to 100 000 years ago in Europe, Asia, and the Middle East. Fossils reveal that Neandertals had thick bones and large faces with prominent noses. The brains of Neandertals were at least as large as those of modern humans.

The fossil records also indicate that Neandertals lived in caves during the ice ages of their time. In addition, the tools, figurines, flowers, pollen, and other evidence from excavation sites, such as burial grounds, suggest that Neandertals may have had religious views and communicated through spoken language.

What happened to Neandertals?

Could Neandertals have evolved into modern humans? No, the fossil record shows that a more modern type of *H. sapiens* spread throughout Europe between 35 000 to 40 000 years ago. This type of *H. sapiens* is called Cro-Magnon (kroh MAG nun). **Cro-Magnons** were identical to modern humans in height, skull structure, tooth structure, and brain size. Paleoanthropologists suggest that Cro-Magnons were toolmakers and artists, as shown in *Figure 16.14.* Cro-Magnons probably also used language, as their skulls contain a bulge that corresponds to the area of the brain that is involved in speech in modern humans.

Did Neandertals evolve into Cro-Magnons? Current genetic and archaeological evidence indicates that this is not the case. Current dates for hominid fossils suggest that modern

Indiana Academic Standards

Pages 434–435: B.1.30, B.1.32

H. sapiens appeared in both South Africa and the Middle East about 100 000 years ago, which was about the same time the Neandertals appeared. In addition, genetic evidence supports the idea of an African origin of modern *H. sapiens*, perhaps as early as 200 000 years ago. This idea suggests that the African *H. sapiens* migrated to Europe and Asia.

Most fossil evidence supports the idea that Neandertals were most likely a sister species of *H. sapiens*, and not an ancestral branch of modern humans. Look at *Figure 16.15* to see one possible evolutionary path to modern humans.

Fossil evidence shows that humans have not changed much anatomically over the last 200 000 years. Humans probably first established themselves in Africa, Europe, and Asia. Then evidence shows that they crossed either by sea or using a land bridge into North America. You can read more about the land bridge theory in the *Connection to Earth Science* at the end of the chapter. By about 10 000 to 8000 years ago, Native Americans had built permanent settlements and were domesticating animals and farming.

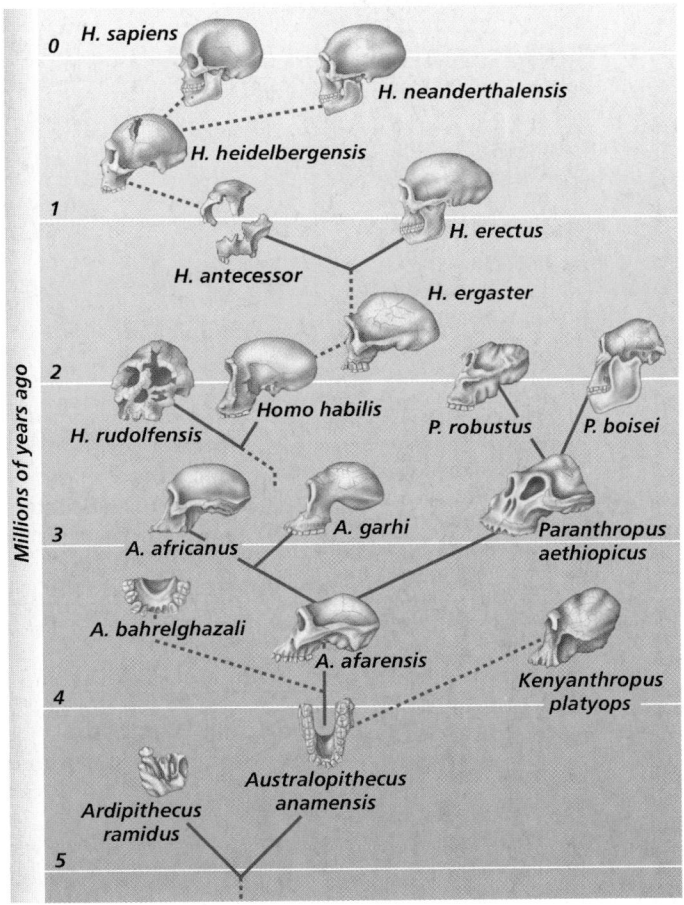

Figure 16.15
This diagram represents one possible pathway for the evolution of *Homo sapiens*. Not all scientists agree on the evolutionary pathway.

Section Assessment

Understanding Main Ideas
1. Describe the history of at least three major discoveries that led to our current understanding of hominid evolution.
2. Why was the development of bipedalism a very important event in the evolution of hominids?
3. What evidence supports the idea that *H. habilis* was an ancestor of *H. erectus*?
4. Identify and describe the evidence that supports the idea that Neandertals were not the ancestors of Cro-Magnon people.

Thinking Critically
5. What kind of animal bones might you expect to find at the site of *Homo habilis* remains if *H. habilis* was a scavenger? A hunter?

SKILL REVIEW
6. **Interpret Scientific Illustrations** Draw a time line to show results of natural selection in the phylogeny or the evolutionary history of hominids. For more help, refer to *Interpret Scientific Illustrations* in the **Skill Handbook**.

in.bdol.glencoe.com/self_check_quiz

16.2 HUMAN ANCESTRY **435**

DAILY INTERVENTION

Check for Understanding
Visual-Spatial Have students construct a time line of the following events: use of fire, bipedal movement, tool use, language, art, burial of the dead. **L1 ELL**

Reteach
Visual-Spatial Have students make a bar graph showing the evolution of human brain size. **L2**

Resources
For more practice, use *Reading Essentials for Biology*, Section 16.2.

Extension
Visual-Spatial Have students illustrate a human phylogenetic tree. **L3**

Assessment

Portfolio Have students write a short essay for their portfolio about the significance of australopithecines in primate evolution. They can conclude their essays with some unanswered questions about australopithecines. **L2**

Section Assessment

1. Early hominids walked upright, had a combination of characteristics similar to modern apes and humans, and several species existed at the same time until recently. Students may select other discoveries.
2. Bipedalism allowed hominids to better scan the horizon for predators and freed their forelimbs for carrying objects.
3. *Homo habilis* was the first hominid to purposefully construct stone tools.
4. Genetic and archaeological evidence suggests that Neandertals were not the ancestors of Cro-Magnon people.
5. If *H. habilis* were scavengers, bones that contain little meat, such as ribs, would be at their sites. If they were hunters, there would be meat-containing bones at their sites.
6. Evaluate the time lines for accuracy.

435

INVESTIGATE BioLab

Time Allotment
one class period

Process Skills
observe and infer, measure in SI, hypothesize, compare and contrast, make and use tables

- Give each student a copy of the skull diagrams from *Unit 5 FAST FILE Resources* to use in this BioLab. These skulls are one-half natural size.
- Alternatively, copy the skull art on this student edition page and increase it by 50% for students to use.

PROCEDURE

Teaching Strategies

- Remind students that australopithecines existed between 1 and 5 million years ago, around the time that African apes and humans probably diverged. Because of their age, australopithecines were probably primitive anatomically.
- To estimate cranial capacities, students should draw circles just inside each skull on the worksheets provided or on the copied and enlarged skulls from the student edition page.
- Estimating cranial capacity by multiplying by the factor of 200 is suitable only for these drawings because the factor is based on the scale of the drawings at one-half natural size.

INVESTIGATE BioLab

Comparing Skulls of Three Primates

Before You Begin
Australopithecines are one of the earliest hominids in the fossil record. In many ways, their anatomy is intermediate between living apes and humans. In this lab, you'll determine the apelike and humanlike characteristics of an australopithecine skull, and compare the skulls of australopithecines, gorillas, and modern humans. The diagrams of skulls shown below are one-fourth natural size. The heavy black lines indicate the angle of the jaw.

PREPARATION

Problem
How do skulls of primates provide evidence for human evolution?

Objectives
In this BioLab, you will:
- **Determine** how paleoanthropologists study early human ancestors.
- **Compare and contrast** the skulls of australopithecines, gorillas, and modern humans.

Materials
metric ruler
protractor
copy of skull diagrams

Skill Handbook
If you need help with this lab, refer to the **Skill Handbook.**

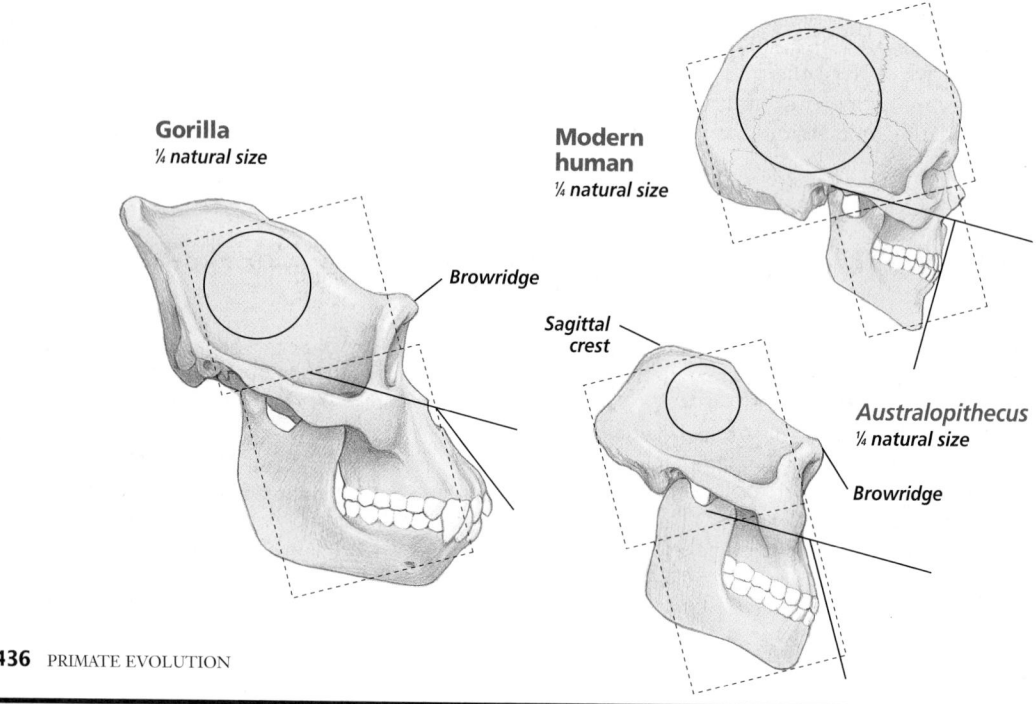

Gorilla
¼ natural size

Modern human
¼ natural size

Browridge

Sagittal crest

Australopithecus
¼ natural size

Browridge

436 PRIMATE EVOLUTION

Data Table

	Gorilla	Australopithecus	Modern human
1. Face area in cm²	32 cm²	19 cm²	12 cm²
2. Brain area in cm²	23 cm²	23 cm²	40 cm²
3. Is the brain area smaller or larger than the face area?	Smaller	Larger	Larger
4. Is brain area 3 times larger than face area?	No	No	Yes
5. Cranial capacity in cm³	600 cm³	600 cm³	1060 cm³
6. Jaw angle °	35°	55°	90°
7. Does lower jaw stick out in front of nose?	Yes	Yes	No
8. Is sagittal crest present?	Yes	Yes	No
9. Is browridge present?	Yes	Yes	No

1. Your teacher will provide copies of the skulls (¼ natural size) of *Australopithecus africanus*, *Gorilla gorilla*, and *Homo sapiens*.
2. The rectangles drawn over the skulls represent the areas of the brain (upper rectangle) and face (lower rectangle). On each skull, determine and record the area of each rectangle (length × width).
3. Measure the diameters of the circles in each skull. Multiply these numbers by 200 cm^2. The result is the cranial capacity (brain volume) in cubic centimeters.
4. The two lines projected on the skulls are used to measure how far forward the jaw protrudes. Use a protractor to measure the acute angle formed by the two lines.
5. Complete the data table.

Data Table

	Gorilla	*Australopithecus*	Modern Human
1. Face area in cm^2			
2. Brain area in cm^2			
3. Is brain area smaller or larger than face area?			
4. Is brain area 3 times larger than face area?			
5. Cranial capacity in cm^3			
6. Jaw angle			
7. Does lower jaw stick out in front of nose?			
8. Is sagittal crest present?			
9. Is browridge present?			

ANALYZE AND CONCLUDE

1. **Compare and Contrast** How would you describe the similarities and differences in face-to-brain area in the three primates?
2. **Interpret Observations** How do the cranial capacities compare among the three skulls? How do the jaw angles compare?
3. **Interpret Data** Identify evidence of the change in the species using anatomical similarities.
4. **ERROR ANALYSIS** What are the possible sources of error in your analysis?

Apply Your Skill

Use Models Obtain diagrams of primate skeletons to determine the similarities and differences using other parts of the skeletons.

 Web Links To find out more about primate evolution, visit in.bdol.glencoe.com/primate_evolution

ANALYZE AND CONCLUDE

1. Humans have a small facial area compared with brain area. Apes have a large facial area compared with brain area. Australopithecines were intermediate between apes and humans but closer to apes.
2. Apes have a small cranial capacity, whereas humans have a large cranial capacity, and that of australopithecines was intermediate but closer to the apes. An ape has a small jaw angle, and a human has a large jaw angle. The jaw angle of australopithecines was intermediate but closer to that of the ape.
3. Each of the items in the data table indicates anatomical similarities that have undergone change.
4. **ERROR ANALYSIS** Possible sources include measuring incorrectly, rounding errors, and errors from measuring a single example rather than taking a mean of many fossil measurements.

Assessment

Discussion Review the similarities and differences between the three skulls. What is the importance of the differences? **L2**

Apply Your Skill

Use Models Obtain illustrations or actual fossil casts of australopithecine limb bones, hands, or feet. Have students compare measurements and other observations of the postcranial skeletons of apes, humans, and australopithecines. **L1**

Indiana Academic Standards

Pages 436–437: B.1.32

437

connection to Earth Science

Purpose

Students will learn about the types of evidence that paleoanthropologists use to propose how modern humans entered the New World.

Teaching Strategies

- Use the illustration on this page, along with a world map or globe, to discuss how human ancestors might have migrated from their African place of origin to the Americas.
- Review radiometric dating.
- Students can prepare wet mounts of pollen from a variety of flowers and, after viewing, draw and label each pollen type.
- Ask students to imagine that they are in the first group of humans crossing the Bering Land Bridge. Have them write an essay about their experiences. **L2**

connection to Earth Science

The Land Bridge to the New World

The Bering Land Bridge, or Beringia, was a strip of land that connected Asia and North America. During the last Ice Age, the Bering Land Bridge was dry land above sea level. The ancestors of Native Americans walked across this land to reach North America.

The 1500 km–wide piece of land known as the Bering Land Bridge is located between the Bering and Chukchi Seas and links northeastern Siberia and northwestern North America. Today, the land bridge is about 267 meters below the ocean's surface. However, during the last ice age, sea level was much lower than it is today. At that time, this land bridge was above the water's surface. Humans could have migrated from Asia to North America across this land bridge. Recent evidence indicates that such a human migration probably occurred about 12 000 years ago.

Dating the land bridge Anthropologists compared two kinds of data to determine the 11 000-year date for human migration across the Bering Land Bridge. They used radiometric dating methods on fossils and gathered information on sea level changes over time. Both data reveal that the Bering Land Bridge was last above sea level about 11 000 years ago.

Pollen reveals plant life Pollen found in sediments dredged from the bottoms of the Bering and Chukchi Seas indicates that the land bridge and the surrounding areas were tundra ecosystems. Willows, birch, sedge tussocks, and spring flowers were the dominant plants of the area, and caribou probably roamed over the frozen soil.

The pollen studies also showed that the temperature at the time was warmer than it is in present-day Alaska. Scientists have used this

finding to propose that perhaps the ice age was ending. The glaciers would have melted in a warming climate and the sea level would have risen, covering the land bridge with water.

A controversial idea Archaeologists have unearthed what they believe to be human artifacts dating back to more than 12 000 years ago in several states. Some archaeologists believe that these artifacts, such as stone spearheads, suggest that humans occupied North America before the land bridge migration. Other archaeologists disagree, citing that no human fossils have been found, contamination of sites could have occurred, and that published reports confirming the dates and documenting the details of most of the sites have not been completed.

Writing About Biology

Infer Study the map shown above. Suggest in a short report another way that prehistoric humans might have entered the New World.

 To find out more about human origins, visit in.bdol.glencoe.com/earth_science

Writing About Biology

Prehistoric humans may have used boats to enter the New World.

Indiana Academic Standards

Pages 438–439: B.1.32

Chapter 16 Assessment

STUDY GUIDE

Section 16.1

Primate Adaptation and Evolution

Key Concepts

- Primates are primarily an arboreal group of mammals. They have adaptations, such as binocular vision, opposable thumbs, and flexible joints, that help them survive in trees.
- There are two groups of primates: strepsirrhines, such as lemurs; and haplorhines, which include tarsiers, monkeys, and hominoids.
- There are two groups of monkeys: New World monkeys and Old World monkeys. New World monkeys live in South America and Central America. Many New World monkeys have a prehensile tail. Old World monkeys are larger and do not have prehensile tails.
- Hominoids are primates that include gorillas, chimpanzees, bonobos, gibbons, orangutans, and humans.
- Fossils indicate that primates appeared on Earth about 66 million years ago. Major trends in primate evolution include an increasing brain size and walking upright.

Vocabulary

anthropoid (p. 424)
opposable thumb (p. 423)
prehensile tail (p. 425)
primate (p. 421)

Section 16.2

Human Ancestry

Key Concepts

- The earliest hominids arose in Africa approximately 5 million years ago. Australopithecine fossils indicate that these individuals were bipedal, but also climbed trees.
- The first hominid to be classified in the genus *Homo* was discovered in Africa in 1964 by Mary and Louis Leakey. The fossil was named *Homo habilis* or "handy human." *Homo habilis* has been radiometrically dated at between 1.5 and 2.5 million years old.
- The appearance of stone tools in the fossil record coincided with the appearance of the genus *Homo* about 2 million years ago.

Vocabulary

australopithecine (p. 430)
bipedal (p. 428)
Cro-Magnon (p. 434)
hominid (p. 428)
hominoid (p. 428)
Neandertal (p. 434)

FOLDABLES
Study Organizer To help you review primate evolution, use the Organizational Study Fold on page 421.

Key Concepts

Summary statements can be used by students to review the major concepts of the chapter.

Biology Online

Visit in.bdol.glencoe.com
/self_check_quiz
/vocabulary_puzzlemaker
/chapter_test
/standardized_test

VOCABULARY PUZZLEMAKER

For additional help with vocabulary, have students access the Vocabulary PuzzleMaker online at in.bdol.glencoe.com/vocabulary_puzzlemaker

FOLDABLES™

Have students use their Foldables to review the content of Section 16.1.

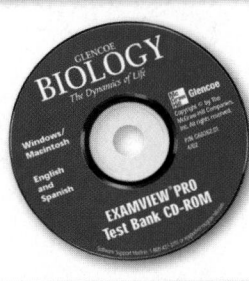

Use the Exam*View*®Pro Test Bank CD-ROM to:

- Create **multiple versions** of tests
- Create **modified** tests with one mouse click for **inclusion** students
- **Edit** existing questions and **add** your own questions
- Build tests aligned with state standards using built-in **State Curriculum Tags**
- Change **English** tests to **Spanish** with one mouse click and vice versa

The Princeton Review *Questions and answers have been aligned and verified by The Princeton Review.*

Vocabulary Review

1. true
2. false—Hominoids
3. false—hominoids
4. true

Understanding Key Concepts

5. D	**8.** A
6. D	**9.** B
7. B	**10.** D

Constructed Response

11. Yes. The first evidence of humans in the Americas dates from about 12 000 years ago. A 25 000-year-old arrowhead would more than double the time that humans are known to be in North America.

12. The adaptations that evolved in nonhuman primates laid the groundwork for adaptations that arose during hominid evolution.

13. Answers could include that scientists compare the DNA of modern humans and that of Neandertals, if such DNA exists. Or scientists could compare the skulls or skeletons of Neandertals and modern humans.

Thinking Critically

14. The time and location of fossil finds will change with time, but most early fossils should be found in African countries. If Neandertal or Cro-Magnon fossils are discovered, they will likely be in European countries. The fossils will fill in gaps of understanding or add support for our present understanding of evolutionary pathways.

440

Vocabulary Review

Review the Chapter 16 vocabulary words listed in the Study Guide on page 439. Determine if each statement is true or false. If false, replace the underlined word with the correct vocabulary word.

1. <u>New World monkeys</u> have prehensile tails.
2. <u>Hominids</u> include humans and the apes.
3. Early hominids that lived in Africa and possessed both apelike and humanlike characteristics are called <u>primates</u>.
4. <u>Bipedal</u> organisms walk upright on two legs.

Understanding Key Concepts

5. The first *Homo sapiens* were _____.
   A. Cro-Magnon people
   B. *Homo erectus*
   C. *Australopithecus afarensis*
   D. Neandertals
6. Which of the following pairs of terms is most closely related?
   A. primate—squirrel
   B. arboreal—gorilla
   C. strepsirrhine—hominid
   D. Cro-Magnon—*Homo sapiens*
7. Primates native to the area indicated by the map below are _____.
   A. Old World monkeys
   B. New World monkeys
   C. apes
   D. strepsirrhines

8. The science of studying the fossils of humans is _____.
   A. paleoanthropology
   B. geology
   C. paleontology
   D. anthropology

9. The earliest primates were most like _____.
   A.   C.
   B.   D.

10. The study of the fossil Lucy helped scientists determine that _____.
    A. both primates and hominids have color vision
    B. hominids are primates with opposable thumbs
    C. hominids had large brains before they walked upright
    D. hominids walked upright before they had large brains

Constructed Response

11. Open Ended Suppose that you were told that a scientist found a 25 000-year-old arrowhead in Arizona. Would you be surprised? Why or why not?

12. Open Ended Why is it important for a paleoanthropologist to know about all primates?

13. Open Ended Some scientists suggest that Neandertals evolved into modern humans. What information should they gather to support their idea?

Thinking Critically

14. **REAL WORLD BIOCHALLENGE** Almost every year the discovery of new fossils provides evidence for the evolution of human ancestors. Visit **in.bdol.glencoe.com** to find out about some of the newest fossil discoveries. When and where were the fossils found? Write an essay to describe how the fossils add to our understanding of primate evolution.

 in.bdol.glencoe.com/chapter_test

15. For an animal to walk erect, its spinal cord must enter the skull at its base. The foramen magnum would be located at the base of the skull not more toward the back as in an animal that uses four appendages for locomotion.

16. Students can design an experiment to test and compare the success of two arboreal animals, a primate and a nonprimate, in a situation unique to arboreal life such as obtaining fruit at the ends of branches.

17. Strepsirrhines are primarily an arboreal group of primates that includes lemurs and tarsiers. Haplorhines include all other primates.

15. Observe and Infer How could you tell from the position of the foramen magnum that an animal walked upright? Explain.

16. Formulate Hypotheses How would you test the idea that opposable thumbs are beneficial adaptations for arboreal mammals?

17. Compare and Contrast Compare and contrast strepsirrhines and haplorhines.

18. Hypothesize Explain why you think there can be different interpretations for the possible pathways of hominid evolution.

End-of-Course Assessment Practice

The assessed Indiana standard appears next to the question.

All questions aligned and verified by *The Princeton Review*

Part 1 Multiple Choice

Use the graph below to answer question 19.

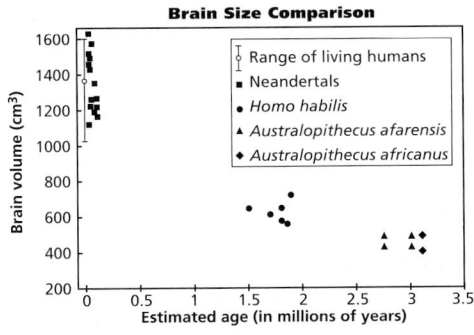

Brain Size Comparison

- Range of living humans
- Neandertals
- *Homo habilis*
- ▲ *Australopithecus afarensis*
- ◆ *Australopithecus africanus*

19. According to the graph, which of the following is a true statement?

B.1.32

A. Hominid brains appear to increase in size as you go back in time.

B. Hominid brains appear to have remained about the same size for the last million years.

C. Hominid brains of the same species are all the same size.

D. Hominid brains have been increasing in size for at least three million years.

Read the following paragraph and use the illustration to answer questions 20 and 21.

Scientists have determined radiometric ages for volcanic materials located near hominid fossils. A cross section showing layered volcanics and sediments containing the fossils is shown above. The location of each hominid fossil is indicated with an "X." Ages of volcanic layers are given as numbers in millions of years ago.

20. Which of the ages represents a maximum age for the fossil hominids? In other words, which is the oldest age that the fossils could be?

B.1.32

A. 233 million years   **C.** 2.33 million years

B. 2.92 million years   **D.** 3.18 million years

21. A minimum age for the fossils is indicated by which age?

B.1.32

A. 233 million years   **C.** 2.33 million years

B. 2.92 million years   **D.** 3.18 million years

Part 2 Constructed Response/Grid In

Record your answers on your answer document.

22. Open Ended Which characteristics are common to all primates? Include in your answer the major function of each characteristic.

B.1.32

23. Open Ended Suppose you found a skull in an area where both Neandertals and Cro-Magnons lived. Explain the types of data you would use to determine which species the skull was from.

 in.bdol.glencoe.com/standardized_test

End-of-Course Assessment Practice

19. D   **21.** B

20. D

22. Characteristics common to primates include relatively large brain volume to body size, stereoscopic vision, opposable thumbs, highly mobile shoulder joints, and feet adapted for grasping.

23. thickness of bones and the prominence of noses and browridges on skulls; Neandertal bones are thicker and their skulls have more prominent noses and larger browridges than Cro-Magnons.

 FAST FILE

Answer Sheet A practice answer sheet can be found on p. 95 of *Unit 5 FAST FILE Resources.*

18. There are fossils of several species of hominids living at the same time. Because the fossil evidence does not indicate a clear pathway for the evolution of these hominids, interpretations of the evidence differ.

RUBRIC

For more help evaluating open-ended assessment questions, see the rubric on p. 9T.

Indiana Academic Standards

Pages 440–441: B.1.30, B.1.32

441

Chapter 17 Organizer

Section Objectives	National Science Standards	State/Local Standards	Advanced Lab and Demo Planning
Section 17.1 1 session, 1/2 block 1. **Evaluate** the history, purpose, and methods of taxonomy. 2. **Explain** the meaning of a scientific name. 3. **Describe** the organization of taxa in a biological classification system.	UCP.1, UCP.2, UCP.4; A.2; C.3, C.5; G.1–3	**Indiana Standards** B.1.35	**Student Labs:** MiniLab 17.1, p. 446: leaves, dichotomous key, glue, several sheets of white paper Problem-Solving Lab 17.1, p. 447
Section 17.2 3 sessions, 2 blocks 4. **Describe** how evolutionary relationships are determined. 5. **Explain** how cladistics reveals phylogenetic relationships. 6. **Compare** the six kingdoms of organisms.	UCP.1, UCP.2, UCP.4, UCP.5; A.1, A.2; C.1, C.3, C.5, C.6; E.1, E.2; G.1–3	**Indiana Standards** B.1.35	**Student Labs:** MiniLab 17.2, p. 453 Additional Lab, p. 454: laboratory glassware (flasks, test tubes, beakers, stirring rods, thermometers, bottle stoppers, pipettes, droppers, funnels, petri dishes, graduated cylinders, jars) Problem-Solving Lab 17.2, p. 456 Investigate BioLab, p. 460: See materials below. **Teacher Demonstration:** Quick Demo, p. 457: pictures of various animal organisms
End of Chapter Assessment Student Edition **Study Guide,** p. 463 **Content Assessment,** pp. 464–465		**Indiana Standards** B.1.35	**Student Lab:** Investigate BioLab, p. 460: sample key from guidebooks, metric ruler

Key to Teaching Strategies

L1 Level 1 activities should be appropriate for students with learning difficulties.

L2 Level 2 activities should be within the ability range of all students.

L3 Level 3 activities are designed for above-average students.

ELL ELL activities should be within the ability range of English Language Learners.

COOP LEARN Cooperative Learning activities are designed for small group work.

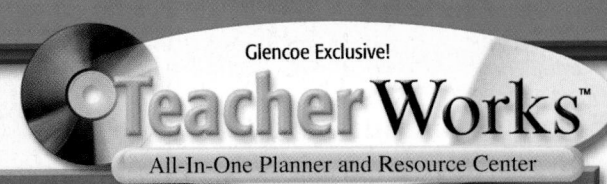

Glencoe Exclusive!

Teacher Works™

All-In-One Planner and Resource Center

Reproducible Masters and Transparencies

Technology

Unit 5 FAST FILE Resources
  MiniLab Worksheet, p. 99
  BioLab Worksheet, pp. 101–102
  Real World BioApplications, pp. 103–104
  Reinforcement and Study Guide in English,
    pp. 105–106
  Reinforcement and Study Guide in Spanish,
    pp. 109–110
  Concept Mapping, p. 113
  Critical Thinking/Problem Solving, p. 114
  Transparency Worksheet, p. 115
Reading Essentials for Biology,
  Section 17.1
Laboratory Manual, pp. 101–104
🔥 **Section Focus Transparency 41**

💿 **Interactive Chalkboard CD-ROM: Section 17.1 Presentation** 🚩
💿 TeacherWorks™ **CD-ROM** 🚩
🎵 **Guided Reading Audio Summaries MP3**

Unit 5 FAST FILE Resources
  MiniLab Worksheet, p. 100
  Reinforcement and Study Guide in English,
    pp. 107–108
  Reinforcement and Study Guide in Spanish,
    pp. 111–112
  Transparency Worksheets, pp. 116, 117–120
Reading Essentials for Biology,
  Section 17.2
Laboratory Manual, pp. 105–108
🔥 **Section Focus Transparency 42**
🔥 **Basic Concepts Transparency 24**
🔥 **Reteaching Skills Transparency 25**

💿 **Interactive Chalkboard CD-ROM: Section 17.2 Presentation** 🚩
💿 TeacherWorks™ **CD-ROM** 🚩
🎵 **Guided Reading Audio Summaries MP3**
💿 **Virtual Labs CD-ROM**
  Virtual Lab: Classifying Using Biotechnology

Unit 5 FAST FILE Resources
  Chapter Assessment, pp. 121–126
  Student Recording Sheet, p. 127

 Reviewing Biology,
pp. 33–34

💿 **Interactive Chalkboard:** 🚩
  Chapter 17 Assessment
💿 **MindJogger Videoquizzes**
  DVD/VHS
💿 **ExamView® Pro Test Bank**
  CD-ROM
💿 TeacherWorks™ **CD-ROM** 🚩
💿 **Succeeding on National Standards CD-ROM**

🖥 in.bdol.glencoe.com
  /self_check_quiz
  /vocabulary_puzzlemaker
  /chapter_test
  /standardized_test

🚩 Indicates materials created specifically for Indiana.

Chapter 17

Organizing Life's Diversity

Short on Time?

BIODIGEST The BioDigest at the end of this unit can be used as a(n):

- preview to introduce important unit concepts.
- overview if time does not permit teaching the entire chapter.
- review of key unit concepts.

Understanding the Photo

This image shows many different species of organisms. There are trees, low-growing plants, a duck, several large carp in the water, and of course, the human feeding the duck. Each organism in the photograph has a scientific name and most have one or more common names. Remind students that not every organism on Earth has been named. This is because new organisms are discovered every year. For more information on why scientists use scientific classification schemes, have students read about biological classification beginning on page 443.

What You'll Learn

- You will identify and compare various methods of classification.
- You will distinguish among six kingdoms of organisms.

Why It's Important

Biologists use a system of classification to organize all living things. Understanding classification helps you study organisms and their evolutionary relationships.

Understanding ▶ the Photo

All of the living organisms in this photo can be classified by biologists. Classification allows living things to be organized according to shared characteristics and how closely related they are to each other.

Biology Online

Visit **in.bdol.glencoe.com** to
- study the entire chapter online
- access Web Links for more information and activities on the diversity of life
- review content with the Interactive Tutor and self-check quizzes

442

Two-Minute Chapter Launcher

Demo Display several photos of organisms. Use a field guide to obtain scientific names beforehand. Ask students to identify them by common name. For each one that students identify, give the scientific name. If possible, explain the derivation of the scientific name so that students can relate the Latin roots with the description of the organism. You also can provide scientific names and have students use a dictionary that shows Greek and Latin roots. From these, students might figure out something about the organism—either its structure or something about its behavior.

Classification

Indiana Standards Standard B.1.35 Explain that the degree of kinship between organisms or species can be estimated from the similarity of their DNA sequences, which often closely matches their classification based on anatomical similarities. Know that amino acid similarities also provide clues to this kinship.

Objectives

Evaluate the history, purpose, and methods of taxonomy.

Explain the meaning of a scientific name.

Describe the organization of taxa in a biological classification system.

Review Vocabulary

species: a group of organisms that can interbreed and produce fertile offspring (p. 7)

New Vocabulary

classification
taxonomy
binomial nomenclature
genus
specific epithet
family
order
class
phylum
division
kingdom

FOLDABLES™
Study Organizer

Classification Systems Make the following Foldable to help you summarize and sequence the classification systems.

STEP 1 **Fold** two vertical sheets of paper in half from top to bottom.

STEP 2 **Turn** both papers horizontally and **cut** the papers in half along the folds. Discard one of the pieces.

STEP 3 **Fold** the three remaining vertical pieces in half from top to bottom.

STEP 4 **Turn** the papers horizontally. **Tape** the short ends of the pieces together (overlapping the edges slightly) to make an accordion book.

STEP 5 **Label** each fold.

Tape

Sequence As you read Chapter 17, arrange the classification systems from oldest to youngest beginning at the far left of the Foldable. Then, write a description of each classification system on the appropriate fold.

How Classification Began

Organizing items can help you understand them better and find them more easily. For example, you probably order your clothes drawers and your CD collection. Biologists want to better understand organisms so they organize them. One tool that they use to do this is **classification**— the grouping of objects or information based on similarities. **Taxonomy** (tak SAH nuh mee) is the branch of biology that groups and names organisms based on studies of their different characteristics. Biologists who study taxonomy are called taxonomists.

Word Origin

taxonomy from the Greek words *taxo*, meaning to "arrange," and *nomy*, meaning "ordered knowledge"; Taxonomy is the science of classification.

Aristotle's system

The Greek philosopher Aristotle (384–322 B.C.) developed the first widely accepted system of biological classification. He classified all the organisms he knew into two groups: plants and animals. He subdivided plants into the three groups, herbs, shrubs, and trees, depending on the size and structure of a plant. He grouped animals according to various characteristics, including their habitat and physical differences.

17.1 CLASSIFICATION **443**

1 Focus

INTERACTIVE CHALKBOARD
PowerPoint® Presentations

Bellringer
Section Focus Transparency 41

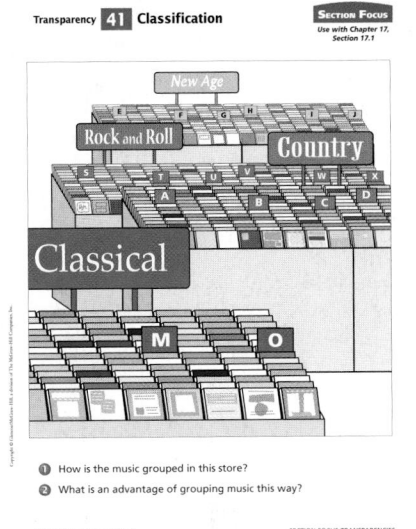

Transparency **41** **Classification**

SECTION FOCUS
Use with Chapter 17, Section 17.1

① How is the music grouped in this store?
② What is an advantage of grouping music this way?

BIOLOGY: The Dynamics of Life

SECTION FOCUS TRANSPARENCIES

INTERACTIVE CHALKBOARD
with Image Bank

PowerPoint® Presentations

This CD-ROM is an editable Microsoft® PowerPoint® presentation that includes:
- Section presentations
- Section checks
- Image bank
- Hot links to Biology Online

FOLDABLES™

For an additional Foldables activity idea, see the Chapter 17 Foldables page in *Unit 5 FAST FILE Resources*.

RESOURCE MANAGER

Unit 5 *FAST FILE* Resources
MiniLab Worksheet, p. 99
BioLab Worksheet, pp. 101–102
Real World BioApplications, pp. 103–104
Reinforcement and Study Guide in English, pp. 105–106
Reinforcement and Study Guide in Spanish, pp. 109–110

Concept Mapping, p. 113
Critical Thinking/Problem Solving, p. 114
Transparency Worksheet, p. 115
Reading Essentials for Biology, Section 17.1
Laboratory Manual, pp. 101–104
 Section Focus Transparency 41

Indiana Academic Standards

Pages 442–443: B.1.35

443

2 Teach

Inquiry

Activity Have students work in groups to role play that they are Aristotle (plants and animals, their behaviors and habitats) or Linnaeus (structural similarities). Have the groups use each system to classify everything that they see in a day. Then have students critique the strengths and weaknesses of each system. **L2**

Visual Learning

Figure 17.1 Ask students to identify features they could use to classify these flowers. Possible answers include the numbers and arrangements of petals or male and female reproductive organs.

Word Origin

Have the students find and define other words using "bi" as part of the root, such as *binocular* and *bicycle*.

Word Origin

binomial nomenclature from the Latin words *bi,* meaning "two," *nomen,* meaning "name," and *calatus,* meaning "list"; The system of binomial nomenclature assigns two words to the name of each species.

If you analyze the basis for Aristotle's groups, you can see it was useful but did not group organisms according to their evolutionary history. According to his system, birds, bats, and flying insects are classified together even though they have little in common besides the ability to fly. As time passed, more organisms were discovered and some did not fit easily into Aristotle's groups, but many centuries passed before Aristotle's system was replaced.

Linnaeus's system of binomial nomenclature

In the late eighteenth century, a Swedish botanist, Carolus Linnaeus (1707–1778), developed a method of grouping organisms that is still used by scientists today. Linnaeus's system was based on physical and structural similarities of organisms. For example, he might use the similarities in flower parts as a basis for classifying flowering plants, *Figure 17.1.* As a result, the groupings revealed the relationships of the organisms.

Eventually, some biologists proposed that structural similarities reflect the evolutionary relationships of species. For example, although bats fly like birds, they also have hair and produce milk for their young. Therefore, bats are classified as mammals rather than as birds, reflecting the evolutionary history that bats share with other mammals. This way of organizing organisms is the basis of modern classification systems.

Modern classification systems use a two-word naming system called **binomial nomenclature** that Linnaeus developed to identify species. In this system, the first word identifies the genus of the organism. A **genus** (JEE nus) (plural, genera) consists of a group of similar species. The second word, which sometimes describes a characteristic of the organism, is called the **specific epithet.** Thus, the scientific name for each species, referred to as the species name, is a combination of the genus name and specific epithet.

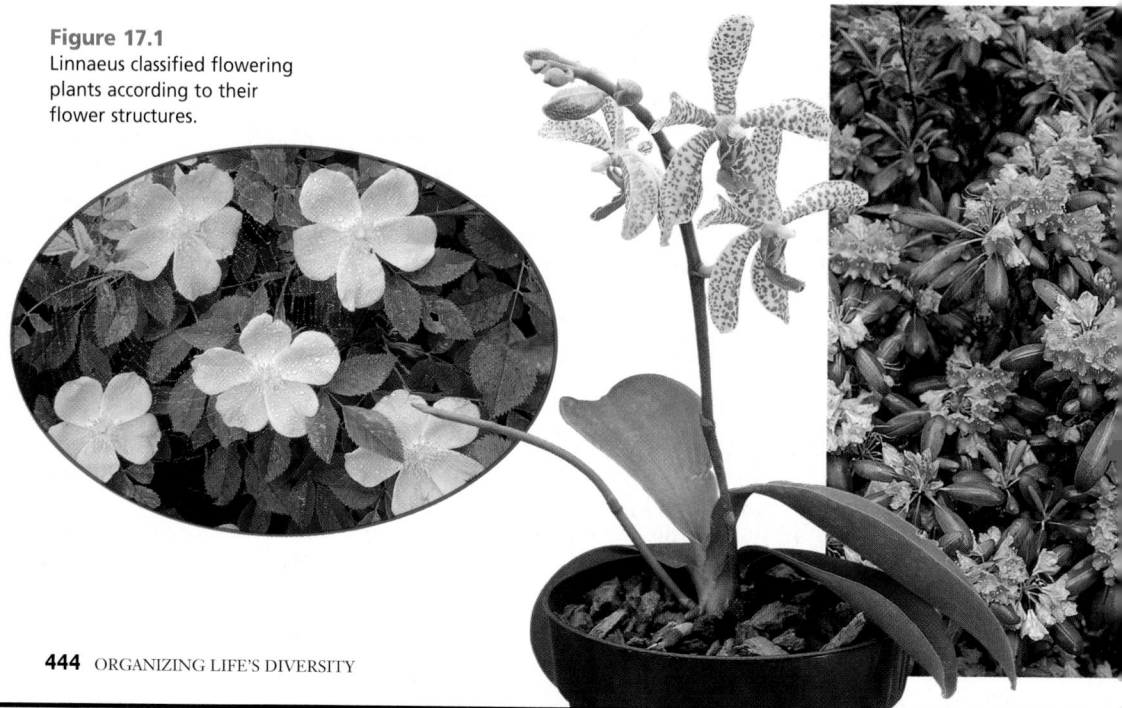

Figure 17.1
Linnaeus classified flowering plants according to their flower structures.

444 ORGANIZING LIFE'S DIVERSITY

INCLUSION STRATEGIES

Learning Disabled Have students use a yellow pages directory to look up three categories, such as automobiles, bakers, and music. (Because these directories vary from place to place, you may want to choose easier categories ahead of time.) Ask them to write lists of the subcategories they find under each of these main heads. Then ask them to write one sentence telling why the yellow pages is a type of classification system. **L1**

For example, the species name of modern humans is *Homo sapiens*. Modern humans are in the genus *Homo*, for example. One of their characteristics is intelligence. The Latin word *sapiens* means "wise."

Scientific and common names

Latin is the language of scientific names. Taxonomists are required to use Latin because the language is no longer used in conversation and, therefore, does not change. Scientific names should be italicized in print and underlined when handwritten. The first letter of the genus name is uppercase, but the first letter of the specific epithet is lowercase.

Although a scientific name gives information about the relationships of an organism and how it is classified, many organisms have common names just like you and your friends might have nicknames. However, a common name can be misleading. For example, a sea horse is a fish, not a horse. In addition, it is confusing when a species has more than one common name. The bird in *Figure 17.2* lives not only in the United States but also in several countries in Europe. It has a different common name in each country. Therefore, if an English scientist uses the bird's English common name in an article, a Spanish scientist looking for information might not recognize the bird as the same species.

Reading Check **Describe** how binomial nomenclature is used to effectively name an organism.

Modern Classification

Expanding on Linnaeus's work, today's taxonomists try to identify the underlying evolutionary relationships of organisms and use the information gathered as a basis for classification.

Figure 17.2
In the United States and England, this bird is called the house sparrow; in Spain, the gorrión doméstico; in Holland, the huismus; and in Sweden, the gråsparv. However, the bird has only one scientific name, *Passer domesticus*.

They compare the external and internal structures of organisms, as well as their geographical distribution and genetic makeup to reveal their probable evolutionary relationships. Grouping organisms on the basis of their evolutionary relationships makes it easier to understand biological diversity.

Taxonomy: A framework

Just as similar food items in a supermarket are stacked together, taxonomists group similar organisms, both living and extinct. Classification provides a framework in which to study the relationships among living and extinct species.

For example, biologists study the relationship between birds and dinosaurs within the framework of classification. Are dinosaurs more closely related to birds or to reptiles? The bones of some dinosaurs have large internal spaces like those in birds. In addition, dinosaur skeletons share many other remarkable similarities with birds. Because of such evidence, they suggest that dinosaurs are more closely related to ostriches, which are birds, than to lizards, which are reptiles.

Taxonomy: A useful tool

Classifying organisms can be a useful tool for scientists who work in agriculture, forestry, and medicine.

INVESTIGATE
BioLab

The BioLab at the end of the chapter can be used at this point in the lesson.

MiniLab 17.1

Purpose
Students will use a dichotomous key to identify organisms.

Process Skills
classify, observe and infer, compare and contrast

Teaching Strategies
- Have students wash their hands after touching the leaves.
- Use keys that identify trees and shrubs by leaf structure.
- Review the features of a dichotomous key (paired statements on a single topic). See pages 810–811 for an example.

Expected Results
Students will identify trees and shrubs based on leaf structure.

Analysis
1. identification of organisms
2. vein and margin structure, leaf shape and size, number of lobes
3. more specific

Assessment
Performance Provide students with several algae and a dichotomous key. Ask them to examine, diagram, and then identify the algae. Use the Performance Task Assessment List for Making and Using a Classification System in **PASC,** p. 121. **L3**

Indiana Academic Standards

Pages 446–447: B.1.35

MiniLab 17.1

Classify

Using a Dichotomous Key in a Field Investigation How could you identify a tree growing in front of your school? You might use a field guide that contains descriptive information or you might use a dichotomous key for trees. A key is made up of sets of numbered statements. Each set deals with a single characteristic of an organism, such as leaf shape or arrangement. Follow the numbered sets until the key reveals the name of the organism.

Procedure
1. Collect a few leaves from local trees. Using a dichotomous key for trees of your area, identify the tree from which each leaf came. To use the key, study one leaf. Then choose the statement from the first pair that most accurately describes the leaf. Continue following the key until you identify the leaf's tree. Repeat the process for each leaf.
2. Glue each leaf on a separate sheet of paper. For each leaf, record the tree's name.

Analysis
1. **Infer** What is the function of a dichotomous key?
2. **Summarize** List three different characteristics used in your key.
3. **Classify** As you used the key, did the characteristics become more general or more specific?

Figure 17.3
Taxonomists can easily distinguish among this poison ivy **(A)** and other plants, such as Virginia creeper **(B),** with which it is often confused.

For example, suppose a child eats berries from a plant in the backyard. The child's parents would probably rush the child and some of the plant and its berries to the nearest hospital. A scientist working at a poison control center could identify the plant, and the physicians would then know how to treat the child.

Anyone can learn to identify many organisms, even similar ones such as shown in **Figure 17.3.** The *MiniLab* on this page will guide you through a way of identifying some organisms using a dichotomous key. Then try the *BioLab* at the end of this chapter.

Taxonomy and the economy
It often happens that the discovery of new sources of lumber, medicines, and energy results from the work of taxonomists. The characteristics of a familiar species are frequently similar to those found in a new, related species. For example, if a taxonomist knows that a certain species of pine tree contains chemicals that make good disinfectants, it's possible that another pine species could also contain these useful substances.

CHALLENGE ACTIVITY

Zoo and Garden Classification Send students to a nearby zoo or botanical garden to find an example of classification. Many exhibits have signs posted that include information about the organism's classification. Have them make a photo or video essay of the example to show to the class. **L3**

How Living Things Are Classified

In any classification system, items are categorized, making them easier to find and discuss. For example, in a newspaper's classified advertisements, you'll find a section listing autos for sale. This section frequently subdivides the many ads into two smaller groups—domestic autos and imported autos. In turn, these two groups are subdivided by more specific criteria, such as different car manufacturers and the year and model of the auto. Although biologists group organisms, not cars, they subdivide the groups on the basis of more specific criteria. A group of organisms is called a taxon (plural, taxa).

Taxonomic rankings

Organisms are ranked in taxa that range from having very broad characteristics to very specific ones. The broader a taxon, the more general its characteristics, and the more species it contains. You can think of the taxa as fitting together like nested boxes of increasing sizes. You already know about two taxa. The smallest taxon is species. Organisms that look alike and successfully interbreed belong to the same species. The next largest taxon is a genus—a group of similar species that have similar features and are closely related.

It is not always easy to determine the species of an organism. For example, over many years, taxonomists have debated how to classify the red wolf, the coyote, and the gray wolf. Some biologists wanted to classify them as separate species, and others wanted to classify them as a single species. Use the *Problem-Solving Lab* on this page to explore the evidence for and against classifying these three organisms as separate species.

Problem-Solving Lab 17.1

Draw a Conclusion

Is the red wolf a separate species? The work of taxonomists results in changing views of species. This is due to both the discovery of new species and the development of new techniques for studying classification.

Red wolf   Coyote   Gray wolf

Solve the Problem

1. The red wolf *(Canis rufus)* can breed and produce offspring with both the coyote *(Canis latrans)* and the gray wolf *(Canis lupus)*. Despite this fact, the three animal types have been classified as separate species.
2. A biologist measured their skulls and concluded that in size and structure, the red wolf's measurements fell midway between gray wolves and coyotes.
3. Based on these data, the biologist concluded that they are separate species.
4. Geneticists, attempting to determine if the three animal types were separate species, found that the nucleotide sequences from the red wolf's DNA were not distinctively different from those of gray wolves or coyotes.
5. The geneticists concluded that the red wolf is a hybrid of the gray wolf and coyote.

Thinking Critically

1. **Infer** A species can be defined as a group of animals that can mate with one another to produce fertile offspring but cannot mate successfully with members of a different group. Does statement (1) support or reject this definition? Explain.
2. **Infer** What type of evidence was the biologist using in (2)? The geneticists in (4)? Explain.
3. **Interpret** A hybrid is the offspring from two species. Which sentence, besides (4) and (5), supports hybrid evidence? Explain.
4. **Analyze** If you supported the biologist's work, would you use the three different scientific names for coyotes, gray wolves, and red wolves? Explain.
5. **Analyze** If you supported the geneticists' conclusions, would you use the three different scientific names? Explain.
6. **Infer** Analyze the relationships among the red wolf, coyote, and gray wolf according to physical and genetic factors.

447

Problem-Solving Lab 17.1

Purpose

Students will analyze why taxonomy can change.

Process Skills

analyze information, apply concepts, define operationally, draw a conclusion, think critically

Background

The red wolf is an endangered species. Programs to reintroduce the red wolf into states, such as North Carolina, have received federal funding. But now that the red wolf is considered a hybrid, some question spending endangered species funds on it.

Teaching Strategies

- Point out that each animal has its own scientific name.
- Use large photos to show the animals' similarities.

Thinking Critically

1. rejects it; The red wolf mates with two other species.
2. biologist, structural; geneticists, biochemical
3. 2; intermediate skull size implies hybridism.
4. Yes; each species must have its own scientific name.
5. No; the red wolf is a hybrid.
6. The physical features appear to be distinctive enough to classify them as different species. The genetic factors indicate that the red wolf is a hybrid of gray wolves and coyotes.

Assessment

Knowledge The red fox's scientific name is *Vulpes vulpes.* Have students classify the red fox and red wolf. Use the Performance Task Assesssment List for Making and Using a Classification System in **PASC**, p. 121. L2

Biology Journal

Organizing Information Provide students with a list of three to five familiar organisms, such as a common fish, amphibian, reptile, bird, and mammal. Have them research how the organisms are classified and use the information to make a table in their journals. L1

Career Path

TECH PREP **Courses in high school:** sciences, mathematics, and English

College: bachelor's degree in biology or another science; master's degree usually required

Career Issue

Ask students whether teachers should be required to follow state or national biology teaching guidelines, or be free to develop their own goals and strategies. Have them explain their answers.

For More Information

For more information about teaching biology, write to:

National Association of
Biology Teachers
12030 Sunrise Valley Drive,
Suite 110
Reston, VA 20191

Visual Learning

Figure 17.4 Ask students how the animals are alike. whiskers, a short face, short ears, similar camouflaging color, four legs, similar body form, short tail

Caption Question Answer
Figure 17.5 (p. 449) Mammalia; Animalia

Reinforcement

Have students use the mnemonic "Dumb King Philip came over from Geneva Switzerland" to remember the order of the taxa.

Indiana Academic Standards

Pages 448–449: B.1.35

CAREERS IN BIOLOGY

Biology Teacher

Are you intrigued by the actions and interactions of plants, animals, and other organisms? Would you like to share this interest with others? Maybe you should become a biology teacher.

Skills for the Job

Biology teachers help students learn about organisms through discussions and activities both inside and outside the classroom. As a biology teacher, you might also teach general science and health. To become a biology teacher, you must earn a bachelor's degree in science, biology, or a closely related field. You sometimes have to spend several months student teaching. Many positions require a master's degree. In many states, you have to pass a national test for teachers. This national test includes a test in biology or in a combination of biology and general science. After all this education, testing, and work, you will be ready to teach others!

 To find out more about careers in related fields, visit in.bdol.glencoe.com/careers

Figure 17.4
Mountain lions **(A)** are not classified in the same genus as lynxes **(B)** and bobcats **(C)**.

In *Figure 17.4,* you can compare the appearance of a lynx, *Lynx canadensis,* a bobcat, *Lynx rufus,* and a mountain lion, *Felis concolor.* The scientific names of the lynx and bobcat tell you that they belong to the same genus, *Lynx.* All species in the genus *Lynx* share the characteristic of having a jaw that contains 28 teeth. Mountain lions and other lions, which are similar to bobcats and lynxes, are not classified in the *Lynx* genus because their jaws contain 30 teeth.

Bobcats, lynxes, lions, and mountain lions belong to the same family called Felidae. **Family,** the next larger taxon in the biological classification system, consists of a group of similar genera. In addition to domesticated cats, bobcats, lynxes, and lions belong to the family Felidae. All members of the cat family share certain characteristics. They have short faces, small ears, forelimbs with five toes, and hindlimbs with four toes. Most can retract their claws.

CHALLENGE ACTIVITY

Discovering New Species: *Linguistic*
Ask students to write in their journals the procedures needed to establish that an insect found in a tropical rain forest is a "new" species that has never before been described. Journal entries will vary but should indicate the use of a key to classify the insect. A detailed description of the insect would be used to identify and classify it. **L3**

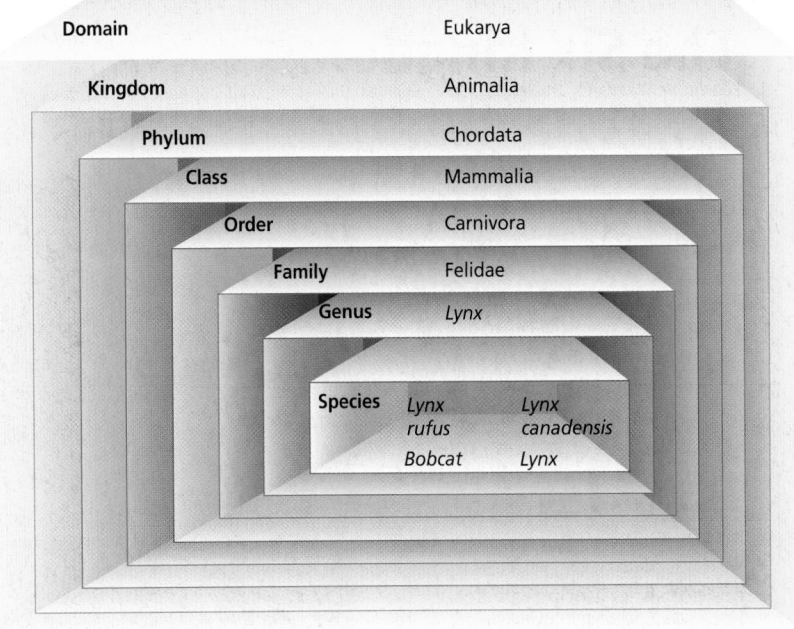

Domain	Eukarya
Kingdom	Animalia
Phylum	Chordata
Class	Mammalia
Order	Carnivora
Family	Felidae
Genus	*Lynx*
Species	*Lynx rufus* Bobcat *Lynx canadensis* Lynx

Figure 17.5
Although the lynx and bobcat are different species, they belong to the same genus, family, order, class, phylum, and kingdom. **Observe and Infer** *What class do the bobcat and lynx belong to? What kingdom do both belong to?*

3 Assess

DAILY INTERVENTION

Check for Understanding
Have students compare and contrast the classification systems of species and library books. Both systems provide a way of organizing information. They differ in the criteria used to create categories and in the number of categories. **L1**

Reteach
Naturalist Have students list the taxa biologists use to classify organisms and describe each taxon they list. **L1**

Resources
For more practice, use *Reading Essentials for Biology*, Section 17.1.

Extension

Naturalist Have students find the scientific names of the wolf, fox, domestic dog, and coyote and explain how the animals are related. **L2**

MODIFIED Assessment

Performance Ask students to work with a partner to collect five plants and use field guides to identify them. **L1**

The larger taxa

There are five larger taxa following family. An **order** is a taxon of similar families. A **class** is a taxon of similar orders. A **phylum** (FI lum) (plural, phyla) is a taxon of similar classes. Plant taxonomists use the taxon **division** instead of phylum. A **kingdom** is a taxon of similar phyla or divisions. A domain contains one or more kingdoms. The six kingdoms are described in the next section.

The bobcat and lynx that were compared earlier are both classified completely in *Figure 17.5*. Although the six-kingdom classification system primarily is used in this textbook, several other classification systems exist. Recently, many taxonomists began including a fifth taxon called domains, which include all six kingdoms. You can learn more about domains and other classification systems on pages 1070–1073 in the *Focus On*.

Section Assessment

Understanding Main Ideas
1. For what reasons are biological classification systems needed?
2. Give two reasons why binomial nomenclature is useful.
3. Describe what Linnaeus contributed to the field of taxonomy.
4. What are the taxa used in biological classification? Which taxon contains the largest number of species? Which taxon contains the fewest number of species?

Thinking Critically
5. Use categories that parallel the taxa of a biological classification system to organize the items you can borrow from a library.

SKILL REVIEW
6. **Classify** Using taxonomic nomenclature, organize the furniture in your home based on function. Develop a model of a hierarchical classification system based on similarities and differences. For more help, refer to *Classify* in the **Skill Handbook**.

in.bdol.glencoe.com/self_check_quiz

17.1 CLASSIFICATION **449**

Section Assessment

1. With them, it is easier to study organisms and their relationships.
2. Common names do not indicate relationships among organisms. The genus name is the same for closely related species; the species name describes the organism.
3. He developed the binomial system for naming organisms and the basis of today's biological classification system.
4. Kingdom, phylum, class, order, family, genus, species; kingdom taxa contain the largest numbers of species, and species taxa contain the fewest.
5. Answers will vary, but students may use categories like reference books, novels, biographies, audiotapes, etc.
6. Suggestion: domain: 1st floor; kingdom: living room; phylum: chairs; order: cushioned; family: single; genus: with foot rest; species: recliner

1 Focus

INTERACTIVE CHALKBOARD
PowerPoint® Presentations

Bellringer
Section Focus Transparency 42

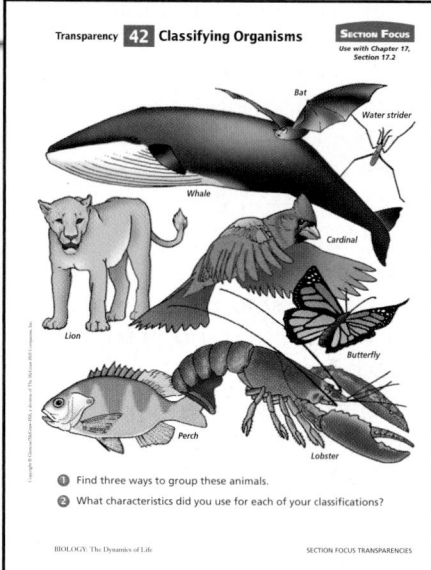

Transparency **42** Classifying Organisms   SECTION FOCUS
Use with Chapter 17, Section 17.2

Bat
Water strider
Whale
Cardinal
Lion
Butterfly
Perch
Lobster

❶ Find three ways to group these animals.
❷ What characteristics did you use for each of your classifications?

BIOLOGY: The Dynamics of Life   SECTION FOCUS TRANSPARENCIES

Using an Analogy
Compare and Contrast Student answers will vary, but may include height, eye or hair color, or similar characteristics; other students will identify these same characteristics as differences. Be aware that some students may not be able to discuss familial characteristics.

Section 17.2

The Six Kingdoms

Indiana Standards Standard B.1.35 Explain that the degree of kinship between organisms or species can be estimated from the similarity of their DNA sequences, which often closely matches their classification based on anatomical similarities. Know that amino acid similarities also provide clues to this kinship.

SECTION PREVIEW

Objectives

Describe how evolutionary relationships are determined.

Explain how cladistics reveals phylogenetic relationships.

Compare the six kingdoms of organisms.

Review Vocabulary
archaebacteria: chemosynthetic prokaryotes that live in harsh environments (p. 384)

New Vocabulary
phylogeny
cladistics
cladogram
eubacteria
protist
fungus

Family Features

Using an Analogy Suppose you entered a room full of strangers and were asked to identify two related people. What clues would you look for? You might listen to hear similar-sounding voices. You might look for similar hair, eye, and skin coloration. You might watch for shared behaviors and mannerisms between individuals. When taxonomists want to identify evolutionary relationships among species, they examine the characteristics of each species.

Compare and Contrast *What physical characteristics do you share with your parents? What physical characteristics make you different from them?*

The Western sword fern *(Polystichum munitum)* and Northern holly fern *(Polystichum lonchitis)* (inset) have a similar structure.

How are evolutionary relationships determined?

Evolutionary relationships are determined on the basis of similarities in structure, breeding behavior, geographical distribution, chromosomes, and biochemistry. Because these characteristics provide the clues about how species evolved, they also reveal the probable evolutionary relationships of species.

Structural similarities

Structural similarities among species reveal relationships. For example, the presence of many shared physical structures implies that species are closely related and may have evolved from a common ancestor. For example, because lynxes and bobcats have structures more similar to each other than to members of any other groups, taxonomists suggest that they share a common ancestor. Likewise, plant taxonomists use structural evidence to classify dandelions and sunflowers in the same family, Asteraceae, because they have similar flower and fruit structures.

450 ORGANIZING LIFE'S DIVERSITY

RESOURCE MANAGER

Unit 5 *Fast File* Resources
MiniLab Worksheet, p. 100
Reinforcement and Study Guide in English, pp. 107–108
Reinforcement and Study Guide in Spanish, pp. 111–112
Transparency Worksheets, pp. 116, 117–120

Reading Essentials for Biology, Section 17.2
Laboratory Manual, pp. 105–108
📖 **Section Focus Transparency 42**
📖 **Basic Concepts Transparency 24**
📖 **Reteaching Skills Transparency 26**

(A)

(B)

If you observe an unidentified animal that can retract its claws, you can infer that it belongs to the cat family. You can then assume that the animal has other characteristics in common with cats. Taxonomists observe and compare features among members of different taxa and use this information to infer their evolutionary history.

Breeding behavior

Sometimes, breeding behavior provides important clues to relationships among species. For example, two species of frogs, *Hyla versicolor* and *Hyla chrysoscelis*, live in the same area and look similar. During the breeding season, however, there is an obvious difference in their mating behavior. The males of each species make different sounds to attract females, and therefore attract and mate only with members of their own group. Scientists concluded that the frogs were two separate species.

Geographical distribution

The location of species on Earth helps biologists determine their relationships with other species. For example, many different species of finches live on the Galápagos Islands off the coast of South America. Biologists propose that in the past some members of a finchlike bird species that lived in South America reached the Galápagos Islands, where they became isolated. These finches probably spread into different niches on the volcanic islands and evolved over time into many

distinct species. The fact that they share a common ancestry is supported by their geographical distribution in addition to their genetic similarities.

Chromosome comparisons

Both the number and structure of chromosomes, as seen during mitosis and meiosis, provide evidence about relationships among species. For example, cauliflower, cabbage, kale, and broccoli look different but have chromosomes that are almost identical in structure. Therefore, biologists propose that these plants are related. Likewise, the similar appearance of chromosomes among chimpanzees, gorillas, and humans suggests a common ancestry.

Biochemistry

Powerful evidence about relationships among species comes from biochemical analyses of organisms. Closely related species have similar DNA sequences and, therefore, similar proteins. In general, the more inherited nucleotide sequences that two species share, the more closely related they are. For example, the DNA sequences in giant pandas and red pandas differ. They differ so much that many scientists suggest that giant pandas are more closely related to bears than to red pandas, such as the one shown in *Figure 17.6.* Read the *Biotechnology* feature at the end of this chapter to learn more about how chemical similarities can reveal evolutionary relationships.

Figure 17.6
DNA sequences in red pandas **(A)** and giant pandas **(B)** suggest that red pandas are more closely related to raccoons, and giant pandas are more closely related to bears.

2 Teach

Activity
Interpersonal Make a set of cards containing the features biologists use to classify organisms. Have a student select a card, describe the feature, and explain why the feature is useful in classification. Return the card to the set and continue until each student has chosen a card. **L2**

Content Background
Red pandas (*Ailurus fulgens*) are found in the Himalaya between 2000 and 4800 m. They are about the size of a large house cat. They are known by several common names, such as wah, hun-ho, and lesser panda.

Visual Learning
Figure 17.6 Ask students in what ways the giant panda and red panda are similar and different. They have similar common names and body shape and features, but have different DNA sequences.

CHALLENGE ACTIVITY

Chromosome Numbers Students who need an additional challenge can research to find numbers of chromosomes and karyotypes of humans, chimpanzees, gorillas, and other primates. They should prepare a poster that compares their findings and propose a phylogeny. **L3**

Indiana Academic Standards
Pages 450–451: B.1.35

Visual Learning

Use Figure 17.7 to explain how cladistics reflects an organism's phylogeny. Provide students with other examples of derived traits, such as tetrapod limbs and mammalian and avian endothermy, that might be used in cladistic analysis.

Inquiry

Discussion Have students brainstorm why taxonomy reflects evolutionary relationships. Review the definition of taxonomy. Review the Word Origin information about *taxonomy* on page 443. When taxonomy accurately reflects an organism's phylogeny, the organism's name provides information about the organism. **L2**

Phylogenetic Classification: Models

Species that share a common ancestor also share an evolutionary history. The evolutionary history of a species is called its **phylogeny** (fy LAH juh nee). A classification system that shows the evolutionary history of species is a phylogenetic classification and reveals the evolutionary relationships of species.

Early classification systems did not reflect the phylogenetic relationships among organisms. As scientists learned more about evolutionary relationships, they modified the early classification schemes to reflect the phylogeny of species.

Cladistics

One biological system of classification that is based on phylogeny is **cladistics** (kla DIHS tiks). Scientists who use cladistics assume that as groups of organisms diverge and evolve from a common ancestral group, they retain some unique inherited characteristics that taxonomists call derived traits. Biologists identify a group's derived traits and use them to make a branching diagram called a

cladogram (KLA deh gram). A cladogram is a model of the phylogeny of a species, and models are important tools for understanding scientific concepts.

Cladograms are similar to the pedigrees, or family trees, you studied in an earlier chapter. Branches on both pedigrees and cladograms show proposed ancestry. In a cladogram, two groups on diverging branches probably share a more recent ancestor than those groups farther away. If two organisms are near each other on a pedigree's branch, they also share an ancestor. However, an important difference between cladograms and pedigrees is that, whereas pedigrees show the direct ancestry of an organism from two parents, cladograms show a probable evolution of a group of organisms from ancestral groups.

In *Figure 17.7,* you see the cladogram for modern birds, such as robins. How was the cladogram developed? First, taxonomists identified the derived traits of modern birds—flight feathers, light bones, a wishbone, down feathers, and feathers with shafts. Next, they identified ancestral species that have at least

Word Origin

phylogeny from the Greek words *phylon,* meaning "related group," and *geny,* meaning "origin"; Organisms are classified based on their phylogeny.

cladistics from the Greek word *klados,* meaning "sprout" or "branch"; Cladistics is based on phylogeny.

Figure 17.7
This cladogram uses the derived traits of a modern bird, such as the robin, to model its phylogeny. Groups that are closer together on the cladogram probably share a more recent common ancestor.

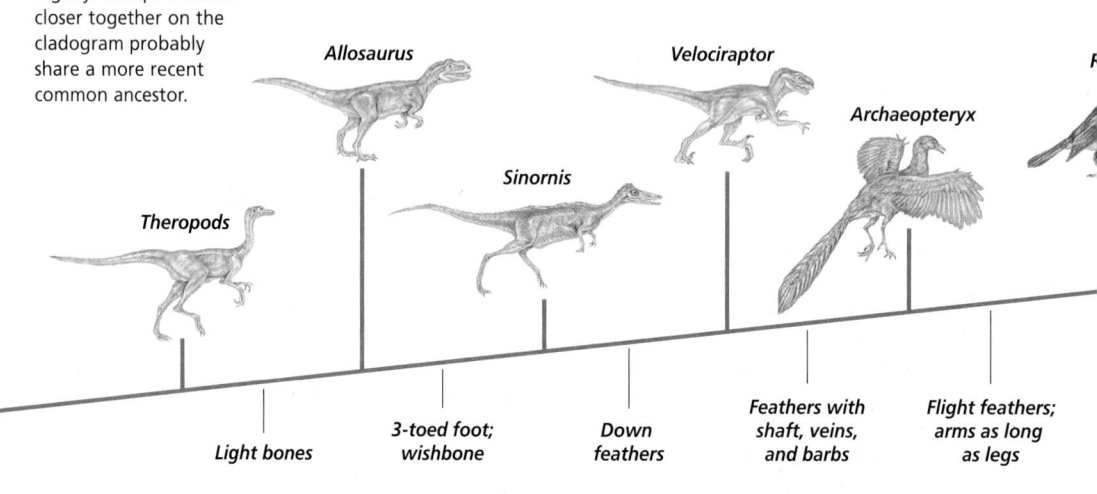

Allosaurus   Velociraptor

Archaeopteryx

Sinornis

Theropods

Light bones   3-toed foot; wishbone   Down feathers   Feathers with shaft, veins, and barbs   Flight feathers; arms as long as legs

452 ORGANIZING LIFE'S DIVERSITY

CHALLENGE ACTIVITY

Domains Pamphlet Students who need an additional challenge can research Woese's system of classification using domains and make an illustrated pamphlet that compares and contrasts this system with the six-kingdom system. **L3**

some of these traits. Most biologists agree that the ancestors of birds are a group of dinosaurs called theropods. Some of these theropods are *Allosaurus, Archaeopteryx, Velociraptor, Sinornis,* and *Protarchaeopteryx.* Each of these ancestors has a different number of derived traits. Some groups share more derived traits than others.

Finally, taxonomists constructed the robin's cladogram from this information. They assume that if groups share many derived traits, they share common ancestry. Thus, *Archaeopteryx* and the robin, which share four derived traits, are on adjacent branches, indicating a recent common ancestor. Use the *MiniLab* on this page to construct a cladogram for another species.

Another type of model

In this book, you will see cladograms and other types of models that provide information about the phylogenetic relationships among species. One type of model resembles a fan. Unlike a cladogram, a fanlike model may communicate the time organisms became extinct or the relative number of species in a group. A fanlike diagram incorporates fossil information and the knowledge gained from anatomical, embryological, genetic, and cladistic studies.

In *Figure 17.8* on the next page, you can see a fanlike model of the six-kingdom classification system. This model includes both Earth's geologic time scale and the probable evolution of organisms during that time span. In addition, this fanlike diagram helps you to find relationships between modern and extinct species.

Groups of organisms that are closer in the same colored ray share more inherited characteristics.

MiniLab 17.2

Classify

Using a Cladogram to Show Relationships Cladograms were developed by Willi Hennig. They use derived characteristics to illustrate evolutionary relationships.

Procedure

1 The following table shows the presence or absence of six derived traits in the seven dinosaurs that are labeled A–G.

2 Use the information listed in the table below to answer the following questions.

Derived Traits of Dinosaurs							
Dinosaur Trait	A	B	C	D	E	F	G
Hole in hip socket	yes	yes	yes	yes	yes	yes	yes
Extension of pubis bone	no	no	no	yes	yes	yes	yes
Unequal enamel on teeth	no	no	no	no	yes	yes	yes
Skull has "shelf" in back	no	no	no	no	no	yes	yes
Grasping hand	yes	yes	yes	no	no	no	no
Three-toed hind foot	yes	yes	no	no	no	no	no

Analysis

1. **Classify** Copy the partially completed cladogram. Complete the missing information on the right side.

2. **Observe** How many traits does dinosaur F share with dinosaur C, with dinosaur D, and with dinosaur E?

3. **Infer** Dinosaurs A and B form a grouping called a clade. The dinosaurs A, B, and C form another clade. What derived trait is shared only by the A and B clade? By the A, B, and C clade? By the D, E, F, and G clade?

4. **Infer** Traits that evolved very early, such as the hole in the hip socket, are called primitive traits. The traits that evolved later, such as a grasping hand, are called derived traits. Are primitive traits typical of broader or smaller clades? Are derived traits typical of broader or smaller clades? Give an example in each case.

MiniLab 17.2

Purpose

Students will make a cladogram.

Process Skills

acquire information, analyze information, apply concepts, classify, compare and contrast, interpret data

Teaching Strategies

- Check student answers to question 1 before they complete the remaining analysis questions.
- Show students pictures of dinosaurs A–G.
  A. *Archaeopteryx*   E. *Allosaurus*
  B. *Plateosaurus*   F. *Stegosarus*
  C. *Parasaurolophus* G. *Triceratops*
  D. *Pachycephalosaurus*

Expected Results

Students will complete the cladogram as follows: node 1 = hole in hip socket, node 4 = extension of pubis bone, node 5 = unequal enamel, node 6 = skull shelf.

Analysis

1. See "Expected Results."
2. 1 trait with C, 2 traits with D, and 3 traits with E.
3. three-toed hind foot; grasping hand; extension of pubis bone
4. broader—hole in hip socket extends to all 7 animals; smaller—three-toed hind foot extends to only 1 clade

Assessment

Performance Ask students to classify the seven dinosaurs according to their external similarities and record their scheme on the chalkboard. Then, show them how a cladogram classifies these dinosaurs. Use the Performance Task Assessment List for Making and Using a Classification System in **PASC**, p. 121. **L2**

USING MODELS

Vertebrate Phylogeny Provide students with the following list of vertebrate classes: birds, reptiles, mammals, amphibians, and fish. Give them a list of derived traits such as legs, feathers, and hair. Have them construct a vertebrate cladogram from the lists. **L3**

Visual Learning

Figure 17.8 Ask the students to explain how time is indicated on the model. Earth's earliest organisms are near the center of the model, and those that appeared later are near the rim.

Critical Thinking

Kingdoms Eubacteria and Archaebacteria contain only unicellular prokaryotes that differ chemically from each other. Kingdom Protista contains eukaryotes that lack complex organ systems. Kingdom Fungi includes heterotrophic eukaryotes that absorb their nutrients. Kingdom Plantae includes multicellular eukaryotes that are photosynthetic. Kingdom Animalia includes multicelluar, eukaryotic heterotrophs with cells that lack cell walls.

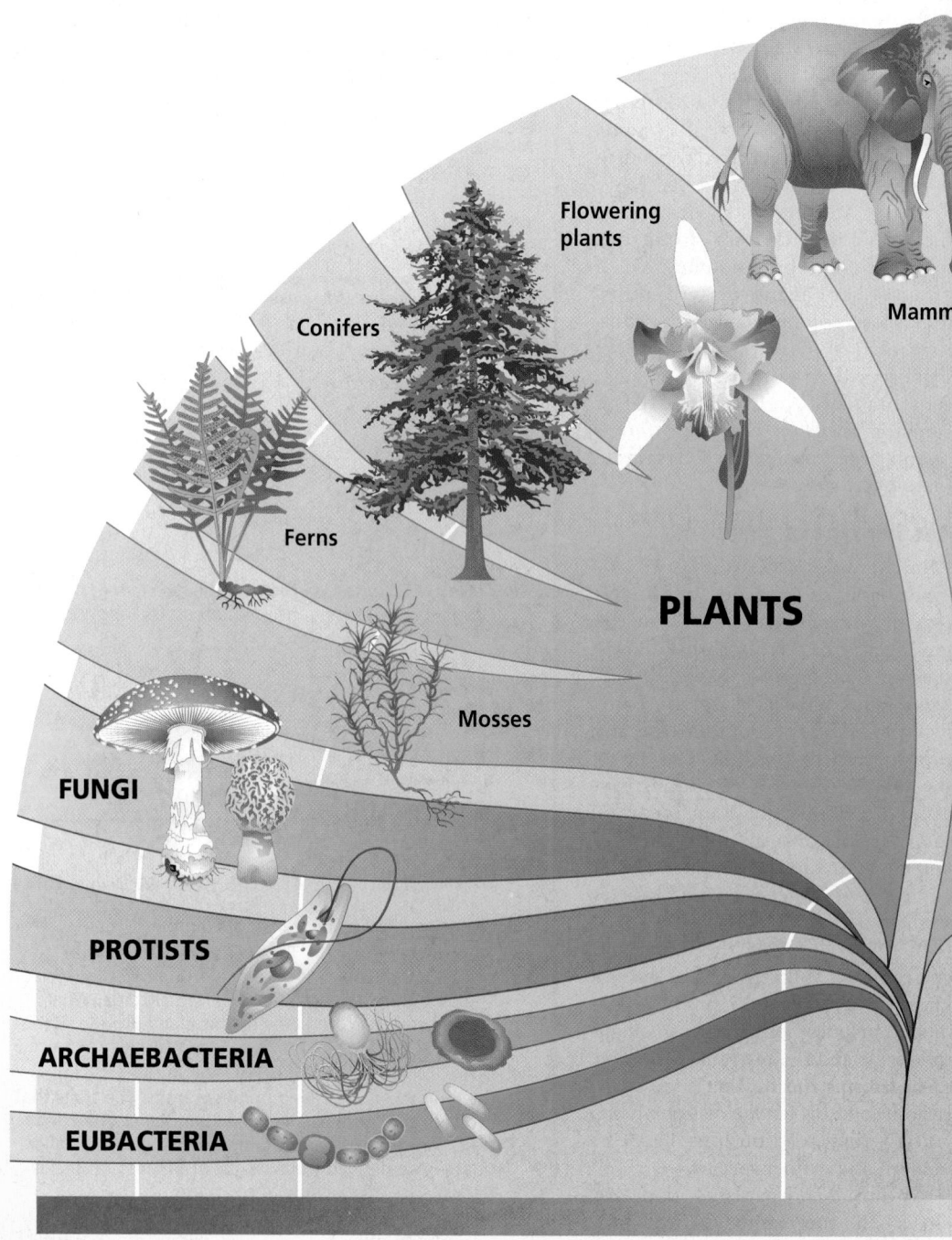

INSIDE STORY

Flowering plants

Conifers

Mamm

Ferns

PLANTS

Mosses

FUNGI

PROTISTS

ARCHAEBACTERIA

EUBACTERIA

Additional Lab

Classification of Glassware

Purpose
Students will classify laboratory glassware.

Materials
laboratory glassware such as flasks, test tubes, beakers, stirring rods, thermometers, bottle stoppers, pipets, droppers, funnels, petri dishes, graduated cylinders, and jars

Procedure
Give students the following directions.
1. Obtain a set of glassware to classify according to its structure and function.

CAUTION: *Handle glassware carefully. Notify your teacher immediately if any glassware breaks. Dispose of broken glass as your teacher directs.*

2. Classify the glassware into two groups. Then subdivide the groups. Note each group's characteristics and the names of its glassware.

Birds

Amphibians
and fishes

tiles

ANIMALS

Sea stars

Arthropods

Mollusks
and worms

Jellyfishes
and sponges

Life's Six Kingdoms

Figure 17.8
In this phylogenetic diagram, six colors represent the six kingdoms of living things. The phylogeny of organisms is represented by a fanlike structure perched on the geologic time scale. The fan's base represents the origin of life during the Precambrian. The fan's rays represent the probable evolution of species from the common origin. The major groups of modern organisms occupy the fan's outer edge, which represents present time. **Critical Thinking** *Identify characteristics of each of the six kingdoms.*

Brainstorming
Have students use Figure 17.8 to identify other organisms that belong in each group. Ask them to explain their choices. **L1**

Time Line
Visual-Spatial Have students make a time line of the evolutionary history of life on Earth using the information in Figure 17.8. Remind students that their time lines represent millions of years. **L1**

Extension
Have interested students research additional information about the former five kingdom classification system. How was it different from the current system? See the *Focus On* feature at the back of the book for help answering this question.

 Indiana Academic Standards

Pages 454–455: B.1.35

3. Place the glassware groups in a phylogenetic model such as in Figure 17.8. Consider how the glassware may have "evolved," and why some groups may be more closely "related" than others. Closely related groups should be closer together on your model.

4. Make a large diagram of your phylogenetic model.

Analysis

1. What glassware features were most useful in your model? Responses are likely to indicate functional traits.

2. How did your phylogenetic model differ from the model in Figure 17.8? The glassware model lacks dates, which would be purely speculative.

Assessment

Portfolio Have students write an essay about the "evolution" of their glassware. They should use the glassware's features to support their statements. Use the Performance Task Assessment List for Writing in Science in **PASC,** p. 159. **L2**

Purpose

Students will determine the approximate number of species in each kingdom.

Process Skills

classify, make and use graphs, use numbers, think critically

Teaching Strategies

■ Have a supply of protractors.
■ Review how to use a protractor and calculate percent.

Background

The number of named species is around 1.4 million, but estimates of as many as 30 million living species have been proposed. Of the species named, about 75% are animals. This value probably does not reflect their relative abundance, but rather their size and accessibility for study.

Thinking Critically

1. Answers should be close to the following: Archaebacteria = 500; Eubacteria = 10 000; Protista = 70 000; Fungi = 110 000; Plants = 510 000; Animals = 2 900 000.
2. Archaebacteria = 0.014%, Eubacteria = 0.3%, Protista = 1.9%, Fungi = 3.1%, Plants = 14.2%, Animals = 80.5%
3. Answers may vary—the number of species may vary due to the extinction and discovery of species.

Assessment

Skill Have students find the approximate number of species that become extinct each day, week, month, and year and summarize their findings in a data table. Then ask them to list the factors that contribute to the loss of species. Use the Performance Task Assessment List for Data Table in **PASC,** p. 109. **L3**

Problem-Solving Lab 17.2

Use Graphs

How many species are there in each kingdom? You may not realize it, but you probably already have seen more than 1000 different species since you were born. How close might you be to having seen all the known different species that exist?

Solve the Problem

The circle graph above shows Earth's six kingdoms. List the approximate number of species for each of the six kingdoms. Each degree of the circle graph is equal to 10 000 species. Archaebacteria represent ½₀ of a degree, and Eubacteria represent 1 degree.

Thinking Critically

1. **Analyze** What is the approximate total number of species for all life-forms on Earth?
2. **Analyze** What approximate percent of the total life-forms on Earth are in each kingdom?
3. **Analyze** Why do the above questions refer to the number of species as "approximate"?

Figure 17.9
Most archaebacteria, such as these salt-loving Halococcus **(A)** live in extreme environments, such as seawater evaporating ponds **(B).**

Color-enhanced TEM Magnification: 40 000×

They are probably more closely related than groups that are farther apart. For example, find the jelly-fishes, the fishes, and the reptiles on the model. Notice that fishes and reptiles are closer to each other than they are to the jellyfishes, indicating that they are more closely related to each other than they are to jellyfishes.

Reading Check **Evaluate** the two models of classification and their adequacy in representing biological events.

The Six Kingdoms of Organisms

As you saw in *Figure 17.8,* the six kingdoms of organisms are archaebacteria, eubacteria, protists, fungi, plants, and animals. In general, differences in cellular structures and methods of obtaining energy are the two main characteristics that distinguish among the members of the six kingdoms. Learn more about the number of species in each kingdom in the *Problem-Solving Lab* on this page.

Prokaryotes

The prokaryotes are microscopic unicellular organisms that lack distinct nuclei bounded by a membrane. Some are heterotrophs and some are autotrophs. In turn, some prokaryotic autotrophs are chemosynthetic whereas others are photosynthetic. There are two kingdoms of prokaryotic organisms: Archaebacteria and Eubacteria. The oldest prokaryotic fossils are about 3.4 billion years old.

There are several hundred species of known archaebacteria and most of them live in extreme environments such as swamps, deep-ocean hydrothermal vents, and seawater evaporating ponds, like the one in *Figure 17.9.*

CHALLENGE ACTIVITY

Gathering Protists For students who want an additional challenge, have them obtain water samples from local ponds. Tell them to scrape the underneath surfaces of rocks into their collecting jars. Have them use a microscope to observe their samples and sketch any protists they see. **L3**

Figure 17.10
Eubacteria are a diverse kingdom of prokaryotes. Both their cellular structure and the way they obtain food vary widely.

LM Magnification: 100×

 The bacteria that cause strep throat are heterotrophs called *Streptococcus*.

Magnification: 40 000×

B Cyanobacteria, such as *Oscillatoria*, live in freshwater and are photosynthetic.

Most of these environments are oxygen-free. The lipids in the cell membranes of archaebacteria, the composition of their cell walls, and the sequence of nucleic acids in their ribosomal RNA differ considerably from those of other prokaryotes. In addition, their genes have a similar structure to those in eukaryotes.

All of the other prokaryotes, about 5000 species of bacteria, are classified in Kingdom Eubacteria. **Eubacteria,** such as those shown in *Figure 17.10,* have very strong cell walls and a less complex genetic makeup than found in archaebacteria or eukaryotes. They live in most habitats except the extreme ones inhabited by the archaebacteria. Although some eubacteria cause diseases, such as strep throat and pneumonia, most bacteria are harmless and many are actually helpful.

Protists: A diverse group

Kingdom Protista contains diverse species, as shown in *Figure 17.11,* that share some characteristics.

Figure 17.11
Although these three protists look different, they are all eukaryotes and live in moist environments.

Magnification: 150×

A Funguslike slime molds often live in damp forests, feeding on microorganisms.

B The paramecium is an animal-like protist that moves through water.

C These kelps are multicellular plantlike protists. Although they look like plants, they do not have organs or organ systems.

17.2   THE SIX KINGDOMS   **457**

Use Figures 17.12 and 17.13 to compare the features of fungi and plants. Have students explain why fungi used to be classified in the plant kingdom. The fungi are plantlike and have cell walls, but, unlike plants, the fungi are not autotrophic.

Inquiry

Activity Display samples or photos of various fungi found in the local environment. Ask students to describe the similarities and differences among the fungi. Use field guides and dichotomous keys to identify each fungi. The differences include the shapes and colors of fruiting bodies, the gills, and other features. Similarities include cell walls made of chitin and heterotrophy. **L3**

Brainstorming

Ask students to brainstorm a list of familiar plants. Be sure they include trees, shrubs, and grasses, as well as annual and perennial garden plants.

Visual Learning

Figure 17.14 Ask students what senses the cheetah uses while running. sight, touch, and smell

Caption Question Answer

Figure 17.12 Fungi are unicellular or multicellular eukaryotes that have chitinous cell walls and are saprobic (absorb nutrients).

458

Figure 17.12
Morels are edible fungi that grow for only a few days in only a few places. **Identify** *What are the characteristics of the fungi kingdom?*

A **protist** is a eukaryote that lacks complex organ systems and lives in moist environments. Fossils of plant-like protists show that protists existed on Earth up to two billion years ago. Although some protists are unicellular, others are multicellular. Some are plantlike autotrophs, some are animal-like heterotrophs, and others are funguslike heterotrophs that produce reproductive structures like those of fungi.

Figure 17.13
A *Hibiscus* is just one kind of flowering plant **(A)**. Tropical tree ferns do not produce flowers **(B)**.

458

Fungi: Earth's decomposers

Organisms in Kingdom Fungi are heterotrophs that do not move from place to place. A **fungus** is either unicellular or multicellular eukaryote that absorbs nutrients from organic materials in the environment. Fungi first appeared in the fossil record over 400 million years ago. There are more than 50 000 known species of fungi, including the one you see in *Figure 17.12*.

Plants: Multicellular oxygen producers

All of the organisms in Kingdom Plantae are multicellular, photosynthetic eukaryotes. None moves from place to place. A plant's cells usually contain chloroplasts and have cell walls composed of cellulose. Plant cells are organized into tissues that in turn, are organized into organs and organ systems. You can see two of the many diverse types of plants in *Figure 17.13*.

The oldest plant fossils are more than 400 million years old.

CULTURAL DIVERSITY

Classifying Lion Tamarins Introduce students to the work of Adelmar Coimbra-Filho, Brazil's leading primatologist. Since the 1960s, Coimbra-Filho has published many articles on the systematics of the lion tamarin, *Leontopithecus,* a newly discovered primate species.

Coimbra-Filho directs Rio de Janeiro's Primate Center. He has coordinated efforts with the World Wildlife Fund to save lion tamarins from extinction. Elicit from students the importance of the work done by taxonomists and systematicists in discovering new species.

Figure 17.14
Many animals have well-developed nervous and muscular systems.

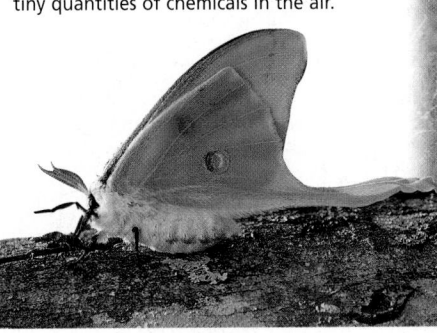

A The luna moth's antennae are sense organs, which are part of its nervous system. The moth's antennae detect tiny quantities of chemicals in the air.

B The cheetah uses many of its organ systems, especially its nervous and muscular systems, to speed through the grasslands, perhaps chasing prey.

However, some scientists propose that plants existed on Earth's land-masses much earlier than these fossils indicate. Plants do not fossilize as often as organisms that contain hard structures, such as bones, which more readily fossilize than soft tissues.

There are more than 250 000 known species of plants. Although you may be most familiar with flowering plants, there are many other types of plants, including mosses, ferns, and evergreens.

Animals: Multicellular consumers

Animals are multicellular heterotrophs. Nearly all are able to move from place to place. Animal cells do not have cell walls. Their cells are organized into tissues that, in turn, are organized into organs and complex organ systems. Some organ systems in animals are the nervous, circulatory, and muscular systems, *Figure 17.14*. Animals first appeared in the fossil record about 600 million years ago.

Check for Understanding
Visual-Spatial Show students pictures of organisms. Ask them to identify the kingdom to which each belongs. **L1**

Reteach
Intrapersonal Have students make flash cards with a photo of an organism on one side and, on the reverse, the name, kingdom, and distinguishing features of the organism. Have them use their cards in groups. **L1**
ELL **COOP LEARN**

Resources
For more practice, use *Reading Essentials for Biology*, Section 17.2.

Extension

Ask students to research the classification of show dogs or cats and explain the additional classification levels that are used. **L2**

✔ Assessment

Performance Set up 15 stations, with numbered specimens. Use microscopes for bacteria and protists and pictures for the larger organisms. Ask students to move among the stations and identify each organism's kingdom. **L1** **ELL**

Section Assessment

Understanding Main Ideas

1. How do members of the different kingdoms obtain nutrients?

2. Make a list of the characteristics that archaebacteria and eubacteria share. Then make a list of their differences.

3. What does it mean for species to have an evolutionary relationship? Identify five ways these relationships are determined. Describe each briefly and give an example for each.

4. How do cladograms and fanlike diagrams differ?

Thinking Critically

5. Why is phylogenetic classification more natural than a system based on characteristics such as medical usefulness, or the shapes, sizes, and colors of body structures?

SKILL REVIEW

6. **Make and Use Tables** Make a table that compares the characteristics of members of each of the six kingdoms. For more help, refer to *Make and Use Tables* in the **Skill Handbook**.

 in.bdol.glencoe.com/self_check_quiz

17.2 THE SIX KINGDOMS **459**

Section Assessment

1. Prokaryotes and protists use photosynthesis or chemosynthesis. Fungi absorb nutrients. The plants photosynthesize. Animals eat other organisms.

2. Both are unicellular prokaryotes with cell walls. They differ in their RNA and cell wall composition.

3. Student answers should reflect information on pages 456–459.

4. Cladograms show phylogeny; fanlike diagrams show evolutionary history in geologic time.

5. Phylogenetic classification relies on inherited features and can provide more reliable information than other systems that do not.

6. Information for tables can be found on pages 456–459.

Time Allotment

one class period

Process Skills

classify, observe and infer, compare and contrast, interpret data, sequence

Alternative Materials

Students can make a key from polystyrene packing pieces or kitchen utensils with a variety of sizes, shapes, and colors.

Making a Dichotomous Key

Before You Begin

Do you remember the first time you saw a beetle? You may have asked someone nearby, "What is it?" You may still be curious to know the names of insects you see. To help identify organisms, taxonomists have developed dichotomous keys. A dichotomous key is a set of paired statements that can be used to identify organisms. When you use a dichotomous key, you choose one statement from each pair that best describes the organism. At the end of each statement you chose, you are directed to the next set of statements to use. Finally, you will reach the name of the organism or the group to which it belongs.

Problem

How is a dichotomous key made?

Objectives

In this BioLab, you will:

- **Classify** organisms on the basis of structural characteristics.
- **Develop** a dichotomous key.

Materials

sample keys from guidebooks
metric ruler

Scarab beetle

Skill Handbook

If you need help with this lab, refer to the **Skill Handbook.**

1. Study the numbered drawings of beetles.
2. Choose one characteristic of the beetles, and classify the beetles into two groups based on that characteristic. Take measurements if you wish.
3. Record the chosen characteristic in a diagram like the one shown. Write the numbers of the beetles in each group on your diagram.
4. Continue to form subgroups within your two groups based on different characteristics. Record the characteristics and numbers of the beetles in your diagram until you have only one beetle in each group.
5. Using the diagram you have just made, make a dichotomous key for the beetles. Remember that each numbered step should contain two choices for classification. Begin with 1A and 1B. For help, examine sample keys provided by your teacher.
6. Exchange dichotomous keys with another team. Use their key to identify the beetles.

Long-horned,
wood-boring
beetle

Teaching Strategies

- Have the students examine samples of dichotomous keys.
- Explain that a well-designed key has contrasting traits from which to chose.
- Point out that after a beetle is identified, its characteristics are not used to develop additional choices.
- Have groups make transparencies of their keys and explain them. Ask students to list the keys' strengths and weaknesses.

1 Variegated mud-loving beetle

2 Mycetaeid beetle

3 Apricot borer

4 Water tiger

5 Predaceous diving beetle

6 Crawling water beetle

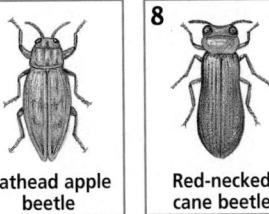
7 Flathead apple beetle

8 Red-necked cane beetle

9 Cucumber snout beetle

10 Whirligig beetle

11 Ironclad beetle

12 Broad-horned flour beetle

13 Red flour beetle

14 Blind ant-beetle

15 False wireworm beetle

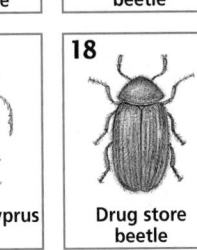
16 White-marked spider beetle

17 Monterey cyprus beetle

18 Drug store beetle

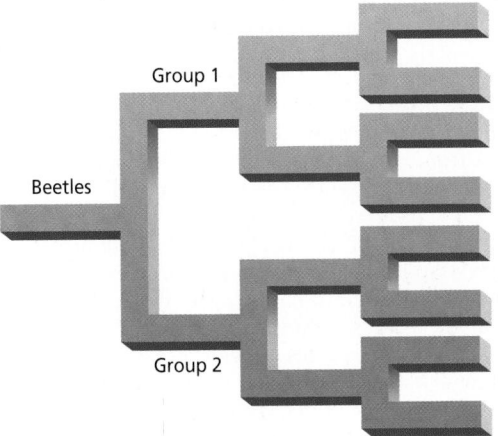

Group 1

Beetles

Group 2

ANALYZE AND CONCLUDE

1. **ERROR ANALYSIS** Was the dichotomous key you constructed exactly like those of other students? Why might they be different?

2. **Analyze Data** What characteristics were most useful for making a classification key for beetles? What characteristics were not useful?

3. **Think Critically** Why do keys typically offer only two choices and not more?

Apply Your Skill

Application Using the same procedure that you just used to make a beetle key, make a dichotomous key to identify the students in your class.

Web Links To find out more about identifying organisms, visit in.bdol.glencoe.com/dichotomous_key

ANALYZE AND CONCLUDE

1. The keys may or may not have been alike. The groups may have first divided the beetles into groups based on different features, such as size rather than color.

2. useful: size, color, and shape of various body parts, number of body sections, and antennae features; not useful: number of legs, number of antennae, habitat.

3. Having only two choices makes it easy to analyze organisms. In many keys, the choice is that the organism either has or does not have a particular characteristic.

Assessment

Performance Give each group a bag of mixed beans. Ask them to make a dichotomous key for the beans. Have the groups exchange their keys to see if they work. Students can place the keys in their portfolios. Use the Performance Task Assessment List for Making and Using a Classification system in **PASC**, p. 121. **L2**

Apply Your Skill

Application Have students use 10–20 features of their classmates, such as hair color or some personal belongings, such as notebooks, shoes, and backpacks, to classify them. You may want to select neutral features in advance to avoid sensitive issues. **L1**

Data and Observations

Have students exchange their keys. If another group can use them successfully, their accuracy is confirmed.

Purpose

Students learn how molecular characteristics can reveal the relative timing of evolutionary events.

Background

In DNA-DNA hybridization, the temperature at which hybrid strands separate indicates the species' DNA similarity. The higher the separation temperature, the stronger the bond, and the more similar are the DNAs. Estimates of the time when types of organisms began evolving assume that mutations occur at a fairly constant, unknown rate. Therefore, DNA sequencing only estimates when major evolutionary events occurred.

Teaching Strategies

- Remind students that molecular analysis adds to traditional morphological information.
- In contrast to distantly related species, closely related species, such as humans and chimpanzees, diverged from a common ancestor fairly recently.

Applying Biotechnology

Students may infer that their order of evolution and relationship was fishes, reptiles, dogs, and lastly humans.

BIO TECHNOLOGY

Molecular Clocks

How long ago did animals first appear on Earth? Did the giant panda evolve along the same family line as bears or raccoons? To help answer questions like these, biologists have learned how to use DNA, proteins, and other biological molecules as "clocks" that reveal details about evolutionary relationships.

Accumulated molecular differences in the DNA of two species can indicate how long they have been separate species. Comparing both the DNA base sequences and the amino acid sequence of a specific protein of two species can indicate the closeness of their relationship.

Comparing DNA One way to compare DNA is to measure how strongly the single strands of DNA from two species will bond. This method is known as DNA-DNA hybridization. Double-stranded DNA from each species is heated to separate the complementary strands. Then the single strands of DNA from each species are mixed and allowed to cool. As the DNA cools, the single strands from the two species bond, or hybridize. If the species are closely related, more of their DNA base pairs will match, and their DNA strands will bond strongly.

Another method of comparing the DNA of species is called DNA sequencing. Biologists select a gene that species have in common and compare the genes' bases. Counting how many base pairs differ can indicate approximately how long ago each species became distinct. Estimates obtained by DNA sequencing show that many of the animal phyla began to appear on Earth about 1.2 billion years ago.

Protein clocks A specific protein is assumed to evolve at about the same rate in all species that contain the protein. Comparing the amino acid sequences of the protein in several species can show about how long ago the species diverged. For example, cytochrome c is a protein in the

Flamingoes and storks are closely related.

cells of aerobic organisms. Both human and chimpanzee cytochrome c have the same amino acid sequence. The cytochrome c of other primates has a different amino acid sequence.

Applications DNA-DNA hybridization has shown that flamingoes are more closely related to storks than they are to geese. Protein clock data suggest that humans and chimpanzees became distinct species recently in the history of Earth. These biotechnological methods are useful in determining phylogenetic relationships.

Applying Biotechnology

Analyze Information The cytochrome c found in humans and chimpanzees differs from that found in dogs by 13 amino acids, in tuna by 31 amino acids, and in rattlesnakes by 20 amino acids. What assumptions can you make based on this information?

 To find out more about molecular clocks, visit in.bdol.glencoe.com/biotechnology

Going Further

Fossil DNA, such as that from mummies or bones, helps scientists determine relationships among living and fossil species. Ask students to research how such work is conducted and what it has revealed.

STUDY GUIDE

Section 17.1

Classification

Key Concepts

■ Although Aristotle developed the first classification system, Linnaeus laid the foundation for modern classification systems by using structural similarities to organize species and by developing a binomial naming system for species.

■ Scientists use a two-word system called binomial nomenclature to give species scientific names.

■ Classification provides an orderly framework in which to study the relationships among living and extinct species.

■ Organisms are classified in a hierarchy of taxa: domain, kingdom, phylum or division, class, order, family, genus, and species.

Vocabulary

binomial nomenclature (p. 444)
class (p. 449)
classification (p. 443)
division (p. 449)
family (p. 448)
genus (p. 444)
kingdom (p. 449)
order (p. 449)
phylum (p. 449)
specific epithet (p. 444)
taxonomy (p. 443)

Section 17.2

The Six Kingdoms

Key Concepts

■ Biologists use similarities in body structures, breeding behavior, geographic distribution, chromosomes, and biochemistry to determine evolutionary relationships.

■ Modern classification systems are based on phylogeny—the evolutionary history of a species.

■ Kingdoms Archaebacteria and Eubacteria contain only unicellular prokaryotes.

■ Kingdom Protista contains eukaryotes that lack complex organ systems.

■ Kingdom Fungi includes heterotrophic eukaryotes that absorb their nutrients.

■ Kingdom Plantae includes multicellular eukaryotes that are photosynthetic.

■ Kingdom Animalia includes multicellular, eukaryotic heterotrophs with cells that lack cell walls.

Vocabulary

cladistics (p. 452)
cladogram (p. 452)
eubacteria (p. 457)
fungus (p. 458)
phylogeny (p. 452)
protist (p. 458)

Magnification: 150×

FOLDABLES™
Study Organizer To help you review the organization of life's diversity, use the Organizational Study Fold on page 443.

 in.bdol.glencoe.com/vocabulary_puzzlemaker

Key Concepts

Summary statements can be used by students to review the major concepts of the chapter.

 Biology Online

Visit in.bdol.glencoe.com
/self_check_quiz
/vocabulary_puzzlemaker
/chapter_test
/standardized_test

VOCABULARY PUZZLEMAKER

 For additional help with vocabulary, have students access the Vocabulary PuzzleMaker online at in.bdol.glencoe.com/vocabulary_puzzlemaker

FOLDABLES™

Have students use their Foldables to review the content of Section 17.1. After reading the chapter, students should write a paragraph on the back of the Foldables that analyzes the importance of using domains and kingdoms to explain evolution.

Use the ExamView® Pro Test Bank CD-ROM to:
• Create **multiple versions** of tests
• Create **modified** tests with one mouse click for **inclusion** students
• **Edit** existing questions and **add** your own questions
• Build tests aligned with state standards using built-in **State Curriculum Tags**
• Change **English** tests to **Spanish** with one mouse click and vice versa

 Indiana Academic Standards

Pages 462–463: B.1.35

Questions and answers have been aligned and verified by The Princeton Review.

Vocabulary Review

1. binomial nomenclature
2. phylum
3. cladistics
4. taxonomy
5. cladogram

Understanding Key Concepts

6. D	8. D	10. A
7. B	9. C	11. C

Constructed Response

12. Aristotle's system used a small number of organisms and criteria that did not reveal phylogenetic relationships. Linnaeus's: large numbers of organisms based on physical similarities that reflect relationships

13. Classification systems change to reflect new information. The changes improve understanding about phylogeny, but can cause problems when researchers are unaware of the revision.

14. Kingdom Fungi; it is eukaryotic, multicellular, not autotrophic, and has cell walls.

Thinking Critically

15. Libraries—by type and content similarities, not by chronology. Classification of organisms is based on both similarities and evolutionary history, a factor that implies chronology.

16. 1. taxonomy; 2. kingdoms; 3. binomial nomenclature; 4. phyla; 5. divisions

17. Taxa will vary. They may choose to learn about phylum chordata, so they would tell about the five classes. The cladogram should show example characteristics separating each class.

464

Vocabulary Review

Review the Chapter 17 vocabulary words listed in the Study Guide on page 463. Match the words with the definitions below.

1. modern classification system using a two-word name

2. large taxon that contains similar classes

3. biological system of classification based on phylogeny

4. branch of biology that groups and names organisms based on their characteristics

5. branching diagram showing derived traits

Understanding Key Concepts

6. Which taxon contains the others?
   A. family
   B. species
   C. order
   D. phylum

7. Unlike a pedigree, a cladogram _____.
   A. shows ancestry
   B. shows hypothesized phylogeny
   C. indicates ancestry from two parents
   D. explains relationships

8. Which of the following pairs of terms are most closely related?
   A. Linnaeus—DNA analysis
   B. Aristotle—binomial nomenclature
   C. protist—prokaryote
   D. taxonomy—classification

9. Linnaeus based most of his classification system on _____.
   A. cell organelles
   B. biochemical comparisons
   C. structural comparisons
   D. embryology

10. A group of prokaryotes that often live in extreme environments is the _____.
    A. archaebacteria
    B. protists
    C. eubacteria
    D. fungi

---

11. Which of the following describes the organism shown to the right?
    A. unicellular consumer
    B. unicellular producer
    C. multicellular consumer
    D. multicellular producer

Constructed Response

12. **Open Ended** Explain why Linnaeus's system of classification is more useful than Aristotle's.

13. **Open Ended** Explain why classification systems continue to be updated with newer versions. What improvements and problems do such updates cause?

14. **Open Ended** You find an unusual organism growing on the bark of a dying tree. Under a microscope, you observe that its cells are eukaryotic, have cell walls, and do not contain chloroplasts. Into what kingdom would you classify this organism? Explain your decision.

Thinking Critically

15. **Compare and Contrast** Compare the classification system of your school library with that of organisms.

16. **Concept Map** Complete the concept map by using the following vocabulary terms: divisions, taxonomy, kingdoms, binomial nomenclature, phyla.

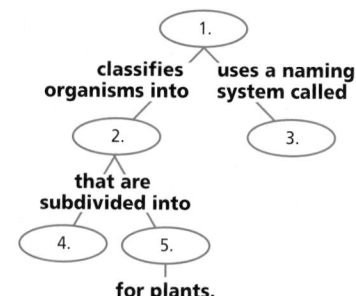

classifies organisms into | uses a naming system called

that are subdivided into

for plants.

 in.bdol.glencoe.com/chapter_test

RUBRIC

Evaluating Open-Ended Questions
Open-ended assessment questions are graded by using a multilevel rubric that guides you in assessing a student's knowledge of a particular concept. The following rubric is a sample scoring device.

17. REAL WORLD BIOCHALLENGE Classification is a system that is both rich and orderly. It lends itself to the Internet. Visit in.bdol.glencoe.com to find out about the classification of a taxon of your choice. What are the major taxa within the one you chose? Create a poster or other illustration displaying a cladogram of your findings. Present your illustration to the class. Explain the characteristics at the nodes.

End-of-Course Assessment Practice

All questions aligned and verified by The Princeton Review

Part 1 Multiple Choice

Use the table below to answer questions 18–20.

Classification of Representative Mammals			
Kingdom	Animalia	Animalia	Animalia
Phylum	Chordata	Chordata	Chordata
Class	Mammalia	Mammalia	Mammalia
Order	Cetacea	Carnivora	Carnivora
Family	Mysticeti	Mustelidae	Felidae
Genus	*Balenopora*	*Mustela*	*Felis*
Species	*B. physalus*	*M. furo*	*F. catus*
Common Name	Blue Whale	Ferret	Domestic cat

18. Which animal is least related to the others?
   A. domestic cat
   B. blue whale
   C. ferret
   D. all equally related

19. At which level does the ferret diverge from the blue whale?
   A. species
   B. genus
   C. family
   D. order

20. At which level does the ferret diverge from the domestic cat?
   A. species
   B. genus
   C. family
   D. order

21. Which of the following is not a species?
   A. *H. sapiens*
   B. *Quercus alba*
   C. bluebird
   D. *M. polyglottis*

Part 2 Open Ended/Grid In

Record your answers on your answer document.

24. Open Ended From the key and the photographs above, identify traits that indicate dragonflies and damselflies may have evolved from a common ancestor.

25. Open Ended What does a dichotomous key tell about an organism? What kinds of information does it not give?

Key	
1A	Front and hind wings similar in size and shape, and folded parallel to the body when at rest . . . . damselflies
1B	Hind wings wider than front wings near base, and extended on either side of the body when at rest . . . . dragonflies

Study the dichotomous key and answer questions 22 and 23.

22. The insect on the right is a damselfly because it has _____.
   A. wings that are opaque
   B. wings folded at rest
   C. smaller eyes
   D. wings not similar in size

23. The insect on the left is a dragonfly because it has _____.
   A. wings that are opaque
   B. wings folded at rest
   C. larger eyes
   D. wings not similar in size

End-of-Course Assessment Practice

18. B
19. D
20. C
21. C
22. B
23. D
24. two pairs of wings located on the same body segment; wings transparent with clearly defined veins; long, thin body; Accept any reasonable answers.
25. A dichotomous key gives paired statements that identify the characteristics of organisms, but it does not give evolutionary history directly.

FAST FILE

Answer Sheet A practice answer sheet can be found on p. 127 of *Unit 5 FAST FILE Resources.*

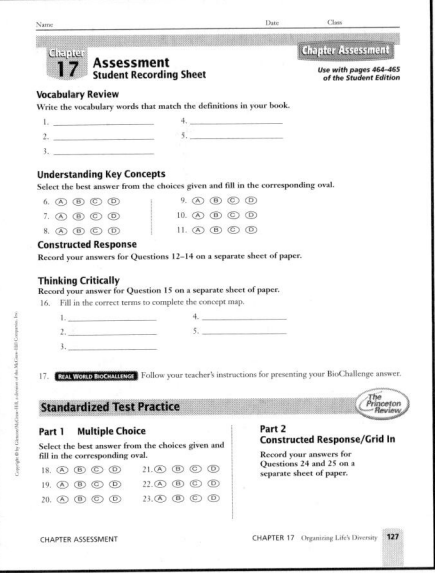

in.bdol.glencoe.com/standardized_test

RUBRIC

SCORE	CRITERIA
4	A correct solution that is supported by well-developed, accurate explanations.
3	A generally correct solution, but may contain minor flaws in reasoning.

SCORE	CRITERIA
2	A partially correct interpretation and/or solution to the problem.
1	A correct solution with no supporting evidence or explanation.
0	An incorrect solution or no solution is given.

Indiana Academic Standards

Pages 464–465: B.1.35

Prepare

Short on Time?

This BioDigest can be used as an overview of the concepts of evolution and classification. If time is limited, you may wish to use this unit summary to teach these concepts in place of the chapters in the change through time unit.

Key Concepts

Students are introduced to the formation of Earth and the origins of life. They learn about the theory of evolution by natural selection and the classification of diverse organisms.

1 Focus

Bellringer

Before beginning the lesson, pass around iron, nickel, and silica sand samples. Ask students to infer why Earth's core contains iron and nickel, and the crust contains silicon and oxygen. Dense elements descended into Earth's core, and lighter materials rose to the crust. **L1**

Indiana Academic Standards

Pages 466–467: B.1.13, B.1.32, B.1.33, B.2.1

Change Through Time

Scientists propose that about five billion years ago Earth was extremely hot. As Earth slowly cooled, water vapor in its atmosphere condensed and fell as rain, forming today's oceans. Life appeared in these oceans betwe 3.9 and 3.4 billion years ago. Since then, millions of species have evolved and then become extinct.

Geologic Time Scale

The four divisions of the geologic time scale span about 4.6 billion years of Earth's history.

The Precambrian

The Precambrian encompasses approximately the first four billion years of the scale. Fossils of prokaryotic cells appear in rocks dated 3.4 billion years old. By the end of the Precambrian, the first eukaryotic cells had evolved.

The Paleozoic Era

The following 300 million years make up the Paleozoic Era. Many plant groups such as ferns and conifers appeared. Animal groups such as worms, insects, fishes, and reptiles evolved.

The Mesozoic Era

From 248 million years ago to 65 million years ago, the Mesozoic Era, reptiles diversified, and mammals and flowering plants evolved. The Mesozoic, the Age of Dinosaurs, ended with a rapid extinction of the dinosaurs.

The Cenozoic Era

The current Cenozoic Era, which has encompassed the previous 65 million years, is often referred to as the Age of Mammals. Primates, including humans, evolved during this era.

The geologic time scale illustrates major events that have occurred during Earth's 4.6-billion-year history. Each era is subdivided into smaller time spans called periods.

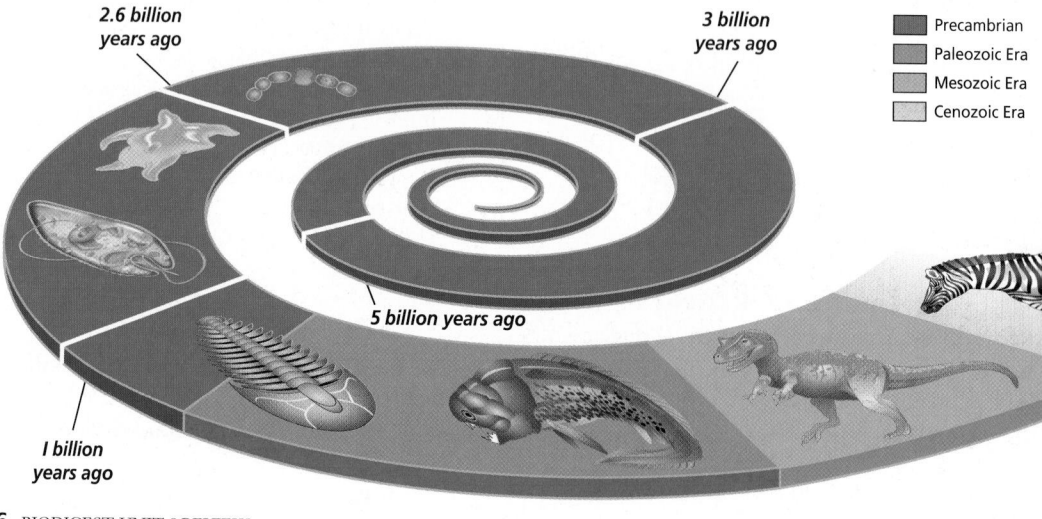

2.6 billion years ago

3 billion years ago

5 billion years ago

1 billion years ago

- Precambrian
- Paleozoic Era
- Mesozoic Era
- Cenozoic Era

RESOURCE MANAGER

Unit 5 FAST FILE Resources
Reinforcement and Study Guide in English, pp. 129–130
Reinforcement and Study Guide in Spanish, pp. 131–132
Student Recording Sheet, p. 133

Origin of Life Theories

People once thought that life was able to arise spontaneously from nonliving material. Two scientists, Francesco Redi and Louis Pasteur, designed controlled experiments to try to disprove spontaneous generation. Their experiments convinced scientists to accept the theory of biogenesis—that life comes only from preexisting life.

Modern Ideas About the Origin of Life

Scientific evidence supports the hypothesis that small organic molecules formed from substances present in Earth's early atmosphere and oceans. At some point, nucleic acids must have formed. Then, clusters of organic molecules might have formed protocells that may have evolved into the first true cells.

Louis Pasteur disproved the idea of spontaneous generation by conducting experiments using broth in swan-necked flasks like this one.

Heterotrophic, anaerobic prokaryotes were probably the earliest organisms to live on Earth. Chemosynthetic prokaryotes evolved over time, followed by oxygen-producing photosynthetic prokaryotes. As the amount of oxygen in the atmosphere increased, aerobically respiring eukaryotes probably evolved.

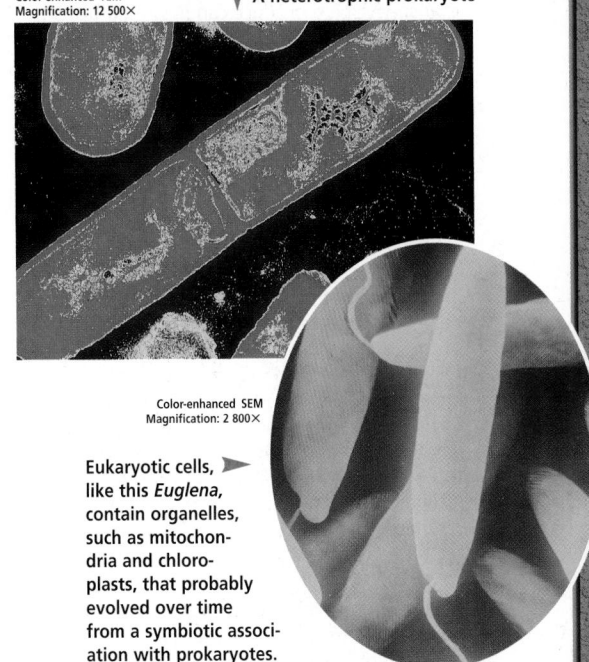

Color-enhanced TEM
Magnification: 12 500×

▼ A heterotrophic prokaryote

Color-enhanced SEM
Magnification: 2 800×

Eukaryotic cells, ▶ like this *Euglena*, contain organelles, such as mitochondria and chloroplasts, that probably evolved over time from a symbiotic association with prokaryotes.

FOCUS ON HISTORY

Pioneers

Two scientists, Stanley Miller and Harold Urey, pioneered work about the origin of Earth's life. Their experiments showed that small molecules can form complex organic materials under conditions that may have existed on early Earth. Other scientists demonstrated how these complex chemicals could form protocells, which are large, organized structures that carry out some activities associated with life, such as growth and division.

The American biologist Lynn Margulis proposed the endosymbiont theory. This theory suggests that cell organelles, such as mitochondria and chloroplasts, may have evolved when small prokaryotes entered larger prokaryotes and began to live symbiotically inside these larger cells.

Lynn Margulis

---

2 Teach

Quick Demo

The Endosymbiont Theory Set up microscopes with slides of *Euglena* showing chloroplasts. Then, use the slides and photos on this page to explain Lynn Margulis's endosymbiont theory.

Activity

Field Trip Arrange a class trip to a local natural history museum where the students can see much of the material discussed in this unit. Ask students to describe how the fossils they observe relate to present-day species. **L2**

Biology Journal

Patterns of Evolution Have students describe the three patterns of evolution using examples other than those presented in the text. Interested students can create posters to share their examples with the rest of the class. **L2**

467

CHALLENGE ACTIVITY

Research During Darwin's expedition on the *Beagle*, he observed the characteristics of various organisms. He noted variations of characteristics of similar species from place to place that eventually led him to believe that evolution had occurred. Have students research the Galápagos finches and tortoises and compare these two examples of divergent evolution. **L3**

Activity

Microscopic Fossils Have students look at slides of diatomaceous earth. Point out that the shells they observe are fossils of protists that lived thousands of years ago. **L1** **ELL**

Inquiry

Discussion Have students make a collection of fossils from the local area. Ask them to identify each type of fossil and the organism that was fossilized and research additional information. **L2**

Biology Journal

Humans of the Future Have students pretend to travel 3000 years into the future. They should describe in their journals what humans look like in the future. Students should also describe why humans look this way, including their ideas about evolution. **L2**

Evidence of Evolution

Charles Darwin and Alfred Wallace proposed natural selection as a mechanism of evolution. Natural selection occurs because all organisms compete for mates, food, space, and other resources. Such competition favors the survival of individuals with variations that help them compete successfully in a specific environment. Individuals that survive to reproduce can pass their traits to the next generation.

Fossil Evidence

The fossil record provides a record of life on Earth and contains evidence for evolution. Fossils come in many forms, such as imprints, the burrow of a worm, or a mineralized bone. By studying fossils, scientists learn how organisms have changed over time.

Scientists use relative and radiometric dating methods to determine the age of fossils and rocks. Relative dating assumes that in undisturbed layers of rock, the deepest rock layers contain the oldest fossils. Radiometric dating analysis compares the known half-lives of radioactive isotopes to a ratio of the amount of radioactive isotope originally in a rock with the amount of the isotope in the rock today. Fossils over 50 000 years old cannot be radiometrically dated, so the rock around them is dated.

Additional Evidence

Similar anatomical structures, called homologous structures, in different organisms might indicate possible shared ancestry. For example, both vertebrate limbs and developmental stages show how vertebrates might be related. In addition, similarities among the nucleic acid sequences of species provide evidence for evolution. Direct evidence for evolution has been observed in the laboratory when species of bacteria have developed resistance to antibiotics.

Mechanics of Evolution

Evolution occurs when a population's genetic equilibrium changes. Mutations, genetic drift, and migration may slightly disrupt the genetic equilibrium of large populations, but they will greatly alter that of small populations. Natural selection affects the genetic equilibrium of all populations.

Three Patterns of Evolution

Three patterns of natural selection lead to speciation. Stabilizing selection favors the survival of a population's average individuals for a feature. Directional selection naturally selects for an extreme feature. Disruptive selection eventually produces two populations, each with one of a feature's extreme characteristics.

Primate Evolution

Primates are a grouping of mammals with adaptations such as binocular vision, opposable thumbs, and mobile skeletal joints. These adaptations help arboreal animals survive in forest trees, where all primates may have originally lived and where most primates still live.

There are two categories of primates: the strepsirrhines, including lemurs and aye-ayes, and the haplorhines, including humans, apes, tarsiers, and monkeys. Monkeys are subdivided further into two groups that are called Old World monkeys and New World monkeys.

Primates first appear in the fossil record in the Cenozoic Era. Fossils indicate that increasing brain size and bipedal locomotion are the two major trends in primate evolution.

The bones that make up a penguin's wings are homologous to those that form the wings of an albatross. The forelimb bones of four-legged vertebrates are also homologous.

CHALLENGE ACTIVITY

Rabbit Adaptations Have students imagine they are studying a rabbit population in a wooded area. After observing a specific area, they find that most of the rabbits are brown. Returning to the same area in twenty years, they find that most of the rabbits are white. What could have happened? What factors could have led to this? Have students write a report discussing their hypotheses. Ask for student volunteers to share their ideas. **L3**

Unlike most Old World monkeys, New World monkeys, such as this howler monkey, have prehensile tails that are used as a fifth limb.

Human Ancestry

Fossils of possible human ancestors called *Australopithecines* were discovered in Africa and date from approximately 4 million years ago. They show that these ancestors were bipedal and climbed trees.

After examining more recently discovered hominid fossils, paleoanthropologists suggest that the increasing efficiency of bipedal locomotion, the decreasing size of jaws and teeth, and increasing brain size were directions of human evolution.

The appearance of both the genus *Homo* and stone tools coincides in the fossil record about 2.5 million years ago. The use of fire, tools, language, and ceremonies developed in later *Homo* species.

Organizing Life's Diversity

Biologists use a classification system to study and communicate about both the millions of species living on Earth today and the many extinct species represented by fossils. Although Aristotle produced the first system of classification, Linnaeus developed the basic structure of the present-day classification system. Linnaeus also developed a naming system, termed binomial nomenclature, that is still used today.

Today's classification uses a hierarchy of taxa to classify organisms. From largest to smallest, this hierarchy is kingdom, phylum or division, class, order, family, genus, and species. The most useful systems of classification show evolutionary relationships among species.

Six Kingdoms of Classification

Species are classified into one of six kingdoms. Prokaryotes belong to Kingdom Archaebacteria or Kingdom Eubacteria. Kingdom Protista contains the eukaryotes that lack complex organ systems and live in moist environments. Kingdom Fungi includes heterotrophic eukaryotes that absorb nutrients. Multicellular autotrophs with complex organ systems are placed in Kingdom Plantae. Kingdom Animalia includes multicellular heterotrophs.

FOCUS ON ADAPTATIONS

Adaptive Radiation in Galápagos Finches

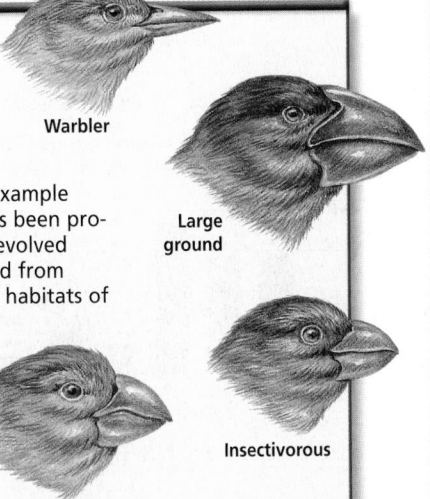

Warbler

Tool-using

Large ground

The finches in the Galápagos Islands are an example of the rapid development of a species. It has been proposed that the 13 species of Galápagos finches evolved from one ancestral species of finches that arrived from South America and colonized the newly formed habitats of these volcanic islands.

The adaptive radiation of finch species occurred as the original finch population adapted to the different niches found in the islands. The pressures of natural selection produced different species, each with their own feeding and habitat adaptations. Six species are shown here.

Cactus ground

Insectivorous

Vegetarian

469

3 Assess

 Indiana Academic Standards

Pages 468–469: B.1.30, B.1.31, B.1.32, B.1.35, B.1.36, B.2.2

This page contains practice questions in the various formats that can be found on the most frequently given standardized tests.

Part 1 Multiple Choice

1. B
2. C
3. D
4. A
5. C
6. D
7. A

FAST FILE

Answer Sheet A practice answer sheet can be found on p. 133 of *Unit 5 FAST FILE Resources.*

Unit 5 Review Standardized Test Practice

End-of-Course Assessment Practice

The assessed Indiana standard appears next to the question.

TEST-TAKING TIP

Prepare for the Test

Find out what the conditions will be for taking the test. Is it timed? Will you be allowed a break? Know these things in advance so that you can practice taking tests under the same conditions.

Part 1 Multiple Choice

1. Which dating method relies on the position of rock layers?
   A. radiometric
   B. relative
   C. absolute
   D. morphology

2. Which of the following was proposed by Charles Darwin?
   B.2.3
   A. endosymbiont hypothesis
   B. biogenesis
   C. natural selection
   D. experimentation

3. Multicellular heterotrophs without cell walls are placed in Kingdom _____.
   A. Protista
   B. Fungi
   C. Plantae
   D. Animalia

Use the following graph to answer questions 4–6.

Leaf Lengths in a Maple Tree Population

4. What was the range of leaf lengths?
   A. 14 cm
   B. 8–22 cm
   C. 20–100 cm
   D. 10–14 cm

5. Which leaf length occurred most often?
   A. 8 cm
   B. 12 cm
   C. 14 cm
   D. 6 cm

6. What type of evolutionary pattern does the graph most closely match?
   A. artificial selection
   B. stabilizing selection
   C. disruptive evolution
   D. directional evolution

Use the following table to help you answer questions 7 and 8.

Some Types of Fossils	
Fossil Type	**Description**
Trace fossil	Structure in sediment that is indirect evidence of an organism
Mold	Empty space in rock that forms when a shell or other part of an organism decays or dissolves
Cast	Minerals fill a mold to make a replica.
Petrified/permineralized fossils	Minerals replace hard parts or fill pores.
Preserved in amber or frozen in permafrost	Original soft parts of organisms often preserved

7. An empty space in a limestone that has the shape of a clam shell is a _____.
   A. mold
   B. cast
   C. trace fossil
   D. petrified fossil

8. A mark on the surface of a layer of sedimentary rock that was made by a trilobite resting on the bottom of the sea is a _____.
   A. mold
   B. cast
   C. trace fossil
   D. fossil in amber

Read the following paragraph and use the diagram to answer questions 9 and 10.

The diagram below represents a cross section of undisturbed rock layers and the species of fossils found in each layer. Use the diagram to answer the following questions.

A	Species 4 & 5
B	Species 3 & 4
C	Species 1 & 2 & 3
D	Species 1 & 2
	Species 1

9. Which environment appears to be most diverse?
  A. environment A
  B. environment B
  C. environment C
  D. environment D

10. Which species survived the longest in this area?
  A. species 5
  B. species 3
  C. species 2
  D. species 1

Use the following diagram to answer questions 11–13.

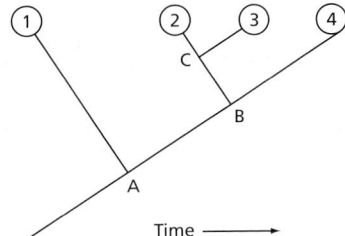

11. Which organism's ancestors diverged first?
  A. 1 **C.** 3
  B. 2 **D.** 4

12. Which organism has traits A and B, but not C?
  A. 1 **C.** 3
  B. 2 **D.** 4

13. Which organism most recently diverged?
  A. 1 **C.** 3
  B. 2 **D.** 4

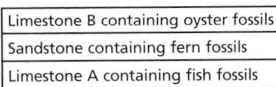 **Constructed Response/Grid In**

Record your answers on your answer document.

14. Open Ended Describe the types of organisms that existed in the Mesozoic Era. In the Cenozoic Era.

15. Open Ended Explain how natural selection might be a mechanism of evolution.

16. Open Ended Why do biologists classify organisms?

The following diagram illustrates a cross section through a sequence of rock units. Use the diagram to answer questions 17 and 18.

Limestone B containing oyster fossils
Sandstone containing fern fossils
Limestone A containing fish fossils

17. Open Ended If the sequence is undisturbed, which rock layer is the oldest? Which is the youngest? Explain your answer.

18. Open Ended Describe the environments in which the rock layers were deposited. Explain the evidence for your answer.

 in.bdol.glencoe.com/standardized_test   UNIT 5 STANDARDIZED TEST PRACTICE **471**

8. C	11. A
9. C	12. D
10. D	13. D

Part 2 Constructed Response/Grid In

14. Reptiles diversified, and mammals and flowering plants evolved in the Mesozoic Era. Primates evolved in the Cenozoic Era and mammals and flowering plants diversified.

15. When natural selection occurs, organisms pass environmentally beneficial traits to their offspring. After a long period of time, a population consists of different organisms.

16. to study and communicate about species

17. Limestone A; Limestone B; The oldest layer is on the bottom and the youngest layer is on the top.

18. Both limestone layers, which contained fossils of marine animals, showed that the location was covered with water. The middle layer of sandstone contains a fern fossil, which grows on land.

RUBRIC

For more help evaluating open-ended assessment questions, see the rubric on p. 9T.

Unit 6

Viruses, Bacteria, Protists, and Fungi

Unit Overview

Chapter 18 introduces students to the forms and characteristics of viruses and to the structures, ecology, and importance of bacteria. **Chapter 19** presents the diversity and classification of protists. **Chapter 20** encourages students to learn about the characteristics and diversity of fungi.

Introducing the Unit

Organize students into groups. Ask each group to estimate how many species live on Earth and to explain their reasoning. To emphasize the diversity of life on Earth, ask students to list all the living things that they see in the photo. **L1**

WebQuest

A WebQuest is an inquiry-based online project in which all information used by students is obtained from the Web. Students evaluate the information to complete the activity. Access the Unit 6 WebQuest at **in.bdol.glencoe.com/webquest**

 Indiana Academic Standards

Pages 472–473: B.1.43

472

History & Biology

Unit 6

| 1500 | 1600 | 1700 |

1761 • Wolfgang Amadeus M[...] composes his first musi[...] piece at age 6.

• **1546** Girolamo Fracastoro theorizes that diseases are caused by invisible organisms.

Viruses, Bacteria, Protists, and Fungi

Indiana Standards
The following standards are covered in Unit 6: B.1.2, B.1.3, B.1.8, B.1.9, B.1.11, B.1.12, B.1.31, B.1.33, B.1.35, B.1.40, B.1.43, B.1.44, B.1.45

What You'll Learn

Chapter 18
Viruses and Bacteria

Chapter 19
Protists

Chapter 20
Fungi

Unit 6 Review
BioDigest & Standardized Test Practice

Why It's Important

Although the world we encounter is largely limited to what we can see, that representation is misleading. Even though the world is filled with plants and animals that are easily distinguishable, much of the real diversity lies in the things we cannot see. We rely on bacteria and fungi to act as decomposers that keep nutrients cycling through the food chain. In addition to bacteria, nonliving things such as viruses act as disease agents on both plants and animals.

> **Understanding the Photo ▶**
> These *Coprinus* mushrooms grow in thick clumps on the forest floor. The mushrooms are the reproductive forms of the fungus, which lives mostly underground and gets nutrition by decomposing the organisms that fall to the forest floor.

472   in.bdol.glencoe.com/webquest

Time Line

Research Have students select an event from the time line above. Using their own knowledge, have them speculate on how the discovery impacted society as a whole. Have students research as necessary to learn what other advances and benefits resulted from the initial discovery. Have them present their findings to the class. **L2**

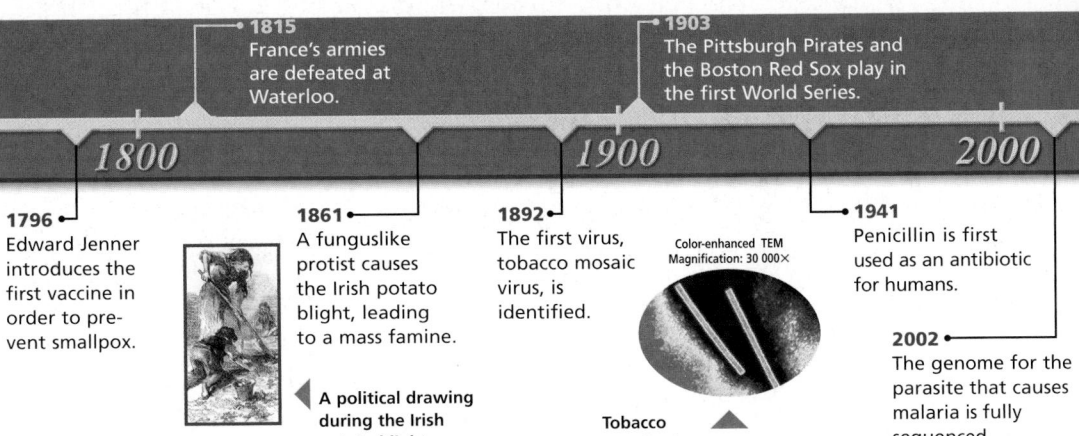

1815
France's armies are defeated at Waterloo.

1903
The Pittsburgh Pirates and the Boston Red Sox play in the first World Series.

1800   1900   2000

1796
Edward Jenner introduces the first vaccine in order to prevent smallpox.

A political drawing during the Irish potato blight

1861
A funguslike protist causes the Irish potato blight, leading to a mass famine.

1892
The first virus, tobacco mosaic virus, is identified.

Color-enhanced TEM
Magnification: 30 000×

Tobacco mosaic virus

1941
Penicillin is first used as an antibiotic for humans.

2002
The genome for the parasite that causes malaria is fully sequenced.

Advance Materials Planning

The following materials may need to be ordered a few weeks in advance of the planned activity.

Chapter 18

■ **MiniLab** (p. 490) prepared slides of cocci, bacilli, and spirilla

■ **BioLab** (p. 496) sterile agar plates, bacterial cultures

Chapter 19

■ **MiniLab** (p. 506) *Paramecium* samples

■ **BioLab** (p. 522) *Paramecium*, *Euglena* samples, methyl cellulose

Chapter 20

■ **MiniLab** (p. 538) mushrooms from a grocery store

■ **BioLab** (p. 544) bromothymol blue solution, yeast, white corn syrup

473

Unit Projects

Make a Poster
Visual-Spatial Design and produce a poster about disease-causing organisms. **L1** **ELL**

Display
Visual-Spatial Make a bulletin board from news articles about beneficial microbes. **L1** **ELL**

Using the Library
Intrapersonal Find out about state and federal laws that regulate food handlers. Report on these laws and how they help to prevent food contamination. **L3**

Section Objectives	National Science Standards	State/Local Standards	Advanced Lab and Demo Planning
Section 18.1 2 sessions, 1/2 block 1. **Identify** the different kinds of viruses and their structures. 2. **Compare** and contrast the replication cycles of viruses.	UCP.1, UCP.2, UCP.3; A.1, A.2; C.4; F.1, F.5, F.6; G.1–3	**Indiana Standards** B.1.43	**Student Labs:** MiniLab 18.1, p. 476 Problem-Solving Lab 18.1, p. 480 **Teacher Demonstration:** Quick Demo, p. 477: 2 nuts, bolt, 3 14-cm pieces of #22 gauge wire
Section 18.2 3 sessions, 1 1/2 blocks 3. **Compare** the types of prokaryotes. 4. **Explain** the characteristics and adaptations of bacteria. 5. **Evaluate** the economic importance of bacteria.	UCP.1, UCP.2, UCP.3; A.1, A.2; C.3, C.4, C.5, C.6; F.1, F.5; G.1, G.3	**Indiana Standards** B.1.2, B.1.3, B.1.8, B.1.12, B.1.33, B.1.36, B.1.43	**Student Labs:** Additional Lab, p. 488: screw-top test tubes; liquid growth medium composed of 445 mL distilled water, 50 mL vinegar, 4 drops Schultz liquid plant food, 0.5 g Accent seasoning, baking soda; 60-watt incandescent lightbulbs; 4 soil samples MiniLab 18.2, p. 490: bacteria slides, microscope Problem-Solving Lab 18.2, p. 492 Design Your Own BioLab, p. 496: See materials below. **Teacher Demonstration:** Quick Demo, p. 493: Swiss cheese, pickles, vinegar, sauerkraut, yogurt, sour cream
End of Chapter Assessment **Student Edition** **Study Guide,** p. 499 **Content Assessment,** pp. 500–501		**Indiana Standards** B.1.2, B.1.8, B.1.9, B.1.40, B.1.43	**Student Lab:** Design Your Own BioLab, p. 496: cultures of bacteria, sterile nutrient agar petri dishes, antibiotic disks, sterile disks of blank filter paper, marking pen, long-handled cotton swabs, forceps, 37°C incubator, metric ruler

Key to Teaching Strategies

L1 Level 1 activities should be appropriate for students with learning difficulties.

L2 Level 2 activities should be within the ability range of all students.

L3 Level 3 activities are designed for above-average students.

ELL ELL activities should be within the ability range of English Language Learners.

COOP LEARN Cooperative Learning activities are designed for small group work.

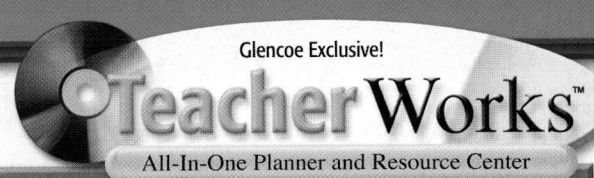

Glencoe Exclusive!

Teacher Works™
All-In-One Planner and Resource Center

Reproducible Masters and Transparencies

Technology

Unit 6 FAST FILE Resources
 MiniLab Worksheet, p. 3
 Reinforcement and Study Guide in English,
  pp. 7–8
 Reinforcement and Study Guide in Spanish,
  pp. 11–12
 Concept Mapping, p. 15
 Transparency Worksheets, pp. 17, 19–22, 25–26
**Reading Essentials for Biology,
 Section 18.1**
Laboratory Manual, pp. 109–112
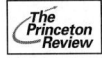 **Section Focus Transparency 43**

 Basic Concepts Transparencies 25–26

 Reteaching Skills Transparency 27

 Interactive Chalkboard CD-ROM: Section 18.1 Presentation ▮
 TeacherWorks™ **CD-ROM** ▮
MP3 **Guided Reading Audio Summaries MP3**
 Virtual Labs CD-ROM
  Virtual Lab: Vaccines in Action

Unit 6 FAST FILE Resources
 MiniLab Worksheet, p. 4
 BioLab Worksheet, pp. 5–6
 Reinforcement and Study Guide in English,
  pp. 9–10
 Reinforcement and Study Guide in Spanish,
  pp. 13–14
 Critical Thinking/Problem Solving, p. 16
 Transparency Worksheets, pp. 18, 23–24, 27–28
**Reading Essentials for Biology,
 Section 18.2**
Laboratory Manual, pp. 113–116
 Inside Story Poster
 Section Focus Transparency 44

 Basic Concepts Transparency 27

 Reteaching Skills Transparency 28

 Interactive Chalkboard CD-ROM: Section 18.2 Presentation ▮
 TeacherWorks™ **CD-ROM** ▮
MP3 **Guided Reading Audio Summaries MP3**

Unit 6 Fast File Resources
 Chapter Assessment, pp. 29–34
 Student Recording Sheet, p. 35

The Princeton Review **Reviewing Biology,** pp. 35–36

 Interactive Chalkboard: ▮
  Chapter 18 Assessment
 **MindJogger Videoquizzes
  DVD/VHS**
 **ExamView® Pro Test Bank
  CD-ROM**
 TeacherWorks™ **CD-ROM** ▮
 Succeeding on National Standards CD-ROM

🖥 in.bdol.glencoe.com
/self_check_quiz
/vocabulary_puzzlemaker
/chapter_test
/standardized_test

▮ Indicates materials created specifically for Indiana.

Chapter 18

Short on Time?

BIODIGEST The BioDigest at the end of this unit can be used as a(n):

- preview to introduce important unit concepts.
- overview if time does not permit teaching the entire chapter.
- review of key unit concepts.

Understanding the Photo

Be sure to refer to this photo when students encounter the phage shape and components of viruses in Figure 18.1. Point out the virus structures—the capsid and the tail—that are distinguishable.

PowerPoint® Presentations

This CD-ROM is an editable Microsoft® PowerPoint® presentation that includes:

- Section presentations
- Section checks
- Image bank
- Hot links to Biology Online
- All transparencies

Viruses and Bacteria

Color-enhanced SEM Magnification 90 000×

What You'll Learn

- You will identify the structures and characteristics of viruses and bacteria.
- You will explain how viruses and bacteria reproduce.
- You will recognize the medical and economic importance of viruses and bacteria.

Why It's Important

Viruses and bacteria are important because many cause diseases in plants and animals. Bacteria play an important role in creating foods and drugs, as well as helping to recycle nutrients.

Understanding ▶ the Photo

Viruses cannot function without a host. This photo, taken with an electron microscope, shows a group of viruses, called phages, infecting an *E. coli* bacterium. The viruses have attached themselves to the outside of the bacterium and are injecting it with their nucleic acid.

Biology Online

Visit in.bdol.glencoe.com to
- study the entire chapter online
- access Web Links for more information and activities on viruses and bacteria
- review content with the Interactive Tutor and self-check quizzes

474

Two-Minute Chapter Launcher

Demo Using a microprojector with a prepared, stained slide of the three shapes of bacteria, have students observe the bacteria under high power or show the students an electronic picture of the three shapes of bacteria.

Have them compare their relative sizes with those of cells they have looked at in Chapter 7. Cells are usually 50 to 100 times bigger. Also have them identify the three common shapes of bacteria. spheres, rods and spirals

Section 18.1

Viruses

Indiana Standards Standard B.1.43 Understand that and describe how organisms are influenced by a particular combination of living and nonliving components of the environment.

Getting a Vaccination

Using Prior Knowledge As a child, you probably received several vaccines. Children are regularly vaccinated against diseases that could otherwise be life threatening. Vaccines are injections of particles of viruses or bacteria that provide the human body with a defense against disease. Thanks to vaccines, many devastating diseases of the past are now rarely encountered.

Research *Make a list of the vaccines you received as a child. Next to each vaccine, list the disease that the vaccine prevents and what microorganism causes the disease.*

Children are vaccinated against several diseases.

SECTION PREVIEW

Objectives

Identify the different kinds of viruses and their structures.

Compare and contrast the replication cycles of viruses.

Review Vocabulary

nucleic acid: a complex macromolecule, either RNA or DNA, that stores genetic information (p. 163)

New Vocabulary

virus
host cell
bacteriophage
capsid
lytic cycle
lysogenic cycle
provirus
retrovirus
reverse transcriptase
prion
viroid

What is a virus?

You've probably had the flu—influenza—at some time during your life. Nonliving particles called viruses cause influenza. **Viruses** are composed of nucleic acids enclosed in a protein coat and are smaller than the smallest bacterium. To appreciate how very tiny viruses are, try the *MiniLab* on the next page.

Most biologists consider viruses to be nonliving because they don't exhibit all the criteria for life. They don't carry out respiration, grow, or develop. All viruses can do is replicate—make copies of themselves—and they can't even do that without the help of living cells. A cell in which a virus replicates is called the **host cell.**

Because they are nonliving, viruses were not named in the same way as organisms. Viruses, such as rabies viruses and polioviruses, were named after the diseases they cause. Other viruses were named for the organ or tissue they infect. For example, scientists first found the adenovirus (uh DEN uh vi ruhs), which is one cause of the common cold, in adenoid tissue between the back of the throat and the nasal cavity.

Today, most viruses are given a genus name ending in the word "virus" and a species name. However, sometimes scientists use code numbers to distinguish among similar viruses that infect the same host. For example, seven similar-looking viruses that infect the common intestinal bacteria, *Escherichia coli*, have the code numbers T1 through T7 (*T* stands for "Type"). A virus that infects a bacterium is called a **bacteriophage** (bak TIHR ee uh fayj), or phage for short.

18.1 VIRUSES **475**

1 Focus

INTERACTIVE CHALKBOARD
PowerPoint® Presentations

Bellringer
Section Focus Transparency 43

Transparency **43** RNA and DNA in Viruses

SECTION FOCUS
Use with Chapter 18, Section 18.1

❶ How is the structure of viral RNA similar to that of viral DNA?
❷ How do the two structures differ?

BIOLOGY: The Dynamics of Life

SECTION FOCUS TRANSPARENCIES

Using Prior Knowledge

Research Students' list of vaccines will likely include DPT vaccine (Diphtheria, Pertussis, Tetanus), Polio, Hepatitis A and Hepatitis B, Hib or *Haemophilus influenza*, MMR, (Measles, Mumps and Rubella) and possibly Chicken Pox. Some students may not be vaccinated for religious reasons.

RESOURCE MANAGER

Unit 6 *FAST FILE* **Resources**
  MiniLab Worksheet, p. 3
  Reinforcement and Study Guide in English, pp. 7–8
  Reinforcement and Study Guide in Spanish, pp. 11–12
  Concept Mapping, p. 15
  Transparency Worksheets, pp. 17, 19–22, 25–26

Reading Essentials for Biology, Section 18.1
Laboratory Manual, pp. 109–112
Section Focus Transparency 43
Basic Concepts Transparencies 25–26
Reteaching Skills Transparency 27

Indiana Academic Standards

Pages 474–475: B.1.43

MiniLab 18.1

Purpose

Students will determine the size of a virus in a TEM photo.

Process Skills

measure in SI, use numbers, collect data

Teaching Strategies

■ Remind students that viruses vary in size, and they will determine the size of only one virus.

■ Use the overhead projector to preview this lab. Using a clear ruler helps to demonstrate what to measure.

■ Use microbiology textbooks for other viruses to measure or order viral electron micrographs from biological supply houses.

■ Have students use calculators.

Expected Results

Students should calculate the size of the poliovirus as follows.

$$\frac{69 \text{ mm}}{5 \text{ mm}} = \frac{0.4 \text{ μm}}{(x)} = 0.029 \text{ μm}$$

Analysis

1. The virus's diameter measures 0.029 μm, less than the 0.2 μm light microscope limit.
2. 3448 viruses (100 μm divided by 0.029 μm)

Assessment

Portfolio Have students look up the size of six viruses on **in.bdol.glencoe.com** and make a scale drawing that shows their relative sizes. Use the Performance Task Assessment List for Scientific Drawing in **PASC**, p. 127. **L2**

MiniLab 18.1

Measure in SI

Measuring a Virus Can you use a light microscope to view a virus? Find out by measuring the size of a polio virus in the photo below and then comparing it to 0.2 μm, the size limit for viewing objects with a light microscope.

Color-enhanced TEM Magnification: 180 000×

Reference line

Procedure

1 Copy the data table below.

Data Table

Values to Measure and Calculate	Measurement
Length of photo line in mm	
Diameter of poliovirus in mm	
Diameter of poliovirus in μm	

2 Examine the photo. The horizontal line you see would measure only 0.4 micrometer (μm) in length if the photo was not magnified 180 000×. Use this line for reference.

3 Calculate the diameter of one poliovirus. First, measure the length of the reference line in millimeters. Record the value in the table. Then, measure the diameter of a poliovirus in millimeters. Record the value in the table.

4 Use the following equation to calculate the actual diameter of the poliovirus (X). Record your answer in the table.

$$\frac{\text{photo line length in mm } (A)}{\text{diameter of virus in mm } (B)} = \frac{0.4 \text{ μm}}{\text{diameter of virus in μm } (X)}$$

Analysis

1. **Interpret Data** Explain why you cannot see viruses with a light microscope. Use specific numbers in your answer.
2. **Use Numbers** An animal cell may be 100 μm in size. How many polioviruses could fit across the top of such a cell?

Viral structure

A virus has an inner core of nucleic acid, either RNA or DNA, and an outer protein coat called a **capsid.** Some relatively large viruses, such as human flu viruses, may have an additional layer called an envelope, surrounding their capsids. Envelopes are composed primarily of the same materials found in the plasma membranes of all cells. You can learn about capsids and envelopes in the *Focus On* on pages 1074–1075.

The core of nucleic acid contains a virus's genetic material. Viral nucleic acid is either DNA or RNA and contains instructions for making copies of the virus. Some viruses have only four genes, while others have hundreds. The arrangement of proteins in the capsid of a virus determines the virus's shape. Four different viral shapes are shown in *Figure 18.1.* The protein arrangement also plays a role in determining what cell can be infected and how the virus infects the cell.

Attachment to a host cell

Before a virus can replicate, it must enter a host cell. Before it can enter, it must first recognize and attach to a receptor site on the plasma membrane of the host cell.

A virus recognizes and attaches to a host cell when one of its proteins interlocks with a molecular shape that is the receptor site on the host cell's plasma membrane. A protein in the tail fibers of the bacteriophage T4, shown in *Figure 18.1,* recognizes and attaches the T4 to its bacterial host cell. In other viruses, the attachment protein is in the capsid or in the envelope. The recognition and attachment process is like two pieces of a jigsaw puzzle fitting together. The process might also remind you of two spaceships docking.

✓ **Reading Check** **Compare and contrast** the structures of viruses to cells.

✓ **Reading Check** Viruses are made of a single strand of nucleic acid, surrounded by a protein coat. Some viruses also have an envelope composed of the same materials as a cell membrane. Cells contain one or more strands of DNA but have a nucleus and organelles, such as mitochondria and Golgi apparatus.

Attachment is a specific process

Each virus has a specifically shaped attachment protein. Therefore, each virus can usually attach to only a few kinds of cells. For example, the T4 phage can infect only certain types of *E. coli* because the T4's attachment protein matches a surface molecule of only these *E. coli*. A T4 cannot infect a human, animal, or plant cell, or even another bacterium. In general, viruses are species specific, and some

Figure 18.1
The different proteins in viral capsids produce a wide variety of viral shapes.

Capsid *Nucleic acid*

Color-enhanced TEM
Magnification: 100 000×

A Polyhedral viruses, such as the papilloma virus that causes warts, resemble small crystals.

Nucleic acid

Capsid

Color-enhanced TEM
Magnification: 34 000×

B The tobacco mosaic virus has a long, narrow helical shape.

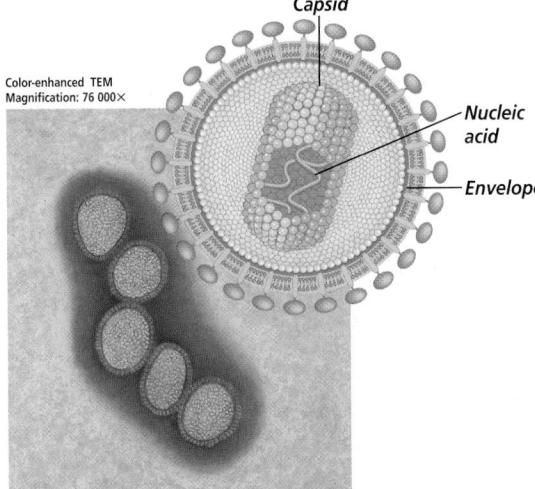

Capsid

Nucleic acid

Envelope

Color-enhanced TEM
Magnification: 76 000×

C An envelope studded with projections covers some viruses, including the influenza virus (photo) and the AIDS-causing virus (inset).

Capsid

Nucleic acid

Tail

Tail fiber

Color-enhanced TEM
Magnification: 65 000×

D This T4 virus, which infects *E. coli*, consists of a polyhedral-shaped head attached to a cylindrical tail with leglike fibers.

477

Uncover the Misconception

Ask students to describe what types of pathogenic microorganisms are treated with antibiotics. They may include viruses in their description. Explain that although antibiotics can treat many bacterial infections, they do not affect viral diseases.

Demonstrate the Concept

Have students research to find the actions of the antibiotics penicillin, tetracycline, bacitracin, vancomycin and gentamicin. Antibiotics are produced naturally by living organisms, mainly molds, against other living organisms, usually bacteria. Most antibiotics work by inhibiting cell wall synthesis or interfering with the function of the ribosomes—inhibiting protein synthesis. Viruses don't have cell walls or function with ribosomes, so they are not affected.

Assess New Knowledge

Ask students to answer what effect antibiotics would have against a viral infection.

Reading Check The attachment protein on the virus is a very specific shape and matches only specific surface molecules on certain types of cells.

also are cell-type specific. For example, polio viruses normally infect only intestinal and nerve cells.

The species specific characteristic of viruses is significant for controlling the spread of viral diseases. For example, by 1980, the World Health Organization had announced that smallpox, which is a deadly human viral disease, had been eradicated. The eradication was possible partly because the smallpox virus infects only humans. A virus such as the one that causes the flu is not species specific and infects animals as well as humans; therefore, it is difficult to eradicate. A virus such as West Nile virus infects mainly birds, horses, and humans.

Reading Check **Summarize** why a virus can attach to only a few specific host cells.

Viral Replication Cycles

Once attached to the plasma membrane of the host cell, the virus enters the cell and takes over its metabolism. Only then can the virus replicate. Viruses have two ways of getting into host cells. The virus may inject its nucleic acid into the host cell like a syringe injects a vaccine into your arm, as shown in *Figure 18.2.* The capsid of the virus stays attached to the outside of the host cell. An enveloped virus enters a host cell in a different way. After attachment, the plasma membrane of the host cell surrounds the virus and produces a virus-filled vacuole inside the host cell's cytoplasm. Then, the virus bursts out of the vacuole and releases its nucleic acid into the cell.

Figure 18.2
In a lytic cycle, a virus uses the host cell's energy and raw materials to make new viruses. A typical lytic cycle takes about 30 minutes and produces about 200 new viruses.

A Attachment

B Entry
The bacteriophage injects its nucleic acid into the bacterial cell.

C Replication
The host's metabolic machinery makes viral nucleic acid and proteins.

D Assembly
New virus particles are assembled.

E Lysis and Release
The host cell breaks open and releases new virus particles.

CHALLENGE ACTIVITY

Viral Time Line Have students make a time line showing the major developments in virology—instrumentation, the discovery of immune system components, the discovery of viral diseases, and vaccine availability. Students could make a separate time line for HIV. **L3**

A Attachment and Entry

B Provirus Formation

Provirus

Bacterial host chromosome

A lysogenic virus injects its nucleic acid into a bacterium.

The viral nucleic acid is called a provirus when it becomes part of the host's chromosome.

C Cell Division

Although the provirus is inactive, it replicates along with the host cell's chromosome.

LYSOGENIC CYCLE

LYTIC CYCLE

The provirus leaves the chromosome.

The cell breaks open releasing viruses.

Viral nucleic acid and proteins are made.

Figure 18.3
In a lysogenic cycle, a virus does not destroy the host cell at once. Rather, the viral nucleic acid is integrated into the genetic material of the host cell and replicates with it for a while before entering a lytic cycle.

Lytic cycle

Once inside the host cell, a virus's genes are expressed and the substances that are produced take over the host cell's genetic material. The viral genes alter the host cell to make new viruses. The host cell uses its own enzymes, raw materials, and energy to make copies of viral genes that along with viral proteins are assembled into new viruses, which burst from the host cell, killing it. The new viruses can then infect and kill other host cells. This process is called a **lytic** (LIH tik) **cycle**. Follow the typical lytic cycle for a bacteriophage shown in *Figure 18.2*.

Lysogenic cycle

Not all viruses kill the cells they infect. Some viruses go through a **lysogenic cycle**, a replication cycle in which the virus's nucleic acid is integrated into the host cell's chromosome. A typical lysogenic cycle for a virus that contains DNA is shown in *Figure 18.3*.

A lysogenic cycle begins in the same way as a lytic cycle. The virus attaches to the host cell's plasma membrane and its nucleic acid enters the cell. However, in a lysogenic cycle, instead of immediately taking over the host's genetic material, the viral DNA is integrated into the host cell's chromosome.

Viral DNA that is integrated into the host cell's chromosome is called a **provirus**. A provirus may not affect the functioning of its host cell, which continues to carry out its own metabolic activity. However, every time the host cell reproduces, the provirus is replicated along with the host cell's chromosome. Therefore, every cell that originates from an infected host

Purpose

Students will analyze data about viruses and decide if the viruses have lytic or lysogenic cycles.

Process Skills

think critically, analyze information, classify, define operationally, interpret data

Background

Measles is caused by the rubeola virus. Shingles is caused by a herpes virus (varicella-zoster virus). Human papillomavirus causes warts. Colds are caused by several viral types—the rhinovirus is the most common. AIDS is caused by the human immunodeficiency virus (HIV).

Teaching Strategies

If necessary, review the two viral replication cycles or ask students to reread these sections.

Thinking Critically

1. short—usually days; long—could be months or years
2. measles, cold; A short incubation implies a short replication cycle.
3. shingles, warts, AIDS; A long incubation implies a long replication cycle.
4. They may be unaware that they're infected and then transmit the disease to others.

Assessment

Performance Ask students to make an informational pamphlet explaining one of these diseases. Use the Performance Task Assessment List for Writing in Science in **PASC**, p. 159. [L2]

Indiana Academic Standards

Pages 480–481: B.1.43

Figure 18.4
Before the influenza virus leaves a host cell, it is wrapped in a piece of the host's plasma membrane, making an envelope with the same structure as the host's plasma membrane.

Color-enhanced TEM Magnification: 17 150×

Problem-Solving Lab 18.1

Analyze Information

What type of virus causes disease? The symptoms and incubation time of a disease can indicate how the virus acts inside its host cell.

Solve the Problem

The table below lists symptoms and incubation times for some viral diseases. Use the table to predict which diseases lytic viruses might cause and which diseases lysogenic viruses might cause.

Characteristics of Some Viral Diseases		
Disease	**Symptom**	**Incubation**
Measles	Rash, fever	9–11 days
Shingles	Pain, itching on skin	Years
Warts	Bumpy areas on skin	Months
Influenza	Body aches, runny nose, fever	1–4 days
HIV	Fatigue, weight loss, fever	2–5 years

Thinking Critically

1. **Observe** How much time is associated with the replication cycle of a lytic virus? A lysogenic virus?
2. **Describe** What diseases may lytic viruses cause? Explain your answer.
3. **Describe** What diseases may lysogenic viruses cause? Explain your answer.
4. **Infer** What is a possible consequence of the fact that a person infected with HIV may have no symptoms for years?

cell has a copy of the provirus. The lysogenic phase can continue for many years. However, at any time, the provirus can be activated and enter a lytic cycle. Then the virus replicates and kills the host cell. Try to distinguish the human diseases caused by lysogenic viruses from those caused by lytic viruses in the *Problem-Solving Lab* on this page.

Disease symptoms of proviruses

The lysogenic process explains the reoccurrence of cold sores, which are caused by the herpes simplex I virus. Even though a cold sore heals, the herpes simplex I virus remains in your cells as a provirus. When the provirus enters a lytic cycle, another cold sore erupts. No one knows what causes a provirus to be activated, but some scientists suspect that physical stress, such as sunburn, and emotional stress, such as anxiety, play a role.

Many disease-causing viruses have lysogenic cycles. Three examples of these viruses are herpes simplex I, herpes simplex II that causes genital herpes, and the hepatitis B virus that causes hepatitis B. Another lysogenic virus is the one that causes chicken pox. Having chicken pox, which usually occurs before age ten, gives lifelong protection from another infection by the virus. However, some chicken pox viruses may remain as proviruses in some of your body's nerve cells. Later in your life, these proviruses may enter a lytic cycle and cause a disease called shingles—a painful infection of some nerve cells.

Release of viruses

Either lysis, the bursting of a cell, or exocytosis, shown in *Figure 18.4*, the active transport process by which materials are expelled from a cell, releases new viruses from the host cell.

INCLUSION STRATEGIES

Learning Disabled Have students create a flip chart of the diseases listed in the Problem-Solving Lab table. Each page should include the name of the disease, symptoms, incubation period, and whether or not it is caused by a lysogenic virus or a lytic virus. [L1]

In exocytosis, a newly produced virus approaches the inner surface of the host cell's plasma membrane. The plasma membrane surrounds the virus, enclosing it in a vacuole that then fuses with the host cell's plasma membrane. Then, the viruses are released to the outside.

Retroviruses

Many viruses, such as the human immunodeficiency virus (HIV) that causes the disease AIDS, are RNA viruses—RNA being their only nucleic acid. The RNA virus with the most complex replication cycle is the **retrovirus** (reh tro VY rus). How can RNA be integrated into a host cell's chromosome, which contains DNA?

Once inside a host cell, the retrovirus makes DNA from its RNA. To do this, it uses **reverse transcriptase** (trans KRIHP tayz), an enzyme it carries inside its capsid. This enzyme helps produce double-stranded DNA from the viral RNA. Then the double-stranded viral DNA is integrated into the host cell's chromosome and becomes a provirus. If reverse transcriptase is found in a

person, it is evidence for infection by a retrovirus. You can see how a retrovirus replicates in its host cell in *Figure 18.5*.

Retrovirus — **Reverse transcriptase** — **Entering cell** — RNA — RNA — **DNA** — *DNA is made from the viral RNA.* — *Provirus in host chromosome* — *mRNA* — *New virus parts* — *New virus forming* — *Exiting cell* — **Retrovirus Cycle**

Figure 18.5
Retroviruses have an enzyme that transcribes their RNA into DNA. The viral DNA becomes a provirus that steadily produces small numbers of new viruses without immediately destroying the cell. **Infer** *How do doctors often discover that someone has a retrovirus infection?*

Discussion

Based on viral structure and replication, have students identify approaches to the production of antiviral vaccines. Vaccines are designed to stimulate the production of antibodies that remain in the system to attack the specific virus. **L2**

Extension

Visual-Spatial Ask students to research and make a table that lists twenty additional viruses not discussed in this section, their type of nucleic acid, structure, method of replication, and host organism. Some examples may include West Nile Virus, Varicella Zoster virus (chicken pox), and Norwalk virus (gastrointestinal illness). **L2**

Indiana Academic Standards

Pages 482–483: B.1.43

HIV: An infection of white blood cells

Once inside a human host, HIV infects white blood cells. Newly made viruses are released into the blood stream by exocytosis and infect other white blood cells. Infected host cells still function normally because the viral genetic material is a provirus that produces only a small number of new viruses at a time. Because the infected cells are still able to function normally, an infected person may not appear sick, but they can still transmit the virus in their body fluids.

An HIV-infected person can experience no AIDS symptoms for a long time. However, most people with an HIV infection eventually get AIDS because, over time, more white blood cells are infected and produce new viruses, *Figure 18.6*. People gradually lose white blood cells because proviruses enter a lytic cycle and kill their host cells. Because white blood cells are part of a body's disease-fighting system, their destruction interferes with the body's ability to protect itself from organisms that cause disease, a symptom of AIDS.

Cancer and Viruses

Some viruses have been linked to certain cancers in humans and animals. For example, the hepatitis B virus has been shown to play a role in causing liver cancer. These viruses disrupt the normal growth and division of cells in a host, causing abnormal growth and creating tumors.

Prions and viroids

Researchers have recently discovered some particles that behave somewhat like viruses and cause infectious diseases. **Prions** are composed of proteins but have no nucleic acid to carry genetic information. Prions are thought to act by causing other proteins to fold themselves incorrectly, resulting in improper functioning. Prions are responsible for many animal diseases, such as mad cow disease and its human equivalent, Creutzfeldt-Jakob disease.

Viroids are composed of a single circular strand of RNA with no protein coat. Viroids have been shown to cause infectious diseases in several plants. The amount of viroid RNA is much less than the amount found in viruses.

Color-enhanced SEM Magnification: 3500×

Figure 18.6
Normal white blood cells are an essential part of a human's immune system **(A)**. In an HIV-infected person, white blood cells are eventually destroyed by HIV proviruses (shown as red objects) that enter lytic cycles **(B)**.

Color-enhanced SEM Magnification 6000

482 VIRUSES AND BACTERIA

Figure 18.7
Tobacco mosaic virus causes yellow spots on tobacco leaves, making them unmarketable **(A)**. In contrast, another virus causes the beautiful stripes of Rembrandt tulips, making them more desirable **(B)**.

Plant viruses

The first virus to be identified was a plant virus, called tobacco mosaic virus, that causes disease in tobacco plants. There are more than 400 viruses that infect a variety of plants. These viruses cause as many as 1000 plant diseases and are named according to their host plant. Viruses can cause stunted growth and yield losses in their host plants. Plant viruses require wounds or insect bites to enter and infect a host, and do not use surface recognition. They do not undergo lytic or lysogenic phases.

Not all viral plant diseases are fatal or even harmful. Some mosaic viruses cause striking patterns of color in the flowers of plants. The infected flowers, like the ones shown

in *Figure 18.7B*, have streaks of vibrant, contrasting colors in their petals. These viruses are easily spread among plants when you cut an infected stem and then cut healthy stems with the same tool.

Origin of Viruses

You might assume that viruses represent an ancestral form of life because of their relatively uncomplicated structure. This is probably not so. For replication, viruses need host cells; therefore, scientists suggest that viruses might have originated from their host cells. Some scientists suggest that viruses are nucleic acids that break free from their host cells while maintaining an ability to replicate parasitically within the host cells.

Check for Understanding
Visual-Spatial Give students out-of-sequence sketches of the steps in the lytic and lysogenic cycles. Have them rearrange the sketches into the correct sequences. **L1**

Reteach
Ask students to make a table that lists each virus discussed in this section, its type of nucleic acid, structure, method of replication, and host organism. **L1**

Resources
For more practice, use *Reading Essentials for Biology*, Section 18.1.

Extension

Visual-Spatial Create and provide students with graphs showing curves of bacterial growth and viral replication. Have students compare the curves and summarize their observations. Point out that, in time, the accumulation of toxic materials leads to bacterial death. The viral curve is steplike. Viral numbers are constant during replication in the host cell and then suddenly rise when the newly made viruses are released. Bacterial growth curves are exponential to a point. **L3**

✓ MODIFIED Assessment

Skill Ask students to compare and contrast viruses and living cells by making a table. **L1**

Section Assessment

Understanding Main Ideas
1. Why is a virus considered to be nonliving?
2. What is the difference between a lytic cycle and a lysogenic cycle?
3. What is a provirus?
4. How do retroviruses convert their RNA to DNA?

Thinking Critically
5. Describe the state of a herpes virus in a person who had cold sores several years ago but who does not have them now.

6. **Make and Use Graphs** A microbiologist added some viruses to a bacterial culture. Every hour from noon to 4:00 P.M., she determined the number of viruses present in a sample of the culture. Her data were 3, 3, 126, 585, and 602. Graph these results. How would the graph look if the culture had initially contained dead bacteria? For more help, refer to *Make and Use Graphs* in the **Skill Handbook**.

in.bdol.glencoe.com/self_check_quiz

18.1 VIRUSES **483**

Section Assessment

1. It does not respire, grow, move, or carry on any life function on its own. Viruses cannot replicate on their own, but must use other living host organisms to make new viruses.
2. In the lytic cycle, viral nucleic acid immediately takes over the cell's machinery and quickly destroys the cell. In the lysogenic cycle, it becomes part of the host cell's DNA and does not quickly kill the cell.
3. viral DNA in a host cell's chromosome
4. using the enzyme reverse transcriptase
5. the virus exists as a provirus in some cells of the person
6. The horizontal axis should be labeled *Time* and the vertical axis *Number of Virus Particles*. Student graphs should show a stepwise increase in the number of viruses. Without living bacteria for viral replication, there would be no replication and thus, no graph.

1 Focus

Bellringer

Section Focus Transparency 44

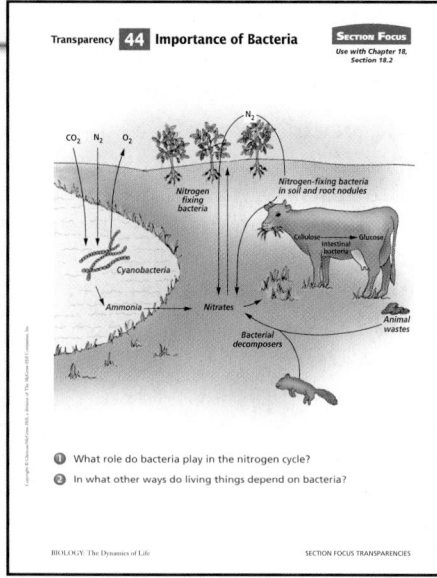

Transparency **44** Importance of Bacteria

SECTION FOCUS
Use with Chapter 18,
Section 18.2

❶ What role do bacteria play in the nitrogen cycle?

❷ In what other ways do living things depend on bacteria?

BIOLOGY: The Dynamics of Life

SECTION FOCUS TRANSPARENCIES

FOLDABLES™

For an additional Foldables activity idea, see the Chapter 18 Foldables page in *Unit 6 FAST FILE Resources.*

Section 18.2

Archaebacteria and Eubacteria

Indiana Standards Standard B.1.12 Compare and contrast the form and function of prokaryotic and eukaryotic cells.

SECTION PREVIEW

Objectives

Compare the types of prokaryotes.

Explain the characteristics and adaptations of bacteria.

Evaluate the economic importance of bacteria.

Review Vocabulary

prokaryote: unicellular organism whose cell lacks a nucleus and internal membrane-bound organelles (p. 173)

New Vocabulary

chemosynthesis
binary fission
conjugation
obligate aerobe
obligate anaerobe
endospore
toxin
nitrogen fixation

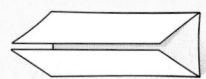
Study Organizer

Viruses and Bacteria Make the following Foldable to help you organize information about viruses and bacteria.

STEP 1 **Fold** one piece of paper lengthwise into thirds.

STEP 2 **Fold** the paper widthwise into six sections.

STEP 3 **Unfold,** lay the paper vertically, and draw lines along the folds.

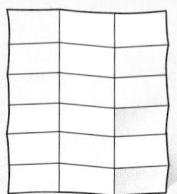

STEP 4 **Label** your table as shown.

	Virus	Bacteria
Structure		
Kinds		
Replication		
Harmful		
Beneficial		

Compare and Contrast As you read Section 18.2, complete the table by describing the characteristics of viruses and bacteria.

Diversity of Prokaryotes

Recall that prokaryotes are unicellular organisms that do not have a nucleus or membrane-bound organelles. They are classified in two kingdoms—archaebacteria and eubacteria. Many biochemical differences exist between these two types of prokaryotes. For example, their cell walls and the lipids in their plasma membranes differ. In addition, the structure and function of the genes of archaebacteria are more similar to those of eukaryotes than to those of eubacteria.

Because they are so different, many scientists propose that archaebacteria and eubacteria arose from a common ancestor several billion years ago.

Archaebacteria: The extremists

There are three types of archaebacteria that live mainly in extreme habitats where there is usually no free oxygen available. You can see some of these environments in *Figure 18.8.* One type of archaebacterium lives

---

RESOURCE MANAGER

Unit 6 *FAST FILE* Resources
  MiniLab Worksheet, p. 4
  BioLab Worksheet, pp. 5–6
  Reinforcement and Study Guide in English, pp. 9–10
  Reinforcement and Study Guide in Spanish, pp. 13–14
  Critical Thinking/Problem Solving, p. 16
  Transparency Worksheets, pp. 18, 23–24, 27–28

Reading Essentials for Biology, Section 18.2
Laboratory Manual, pp. 113–116
Inside Story Poster
Section Focus Transparency 44

Basic Concepts Transparency 27

Reteaching Skills Transparency 28

n oxygen-free environments and produces methane gas. These methane-producing archaebacteria live in marshes, lake sediments, and the digestive tracts of some mammals, such as cows. They also are found at sewage disposal plants, where they play a role in the breakdown of sewage.

A second type of archaebacterium lives only in water with high concentrations of salt, such as in Utah's Great Salt Lake and the Middle East's Dead Sea. A third type lives in the hot, acidic waters of sulfur springs.

This type of anaerobic archaebacterium also thrives near cracks deep in the ocean floor, where it is the autotrophic producer for a unique animal community's food chain.

Eubacteria: The heterotrophs

Eubacteria, the other kingdom of prokaryotes, includes those prokaryotes that live in places more hospitable than archaebacteria inhabit and that vary in nutritional needs. The heterotrophic eubacteria live almost everywhere and use organic molecules as their food source.

Figure 18.8
Archaebacteria live in extreme environments.

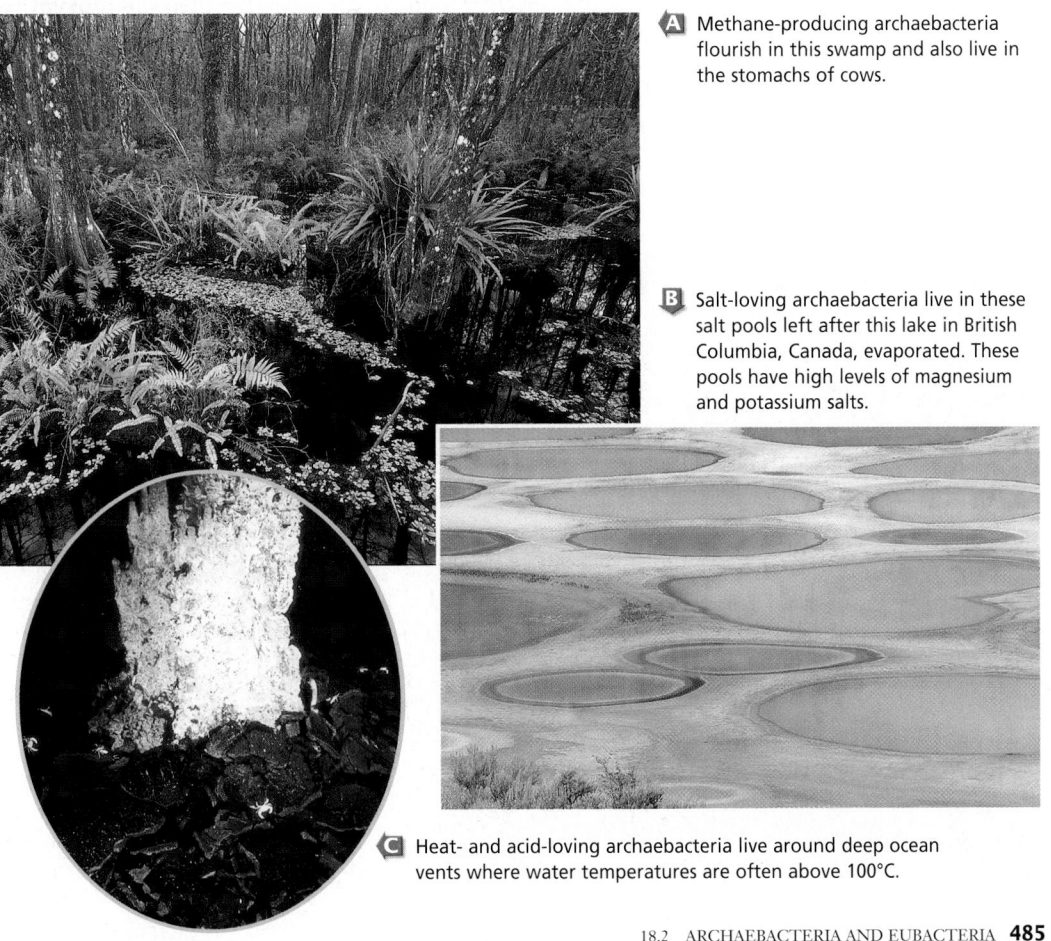

Ⓐ Methane-producing archaebacteria flourish in this swamp and also live in the stomachs of cows.

Ⓑ Salt-loving archaebacteria live in these salt pools left after this lake in British Columbia, Canada, evaporated. These pools have high levels of magnesium and potassium salts.

Ⓒ Heat- and acid-loving archaebacteria live around deep ocean vents where water temperatures are often above 100°C.

2 Teach

Activity

Ask students to make a wet mount of a period cut from a newspaper. Remind them to handle glass microscope slides carefully. Have them estimate the period's size given that the average low-power objective field of view of a microscope is 1.44 mm. about 0.35 mm Ask them to calculate how many bacteria that measure 0.002 mm could fit on the period. about 175 **L2**

Activity

Logical-Mathematical Give students slides of heterotrophic and photoautotrophic bacteria. Ask them to observe the slides under high power and sketch them. Remind students to use care when handling a microscope and glass slides and to use special care not to break the slide when viewing it under the high-power objective. Have students estimate the bacterial sizes if their high-power field of view is 0.35 mm. Then, ask them to write a comparison of the two types of bacteria. **L2**

INCLUSION STRATEGIES

Learning Disabled For students having trouble with the difference between archaebacteria and eubacteria, place pictures of habitats such as a freshwater pond, hot spring, thermal vent, and cheese on an overhead projector or on the board. Have students indicate which type of bacteria would be found in each habitat. **L1**

Kinesthetic Thin yogurt containing live bacterial cultures with distilled water. Have students make a wet mount of the yogurt, adding a drop of methylene blue, and look for bacteria on their slides. The bacteria should be visible under the high power. Remind students to use care when handling a microscope and glass slides and to use special care not to break the slide when viewing it under the high-power objective. Caution students that stains may be permanent on their clothing. Have them rinse their skin immediately if they spill stain on it. **L1** **ELL**

Biology Journal

Bacteria Making Headlines Ask students to bring in newspaper and magazine articles about bacterial illnesses and summarize the articles in their journals. **L2**

Indiana Academic Standards

Pages 486–487: B.1.2, B.1.12, B.1.43

486

Word Origin

cyanobacterium from the Greek words *kyanos*, meaning "blue," and *bakterion*, meaning "small rod"; The cyanobacteria are blue-green bacteria.

Figure 18.9
Cyanobacteria, such as *Anabaena*, are photosynthetic and have a blue-green color.

LM Magnification: 250×

Some bacterial heterotrophs are parasites, obtaining their nutrients from living organisms. They are not adapted for trapping food that contains organic molecules or for making organic molecules themselves. Others are saprophytes—organisms that feed on dead organisms or organic wastes. Recall that saprophytes break down and recycle the nutrients locked in the body tissues of dead organisms.

Eubacteria:
Photosynthetic autotrophs

A second type of eubacterium is the photosynthetic autotroph. These eubacteria live in places with sunlight because they need light to make the organic molecules that are their food. Cyanobacteria are photosynthetic autotrophs. They contain the pigment chlorophyll that traps the sun's energy, which they then use in photosynthesis. Most cyanobacteria, like the *Anabaena* shown in *Figure 18.9*,

are blue-green and some are red or yellow in color. Cyanobacteria commonly live in ponds, streams, and moist areas of land. They are composed of chains of independent cells.

Eubacteria:
Chemosynthetic autotrophs

A third type of eubacterium is the chemosynthetic autotroph. Like photosynthetic bacteria, these bacteria make organic molecules that are their food. However, unlike the photosynthetic bacteria, the chemosynthetic bacteria do not obtain the energy they need to make food from sunlight. Instead, they break down and release the energy of inorganic compounds containing sulfur and nitrogen in the process called **chemosynthesis** (kee moh SIHN thuh sus). Some chemosynthetic bacteria are very important to other organisms because they are able to convert atmospheric nitrogen into the nitrogen-containing compounds that plants need.

What is a bacterium?

A bacterium consists of a very small cell. Although tiny, a bacterial cell has all the structures necessary to carry out its life functions.

The structure of bacteria

Prokaryotic cells have ribosomes, but their ribosomes are smaller than those of eukaryotes. They also have genes that are located for the most part in a single circular chromosome, rather than in paired chromosomes. What structures can protect a bacterium? Look at *Figure 18.10* on the next page to learn about other structures located in bacterial cells.

One structure that supports and protects a bacterium is the cell wall. The cell wall protects the bacterium by preventing it from bursting.

INCLUSION STRATEGIES

Learning Disabled To help students learn the names, shapes, and arrangements of bacteria, have them create flash cards. Students can show a bacterium on one side and its function on the other side. Later, students can add the name of the bacterium on one side and the shape on the other. They also can make cards that show bacterial arrangements—clusters, chains, and pairs—to practice using the correct prefixes. **L1**

A Typical Bacterial Cell

Figure 18.10
Bacteria are microscopic, prokaryotic cells. Bacteria are unicellular. A typical bacterium, such as *Escherichia coli* shown at the right, would have some or all of the structures shown in this diagram of a bacterial cell.
Critical Thinking *Which structures of bacteria are involved in reproduction?*

Color-enhanced TEM Magnification: 3000×

Escherichia coli

A **Capsule** Some bacteria have a sticky gelatinous capsule around the cell wall. A bacterium with a capsule is more likely to cause disease than a bacterium without a capsule.

B **Cell wall** A cell wall surrounds the plasma membrane. It gives the cell its shape and prevents osmosis from bursting the cell.

C **Chromosome** A single DNA molecule, arranged as a circular chromosome and not enclosed in a nucleus, contains most of the bacterium's genes.

G **Plasma membrane** A plasma membrane surrounds the cell and regulates what enters and leaves the cell.

D **Flagellum** Some bacteria have long, whiplike protrusions called flagella (singular, flagellum) that enable them to move.

F **Pilus** Some bacteria have pili—hairlike structures emerging from the cell surface. A hairlike pilus helps a bacterium stick to a surface. It is also like a bridge through or on which two bacteria can exchange DNA.

E **Plasmid** A few genes are located in a small circular chromosome piece called a plasmid. A bacterium may have one or more plasmids.

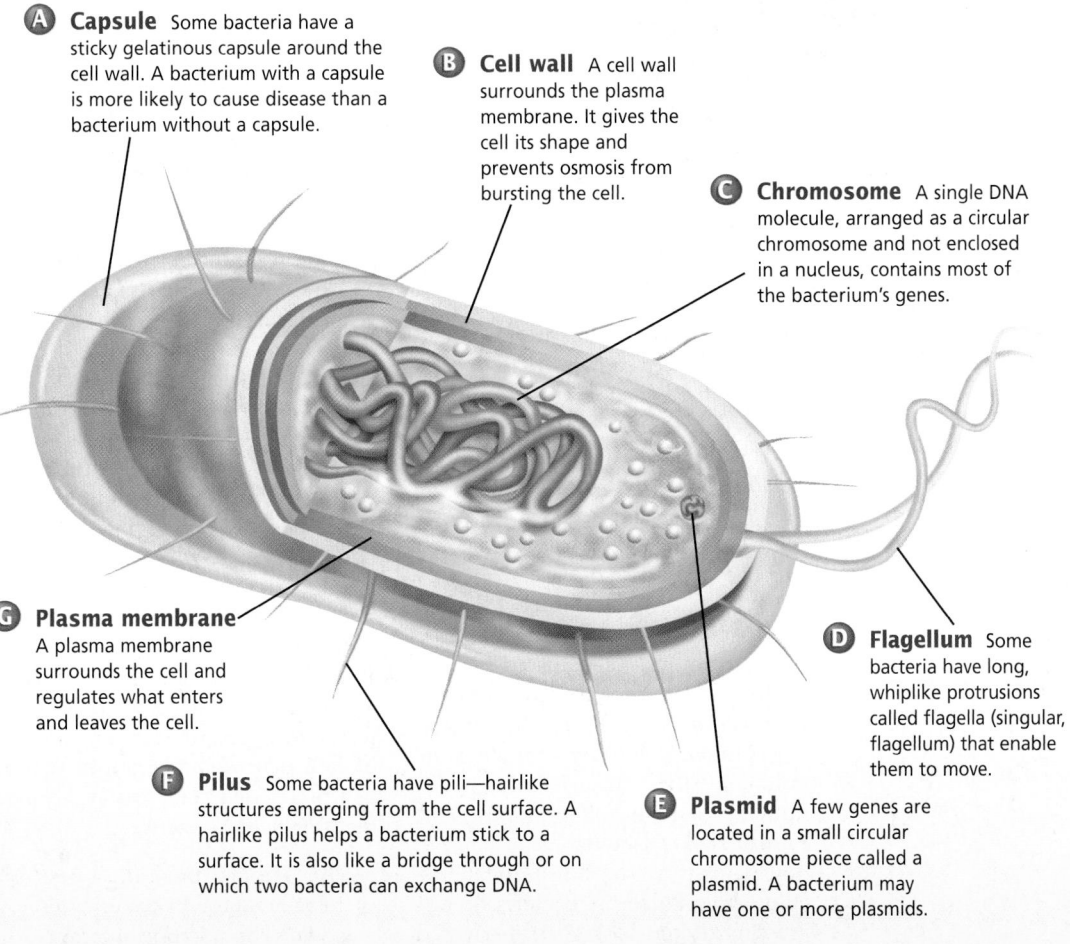

Purpose
Students will learn about both the structures and adaptations of a generalized bacterium.

Teaching Strategies
To demonstrate some conditions that inhibit bacterial growth, pour 100 mL of boiled beef broth into each of four sterile beakers. Label the beakers *1*, *2*, *3*, and *4* and add respectively to each 1 tsp salt, 1 tsp sugar, 1 tsp vinegar, and 1 tsp distilled water. Have students observe and record the clarity and color of the broth in each beaker initially and again after three days. Explain that bacterial growth clouds the broth. Ask students to explain how salt, sugar, and acid (vinegar) affected bacterial growth. Salt and acids inhibit growth; sugar aids it. **L1**

Visual Learning
- Name the bacterial structures shown in The Inside Story. As you name each structure, have a student summarize its function. Repeat until all structures have been discussed. **L1**
- Challenge students to identify bacterial cell structures that are shared and not shared by plant and/or animal cells. **L1**

Critical Thinking
Students might say the chromosome, pili, and maybe plasmids.

CHALLENGE ACTIVITY

Discovering Penicillin: *Interpersonal*
Ask groups to write a skit about penicillin, including the details of Fleming's discovery, how medicine changed after its discovery, and the problem of penicillin-resistant bacteria. **L3** **COOP LEARN**

Extension

Linguistic Have students research different bacteria and list whether or not each is Gram-positive or Gram-negative.

Figure 18.11
The mold known as *Penicillium notatum*, shown above in its growth stages, produces the antibiotic penicillin.

Because most bacteria live in a hypotonic environment, one in which there is a higher concentration of water molecules outside than inside the cell, water is always trying to enter a bacterial cell. A bacterial cell remains intact, however, and does not burst open as long as its cell wall is intact. If the cell wall is damaged, water will enter the cell by osmosis, causing the cell to burst. Scientists used a bacterium's need for an intact cell wall to develop a weapon against bacteria that cause disease.

In 1928, Sir Alexander Fleming accidentally discovered penicillin, the first antibiotic—a substance that destroys bacteria—used in humans. He was growing bacteria when an airborne mold, *Penicillium notatum*, contaminated his culture plates. He noticed that the mold, shown in ***Figure 18.11***, secreted a substance—now known as the antibiotic penicillin—that killed the bacteria he was growing. Later, biologists discovered that penicillin can interfere with the

ability of some bacteria to make cell walls. When such bacteria grow in penicillin, holes develop in their cell walls, water enters their cells, and they rupture and die.

Identifying bacteria

Scientists have developed ways to distinguish among bacteria. For example, one trait that helps categorize bacteria is how they react to Gram stain. Gram staining is a technique that distinguishes two groups of bacteria because the stain reflects a basic difference in the composition of bacterial cell walls. The cell walls of all bacteria are made of interlinked sugar and amino acid molecules that differ in arrangement and react differently to Gram stain. After staining Gram-positive bacteria are purple and Gram-negative bacteria are pink. Gram-positive bacteria are affected by different antibiotics than those that affect Gram-negative bacteria.

Not only do bacterial cell walls react differently to Gram stain, but they also give bacteria different shapes. Shape is another way to categorize bacteria. The three most common shapes are spheres, called cocci; rods, called bacilli; and spirals called spirilla. An example of each shape is shown in ***Figure 18.12***. In addition to having one of these shapes, bacterial cells often grow in characteristic patterns that provide another way of categorizing them. *Diplo-* is a prefix that refers to a paired arrangement of cell growth. The prefix *staphylo-* describes an arrangement of cells that resemble grapes. *Strepto-* is a prefix that refers to an arrangement of chains of cells.

Reading Check **Describe** what shape and growth pattern you would expect *Staphylococcus* bacteria to have.

Additional Lab

Photosynthetic Bacteria

Purpose
Students will isolate photosynthetic bacteria from a variety of soil samples.

Safety Precautions
Remind students to wear safety goggles, a lab apron, and disposable latex gloves and to avoid skin, eye, and mouth contact with the materials used in this activity. Caution them to handle glass tubes carefully and to dispose of broken glass as you direct. Remind them not to handle electrical equipment with wet hands and to wash their hands thoroughly after this activity.

Materials
screw-top test tubes; liquid growth medium composed of 445 mL distilled water, 50 mL vinegar, 4 drops Schultz liquid plant food, 0.5 g Accent seasoning, and enough baking soda to bring the pH to 7.0 (about 4.5 g); 60-watt incandescent lightbulbs; four soil samples

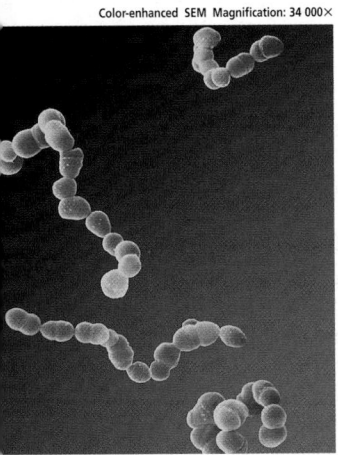

Color-enhanced SEM Magnification: 34 000×

A These spherical, Gram-positive *Streptococcus pneumoniae* bacteria cause pneumonia.

Color-enhanced SEM Magnification: unavailable

B This rodlike, Gram-positive bacterium, *Bacillus anthracis,* commonly exists in the soil. It can cause anthrax in cattle, sheep, and humans.

LM Magnification: 250×

C This spiral-shaped, Gram-negative *Spirillum volutans* bacterium has flagella.

Figure 18.12
Bacteria exist in three main shapes.

Reproduction by binary fission

Bacteria cannot reproduce by mitosis or meiosis because they have no nucleus, and instead of pairs of chromosomes, they have one circular chromosome and varying numbers of smaller circular pieces of DNA called plasmids. Therefore, they have other ways to reproduce.

Bacteria reproduce asexually by a process known as **binary fission.** To reproduce in this way, a bacterium first copies its chromosome. Then the original chromosome and the copy become attached to the cell's plasma membrane for a while. The cell grows larger, and eventually the two chromosomes separate and move to opposite ends of the cell. Then, a partition forms between the chromosomes, as shown in *Figure 18.13*. This partition separates the cell into two similar cells. Because each new cell has either the original or the copy of the chromosome, the resulting cells are genetically identical.

Bacterial reproduction can be rapid. In fact, under ideal conditions, some bacteria can reproduce every 20 minutes, producing enormous numbers of bacteria quickly. If bacteria always reproduced this fast, they would cover the surface of Earth within a few weeks. But bacteria don't always have ideal growing conditions. They run out of nutrients and water,

Figure 18.13
This *Escherichia coli* cell is starting to divide. The newly forming partition is visible in the center of the cell.

Color-enhanced TEM Magnification: 16 500×

Visual Learning
Figure 18.13 Ask students why cell growth is needed for binary fission. for chromosome duplication and separation

Discussion
Ask students if they would rather have $10 every 20 minutes for 13 hours or one penny doubled every 20 minutes for 13 hours. The first choice would equal $400 and the second choice would be more than $5 million by exponential growth. Point out that the growth rate for bacteria as they undergo asexual reproduction is like the second example.

Procedure
Give students the following directions.
1. Place 1 to 2 cm of each soil in a test tube. Add growth medium, screw on the test tube's top, and shake well.
2. Place the tubes about 60 cm away from a lightbulb and do not disturb.
3. Hypothesize where bacteria will grow.
4. Examine the cultures daily for two weeks. Red, rust, pink, and orange colors indicate photosynthetic bacteria.

Analysis
1. In which tubes did you find photosynthetic bacteria? from all to none
2. Was your hypothesis supported by your data? Speculate why or why not. Data will vary. There are hundreds of photosynthetic bacteria and only some may have been able to grow.
3. What caused the colors you saw in the test tubes? photosynthetic pigments

Assessment
Performance Have students experiment to determine the best temperature for the growth of their isolated bacteria. They must subculture every two weeks to maintain the culture. Use the Performance Task Assessment List for Assessing a Whole Experiment and Planning the Next Experiment in **PASC,** p. 105. **L3**

Purpose

Students will examine three typical shapes of bacteria.

Process Skills

compare and contrast, classify, observe and infer

Teaching Strategies

- Provide students with their microscopes' high-power field of view diameter.
- Encourage students to identify bacterial arrangements.
- Caution students to work carefully with microscopes, slides, and coverslips especially when viewing slides under a high-power objective.

Expected Results

Students will observe spherical, rod-, and spiral-shaped bacteria.

Analysis

1. The spherical bacteria were smallest. The spirilla were most likely largest.
2. the pink bacteria
3. exchange information and nuclear material

Modified Assessment

Performance Give students a prepared slide of unfamiliar bacteria. Ask them to identify the bacteria's shape and arrangement. Use the Performance Task Assessment List for Making Observations and Inferences in **PASC**, p. 89. **L1**

Indiana Academic Standards

Pages 490–491: B.1.3, B.1.8, B.1.33

Observe

Bacteria Have Different Shapes Bacteria come in three shapes: spherical (coccus), rodlike (bacillus), and spiral shaped (spirillum). They may appear singly or in pairs, chains, or clusters. Each species has a typical shape and reaction to Gram stain.

Color-enhanced SEM Magnification: 50 000×

Staphylococcus **bacteria**

Procedure

1. Obtain slides of bacteria from your teacher.
2. Using low power, locate bacteria of one shape. Switch to high power. Look for individual cells and observe their shape. Also observe the size of the cells and their color. Then look for groups of bacterial cells to determine their arrangement. **CAUTION:** *Use caution when working with a microscope and microscope slides.*
3. Repeat step 2 for bacteria with the other shapes. Then, compare the sizes of the bacteria.
4. Draw a diagram of each type of bacteria.

Analysis

1. **Measure** How do the sizes of the three bacteria compare?
2. **Classify** Which of the bacteria were Gram negative?
3. **Explain** What adaptive advantage might there be for bacteria to form groups of cells?

Figure 18.14

The *E. coli* at the bottom is attached to the other bacteria by pili, through or on which genetic material is being transferred. **Infer** *How would conjugation be a useful addition to binary fission?*

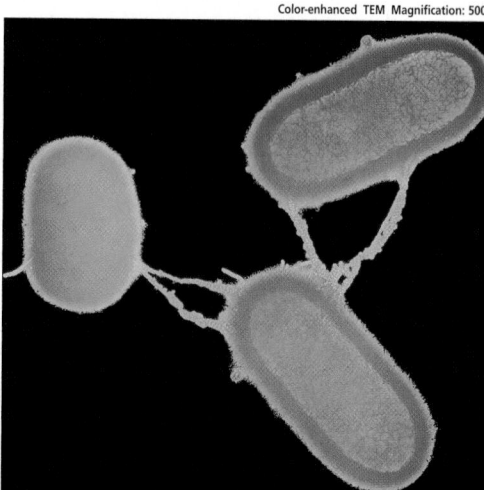

Color-enhanced TEM Magnification: 5000×

they poison themselves with their own wastes, and predators eat them.

Sexual reproduction

In addition to binary fission, some bacteria have a form of sexual reproduction called conjugation. During **conjugation** (kahn juh GAY shun), one bacterium transfers all or part of its chromosome to another cell through or on a bridgelike structure called pilus (plural, pili) that connects the two cells. In *Figure 18.14,* you can see how this genetic transfer occurs. Conjugation results in a bacterium with a new genetic composition. This bacterium can then undergo binary fission, producing more cells with the same genetic makeup.

Try the *MiniLab* on this page to see some bacterial staining reactions, cell shapes, and patterns of growth.

Adaptations in Bacteria

Based on fossil evidence, some scientists propose that anaerobic bacteria were probably among the first photosynthetic organisms, producing not only their own food but also oxygen. As the concentration of oxygen increased

Caption Question Answer
Figure 18.14 Conjugation is a form of sexual reproduction, allowing a new genetic recombination, whereas binary fission produces only duplicate copies of the genetic material.

Color-enhanced TEM Magnification: 12 500×

in Earth's atmosphere, some bacteria probably adapted over time to use oxygen for respiration.

Diversity of metabolism

Recall that breaking down food to release its energy is called cellular respiration. Modern bacteria have diverse types of respiration.

Many bacteria require oxygen for respiration. These bacteria are called **obligate aerobes.** *Mycobacterium tuberculosis,* the organism that causes the lung disease called tuberculosis, is an obligate aerobe. There are other bacteria, called **obligate anaerobes,** that are killed by oxygen. Among bacteria that are obligate anaerobes is the bacterium *Treponema pallidum* that causes syphilis, a sexually transmitted disease, and the bacterium that causes botulism, a type of food poisoning that you will learn more about soon. There are still other bacteria that can live either with or without oxygen, releasing the energy in food aerobically by cellular respiration or anaerobically by fermentation.

A survival mechanism

Some bacteria, when faced with unfavorable environmental conditions, produce endospores, shown in *Figure 18.15*. An **endospore** is a tiny structure that contains a bacterium's DNA and a small amount of its cytoplasm, encased by a tough outer covering that resists drying out, temperature extremes, and harsh chemicals. As an endospore, the bacterium rests and does not reproduce. When environmental conditions improve, the endospore germinates, or produces a cell that begins to grow and reproduce. Some endospores have germinated after thousands of years in the resting state.

Although endospores are useful to bacteria, they can cause problems for people. Endospores can survive a temperature of 100°C, which is the boiling point of water. To kill endospores, items must be sterilized—heated under high pressure in either a pressure cooker or an autoclave. Under pressure, water will boil at a higher temperature than its usual 100°C, and this higher temperature kills endospores.

18.2 ARCHAEBACTERIA AND EUBACTERIA **491**

Purpose

Students are asked to apply information about one type of food poisoning.

Process Skills

think critically, analyze information, hypothesize

Background

Endospores of *Clostridium botulinum* that are left undestroyed on a vegetable being canned can germinate after the jar is sealed. The bacteria grow in the jar's anaerobic conditions, producing a powerful endotoxin that can result in respiratory failure if ingested by humans.

Teaching Strategies

Have students review the meaning of the terms *obligate anaerobe*, *endospore*, *anaerobic conditions*, *germinate*, *toxin*. **L1** **ELL**

Thinking Critically

1. Answers may vary. Endospores won't germinate in oxygen.
2. Answers may vary. Spores in soil cling to the plant.
3. Answers may vary. A high enough temperature may not have been reached during canning.
4. The jars contain no oxygen.

Assessment

Knowledge Ask students to make a poster comparing the characteristics, problems, symptoms and general nature of the diseases caused by *Clostridium tetani* (tetanus) and *Clostridium botulinum*. Use the Performance Task Assessment List for Poster in **PASC**, p. 145. **L2**

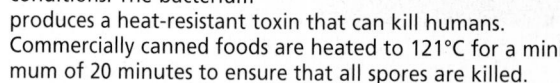

Problem-Solving Lab 18.2

Hypothesize

Can you get food poisoning from eating home-canned foods? *Clostridium botulinum* is a bacterial species that causes food poisoning.

Solve the Problem

C. botulinum is an obligate anaerobic soil bacterium, and it easily spreads onto plants. It forms endospores that are highly heat-resistant and germinate only in anaerobic conditions. The bacterium produces a heat-resistant toxin that can kill humans. Commercially canned foods are heated to 121°C for a minimum of 20 minutes to ensure that all spores are killed.

Thinking Critically

1. **Hypothesize** Why don't you get food poisoning if you eat fresh vegetables that are contaminated with the endospores of *C. botulinum*?
2. **Hypothesize** How do the endospores of *C. botulinum* get into home-canned vegetables?
3. **Hypothesize** How can *C. botulinum* endospores survive inadequate home-canning procedures?
4. **Explain** Why do endospores of *C. botulinum* germinate inside canning jars?

Figure 18.16
CAUTION: When a foil-wrapped potato is baked, any *Clostridium botulinum* spores on its skin can survive. If the potato is eaten immediately, the spores cannot germinate. However, if the still-wrapped potato cools at room temperature, the spores can germinate in the anaerobic environment of the foil, and the bacteria will produce their deadly toxin.

Canned foods must be sterilized and acidified. This is because the endopores of the bacterium called *Clostridium botulinum* easily get into foods being canned. These bacteria belong to the group clostridia—all obligate anaerobic bacteria that form endospores. If the endospores of *C. botulinum* get into improperly sterilized canned food, they germinate. Bacteria grow in the anaerobic environment of the can and produce a powerful and deadly poison, called a **toxin,** as they grow. This deadly toxin saturates the food and, if eaten, causes the disease called botulism. Although rare, botulism is often fatal, and it can be transmitted in many ways other than poorly canned food, as shown in *Figure 18.16.* Try the *Problem-Solving Lab* on this page to learn more about *C. botulinum.*

A different bacterium, *Bacillus anthracis*, lives in the soil. *B. anthracis* causes anthrax, a disease that commonly infects cattle and sheep, but can also infect humans. Most human anthrax infections are fairly harmless and occur on the skin as a result of handling animals. The bacterial spores can become airborne, however, and if inhaled in large amounts, can

---

INCLUSION STRATEGIES

English Language Learners: *Visual-Spatial* Give students a diagram of bacteria with different shapes and arrangements. Include a key of the meanings of the word parts needed to name each bacterial type. Ask students to write the correct bacterial name below each drawing. **L1** **ELL**

Figure 18.17
Soybean plants have swellings, called nodules, on their roots (**A**). The nodules (**B**) contain bacteria called *Rhizobium* (**C**) that convert nitrogen gas into ammonia. In this symbiotic association, the plant gains usable nitrogen, and the bacteria gain food.

Color-enhanced SEM
Magnification: 7400×

Quick Demo

Useful Bacteria Bring to class some foods that require bacteria for processing. Include Swiss cheese, pickles, vinegar, sauerkraut, yogurt, and sour cream. Explain the importance of bacteria to each food.

Enrichment
Explain that some bacteria produce methane gas, which is the major component of natural gas. On the chalkboard, sketch the structural formula of methane and write its molecular formula, CH_4. Light a Bunsen burner to illustrate methane's properties. Tell students that natural gas companies add chemicals with odors that warn their customers of a fuel leak. Have students brainstorm advantages resulting from utilizing bacteria that produce methane. **L3**

...rminate in a person's lungs, causing ...n infection. This infection is more ...erious than a skin infection and often ...tal. The infection harms the lungs by ...roducing toxins that damage lung tis-...ue and the circulatory system. Because ...nthrax can be easily spread through ...e air, it has been used to intentionally ...arm people as a biological weapon.

The Importance of Bacteria

When you think about bacteria, ...our first thought may be disease. But ...isease-causing bacteria are few com-...ared with the number of harmless ...nd beneficial bacteria on Earth. ...acteria help to fertilize fields, to ...ecycle nutrients on Earth, and to ...roduce foods and medicines.

Nitrogen fixation

Most of the nitrogen on Earth ...exists in the form of nitrogen gas, N_2, ...which makes up about 80 percent of the atmosphere. All organisms need nitrogen because the element is a component of their proteins, DNA, RNA, and ATP. Yet few organisms, including most plants, can directly use nitrogen from the air.

Several species of bacteria have enzymes that convert N_2 into ammonia (NH_3) in a process known as **nitrogen fixation.** Other bacteria then convert the ammonia into nitrite (NO_2^-) and nitrate (NO_3^-), which plants can use. Bacteria are the only organisms that can perform these chemical changes.

Some nitrogen-fixing bacteria live symbiotically within the roots of some trees and legumes—plants such as peas, peanuts, and soybeans—in swollen areas called nodules. You can see some nodules in *Figure 18.17.* Farmers grow legume crops after the harvesting of crops such as corn, which depletes the soil of nitrogen. Not only do legumes replenish the soil's nitrogen supply, they are an economically useful crop.

Physical Science Connection

Classify everyday matter Elements are substances with the same number of protons in the nucleus of their atoms. For example, all nitrogen atoms (N) in nitrogen gas (N_2) have 7 protons. Compounds, such as ammonia (NH_3), consist of more than one element present in fixed proportions. The ratio of nitrogen to hydrogen atoms in ammonia always is 1 to 3.

Physical Science Connection

Review with students that the number of protons in an element is equal to its atomic number. Nitrogen's atomic number is 7. Therefore, it has 7 protons in its nucleus.

PROJECT

Bacteria of Decay: *Kinesthetic* Have students model a landfill in a jar containing moist soil. Instruct them to bury carrot shavings, paper, aluminum foil, and other items that are in landfills. Do not bury any animal products.

After two weeks, have them unearth the items they buried and compare the way they look with their pre-burial appearances. Ask students to record their observations and discuss the importance of the recycling that bacteria do.

Have students wear a lab apron, disposable latex gloves, and safety goggles. Remind them to wash their hands thoroughly. **L2**

Indiana Academic Standards

Pages 492–493: B.1.43

Recycling of nutrients

You learned that life could not exist if decomposing bacteria did not break down the organic materials in dead organisms and wastes, returning nutrients, both organic materials and inorganic materials, to the environment. Autotrophic bacteria and also plants and algae, which are at the bottom of the food chains, use the nutrients in the food they make.

This food is passed from one heterotroph to the next in food chains and webs. In the process of making food, many autotrophs replenish the supply of oxygen in the atmosphere. You can see from all this that other life depends on bacteria.

Food and medicines

Some foods that you eat—mellow Swiss cheese, shown in *Figure 18.18,* crispy pickles, tangy yogurt—would not exist without bacteria. During respiration, different bacteria produce diverse products, many of which have distinctive flavors and aroma. As a result, specific bacteria are used to make different foods, such as vinegar, cheeses, and sauerkraut. Bacteria also inhabit your intestines and produce vitamins and enzymes that help digest food.

In addition to food, some bacteria produce important antibiotics that destroy other types of bacteria. Streptomycin, erythromycin, bacitracin, and neomycin are some of these antibiotics. How do you know which antibiotic you need when you are sick? The *BioLab* at the end of the chapter will help you learn how scientists have obtained such information.

Bacteria cause disease

Bacteria cause diseases in plants and animals, causing crops and livestock losses that impact humans indirectly.

Figure 18.18
Bacteria not only give Swiss cheese **(A)** its flavor but also its holes as they produce carbon dioxide that bubbles through the cheese **(B)**. Useful bacteria are grown in large industrial fermenting vats **(C)**.

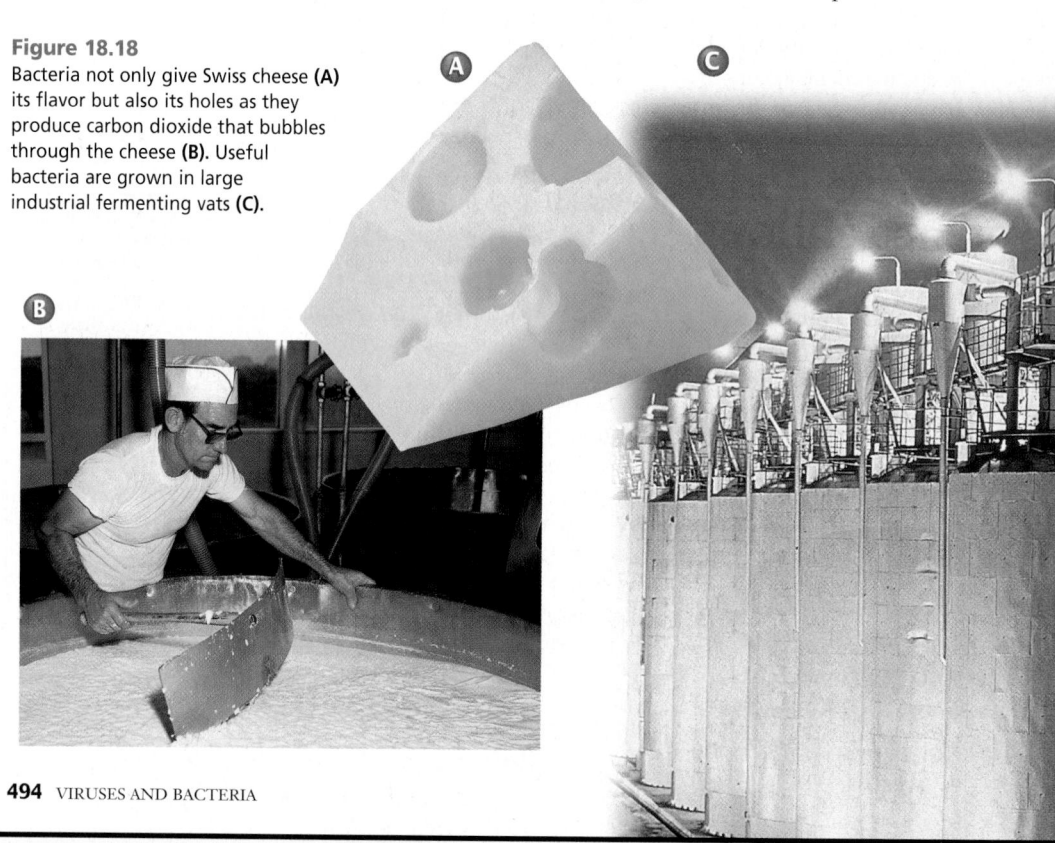

494 VIRUSES AND BACTERIA

Table 18.1 Diseases Caused by Bacteria

Disease	Transmission	Symptoms	Treatment
Strep throat (*Streptococcus*)	Inhale or ingest through mouth	Fever, sore throat, swollen neck glands	Antibiotic
Tuberculosis	Inhale	Fatigue, fever, night sweats, cough, weight loss, chest pain	Antibiotic
Tetanus	Puncture wound	Stiff jaw, muscle spasms, paralysis	Open and clean wound, antibiotic; give antitoxin
Lyme disease	Bite of infected tick	Rash at site of bite, chills, body aches, joint swelling	Antibiotic
Dental cavities (caries)	Bacteria in mouth	Destruction of tooth enamel, toothache	Remove and fill the destroyed area of tooth
Diphtheria	Inhale or close contact	Sore throat, fever, heart or breathing failure	Vaccination to prevent, antibiotics

Bacteria also cause many human diseases, some of which you can see listed in *Table 18.1*. Disease-causing bacteria can enter human bodies through openings, such as the mouth. They are carried in air, food, and water and sometimes invade humans through skin wounds. Bacterial diseases harm people in two ways. The growth of the bacteria can interfere with the normal function of body tissue, or it can release a toxin that directly attacks the host.

In the past, bacterial illnesses had a greater effect on human populations than they do now. As recently as 1900, life expectancy in the United States was only 47 years. The most dangerous diseases at that time were the bacterial illnesses tuberculosis and pneumonia. In the last 100 years, human life expectancy has increased to about 75 years. This increase is due to many factors, including better public health systems, improved water and sewage treatment, better nutrition, and better medical care. These improvements, along with antibiotics, have reduced the death rates from bacterial diseases to low levels. However, this is starting to change as you can read in the *Biology and Society* feature at the end of this chapter.

3 Assess

DAILY INTERVENTION

Check for Understanding
Have students list the common characteristics of the major groups of bacteria. **L1**

Reteach
Linguistic Ask students to outline this section of the chapter using standard outline format. Beneath each of their outline heads, have students write a short summary of the section. **L2**

Resources
For more practice, use *Reading Essentials for Biology*, Section 18.2.

Extension

Linguistic Ask a group of students to write to the Centers for Disease Control and Prevention in Atlanta, Georgia, to get recent copies of the "Morbidity and Mortality Weekly Report" (MMWR). Have them summarize the information about diseases that are currently monitored in the United States and around the world. **L3**

✓ MODIFIED Assessment

Portfolio Have students make labeled diagrams of the bacteria they have studied in this chapter. Ask them to include captions that describe their adaptations. **L1**

Section Assessment

Understanding Main Ideas
1. Describe six parts of a typical bacterial cell. State the function of each.
2. What are endospores? How do they help bacteria survive?
3. Explain how penicillin affects a bacterial cell.
4. Explain how bacteria avoid osmotic rupture.

Thinking Critically
5. Some scientists have proposed that bacterialike cells were probably among the earliest organisms to live on Earth. Draw up a list of reasons why such a suggestion is feasible. Then explain each reason on your list.

SKILL REVIEW

6. **Make and Use Tables** Construct a table comparing and contrasting archaebacteria and eubacteria. Include at least three ways they are alike and three ways they are different. For more help, refer to *Make and Use Tables* in the **Skill Handbook**.

in.bdol.glencoe.com/self_check_quiz

18.2   ARCHAEBACTERIA AND EUBACTERIA   **495**

Section Assessment

1. Chromosome has genetic information; plasma membrane regulates entry and exit; cell wall prevents osmotic rupture and gives shape; capsule protects; flagella move; pili help it adhere and conjugate.
2. survival structures; Endospores protect bacteria from dryness, chemicals, etc.
3. It interferes with the construction and repair of bacterial cell walls.
4. Cell walls protect them.
5. The oldest fossils are bacterialike. The prokaryotic cell is not complex. Today, some bacteria live in extreme conditions.
6. differences: plasma membrane and cell wall structure, tRNA and rRNA base sequences, reactions to antibiotics; similarities: prokaryotes, unicellular, one circular chromosome

DESIGN YOUR OWN

BioLab

PREPARATION

Time Allotment

initial session: one class period; followup session: 15 minutes, 48 hours after lab is begun

Process Skills

compare and contrast, observe and infer, recognize cause and effect, form a hypothesis, interpret data

Safety Precautions

Have students wear a lab apron, safety goggles, and disposable latex gloves during this lab. Students should wash their hands with soap after handling bacterial cultures. When students complete the lab, they should clean their work areas with disinfectant. Used swabs and petri dishes should be disposed of after autoclaving or by incineration.

If students are transferring bacteria from an agar culture, they should use sterile technique. Remind them that even though *E. Coli* is not pathogenic under normal conditions, it is wise to treat cultures with caution.

PREPARATION

■ Arrange for delivery of the culture of *E. coli* and the petri dishes shortly before the students will do the lab.

■ Purchase disks that contain antibiotics with which students are likely to be familiar.

DESIGN YOUR OWN

BioLab

INQUIRY **Before You Begin**

Doctors must know which antibiotic kills each type of disease-causing bacterium. You can use a test similar to the one in this *BioLab* to discover this information. You will use sterile, agar-containing petri dishes and sterile, antibiotic disks. When you place a disk on the agar, the antibiotic diffuses into the agar. A clear ring that develops around a disk—a zone of inhibition—is where the antibiotic killed susceptible bacteria.

How sensitive are bacteria to antibiotics?

PREPARATION

Problem

How can you determine which antibiotic most effectively kills specific bacteria?

Hypotheses

Decide on one hypothesis that you will test. Your hypothesis might be that the antibiotic with the widest zone of inhibition most effectively inhibits growth of that bacteria.

Objectives

In this BioLab, you will:

■ **Compare** how effectively different antibiotics kill specific bacteria.

■ **Determine** the most effective antibiotic to treat an infection that these bacteria might cause.

Possible Materials

cultures of bacteria
sterile nutrient agar
  petri dishes
antibiotic disks
sterile disks of blank
  filter paper

marking pen
long-handled cotton swabs
forceps
37°C incubator
metric ruler

Safety Precautions

CAUTION: *Always wear goggles in the lab. Although the bacteria you will work with are not disease-causing, do not spill them. Wash your hands with antibacterial soap immediately after handling any bacterial culture. Clean your work area after you finish. Follow your teacher's instructions about disposal of your swabs, cultures, and petri dishes.*

Skill Handbook

If you need help with this lab, refer to the **Skill Handbook**.

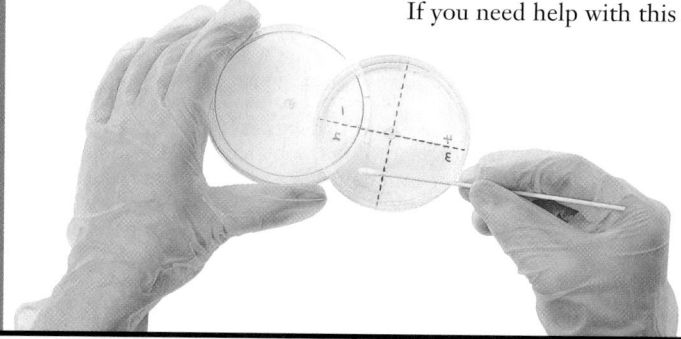

PROCEDURE

Teaching Strategies

■ Show students a petri dish that you inoculated with *E. coli* and then incubated two days before they begin this lab.

■ Teach students sterile technique. Have them practice with a sterile loop on plain agar before working with live cultures. A

loop and solid cultures are harder to use than a cotton swab and a liquid culture.

■ Have students hold the dish to the light to examine the clear zones of inhibition.

■ Explain that the *E. coli* that is a common, harmless intestinal dweller can cause disease in other body areas.

Possible Procedures

■ Students will likely divide the dish into four quadrants and place different antibiotic disks in each of three quadrants and a plain sterile disk in the fourth.

1. Examine the materials provided by your teacher, and study the photos in this lab. As a group, agree on one way that your group could investigate your hypothesis. Design an experiment in which you can collect quantitative data.

2. Make a list of numbered directions and include the amounts of each material you will need. If possible, use no more than one petri dish for each person.

3. Design and construct a table for recording data. To do this, carefully consider what data you need to record and how you will measure the data. For example, how will you measure what happens around the antibiotic disks as the antibiotic diffuses into the agar?

Check the Plan

Discuss the following points with other group members.

1. How will you set up your petri dishes? How many antibiotics can you test on one petri dish? How will you measure the effectiveness of each antibiotic? What will be your control?

2. Will you add the bacteria or the antibiotic disks first?

3. What will you do to prevent other bacteria from contaminating the petri dishes?

4. How often will you observe the petri dishes?

5. *Make sure your teacher has approved your experimental plan before you proceed further.*

6. Carry out your experiment. CAUTION: *Wash your hands with antibacterial soap and water after handling dishes of bacteria.*

7. CLEANUP AND DISPOSAL Consult with your teacher in order to make wise choices in the disposal of bacterial cultures and antibiotics.

ANALYZE AND CONCLUDE

1. **Measure in SI** How did you measure the zones of inhibition? Why did you do it this way?

2. **Draw Conclusions** Suppose you were a physician treating a patient infected with these bacteria. Which antibiotic would you use? Why?

3. **Analyze the Procedure** What limitations does this technique have? If these bacteria were infecting a person, what other tests might increase your confidence about treating the person with the most effective antibiotic?

Apply Your Skill

Application Use a similar procedure to test the effectiveness of four commercial antibacterial soaps and evaluate their promotional claims. Check your plan with your teacher, then prepare your disks by soaking them in the different soap solutions.

Web Links To find out more about antibiotics, visit in.bdol.glencoe.com/antibiotics

18.2 ARCHAEBACTERIA AND EUBACTERIA **497**

Possible Hypotheses

If antibiotic disks are in a bacterial culture, no bacteria will grow. If no antibiotic disks are present, bacterial growth will be great.

ANALYZE AND CONCLUDE

1. Most students will measure the diameter of the zone of inhibition and use the value as a basis of comparison.

2. Use the one with the largest zone of inhibition, which best inhibits bacterial growth.

3. The antibiotic may work in an agar culture, but not in human tissue. A doctor might also do blood tests to examine the kinds of white blood cells present, or look for the bacteria themselves.

Assessment

Portfolio Ask students to write a paragraph about the following event: A man arrives at his doctor's office with a bacterial infection in a cut. The doctor can prescribe one of ten antibiotics. How can she learn which antibiotic will work best for the patient? Use the Performance Task Assessment List for Writing in Science in **PASC**, p. 159. **L2**

Apply Your Skill

Application Students can use liquid soaps or a solution of distilled water and shavings of bar soap. They may need to vary the concentrations of the soap solutions.

■ After incubating the dish for two days, students can measure the diameter of the clear areas that surround the disks.

Data and Observations

Most antibiotic disks should show some inhibition. Results will vary depending on the antibiotic disks used. The untreated disks should show no zone of inhibition.

Purpose

Students learn why drug-resistant bacteria develop and how this threatens public health.

Background

Low levels of antibiotics in the environment promote natural selection for resistant bacteria. Without antibiotics, larger populations of nonresistant bacteria thrive because they usually outcompete resistant strains. Therefore, the presence of nonresistant bacteria might help slow the development of drug resistance.

Teaching Strategies

- Remind students that common antibiotics include penicillin, ampicillin, and tetracycline.
- Explain that patients who take fewer than the prescribed number of daily pills maintain low drug levels that kill nonresistant cells in their bodies.
- Tell students that some bacteria produce substances called bacteriocins that are toxic to closely related bacteria. Sometimes bacteriocins can replace antibiotics to control bacteria that can cause food poisoning.
- Explain that responsible use can prolong the effectiveness of current antibiotics while new ones are being tested.

Investigating the Issue

Bacteria can be genetically engineered to produce antibiotics that attack specific disease-causing bacteria.

Biology and Society

Superbugs Defy Drugs

Antibiotics have prevented millions of deaths from bacterial diseases in the past century. Today, however, many disease-causing bacteria have developed resistance to the antibiotics that used to kill them. The spread of antibiotic-resistant bacteria carries with it the threat of incurable disease. Microbiologists are working to develop new drugs to defeat these "superbugs."

Perspectives During the past 50 years, antibiotics have been used for preventive medical reasons and in agriculture. With the development of resistant bacteria, these uses are being reassessed.

How much is too much? Because antibiotics have worked well and had few side effects, some physicians prescribe them for preventive reasons. For example, physicians may prescribe antibiotics before surgery to prevent the chance of infection from bacteria during the surgery. In addition, some physicians prescribe antibiotics for patients with viral infections because a viral infection makes a body vulnerable to a bacterial infection.

Because antibiotics hasten the growth of healthy cattle, chickens, and other domestic animals, many animal feeds contain small amounts of antibiotics. Similarly, antibiotics are used to coat fruit and other agricultural products. These antibiotics may produce resistant bacteria, which pass to people when they eat the food.

Emerging resistance Many antibiotics are available, and several bacteria that they once killed are now resistant to one or more of them.

Prescription antibiotics

Tuberculosis, for example, is a deadly, highly contagious disease that a combination of antibiotics usually treats effectively. But strains of resistant tuberculosis bacteria have appeared, and the disease continues to claim lives after once being targeted for elimination through antibiotic use.

Some *Staphylococcus* bacteria, which cause serious infections in hospital patients, were previously resistant to all antibiotics except vancomycin, an antibiotic usually reserved as a last-resort antibiotic. Now vancomycin resistance has turned up in another common "hospital bug," *Enterococcus*. Resistance genes spread easily among bacteria, and vancomycin-resistant staphylococcus infections have recently appeared.

Developing better antibiotics Microbiologists are experimenting with bacterial viruses, or bacteriophages, to develop new antibiotics. Bacteriophages, commonly called phages prevent bacteria from building outer cell walls, weakening and killing the bacteria. Researchers believe phage DNA can be used to produce antibiotics that would attack bacterial cell walls. When bacterial strains develop resistance, the phage's DNA code could be manipulated to create an antibiotic that attacks a different point in the cell wall.

Genetics may provide another weapon in the fight against disease. One bacterium, *Streptomyces coelicolor*, is used to produce several antibiotics. The recent sequencing of its genome could lead to new antibiotics as researchers mix and match the genes to produce new compounds and medicines.

Investigating the Issue

Think Critically Not all bacteria are harmful. How might microbiologists use genetics to target specific disease-causing bacteria with new antibiotics?

 To find out more about bacteria that are antibiotic-resistant, visit in.bdol.glencoe.com/biology_society

Going Further

Encourage students to explore recent developments in the use of bacteriocins to battle food-borne bacteria, the search for new antibiotics, and the occurrence of diseases that are drug-resistant.

STUDY GUIDE

Section 18.1

Viruses

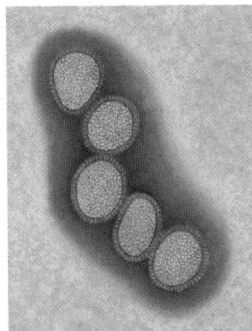

Color-enhanced TEM Magnification: 76 000×

Key Concepts

- Viruses are nonliving particles that have a nucleic acid core and a protein-containing capsid.

- To replicate, a virus must first recognize a host cell, then attach to it, and finally enter the host cell and take over its metabolism.

- During a lytic cycle, a virus replicates and kills the host cell. In a lysogenic cycle, a virus's DNA is integrated into a chromosome of the host cell, but the host cell does not die.

- Retroviruses contain RNA. Reverse transcriptase is an enzyme that helps convert viral RNA to DNA, which is then integrated into the host cell's chromosome.

- Prions and viroids are virus-like particles. Prions are composed of only a protein, while a viroid is a singular strand of RNA.

- Viruses probably originated from their host cells.

Vocabulary

bacteriophage (p. 475)
capsid (p. 476)
host cell (p. 475)
lysogenic cycle (p. 479)
lytic cycle (p. 479)
prion (p. 482)
provirus (p. 479)
retrovirus (p. 481)
reverse transcriptase
  (p. 481)
viroid (p. 482)
virus (p. 475)

Section 18.2

Archaebacteria and Eubacteria

Key Concepts

- There are two kingdoms of prokaryotes: archaebacteria and eubacteria. Archaebacteria inhabit extreme environments. Eubacteria live almost everywhere else. They probably arose separately from a common ancestor billions of years ago.

- Bacteria are varied. Some are heterotrophs, some are photosynthetic autotrophs, and others are chemosynthetic autotrophs. Bacteria can be obligate aerobes, obligate anaerobes, or both aerobic and anaerobic.

- Bacteria usually reproduce by binary fission. Some have a type of sexual reproduction called conjugation. Some bacteria form endospores that enable them to survive when conditions are unfavorable.

Vocabulary

binary fission (p. 489)
chemosynthesis (p. 486)
conjugation (p. 490)
endospore (p. 491)
nitrogen fixation
  (p. 493)
obligate aerobe (p. 491)
obligate anaerobe
  (p. 491)
toxin (p. 492)

LM Magnification: 250×

FOLDABLES™
Study Organizer To help you review viruses and bacteria, use the Organizational Study Fold on page 484.

 in.bdol.glencoe.com/vocabulary_puzzlemaker

CHAPTER 18 ASSESSMENT **499**

Key Concepts

Summary statements can be used by students to review the major concepts of the chapter.

Biology Online

Visit in.bdol.glencoe.com
  /self_check_quiz
  /vocabulary_puzzlemaker
  /chapter_test
  /standardized_test

VOCABULARY PUZZLEMAKER

For additional help with vocabulary, have students access the Vocabulary PuzzleMaker online at in.bdol.glencoe.com/vocabulary_puzzlemaker

FOLDABLES™
Have students use their Foldables to review the content of Section 18.2.

Use the ExamView®Pro Test Bank CD-ROM to:

- Create **multiple versions** of tests
- Create **modified** tests with one mouse click for **inclusion** students
- **Edit** existing questions and **add** your own questions
- Build tests aligned with state standards using built-in **State Curriculum Tags**
- Change **English** tests to **Spanish** with one mouse click and vice versa

Indiana Academic Standards

Pages 498–499: B.1.12, B.1.33, B.1.36, B.1.43

Questions and answers have been aligned and verified by The Princeton Review.

Vocabulary Review

1. host cell
2. reverse transcriptase
3. provirus
4. binary fission
5. endospore

Understanding Key Concepts

6. D	9. B	12. D
7. C	10. D	13. D
8. C	11. A	14. A

Constructed Response

15. Scientists cannot study or conduct experiments on the majority of the bacteria populations to discover their characteristics or requirements.

16. Viruses contain genetic material (DNA or RNA) and are able to replicate. Viruses are not composed of cells, and they do not grow or develop.

17. Many bacteria help to fertilize fields, recycle nutrients on Earth, and produce foods and medicines. Others cause disease in plants and animals, causing crops and livestock losses that impact humans directly.

Thinking Critically

18. Prions behave similar to viruses, but are comprised of only a protein, without genetic material. They appear to be a modified host protein that can transmit disease. The U.S. has instituted various regulations, such as airport checks on travelers from infected countries; bans on animal feed containing bovine tissue; and other regulations.

500

Vocabulary Review

Review the Chapter 18 vocabulary words listed in the Study Guide on page 499. Match the words with the definitions below.

1. a cell in which a virus replicates
2. retrovirus uses this enzyme to make DNA from its RNA
3. viral DNA that is integrated into the host cell's chromosome
4. method bacteria use to reproduce asexually
5. tiny structure that contains bacterial DNA encased by a tough outer covering

Understanding Key Concepts

6. A _____ is never a part of a virus.
   A. nucleic acid   C. viral envelope
   B. protein coat   D. cell wall

7. Which of the following is NOT a common bacterial shape?
   A.   B.   C.   D.

8. What characteristic do viruses share with all living organisms?
   A. respiration   C. replication
   B. metabolism   D. movement

9. During a lytic cycle, after a virus enters the cell, the virus _____.
   A. forms a provirus
   B. replicates
   C. dies
   D. becomes inactive

10. Prokaryotic cells have _____.
   A. organelles
   B. a nucleus
   C. mitochondria
   D. a cell wall

11. In _____, bacteria convert gaseous nitrogen into ammonia, nitrates, and nitrites.
   A. nitrogen fixation
   B. binary fission
   C. conjugation
   D. attachment

12. Bacteria that require _____ for respiration are called _____.
   A. food—obligate saprophytes
   B. hydrogen—archaebacteria
   C. oxygen—obligate anaerobes
   D. oxygen—obligate aerobes

13. Some bacteria, when faced with unfavorable environmental conditions, produce structures called _____.
   A. pili   C. toxins
   B. capsules   D. endospores

14. Which of the following would be most likely to live in Utah's Great Salt Lake?
   A. archaebacteria
   B. staphylococci
   C. eubacteria
   D. viruses

Constructed Response

15. **Open Ended** Scientists cannot grow about 99 percent of all bacteria in the laboratory. How might this inability interfere with understanding bacteria?

16. **Compare and Contrast** What characteristics of life do viruses have? Describe the ways in which viruses differ from living cells.

17. **Open Ended** Summarize the role of microorganisms such as bacteria in maintaining and disrupting equilibrium, including diseases in plants and animals.

Thinking Critically

18. **REAL WORLD BIOCHALLENGE** In addition to viruses, prions, such as bovine spongiform encephalopathy (mad cow disease), can cause diseases. Like viruses, prions are nonliving particles. What restrictions and regulations does the United States government have in place to prevent mad cow disease from coming to the U.S.? Research the answers and report back to your class by making a poster discussing the prevention of this disease in the U.S.

 in.bdol.glencoe.com/chapter_test

RUBRIC

Evaluating Open-Ended Questions
Open-ended assessment questions are graded by using a multilevel rubric that guides you in assessing a student's knowledge of a particular concept. The following rubric is a sample scoring device.

End-of-Course
Assessment Practice

All questions aligned and verified by *The Princeton Review*

Part 1 Multiple Choice

Use the diagram to answer questions 19 and 20.

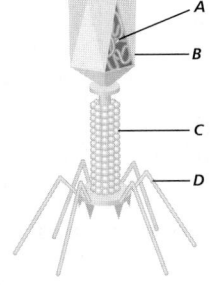

19. Which structure is the genetic material of the virus?
    - **A.** A
    - **B.** B
    - **C.** C
    - **D.** D

20. Which structure is used for attachment to a host bacterium?
    - **A.** A
    - **C.** C
    - **B.** B
    - **D.** D

21. Complete the concept map by using the following vocabulary terms: host cells, viruses, lysogenic cycle, bacteriophages, lytic cycle.

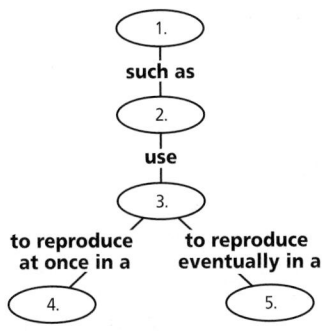

Part 2 Constructed Response/Grid In

Record your answers on your answer document.

25. **Open Ended** Describe the role of viruses in causing diseases and conditions such as acquired immune deficiency syndrome and smallpox.

26. **Open Ended** Bacteria interact with humans in several ways. Identify and describe the role of bacteria in both maintaining health, such as digestion, and causing disease in humans. Cite specific examples.

 in.bdol.glencoe.com/standardized_test

One milliliter of *E. coli* culture was added to each of three petri dishes (I, II, and III). The dishes were incubated for 36 hours, and then the number of bacterial colonies on each were counted.

Growth of *E. coli* Under Various Conditions		
Petri Dish Number	Medium	Colonies Per Dish
I	Agar and carbohydrates	35
II	Agar, carbohydrates, and vitamins	250
III	Agar and vitamins	0

Study the table and the paragraph above and answer questions 22–24.

22. Which of the above dishes demonstrate that carbohydrates are necessary for the growth of *E. coli?*
    - **A.** dish I alone
    - **B.** dishes I and II
    - **C.** dishes II and III
    - **D.** dish III

23. Which of the above dishes demonstrate that vitamins enhance the growth of *E. coli?*
    - **A.** dishes I and II
    - **B.** dishes II and III
    - **C.** dishes I and III
    - **D.** none of the dishes

24. Which is an independent variable in this experiment?
    - **A.** *E. coli*
    - **B.** agar
    - **C.** carbohydrates
    - **D.** number of colonies

CHAPTER 18 ASSESSMENT **501**

End-of-Course Assessment Practice

19. A   20. D
21. 1. viruses; 2. bacteriophages; 3. host cells; 4. lytic cycle; 5. lysogenic cycle
22. B   23. A   24. C
25. All viruses replicate in a host cell. Viruses such as smallpox, infect only humans and cause deadly diseases. Many disease-causing viruses have lysogenic cycles that allow them to stay in the host for long periods of time. Examples are herpes simplex I and II, hepatitis B, and chicken pox. Retroviruses make DNA from their RNA and are responsible for diseases such as AIDS.
26. Bacteria are part of the normal organisms living in our body, including the skin and intestinal tract. As a part of the intestinal tract, bacteria produce certain vitamins. Disease-causing bacteria enter the body and invade human tissue. The bacterial growth can interfere with the normal function of the tissue and the bacteria can produce toxins which directly attack the host. Examples may vary but might include syphilis, botulism, anthrax, strep throat, tuberculosis, tetanus, Lyme disease, or cholera.

 FAST FILE

Answer Sheet A practice answer sheet can be found on p. 35 of *Unit 6 FAST FILE Resources*.

 Indiana Academic Standards

Pages 500–501: B.1.2, B.1.8, B.1.9, B.1.40, B.1.43

RUBRIC

SCORE	CRITERIA
4	A correct solution that is supported by well-developed, accurate explanations.
3	A generally correct solution, but may contain minor flaws in reasoning.

SCORE	CRITERIA
2	A partially correct interpretation and/or solution to the problem.
1	A correct solution with no supporting evidence or explanation.
0	An incorrect solution or no solution is given.

Chapter 19 Organizer

Section Objectives	National Science Standards	State/Local Standards	Advanced Lab and Demo Planning
Section 19.1 1 session, 1 block 1. **Identify** the characteristics of the Kingdom Protista. 2. **Compare and contrast** the four groups of protozoans.	UCP.2, UCP.4, UCP.5; A.1, A.2; C.1, C.3, C.4, C.5, C.6; E.1; F.4; G.1	**Indiana Standards** B.1.2, B.1.3, B.1.43	**Student Labs:** MiniLab 19.1, p. 506: *Paramecium* culture, crushed wheat seed particles, dropper, water, microscope slide, coverslip, microscope Problem-Solving Lab 19.1, p. 508: pH paper, liquids with different pHs. **Teacher Demonstration:** Quick Demo, p. 505: slides of amoebas, foraminiferans, radiolarians
Section 19.2 1 session, 1 block 3. **Compare and contrast** the variety of plantlike protists. 4. **Explain** the process of alternation of generations in algae.	UCP.2; A.1, A.2; C.1, C.4, C.6; F.4, F.5; G.1, G.2	**Indiana Standards** B.1.2, B.1.3, B.1.8, B.1.11, B.1.43	**Student Labs:** MiniLab 19.2, p. 511: dropper, pond water, glass slide, coverslip, microscope Problem-Solving Lab 19.2, p. 514 **Teacher Demonstration:** Quick Demo, p. 515: agar, petri dish, label from an ice cream carton
Section 19.3 2 sessions, 1/2 block 5. **Contrast** the cellular differences and life cycles of the two types of slime molds. 6. **Discuss** the economic importance of the downy mildews and water molds.	UCP.2, UCP.4; A.1, A.2; C.1, C.4; E.1, E.2; F.3, F.4, F.5; G.1, G.2	**Indiana Standards** B.1.2, B.1.8, B.1.11, B.1.35, B.1.43	**Student Labs:** Problem-Solving Lab 19.3, p. 518 Additional Lab, p. 518: petri dish with plasmodium stage for *Physarum polycephalum*, stereomicroscope Design Your Own BioLab, p. 522: See materials below.
End of Chapter Assessment **Student Edition** **Study Guide,** p. 525 **Content Assessment,** pp. 526–527		**Indiana Standards** B.1.2, B.1.3, B.1.8, B.1.43	**Student Lab:** Design Your Own BioLab, p. 522: *Euglena* culture, *Paramecium* culture, microscope, microscope slides, dropper, methylcellulose, coverslips, metric ruler, index cards, scissors, toothpicks

Key to Teaching Strategies

L1 Level 1 activities should be appropriate for students with learning difficulties.

L2 Level 2 activities should be within the ability range of all students.

L3 Level 3 activities are designed for above-average students.

ELL ELL activities should be within the ability range of English Language Learners.

COOP LEARN Cooperative Learning activities are designed for small group work.

Legend

🕯 Transparency   💿 CD-ROM   🎵 MP3   📼 Videocassette   💿 DVD

Glencoe Exclusive!

TeacherWorks™
All-In-One Planner and Resource Center

Reproducible Masters and Transparencies

Technology

Unit 6 *FAST FILE* **Resources**
  MiniLab Worksheet, p. 39
  Reinforcement and Study Guide in English, p. 45
  Reinforcement and Study Guide in Spanish, p. 49
  Critical Thinking/Problem Solving, p. 54
  Transparency Worksheets, pp. 55, 65–68
Laboratory Manual, pp. 117–120
🕯 **Section Focus Transparency 45**
🕯 **Reteaching Skills Transparencies 29, 30**

💿 **Interactive Chalkboard CD-ROM: Section 19.1 Presentation** 🏴
💿 TeacherWorks™ **CD-ROM** 🏴
🎵 **Guided Reading Audio Summaries MP3**

Unit 6 *FAST FILE* **Resources**
  MiniLab Worksheet, p. 40
  BioLab Worksheet, pp. 41–42
  Real World BioApplications, pp. 43–44
  Reinforcement and Study Guide in English,
    pp. 46–47
  Reinforcement and Study Guide in Spanish,
    pp. 50–51
  Transparency Worksheets, pp. 56, 59–60, 63–64
Laboratory Manual, pp. 121–124
🕯 **Section Focus Transparency 46**
🕯 **Basic Concepts Transparencies 28, 30**

💿 **Interactive Chalkboard CD-ROM: Section 19.2 Presentation** 🏴
💿 TeacherWorks™ **CD-ROM** 🏴
🎵 **Guided Reading Audio Summaries MP3**

Unit 6 *FAST FILE* **Resources**
  Reinforcement and Study Guide in English, p. 48
  Reinforcement and Study Guide in Spanish, p. 52
  Concept Mapping, p. 53
  Transparency Worksheets, pp. 57, 61–64
🕯 **Section Focus Transparency 47**
🕯 **Basic Concepts Transparencies 29, 30**

💿 **Interactive Chalkboard CD-ROM: Section 19.3 Presentation** 🏴
💿 TeacherWorks™ **CD-ROM** 🏴
🎵 **Guided Reading Audio Summaries MP3**

Unit 6 *FAST FILE* **Resources**
  Chapter Assessment, pp. 69–74
  Student Recording Sheet, p. 75
The Princeton Review **Reviewing Biology,** pp. 37–38

💿 **Interactive Chalkboard:** 🏴
  Chapter 19 Assessment
💿 **MindJogger Videoquizzes DVD/VHS**
💿 **Exam*View*® Pro Test Bank CD-ROM**
💿 TeacherWorks™ **CD-ROM** 🏴
💿 **Succeeding on National Standards CD-ROM**

💻 in.bdol.glencoe.com
  /self_check_quiz
  /vocabulary_puzzlemaker
  /chapter_test
  /standardized_test

🏴 Indicates materials created specifically for Indiana.

Short on Time?

BIODIGEST The BioDigest at the end of this unit can be used as a(n):

- preview to introduce important unit concepts.
- overview if time does not permit teaching the entire chapter.
- review of key unit concepts.

Understanding the Photo

Slime molds have both animal-like and funguslike characteristics. They move like animals, but they form spores like fungi. Slime molds have been placed in the Kingdom Protista because they are so different from both animals and fungi. The common name for this particular slime mold is pretzel slime mold (*Hemitrichia serpula*) for its resemblance to a pretzel.

Content Background

Cell Models Use models of plant and animal cells available from biological supply houses or diagrams in Chapter 7 to review these typical cell types. As you discuss plantlike and animal-like protists, compare them to plant and animal cells.

Chapter 19

Protists

What You'll Learn

- You will differentiate among the major groups of protists.
- You will recognize the ecological niches of protists.
- You will identify some human diseases and the protists responsible for them.

Why It's Important

Because protists are responsible for much of the oxygen in the atmosphere, and are the base for most food chains in aquatic environments, most other organisms depend on protists for their own existences.

Understanding ▶ the Photo

This pretzel slime mold is a multicellular protist that grows on logs and branches. Its appearance and growth are similar to those of a fungus.

Biology Online

Visit **in.bdol.glencoe.com** to
- study the entire chapter online
- access Web Links for more information and activities on protists
- review content with the Interactive Tutor and self-check quizzes

502

Two-Minute Chapter Launcher

Demo Set up several microscopes with slides of different protozoans (such as *Paramecium, Euglena,* and *Amoeba*) in each. The slides may be prepared or wet mounts for the demonstration. Have students look at each slide. Ask students to compare and contrast the organisms they observe. Students should indicate that the organisms are unicellular and have different methods for movement and have some characteristics of plants and/or animals. **L2**

Section 19.1

The World of Protists

Indiana Standards Standard B.1.2 Explain that every cell is covered by a membrane that controls what can enter and leave the cell… In addition, understand that flagella and/or cilia may allow some Protista, some Monera, and some animal cells to move.

How do you classify these things?

Using Prior Knowledge You have learned that the six kingdom classification system includes many obviously distinct kingdoms, such as animals, plants, and fungi. Although most of the organisms in these kingdoms are very different from each other, Kingdom Protista contains organisms that are often almost impossible to tell apart from animals, plants, or fungi. This kingdom includes an amazingly diverse group, many of which move like an animal, photosynthesize like a plant, or produce spores like a fungus.

Explain *Read Section 19.1 and decide how you would define a protist.*

Color-enhanced LM Magnification: 120×

A protist in a water environment

What is a protist?

Kingdom Protista contains the most diverse organisms of all the kingdoms. Protists may be unicellular or multicellular, microscopic or very large, and heterotrophic or autotrophic. In fact, there is no such organism as a typical protist. When you look at different protists, you may wonder how they could be grouped together. The characteristic that all protists share is that, unlike bacteria, they are all eukaryotes, which means that most of their metabolic processes occur inside their membrane-bound organelles.

Although there are no typical protists, some resemble animals in the way they get food. The animal-like protists are called **protozoa** (proh tuh ZOH uh) (singular, protozoan). Unlike animals, though, all protozoans are unicellular. Other protists are plantlike autotrophs, using photosynthesis to make their food. Plantlike protists are called **algae** (AL jee) (singular, alga). Unlike plants, algae do not have organs such as roots, stems, and leaves. Still other protists are more like fungi because they decompose dead organisms. However, unlike fungi, funguslike protists are able to move at some point in their life and do not have chitin in their cell walls.

It might surprise you to learn how much protists affect other organisms. Some protists cause diseases, such as malaria and sleeping sickness, that result in millions of human deaths throughout the world every year.

19.1 THE WORLD OF PROTISTS **503**

SECTION PREVIEW

Objectives

Identify the characteristics of Kingdom Protista.

Compare and contrast the four groups of protozoans.

Review Vocabulary
eukaryote: unicellular or multicellular organism whose cells contain membrane-bound organelles (p. 173)

New Vocabulary
protozoan
alga
pseudopodia
asexual reproduction
flagellate
ciliate
sporozoan
spore

Word Origin

protozoa from the Greek words *protos,* meaning "first," and *zoa,* meaning "animals"; Protozoa are animal-like protists.

---

1 Focus

INTERACTIVE CHALKBOARD
PowerPoint® Presentations

Bellringer
Section Focus Transparency 45

Transparency **45** Protists

SECTION FOCUS
Use with Chapter 19, Section 19.1

This Amoeba is surrounding its food.

The Didinium is feeding on a Paramecium.

This Euglena moves by whipping its flagellum.

Beating cilia draw food into the mouth of this Stentor.

❶ What life characteristic is each of these organisms exhibiting?

❷ How are these organisms alike and different?

BIOLOGY: The Dynamics of Life   SECTION FOCUS TRANSPARENCIES

INTERACTIVE CHALKBOARD
with Image Bank

PowerPoint® Presentations

This CD-ROM is an editable Microsoft® PowerPoint® presentation that includes:
- Section presentations
- Section checks
- Image bank
- Hot links to Biology Online
- All transparencies

Using Prior Knowledge

Explain Protists are eukaryotes that show variety in feeding relationships (some are autotrophic, many are decomposers, some are parasitic), reproduction (both asexual and sexual, many times within the same group), and movement.

RESOURCE MANAGER

Unit 6 *FAST FILE* Resources
MiniLab Worksheet, p. 39
Reinforcement and Study Guide in English, p. 45
Reinforcement and Study Guide in Spanish, p. 49
Critical Thinking/Problem Solving, p. 54
Transparency Worksheets, pp. 55, 65–68

Reading Essentials for Biology, Section 19.1
Laboratory Manual, pp. 117–120
Section Focus Transparency 45
Reteaching Skills Transparencies 29, 30

503

2 Teach

Activity

Visual-Spatial After students have read about the characteristics of protists, have them diagram a generalized protist cell. They should draw their diagrams to scale and label the cell organelles. Then have students draw and label a bacterial cell (see Chapter 18) for comparison. This activity should initiate a useful discussion about the characteristics of protists. **L2** **ELL**

Tying to Prior Knowledge

Ask students to compare and contrast the terms in the word pairs that follow: eukaryotes and prokaryotes, heterotrophs and autotrophs, and motile and nonmotile. Eukaryotes have membrane-bound organelles; the prokaryotes lack membrane-bound organelles. Heterotrophs take in food from the environment; autotrophs produce their own food. A motile organism can move; a nonmotile organism cannot move. **L2** **ELL**

✓**Reading Check** Animal-like protists are all unicellular and lack cell walls. Plantlike protists are autotrophic, but do not develop organs. Funguslike protists develop spores like fungi, but do not contain chitin in their cell walls.

Unicellular algae produce much of the oxygen in Earth's atmosphere and are the basis of aquatic food chains. Slime molds and water molds decompose a significant amount of organic material, making the nutrients available to living organisms. Protozoans, algae, and funguslike protists play important roles on Earth. Look at ***Figure 19.1*** to see some protists.

✓**Reading Check** **Describe** the characteristics of animal-like, plantlike, and funguslike protists.

What is a protozoan?

If you sat by a pond, you might notice clumps of dead leaves at the water's edge. Under a microscope, a piece of those wet decaying leaves reveals a small world, probably inhabited by animal-like protists. Although a diverse group, all protozoans are unicellular heterotrophs that feed on other organisms or dead organic matter. They usually reproduce asexually, but some also reproduce sexually.

Figure 19.1
Members of Kingdom Protista are animal-like, plantlike, and funguslike.

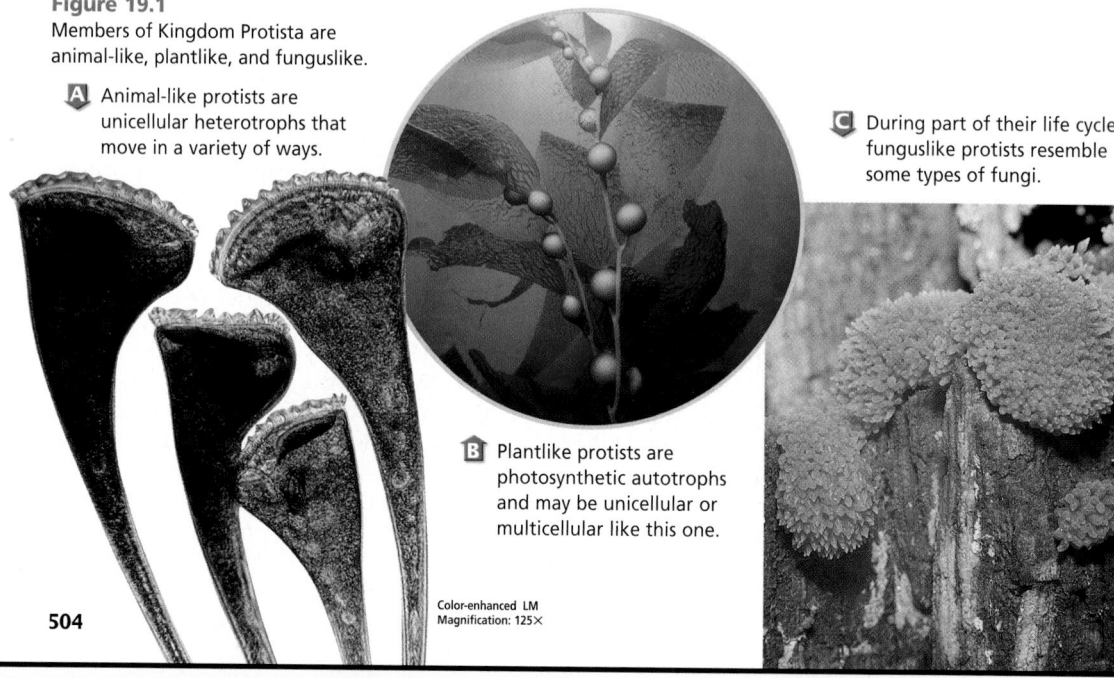

A Animal-like protists are unicellular heterotrophs that move in a variety of ways.

B Plantlike protists are photosynthetic autotrophs and may be unicellular or multicellular like this one.

C During part of their life cycle, funguslike protists resemble some types of fungi.

Color-enhanced LM
Magnification: 125×

504

Diversity of Protozoans

Many protozoans are grouped according to the way they move. Some protozoans use cilia or flagella to move. Others move and feed by sending out cytoplasm-containing extensions of their plasma membranes. These extensions are called **pseudopodia** (sew duh POH dee uh). Other protozoans are grouped together because they are parasites. There are four main groups of protozoans: the amoebas (uh MEE buz), the flagellates, the ciliates, and the sporozoans (spor uh ZOH unz).

Amoebas: Shapeless protists

The phylum Rhizopoda includes hundreds of species of amoebas and amoebalike organisms. Amoebas have no cell wall and form pseudopodia to move and feed. As a pseudopod forms, the shape of the cell changes and the amoeba moves. Amoebas form pseudopodia around their food, as you can see in ***Figure 19.2***. Although most amoebas live in salt water, there are freshwater ones that

---

INCLUSION STRATEGIES

Visually Impaired: *Kinesthetic* Have students build tactile models to demonstrate the difference between cilia and flagella. A piece of terry cloth or shag carpeting wrapped around a bar of soap can model cilia. Pieces of string 6 to 12 inches long taped to a ball can be used to simulate flagella. A plastic baseball with holes in it can be used to illustrate foraminiferans and radiolarians. **L1** **ELL**

Figure 19.2
An amoeba feeds on small organisms such as bacteria.

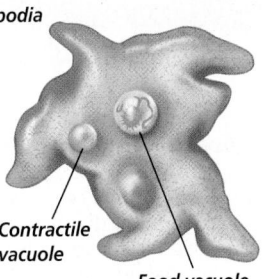

Nucleus

Cytoplasm

Pseudopodia

Contractile vacuole

Food vacuole

LM Magnification: 160×

A As an amoeba approaches food, pseudopodia form and eventually surround the food.

B The food becomes enclosed in a food vacuole.

C Digestive enzymes break down the food, and the nutrients diffuse into the cytoplasm.

live in the ooze of ponds, in wet patches of moss, and even in moist soil. Because amoebas live in moist places, nutrients dissolved in the water around them can diffuse directly through their cell membranes. However, because freshwater amoebas live in hypotonic environments, they constantly take in water. Their contractile vacuoles collect and pump out excess water.

Two groupings of mostly marine amoebas, the foraminiferan (foh ram uh NIH fer in) and radiolarian shown in *Figure 19.3*, have shells. Foraminiferans, which are abundant on the sea floor, have hard shells made of calcium carbonate. Fossil forms of these protists help geologists determine the ages of some rocks and sediments. Unlike foraminiferans, radiolarians have shells made of silica. Under a microscope, you can see the complexity of these shells. In addition, radiolarians are an important part of marine plankton—an assortment of microscopic organisms that float in the ocean's photic zone and form the base of marine food chains.

Most amoebas commonly reproduce by **asexual reproduction,** in which a single parent produces one or more identical offspring by dividing into two cells. When environmental conditions become unfavorable, some types of amoebas form cysts that can survive extreme conditions.

A

B

Color-enhanced LM Magnification: 100×

SEM Magnification: unavailable

Figure 19.3
Foraminiferans **(A)** and radiolarians **(B)** are amoebas that extend pseudopodia through tiny holes in their shells. Pseudopodia act like sticky nets that trap food. **Explain** *What are pseudopodia composed of?*

19.1 THE WORLD OF PROTISTS **505**

MiniLab 19.1

Purpose
Students will discover how a *Paramecium* species responds when it contacts a solid object.

Process Skills
observe and infer, draw a conclusion

Teaching Strategies
- Using methylcellulose to slow the protists interferes with *Paramecium's* normal response.
- Toothbrush bristles or small pieces of cotton may be used to block the path of *Paramecium*.
- Remind students to use caution when working with microscopes, slides, and coverslips.
- Have students wash their hands thoroughly with soap after handling cultures.

Expected Results
Paramecium typically reverses the direction in which its cilia are beating and backs away from a solid object that it contacts.

Analysis
1. it backs up, then proceeds forward in a new direction
2. briefly
3. The cell turns on its long axis, and can fold.

Modified Assessment
Portfolio Have students draw what occurs when *Paramecium* encounters solid objects and write captions for the events. Use the Performance Task Assessment List for Scientific Drawing in **PASC,** p. 127. **L1**

MiniLab 19.1

Observe and Infer

Observing Ciliate Motion The cilia on the surface of a paramecium move so that the cell normally swims through the water with one end directed forward. But when this end bumps into an obstacle, the paramecium responds by changing direction.

Observing a paramecium

Procedure
1. Observe a paramecium culture that has had boiled, crushed wheat seeds in it for several days.
2. Carefully place a drop of water containing wheat seed particles on a microscope slide. Gently add a coverslip.
3. Using low power, locate a paramecium near some wheat seed particles. **CAUTION: Use caution when working with a microscope, glass slides, and coverslips.**
4. Watch the paramecium as it swims around among the particles. Record your observations of the organism's responses each time it contacts a particle.

Analysis
1. **Describe** What does a paramecium do when it encounters an obstacle?
2. **Observe** How long does the paramecium's response last?
3. **Describe** How does the shape of the paramecium change as it moves among the particles?

Figure 19.4
The flagellated protozoans **(A)** that live in the guts of termites **(B)** produce enzymes that digest wood, making nutrients available to their hosts.

LM Magnification: 120×

506 PROTISTS

Flagellates: Protozoans with flagella

The phylum Zoomastigina consists of protists called **flagellates,** which have one or more flagella. Flagellate protists move by whipping their flagella from side to side.

Some flagellates are parasites that cause diseases in animals, such as African sleeping sickness in humans. Other flagellates are helpful. For example, termites like those you see in *Figure 19.4B* survive on a diet of wood. Without the help of a certain species of flagellate that lives in the guts of termites, some termites could not survive on such a diet. In a mutualistic relationship, flagellates convert cellulose from wood into a carbohydrate that both they and their termite hosts can use.

Ciliates: Protozoans with cilia

The roughly 8000 members of the protist phylum Ciliophora, known as **ciliates,** use the cilia that cover their bodies to move. Use the *MiniLab* on this page to observe a typical ciliate motion. Ciliates live in every kind of aquatic habitat—from ponds and streams to oceans and sulfur springs. What does a typical ciliate look like? To find out, look at *Figure 19.5* on the next page.

TECH PREP

Charting Protist Diseases: *Visual-Spatial* Have students make a table about the agents and symptoms of the following diseases: malaria, sleeping sickness, Chagas' disease, giardiasis, and amoebic dysentery. Column headings can be: *Kingdom, Phylum, Means of Locomotion, Method of Transmission,* *Parasitic or Free-living, Disease Symptoms,* and *Comments.* In the comments column, students can indicate dates of famous outbreaks, countries in which the disease is located, how many people are affected each year and/or methods of treatment available. **L2**

A Paramecium

Figure 19.5
Paramecia are unicellular organisms, but their cells are quite complex. Within a paramecium are many organelles and structures that are each adapted to carry out a distinct function. **Critical Thinking** *How might the contractile vacuoles of a paramecium respond if the organism were placed in a dilute salt solution?*

LM Magnification: 110✕

Paramecium caudatum

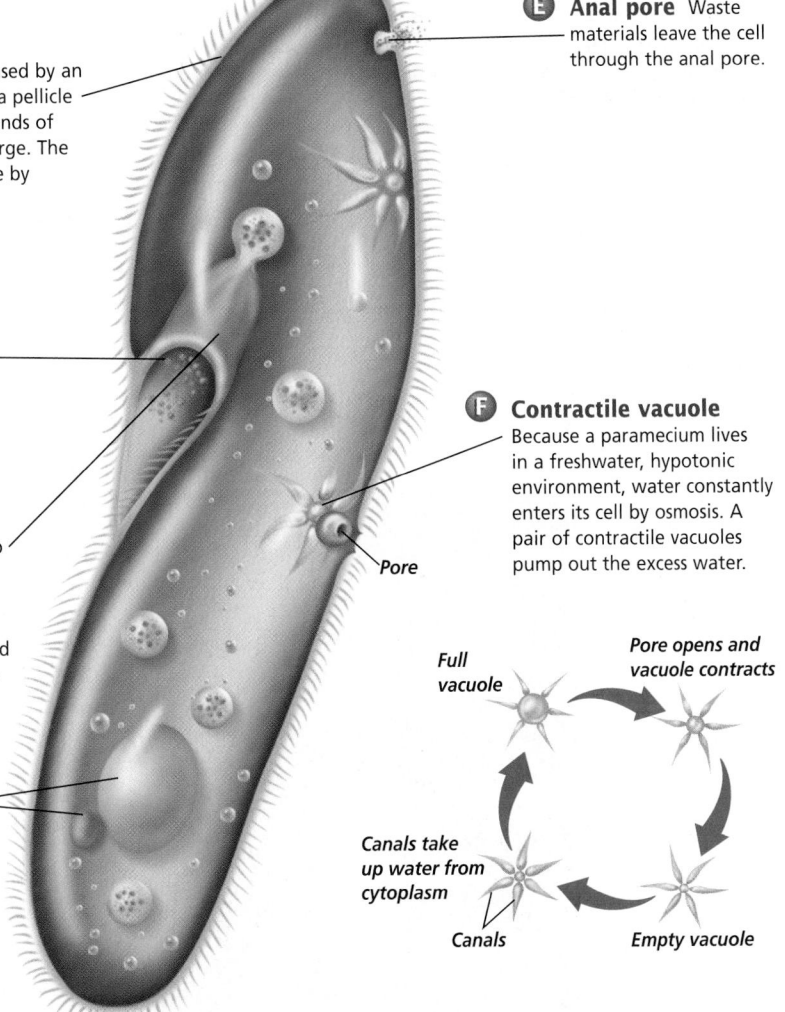

Ⓐ Cilia The cell is encased by an outer covering called a pellicle through which thousands of tiny, hairlike cilia emerge. The paramecium can move by beating its cilia.

Ⓑ Oral groove Paramecia feed primarily on bacteria that are swept into the gullet by cilia that line the oral groove.

Ⓒ Gullet Food moves into the gullet, becoming enclosed at the end in a food vacuole. Enzymes break down the food, and the nutrients diffuse into the cytoplasm.

Ⓓ Micronucleus and macronucleus The small micronucleus plays a major role in sexual reproduction. The large macronucleus controls the everyday functions of the cell.

Ⓔ Anal pore Waste materials leave the cell through the anal pore.

Ⓕ Contractile vacuole Because a paramecium lives in a freshwater, hypotonic environment, water constantly enters its cell by osmosis. A pair of contractile vacuoles pump out the excess water.

Pore

Full vacuole

Pore opens and vacuole contracts

Canals take up water from cytoplasm

Canals

Empty vacuole

19.1 THE WORLD OF PROTISTS **507**

Purpose
Students learn about the role of *Paramecium's* organelles.

Teaching Strategies
Ask students to explain the action of the contractile vacuoles.

Visual Learning
- Have students describe the location, shape, and function of each organelle. **L1**
- Have students make a table with the headings Function and Organelle. Beneath the Function head, have students list: Digestion, Locomotion, Protection, Excretion, Homeostasis, and Reproduction. Instruct the students to use the diagram to complete their tables. **L2**

Critical Thinking
Just about anything aside from pure water has some salt content, so that the terms *salt water* and *freshwater* are relative terms. If the medium in which the paramecium is swimming is more dilute than the cytoplasm inside the paramecium, or any water in the contractile vacuole, then water will tend to move into the paramecium and the contractile vacuole will contract less frequently. See the discussion in Chapter 8 (Figures 8.2 through 8.4) on isotonic, hypotonic, and hypertonic solutions.

CHALLENGE ACTIVITY

Observing Paramecia Provide students with cultures of live *Paramecium*. Have students make wet mount slides and using careful techniques, observe the activities of the organism. Have students draw one *Paramecium* and label the drawing from observations of one or more of the organisms. In particular, help students to focus on the surface of the organism to see cilia. Students can describe movements. Live paramecia are active and may need to be slowed down. Cilia are lined up in orderly fashion. **L3**

Purpose

Analyze the role of digestive enzymes in *Paramecium*.

Process Skills

observe and infer, interpret scientific illustrations, recognize cause and effect

Teaching Strategies

Review pH. Inform students that there are both liquid and paper pH indicators.

Thinking Critically

The pH in a food vacuole forming at the end of the gullet is above 5. As digestion begins, the pH drops to below 3 and changes again as digestion progresses. As digestion nears completion, the pH increases until it is above 5 again.

Assessment

Performance Give students liquids with different pHs. Have them use pH paper to find which liquids match the pH in *Paramecium's* food vacuole at the start and end of digestion. Use the Performance Task Assessment List for Carrying Out a Strategy and Collecting Data in **PASC,** p. 97. **L2** **ELL**

Inquiry

Activity Have students research and write a report on the correlation between the genetic disease sickle-cell anemia and malaria. They should include the evolutionary significance of such a relationship. **L3**

Problem-Solving Lab 19.1

Draw a Conclusion

How do digestive enzymes function in paramecia? Paramecia ingest food particles and enclose them in food vacuoles.

Each food vacuole circulates in the cell as the food is digested by enzymes that enter the vacuole. Digested nutrients are absorbed into the cytoplasm.

Solve the Problem

1. Some digestive enzymes function best at high pH levels, while others function best at low (more acidic) pH levels.
2. Congo red is a pH indicator dye; it is red when the pH is above 5 and blue when the pH is below 3 (very acidic).
3. Yeast cells that contain Congo red can be produced by adding dye to the solution in which the cells are growing.
4. When paramecia feed on dyed yeast cells, the yeast is visible inside food vacuoles.
5. Examine the drawing above. The appearance of a yeast-filled food vacuole over time is indicated by the colored circles inside the paramecium. Each arrow indicates movement and the passing of time.

Thinking Critically

Observe and Infer What happens to the pH in the food vacuole over time? Explain what sequence of digestive enzymes might function in a paramecium.

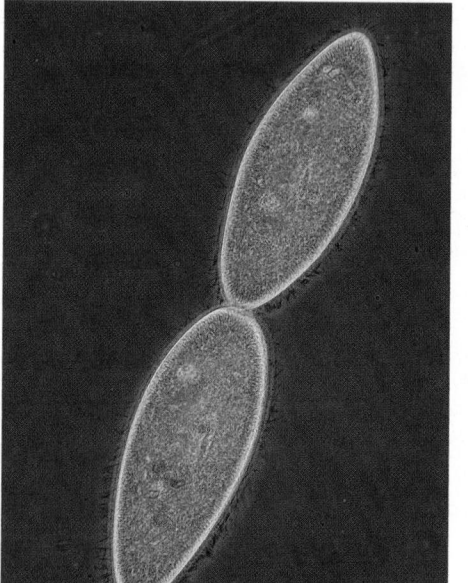

Color-enhanced LM Magnification: 84×

Figure 19.6
A paramecium reproduces by dividing into two identical daughter cells.

508 PROTISTS

Many structures found in ciliates' cells may work together to perform just one important life function. For example, a *paramecium* uses its cilia, oral groove, gullet, and food vacuoles in the process of digestion. Use the *Problem-Solving Lab* on this page to explore how a paramecium digests the food in a vacuole.

A paramecium usually reproduces asexually by dividing crosswise and separating into two daughter cells, as you can see in *Figure 19.6.* Whenever their food supplies dwindle or their environmental conditions change, paramecia usually undergo a form of conjugation. In this complex process, two paramecia join and exchange genetic material. Then they separate, and each divides asexually, passing on its new genetic composition.

Sporozoans: Parasitic protozoans

Protists in the phylum Sporozoa are often called **sporozoans** because most produce spores. A **spore** is a reproductive cell that forms without fertilization and produces a new organism.

All sporozoans are parasites. They live as internal parasites in one or more hosts and have complex life cycles. Sporozoans are usually found in a part of a host that has a ready food supply, such as an animal's blood or intestines. *Plasmodium*, members of the sporozoan genus, are organisms that cause the disease malaria in humans and other mammals and in birds.

Sporozoans and malaria

Throughout the world today, more than 300 million people have malaria, a serious disease that usually occurs in places that have tropical climates. The *Plasmodium* that mosquitoes transmit to people cause human malaria. As you can see in *Figure 19.7,* the

---

CHALLENGE ACTIVITY

Malaria Drugs Students can research the efforts to produce new drugs to prevent malaria. After doing research, they can write an illustrated newspaper article that describes what they have learned. **L3**

Indiana Academic Standards
Pages 508–509: B.1.2, B.1.3, B.1.43

malaria-causing *Plasmodium* live in both humans and mosquitoes.

Until World War II, the drug quinine was used to treat malaria. Today, a combination of the drugs chloroquine and primaquine are most often used to treat this disease because they cause few serious side effects in humans. But some species of *Plasmodium* have begun to resist these drugs. Therefore, new drugs are under development to treat malaria.

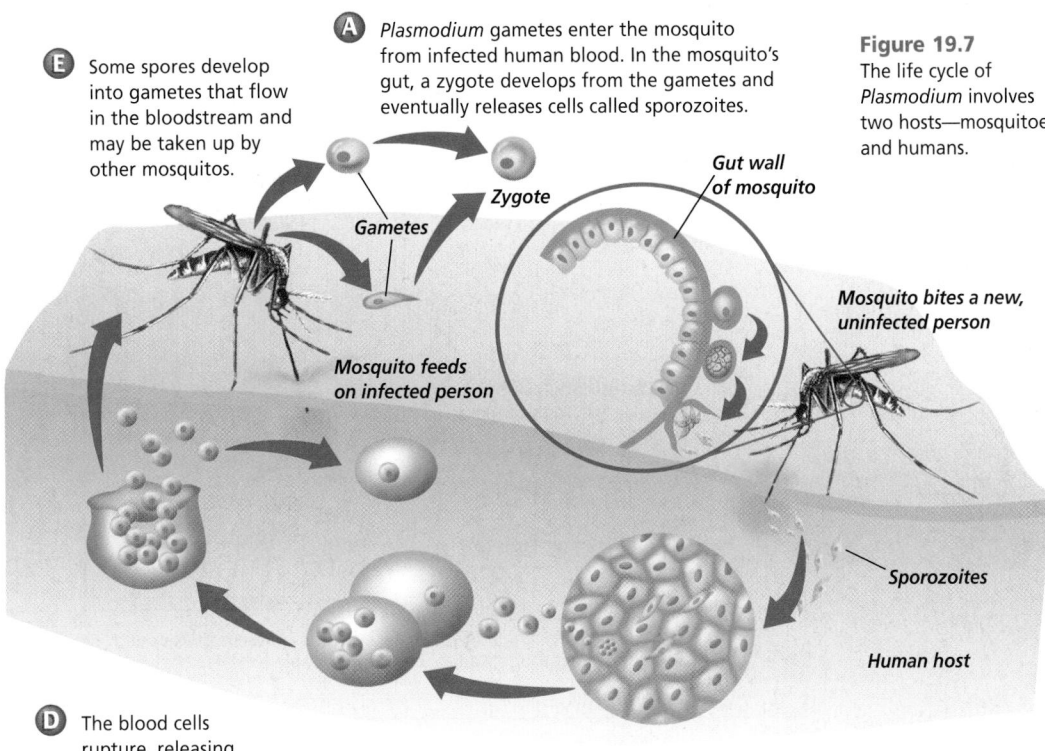

E Some spores develop into gametes that flow in the bloodstream and may be taken up by other mosquitos.

A *Plasmodium* gametes enter the mosquito from infected human blood. In the mosquito's gut, a zygote develops from the gametes and eventually releases cells called sporozoites.

Gametes

Zygote

Gut wall of mosquito

Mosquito feeds on infected person

Mosquito bites a new, uninfected person

Sporozoites

Human host

Figure 19.7
The life cycle of *Plasmodium* involves two hosts—mosquitoes and humans.

D The blood cells rupture, releasing both toxins and new spores that infect more red blood cells and multiply.

C The sporozoites reproduce asexually in the human's liver, forming sporelike cells that enter the human's red blood cells and multiply rapidly.

B Sporozoites enter the mosquito's salivary gland and are injected into the mosquito's human host.

Section Assessment

Understanding Main Ideas
1. Describe the characteristics of the protist kingdom. Then compare the characteristics of the four major groups of protozoans. How is each group of protozoans animal-like?
2. How do amoebas obtain food?
3. Explain any differences that exist between ciliates and flagellates.
4. What makes a sporozoan different from other protozoan groups?

Thinking Critically
5. What role do contractile vacuoles play in helping freshwater protozoans maintain homeostasis?

SKILL REVIEW
6. **Sequence** Trace the life cycle of a Plasmodium that causes human malaria. Identify all forms of the sporozoan and the role each plays in the disease. For more help, refer to *Sequence* in the **Skill Handbook**.

 in.bdol.glencoe.com/self_check_quiz

3 Assess

DAILY INTERVENTION

Check for Understanding
Visual-Spatial Have students make a concept map showing Kingdom Protista's three subgroups. Ask them to expand their maps to include the four protozoan phyla. **L2**

Reteach
Have students list five general protist traits and then make a second list of protozoan-specific traits. **L1**

Resources
For more practice, use *Reading Essentials for Biology*, Section 19.1.

Extension
Have students research the phylum of the organism *Trypanosoma cruzi*. Ask them to draw and label this protist. **L2**

✓ Assessment

Knowledge Have students identify the unrelated word in each of the following groups:
1. amoeba, foraminiferan, *Paramecium*, radiolarian;
2. pseudopodia, cilia, oral groove, pellicle;
3. dysentery, AIDS, sleeping sickness, Chagas' disease. **L2**

Section Assessment

1. Protists are eukaryotes without tissues. Protozoans are unicellular, heterotrophic protists. Rhizopods have pseudopodia, Ciliophorans have cilia, and flagella propel Mastigophorans. Sporozoans are parasites.
2. Pseudopodia entrap prey.
3. Flagellates have long, whiplike flagella. Ciliates have many short, hairlike cilia.
4. All are parasitic, many produce spores, and some cannot move.
5. Contractile vacuoles pump out excess water that enters the cell by osmosis.
6. Student answers should include the information in Figure 19.7. Both the human and mosquito hosts and the forms that *Plasmodium* take in each host should be distinguished.

1 Focus

Bellringer
Section Focus Transparency 46

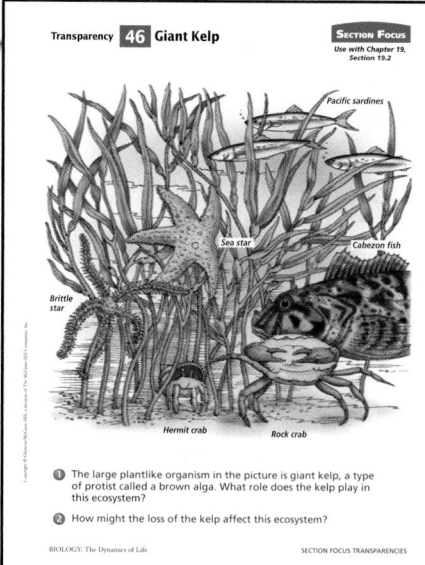

Transparency **46** Giant Kelp

SECTION FOCUS
Use with Chapter 19, Section 19.2

Pacific sardines

Sea star

Cabezon fish

Brittle star

Hermit crab   *Rock crab*

① The large plantlike organism in the picture is giant kelp, a type of protist called a brown alga. What role does the kelp play in this ecosystem?

② How might the loss of the kelp affect this ecosystem?

BIOLOGY: The Dynamics of Life   SECTION FOCUS TRANSPARENCIES

Biology Journal

Protozoans and Algae Have students prepare a table that compares and contrasts protozoans and algae. Suggest that they use the headings *Similarities* and *Differences*. The rows can include topics such as *cell organization*, *nutrition*, and *cell structures*. **L2**

FOLDABLES™

For an additional Foldables activity idea, see the Chapter 19 Foldables page in *Unit 6 FAST FILE Resources*.

Indiana Academic Standards

Pages 510–511: B.1.2, B.1.3

Section 19.2

Algae: Plantlike Protists

SECTION PREVIEW

Objectives
Compare and contrast the variety of plantlike protists.

Explain the process of alternation of generations in algae.

Review Vocabulary
photosynthesis: process by which autotrophs trap energy from sunlight with chlorophyll and convert carbon dioxide and water into simple sugars (p. 225)

New Vocabulary
thallus
colony
fragmentation
alternation of generations
gametophyte
sporophyte

FOLDABLES™
Study Organizer

Protists Make the following Foldable to help identify and study the characteristics of each type of algae.

STEP 1 **Fold** a vertical sheet of paper from side to side. Make the back edge about 1.5 cm longer than the front edge.

STEP 2 **Turn** lengthwise and **fold** into six sections.

STEP 3 **Unfold and cut** only the top layer along all five folds to make six tabs.

STEP 4 **Label** each tab as follows: *Euglenoids, Diatoms, Dinoflagellates, Red Algae, Brown Algae, Green Algae.* Label the edge as *Unicellular and Multicellular Algae.*

Read and Write As you read Section 19.2, list the characteristics of each type of algae under the appropriate tab. Use your foldable to take notes and as a study guide.

What are algae?

Photosynthesizing protists are called algae. All algae contain up to four kinds of chlorophyll as well as other photosynthetic pigments. These pigments produce a variety of colors in algae, including purple, rusty-red, olive-brown, yellow, and golden-brown, and are a way of classifying algae into groups.

Algae include both unicellular and multicellular organisms. The photosynthesizing unicellular protists, known as phytoplankton (fi toh PLANK tun), are so numerous that they are one of the major producers of nutrients and oxygen in aquatic ecosystems in the world. Through photosynthesis, algae produce much of the oxygen used on Earth. Although multicellular algae may look like plants because they are large and sometimes green, they have no roots, stems, or leaves. Use the *MiniLab* on the next page to observe algae.

510 PROTISTS

RESOURCE MANAGER

Unit 6 *FAST FILE* Resources
MiniLab Worksheet, p. 40
BioLab Worksheet, pp. 41–42
Real World BioApplications, pp. 43–44
Reinforcement and Study Guide in English, pp. 46–47
Reinforcement and Study Guide in Spanish, pp. 50–51

Transparency Worksheets, pp. 56, 59–60, 63–64
Reading Essentials for Biology, Section 19.2
Laboratory Manual, pp. 121–124
Section Focus Transparency 46
Basic Concepts Transparencies 28, 30

Diversity of Algae

Algae are classified into six phyla. Three of these phyla—the euglenoids, diatoms, and dinoflagellates—include only unicellular species. However, in the other three phyla, which are the green, red, and brown algae, most species are multicellular.

Euglenoids: Autotrophs and heterotrophs

Hundreds of species of euglenoids (yoo GLEE noydz) make up the phylum Euglenophyta. Euglenoids are unicellular, aquatic protists that have both plant and animal characteristics. Unlike plant cells, they lack a cell wall made of cellulose. However, they do have a flexible pellicle made of protein that surrounds the cell membrane. Euglenoids are plantlike in that most have chlorophyll and photosynthesize. However, they are also animal-like because, when light is not available, they can ingest food in ways that might remind you of some protozoans. In other words, euglenoids can be heterotrophs. *In Figure 19.8,* you can see a typical euglenoid.

Euglenoids might also remind you of protozoans because they have one or more flagella to move.

MiniLab 19.2

Observe

Going on an Algae Hunt Pond water may be teeming with organisms. Some are macroscopic organisms, but the majority are microscopic. Some may be heterotrophs, and others autotrophs. How can you tell them apart?

Procedure

1. Copy the data table.

Data Table		
Diagram	**Motile/Nonmotile**	**Unicellular/Multicellular**

2. Place a drop of pond water onto a glass slide and add a coverslip. **CAUTION:** *Use caution when working with a microscope, glass slides, and coverslips.*
3. Observe the pond water under low magnification of your microscope, and look for algae that may be present. Algae from a pond will usually be green or yellow-green in color.
4. Diagram several different species of algae in your data table and indicate if each is motile or nonmotile. Indicate if the algae are unicellular or multicellular.

Analysis

1. **Analyze** What characteristic distinguished algae from any protozoans that may have been present?
2. **Describe** Explain how the characteristic in question 1 categorizes algae as autotrophs.
3. **Observe** Did you observe any relationship between movement and size? Explain your answer.

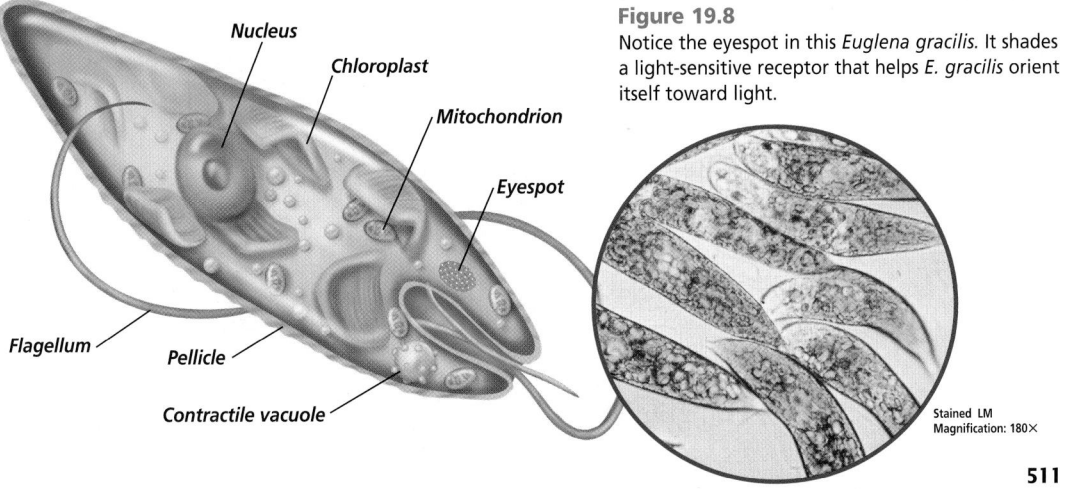

Figure 19.8
Notice the eyespot in this *Euglena gracilis.* It shades a light-sensitive receptor that helps *E. gracilis* orient itself toward light.

Nucleus
Chloroplast
Mitochondrion
Eyespot
Flagellum
Pellicle
Contractile vacuole

Stained LM
Magnification: 180×

511

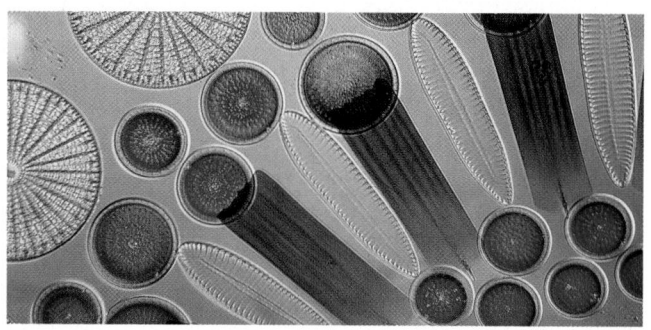

Figure 19.9
Diatom shells have many shapes.

Color-enhanced LM Magnification: 450×

They use their flagella to move toward light or food. In the *BioLab* at the end of this chapter, you can learn more about how a euglenoid responds to light.

Diatoms: The golden algae

Diatoms (DI uh tahmz), members of the phylum Bacillariophyta, are unicellular photosynthetic organisms with shells composed of silica. They make up a large component of the phytoplankton population in both marine and freshwater ecosystems.

The delicate shells of diatoms, like those you see in *Figure 19.9*, might remind you of boxes with lids. Each species has its own unique shape, decorated with grooves and pores.

Diatoms contain chlorophyll as well as other pigments called carotenoids (ke RUH tuhn oydz) that usually give them a golden-yellow color. The food that diatoms make is stored as oils rather than starch. These oils give fishes that feed on diatoms an oily taste. They also give diatoms buoyancy so that they float near the surface where light is available.

When diatoms reproduce asexually, the two halves of the box separate. Each half then produces a new half to fit inside itself. This means that half of each generation's offspring are smaller than the parent cells. When diatoms

Figure 19.10
Diatoms reproduce asexually for several generations before reproducing sexually. **Infer** *How is the size of the diatom related to its mode of reproduction?*

Mitosis

Wall formation around cell

Asexual reproduction

Meiosis

Sexual reproduction

Zygote

Gametes

Fusion of gametes

Sperm released

512 PROTISTS

Color-enhanced SEM Magnification: 12 000×

Figure 19.11
Red tides, such as the one shown here **(A)**, are often caused by dinoflagellates such as this one called *Gonyaulax* **(B)**.

are about one-quarter of their original size, they reproduce sexually by producing gametes that fuse to form zygotes. The zygote develops into a full-sized diatom, which will divide asexually for a while. You can see both the asexual and sexual reproductive processes of diatoms in *Figure 19.10.*

When diatoms die, their shells sink to the ocean floor. The deposits of diatom shells—some of which are millions of years old—are dredged or mined, processed, and used as abrasives in tooth and metal polishes, or added to paint to give the sparkle that makes pavement lines more visible at night.

Dinoflagellates: The spinning algae

Dinoflagellates (di nuh FLA juh layts), members of the phylum Dinoflagellata, have cell walls that are composed of thick cellulose plates. They come in a great variety of shapes and styles—some even resemble helmets, and others look like suits of armor.

Dinoflagellates contain chlorophyll, carotenoids, and red pigments. They have two flagella located in grooves at right angles to each other. The cell spins slowly as the flagella beat. A few species of dinoflagellates live in freshwater, but most are marine and, like diatoms, are a major

component of phytoplankton. Many species live symbiotically with jellyfishes, mollusks, and corals. Some free-living species are bioluminescent, which means that they emit light.

Several species of dinoflagellates produce toxins. One toxin-producing dinoflagellate, *Pfiesteria piscicida*, that some North Carolina researchers discovered in 1988, has caused a number of fish kills in the coastal waters from Delaware to North Carolina.

Another toxic species, *Gonyaulax catanella*, produces an extremely strong nerve toxin that can be lethal. In the summer, these organisms may become so numerous that the ocean takes on a reddish color as you can see in *Figure 19.11.* This population explosion is called a red tide. In some red tides, there can be as many as 40 to 60 million dinoflagellates per liter of seawater.

The toxins produced during a red tide may make humans ill. During red tides, the harvesting of shellfish is usually banned because shellfish feed on the toxic algae and the toxins concentrate in their tissues. People who eat such shellfish risk being poisoned. You can learn more about the causes and effects of red tides in the *Problem-Solving Lab* on the next page.

19.2 ALGAE: PLANTLIKE PROTISTS **513**

Purpose

Students will analyze real-life events associated with red tides.

Process Skills

think critically, acquire information, draw a conclusion, recognize cause and effect

Teaching Strategies

■ Have students work in small groups, discussing each event thoroughly.

■ Have groups share answers.

Thinking Critically

1. **a.** statements 1 or 2—Toxins accumulate in shellfish that humans eat; mackerel eat dinoflagellates and whales eat the mackerel.
   b. statement 5—Autotrophs use sunlight and nutrients to grow.
   c. statement 3—Human population growth correlates with the frequency of red tides.

2. No, statement 3 indicates a correlation between human activity and the frequency of red tides but it does not prove human responsibility.

Modified Assessment

Portfolio Have students diagram dinoflagellates they observe on prepared slides or from photographs or illustrations you provide. Have students write a statement as to why they are called dinoflagellates. They each have a pair of flagella. Use the Performance Task Assessment List for Scientific Drawing in **PASC**, p. 127. **L1**

Problem-Solving Lab 19.2

Recognize Cause and Effect

Why is the number of red tides increasing? Scientists have been aware of red tide poisoning of birds, fishes, and mammals such as whales and humans for years. Could the rise in red tide poisoning be related to human activities?

A sperm whale's carcass

Solve the Problem

The following events are associated with the appearance of red tides.

1 The dinoflagellate toxin that causes illness and sometimes death in humans accumulates in the body tissues of shellfish, such as clams and oysters.

2 Within five weeks, 14 humpback whales died on beaches in Massachusetts. The whales' stomachs contained mackerel with high levels of dinoflagellate toxin.

3 Between 1976 and 1986, the human population of Hong Kong increased sixfold, and its harbor had an eightfold increase in red tides. Human waste water was commonly emptied into the harbor.

4 Studies show that red tides are increasing worldwide.

5 An algal bloom occurs when algae, using sunlight and abundant nutrients, increase rapidly in number to hundreds of thousands of cells per milliliter of water.

Thinking Critically

1. **Think Critically** Which statement above provides evidence that supports each of the following ideas? Explain each answer.
   a. Dinoflagellate poisons flow through the food chain.
   b. Dinoflagellates are autotrophs.
   c. There is a correlation between human activities and algae growth.

2. **Think Critically** Based on the evidence presented above, can you conclude that human activity is responsible for the increase in red tides? Why or why not?

Red algae

Red algae, members of the phylum Rhodophyta, are mostly multicellular marine seaweeds. The body of a seaweed, as well as that of some plants and other organisms, is called a **thallus** and lacks roots, stems, or leaves. Red algae use structures called holdfasts to attach to rocks. They grow in tropical waters or along rocky coasts in cold water. You can see a red alga in *Figure 19.12.*

In addition to chlorophyll, red algae also contain photosynthetic pigments called phycobilins. These pigments absorb green, violet, and blue light—the only part of the light spectrum that penetrates water below depths of 100 m. Therefore, the red algae can live in deep water where most other seaweeds cannot thrive.

Brown algae

About 1500 species of multicellular brown algae make up the phylum Phaeophyta. Almost all of these species live in salt water along rocky coasts in cool areas of the world. Brown algae contain chlorophyll as well as a yellowish-brown carotenoid called fucoxanthin, which gives them their brown color. Many species of brown algae have air bladders that keep their bodies floating near the surface, where light is available.

The largest and most complex of brown algae are kelp. In kelp, the thallus is divided into the holdfast,

Figure 19.12
This Coralline alga is only one of about 4000 species of red algae. Some species are popular foods in Japan and other countries.

CULTURAL DIVERSITY

Algae Harvesting in Japan Inform students that people in many areas of the world, particularly Asia, eat certain algae. Point out that algae contain nutrients, such as protein, and many vitamins and minerals. Algae are eaten fresh, boiled, or fried in many Asian recipes. One edible alga used in Japanese cooking is *Porphyra*, a red alga commonly called *nori*. Since the seventeenth century, the Japanese have harvested nori from Tokyo Bay. Have students research how the Japanese harvest algae. Bring in some Japanese foods that contain algae for the class to see. **L3**

ipe, and blade. The holdfasts anchor elp to rocks or the sea bottom. Some iant kelp may grow up to 60 meters ng. In some parts of the world, ich as off the California coast, giant elps form dense, underwater forests. hese kelp forests are rich ecosystems id provide a wide variety of marine rganisms with their habitats.

reen algae

Green algae make up the phylum chlorophyta. The green algae are le most diverse algae, with more han 7000 species. The major pig-lent in green algae is chlorophyll, ut some species also have yellow igments that give them a yellow-reen color. Most species of green lgae live in freshwater, but some live 1 the oceans, in moist soil, on tree runks, in snow, and even in the fur of loths—large, slow-moving mammals hat live in the tropical rain forest anopy.

Green algae can be unicellular, olonial, or multicellular in organiza-on. As you can see in *Figure 19.13,*

Chlamydomonas is a unicellular and flagellated green alga. *Spirogyra* is a multicellular species that forms slen-der filaments. *Volvox* is a green alga that can form a **colony,** a group of cells that lives together in close association.

A *Volvox* colony is composed of hundreds, or thousands, of flagel-lated cells arranged in a single layer forming a hollow, ball-shaped struc-ture. The cells are connected by strands of cytoplasm, and the fla-gella of individual cells face out-ward. The flagella can beat in a coordinated fashion, spinning the colony through the water. Small balls of daughter colonies form inside the large sphere. The wall of the large colony will eventually break open and release the daughter colonies.

Green algae can reproduce both asexually and sexually. For example, *Spirogyra* can reproduce asexually through fragmentation. During **fragmentation,** an individual breaks up into pieces and each piece grows into a new individual.

Reading Check (p. 516)
Chlorophytes are green algae that live in both salt water and freshwater. Euglenophytes are unicellu-lar algae that have pellicles and flagella. Bacillariophytes are diatoms that have silica cell walls. Phaeophytes are brown algae that can grow very large. Rhodophytes are multicellular red algae that survive at great depths in marine environments. Dino-flagellates are marine unicel-lular algae that can cause red tides.

Assessment

Portfolio Have students make a flowchart of the life cycle of *Ulva* and include the terms: alternation of generations, gametophyte, sporophyte, mitosis, meiosis, zygote, and gamete. **L2**

Physical Science Connection

Inform students that the colors of some gemstones also are due to absorption of light. The green hues in emerald and the red hues in ruby are due to the wavelengths of visible light absorbed by them. In emerald, red and blue wavelengths are selectively absorbed, while in ruby, violet and yellow-green wavelengths are absorbed. The wavelengths that are not absorbed cause the colors that are seen.

Color-enhanced LM Magnification: unavailable

Color-enhanced LM Magnification: 15×

igure 19.13
hlamydomonas is a unicellular pecies of green algae **(A)**, while *pirogyra* is a multicellular form **(B)**. he wall of a *Volvox* colony contains undreds of cells **(C)**. The smaller balls iside the sphere are daughter olonies.

agnification: unavailable

515

Quick Demo

Explore Algae Allow students to feel the texture of agar in a petri dish. Then, display an ingredient label from an ice cream carton that lists alginate, agar, or carrageenan, a protein found in red algae. Discuss why algal products are used in ice cream and agar. Encourage students to think of other products that might have a similar alga ingredient. **L1**

3 Assess

Extension

Ask students to compile a list of foods that contain algae. **L2**

 Assessment

Knowledge Make six line drawings showing an alga from each of the six phyla. Give students sets of the drawings and ask them to list three facts or ideas about each alga. **L2**

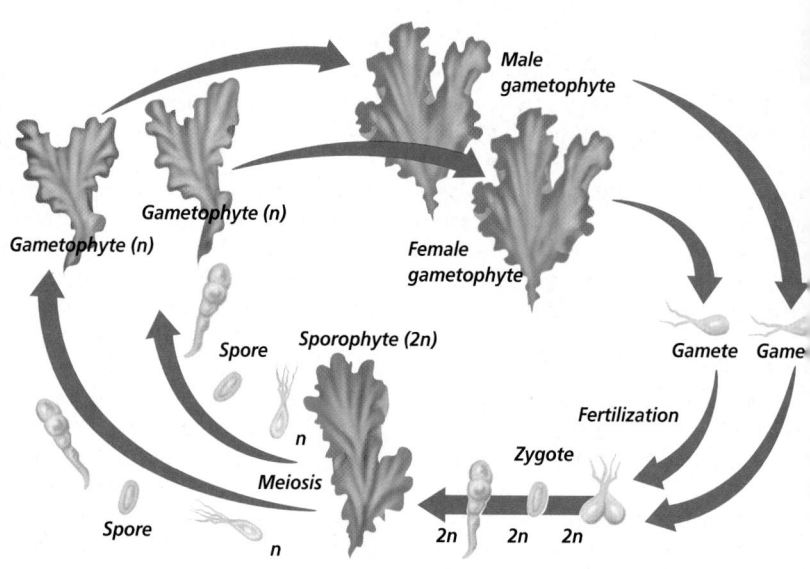

Figure 19.14
In the life cycle of the sea lettuce *(Ulva)*, the generations alternate between haploid (gametophyte) and diploid (sporophyte). Both fungi and plants also alternate generations.

Green algae, and some other types of algae, have a complex life cycle. This life cycle consists of individuals that alternate between producing spores and producing gametes.

Alternation of Generations

The life cycles of some of the algae and all plants have a pattern called **alternation of generations.** An organism that has this pattern alternates between existing as a haploid and a diploid organism, creating two different generations.

The haploid form of the organism is called the **gametophyte** because produces gametes. The gametes fuse to form a zygote from which the diploid form of the organism, which is called the **sporophyte,** develops. Certain cells in the sporophyte undergo meiosis. Eventually, these cells become haploid spores that can develop into a new gametophyte. Look at *Figure 19.14* to see the life cycle of *Ulva,* a multicellular green alga.

Reading Check **List and describe** the different types of algae.

Section Assessment

Understanding Main Ideas

1. In what ways are algae important to all living things on Earth?
2. Give examples that show why the green algae are considered to be the most diverse of the six phyla of algae.
3. In what ways do the sporophyte and gametophyte generations of an alga such as *Ulva* differ from each other?
4. Why are phycobilins an important pigment in red algae?

Thinking Critically

5. Use a table to list the reasons why euglenoids should be classified as protozoans and also as algae.

SKILL REVIEW

6. **Make and Use Tables** Construct a table listing the different phyla of algae. Indicate whether they have one or more cells, their color, and give an example of each. For more help, refer to *Make and Use Tables* in the **Skill Handbook.**

 in.bdol.glencoe.com/self_check_quiz

Section Assessment

1. They are producers of oxygen and the primary autotrophs of many food chains.
2. *Chlamydomonas* is a unicellular example. *Volvox* is a colonial form. *Ulva* is a multicellular alga.
3. Haploid gametophytes form gametes and diploid sporophytes form spores.
4. They can absorb the green, violet, and blue light that penetrates deep water.
5. Their chloroplasts are algaelike and their locomotion is protozoanlike.
6. Euglenophyta—one, green, euglena; Bacillariophyta—one, golden, diatom; Dinoflagellata—one, green, yellow, and red, dinoflagellate; Rhodophyta— many, red, red seaweed; Phaeophyta— many, brown, brown seaweed; Chlorophyta—one or many, green, green algae

Slime Molds, Water Molds, and Downy Mildews

Why aren't they fungi?

Finding the Main Idea Until recently, many of the funguslike protists were classified as fungi. Slime molds, water molds, and downy mildews can often look and act like fungi, and many cause diseases in plants the way fungi do.

Describe *As you read the section, write a description or draw your perception of how the funguslike protists appear physically and how they live. Compare and contrast these descriptions with how you would describe fungi.*

A plasmodial slime

What are funguslike protists?

Certain groups of protists, the slime molds, the water molds, and the downy mildews, consist of organisms with some funguslike features. Recall that fungi are heterotrophic organisms that decompose organic materials to obtain energy. Like fungi, the funguslike protists decompose organic materials.

There are three phyla of funguslike protists. Two of these phyla consist of slime molds. Slime molds have characteristics of both protozoans and fungi and are classified by the way they reproduce. Water molds and downy mildews make up the third phylum of funguslike protists. Although funguslike protists are not an everyday part of human lives, some disease-causing species damage vital crops.

Slime Molds

Many slime molds are beautifully colored, ranging from brilliant yellow or orange to rich blue, violet, and jet black. They live in cool, moist, shady places where they grow on damp, organic matter, such as rotting leaves or decaying tree stumps and logs.

---

1 Focus

INTERACTIVE CHALKBOARD
PowerPoint® Presentations

Bellringer
Section Focus Transparency 47

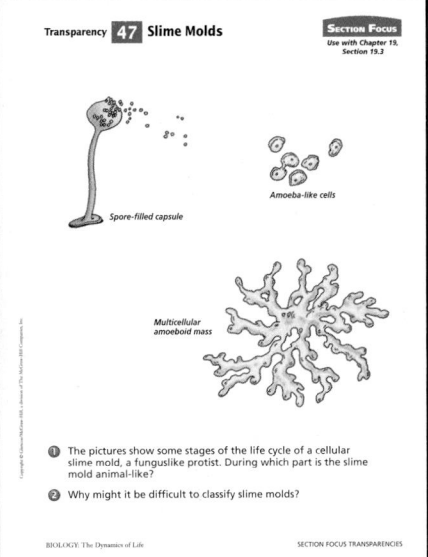

Transparency **47** Slime Molds

SECTION FOCUS
Use with Chapter 19, Section 19.3

Spore-filled capsule

Amoeba-like cells

Multicellular amoeboid mass

1 The pictures show some stages of the life cycle of a cellular slime mold, a funguslike protist. During which part is the slime mold animal-like?

2 Why might it be difficult to classify slime molds?

BIOLOGY: The Dynamics of Life   SECTION FOCUS TRANSPARENCIES

Finding the Main Idea

Describe Funguslike protists may be slimy or fuzzy in appearance. Water molds, with their fuzzy appearance, look much like the hyphae of fungi.

Using Science Terms

English Language Learners:
Linguistic Reinforce terms students can use to recall the three groups of protists. For animal-like protists, use unicellular, motile, and heterotroph. For plantlike protists, use photosynthetic, autotroph, unicellular, and multicellular. For funguslike protists, use heterotroph and decomposer. **ELL** **L1**

---

2 Teach

Purpose

Students will relate cell division to a slime mold's life cycle.

Process Skills

apply concepts, interpret scientific illustrations, think critically

Teaching Strategies

■ Grow slime molds and have students observe them with a stereomicroscope.
■ Review mitosis, meiosis, fertilization, and spore formation.

Thinking Critically

1. mitosis—cell growth; meiosis—haploid gamete formation (gametes form at C)
2. D—two gamete cells join; C—cells with flagella; E—results from fertilization
3. growth stage—organisms use food to grow

Assessment

Performance Have students grow slime molds from purchased spores. Use the Performance Task Assessment List for Carrying Out a Strategy and Collecting Data in **PASC,** p. 97. **L3 ELL**

Caption Question Answer

Figure 19.15 Plasmodial slime molds creep over the surfaces of decaying logs or leaves, engulfing microorganisms, usually bacteria, as they move along.

Problem-Solving Lab 19.3

Predict

What changes occur during a slime mold's life cycle?
Plasmodial slime molds undergo a number of different stages during their life cycle. The most visible stage is the plasmodial stage, where the organism looks like a slimy mass of material. The plasmodium changes into a reproductive stage that is microscopic and, therefore, less visible.

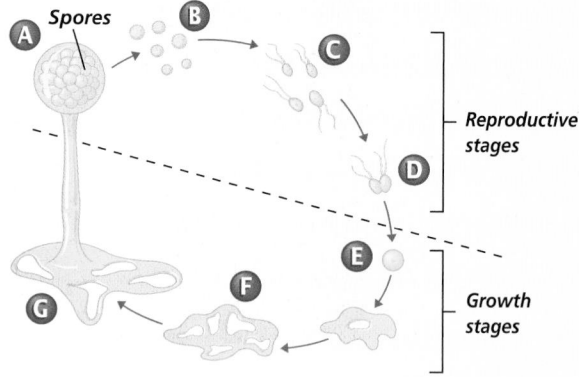

Solve the Problem

Examine the life cycle of a plasmodial slime mold. The structures below the dashed line are diploid in chromosome number. Based on the diagram and your understanding of mitosis and meiosis, answer the questions below.

Thinking Critically

1. **Explain** What cell process, mitosis or meiosis, takes place between F and G? Explain why. Between A and B? Explain why.
2. **Explain** What letter best shows fertilization occurring? Motile spores? An embryo? Explain why in each case.
3. **Observe** During which stage does the slime mold feed? Explain.

Figure 19.15
The moving, feeding form of a plasmodial slime mold is a multinucleate blob of cytoplasm. **Infer** *How does a plasmodial slime mold acquire food?*

518 PROTISTS

There are two major types of slime molds—plasmodial slime molds and cellular slime molds. The plasmodial slime molds belong to the phylum Myxomycota, and the cellular slime molds make up another grouping, the phylum Acrasiomycota.

Slime molds are animal-like during much of their life cycle, moving about and engulfing food in a way similar to that of amoebas. However, like fungi, slime molds make spores to reproduce. Use the *Problem-Solving Lab* on this page to learn more about the life cycle of a slime mold.

Plasmodial slime molds

Plasmodial slime molds get their name from the fact that they form a **plasmodium** (plaz MOH dee um), a mass of cytoplasm that contains many diploid nuclei but no cell walls or membranes. This slimy, multinucleate mass, like the one you see in *Figure 19.15,* is the feeding stage of the organism. The plasmodium creeps like an amoeba over the surfaces of decaying logs or leaves. Some quicker plasmodiums move at the rate of about 2.5 centimeters per hour, engulfing microscopic organisms and digesting them in food vacuoles. At that rate, a plasmodium would cross your textbook page in eight hours.

A plasmodium may reach more than a meter in diameter and contain thousands of nuclei. However, when moisture and food become

---

Additional Lab

Observing Slime Mold

Purpose

Allow students to observe a plasmodium-type slime mold.

Materials 🔬🧤☣️🧤

petri dish with plasmodium stage of

518

Physarum polycephalum (Prepare subcultures two days in advance by cutting sections from the culture, putting the pieces on plastic agar plates that contain a few flakes of oat cereal moistened with distilled water.); stereomicroscope

Procedure

Give students the following directions.

1. Wear a lab apron, gloves, and safety goggles during this lab.
2. Observe the slime mold.
3. Design a way to determine if the organism moves or not.
4. Record your macroscopic observations.
5. Use a stereomicroscope to observe the slime mold. Record your observations about its microscopic appearance and behavior.

Figure 19.16
The reproductive cycle of a cellular slime mold is complex (A). Single cells clump and form a structure that resembles a small garden slug (B). Eventually, the clump forms a stalked reproductive structure that produces spores (C).

A

Spores

Amoeba-like cells released

Cells feed, grow, and divide

Cells gather

Multicellular amoeboidlike mass forms

Spore-filled capsule on a stalk forms

The sluglike structure migrates

The mass compacts and forms a sluglike structure

C

Color-enhanced LM Magnification: 50×

B

Color-enhanced LM Magnification: 50×

scarce in its surroundings, a plasmodium transforms itself into many separate, stalked, spore-producing structures. Meiosis takes place within these structures and produces haploid spores, which the wind disperses. A spore germinates into either a flagellated or an amoeboid cell, or a gamete, that can fuse with another cell to form a zygote. The diploid zygote grows into a new plasmodium.

Cellular slime molds

Unlike plasmodial slime molds, cellular slime molds spend part of their life cycle as an independent amoeboid cell that feeds, grows, and divides by cell division, as shown in *Figure 19.16*. When food becomes

scarce, these independent cells join with hundreds or thousands of others to reproduce. Such an aggregation of amoeboid cells resembles a plasmodium. However, this mass of cells is multicellular—made up of many individual amoeboid cells, each with a distinct cell membrane. Cellular slime molds are haploid during their entire life cycle.

✓ **Reading Check** **Compare and contrast** the two types of slime molds.

Word Origin

plasmodium from the Greek word *plassein*, meaning "mold," and the Latin word *odiosus*, meaning "hateful"; One form of a slime mold is a plasmodium.

---

6. Dispose of the slime mold as your teacher directs. Wash your hands thoroughly with soap when you finish.

Analysis

1. Describe the slime mold's appearance and behavior. Is it a plasmodial or cellular slime mold? yellow, bloblike, stringy, moves very slowly; plasmodium

2. Describe the slime mold's microscopic appearance and behavior. Material flows within the slime mold, stops, then flows in the opposite direction.

519

Discussion Ask students to research the different protist phyla shown in Figure 19.17. Have students discuss the statement from page 504 that says, "Slime molds and water molds decompose a significant amount of organic material, making nutrients available to living organisms." You can also have students make a connection between this statement and the energy pyramid in Figure 2.14 in Chapter 2. **L2**

Extension

Visual-Spatial Have students make flowcharts of the life cycles of Myxomycota and Acrasiomycota organisms and include the chromosome number for each stage. Have students include a summary statement that compares the two organisms. **L3**

Indiana Academic Standards

Pages 520–521: B.1.35, B.1.43

520

Water Molds and Downy Mildews

Water molds and downy mildews are both members of the phylum Oomycota. Most members of this large and diverse group of funguslike protists live in water or moist places. As shown in *Figure 19.17,* some feed on dead organisms and others are plant parasites.

Most water molds appear as fuzzy, white growths on decaying matter. They resemble some fungi because they grow as a mass of threads over a food source, digest it, and then absorb the nutrients. But at some point in their life cycle, water molds produce flagellated reproductive cells—something that fungi never do. This is why water molds are classified as protists rather than fungi.

One economically important member of the phylum Oomycota is a downy mildew that causes disease in many plants. A downy mildew called *Phytophthora infestans* affected the lives of the people of Ireland by destroying their major food crop of potatoes. The famine that followed caused a mass immigration to America.

Origin of Protists

How are the many different kinds of protists related to each other and to fungi, plants, and animals? You can see the relationships of protists to each other in *Figure 19.18.*

Although taxonomists are now comparing the RNA and DNA of these groups, there is little conclusive evidence to indicate whether ancient protists were the evolutionary ancestors of fungi, plants, and animals or whether protists emerged as evolutionary lines that were separate. Because of evidence from comparative RNA sequences in modern green algae and plants, many biologists agree that ancient green algae were probably ancestral to modern plants.

Figure 19.17
Water molds and downy mildews live in moist places and cause both plant and animal diseases.

A The downy mildew *Phytophthora infestans* is killing this potato plant.

B The water mold growing on this insect is decomposing the insect's tissues and absorbing the nutrients.

520 PROTISTS

CHALLENGE ACTIVITY

Protists Have students select one protist group in Figure 19.18 to research for a two-page report. While reports will vary, students should include a statement that defends the placement of their selected group in Kingdom Protista. **L3**

Figure 19.18
This fanlike diagram shows the relationships of the different protist phyla.

PROTISTS

Chlorophytes
7000 species

Rhizopods
11 500 species

Flagellates
2500 species

Ciliates
8000 species

Phaeophytes
1500 species

Rhodophytes
4000 species

Bacillariophytes
10 000 species

Euglenophytes
800 species

Sporozoans
3900 species

Dinoflagellates
1000 species

Acrasiomycotes
65 species

Myxomycotes
450 species

Oomycotes
175 species

Animals

Plants

Fungi

Species numbers are approximate and subject to change pending discoveries or extinctions.

---

3 Assess

DAILY INTERVENTION

Check for Understanding
Naturalist Have students compare and contrast the three funguslike protist phyla. Ask them to explain why these organisms are classified as protists and not fungi. **L2**

Reteach
Naturalist Have student groups prepare charts that compare and contrast the phyla Myxomycota, Acrasiomycota, and Oomycota. **L2** **COOP LEARN**

Resources
For more practice, use *Reading Essentials for Biology*, Section 19.3.

Extension

Summarize how slime molds are like both protozoans and fungi. Describe how they are classified.

✔ Assessment

Knowledge Ask students to list several protozoanlike traits and several funguslike traits of the funguslike protists. **L2**

Section Assessment

Understanding Main Ideas

1. Describe the protozoan and funguslike characteristics of slime molds.
2. Why might some biologists refer to plasmodial slime molds as acellular slime molds? (Hint: Look in the **Skill Handbook** for the origins of scientific terms.)
3. How could a water mold eventually kill a fish?
4. How does a plasmodial slime mold differ from a cellular slime mold?

Thinking Critically

5. In what kinds of environments would you expect to find slime molds? Explain your answer.

SKILL REVIEW

6. **Observe and Infer** If you know that a plasmodium consists of many nuclei within a single cell, what can you infer about the process that formed the plasmodium? For more help, refer to *Observe and Infer* in the **Skill Handbook**.

 in.bdol.glencoe.com/self_check_quiz   19.3 SLIME MOLDS, WATER MOLDS, AND DOWNY MILDEWS **521**

Section Assessment

1. They are protozoanlike in that at different stages they have flagella and the ability to move like amoebas. They are funguslike in that they produce spores, and many are saprophytic decomposers.
2. The plasmodium is a mass of cytoplasm containing many nuclei but no cell walls or membranes that separate cells.
3. The mold digests its tissues.
4. Plasmodial slime molds feed as a multinucleated plasmodium, but cellular slime molds feed as amoeboid cells.
5. Slime molds should live in warm, moist environments where the moisture would prevent dehydration and provide the conditions their food supply needs to thrive.
6. The process suggests mitosis without cell division.

Time Allotment
one class period

Process Skills
observe and infer, experiment, form a hypothesis, identify and control variables

Safety Precautions
Remind students to use special care when viewing a slide under high power. Have students wash their hands thoroughly with soap and water after finishing the lab and cleanup.

PREPARATION

Cover a test tube containing *Euglena* with black paper containing a narrow, slitlike opening. Leave the tube in bright light for 12 hours and then remove the paper. Students should observe a green band of *Euglena*. Cover half of a test tube containing *Paramecium* with black paper, place the tube on its side in bright light for 12 hours. *Paramecium* should congregate in the covered side.

Possible Hypotheses
If *Paramecium* are attracted to light, then they will move to the light zone on a glass slide containing both light and dark zones.

If *Euglena* are attracted to light, then they will move to the light zone on a glass slide containing both light and dark zones.

PLAN THE EXPERIMENT

Teaching Strategies
■ Provide time for students to observe the organisms' size, speed, and mobility under a microscope before they begin.
■ Have students use low power to observe *Paramecium* (a 4× objective works best) and high power to observe *Euglena*.

■ Advise students that they must count organisms quickly.

Possible Procedures
■ Index cards can provide a light and dark microscope zone. Cut the cards to fit over part of the coverslip. Students

should focus on the edge of the card to observe each organism's direction of movement. If possible, use coverslips (22 × 30 mm or 22 × 40 mm) that cover a large area.
■ Prepare or purchase methylcellulose.

DESIGN YOUR OWN
BioLab

Before You Begin

Members of the genus *Paramecium* are ciliated protozoans—unicellular, heterotrophic protists that move around in search of small food particles. *Euglena* are unicellular algae—autotrophic protists that usually contain numerous chloroplasts. In this *BioLab*, you'll investigate how these two protists respond to light in their environment.

How do *Paramecium* and *Euglena* respond to light?

PREPARATION

Problem
Do both *Paramecium* and *Euglena* respond to light, and do they respond in different ways? Decide on one type of protist activity that would constitute a response to light.

Hypotheses
Decide on one hypothesis that you will test. Your hypothesis might be that *Paramecium* will not respond to light and *Euglena* will respond, or that *Paramecium* will move away from light and *Euglena* will move toward light.

Objectives
In this BioLab, you will:
■ **Prepare** slides of *Paramecium* and *Euglena* cultures and observe swimming patterns in the two organisms.
■ **Compare** how these two different protists respond to light.

Possible Materials
Euglena culture	coverslips
Paramecium culture	metric ruler
microscope	index cards
microscope slides	scissors
dropper	toothpicks
methyl cellulose	

Safety Precautions
CAUTION: *Always wear goggles in the lab. Use caution when working with a microscope, glass slides, and coverslips. Wash your hands with soap and water immediately after working with protists and chemicals.*

Skill Handbook
If you need help with this lab, refer to the **Skill Handbook**.

PLAN THE EXPERIMENT

1. Decide on an experimental procedure that you can use to test your hypothesis.
2. Record your procedure, step-by-step, and list the materials you will be using.
3. Design a data table in which to record your observations and results.

Check the Plan

Discuss all the following points with other group members to determine your final procedure.

1. What variables will you have to measure? What will be your control?

2. What will be the shape of the light-controlled area(s) on your microscope slide?

3. Decide who will prepare materials, make observations, and record data.

4. *Make sure your teacher has approved your experimental plan before you proceed further.*

5. To mount drops of *Paramecium* culture and *Euglena* culture on microscope slides, use a toothpick to place a small ring of methyl cellulose on a clean microscope slide. Place a drop of *Paramecium* or *Euglena* culture within this ring. Place a coverslip over the ring and culture. The thick consistency of methyl cellulose should slow down the organisms for easy observation.

6. Make preliminary observations of swimming *Paramecium* and *Euglena*. Then think again about the observation times that you have planned. Maybe you will decide to allow more or less time between your observations.

7. Carry out your experiment.

8. **CLEANUP AND DISPOSAL** Work with your teacher to make wise choices concerning disposal of materials.

ANALYZE AND CONCLUDE

1. **Compare and Contrast** Compare and contrast all the responses of the *Paramecium* and *Euglena* to both light and darkness. What explanations can you suggest for their behavior?

2. **Make Inferences** Can you use your results to suggest what sort of responses to light and darkness you might observe using other heterotrophic or autotrophic protists?

3. **ERROR ANALYSIS** Did your data support your hypothesis? Why or why not?

Apply Your Skill

Project You may want to extend this experiment by varying the shapes or relative sizes of light and dark areas or by varying the brightness or color of the light. In each case, make hypotheses before you begin. Keep your data in a notebook, and draw up a table of your results at the end of your investigations.

Web Links To find out more about protists, visit
in.bdol.glencoe.com/protists

ANALYZE AND CONCLUDE

1. *Euglena* are attracted to light. *Paramecia* avoid bright light. *Euglena* need light to make food. Being heterotrophic, *Paramecia* can find food in dim and dark places.

2. Most autotrophs show a positive response to light whereas most heterotrophs show a negative response.

3. **ERROR ANALYSIS** Answers may vary. Data must be used to either support or reject student hypotheses. Advise students to do several trials for each organism. Ask them to explain why this is important.

Assessment

Portfolio Have students write an evaluation of what they learned in this investigation. Use the Performance Task Assessment List for Writing in Science in **PASC**, p. 159. **L2**

Apply Your Skill

Project Students may wish to test the response of these protists to other factors, such as different concentrations of salt solutions. **L3 ELL**

Data and Observations

Data should indicate that *Euglena* are attracted to light; *Paramecium* are not.

CLEANUP AND DISPOSAL

Microscope coverslips and slides may be washed thoroughly with soap and water or sterilized and reused. Protozoans may be returned to a holding jar for use in making a stock culture.

Purpose

Students learn about some properties and uses of diatoms, how these algae are used in forensics, and their potential in fighting some forms of cancer.

Teaching Strategies

- Diatomite is available at large nurseries. Diatomaceous earth is available from scientific supply companies.

- Have students mix a drop of water and a pinch of diatomite on a microscope slide, cover with a coverslip, and examine on a microscope under low, then high power to determine porosity. Porosity is determined by estimating the amount of open space among diatom shells in a field of view. Most diatomite has a porosity of about 80–85 percent by volume.

- Mined diatomite is highly absorbent and is dehydrated before it is transported. Most diatomite will absorb up to 1 times its weight and still be a dry powder.

Applying Biotechnology

Based on the information provided, students can deduce that the person did not drown in the pond. If so, large numbers of diatoms would have been in the lungs, especially in the spring when the diatom populations thrive. The person may have drowned in a swimming pool where the chlorine would have killed most of the organisms.

The Diversity of Diatoms

What do most swimming pool filters, fine porcelain, metal polishes, and some insecticides have in common? All contain the remains of millions of single-celled algae known as diatoms. In addition to their many industrial uses, diatoms can be used to solve crimes and may someday aid in fighting cancer.

Diatoms are unicellular algae enclosed in hard, perforated shells made of silica. Each half of a diatom's shell resembles the top or bottom of a miniature circular box. When diatoms die, their shells fall to the bottom of the water body in which they lived. Over time, the shells undergo physical changes to become diatomite—a very porous, highly absorbent, powdery rock with many uses.

Some industrial uses for diatoms As a result of the structure and composition of diatoms' shells, diatomite is extremely absorbent and essentially chemically inert. Thus, diatomite is a common component in many industrial absorbents used to clean up chemical spills. Diatomite is also a critical ingredient in some types of pet litter and potting soils and can also be added to fertilizers and pesticides to prevent caking.

Another important use of diatomite is as an insecticide. When added to stored grains, the razor-sharp diatom shells in diatomite can pierce the cuticles of insects that may be in the silo, causing them to dehydrate and die. Diatomite is nontoxic to most other animals, and thus does not have to be removed before the grain is used.

Diatomite can also be cut into blocks and bricks and used for thermal and acoustic insulation. It can be ground up to produce filters that are used in swimming pools and in the processing of some beverages. Ground diatomite is also used as filler in many kinds of paints, plastics, cements, pesticides, and pharmaceuticals, and is a major component of most fine porcelain and many mild abrasives.

Color-enhanced SEM Magnification: 16

Diatoms

Diatoms and forensics In addition to their many industrial uses, diatoms may be used in forensics. Forensic biology is a science that uses biological evidence in court to support or disprove guilt. Diatoms can be collected from the shoes or clothing of persons involved or suspected in a crime in order to identify the criminal(s) and/or the scene of the crime. Diatoms can also pinpoint the time of year during which a crime occurred.

Diatoms—Possible cancer drugs In nature, certain species of diatoms produce substances that kill the developing embryos of copepods and sea urchins. In the lab, these same substances have been shown to prevent some human cancer cells from dividing. Such studies suggest that a drug made from certain types of diatoms might be able to slow down or even prevent the abnormal reproduction of some kinds of cancer cells.

Applying Biotechnology

Draw Conclusions Suppose that police find a dead body at the edge of a pond in early May. Examination of the body showed drowning as the cause of death. The time of death was estimated to have been about two weeks prior to the discovery of the body. Very few diatoms were found in the water that filled the person's lungs. Did this person drown in the pond? Explain.

 To find out more about diatoms, visit in.bdol.glencoe.com/biotechnology

Going Further

Have students find out how diatoms are used in Earth science studies. Fossilized diatoms can be used to determine ancient climates. Their sensitivity to changes in salinity, temperature, and nutrients makes them useful in reconstructing large (ice ages, tectonic activity) and small scale (El Niño) oceanic changes. Coastal and estuarian diatom populations can be used to evaluate the impact of clear-cutting, fertilizer usage, and the damming of rivers.

STUDY GUIDE

Section 19.1

The World of Protists

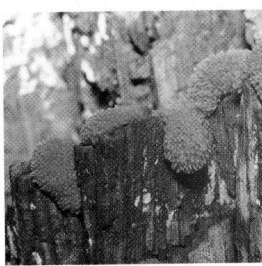

Key Concepts

- Kingdom Protista is a diverse group of living things that contains animal-like, plantlike, and funguslike organisms.
- Some protists are heterotrophs, some are autotrophs, and some get their nutrients by decomposing organic matter.
- Amoebas move by extending pseudopodia. The flagellates use one or more flagella to move. The beating of cilia produces cilliate movement. Sporozoans live as parasites and produce spores.

Vocabulary

alga (p. 503)
asexual reproduction (p. 505)
ciliate (p. 506)
flagellate (p. 506)
protozoan (p. 503)
pseudopodia (p. 504)
spore (p. 508)
sporozoan (p. 508)

Section 19.2

Algae: Plantlike Protists

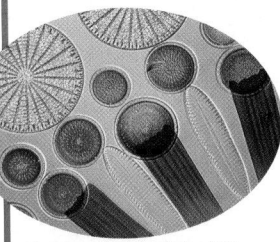

Color-enhanced LM Magnification: 450×

Key Concepts

- Algae are unicellular and multicellular photosynthetic autotrophs. Unicellular species include the euglenoids, diatoms, dinoflagellates, and some green algae. Multicellular species include red, brown, and green algae.
- Green, red, and brown algae, often called seaweeds, have complex life cycles that alternate between haploid and diploid generations.

Vocabulary

alternation of generations (p. 516)
colony (p. 515)
fragmentation (p. 515)
gametophyte (p. 516)
sporophyte (p. 516)
thallus (p. 514)

Section 19.3

Slime Molds, Water Molds, and Downy Mildews

Color-enhanced LM Magnification: 50×

Key Concepts

- Slime molds, water molds, and downy mildews are funguslike protists that decompose organic material to obtain nutrients.
- Plasmodial and cellular slime molds change in appearance and behavior before producing reproductive structures.

Vocabulary

plasmodium (p. 518)

FOLDABLES™ Study Organizer To help you review protists, use the Organizational Study Fold on page 510.

in.bdol.glencoe.com/vocabulary_puzzlemaker   CHAPTER 19 ASSESSMENT **525**

Key Concepts

Summary statements can be used by students to review the major concepts of the chapter.

Biology Online

Visit in.bdol.glencoe.com
/self_check_quiz
/vocabulary_puzzlemaker
/chapter_test
/standardized_test

VOCABULARY PUZZLEMAKER

For additional help with vocabulary, have students access the Vocabulary PuzzleMaker online at in.bdol.glencoe.com/vocabulary_puzzlemaker

FOLDABLES™

Have students use their Foldables to review the content of Section 19.2. On the back of the paper, compare and contrast algae and protozoa.

Use the ExamView®Pro Test Bank CD-ROM to:

- Create **multiple versions** of tests
- Create **modified** tests with one mouse click for **inclusion** students
- **Edit** existing questions and **add** your own questions
- Build tests aligned with state standards using built-in **State Curriculum Tags**
- Change **English** tests to **Spanish** with one mouse click and vice versa

Indiana Academic Standards

Pages 524–525: B.1.2, B.1.43

Vocabulary Review

1. pseudopodia
2. gametophyte
3. plasmodium
4. sporophyte
5. colony

Understanding Key Concepts

6. A	10. D	14. C
7. C	11. B	15. B
8. A	12. B	16. D
9. B	13. A	

Constructed Response

17. oak forest; dry conditions stimulate spore-producing structures
18. Answers will vary, but may include cilia, pseudopodia, flagella, eyespots, contractile vacuoles, or others.
19. Mosquitoes breed in water. The elimination of breeding grounds reduces the mosquito population and reduces the risk of contracting malaria.

Thinking Critically

20. 1. protozoans; 2. amoebas; 3. ciliates; 4. flagellates; 5. sporozoans
21. Malaria alternates between invertebrate hosts, mosquitoes of the genus *Anopheles,* and a vertebrate host, such as humans in the case of human malaria.
    Discussion answers will vary. Currently, more than one million people die annually from malaria, so a preventative vaccine could save significant numbers of people.

Vocabulary Review

Review the Chapter 19 vocabulary words listed in the Study Guide on page 525. Match the words with the definitions below.

1. cytoplasm-containing extensions of protozoan plasma membranes
2. haploid form of an alga that produces gametes
3. mass of cytoplasm that contains many diploid nuclei but no separating cell walls or membranes
4. diploid form of an alga that contains cells that undergo meiosis
5. a group of cells that lives together in close association

Understanding Key Concepts

6. Which organisms may cause red tides?
   A. dinoflagellates   C. green algae
   B. euglenoids   D. red algae
7. Which organelle in protists is able to eliminate excess water?
   A. anal pore   C. contractile vacuole
   B. mouth   D. gullet
8. Producers in aquatic food chains include _____.
   A. algae   C. slime molds
   B. protozoans   D. amoebas
9. Protists are classified on the basis of their _____.
   A. nutrition
   B. method of locomotion
   C. reproductive abilities
   D. size
10. Euglenoids are unique algae because of their _____.
    A. flagella
    B. cilia
    C. silica walls
    D. heterotrophic nature

11. Which of the following is not a protist?

A.   B.   C.   D.

12. The algae that can survive in the deepest water are the _____.
    A. brown algae   C. diatoms
    B. red algae   D. green algae
13. The largest and most complex of brown algae are the _____.
    A. kelp   C. sea lettuce
    B. *Chlamydomonas*   D. *Spirogyra*
14. Which of the following are protected by armored plates?
    A. kelp   C. dinoflagellates
    B. fire algae   D. diatoms
15. Unlike bacteria, all protists are _____.
    A. prokaryotes   C. nonliving
    B. eukaryotes   D. both prokaryotic and eukaryotic
16. What type of structure does the protist shown to the right use to move?
    A. cilium
    B. gullet
    C. pellicle
    D. flagellum

Constructed Response

17. **Infer** In which ecosystem would a plasmodial slime mold transform itself into spore-producing structures more frequently: a rainy forest in the Pacific Northwest or a dry, oak forest in the Midwest? Explain.
18. **Infer** Give three examples of organelles that help protists maintain homeostasis.
19. **Explain** To fight malaria, wetlands were often drained. How did this cut down on malaria cases?

in.bdol.glencoe.com/chapter_test

RUBRIC

Evaluating Open-Ended Questions
Open-ended assessment questions are graded by using a multilevel rubric that guides you in assessing a student's knowledge of a particular concept. The following rubric is a sample scoring device.

Thinking Critically

20. Concept Map Complete the concept map with the terms: amoebas, sporozoans, flagellates, protozoans, ciliates.

Animal-like protists are called

1.

which include — which include — which include — which include

2. — 3. — 4. — 5.

that use pseudopods to move. — that use cilia to move. — that use flagella to move. — that produce spores and are parasites.

21. **REAL WORLD BIOCHALLENGE** More than two million people worldwide die from malaria infections transmitted by just four species of the sporozoan *Plasmodium*. Recent attempts to decrease deaths caused by malaria are yielding promising new methods of prevention. Visit **in.bdol.glencoe.com** to discover the potential of this research. What are the hosts of the malaria parasite? Discuss with your classmates how the number of people who die from malaria could be reduced.

End-of-Course Assessment Practice

22. B   **24.** D
23. A   **25.** A
26. Protozoa eliminate water through canals connected to contractile vacuoles. As water enters the cells by osmosis, it is collected in the contractile vacuoles.

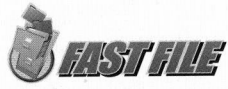 **FAST FILE**

Answer Sheet A practice answer sheet can be found on p. 75 of *Unit 6 FAST FILE Resources.*

The assessed Indiana standard appears next to the question.

All questions aligned and verified by *The Princeton Review*

Part 1 — Multiple Choice

Use the graph to answer questions 22 and 23.

A group of high school students studied unicellular algae in the middle of a pond. For two days they measured the number of cells in the water at various depths. They produced the following graph based on their data.

Locations of Diatoms

Location of highest concentration of diatoms

Surface

50 cm

100 cm

12 A.M.   12 P.M.   12 A.M.   12 P.M.   12 A.M.

Times in hours

22. At what time were the highest concentrations of diatoms at the surface?
   A. midnight   **C.** 3 A.M.
   B. noon   **D.** 6 P.M.

23. At what time were the highest concentrations of diatoms about a meter below the surface?
   A. midnight   **C.** 3 A.M.
   B. noon   **D.** 6 P.M.

Study the diagram and answer questions 24 and 25.

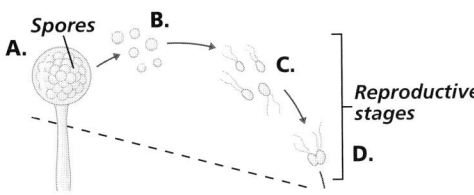

Spores

A. **B.** **C.**

Reproductive stages

D.

24. Which of the following represents
B.1.15 fertilization?
   A. A   **C.** C
   B. B   **D.** D

25. Cells in stage C have _____
B.1.8 chromosomes.
   A. *n*   **C.** a diploid number of
   B. *2n*   **D.** no

Part 2 — Constructed Response/Grid In

Record your answer on your answer document.

26. Open Ended Describe how protozoa eliminate excess water from their internal environments.

 in.bdol.glencoe.com/standardized_test

CHAPTER 19 ASSESSMENT **527**

RUBRIC

SCORE	CRITERIA
4	A correct solution that is supported by well-developed, accurate explanations.
3	A generally correct solution, but may contain minor flaws in reasoning.

SCORE	CRITERIA
2	A partially correct interpretation and/or solution to the problem.
1	A correct solution with no supporting evidence or explanation.
0	An incorrect solution or no solution is given.

 Indiana Academic Standards

Pages 526–527: B.1.2, B.1.3, B.1.8, B.1.43

Chapter 20 Organizer

Section Objectives	National Science Standards	State/Local Standards	Advanced Lab and Demo Planning
Section 20.1 1 session, 1 block 1. **Identify** the basic characteristics of the fungi kingdom. 2. **Explain** the role of fungi as decomposers and how this role affects the flow of both energy and nutrients through food chains.	UCP.1–3; A.1, A.2; UCP.1, UCP.2, UCP.5; A.1, A.2; C.1, C.4, C.5, C.6; F.5	**Indiana Standards** B.1.8, B.1.11, B.1.13, B.1.43, B.1.44	**Student Labs:** MiniLab 20.1, p. 530: fresh bakery bread, water, plastic bag, forceps, coverslip, microscope Additional Lab, p. 530: small paper cups, macaroni, aluminum foil, water, cardboard pieces, oatmeal flakes, swab with mold spores, plastic wrap Problem-Solving Lab 20.1, p. 534 **Teacher Demonstration:** Quick Demo, p. 531: mushrooms
Section 20.2 2 sessions, 1/2 block 3. **Identify** the four major phyla of fungi. 4. **Distinguish** among the ways spores are produced in zygomycotes, ascomycotes, and basidiomycotes. 5. **Summarize** the ecological roles of lichens and mycorrhizae.	UCP.1–5; A.1, A.2; C.1, C.3, C.4, C.5, C.6; F.1, F.4, F.5; G.1–3	**Indiana Standards** B.1.11, B.1.35, B.1.40, B.1.43, B.1.44	**Student Labs:** MiniLab 20.2, p. 538: mushrooms, paper bag, white sheet of paper Problem-Solving Lab 20.2, p. 542 Internet BioLab, p. 544: See materials below. **Teacher Demonstration:** Quick Demo, p. 537: *Peziza*, water, microscope slides, coverslips, microscope
End of Chapter Assessment Student Edition **Study Guide,** p. 547 **Content Assessment,** pp. 548–549		**Indiana Standards** B.1.2, B.1.31, B.1.43, B.1.44	**Student Lab:** Internet BioLab, p. 544: bromothymol blue solution (BTB), straw, 4 small test tubes, 3 large test tubes, 3 one-hole stoppers with glass tube inserts for large test tubes, yeast/white corn syrup mixture, water/white corn syrup mixture, water/yeast mixture, test-tube rack, 3 250-mL beakers, ice cubes, Celsius thermometer, hot plate, 50-mL graduated cylinder, glass marking pencil, 3 pieces of 10-cm rubber tubing, aluminum foil

Key to Teaching Strategies

L1 Level 1 activities should be appropriate for students with learning difficulties.

L2 Level 2 activities should be within the ability range of all students.

L3 Level 3 activities are designed for above-average students.

ELL ELL activities should be within the ability range of English Language Learners.

COOP LEARN
Cooperative Learning activities are designed for small group work.

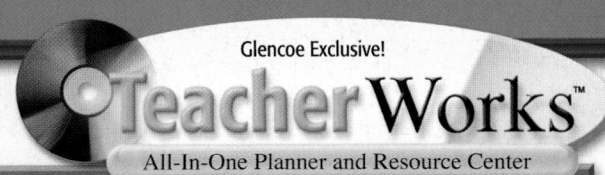

Glencoe Exclusive!

Teacher Works™
All-In-One Planner and Resource Center

Reproducible Masters and Transparencies

Technology

Unit 6 *FAST FILE* Resources
  MiniLab Worksheet, p. 79
  Real World BioApplications, pp. 83–84
  Reinforcement and Study Guide in English,
    pp. 85–86
  Reinforcement and Study Guide in Spanish,
    pp. 89–90
  Concept Mapping, p. 93
  Critical Thinking/Problem Solving, p. 94
  Transparency Worksheet, p. 95
**Reading Essentials for Biology,
  Section 20.1**
Laboratory Manual, pp. 117–120
 Section Focus Transparency 48

💿 **Interactive Chalkboard CD-ROM: Section 20.1 Presentation**
💿 TeacherWorks™ **CD-ROM**
🎵 **Guided Reading Audio Summaries MP3**

Unit 6 *FAST FILE* Resources
  MiniLab Worksheet, p. 80
  BioLab Worksheet, pp. 81–82
  Reinforcement and Study Guide in English,
    pp. 87–88
  Reinforcement and Study Guide in Spanish,
    pp. 91–92
  Transparency Worksheets, pp. 96, 97–102
**Reading Essentials for Biology,
  Section 20.2**
Laboratory Manual, pp. 121–124
 Section Focus Transparency 49
 Basic Concepts Transparencies 31, 32
 Reteaching Skills Transparency 31

💿 **Interactive Chalkboard CD-ROM: Section 20.2 Presentation**
💿 TeacherWorks™ **CD-ROM**
🎵 **Guided Reading Audio Summaries MP3**

Unit 6 *FAST FILE* Resources
  Chapter Assessment, pp. 103–108
  Student Recording Sheet, p. 109

The Princeton Review **Reviewing Biology,** pp. 39–40

💿 **Interactive Chalkboard:
  Chapter 20 Assessment**
💿 **MindJogger Videoquizzes
  DVD/VHS**
💿 **Exam*View*® Pro Test Bank
  CD-ROM**
💿 TeacherWorks™ **CD-ROM**
💿 **Succeeding on National Standards CD-ROM**

🖱 in.bdol.glencoe.com
  /self_check_quiz
  /vocabulary_puzzlemaker
  /chapter_test
  /standardized_test

Indicates materials created specifically for Indiana.

Fungi

Short on Time?

 The BioDigest at the end of this unit can be used as a(n):

- preview to introduce important unit concepts.
- overview if time does not permit teaching the entire chapter.
- review of key unit concepts.

Understanding the Photo

Kingdom Fungi contains many species of mushrooms that can be consumed for food, but others are poisonous and deadly. Many species in this kingdom do not form mushrooms at all.

What You'll Learn

- You will identify the characteristics of the fungi kingdom.
- You will differentiate among the phyla of fungi.

Why It's Important

Fungi decompose organic matter, cleaning the environment and recycling nutrients. They create food products and medicines. However, fungi can also cause significant diseases in humans and plants.

Understanding ▶ the Photo

This white ogre mushroom (*Amanita virgineoides*) is native to Japan. It grows on forest floors, where it feeds on decomposing leaves.

Biology Online

Visit in.bdol.glencoe.com to
- study the entire chapter online
- access Web Links for more information and activities on fungi
- review content with the Interactive Tutor and self-check quizzes

528

Indiana Academic Standards

Pages 528–529: B.1.43

Two-Minute Chapter Launcher

Demonstrate Show students examples of mushrooms purchased from a supermarket, baking yeast, bread molds in a plastic bag, and other examples of fungi that are available, and slime molds. Have students diagram each example presented and then describe what they all have in common. Students may indicate that each one looks different than the others. Some are easily seen with the unaided eye, but others should be viewed under a microscope to see their features. All of the examples are various species of fungi.

What is a fungus?

Bellringer
Section Focus Transparency 48

SECTION PREVIEW

Objectives
Identify the basic characteristics of the fungi kingdom.

Explain the role of fungi as decomposers and how this role affects the flow of both energy and nutrients through food chains.

Review Vocabulary
decomposer: organism that breaks down and absorbs nutrients from dead organisms (p. 47)

New Vocabulary
hypha
mycelium
chitin
haustoria
budding
sporangium

Mysterious Rings of Mushrooms

Using Prior Knowledge
Have you ever seen mushrooms that grow in a ring like the one shown here? The visible mushrooms are only one part of the fungus. Beneath the soil's surface are threadlike filaments that may grow a long distance away from the above-ground ring of mushrooms. These filaments can grow for a long time before they produce the surface mushrooms. Mushrooms that grow in rings are only one of many types of fungi, all of which share certain characteristics.

Infer *Why does a mushroom fairy ring, such as the one shown in the photo, take on a ring shape?*

A ring of mushrooms

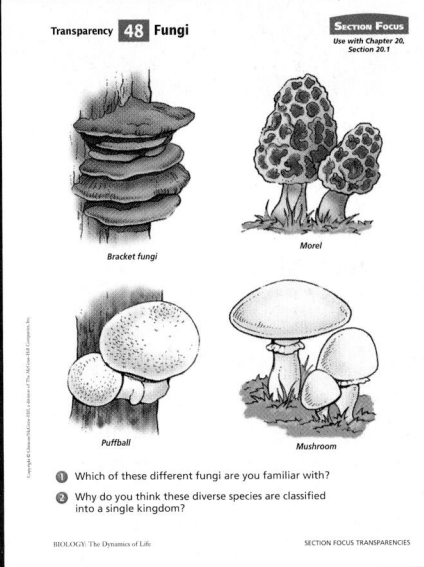

The Characteristics of Fungi

Fungi are everywhere—in the air and water, on damp basement walls, in gardens, on foods, and sometimes even between people's toes. Some fungi are large, bright, and colorful, whereas others are easily overlooked, as shown in **Figure 20.1.** Many have descriptive names such as stinkhorn,

Figure 20.1
Fungi vary in form, size, and color.

PowerPoint® Presentations
This CD-ROM is an editable Microsoft® PowerPoint® presentation that includes:
• Section presentations
• Section checks
• Image bank
• Hot links to Biology Online
• All transparencies

A Bird's nest fungi look like nests, complete with eggs.

B Brightly colored coral fungi resemble ocean corals.

C A fungus killed this insect by feeding on its tissues.

20.1   WHAT IS A FUNGUS?   **529**

Using Prior Knowledge

Infer Mushrooms are fruiting bodies that appear at the edges of the fungal colony. They began growing in one spot and the underground mycellium grew outward until the mushrooms grew above the surface.

RESOURCE MANAGER

Unit 6 FAST FILE Resources
MiniLab Worksheet, p. 79
Real World BioApplications, pp. 83–84
Reinforcement and Study Guide in English, pp. 85–86
Reinforcement and Study Guide in Spanish, pp. 89–90

Concept Mapping, p. 93
Critical Thinking/Problem Solving, p. 94
Transparency Worksheet, p. 95
Reading Essentials for Biology, Section 20.1
Laboratory Manual, pp. 117–120
Section Focus Transparency 48

2 Teach

MiniLab 20.1

Purpose
Students will identify a requirement for bread mold to grow.

Process Skills
observe and infer, investigate

Teaching Strategies
■ Parents should be notified ahead of time that students will be working with bread mold.
■ Mold grows quickly on bakery bread that lacks preservatives.
■ Identify calcium propionate on bread ingredient labels as a mold inhibitor.
■ Autoclave or incinerate all fungal samples to destroy them.

Expected Results
After 4–6 days, mold will grow only on moist bread slices.

Analysis
1. Only moist bread had mold. It suggests that there might be spores in the classroom air.
2. Molds require water and food for growth.

Assessment
Performance Have students design an experiment to show that air contains mold spores that will grow on bread. Use the Performance Task Assessment List for Designing an Experiment in **PASC**, p. 95. **L2**

MiniLab 20.1

Observe and Infer

Growing Mold Spores Any mold spore that arrives in a favorable place can germinate and produce hyphae. Can you identify a condition necessary for the growth of bread mold spores?

Procedure ▢▢▢▢▢▢
1. Place two slices of freshly baked bakery bread on a plate. Sprinkle some water on one slice to moisten its surface. Leave both slices uncovered for several hours.
2. Sprinkle a little more water on the moistened slice, and place both slices in their own plastic, self-seal bags. Trap air in each bag so that the plastic does not touch the bread's surface. Then seal the bags and place them in a darkened area at room temperature.
3. After five days, remove the bags and look for mold.
4. Remove a small piece of mold with a forceps, place it on a slide in a drop of water, and add a coverslip. Observe the mold under a microscope's low power and high power. **CAUTION: *Use caution when working with a microscope, glass slides, and coverslips. Wash your hands with soap and water after working with mold. Dispose of the mold as your teacher directs.***

Analysis
1. **Observe and Infer** Did you observe mold growth on the moistened bread? On the dry bread? How does this experiment demonstrate that there are mold spores in your classroom?
2. **Draw Conclusions** What conclusions can you draw about the conditions necessary for the growth of a bread mold?

Figure 20.2
A germinating fungal spore produces hyphae that branch to form a mycelium. **Describe** *What other tasks do hyphae carry out?*

Spore   Germinating spore   Mycelium

Food source

puffball, rust, or ringworm. Many species grow best in moist environments at warm temperatures between 20°C and 30°C. You are, however, probably familiar with molds that grow at much lower temperatures on left-over foods in your refrigerator.

Fungi used to be classified in the plant kingdom because, like plants, many fungi grow anchored in soil and have cell walls. However, as biologists learned more about fungi, they realized that fungi belong in their own kingdom.

The structure of fungi

Although there are a few unicellular types of fungi, such as yeasts, most fungi are multicellular. The basic structural units of multicellular fungi are their threadlike filaments called **hyphae** (HI fee) (singular, hypha), which develop from fungal spores, as shown in *Figure 20.2*. Hyphae elongate at their tips and branch extensively to form a network of filaments called a **mycelium** (mi SEE lee um). There are different types of hyphae in a mycelium. Some anchor the fungus, some invade the food source, and others form fungal reproductive structures. Use the *MiniLab* on this page to observe the hyphae of some bread mold you grow.

530 FUNGI

Additional Lab

Mold Growth

Purpose
Students will show that mold grows on moist, organic material.

Materials ▢▢▢
small paper cups, macaroni, aluminum foil, water, cardboard pieces, oatmeal flakes, swab with mold spores, plastic wrap

Procedure
Be aware that some students may have allergies to mold.
1. Number eight small paper cups 1–8 and label each with your name and date.

Add the following to each cup (1/8 full): cup #1 cardboard, #2 moist cardboard, #3 oatmeal, #4 moist oatmeal, #5 macaroni, #6 moist macaroni, #7 aluminum foil ball, #8 wet aluminum foil ball.
2. Rub a cotton swab with mold spores on the surface of each cup's contents.
3. Cover each cup with plastic wrap and place the cups in a designated area. Wash your hands with soap and water.

You can use a magnifying glass to see individual hyphae in molds that grow on bread. However, the hyphae of mushrooms are much more difficult to see because they are tightly packed, forming a dense mass.

Unlike plants, which have cell walls made of cellulose, the cell walls of most fungi contain a complex carbohydrate called **chitin** (KI tun). Chitin gives the fungal cell walls both strength and flexibility.

Inside hyphae

In many types of fungi, cross walls called septa (singular, septum) divide hyphae into individual cells that contain one or more nuclei, *Figure 20.3*. Septa are usually porous, allowing cytoplasm and organelles to flow freely and nutrients to move rapidly from one part of a fungus to another.

Some fungi consist of hyphae with no septa. Under a microscope, you see hundreds of nuclei streaming along in a continuous flow of cytoplasm. As in hyphae with septa, the flow of cytoplasm quickly and efficiently disperses nutrients and other materials throughout the fungus.

Adaptations in Fungi

Fungi can be harmful. Some cause food to spoil. Some cause diseases, and some are poisonous. However, they play an important and beneficial role. In a world without fungi, huge amounts of wastes, dead organisms, and debris, which consist of complex organic substances, would litter Earth. Many fungi, along with some bacteria and protists, are decomposers. They break down complex organic substances into raw materials that other living organisms need. Thanks to these organic decomposers, fallen leaves, animal carcasses, and other wastes are eliminated.

Figure 20.3
Hyphae differ in structure.

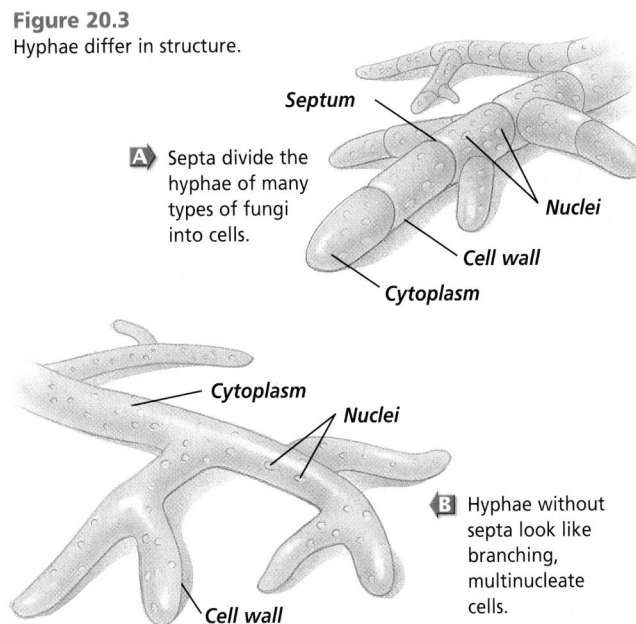

A Septa divide the hyphae of many types of fungi into cells.

Septum

Nuclei

Cell wall

Cytoplasm

Cytoplasm

Nuclei

B Hyphae without septa look like branching, multinucleate cells.

Cell wall

How fungi obtain food

Unlike plants and some protists, fungi cannot produce their own food. Fungi are heterotrophs, and they use a process called extracellular digestion to obtain nutrients. In this process, food is digested outside a fungus's cells, and the digested products are then absorbed. For example, as some hyphae grow into the cells of an orange, they release digestive enzymes that break down the large organic molecules of the orange into smaller molecules. These small molecules diffuse into the fungal hyphae and move in the free-flowing cytoplasm to where they are needed for growth, repair, and reproduction. The more a mycelium grows, the more surface area becomes available for nutrient absorption.

✓ **Reading Check** **Summarize** the role of fungi in maintaining equilibrium, including decay in an ecosystem.

20.1 WHAT IS A FUNGUS? **531**

 Quick Demo

Describe Mushrooms Provide small student groups with mushrooms purchased from a supermarket and ask them to record their observations. After four or five minutes, have the groups share their lists.
L1 **COOP LEARN**

✓ **Reading Check** By decomposing waste materials, fungi are important in recycling nutrients for other organisms in the ecosystem.

Activity

Kinesthetic Use any mold that grows on food to illustrate the appearance of hyphae. Have students prepare some wet mounts of the mold and view it under low- and then high-power magnification. Have students wear aprons, gloves, and goggles and wash their hands after handling the fungal samples and after they clean up. Caution them to use care when working with glass slides and coverslips and when viewing a slide under high power.
L2 **ELL**

Portfolio

Fungi Adaptations Ask students to diagram the fungi they observed in the Activity above and compare them in writing, explaining their adaptations and feeding relationships. **L2**

Indiana Academic Standards

Pages 530–531: B.1.8, B.1.13, B.1.44

---

4. Check the cups, without disturbing the growth, each day for a week.
5. Design a data table to record your observations, including the amount of mold growth.
6. As directed by your teacher, dispose of any mold that grows.

Analysis
1. **What evidence suggests that mold feeds on organic matter?** All organic materials showed mold growth. The only inorganic material (aluminum foil) showed no growth.
2. **Explain the role of the cups without water.** They were controls, showing that molds require moisture to grow.

Assessment
Knowledge Have the students hypothesize whether the following items will support mold growth and explain why: dry cereal, penny, wet penny, wet cracker, cooked and uncooked rice. Use the Performance Task Assessment List for Formulating a Hypothesis in **PASC**, p. 93. **L2**

Have students compare the terms *extracellular digestion* and *intracellular digestion* and provide an example of each. **L2**

Revealing Misconceptions

Many students will only be familiar with edible mushrooms and toadstools and be unaware of the variety of organisms found in Kingdom Fungi. Point out that only about 25% of all fungi are in the same phyla as mushrooms.

Uncover the Misconception

Place a mushroom, moldy bread or fruit, blue cheese, and dried yeast in separate petri dishes. Ask students to identify which one is a fungus. Most students will choose the mushroom. Explain that although they are very different in appearance, all of the organisms are fungi.

Demonstrate the Concept

Prepare a flip chart that shows each of the phyla of fungi. Each page of the chart should show an example of each and include the reproductive method or other differences. Go over these with the students.

Assess New Knowledge

Have students identify other fungi that they may not have thought about when first questioned.

532

Different feeding relationships

Fungi have different types of food sources. A fungus may be a saprophyte, a mutualist, or a parasite depending on its food source.

Saprophytes are decomposers and feed on waste or dead organic material. Mutualists live in a symbiotic relationship with another organism, such as an alga. Parasites absorb nutrients from the living cells of their hosts. Parasitic fungi may produce specialized hyphae called **haustoria**, (huh STOR ee uh), which penetrate and grow into host cells where they directly absorb the host cells' nutrients. You can see a diagram of haustoria invading host cells in *Figure 20.4.*

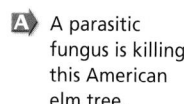

Word Origin

haustoria from the Latin word *haurire*, meaning "to drink"; The hyphae that invade the cells of a host to absorb nutrients are called haustoria.

Figure 20.4
Fungi may be parasites, mutualists, or saprophytes.

Fungal hypha

Haustorium　　　*Host cell*

B Fungi can produce haustoria that grow into host cells and absorb their nutrients.

A A parasitic fungus is killing this American elm tree.

C The saprophytic turkey-tail fungus (*Trametes versicolor*) decomposes the tissues in this dead tree branch.

532 FUNGI

Reproduction in Fungi

Depending on the species and on environmental conditions, a fungus may reproduce asexually or sexually. Fungi reproduce asexually by fragmentation, budding, or producing spores.

Fragmentation and budding

In fragmentation, pieces of hyphae that are broken off a mycelium grow into new mycelia. For example, when you prepare your garden for planting, you help fungi in the soil reproduce by fragmentation. This is because, every time you dig into the soil, your shovel slices through mycelia, fragmenting them. Most of the fragments will grow into new mycelia.

CHALLENGE ACTIVITY

Toxic Fungi Students who need an additional challenge can research *Aspergillus flavus,* which invades stores of grains and nuts. They can produce a brochure that contains information about the fungus and the dangers posed by the chemical (aflatoxin, a carcinogen that can destroy the liver if ingested) that it produces. The students may include identification procedures to determine if grains or nuts have been contaminated. See *BioChallenges and Enrichment* for additional projects and activities. **L3**

Figure 20.5
Fungi reproduce asexually by budding, fragmentation, or spore production.

A Most yeasts reproduce asexually by budding.

Color-enhanced SEM Magnification: 2 250×

B Many fungi, such as this bread mold, can produce spores asexually.

The unicellular fungi called yeasts often reproduce by a process called **budding**—a form of asexual reproduction in which mitosis occurs and a new individual pinches off from the parent, matures, and eventually separates from the parent. You can see a yeast cell and its bud in *Figure 20.5*.

Reproducing by spores

Recall that a spore is a reproductive cell that can develop into a new organism. Most fungi produce spores. When a fungal spore is transported to a place with favorable growing conditions, a threadlike hypha emerges and begins to grow, eventually forming a new mycelium. The mycelium becomes established in the food source.

In some fungi, after a while, specialized hyphae grow away from the rest of a mycelium and produce a spore-containing structure called a **sporangium** (spuh RAN jee uhm) (plural, sporangia)—a sac or case in which spores are produced. The tiny black spots you see in a bread mold's mycelium are a type of sporangium.

In fact, for most fungi, the specialized reproductive hyphal structures where the fungal spores are produced are usually the only part of a fungus you can see, and the sporangia often make up only a very small fraction of the total organism.

Many fungi can produce two types of spores—one type by mitosis and the other by meiosis—at different times during their life cycles. One important criterion for classifying fungi into divisions is their patterns of reproduction, especially sexual reproduction, during the life cycle.

The adaptive advantages of spores

Many adaptive advantages of fungi involve spores and their production. First, the sporangia protect spores and, in some cases, prevent them from drying out until they are ready to be released. Second, most fungi produce a large number of spores at one time. For example, a puffball that measures only 25 cm in circumference can produce about 1 trillion spores.

20.1 WHAT IS A FUNGUS? **533**

3 Assess

DAILY INTERVENTION

Check for Understanding
Have students explain how the following are related. **L1**
- hyphae—mycelium
- cell wall—chitin
- decomposers—extracellular digestion
- reproduction—sporangium
- spores—budding

Reteach
Naturalist Have students outline fungal characteristics, including structure, nutrition, and reproduction. **L1**

Resources
For more practice, use *Reading Essentials for Biology,* Section 20.1.

Extension

Yeast cells respire aerobically and undergo fermentation anaerobically. Review the processes and ask students to compare and contrast them. **L1**

✓ MODIFIED Assessment

Skill Have students make a table that compares the cellular organizations, methods of obtaining food, cell wall compositions, and habitats of fungi and plants. **L1**

Purpose

Students will analyze information about chestnut blight fungus.

Process Skills

analyze information, draw a conclusion, apply concepts

Teaching Strategies

■ Compare the chestnut blight and Dutch Elm disease.
■ Explain the role of a plant's vascular tissue.
■ Review the meanings of fungal strain, canker, and fungicide.

Thinking Critically

1. Answers will vary. It's hard to keep trees free of insects, birds, wind, and rain.
2. The fungus grows under the bark.
3. Answers will vary: import some Japanese chestnut trees and breed *dentata* species with *crenata* species. DNA technology may help create resistant trees.

Assessment

Portfolio Ask students to find the derivation of the word *canker* and explain why it so well describes chestnut blight symptoms. Use the Performance Task Assessment List for Oral Presentation in **PASC,** p. 143. **L2**

Problem-Solving Lab 20.1

Analyze Information

Why are chestnut trees so rare? The American chestnut tree (*Castanea dentata*) has almost disappeared from the United States, Italy, and France because of a disease known as chestnut blight, which is caused by the fungus *Cryphonectria parasitica.* Since 1900, three to four billion trees have been lost to chestnut blight.

Solve the Problem

Fact: Spores of *C. parasitica* land on the bark of American chestnut trees and germinate. Hyphae grow below the bark and form a canker (diseased tissue) that spreads, producing large areas of dead tissue. Eventually, the nutrient and water supplies of the tree are cut off, and the tree dies.
Fact: *C. parasitica* reproduces by forming spores that are carried by wind, insects, birds, and rain to other trees that then become infected.
Fact: The Japanese chestnut tree *Castanea crenata* is resistant to the *C. parasitica* fungus. This resistance is partially due to the existence of weak fungal strains that cannot kill their host.

Thinking Critically

1. **Predict** Why would it be difficult to control the disease by preventing spores from landing on healthy trees?
2. **Interpret Data** Based on how this fungus grows, why can't fungicides applied to the bark of an infected tree kill the fungus?
3. **Describe** Suggest a solution to the problem in the United States knowing about the resistance of the Japanese chestnut species and the existence of weak disease-causing fungal strains. (Hint: Think about DNA technology.)

Figure 20.6
A passing animal or the pressure of raindrops may have caused these puffballs to discharge the cloud of spores that will be dispersed by the wind.

Producing so many spores increases the germination rate and improves the species survival chances.

Finally, fungal spores are small and lightweight and can be dispersed by wind, water, and animals such as birds and insects. The wind will disperse the spores that the puffballs you see in *Figure 20.6* are releasing. Spores dispersed by wind can travel hundreds of kilometers. In the *Problem-Solving Lab* on this page, you can learn about the dispersal methods of a plant fungus that causes the disease called chestnut blight in chestnut trees.

Section Assessment

Understanding Main Ideas
1. Identify the characteristics of the fungi kingdom.
2. Describe how a fungus obtains nutrients.
3. What role do fungi play in food chains?
4. How are the terms *hypha* and *mycelium* related?

Thinking Critically
5. Imagine you are a mycologist (scientist who studies fungi) who finds an inhabited bird's nest.

Explain why you would expect to find several different types of fungi growing in the nest.

SKILL REVIEW

6. **Measure in SI** Outline the steps you would take to calculate the approximate number of spores in a puffball fungus with a circumference of 10 cm. For more help, refer to *Measure in SI* in the **Skill Handbook.**

534 FUNGI

 in.bdol.glencoe.com/self_check_quiz

Section Assessment

1. Fungi are mostly multicellular, eukaryotic organisms. All fungi have chitin in their cell walls and are heterotrophic.
2. Hyphae invade a food source where they release enzymes that digest the food. The hyphae absorb digested foods.

3. Fungi are decomposers that break down and recycle dead organic material, providing nutrients for autotrophs.
4. A mycelium is made up of hyphae.
5. Fungi use a variety of organic materials for food. Fungi may feed on feathers, excrement, or twigs in the nest.

6. Divide a puffball into many small similar-sized sections. Use a sampling technique to estimate the number of spores in one small section. Multiply the estimate by the number of remaining sections.

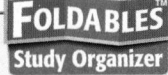

Section 20.2

The Diversity of Fungi

Indiana Standards Standard B.1.35 Explain that the degree of kinship between organisms or species can be estimated from the similarity of their DNA sequences, which often closely matches their classification based on anatomical similarities...

SECTION PREVIEW

Objectives

Identify the four major phyla of fungi.

Distinguish among the ways spores are produced in zygomycotes, ascomycotes, and basidiomycotes.

Summarize the ecological roles of lichens and mycorrhizae.

Review Vocabulary

spore: type of haploid (*n*) reproductive cell that forms a new organism without the fusion of gametes (p. 508)

New Vocabulary

stolon
rhizoid
zygospore
gametangium
ascus
ascospore
conidiophore
conidium
basidium
basidiospore
mycorrhiza
lichen

Fungi Make the following Foldable to help you organize the main characteristics of the four major phyla of fungi.

STEP 1 **Draw** a mark at the midpoint of a sheet of paper along the side edge. Then **fold** the top and bottom edges in to touch the midpoint.

STEP 2 **Fold** in half from side to side.

STEP 3 **Open and cut** along the inside fold lines to form four tabs.

STEP 4 **Label** each tab as shown.

| Zygomycotes | Ascomycotes |
| Basidiomycotes | Deuteromycotes |

Classify As you read Section 20.2, list the characteristics of the four major phyla of fungi under the appropriate tab.

Zygomycotes

Have you ever taken a slice of bread from a bag and seen some black spots and a bit of fuzz on the bread's surface? If so, then you have probably seen *Rhizopus stolonifer*, a common bread mold. *Rhizopus* is probably the most familiar member of the phylum Zygomycota (zy goh mi KOH tuh). Many other members of about 1000 species of zygomycotes are also decomposers. Zygomycotes reproduce asexually by producing spores. They produce a different type of spore when they reproduce sexually. The hyphae of zygomycotes do not have septa that divide them into individual cells.

Growth and asexual reproduction

When a *Rhizopus* spore settles on a moist piece of bread, it germinates and hyphae begin to grow. Some hyphae called **stolons** (STOH lunz) grow horizontally along the surface of the bread, rapidly producing a mycelium. Some other hyphae form **rhizoids** (RI zoydz) that penetrate the food and anchor the mycelium in the bread. Rhizoids secrete enzymes needed for extracellular digestion and absorb the digested nutrients.

Asexual reproduction begins when some hyphae grow upward and develop sporangia at their tips. Asexual spores develop in the sporangia. When a sporangium splits open, hundreds of spores are released.

20.2   THE DIVERSITY OF FUNGI   **535**

2 Teach

Reinforcement

Explain that hyphae have different names, depending on their function. Examples are rhizoids, stolons, and sporangia. Have students describe the role of each of these hyphae and then the role of the hyphae called a *mycelium*.

Using Science Terms

Have students find the meanings of the four terms *sporangium, gametangium, zygospore,* and *ascospore* and explain how the name of each structure suits its function.

Enrichment

Linguistic Ask students to research and report on the medical use of cyclosporine, a chemical produced from the soil fungus *Tolypocladium inflatum.* This chemical suppresses the immunity that causes the rejection of transplanted organs. More than 90% of transplant patients survive rejection today because of cyclosporine. **L2**

Activity

Visual-Spatial Have students construct a concept map that uses the following structures and functions: stolons, sporangia, rhizoids, absorb nutrients, form spores, and produce mycelia. **L1**

Indiana Academic Standards

Pages 536–537: B.1.11, B.1.43

Those that land on a moist food supply germinate, form new hyphae, and reproduce asexually again.

Producing zygospores

Suppose that the bread on which *Rhizopus* was growing began to dry out. This unfavorable environmental condition could trigger the fungus to reproduce sexually. When zygomycotes reproduce sexually, they produce **zygospores** (ZI guh sporz), which are thick-walled spores that can withstand unfavorable conditions.

Sexual reproduction in *Rhizopus* occurs when haploid hyphae from two compatible mycelia, called plus and minus mating strains, grow together and fuse. Where the haploid hyphae fuse, they each form a **gametangium** (ga muh TAN ghee uhm), a structure containing a haploid nucleus. When the haploid nuclei of the two gametangia fuse, a diploid zygote forms. The zygote develops a thick wall, becoming a dormant zygospore.

A zygospore may remain dormant for many months, surviving periods of drought, cold, and heat. When environmental conditions are favorable, the zygospore absorbs water, undergoes meiosis, and germinates to produce a hypha with a sporangium. Each haploid spore formed in the sporangium can grow into a new mycelium. Look at *Figure 20.7* to see how *Rhizopus* reproduces both sexually and asexually.

Figure 20.7
During its life cycle, the black bread mold, *Rhizopus stolonifera,* reproduces both asexually and sexually.

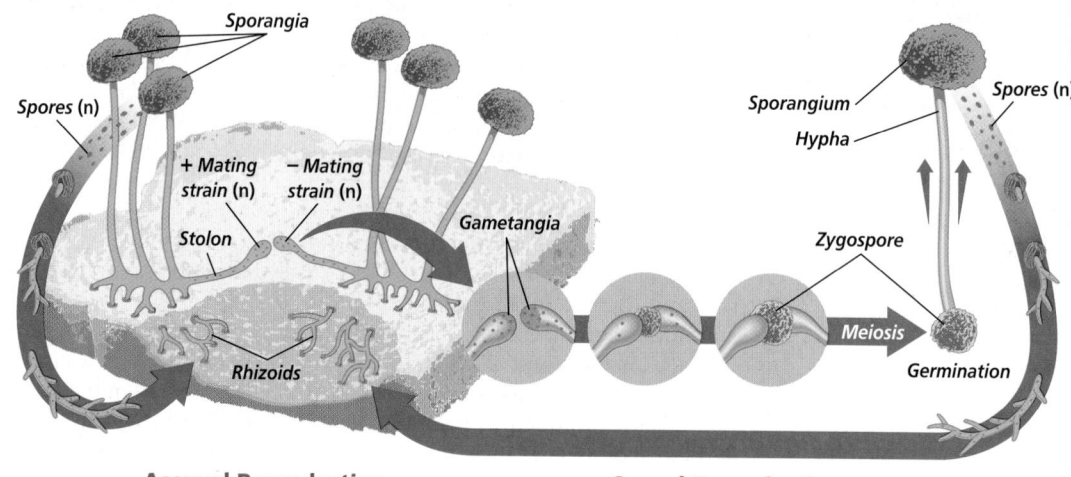

A Zygospores form where gametangia have fused.

LM Magnification: 100×

B These *Rhizopus* sporangia are filled with thousands of haploid spores.

LM Magnification: 27×

Sporangia

Spores (n)

+ Mating strain (n)   − Mating strain (n)

Stolon

Gametangia

Rhizoids

Meiosis

Germination

Zygospore

Sporangium

Hypha

Spores (n)

Asexual Reproduction   **Sexual Reproduction**

536 FUNGI

USING MODELS

Examining Fungi Use models of fungi (available from biological supply houses or produced by previous students from locally available materials) to review and reinforce knowledge of fungal structures. Students may want to make their own models. Make sure they include structures such as hyphae, mycelium, sporangium, and the fruiting body. **L1**

Ascomycotes

The Ascomycota is the largest phylum of fungi, containing about 30 000 species. The ascomycotes are also called sac fungi. Both names refer to tiny saclike structures, each called an **ascus,** in which the sexual spores of the fungi develop. Because they are produced inside an ascus, the sexual spores are called **ascospores.**

During asexual reproduction, ascomycotes produce a different kind of spore. Fungal hyphae grow up from the mycelium and elongate to form **conidiophores** (kuh NIH dee uh forz). Chains or clusters of asexual spores called **conidia** develop from the tips of conidiophores. Wind, water, and animals disperse these haploid spores. Some conidia and conidiophores are shown in *Figure 20.8.*

Important ascomycotes

You've probably encountered a few types of sac fungi in your refrigerator in the form of blue-green, red, and brown molds on decaying foods. Other sac fungi are familiar to farmers and gardeners because they cause plant diseases such as apple scab and ergot of rye. Learn more about the dangers of fungi in the *Connection to Social Studies* at the end of this chapter.

Not all sac fungi have a bad reputation. Ascomycotes can have many different forms, as you can see in *Figure 20.9.* Morels and truffles are two edible members of this phylum. Perhaps the most economically important ascomycotes are the yeasts.

Yeasts are unicellular sac fungi that rarely produce hyphae and usually reproduce asexually by budding. Yeasts are anaerobes and ferment sugars to produce carbon dioxide and ethyl alcohol. Because yeasts produce alcohol, they are used to make wine and beer. Other yeasts are used in

Color-enhanced SEM Magnification: 305×

baking because they produce carbon dioxide, the gas that causes bread dough to rise and take on a light, airy texture. Use the *BioLab* at the end of this chapter to experimentally determine the temperature at which yeasts function most efficiently.

Yeasts are also important tools for research in genetics because they have large chromosomes. A vaccine for the disease hepatitis B is produced by splicing human genes with those of yeast cells. Because yeasts multiply rapidly, they are an important source of the vaccine.

Figure 20.8
Most ascomycotes reproduce asexually by producing conidia in structures called conidiophores.

Figure 20.9
Many ascomycotes are cup shaped or have cup-shaped indentations that are lined with asci.

A Morels are prized for their flavor.

B The orange cuplike structures of this ascomycote are visible on the dead bark.

537

Purpose

Students will observe the arrangement of mushroom gills.

Process Skills

observe and infer, experiment

Teaching Strategies

- Have students wear aprons, gloves, and goggles and wash their hands after they finish the activity and clean up.
- Find an area where nothing will disturb the caps overnight.
- Have students make wet mounts of the spores, examine them under low- and high-power magnification, and sketch their observations. **L2** **ELL**

Expected Results

Spores will form a pattern on the paper corresponding to the gills' locations.

Analysis

1. brown
2. Spores are formed toward the edges of the gills. The patterns are the same.

Modified Assessment

Skill Give students spore patterns from different mushrooms and use them to reconstruct the gill arrangements. Use the Performance Task Assessment List for Scientific Drawing in **PASC**, p. 127. **L1** **ELL**

MiniLab 20.2

Classify

Examining Mushroom Gills
Spore prints can often help in mushroom identification by revealing the pattern of a mushroom's gills and the color of its spores. Use this technique to see how a mushroom's gills are arranged.

Procedure

1. Break off the stalks from some grocery store mushrooms. Place the caps in a paper bag for a few days.
2. When the undersides of the caps are very dark brown, set the caps, gill side down, on a white sheet of paper. Be sure that the gills are touching the surface of the paper.
3. After leaving the caps undisturbed overnight, carefully lift the caps from the paper and observe the results.
4. Wash your hands with soap and water. Dispose of fungi as your teacher directs.

Analysis

1. **Observe** What color are the spores on the paper?
2. **Compare** How does the pattern of spores on the paper compare with the arrangement of gills on the underside of the mushroom cap that produced it?

Basidiomycotes

Of all the diverse kinds of fungi, you are probably most familiar with some of the about 25 000 species in the phylum Basidiomycota. Mushrooms, puffballs, stinkhorns, bird's nest fungi, and bracket fungi are all basidiomycotes. So are the rust and smut fungi. Use the *MiniLab* to distinguish some mushroom species.

Basidia and basidiospores

Basidiomycotes have club-shaped hyphae called **basidia** (buh SIHD ee uh) that produce spores and give them their common name—club fungi. Basidia usually develop on short-lived, visible reproductive structures that have varied shapes and sizes, as you can see in *Figure 20.10*. Spores called **basidiospores** are produced in basidia during reproduction.

A basidiomycote, such as a mushroom, has a complex reproductive cycle. How does a mushroom reproduce? Study *Figure 20.11* to find out.

Figure 20.10
Basidiomycotes have many different forms, and what you see are their reproductive structures.

A Smuts are parasites that attack plants such as corn.

B Shelf fungi, such as this sulfur shelf, often grow on tree branches and fallen logs.

C A typical mushroom, such as this *Mycena*, has a cap that sits on top of a stalk.

TECH PREP

Mushrooms: *Naturalist* Provide students with an assortment of store-bought mushrooms and a mushroom field guide. Ask them to identify each mushroom. **L3** **ELL**

The Life of a Mushroom

Figure 20.11

What you call a mushroom is a reproductive structure of the fungus. Most of the fungus is underground and not visible. A single mushroom can produce hundreds of thousands of spores as a result of sexual reproduction. Most types of mushrooms have no asexual reproductive stages in their life cycle. **Critical Thinking** *Why are spores of mushrooms produced above ground?*

Mycena pura

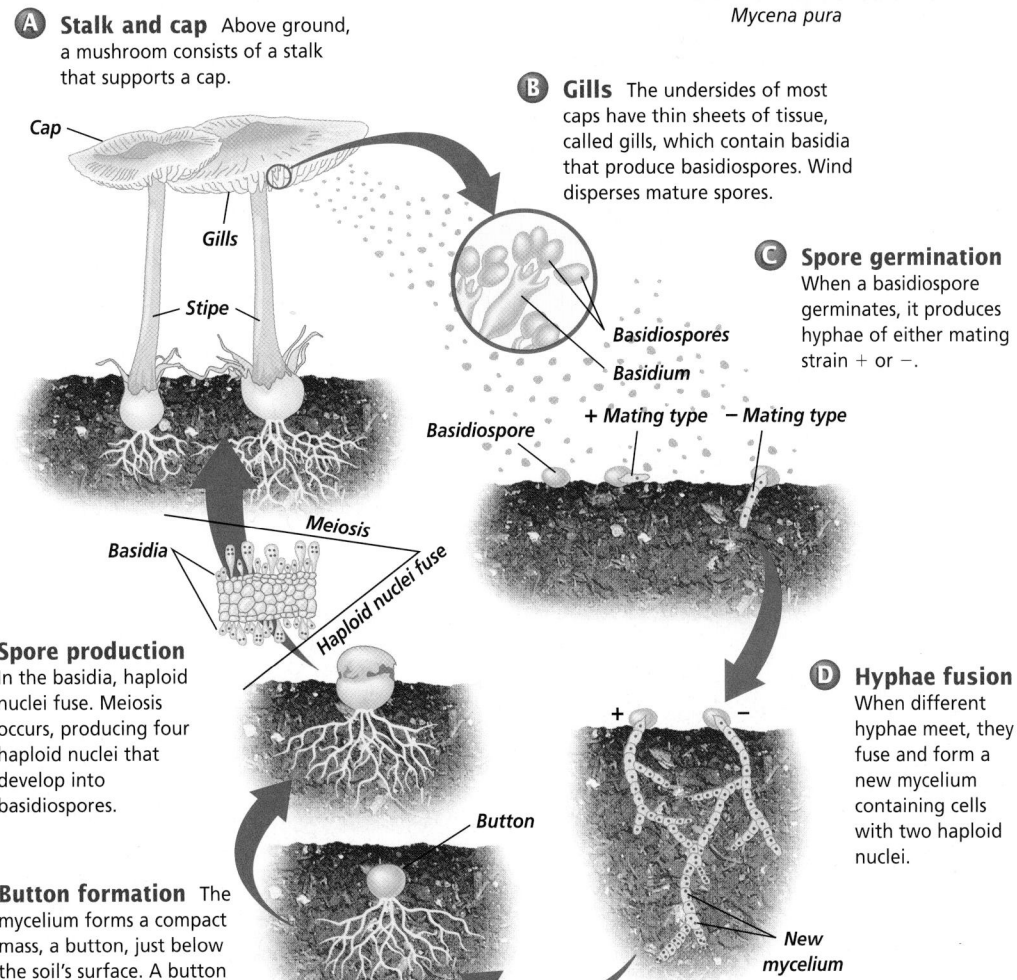

A **Stalk and cap** Above ground, a mushroom consists of a stalk that supports a cap.

Cap

Gills

Stipe

B **Gills** The undersides of most caps have thin sheets of tissue, called gills, which contain basidia that produce basidiospores. Wind disperses mature spores.

Basidiospores

Basidium

C **Spore germination** When a basidiospore germinates, it produces hyphae of either mating strain + or −.

Basidiospore   *+ Mating type*   *− Mating type*

Meiosis

Basidia

Haploid nuclei fuse

F **Spore production** In the basidia, haploid nuclei fuse. Meiosis occurs, producing four haploid nuclei that develop into basidiospores.

E **Button formation** The mycelium forms a compact mass, a button, just below the soil's surface. A button develops into a stalk and cap.

Button

D **Hyphae fusion** When different hyphae meet, they fuse and form a new mycelium containing cells with two haploid nuclei.

New mycelium

20.2   THE DIVERSITY OF FUNGI   **539**

Purpose

Students will follow the steps in the life cycle of a mushroom.

Teaching Strategies

Remind students that Basidiomycetes spores result from sexual reproduction.

Visual Learning

■ Point out that in step 4, the nuclei from each original + and − type are in the same cell but not fused. Ask if the cells are haploid, diploid, or haploid + haploid in chromosome number. haploid + haploid

■ Ask students to use the diagram to explain when fertilization occurs. just prior to spore formation in the basidium

■ Have students explain the adaptive value of producing many basidiospores. Many spores ensure the continued life cycle of the fungus.

Critical Thinking

The spores are produced aboveground so that they can be easily dispersed by air currents.

Indiana Academic Standards

Pages 538–539: B.1.11, B.1.43

Tell students that, to avoid poisonous mushrooms, they should never eat ones collected from fields. Explain that even mycologists may be unsure of the identity of some mushrooms. You may want to show photos of two similar looking species of mushrooms such as morels (*Morchella elata*) that are edible and false morels (*Gyromitra esculenta*), which are poisonous.

Enrichment

Linguistic Have interested students research mushroom folklore. One good reference is: "Who put the toad in toadstools?" A. Morgan, *New Scientist*, vol. 112, December 1986/January 1987. **L3**

Reinforcement

Review the methods by which zygomycotes, ascomycotes, and basidiomycotes reproduce sexually. Emphasize that deuteromycotes form a separate group mainly because nobody has observed them reproduce sexually.

Enrichment

Have students research the discovery of penicillin and explain how it affected the medical field. **L2**

Deuteromycotes

There are about 25 000 species of fungi classified as deuteromycotes, which have no known sexual stage in their life cycle, unlike the zygomycotes, ascomycotes, and basidiomycotes. Although the deuteromycotes may only be able to reproduce asexually, another possibility is that their sexual phase has not yet been observed by mycologists, biologists who study fungi.

Word Origin

mycorrhiza from the Greek words *mykes*, meaning "fungus," and *rhiza*, meaning "root"; Mycorrhizae are mutualistic relationships between fungi and plants.

Diverse deuteromycotes

If you've ever had strep throat, pneumonia, or other kinds of bacterial infection, your doctor may have prescribed penicillin—an antibiotic produced from a deuteromycote that is commonly seen growing on fruit, as shown in *Figure 20.12*. Other deuteromycotes are used in the making of foods, such as soy sauce and some kinds of blue-veined cheese. Still other deuteromycotes are used commercially to produce substances such as citric acid, which gives jams, jellies, soft drinks, and fruit-flavored candies a tart taste.

Figure 20.12 Many deuteromycotes are useful.

A Bleu cheese has a distinctive flavor. The blue splotches are patches of fungal spores.

B The antibiotic penicillin is derived from *Penicillium* mold, shown here growing on an orange.

Mutualism: Mycorrhizae and Lichens

Certain fungi live in a mutualistic association with other organisms. Two of these mutualistic associations that are also symbiotic are called mycorrhizae and lichens.

Mycorrhizae

A **mycorrhiza** (my kuh RHY zuh) is a mutualistic relationship in which a fungus lives symbiotically with a plant. Most of the fungi that form mycorrhizae are basidiomycotes, but some zygomycotes also form these important relationships.

How does a plant benefit from a mycorrhizal relationship? Fine, thread-like hyphae grow harmlessly around or into the plant's roots, as shown in *Figure 20.13*. The hyphae increase the absorptive surface of the plant's roots, resulting in more nutrients entering the plant. Phosphorus, copper, and other minerals in the soil are absorbed by the hyphae and then released into the roots. In addition, the

CULTURAL DIVERSITY

A Fungus Called Ergot The fungus ergot produces many chemicals, including ergotamine. In ancient Greece and Peru and also during the Middle Ages in Europe, ergot was used in small quantities for spiritual and medicinal purposes.

Ergot grows on rye and causes severe symptoms if it is milled in flour that people ingest. Eating ergot causes Saint Anthony's fire, a disease with symptoms that include uncontrolled behavior, hallucinations, hysteria, and facial redness. Some historians suggest that ergot may have caused the bizarre behavior of the people tried for witchcraft in Salem, Massachusetts, during colonial times.

Visual-Spatial Soak lichens over-night in water. Have students examine the water with a stereomicroscope. They should observe many tiny animals called "water bears" or tardigrades. Have students diagram the tardigrades and research them. **L3** **ELL**

Inquiry

Discussion Have students hypothesize the effects of acid rain on fungal growth. Ask them to verbally design a procedure that tests their hypothesis. Remind students to include experimental controls. **L2**

Figure 20.13
The fungal part of a mycorrhiza surrounds plant roots **(A)**. The red filaments in the plant cells are fungal hyphae **(B)**. *Infer How does mycorrhiza benefit a host plant?*

Caption Question Answer
Figure 20.13 Mycorrhizae help to provide additional surface area for absorption of water and nutrients.

Struggling Learners

Have students make a table that compares mycorrhizae and lichens. The left side of the table should list the two symbiotic relationships. The column heads should include: *Type of Relationship, Organisms Involved, Habitat, Advantage to the Organisms.* **L2** **ELL**

Stained LM Magnification: 100×

Fungus

fungus also may help to maintain water in the soil around the plant. In turn, the mycorrhizal fungus benefits by receiving organic nutrients, such as sugars and amino acids, from the plant.

About 80 to 90 percent of all plant species have mycorrhizae associated with their roots. Plants of a species that have mycorrhizae grow larger and are more productive than those that don't. In fact, some species cannot survive without mycorrhizae. Some orchid seeds, for example, usually do not germinate without a symbiotic fungus to provide water and nutrients.

Lichens

It's sometimes hard to believe that the orange, green, and black blotches that you see on rocks, trees, and stone walls are alive. The blotches may look like flakes of old paint or pieces of dried moss, but they are forms of lichens. See *Figure 20.14.*

Figure 20.14
Lichens have a variety of forms.

A Some lichens form crust-like growths on bare rocks and stone walls.

B Each stalk of these British soldier lichens is about 3 cm tall.

C Some lichens resemble leaves, like these lichens growing on a dead twig.

CHALLENGE ACTIVITY

Classifying Deuteromycotes Students who need an additional challenge can research the classification of the Deuteromycotes in the various classification schemes. After determining reasons for the different classification structures, they can prepare a chart that compares and contrasts the systems. **L3**

Purpose

Students will differentiate between a lichen's fungal and algal components.

Process Skills

compare and contrast, think critically, design an experiment, interpret scientific diagrams

Teaching Strategies

■ Make sure that students are familiar with the composition of lichens before doing this activity.

■ Review symbiosis and discuss the life styles, including mutualism, that the term includes.

Thinking Critically

1. Structure B is the algal part because it is green, the color of chlorophyll. Structure A is the fungal part because it is not green and probably cannot make its own food.

2. Structure C shows a sac or ascus that contains spores.

3. Answers will vary. Separate the algae and fungi and try to maintain each part separately by providing nutrients and water to the fungus and light, carbon dioxide, and water to the alga.

Assessment

Knowledge Have students research and write a report about the consequences of Norwegian lichens absorbing radioactive elements after the Chernobyl nuclear accident in Russia. Use the Performance Task Assessment List for Writing in Science in **PASC**, p. 159. **L3**

√**Reading Check** Lichens are composed of a fungus and algae or cyanobacteria. The fungus provides an anchor for the algae or cyanobacteria and helps to catch water. The algae or cyanobacteria provides food for the fungus as a result of photosynthesis.

542

Problem-Solving Lab 20.2

Think Critically

What's inside a lichen?
A lichen consists of a fungus and an alga or cyanobacterium that live symbiotically. The prefix *sym* means "together," and *biotic* means "life." The word *symbiosis* describes the fact that there are two different life forms living together.

Solve the Problem

You find a lichen and make a thin slice through it. You magnify the slice under the microscope and draw what you observe—the diagram above.

Thinking Critically

1. **Outline** Using color as a clue, list the letters that identify the algal and fungal parts of the lichen.
2. **Explain** Structure C is a reproductive part. After examining it, you conclude that this is a reproductive structure of an ascomycote. Explain how you knew this.
3. **Experiment** Scientists have wondered if the parts of a lichen can survive by themselves. Describe an experiment that might answer this question.

Figure 20.15
Cladina stellaris is a common lichen on the tundra and a favorite food of caribou and reindeer.

542 FUNGI

A **lichen** (LI kun) is a symbiotic association between a fungus, usually an ascomycote, and a photosynthetic green alga or a cyanobacterium, which is an autotroph.

The fungus portion of the lichen forms a dense web of hyphae in which the algae or cyanobacteria grow. Together, the fungus and its photosynthetic partner form a structure that looks like a single organism. Use the *Problem-Solving Lab* to find out more about a lichen's structure.

Lichens need only light, air, and minerals to grow. The photosynthetic partner provides the food for both organisms. The fungus, in turn, provides its partner with water and minerals that it absorbs from rain and the air, and protects it from changes in environmental conditions.

There are about 20 000 species of lichens. They range in size from less than 1 mm to several meters in diameter. Most lichens grow slowly, increasing in diameter only 0.1 to 10 mm per year. Some lichens may be thousands of years old.

Found worldwide, lichens are pioneers, being among the first to colonize a barren area. Lichens live in arid deserts, on bare rocks exposed to bitter-cold winds, and just below the timberline on mountain peaks. On the arctic tundra, lichens, such as the one shown in *Figure 20.15*, are the dominant form of vegetation. Both caribou and musk oxen graze on lichens there, much like cattle graze on grass elsewhere.

Not only are lichens pioneers, but they are also indicators of pollution levels in the air. The fungus readily absorbs materials from the air. If pollutants are present, they kill the fungus. Without the fungal part of a lichen, the photosynthetic partner also dies.

√**Reading Check** **Describe** the components that make up a lichen and what each contributes.

CHALLENGE ACTIVITY

Observe Fungus Have students prepare wet mount slides of the fungus in blue cheese and observe it under a microscope. Remind them to wear goggles, gloves, an apron, and to be careful when working with microscopes and slides. Have them wash their hands with soap and water after preparing their slides. Ask them to diagram and describe their observations. **L3**

Figure 20.16
This diagram shows the relationships of fungi.

Ascomycotes
30 000 species

Lichens
20 000 species

Deuteromycotes
25 000 species

FUNGI

Basidiomycotes
25 000 species

Zygomycotes
1000 species

Protists

Archaebacteria

Eubacteria

Species numbers are approximate and subject to change pending discoveries or extinctions.

Origins of Fungi

Mycologists hypothesize that the ascomycotes and the basidiomycotes evolved from a common ancestor and that the zygomycotes evolved earlier, as you can see in *Figure 20.16*.

Although fossils can provide clues as to how organisms evolved, fossils of fungi are rare because fungi are composed of soft materials. The oldest fossils that have been identified as fungi are over 400 million years old.

Section Assessment

Understanding Main Ideas
1. What occurs underground between the time a basidiospore germinates and a mushroom button forms?
2. Explain how the deuteromycotes differ from members of the other divisions of fungi. Explain how they are all similar.
3. Who are the partners in a mycorrhizae? Describe how each partner benefits in a mycorrhizal relationship.
4. How does a hyphae called a stolon differ from a rhizoid?

Thinking Critically
5. You are working with a team of environmental engineers to monitor air pollution levels. How might you use lichens to collect data and determine the air quality?

SKILL REVIEW
6. **Compare and Contrast** What are the similarities and differences between the fungal reproductive structures, ascospores and conidiophores? For more help, refer to *Compare and Contrast* in the **Skill Handbook**.

in.bdol.glencoe.com/self_check_quiz

20.2   THE DIVERSITY OF FUNGI   **543**

3 Assess
DAILY INTERVENTION
Check for Understanding
Have students explain the following relationships. **L1**
- stolon, rhizoid, hyphae
- mating types, zygospores, zygomycota
- ascomycota, asci, spores
- basidiomycota, basidia spores
- penicillin, deuteromycota
- lichen, mycorrhiza, mutualism

Reteach
Naturalist Have student groups explain how each division's fungi obtain food, reproduce, and enter into symbiotic relationships. **L1**
COOP LEARN

Resources
For more practice, use *Reading Essentials for Biology,* Section 20.2.

Extension
Have students compile a list of foods derived from fungi. **L2**

✔ Assessment
Knowledge Ask students for an example, a description of the spore-forming structures, and the economic importance of each fungal division. **L2**

Indiana Academic Standards
Pages 542–543: B.1.35, B.1.43

Section Assessment

1. The hyphae of opposite mating types fuse and form a mycelium. Eventually, the mycelium forms a compact mass called a button.
2. Deuteromycotes have no known means of reproducing sexually. They share the same characteristics of other fungi such as chitinous cell walls and being heterotrophs.
3. The plant receives additional minerals and water absorbed by the fungus. The fungus receives the plant's excess food.
4. A stolon grows on a food's surface; a rhizoid invades a food source.
5. The population of lichens is directly proportional to the atmosphere's cleanliness. As the air becomes more polluted, the population of lichens declines.
6. Both are reproductive structures. Ascospores are the sexually produced spores while condiophores are the structures that will produce the asexual conidiospores.

Time Allotment

initial session: 20 minutes to review procedure and do the setup; second session: class period

Process Skills

design an experiment, observe and infer, record data, relate cause and effect, communicate

PREPARATION

■ Prepare BTB solution as follows: add 0.5 g BTB powder to 500 mL distilled water to make stock. Dilute 10 mL of stock in 500 mL distilled water for students to use.

■ Pretest diluted BTB solution by exhaling into it through a straw. If its color fails to change from blue to dark or light green within 60 seconds, carefully adjust the pH by adding a drop of concentrated hydrochloric acid to the stock, diluting again, and retesting. Repeat until the change occurs within 60 seconds. If the stock turns green, mix in one or two drops of concentrated ammonium hydroxide.

■ Add a packet of yeast and 20 mL white corn syrup to 250 mL water to make a yeast/corn syrup mixture 20–30 minutes before class.

Alternative Materials

Use a solution of 20% sucrose instead of corn syrup. Use yeast cake (found in supermarkets), which begins to ferment faster than packet yeast.

Before You Begin

Does temperature affect the rate of carbon dioxide production by yeast? Look at the experimental setup pictured at the right. As yeast metabolizes in the stoppered container, the carbon dioxide that is produced is forced out through the bent tube into the open tube, which contains a solution of bromothymol blue (BTB). Carbon dioxide causes chemical reactions that result in a color change in the BTB. Differences in the time required for this color change to occur indicate the relative rates of carbon dioxide production by yeasts.

Color-enhanced SEM Magnification: 2270×

Yeast cells

Does temperature affect yeast metabolism?

PREPARATION

Problem

How can you determine the affect of temperature on the metabolism of yeast? Brainstorm ideas among the members of your group.

Hypotheses

Decide on one hypothesis that you will test. Your hypothesis might be that low temperature slows down the metabolic activity of yeast, or that a high temperature speeds up the metabolic activity of yeast.

Objectives

In this BioLab, you will:

■ **Measure** the rate of yeast metabolism using a BTB color change as a rate indicator.

■ **Compare** the rates of yeast metabolism at several temperatures.

■ **Use the Internet** to collect and compare data from other students.

Possible Materials

bromothymol blue solution (BTB)	water/yeast mixture
straw	test-tube rack
small test tubes (4)	250-mL beakers (3)
large test tubes (3)	ice cubes
one-hole stoppers with glass tube inserts for large test tubes (3)	Celsius thermometer or temperature probe
	hot plate
yeast/white corn syrup mixture	graduated cylinder
water/white corn syrup mixture	glass-marking pencil
	10 cm of rubber tubing (3)
	aluminum foil

Safety Precautions

CAUTION: *Always wear goggles in the lab. Be careful in attaching rubber tubing to the glass tube inserts in the stoppers. Avoid touching the top of the hot plate. Wash your hands thoroughly at the end of your experiments.*

Skill Handbook

If you need help with this lab, refer to the **Skill Handbook**.

PROCEDURE

Teaching Strategies

■ Have students wear aprons and goggles and wash their hands with soap and water at the the end of the lab. Caution them to use care when working with chemicals.

■ BTB is an acid indicator. Carbon dioxide reacts with water to produce carbonic acid.

■ Students can measure the amount of gas collected in each tube rather than rely on BTB color change. Carbon dioxide gas will collect through water displacement in an inverted tube filled with water and placed in the beaker of water with a rubber tube inserted into its mouth.

Possible Procedures

Control tubes may consist of stoppered tubes with no yeast/corn syrup mixture.

1. Answers will vary. The warmer the water, the more rapid the color change of BTB.
2. Answers will vary depending on the experimental design chosen. Data should be similar.
3. It is the food for yeast.
4. The volume of water/corn syrup and the amount of yeast used were variables and had to be kept constant.
5. Because controls will vary, such as a tube with no yeast/corn syrup, some data will show more difference than other data.
6. **ERROR ANALYSIS** Errors may include timing, inaccurate measurement of gas produced, or materials used.

PLAN THE EXPERIMENT

1. Decide on ways to test your group's hypothesis.
2. Record your procedure, and list the materials and amounts of solutions that you will use. Design a data table for recording your observations.
3. Pour 5 mL of BTB solution into a test tube. Use a straw to blow gently into the tube until you observe a series of color changes. Cover this tube with aluminum foil, and set it aside in a test-tube rack. Record your observations of the color changes caused by carbon dioxide in your breath.

Check the Plan
Discuss the following to decide on your procedure.
1. What data on color change and time will you collect? How will you record your data?
2. What variables will you control?
3. What control will you use?
4. Assign tasks for each member of your group.
5. *Make sure your teacher has approved your experimental plan before you proceed further.*
6. Carry out your experiment. Visit **in.bdol.glencoe.com/internet_lab** to post your data.
7. **CLEANUP AND DISPOSAL** Check with your teacher for instructions on disposal of yeast and BTB.

5 mL bromothymol blue solution

30 mL yeast/corn syrup solution

ANALYZE AND CONCLUDE

1. **Check Your Hypothesis** Explain whether your data support your hypothesis. Use your experimental data to support or reject your hypothesis concerning temperature effects on the rate of yeast metabolism.
2. **Use the Internet** How did the data you collected compare with that of other students? Compare experimental designs. Did differences in experimental design account for any differences in data collected?
3. **Make Inferences** What must be the role of white corn syrup in this experiment?
4. **Identify Variables** Describe some variables that your group had to control in this experiment. Explain how you controlled each variable.
5. **Draw Conclusions** Did your experiment clearly show that differences in rates of yeast metabolism were due to temperature differences?
6. **ERROR ANALYSIS** What errors did your group make? How could you improve the experiment?

Share Your Data
Find this BioLab using the link below, and post your data in the data table provided for this activity. Using the additional data from other students on the Internet, analyze the combined data and briefly describe your experimental design.

in.bdol.glencoe.com/internet_lab

Assessment
Performance Have students design an experiment to measure the actual volume of gas given off by a yeast/corn syrup solution at different temperatures. Use the Performance Task Assessment List for Designing an Experiment in **PASC,** p. 95. **L2**

Share Your Data
To navigate the Internet BioLabs, go to **in.bdol.glencoe.com/ internet_lab.** Students should pool data only from identical temperatures. If data from different temperatures are pooled inadvertently, the results will be inaccurate.

Data and Observations
More carbon dioxide gas is produced by yeast immersed in warm water temperatures. These tubes change color more rapidly than those at cooler temperatures.

CLEANUP AND DISPOSAL
 Yeast and BTB can be safely discarded in the sink if flushed with plenty of water. All glassware should be sterilized or cleaned in hot, soapy water by the instructor.

Indiana Academic Standards
Pages 544–545: B.1.45

connection to *Social Studies*

Students will learn how fungi have influenced some historical events.

Teaching Strategies

■ Ask students to discuss criteria for deciding whether an organism is beneficial or detrimental to humans. For example, fungi that are considered pests in one culture may be used as a food in another.

■ Discuss how events that at first seem negative can lead to positive outcomes. The discovery of penicillin and the development of iron ships are examples.

■ Discuss the Cultural Diversity information on p. 540, which describes the problems that ergot has caused throughout history.

Indiana Academic Standards

Pages 546–547: B.1.40, B.1.43, B.1.44

connection to *Social Studies*

The Dangers of Fungi

Fungi are both friend and foe. Some, such as mushrooms, provide food. Other fungi produce antibiotics such as penicillin. Many others break down dead tissue and recycle organic molecules, thereby keeping Earth from being buried under tons of unusable organic debris. Yet, fungi also damage crops, buildings, and animals.

Fungi cause many plant diseases that can kill plants and cause sickness and death in animals that feed on infected plants. Fungi also directly cause some human diseases.

Plant pathogens Fungi that cause the plant diseases called rusts are difficult to control. Rusts are successful because they are pleomorphic—each species produces many kinds of spores that can infect different hosts. The wind can spread their spores over hundreds of miles. For example, *Puccinia graminis* is a fungus that causes black stem rust in cereal grains, such as rice and wheat. *P. graminis* produces five kinds of spores, some of which also infect barberry plants.

Rye, another cereal plant, can host the fungus *Claviceps purpurea*, which causes a disease called ergot. Animals contract ergot after eating infected rye. Human epidemics of ergot poisoning have occurred throughout history after people ate food made from grain infected by *C. purpurea*.

Fungi can also cause major losses of timber. For example, near the end of the nineteenth century, chestnut seedings infected with the fungus *Endothia parasitica* were brought into the United States. By 1950, *E. parasitica* had destroyed most of the country's chestnut trees. Other fungi have devastated the North American populations of elm trees and eastern and western white pines.

In addition to infecting live trees, fungi damage structures built of wood. When ships

546 FUNGI

Wheat attacked by the fungus *Puccinia graminis*

were primarily wooden, dry rot always threatened their loss. Fungi cause dry rot when they grow in moist wooden structures.

Human pathogens Although bacteria and viruses cause most human diseases, fungi cause their share. Most fungi are dermatophytes, that is, they invade skin, nails, and hair. Among the more common human fungal infections are ringworm and athlete's foot. Some fungal spores can be inhaled into the lungs where they can establish an infection that can spread throughout the body.

Fungi can cause substantial economic loss, disease, and even death. But their critical role in recycling organic matter and their benefit as a source of food and medicinal drugs are essential to human survival on Earth.

Writing About Biology

Reproduction Many fungi reproduce both asexually and sexually. In a short report, discuss the advantage of having two kinds of reproduction.

 To find out more about fungi, visit in.bdol.glencoe.com/social_studies

Writing About Biology

Asexual spores provide fungi with an adaptive advantage. Spores can resist drought, are produced in large numbers, and are small and lightweight, making them easy to disperse by wind, water, and animals. Sexual reproduction leads to genetic diversity.

STUDY GUIDE

Section 20.1

What is a fungus?

Key Concepts

- The structural units of a fungus are hyphae, which grow and form a mycelium.
- Fungi are heterotrophs that carry out extracellular digestion. A fungus may be a saprophyte, a parasite, or a mutualist in a symbiotic relationship with another organism.
- Many fungi produce both asexual and sexual spores. One criterion for classifying fungi is by their patterns of reproduction, especially sexual reproduction, during the life cycle.

Vocabulary

budding (p. 533)
chitin (p. 531)
haustoria (p. 532)
hypha (p. 530)
mycelium (p. 530)
sporangium (p. 533)

Section 20.2

The Diversity of Fungi

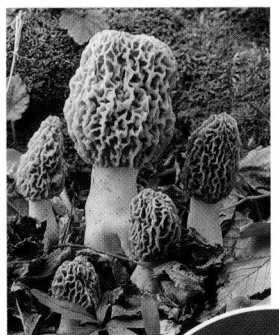

Key Concepts

- Zygomycotes form asexual spores in a sporangium. They reproduce sexually by producing zygospores.
- Ascomycotes reproduce asexually by producing spores called conidia and sexually by forming ascospores.
- In basidiomycotes, sexual spores are produced on club-shaped structures called basidia.
- Deuteromycotes may reproduce only asexually.
- Fungi play an important role in decomposing organic material and recycling the nutrients on Earth.
  - Certain fungi associate with plant roots to form mycorrhizae, a symbiotic relationship between a fungus and a plant.
  - A lichen, a symbiotic association of a fungus and an alga or cyanobacterium, survives in many inhospitable habitats.

Vocabulary

ascospore (p. 537)
ascus (p. 537)
basidiospore (p. 538)
basidium (p. 538)
conidiophore (p. 537)
conidium (p. 537)
gametangium (p. 536)
lichen (p. 542)
mycorrhiza (p. 540)
rhizoid (p. 535)
stolon (p. 535)
zygospore (p. 536)

 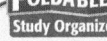

FOLDABLES™
Study Organizer To help you review the phyla of Fungi, use the Organizational Study Fold on page 535.

CHAPTER 20 ASSESSMENT **547**

Key Concepts

Summary statements can be used by students to review the major concepts of the chapter.

Biology Online

Visit in.bdol.glencoe.com
/self_check_quiz
/vocabulary_puzzlemaker
/chapter_test
/standardized_test

VOCABULARY PUZZLEMAKER

For additional help with vocabulary, have students access the Vocabulary PuzzleMaker online at in.bdol.glencoe.com/vocabulary_puzzlemaker

FOLDABLES™

Have students use their Foldables to review the content of Section 20.2. On the back of the paper, make a dichotomous key that could be used to classify fungi into phyla.

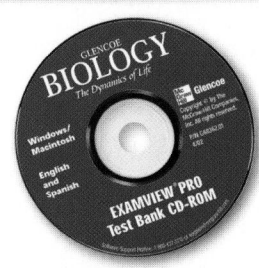

Use the ExamView®Pro Test Bank CD-ROM to:

- Create **multiple versions** of tests
- Create **modified** tests for **inclusion** students with one mouse click
- **Edit** existing questions and **add** your own questions
- Build tests aligned with state standards using built-in **State Curriculum Tags**
- Change **English** tests to **Spanish** with one mouse click and vice versa

The Princeton Review *Questions and answers have been aligned and verified by The Princeton Review.*

Vocabulary Review

1. true
2. true
3. false—lichen
4. false—ascus
5. true

Understanding Key Concepts

6. C	10. C	14. D
7. B	11. D	15. D
8. A	12. B	
9. B	13. A	

Constructed Response

16. The bulk of the mushroom lies below ground and therefore cannot be destroyed this way.

17. This may provide spores with an opportunity to land on new or different food sources.

18. This could prevent destruction and disruption of any mycorrhiza that may be present.

Thinking Critically

19. 1. hyphae; 2. stolons; 3. rhizoids; 4. sporangia; 5. mycelium

20. The development of penicillin occurred during World War II and had a major role in the treatment of soldiers wounded in the war. Since then a variety of other antibiotics have been developed from fungi or based on substances first found in fungi. Students should relate at least one of these new antibiotics.

Vocabulary Review

Review the Chapter 20 vocabulary words listed in the Study Guide on page 547. Determine if each word is true or false. If false, replace the underlined word with the correct vocabulary word.

1. <u>Hyphae</u> are threadlike filaments that develop from fungal spores.

2. Club-shaped hyphae that produce spores are called <u>basidia</u>.

3. A <u>mychorrhiza</u> is a symbiotic association between a fungus and a photosynthetic green alga or cyanobacterium.

4. The saclike structure in which sexual spores develop is called a <u>conidiophore</u>.

5. A network of hyphae filaments make up a <u>mycelium</u>.

Understanding Key Concepts

6. Most fungi function as _____ in their environments.
   A. consumers   C. decomposers
   B. producers   D. autotrophs

7. Which of the following is a type of asexual reproduction in fungi?
   A. sporangium   C. mycelium
   B. budding   D. haustoria

8. Mushrooms, puffballs, and bracket fungi belong to the group called _____.
   A. club fungi   C. Zygomycota
   B. sac fungi   D. Deuteromycota

9. Which drawing represents a zygospore?

   A.   B.   C.   D.

10. Fungi sometimes live in a mutualistic relationship with a plant. They might help their host by _____.
    A. using the food supplied by the host
    B. using energy made by the host
    C. supplying water to the host
    D. providing the host with spores

11. Soy sauce, citric acid, and penicillin all come from _____.
    A. club fungi
    B. sac fungi
    C. zygomycotes
    D. deuteromycotes

12. The basic structural unit of a multicellular fungus is a _____.
    A. spore
    B. hyphae
    C. stalk
    D. mycellium

13. The complex carbohydrate found in the cell walls of most fungi is _____.
    A. chitin
    B. cellulose
    C. glycogen
    D. starch

14. Unlike other fungi, _____ are known to reproduce only asexually.
    A. zygomycotes   C. basidiomycotes
    B. ascomycotes   D. deuteromycotes

15. The photo at right shows bread mold structures that are called _____.
    A. hyphae
    B. rhizoids
    C. zygospores
    D. sporangia

    LM Magnification: 27×

Constructed Response

16. **Open Ended** Your neighbor is pulling up mushrooms that are growing in his lawn. He tells you that he heard mushrooms won't come back again if they are quickly removed. What would you tell him?

17. **Infer** Why is being able to produce spores that can be widely dispersed such an important adaptation for fungi?

18. **Describe** When you transplant flowers, shrubs, or trees, why is it a good idea to leave the soil intact around a plant's roots?

 in.bdol.glencoe.com/chapter_test

RUBRIC

Evaluating Open-Ended Questions
Open-ended assessment questions are graded by using a multilevel rubric that guides you in assessing a student's knowledge of a particular concept. The following rubric is a sample scoring device.

Thinking Critically

19. Concept Map Use the following terms: sporangia, rhizoids, hyphae, stolons, mycellium.

Bread mold consists of

```
                    ┌─────────┐
                    │   1.    │
                    └─────────┘
         ┌──────────────┼──────────────────┐
      called         called        that grow upward
                                      and end in
     ┌────────┐    ┌────────┐       ┌────────┐
     │   2.   │    │   3.   │       │   4.   │
     └────────┘    └────────┘       └────────┘
  that grow        that            
  horizontally     absorb          
  and produce a    food            
     ┌────────┐                    
     │   5.   │                    
     └────────┘                    
```

20. **REAL WORLD BIOCHALLENGE** Since the introduction of penicillin, fungi have played a major role in the development of antibiotic medicines. Visit **in.bdol.glencoe.com** to find out more about some examples of fungi that have been used in the development of antibiotics. Why was the development of penicillin so important to the United States? Write an essay that explains what you find out about the development of antibiotics. Share your information with the class.

The assessed Indiana standard appears next to the question.

All questions aligned and verified by *The Princeton Review*

End-of-Course Assessment Practice

Part 1 Multiple Choice

Use the diagram to answer questions 21 and 22.

21. Structure A and structure B
B.1.15 represent a _____ and _____.

    A. fungal capsule—mycelium
    B. spore—hypha
    C. hypha—lichen
    D. lichen—mycelium

22. The process illustrated is called _____.
B.1.15   **A.** photosynthesis   **C.** germination
    B. fertilization   **D.** host invasion

23. Which group of fungi produces sexual spores on a clublike structure?
    A. zygomycotes   **C.** basidiomycotes
    B. ascomycotes   **D.** deuteromycotes

24. Which fungi reproduce only asexually?
    A. zygomycotes   **C.** basidiomycotes
    B. ascomycotes   **D.** deuteromycotes

Part 2 Constructed Response/Grid In

Record your answers on your answer document.

28. Open Ended Describe the ways that fungi reproduce.

29. Open Ended Summarize the role of fungi in maintaining and disrupting equilibrium, including diseases in plants and animals.

 in.bdol.glencoe.com/standardized_test

Use the information below and your knowledge of science to answer questions 25–27.
The metabolic activity of yeasts at various temperatures is shown in the table below. A chemical indicator added to the yeast solution changed color when yeast cells were metabolizing.

Metabolic Activity of Yeasts	
Temperature of Yeast Solution	Time Needed for Color Change
2°C	No color change
25°C	44 minutes
37°C	22 minutes

25. The yeasts were most active at _____.
    A. 2°C   **C.** 37°C
    B. 25°C   **D.** 22°C

26. Yeast cells were metabolizing at _____.
    A. 2°C and 25°C   **C.** 2°C
    B. 2°C and 37°C   **D.** 25°C and 37°C

27. The rate of a chemical reaction is not affected by _____.
    A. temperature   **C.** a catalyst
    B. reactant concentration **D.** buoyancy

CHAPTER 20 ASSESSMENT **549**

Chapter 20 Assessment

End-of-Course Assessment Practice

21. B   **24.** D   **27.** D
22. C   **25.** C
23. C   **26.** D

28. Fungi reproduce sexually or asexually by spores. They may also reproduce by fragmentation. Spores may be produced sexually on basidia, conidiophores, or in an ascus.

29. Fungi maintain equilibrium in an ecosystem by decomposing dead organisms; mycorrhizae help some plants live by providing additional surface area for water and nutrient absorption. They can disrupt an ecosystem by causing diseases in plants and animals.

FAST FILE

Answer Sheet A practice answer sheet can be found on p. 109 of *Unit 6 FAST FILE Resources.*

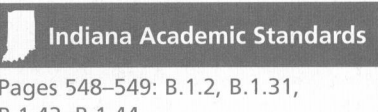

Indiana Academic Standards

Pages 548–549: B.1.2, B.1.31, B.1.43, B.1.44

RUBRIC

SCORE	CRITERIA
4	A correct solution that is supported by well-developed, accurate explanations.
3	A generally correct solution, but may contain minor flaws in reasoning.

SCORE	CRITERIA
2	A partially correct interpretation and/or solution to the problem.
1	A correct solution with no supporting evidence or explanation.
0	An incorrect solution or no solution is given.

Prepare

Short on Time?

This BioDigest can be used for an overview of viruses and bacteria, protists, and fungi. You may wish to use this summary to teach about viruses and the three types of organisms in place of the chapters in the viruses, bacteria, protists, and fungi unit.

Key Concepts

Students learn about the structures and functions of viruses. They study the diversity of life in four kingdoms: bacteria, archaebacteria, protists, and fungi, including the ecology and classification of organisms within these kingdoms.

1 Focus

Bellringer

To begin, have students compare and contrast a bacterial culture in a petri dish, *Spirogyra* in a test tube, and a bracket fungus. Each is alive and made of cells. They do not look like each other. **L1** **ELL**

Viruses, Bacteria, Protists, and Fungi

Archaebacteria and eubacteria occupy most habitats on Earth, and protists and fungi are almost as diverse. But, viruses enter and take over their cells and the cells of all other organisms.

Viruses

There are many kinds of viruses, nonliving particles, most of which can cause diseases in the organisms they infect. Most viruses are much smaller than the smallest bacterium, and none respire or grow.

Structure

Viruses consist of a core of DNA or RNA surrounded by a protein coat, called a capsid. The capsid may be enclosed by a layer called an envelope that is made of phospholipids and proteins. Depending on their nucleic acid content, viruses are classified as either DNA or RNA viruses.

Replication

Viruses replicate only inside cells. First, a virus attaches to a specific molecule on a cell's membrane. Then, it enters the cell where it begins either a lytic or a lysogenic cycle. In the lytic cycle, the viral nucleic acid causes the host to produce new virus particles that are then released, killing the host. In the lysogenic cycle, the viral DNA becomes part of the host's chromosome for a while, and later may enter a lytic cycle.

Bacteria

A bacterium is a unicellular prokaryote. Most of its genes are contained in a circular chromosome in the cytoplasm. A cell wall surrounds its plasma membrane. Bacteria may be heterotrophs, photosynthetic autotrophs, or chemosynthetic autotrophs. They reproduce asexually by binary fission and sexually by conjugation.

Color-enhanced SEM Magnification: 1445×

Bacteria occur in three basic shapes: spheres, rods, and spirals.

Color-enhanced SEM Magnification: 625×

Adaptations

Many bacteria are obligate aerobes, needing oxygen to respire. Some bacteria called obligate anaerobes are killed by oxygen. Still other bacteria can live either with or without oxygen. Some bacteria can produce endospores to help them survive unfavorable environmental conditions.

Importance

Some bacteria cause diseases. Other bacteria fix nitrogen, recycle nutrients, and help make food products and medicines.

RESOURCE MANAGER

Unit 6 FAST FILE Resources
Reinforcement and Study Guide in English, pp. 111–112
Reinforcement and Study Guide in Spanish, pp. 113–114
Student Recording Sheet, p. 115

Protists

Kingdom Protista is a diverse group of heterotrophic, autotrophic, parasitic, and saprophytic eukaryotes. Although many protists are unicellular, some are multicellular. They all live in aquatic or very moist places.

Protozoans: Animal-like protists

Animal-like protists known as protozoans are unicellular, heterotrophic organisms. Many protozoans are classified based on their adaptations for locomotion in the environment.

Phylum Rhizopoda is composed of the protozoans called amoebas that use pseudopodia, extensions of their plasma membrane, to move and engulf prey. Phylum Mastigophora is composed of protozoans that use flagella to move around. Some parasitic protozoan species that have flagella cause disease, but other flagellated species are helpful. Members of the phylum

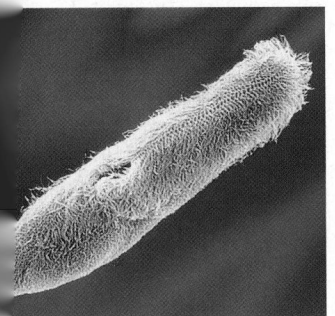

Color-enhanced TEM Magnification: 4000×

The beating cilia of a *paramecium* produce water currents for collecting food.

Color-enhanced SEM Magnification: 130×

Plasmodium may infect more than one hundred million people every year in African and South American countries.

Ciliophora move by beating hairlike projections called cilia. *Paramecium* is a widely studied ciliate.

Sporozoans are grouped together because they are all parasites and many produce spores. Most have very complex life cycles with different stages. *Plasmodium*, the protozoans that cause the disease malaria, have a sexual stage in mosquitoes and an asexual stage in humans.

VITAL STATISTICS

Protists

Distribution: worldwide in aquatic and moist habitats
Niches: producers, herbivores, predators, parasites, and decomposers
Number of species: more than 60 000
Size range: less than 2 micrometers in length to greater than 100 meters (328 feet) in length

FOCUS ON ADAPTATIONS

Archaebacteria: The Extremists

Archaebacteria are unicellular prokaryotes, most of which survive in extremely harsh environments. A group of archaebacteria that produce methane live in the intestinal tracts of animals and in sewage treatment plants. A second group thrives in hot, acidic environments, such as in the thermal springs of Yellowstone National Park or around the hot vents on ocean floors. A third group survive in extremely salty water such as that found in Utah's Great Salt Lake.

Utah's Great Salt Lake

551

CHALLENGE ACTIVITY

Bacteria and the Nitrogen Cycle
Review the biogeochemical cycles discussed in Chapter 2. Then discuss how bacteria are important in nitrogen fixation and nutrient cycling. **L3**

2 Teach

Activity

Visual-Spatial Have students view prepared slides of bacteria that show the three most common bacterial shapes: spherical, rodlike, and spiral-shaped. **L2** **ELL**

Visual Learning

■ Ask students to look at the Focus On Adaptations on page 551 and explain why archaebacteria are often considered extremists.

■ Have students use the information in the photos and the vital statistics box on this page to explain why protozoans are important.

Struggling Learners

Linguistic For students who need extra practice with the English language, have them rewrite a summary of the BioDigest information in both their native language and English. **L2** **ELL**

Activity

Visual-Spatial Have students use a microscope to look at slides of pond water. Ask them to use guides to identify the protists they see. Remind them to be careful when using microscopes and slides. **L2** **ELL**

Bulletin Board Display

Visual-Spatial Have students make a display of all the viruses, bacteria, and protists they can find throughout Chapters 18 and 19. Ask them to draw and label each one. **L2** **ELL**

Inquiry

The Diversity of Protists Have students describe and create questions about the protists they observed when they viewed slides of pond water in the Activity. **L1**

LM Magnification: 400×

▲ Euglenas use one or two flagella to move.

◄ The shells of diatoms contain silica.

Color-enhanced LM Magnification: 200×

Algae: Plantlike Protists

Autotrophic protists are called algae. They are grouped on the basis of body structure and the pigments they contain. Photosynthetic algae produce a great deal of Earth's atmospheric oxygen. They are unicellular and multicellular.

Euglenas

Unicellular algae that can be both autotrophs and heterotrophs are classified in the phylum Euglenophyta. Most species have chlorophyll for photosynthesis. When there is no light, some euglenas can ingest food.

Diatoms

Unicellular algae called diatoms are classified in phylum Bacillariophyta. In addition to chlorophyll, diatoms contain carotenoids, pigments with a golden-yellow color. Diatoms live in both saltwater and freshwater environments.

Dinoflagellates

Dinoflagellates, members of the phylum Dinoflagellata, are unicellular algae surrounded by hard, armorlike plates and propelled by flagella. They may contain a variety of pigments, including chlorophyll, caretenoids, and red pigments. Marine blooms of dinoflagellates can cause toxic red tides.

Red Algae

Members of the phylum Rhodophyta are multicellular marine algae. Because of their red and blue pigments, some species can grow at depths of 100 meters.

Brown Algae

About 1500 species of algae are classified in phylum Phaeophyta and all contain a brown pigment. The largest brown algae are the giant kelps that can grow to about 60 meters in length.

Magnification: 8×

A chocolate slime mold

FOCUS ON ADAPTATIONS

Mycorrhizae

Some plants live in association with mutualistic fungi. These relationships, called mycorrhizae (my kuh RHY zuh), benefit both the fungi and the plants. The hyphae of the fungus are entwined with the roots of the plant, and absorb sugars and other nutrients from the plant's root cells. In turn, the fungus increases the surface area of the plant's roots, allowing the roots to absorb more water and minerals.

The relationship enables the fungus to obtain food and the plant to grow larger. Some plants have grown so dependent on their mychorrhizal relationships that they cannot grow without them.

Hyphae of fungus

Plant cell

Fungal hyphae can grow among a plant's root cells.

552

Quick Demo

Lichens Collect some lichens and discuss how they differ with students.

Indiana Academic Standards
Pages 552–553: B.1.2, B.1.43, B.1.44

CHALLENGE ACTIVITY

Kelp For students who need an additional challenge, have them research the life cycle of giant kelps. Ask students to make a diagram showing the life cycle and include how kelps are used for food and other products. **L3**

Green Algae

The green algae in the phylum Chlorophyta, may be unicellular, colonial, or multicellular. The major pigment in their cells is chlorophyll, and some also have yellow pigments.

Funguslike Protists

Funguslike protists include the slime molds, water molds, and downy mildews. They are saprophytes, decomposing organic material to obtain its nutrients.

Fungi

Members of Kingdom Fungi are mostly multicellular, eukaryotic organisms that have cell walls made of chitin. The structural units of a fungus are hyphae. Fungi secrete enzymes into a food source to digest the food and then absorb the digested nutrients.

Fungi may be saprophytes, parasites, or mutualists. They play a major role in decomposing organic material and recycling Earth's nutrients.

These mushrooms have gills containing basidia on the underside of their caps.

Club Fungi

Club fungi include mushrooms, puffballs, and bracket fungi, and all are members of phylum Basidiomycota. Club fungi have club-shaped structures called basidia in which their sexual spores are produced.

Zygospore-Forming Fungi

Members of phylum Zygomycota produce thick-walled, sexual spores called zygospores. Zygomycotes also form many asexual spores in sporangia.

Some of this bread mold's hyphae (HI fee) form a mat called a mycelium that is anchored in the food source by other hyphae called rhizoids.

Sac Fungi

Fungi that produce sexual spores called ascospores in saclike structures called asci are classified in phylum Ascomycota. Sac fungi produce asexual spores, called conidiospores, which develop in chains or clusters from the tips of elongated hyphae called conidiophores.

Lichens

A lichen is a symbiotic association of a mutualistic fungus and a photosynthetic alga or cyanobacterium. Lichens live in many inhospitable areas, such as cold climates and high altitudes, but they are sensitive to pollution and do not grow well in polluted areas.

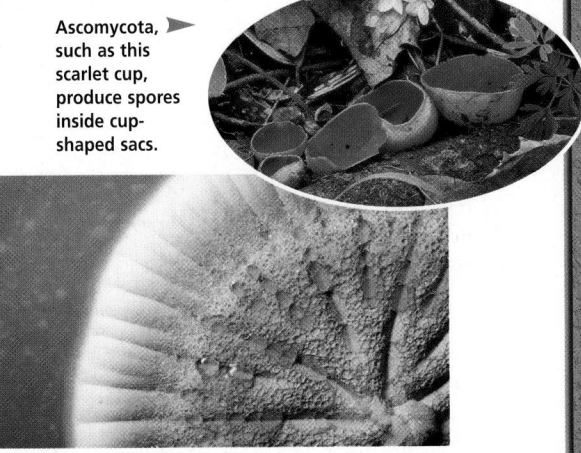

Ascomycota, such as this scarlet cup, produce spores inside cup-shaped sacs.

▲ Imperfect fungi, such as this *Penicillium* mold, are classified in phylum Deuteromycota. Sexual reproduction has never been observed in imperfect fungi.

VIRUSES, BACTERIA, PROTISTS, AND FUNGI **553**

3 Assess

DAILY INTERVENTION

Check for Understanding
Naturalist Have students differentiate among viruses, bacteria, protists, and fungi using examples and the unique characteristics of each.

Reteach
Have students prepare a table that includes examples, unique characteristics, and general information about viruses and the archaebacteria, eubacteria, protists, and fungi. **L2**

Extension

Have students work in groups, using information on pages 540–542, to explain the symbiotic relationships of lichens and mycorrhizae. **L2** **COOP LEARN**

✔ Assessment

Knowledge Provide students with pictures of viruses, bacteria, protists, and fungi from magazines, journals, or drawings. Have them identify what each picture depicts. **L1** **ELL**

Portfolio

Types of Algae Have students make a table of algae phyla. The table should include information, such as the phylum's name, its characteristics, general information, and an example. **L2**

USING MODELS

Protozoan movement Have students construct models that show how protozoans move. For example, students could construct a small row boat with many oars to demonstrate ciliates.

Students could also make clay models of amoebas and their pseudopods. The flagella of other organisms could be represented by yarn or pipe cleaners. **L1** **ELL** **COOP LEARN**

This page contains practice questions in the various formats that can be found on the most frequently given standardized tests.

 Part 1 Multiple Choice

1. B	**8.** B	**15.** A
2. A	**9.** C	**16.** A
3. C	**10.** A	**17.** C
4. A	**11.** C	**18.** D
5. A	**12.** A	**19.** B
6. B	**13.** D	
7. D	**14.** B	

FAST FILE

Answer Sheet A practice answer sheet can be found on p. 115 of *Unit 6 Fast File Resources.*

 End-of-Course Assessment Practice The assessed Indiana standard appears next to the question.

 TEST-TAKING TIP
Investigate
Ask what kinds of questions to expect on the test. Ask for practice tests so that you can become familiar with the test-taking materials.

Part 1 Multiple Choice

1. The core of a virus contains _____.
  A. phospholipids   **C.** amino acids
  B. nucleic acids   **D.** proteins

2. Photosynthetic bacteria include _____.
B.1.12   **A.** cyanobacteria   **C.** methanogens
  B. anaerobes   **D.** chemoautotrophs

3. The most likely place to find archaebacteria would be in _____.
  A. food
  B. a DNA lab
  C. a hot sulfur spring
  D. a fast flowing stream

4. The bacterial name associated with a rod shape is _____.
  A. bacillus
  B. coccus
  C. spirillum
  D. nucleic acid

5. A key enzyme utilized by an RNA virus is _____.
  A. reverse transcriptase
  B. provirus
  C. attachment protein
  D. capsid

6. Penicillin kills bacteria by interfering with the enzymes that link the sugar chains in the _____.
  A. nucleus
  B. cell wall
  C. plasmid
  D. capsule

7. In the _____ cycle, viruses use the cell's energy and raw materials to copy themselves, then burst from the cell.
  A. cell
  B. lysogenic
  C. plasmid
  D. lytic

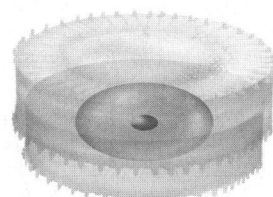

8. In the illustration of a diatom above, the shell is made of _____.
  A. protein
  B. silica
  C. carbohydrate
  D. lipid

9. A population explosion of dinoflagellates that produces a strong nerve toxin is _____.
  A. only possible in freshwater
  B. *Pfiesteria piscicida*
  C. a red tide
  D. rare in warm, polluted waters

10. A student finds a species of autotrophic
B.1.2   algae with a long filament that propels it through the water. The filament is a _____.
  A. flagellum
  B. pseudopod
  C. cilium
  D. microtubule

11. The major pigment of green algae is _____.
  A. red
  B. carotene
  C. chlorophyll
  D. a chloroplast

Indiana Academic Standards
Pages 554–555: B.1.2, B.1.9, B.1.35, B.1.43

12. Mushrooms are classified in phylum _____.
   - **A.** Basidiomycota
   - **B.** Zygomycota
   - **C.** Ascomycota
   - **D.** Deuteromycota

13. Cell walls of fungi contain _____.
   - **A.** cellulose
   - **B.** spores
   - **C.** hyphae
   - **D.** chitin

14. A puffball is a type of _____.
   - **A.** sac fungus
   - **B.** club fungus
   - **C.** lichen
   - **D.** imperfect fungus

15. Lichens are sensitive to _____.
   - **A.** pollution
   - **B.** cold
   - **C.** drought
   - **D.** predators

Use the information below and your knowledge of science to answer questions 16–19.

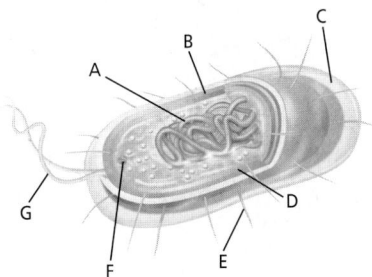

16. The organism pictured is _____.
B.1.12
   - **A.** prokaryotic
   - **B.** eukaryotic
   - **C.** multicellular
   - **D.** not a living organism

17. The component designated as C is most commonly found in _____.
B.1.12
   - **A.** disease causing viruses
   - **B.** harmless viruses
   - **C.** disease causing bacteria
   - **D.** harmless bacteria

18. Component F is a _____.
   - **A.** ribosome
   - **B.** pilus
   - **C.** nucleus
   - **D.** plasmid

19. The physical law that best explains why component G causes the organism to move is _____.
   - **A.** Newton's first law of motion
   - **B.** Newton's third law of motion
   - **C.** Ohm's law
   - **D.** Boyle's law

Part 2 Constructed Response/Grid In

Record your answers on your answer document.

20. **Open Ended** Compare and contrast the structures and functions of viruses to those of cells. Why are viruses not considered to be living?

21. **Open Ended** In agricultural regions where farmers use large amounts of nitrogen fertilizers in their
B.1.37, fields, local ponds and lakes often develop a thick, green scum containing algae in late summer.
B.1.41 Hypothesize why this happens.

22. **Open Ended** Both fungi and animals are heterotrophs. Contrast the interactions of fungi and plants with the interactions of animals and plants.

23. **Open Ended** Describe some vastly different characteristics among organisms in the Kingdom Protista. What common characteristics link them as protists?

 in.bdol.glencoe.com/standardized_test

UNIT 6 STANDARDIZED TEST PRACTICE **555**

Part 2 Constructed Response/Grid In

20. Viruses and cells are similar in that both have genetic material as either DNA or RNA and both reproduce. Viruses are not considered living things because, unlike cells, they do not grow or develop. In addition, viruses do not maintain homeostasis or contain organelles that cells do.

21. The nitrogen fertilizers run off into water sources, where they stimulate the growth and reproduction of algae.

22. A few fungal species are mutualists, but fungi are mainly decomposers or parasites. They live off dead or living organic material. Plants are autotrophs and supply the food used by most fungi. Animals are consumers, depending on plants directly or indirectly for their food.

23. Organisms of Kingdom Protista can be autotrophic or heterotrophic. They may be one-celled or multicellular. Protists can have characteristics that are animal-like, plantlike, or funguslike. Regardless of these differences, all protists are eukaryotes.

RUBRIC

For more help evaluating open-ended assessment questions, see the rubric on p. 9T.

Plants

Unit Overview

Unit 7 surveys the plant kingdom. **Chapter 21** includes a brief discussion of plant origins and the adaptations of plants to life on land. Plant divisions are introduced. **Chapter 22** introduces the major characteristics of each plant division. **Chapter 23** presents plant cells and tissues and describes root, stem, and leaf anatomy. Plant responses to the environment also are explained. **Chapter 24** examines reproduction in plants.

Introducing the Unit

Use this photograph to initiate a class discussion about plants as living organisms and the vital role plants play in Earth's biomes.

A WebQuest is an inquiry-based online project in which all information used by students is obtained from the Web. Students evaluate the information to complete the activity. Access the Unit 7 WebQuest at **in.bdol.glencoe.com/webquest**

History & Biology

1609–1610 • Spaniards establish a settlement that will become present-day Santa Fe, New Mexico.

9000 B.C.   **1600**

9000–8001 B.C. Wheat and barley are the first plants grown as food crops.

300–291 B.C. Theophrastus, often called the "Father of Botany," describes more than 500 plants in his book *History of Plants.*

1667 • Seed plants are classified as monocots or dicots according to the number of seed leaves (1 or 2) in their seeds.

Plants

What You'll Learn

Chapter 21
What is a plant?

Chapter 22
The Diversity of Plants

Chapter 23
Plant Structure and Function

Chapter 24
Reproduction in Plants

Unit 7 Review
BioDigest and Standardized Test Practice

Why It's Important

Although plants have different forms, they have common structures and functions. Over time, adaptations of these structures and functions resulted in the diversity of plants found in the land and water biomes on Earth. In these biomes, plants are an essential resource for many of the other organisms that live there, including humans. These organisms depend on plants for oxygen and, directly or indirectly, for food.

Indiana Standards
The following standards are covered in Unit 7:
B.1.1, B.1.2, B.1.3, B.1.7, B.1.8, B.1.11, B.1.15, B.1.18, B.1.31, B.1.32, B.1.35, B.1.43, B.1.45

Understanding the Photo ▶
Plant heights vary from a few millimeters to many meters. These conifer trees can grow to be hundreds of times taller than the ferns on the forest floor.

Time Line

Activity Students will be aware that in addition to wheat and barley, other plants are grown as food crops. Have students research the origins of food crops such as other grains, fruits, vegetables, and nuts. Each student should prepare a written and illustrated report of his or her research. In the classroom, mark on a world map the location of each food crop's origin. Also, create a classroom time line of food crop origins. **L2**

Indiana Academic Standards

Pages 556–557: B.1.43

1791
The Bill of Rights is ratified.

1930
The first packaged, sliced bread is introduced in the U.S.

1800   *1900*   *2000*

1851
It is discovered that alternation of generations is part of the life cycle of plants, such as mosses.

1967
Ten thousand-year-old frozen lupine seeds are discovered in the Yukon Territory of Canada. They germinate within 48 hours after they thaw.

1986
The first field trials of a genetically altered plant (tobacco) are carried out.

Unit 7

Advance Materials Planning

The following materials may need to be ordered a few weeks in advance of the planned activity.

Chapter 21

- **Additional Lab** (p. 560) radish seeds
- **MiniLab 21.1** (p. 561) *Marchantia*
- **MiniLab 21.2** (p. 566) *Lycopodium* and *Equisetum*

Chapter 22

- **MiniLab 22.1** (p. 586) sporangia
- **MiniLab 22.2** (p. 589) seeds

Chapter 23

- **MiniLab 23.1** (p. 608) celery
- **Internet BioLab** (p. 626) green onions
- **Quick Demo** (p. 623) place a broad leaf houseplant near a sunny window

Chapter 24

- **MiniLab 24.1** (p. 634) garlic, carrots, and white potatoes
- **MiniLab 24.2** (p. 657) corn and bean seeds
- **BioLab** (p. 658) carnations

557

Unit Projects

Experimenting

Logical-Mathematical Have students design and perform an experiment to test one aspect of plant growth. **L2**

Interviewing

Linguistic Have students interview a florist or nursery worker to learn how they keep flowers and plants fresh and healthy. **L1**

Final Report

Have student groups present their findings about plant uses in construction as a pamphlet that could be presented to students at your local middle schools. **L3**
COOP LEARN

Chapter 21 Organizer

Section Objectives	National Science Standards	State/Local Standards	Advanced Lab and Demo Planning
Section 21.1 1 session, 1 block 1. **Compare and contrast** characteristics of algae and plants. 2. **Identify and evaluate** structural adaptations of plants to their land environments. 3. **Describe** the alternation of generation in land plants.	UCP.1, UCP.3–5; A.1, A.2; B.3; C.3–5; G.1–3	**Indiana Standards** B.1.31, B.1.32, B.1.35, B.1.43, B.1.45	**Student Labs:** MiniLab 21.1, p. 561: living or preserved sample of *Marchantia,* protective gloves, dissecting microscope or hand lens Problem-Solving Lab 21.1, p. 563 Additional Lab, p. 560: petri dish, black paper, scissors, microscope, hand lens, glass slide, coverslip, water, forceps, radish seeds, label **Teacher Demonstration:** Quick Demo, p. 560: pictures of green algae, pictures of land plants
Section 21.2 2 sessions, 1 block 4. **Describe** the phylogenic relationships among divisions of plants. 5. **Identify** the twelve plant kingdom divisions.	UCP.2, UCP.4, UCP.5; A.1, A.2; B.3; C.3–5; E.1, E.2; F.1, F.3, F.6; G.1–3	**Indiana Standards** B.1.31, B.1.32, B.1.35, B.1.43	**Student Labs:** MiniLab 21.2, p. 566: living or preserved club mosses and horsetails, protective gloves Problem-Solving Lab 21.2, p. 567 Design Your Own BioLab, p. 570. See materials below. **Teacher Demonstration:** Quick Demo, p. 565: pine needles, broad leaves
End of Chapter Assessment Student Edition **Study Guide,** p. 573 **Content Assessment,** pp. 574–575		**Indiana Standards** B.1.11, B.1.21, B.1.35, B.1.43	**Student Lab:** Design Your Own BioLab, p. 570: conifer twigs, conifer branches, conifer cones

Key to Teaching Strategies

L1 Level 1 activities should be appropriate for students with learning difficulties.

L2 Level 2 activities should be within the ability range of all students.

L3 Level 3 activities are designed for above-average students.

ELL ELL activities should be within the ability range of English Language Learners.

COOP LEARN Cooperative Learning activities are designed for small group work.

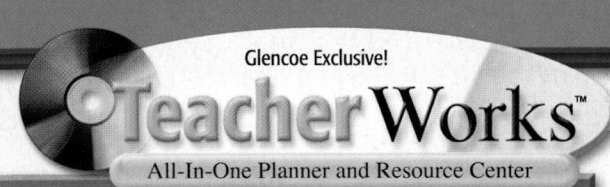

Glencoe Exclusive!
Teacher Works™
All-In-One Planner and Resource Center

Reproducible Masters and Transparencies	Technology

Unit 7 FAST FILE Resources
  MiniLab Worksheet, p. 3
  Reinforcement and Study Guide in English,
    pp. 7–8
  Reinforcement and Study Guide in Spanish,
    pp. 11–12
  Concept Mapping, p. 15
  Transparency Worksheet, p. 17
**Reading Essentials for Biology,
  Section 21.1**
Laboratory Manual, pp. 129–132
Probeware Labs, pp. 17–20
🔥 **Section Focus Transparency 50**

💿 **Interactive Chalkboard CD-ROM: Section 21.1 Presentation**
💿 TeacherWorks™ **CD-ROM**
🎵 **Guided Reading Audio Summaries MP3**
💿 **Virtual Labs CD-ROM**
  Virtual Lab: Survey of the Plant Kingdom

Unit 7 FAST FILE Resources
  MiniLab Worksheet, p. 4
  BioLab Worksheet, pp. 5–6
  Reinforcement and Study Guide in English,
    pp. 9–10
  Reinforcement and Study Guide in Spanish,
    pp. 13–14
  Critical Thinking/Problem Solving, p. 16
  Transparency Worksheets, pp. 18–20
**Reading Essentials for Biology,
  Section 21.2**
🔥 **Section Focus Transparency 51**
🔥 **Basic Concepts Transparency 33**

💿 **Interactive Chalkboard CD-ROM: Section 21.2 Presentation**
💿 TeacherWorks™ **CD-ROM**
🎵 **Guided Reading Audio Summaries MP3**

Unit 7 FAST FILE Resources
  Chapter Assessment, pp. 21–26
  Student Recording Sheet, p. 27

  The Princeton Review **Reviewing Biology,**
  pp. 41–42

💿 **Interactive Chalkboard:
  Chapter 21 Assessment**
💿 **MindJogger Videoquizzes
  DVD/VHS**
💿 **ExamView® Pro Test Bank
  CD-ROM**
💿 TeacherWorks™ **CD-ROM**
💿 **Succeeding on National Standards CD-ROM**

🖥 **in.bdol.glencoe.com**
  /self_check_quiz
  /vocabulary_puzzlemaker
  /chapter_test
  /standardized_test

Indicates materials created specifically for Indiana.

Short on Time?

BIODIGEST The BioDigest at the end of this unit can be used as a(n):

- preview to introduce important unit concepts.
- overview if time does not permit teaching the entire chapter.
- review of key unit concepts.

Understanding the Photo

Seed plants are classified into five divisions. The division of flowering plants is Anthophyta. Anthophytes bear their seeds in fruits. The trees in the background are conifers. They belong to the division Coniferophyta and bear their seeds in cones.

with Image Bank

PowerPoint® Presentations

This CD-ROM is an editable Microsoft® PowerPoint® presentation that includes:

- Section presentations
- Section checks
- Image bank
- Hot links to Biology Online
- All transparencies

Chapter 21

What is a plant?

What You'll Learn

- You will identify and evaluate the structural adaptations of plants to their land environments.
- You will survey and identify the major divisions of plants.

Why It's Important

Plants were the first multicellular organisms to inhabit land over 440 million years ago. Since then, plants have developed into a diverse group of organisms that help provide us with food, oxygen, and shelter.

Understanding ▶ the Photo

Because of plant adaptations over time, different plant species grow in the different biomes on Earth. The flowering plants and others growing in this mountain meadow have structural and physiological adaptations that ensure their long-term survival in this environment.

 Biology Online

Visit in.bdol.glencoe.com to
- study the entire chapter online
- access Web Links for more information and activities on plants
- review content with the Interactive Tutor and self-check quizzes

558

 Two-Minute Chapter Launcher

Demo Have students examine a variety of local plant materials, such as seeds, flowers, fruits, leaves, and roots, as well as mosses and ferns if they grow in your area. Ask students to infer how these plant structures are adaptations to the local environment. Answers will vary depending on region and plant materials available.

Section 21.1

Adapting to Life on Land

SECTION PREVIEW

Objectives

Compare and contrast characteristics of algae and plants.

Identify and evaluate structural adaptations of plants to their land environments.

Describe the alternation of generations in land plants.

Review Vocabulary
adaptation: any structure, behavior, or internal process that enables an organism to respond to stimuli and better survive in an environment (p. 9)

New Vocabulary
cuticle
leaf
root
stem
vascular tissue
vascular plant
nonvascular plant
seed

Study Organizer

Alternation of Generations Make the following Foldable to help you illustrate and explain how the lives of all plants have two alternating stages.

STEP 1 Draw a mark at the midpoint of a vertical sheet of paper along the side edge.

STEP 2 Fold the outside edges in to touch at the midpoint mark.

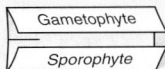

Gametophyte

Sporophyte

STEP 3 Label the tabs as shown.

Illustrate and Explain As you read Section 21.1, illustrate and explain each stage under its tab.

Word Origin

cuticle from the Latin word *cutis*, meaning "skin"; The cuticle is the outermost covering of most plants.

Origins of Plants

What is a plant? A plant is a multicellular eukaryote. Most plants can produce their own food in the form of glucose through the process of photosynthesis. In addition, plant cells have thick cell walls made of cellulose. The stems and leaves of most plants have a waxy waterproof coating called a **cuticle** (KYEWT ih kul).

Fossils and other geological evidence suggest that a billion years ago, plants had not yet begun to appear on land. No ferns, mosses, trees, grasses, or wildflowers existed. The land was barren except for some algae at the edges of inland seas and oceans. However, the shallow waters that covered much of Earth's surface at that time were teeming with bacteria, algae and other protists, as well as simple animals such as corals, sponges, jellyfish, and worms. Evidence indicates that green algae eventually became adapted to life on land.

Scientists hypothesize that all plants probably evolved from filamentous green algae that lived in the ancient oceans. Some of the evidence for their relationship can be found in modern members of both groups. Green algae and plants have cell walls that contain cellulose. Both groups have the same types of chlorophyll used in photosynthesis and store food in the form of starch. All other major groups of organisms store food in the form of glycogen and other complex sugars, and/or lipids.

21.1 ADAPTING TO LIFE ON LAND **559**

1 Focus

Bellringer
Section Focus Transparency 50

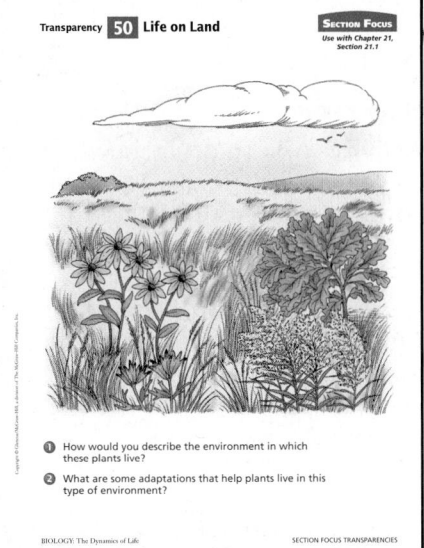

Transparency **50** Life on Land

SECTION FOCUS
Use with Chapter 21, Section 21.1

❶ How would you describe the environment in which these plants live?

❷ What are some adaptations that help plants live in this type of environment?

BIOLOGY: The Dynamics of Life   SECTION FOCUS TRANSPARENCIES

Word Origin

Have students use a dictionary to discover the connection between *cuticle* and *cutin*. Cuticle is made of cutin.

FOLDABLES™

For an additional Foldables activity idea, see the Chapter 21 Foldables page in *Unit 7 FAST FILE Resources*.

RESOURCE MANAGER

Unit 7 FAST FILE Resources
MiniLab Worksheet, p. 3
Reinforcement and Study Guide in English, pp. 7–8
Reinforcement and Study Guide in Spanish, pp. 11–12
Concept Mapping, p. 15
Transparency Worksheet, p. 17

Reading Essentials for Biology, Section 21.1
Laboratory Manual, pp. 129–132
Probeware Labs, pp. 17–20
Section Focus Transparency 50

Indiana Academic Standards
Pages 558–559: B.1.31, B.1.32, B.1.35

2 Teach

✓ **Reading Check** Early land plants may have helped break down rock to form soil, which allowed other plants to grow there.

Inquiry

Activity Ask students how they could demonstrate that a thin waxy covering prevents water loss. **L1**

Caption Question Answer
Figure 21.2 The larger surface area of a broad leaf allows a greater number of chloroplasts to be exposed to sunlight.

Quick Demo

Compare Algae and Plants Show students pictures of green algae and land plants. Ask them to describe the different conditions under which each organism exists. **L2**

Virtual Lab

CD-ROM Students will expose a plant to nature's elements in *Survey of the Plant Kingdom.*

Indiana Academic Standards

Pages 560–561: B.1.31, B.1.32, B.1.43, B.1.45

Figure 21.1
This fossil of *Cooksonia* is more than 400 million years old **(A)**. *Cooksonia* was probably one of the first vascular plants. The plant had leafless stems **(B)**.

The first evidence of plants in the fossil record began to appear over 440 million years ago. These early plants were simple in structure and did not have leaves. They were probably instrumental in turning bare rock into rich soil. The earliest known plant fossils are those of psilophytes (SI luh fites), such as those shown in *Figure 21.1.*

✓ **Reading Check** **Explain** how early land plants contributed to the movement of other plants to land.

Adaptations in Plants

Life on land has advantages as well as challenges. All organisms need water to survive. A filamentous green alga floating in a pond does not need to conserve water. The alga is completely immersed in a bath of water and dissolved nutrients, which it can absorb directly into its cells. For most land plants, the only available supply of water and minerals is in the soil, and only the portion of the plant that penetrates the soil can absorb these nutrients.

When you studied protists, you learned that algae reproduce by releasing unprotected unicellular gametes

into the water, where fertilization and development take place. Land plants evolved structural and physiological adaptations that help protect the gametes from drying out. In some plants, the sperm are released near the egg so they only have to travel a short distance. Other plants have protective structures to ensure the survival of the gametes. Land plants must also withstand the forces of wind and weather and be able to grow against the force of gravity. Over the past 443 million years or so, plants have developed a huge variety of adaptations that reflect both the challenges and advantages of living on land.

Preventing water loss

If you run your fingers over the surface of an apple, a maple leaf, or the stem of a houseplant, you'll probably find that it is smooth and slightly slippery. Most fruits, leaves, and stems are covered with a protective, waxy layer called the cuticle. Waxes and oils are lipids, which are biomolecules that do not dissolve in water. The waxy cuticle creates a barrier that helps prevent the water in the plant's tissues from evaporating into the atmosphere.

Figure 21.2
There is great diversity in leaf shapes and sizes. **Infer** *What advantage would a broad leaf, like this cottonwood leaf, have over a narrow leaf, like a pine needle?*

Additional Lab

Root Hairs

Purpose
This lab will allow students to examine the number and nature of root hairs.

Materials
CAUTION: *If mold grows in dishes, it can cause a respiratory reaction.*
petri dish, black paper, microscope, scissors, hand lens, glass slide, coverslip, water, forceps, radish seeds, label

Procedure
1. Cut several thicknessess of black paper to fit inside the bottom of a petri dish.
2. Moisten the paper and add 10 radish seeds to the dish and cover. Label your dish.
3. Examine the dish daily. Use a hand lens to check for root hairs. Wash your hands. Record your observations with diagrams.
4. After several days, use forceps to remove several root hairs. Prepare a wet mount of the hairs and examine them under a microscope. Determine if root hairs are multicellular or unicellular. Wash your hands.

Carrying out photosynthesis

The **leaf**, like the one in *Figure 21.2*, is a plant organ that grows from a stem and usually is where photosynthesis occurs. Leaves differ greatly in size and shape and they can vary on the same plant. Each plant division has unique leaves or leaflike structures.

Putting down roots

Most plants depend on the soil as their primary source for water and other nutrients. Plants can take in water and nutrients from the soil with their roots. In most plants, a **root** is a plant organ that absorbs water and minerals usually from the soil. Roots contain tissues that transport those nutrients to the stem. Roots anchor a plant usually in the ground. Some roots, such as those of radishes or sweet potatoes, accumulate starch and function as organs of storage. Many people use these storage roots as a food source. Find out more about the uses of plants on pages 1076–1079 in the *Focus On*.

In the *MiniLab* on this page, explore and evaluate some structural adaptations of plants that allow them to survive on land. Also, practice your lab skills by using a dissecting microscope.

Transporting materials

Water moves from the roots of a tree to its leaves, and the sugars produced in the leaves move to the roots through the stem. A **stem** is a plant organ that provides support for growth, as shown in *Figure 21.3*. It contains tissues for transporting food, water, and other materials from one part of the plant to another. Stems also can serve as organs for food storage. In green stems, some cells contain chlorophyll and can carry out photosynthesis.

MiniLab 21.1

Apply Concepts

Examining Land Plants
Liverworts are considered to be one of the simplest of all land plants. They show many of the adaptations that other land plants have evolved that enable them to survive on a land environment.

Marchantia

Procedure

1. Examine a living or preserved sample of *Marchantia*. **CAUTION:** *Wear protective gloves when handling preserved materials.*

2. Note and record the following observations. Is the plant unicellular or multicellular? Does it have a top and bottom? How do these differ? Is it one cell in thickness or many cells thick? Does the plant seem to grow upright like a tree or close to the ground?

3. Use a dissecting microscope to examine its top and bottom surfaces. Are tiny holes or pores present? If you answer "yes," which surface has pores?

Analysis

1. **Predict** How might having a multicellular, thick body be an advantage to life on land?

2. **Observe** Are rootlike structures present? Evaluate the significance of this adaptation to a land environment.

3. **Infer** What might be the role of any pores observed on the plant? Why is the location of the pores critical to surviving on a land environment?

Figure 21.3
Stems can be soft and flexible like the basil stem shown here **(A)**. Other plants, such as this sugar maple tree, have strong, thick stems that provide support and allow the tree to grow to great heights **(B)**.

MiniLab 21.1

Purpose

Students will analyze diagrams and detect errors in labeling.

Background

Review the concept of alternation of generations prior to this lab.

Process Skills

analyze information, concept mapping, interpret scientific illustrations, sequence, think critically

Teaching Strategies

■ Form small student groups.
■ Review the terms haploid and diploid with students.
■ Point out that *gamet*ophytes always form *gametes* while *sporo*phytes always form *spores*.

Thinking Critically

1. Gametophytes always form gametes by the processes of mitosis and cell division; gametophytes and gametes are haploid, not diploid.
2. Sporophytes always form spores by meiosis; chromosome number of spores will be haploid or 6.
3. Diagram B follows A with an arrow connecting spores to gametophyte stage and an arrow connecting gametes to sporophyte stage. Students may also indicate fertilization of gametes prior to forming sporophyte.

Assessment

Performance Ask students to draw and label as in diagrams A and B, a complete life cycle of a plant with $2n=20$. Use the Performance Task Assessment List for Scientific Drawing in **PASC,** p. 127. **L2** **ELL**

Indiana Academic Standards

Pages 562–563: B.1.31, B.1.35

Figure 21.4
A seed consists of an embryo, a food supply, and a protective seed coat.

Embryo

Seed coat

Food supply

The stems of most plants contain vascular tissues. **Vascular tissues** (VAS kyuh lur) are made up of tubelike, elongated cells through which water, food, and other materials are transported. Plants that possess vascular tissues are known as **vascular plants.** Most of the plants you are familiar with, including pine and maple trees, ferns, rhododendrons, rye grasses, English ivy, and sunflowers, are vascular plants.

Mosses and several other small, less-familiar plants called hornworts and

Figure 21.5
The lives of all plants consist of two generations.

Spores (*n*)

Male gamete (*n*)

Female gamete (*n*)

Meiosis

GAMETOPHYTE (*n*)

Fertilization

SPOROPHYTE (2*n*)

Mitosis and cell division

562 WHAT IS A PLANT?

liverworts are usually classified as non vascular plants. **Nonvascular plant** do not have vascular tissues. The bodies of nonvascular plants are usually no more than a few cells thick, and water and nutrients travel from one cell to another by the processes of osmosis and diffusion.

The evolution of vascular tissue was an important structural adaptation for plants that allowed them to survive in the many habitats on land. Vascular plants can live farther away from water than nonvascular plants. Also, because vascular tissues include thickened cells called fibers that help support growth, vascular plants can grow much larger than nonvascular plants.

Reproductive strategies

Adaptations in some land plants include the evolution of seeds. A **seed** is a plant organ that contains an embryo, along with a food supply, and is covered by a protective coat, as shown in *Figure 21.4*. A seed protects the embryo from drying out and also can aid in its dispersal. Recall that a spore consists only of a haploid cell with a hard, outer wall. Land plants reproduce by either spores or seeds.

In non-seed plants, which include mosses and ferns, the sperm require a film of water on the gametophyte plant to reach the egg. In seed plants, which include all conifers and flowering plants, sperm reach the egg without using a film of water. This difference is one reason why non-seed plants require wetter habitats than most seed plants.

Alternation of generations

As in algae, the lives of all plants include two stages, or alternating generations, as shown in *Figure 21.5*. The gametophyte generation of a plant results in the development of gametes. All cells of the gametophyte, including the gametes, are haploid (*n*). The sporophyte generation begins with fertilization. All cells of the sporophyte are diploid (2*n*) and are produced by mitosis and cell division. The spores are produced in the sporophyte plant body by meiosis, and are therefore haploid (*n*).

In non-seed vascular plants such as ferns, spores have hard outer coverings. Spores are released into the environment where they can grow into haploid gametophyte plants. These plants produce male and female gametes. Following fertilization, the sporophyte plant develops and grows from the gametophyte plant.

In seed plants, such as conifers and flowering plants, spores develop inside the sporophyte and become the gametophytes. The gametophytes consist of only a few cells. Male and female gametes are produced by these gametophytes. After fertilization, a new sporophyte develops within a seed. The seed eventually is released and the new sporophyte plant grows.

Use the *Problem-Solving Lab* on this page to explore further the differences between the gametophyte and sporophyte generations of plants.

Problem-Solving Lab 21.1

Analyze Information

How do gametophytes and sporophytes compare?
A plant has two stages in its life cycle. The stages are called the gametophyte generation and the sporophyte generation.

Solve the Problem

Diagram A shows the gametophyte generation of a plant. This plant has a haploid chromosome number of 6. Examine the diagram carefully and look for errors.

Diagram B shows the sporophyte generation of a plant. This plant has a diploid chromosome number of 12. Examine the diagram carefully and look for errors.

Thinking Critically

1. **Observe** Analyze diagram A, identify errors, and explain why they are incorrect.
2. **Observe** Analyze diagram B, identify errors, and explain why they are incorrect.
3. **Use Models** Illustrate diagrams A and B correctly so that they connect to one another and form a complete life cycle diagram of a plant.

3 Assess

DAILY INTERVENTION

Check for Understanding
Have students explain the differences between the following word groups. **L2** **ELL**
a. seed—spore
b. vascular—nonvascular
c. sporophyte—gametophyte

Reteach
Have students prepare an outline that shows: (a) evidence that land plants evolved from green algae, (b) adaptations of land plants that enable them to survive on land, and (c) the major functions of leaves, roots, and stems. **L2**

Resources
For more practice, use *Reading Essentials for Biology*, Section 21.1.

Extension

Visual-Spatial Have students observe a plant growing outside the school, and list traits that allow it to live on land. **L2**

Knowledge Have student groups discuss then explain how each of the following help plants survive on land: (a) thin leaves, (b) waxy cuticle, (c) roots, (d) supportive tissue in stems, (e) thick covering around gametes. **L1**

Section Assessment

Understanding Main Ideas
1. Identify three characteristics that plants share with algae.
2. Explain how the development of the cuticle and the vascular system influenced the evolution of plants on land.
3. How do seeds and spores differ? What are the benefits of producing seeds?
4. List the sequence of events involved in the alternation of generations in land plants. Do all plants have alternation of generations?

Thinking Critically
5. Explain why vascular plants are more likely to survive in a dry environment than nonvascular plants.

SKILL REVIEW
6. **Make and Use Tables** Make a table of the different structural adaptations plants evolved that allow them to live on land. Include an evaluation of how each specific adaptation helped plants survive on land. For more help, refer to *Make and Use Tables* in the **Skill Handbook**.

 in.bdol.glencoe.com/self_check_quiz

21.1 ADAPTING TO LIFE ON LAND **563**

Section Assessment

1. cell walls composed of cellulose, the same types of chlorophyll for photosynthesis, and storage of food as starch
2. A cuticle reduces water loss and a vascular system transports food, water, and minerals to all parts of the plant.
3. Seeds have a protective coat and contain a diploid embryo. Spores are a single haploid cell with a hard, outer wall. Seeds protect an embryo from drying out and aid in dispersal.
4. Sporophytes form spores via meiosis, spores form gametophytes that form gametes via mitosis, gametes fuse to form a new sporophyte. Yes, all land plants have alternation of generations.
5. Vascular plants have tubelike tissues that transport water and nutrients, whereas nonvascular plants use osmosis and diffusion, which requires a close association with water.
6. Table should include the following: cuticle reduces water loss; leaves carry out photosynthesis; roots anchor and absorb; vascular tissues transport materials; reproductive strategies that protect spores.

1 Focus

Bellringer

Section Focus Transparency 51

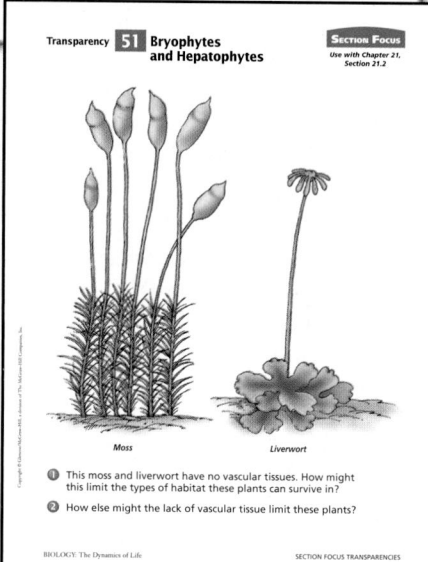

Transparency **51** Bryophytes and Hepatophytes

SECTION FOCUS
Use with Chapter 21, Section 21.2

Moss   *Liverwort*

❶ This moss and liverwort have no vascular tissues. How might this limit the types of habitat these plants can survive in?

❷ How else might the lack of vascular tissue limit these plants?

BIOLOGY: The Dynamics of Life   SECTION FOCUS TRANSPARENCIES

Using Prior Knowledge

Infer Some cacti store water for drier months. Modified leaves can be small or thornlike, thus reducing surface areas and reducing water loss. Some cacti have stems with waxy coatings that help reduce water loss. Mosses are small nonvascular plants that live in moist environments. Movement of materials by osmosis is satisfactory because of their small size.

Physical Science Connection

Earth's plates move at speeds that range from about 2 cm/yr to about 18 cm/yr. Geologists now use the global positioning system (GPS) to measure plate motion over several years. The measured speeds generally agree with plate motions over the past several million years, inferred from geological evidence. This suggests that, on average, these speeds appear remarkably constant over millions of years.

564

Section 21.2

Survey of the Plant Kingdom

SECTION PREVIEW

Objectives

Describe the phylogenic relationships among divisions of plants.

Identify the plant kingdom divisions.

Review Vocabulary
evolution: gradual change in an organism through adaptations over time (p. 10)

New Vocabulary
frond
cone

Physical Science Connection

Movement of landmasses
Landmasses continually move over Earth's surface. Earth's outer layer is broken into huge sections called plates. These plates move slowly over the material underneath. Many scientists think that the motion of hot material deep within Earth generates the forces that cause plates to move.

Different Plants in Different Places

Using Prior Knowledge Members of the plant kingdom are found worldwide. Plants survive on the cold tundra, in arid deserts, in oceans, in freshwater lakes, and in your community. If you have ever traveled far from home, you may have seen plants that do not grow naturally where you live. Even near your home you may have noticed that some plants grow only in sunny locations and others thrive in shady, damp areas.

Infer *What structural and physiological adaptations do plants, such as the cactus and mosses shown here, have that would allow them to survive in different biomes on Earth? Compare and then evaluate the significance of these adaptations.*

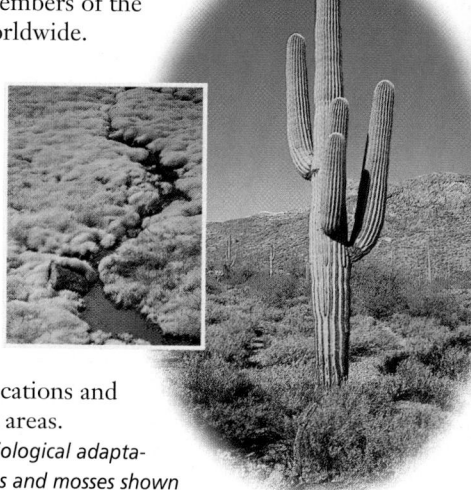

A *Saguaro* cactus (right) and mosses (left)

Phylogeny of Plants

Many geological and climate changes have taken place since the first plants became adapted to life on land. Landmasses have moved from place to place over Earth's surface, climates have changed, and bodies of water have formed and disappeared. Hundreds of thousands of plant species evolved, and countless numbers of these became extinct as conditions continually changed. These processes of evolution and extinction continue to be affected by local and global changes. As plant species evolved in this changing landscape, they retained many of their old characteristics and also developed new ones. These processes of evolution and extinction continue today.

Some botanists use plant characteristics to classify plants into divisions. Recall that a plant division is similar to a phylum in other kingdoms. The highlights of plant evolution include origins of plants from green algae, the production of a waxy cuticle, the development of vascular tissue and roots, and the production of seeds. The production of seeds can be used as a basis to separate the divisions into two groups—non-seed plants and seed plants.

564 WHAT IS A PLANT?

RESOURCE MANAGER

Unit 7 *FAST FILE* Resources
MiniLab Worksheet, p. 4
BioLab Worksheet, pp. 5–6
Reinforcement and Study Guide in English, pp. 9–10
Reinforcement and Study Guide in Spanish, pp. 13–14
Critical Thinking/Problem Solving, p. 16
Transparency Worksheets, pp. 18–20

Reading Essentials for Biology, Section 21.2
Section Focus Transparency 51
Basic Concepts Transparency 33

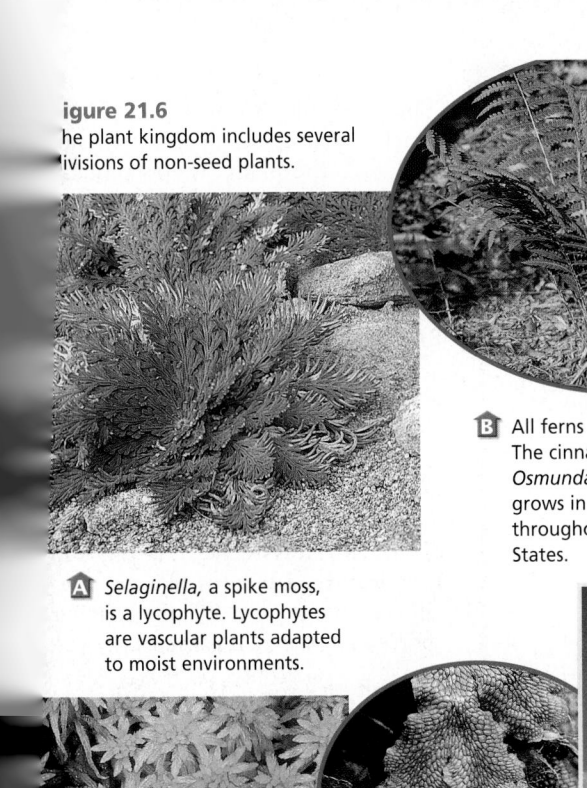

Figure 21.6
The plant kingdom includes several divisions of non-seed plants.

B All ferns are pterophytes. The cinnamon fern, *Osmunda cinnamomea*, grows in swampy habitats throughout the United States.

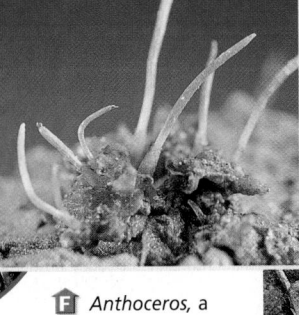

C *Equisetum* is an arthrophyte. It has roots, stems, and leaves, but the stems are hollow and appear jointed.

A *Selaginella*, a spike moss, is a lycophyte. Lycophytes are vascular plants adapted to moist environments.

E *Marchantia* is a hepaticophyte. It is found on damp rocks.

F *Anthoceros*, a hornwort, is an anthocerophyte. It is found in moist, shady habitats.

D *Sphagnum* is a bryophyte. It grows in peat bogs.

G *Psilotum* sporophytes have simple stems but no leaves or roots.

Non-seed Plants

The divisions of non-seed plants are shown in *Figure 21.6*. These plants produce hard-walled reproductive cells called spores. Non-seed plants include vascular and nonvascular organisms.

Hepaticophyta

Hepaticophytes (heh PAH tih koh fites) include small plants commonly called liverworts. Their flattened bodies resemble the lobes of an animal's liver. Liverworts are nonvascular plants that grow only in moist environments. Water and nutrients move throughout a liverwort by osmosis and diffusion. Studies comparing the biochemistry of different plant divisions suggest that liverworts may be the ancestors of all plants.

There are two kinds of liverworts: thallose liverworts and leafy liverworts. Thallose liverworts have a broad body that looks like a lobed leaf. Leafy liverworts are creeping plants with three rows of thin leaves attached to a stem.

Anthocerophyta

Anthocerophytes (an THOH ser oh fites) are also small thallose plants.

> **Word Origin**
>
> hepato- from the Greek word *hepar*, meaning "liver"; Hepaticophytes have liver-shaped gametophytes.

MiniLab 21.2

Purpose
Students will compare two living plants with their fossil relatives.

Process Skills
collect data, compare and contrast, draw a conclusion, measure in SI, observe and infer

Safety Precautions
Be sure that students wear protective gloves when handling specimen. If using latex gloves, check with students for latex sensitivity. Caution students about rubbing their eyes when working with preserved materials. Wash hands after the activity.

Teaching Strategies
■ Living and preserved club mosses and horsetails are available from biological supply houses.
■ Student observations can be both qualitative and quantitative. Review the meaning of these terms.
■ Review conversion from meters to centimeters if necessary.

Expected Results
Students' comparisons between the living plants and their fossil relatives will vary.

Analysis
1. similarities—green, grow upright, have scalelike leaves; differences—tall thick fossil stem with ridged surface, short thin living stem, leaves on top of fossil stem, leaves on living stem; Student answers on the closeness of the relationship may vary, but, may agree that they are closely related. If using the total number of similarities and differences, students may disagree.

MiniLab 21.2

Compare and Contrast

Looking at Modern and Fossil Plants Many modern plants have relatives that are known only from the fossil record. Are modern plants similar to their fossil relatives? Are there any differences?

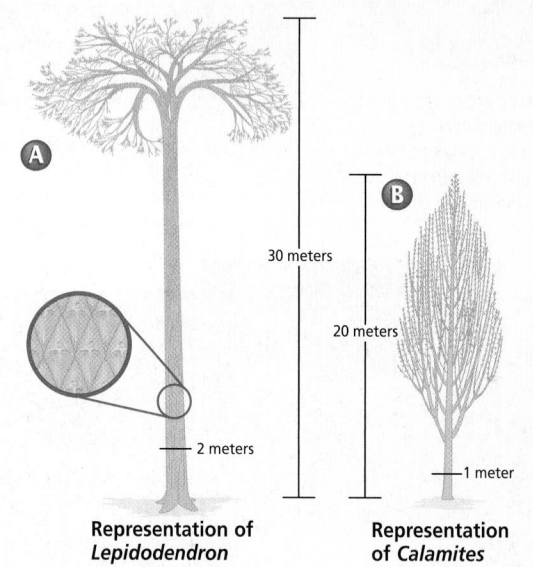

30 meters
20 meters
2 meters
1 meter

Representation of Lepidodendron

Representation of Calamites

Procedure
1. Examine a preserved or living sample of *Lycopodium*, a club moss. **CAUTION:** *Wear protective gloves when handling preserved material.*
2. Note and record the following observations:
   a. Does the plant grow flat or upright like a tree?
   b. Describe the appearance of its leaves and its stem.
   c. Measure the plant's height and diameter in centimeters.
3. Repeat step 2 for diagram A, a fossil relative.
4. Repeat steps 1–3 using a preserved or living sample of *Equisetum*, a horsetail and diagram B, a fossil relative.

Analysis
1. **Compare and Contrast** Describe the similarities and differences between *Lycopodium* and *Lepidodendron*. Do your observations justify their closeness as relatives? Explain.
2. **Compare and Contrast** Describe the similarities and differences between *Equisetum* and *Calamites*. Do your observations justify their closeness as relatives? Explain.

566 WHAT IS A PLANT?

The sporophytes of these plant which resemble the horns of an animal, give the plants their common name—hornworts. These nonvascular plants grow in damp, shady habitats and rely on osmosis and diffusion to transport nutrients.

Bryophyta
Bryophytes (BRI uh fites), th mosses, are nonvascular plants th rely on osmosis and diffusion transport materials. However, son mosses have elongated cells that conduct water and sugars. Moss plan are usually less than 5 cm tall ar have leaflike structures that are usually only one to two cells thick. The spores are formed in capsules.

Psilophyta
Psilophytes, known as whisk fern consist of thin, green stems. Th psilophytes are unique vascular plan because they have neither roots n leaves. Small scales that are flat, rigi overlapping structures cover eac stem. The two known genera psilophytes are tropical or subtrop cal. Only one genus is found in th southern United States.

Reading Check **Describe** the main difference between bryophytes an psilophytes.

Lycophyta
Lycophytes (LI koh fites), the clu mosses, are vascular plants adapte primarily to moist environment Lycophytes have stems, roots, ar leaves. Their leaves, although ve small, contain vascular tissue. Speci existing today are usually less tha 25 cm high, but their ancestors gre as tall as 30 m and formed a large pa of the vegetation of Paleozoic forest The plants of these ancient fores have become part of the coal tha is now used by people for fue

2. similarities—green, grow upright, leaves are in whorls, leaves are small, rings on stem; differences—fossil has branches while living is one single stem, fossil is taller and thicker, living plant leaves appear to be much smaller than fossil; See explanation in answer to question #1.

Assessment
Knowledge Ask students to find out how long ago the fossil plant examples used in this MiniLab lived on Earth. Use the Performance Task Assessment List for Using Math in Science in **PASC**, p. 101. **L2**

Try *MiniLab 21.2* to explore the similarities and differences between modern and fossil lycophytes.

Arthrophyta

Arthrophytes (AR throh fites), the horsetails, are vascular plants. They have hollow, jointed stems surrounded by whorls of scalelike leaves. The cells covering the stems of some arthrophytes contain large deposits of silica. Although primarily a fossil group, about 15 species of arthrophytes exist today. All modern horsetails are small, but their fossil relatives were the size of trees.

Pterophyta

Pterophytes (TER oh fites), ferns, are the most well-known and diverse group of non-seed vascular plants. Ferns were abundant in Paleozoic and Mesozoic forests. They have leaves called **fronds** that vary in length from 1 cm to 500 cm. The large size and complexity of fronds is one difference between pterophytes and other groups of seedless vascular plants. Although ferns are found nearly everywhere, most grow in the tropics.

Seed Plants

Seed plants produce seeds, which in a dry environment are a more effective means of reproduction than spores. A seed consists of an embryonic plant and a food supply covered by a hard protective seed coat. All seed plants have vascular tissues. In *Problem-Solving Lab 21.2*, you can compare a characteristic common to seed plants and non-seed plants.

Cycadophyta

Cycads (SI kuds) were abundant during the Mesozoic Era. Today, there are about 100 species of cycads. They are palmlike trees with scaly

trunks and can be short or more than 20 m in height. Cycads produce male and female cones on separate trees. **Cones** are scaly structures that support male or female reproductive structures. Cycad cones can be as long as 1 m. Seeds are produced in female cones. Male cones produce clouds of pollen.

Problem-Solving Lab 21.2

Apply Concepts

What trend in size is seen with gametophyte and sporophyte generations? All plants undergo alternation of generations. There is a specific trend, however, that occurs in size as one goes from one plant division to the next.

Solve the Problem

The following graph shows the trend that occurs within the plant kingdom as one compares the size of sporophyte and gametophyte generations in three major divisions.

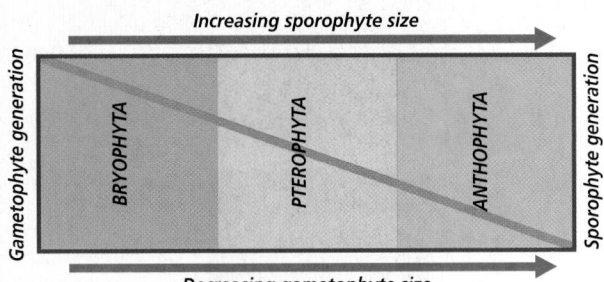

Increasing sporophyte size

Gametophyte generation — BRYOPHYTA — PTEROPHYTA — ANTHOPHYTA — Sporophyte generation

Decreasing gametophyte size

Thinking Critically

1. **Analyze** Describe the trend that occurs to the size of the gametophyte generation as one moves from bryophytes to anthophytes.
2. **Analyze** Describe the trend that occurs to the size of the sporophyte generation as one moves from bryophytes to anthophytes.
3. **Predict** Estimate the size of the gametophyte generation compared with the sporophyte generation in:
   a. Coniferophyta. Explain.
   b. Lycophyta. Explain.
4. **Infer** You are looking at a giant redwood tree. Which generation is it and how do you know?

Problem-Solving Lab 21.2

Purpose

Students will analyze a graph and detect trends in the size of the gametophyte and sporophyte generations of various plant divisions.

Process Skills

apply concepts, think critically, compare and contrast, draw a conclusion

Teaching Strategies

Ask students to sequence the plant divisions from Bryophyta to Anthophyta prior to doing this lab. This will allow them to refer to their lists as they complete the analysis section.

Thinking Critically

1. gametophyte generation becomes smaller
2. sporophyte generation becomes larger
3. a. large sporophyte, small gametophyte; it would be located directly to the left of Anthophytes
   b. large gametophyte, small sporophyte; it would be located close to the right of Bryophyta
4. Redwoods are conifers and the large generation is the sporophyte.

Modified Assessment

Knowledge Ask students to list the laboratory tools needed to study the gametophyte and sporophyte generations of a moss plant and a rose. Use the Performance Task List for Designing an Experiment in **PASC**, p. 95. **L1**

 Indiana Academic Standards

Pages 566–567: B.1.31, B.1.32, B.1.43

Display

Visual-Spatial Have students photograph a variety of plants or bring in pictures of various plants cut from magazines. As a class, develop a bulletin board display that places each plant pictured, along with its name, in its correct division. Use the completed display as a teaching tool throughout the unit. **L1** **COOP LEARN**

Struggling Learners

Have students use Table 21.1 and the text to make a table that compares conifers and anthophytes. The table should have two columns labeled Similarities and Differences. Have students include physical differences and similarities. **L2** **ELL**

Caption Question Answer
Figure 21.7 Student answers will vary; however, all responses should be plant organs that developed from a flower or flowers.

Table 21.1 Seed Plant Divisions

Division	Example	Common Names	Characteristics
Cycadophyta		Sago palm, cycad, zamia, dioon	Cycads grow in tropical or subtropical environments. These plants are slow-growing trees with unbranched trunks. Their leaves are palmlike. Seeds are produced in cones on female plants.
Gnetophyta		Joint fir, *Gnetum*, *Welwitschia*	Gnetophytes are usually found in desert or arid environments, but some are tropical. They exhibit diverse growth habits from vines to low-growing forms. These plants produce seeds in conelike structures.
Ginkgophyta		Ginkgo, maidenhair tree	Ginkgoes are tolerant of a wide range of habitats from urban to open environments. These trees drop their leaves in the fall. Their seeds are surrounded by soft, fruitlike structures.
Coniferophyta		Pine, spruce, juniper, redwood, fir, yew, hemlock, arborvitae, cedar	Conifers grow in a wide range of habitats. Depending on the species, conifers can be tall trees or ground-covering shrubs. The leaves of conifers are needlelike or scalelike. Seeds develop in cones or berrylike structures.
Anthophyta		Rice, tomato, rose, corn, basil, apple, oak, grass, cattail, grape, bluebell	Anthophytes are found worldwide. The division includes a great diversity of growth habits, forms, and sizes. All anthophytes produce flowers from which dry or fleshy fruits with one or more seeds develop.

Gnetophyta

There are three genera of gnetophytes (NEE toh fites) and each has distinct characteristics. *Gnetum* (NEE tum) includes about 30 species of tropical trees and climbing vines. There are about 35 *Ephedra* (eh FEH dra) species that grow as shrubby plants in desert and arid regions. *Welwitschia* (wel WITCH ee uh) has only one species, which is found in the deserts of southwest Africa. Its leaves grow from the base of a short stem that resembles a large, shallow cap.

CHALLENGE ACTIVITY

Logging Have students prepare a detailed diagram of the harvest and lumber production processes of a specific conifer. Have them make another diagram that compares modern methods to methods used in the early twentieth century. **L3**

Indiana Academic Standards
Pages 568–569: B.1.31, B.1.35

Ginkgophyta

This division has only one living species, *Ginkgo biloba*, a distinctive tree with small, fan-shaped leaves. Like cycads, ginkgoes (GING kohs) have male and female reproductive structures on separate trees. The seeds produced on female trees have an unpleasant smell, so ginkgoes planted in city parks are usually male trees. Ginkgoes are hardy and resistant to insects and to air pollution.

Coniferophyta

These are the conifers (KAH nuh furz), cone-bearing trees such as pine, fir, cypress, and redwood. Conifers are vascular seed plants that produce seeds in cones. Species of conifers can be identified by the characteristics of their cones or leaves that are needle-like or scaly. You can learn more about how to identify conifers in the *BioLab* at the end of the chapter.

Bristlecone pines, the oldest known living trees in the world, are members of this plant division. Another type of conifer, the Pacific yew, is a source of cancer-fighting drugs. Read more about medicinal plants in the *Connection to Health* at the end of this chapter.

Anthophyta

Anthophytes (AN thoh fites), commonly called the flowering plants,

Figure 21.7
These fruits and seeds developed from flowers.
List *Can you name three vegetables that are really fruits?*

are the largest, most diverse group of seed plants living on Earth. There are approximately 250 000 species of anthophytes. Fossils of the Anthophyta date to early in the Cretaceous Period. Unlike conifers, anthophytes produce flowers from which fruits develop, like those in *Figure 21.7*. A fruit usually contains one or more seeds. This division has two classes: the monocotyledons (mah nuh kah tul EE dunz) and dicotyledons (di kah tul EE dunz). You will learn more about the distinctions between monocots and dicots when you read about anthophyte tissues in Chapter 23.

Table 21.1 lists some information about the divisions of seed plants. Do you recognize any of the common names of the plants? Can you add to the list of common names?

Word Origin

conifero- from the Latin word *conifer*, meaning "cone bearing"; Many plants in the division Coniferophyta produce their seeds on cones.

3 Assess

DAILY INTERVENTION

Check for Understanding
Quiz students orally about the major characteristics of the plant divisions.

Reteach
Visual-Spatial Have students construct a table organizing plant divisions under two headings: non-seed plants and seed plants. **L2**

Resources
For more practice, use *Reading Essentials for Biology*, Section 21.2.

Extension

Have students prepare a key that will enable them to distinguish among the plant divisions. Encourage students to photocopy their keys and share them with their classmates. **L3**

✔ **Assessment**

Knowledge Using the photos in Figures 21.6 and Table 21.1, have students explain why each plant belongs to its particular division. **L2**

The BioLab at the end of the chapter can be used at this point in the lesson.

Section Assessment

Understanding Main Ideas
1. What is the primary difference between the seeds of conifers and anthophytes?
2. Why are seeds an important structural adaptation? What plant divisions produce seeds? Which plant divisions do not produce seeds?
3. What structural adaptation allows pterophytes to grow larger than bryophytes?
4. Compare and contrast anthophytes and anthocerophytes.

Thinking Critically
5. In which division would you expect to find apple trees? Why?

SKILL REVIEW
6. **Get the Big Picture** Make a table of the plant divisions. Label columns: Division, Seed Plants, Non-seed Plants, Vascular Plants, Nonvascular Plants, and Seeds in Fruits. For more help, refer to *Get the Big Picture* in the **Skill Handbook**.

in.bdol.glencoe.com/self_check_quiz

Section Assessment

1. Anthophyte seeds are encased in fruits; conifer seeds are produced on cones.
2. Seeds protect and supply food for the embryo and aid in dispersal. seed: Cycadophyta, Gnetophyta, Ginkgophyta, Coniferophyta, and Anthophyta; non-seed: Anthocerophyta, Hepaticophyta, Bryophyta, Psilophyta, Lycophyta, Arthrophyta, and Pterophyta
3. Ferns have vascular tissues that transport water and provide support.
4. Both show alternation of generations and are land plants. Anthocerophytes are non-seed, nonvascular plants; anthophytes are vascular seed plants.
5. Anthophyta; They have flowers and fruit.
6. non-seed, nonvascular: Anthocerophytes, Hepaticophytes, and Bryophytes; non-seed, vascular: Psilophytes, Lycophytes, Arthrophytes, and Pterophytes; seed, vascular: Cycadophytes, Gnetophytes, Ginkgophyte, Coniferophytes; Anthophytes; seeds in fruits, vascular: Anthophytes

Time Allotment
one class period

Process Skills
observe and infer, classify, compare and contrast, organize data

Safety Precautions
Some of the needle and cone specimens are very sharp. Warn students of the possibility of sticking themselves with the pointed ends. Don't touch face during lab. Wash hands after lab.

PREPARATION

Alternative Materials
Specimens should contain both needles and cones. If unavailable, substitute scale diagrams of a variety of conifer needle and cone specimens.

Possible Hypotheses
- The number of needles per bundle, length of needles, shape of needles, color of needles, and appearance of the sheath at the base of the needles are useful in classifying conifers.
- Cone shape, length, and diameter may be used to classify conifers.

DESIGN YOUR OWN
BioLab

INQUIRY
Before You Begin
Each conifer species has a unique cone. The leaves of conifer species also have different characteristics. How would you identify a conifer? You would probably use a dichotomous key. Dichotomous keys list features of related organisms in a way that allows you to determine each organism's scientific name. Below is an example from a dichotomous key that might be used to identify trees.

Needles grouped in bundles
Needles not grouped in bundles
Needlelike leaves
Flat, thin leaves
Leaves composed of three or more leaflets
Leaves not made up of leaflets

Arborvitae

How can you make a key for identifying conifers?

PREPARATION

Problem
What characteristics can be used to create a dichotomous key for identifying different kinds of conifers?

Hypotheses
State your hypothesis according to the kinds of characteristics you predict will best serve to distinguish among several conifer groups. Explain your reasoning.

Objectives
In this BioLab, you will:
- **Compare** structures of several different conifer specimens.
- **Identify** which characteristics can be used to distinguish one conifer from another.
- **Develop a model** of a hierarchical classification system (division, genus, species) based on similarities and differences using taxonomic nomenclature.

Pine needles

Possible Materials
twigs, branches, and cones from several different conifers that have been identified for you

Safety Precautions 🔬🥽👕
CAUTION: *Always wash your hands after handling biological materials. Always wear goggles in the lab.*

Skill Handbook
If you need help with this lab, refer to the **Skill Handbook**.

Hemlock

PLAN THE EXPERIMENT

Teaching Strategies
- Label the samples with either their scientific names or generic names such as Conifer A, Conifer B, etc. This will allow students to establish whether or not a key actually works when identification is attempted by another group.

- Illustrate on the chalkboard or an overhead what an ideal key may look like. Point out that trait options are shown at each step.

Possible Procedures
Student procedures will vary. However, the general organization of the key itself will be similar from group to group. Making branches with opposite characteristics will help with the key design.

PLAN THE EXPERIMENT

1. Make a list of characteristics that could be included in your key. You might consider using shape, color, size, habitat, or other factors.

2. Determine which of those characteristics would be most helpful in classifying your conifers.

3. Determine in what order the characteristics should appear in your key.

4. Decide how to describe each characteristic.

Check the Plan

1. The traits described at each step in a key are often pairs of contrasting characteristics. For example, the first step in a key to conifers might compare "needles grouped in bundles" with "needles attached singly."

2. Someone who is not familiar with conifer identification should be able to use your key to correctly identify any conifer it includes.

3. *Make sure your teacher has approved your experimental plan before you proceed further.*

4. Carry out your plan by creating your key.

5. **CLEANUP AND DISPOSAL** Return all conifer specimens to the location specified by your teacher for reuse by other students. Wash your hands thoroughly.

Spruce

ANALYZE AND CONCLUDE

1. **Check Your Hypothesis** Have someone outside your lab group use your key to identify a conifer specimen. If he or she cannot identify it, try to determine what the problem is and make improvements to your key.

2. **Relate Concepts** Give one or more examples of situations in which a dichotomous key would be a useful tool.

3. **ERROR ANALYSIS** Is there only one correct way to design a dichotomous key for your specimens? Explain why or why not.

Apply Your Skill

Project Design a different dichotomous key that would also work to identify your specimens. You may expand your key to include additional conifers.

 Web Links To find out more about conifers, visit in.bdol.glencoe.com/conifers

ANALYZE AND CONCLUDE

1. By using student key design on the overhead, the entire class can determine whether or not the key works.

2. It can distinguish poisonous from nonpoisonous plants, and harmful from nonharmful insects.

3. **ERROR ANALYSIS** Student key designs placed on the overhead will illustrate the diversity of student trait choices used to organize and design each key. Make sure students understand that their keys must distinguish among several similar conifers, each of which must be uniquely identified. Each fork in their key must be specific and identifiable.

Assessment

Performance Provide students with a bag of common laboratory items such as: glass slide, coverslip, paper clip, thumbtack, rubber band, staple, and dissecting needle. Ask them to prepare a key that identifies each item. Use the Performance Task Assessment List for Making and Using a Classification System in **PASC**, p. 121. **L1**

Apply Your Skill

Project Ask students to explain why a key design based on leaf odor or habitat may not be workable or practical.

Data and Observations

Have students record their keys and turn them in at the end of class. Make transparencies of sample keys and use them in class the following day as a means for illustrating correct and incorrect key design.

CLEANUP AND DISPOSAL

Make sure that students make wise choices in the use and conservation of resources and the disposal or recycling of materials.

connection to Health

Medicines from Plants

Madagascar rosy periwinkle

What comes to mind when you hear the word *plant?* A vase full of flowers? A fruit and vegetable garden? An evergreen forest? Although these examples are what most people think of when they hear the word *plant*, plants provide us with much more than bouquets, food, and lumber. Nearly 80 percent of the world's population relies on medications derived from plants. In fact, just fewer than 100 plants provide the active ingredients used in the ten dozen or so plant-derived medicines currently on the market.

For thousands of years, the words *plants* and *medicines* were used synonymously. In the fifth century A.D., doctors of the Byzantine Empire used the autumn crocus to effectively treat rheumatism and arthritis. Hundreds of years ago, certain groups of Native North Americans used the rhizomes of the mayapple as a laxative, a remedy for intestinal worms, and as a topical treatment for warts and other skin growths. The oils from peppermint leaves have long been used to settle an upset stomach. Lotions containing the liquid from the plant *Aloe vera* are often used to relieve the pain associated with minor burns, including sunburn. "Herbal" medicines have again begun to play an important role in so-called modern medicine.

Aspirin—The wonder drug Evidence suggests that almost 2500 years ago, a Greek physician named Hippocrates used a substance from the bark of a white willow tree to treat minor pains and fever. The substance, which is called salicin, unfortunately upset the stomach. Research in the late 1800s led to the discovery of acetylsalicylic acid (ah SEE till sa lih SIH lick • A sid), or aspirin. Aspirin originally was developed by chemist Felix Hoffmann to relieve the joint discomfort associated with rheumatism. Salicylic

acid—a major component of aspirin—was finally synthesized in the laboratory in the early 1900s. Since then, aspirin's use has become widespread.

New drugs for cancer Drugs that fight two types of cancer—Hodgkin's disease and leukemia—have been derived from the Madagascar rosy periwinkle. Drugs produced from the needles and bark of the Pacific yew have been used to treat breast, ovarian, lung, and other cancers. Although the interest in medicinal plants by consumers, medical experts, and pharmaceutical companies is growing, it is estimated that less than five percent of the 250 000 different flowering plant species have been studied for their potential use in the field of medicine.

Researching in Biology

Project Identify a plant not mentioned in this feature that is known to have medicinal properties. Research the plant's geographic distribution on Earth, its use(s), the active ingredient derived from the plant, and whether or not a synthetic form of the active ingredient is available for use. As a class, compile all findings and create a classroom display.

 To find out more about medicines derived from plants, visit in.bdol.glencoe.com/health

Researching in Biology

Responses might include the potent analgesic morphine, which is derived from the opium poppy; the antimalarial drug quinine, which is made by boiling the bark of cinchona trees; and the heart stimulant digitalis, which is made from the leaves of foxgloves.

STUDY GUIDE

Section 21.1

Adapting to Life on Land

Key Concepts

- Plants are multicellular eukaryotes with cells that have cell walls containing cellulose. A waterproof cuticle covers the outer surface of most plants. Most plants undergo photosynthesis, which produces glucose, a form of food.

- All plants on Earth probably evolved from filamentous green algae that lived in ancient oceans. The first plants to eventually move from water to land probably were leafless forms.

- Adaptations for life on land include a cuticle; the development of leaves, roots, stems, and vascular tissues; alternation of generations; and the evolution of the seed.

Vocabulary

cuticle (p. 559)
leaf (p. 561)
nonvascular plant (p. 562)
root (p. 561)
seed (p. 562)
stem (p. 561)
vascular plant (p. 562)
vascular tissue (p. 562)

Section 21.2

Survey of the Plant Kingdom

Key Concepts

- The plant kingdom is grouped into major categories called divisions.

- Nonvascular plants are in the divisions Anthocerophyta, Hepaticophyta, and Bryophyta. They reproduce mainly by using spores. Nonvascular plants do not produce seeds.

- Non-seed vascular plants are in the divisions Psilophyta, Lycophyta, Arthrophyta, and Pterophyta. These plants have tissues that conduct water and other materials and reproduce mainly by spores.

- Vascular seed plants in the divisions Cycadophyta, Gnetophyta, Ginkgophyta, and Coniferophyta produce seeds on cones. Male cones and female cones can be on separate plants or the same plant.

- The division Anthophyta includes vascular, seed-producing plants that flower. Fruits with seeds develop from flowers. Anthophytes are divided into two groups—monocotyledons and dicotyledons.

Vocabulary

cone (p. 567)
frond (p. 567)

FOLDABLES
Study Organizer To help you review plant adaptations to land, use the Organizational Study Fold on page 559.

in.bdol.glencoe.com/vocabulary_puzzlemaker

Key Concepts

Summary statements can be used by students to review the major concepts of the chapter.

Biology Online

Visit in.bdol.glencoe.com
/self_check_quiz
/vocabulary_puzzlemaker
/chapter_test
/standardized_test

VOCABULARY PUZZLEMAKER

For additional help with vocabulary, have students access the Vocabulary PuzzleMaker online at in.bdol.glencoe.com/vocabulary_puzzlemaker

FOLDABLES™

Have students use their Foldables to review the content of Section 21.1. On the back of their Foldable, have students infer how alternation of generations is advantageous for plants.

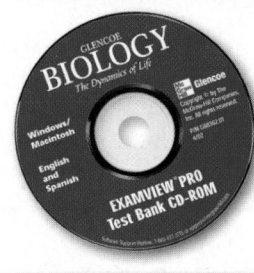

Use the Exam*View*®Pro Test Bank CD-ROM to:
- Create **multiple versions** of tests
- Create **modified** tests with one mouse click for **inclusion** students
- **Edit** existing questions and **add** your own questions
- Build tests aligned with state standards using built-in **State Curriculum Tags**
- Change **English** tests to **Spanish** with one mouse click and vice versa

Chapter 21 Assessment

 The Princeton Review **Questions and answers have been aligned and verified by The Princeton Review.**

Vocabulary Review

1. nonvascular plant
2. root
3. cone
4. leaf
5. vascular tissue

Understanding Key Concepts

6. A   9. D   12. D
7. C   10. D
8. C   11. A

Constructed Response

13. Studies that compare the biochemistry of different plants suggest that the earliest plants were most similar to liverworts. Also, plants to grow first during succession often are liverworts. Adaptations that allow growth in barren land environments may be the same adaptations that allowed for survival from a water to a land environment.

14. Flowering plants produce seeds in which the embryo plant is protected. Seeds are enclosed in fruits, which ensure greater survival and distribution. They have vascular tissues enabling them to efficiently transport food, water and other materials.

15. The transport of food, water, and other substances from one cell to another by osmosis and diffusion is possible for hepaticophytes and bryophytes because their leaflike structures are small and thin. If leaves were large and thick, water and food would not be able to move quickly enough for cells to maintain homeostasis.

574

Vocabulary Review

Review the Chapter 21 vocabulary words listed in the Study Guide on page 573. Match the words with the definitions below.

1. plants in which the transport of water and other substances is mainly by osmosis and diffusion from cell to cell

2. the organ that anchors a plant and absorbs most of the water and minerals used by a plant

3. for plants such as pines and spruces, it is the organ that contains reproductive structures

4. the plant organ that is usually the site of photosynthesis

5. a group of tubelike, elongated cells through which water and other materials are transported throughout a plant

Understanding Key Concepts

6. Which of these traits is NOT common to plants and green algae?
   A. reproduce by fission
   B. contain cellulose in cell walls
   C. store food as starch
   D. contain the same kind of chlorophyll

7. Vascular tissues are found in _____.
   A. bacteria   C. ferns
   B. algae   D. hornworts

8. Which of the following characteristics is NOT found in plants?
   A. eukaryotic cells   C. prokaryotic cells
   B. cellulose cell walls   D. waxy cuticle

9. The plant organ in the photo to the right is from a plant in division _____.
   A. Anthocerophyta
   B. Coniferophyta
   C. Lycophyta
   D. Anthophyta

10. Which group of organisms is probably the ancestor of land plants?
    A. cyanobacteria   C. bryophytes
    B. archaebacteria   D. green algae

11. Seeds enclosed in a fruit is a structural adaptation of _____.
    A. Anthophytes   C. Coniferophytes
    B. Bryophytes   D. Pterophytes

12. The fern structure to the right is called a _____.
    A. rhizome
    B. root
    C. gametophyte
    D. frond

Constructed Response

13. **Open Ended** Explain why biologists hypothesize that the first plants to adapt to life on land may have been similar to liverworts.

14. **Open Ended** Anthophytes are found worldwide and include the greatest number of known plant species. Identify, describe, and evaluate characteristics of this division that were important to its success. Explain your choices.

15. **Open Ended** Observe the plants in *Figure 21.6 D* and *E*. Describe the structural adaptations that contribute to their long-term survival in moist environments.

Thinking Critically

16. **Concept Map** Copy the concept map below then complete it the using the following terms: leaves, roots, stems, vascular tissue, vascular plant.

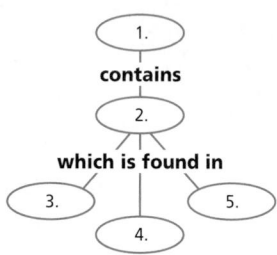

1.

contains

2.

which is found in

3.   4.   5.

in.bdol.glencoe.com/chapter_test

Thinking Critically

16. 1. vascular plant; 2. vascular tissue; 3. roots; 4. stems; 5. leaves; (3, 4, & 5 in any order)

17. Factors to consider: rainfall per year, sun or shade, soil type, climatic variations, slope, specialized care needed, annual vs. perennial plants; Plant selections will vary depending on climate, soil type, and other local conditions.

RUBRIC

Evaluating Open-Ended Questions
Open-ended assessment questions are graded by using a multilevel rubric that guides you in assessing a student's knowledge of a particular concept. The following rubric is a sample scoring device.

17. **REAL WORLD BIOCHALLENGE** You are appointed to a committee at school that is to plan and plant a flower garden. What factors must be considered when selecting plants for this garden? Visit in.bdol.glencoe.com to research plants and plan the garden. Sketch a plan and list your plant selections. Explain why each plant was chosen.

The assessed Indiana standard appears next to the question.

All questions aligned and verified by *The Princeton Review*

Part 1 ▶ Multiple Choice

Study the cladogram below and answer questions 18–20.

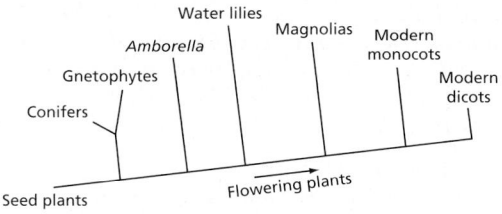

18. The cladogram shows the evolution of some
1.30 flowering plants. According to the clado-gram, modern monocots developed _____ *Amborella*.
A. at the same time as   **C.** after
B. before   **D.** none of these

19. *Amborella* is most closely related to _____.
A. modern monocots   **C.** water lilies
B. modern dicots   **D.** magnolias

20. Which of the following plant types evolved before *Amborella*?
A. gnetophytes   **C.** magnolias
B. modern dicots   **D.** water lilies

Use the diagram below to answer questions 21 and 22.

21. The sporophyte produces spores by the
B.1.8 process of _____.
A. mitosis   **C.** fission
B. meiosis   **D.** fertilization

22. Which of the following would NOT have a
B.1.8 haploid or *n* number of chromosomes?
A. gametophyte   **C.** sporophyte
B. spore   **D.** gamete

Part 2 ▶ Constructed Response/Grid In

Record your answers or fill in the bubbles on your answer document using the correct place value.

23. Grid In The sporophyte of corn has 20 chromosomes. How many chromosomes would you expect to find in corn gametes?

24. Open Ended Describe the differences between seed and non-seed plants. Considering structural
1.31 and physiological adaptations of these two plant types, infer why seed plants are found in more diverse environments than non-seed plants.

 in.bdol.glencoe.com/standardized_test

End-of-Course Assessment Practice

18. C	**21.** B
19. C	**22.** C
20. A	**23.** 10

24. The embryos of seed plants are protected from adverse conditions, offering more chance for survival and distribution to new areas. Non-seed plants reproduce by spores and require a moist environment for reproduction. Non-seed plants are limited in their distribution to moist environments while many seed plants are not.

FAST FILE

Answer Sheet A practice answer sheet can be found on p. 27 of *Unit 7 FAST FILE Resources*.

RUBRIC

SCORE	CRITERIA
4	A correct solution that is supported by well-developed, accurate explanations.
3	A generally correct solution, but may contain minor flaws in reasoning.
2	A partially correct interpretation and/or solution to the problem.
1	A correct solution with no supporting evidence or explanation.
0	An incorrect solution or no solution is given.

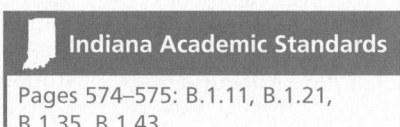

Indiana Academic Standards

Pages 574–575: B.1.11, B.1.21, B.1.35, B.1.43

Chapter 22 Organizer

Section Objectives	National Science Standards	State/Local Standards	Advanced Lab and Demo Planning
Section 22.1 1 session 1. **Identify** the structures of nonvascular plants. 2. **Compare and contrast** characteristics of the different groups of nonvascular plants.	UCP.1, UCP.2, UCP.5; A.1, A.2; C.3, C.4; D.2; F.3, F.4; G.1, G.2	**Indiana Standards** B.1.35, B.1.43	**Student Lab:** Problem-Solving Lab 22.1, p. 578 **Teacher Demonstration:** Quick Demo, p. 579: water, one flowerpot containing sand, one flowerpot containing sand and peat moss
Section 22.2 1 session 3. **Evaluate** the significance of plant vascular tissue to life on land. 4. **Identify and analyze** the characteristics of the non-seed vascular plant divisions.	UCP.1–5; A.1, A.2; C.3, C.4, C.5, C.6; F.3; G.1, G.2, G.3	**Indiana Standards** B.1.15, B.1.32, B.1.35, B.1.43, B.1.45	**Student Labs:** Problem-Solving Lab 22.2, p. 584 MiniLab 22.1, p. 586: water, glycerin, glass slide, forceps, 2 sori from a frond, 2 coverslips, microscope **Teacher Demonstration:** Quick Demo, p. 582: capillary tube, petri dish, colored water
Section 22.3 2 sessions, 1 1/2 blocks 5. **Identify and analyze** the characteristics of seed plants. 6. **Analyze** the advantages of seed and fruit production.	UCP.1–5; A.1, A.2; C.3–6; E.1, E.2; F.1–6; G.1–3	**Indiana Standards** B.1.15, B.1.32, B.1.41, B.1.45	**Student Labs:** MiniLab 22.2, p. 589: lima beans, rice, peas, rye, forceps, iodine stain Additional Lab, p. 592: microscope, prepared slide of conifer leaf cross section Internet BioLab, p. 598: See materials below. **Teacher Demonstration:** Quick Demo, p. 591: cones
End of Chapter Assessment **Student Edition** **Study Guide,** p. 601 **Content Assessment,** pp. 602–603		**Indiana Standards** B.1.15, B.1.32, B.1.43	**Student Lab:** Internet BioLab, p. 598: Internet access

Key to Teaching Strategies

L1 Level 1 activities should be appropriate for students with learning difficulties.

L2 Level 2 activities should be within the ability range of all students.

L3 Level 3 activities are designed for above-average students.

ELL ELL activities should be within the ability range of English Language Learners.

COOP LEARN Cooperative Learning activities are designed for small group work.

Glencoe Exclusive!

Teacher Works™
All-In-One Planner and Resource Center

Reproducible Masters and Transparencies

Technology

Unit 7 FAST FILE Resources
Reinforcement and Study Guide in English, p. 35
Reinforcement and Study Guide in Spanish, p. 39
Transparency Worksheet, p. 45
Reading Essentials for Biology, Section 22.1
☞ **Section Focus Transparency 52**

◉ **Interactive Chalkboard CD-ROM: Section 22.1 Presentation** 🔖
◉ TeacherWorks™ **CD-ROM** 🔖
🎵 **Guided Reading Audio Summaries MP3**

Unit 7 FAST FILE Resources
MiniLab Worksheet, p. 31
Reinforcement and Study Guide in English, pp. 36–37
Reinforcement and Study Guide in Spanish, pp. 40–41
Transparency Worksheet, p. 46
Reading Essentials for Biology, Section 22.2
Laboratory Manual, pp. 133–136
☞ **Section Focus Transparency 53**

◉ **Interactive Chalkboard CD-ROM: Section 22.2 Presentation** 🔖
◉ TeacherWorks™ **CD-ROM** 🔖
🎵 **Guided Reading Audio Summaries MP3**

Unit 7 FAST FILE Resources
MiniLab Worksheet, p. 32
BioLab Worksheet, pp. 33–34
Reinforcement and Study Guide in English, p. 38
Reinforcement and Study Guide in Spanish, p. 42
Concept Mapping, p. 43
Critical Thinking/Problem Solving, p. 44
Transparency Worksheets, pp. 47, 49–52
Reading Essentials for Biology, Section 22.3
Laboratory Manual, pp. 137–140
☞ **Section Focus Transparency 54**
☞ **Basic Concepts Transparencies 34, 35**

◉ **Interactive Chalkboard CD-ROM: Section 22.3 Presentation** 🔖
◉ TeacherWorks™ **CD-ROM** 🔖
🎵 **Guided Reading Audio Summaries MP3**

Unit 7 FAST FILE Resources
Chapter Assessment, pp. 53–58
Student Recording Sheet, p. 59

The Princeton Review **Reviewing Biology,** pp. 43–44

◉ **Interactive Chalkboard: Chapter 22 Assessment** 🔖
◉ **MindJogger Videoquizzes DVD/VHS**
◉ **ExamView® Pro Test Bank CD-ROM**
◉ TeacherWorks™ **CD-ROM** 🔖
◉ **Succeeding on National Standards CD-ROM**

🖥 **in.bdol.glencoe.com**
/self_check_quiz
/vocabulary_puzzlemaker
/chapter_test
/standardized_test

🔖 Indicates materials created specifically for Indiana.

Short on Time?

BIODIGEST The BioDigest at the end of this unit can be used as a(n):
- preview to introduce important unit concepts.
- overview if time does not permit teaching the entire chapter.
- review of key unit concepts.

Understanding the Photo

The Olympic National Park in northwestern Washington includes three distinct ecosystems—glacier-capped mountains, Pacific coast, and a temperate rain forest. There is an abundance and great diversity of plants within the park. In the rain forest, ferns and mosses cover the ground and gigantic conifers tower above the forest floor.

The Diversity of Plants

What You'll Learn

- You will identify the characteristics of the major plant groups.
- You will identify and compare the distinguishing features of vascular and nonvascular plants.
- You will analyze the advantages of seed production.

Why It's Important

You can classify plants according to their diverse characteristics. Knowing about these characteristics of plants will help you analyze the relationships among plant divisions.

Understanding ▶ the Photo

Plants can be categorized as either non-seed plants or seed plants. The ferns and mosses covering the ground in this forest are non-seed plants. The trees and woody shrubs are seed plants.

Biology Online

Visit in.bdol.glencoe.com to
- study the entire chapter online
- access Web Links for more information and activities on diversity of plants
- review content with the Interactive Tutor and self-check quizzes

Two-Minute Chapter Launcher

Activity Form groups of students and give each group pictures or live samples of a variety of vascular and nonvascular plants that grow locally. Ask students to compare and contrast the plants and infer how each is adapted to the local environment. Provide each group with at least one vascular plant and one nonvascular plant. **L2** **ELL** **COOP LEARN**

Indiana Academic Standards

Pages 576–577: B.1.43

Nonvascular Plants

SECTION PREVIEW

Objectives

Identify the structures of nonvascular plants.

Compare and contrast characteristics of the different groups of nonvascular plants.

Review Vocabulary
fertilization: fusion of male and female gametes (p. 253)

New Vocabulary
antheridium
archegonium

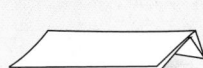 **FOLDABLES™**
Study Organizer

Diversity Make the following Foldable to help you organize information about the diversity of plants.

STEP 1 **Fold** one piece of paper in half lengthwise twice.

STEP 2 **Fold** the paper widthwise into fourths.

STEP 3 **Unfold,** lay the paper lengthwise, and draw lines along the folds.

STEP 4 **Label** your table as shown.

Plants	Divisions	Origins	Adaptations
Nonvascular			
Non-seed vascular			
Seed vascular			

Make a Table As you read Chapter 22, complete the table about the diversity of plants.

What is a nonvascular plant?

Nonvascular plants are not as common or as widespread in their distribution as vascular plants because life functions, including photosynthesis and reproduction, require a close association with water. Because a steady supply of water is not available everywhere, nonvascular plants are limited to moist habitats by streams and rivers or in temperate and tropical rain forests. Recall that a lack of vascular tissue also limits the size of a plant. In drier soils, there is not enough water to meet the needs of most nonvascular plants. Their long-term survival in dry environments is limited by this resource—water. However, nonvascular plants, such as the moss in *Figure 22.1*, are successful in habitats with adequate water.

Figure 22.1
Bryum is a type of moss frequently found in moist forest habitats.

Alternation of generations

As in all plants, the life cycle of nonvascular plants includes an alternation of generations between a diploid sporophyte and a haploid gametophyte. However, nonvascular plant divisions include the only plants that have a dominant gametophyte generation. Sporophytes grow attached to and depend on gametophytes to take in water and other substances.

1 Focus

 INTERACTIVE CHALKBOARD
PowerPoint® Presentations

Bellringer
Section Focus Transparency 52

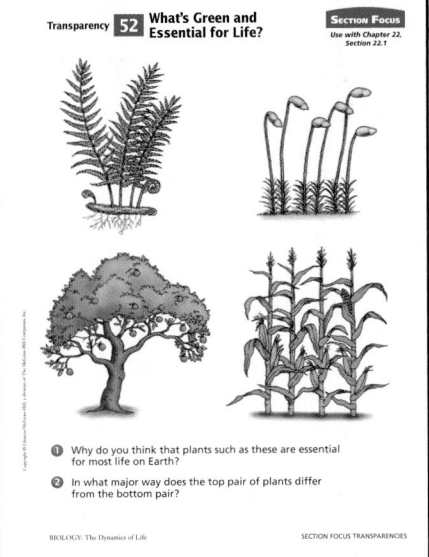

Transparency **52** What's Green and Essential for Life?   **SECTION FOCUS** Use with Chapter 22, Section 22.1

① Why do you think that plants such as these are essential for most life on Earth?

② In what major way does the top pair of plants differ from the bottom pair?

BIOLOGY: The Dynamics of Life   SECTION FOCUS TRANSPARENCIES

 INTERACTIVE CHALKBOARD
with Image Bank

PowerPoint® Presentations

This CD-ROM is an editable Microsoft® PowerPoint® presentation that includes:
- Section presentations
- Section checks
- Image bank
- Hot links to Biology Online
- All transparencies

FOLDABLES™

For an additional Foldables activity idea, see the Chapter 22 Foldables page in *Unit 7 FAST FILE Resources.*

RESOURCE MANAGER

Unit 7 *FAST FILE* Resources
Reinforcement and Study Guide in English, p. 35
Reinforcement and Study Guide in Spanish, p. 39
Transparency Worksheet, p. 45

 Reading Essentials for Biology, Section 22.1
Section Focus Transparency 52

2 Teach

Purpose

Students will interpret a graph of the number of moss species in south Texas counties.

Process Skills

interpret data, analyze, draw conclusions, calculate, infer

Background

Mosses are nonvascular plants that require water for reproduction.

Teaching Strategies

■ Students may confuse the number of moss species with the number of mosses. The variety of species is what the graph shows, not the actual number of moss plants.

■ Make students aware of the fact that the spaces between the bars on the graph indicate that there were no moss species found between 15 and 21.

Thinking Critically

1. The number of counties in South Texas that have few moss species is greater than counties that have many moss species.
2. 65%
3. 13.5%
4. Counties with more moss species may have rivers or streams that provide suitable wet habitats for mosses.

Error Analysis

Students may confuse the vertical axis, the number of counties, with the horizontal axis, the number of moss species. Students may also have trouble calculating percentages.

Problem-Solving Lab 22.1

Interpret Data

Do bryophytes grow in South Texas? The presence and distribution of moss species in South Texas are displayed in the graph below.

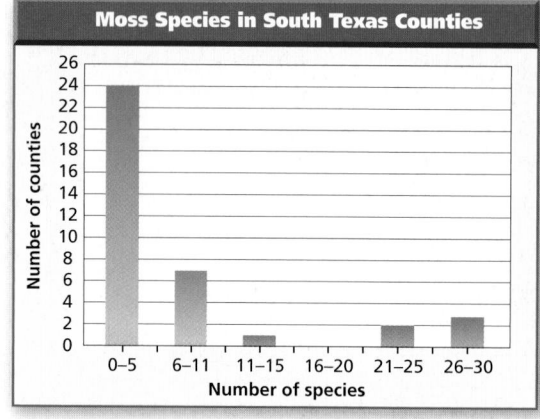

Moss Species in South Texas Counties

(Bar graph: y-axis "Number of counties" from 0 to 26; x-axis "Number of species" with categories 0–5, 6–11, 11–15, 16–20, 21–25, 26–30)

Solve the Problem

Bryophytes need a moist environment and South Texas can be very hot and dry. Interpret the data and infer why the distribution of the numbers of moss species in South Texas counties is so varied.

Thinking Critically

1. **Estimate** Which is greater, counties in South Texas that have many moss species or counties in South Texas that have few moss species?
2. **Calculate** What percentage of counties in South Texas have five or fewer moss species?
3. **Calculate** What percentage of counties in South Texas have more than 20 moss species?
4. **Infer** How might the environment or geography in counties that have more than 20 moss species be different from the environment of counties that have no or very few moss species?

B Moss species sometimes are referred to as pioneer species because they often are some of the first species to inhabit newly formed or disturbed environments. These mosses are growing on the damp surfaces of fallen trees. **Analyze** *Describe the flow of matter between these mosses, trees, and the environment.*

578 THE DIVERSITY OF PLANTS

Modified Assessment

If the number of moss species in County A is 10, County B is 30, and County C is 50, infer which county has the wettest habitat. Explain.

Non-photosynthetic sporophytes, like those shown in *Figure 22.2A,* depend on their gametophytes for food.

Gametophytes of nonvascular plants produce two kinds of sexual reproductive structures. The **antheridium** (an thuh RIH dee um) is the male reproductive structure in which sperm are produced. The **archegonium** (ar kih GOH nee um) is the female reproductive structure in which eggs are produced. Fertilization, which begins the sporophyte generation, occurs in the archegonium.

Adaptations in Bryophyta

There are several divisions of nonvascular plants. The first division you'll study are the mosses, or bryophytes.

Figure 22.2
Mosses usually grow as carpets of small green plants that cover damp soil or other damp surfaces.

A Brown stalks with spore capsules, the sporophyte generation, grow from the green, leafy gametophyte.

Bryophytes are the most familiar of the nonvascular plant divisions. Mosses are small plants with leafy stems. The leaves of mosses are usually one cell thick. Mosses have rhizoids, colorless multicellular structures, which help anchor the stem to the soil. Although mosses do not contain true vascular tissue, some species do have a few, long water-conducting cells in their stems.

Mosses usually grow in dense carpets of hundreds of plants, as shown in *Figure 22.2B.* Some have upright stems; others have creeping stems that hang from steep banks or tree branches. Some mosses form extensive mats that help retard erosion on exposed rocky slopes.

Mosses grow in a wide variety of habitats, as stated in the *Problem-Solving Lab* on the opposite page. They even grow in the arctic during the brief growing season where sufficient moisture is present.

A well-known moss is *Sphagnum,* also known as peat moss. This plant thrives in acidic bogs in northern regions of the world. It is harvested for use as fuel and is a commonly used soil additive. Dried peat moss absorbs large amounts of water, so florists and gardeners use it to increase the water-holding ability of some soils.

Adaptations in Hepaticophyta

Another division of nonvascular plants is the liverworts, or hepaticophytes. Like mosses, liverworts are small plants that usually grow in clumps or masses in moist habitats. The name of the division is derived from the word *hepar,* which refers to the liver. The flattened body of a liverwort gametophyte is thought to resemble the shape of the lobes of an animal's liver. Liverworts occur in many environments worldwide.

Figure 22.3
Liverworts may have a flattened plant body called a thallus **(A)** or leafy stems **(B)**.

A liverwort can be categorized as either thallose or leafy, as shown in *Figure 22.3.* The body of a thallose liverwort is called a thallus. It is broad and ribbonlike and resembles a fleshy, lobed leaf. Thallose liverworts like *Marchantia,* shown in *Figure 22.3A,* are usually found growing on damp soil. Leafy liverworts grow close to the ground and usually are common in tropical jungles and areas with persistent fog. Their stems have flat, thin leaves arranged in three rows—a row along each side of the stem and a row of smaller leaves on the stem's lower surface. Liverworts have rhizoids that are composed of only one elongated cell.

Reading Check **Examine** a hepaticophyte's method of growth. Evaluate its significance as an adaptation to a hepaticophyte's environment.

Word Origin

antheridium from the Medieval Latin word *anthera,* meaning "pollen"; Sperm are produced in the antheridium.

archegonium from the Greek word *archegonos,* meaning "originator"; Eggs are produced in the archegonium.

22.1 NONVASCULAR PLANTS **579**

Caption Question Answer
Figure 22.2 Moss living on the fallen trees causes breakdown of the tree trunk to soil in which seeds fall and grow into new trees.

Quick Demo

Water Absorption by Mosses Show students the water absorption capabilities of peat moss by pouring water into two flowerpots: one containing sand and the other containing a mix of sand and peat moss.

Portfolio

Alternation of Generations Have students prepare a simple flowchart diagram that depicts alternation of generations. The diagram must include these terms: *gametophyte generation, sporophyte generation, spore, gamete, diploid,* and *haploid.* Have students place the flowchart in their portfolio. **L2**

Reading Check Liverworts grow close to the ground, an adaptation that enables them to get water easily and not have to transport it far to all cells of the plant.

USING MODELS

Modeling Nonvascular Plants Students may not be as familiar with nonvascular plants as they are with vascular plants. It will help them to make out of clay, modeling dough, or salt dough a three-dimensional representation of each of the following plant divisions: hepaticophytes, anthocerophytes, and bryophytes. Ask each group of students to make a model of each plant and be prepared to describe the characteristic features of each of their models as you move from group to group. **L2**
COOP LEARN

 Indiana Academic Standards
Pages 578–579: B.1.43

3 Assess

Figure 22.4
The upright sporophyte of the hornwort resembles an animal horn and gives the plant its common name.

Sporophyte with sporangium (2n)

Gametophyte (n)

Adaptations in Anthocerophyta

Anthocerophytes are the smallest division of nonvascular plants, currently consisting of only about 100 species. Also known as hornworts, these nonvascular plants are similar to liverworts in several respects. Like some liverworts, hornworts have a thallose body. The sporophyte of a hornwort resembles the horn of an animal, as shown in *Figure 22.4,* which is why members of this division are commonly called "hornworts." Another feature unique to hornworts is the presence of one to several chloroplasts in each cell of the sporophyte depending upon the species. Unlike other nonvascular plants, the hornwort sporophyte, not the gametophyte, produces most of the food used by both generations.

Origins of Nonvascular Plants

Fossil and genetic evidence suggests that liverworts were the first land plants. Fossils that have been positively identified as nonvascular plants first appear in rocks from the early Paleozoic Era, more than 440 million years ago. However, paleobotanists suspect that nonvascular plants were present earlier than current fossil evidence suggests. Both nonvascular and vascular plants probably share a common ancestor that had alternating sporophyte and gametophyte generations, cellulose in their cell walls, and chlorophyll for photosynthesis.

Section Assessment

Understanding Main Ideas
1. Compare and contrast a leafy liverwort and a thallose liverwort.
2. Explain how the bryophyte sporophyte generation is dependent on the bryophyte gametophyte generation.
3. Identify characteristics shared by all nonvascular plants.
4. Evaluate the significance of nonvascular plant adaptations to their moist environments.

Thinking Critically
5. Identify the growth and development methods of mosses. Explain why these are advantageous in their environments.

SKILL REVIEW

6. **Compare and Contrast** Describe the variations in gametophyte and sporophyte generations of nonvascular plants. For more help, refer to *Compare and Contrast* in the **Skill Handbook**.

580 THE DIVERSITY OF PLANTS

 in.bdol.glencoe.com/self_check_quiz

Section Assessment

1. Thallose liverworts have a broad, ribbonlike body that resembles a fleshy, lobed leaf. Leafy liverworts have three rows of flat, thin leaflike structures attached to a stem.
2. The sporophyte generation is small and obtains food, water, and minerals from the larger gametophyte generation.

3. Nonvascular plants lack vascular tissue, are typically small in size, have a dominant gametophyte generation, and grow in moist, shady areas.
4. Since these plants rely on diffusion and osmosis for the transport of water and minerals, they tend to be found in areas where water is plentiful.
5. The dense mats retain water and help reduce evaporation.

6. The gametophyte and sporophyte generations are both stages of the nonvascular plant life cycle. The sporophyte generation is smaller and dependent upon the gametophyte. The gametophyte generation is haploid and produces gametes, whereas the sporophyte generation is diploid and produces spores.

Section 22.2

Non-Seed Vascular Plants

Plants with Pipes

Using an Analogy You take a drink from a water fountain then watch the unused water flow down the drain. In the lab, another student turns a tap to get 50 mL of water for an investigation. These activities are possible because your school has plumbing that delivers water and carries away wastes. Plants, such the tree fern and others shown to the right, have plumbing too. This plant plumbing—called vascular tissues—distributes water and other dissolved substances throughout a plant.

Concept Map *After you read about non-seed vascular plants, make a concept map that identifies and analyzes the relationships among these organisms.*

Tree fern

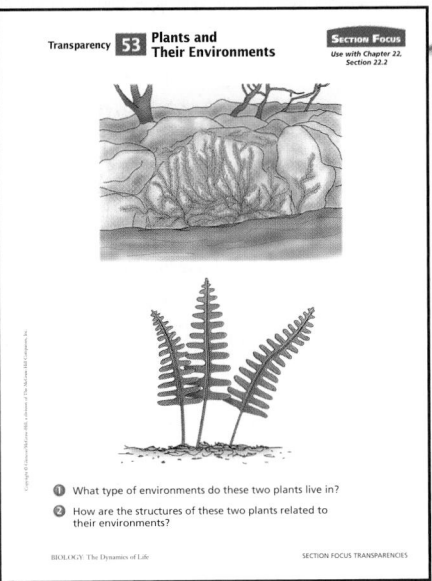

SECTION PREVIEW

Objectives

Evaluate the significance of plant vascular tissue to life on land.

Identify and analyze the characteristics of the non-seed vascular plant divisions.

Vocabulary Review
alternation of generations: type of life cycle found in some algae, fungi, and all plants where an organism alternates between a haploid (*n*) gametophyte generation and a diploid (2*n*) sporophyte generation (p. 516)

New Vocabulary
strobilus
prothallus
rhizome
sorus

What is a non-seed vascular plant?

The obvious difference between a vascular and a nonvascular plant is the presence of vascular tissue. As you may remember, vascular tissue is made up of tubelike, elongated cells through which water and sugars are transported. Vascular plants are able to adapt to changes in the availability of water, and thus are found in a variety of habitats. You will learn about three divisions of non-seed vascular plants: Lycophyta, Arthrophyta, and Pterophyta.

Alternation of generations

Vascular plants, like all plants, exhibit an alternation of generations. Unlike nonvascular plants, the spore-producing vascular sporophyte is dominant and larger in size than the gametophyte, as shown in *Figure 22.5*. The mature sporophyte does not depend on the gametophyte for water or nutrients.

Figure 22.5
In non-seed vascular plants, the sporophyte generation is dominant.

Sporophyte (2n)

Gametophyte (n)

Using an Analogy

Concept Map Ask students to make a list of ways in which the "plant plumbing" analogy is NOT like the vascular system of plants.

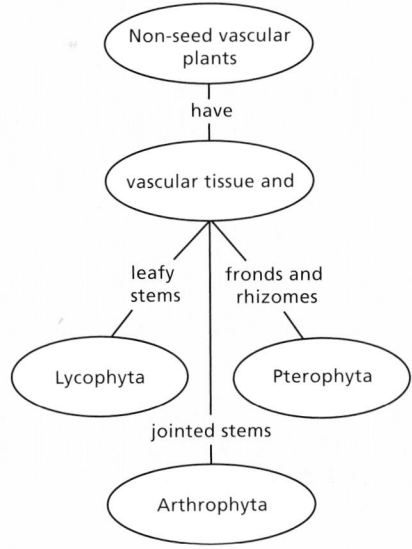

RESOURCE MANAGER

Unit 7 *FAST FILE* Resources
MiniLab Worksheet, p. 31
Reinforcement and Study Guide in English, pp. 36–37
Reinforcement and Study Guide in Spanish, pp. 40–41
Transparency Worksheet, p. 46

Reading Essentials for Biology, Section 22.2
Laboratory Manual, pp. 133–136
Section Focus Transparency 53

Indiana Academic Standards

Pages 580–581: B.1.15, B.1.35, B.1.43, B.1.45

2 Teach

Capillary Action in Plants
Stand a capillary tube in a petri dish filled with colored water. Have students note the rise of water within the tube. Explain that this movement occurs due to capillary action. Ask students to correlate the movement of water in the glass tube to the movement of water in vascular plants. Use this demonstration to explain the relationship between the evolution of vascular tissue and the increased size of plants, and the efficiency of water and mineral movement throughout the plants.

Biology Journal

Spike and Club Moss Question
Have students write a brief essay to explain why club mosses are not common in desert habitats and why most people never see the gametophyte generation of these plants. Have students explain why these plants are not related to the mosses that were discussed in Section 22.1. **L3**

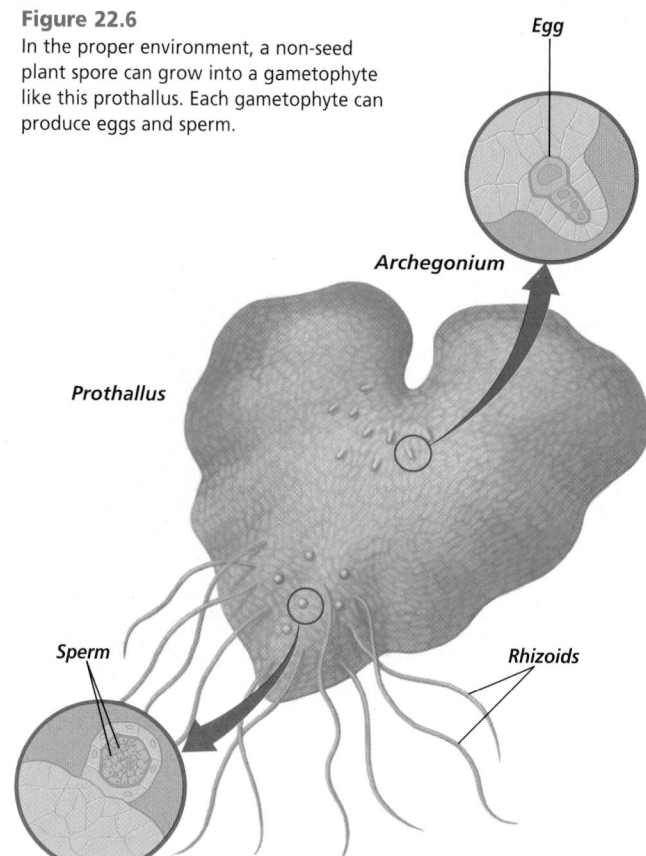

Figure 22.6
In the proper environment, a non-seed plant spore can grow into a gametophyte like this prothallus. Each gametophyte can produce eggs and sperm.

Egg

Archegonium

Prothallus

Sperm

Rhizoids

Antheridium

Figure 22.7
Selaginella species inhabit a variety of environments, from damp greenhouse floors to tropical forests. The resurrection plant, *Selaginella lepidophylla*, is adapted to survive extreme drought **(A)**. When moisture returns, the plant resumes normal functions **(B)**.

A major advance in this group of vascular plants was the adaptation of leaves to form structures that protect the developing reproductive cells. In some non-seed vascular plants, spore-bearing leaves form a compact cluster called a **strobilus** (stroh BIH lus). The spores are released from the strobilus and can grow to form gametophytes. A fern gametophyte is called a **prothallus** (proh THA lus). Gametophytes are relatively small and live in or on the soil. Antheridia and archegonia develop on the gametophyte, as illustrated in *Figure 22.6*. Sperm are released from antheridia and require a continuous film of water to reach eggs in the archegonia. If fertilization occurs, a zygote can grow into a large, dominant sporophyte.

Adaptations in Lycophyta

From fossil evidence it is known that tree-sized lycophytes were members of the early forest community. Modern lycophytes, like the one in *Figure 22.7*, are much smaller than their early ancestors. Lycophytes are commonly called club mosses and spike mosses. Their leafy stems resemble moss gametophytes, and their reproductive structures are club or spike shaped. However, unlike mosses, the sporophyte generation of the lycophytes is dominant. It has roots, stems, and small leaflike structures. A single vein of vascular tissue runs through each leaflike structure. The stems of lycophytes may be upright or creeping and have roots growing from the base of the stem.

English Language Learners Pair students with limited English proficiency and students with strong English skills. Have them review together the life cycles of vascular plants—pterophytes, coniferophytes and anthophytes. Ask students to draw and label a diagram that illustrates alternation of generations for one of the vascular plant groups. **L1 ELL COOP LEARN**

Figure 22.8
The sporophyte generation of a horsetail, *Equisetum,* has thin, narrow leaflike structures that circle each joint of the slender, hollow stem. Spore-producing stems are not photosynthetic.

The club moss, *Lycopodium,* is commonly called ground pine because it is evergreen and resembles a miniature pine tree. Some species of ground pine have been collected for decorative uses in such numbers that the plants have become endangered.

Reading Check **Explain** why water limits the long-term survival of non-seed vascular plants.

Adaptations in Arthrophyta

Arthrophytes, or horsetails, represent a second group of ancient vascular plants. Like the lycophytes, early horsetails were tree-sized members of the forest community. Today's arthrophytes are much smaller than their ancestors, usually growing to about 1 m tall. There are only about 15 species in existence, all of the genus *Equisetum.*

The name horsetail refers to the bushy appearance of some species. These plants also are called scouring rushes because they contain silica, an abrasive substance, and were once used to scour cooking utensils. If you run your finger along a horsetail stem, you can feel how rough it is.

Most horsetails, like the ones shown in *Figure 22.8,* are found in marshes, in shallow ponds, on stream banks, and other areas with damp soil. Some species are common in the drier soil of fields and roadsides. The stem structure of horsetails is unlike most other vascular plants; it is ribbed and hollow, and appears jointed. At each joint, there is a whorl of tiny, scalelike leaves.

Like lycophytes, arthrophyte spores are produced in strobili that form at the tips of non-photosynthetic stems. After the spores are released, they can grow into gametophytes with antheridia and archegonia.

Word Origin

strobilus from the Greek word *strobos,* meaning "whirling"; Spore-bearing leaves form a compact cluster called a strobilus.

22.2 NON-SEED VASCULAR PLANTS **583**

Visual Learning
Figure 22.8 Point out that the strobili at the tips of the horsetail stems are formed by leaves with spores. Have students use the appearance of the plant to speculate as to why it was named a horsetail. The plant looks roughly like the tail of a horse.

Enrichment
Kinesthetic Purchase a resurrection plant *(Selaginella lepidophylla).* Have students examine the plant and decide if it is still alive. Soak the plant in water overnight and place it beneath a plant light. Have students observe the plant again and consider if they should revise their original conclusion about whether or not the plant is alive. **L1**

Reading Check Sperm must swim in water to the egg. Without water, the sperm cannot reach the egg.

Word Origin

Using the information given, have students infer how "strobe lights" got their name.

CHALLENGE ACTIVITY

Horsetails Cross Section Have students use information they have read about horsetails to prepare what they believe would be cross-section diagrams of the stem of this plant. Have them add appropriate labels to structures where needed. **L3**

 Indiana Academic Standards

Pages 582–583: B.1.15, B.1.32, B.1.43

Purpose

Students will review the need for water in the process of fertilization among certain plant divisions.

Process Skills

think critically, acquire information, apply concepts, predict

Teaching Strategies

■ Students will have to consult their text to determine the answers to the column marked "Sperm must swim to egg?" You may wish to advise them of the page references to be used in researching the answer.

■ A "yes" or "no" answer is required for the completion of both columns.

■ All correct answers should be "yes."

Thinking Critically

1. yes to all
2. Sperm can swim only in a film of water. Therefore, this column must also be marked with a yes.
3. Water is needed for fertilization. Therefore, these plants must grow in areas with sufficient moisture.
4. wind, insects, birds, mammals

Assessment

Skill Ask students to review the need for a film of water for fertilization of the bryophytes. With the answer in mind, have them hypothesize the general environment surrounding these plants millions of years ago. Use the Performance Task Assessment List for Formulating a Hypothesis in **PASC**, p. 93. **L3**

Problem-Solving Lab 22.2

Apply Concepts

Is water needed for fertilization? Non-seed vascular plants have a number of shared characteristics. One of these characteristics is related to certain requirements needed for reproduction.

Solve the Problem

Examine the following data table. Notice that some of the information is incomplete.

Data Table			
Division	Example	Sperm Must Swim to Egg?	Water Needed for Fertilization?
Lycophyta	Club moss		
Arthrophyta	Horsetail		
Pterophyta	Ferns		

Thinking Critically

1. **Explain** How would you complete the column titled "Sperm Must Swim to Egg?"
2. **Explain** How is the column titled "Water Needed for Fertilization?" related to answers in the previous column?
3. **Describe** What environment is required for the growth of these three plant divisions?
4. **Predict** What other means might be possible for plant sperm delivery to eggs without the use of water?

A The center of this fern, where the fronds form, resembles a bird's nest. Bird's nest ferns often are grown as houseplants.

B The clover fern is an aquatic plant. Its roots grow underground at the muddy bottom of a body of water.

584 THE DIVERSITY OF PLANTS

Adaptations in Pterophyta

According to fossil records, ferns—division Pterophyta—first appeared nearly 375 million years ago during the time when club mosses and horsetails were the predominant members of Earth's plant population. Ancient ferns grew tall and treelike and formed vast forests. Over time, ferns evolved into many species, adapted to different environments, and today are more abundant than club mosses or horsetails.

Ferns range in size from a few meters tall, like tree ferns, to small, floating plants that are only a few centimeters in diameter, such as those in *Figure 22.9*. You may have seen shrub-sized ferns on damp forest floors or along stream banks. Some ferns inhabit dry areas, becoming dormant when moisture is scarce and resuming growth and reproduction only when water is available again. Explore the relationship between water and non-seed vascular plants in the *Problem-Solving Lab* on this page.

Figure 22.9
Today there are about 12 000 species of living ferns. Ferns occupy widely diverse habitats and have a variety of different forms and sizes.

C Many species of tall tree ferns exist in the tropics.

INCLUSION STRATEGIES

Visually Impaired Have visually impaired students examine a frond that has a raised sori on its underside. Have students touch the sori. Ask students what makes up these groups of sori, and if any other vascular non-seed plants have these structures. **L1** **ELL**

Figure 22.10
Fern sporophyte structures include a rhizome, fronds, and roots. **Compare and Contrast** *In general, how do the sizes of fern sporophytes and gametophytes compare?*

A The fern rhizome is an underground stem. Roots and fronds grow from nodes along the rhizome.

Fronds

Root

Rhizome

Fern structures

As with most vascular plants, it is the sporophyte generation of the fern that has roots, stems, and leaves. The part of the fern plant that we most commonly recognize is the sporophyte generation. The gametophyte in most ferns is a thin, flat structure that is independent of the sporophyte. In most ferns, the main stem is underground. This thick, underground stem is called a **rhizome.** It contains many starch-filled cells for storage. The leaves of a fern are called fronds and grow upward from the rhizome, as shown in *Figure 22.10.* The fronds are often divided into leaflets called pinnae, which are attached to a central rachis. Ferns are the first of the vascular plants to have evolved leaves with branching veins of vascular tissue. The branched veins in ferns transport water and food to and from all the cells.

B The form of fern fronds varies from species to species. Some fronds are broad, flat structures and others are finely divided into leaflets. Fronds are supported by a stemlike structure called a rachis.

C New fern fronds are called fiddleheads because their shape is similar to the neck of a violin.

Display
Add pictures of non-seed vascular plants to the bulletin board display.

Chalkboard Activity
Logical-Mathematical Ask students to use information about the number of plant species to prepare a bar graph. On the chalkboard, write the following information.

Bryophyta = 20 000
Hepaticophyta = 6500
Anthocerophyta = 100
Lycophyta = 1150
Arthrophyta = 15
Pterophyta = 11 000

Tell students that these numbers represent the approximate number of living species for each non-seed plant division studied so far. **L2**

PROJECT

Growing Fern Prothallia from Spores:
Kinesthetic Have students grow fern prothallia by following the procedure given. C-Fern spores and growing media are available from biological supplies catalogs. Spores will germinate within five days and prothallia will grow within eight to twelve days. Students can design an experiment to determine the effect of environment on spore germination and prothallia development. These cultures can be maintained and used to study fern reproduction in Chapter 24. **L3**

 Indiana Academic Standards
Pages 584–585: B.1.15, B.1.32, B.1.43

Purpose

Students will observe the release of spores from a sporangium.

Process Skills

compare and contrast, hypothesize, observe and infer

Teaching Strategies

- Ferns with sori may be obtained from a biological supply company.
- Glycerin will cause sporangia to enlarge and break open, releasing spores. This event can be observed if students exercise patience while viewing sporangia under the microscope. Glycerin will cause both fresh and preserved sporangia to break open. Students should avoid skin contact with glycerin.
- Use of a single-edged razor rather than a forceps to lift sori will reduce the amount of rupture to the sporangia. Caution students to use extreme care when working with a razor blade.

Troubleshooting

Make sure that glycerin and water are at room temperature. Also, glycerin must be relatively new—colorless and clear.

Expected Results

Students will see a few spores released from sporangia under water but should see many more in glycerin.

Analysis

1. Spores are more easily seen in glycerin.
2. Glycerin caused the sporangia to break open.
3. Student answers may vary—drying out of sporangium, absorption of water.
4. Student answers may vary—glycerin causes osmotic imbalance.

Experiment

Identifying Fern Sporangia When you admire a fern growing in a garden or forest, you are admiring the plant's sporophyte generation. Upon further examination, you should be able to see evidence of spores being formed. Typically, the evidence you are looking for can be found on the underside of the fern's fronds.

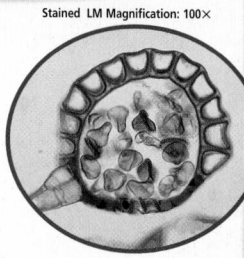

Stained LM Magnification: 100×

Fern sporangium

Procedure

CAUTION: *Use caution when handling a microscope, glass slides, and coverslips.*

1. Place a drop of water and a drop of glycerin at opposite ends of a glass slide.
2. Use forceps to gently pick off one sorus from a frond. Place it in the drop of water and add a coverslip.
3. Add a second sorus to the glycerin and add a coverslip.
4. Observe both preparations under low-power magnification and note any similarities and differences. Look for large sporangia (resembling heads on a stalk) and spores (tiny round bodies released from a sporangium).

Analysis

1. **Compare and Contrast** How does the appearance of spores in water and in glycerin differ?
2. **Explain** How did the glycerin affect the sporangium?
3. **Form a Hypothesis** Explain how sporangia naturally burst.
4. **Form a Hypothesis** Explain how sporangia were affected by glycerin.

Figure 22.11
Sori found on the underside of fern fronds look like brown or rust-colored dust.

B Some species of ferns have sori on the edges of fronds.

A Most sori are found as round clusters. The shape, color, and arrangement of clusters on a frond vary with fern species.

586

Modified Assessment

Knowledge Ask students to describe the events that would follow the release of fern spores. Use the Performance Task Assessment List for Events Chain in **PASC**, p. 163. **L1**

The fern life cycle is representative of other non-seed vascular plants. Fern spores are produced in structures called sporangia. Clusters of sporangia form a structure called a **sorus** (plural, sori). Sori are usually found on the undersides of fronds, as shown in *Figure 22.11*, but in some ferns, spores are borne on modified fronds. Practice your lab skills and learn more about fern spores and sporangia in the *MiniLab* on this page.

Origins of Non-Seed Vascular Plants

The earliest evidence of non-seed vascular plants is found in fossils from early in the Devonian Period, around 375 million years ago. Large tree-sized lycophytes, arthrophytes, and pterophytes were extremely abundant in the warm, moist forests that dominated Earth during the Carboniferous Period. Ancient lycophyte species grew as tall as 30 m. Many of these species of non-seed vascular plants died out about 280 million years ago—a time when Earth's climate was cooler and drier. Today's non-seed

Figure 22.12
The divisions of non-seed vascular plants and nonvascular plants are closely related.

Pterophytes
11 000 species

Lycophytes
1150 species

Psilophytes
6 species

Arthrophytes
15 species

Anthocerophytes
100 species

Bryophytes
20 000 species

Lepidodendron

Calamites

Hepaticophytes
6500 species

Protists

Species numbers are approximate and subject to change pending discoveries or extinctions.

nonvascular plants are much smaller and less widespread in their distribution than their prehistoric ancestors.

The evolution of vascular tissue enabled these plants to live on land and to maintain larger body sizes in comparison with nonvascular plants. As you can infer from *Figure 22.12,* non-seed vascular plants are closely related to nonvascular plants.

Section Assessment

Understanding Main Ideas
1. Explain why most non-seed vascular plants live in moist habitats.
2. Identify and analyze the characteristics of lycophyte and pterophyte sporophytes.
3. Compare and contrast non-seed vascular plants that exist today and those that lived in ancient forest communities.
4. What are the similarities and differences between the sporophyte of a non-seed vascular plant and the sporophyte of a nonvascular plant?
5. List the three structures common to all fern sporophytes and describe the function of each.

Thinking Critically
6. Hypothesize why there are fewer non-seed vascular plants today than there were 300 million years ago. Analyze, critique, and review your hypothesis as to its strengths and weaknesses based on scientific information.

SKILL REVIEW
7. **Observe and Infer** How do you think the presence of silica in the stems of arthrophytes might protect these plants from being eaten by animals? For more help, refer to *Observe and Infer* in the **Skill Handbook.**

 in.bdol.glencoe.com/self_check_quiz

22.2 NON-SEED VASCULAR PLANTS **587**

3 Assess

DAILY INTERVENTION

Check for Understanding
Have students explain how the terms in each of the following groups are related. **L2 ELL**
a. strobilus—arthrophytes
b. prothallus—gametophyte—fern
c. sporophyte—dominant—lycophytes

Reteach
Have students list three characteristics for each division: Lycophyta, Arthrophyta, and Pterophyta. **L1**

Resources
For more practice, use *Reading Essentials for Biology,* Section 22.2.

Extension
Visual-Spatial Have students make a concept map to explain the changes in size in the sporophyte and gametophyte generations of Bryophyta, Lycophyta, and Pterophyta. **L3**

✓ **MODIFIED Assessment**

Knowledge Show students unlabeled photos or drawings of gametophytes and sporophytes of each non-seed vascular division. Have students identify them. **L1**

Indiana Academic Standards
Pages 586–587: B.1.15, B.1.32, B.1.35

Section Assessment

1. Sperm cells swim through a continuous film of water to fertilize egg cells.
2. Lycophytes are small, grow close to the ground, and have stems covered by small, narrow leaves. Roots are present also. Pterophytes have roots underground, stems, and leaves called fronds usually with sori on their undersides. Spores are found within sori.
3. Ancient species were much larger and more abundant.
4. The sporophyte of a vascular plant is larger and not dependent on the gametophyte generation; both sporophytes are diploid.
5. fronds—photosynthesis and reproduction; rhizome—support and storage; roots—anchorage and absorption
6. Earth's climate has changed decreasing the number of areas in which non-seed vascular plants can survive. Students should cite sources of information that support their hypotheses.
7. Stems would be hard to digest and silica might cut delicate digestive tissues.

587

1 Focus

INTERACTIVE CHALKBOARD
PowerPoint® Presentations

Bellringer
Section Focus Transparency 54

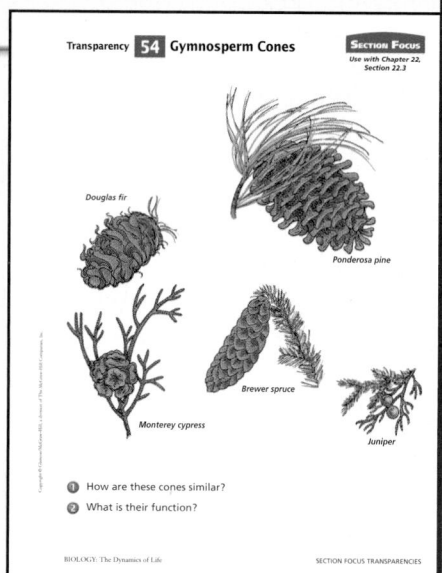

Transparency **54** Gymnosperm Cones

Section Focus
Use with Chapter 22, Section 22.3

Douglas fir

Ponderosa pine

Brewer spruce

Monterey cypress

Juniper

① How are these cones similar?
② What is their function?

BIOLOGY: The Dynamics of Life

SECTION FOCUS TRANSPARENCIES

Using Prior Knowledge

Creative Writing Items derived from seed plants might include books, dyes in clothing, pencils, furniture, baskets, rope, cosmetics, medicines, preservatives, items made of rubber, poster board, file folders, fragrance in candles, sporting equipment, and certain buildings. Tell students that the story they write should reflect their knowledge of seed plant structure and function and should be imaginative and use creativity.

Indiana Academic Standards

Pages 588–589: B.1.15

Section 22.3

Seed Plants

SECTION PREVIEW

Objectives

Identify and analyze the characteristics of seed plants.

Analyze the advantages of seed and fruit production.

Review Vocabulary
reproduction: production of offspring by an organism; a characteristic of all living things (p. 7)

New Vocabulary
pollen grain
ovule
embryo
cotyledon
fruit
deciduous plant
monocotyledon
dicotyledon
annual
biennial
perennial

. . . they're everywhere, they're everywhere . . .

Using Prior Knowledge Items derived from seed plants are a significant part of everyone's life. Cotton fabrics are woven from processed cottonseed fibers. Most paper begins as wood pulp, a product of seed plants. You eat seed plants and drink their products. Other organisms that eat seed plants are part of most diets. Products of seed plants are used in construction and manufacturing. Without seed plants, life on Earth would be impossible for most organisms.

Creative Writing As a class, brainstorm and record items you use that are either seed plants or are derived from seed plants. Identify the seed plant(s) for each item. After reviewing your list, write a story about what your life would be like without seed plants.

These girls are surrounded by items that are derived from seed plants.

What is a seed plant?

Some vascular plants produce seeds in which reduced sporophyte plants are enclosed within a protective coat. The seeds may be surrounded by a fruit or carried on the scales of a cone.

Seed plants produce spores

In seed plants, as in all other plants, spores are produced by the sporophyte generation. These spores develop into the male and female gametophytes. The male gametophyte develops inside a structure called a **pollen grain** that includes sperm cells, nutrients, and a protective outer covering. The female gametophyte, which produces the egg cell, is contained within a sporophyte structure called an **ovule.**

Fertilization and reproduction

The union of the sperm and egg, called fertilization, forms the sporophyte zygote. In most seed plants, this process does not require a continuous film of water as required by nonvascular and non-seed vascular plants. Remember that in non-seed plants, the sperm must swim through a continuous film of water in order to reach eggs in the archegonia of a gametophyte. Because they do not require a continuous film of water for fertilization, seed plants are able to grow and reproduce in a wide variety of habitats that have limited water availability.

RESOURCE MANAGER

Unit 7 FAST FILE Resources
MiniLab Worksheet, p. 32
BioLab Worksheet, pp. 33–34
Reinforcement and Study Guide in English, p. 38
Reinforcement and Study Guide in Spanish, p. 42
Concept Mapping, p. 43

Critical Thinking/Problem Solving, p. 44
Transparency Worksheets, pp. 47, 49–52
Reading Essentials for Biology, Section 22.3
Laboratory Manual, pp. 137–140
🔖 **Section Focus Transparency 54**
🔖 **Basic Concepts Transparencies 34, 35**

After fertilization, the zygote develops into an embryo. An **embryo** is an early stage of development of an organism. In plants, an embryo is the young diploid sporophyte stage of the plant. Embryos of seed plants include one or more cotyledons. **Cotyledons** (kah tuh LEE dunz) usually store or absorb food for the developing embryo. In conifers and many flowering plants, cotyledons are the leaflike structures on the plant's stem when the plant emerges from the soil.

Advantages of seeds

A seed consists of an embryo and its food supply enclosed in a tough, protective coat, as shown in *Figure 22.13*. Seed plants have several important advantages over non-seed plants. The seed contains a supply of food to nourish the young plant during the early stages of growth. This food is used by the plant until its leaves are developed enough to carry out photosynthesis. In conifers and some flowering plants, the embryo's food supply is stored in the cotyledons. The embryo is protected during harsh conditions by a tough seed coat. The seeds of many species are also adapted for easy dispersal to new areas. Then the new plants do not have to compete with their parent plant for sunlight, water, soil nutrients, and living space. You can learn more about seed structure in *MiniLab 22.2*.

Figure 22.13
Seeds exhibit a variety of structural adaptations.

A A tough seed coat protects some pine seeds until favorable conditions exist for germination. As growth begins, the seed coat breaks down and eventually drops off.

B The feathery tuft attached to milkweed seeds aids in their dispersal.

22.3 SEED PLANTS **589**

MiniLab 22.2

Compare and Contrast

Comparing Seed Types Anthophytes are classified into two classes, the monocotyledons (monocots) and dicotyledons (dicots) based on the number of cotyledons.

Procedure

1. Copy the data table shown below.
2. Examine the variety of seeds given to you. Use forceps to gently remove the seed coat or covering from each seed if one is present.
3. Determine the number of cotyledons present. If two cotyledons are present, the seed will easily separate into two equal halves. If one cotyledon is present, it will not separate into halves. Record your observations in the data table.
4. Add a drop of iodine to each seed. Note the color change. Record your observations in the data table. **CAUTION:** *Wash your hands with soap and water after handling chemicals.*

Data Table			
Seed Name	Number of Cotyledons	Monocot or Dicot	Color with Iodine
Lima bean			
Rice			
Pea			
Rye			

Analysis

1. **Observe** Starch turns purple when iodine is added to it. Describe the color change when iodine was added to each seed.
2. **Form a Hypothesis** Why do seeds contain stored starch?

MiniLab 22.2

Purpose

Students will determine how to tell if a seed is from a monocot or dicot plant and test for the presence of starch in seeds.

Process Skills

acquire information, apply concepts, classify, compare and contrast, predict

Teaching Strategies

■ Presoak all seeds overnight so that seed coats come off easily. Do not soak seeds more than 12 h.
■ Supply single-edged razor blades to remove seed coats.
■ Seeds are available from grocery stores, hardware stores (rye), or pet shops (bird feed). Seeds should not be chemically treated.
■ Use a dilute iodine solution when testing for starch (3 g potassium iodide and 1 g iodine to 300 mL of water). Be sure iodine is not old. Place in dropper bottles for ease in student dispensing. Caution students that iodine is toxic and an eye irritant. If it is spilled on skin or clothing it should be washed immediately.
■ Students should wear goggles during this activity.

Expected Results

The lima bean, pea, and sunflower are dicots. All others are monocots. Rice and lima beans will turn purple.

Analysis

1. The seeds turn purple.
2. Starch is food for a growing embryo.

Assessment

Portfolio Have students diagram the lima bean seeds they dissected and color in the area that stained purple. Ask students to write a paragraph about the advantages of seed production beneath their diagram and place their work in their portfolios. Use the Performance Task Assessment List for Scientific Drawing in **PASC**, p. 127. **L2**

Concept Development

Ask students to compare and contrast Gnetophyta with Ginkgophyta. As a means for doing this, have students prepare a chart with the headings "Gnetophyta and Ginkgophyta Similarities" and "Gnetophyta and Ginkgophyta Differences." Have students include comparisons of reproductive structures as well as general traits. Ask them also to include where each plant is found in the world, the number of species alive today, the number of genera present today, and economic uses of these plants. **L2**

Enrichment

Intrapersonal The drug ephedrine has been used by the Chinese for more than five thousand years. It is called *ma huang*, which means "astringent" and "yellow." The words refer to the drug's taste and color. Ephedrine increases cardiac muscle action, raises blood pressure, dilates the pupils, and reduces congestion. Have interested students research this drug and write a report on its uses and its source. **L3**

Figure 22.14
Cycads have a terminal rosette of leaves. Male cones (A) produce pollen grains that are released in great masses into the air. Female cones (B) contain ovules with eggs.

Diversity of seed plants

In some plants, seeds develop on the scales of woody strobili called cones. This group of plants is sometimes referred to as gymnosperms. The term gymnosperm means "naked seed" and is used with these plants because their seeds are not protected by a fruit. The gymnosperm plant divisions you will learn about are Cycadophyta, Ginkgophyta, Gnetophyta, and Coniferophyta.

Flowering plants, also called angiosperms, produce seeds enclosed within a fruit. A **fruit** includes the ripened ovary of a flower. The fruit provides protection for seeds and aids in seed dispersal. The Anthophyta division contains all species of flowering plants.

Figure 22.15
Unlike cycads, the seeds of the ginkgo develop a fleshy outer covering (A). The ginkgo is sometimes called the maidenhair tree because its lobed leaves (B) resemble the fronds of a maidenhair fern.

590

Adaptations in Cycadophyta

About 100 species of cycads exist today, exclusively in the tropics and subtropics. The only present-day species that grows wild in the United States is found in Florida, although you may see cycads cultivated in greenhouses or botanical gardens.

Cycads have male and female reproductive systems on separate plants, as shown in *Figure 22.14*. The male system includes cones that produce pollen grains, which produce motile sperm. Cycads are one of the few seed plants that produce motile sperm. The female system includes cones that produce ovules. The trunks and leaves of many cycads resemble those of palm trees, but cycads and palms are not closely related because palms are anthophytes.

Adaptations in Ginkgophyta

Today, this division is represented by only one living species, *Ginkgo biloba*. All ginkgoes are cultivated trees, and they are not known to exist in the wild. Like cycads, ginkgo male and female reproductive systems are on separate plants. The male ginkgo produces pollen grains in strobiluslike cones that grow from the bases of leaf clusters. Also like cycads, ginkgo pollen grains produce motile sperm. The female ginkgo produces ovules which, when fertilized, develop fleshy, apricot-colored seed coats, as shown in *Figure 22.15*. These soft seed coats give off a foul odor when broken or crushed. Ginkgoes often are planted in urban areas because they tolerate smog and pollution. Gardeners and landscapers usually only plant male gingkoes because they do not produce seeds with soft

Indiana Academic Standards

Pages 590–591: B.1.15

CHALLENGE ACTIVITY

Is it a cycad? Have students imagine that they are traveling through Florida with a friend. Their friend identifies a plant as a cycad that is forming seeds. They search the surrounding area for more cycads but find none within a 20-kilometer radius. Have students write in their journals as many reasons as possible to explain why they believe their friend incorrectly identified the plant as a cycad. Cycads are either male or female; therefore, the male plant must be close to the female to provide pollen. Palms can self-fertilize—being both male and female—and can grow alone and reproduce. Thus it is likely that this plant was a palm. **L3**

seed coats. Do the *BioLab* at the end of this chapter to explore what other trees are planted in urban areas.

✓ **Reading Check** **Infer** what structural adaptations give ginkgoes a tolerance of urban environments.

Adaptations in Gnetophyta

Most living gnetophytes can be found in the deserts or mountains of Asia, Africa, North America, and Central and South America. The division Gnetophyta contains only three genera, which have different structural adaptations to their environments. The genus *Gnetum* is composed of tropical climbing plants. The genus *Ephedra* contains shrublike plants and is the only gnetophyte genus found in the United States. The third genus, *Welwitschia*, is a bizarre-looking plant found only in South Africa. It grows close to the ground, has a large tuberous root, and may live 1000 years. *Ephedra* and *Welwitschia* are pictured in *Figure 22.16*.

Adaptations in Coniferophyta

The sugar pine is one of many familiar forest trees that belong to the division Coniferophyta. The conifers are trees and shrubs with needlelike

Figure 22.16
Most gnetophytes have separate male and female plants.

A Members of the genus *Ephedra* are a source of ephedrine, a medicine used to treat asthma, emphysema, and hay fever.

B *Welwitschia* may live 1000 years. The plant has only two leaves, which continue to lengthen as the plant grows older.

or scalelike leaves. They are abundant in forests throughout the world, and include pine, fir, spruce, juniper, cedar, redwood, yew, and larch.

The reproductive structures of most conifers are produced in cones. Most conifers have male and female cones on different branches of the same tree. The male cones produce pollen. They are small and easy to overlook. Female cones are much larger. They stay on the tree until the seeds have matured. Examples of both types of cones are shown in *Figure 22.17*.

Figure 22.17
Male and female cones of conifers differ in structure and function.

A Male cones are made up of thin papery scales that disintegrate soon after the cones open and shed clouds of pollen grains.

B In many conifers, including spruce, two seeds develop at the base of each of the woody scales that make up a female cone.

591

✓ **Reading Check** To survive in an urban environment, adaptations such as a thick cuticle on leaves and thick bark on the trunk that reduce water loss would be advantageous. Ginkgoes tolerate smog and pollution.

Quick Demo

Examining Cones Provide students with a variety of cones. Ask them to describe what might be found within or upon each wooden scale. Some students may say seeds. Have them gently pry the scales open to reveal the seeds within. **L1** **ELL**

Portfolio

Scientific Names Have students use references to determine and record the scientific names for all conifers listed in this section. **L2** **ELL**

INTERNET BioLab The BioLab at the end of the chapter can be used at this point in the lesson.

CULTURAL DIVERSITY

Importance of Non-flowering Seed Plants: *Linguistic* Many species of non-flowering seed plants play significant roles as timber trees, food plants, and sources of essential oils and soaps in the economies of countries. Initiate a discussion about the cultural importance of the ginkgo tree in China and Japan. *Ginkgo biloba* is the only living represen-

tative of the Ginkgophyta division and no longer exists in the wild. It has been cultivated for thousands of years for use as an ornamental plant in Chinese and Japanese temple gardens. Have students choose different types of non-flowering seed plants and present reports on their economic value or cultural significance in different countries. **L3**

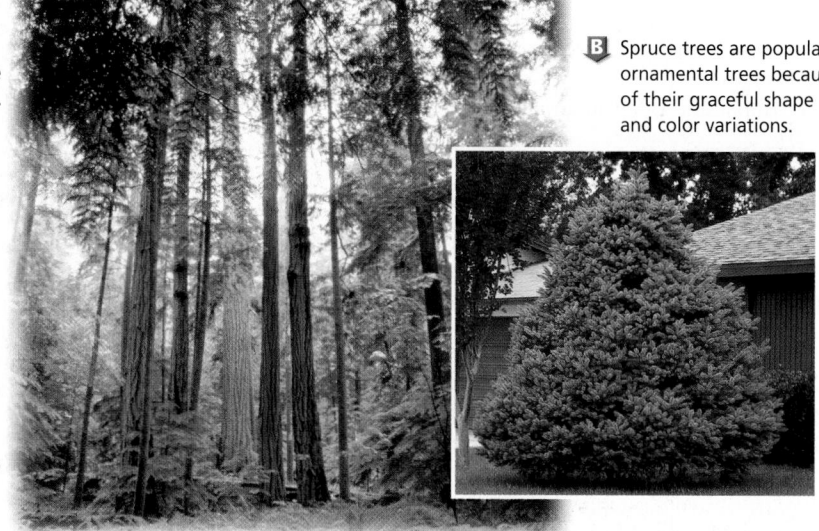

Figure 22.18
Most conifers are evergreen plants.

A The Douglas fir is one of the most important lumber trees in North America. It grows straight and tall, to a height of about 100 m.

B Spruce trees are popular ornamental trees because of their graceful shape and color variations.

Evergreen conifers

Most conifers, like those pictured in *Figure 22.18,* are evergreen plants—plants that retain some of their leaves for more than one year. Although individual leaves drop off as they age or are damaged, the plant never loses all of its leaves at one time.

Plants that retain some of their leaves year-round can photosynthesize whenever favorable environmental conditions exist. This is an advantage in environments where the growing season is short. Another advantage of leaf retention is that a plant's food reserves are not depleted each spring to produce a whole set of new leaves.

Evergreen leaves usually have a heavy coating of cutin, a water-insoluble, waxy material that helps reduce water loss. For conifers, leaf shape—needlelike or scalelike—also helps reduce water loss. To learn more about conifer needles, see *Figure 22.20* on the next page.

Deciduous trees lose their leaves

A few conifers, including larches and bald cypress trees, are deciduous, *Figure 22.19.* **Deciduous plants** drop all their leaves each fall or when water is scarce or unavailable as in the tundra or in deserts. Plants lose most of their water through the leaves; very little is lost through bark or roots. Dropping all leaves is an adaptation for reducing water loss. However, a tree with no leaves cannot photosynthesize and must remain dormant during this time.

Figure 22.19
Some trees, including these bald cypress trees, lose their leaves in the fall as an adaptation for reducing water loss.

Word Origin

deciduous from the Latin word *decidere,* meaning to "fall off"; Deciduous trees drop all of their leaves at the end of the growing season.

592   THE DIVERSITY OF PLANTS

Additional Lab

The Conifer Leaf

Purpose
Students will observe, diagram, and label the structures of a typical conifer leaf.

Materials 🖉
microscope, prepared slide of conifer leaf cross section

Procedure
Give students the following directions.
1. Observe the slide under low power.
2. Diagram what you see. Label the following structures using these descriptions as a guide: (a) cuticle—noncellular layer, thin covering over leaf; (b) epidermis—below cuticle, one cell in thickness; (c) mesophyll (spongy layer)—large cells, thick layer just below epidermis; (d) endodermis—one-cell-layer thick, surrounds large oval central area; (e) palisade layer—many cells in thickness, surrounded by endodermis; (f) vascular tissue—very center of leaf, two types are present.
3. Look again at the leaf using the microscope. Check for evidence of stomata on the epidermis and the presence of

Pine Needles

Figure 22.20
When you look at a snow-covered pine forest, you may be surprised to learn that winter can be considered a dry time for plants. The cold temperature means that the soil moisture is unavailable because it is frozen. The needles of pines have several adaptations that enable the plants to conserve water during the cold dry winter and the dry heat of the summer. **Critical Thinking** *How does the structure of pine needles enhance the survival of conifers during hot and dry summers as well as cold and snowy winters?*

Cross section of needle bundle

Papery sheath

Needle

A Modified leaf cells There are leaf-cell modifications in pine needles that help reduce water loss. The outermost layer of cells, called the epidermis, has a thick, waxy, waterproof coating called a cuticle. Sometimes the cuticle is so thick that it gives needles a grayish color. The layer of cells just below the epidermis has thick cell walls that also help to reduce water loss.

B Bundles of needles The needles of pines usually grow in bundles of two, three, or five needles. The number of needles per bundle and the shape of needles are genetically determined. A papery sheath surrounds the base of each bundle.

Epidermis

Stoma

C Recessed stomata A pine-needle stoma is located in a recessed cavity of the epidermis. This position provides more protection from harsh environmental conditions than on the surface of the epidermis. The result is reduced water loss from leaf tissues.

22.3 SEED PLANTS **593**

Purpose
Students examine the adaptations that enable conifers to survive in harsh environments.

Teaching Strategies
Have students describe common everyday structures or objects that are analogous to structures found in pine needles. Students may correlate cuticle to wax paper, or stomata to skin pores. **L2**

Visual Learning
Have students examine a prepared slide of the cross section of a pine needle. **L1 ELL**

Critical Thinking
Pine needles have several structural adaptations that reduce evaporation. These features help conifers survive times when water is scarce.

Indiana Academic Standards
Pages 592–593: B.1.15, B.1.45

---

several ringlike parts, called resin ducts, in the mesophyll. Add these parts and labels to your diagram.

Analysis
1. How does the cross-section view of a conifer leaf differ from what you would see in a deciduous tree leaf? round rather than flat and long

2. What may be the role of the normally green mesophyll and palisade layers? responsible for food production

3. What is the function of the cuticle and vascular tissue? retain water, transport materials

Assessment
Skill Diagram or describe how a cross-section slice of a conifer leaf would be made. Use the Performance Task Assessment List for Model in **PASC**, p. 123. **L2**

Figure 22.21
A florist's display is a good place to see an assortment of flowering plants.

of people have different viewpoints on preserving this rich habitat.

Fruit production

Anthophyta is unique among plant divisions. It is the only division in which plants have flowers and produce fruits. A fruit develops from a flower's female reproductive structure(s). Sometimes, other flower parts become part of the fruit and, as in pineapples, the fruit develops from more than one flower. A fruit usually contains one or more seeds. One of the advantages of fruit-enclosed seeds is the added protection the fruit provides for the young embryo.

Fruits often aid in the dispersal of seeds. Animals may eat them or carry them off to store for food. Seeds of some species that are eaten pass through the animal's digestive tract unharmed and are distributed as the animal wanders. In fact, some seeds must pass through a digestive tract before they can begin to grow a new plant. Some fruits have structural adaptations that help disperse the seed by wind or water. Some examples of fruits are illustrated in *Figure 22.22*.

Adaptations in Anthophyta

Flowering plants are classified in the division Anthophyta. They are the most well-known plants on Earth with more than 250 000 identified species. See if you are familiar with some of the plants in *Figure 22.21*. Like other seed plants, anthophytes have roots, stems, and leaves. But unlike the other seed plants, anthophytes produce flowers and form seeds enclosed in a fruit. Many different species of flowering plants inhabit tropical forests. As you will discover in *Biology and Society* at the end of this chapter, different groups

Figure 22.22
Fruits exhibit a wide variety of structural adaptations that aid in seed protection and dispersal.

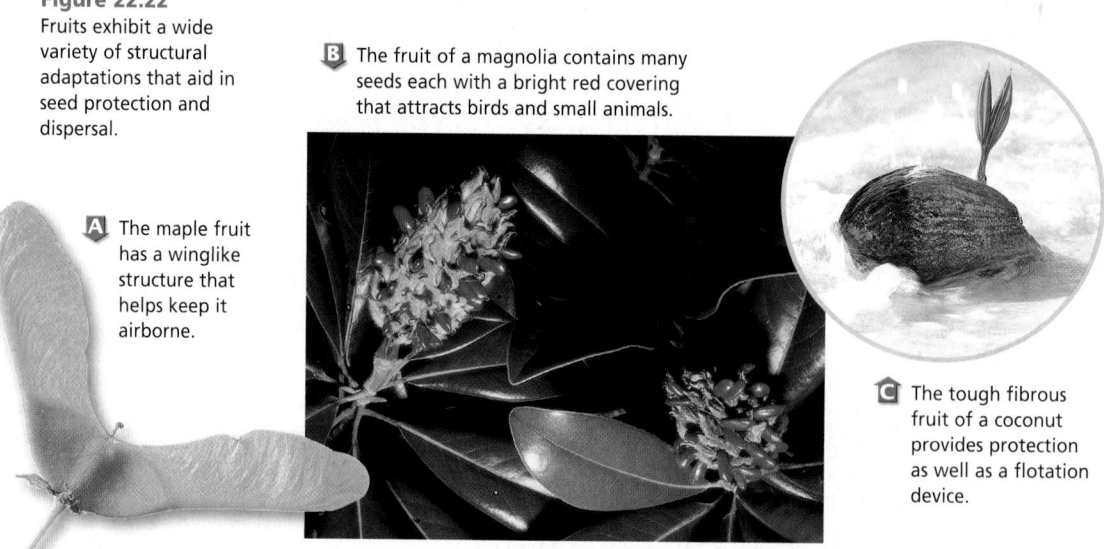

A The maple fruit has a winglike structure that helps keep it airborne.

B The fruit of a magnolia contains many seeds each with a bright red covering that attracts birds and small animals.

C The tough fibrous fruit of a coconut provides protection as well as a flotation device.

594 THE DIVERSITY OF PLANTS

Monocots and dicots

The division Anthophyta is divided into two classes: monocotyledons and dicotyledons. The two classes are named for the number of cotyledons in the seed. **Monocotyledons** (mah nuh kah tuh LEE dunz) have one seed leaf; **dicotyledons** (di kah tuh LEE dunz) have two seed leaves. These two classes often are called monocots and dicots. *Table 22.1* compares the characteristics of monocots and dicots. About 65 000 species of monocots have been identified and include grasses, orchids, lilies, and palms. Identified dicot species number about 185 000. They include nearly all of the familiar shrubs and trees (except conifers), cacti, wildflowers, garden flowers, vegetables, and herbs.

Life spans of anthophytes

Why do some plants live longer than people, and others live only a few weeks? The life span of a plant is genetically determined and reflects strategies for surviving periods of harsh conditions.

Annual plants live for only a year or less. They sprout from seeds, grow, reproduce, and die in a single growing season. Most annuals are herbaceous, which means their stems are green and do not contain woody tissue. Many food plants such as corn, wheat, peas, beans, and squash are annuals, as are many weeds of the temperate garden. Annuals form drought-resistant seeds that can survive the winter.

Biennial plants have life spans that last two years. Many biennials develop large storage roots, such as carrots, beets, and turnips. During the first year, biennials grow many leaves and develop a strong root system. Over the winter, the aboveground portion of the plant dies back, but the roots remain alive. Under ground roots are able to survive conditions that leaves and stems cannot endure. During the second spring, food stored in the root is used to produce new shoots that produce flowers and seeds.

Table 22.1 Distinguishing Characteristics of Monocots and Dicots				
	Seed Leaves	**Vascular Bundles in Leaves**	**Vascular Bundles in Stems**	**Flower Parts**
Monocots	One cotyledon	Usually parallel	Scattered	Multiples of three
Dicots	Two cotyledons	Usually netlike	Arranged in ring	Multiples of four and five

Career Path

Courses in high school: mathematics, electronics, shop courses involving machinery

College: courses in forestry or logging; two-year degree to become a forest technician

Other education sources: on-the-job training

Career Issue

Jobs for traditional lumberjacks are decreasing. One reason is because of increased mechanization. Have students research the pros and cons of using machines instead of traditional logging techniques. Hold a class debate following their research.

For More Information

For more information about working in the logging industry, students can write to:

Society of American Foresters
5400 Grosvenor Lane
Bethesda, MD 20814

Lumberjack

If you like to spend time in the forest, consider a career as a lumberjack or a logging industry worker. Besides being outdoors, you will get lots of exercise.

Skills for the Job

The logging industry now includes many different workers. Cruisers choose which trees to cut. Fallers use chainsaws and axes to cut, or "fell," the chosen trees. Buckers saw off the limbs and cut the trunk into pieces. Logging supervisors oversee these tasks. Other workers turn the tree into logs or wood chips that are used to make paper. After finishing high school, most loggers learn on the job. However, with a two-year degree, you can become a forest technician. A four-year degree qualifies you as a professional forester who manages the forest resources. Most logging jobs are in the Northwest, Northeast, South, and Great Lakes regions.

For more careers in related fields, visit in.bdol.glencoe.com/careers

Perennials live for several years, producing flowers and seeds periodically—usually once each year. Some survive harsh conditions by dropping their leaves or dying back to soil level, while their woody stems or underground storage organs remain intact and dormant. Examples of plants with different lifespans are shown in *Figure 22.23*.

Origins of Seed Plants

Seed plants first appeared about 360 million years ago during the Paleozoic Era. Some seed plants, such as ancient relatives of cycads and ginkgoes, shared Earth's forest with

B Some woody perennials, like brambles, drop their leaves and become dormant during the winter.

Figure 22.23
Anthophytes may be annuals, biennials, or perennials.

A Vegetable gardeners grow biennial parsley for its leaves.

D Herbaceous perennials often have underground storage organs used for overwintering.

C These tomatoes are annual plants.

Indiana Academic Standards

Pages 596–597: B.1.15, B.1.32

596

TECH PREP

Monoculture Tree Farms Monoculture tree farms allow foresters to more efficiently manage growing trees, which are needed to meet the increased demand for wood and wood products. Monoculture refers to the practice of growing only one species of tree. Plants grown in monocultures must be carefully monitored because diseases and insect infestations can occur quickly and devastate the crop. Have interested students research the types of trees harvested by foresters in their region of the United States. Ask students to find out if any of these trees are grown in monoculture stands. Have students give an oral report based on their findings. **L3**

Figure 22.24
The seed plant divisions are closely related to each other.

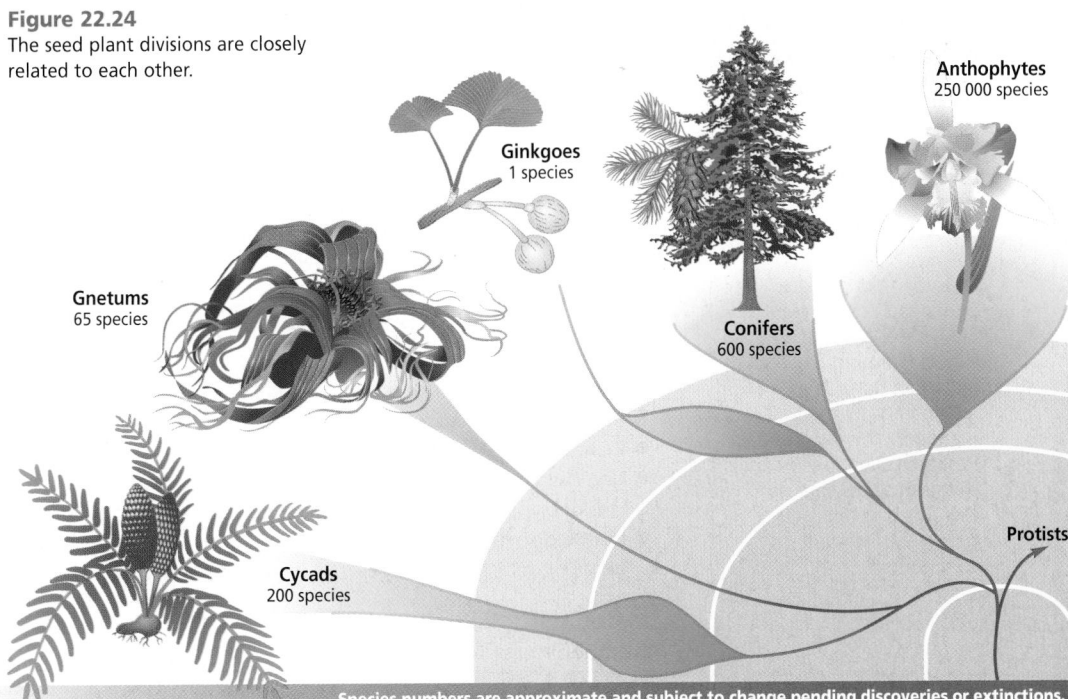

Ginkgoes
1 species

Anthophytes
250 000 species

Gnetums
65 species

Conifers
600 species

Protists

Cycads
200 species

Species numbers are approximate and subject to change pending discoveries or extinctions.

3 Assess

DAILY INTERVENTION

Check for Understanding
Have students explain the differences between: fruits and cones; deciduous and evergreen; monocot and dicot; annual and perennial; and gymnosperm and angiosperm. **L2**

Reteach
Have students name plants that are examples of each of the terms listed in Check for Understanding. **L1**

Resources
For more practice, use *Reading Essentials for Biology,* Section 22.3.

the dinosaurs during the Mesozoic Era. However, about 65 million years ago, most members of the Ginkgophyta died out along with many organisms during a mass extinction.

According to fossil evidence, the first conifers emerged around 250 million years ago. During the Jurassic Period, conifers became predominant forest inhabitants and remain so today.

Anthophytes first appeared about 140 million years ago late in the Jurassic Period of the Mesozoic Era.

The evolutionary relationships among the divisions of vascular seed plants are illustrated in *Figure 22.24.*

Extension

Visual-Spatial Have students prepare an illustrated report that depicts uses for five types of nonflowering seed plants. Have students identify each plant with its common and scientific name. **L3**

✔ Assessment

Skill Have students describe the adaptations for survival that are exhibited by seed plants in a land environment. **L2**

Section Assessment

Understanding Main Ideas
1. Identify two adaptations that help seed plants reproduce on land.
2. Explain why needlelike leaves are an adaptation in climates where water may be a limited resource.
3. What adaptations help make flowering plants so successful?
4. Compare and contrast characteristics of anthophytes and coniferophytes.

Thinking Critically
5. Infer why the development of the seed might have affected the lives of herbivorous animals living in Earth's ancient forests.

SKILL REVIEW
6. **Get the Big Picture** Compare the formation of a spore in ferns and a seed in conifers. For more help, refer to *Get the Big Picture* in the **Skill Handbook.**

in.bdol.glencoe.com/self_check_quiz

22.3 SEED PLANTS **597**

Section Assessment

1. Seeds contain a food supply for the developing embryo and protect the embryo from harsh conditions.
2. The thick cuticle, reduced surface area, and sunken stomata limit evaporation.
3. Flowering plants produce fruits that protect the seeds and aid in seed dispersal.

4. Anthophytes produce flowers and fruits. Coniferophytes do not. They both produce seeds.
5. Seeds contain a high-energy food source. By eating seeds, herbivores could obtain more energy per gram of food. Also, seeds ensured the survival of plants in drier environments where

spore-reproducing plants could not survive. Therefore, herbivores' food supply increased in drier environments.
6. Fern spores are produced in sporangia. Clusters of sporangia form sori that are found on the pinnae. Conifer seeds are produced on the scales of the cone.

INTERNET BioLab

Time Allotment

two class periods (if enough computers are available in class); two hours if done at home

Process Skills

acquire information, analyze information, collect data, define operationally, think critically, draw a conclusion, interpret data, apply concepts

PREPARATION

Prepare different tree lists in advance for your students. This may help to speed up the initial student selection process.

Alternative Materials

If internet resources are not available, students can still complete this BioLab through conventional library research using books and periodicals.

INTERNET BioLab

Before You Begin

Imagine that you are employed as a forester in a city's department of Urban Planning. You have just been handed an assignment by the city manager. The assignment? Research the types of trees that would be most suitable for planting along the streets of your community.

Researching Trees on the Internet

PREPARATION

Problem

Use the Internet to find different tree species that would be suitable for planting along the streets in your community.

Objectives

In this BioLab, you will:
- **Research** the characteristics of five different tree species.
- **Use the Internet** to collect and compare data from other students.
- **Conclude** which tree species would be most suitable for planting along the streets in your community.

Materials

Internet access

Skill Handbook

If you need help with this lab, refer to the **Skill Handbook.**

PROCEDURE

1. Make a copy of the data table.
2. Pick five tree species that you wish to research. (Note: Your teacher may provide you with suggestions if necessary.)
3. Visit **in.bdol.glencoe.com/internet_lab** to find links to information needed for this BioLab.
4. Record the information in your data table.

California redbud, *Cercis occidentalis*

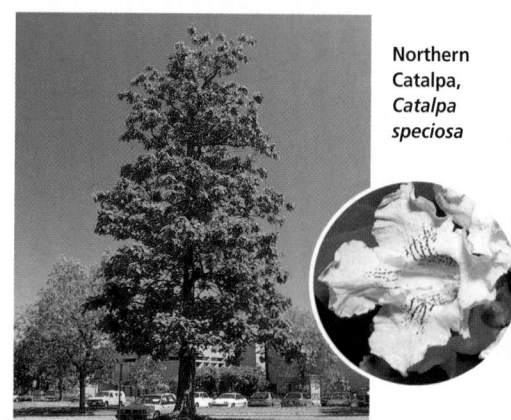

Northern Catalpa, *Catalpa speciosa*

PROCEDURE

Teaching Strategies

- Suggest to students that they modify the space allowed in the data table to accommodate information or diagrams. The category marked "Additional Information" could be used to describe trees' tolerances to pollutants.

- Encourage students to complete this BioLab at home as a homework assignment if they have computers with Internet access available there.
- Limit the selection of conifers to one or two species out of the five selected for study.

- To find this Internet BioLab, visit **in.bdol.glencoe.com/internet_lab**. Click on Chapter Resources, then the chapter number, and then Internet BioLab.

Data Table

	1	2	3	4	5
Tree name (common name)					
Scientific name					
Division					
Soil/Water preference					
Temperature tolerance					
Height at maturity					
Rate of growth					
General shape					
Diseases/Pests					
Special care					
Deciduous or evergreen					
Additional information					

Flowering dogwood,
Cornus florida

Southern Magnolia,
Magnolia grandiflora

ANALYZE AND CONCLUDE

1. **Define Operationally** Explain the difference between trees classified as either Coniferophyta or Anthophyta.

2. **Analyze** Was the information provided on the Internet helpful in completing your data table? Explain your answer.

3. **Think Critically** What do you consider to be the most important characteristic when deciding on the most suitable tree for your community? Explain your answer.

4. **Use the Internet** Using the information you gathered from the Internet, which tree species would most likely be the:

   a. most suitable along a street in your community? Explain your answer.

   b. least suitable along a street in your community? Explain your answer.

5. **Apply** Explain why tree selections would differ if your community were located in:

   a. a desert biome

   b. a taiga biome

   c. a tropical rain forest biome

Share Your Data

Classify Find this BioLab using the link below, and post your findings in the table provided for this activity. Using the additional data from other students on the Internet, prepare a dichotomous key that allows you to identify your five trees.

 in.bdol.glencoe.com/internet_lab

ANALYZE AND CONCLUDE

1. Coniferophytes are cone-bearing trees, seeds formed on cones; anthophytes are flowering plants, seeds formed within a fruit.

2. Student answers will vary. The Internet (if used) will provide information for the data table.

3. Student answers will vary. Students may select rate of growth, temperature tolerance, or disease resistance as the most important qualities.

4. **a.** Student answers will vary.

   b. Student answers will vary.

5. **a.** High summer temperature and drought tolerance would be important factors.

   b. Long periods of drought during the summer would be an important factor.

   c. Temperature tolerance during the winter would be an important factor.

Share Your Data

To navigate the Internet BioLabs, go to **in.bdol.glencoe.com/ internet_lab**. Make sure students' keys are truly dichotomous and are logical.

Data and Observations

Student data tables will vary depending on the initial trees selected for study.

Assessment

Skill Provide students with data on two or three tree species. Ask them to determine the best national site for these tree species. Use the Performance Task Assessment List for Analyzing the Data in **PASC**, p. 99. **L2**

599

600

Biology and Society

Environment: Keeping a Balance

Tropical rain forests are Earth's most biologically diverse ecosystems. Many people live within areas of tropical rain forests and most depend directly or indirectly on the extraction of resources from them through mining, growing crops, ranching, and timber harvesting. This has resulted in the loss of large areas of these forests each year.

Agriculture in rain forests Traditional methods of growing crops, ranching, and tree harvesting involved clearing land of tropical rain forest vegetation in order to provide space to grow crops, allow plants to grow as food for cattle, or to remove the most economically valuable trees. Often referred to as slash-and-burn agriculture, the land was cleared then used for agriculture until the soil's nutrients were depleted, after which it was abandoned to allow the regrowth of trees and other plants. This system worked as long as the removal rate of the forest vegetation did not exceed the recovery rate of the forest vegetation.

Logged rain forest

A sustainable harvest Thousands of plant species grow in tropical rain forests, yet only a few species are considered valuable. Many ecologists and conservation groups are working to promote more sustainable alternatives to obtaining resources from tropical rain forests. Agroforestry—an ecological approach to land use that integrates the use of trees on individual farms and in entire regions—has been used for centuries to manage land for trees, crops, and animals together. The philosophy behind agroforestry is to maintain more of the tropical rain forest's structure and function while providing food and other resources for the farmer, such as wood that can be used or sold. In many areas where trees have been removed, new trees have been planted that do not compete with crops. This creates a more diverse and sustainable system. While agroforestry does not prevent the loss of species, it is hoped that by using more sustainable agricultural methods less tropical rain forest will be slashed and burned in the future.

Perspectives Only a small fraction of the world's tropical rain forests are managed sustainably. Efforts are being made to promote agroforestry and other agricultural practices. However, not all trees and crops are suited to an agroforestry system, and agroforestry still results in a reduction of biodiversity because many plants are removed from the understory to prevent competition with crops.

Forming Your Opinion

Analyze Brainstorm in groups for reasons why some trees may be suited for agroforestry while others are not. Discuss the link between agriculture and the loss of tropical forests. How might more sustainable agricultural methods decrease rain forest destruction? Analyze, critique, and review your explanations as to their strengths and weaknesses using scientific information and evidence.

 To find out more about rain forest destruction and sustainable forestry, visit
in.bdol.glencoe.com/biology_society

STUDY GUIDE

Section 22.1

Nonvascular Plants

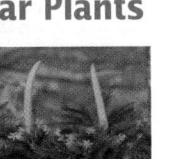

Key Concepts

- Nonvascular plants lack vascular tissue and reproduce by producing spores. The gametophyte generation is dominant.
- There are three divisions of nonvascular plants: Bryophyta, Hepaticophyta, and Anthocerophyta.

Vocabulary

archegonium (p. 578)
antheridium (p. 578)

Section 22.2

Non-Seed Vascular Plants

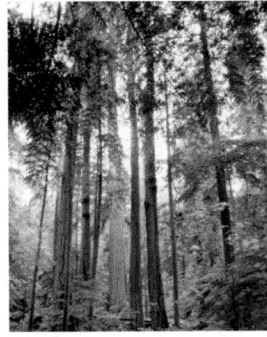

Key Concepts

- The non-seed vascular plants were predominant in Earth's ancient forests. They are represented by modern species.
- Vascular tissues provide the structural support that enables vascular plants to grow taller than nonvascular plants.
- There are three divisions of non-seed vascular plants: Lycophyta, Arthrophyta, and Pterophyta.

Vocabulary

prothallus (p. 582)
rhizome (p. 585)
sorus (p. 586)
strobilus (p. 582)

Section 22.3

Seed Plants

Key Concepts

- Seeds contain a supply of food to nourish the young plant, protect the embryo during harsh conditions, and provide methods of dispersal.
- There are four divisions of vascular plants that produce naked seeds: Cycadophyta, Gnetophyta, Ginkgophyta, and Coniferophyta.
- Anthophytes produce flowers and have seeds enclosed in a fruit.
- Fruits provide protection for the seeds and aid in their dispersal.
- Anthophytes are either monocots or dicots based on the number of cotyledons present in the seed.
- Anthophytes may be annuals, biennials, or perennials.

Vocabulary

annuals (p. 595)
biennials (p. 595)
cotyledon (p. 589)
deciduous plant (p. 592)
dicotyledons (p. 595)
embryo (p. 589)
fruit (p. 590)
monocotyledons (p. 595)
ovule (p. 588)
perennials (p. 596)
pollen grain (p. 588)

FOLDABLES™
Study Organizer To help you review the diversity of plants, use the Organizational Study Fold on page 577.

 in.bdol.glencoe.com/vocabulary_puzzlemaker

CHAPTER 22 ASSESSMENT **601**

Key Concepts

Summary statements can be used by students to review the major concepts of the chapter.

 Biology Online

Visit in.bdol.glencoe.com
/self_check_quiz
/vocabulary_puzzlemaker
/chapter_test
/standardized_test

VOCABULARY PUZZLEMAKER

 For additional help with vocabulary, have students access the Vocabulary PuzzleMaker online at in.bdol.glencoe.com/ vocabulary_puzzlemaker

FOLDABLES™

Have students use their Foldables to review the content of Section 22.1.

Use the ExamView®Pro Test Bank CD-ROM to:

- Create **multiple versions** of tests
- Create **modified** tests with one mouse click for **inclusion** students
- **Edit** existing questions and **add** your own questions
- Build tests aligned with state standards using built-in **State Curriculum Tags**
- Change **English** tests to **Spanish** with one mouse click and vice versa

 Indiana Academic Standards

Pages 600–601: B.1.15, B.1.41

Questions and answers have been aligned and verified by The Princeton Review.

Vocabulary Review

1. rhizome
2. archegonium
3. prothallus
4. cotyledon
5. biennial

Understanding Key Concepts

6. C	10. B
7. D	11. D
8. A	12. A
9. C	13. D

Constructed Response

14. Fertilization may occur at any time and in drier environments because it is no longer dependent on water.

15. Needlelike leaves are adaptations to the northern biomes where it is cold and water not available during the winter. Cycads and ginkgoes live in temperate or tropical biomes in which water loss from a broad leaf can be quickly replaced by water in the habitat. Greater leaf surface areas allow for greater food production, which is needed when a plant does not have a period of reduced activity or dormancy.

16. The sporophyte will have more of a chance of survival when attached to the gametophyte. It cannot be washed away in water as it is attached to a gametophyte anchored in the soil.

Thinking Critically

17. By being recessed, stomata are sheltered from drying winds and shaded from the heat of sunlight, thus, helping to reduce water loss.

602

Vocabulary Review

Review the Chapter 22 vocabulary words listed in the Study Guide on page 601. Match the words with the definitions below.

1. the thick underground stem of a fern
2. gametophyte's female reproductive structure in which eggs develop
3. gametophyte of a fern
4. seed structure that stores food for the embryo
5. anthophyte that has a life span of two years

Understanding Key Concepts

6. Bryophytes, hepaticophytes, and anthocerophytes are the three divisions of _____ plants.
   A. vascular   C. nonvascular
   B. seed   D. evergreen

7. Lycophytes include _____.
   A. ferns   C. mosses
   B. conifers   D. club mosses

8. Anthophytes and coniferophytes are divisions that are BOTH _____.
   A. vascular and seed-producing
   B. vascular and non-seed
   C. nonvascular and non-seed
   D. nonvascular and seed-producing

9. Vascular tissue is important to a plant because it _____.
   A. anchors it in the soil
   B. reproduces
   C. transports water and nutrients
   D. photosynthesizes

10. The plant in the photograph is a(n) _____.
    A. Anthophyte
    B. Pterophyte
    C. Arthrophyte
    D. Gnetophyte

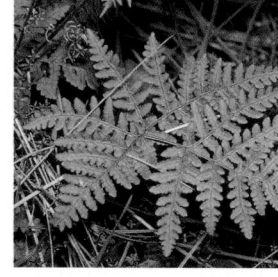

11. The gametophyte generation is dominant in which of the following plants?
    A. pine trees   C. apple trees
    B. ferns   D. mosses

12. Which of the following is NOT a part of a seed?
    A. gametophyte   C. food supply
    B. protective coat   D. embryo

13. An orange tree would be classified in the same division as which of the following?
    A. pine tree   C. cycad
    B. moss   D. sunflower

Constructed Response

14. **Open Ended** Evaluate the significance of the adaptation—fertilization that does not require a film of water for sperm to reach the egg—for land plants.

15. **Open Ended** Cycads and ginkgoes do not have needlelike leaves like pines and spruces do. For these coniferophytes, explain the significance of leaf shape as an adaptation to the biomes in which they grow.

16. **Open Ended** What might be the advantage of having the sporophyte dependent on the gametophyte?

Thinking Critically

17. **Observe and Infer** Examine the needle cross section in *Figure 22.20*. Infer how the position of stomata helps reduce water loss.

18. **REAL WORLD BIOCHALLENGE** Forests are essential to our economy and for the preservation of biodiversity. Visit in.bdol.glencoe.com to investigate what is being done to preserve biodiversity of forest resources near you. Make a map of one area and indicate where projects are planned or are in place that help preserve biodiversity.

19. **Concept Map** Construct a concept map that shows the relationships among the following terms: eggs, prothallus, archegonia, antheridia, sperm, fern, gametophyte.

 in.bdol.glencoe.com/chapter_test

18. Answers will vary depending on the region and forest selected.

RUBRIC

For more help evaluating open-ended assessment questions, see the rubric on p. 9T.

End-of-Course
Assessment Practice

All questions aligned and verified by The Princeton Review

Part 1 Multiple Choice

Russian olive is an introduced, nonnative seed plant that is crowding out native plants in certain parts of the United States. Study the graph below and answer questions 20–22.

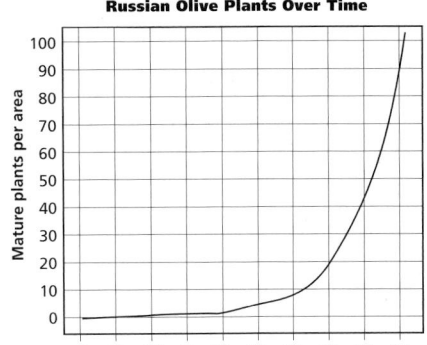

Russian Olive Plants Over Time

20. How many years does it take for there to be 50 mature Russian olive plants in an area?
   A. 45   **C.** 40
   B. 100   **D.** none of these

21. After an area has 50 mature plants, how many years must pass before there are 100 mature plants?
   A. 45   **C.** 15
   B. 5   **D.** 25

22. The general pattern of development and establishment of Russian olive plants in an area can be described as _____.
   A. fast for many years then slow thereafter
   B. slow for many years then a rapid increase
   C. steady throughout its time in an area
   D. very rapid from the start

Use the graph below to answer questions 23 and 24.

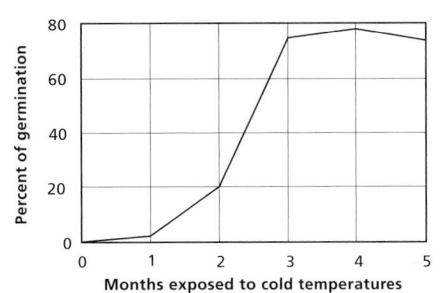

Seed Germination Rate After Exposure to Cold

23. What would be the minimum time you would keep the experimental seeds under refrigeration before planting?
   A. 1 month   **C.** 6 months
   B. 3 months   **D.** 80 months

24. How long does it take to get 50 percent germination?
   A. 2½ months   **C.** 1 month
   B. 6 months   **D.** 4 months

Part 2 Constructed Response/Grid In

Record your answers on your answer document.

25. **Open Ended** Which two plant divisions do you think are the most important? Why?

26. **Open Ended** On gametophytes of certain mosses, the outer surfaces of cells are curved, as shown to the right. Describe the environment of mosses with such an adaptation.

 ← Light →

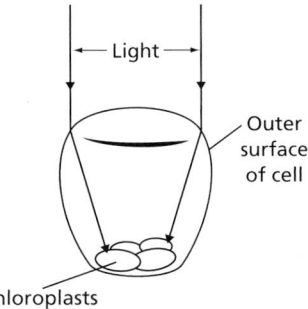

Outer surface of cell

Chloroplasts

End-of-Course Assessment Practice

20. C   22. B
21. B   23. B   24. A
25. flowering plants because of the food, fiber, and other materials they supply for humans and animals; conifers because of their economic and medicinal value for humans and the habitat and niches provided for numerous plants and animals
26. The curved surfaces act like lenses, focusing light on the chloroplasts. These mosses can grow in low-light environments.

FAST FILE

Answer Sheet A practice answer sheet can be found on p. 59 of *Unit 7 FAST FILE Resources.*

19.

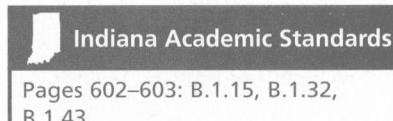

Fern —spores produce the→ gametophyte —that is called the→ prothallus —that contains→ antheridia —that produces→ sperm.
                                                               prothallus —that contains→ archegonia —that produces→ eggs.

Indiana Academic Standards

Pages 602–603: B.1.15, B.1.32, B.1.43

Chapter 23 Organizer

Section Objectives	National Science Standards	State/Local Standards	Advanced Lab and Demo Planning
Section 23.1 1 session, 1/2 block 1. **Identify** the major types of plant cells. 2. **Distinguish** among the functions of the different types of plant tissues.	UCP.1, UCP.2, UCP.5; A.1, A.2; C.1, C.4, C.5; F.3	**Indiana Standards** B.1.1, B.1.2, B.1.3, B.1.15	**Student Labs:** MiniLab 23.1, p. 608: celery stalk, 2 glass slides, water, coverslip, microscope Additional Lab, p. 608: garden trowel, metric balance Problem-Solving Lab 23.1, p. 611 Internet BioLab, p. 626: See materials below. **Teacher Demonstration:** Quick Demo, p. 606: apple, celery, pear
Section 23.2 1 session, 1 block 3. **Identify and compare** the structures of roots, stems, and leaves. 4. **Describe and compare** the functions of roots, stems, and leaves.	UCP.1, UCP.2, UCP.5; A.1, A.2; C.1, C.4–6	**Indiana Standards** B.1.1, B.1.15	**Student Labs:** Problem-Solving Lab 23.2, p. 619 MiniLab 23.2, p. 620: leaves of 5 different plants or preserved leaves, paper, pencil **Teacher Demonstration:** Quick Demo, p. 615: iodine stain, potato
Section 23.3 2 sessions, 1 block 5. **Identify** the major types of plant hormones. 6. **Identify and analyze** the different types of plant responses.	UCP.1, UCP.2, UCP.5; A.1, A.2; B.3; C.1, C.4–6; E.2; G.1–3	**Indiana Standards** B.1.1, B.1.7, B.1.15, B.1.18, B.1.45	**Student Lab:** Problem-Solving Lab 23.3, p. 624 **Teacher Demonstration:** Quick Demo, p. 623: broadleaf houseplants
End of Chapter Assessment Student Edition **Study Guide,** p. 629 **Content Assessment,** pp. 630–631		**Indiana Standards** B.1.15, B.1.16, B.1.37	**Student Lab:** Internet BioLab, p. 626: microscope, glass slide, water, dropper, single-edged razor blade, ruler, coverslip, green leaf from an onion plant

Key to Teaching Strategies

L1 Level 1 activities should be appropriate for students with learning difficulties.

L2 Level 2 activities should be within the ability range of all students.

L3 Level 3 activities are designed for above-average students.

ELL ELL activities should be within the ability range of English Language Learners.

COOP LEARN Cooperative Learning activities are designed for small group work.

Legend

 Transparency   CD-ROM   MP3   Videocassette   DVD

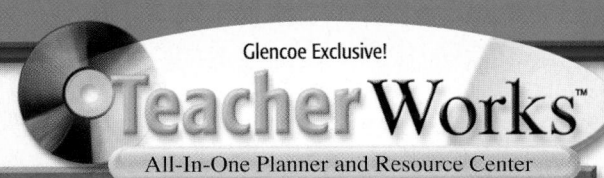

Glencoe Exclusive!
TeacherWorks™
All-In-One Planner and Resource Center

Reproducible Masters and Transparencies	Technology

Reproducible Masters and Transparencies

Unit 7 *FAST FILE* Resources
MiniLab Worksheet, p. 63
BioLab Worksheet, pp. 65–66
Reinforcement and Study Guide in English, p. 67
Reinforcement and Study Guide in Spanish, p. 71
Concept Mapping, p. 75
Transparency Worksheets, pp. 77, 85–86
Reading Essentials for Biology,
  Section 23.1
Section Focus Transparency 55
Reteaching Skills Transparency 32

Unit 7 *FAST FILE* Resources
MiniLab Worksheet, p. 64
Reinforcement and Study Guide in English,
  pp. 68–69
Reinforcement and Study Guide in Spanish,
  pp. 72–73
Critical Thinking/Problem Solving, p. 76
Transparency Worksheets, pp. 78, 81–84, 87–90
Reading Essentials for Biology,
  Section 23.2
Laboratory Manual, pp. 141–146, 147–150
Section Focus Transparency 56
Basic Concepts Transparencies 36, 37
Reteaching Skills Transparencies 33, 34

Unit 7 *FAST FILE* Resources
Reinforcement and Study Guide in English, p. 70
Reinforcement and Study Guide in Spanish, p. 74
Transparency Worksheet, p. 79
Reading Essentials for Biology,
  Section 23.3
Section Focus Transparency 57

Unit 7 *FAST FILE* Resources
Chapter Assessment, pp. 91–96
Student Recording Sheet, p. 97
The Princeton Review **Reviewing Biology,** pp. 45–46

Technology

Interactive Chalkboard CD-ROM: Section 23.1 Presentation
TeacherWorks™ CD-ROM
Guided Reading Audio Summaries MP3

Interactive Chalkboard CD-ROM: Section 23.2 Presentation
TeacherWorks™ CD-ROM
Guided Reading Audio Summaries MP3
Virtual Labs CD-ROM
Virtual Lab: Plant Transpiration

Interactive Chalkboard CD-ROM: Section 23.3 Presentation
TeacherWorks™ CD-ROM
Guided Reading Audio Summaries MP3

Interactive Chalkboard:
Chapter 23 Assessment
MindJogger Videoquizzes DVD/VHS
ExamView® Pro Test Bank CD-ROM
TeacherWorks™ CD-ROM
Succeeding on National Standards CD-ROM

in.bdol.glencoe.com
/self_check_quiz
/vocabulary_puzzlemaker
/chapter_test
/standardized_test

Indicates materials created specifically for Indiana.

Short on Time?

BIODIGEST The BioDigest at the end of this unit can be used as a(n):
- preview to introduce important unit concepts.
- overview if time does not permit teaching the entire chapter.
- review of key unit concepts.

Understanding the Photo

Plants are composed of cells, tissues, and organs. Seed plants have three basic cell types: parenchyma, with thin walls found throughout the plant; collenchyma, with unevenly thickened walls found in growing parts of plants; and sclerenchyma with thick walls found in supporting tissue. Plants have four basic kinds of tissues: dermal, meristematic, ground, and vascular—all of which make up the basic organs: roots, stems, and leaves.

What You'll Learn

- You will describe and compare the major types of plant cells and tissues.
- You will identify and analyze the structure and functions of roots, stems, and leaves.
- You will identify plant hormones and determine the nature of plant responses.

Why It's Important

Humans and the organisms around them, including plants, share an environment. By knowing about plant structure and how plants function, you can better understand how humans and plants interact.

Understanding ▶ the Photo

These pitcher plants look different from the plants that surround them. However, they and the other plants have similar plant systems and subsystems.

 Biology Online

Visit in.bdol.glencoe.com to
- study the entire chapter online
- access Web Links for more information and activities on plant structure and function
- review content with the Interactive Tutor and self-check quizzes

604

Plant Structure and Function

 Two-Minute Chapter Launcher

Activity Divide students into groups. Give each group of students a potted plant. Ask students to examine stems and leaves. Demonstrate how to remove the plant from the pot to examine the roots. Instruct students not to disturb the root ball, and show them how to return the plant to the pot. They should infer the functions of each plant organ. **L2**

Section 23.1

Plant Cells and Tissues

Indiana Standards Standard B.1.1 Recognize that and explain how the many cells in an individual can be very different from one another, even though they are all descended from a single cell and thus have essentially identical genetic instructions. Understand that different parts of the genetic instructions are used in different types of cells and are influenced by the cell's environment and the past history.

SECTION PREVIEW

Objectives
Identify the major types of plant cells.

Distinguish among the functions of the different types of plant tissues.

Review Vocabulary
vacuole: membrane-bound, fluid-filled space in the cytoplasm of cells used for the temporary storage of materials (p. 183)

New Vocabulary
parenchyma
collenchyma
sclerenchyma
epidermis
stomata
guard cell
trichome
xylem
tracheid
vessel element
phloem
sieve tube member
companion cell
meristem
apical meristem
vascular cambium
cork cambium

FOLDABLES™
Study Organizer

Plants Cells and Tissues Make the following Foldable to help you compare the types of plant cells and tissues.

STEP 1 **Fold** a vertical sheet of paper in half from top to bottom.

STEP 2 **Fold** in half from side to side with the fold at the top.

STEP 3 **Unfold** the paper once. **Cut** only the fold of the top flap to make two tabs.

STEP 4 **Turn** the paper vertically and **label** the front tabs as shown.

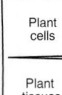

Plant cells

Plant tissues

Identify and Describe As you read Chapter 23, identify and describe the types of plant cells and plant tissues under each tab.

Types of Plant Cells

Like all organisms, plants are composed of cells. Plant cells are different from animal cells because they have a cell wall, a central vacuole, and can contain chloroplasts. *Figure 23.1* shows a typical plant cell. Plants, just like other organisms, are composed of different cell types.

Central vacuole

Chloroplast

Cell wall

Figure 23.1
Plant cells have several distinguishing features, such as a cell wall, chloroplasts, and a large central vacuole.

Parenchyma

Parenchyma (puh RENG kuh muh) cells are the most abundant kind of plant cell. They are found throughout the tissues of a plant. These spherical cells have thin, flexible cell walls. Most parenchyma cells usually have a large central vacuole, which sometimes contains a fluid called sap.

23.1 PLANT CELLS AND TISSUES **605**

Section 23.1

1 Focus

INTERACTIVE CHALKBOARD
PowerPoint® Presentations

Bellringer
Section Focus Transparency 55

Transparency **55** Plant Cells and Tissues

Section Focus
Use with Chapter 23, Section 23.1

Tree cross section

Apple cross section

Leaf cross section

① What different types of tissues are found in these plants?
② What is the function of these different tissues?

BIOLOGY: The Dynamics of Life

SECTION FOCUS TRANSPARENCIES

INTERACTIVE CHALKBOARD
with Image Bank

PowerPoint® Presentations
This CD-ROM is an editable Microsoft® PowerPoint® presentation that includes:
- Section presentations
- Section checks
- Image bank
- Hot links to Biology Online
- All transparencies

FOLDABLES™
For an additional Foldables activity idea, see the Chapter 23 Foldables page in *Unit 7 FAST FILE Resources.*

RESOURCE MANAGER

Unit 7 *FAST FILE* Resources
MiniLab Worksheet, p. 63
BioLab Worksheet, pp. 65–66
Reinforcement and Study Guide in English, p. 67
Reinforcement and Study Guide in Spanish, p. 71

Concept Mapping, p. 75
Transparency Worksheets, pp. 77, 85–86
Reading Essentials for Biology, Section 23.1
Section Focus Transparency 55
Reteaching Skills Transparency 32

Indiana Academic Standards

Pages 604–605: B.1.2, B.1.3, B.1.15

605

2 Teach

Cell Types Provide students with slices of apple, celery, and pear. Point out to the students that the soft fleshy tissue of each specimen is composed mostly of parenchyma cells, the stringy fibers in the celery are composed of collenchyma cells, and the gritty particles in the pear are clusters of sclerenchyma cells.

✓**Reading Check** Parenchyma cells are thin-walled and store sap in vacuoles. Collenchyma cells are long with unevenly thick walls that provide support for the plant. Sclerenchyma cells are very thick-walled and provide support and are also associated with transport of cellular materials.

Word Origin

par- from the Greek word *para*, meaning "beside"

coll- from the Greek word *kolla*, meaning "glue"

scler- from the Greek word *skleros*, meaning "hard"

Parenchyma, collenchyma, and sclerenchyma are all types of plant tissues.

Figure 23.2
Plants are composed of three basic types of cells, which are shown here stained with dyes.

Parenchyma cells, as shown in *Figure 23.2A*, have two main functions: storage and food production. The large vacuole found in these cells can be filled with water, starch grains, or oils. The edible portions of many fruits and vegetables are composed mostly of parenchyma cells. Parenchyma cells also can contain numerous chloroplasts that produce glucose during photosynthesis.

Collenchyma

Collenchyma (coh LENG kuh muh) cells are long cells with unevenly thickened cell walls, as illustrated in *Figure 23.2B*. The structure of the cell wall is important because it allows the cells to grow. The walls of collenchyma cells can stretch as the cells grow while providing strength and support. These cells are arranged in tubelike strands or cylinders that provide support for surrounding tissue. The long tough strands you may have noticed in celery are composed of collenchyma.

Sclerenchyma

The walls of **sclerenchyma** (skle RENG kuh muh) cells are very thick and rigid. At maturity, these cells often die. Although their cytoplasm disintegrates, their strong, thick cell walls remain and provide support for the plant. Sclerenchyma cells can be seen in *Figure 23.2C*. Two types of sclerenchyma cells commonly found in plants are fibers and sclerids (SKLER idz). Fibers are long, thin cells that form strands. They provide support and strength for the plant and are the source of fibers used for making linen and rope. A type of fiber is associated with vascular tissue, which you will learn about later in this section. Sclerids are irregularly shaped and usually found in clusters. They are the gritty texture of pears and a major component of the pits found in peaches and other fruits.

✓**Reading Check** **Compare and contrast** the structures and functions of parenchyma, collenchyma, and sclerenchyma.

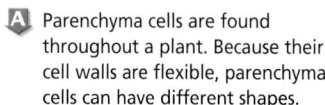

A Parenchyma cells are found throughout a plant. Because their cell walls are flexible, parenchyma cells can have different shapes.

B Collenchyma cells often are found in parts of the plant that are still growing. Notice the unevenly thickened cell walls.

C The walls of sclerenchyma cells are very thick. These dead cells are able to provide support for the plant.

LM Magnification: 54×

LM Magnification: 80×

LM Magnification: 120×

 Indiana Academic Standards

Pages 606–607: B.1.1, B.1.3, B.1.15

INCLUSION STRATEGIES

Learning Disabled: *Visual-Spatial* Have students prepare a table to summarize the characteristics of plant cells. Organizing these characteristics into a table will help students with learning disabilities to distinguish these cell types. Headings across the top could include: Shape of Cells, Nature of Cell Wall, and Function. Headings down the side of the table should be: Parenchyma, Collenchyma, and Sclerenchyma. **L1**

Plant Tissues

Recall that a tissue is a group of cells that function together to perform an activity. Tissues can be referred to as plant subsystems. There are several different tissue types in plants.

Dermal tissues

The dermal tissue, or **epidermis**, is composed of flattened cells that cover all parts of the plant. It functions much like the skin of an animal, covering and protecting the body of a plant. As shown in *Figure 23.3*, the cells that make up the epidermis are tightly packed and often fit together like a jigsaw puzzle. The epidermal cells produce the waxy cuticle that helps prevent water loss.

Another structure that helps control water loss from the plant, a stoma, is part of the epidermal layer. **Stomata** (STOH mah tuh) (singular, stoma) are openings in leaf tissue that control the exchange of gases. Stomata are found on green stems and on the surfaces of leaves. In many plants, fewer stomata are located on the upper surface of the leaf as a means of conserving water. Cells called **guard cells** control the opening and closing of stomata. The

Stained LM Magnification: 100×

Figure 23.3
The cells of the epidermis fit together tightly, which helps protect the plant and prevents water loss.

opening and closing of stomata regulates the flow of water vapor from leaf tissues. You can learn more about stomata in the *BioLab* at the end of this chapter.

The dermal tissue of roots may have root hairs. Root hairs are extensions of individual cells that help the root absorb water and dissolved minerals. On the stems and leaves of some plants, there are structures called trichomes. **Trichomes** (TRI kohmz) are hairlike projections that give a stem or a leaf a "fuzzy" appearance. They help reduce the evaporation of water from the plant. In some cases, trichomes are glandular and secrete toxic substances that help protect the plant from predators. Stomata, root hairs, and trichomes are shown in *Figure 23.4.*

Figure 23.4
A root hair **(A)** is an extension of a root epidermal cell. A trichome **(B)** is unicellular or multicellular growth from an epidermal cell. Stomata **(C)** are openings in the leaf epidermis. Each stoma is surrounded by two guard cells.

Color-enhanced SEM Magnification: 715×

Color-enhanced SEM Magnification: 200×

Color-enhanced SEM Magnification: 63×

607

Microscope Activity

Visual-Spatial Students can see xylem cells under the microscope if they prepare wet mounts of wood shavings from the pencil sharpener. **L1** **ELL**

INTERNET
BioLab

The BioLab at the end of the chapter can be used at this point in the lesson.

Portfolio

Mapping Cells and Tissues Have students construct a concept map showing the relationship between the different types of plant cells and tissues. Have students include their completed concept map in their portfolio. **L3**

Biology Journal

Building a Plant Have students imagine that they are going to build a plant using traditional building materials such as wood, brick, mortar, insulation, etc. Have them describe what materials they would use to build each type of tissue in the plant. **L2**

USING MODELS

Xylem and Phloem Cells: *Kinesthetic*
Provide students with scissors, a dissecting needle, tape, and several paper straws. Ask them to use these materials to construct models of vessel elements and sieve tube members with their companion cells. Have students draw the nuclei on the straw cells that contain them. Advise students that most xylem cells are dead and, therefore, lack a nucleus. Have students add labels to the straw to identify each type. Models should have open ends on vessels and closed ends with holes on sieve cells with a companion cell taped next to it. **L2** **ELL**

Purpose

Students will prepare, observe, and determine the function of two plant tissue types.

Process Skills

draw a conclusion, interpret data, observe and infer, predict

Safety Precautions

To reduce possible injuries, have each student place several layers of paper toweling between his or her thumb and the top glass slide before pressing down on it. Provide a labeled container for broken glass.

Teaching Strategies

- One bunch of celery will be sufficient for all classes.
- Be sure students do not put too much "stringy tissue" on the slide because it will appear as a dark mass since light cannot pass through it.
- Demonstrate the safe way of using a scalpel or single-edged razor blade to remove soft tissue.

Expected Results

The stringy tissue will appear as nongreen tissue that resembles a track, or roadway. The soft tissue will appear green and cubelike in shape.

Analysis

1. tubelike, pipelike, stringlike, nongreen or colorless
2. cubelike, square, or irregular shapes, green in color
3. yes; Long, narrow cells are ideal for transporting water and nutrients. Cubelike cells would be most suitable for food storage.

Assessment

Performance Have students prepare slide squashes of banana "strings" that are on the fruit after peeling. Use the Performance Task Assessment List for Making Observations and Inferences in **PASC**, p. 89. **L1 ELL**

608

Observe

Examining Plant Tissues Pipes are hollow. Their shape or structure allows them to be used efficiently in transporting water. Plant vascular tissues have this same efficiency in structure.

Procedure

1. Snap a celery stalk in half and remove a small section of "stringy tissue" from its inside.
2. Place the material on a glass slide. Add several drops of water. Place a second glass slide on top. **CAUTION: Use caution when handling a microscope and glass slides.**
3. Press down evenly on the top glass slide with your thumb directly over the plant material.
4. Remove the top glass slide. Add more water if needed. Add a coverslip.
5. Examine the celery material under low-and high-power magnification. Diagram what you see.
6. Repeat steps 2–5 using some of the soft tissue inside the celery stalk.

Analysis

1. **Describe** Write a description of the stringy tissue under low- and high-power magnification.
2. **Describe** Write a description of the soft tissue under low- and high-power magnification.
3. **Explain** Does the structure of these tissues suggest their functions?

Figure 23.5
Tracheids and vessel elements are the conducting cells of the xylem. These cells die when they mature but their cell walls remain.

Vessel element

Tracheid

608 PLANT STRUCTURE AND FUNCTION

Vascular tissues

Food, dissolved minerals, and water are transported throughout the plant by vascular tissue. Xylem and phloem are the two types of vascular tissues. **Xylem** is plant tissue composed of tubular cells that transports water and dissolved minerals from the roots to the rest of the plant. In seed plants, xylem is composed of four types of cells—tracheids, vessel elements, fibers, and parenchyma.

Tracheids (TRA kee uhdz) are tubular cells tapered at each end. The cell walls between adjoining tracheids have pits through which water and dissolved minerals flow.

Vessel elements are tubular cells that transport water throughout the plant. They are wider and shorter than tracheids and have openings in their end walls, as shown in *Figure 23.5*. In some plants, mature vessel elements lose their end walls and water and dissolved minerals flow freely from one cell to another.

Although almost all vascular plants have tracheids, vessel elements are most commonly found in anthophytes. Conifers have tracheids but no vessel elements in their vascular tissues. This difference in vascular tissues could be one reason why anthophytes are the most successful plants on Earth. Anthophyte vessel elements are thought to transport water more efficiently than tracheids because water can flow freely from vessel element to vessel element through the openings in their end walls.

You can learn more about vascular tissues in the *MiniLab* on this page. What other types of tissues are found in vascular plants? To answer this question, look at *Figure 23.6* on the next page.

Sugars and other organic compounds are transported throughout a vascular plant within the phloem.

Additional Lab

Comparing Root Types

Purpose

This field investigation will allow students to compare taproots and fibrous roots.

Preparation

Locate areas of grass and dandelions.

Materials

garden trowel, metric balance

Procedure

Give students the following directions.

1. Examine pictures of taproots and fibrous roots in your textbook. Which type of root do you think contains more root hairs?
2. Using a trowel, loosen the soil around a dandelion plant and gently pull it out. Repeat this process with a clump of grass.

A Plant's Body Plan

Figure 23.6
There seems to be an almost endless variety of vascular plants. Regardless of their diversity and numerous adaptations, all vascular plants have the same basic body plan. They are composed of cells, tissues, and organs. **Critical Thinking** *What are the different types of meristems, and how do they help produce new plant systems and subsystems?*

A **Cells** Most new plant cells are produced by cell divisions in regions of a plant called meristems. Meristematic cells continually divide. After each cell division, one of the two new cells remains meristematic and the other begins to differentiate. Two types of meristems—apical and lateral—produce different cell types. Apical meristems produce cells that add length to stems and roots. Lateral meristems produce cells that increase stem and root diameters.

B **Tissues** Plants have four types of tissues: dermal, vascular, ground, and meristematic. Dermal tissues cover the plant body. Vascular tissues transport water, food, and dissolved substances throughout the plant. Photosynthesis, storage, and secretion are functions of ground tissue. Meristematic tissues produce most of a plant's new cells.

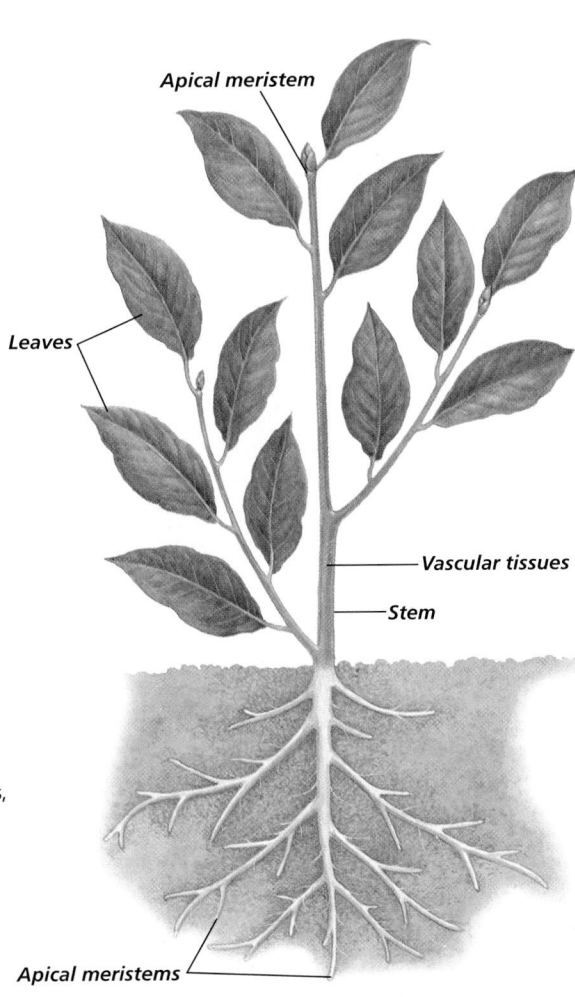

Apical meristem

Leaves

Vascular tissues

Stem

Apical meristems

Vascular plants

C **Organs** The major plant organs are stems, leaves, and roots. They differ in structure among plant divisions but share common functions. A stem is a plant organ that provides structural support and contains vascular tissues. Leaves and reproductive structures grow from stems. Usually, leaves are the organs in which photosynthesis occurs. Leaf form differs among plants. Roots anchor a plant in soil or on another plant or structure. Most roots absorb water and dissolved substances that then are transported in vascular tissues throughout the plant.

Purpose
Students will study the basic body plan of a plant.

Teaching Strategies
Ask students to describe the functions of the four tissue types. **L2**

Visual Learning
■ Ask students to bring in samples or pictures of leaves, stems, and roots. Have them describe the similarities and differences among the different organs. **L2**
■ Have students examine a prepared slide of an onion root tip. Point out that apical meristems produce new cells through the process of mitosis. **L1**

Critical Thinking
Apical meristems are located at the tips of stems and roots. They increase the height of the plant by producing new cells. The vascular cambium produces new phloem and xylem cells. The cork cambium produces the outer layers of bark.

 Indiana Academic Standards

Pages 608–609: B.1.1, B.1.15

---

3. Record the mass of each plant with its clinging soil. Carefully, rinse away the soil. Record the mass of the plants again.
4. Divide each plant's mass by its mass plus soil. Record this ratio.
5. **CLEANUP AND DISPOSAL** Clean all equipment as instructed by your teacher and return everything to its proper place. Make wise choices in the recycling of plant material.

Expected Results
The fibrous roots should hold more soil in close contact to its roots.

Analysis
1. Based on your ratio, which root type holds more soil in close contact to its roots? fibrous roots
2. Which root type would have a greater surface area for water absorption? fibrous roots

Assessment
Performance Have students write a report summarizing this lab. Use the Performance Task Assessment List for Lab Report in **PASC**, p. 119. **L3**

Purpose

Students will determine that water and minerals move upward through stems while sugar moves downward through stems.

Process Skills

analyze information, apply concepts, interpret data, predict, recognize cause and effect

Teaching Strategies

■ Review the nature of vascular tissue within the stem of anthophytes but do not specifically mention the role of xylem and phloem.

■ Point out to students that many trees are anthophytes.

■ Diagrams may be consulted to show that vascular tissue is continuous through a plant's stem.

Thinking Critically

1. transports food throughout a plant; flow of sugar was blocked, causing sugar to accumulate above the metal sheet

2. transports water and dissolved minerals throughout a plant; flow of water and dissolved minerals was blocked, causing them to accumulate below the metal sheet

3. Water and dissolved minerals would not be blocked, but sugars would be blocked because phloem is located just inside the bark.

Modified Assessment

Skill Ask students to predict the concentrations of water, dissolved minerals, and sugars 24 hours after inserting a metal sheet all the way through the stem. Use the Performance Task Assessment List for Making Observations and Inferences in **PASC**, p. 89. **L1**

Phloem is made up of tubular cells joined end to end, as shown in *Figure 23.7*. It is similar to xylem because phloem also has long cylindrical cells. However these cells, called **sieve tube members,** are alive at maturity. Sieve tube members are unusual because they contain cytoplasm but do not have a nucleus or ribosomes. Next to each sieve tube member is a companion cell. **Companion cells** are nucleated cells that help with the transport of sugars and other organic compounds through the sieve tubes of the phloem. In anthophytes, the end walls between two sieve tube members are called sieve plates. The sieve plates have large pores that allow sugar and organic compounds to move from sieve tube member to sieve tube member. Phloem can transport materials from the roots to the leaves also. You can learn more about vascular tissues in *Problem-Solving Lab 23.1.*

The vascular phloem tissue of many plants contains fibers. Although the fibers are not used for transporting materials, they are important because they provide support for the plant.

Figure 23.7
Phloem tissue carries sugars and other organic compounds throughout the plant.

Sieve tube member

Companion cell

Sieve plate

Figure 23.8
The numerous chloroplasts in this ground tissue produce food for the plant.

Chloroplasts

Color-enhanced LM
Magnification: 400×

Ground tissue

Ground tissue is composed mostly of parenchyma cells but it may also include collenchyma and sclerenchyma cells. It is found throughout a plant and often is associated with other tissues. The functions of ground tissue include photosynthesis, storage, and support. The cells of ground tissue in leaves and some stems contain numerous chloroplasts that carry on photosynthesis. Ground tissue cells in some stems and roots contain large vacuoles that store starch grains and water. Cells, such as those shown in *Figure 23.8,* are often seen in ground tissue.

610 PLANT STRUCTURE AND FUNCTION

CULTURAL DIVERSITY

Origin and Cultural Significance of Corn Corn was one of the earliest crops to be domesticated, and has been a major food source for Native Americans of both North and South America for about 7000 years. In addition to its importance as a food source, corn also occupies a symbolic place in the culture of many Native American tribes. Ask students working in groups to research uses for corn other than as a food source. Ask each group to prepare an illustrated essay of its findings. **L2**
COOP LEARN

Meristematic tissues

A growing plant produces new cells in areas called meristems. **Meristems** are regions of actively dividing cells. Meristematic cells are differently shaped parenchyma cells with large nuclei. There are several types of meristems; two types are shown in *Figure 23.6* on page 609.

Apical meristems are found at or near the tips of roots and stems. They produce cells that allow the roots and stems to increase in length. Lateral meristems are cylinders of dividing cells located in roots and stems. The production of cells by the lateral meristems results in an increase in root and stem diameters. Most woody plants have two kinds of lateral meristems—vascular cambium and cork cambium. The **vascular cambium** produces new xylem and phloem cells in the stems and roots. The **cork cambium** produces cells with tough cell walls. These cells cover the surface of stems and roots. The outer bark of a tree is produced by the cork cambium.

A third type of lateral meristem is found in grasses, corn, and other monocots. This meristem adds cells that lengthen the part of the stem between the leaves. These plants do not have a vascular or a cork cambium.

Problem-Solving Lab 23.1

Apply Concepts

What happens if vascular tissue is interrupted? Anthophytes have tissues within their organs that transport materials from roots to leaves and from leaves to roots. What happens if this pathway is experimentally interrupted?

Solve the Problem

A thin sheet of metal was inserted halfway through the stem of a living tree as shown in the diagram. One day later, the following analysis was made:

- Concentration of water and dissolved minerals directly below the metal sheet was higher than above the metal sheet.
- Concentration of sugar directly above the metal sheet was higher than directly below the metal sheet.

Higher sugar levels

Metal plate

Higher water and dissolved mineral levels

Thinking Critically

1. **Explain** What is the function of phloem? Why was the concentration of sugars different on either side of the metal sheet?
2. **Explain** What is the function of xylem? Why was the concentration of dissolved minerals and water different on either side of the metal sheet?
3. **Analyze** How would the experimental findings differ if the metal sheet were inserted only into the bark of the tree?

Section Assessment

Understanding Main Ideas

1. Describe the distinguishing characteristics of the three types of plant cells.
2. Identify and analyze the function of vascular tissue. Name the two different types of vascular tissue.
3. Explain the function of stomata.
4. Draw a plant and identify and indicate where the apical meristems would be located. How do they function differently from lateral meristems in the development of a plant?

Thinking Critically

5. Explain what type of plant cell you would expect to find in the photosynthetic tissue of a leaf. What is another name for the photosynthetic tissue?

SKILL REVIEW

6. **Compare and Contrast** Compare and contrast the cells that make up the xylem and the phloem. For more help, refer to *Compare and Contrast* in the **Skill Handbook**.

in.bdol.glencoe.com/self_check_quiz

23.1   PLANT CELLS AND TISSUES   **611**

3 Assess

Extension

Ask students what tissues or organs in humans are analogous to plant tissues. **L3**

MODIFIED Assessment

Skill Have students draw a simple diagram of a plant with roots, stems, and leaves. Have them label the location of the four types of plant tissues. **L1** **ELL**

Indiana Academic Standards

Pages 610–611: B.1.1, B.1.15

Section Assessment

1. Parenchyma are spherical, thin-walled cells. Collenchyma are cells with unevenly thickened cell walls. Sclerenchyma cells have very thick cell walls.
2. Vascular tissue transports water, food, and dissolved minerals throughout the plant. xylem and phloem
3. Stomata control the exchange of gases.
4. Apical meristems are found at the tips of stems and roots. Lateral meristems increase stem and root diameter; apical meristems increase root and stem length.
5. parenchyma; because it can contain chloroplasts, but sclerenchyma and collenchyma do not; ground tissue
6. Xylem and phloem are both composed of cylindrical cells. Xylem cells are dead at maturity, whereas phloem cells are alive.

1 Focus

Bellringer
Section Focus Transparency 56

Transparency **56** Angiosperm Structures

SECTION FOCUS
Use with Chapter 23, Section 23.2

① What are the main parts of this tree?
② What is the function of each part?

BIOLOGY: The Dynamics of Life
SECTION FOCUS TRANSPARENCIES

Using Prior Knowledge

Experiment Students might decide to investigate how colored water moves from the root through a plant stem to the leaf or flower. They might select celery, a white carnation plant, or other light colored plant using dark food coloring for their investigation. When you examine their plan, make sure they have incorporated a control and are planning to collect quantitative data.

Section 23.2

Roots, Stems, and Leaves

Indiana Standards Standard B.1.15 Understand and explain that, in biological systems, structure and function must be considered together.

SECTION PREVIEW

Objectives
Identify and compare the structures of roots, stems, and leaves.
Describe and compare the functions of roots, stems, and leaves.

Review Vocabulary
organ: group of two or more tissues organized to perform complex activities within an organism (p. 210)

New Vocabulary
cortex
endodermis
pericycle
root cap
sink
translocation
petiole
mesophyll
transpiration

Do you like to eat plant organs?

Using Prior Knowledge The next time you eat a salad, look closely at its contents. Did you know that most of the items you are eating are plant organs? Lettuce and spinach are leaves. Carrots and radishes are roots. Asparagus is a stem. Bean and alfalfa sprouts include immature leaves, stems, and roots. There are more than one-quarter million kinds of plants on Earth, and their organs exhibit an amazing variety.

Experiment *After reading the first two sections of this chapter, design an investigation to demonstrate how vascular tissue is common to roots, stems, and leaves. Show your plan to your teacher and get permission to perform the investigation. Be sure to follow all laboratory safety rules. Share your findings with your class.*

Salad of roots, stems, and leaves

Roots

Roots are plant organs that anchor a plant, usually absorb water and dissolved minerals, and contain vascular tissues that transport materials to and from the stem. As shown in *Figure 23.9*, roots may be short or long, and thick and massive or thin and threadlike. The surface area of a plant's roots can be as much as 50 times greater than the surface area of its leaves. Most roots grow in soil but some do not.

The type of root system is genetically determined but can vary because of environmental factors such as soil type, moisture, and temperature. There are two main types of root systems—taproots and fibrous roots. Carrots and beets are taproots, which are single, thick structures with smaller branching roots. Taproots accumulate and store food. Fibrous roots systems have many, small branching roots that grow from a central point.

Some plants, such as the corn in *Figure 23.10*, have a type of root

Figure 23.9
The taproot of a carrot plant can store large quantities of food and water **(A)**. The fibrous roots of grasses absorb water and anchor the plant **(B)**.

Ⓐ

Ⓑ

612 PLANT STRUCTURE AND FUNCTION

RESOURCE MANAGER

Unit 7 *FAST FILE* Resources
MiniLab Worksheet, p. 64
Reinforcement and Study Guide in English, pp. 68–69
Reinforcement and Study Guide in Spanish, pp. 72–73
Critical Thinking/Problem Solving, p. 76
Transparency Worksheets, pp. 78, 81–84, 87–90

Reading Essentials for Biology, Section 23.2

Laboratory Manual, pp. 141–146, 147–150
Section Focus Transparency 56
Basic Concepts Transparencies 36, 37
Reteaching Skills Transparencies 33, 34

called prop roots, which originate above ground and help support a plant. Many climbing plants have aerial roots that cling to objects such as walls and provide support for climbing stems. When bald cypress trees grow in swampy soils, they produce modified roots called pneumatophores, which are referred to as "knees." The knees grow upward from the mud, and eventually, out of the water. Knees help supply oxygen to the roots.

The structure of roots

If you look at the diagram of a root in *Figure 23.11,* you can see that a root hair is a tiny extension of an epidermal cell. Root hairs increase the surface area of a root that contacts the soil. They absorb water, oxygen, and dissolved minerals. The next layer is a part of the ground tissue called the **cortex,** which is involved in the transport of water and dissolved minerals into the vascular tissues. The cortex is

Figure 23.10
As a corn plant grows, prop roots grow from the stem and help keep the tall and top-heavy plant upright.

made up of parenchyma cells that sometimes store food and water.

At the inner limit of the cortex lies the **endodermis,** a layer of cells with waterproof cell walls that form a seal around the root's vascular tissues.

Figure 23.11
Water and dissolved minerals move into the root along two pathways.

Pericycle
Endodermis
Cortex
Epidermis

A Dissolved minerals and water enter root hairs and travel through and between the cells of the cortex.

Root hair

Endodermal cells Waterproof seal

B Minerals dissolved in water can flow between the parenchyma cells, directly into the root cortex, then through the cells of the endodermis.

23.2 ROOTS, STEMS, AND LEAVES **613**

2 Teach

Enrichment

Portfolio Tell students to imagine themselves as a drop of water trying to get from the soil to the central vascular tissue of a root. Have them write a paragraph describing their journey. **L2**

Activity

Kinesthetic Form groups of four students and provide each group with colored markers and a large sheet of paper. Have them compare water entering a root to an everyday life process. Students are to diagram the everyday life process and label the diagram with the science terms in Figure 23.11. Make sure that students have time to brainstorm ideas before beginning and that all group members contribute to the diagram.

Enrichment

Portfolio Ask a group of students to prepare a multimedia presentation about roots. They should include material about fibrous roots, taproots, and specialized roots such as prop roots and "knees." Have them present their projects to the class.

INCLUSION STRATEGIES

Learning Disabled: *Interpersonal*
Provide each student group with a transparency and washable transparency markers. Students should take turns tracing Figure 23.11 until the image is copied. Each student should spend about 30 seconds drawing before handing the marker to another student in the group. All group members should participate. Ask students to comment on each other's work as they progress, first positive comments, and then corrective suggestions. If time permits, have them use the overhead projector to explain their transparency.

Figure 23.12
The root structures of dicots and monocots differ in the arrangement of xylem and phloem.

Xylem

Phloem

Parenchyma

Stained LM Magnification: 20×

Stained LM Magnification: 15×

A The xylem in this dicot root is arranged in a central star-shaped fashion. The phloem is found between the points of the star.

B In this monocot, there are alternating strands of xylem and phloem that surround a core of parenchyma cells.

Word Origin

pericycle from the Greek words *peri,* meaning "around," and *kykos,* meaning "circle"; In vascular plants, the pericycle can produce lateral roots.

endodermis from the Greek words *endon,* meaning "within," and *dermis,* meaning "skin"; In vascular plants, the endodermis is the innermost layer of cells of the root cortex.

The waterproof seal of the endodermis forces water and dissolved minerals that enter the root to pass through the cells of the endodermis. Thus, the endodermis controls the flow of water and dissolved minerals into the root. Next to the endodermis is the **pericycle.** It is the tissue from which lateral roots arise as offshoots of older roots.

Xylem and phloem are located in the center of the root. The arrangement of xylem and phloem tissues, as shown in *Figure 23.12,* accounts for one of the major differences between monocots and dicots. In dicot roots, the xylem forms a central star-shaped mass with phloem cells between the rays of the star. Monocot roots usually have strands of xylem that alternate with strands of phloem. There is sometimes a central core of parenchyma cells in the monocot root called a pith.

Root growth

There are two areas of rapidly dividing cells in roots where the production of new cells initiates growth. The root apical meristem produces cells that

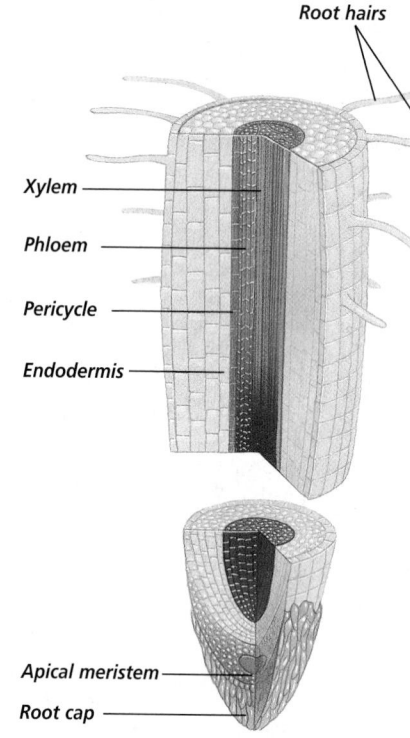

Root hairs

Xylem

Phloem

Pericycle

Endodermis

Apical meristem

Root cap

Figure 23.13
Roots develop by both cell division and elongation. As the number and size of cells increases, the root grows in length and width.

CHALLENGE ACTIVITY

Do roots respire? Have student groups carry out the following experiment to answer the question: Do roots carry out respiration and release carbon dioxide? Have students germinate bean seeds and grow young plants (this takes about 10 days). Have students remove plants from soil and place the roots into tubes of bromothymol blue (BTB) solution, then seal the tubes using a cotton or clay plug. Suggest that they use a control tube. Advise students that BTB turns from blue to light blue or green/yellow in the presence of an acid. Have students observe the liquid after 24 hours. Ask them to write a report summarizing what conclusions can be made regarding root tissue respiration. **L3** **ELL** **COOP LEARN**

cause a root to increase in length. As these cells begin to mature, they differentiate into different types of cells. In dicots, the vascular cambium develops between the xylem and phloem and contributes to a root's growth by adding cells that increase its diameter.

Each layer of new cells produced by the root apical meristem is left farther behind as new cells are added and the root grows forward through the soil. The tip of each root is covered by a protective layer of parenchyma cells called the **root cap.** As the root grows through the soil, the cells of the root cap wear away. Replacement cells are produced by the root apical meristem so the root tip is never without its protective covering. Examine *Figure 23.13* on the previous page to see if you can locate all the structures of a root.

Stems

Stems usually are the aboveground parts of plants that support leaves and flowers. They have vascular tissues that transport water, dissolved minerals, and sugars to and from roots and leaves. Their form ranges from the thin, herbaceous stems of basil plants to the massive, woody trunks of trees. Green, herbaceous stems are soft and flexible and usually carry out some photosynthesis. Petunias, impatiens, and carnations are other examples of plants with herbaceous stems. Trees, shrubs, and some other perennials have woody stems. Woody stems are hard and rigid and have cork and vascular cambriums.

Some stems are adapted to storing food. This can enable the plant to survive drought or cold, or grow from year to year. Stems that act as food-storage organs include corms, tubers, and rhizomes. A corm is a short, thickened, underground stem

Figure 23.14
Plants can use food stored in stems to survive when conditions are less than ideal.

A A white potato is a tuber.

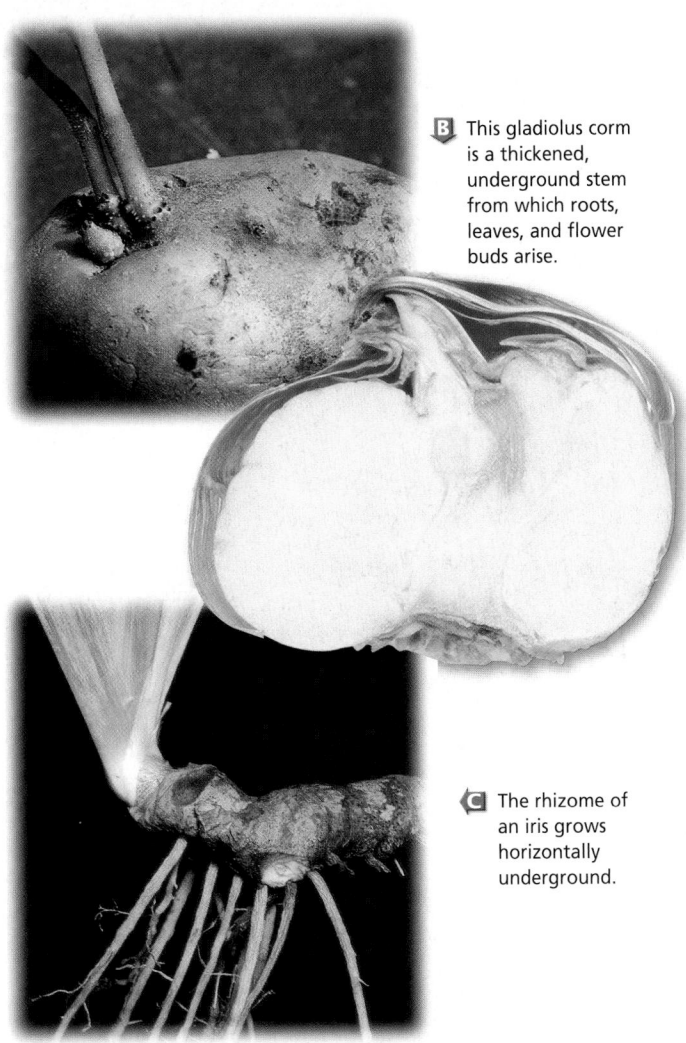

B This gladiolus corm is a thickened, underground stem from which roots, leaves, and flower buds arise.

C The rhizome of an iris grows horizontally underground.

surrounded by leaf scales. A tuber is a swollen, underground stem that has buds from which new plants can grow. Rhizomes also are underground stems that store food. Some examples of these food-storing stems are shown in *Figure 23.14.*

23.2 ROOTS, STEMS, AND LEAVES **615**

Enrichment

Linguistic Hydroponics is an agricultural process in which plants are grown in a nutrient solution rather than soil. Interest in commercial hydroponics began in 1925. Today, in regions where there are environmental concerns about groundwater pollution from agricultural chemical runoff, commercial hydroponics is a viable alternative to field production.

Ask students to research hydroponics, make a list of all the necessary nutrients and supplies required for a hydroponics garden, and to evaluate the pros and cons of this growth method. **L3**

Quick Demo

Storage Stems Demonstrate starch storage in tubers by adding a few drops of an iodine stain to several slices of potato tuber. Explain that the blue-black color indicates the presence of starch.

Indiana Academic Standards

Pages 614–615: B.1.15

Which fertilizers work best? Use liquid fertilizer to prepare solutions of the following percentages: 100, 80, 60, 40, 20, and 0. For preparation instructions, see pages 16T–17T of the Teacher Guide. Assign each student a concentration. Have students plant seeds (turnip or mustard seeds work well) in disposable 3-ounce cups filled with moist potting soil. Make drainage holes in the bottoms of cups. Place cups in a sunny location or under fluorescent lights. Students should water their plants as needed. Once a week, students should add 5 mL of their concentration, make observations of plant height and appearance, and record data. After several weeks, students should compile their observations and draw conclusions. **L2** **ELL**

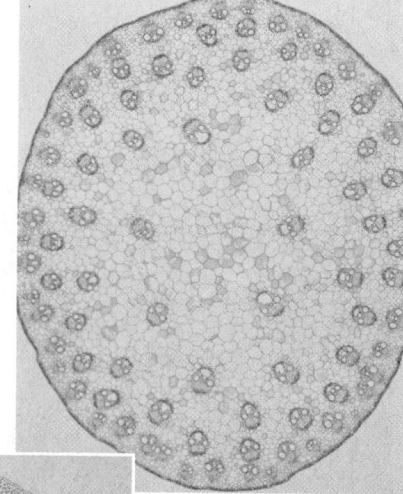

Figure 23.15 Stems have vascular bundles.

A The vascular bundles in a monocot are scattered throughout the stem as seen in this cross section.

Color-enhanced LM Magnification: 4×

Color-enhanced LM Magnification: 2×

B As seen in this cross section, young herbaceous dicot stems have separate bundles of xylem and phloem that form a ring. In older stems, the vascular tissues form a continuous cylinder.

C Woody stems are composed primarily of dead xylem cells.

Annual growth rings

Cork

Phloem

Vascular cambium

Xylem

616 PLANT STRUCTURE AND FUNCTION

Internal structure

Both stems and roots have vascular tissues. However, the vascular tissues in stems are arranged differently from that of roots. Stems have a bundled arrangement or circular arrangement of vascular tissues within a surrounding mass of parenchyma tissue. As you can see in *Figure 23.15A* and *B*, monocots and dicots differ in the arrangement of vascular tissues in their stems. In most dicots, xylem and phloem are in a circle of vascular bundles that form a ring in the cortex. The vascular bundles of most monocots are scattered throughout the stem.

Woody stems

Many conifers and perennial dicots produce thick, sturdy stems, as shown in *Figure 23.15C,* that may last several years, or even decades. As the stems of woody plants grow in height, they also grow in thickness. This added thickness, called secondary growth, results from cell divisions in the vascular cambium of the stem. The xylem tissue produced by secondary growth is also called wood. In temperate regions, a tree's annual growth rings are the layers of vascular tissue produced each year by secondary growth. These annual growth rings can be used to estimate the age of the plant. The vascular tissues often contain sclerenchyma fibers that provide support for the growing plant.

As secondary growth continues, the outer portion of a woody stem develops bark. Bark is composed of phloem cells and the cork cambium. Bark is a tough, corky tissue that protects the stem from damage by burrowing insects and browsing herbivores.

Stems transport materials

Water, sugars, and other compounds are transported within the stem. Xylem transports water and dissolved minerals from the roots to the leaves. Water that is lost through the leaves is continually replaced by water moving in the xylem. Water forms an unbroken column within the xylem. As water moves up through the xylem, it also carries dissolved minerals to all living plant cells.

The contents of phloem are primarily dissolved sugars but phloem also can transport hormones, viruses, and other substances. The sugars originate in photosynthetic tissues that are usually in leaves. Any portion of the plant that stores these sugars is called a **sink,** such as the parenchyma cells that make up the cortex in the root. The movement of sugars in the phloem is called **translocation** (trans loh KAY shun). *Figure 23.16* shows the movement of materials in the vascular tissues of a plant.

Growth of the stem

Primary growth in a stem is similar to primary growth in a root. This increase in length is due to the production of cells by the apical meristem, which lies at the tip of a stem. As mentioned earlier, secondary growth or an increase in diameter is the result of cell divisions in the vascular cambium or lateral meristem. Meristems located at intervals along the stem, called nodes, give rise to leaves and branches.

Leaves

The primary function of the leaves is photosynthesis. Most leaves have a relatively large surface area that receives sunlight. Sunlight passes through the transparent cuticle and epidermis into the photosynthetic tissues just beneath the leaf surface.

Leaf variation

When you think of a leaf, you probably think only of a flat, broad, green structure. This part of the leaf is called the leaf blade. Sizes, shapes, and types of leaves vary enormously. The giant Victoria water lily that grows in some of the rivers of Guyana has floating, circular leaves that can be more than two meters in diameter.

Figure 23.16
Xylem carries water up from roots to leaves. Phloem transports sugars from photosynthetic tissues to sinks located throughout the plant.

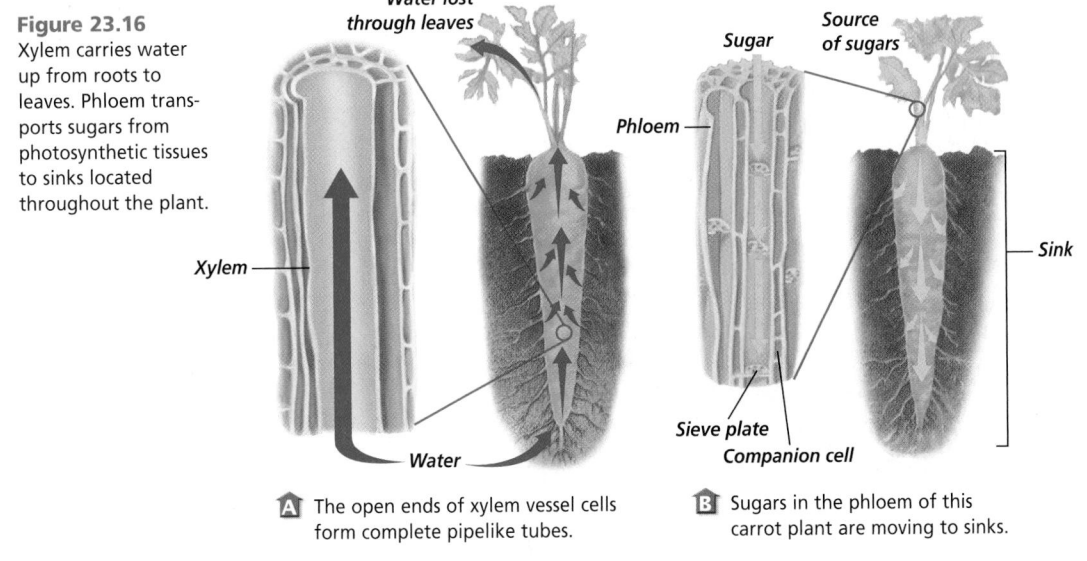

A The open ends of xylem vessel cells form complete pipelike tubes.

B Sugars in the phloem of this carrot plant are moving to sinks.

23.2 ROOTS, STEMS, AND LEAVES **617**

Microscope Activity

Visual-Spatial Students can view prepared slides of leaf cross sections. Have them compare the slides to the leaf cross section in Figure 23.19. Encourage students to draw a diagram of the cross section and label the external and internal structures of the leaf. **L2**
ELL

Biology Journal

A Leaf Analogy Ask students to describe in their journals how a cross-sectional view of a leaf can be represented by a sandwich. Ask students to describe the makeup of a sandwich and relate its component parts to those in the leaf. To get started, tell them to compare the upper epidermis to the top slice of bread. **L1**

Virtual Lab

CD-ROM Students will investigate the factors that affect transpiration rates in *Plant Transpiration.*

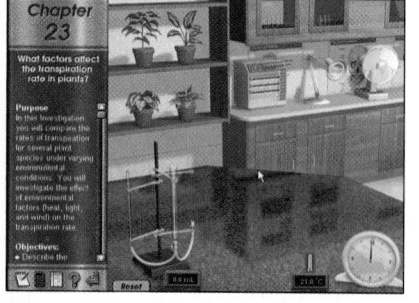

Indiana Academic Standards

Pages 618–619: B.1.15

618

A The leaves of the walnut are compound with many leaflets.

B The needlelike leaves of the evergreen yew can receive sunlight year round.

C The tulip poplar is a deciduous tree with broad, distinctive, simple leaves.

Figure 23.17
Leaf shapes vary, but most are adapted to receive sunlight.

The leaves of duckweed, a common floating plant of ponds and lakes, are measured in millimeters. Some plant species commonly produce different forms of leaves on one plant.

Some leaves, such as grass blades, are joined directly to the stem. In other leaves, a stalk joins the leaf blade to the stem. This stalk, which is part of the leaf, is called the **petiole** (PE tee ohl). The petiole contains vascular tissues that extend from the stem into the leaf and form veins. If you look closely, you will notice these veins as lines or ridges running along the leaf blade.

Leaves vary in their shape and arrangement on the stem. A simple leaf is one with a blade that is not divided. When the blade is divided into leaflets, it is called a compound leaf. *Figure 23.17* gives some examples of the variety of leaf shapes.

The arrangement of leaves on a stem can vary. Leaves can grow from opposite sides of the stem in an alternating arrangement. If two leaves grow opposite each other on a stem, the arrangement is called opposite. Three or more leaves growing around a stem at the same position is called a whorled arrangement.

Leaf structure

The internal structure of a typical leaf is shown in *Figure 23.18*. The vascular tissues are located in the midrib and veins of the leaf. Just beneath the epidermal layer are two layers of mesophyll. **Mesophyll** (MEH zuh fihl) is the photosynthetic tissue of a leaf. It is usually made up of two types of parenchyma cells—palisade mesophyll and spongy mesophyll. The palisade mesophyll is made up of column-shaped cells containing many chloroplasts. These cells are found just under the upper epidermis

Figure 23.18
The tissues of a leaf are adapted for photosynthesis, gas exchange, limiting water loss, and transporting water and sugars.

Cuticle
Upper epidermis
Palisade mesophyll
Vascular bundle
Xylem
Phloem
Lower epidermis
Spongy mesophyll
Guard cell
Stomata

INCLUSION STRATEGIES

Visually Impaired Use two long, inflated balloons as a model of guards cells for visually impaired students. Fasten their ends together and place the balloons next to each other. Typically, a bow will exist in the center to simulate the stoma opening. Allow students to examine the component parts, guard cells and stoma opening, as you explain what they represent. Push the two balloons together to close the stoma and allow students to reexamine the model. **L1** **ELL**

and receive maximum exposure to sunlight. Most photosynthesis takes place in the palisade mesophyll. Below the palisade mesophyll is the spongy mesophyll, which is composed of loosely packed, irregularly shaped cells. These cells usually are surrounded by many air spaces that allow carbon dioxide, oxygen, and water vapor to freely flow around the cells. Gases can also move in and out of a leaf through the stomata, which are located in the upper and/or lower epidermis.

Transpiration

You read previously that leaves have an epidermis with a waxy cuticle and stomata that help reduce water loss. Guard cells are cells that surround and control the size of a stoma, as shown in *Figure 23.19*. The loss of water through the stomata is called **transpiration**. Learn more about how a plant's surroundings may influence rate of transpiration in *Problem-Solving Lab 23.2* on this page.

Figure 23.19
Guard cells regulate the size of the opening of the stomata according to the amount of water in the plant.

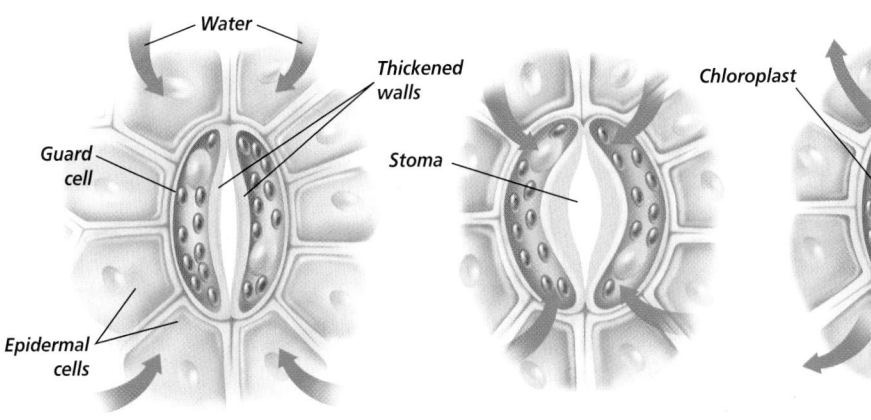

Water

Thickened walls

Guard cell

Stoma

Chloroplast

Epidermal cells

A The guard cells have flexible cell walls.

B When water enters the guard cells, the pressure causes them to bow out, opening the stoma.

C As water leaves the guard cells, the pressure is released and the cells come together, closing the stoma.

Problem-Solving Lab 23.2

Draw Conclusions

What factors influence the rate of transpiration? Plants lose large amounts of water during transpiration. This process aids in pulling water up from roots to stem to leaves where it can be used in photosynthesis.

Solve the Problem
A student was interested in seeing if a plant's surroundings might affect its rate of water loss. A geranium plant was set up as a control. A second geranium was sealed within a plastic bag and a third geranium was placed in front of a fan. All three plants were placed under lights. The student's experimental data are shown in the graph.

Rate of Water Loss

Water loss

Time

Thinking Critically
1. **Infer** Which line, A, B, or C, might best represent the student's control data? Explain.
2. **a. Infer** Which line might best represent the data with the plant sealed within a bag? Explain.
   b. Identify What abiotic environmental factor was being tested?
3. **Infer** Which line might best represent the data with the plant in front of a fan? Explain.
4. **Conclude** Write a conclusion for the student's experiment.

Assessment

Performance Have students perform this experiment. Ask them to prepare an outline of their experimental procedure. Use the Performance Task Assessment List for Carrying Out a Strategy and Collecting Data in **PASC**, p. 97. **L2**

Problem-Solving Lab 23.2

Purpose
Students will analyze a graph and relate it to factors that influence transpiration rates.

Process Skills
analyze information, compare and contrast, identify and control variables, design an experiment, draw a conclusion, hypothesize, interpret data, make and use graphs, recognize cause and effect, think critically

Teaching Strategies
■ Students must be able to correlate sealing of a plant within a plastic bag with a corresponding rise in humidity within the bag. Discuss this idea with students prior to starting this activity. Based on their own experience, does perspiration evaporate from their skin more quickly on a humid day or a less humid day?

■ Students must also be able to correlate presence of wind with an increase in water loss through evaporation. Discuss this idea with students prior to starting this activity. Based on their own experience, why is it cooling to sit in front of a fan?

Thinking Critically
1. B; Water loss from a fan would be highest, water loss inside the plastic bag would be lowest.
2. **a.** C; Transpiration is reduced due to high humidity inside of the bag.
   b. amount of humidity or moisture in air
3. A; Transpiration is accelerated due to presence of wind.
4. A plant's transpiration rate is related to environmental conditions. High humidity reduces the rate of transpiration. Windy conditions increase the rate of transpiration.

619

MiniLab 23.2

Purpose

Students will examine leaves and compare and contrast the leaf type, venation, and arrangement for each leaf.

Process Skills

compare and contrast, observe, classify, infer, analyze

Safety Precautions

Caution students that some leaves can irritate their skin and that they should not touch their eyes, face, or mouths when handling leaves. Students should wash their hands thoroughly with soap and water after they complete the activity and clean up. Caution students if poisonous plants, such as poison ivy and poison oak, are in your area.

Teaching Strategies

■ If leaves are not available, you might use pictures of leaves from tree identification books.
■ Students may confuse compound leaflets with leaves. Explain that leaflets of compound leaves do not grow directly from buds as leaves do.
■ If you do this MiniLab during class time, provide students with clipboards and paper when they go outside.

Expected Results

Students will find simple and compound leaves, leaves with pinnate, palmate, and parallel venation, and leaves that are opposite, alternate, and whorled.

Analysis

1. Class results will differ.
2. to identify plants or to understand how they might be related to other plant species

Modified Assessment

Interpret Scientific Illustrations Provide students with photocopies of leaves they have not seen and ask them to identify their features: leaf type, venation, and leaf arrangement. **L1** **ELL**

620

MiniLab 23.2

Compare and Contrast

Observing Leaves Identifying leaf characteristics can help you identify plants. Use these leaf images to complete this field investigation.

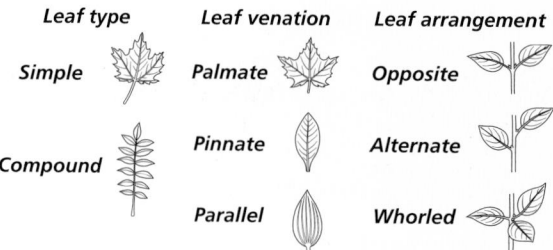

Leaf type — Simple, Compound
Leaf venation — Palmate, Pinnate, Parallel
Leaf arrangement — Opposite, Alternate, Whorled

Procedure

CAUTION: *Keep your hands away from your mouth while doing this investigation. Wash your hands thoroughly after you complete your work.*

1 With your teacher's permission, examine leaves on five different plants on your school campus, or observe preserved leaves. Do not use conifers.

2 Sketch a leaf from each plant. Beside each sketch, label the leaf as simple or compound, list its venation, and write the word that describes its arrangement on the stem.

Analysis

1. **Collect and Organize Data** As a class, place leaves having the same three characteristics into groups. List the characteristics and count the number of leaves in each group. Display class results in a bar graph.
2. **Infer** Why would a botanist compare and contrast leaf structure?

Figure 23.20
Leaf venation patterns help distinguish between monocots and dicots. Leaves of corn plants have parallel veins **(A)**, a characteristic of many monocots. Leaves of lettuce plants are netlike **(B)**, a characteristic of many dicots. Leaves of ginkgoes are dichotomously veined **(C)**.

Indiana Academic Standards

Pages 620–621: B.1.15

The opening and closing of guard cells regulate transpiration. As you read about how guard cells work, look again at the diagrams in *Figure 23.19*. Guard cells are cells scattered among the cells of the epidermis. The walls of these cells contain fiberlike structures. When there is more water available in surrounding cells than in guard cells, water enters guard cells by osmosis. These fiberlike structures in the cell walls of guard cells prevent expansion in width, not in length. Because the two guard cells are attached at either end, this expansion in length forces them to bow out and the stoma opens. When there is less water in surrounding tissues, water leaves the guard cells. The cells return to their previous shape, which reduces the size of the stoma. The proper functioning of guard cells is important because plants lose up to 90 percent of all the water they transport from the roots by transpiration.

Venation patterns

One way to distinguish among different groups of plants is to examine the pattern of veins in their leaves. The veins of vascular tissue run through the mesophyll of the leaf. As shown in *Figure 23.20*, leaf venation patterns may be parallel, netlike, or dichotomous. You can learn more about leaf venation in the *MiniLab* shown here.

A The surface of a tomato leaf has glandular hairs that help repel insects and other predators.

B The leaves of the pitcher plant are modified for trapping insects.

C The leaves of *Aloe vera* are adapted to store water in a dry desert environment.

Figure 23.21
Modified leaves serve many functions in addition to photosynthesis.

Leaf modifications

Many plants have leaves with structural adaptations for functions besides photosynthesis. Some plant leaves have epidermal growths, as shown in *Figure 23.21A,* that release irritants when broken or crushed. Animals, including humans, learn to avoid plants with such leaves. Cactus spines are modified leaves that help reduce water loss from the plant and provide protection from predators.

Carnivorous plants, like the pitcher plant in *Figure 23.21B,* have leaves with adaptations that can trap insects or other small animals. Other leaf modifications include tendrils, the curly structures on sweet peas, the overlapping scales that enclose and protect buds, and the colorful bracts of poinsettias.

Leaves often function as water or food storage sites. The leaves of *Aloe vera,* shown in *Figure 23.21C,* store water. This adaptation ensures the long-term survival of the plant when water resources are scarce. A bulb consists of a shortened stem, a flower bud, and thickened, immature leaves. Food is stored in the bases of the leaves. Onions, tulips, narcissus, and lilies all grow from bulbs.

Reading Check **Evaluate** the significance of leaf structural adaptations to their environments.

Section Assessment

Understanding Main Ideas

1. Compare and contrast the arrangement of xylem and phloem in dicot roots and stems.
2. Infer where you would expect to find stomata in a plant with leaves that float on water, such as a water lily. Explain.
3. Describe the primary function of most leaves. List some other functions of leaves.
4. Explain how guard cells function and regulate the size of a stoma.

Thinking Critically

5. Compare and contrast the function and structure of the epidermis and the endodermis in a vascular plant.

SKILL REVIEW

6. **Get the Big Picture** Construct a table that summarizes the structure and functions of roots, stems, and leaves. For more help, refer to *Get the Big Picture* in the **Skill Handbook.**

in.bdol.glencoe.com/self_check_quiz

23.2 ROOTS, STEMS, AND LEAVES **621**

---

3 Assess

DAILY INTERVENTION

Check for Understanding
Have students explain the difference between the terms of the following word groups. **L2**
a. transpiration—translocation
b. palisade mesophyll—spongy mesophyll

Reteach
Have students explain how the words in each pair listed above are alike or related. **L2**

Resources
For more practice, use *Reading Essentials for Biology,* Section 23.2.

Extension

Visual-Spatial Provide students with black line drawings of cross sections of roots, stems, and leaves. Have students label the drawings using terms from the text. **L1**

 Assessment

Skill Have students list in a table differences and similarities between monocots and dicots. Differences should include vein patterns and the pattern of vascular bundles. Similarities are anatomy, multicellular, and photosynthesis. **L2**

Section Assessment

1. In dicot roots, xylem forms a star-shaped figure in the center with phloem between the star rays. In stems, xylem and phloem are arranged in bundles that form a circle with the phloem outside of the xylem.
2. Stomata would be on the upper surface that is exposed to the air. This will allow for gas exchange.
3. The primary function is to trap light energy for photosynthesis. Some are modified for storage and protection.
4. When filled with water, guard cells swell and bow out, opening the stoma.
5. The endodermis and epidermis both control water movement. Endodermal cells are within the root and have waterproof walls. The flattened epidermal cells form the outer covering of a plant.
6. Roots anchor the plant, absorb water and dissolved minerals, and transport material up to the stem. Stems provide support and transport water, dissolved minerals, and sugars to and from roots and leaves. Leaves function in photosynthesis and gas exchange.

621

1 Focus

INTERACTIVE CHALKBOARD
PowerPoint® Presentations

Bellringer
Section Focus Transparency 57

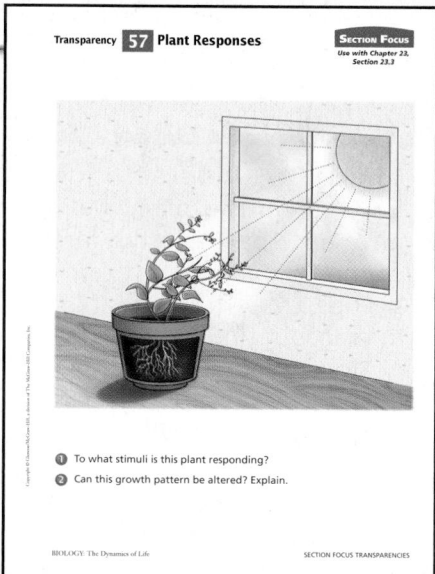

Transparency **57** Plant Responses

SECTION FOCUS
Use with Chapter 23, Section 23.3

❶ To what stimuli is this plant responding?
❷ Can this growth pattern be altered? Explain.

BIOLOGY: The Dynamics of Life

SECTION FOCUS TRANSPARENCIES

Using an Analogy
Make and Use Tables

Stimulus	Response
Gravity	Roots grow down, stems grow up
Light	Leaves and stems grow toward light
Touch	Tendrils coil around fence; mimosa leaves fold; flytrap's leaves snap shut
Hormones	Fruit ripening; growth; cell division

Section 23.3

Plant Responses

Indiana Standards Standard B.1.7 Explain that complex interactions among the different kinds of molecules in the cell cause distinct cycles of activities, such as growth and division. Note that cell behavior can also be affected by molecules from other parts of the organism, such as hormones.

SECTION PREVIEW

Objectives
Identify the major types of plant hormones.
Identify and analyze the different types of plant responses.

Review Vocabulary
stimulus: anything in an organism's internal or external environment that causes the organism to react (p. 9)

New Vocabulary
hormone
auxin
gibberellin
cytokinin
ethylene
tropism
nastic movement

Humans and Plants Respond to Sunlight

Using an Analogy You step outside into the bright sunlight and immediately raise your hand to shade your eyes. You react quickly to the bright sunlight. Plants react to sunlight, too. Often, however, plant responses to things in their environment are so slow that they can only be captured by time-lapse photography. When filmed in this way, the flower heads of sunflowers can be seen moving with the sun's apparent movement across the sky. In this section, you will read about other plant stimuli and responses.

Make and Use Tables As you read this section, make a table of plant stimuli and responses. Include the source of the stimulus and describe how the plant responds. When studying this chapter, use the table to review this section.

Sunflowers

Figure 23.22
Auxin produced in the tip of the main shoot inhibits the growth of side branches **(A)**. Once the tip is removed, the side branches start to grow **(B)**.

Shoot tip
Buds inhibited
Shoot tip removed
Buds grow into side branches

Ⓐ Ⓑ

Plant Hormones

Plants, like animals, have hormones that regulate growth and development. A **hormone** is a chemical that is produced in one part of an organism and transported to another part, where it causes a physiological change. Only a small amount of the hormone is needed to make this change.

Auxins cause stem elongation

The group of plant hormones called **auxins** (AWK sunz) promotes cell elongation. Indoleacetic (in doh luh SEE tihk) acid (IAA)—a naturally occurring auxin—is produced in apical meristems of plant stems. IAA weakens the connections between the cellulose fibers in the cell wall, which allows a cell to stretch and grow longer. The combination of new cells from the apical meristem and increasing cell lengths leads to stem growth. Auxin is not transported in the vascular system. It moves from one parenchyma cell to the next by active transport.

622 PLANT STRUCTURE AND FUNCTION

RESOURCE MANAGER

Unit 7 FAST FILE Resources
Reinforcement and Study Guide in English, p. 70
Reinforcement and Study Guide in Spanish, p. 74
Transparency Worksheet, p. 79

Reading Essentials for Biology, Section 23.3
Section Focus Transparency 57

Auxins have other effects on plant growth and development. Auxin produced in the apical meristem inhibits the growth of side branches. Removing the stem tip reduces the amount of auxin present and allows the development of branches, as shown in *Figure 23.22*.

Auxin also delays fruit formation and inhibits the dropping of fruit from the plant. When auxin concentrations decrease, the ripened fruits of some trees fall to the ground and deciduous trees begin to shed their leaves.

✓ Reading Check **Infer** how a fruit grower might use auxins.

Gibberellins promote growth

The group of plant growth hormones called **gibberellins** (jih buh REH lunz) causes plants to grow taller because, like auxins, they stimulate cell elongation. Unlike auxins, gibberellins are transported in vascular tissue. Many dwarf plants, such as those in *Figure 23.23*, are short because the plant does not produce gibberellins or its cells are not receptive to the hormone. If gibberellins are applied to the tip of a dwarf plant, it will grow taller. Gibberellins also increase the rate of seed germination and bud development. Farmers have learned to use gibberellins to enhance fruit formation. Florists often use gibberellins to induce flower buds to open.

Cytokinins stimulate cell division

The hormones called **cytokinins** (si tuh KI nihnz) stimulate mitosis and cell division. Cytokinins stimulate the production of proteins needed for mitosis and cell division. Most cytokinins are produced in root meristems. This hormone travels up the xylem to other parts of the plant. The effects of cytokinins are often enhanced by the presence of other hormones.

Figure 23.23
The bean plants in this picture are genetic dwarfs. The two plants on the right were treated with gibberellin and have grown to a normal height.

Ethylene gas promotes ripening

The plant hormone **ethylene** (EH thuh leen) is a simple, gaseous compound composed of carbon and hydrogen. It is produced primarily by fruits, but also by leaves and stems. Ethylene is released during a specific stage of fruit ripening. It causes cell walls to weaken and become soft. Ethylene speeds the ripening of fruits and promotes the breakdown of complex carbohydrates to simple sugars. If you have ever enjoyed a ripe red apple you know that it tastes sweeter than an immature fruit.

Many farmers use ethylene to ripen green fruits or vegetables after they have been picked, as shown in *Figure 23.24*.

Word Origin
auxin from the Greek word *auxein*, meaning "to increase"; Auxin causes stem elongation by increasing cell length.

Figure 23.24
Tomatoes are usually picked when they are green then they are treated with ethylene. Most of the tomatoes you see in grocery stores have been ripened in this manner.

2 Teach

Quick Demo

Phototropism Show students broadleaf houseplants that have been on a sunny windowsill long enough to show a phototropism. Ask them if they notice anything special about the leaves. Direct their attention to the orientation of the leaves. Ask students to propose ideas as to why the leaves are all facing the same direction. **L1**

✓ Reading Check A fruit grower might use high concentrations of auxin to promote fruit formation and inhibit the premature dropping of fruit.

Microscope Activity

Visual-Spatial Students can view the numerous cells in various stages of mitosis in onion root tip slides. Remind students that cytokinins produced in the root tip stimulate this cell division. **L1**

⊚ CHALLENGE ACTIVITY

Design an Experiment Have students research and design an experiment to test the effect of different concentrations of gibberellins on dwarf plants. Dwarf peas and the rosette variety of Wisconsin Fast Plants work well for this type of experiment. **L3**

Indiana Academic Standards

Pages 622–623: B.1.7

Purpose

Students will conclude from experimental evidence that light and the tip end of a young stem are needed for phototropism.

Process Skills

predict, think critically, analyze information, compare and contrast, draw a conclusion, hypothesize, interpret data, recognize cause and effect

Teaching Strategies

- Explain to students that the seed in each diagram is below the soil surface.
- Review the meaning of "opaque."
- Use the term *coleoptile* to refer to the young oat stem.

Thinking Critically

1. A and C; If there is no light source or the stem tip is not able to detect light, there is no phototropic response.
2. Student answers may vary. When the stem tip is intact (as in A), there is a phototropic response. However, when the stem tip is missing, there is no phototropic response.
3. stem tip; When the stem tip is removed, phototropism does not occur.

Assessment

Portfolio Ask students to design an experiment to test the hypothesis that the stem tip of a young stem does indeed contain a chemical that influences phototropism. Students should place their plan in their portfolio. Use the Performance Task Assessment List for Assessing a Whole Experiment and Planning the Next Experiment in **PASC**, p. 105. **L3**

Indiana Academic Standards

Pages 624–625: B.1.7, B.1.18, B.1.45

624

Problem-Solving Lab 23.3

Draw a Conclusion

How do plant stems respond to light? While working with young oat plants, Charles Darwin made discoveries about the response of young plant stems to light that helped explain why plants undergo phototropism. Scientists now know that this response is the result of an auxin that causes rapid cell elongation to occur along one side of a young plant stem. However, auxins were unknown during Darwin's time.

Solve the Problem

Study the before and after diagrams. The three plants are young oat stems. Note that the light source is directed at the plants from one side.

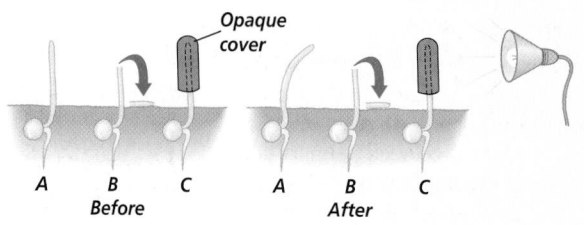

Opaque cover

A   B   C   A   B   C
   Before   After

Thinking Critically

1. **Interpret Scientific Illustrations** Which diagram (or diagrams) supports the conclusion that light is the stimulus for phototropism? Explain.
2. **Interpret Scientific Illustrations** Which diagram (or diagrams) supports the conclusion that the stem tip is the stimulus for phototropism? Explain.
3. **Conclude** Where might the auxin responsible for phototropism be produced? Explain.

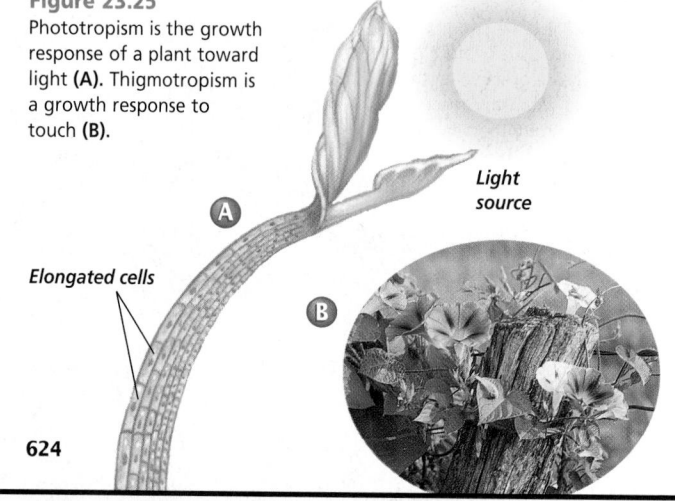

Figure 23.25
Phototropism is the growth response of a plant toward light (**A**). Thigmotropism is a growth response to touch (**B**).

Light source

Elongated cells

A

B

624

Plant Responses

Why do roots grow down and most stems grow up? Although a plant lacks a nervous system and usually cannot make quick responses to stimuli, it does have mechanisms that enable it to respond to its environment. Plants grow, reproduce, and reposition their roots, stems, and leaves in response to environmental conditions, such as gravity, light, temperature, and amount of darkness.

Tropic responses in plants

At the beginning of this section, you read that the flower heads of sunflowers slowly respond to the sun's apparent movement across the sky. **Tropism** is a plant's response to an external stimulus. The tropism is called positive if the plant grows toward the stimulus. The tropism is called negative if the plant grows away from the stimulus.

The growth of a plant toward light is called phototropism. It is caused by an unequal distribution of auxin in the plant's stem. There is more auxin on the side of the stem away from the light. This results in cell elongation, but only on that side. As these cells lengthen, the stem bends toward the light, as shown in *Figure 23.25A*. You can learn more about phototropism in the *Problem-Solving Lab* on this page.

There is another tropism associated with the upward growth of stems and the downward growth of roots. Gravitropism is plant growth in response to gravity. Gravitropic responses are beneficial to plants. Roots that grow down into the soil are able to anchor the plant and can take in water and dissolved minerals. Stems usually exhibit a negative gravitropism.

Some plants exhibit another tropism called thigmotropism, which is a growth response to touch. The tendrils of the vine in *Figure 23.25B* have coiled around a fence after making contact during early growth.

Because tropisms involve growth, they are not reversible. The position of a stem that has grown several inches in a particular direction cannot be changed. But, if the direction of the stimulus is changed, the stem will begin growing in another direction.

Nastic responses in plants

A responsive movement of a plant that is not dependent on the direction of the stimulus is called a **nastic movement.** An example of a nastic movement is the movement of *Mimosa pudica* leaflets when they are touched, as shown in *Figure 23.26A*. This is caused by a change in water pressure in the cells at the base of each leaflet. A dramatic drop in pressure causes the cells to become limp and the leaflets to change orientation.

Another example of a nastic response is the sudden closing of the hinged leaf of a Venus's-flytrap, *Figure 23.26B.* If an insect triggers sensitive hairs on the inside of the leaf, the leaf snaps shut. Nastic responses that are due to changes in cellular water pressure are reversible because they do not involve growth. The *Mimosa pudica* and Venus's-flytrap leaves return to their original positions once the stimulus ends.

Figure 23.26
When leaflets of *Mimosa pudica* are touched, they move inward **(A)**. Trigger hairs must be touched to close the hinged leaf of a Venus's-flytrap **(B)**.
Infer *How do these adaptations help ensure the long-term survival of each species?*

3 Assess

DAILY INTERVENTION

Check for Understanding
Have students explain how the words in each of the following pairs are related. **L2**
a. auxin—hormone
b. cytokinin—cell division
c. ethylene—ripe fruit
d. tropic response—nastic response

Reteach
Linguistic Have students write sentences correctly using each of the groups of words in Check for Understanding. **L2**

Resources
For more practice, use *Reading Essentials for Biology,* Section 23.3.

Extension

Have students do research on the use of plant hormones in agriculture. **L3**

 Assessment

Knowledge Show students pictures of different plant responses and ask them to identify the type of response. **L1**

Section Assessment

Understanding Main Ideas
1. Define a hormone.

2. Compare and contrast tropic responses and nastic movements.

3. Explain how a plant can bend toward sunlight. What term describes this response?

4. Name one plant hormone and describe how it functions.

5. Explain why gardeners often remove stem tips of chrysanthemum plants during early summer.

Thinking Critically
6. One technique that has been used for years to ripen fruit is to put a ripened banana in a paper bag with the unripe fruit. Infer what happens inside the bag.

SKILL REVIEW
7. **Experiment** Explain how you would design an experiment to investigate the effects of different colors of light on the phototropism of a plant. For more help, refer to *Experiment* in the **Skill Handbook.**

 in.bdol.glencoe.com/self_check_quiz

Section Assessment

1. A hormone is a chemical produced in one part of an organism and transported to another part, where it then causes a physiological change.

2. Nastic movements are reversible, whereas tropic responses are not. Nastic movements are not dependent upon the direction of the stimulus, whereas tropic responses are.

3. A plant can bend toward the light as a result of cell elongation on the side of the stem away from the light. phototropism

4. Possible answers: auxins cause stem elongation; gibberellins promote growth; cytokinins stimulate cell division; and ethylene gas promotes fruit ripening.

5. to promote lateral branching, which increases the number of flowering stems

6. Ripe fruits release ethylene gas that stimulates the ripening of other fruits.

7. Expose identical plants to different colors of light for 24 hours and measure the response. Be sure to have a control.

Time Allotment

one class period

Process Skills

collect data, communicate, interpret data, recognize cause and effect, draw a conclusion, compare and contrast, measure in SI, observe and infer, use numbers

Safety Precautions

Review safety when working with single-edged razor blades. Remind students to cut away from their bodies. Remind students to use only the fine adjustment knob when viewing slides under high-power. Have students wash their hands after handling plants.

Before You Begin

If asked to count the total number of stomata on a leaf, you might answer by saying "that's an impossible task." It may not be necessary for you to count each and every stoma. Sampling is a technique that is used to arrive at an answer that is close to the actual number. You will use a sampling technique in this *BioLab*.

Determining the Number of Stomata on a Leaf

PREPARATION

Problem

How can you count the total number of stomata on a leaf?

Objectives

In this BioLab, you will:
- **Measure** the area of a leaf.
- **Observe** the number of stomata seen under a high-power field of view.
- **Calculate** the total number of stomata on a leaf.
- **Use the Internet** to collect and compare data from other students.

Materials

microscope
glass slide
water and dropper
single-edged razor blade

ruler
coverslip
green leaf from an onion
plant

Safety Precautions

CAUTION: *Wear latex gloves when handling an onion.*

Skill Handbook

If you need help with this lab, refer to the **Skill Handbook**.

PROCEDURE

1. Copy Data Table 1 and Data Table 2.

2. To calculate the area of the high-power field of view for your microscope, go to *Math Skills* in the **Skill Handbook**. Enter the area in Data Table 2.

3. Obtain an onion leaf and carefully cut it open lengthwise using a single-edged razor blade. **CAUTION:** *Be careful when cutting with a razor blade.*

4. Measure the length and width of your onion leaf in millimeters. Record these values in Data Table 2.

5. Remove a small section of leaf and place it on a glass slide with the dark green side facing DOWN.

6. Add several drops of water and gently scrape away all green leaf tissue using the razor blade. An almost transparent layer of leaf epidermis will be left on the slide.

PREPARATION

Alternative Materials

- Any type of leaf may be substituted. Green onion is ideal because it is readily available in supermarkets. It also is easily scraped with the razor blade to yield a clear epidermis.
- Other leaves may be used. Students will have to calculate the area of differently shaped leaves. Step 3 will no longer be valid if other leaves are used. Geranium and ficus leaves also work well.

Data Table 1

Trial	Number of Stomata
1	
2	
3	
4	Data will vary.
5	
Total	
Average	

PROCEDURE

Teaching Strategies

- You may find that students will need to use a calculator.
- Review how to calculate an average using sample data on the overhead projector.

Troubleshooting

- Students may have difficulty observing the stomata. Most problems are the result of not having scraped away enough of the spongy layer of the leaf.
- On occasion, the epidermis will tear when students scrape too vigorously. Have students discard their wet

mounts and try a new sample of leaf material.

- Failure to see or find any stomata may be due to the fact that students did not place their leaf sample with the dark side down. Green onions do not have stomata on their inside surfaces.

7. Add water and a coverslip to the epidermis. Observe under low-power magnification and locate an area where guard cells and stomata can be seen clearly. **CAUTION:** *Use caution when handling a microscope, microscope slides, and coverslips.*

8. Switch to high-power magnification.

9. Count the number of stomata in your field of view. This is Trial 1. Record your count in Data Table 1.

10. Move the slide to a different area. Count the number of stomata in this field of view. This is Trial 2. Record your count in Data Table 1.

11. Repeat step 10 for Trials 3, 4, and 5. Calculate the average number of stomata observed.

12. Calculate the total number of stomata on the entire onion leaf by following the directions in Data Table 2.

13. **CLEANUP AND DISPOSAL** Clean all equipment as instructed by your teacher, and return everything to its proper place. Dispose of leaf tissue and coverslips properly. Wash your hands thoroughly.

LM Magnification: 200×

Data Table 2

Area of high-power field of view	= __*__ mm²
Length of leaf portion in mm	= __*__ mm
Width of leaf portion in mm	= __*__ mm
Calculate area of leaf (length × width)	= __*__ mm²
Calculate number of high-power fields of view on leaf (area of leaf ÷ the area of one high-power field of view)	= __*__
Calculate total number of stomata (number of high-power fields of view × average number of stomata from Data Table 1)	= ____ *

* Answer will vary.

ANALYZE AND CONCLUDE

1. **Communicate** Compare your data with those of your classmates. Offer several reasons why your total number of stomata for the leaf may not be identical to your classmates.

2. **Predict** Would you expect all plants to have the same number of stomata per high-power field of view? Explain your answer.

3. **Compare and Contrast** What are the advantages to using sampling techniques? What are some limitations?

4. **ERROR ANALYSIS** Analyze the following procedures from this experiment and explain how you can change them to improve the accuracy of your data.
   a. five trials in Data Table 1
   b. calculating the area of your high-power field of view

Share Your Data

Interpret Data Find this BioLab using the link below, and post your data in the data tables provided for this activity. Using the additional data from other students on the Internet, analyze the combined data and complete your graph.

 in.bdol.glencoe.com/internet_lab

23.3 PLANT RESPONSES **627**

connection to Art

Purpose

to illustrate the relationship between nature and art

Teaching Strategies

Posters of O'Keeffe's works are available in art shops and museum gift shops. Bring in several examples to illustrate more of her work.

Have students visit an art gallery to view paintings by artists who use flowers as their subject matter. As an alternative, have students examine art books to find the names of artists who use flowers. Ask students to present oral reports on their findings. **L1**

Visual Learning

Ask students what plant hormone may have influenced the flowering of the red poppy.

Red Poppy
by Georgia O'Keeffe (1887–1986)

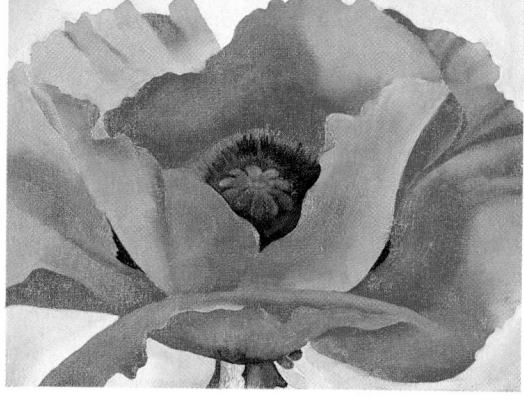

"When you take a flower in your hand and really look at it," O'Keeffe said, cupping her hand and holding it close to her face, "it's your world for the moment. I want to give that world to someone else. Most people in the city rush around so, they have no time to look at a flower. I want them to see it whether they want to or not."

American artist Georgia O'Keeffe attracted much attention when the first of her many floral scenes was exhibited in New York in 1924. Everything about these paintings—their color, size, point of view, and style—overwhelmed the viewer's senses, just as their creator had intended.

In describing her huge paintings of solitary flowers, Georgia O'Keeffe said: "I decided that I wasn't going to spend my life doing what had already been done." Indeed, she did do what had not been done by painting enormous poppies, lilies, and irises on giant canvases. Her use of colors and emphasis on shapes suggests nature rather than copying it with photographic realism. Her work can be described as abstract. "I found that I could say things with color and shapes that I couldn't say in any other way—things that I had no words for," she said.

The viewer's eye is drawn into the flower's heart In this early representation of one of her familiar poppies, O'Keeffe directed the viewer's eye down into the poppy's center by contrasting the light tints of the outer ring of petals with the darkness of the poppy's center.

The viewer's eye is drawn to the center of the flower, much as the flower naturally attracts an insect for reproduction purposes. The overwhelming size and detailed interiors of O'Keeffe's flowers give an effect similar to a photographer's close-up camera angle.

During her long life, O'Keeffe created hundreds of paintings. Her subjects included the flowers for which she is perhaps most famous, as well as other botanical themes. Her paintings of New Mexico deserts are characterized by sweeping forms that portray sunsets, rocks, and cliffs.

Georgia O'Keeffe died in New Mexico in 1986. She is remembered for her bold, vivid paintings that are, indeed, larger than life.

Writing About Biology

Critique It's easy to identify the flowers in O'Keeffe's paintings, but can they be considered scientific models? Look at the poppy flower photograph on page 957 of this book. Write a critique that evaluates each of these models—O'Keeffe's poppy and the photograph—according to its adequacy in representing a poppy flower.

 To find out more about Georgia O'Keeffe, visit in.bdol.glencoe.com/art

Writing About Biology

O'Keeffe's paintings are her interpretations of flowers. They are not accurate depictions of flowers or reliable references for studying flower structure. The photo of a flower can be used to identify visible flower structures. Neither image can show all of a flower's structures.

 Indiana Academic Standards

Pages 628–629: B.1.1, B.1.7, B.1.15, B.1.18

STUDY GUIDE

Section 23.1

Plant Cells and Tissues

Color-enhanced SEM Magnification: 200×

Key Concepts

- Most plant tissues are composed of parenchyma cells, collenchyma cells, and sclerenchyma cells.
- Dermal tissue is a plant's protective covering.
- Xylem moves water and dissolved minerals up from roots and throughout the plant. Phloem transports sugars and organic compounds throughout the plant.
- Ground tissue often functions in food production and storage.
- Meristematic tissues undergo cell divisions. Most plant growth results from new cells produced in the meristems.

Vocabulary

apical meristem (p. 611)
collenchyma (p. 606)
companion cell (p. 610)
cork cambium (p. 611)
epidermis (p. 607)
guard cell (p. 607)
meristem (p. 611)
parenchyma (p. 605)
phloem (p. 610)
sclerenchyma (p. 606)
sieve tube member (p. 610)
stomata (p. 607)
tracheid (p. 608)
trichome (p. 607)
vascular cambium (p. 611)
vessel element (p. 608)
xylem (p. 608)

Section 23.2

Roots, Stems, and Leaves

Key Concepts

- Roots anchor plants and contain vascular tissues. Root hairs absorb water, oxygen, and dissolved minerals. A root cap covers and protects each root tip.
- Stems provide support, contain vascular tissues, and produce leaves. Some stems are underground.
- Leaves undergo photosynthesis. A stoma is an opening in the leaf epidermis, is surrounded by two guard cells, and takes in and releases gases. Veins in leaves are bundles of vascular tissues.

Vocabulary

cortex (p. 613)
endodermis (p. 613)
mesophyll (p. 618)
pericycle (p. 614)
petiole (p. 618)
root cap (p. 615)
sink (p. 617)
translocation (p. 617)
transpiration (p. 619)

Section 23.3

Plant Responses

Key Concepts

- Plant hormones affect plant growth and functions.
- Tropisms are growth responses to external stimuli.
- Some nastic responses are caused by changes in cell pressure.

Vocabulary

auxin (p. 622)
cytokinin (p. 623)
ethylene (p. 623)
gibberellin (p. 623)
hormone (p. 622)
nastic movement (p. 625)
tropism (p. 624)

FOLDABLES
Study Organizer To help you review plant structure and function, use the Organizational Study Fold on page 605.

Key Concepts
Summary statements can be used by students to review the major concepts of the chapter.

 Biology Online

Visit in.bdol.glencoe.com
/self_check_quiz
/vocabulary_puzzlemaker
/chapter_test
/standardized_test

VOCABULARY PUZZLEMAKER

 For additional help with vocabulary, have students access the Vocabulary PuzzleMaker online at in.bdol.glencoe.com/vocabulary_puzzlemaker

FOLDABLES™
Have students use their Foldables to review the content of Section 23.1. On the back of their Foldables, have students analyze how plant tissues function together.

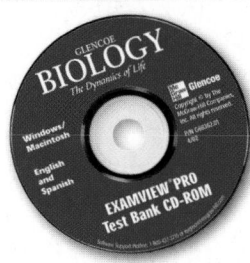

Use the ExamView®Pro Test Bank CD-ROM to:
- Create **multiple versions** of tests
- Create **modified** tests with one mouse click for **inclusion** students
- **Edit** existing questions and **add** your own questions
- Build tests aligned with state standards using built-in **State Curriculum Tags**
- Change **English** tests to **Spanish** with one mouse click and vice versa

Questions and answers have been aligned and verified by The Princeton Review.

Vocabulary Review

1. Apical meristem; it is not a type of cell.
2. Vessel element; it is found in xylem but the other two are found in phloem.
3. Vascular cambium; stomata are located in the epidermis.
4. Root cap; the movement of sugars to a sink is called translocation.
5. Tropism; cytokinin is a hormone.

Understanding Key Concepts

6. D   9. A   12. A
7. C   10. B
8. C   11. A

Constructed Response

13. Sap is dissolved sugar that was made and stored in the roots while the tree had leaves. It is being transported in the trunk's vascular system. The tissue or subsystem is called phloem.
14. The endodermis creates a barrier to the flow of water and ions, forcing them to flow through the endodermal cells thus regulating their movement.

Thinking Critically

15. Three main organs (systems):
    A. Leaves carry out photosynthesis and have vascular tissues (subsystem) in veins; a mesophyll layer (subsystem) consists of cells that contain chloroplasts; covered by an epidermis that contains stomata that control gas exchange; and are covered by a protective cuticle.
    B. Roots take in water and dissolved minerals; have

Vocabulary Review

Review the Chapter 23 vocabulary words listed in the Study Guide on page 629. For each set of vocabulary words, choose the one that does not belong. Explain why it does not belong.

1. parenchyma—sclerenchyma—apical meristem
2. vessel element—sieve tube member—companion cell
3. stomata—vascular cambium—epidermis
4. root cap—translocation—sink
5. cytokinin—hormone—tropism

Understanding Key Concepts

6. The tissue that makes up the protective covering of a plant is _____ tissue.
   A. vascular   C. ground
   B. meristematic   D. dermal

7. This root cross section with a core of vascular tissue is typical of _____ plants.
   A. horsetail
   B. monocot
   C. dicot
   D. moss

8. A cambium and a meristem are examples of _____ tissues.
   A. support   C. growth
   B. protective   D. transport

9. One of the primary structural differences between dicot roots and stems is the _____.
   A. arrangement of vascular tissues in roots and stems
   B. presence of stomata in roots
   C. lack of an epidermis in stems
   D. presence of an apical meristem in stems only

10. The ripening of fruit is stimulated by the presence of _____.
    A. gibberellin
    B. ethylene
    C. auxin
    D. cytokinin

---

11. Which diagram correctly shows the functioning of guard cells?

A.

Water

B.

Water

12. Which terms complete this concept map?
    A. tracheids and vessel elements
    B. companion cells and fibers
    C. tracheids and sieve tubes
    D. companion cells and sieve tubes

Water is transported in

xylem

is composed of

Constructed Response

13. **Open Ended** In late winter, some sugar maple trees have holes drilled in their trunks in order to collect their sap, a sugary fluid. This sap is processed to make maple syrup. Explain the source of the sap, and identify the plant system and subsystem that contains it.

14. **Open Ended** How does the endodermis control the flow of water and ions into root vascular tissues?

Thinking Critically

15. **Compare and Contrast** Identify and analyze characteristics of plant systems and subsystems.

16. REAL WORLD BIOCHALLENGE More than 5000 products are made from the vascular tissues of about 1000 tree species in the United States. Investigate the production of lumber, paper, fuel, charcoal and its products, fabrics, maple syrup, spices, dyes, and drugs that come from vascular tissues. Visit in.bdol.glencoe.com to research these topics. Prepare and present a poster or multimedia presentation of your findings.

 in.bdol.glencoe.com/chapter_test

---

vascular tissue (subsystem); cortex that moves water and dissolved minerals into the vascular tissue; also may be a storage area and an epidermis protects the root.

C. Stems transport water, nutrients, and dissolved minerals and have vascular tissue (subsystem) and support tissue.

16. Answers will vary as there are a variety of production processes for each product.

End-of-Course Assessment Practice

The assessed Indiana standard appears next to the question.

All questions aligned and verified by The Princeton Review

Part 1 Multiple Choice

Use data in the graph below to answer questions 17 and 18.

Stem Woodiness

(y-axis: Rating, 0–4; x-axis: Copper concentration parts per million (ppm), 0–4)

17. Copper is an important soil micronutrient
B.1.43 for plants. According to the graph, the copper concentration that resulted in the woodiest stem is _____.
  A. 3 ppm
  B. 0.5 ppm
  C. 1.5 ppm
  D. 4 ppm

18. Without enough copper, branches of some
B.1.43 conifers twist as they grow. If you were a tree grower and some of your conifer trees' branches were twisted and bent, what is the correct course of action to take first?
  A. Water the trees more.
  B. Apply fertilizer.
  C. Test the soil to determine nutrient levels.
  D. Apply a pesticide.

Leaf samples from the same plant species were collected from four different locations. Stomata were counted and averaged, and the data were graphed as shown below. Use the graph to answer questions 19 and 20.

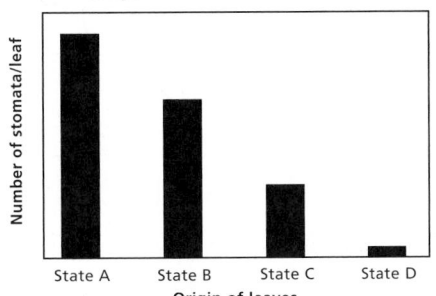

Comparison of Numbers of Stomata

(y-axis: Number of stomata/leaf; x-axis: Origin of leaves — State A, State B, State C, State D)

19. In which location might there be the most rainfall?
  A. State A
  B. State B
  C. State C
  D. State D

20. How might the number of stomata correlate with the amount of rainfall?
  A. more stomata, less rainfall
  B. no stomata, no rainfall
  C. more stomata, more rainfall
  D. fewer stomata, more rainfall

Part 2 Constructed Response/Grid In

Record your answers on your answer document.

21. Open Ended Sometimes foresters kill selected trees to reduce competition for limited environmental resources. They often use a process called girdling that involves removing a band of bark and some wood from around the trunk of a tree. Once this circle of material is removed, the tree eventually dies. Explain why this can happen.

22. Open Ended In the last decade, over three million acres of privately owned, forested land has
B.1.37 been converted to agricultural uses, real estate development, and other uses. Describe what might be the biological and ecological results of these changes.

 in.bdol.glencoe.com/standardized_test

End-of-Course Assessment Practice

17. A **19.** A
18. C **20.** C
21. Girdling interrupts the flow of sugars in phloem and water and dissolved minerals in xylem. Roots do not receive food and the rest of the tree does not receive enough water and dissolved minerals thus, the tree eventually dies.
22. Decrease in biodiversity and diminished ecological function might result. Possible results include: wildlife habitat loss, decline in species numbers, nonnative species replace natives, invasion of undesirable pests, and runoff contaminating streams and lakes limiting aquatic life.

 FAST FILE

Answer Sheet A practice answer sheet can be found on p. 97 of *Unit 7 Fast File Resources.*

RUBRIC

For more help evaluating open-ended assessment questions, see the rubric on p. 9T.

 Indiana Academic Standards

Pages 630–631: B.1.15, B.1.16, B.1.37

Chapter 24 Organizer

Section Objectives	National Science Standards	State/Local Standards	Advanced Lab and Demo Planning
Section 24.1 1 session 1. **Review** the steps of alternation of generations. 2. **Survey and identify** methods of reproduction and the life cycles of mosses, ferns, and conifers.	UCP.1, UCP.2, UCP.5; A.1, A.2; C.1, C.4–6	**Indiana Standards** B.1.8, B.1.11	**Student Labs:** MiniLab 24.1, p. 634: garlic bulb, water, test tube, carrot root, potato with eye (stem and buds), toothpick, beaker Problem-Solving Lab 24.1, p. 640 **Teacher Demonstration:** Quick Demo, p. 637: pictures of moss, fern, and conifer gametophytes (with magnification noted on photo)
Section 24.2 1 session, 1/2 block 3. **Identify** the organs of a flower. 4. **Examine** how photoperiodism influences flowering.	UCP.1, UCP.2, UCP.5; A.1, A.2; C.1, C.5; G.1, G.2	**Indiana Standards** B.1.15, B.1.18	**Student Lab:** Problem-Solving Lab 24.2, p. 644 **Teacher Demonstration:** Quick Demo, p. 643: flower
Section 24.3 2 sessions, 1 block 5. **Survey and identify** the methods of reproduction, growth, and development in flowering plants. 6. **Outline** the processes in which cells differentiate during the formation of seeds and fruits and during seed germination.	UCP.1, UCP.2, UCP.5; C.1, C.4–6; E.1, E.2; F.3; G.1–3	**Indiana Standards** B.1.11, B.1.15, B.1.18, B.1.21, B.1.23, B.1.35, B.1.43	**Student Labs:** Additional Lab, p. 654: canned kidney beans, paper cup, water, dried kidney beans, wax paper, labels, 2,3,5-triphenyl tetrazolium chloride solution, dark dropper bottles MiniLab 24.2, p. 657: soaked and ungerminated corn kernel, bean seed, germinated corn kernel and bean seeds, microscope Investigate BioLab, p. 658: See materials below. **Teacher Demonstrations:** Quick Demo, p. 647: peanut Quick Demo, p. 651: tomato, peach
End of Chapter Assessment Student Edition **Study Guide,** p. 661 **Content Assessment,** pp. 662–663		**Indiana Standards** B.1.11, B.1.15, B.1.19, B.1.35	**Student Lab:** Investigate BioLab, p. 658: complete dicot flower, hand lens or dissecting microscope, colored pencils (red, green, blue), microscope, 2 microscope slides, 2 coverslips, single-edged razor blade, dropper, water, forceps or tweezers

Key to Teaching Strategies

L1 Level 1 activities should be appropriate for students with learning difficulties.

L2 Level 2 activities should be within the ability range of all students.

L3 Level 3 activities are designed for above-average students.

ELL ELL activities should be within the ability range of English Language Learners.

COOP LEARN
Cooperative Learning activities are designed for small group work.

Legend

 Transparency   ⊙ CD-ROM   MP3   ▥ Videocassette   ⊙ DVD

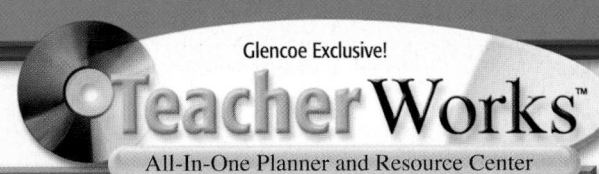

Glencoe Exclusive!
TeacherWorks™
All-In-One Planner and Resource Center

Reproducible Masters and Transparencies	Technology
Unit 7 FAST FILE Resources MiniLab Worksheet, p. 101 Reinforcement and Study Guide in English, pp. 105–106 Reinforcement and Study Guide in Spanish, pp. 109–110 Concept Mapping, p. 113 Transparency Worksheets, pp. 115, 119–124, 131–134 🔖 **Section Focus Transparency 58** 🔖 **Basic Concepts Transparencies 38, 39, 40** 🔖 **Reteaching Skills Transparencies 35, 36**	⊙ **Interactive Chalkboard CD-ROM: Section 24.1 Presentation** 🚩 ⊙ **TeacherWorks™ CD-ROM** 🚩 ♫ **Guided Reading Audio Summaries MP3**
Unit 7 FAST FILE Resources BioLab Worksheet, pp. 103–104 Reinforcement and Study Guide in English, p. 107 Reinforcement and Study Guide in Spanish, p. 111 Transparency Worksheets, pp. 116, 125–130, 135–136 **Inside Story Poster** 🔖 **Section Focus Transparency 59** 🔖 **Basic Concepts Transparencies 41, 42, 43** 🔖 **Reteaching Skills Transparency 37**	⊙ **Interactive Chalkboard CD-ROM: Section 24.2 Presentation** 🚩 ⊙ **TeacherWorks™ CD-ROM** 🚩 ♫ **Guided Reading Audio Summaries MP3**
Unit 7 FAST FILE Resources MiniLab Worksheet, p. 102 Reinforcement and Study Guide in English, p. 108 Reinforcement and Study Guide in Spanish, p. 112 Critical Thinking/Problem Solving, p. 114 Transparency Worksheet, p. 117 **Laboratory Manual,** pp. 151–154, 155–158 🔖 **Section Focus Transparency 60**	⊙ **Interactive Chalkboard CD-ROM: Section 24.3 Presentation** 🚩 ⊙ **TeacherWorks™ CD-ROM** 🚩 ♫ **Guided Reading Audio Summaries MP3**
Unit 7 FAST FILE Resources Chapter Assessment, pp. 137–142 Student Recording Sheet, p. 143 The Princeton Review **Reviewing Biology,** pp. 47–48	⊙ **Interactive Chalkboard:** 🚩 **Chapter 24 Assessment** ⊙ **MindJogger Videoquizzes DVD/VHS** ⊙ **ExamView® Pro Test Bank CD-ROM** ⊙ **TeacherWorks™ CD-ROM** 🚩 ⊙ **Succeeding on National Standards CD-ROM** 🖥 **in.bdol.glencoe.com** /self_check_quiz /vocabulary_puzzlemaker /chapter_test /standardized_test

🚩 Indicates materials created specifically for Indiana.

Understanding the Photo

This SEM color-enhanced image of anthophyte pollen grains has a magnification of 725×. Have students determine how many species are represented (based on form, not color). 6 Included in the photo are pollen grains of hollyhock, sunflower, morning glory, lily, castor bean, and primrose.

Chapter 24

Reproduction in Plants

What You'll Learn

- You will compare and contrast the life cycles of mosses, ferns, and conifers.
- You will sequence the life cycle of a flowering plant.
- You will describe the characteristics of flowers, seeds, and fruits.

Why It's Important

Much of life on Earth, including you, depends on plants. Humans eat plants and some people eat organisms that eat plants. If plants did not reproduce and continue their species, the food sources for much of life on Earth would disappear.

Understanding ▶ the Photo

Pollen grains of seed plants—coniferophytes and anthophytes—contain male reproductive cells. Botanists and paleobotanists can use the unique structures of pollen grains to identify living or extinct seed-plant species. This color-enhanced SEM photograph shows pollen grains from several species of living anthophytes.

Color-enhanced SEM Magnification: 1800×

 Two-Minute Chapter Launcher

Activity Provide students with complete flowers—those with petals, sepals, stamen, and pistil(s)—and the reproductive structures of mosses, ferns and conifers. If live material is not available, provide preserved specimens or pictures. Ask students to compare and contrast the reproductive structures of anthophytes to those of mosses, ferns, and conifers. **L2**

Section 24.1

Life Cycles of Mosses, Ferns, and Conifers

SECTION PREVIEW

Objectives
Review the steps of alternation of generations.
Survey and identify methods of reproduction and the life cycles of mosses, ferns, and conifers.

Review Vocabulary
gametophyte: haploid form of an organism in alternation of generations that produces gametes (p. 516)

New Vocabulary
vegetative reproduction
protonema
megaspore
microspore
micropyle

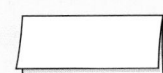 **FOLDABLES™ Study Organizer**

Life Cycles Make the following Foldable to help you organize events in the life cycles of mosses, ferns, and conifers.

STEP 1 **Fold** a sheet of paper in half lengthwise. Make the back part about 5 cm longer than the front part.

STEP 2 **Turn** the paper so the fold is on the bottom, then **fold** it into thirds.

STEP 3 **Unfold and cut** only the top layer along each fold to make three tabs.

STEP 4 **Label** the Foldable as shown.

Life Cycles
| Mosses | Ferns | Conifers |

Illustrate and Write As you read Chapter 24, illustrate and write about the life cycles of each group of plants behind the appropriate tab.

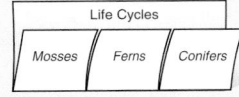

Transparency **58** Fern Life Cycle

SECTION FOCUS
Use with Chapter 24, Section 24.1

— New sporophyte
— Gametophyte
— Sporophyte

① Which generation is dominant in the life cycle of this fern?
② How does this compare with the life cycle of mosses?

BIOLOGY: The Dynamics of Life   SECTION FOCUS TRANSPARENCIES

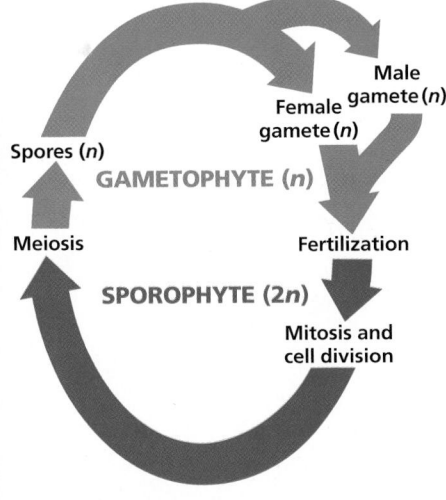

Figure 24.1
In an alternation of generations, the gametophyte *(n)* stage produces gametes, and the sporophyte *(2n)* produces spores.

Alternation of Generations

As you learned earlier, plant life cycles include an alternation of generations. As shown in *Figure 24.1,* an alternation of generations consists of a sporophyte stage and a gametophyte stage.

All cells of a sporophyte are diploid. Certain cells of a sporophyte undergo meiosis, which produces haploid spores. These spores undergo cell divisions and form a multicellular, haploid gametophyte. Some cells of a gametophyte differentiate and form haploid gametes. The female gamete is an egg and the male gamete is a sperm. When a sperm fertilizes an egg, a diploid zygote forms. This is sexual reproduction. The zygote can undergo cell divisions and form an embryo sporophyte. If the embryo develops to maturity, the cycle can begin again.

This basic life cycle pattern is the same for most plants. However, there are many variations on this pattern within the plant kingdom. For instance, recall that in mosses the gametophyte is the familiar form, not the sporophyte.

24.1   LIFE CYCLES OF MOSSES, FERNS, AND CONIFERS   **633**

INTERACTIVE CHALKBOARD with Image Bank

PowerPoint® Presentations

This CD-ROM is an editable Microsoft® PowerPoint® presentation that includes:
• Section presentations
• Section checks
• Image bank
• Hot links to Biology Online
• All transparencies

FOLDABLES™
For an additional Foldables activity idea, see the Chapter 24 Foldables page in *Unit 7 FAST FILE Resources.*

 Indiana Academic Standards

Pages 632–633: B.1.11

RESOURCE MANAGER

Unit 7 *FAST FILE* Resources
MiniLab Worksheet, p. 101
Reinforcement and Study Guide in English, pp. 105–106
Reinforcement and Study Guide in Spanish, pp. 109–110
Concept Mapping, p. 113
Transparency Worksheets, pp. 115, 119–124, 131–134

Reading Essentials for Biology, Section 24.1
📖 **Section Focus Transparency 58**
📖 **Basic Concepts Transparencies 38, 39, 40**
📖 **Reteaching Skills Transparencies 35, 36**

2 Teach

Purpose

Students will use different plant parts to demonstrate asexual reproduction.

Process Skills

experiment, analyze information, collect data, compare and contrast, draw a conclusion

Teaching Strategies

■ Have students work in small groups to conserve materials.
■ Make sure that the root end of the garlic clove is in water. One garlic bulb should supply enough cloves for an entire class.
■ Both garlic and potato may be suspended over water using toothpicks as bracing. Small plastic or glass containers may be used in place of beakers or test tubes.
■ Make sure that students identify their plants and label their jars and/or dishes.
■ Tell students to replace any lost water from the containers.
■ Some potatoes are chemically treated to inhibit growth. This may account for slow or no new growth.

Expected Results

All plant tissues should produce new growth.

Analysis

1. a. Different plant parts generated new growth.
   b. New growth occurred within several days.
   c. Only one plant was used for each experimental setup.
2. Answers may include faster growth and that all offspring are identical to parent.

In others, such as flowering plants, the gametophyte is microscopic. Most people have never even seen the female gametophyte of a flowering plant. Botanists usually refer to the bigger, more obvious plant as the dominant generation. The dominant generation lives longer and can survive independently of the other generation. In most plant species the sporophyte is the dominant plant.

Asexual reproduction

Most plants also can reproduce asexually by a process called **vegetative reproduction.** In this type of reproduction, new plants are produced from existing plant organs or parts of organs. The new plants have the same genetic makeup as the original plant. For example, some thallose liverwort gametophytes can produce cuplike structures, as shown in *Figure 24.2*. Inside, minute pieces of tissue called gemmae (JEH mee) develop. If gemmae fall from the cup, they can grow into other liverwort gametophytes that are genetically identical to the thallus. You can learn more about asexual reproduction in *MiniLab 24.1*.

✓ **Reading Check** **Compare** the genetic makeups of plants produced from one plant by asexual reproduction to each other and the original plant.

MiniLab 24.1

Experiment

Growing Plants Asexually Plants are capable of reproducing asexually. Reproductive cells such as egg or sperm are not needed in asexual reproduction. Plant organs such as roots, stems, and even leaves can produce new offspring.

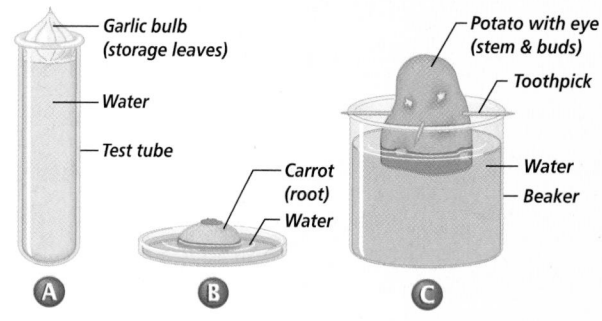

- Garlic bulb (storage leaves)
- Water
- Test tube
- Carrot (root)
- Water
- Potato with eye (stem & buds)
- Toothpick
- Water
- Beaker

Ⓐ Ⓑ Ⓒ

Procedure

1. Prepare three different plant parts for study using diagrams A, B, and C as a guide.
2. Design a data table in which you can diagram your observations and list the number of days since the experiment began.
3. Diagram the plant parts and label them as *Day 1.*
4. Make and record observations every three days. Replace any lost water as needed.
5. Observe any changes that occur to your plants over the next two weeks.

Analysis

1. **Observe** What experimental evidence do you have that:
   a. plants can use different structures for asexual reproduction?
   b. asexual reproduction is a rapid process?
   c. asexual reproduction requires only one parent?
2. **List** Describe advantages of asexual reproduction in plants.

634 REPRODUCTION IN PLANTS

Figure 24.2
Small cups filled with tiny gemmae have formed on the thallus of this liverwort.

Assessment

Performance Provide students with *Kalanchoe* (available at flower or garden shops). Have students conduct an experiment to determine what conditions stimulate the growth of new plants along the leaf's edge. Use the Performance Task Assessment List for Carrying Out a Strategy and Collecting Data in **PASC,** p. 97. **L3**

Life Cycle of Mosses

The gametophyte stage is the dominant generation in mosses. A haploid moss spore can germinate and grow to form a **protonema** (proh tuh NEE muh). It is a small green filament of cells that can develop into the gametophyte. In some mosses, male and female reproductive structures form on separate gametophytes, but in others, male and female reproductive structures are on the same gametophyte. Recall that the egg-producing, female reproductive structure is an archegonium, and the sperm-producing, male reproductive structure is an antheridium.

Motile sperm from an antheridium swim in a continuous film of water to an egg in an archegonium. If fertilization occurs, a diploid zygote forms. The zygote undergoes cell divisions forming the sporophyte that consists of a stalk with a capsule at the top. The sporophyte remains attached to and dependent on the gametophyte. Cells in the capsule undergo meiosis, producing haploid spores. When the capsule matures, it bursts open and releases spores. If the spores land in a favorable environment, they can germinate and the cycle repeats, as shown in *Figure 24.3.*

Figure 24.3
The moss gametophyte produces gametes that join to form a zygote. The zygote develops into the sporophyte that produces spores. Spores can germinate and grow into a gametophyte, completing the moss's life cycle.

Mitosis

Developing sporophyte

Zygote (2n)

Sporophyte (2n)

Gametophyte (n)

Fertilization

Capsule

Sperm

Egg

SPOROPHYTE GENERATION 2n

Meiosis

Capsule opens releasing spores

GAMETOPHYTE GENERATION n

Germinating spores

Male gametophyte (n)

Female gametophyte (n)

Protonema

Revealing Misconceptions

Students learned that haploid gametes form by meiosis. They may think that this is true for all sexually reproducing organisms.

Uncover the Misconception

In plants, spores are produced by meiosis. Mitosis and cell division of these haploid cells, however, produce gametes. Plants have alternation of generations. In this process, meiosis forms haploid spore cells, the beginning of the gametophyte generation.

Demonstrate the Concept

Ask students to make a Foldable that illustrates Figure 24.3.

Assess New Knowledge

Ask students to draw from memory a diagram that illustrates the development of haploid spores and haploid gametes in alternation of generations.

✓ **Reading Check** Plants produced by asexual reproduction from one plant will be genetically identical and have the same genetic make-up as the parent.

INCLUSION STRATEGIES

Learning Disabled: *Linguistic* Have students review terms associated with alternation of generations by reinforcing the correlation between the name of each generation and its function. For example, *sporo*phytes form *spores*, while *gameto*phytes form *gametes*. **L1** **ELL**

 Indiana Academic Standards

Pages 634–635: B.1.8, B.1.11

Students may think the sori on the underside of fern fronds are some kind of insect infestation.

Uncover the Misconception

Sori are clusters of sporangia. Within the sporangia, spores are produced by meiosis.

Demonstrate the Concept

Have students prepare slides of sporangia and view them under a microscope.

Assess New Knowledge

Ask students to draw diagrams of what they see under the microscope and explain what a sorus is.

Caption Question Answer

Figure 24.4A In mosses, the dominant stage is the photosynthetic gametophyte. The moss sporophyte grows from the gametophyte and depends on it for water and nutrients. Mosses are nonvascular, low growing plants. The fern sporophyte is dominant, photosynthetic, and independent of the gametophyte. The fern gametophyte grows from a spore and is independent. Ferns are vascular plants and most are much larger than mosses.

Chalkboard Activity

Have students write a simple moss life cycle sequence on the board. Help them get started by showing them what the cycle may look like by providing them with this sample: sporophyte ⇒ spores by meiosis ⇒ protonema ⇒ etc. **L2**

Figure 24.4
Fern sporophytes are common in a forest. However, a fern gametophyte is rarely seen.

A Most fern sporophytes can grow 25 cm or taller. **Differentiate** *How is a fern's method of growth different from a moss's?*

B Each round cluster of sporangia on the underside of a fern frond is called a sorus. Each sporangium contains spores that are released, sometimes in dramatic fashion.

C The heart-shaped fern gametophyte is usually 5 mm–6 mm across.

Stained LM Magnification: 25×

Some moss gametophytes also reproduce by vegetative reproduction. They can break into pieces when dry and brittle then, when moisture returns, each piece can grow and form a protonema then a gametophyte.

Life Cycle of Ferns

Unlike mosses, the dominant stage of the fern life cycle is the sporophyte stage. The fern sporophyte includes the familiar fronds you see in *Figure 24.4A*. Fern fronds grow from a rhizome, which is an underground stem. On the underside of some fronds are sori, which are clusters of sporangia. Meiosis occurs within the sporangia, producing haploid spores. When environmental conditions are right, the sporangia open and release haploid spores, as shown in *Figure 24.4B*.

A spore can germinate to form a heart-shaped gametophyte called a prothallus, as shown in *Figure 24.4C*. The prothallus produces both archegonia and antheridia on its surface. The flagellated sperm released by antheridia swim through a film of water to eggs in archegonia. If fertilization occurs, the diploid zygote can develop into the sporophyte. Initially, this developing sporophyte depends upon the gametophyte for its nutrition. However, once the sporophyte produces green fronds, it can carry on

CHALLENGE ACTIVITY

Chemistry in Biology: *Linguistic*
Have students do research and prepare a report about the role of chemotaxis in moss and fern reproduction. **L3**

Figure 24.5
In the life cycle of a fern, the sporophyte generation becomes independent of the gametophyte.

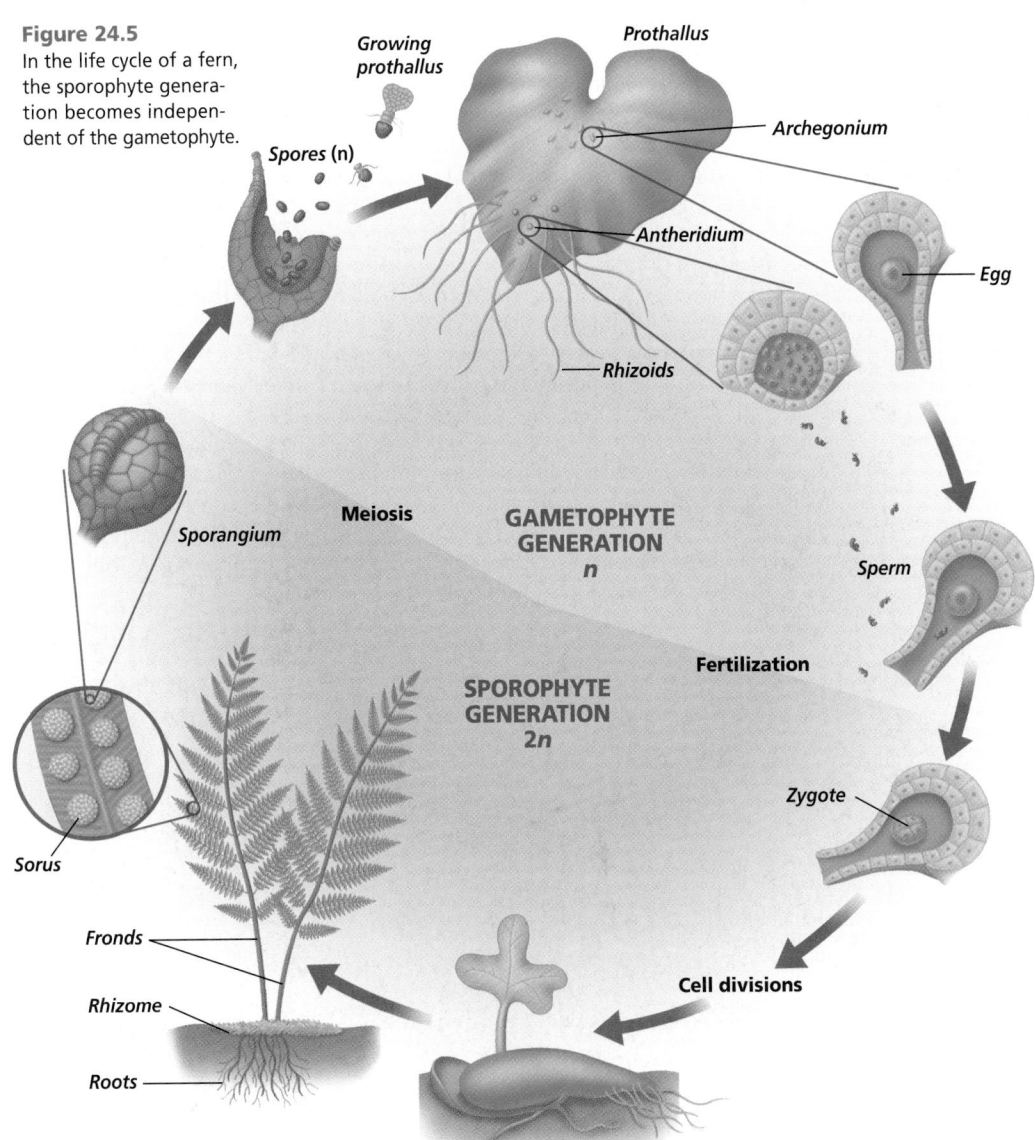

Growing prothallus

Prothallus

Spores (n)

Archegonium

Antheridium

Egg

Rhizoids

Sporangium

Meiosis

GAMETOPHYTE GENERATION
n

Sperm

Fertilization

SPOROPHYTE GENERATION
2n

Zygote

Sorus

Fronds

Rhizome

Roots

Cell divisions

Quick Demo

Size of a Gametophyte
Give students pictures of moss, fern, and conifer gametophytes that have the magnification noted on the photo. Have them calculate the size of each gametophyte. The size of the drawing (in millimeters) divided by the magnification equals the size of the original gametophyte (in millimeters). Students will then be able to compare the size of the gametophytes. **L3**

Chalkboard Activity

Write the following terms on the chalkboard: *spore, zygote, egg, sporophyte,* and *sperm.* Have students identify whether each structure is haploid or diploid. **L2**

Biology Journal

Fern Life Cycle Have students diagram the stages of the fern life cycle in their journals for review. Encourage students to divide the diagram so that all sporophytes are on one side and all gametophytes are on the other. Have them label the diagram *Sporophyte Stages, Gametophyte Stages.* **L1**
ELL

photosynthesis and survive on its own. The prothallus dies and decomposes as the sporophyte matures. The mature fern sporophyte consists of a rhizome from which roots and fronds grow. If pieces of rhizome break away, new fern plants can develop from them by vegetative reproduction. Sporangia can develop on the fronds, spores can be released, and the cycle can begin again. The life cycle of the fern is summarized in *Figure 24.5*.

24.1 LIFE CYCLES OF MOSSES, FERNS, AND CONIFERS **637**

CULTURAL DIVERSITY

Ferns as Food Considered a gourmet delicacy by some, humans have eaten cooked and raw fern fiddleheads for centuries. In the past, it is known that Native Americans often dug rhizomes of some ferns, baked them, and then ate the starchy tissue inside. In many places in Asia, the oriental water fern is still planted in rice patties, harvested, then eaten raw or cooked.

 Indiana Academic Standards

Pages 636–637: B.1.11

The Life Cycle of Conifers

The dominant stage in conifers is the sporophyte generation. One of the more familiar conifer sporophytes is shown in *Figure 24.6A*. The adult conifer produces male and female cones on separate branches of one plant. Cones contain spore-producing structures, or sporangia, on their scales.

Female cones, which are larger than the male cones, develop two ovules on the upper surface of each cone scale. Each ovule contains a sporangium with a diploid cell that undergoes meiosis and produces four megaspores. A **megaspore** is a female spore that eventually can become the female gametophyte. One of the four megaspores survives and grows by cell divisions

into the female gametophyte. It consists of hundreds of cells and is dependent on the sporophyte for protection and nutrition. Within the female gametophyte are two or more archegonia, each containing an egg.

Male cones have sporangia that undergo meiosis to produce male spores called **microspores.** Each microspore can develop into a male gametophyte, or pollen grain. Each pollen grain, with its hard, water-resistant outer covering, is a male gametophyte. Examples of male and female conifer gametophytes are shown in *Figure 24.7*.

In conifers, pollination is the transfer of pollen grains from the male cone to the female cone. Pollination can occur when a wind-borne pollen grain falls near the opening in one of the

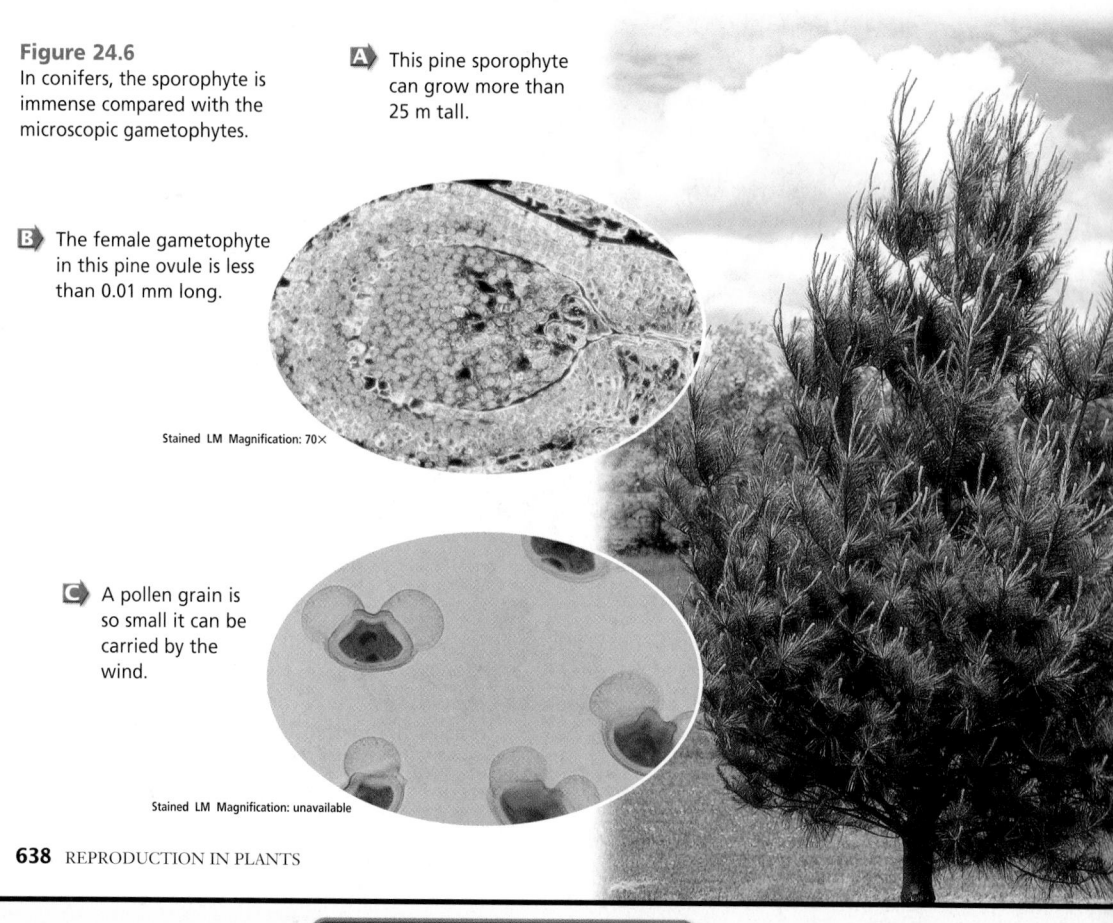

Figure 24.6
In conifers, the sporophyte is immense compared with the microscopic gametophytes.

A This pine sporophyte can grow more than 25 m tall.

B The female gametophyte in this pine ovule is less than 0.01 mm long.

Stained LM Magnification: 70×

C A pollen grain is so small it can be carried by the wind.

Stained LM Magnification: unavailable

638 REPRODUCTION IN PLANTS

INCLUSION STRATEGIES

Learning Disabled: *Visual-Spatial*
Prepare individual cards with a drawing on each showing one single stage of the life cycle of the pine. Provide a packet of cards to students who are

learning disabled. Have students arrange the cards in proper sequence to illustrate the complete life cycle for a typical pine. **L1** **ELL**

Figure 24.7
The life cycle of a conifer includes the production of two types of spores by the sporophyte. These spores develop into the male and female gametophytes.

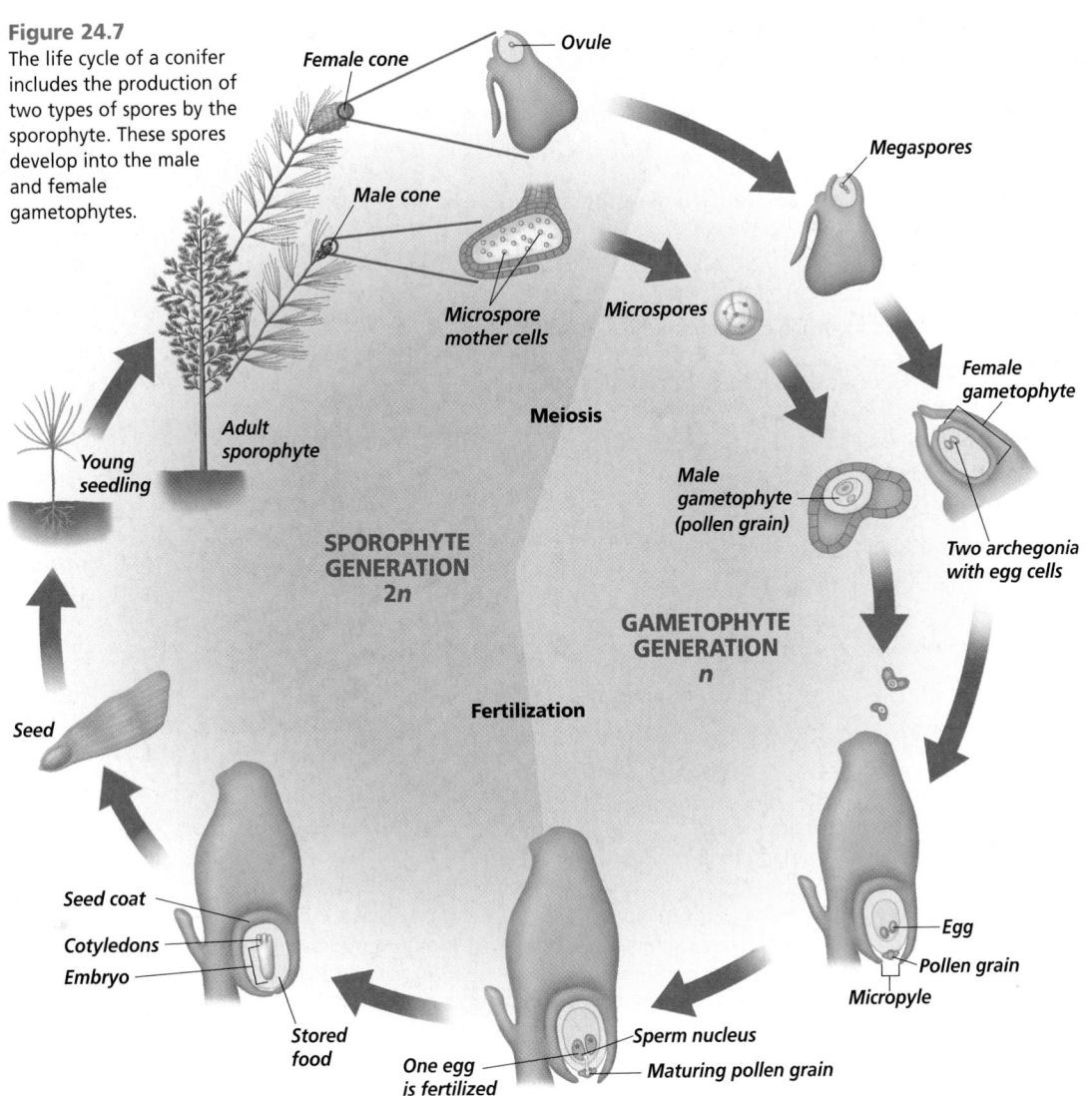

Ovule
Female cone
Megaspores
Male cone
Microspore mother cells
Microspores
Female gametophyte
Meiosis
Male gametophyte (pollen grain)
Two archegonia with egg cells
Adult sporophyte
Young seedling
SPOROPHYTE GENERATION 2*n*
GAMETOPHYTE GENERATION *n*
Fertilization
Seed
Egg
Pollen grain
Micropyle
Seed coat
Cotyledons
Embryo
Stored food
One egg is fertilized
Sperm nucleus
Maturing pollen grain

ovules of the female cone. The opening of the ovule is called the **micropyle** (MI kruh pile). The pollen grain adheres to a sticky drop of fluid that covers the micropyle. As the fluid evaporates, the pollen grain is drawn closer to the micropyle. Although pollination has occurred, fertilization does not take place for at least a year. The pollen grain and the female gametophyte will mature during this time.

As the pollen grain matures, it produces a pollen tube that grows through the micropyle and into the ovule. A sperm nucleus from the male gametophyte moves through the pollen tube to the egg. If fertilization occurs, a zygote forms. It is nourished by the female gametophyte and can develop into an embryo with several cotyledons. The cotyledons will nourish the sporophyte after germination.

24.1 LIFE CYCLES OF MOSSES, FERNS, AND CONIFERS **639**

Visual Learning
Figure 24.7 To reinforce the concept of diploid versus haploid, ask students to assign a specific chromosome number to each stage in Figure 24.7. Explain that the diploid number for this species is 24. **L2**

Biology Journal
Gametophytes and Sporophytes
Have students compare and contrast gametophyte and sporophyte generations of mosses, ferns, and conifers. **L2**

Problem-Solving Lab 24.1

Problem-Solving Lab 24.1 on p. 640.

Purpose
Students will categorize traits of mosses, ferns, and pines.

Process Skills
compare and contrast, think critically, analyze information, apply concepts, predict

Teaching Strategies
Allow students to work in groups and to use their text as a reference.

Thinking Critically
1. most—moss, fern; least—moss, conifer
2. a. no; yes; Gametophytes are in male and female cones.
   b. no; yes; sporophyte is large, gametophyte is minute
3. Student answers should agree with the table.

Assessment
Performance Have students grow ferns from spores, which are available from biological supply houses. Use the Performance Task Assessment List for Carrying Out a Strategy and Collecting Data in **PASC**, p. 97. **L3** **ELL**

PROJECT

Dichotomous Keys Have students prepare a dichotomous key to identify mosses, ferns, and conifers based on plant life cycles. Students should test their keys by exchanging them with other students. **L2**

3 Assess

Problem-Solving Lab 24.1

Make and Use Tables

What characteristics do mosses, ferns, and conifers share?
It can help to organize information in a table, because characteristics, similarities, and differences are shown in a simple format.

Solve the Problem
Copy and complete the following data table using "yes" or "no."

Data Table			
Trait	Moss	Fern	Conifer
Has alternation of generations			
Film of water needed for fertilization			
Dominant gametophyte			
Dominant sporophyte			
Sporophyte is photosynthetic			
Produces seeds			
Produces sperm			
Produces pollen grains			
Produces eggs			

Thinking Critically

1. **Identify** Which two plant groups share the most characteristics? Which two share the fewest?
2. **Describe** While on a woodland trail, would you easily observe:
   a. a pine gametophyte? Sporophyte? Explain.
   b. a fern gametophyte? Sporophyte? Explain.
3. **Compare and Contrast** Using information from your table, compare and contrast reproduction among mosses, ferns, and conifers.

Figure 24.8
Conifer seeds germinate into new, young sporophytes such as the pine tree seedling shown here.

A seed coat forms around the ovule as the mature seed is produced. Mature seeds are released when the female cone opens.

When conditions are favorable, a released seed can germinate and grow into a new, young sporophyte, as shown in *Figure 24.8*. Review the stages of a conifer's life cycle in *Figure 24.7*. Use the *Problem-Solving Lab* on this page to further explore the characteristics of the life cycles of mosses, ferns, and conifers.

Section Assessment

Understanding Main Ideas
1. Explain how vegetative reproduction can produce a new plant. Provide an example.
2. How is the sporophyte generation of a moss dependent on the gametophyte generation?
3. Interpret the function of a plant's reproductive system.
4. Compare and contrast the life cycle of a fern and a conifer.

Thinking Critically
5. Why is the term alternation of generations appropriate to describe the life cycle of a plant?

SKILL REVIEW

6. **Sequence** Make an events-chain concept map of the life cycle of a fern, beginning with the prothallus. For more help, refer to *Sequence* in the Skill Handbook.

640 REPRODUCTION IN PLANTS

 in.bdol.glencoe.com/self_check_quiz

Section Assessment

1. A new plant grows from a plant organ or part of it; liverwort gemmae
2. for support and most of its nutrients
3. continuation of the species
4. The sporophyte is dominant in both. The fern gametophyte grows from a spore, produces male and female gametes, and is separate from the sporophyte. Conifer gametophytes are within male and female sporophyte cones. Conifers grow from seeds.
5. The sporophyte generation (2n) alternates with the gametophyte generation (n).
6. Prothallus→gametes→fertilization→ sporophyte→spore→prothallus

Section 24.2

Flowers and Flowering

Indiana Standards Standard B.1.15 Understand and explain that, in biological systems, structure and function must be considered together.

SECTION PREVIEW

Objectives
Identify the organs of a flower.

Examine how photoperiodism influences flowering.

Review Vocabulary
response: an organism's reaction to a change in its internal or external environment (p. 9)

New Vocabulary
petal
sepal
stamen
anther
pistil
ovary
photoperiodism
short-day plant
long-day plant
day-neutral plant

A Flower by Any Other Name

Using Prior Knowledge When you hear the word *flower*, what image comes to mind? Is it a fragrant rose, a yellow daisy, or a trumpet-shaped lily? These flowers have characteristics that are similar and others that are different. You may know that they all have petals, but what other parts are found in each of them? In this section you will read about a flower's organs, their functions, and how they vary from species to species. You also will learn how an external stimulus affects flowering times.

Assemble For one week, find images of flowers in magazines and other periodicals. With permission, cut them out and bring them to class. Try not to duplicate your selections. Create a class list of the name of each flower and assemble a classroom collage of the flower images.

Flowers display a variety of shapes and colors.

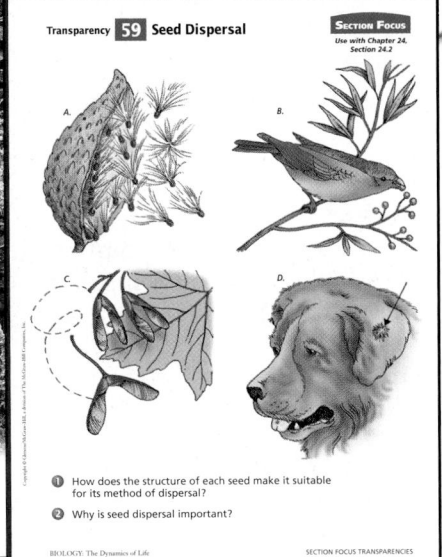

Transparency 59 Seed Dispersal

A. B. C. D.

❶ How does the structure of each seed make it suitable for its method of dispersal?

❷ Why is seed dispersal important?

BIOLOGY: The Dynamics of Life   SECTION FOCUS TRANSPARENCIES

What is a flower?

The process of sexual reproduction in flowering plants takes place in a flower, which is a complex structure made up of several organs. Some organs of the flower are directly involved in fertilization and seed production. Other floral organs function in pollination. There are probably as many different shapes, sizes, colors, and configurations of flowers as there are species of flowering plants. In fact, flower characteristics are often used in plant identification.

The structure of a flower

Even though there is an almost limitless variation in flower shapes and colors, all flowers share a basic structure. A flower's structure is genetically determined and usually made up of four kinds of organs: sepals, petals, stamens, and pistils. The flower parts you are probably most familiar with are the petals. **Petals** are usually the colorful structures at the top of a flower stem. The flower stem is called the peduncle. **Sepals** are usually leaflike and encircle the peduncle below the petals.

Inside the petals are the stamens. A **stamen** is the male reproductive organ of a flower. At the tip of the stamen is the **anther.** The anther produces pollen that eventually contains sperm.

Using Prior Knowledge

Assemble Lists of names will vary as will the collages created. Students might group their flowers by color, size, shape, numbers of flower parts, or whether the reproductive structures are obvious or not. Ask students what flower structures might be used by botanists to classify flowering plants.

24.2 FLOWERS AND FLOWERING **641**

Unit 7 *FAST FILE* Resources
BioLab Worksheet, pp. 103–104
Reinforcement and Study Guide in English, p. 107
Reinforcement and Study Guide in Spanish, p. 111
Transparency Worksheets, pp. 116, 125–130, 135–136

Reading Essentials for Biology, Section 24.2
Inside Story Poster
🖐 **Section Focus Transparency 59**
🖐 **Basic Concepts Transparencies 41, 42, 43**
🖐 **Reteaching Skills Transparency 37**

Purpose

to describe flower anatomy and identify the role flower parts play in reproduction

Teaching Strategies

Elicit what role is played by flower organs that are not important in fertilization. These organs attract pollinators or protect young or immature fertile flower parts. **L2**

Visual Learning

Ask students to use the captions to explain how the following pairs of terms are related: (a) sepals and calyx; (b) petals and corolla; (c) stamen and anther; (d) stigma and style; (e) ovary and ovule. **L1**

Critical Thinking

The shape of a flower may promote different pollination methods. For example, tubular flowers are probably pollinated by animals.

Chalkboard Activity

Write the following phrases on the chalkboard: contains chlorophyll, where meiosis takes place, contains gametophyte, is part of the sporophyte, contains diploid cells, forms spores, forms microspores, forms megaspores. Ask students to identify the flower organ or organs described by each phrase. **L2**

 Indiana Academic Standards

Pages 642–643: B.1.15

INSIDE STORY

Identifying Organs of a Flower

Figure 24.9
Of the four major organs of a flower, only two—the stamens and pistils—are reproductive organs directly involved in seed development. Sepals and petals support and protect the reproductive organs and help attract pollinators. The structure of a typical flower is illustrated here. **Critical Thinking** *How are different flower shapes important to a plant's survival?*

St.-John's-Wort

A **Petals** These are usually brightly colored and often have perfume or nectar at their bases to attract pollinators. In many flowers, the petal also provides a surface for insect pollinators to rest on while feeding. All of the petals of a flower are called the corolla.

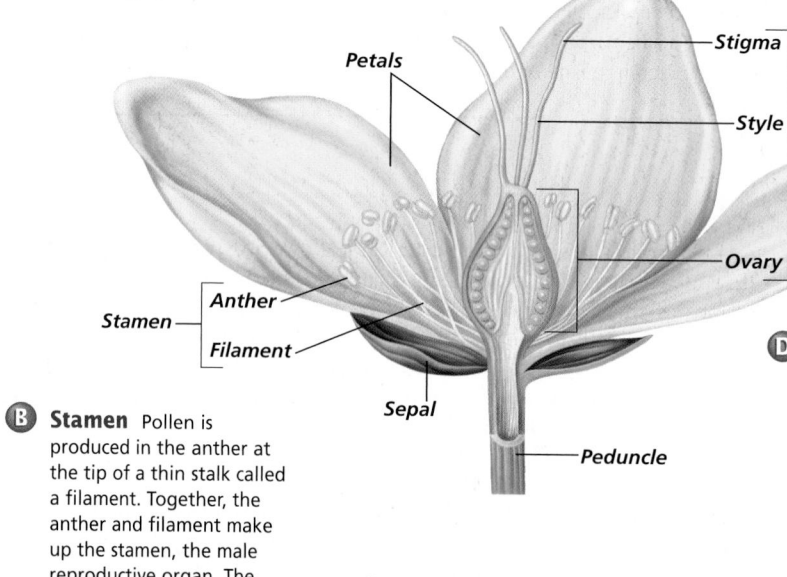

B **Stamen** Pollen is produced in the anther at the tip of a thin stalk called a filament. Together, the anther and filament make up the stamen, the male reproductive organ. The number of stamens in flowers varies from none to many, like the flower shown here.

C **Sepals** A ring of sepals makes up the outermost portion of the flower. Sepals serve as a protective covering for the flower bud. They sometimes are colored and resemble petals. All of the sepals of a flower are called the calyx.

D **Pistil** The female reproductive organ of a flower is the pistil. At the top of the pistil is the stigma that receives the pollen. The style is a slender stalk that connects the stigma to the ovary in which ovules grow. Each ovule can produce an egg. If fertilization occurs, the ovule develops into the seed. The number of pistils in flowers varies from none to many.

INCLUSION STRATEGIES

English Language Learners/Learning Disabled Have students create a table with the heads *Male, Female, Neither Male nor Female.* Ask students to list the following structures beneath the appropriate head: stamen, pistil, anther, calyx, corolla, ovary, stigma, petal, sepal, pollen, egg, ovule, style. **L1** **ELL**

At the center of the flower, attached to the top of the peduncle, is usually one or more pistils. The **pistil** is the female organ of the flower. The bottom portion of the pistil is the **ovary,** a structure with one or more ovules, each usually contains one egg. As you read in the previous section, the female gametophyte develops inside the ovule. You can learn more about floral structure and practice your lab skills in the *BioLab* at the end of this chapter.

Modifications in flower structure

A flower that has all four organs—sepals, petals, stamens, and pistils—is called a complete flower, as shown in *Figure 24.9.* The morning glory, shown in *Figure 24.10A,* is another example of a complete flower. A flower that lacks one or more organs is called an incomplete flower. For example, walnut trees have separate

male and female flowers. The male flowers, as shown in *Figure 24.10B,* have stamens but no pistils; the female flowers bear pistils but no stamens.

The flowers of plants such as sweet corn, as shown in *Figure 24.10C,* and grasses, have no petals and are adapted for pollination by wind rather than by animals. You can explore flower adaptations further in the *Problem-Solving Lab* on the next page.

Photoperiodism

The relative lengths of daylight and darkness each day have a significant effect on the rate of growth and the timing of flower production in many species of flowering plants. For example, some chrysanthemum plants produce flowers only during the fall, when the length of daylight is getting shorter and the length of darkness is getting longer daily.

Word Origin

photoperiodism from the Greek words *photos,* meaning "light," and *periodos,* meaning "a period"; The flowering response of a plant to periods of dark and light is photoperiodism.

Figure 24.10
The diversity of flower forms is evidence of the success of flowering plants.

A The petals of the morning glory are fused together to form a bell shape.

C The tassels at the top of a corn plant are male flowers.

B The male flowers of the walnut tree form long structures called catkins.

643

Purpose

Students will study and interpret diagrams of flower cross sections.

Process Skills

think critically, compare and contrast, interpret scientific illustrations

Teaching Strategies

■ Review the basic anatomy of a flower before this activity.

■ Make sure that students understand the differences between complete and incomplete flowers.

■ Review the characteristics of monocots and dicots.

■ Illustrate a "cross-section" cut using an apple as an example.

Thinking Critically

1. a. monocot; flower parts in a multiple of three
   b. dicot; flower parts in a multiple of four
   c. dicot; flower parts in a multiple of four
2. B and C are complete flowers. D and E are incomplete flowers.
3. B and C have both stamens and pistils.
4. E requires cross-pollination; it does not have stamen. D cannot be pollinated; it does not have a pistil.

Modified Assessment

Performance Have students copy diagrams C, D, and E and label the flower parts. Use the Performance Task Assessment List for Scientific Drawing in PASC, p. 127. **L1** **ELL**

✓**Reading Check** In midsummer, the amount of darkness daily is not enough to induce flowering.

644

Problem-Solving Lab 24.2

Interpret Scientific Illustrations

How do flowers differ? There is great variation in flower shape. This variation occurs when certain flower parts are fused together, parts are rearranged, or when parts may be totally missing. Almost all dicot plants will have flower parts that are in multiples of four or five. For example, a plant having eight or ten petals would be a dicot. Almost all monocot plants have flower parts in multiples of three.

Solve the Problem

Diagram A shows a flower with its parts labeled. Imagine that the flower has been cut along the dashed line. Diagram B is an enlarged cross-section view of the bottom half. The flower is from a dicot plant because there are five sepals, petals, and stamens.

Pistil
Stamen
Petal
Sepal

Thinking Critically

Use diagrams B, C, D, and E to answer the following questions.

1. **Determine** Diagrams C, D, and E also are diagrammatic cross-section views of flowers. Is diagram:
   a. C a monocot or dicot? Explain.
   b. D a monocot or dicot? Explain.
   c. E a monocot or dicot? Explain.
2. **Infer** Which diagrams are complete flowers, and which are incomplete flowers?
3. **Predict** Which flowers might be capable of self-pollination? Explain.
4. **Predict** Which flowers require another flower for pollination? Explain.

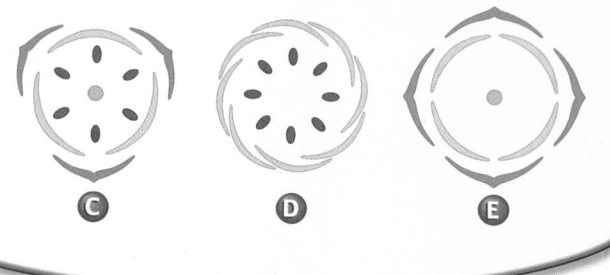

644 REPRODUCTION IN PLANTS

A grower who wants to produce these chrysanthemum flowers during the middle of summer must artificially increase the length of darkness. The grower can do this by draping a black cloth over and around the chrysanthemum plants before sunset each day, and then removing it the following morning. The response of flowering plants to daily daylight-darkness conditions is called **photoperiodism.**

Plant biologists originally thought that the length of daylight controlled flowering. However, they now know that it is the length of darkness that controls flowering, and that the darkness must be uninterrupted. Each plant species has a critical period—specific daylight-darkness conditions that will initiate flowering. Plants can be placed in one of four categories depending on the daylight-darkness conditions that they require for flower production. Plants are short-day plants, long-day plants, day-neutral plants, or intermediate day plants.

A **short-day plant** flowers when the number of daylight hours is shorter than that of its critical period. Short-day plants usually flower sometime during late summer, fall, winter, or spring. Examples of short-day plants include asters, poinsettias, strawberries, ragweed, and pansies, as shown in *Figure 24.11A.*

✓**Reading Check** **Explain** why pansies stop flowering in midsummer.

A **long-day plant** flowers when the number of daylight hours is longer than that of its critical period. Long-day plants usually flower in summer, but also will flower if lighted continually. Carnations, petunias, potatoes, spinach, and wheat are long-day plants, as well as the lettuce shown in *Figure 24.11B.*

CHALLENGE ACTIVITY

Design an Experiment Advise students that the light that triggers flower production does not have to reach the plant's flower buds, but must reach and be detected by the leaves. Have students design an experiment to prove that it is the leaf that must be stimulated by light for the plant to achieve flowering. Suggest that it is possible to place parts of the plant behind light barriers while other parts of the same plant are exposed to light. **L3**

Figure 24.11
Photoperiodism refers to a plant's response to the changing length of night.

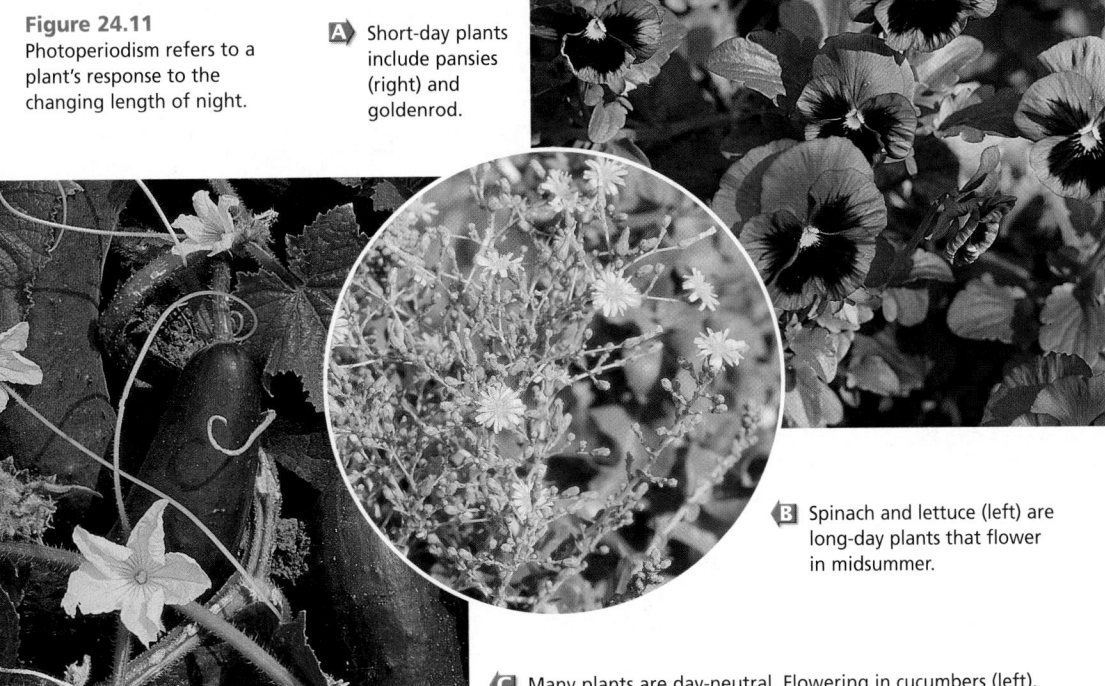

A Short-day plants include pansies (right) and goldenrod.

B Spinach and lettuce (left) are long-day plants that flower in midsummer.

C Many plants are day-neutral. Flowering in cucumbers (left), tomatoes, and corn is not influenced by a dark period.

As long as the proper growing conditions exist, some plants will flower over a range in the number of daylight hours. These plants are called **day-neutral plants**. This category includes many tropical plants, roses, cotton, dandelions and many other weeds, as well as the cucumbers shown in *Figure 24.11C*.

An intermediate-day plant will not flower if days are shorter or longer than its critical period. Several grasses and sugarcane are in this category.

Photoperiodism is a physiological adaptation of all flowering plants that ensures the production of flowers at a time when there is an abundant population of pollinators. This is important because pollination is a critical event in the life cycles of all flowering plants.

Section Assessment

Understanding Main Ideas

1. Compare and contrast sepals and petals.
2. Describe the male and female reproductive organs of a flower.
3. Explain why walnut flowers are considered incomplete flowers.
4. Discuss how photoperiodism influences flowering.
5. Infer why a gardener's holly plant flowers every spring but never produces holly berries.

Thinking Critically

6. In the middle of the summer a florist receives a large shipment of short-day plants. Infer what the florist must do to induce flowering.

SKILL REVIEW

7. **Get the Big Picture** Explain why the structure of a wind-pollinated flower is often different from that of an insect pollinated flower. For more help, refer to *Get the Big Picture* in the **Skill Handbook**.

 in.bdol.glencoe.com/self_check_quiz

---

3 Assess

DAILY INTERVENTION

Check for Understanding
Ask students to explain the relationships of the following word groups. **L2** **ELL**
a. stamen—anther
b. pistil—stigma—ovary
c. ovary—ovule

Reteach
Obtain a flower model. As you point out structures on the model, have students name each structure and explain its function. **L1**

Resources
For more practice, use *Reading Essentials for Biology,* Section 24.2.

Extension

Linguistic Have students determine the meaning of the terms *androecium, gynoecium,* and *perianth.* Have them assign the term *sterile* or *nonsterile* to each flower part. **L3**

✔ **Assessment**

Performance Provide students with a diagram of a typical flower. Have them label the parts of the flower and identify reproductive parts. **L1**

Indiana Academic Standards

Pages 644–645: B.1.15, B.1.18

Section Assessment

1. Both are leaflike structures. Petals are bright colors. Sepals are usually green.
2. male—the stamen, which consists of the anther and filament; female—the pistil, which consists of a stigma, style, and ovary
3. Walnut flowers are incomplete because they do not have both pistils and stamens.
4. Flowering is controlled by photoperiodism.
5. The plant has female flowers and there is no plant nearby with male flowers, or it has male flowers.
6. The florist should cover the greenhouse with tarps each afternoon to shorten the day and lengthen the night.
7. Wind-pollinated flowers are small and lack petals. Insect-pollinated flowers have brightly colored petals and nectar.

1 Focus

Bellringer
Section Focus Transparency 60

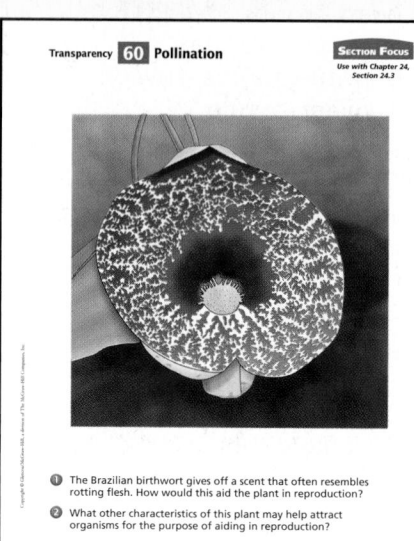

Transparency **60** Pollination

SECTION FOCUS
Use with Chapter 24, Section 24.3

❶ The Brazilian birthwort gives off a scent that often resembles rotting flesh. How would this aid the plant in reproduction?

❷ What other characteristics of this plant may help attract organisms for the purpose of aiding in reproduction?

BIOLOGY: The Dynamics of Life

SECTION FOCUS TRANSPARENCIES

Finding Main Ideas

Outline Students' outlines will vary. Make sure they use the red and blue titles in the section to guide their outlining. Struggling students may be confused by the traditional outline with Roman numerals followed by uppercase letters, numbers, and lowercase letters. Ask these students to make a simple numbered list of important concepts under each heading.

Section 24.3

The Life Cycle of a Flowering Plant

Indiana Standards Standard B.1.15 Understand and explain that, in biological systems, structure and function must be considered together.

SECTION PREVIEW

Objectives
Survey and identify the methods of reproduction, growth, and development in flowering plants.
Outline the processes in which cells differentiate during the formation of seeds and fruits and during seed germination.

Review Vocabulary
pollination: transfer of pollen grains from male reproductive organs to female reproductive organs in plants; usually within the same species (p. 254)

New Vocabulary
polar nuclei
double fertilization
endosperm
dormancy
germination
radicle
hypocotyl

"Tall oaks from little acorns grow." —David Everett (1769–1813)

Finding Main Ideas On a piece of paper, construct an outline about the life cycle of a flowering plant, such as the bee orchid shown to the right. Use the red and blue titles in this section as a guideline. As you read the paragraphs that follow the titles, add important information and vocabulary words to your outline.

Example:

I. The Life Cycle of an Anthophyte
  A. Development of the female gametophyte
   1. Occurs in ovule
   2. Involves meiosis
   3. Polar nuclei formed

Use your outline to help you answer questions in the Section Assessment on page 657. For more help, refer to *Outline* in the **Skill Handbook.**

Bee orchid, *Ophrys speculum*

The Life Cycle of an Anthophyte

The life cycle of flowering plants is similar to that of conifers in many ways. In both coniferophytes and anthophytes, the gametophyte generation is contained within the sporophyte. Many of the reproductive structures are also similar. However, anthophytes are the only plants that produce flowers and fruits. *Figure 24.12* summarizes the life cycle of a flowering plant.

Development of the female gametophyte

In anthophytes, the female gametophyte is formed inside the ovule within the ovary. In the ovule, a cell undergoes meiosis and produces haploid megaspores. One of these megaspores can develop into the female gametophyte, but the other three spores usually die. In most flowering plants, the megaspore's nucleus undergoes mitosis three times, producing eight haploid nuclei. These eight nuclei make up the female gametophyte. Cell walls form around each of six nuclei, one of which is now called the egg cell.

RESOURCE MANAGER

Unit 7 *FAST FILE* Resources
  MiniLab Worksheet, p. 102
  Reinforcement and Study Guide in English, p. 108
  Reinforcement and Study Guide in Spanish, p. 112
  Critical Thinking/Problem Solving, p. 114
  Transparency Worksheet, p. 117

Reading Essentials for Biology, Section 24.3
Laboratory Manual, pp. 151–154, 155–158
 Section Focus Transparency 60

Figure 24.12
In the life cycle of a flowering plant, the sporophyte generation nourishes and protects the developing gametophyte.

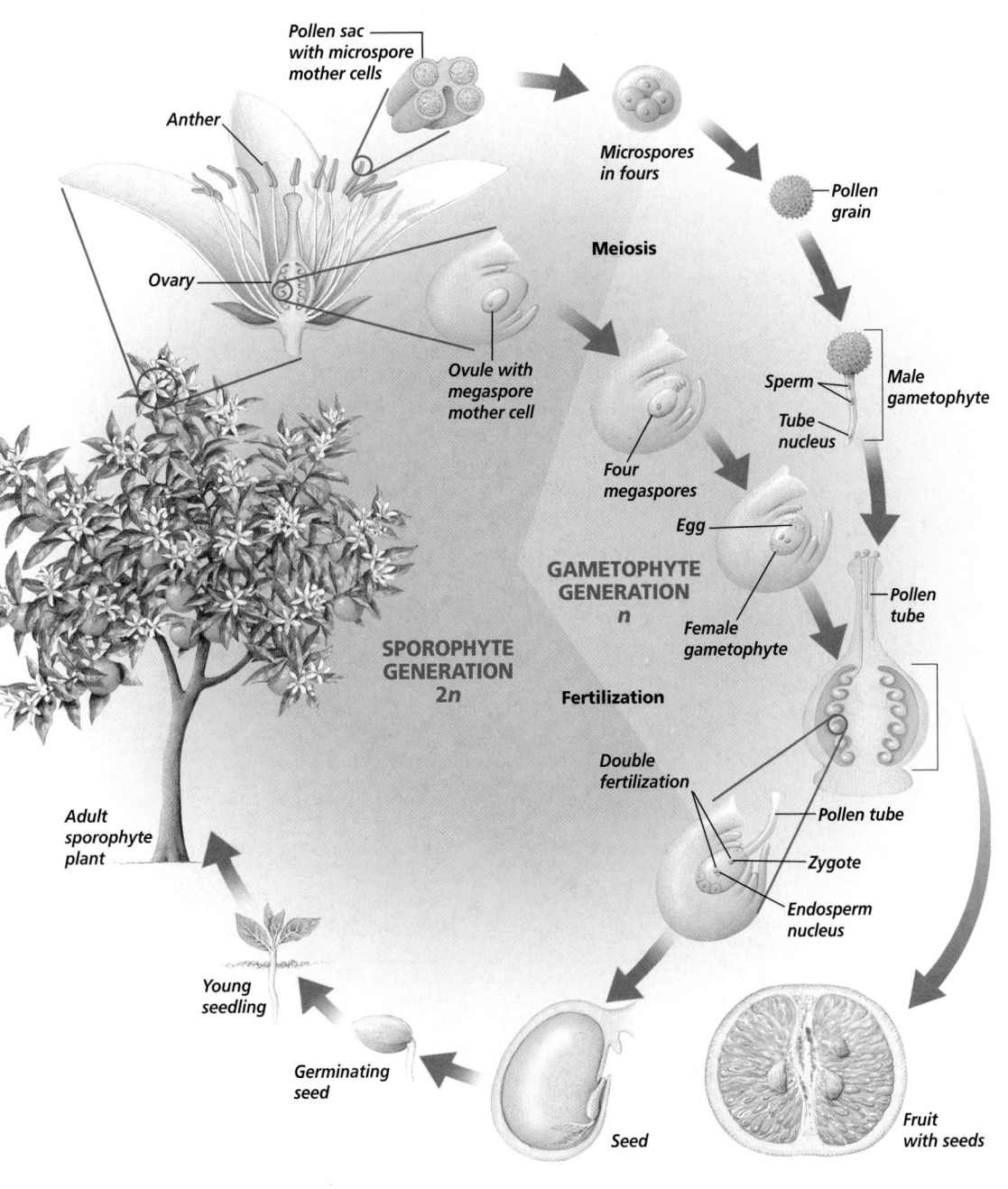

Pollen sac with microspore mother cells

Anther

Ovary

Ovule with megaspore mother cell

Microspores in fours

Meiosis

Pollen grain

Sperm

Tube nucleus

Male gametophyte

Four megaspores

Egg

GAMETOPHYTE GENERATION *n*

Female gametophyte

Pollen tube

SPOROPHYTE GENERATION 2*n*

Fertilization

Double fertilization

Pollen tube

Zygote

Endosperm nucleus

Adult sporophyte plant

Young seedling

Germinating seed

Seed

Fruit with seeds

2 Teach

Seed Structure Show students the new sporophyte inside a peanut. It is the structure with two tiny leaves. **CAUTION:** *Do not allow students to eat the peanuts as some students may be allergic to them.*

Microscope Activity
Visual-Spatial Have students view prepared slides of *Lilium* ovaries. Ask students to draw and label an ovule. **L1**

Biology Journal
Flowering Plant Life Cycle Have students write a paragraph in their journal outlining the steps of a flowering plant's life cycle. Encourage them to illustrate the concepts with drawings. **L2**

INCLUSION STRATEGIES

Learning Disabled Provide students with a black-line drawing of the life cycle of a flowering plant. Using colored pencils, have them shade in the gametophyte stage and the sporophyte stage in two different colors. **L1 ELL**

Figure 24.13 The nuclei in the ovule are haploid while the nuclei in leaf cells are diploid.

Reinforcement

Show students a flower pistil that has been cut open to reveal the ovary. Ask them to point to where the following occur: growth of pollen tube, development of female gametophyte, and double fertilization. **L2**

Discussion

Linguistic Discuss the following ideas with your students.
1. Go over the use of the term *double fertilization.* Point out that the same egg cell is not fertilized twice.
2. What is the function of an endosperm? a food supply for the plant embryo
3. What can develop from a fertilized ovule? a seed
4. What can develop from a newly formed seed? a new plant **L1**

Figure 24.13
The eight nuclei produced by the megaspore form the female gametophyte inside an ovule of an anthophyte's flower. **Differentiate** *How do these nuclei differ from those in the leaf cells of this anthophyte?*

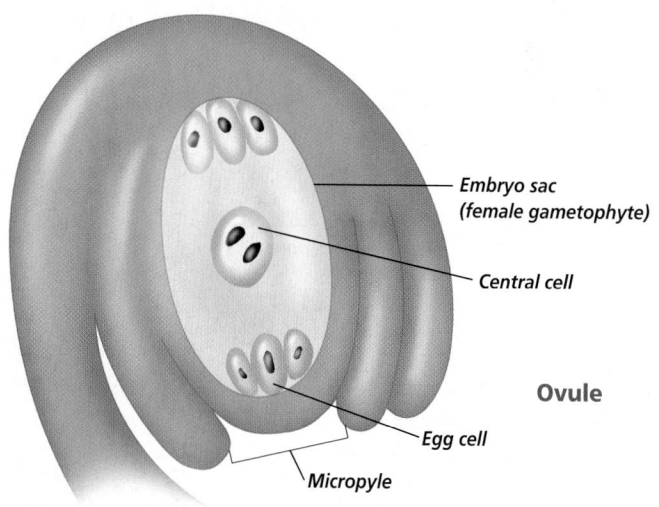

Embryo sac (female gametophyte)

Central cell

Ovule

Egg cell

Micropyle

The two remaining nuclei, which are called **polar nuclei,** are enclosed in one cell. This cell, the central cell, is located at the center of the female gametophyte. The egg cell is near the micropyle, as shown in *Figure 24.13.* The other five cells eventually disintegrate.

Development of the male gametophyte

The formation of the male gametophyte begins in the anther, as seen in *Figure 24.14.* Haploid microspores are produced by meiosis within the pollen sac. The nucleus of each microspore undergoes mitosis. A thick, protective wall surrounds these two nuclei. This structure is the immature male gametophyte, or pollen grain. The nuclei within the pollen grain are the tube nucleus and the generative nucleus. When the pollen grains mature, the anther usually splits open.

Figure 24.14
Meiotic division of each of many cells within the anther produces four microspores. These microspores develop into male gametophytes or pollen grains.

Pollen sacs

Microspore mother cell (2n)

MEIOSIS

Tube nucleus

Generative nucleus

ANTHER

Pollen grain (male gametophyte)

Microspores (n)

648 REPRODUCTION IN PLANTS

USING MODELS

Double Fertilization: *Kinesthetic* Use a plastic sandwich bag to represent a female gametophyte. Place eight small balls of clay of the same color within the bag and explain what each ball represents. Arrange the eight balls to model the female gametophyte shown in Figure 24.13. Introduce two small balls of clay of a different color to the bag. Explain that each ball represents the two sperm nuclei that enter the female gametophyte. Fuse one sperm with the egg and explain that this represents the zygote, which is now diploid. Fuse the other with the central cell, double fertilization. Explain that this structure is triploid and forms endosperm. **L1**

Figure 24.15
The shape, color, and size of a flower reflect its relationship with a pollinator.

A Ragweed's wind-pollinated flowers are small and green and lack structures that would block wind currents.

B A butterfly can be a pollinator when it visits a flower to sip nectar.

C Flowers pollinated by hummingbirds are often tubular and colored bright red or yellow but may have little scent.

D The ultraviolet markings of some flowers guide pollinating insects to a flower's nectar.

Pollination

In anthophytes, pollination is the transfer of the pollen grain from the anther to the stigma. Depending on the type of flower, the pollen can be carried to the stigma by wind, water, or animals. Plant reproduction is most successful when the pollination rate is high, which means that the pistil of a flower receives enough pollen of its own species to fertilize the egg in each ovule. Although it may seem wasteful for wind-pollinated plants to produce such large amounts of pollen, it does help ensure pollination. Many

anthophytes have elaborate mechanisms that help ensure that pollen grains are deposited in the right place at the right time. Some of these are shown in *Figure 24.15*.

Most anthophytes that are pollinated by animals produce nectar in their flowers. Nectar is a highly concentrated food sought by visitors to these flowers. It is a liquid made up of proteins and sugars and usually collects in the cuplike area at the base of petals. Animals, such as insects and birds, brush up against the anthers while trying to get to the nectar.

Ask students to answer the following questions. (a) Why is pollen needed for fertilization? It contains sperm cells. (b) Why must the pollen that fertilizes a flower be from the same species as the female flower? Chromosome numbers and alleles must be identical for fertilization to occur. (c) What will happen if pollen lands on the wrong species of flower? No pollen tube will form and fertilization will not occur. **L2**

Inquiry

Discussion Form student groups and ask them to make lists of advantages and disadvantages of cross-pollination and self-pollination. Ask them to predict what environmental factors might contribute to the success of each type of pollination. Have a class discussion about the predictions of each group. **L2 COOP LEARN**

Portfolio

Cross- and Self-Pollination Have students create drawings that explain the concepts of cross-pollination and self-pollination. Instruct students to include proper labels and titles for the drawings. Non-artistic students may be provided with a flower outline that they can trace for their diagrams. **L2 ELL**

PROJECT

Are bees the best?: *Intrapersonal*
Members of the *Brassica* genus can be pollinated with cotton swabs, paint brushes, and dried bees. Have students design an experiment to determine whether or not bees are the most efficient pollinators. **L3**

Students may think that "hay fever" is an allergy to hay.

Uncover the Misconception

Hay fever is a term used to describe an allergic reaction to the protein present in pollen. Often, the pollen is from plants that flower in the early fall or spring.

Demonstrate the Concept

Ask students to research what kinds of plants commonly cause hay fever. They should also determine if those plants are common in their environment.

Assess New Knowledge

Have students write a short essay about the common causes of hay fever in their environment.

Concept Development

Corn has male and female flowers on different parts of the same plant. Have students explain what a corn tassel is, where the female corn flower is located, and what corn silk is. The corn tassel is composed of all the stamens of many male flowers. The corn silk is composed of all the styles of many female flowers. The corn kernels on the cob are fertilized fruits of the plant.

The pollen that attaches to them can be carried to another flower, resulting in pollination. Some insects also gather pollen to use as food. By producing nectar and attracting animal pollinators, animal-pollinated plants are able to promote pollination with lesser amounts of pollen.

Some nectar-feeding pollinators are attracted to a flower by its color or scent or both. Some of the bright, vivid flowers attract pollinators, such as butterflies and bees. Some of these flowers have markings that are invisible to the human eye but are easily seen by insects, as shown in *Figure 24.15D*. Flowers that are pollinated by beetles and flies have a strong scent but are often dull in color.

Many flowers have structural adaptations that favor cross-pollination—pollination between two plants of the same species. This results in greater genetic variation because a sperm from one plant fertilizes an egg from another. For example, the flowers of certain species of orchids resemble female wasps. A male wasp visits the flower and attempts to mate with it and becomes covered with pollen, which is deposited on orchids it may visit in the future.

Fertilization

Once a pollen grain has reached the stigma of the pistil, several events take place before fertilization occurs. Inside each pollen grain are two haploid nuclei, the tube nucleus and the generative nucleus. The tube nucleus directs the growth of the pollen tube down through the pistil to the ovary, as shown in *Figure 24.16*. The generative nucleus divides by mitosis, producing two sperm nuclei. The sperm nuclei move through the pollen tube to a tiny opening in the ovule called the micropyle.

Within the ovule is the female gametophyte. One of the sperm unites with the egg forming a diploid zygote, which begins the new sporophyte generation. The other sperm nucleus fuses with the central cell, which

Figure 24.16
In flowering plants, part of the male gametophyte grows through the pistil to reach the female gametophyte. Double fertilization involves two sperm nuclei. A zygote (2n) and endosperm (3n) are formed.

Pollen grain

Stigma

Style

Ovary

Central cell

Ovule

Egg cell

Two sperm nuclei

Pollen tube

Tube nucleus

Double Fertilization

One sperm fertilizes the central cell (3n)

One sperm fertilizes the egg cell (2n)

650   REPRODUCTION IN PLANTS

CHALLENGE ACTIVITY

Pollination Guaranteed There are many different mechanisms to ensure pollination. Tell students about the carrion flowers that have a fragrance similar to rotting flesh that attracts its pollinators—flies and beetles. One species of aquatic plant releases its pollen in a "pollen boat" that floats on the water's surface until it slides down the dimple created by the surface tension around nearby flowers. Have students research other unique pollination strategies and present their findings in an illustrated report. **L3**

Figure 24.17
A fruit usually consists of seeds and the surrounding mature ovary of a flowering plant.

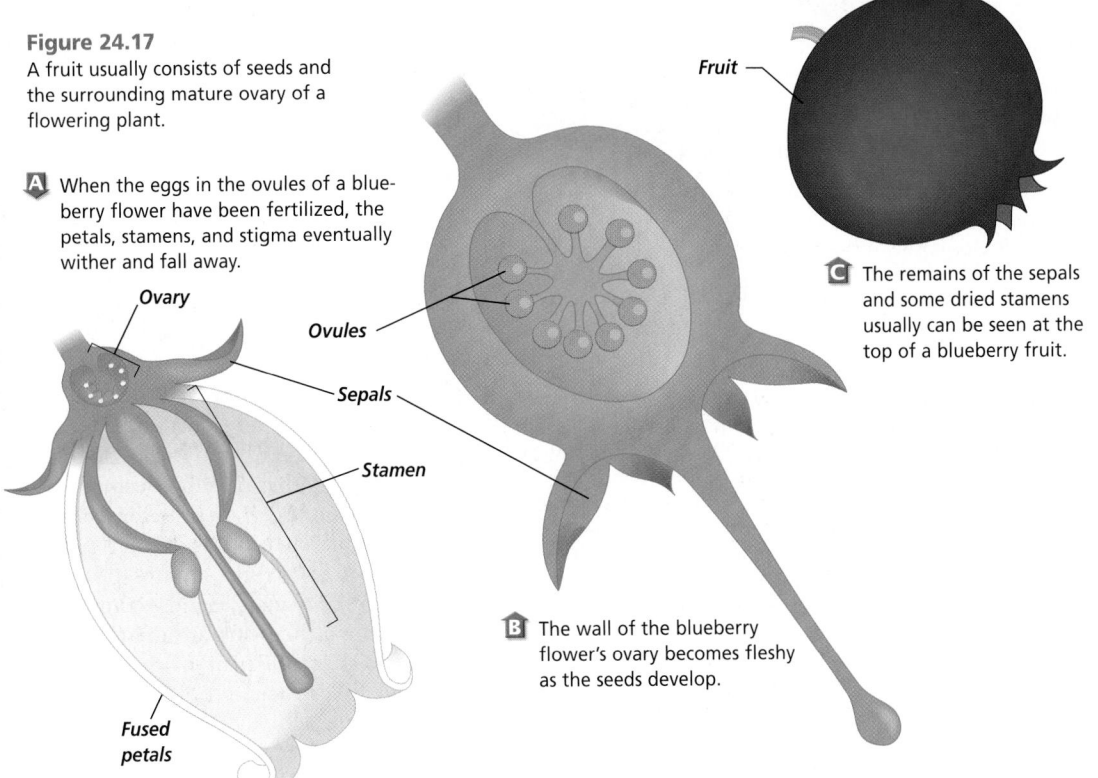

A When the eggs in the ovules of a blueberry flower have been fertilized, the petals, stamens, and stigma eventually wither and fall away.

Ovary

Ovules

Sepals

Stamen

Fused petals

Fruit

C The remains of the sepals and some dried stamens usually can be seen at the top of a blueberry fruit.

B The wall of the blueberry flower's ovary becomes fleshy as the seeds develop.

contains the polar nuclei, to form a cell with a triploid (3*n*) nucleus. This process, in which one sperm fertilizes the egg and the other sperm joins with the central cell, is called **double fertilization.** Double fertilization is unique to anthophytes and is illustrated in *Figure 24.16.* The triploid nucleus will divide many times, eventually forming the endosperm of the seed. The **endosperm** is food storage tissue that supports development of the embryo in anthophyte seeds.

Many flower ovaries contain more than one ovule. For each ovule to become a seed, at least one pollen grain must land on the stigma for each ovule contained in the ovary. In a watermelon plant, for example, hundreds of pollen grains are required to pollinate a

flower if each ovule is to be fertilized. You are probably familiar with the hundreds of seeds in a watermelon that are the result of this process.

Seeds and Fruits

The embryo contained within a seed is the next sporophyte generation. The formation of seeds and the fruits that enclose them, as shown in *Figure 24.17,* help ensure the survival of the next generation.

Seed formation

After fertilization takes place, seed development begins. Inside the ovule, the zygote divides and develops into the embryo plant. The triploid central cell develops into the seed's endosperm.

Word Origin

endosperm from the Greek words *endon*, meaning "within," and *sperma*, meaning "seed"; The endosperm is storage tissue found in the seeds of many anthophytes.

Concept Development
Show students an apple. Explain that unlike most fruits, which form from the ovary wall, the fleshy part of an apple forms from the swollen receptacle.

Activity
Visual-Spatial Have students prepare a chart comparing the amount of fiber in five fruits. They should explain why a high fiber diet is considered beneficial. **L2**

Career Path
TECH PREP **Courses in high school:** biology, botany, chemistry, mathematics
College: two- or four-year degree to become a crew supervisor
Other education sources: on-the-job training

Career Issue

With many issues and problems in the world, ask students if they think anyone should be concerned about the quality of a golf course. Have them explain the reasons for their opinions.

For More Information

For more information on becoming a greens keeper, students can write to:

Professional Grounds
    Management Society
Suite 104
120 Cockeysville Road
Hunt Valley, MD 21031

Enrichment

Visual-Spatial Have students research the different types of fruits: cypsela, berry, pome, follicle, legume, capsule, and aggregate. Ask them to create a visual that defines each fruit type and shows examples of each. **L3**

Greens Keeper

Do you like to work outside? Is golf your favorite sport? Then you already know the value of a well-manicured golf fairway. Maintaining golf fairways is one of the responsibilities of a greens keeper.

Skills for the Job

A greens keeper maintains both the playing quality and the beauty of a golf course. Beginning greens keepers usually learn on the job and spend their days mowing the greens. Greens keepers who want to manage large crews will need a two- or four-year degree in turf management and a certificate in grounds management. They must be thoroughly familiar with different types of grasses, the growing conditions that each require, and the pests, diseases, and environmental factors that can affect them. Greens keepers also must know what corrective measures to take when something affects the grasses so that fairways can be kept in excellent condition. Other careers in turf management include maintaining the grounds of shopping centers, schools, sports playing fields, cemeteries, office buildings, and other locations.

 For more careers in related fields, visit in.bdol.glencoe.com/careers

The wall of the ovule becomes the seed coat, which can aid in seed dispersal and help protect the embryo until it begins growing.

Fruit formation

As the seeds develop, the surrounding ovary enlarges and becomes the fruit. Sometimes other flower organs become part of the fruit. A fruit is the structure that contains the seeds of an anthophyte.

A fruit is as unique to an anthophyte as is its flower, and many anthophytes can be identified by examining their fruit. You are familiar with plants that develop fleshy fruits, such as apples, grapes, melons, tomatoes, and cucumbers. Other plants develop dry fruits such as peanuts, sunflower "seeds," and walnuts. In dry fruits, the ovary around the seeds hardens as the fruit matures. Some plant foods that we call vegetables or grains are actually fruits, as shown in ***Figure 24.18***.

Figure 24.18
A fruit is usually the ripened ovary of a flower that can contain one or more seeds. The most familiar fruits are those we consume as food.

B Fleshy fruits are juicy and full of water and sugars.

A Dry fruits have dry fruit walls. The ovary wall may start out with a fleshy appearance, as in hickory nuts or bean pods, but when the fruit is fully matured, the ovary wall is dry.

 Indiana Academic Standards
Pages 652–653: B.1.11, B.1.15

CULTURAL DIVERSITY

The History of Chocolate *Theobroma cacao* is a native tree from Central America. Its flowers grow from the tree's trunk. After pollination, large pods are produced that contain about 40 cacao beans. Because of its seeds, cacao was domesticated by the Mayas and Aztecs who turned the seeds into a rich brown drink called chocolate. Research about chocolate "addiction" indicates that it has both physiological and psychological bases.

Figure 24.19
A wide variety of seed-dispersal mechanisms have evolved among flowering plants.

Clinging fruits, like those of the cocklebur and burdock, are covered by hooks that stick to the hair, fur, or feathers of passing animals or the clothes of passing humans.

C Wind-dispersed seeds have structural adaptations that enable them to be held aloft while they drift away from their parent.

A The ripe pods of violets snap open with a pop, which sends a shower of small seeds in all directions.

Can you think of any vegetables that are actually fruits? For example, green peppers are fleshy fruits that are often referred to as vegetables.

Seed dispersal

A fruit not only protects the seeds inside it, but also may aid in dispersing those seeds away from the parent plant and into new habitats. The dispersal of seeds, as shown in *Figure 24.19,* is important because it reduces competition for sunlight, soil, and water between the parent plant and its offspring. Animals such as raccoons, deer, bears, and birds help distribute many seeds by eating fruits. They can carry the fruit some distance away from the parent plant before consuming it and spitting out the seeds. Or they may eat the fruit, seeds and all. Seeds that are eaten usually pass through the digestive system undamaged and are deposited in the animal's wastes. Squirrels, birds, and other nut gatherers may drop and lose seeds they collect, or even bury them only

to forget where. These seeds can then germinate far from the parent plant.

Plants, such as water lilies and coconut palms that grow in or near water, produce fruits or seeds with air pockets in the walls that enable them to float and drift away from the parent plant. The ripened fruits of many plants split open to release seeds with structural adaptations for dispersal by wind or by clinging to animal fur. Orchid seeds are so tiny that they can become airborne. The fruit of the poppy flower forms a seed-filled capsule that bobs about in the wind and sprinkles its tiny seeds like a salt shaker. Tumbleweed seeds are scattered as the plant rolls along the ground.

Seed germination

At maturity, seeds are fully formed. The seed coat dries and hardens, enabling the seed to survive environmental conditions that are unfavorable to the parent plant. The seeds of some plant species must germinate within a short period of time or die.

Activity

Logical Mathematical Water must be absorbed by seeds prior to germination in a process called imbibition. The volume change that occurs during imbibition can be measured through water displacement.

Place 50 mL of water in a graduated cylinder. Add 10 bean seeds. The new level of water less the original volume equals the volume of the 10 seeds. Remove the seeds from the cylinder and soak them in water overnight. The following day, add 50 mL of water to the graduated cylinder. Add the soaked beans and calculate their new volume. Have students use the water-displacement technique to calculate the percent of volume change that occurs through imbibition. **L2** **ELL**

Indiana Academic Standards

Pages 654–655: B.1.15, B.1.18

Figure 24.20
Seeds can remain dormant for long periods of time. Lupine seeds like these can germinate after remaining dormant for decades.

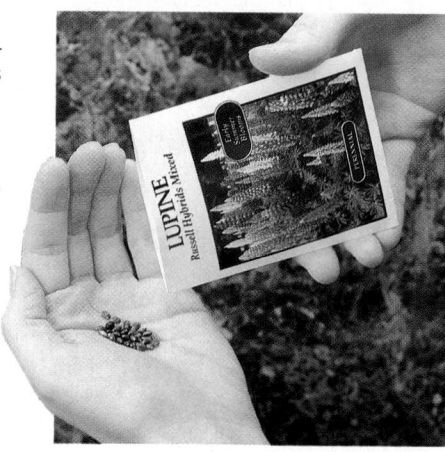

However, the seeds of some plant species can remain in the soil until conditions are favorable for growth and development of the new plant. This period of inactivity in a mature seed is called **dormancy.** The length of time a seed remains dormant can vary from one species to another. Some seeds, such as willow, magnolia, and maple remain dormant for only a few weeks after they mature. These

seeds cannot survive harsh conditions for long periods of time. Other plants produce seeds, like those shown in *Figure 24.20,* that can remain dormant for remarkably long periods of time. Even under harsh conditions, the seeds of desert wildflowers and some conifers can survive dormant periods of 15 to 20 years. Scientists discovered ancient seeds of the East Indian Lotus, *Nelumbo nucifera,* in China, which they have radiocarbon dated to be more than a thousand years old. Imagine their amazement when these seeds germinated!

Requirements for germination

Dormancy ends when the seed is ready to germinate. **Germination** is the beginning of the development of the embryo into a new plant. The absorption of water and the presence of oxygen and favorable temperatures usually end dormancy, but there may be other requirements.

Water is important because it activates the embryo's metabolic system. Once metabolism has begun, the seed must continue to receive water or it will die. Just before the seed coat breaks open, the rate of respiration in the plant embryo increases rapidly.

Many seeds germinate best at temperatures between 25°C and 30°C. At temperatures below 0°C or above 45°C, most seeds won't germinate at all.

Some seeds have specific requirements for germination. For example, some germinate more readily after they have passed through the acid environment of an animal's digestive system. Others require a period of freezing temperatures, such as apple

Figure 24.21
Many wildflower seeds require fire to germinate. This is especially true in prairie environments where fires are periodically set to induce the germination of prairie wildflower seeds.

Additional Lab

Respiring Seeds

Purpose
to compare the rate of respiration in germinating and nongerminating seeds

Materials
canned kidney beans, paper cup, water, dried kidney beans, wax paper, labels, tetrazolium solution in dark dropper bottles (add 1 g of 2,3,5-triphenyl tetrazolium chloride to 100 mL distilled water)

Procedure
Give the following directions to students.
1. Soak ten kidney bean seeds overnight in water. The next day, split each seed in half and place them split-side up on a labeled sheet of waxed paper.
2. Split ten canned kidney beans and place them split-side up on a labeled sheet of waxed paper.
3. Add a drop of the tetrazolium solution to each cut surface. Wait 20–30 minutes. Record in which seeds and where in the seeds a pink color appears. (Note: Tetrazolium can be diluted and discarded

Figure 24.22
Germination of a bean seed is stimulated by warm temperatures and water, which softens the seed coat.

A The radicle will become the primary root.

Hypocotyl

Radicle

Cotyledon

Seed coat

Primary root

B The hypocotyl is the first part of the stem to appear.

Epicotyl

Withered cotyledons

Hypocotyl

Cotyledon

C As the hypocotyl straightens, the plant's first leaves are exposed to sunlight.

Secondary roots

D As new leaves mature, the cotyledons wither and fall away.

seeds, extensive soaking in saltwater, such as coconut seeds, or certain day lengths. The seeds of some conifers will not germinate unless they have been exposed to fire. The same is true of certain wildflower species, including lupines and gentians, as shown in *Figure 24.21*.

The germination of a typical dicot embryo is shown in *Figure 24.22*. Once the seed coat has been softened by water, the embryo starts to emerge from the seed. The first part of the embryo to appear is the embryonic root called the **radicle** (RA dih kul). The radicle grows down into the soil

and develops into a root. The portion of the stem nearest the seed is called the **hypocotyl** (HI poh kah tul). In some plants, the first part of the stem to push above ground is an arched portion of the hypocotyl. As the hypocotyl continues growing, it straightens, bringing with it the cotyledons and the plant's first leaves. In monocots, the cotyledon remains below the soil's surface. As growth continues, the leaves turn green, and the plant produces its own food through photosynthesis. To learn more about germinating seeds, try the *MiniLab* on page 657.

Physical Science Connection

Forces exerted by seedlings
When a seedling emerges from a seed, its stem pushes upward through the soil. This push or force results from water pressure inside the seedling's cells. Also, the number of cells within the seedling increases as it grows. Therefore, the total force exerted on the soil by the seedling increases as the seedling grows.

Physical Science Connection

Both the seedling and gravity exert forces on soil particles that surround the seed. Have students use Newton's laws of motion to explain whether the forces acting on these soil particles are balanced or unbalanced as the seedling grows. According to the first law of motion, the motion of an object changes only if an unbalanced force acts on the object. If the seedling pushes a soil particle out of the way, the motion of the particle changes and the forces acting on it must be unbalanced.

Discussion
Relate the following questions to the events associated with seed germination. Why is oxygen needed by a seed? How does soil contribute oxygen to plants? Why do seeds typically germinate in the spring and not in the late fall or winter? **L1** **COOP LEARN**

down the sink, but the bean seeds cannot be discarded in the sink.) Caution students to use care when working with chemicals.
4. Wash hands thoroughly with soap and water after completing this lab.

Analysis
1. Tetrazolium solution indicates cell respiration when it turns pink. Which seed

treatment carried on cell respiration? Why? Uncanned seeds are alive; canned seeds are dead.
2. The darker the pink color, the greater the rate of respiration. Which seed part carries on the greatest rate of respiration? Why? Embryo; rapid growth requires more energy.

Assessment
Portfolio Design an experiment to determine how many seeds in a seed packet are alive. Use the Performance Task Assessment List for Designing an Experiment in **PASC**, p. 95. **L3**

MiniLab 24.2

Purpose
to compare dormant and germinating monocot and dicot seed embryos

Process Skills
observe and infer, compare and contrast

Teaching Strategies
Soak some seeds 24 hours and others 72 hours prior to use. After the 72-hour seeds have been soaking for 24 hours, wrap them in moist paper towels and place them in sealed plastic bags.

Expected Results
Germinating seeds have larger embryos.

Analysis
1. Labels should include cotyledon(s), embryo. Dicot diagrams should include cotyledons, embryo, epicotyl, radicle, plumule, and hypocotyl. Monocot diagrams should include only cotyledon and embryo.
2. monocot—one cotyledon, small embryo, is slow to germinate, and its embryo parts are hard to differentiate; dicot—two cotyledons, larger embryo, and easily seen embryo parts

Modified Assessment
Performance Provide students with seeds. Have students classify each seed after removing the seed coat. Use the Performance Task Assessment List for Making and Using a Classification System in **PASC,** p. 121. **L1**

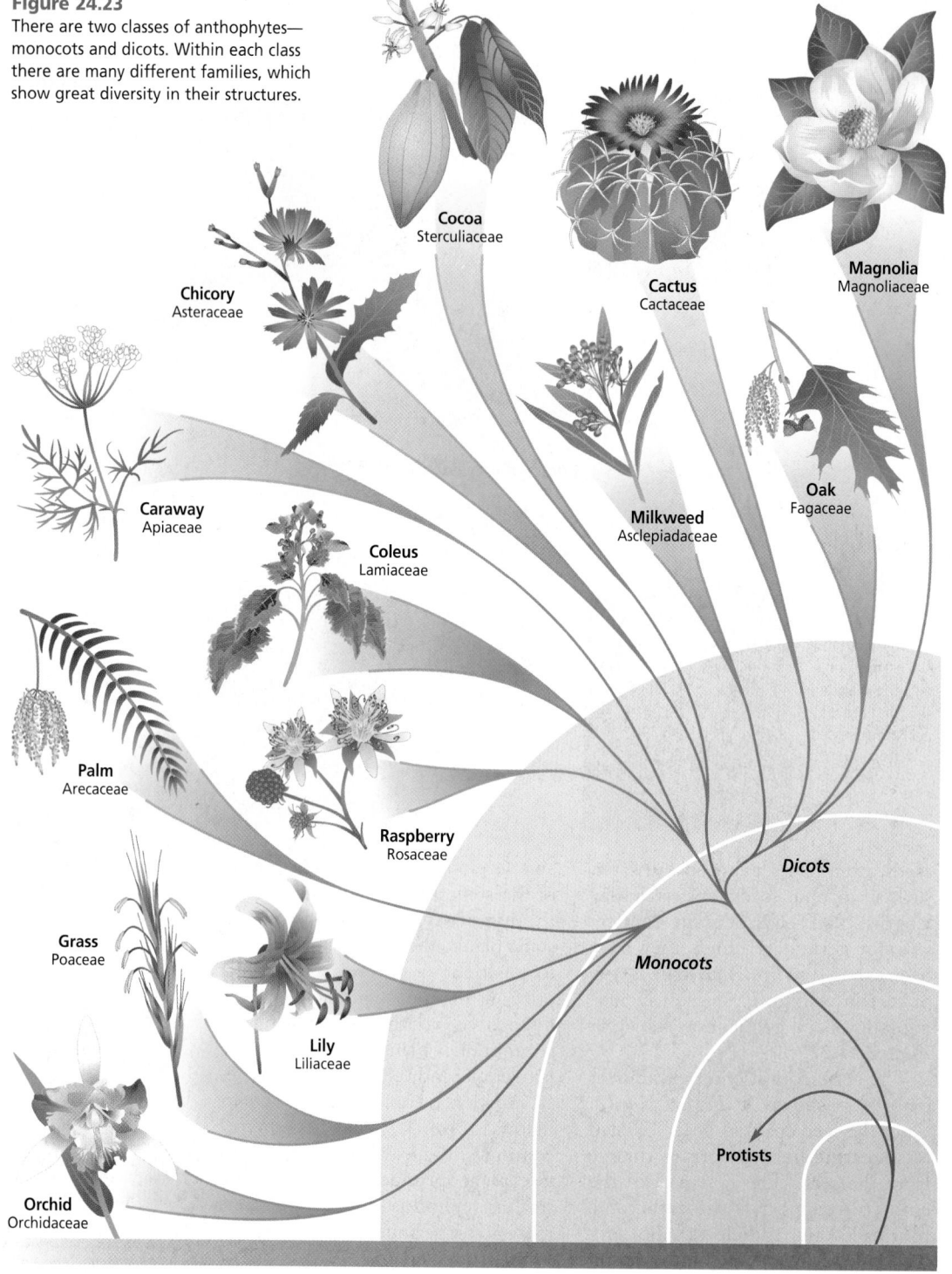

Figure 24.23
There are two classes of anthophytes— monocots and dicots. Within each class there are many different families, which show great diversity in their structures.

Cocoa
Sterculiaceae

Cactus
Cactaceae

Magnolia
Magnoliaceae

Chicory
Asteraceae

Caraway
Apiaceae

Coleus
Lamiaceae

Milkweed
Asclepiadaceae

Oak
Fagaceae

Palm
Arecaceae

Raspberry
Rosaceae

Grass
Poaceae

Lily
Liliaceae

Dicots

Monocots

Protists

Orchid
Orchidaceae

INCLUSION STRATEGIES

Learning Disabled Ask students to prepare a concept map that deals only with the structures present in a bean seed. The following terms must be included in the map: *cotyledon, hypocotyl, epicotyl, radicle,* and *meristem.* Allow students to work either independently or in cooperative groups. **L1** **COOP LEARN**

Vegetative reproduction

The roots, stems, and leaves of plants are called vegetative structures. When these structures produce a new plant, it is called vegetative reproduction. Vegetative reproduction is common among anthophytes. Some modified stems of anthophytes, such as potato tubers, can produce a new plant from each "eye" or bud. Farmers make use of this feature when they cut potato tubers into pieces and plant them.

Although cloning animals is a relatively new phenomenon, for years gardeners have relied on cloning to reproduce plants. Using vegetative reproduction to grow numerous plants from one plant is frequently referred to as vegetative propagation. Some plants, such as begonias, can be propagated by planting cuttings, which are pieces of the stem or a leaf that has been cut off another begonia. Even smaller pieces of plants can be used to grow plants by tissue culture. Minute pieces of plant tissue are placed on nutrient agar in test tubes or petri dishes. The plants grown from cuttings and tissue cultures have the same genetic makeup as the plants from which they came and are botanical clones.

There is great diversity in the flowers, seeds, fruits, and vegetative structures of anthophytes. Anthophytes are divided into families based on these differences. The relationships among these families are shown in *Figure 24.23* on the opposite page. Which of the families is part of your environment?

MiniLab 24.2

Observe

Looking at Germinating Seeds
Seeds are made up of a plant embryo, a seed coat, and in some plants, a food-storage tissue. Monocot and dicot seeds differ in structure.

Corn seed germination

Procedure

1. Obtain from your teacher a soaked, ungerminated corn kernel (monocot), a bean seed (dicot), and germinating corn and bean seeds.
2. Remove the seed coats from each of the ungerminated seeds. Examine the seed's structures under a microscope using low-power magnification. Locate and identify the embryo's structures and other seed structures.
3. Examine the germinating seeds. Locate and identify the structures you observed in the dormant seeds.

Analysis

1. **Diagram** Draw the dormant embryos in the soaked seeds, and label their structures. Draw the germinating seeds, and label their structures.
2. **Distinguish** List at least three major differences you observed in the internal structures of the corn and bean seeds.

Section Assessment

Understanding Main Ideas
1. Explain the relationship between the pollination of a flower and the production of one or more seeds.
2. Name the part(s) of an anthophyte flower that becomes the fruit.
3. Describe the process of double fertilization in anthophytes.
4. Infer how the production of nectar could enhance the pollination of a flowering plant.

Thinking Critically
5. Sequence the formation of the female gametophyte in a flowering plant using illustrations.

SKILL REVIEW

6. **Make and Use Tables** Make a table that identifies whether each organ of a flower is involved in pollination, fruit formation, seed production, or seed dispersal. For more help, refer to *Make and Use Tables* in the **Skill Handbook.**

 in.bdol.glencoe.com/self_check_quiz

24.3   THE LIFE CYCLE OF A FLOWERING PLANT   **657**

Section Assessment

1. One pollen grain is required for the production of each seed.
2. usually the ovary
3. Double fertilization occurs when one sperm unites with the egg cell, forming the 2*n* zygote and the other sperm cell fuses with the central cell to form a 3*n* cell.
4. Nectar attracts animals such as insects and bats; they get pollen on them as they try to reach the nectar. As these animals travel from flower to flower, they cross-pollinate the flowers.
5. In the ovule, meiosis produces four haploid megaspores. One of these will undergo three mitotic divisions. The eight nuclei make up the embryo sac or female gametophyte.
6. pollination: stamen, pistil; fruit formation: pistil, sometimes other flower organs; seed production: pistil; seed dispersal: pistil

INVESTIGATE BioLab

Time Allotment

one class period

Process Skills

observe and infer, use the microscope, compare and contrast, interpret data

Safety Precautions

■ Handle the razor blade with extreme caution. Always cut away from the body.

■ Some students may be allergic to the chemicals used in preserved specimens. Caution students against rubbing their eyes because of the preservative. Always have students wash their hands thoroughly after handling preserved specimens.

Alternative Materials

■ Do not use composite species of flowers such as sunflower, daisy, or dandelion.

■ Preserved slides that show eggs within the ovule are available from supply houses.

■ Preserved flowers are available from biological supply houses. A disadvantage to such flowers is that the preservative can discolor flower parts. Petals and sepals appear dull green as a result.

INVESTIGATE BioLab

Before You Begin

Flowers are the reproductive structures of anthophytes. They come in many colors and shapes. Often their colors or shapes are related to the manner in which pollination takes place. The major organs of a flower include the petals, sepals, stamens, and pistils. Some flowers are incomplete, which means they do not have all four kinds of organs. You will study a complete flower.

658 REPRODUCTION IN PLANTS

Examining the Organs of a Flower

PREPARATION

Problem

What do the organs of a flower look like? How are they arranged?

Objectives

In this BioLab, you will:

■ **Observe** the organs of a flower.
■ **Identify** the functions of flower organs.

Materials

flower—any complete dicot flower that is available locally, such as phlox, carnation, or tobacco flower
hand lens (or dissecting microscope)
colored pencils (red, green, blue)
microscope slides (2)

microscope
single-edged razor blade
coverslips (2)
dropper
water
forceps (or tweezers)

Safety Precautions

CAUTION: *Handle the razor blade with extreme caution. Always cut away from you. Use caution when handling a microscope, slides, and coverslips.*

Skill Handbook

If you need help with this lab, refer to the **Skill Handbook.**

PROCEDURE

1. Examine your flower. Locate the sepals and petals. Note their numbers, size, color, and arrangement. Record this data. Remove the sepals and petals from your flower by gently pulling them off the stem.

2. Using the hand lens, locate the stamens, each of which consists of a thin filament with an anther on the tip. Note and record the number of stamens.

3. Locate the pistil. The stigma at the top of the pistil is often sticky. The style is a long, narrow structure that leads from the stigma to the ovary.

PROCEDURE

Teaching Strategies

■ If necessary, review proper use of the microscope.

■ Students can work in groups of two to three for this BioLab.

■ Show students how to remove the petals and sepals.

■ When preparing the anther wet mount, have students squash the anther using their thumb and a piece of lens paper over the coverslip. Advise students to press evenly to avoid cracking the coverslip, or use plastic coverslips.

■ Students should not attempt to observe egg cells in ovules under the microscope.

4. Place an anther onto a microscope slide and add a drop of water. Cut the anther into several pieces with the razor blade. Place a coverslip over the cut-up anther. **CAUTION:** *Always take care when using a razor blade.*

5. Examine the anther under low and high power of your microscope. The small, dotlike structures are pollen grains. Remove the slide from the stage of the microscope.

6. Slice the pistil in half lengthwise with the razor blade. Mount one half, cut side facing up, on a microscope slide.

7. Identify and examine the pistil's ovary with a hand lens or dissecting microscope. The many dotlike structures in the ovary are ovules. A tiny stalk connects each ovule to the wall of the ovary.

8. Make a diagram of the flower, labeling all its parts. Color the female reproductive parts red. Color the male reproductive parts green. Color the remaining parts blue.

9. **CLEANUP AND DISPOSAL** Clean all equipment as instructed by your teacher, and return everything to its proper place. Properly dispose of coverslips and flower organs. Wash your hands thoroughly.

ANALYZE AND CONCLUDE

1. **Observe** How many stamens are present in your flower? How many pistils, ovaries, sepals, and petals?

2. **Compare and Contrast** Make a reasonable estimate for your flower of the number of pollen grains in the anther and the number of ovules in the ovary. Calculate the class average of the estimated number of pollen grains and estimated number of ovules.

3. **Interpret Data** Which number is greater? Pollen grains in one anther or ovules in one ovary? Give a possible explanation for your answer.

Apply Your Skill

Field Investigation Use a field guide to identify common wildflowers in your area. Most field guide identifications are made on the basis of color, shape, numbers, and arrangement of flower parts. If collecting is permitted, pick a few common flowers to press and make into a display of local flora.

 Web Links To find out more about flowers, visit in.bdol.glencoe.com/flowers

ANALYZE AND CONCLUDE

1. Organs will be in a multiple of 3 if a monocot, or a multiple of 4 or 5 if a dicot.

2. Answers will vary.

3. pollen grains in an anther; The probability of pollen landing on the stigma increases when there is a large number of pollen grains.

Assessment

Knowledge Provide students with diagrams of a flower other than that used in this BioLab. Have them label and indicate the general function of all important structures. Use the Performance Task Assessment List for Making Observations and Inferences in **PASC**, p. 89. **L1**

Apply Your Skill

Field Investigation Have students compile a list of the flowers that they identify. Make a table with all of the flower names in the first column, and title the other columns: *Complete, Incomplete, Monocot,* and *Dicot.* Have students correctly categorize the list of flowers. **L2**

Data and Observations

Student diagrams, when colored properly, should show the petals and sepals as blue, pistil as red, and stamens as green.

CLEANUP AND DISPOSAL

 Direct students to wash slides, place razor blades in a designated beaker, and dispose of flower parts in the trash can. Place plastic coverslips in the trash can, or place glass coverslips in the glass waste container. Have students wash their hands thoroughly after completing this lab.

Indiana Academic Standards

Pages 658–659: B.1.18

BIO TECHNOLOGY

Hybrid Plants

For thousands of years, humans have influenced the breeding of plants, especially food crops and flowers. Today's plant breeders create hybrid strains with a variety of desired characteristics, such as more colorful or fragrant flowers, tastier fruit, higher yields, or increased resistance to diseases and pests.

Technician performing hybridization studies

The perfect ear of corn The first step in creating a hybrid is the selection of parent plants with desirable characteristics. A breeder might select a corn plant that ripens earlier in the season, one that can be sown earlier in the spring because its seeds germinate well in cool, moist soil, or one with more kernels per ear.

The next step is to grow several self-pollinated generations of each plant to form a true-breeding line—plants that produce offspring that always show the desired characteristic. To do this, each plant must be prevented from cross-pollinating with other corn. The female flowers, called silks, grow on cobs near the middle of the corn stalk. The breeder covers the silks to prevent wind-borne pollen from fertilizing them. The pollen-producing male tassels are removed, and the breeder uses selected pollen to hand-pollinate each silk.

Once each true-breeding line has been established, the real experimentation begins. Breeders cross different combinations of true-breeding lines to see what characteristics the resulting F_1 hybrids will have. These trials show which of the true-breeding lines reliably pass their desired characteristic to hybrid offspring, and which crosses produce seeds that the breeder can market as a new, improved variety of corn.

Plant breeding today Cell culture and genetic engineering technologies are new plant breeding techniques. Protoplast fusion removes the cell walls from the cells of leaves or seedlings, then uses electricity or chemicals to fuse cells of two different species. Some of these fused cells have been successfully cultured in the lab and grown into adult plants, though none have produced seeds.

Recombinant DNA technology has been used to insert specific genes into the chromosomes of a plant. This technique helps produce plants that are resistant to frost, drought, or disease.

Applying Biotechnology

Form an Opinion Scientists have genetically engineered hybrid corn to produce an insecticide that kills one of corn's most damaging insects, the European corn borer. The hybrid corn produces Bt delta endotoxin. Since its introduction in 1996, Bt-corn has been the subject of much controversy. Research this topic and form an opinion for or against the growing of Bt-corn. Create a file of scientific articles and information that supports your position. Discuss this topic with someone of the opposite opinion.

 To find out more about hybrid seeds, visit in.bdol.glencoe.com/biotechnology

STUDY GUIDE

Section 24.1

Life Cycles of Mosses, Ferns, and Conifers

Key Concepts

- The gametophyte generation is dominant in mosses. Archegonia and antheridia form on separate or the same gametophyte. Fertilization requires a film of water on the gametophyte.

- Archegonia and antheridia develop on a prothallus, the fern gametophyte. Fertilization requires a film of water on the gametophyte. The sporophyte generation is dominant in ferns.

- Conifers have cones in which a male or female gametophyte forms. Sperm nuclei form in pollen grains and eggs form in ovules. The embryo is protected in a seed.

Vocabulary

megaspore (p. 638)
micropyle (p. 639)
microspore (p. 638)
protonema (p. 635)
vegetative reproduction (p. 634)

Section 24.2

Flowers and Flowering

Key Concepts

- Flowers are made up of four organs: sepals, petals, stamens, and pistils. A flower lacking any organ is called incomplete. Complete flowers have all four organs.

- Photoperiodism—responses of flowering plants to daylight-darkness conditions—affects flower production. Plants are called short-day, long-day, day-neutral, or intermediate depending upon their photoperiodic response.

Vocabulary

anther (p. 641)
day-neutral plant (p. 645)
long-day plant (p. 644)
ovary (p. 643)
petals (p. 641)
photoperiodism (p. 644)
pistil (p. 643)
sepals (p. 641)
short-day plant (p. 644)
stamen (p. 641)

Section 24.3

The Life Cycle of a Flowering Plant

Key Concepts

- The male gametophyte develops from a microspore in the anther. The female gametophyte develops from a megaspore in the ovule.

- Double fertilization occurs when a sperm nucleus joins with an egg to form a zygote. The second sperm nucleus joins the central cell to form endosperm.

- Fruits and seeds are modified for dispersal. Seeds can stay dormant for a long time before they germinate.

Vocabulary

dormancy (p. 654)
double fertilization (p. 651)
endosperm (p. 651)
germination (p. 654)
hypocotyl (p. 655)
polar nuclei (p. 648)
radicle (p. 655)

FOLDABLES
Study Organizer To help you review the life cycles of mosses, ferns, and conifers, use the Organizational Study Fold on page 633.

 in.bdol.glencoe.com/vocabulary_puzzlemaker

CHAPTER 24 ASSESSMENT **661**

Key Concepts
Summary statements can be used by students to review the major concepts of the chapter.

 Biology Online

Visit in.bdol.glencoe.com
/self_check_quiz
/vocabulary_puzzlemaker
/chapter_test
/standardized_test

VOCABULARY PUZZLEMAKER

For additional help with vocabulary, have students access the Vocabulary PuzzleMaker online at in.bdol.glencoe.com/vocabulary_puzzlemaker

FOLDABLES™
Have students use their Foldables to review the content of Section 24.1. On the back of their Foldables, have students infer how dominant gametophytes and dominant sporophytes are adapted to their environments.

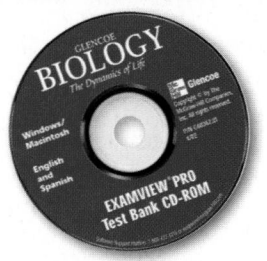

Use the ExamView®Pro Test Bank CD-ROM to:
- Create **multiple versions** of tests
- Create **modified** tests with one mouse click for **inclusion** students
- **Edit** existing questions and **add** your own questions
- Build tests aligned with state standards using built-in **State Curriculum Tags**
- Change **English** tests to **Spanish** with one mouse click and vice versa

 Indiana Academic Standards

Pages 660–661: B.1.11, B.1.15, B.1.18, B.1.21, B.1.23

The Princeton Review Questions and answers have been aligned and verified by The Princeton Review.

Vocabulary Review

1. micropyle
2. stamen
3. hypocotyl
4. protonema
5. long-day plant

Understanding Key Concepts

6. B	9. C	12. D
7. B	10. B	13. A
8. C	11. A	

Constructed Response

14. Seeds are mostly stored food intended for use by the embryo plant.

15. It allows seeds to remain alive until water becomes available for germination.

16. The root anchors the seed and obtains needed water from the soil for further growth and development of the plant.

Thinking Critically

17. The prickly seed can stick to animals and be carried to another location. A seed with a winglike structure can be transported by wind. A minute seed could get wedged in an animal's foot or a human's shoes, or be carried on air currents.

18. Depending on endangered plant species chosen, measures to preserve them may include preserving habitats as parks or as wilderness areas, and educating the public about the importance of preserving endangered plants to maintain biodiversity. Because plants are the basis of food chains,

---

Vocabulary Review

Review the Chapter 24 vocabulary words listed in the Study Guide on page 661. Match the words with the definitions below.

1. in seed plants, the opening in the ovule through which the pollen tube enters
2. male reproductive organ of a flower that consists of an anther and a filament
3. the first part of the stem to push above ground from a germinating seed
4. in mosses, the small green filament of haploid cells that develops from a spore
5. plants that produce flowers only after exposure to short nights

Understanding Key Concepts

6. Moss gametophytes are _____ and form gametes by _____.
   A. diploid—meiosis C. diploid—mitosis
   B. haploid—mitosis D. haploid—meiosis

7. Which of the following structures can develop as part of an anthophyte?
   A.   C.

   B.   D.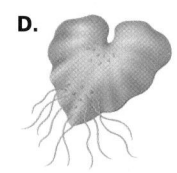

8. The endosperm of an anthophyte seed is _____.
   A. haploid   C. triploid
   B. monoploid   D. diploid

9. Producing a new plant from part of another plant is _____.
   A. photoperiodism
   B. double fertilization
   C. vegetative reproduction
   D. germination

---

10. A flower that naturally has eight petals and four sepals and four pistils is called _____.
    A. asexual   C. complete
    B. incomplete   D. partial

11. The male gametophyte of a conifer is called a _____.
    A. pollen grain C. cone
    B. needle   D. cotyledon

12. Meiosis begins the _____ stage in a plant's life cycle.
    A. bryophyte   C. sporophyte
    B. pterophyte   D. gametophyte

13. Ferns produce male gametes in _____.
    A. antheridia   C. rhizomes
    B. protonemas   D. archegonia

Constructed Response

14. **Open Ended** Many animals, including humans, eat seeds such as peas, beans, peanuts, and almonds. Why are seeds a good food source?

15. **Open Ended** How does dormancy help the survival of a plant species in a desert biome?

16. **Open Ended** The root is usually the first organ to emerge from a germinating seed. Evaluate how this benefits the plant more than if another organ emerged first.

Thinking Critically

17. **Predict** You are given three seeds. One is prickly, another has a winglike structure, and the third is tiny. How might each of the seeds be dispersed?

18. **REAL WORLD BIOCHALLENGE** The U.S. Fish and Wildlife Service has a list of endangered or threatened flowering plant species. Visit in.bdol.glencoe.com to investigate five plants on this list. Determine why they are considered endangered and what is being done to preserve them. What might result if one of your plants became extinct? Prepare a poster or give multimedia presentation of your results to your class.

 in.bdol.glencoe.com/chapter_test

---

the extinction of a plant species disrupts a food chain and could lead to the extinction of other organisms in that food chain.

RUBRIC

Evaluating Open-Ended Questions
Open-ended assessment questions are graded by using a multilevel rubric that guides you in assessing a student's knowledge of a particular concept. The following rubric is a sample scoring device.

Chapter 24 Assessment

End-of-Course Assessment Practice

All questions aligned and verified by The Princeton Review

Part 1 Multiple Choice

Desert mistletoe grows on a desert plant named catclaw, *Acacia greggii*. Predict a trend from the data to answer question 19. Analyze the graph and answer questions 20 and 21.

Mistletoe Infection and Catclaw Fruit Production

19. The data was collected during a drought. When drought is not severe, mistletoe infestation does not reduce fruit production. A graph of this situation would show _____.
    A. bars unequal in height
    B. bars much lower than the bars in the graph above
    C. two high bars and one low bar
    D. all bars the same height

20. As infection of catclaw becomes more severe, _____.
    A. fruit production increases
    B. fruit production decreases
    C. fruit production remains unchanged
    D. catclaw plants die

21. If the rate of infestation by mistletoe of catclaw increases over the years, catclaw numbers may _____.
    A. decrease   C. remain the same
    B. increase   D. decrease, then increase

Analyze and evaluate the graph below to answer questions 22–24.

Germination of Beans After Exposure to Radiation

22. Which group of beans had the highest percentage of germination?
    A. control   C. medium-exposure level
    B. high-exposure   D. low-exposure level level

23. As the radiation dose increases, germination _____.
    A. increases   C. stops
    B. decreases   D. is not affected

24. When beans are given a low dose of radiation, about _____ germinate.
    A. 25 percent   C. none
    B. 50 percent   D. 100 percent

Part 2 Constructed Response/Grid In

Record your answer on your answer document.

25. **Open Ended** Plant geneticists have learned that about one-third of the genes in two different plant genomes are not found in any sequenced fungus or animal genome. Infer why plants have many genes that do not have counterparts in the fungus kingdom or the animal kingdom.

 in.bdol.glencoe.com/standardized_test

CHAPTER 24 ASSESSMENT **663**

End-of-Course Assessment Practice

19. D   **21.** A   **23.** B
20. B   **22.** D   **24.** A
25. Plants carry on photosynthesis and other light related processes that animals and fungi do not perform.

 FAST FILE

Answer Sheet A practice answer sheet can be found on p. 143 of *Unit 7 FAST FILE Resources.*

RUBRIC

SCORE	CRITERIA
4	A correct solution that is supported by well-developed, accurate explanations.
3	A generally correct solution, but may contain minor flaws in reasoning.

SCORE	CRITERIA
2	A partially correct interpretation and/or solution to the problem.
1	A correct solution with no supporting evidence or explanation.
0	An incorrect solution or no solution is given.

 Indiana Academic Standards

Pages 662–663: B.1.11, B.1.15, B.1.19, B.1.35

Prepare

Short on Time?

This BioDigest can be used as an introduction to or an overview of the structures and functions of plants. If time is limited, you may wish to use this unit summary to teach about plants in place of the chapters in the plants unit.

Key Concepts

Students learn about the characteristics of the major plant divisions. They are introduced to the alternation of generations; the distinctions between non-seed and seed plants; pollination and fertilization; and the adaptive value of flowers, seeds, and fruits.

1 Focus

Bellringer

Visual-Spatial Bring an assortment of live plants into the classroom, including mosses, horsetails, and club mosses, if available. Include a small potted pine or other conifer, and several potted flowering plants. Ask students to observe each plant and make a list of its characteristics in their journals. **L1**

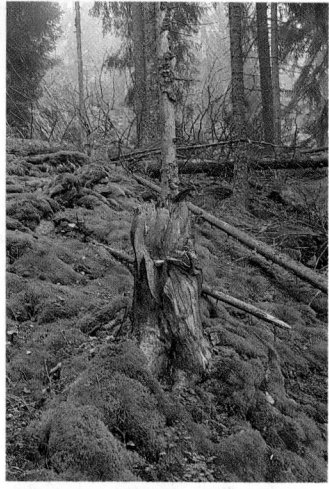

Mosses often grow in masses that form thick carpets.

Plants

Plants provide food and shelter for most of Earth's organisms. Through the process of photosynthesis, they transform the radiant energy in light into chemical energy in food and release oxygen. All plants are multi-cellular eukaryotes whose cells are surrounded by a cell wall made of cellulose.

Non-Seed Plants

Non-seed plants reproduce by forming spores. A spore is a haploid (*n*) reproductive cell, produced by meiosis, which can withstand harsh environmental conditions. When conditions become favorable, a spore can develop into the haploid, gametophyte generation of a plant.

Mosses, Liverworts, and Hornworts

Bryophyta (mosses), Hepaticophyta (liverworts), and Anthocerophyta (hornworts) are divisions of non-seed nonvascular plants that live in cool, moist habitats. These plant groups have no vascular tissues to move water and nutrients from one part of the plant to another. They usually grow no more than several centimeters tall.

Club Mosses

Club mosses are non-seed vascular plants in the division Lycophyta. They are found primarily in moist environments and are usually only a few centimeters high. Fossil lycophytes grew as high as 30 m and formed a large part of the vegetation of Paleozoic forests.

FOCUS ON ADAPTATIONS
Alternation of Generations

The leafy moss gametophyte is haploid. The spore stalks and capsules are diploid.

The life cycles of plants have two stages, called generations. The diploid (2*n*) stage is called the sporophyte generation. It produces haploid (*n*) spores that develop into the gametophyte generation. The gametophyte generation produces male and female gametes that can unite and begin a new sporophyte generation.

In nonvascular plants, the sporophyte is smaller than the gametophyte, and usually remains attached to the gametophyte. The nonvascular sporophyte is dependent upon the nonvascular gametophyte for water and its nutrition. In vascular plants, the sporophyte is dominant and independent of the gametophyte. Vascular gametophytes are minute and usually are buried in soil or are enclosed within the vascular sporophyte.

664

RESOURCE MANAGER

Unit 7 *FAST FILE* Resources
Reinforcement and Study Guide in English, pp. 145–146
Reinforcement and Study Guide in Spanish, pp. 147–148
Student Recording Sheet, p. 149

Horsetails

Horsetails are non-seed vascular plants in the division Arthrophyta. They are common in areas with damp soil, such as stream banks and sometimes along roadsides. Present-day horsetails are small, but their ancestors were treelike.

Ferns

Ferns, division Pterophyta, are diverse non-seed vascular plants. They have leaves called fronds that grow up from an underground stem called the rhizome. Ferns are found in many different habitats, including shady forests, stream banks, roadsides, and abandoned pastures.

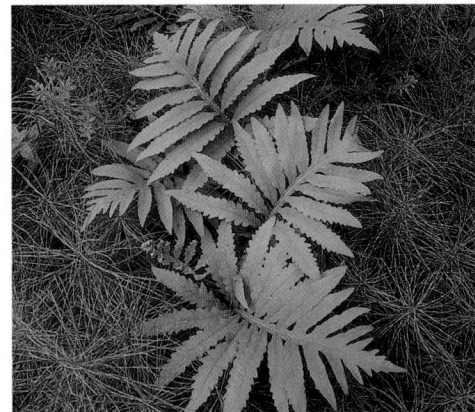

Fern fronds are sometimes divided into leaflets.

Seed Plants

A seed is a reproductive structure that contains a sporophyte embryo and a food supply that are enclosed in a protective coating. The food supply nourishes the young plant during the first stages of growth. Like spores, seeds can survive harsh conditions. The seed develops into the sporophyte generation of the plant. Seed plants include conifers and flowering plants.

Cycads, Ginkgoes, and Joint Firs

Plants in divisions Cycadophyta (cycads), Ginkgophyta (ginkgoes), and Gnetophyta (joint firs), along with those in Coniferophyta, are sometimes called gymnosperms. Seeds of these plants

Seeds of conifers develop at the base of each woody scale of female cones.

are not part of a fruit. Their male and female reproductive organs are in separate structures. Seeds develop in the female reproductive structure. These plants have different forms and grow in diverse environments.

Conifers

Conifers, division Coniferophyta, produce seeds, usually in woody strobili called cones, and have needle-shaped or scalelike leaves. Most conifers are evergreen plants, which means they bear leaves all year round.

Conifers are common in cold or dry habitats. Their needles have a compact shape and a thick, waxy covering that helps reduce water loss. Conifer stems are covered with a thick layer of bark that insulates the tissues inside. These structural adaptations enable conifers to survive below freezing temperatures.

VITAL STATISTICS

Conifers

Examples: Pine, spruce, fir, larch, yew, redwood, juniper.
Plant giants: Giant sequoias of central California, to 99 m tall, the most massive organisms in the world; coast redwoods of California, to 117 m, the tallest trees in the world.

---

2 Teach

Quick Demo

Horsetail Stems If horsetails grow in your area, bring several stems into the classroom. Show students that the hollow stems come apart fairly easily at the nodes. Have them examine the strobili, if present. Point out that the silica in the stems gives horsetails a scouring-pad quality and is the source of the common name "scouring rush."

Guest Speaker

Have a pharmacist or physician visit the class to discuss plants that are important in the production of medicines.

INCLUSION STRATEGIES

Learning Disabled: *Kinesthetic* Bring to class and allow students to handle several varieties of conifer cones. Include male cones if available. Tell students the common name and/or Latin name of the tree each cone is from. Ask students to record their observations of each species—sketches and/or description—in their journals. As a class, create a table that compares and contrasts the cones. **L1**

Inquiry

Discussion Ask students to compare and contrast pollination and fertilization in conifers and flowering plants. In conifers, pollen is carried by wind to the female cone. In flowers, pollen may also be transported by animals. In flowers, the pollen is carried to the stigma. In both conifers and flowers, the pollen grows a tube through which the sperm travels to reach the ovary. In both, sperm and egg unite to form a zygote that develops into a seed. **L2**

Visual Learning

Linguistic Bring into the classroom several different fruits, including both dry and fleshy varieties. Have students examine the exterior of each fruit, then cut it open to observe the arrangement of seeds. Ask students to describe their observations in their journals. **L1**

Biology Journal

Identifying and Classifying Plants Have students collect pictures of different types of plants. They should identify the plants and classify them as vascular or nonvascular and non-seed or seed producing. **L2** **ELL**

Indiana Academic Standards

Pages 666–667: B.1.15, B.1.18, B.1.43

Plants

Flowering Plants

The flowering plants, division Anthophyta, form the largest and most diverse group of plants on Earth today. They provide much of the food eaten by humans. Anthophytes produce flowers and develop seeds that are part of a fruit.

Monocots and Dicots

The anthophytes are in two classes: the monocotyledons and the dicotyledons. Cotyledons, or "seed leaves," are part of the seed along with the plant embryo. Monocots have one seed leaf and dicots have two seed leaves.

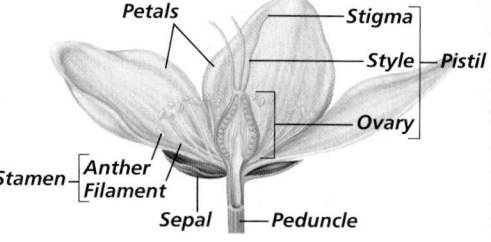

Flowers

Flowers are the organs of reproduction in anthophytes. The pistil is the female reproductive organ. At the base of the pistil is the ovary. Inside the ovary are the ovules. Ovules contain the female gametophyte. A female gamete—an egg cell—forms in each ovule. The stamen is the male reproductive organ of a flower. Pollen grains that form inside the anther eventually contain male gametes called sperm.

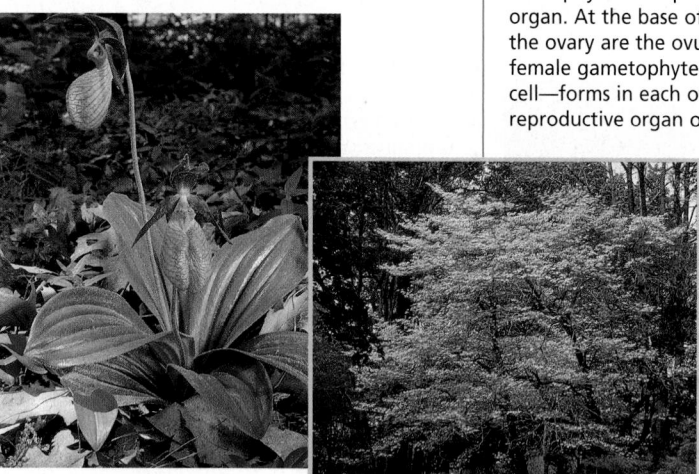

Monocots include grasses, orchids (left photo), and palms. Dicots include many flowering trees (right photo) and wildflowers.

FOCUS ON ADAPTATIONS
Moving from Water to Land

LM Magnification: 400×

Plants probably evolved from filamentous green algae.

All plants probably evolved from filamentous green algae that lived in nutrient-rich waters of Earth's ancient oceans. Water and dissolved minerals can diffuse directly into the cells of an ocean-dwelling alga. As land plants evolved, new structures developed that allowed water and dissolved minerals to be taken in from the environment and to be transported to all parts of the plant.

Nonvascular plants In nonvascular plants, water and nutrients travel from one cell to another by the processes of osmosis and diffusion. As a result, nonvascular plants are limited to moist environments.

INCLUSION STRATEGIES

Visually Impaired Have students with visual impairments handle the plants collected for the Bellringer activity. Break off small parts for them to handle. Ask them to describe what they feel as their partners write down their observations. Make sure students don't injure themselves by handling the plants. **L1**

Plants that depend on the wind to carry pollen from anther to stigma tend to have small, inconspicuous flowers. The pollen of corn is carried by the wind from these male flowers to female flowers that make up an ear of corn.

Pollen

In seed plants, the sperm develop inside of the thick-coated pollen grains. Pollen is an important structural adaptation that has enabled seed plants to live in diverse land habitats. Pollination is the transfer of pollen grains from the anther to the stigma of the pistil.

Pollinators

Pollen can be transferred by wind, insects, birds, and even bats. Some flowers have colorful or perfumed petals that attract pollinators. Flowers also can contain sweet nectar, as well as pollen, which provides pollinators with food.

Vascular plants The stems of most plants contain vascular tissues made up of tubelike, elongated cells through which water, food, and other materials move from one part of the plant to another. One reason vascular plants can grow larger than nonvascular plants is that vascular tissue allows a more efficient method of internal transport than osmosis and diffusion. In addition, vascular tissues include thickened fibers that can support upright growth.

An unbroken column of water travels from the roots in xylem tissues. Sugars formed by photosynthesis travel throughout the plant in phloem tissues.

Fruit

Following fertilization, a fruit with seeds can develop. Fruits help protect seeds until they are mature. Some flowering plants develop fleshy fruits, such as apples, melons, tomatoes, or squash. Other flowering plants develop dry fruits, such as peanuts, walnuts, or sunflowers. Fruits also can help disperse seeds.

Plant Responses

Plants respond to stimuli in their environment such as light, temperature, and water availability. Chemicals called hormones control some of these responses by increasing cell division and growth.

The phototropic response shown here is the result of increased cell growth on the side of the stem away from the light.

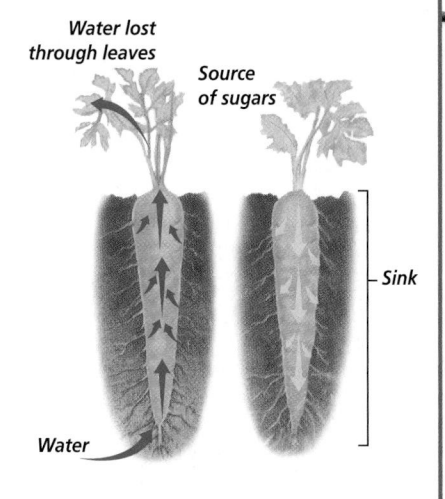

Water lost through leaves

Source of sugars

Sink

Water

667

3 Assess

DAILY INTERVENTION

Check for Understanding
Have students explain the difference between the terms in each of the following word pairs. **L2**
a. seed—spores
b. vascular—nonvascular
c. cone—fruit
d. monocot—dicot

Reteach
Have students name plants that are or produce structures, listed in the word pairs of the Check for Understanding. Ask them to explain why each plant is representative of the term. **L2**

Extension

Linguistic Have students research one plant division of their choice and present a brief oral report to the class. **L3**

✔ Assessment

Skill Have students prepare a chart that shows the different types of plants and their major characteristics. **L2**

Street-Tree Census Have students conduct a street-tree census in their community. Provide students with tree identification field guides to help them identify trees. They can analyze the results of the census and submit a class report to the community government with suggestions of where additional trees could be planted. **L3**
COOP LEARN

This page contains practice questions in the various formats that can be found on the most frequently given standardized tests.

Part 1 ▶ Multiple Choice

1. D   4. A
2. B   5. C
3. C   6. A

Answer Sheet A practice answer sheet can be found on p. 149 of the *Unit 7 FAST FILE Resources.*

■ End-of-Course
Assessment Practice

TEST-TAKING TIP

Plan Your Work and Work Your Plan

Set up a study schedule for yourself well in advance of your test. Plan your workload so that you do a little each day rather than a lot all at once. The key to retaining information is to repeatedly review and practice it. There is truth in the saying, "Use it or lose it."

Part 1 ▶ Multiple Choice

Blueberry plants grow best and have optimal berry production in soils that have a pH range of 4.0–5.2. Recall that a substance with a pH less than 7 is called acidic. Scientists tested the soils on 104 commercial blueberry farms, then compiled their data. Analyze the graph of their data below to answer questions 1 and 2.

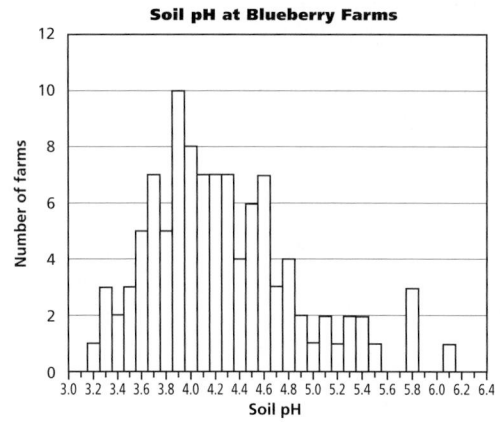

1. Which of the following statements best describes the soils at most blueberry farms?
   A. within the pH range for optimal berry production
   B. lower than the pH range for optimal berry production
   C. higher than the pH range for optimal berry production
   D. both lower and higher than the pH range for optimal berry production

2. What percentage of the blueberry farms have soils too acidic for optimal berry production?
   A. 57%
   B. 35%
   C. 100%
   D. 9%

Study the graph below about seed production responses of purple needlegrass in California to answer questions 3–5.

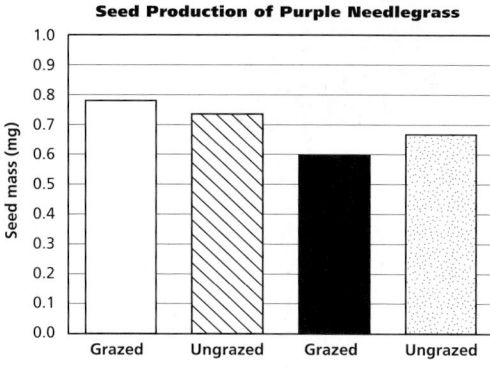

3. The largest seed mass of purple needlegrass occurs when the habitat is _____.
   A. grazed and unburned
   B. ungrazed and unburned
   C. grazed and burned
   D. ungrazed and burned

4. The smallest seed mass of purple needle grass occurs when the habitat is _____.
   A. grazed and unburned
   B. ungrazed and unburned
   C. grazed and burned
   D. ungrazed and burned

5. If you wanted to grow purple needlegrass with seeds with larger mass, how would you manage your land?
   A. graze only
   B. burn only
   C. graze and burn
   D. neither graze nor burn

Indiana Academic Standards

Pages 668–669: B.1.15, B.1.18

The roots of some nonnative plants produce chemicals that interfere with the growth of native grasses. Analyze the graph below to answer questions 6 and 7.

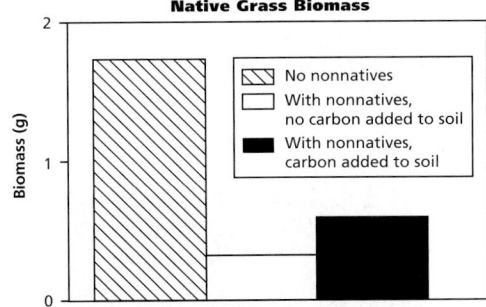

Native Grass Biomass

Legend:
- No nonnatives
- With nonnatives, no carbon added to soil
- With nonnatives, carbon added to soil

Y-axis: Biomass (g), 0 to 2

6. In this study, the effect of carbon on native plants _____.
  - **A.** is somewhat beneficial
  - **B.** is harmful
  - **C.** completely counteracts the effect of the chemical given off by the roots of the nonnative plants
  - **D.** cannot be determined by analyzing the graph

7. When native grasses are grown with nonnative plants nearby and carbon is not added to the soil, the biomass of the native grasses is _____.
  - **A.** less than grasses grown without the nonnative plants nearby regardless of whether carbon is added to the soil
  - **B.** greater than without nonnative plants nearby
  - **C.** not affected by the addition of carbon to the soil
  - **D.** less than without nonnatives nearby, but greater than when carbon is added to the soil

8. Mosses, ferns, and club mosses are alike because they _____.
  - **A.** require water for fertilization
  - **B.** have adaptations for conserving water
  - **C.** need insects for pollination
  - **D.** grow best in warm, sunny, and dry habitats

9. Club mosses, horsetails, and conifers have specialized leaves that form reproductive structures known as _____.
  - **A.** sori
  - **B.** flowers
  - **C.** protonema
  - **D.** strobili

Part 2 Constructed Response/Grid In

Record your answers or fill in the bubbles on your answer document using the correct place value.

10. Open Ended Snow buttercups in the alpine tundra have flowers that orient themselves toward and track the apparent movement of the sun across the sky. Biologists hypothesized that this response was stimulated by the blue wavelength component of light. It is known that red filters can block blue wavelengths. Describe an experiment that would test this hypothesis.

11. Open Ended Why do vascular plants have an adaptive advantage over nonvascular plants?

12. Open Ended Using the table to the right, choose two geographic areas and infer why the number of seed plants in the two areas differ.

Estimated Number of Seed Plants in Geographical Areas	
Geographic Area	**Estimated Number**
Europe	13 638
Africa	74 232
Australia/ New Zealand	81 876
Pacific Islands	10 758
Northern America	34 455
Southern America	115 242

13. Grid In A change in pH of one represents a 10-times change in the hydrogen ion concentration of a substance. A change in pH of two represents a 100-times change in the hydrogen ion concentration of a substance. Using the graph about soil pH on page 668 for questions 1 and 2, find to the nearest whole number the change in soil pH from the lowest to the highest recorded number. This number represents a _____-times change in hydrogen ion concentration.

 in.bdol.glencoe.com/standardized_test

---

7. A **9.** D

8. A

Part 2 Constructed Response/Grid In

10. Student answers will vary. Be sure student designs include a control and that they are testing only one variable. For example, cover a group of buttercups with red filters, another group with blue filters, and a control group with clear filters and observe how the buttercups track the sun.

11. Vascular plants do not depend on the presence of water in their environment for sexual reproduction. They are covered with a cuticle that helps to reduce water loss. Vascular tissues allow for more efficient distribution of materials within the plant. There is a greater variety of plant forms among vascular plants that are adapted to different environments.

12. Student answers will vary depending on areas chosen. In most cases, the greater number of seed plants is directly related to the amount of land in an area covered by vegetation and whether or not the area has a climate favorable for plant growth.

13. 1000

RUBRIC

For more help evaluating open-ended assessment questions, see the rubric on p. 9T.

Unit 8

Invertebrates

Unit Overview

Unit 8 familiarizes students with invertebrate animals.

Chapter 25 introduces characteristics of animals and describes body plans.

Chapter 26 examines structures, adaptations, ecology, and phylogeny of sponges, cnidarians, flatworms, and roundworms.

Chapter 27 examines the characteristics, ecology, and phylogeny of mollusks and segmented worms.

Chapter 28 explores arthropod diversity and explains adaptations that allowed arthropods to become land dwellers.

Chapter 29 presents characteristics of echinoderms and introduces invertebrate chordates.

Introducing the Unit

Ask students to examine the photo of the coral reef and identify the organisms shown. Have the class brainstorm to create lists of how these organisms are alike and how they are different. **L2**

WebQuest

A WebQuest is an inquiry-based online project in which all information used by students is obtained from the Web. Students evaluate the information to complete the activity. Access the Unit 8 WebQuest at **in.bdol.glencoe.com/webquest**

670

Unit 8

History & Biology

Time Line: 400 B.C. — 1450 1500 — 1600

- **350 B.C.** Aristotle classifies all known animals into eight groups.
- **1452–1455** Gutenberg prints about 180 copies of the Bible.
- **1551** The first of five volumes titled *Historia Animalium* is published—the beginning of the science of zoology.
- **1564** William Shakespeare is born.
- **1669** First description of invertebrate anato[my] published in Malpi[ghi's] *Silkworms.*

Invertebrates

Elephant from *Historia Animalium*

What You'll Learn

Chapter 25
What is an animal?

Chapter 26
Sponges, Cnidarians, Flatworms, and Roundworms

Chapter 27
Mollusks and Segmented Worms

Chapter 28
Arthropods

Chapter 29
Echinoderms and Invertebrate Chordates

Unit 8 Review
BioDigest & Standardized Test Practice

> **Indiana Standards**
> The following standards are covered in Unit 8:
> B.1.1, B.1.7, B.1.8, B.1.11, B.1.14, B.1.15, B.1.16, B.1.17, B.1.18, B.1.19, B.1.30, B.1.31, B.1.32, B.1.34, B.1.38, B.1.43

Why It's Important

About 95 percent of all animals are invertebrates—animals without backbones. These animals exhibit variations, tolerances, and adaptations to nearly all of Earth's biomes. Understanding how these organisms develop and function helps humans to better understand themselves.

> **Understanding the Photo** ▶
> This reef was built over many centuries as corals completed their life cycles. Today, it is home to a great diversity of organisms. The corals, crinoids, and sponges shown here are three types of the countless invertebrate animals on Earth.

670 in.bdol.glencoe.com/webquest

Time Line

Discussion Direct students' attention to the image of the elephant below the time line. Show students other images from Gesner's *Historia Animalium.* If Gesner's books are not available from a library, use the Internet links at to download and print images. Ask students to propose explanations about why many of the animal illustrations in Gesner's books are not realistic. In most cases, the illustrator drew the animal from a written or verbal description.

1769 Patent for the steam engine issued.

1925 The quick-freeze machine is invented—the beginning of the frozen food industry.

1700 • 1800 • 1900 • 2000

1711 Corals are reclassified as animals instead of plants.

1822 The first book in which vertebrate and invertebrate animals are distinguished is published.

1899 A scientist raises unfertilized sea urchin eggs to maturity by altering their environment.

1997 A new species of marine worms is found living 450 m deep in the Gulf of Mexico.

1977 New species of giant clams, marine worms, and other organisms are discovered living around deep-sea vents near the Galápagos Islands.

Marine worms ▶

Advance Materials Planning

The following materials may need to be ordered a few weeks in advance of the planned activity.

Chapter 25
- ■ **MiniLab** (p. 675) rotifers
- ■ **MiniLab** (p. 683) vinegar eels
- ■ **BioLab** (p. 686) zebra fishes (males and females), prepared aquarium

Chapter 26
- ■ **MiniLab** (p. 702) hydra
- ■ **MiniLab** (p. 712) slides of *Trichinella* larvae
- ■ **BioLab** (p. 714) live planarians

Chapter 27
- ■ **Additional Lab** (p. 724) land snails
- ■ **BioLab** (p. 734) live earthworms

Chapter 28
- ■ **MiniLab** (p. 743) preserved lobster
- ■ **MiniLab** (p. 754) grasshopper life stages specimens
- ■ **BioLab** (p. 756) brine shrimp eggs

Chapter 29
- ■ **MiniLab** (p. 764) slides of sea star pedicellariae
- ■ **MiniLab** (p. 773) lancelet
- ■ **BioLab** (p. 776) preserved specimens of sea star, sea urchin, sand dollar, sea cucumber

671

Unit Projects

Using the Library
Intrapersonal Ask students to research information about butterfly metamorphosis. **L2**

Design and Build
Kinesthetic Have students obtain the materials and develop an enclosure to observe butterfly metamorphosis. **L1** **ELL**

Make a Map
Visual-Spatial Have students map the migration of monarch butterflies. **L3**

Chapter 25 Organizer

Section Objectives	National Science Standards	State/Local Standards	Advanced Lab and Demo Planning
Section 25.1 1 session, 1/2 block 1. **Identify** the characteristics of animals. 2. **Identify** cell differentiation in the development of a typical animal. 3. **Sequence** the development of a typical animal.	UCP.1–5; A.1, A.2; C.1, C.3–6; E.2; F.3, F.6; G.1, G.2	**Indiana Standards** B.1.1, B.1.11, B.1.16, B.1.30	**Student Labs:** MiniLab 25.1, p. 675: toothbrush bristles, glass slide, water, rotifers, coverslip, microscope Problem-Solving Lab 25.1, p. 676 Internet BioLab, p. 686: See materials list below. **Teacher Demonstration:** Quick Demo, p. 674: various prepared slides of animal cells (nerve, muscle, blood, and cells lining the stomach)
Section 25.2 2 sessions, 1 1/2 blocks 4. **Compare and contrast** radial and bilateral symmetry with asymmetry. 5. **Trace** the phylogeny of animal body plans. 6. **Distinguish** among the body plans of acoelomate, pseudocoelomate, and coelomate animals.	UCP.1–5; A.1, A.2; C.1, C.3, C.5, C.6; E.1, E.2; F.1; G.1, G.2	**Indiana Standards** B.1.1, B.1.15, B.1.16, B.1.32	**Student Labs:** Problem-Solving Lab 25.2, p. 682 Additional Lab, p. 682: microscope, prepared slides of cross sections of hydra, planarian, nematode, earthworm MiniLab 25.2, p. 683: vinegar eels, microscope, glass slide, water, coverslip, clock or stopwatch with second hand **Teacher Demonstration:** Quick Demo, p. 681: dried bodies of marine sponges, goldfish, large, preserved jellyfish
End of Chapter Assessment Student Edition **Study Guide,** p. 689 **Content Assessment,** pp. 690–691		**Indiana Standards** B.1.1, B.1.7, B.1.15, B.1.16	**Student Lab:** Internet BioLab, p. 686: zebra fishes (males and females), prepared aquarium, binocular microscope, petri dish, wax pencil, bulb baster, beaker, dropper

Key to Teaching Strategies

L1 Level 1 activities should be appropriate for students with learning difficulties.

L2 Level 2 activities should be within the ability range of all students.

L3 Level 3 activities are designed for above-average students.

ELL ELL activities should be within the ability range of English Language Learners.

COOP LEARN Cooperative Learning activities are designed for small group work.

Legend

 Transparency   ⬤ CD-ROM   MP3 MP3   ▣ Videocassette   ⬤ DVD

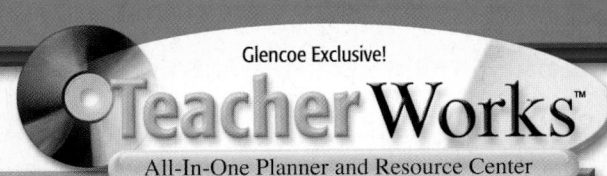

Glencoe Exclusive!
TeacherWorks™
All-In-One Planner and Resource Center

Reproducible Masters and Transparencies	Technology

Reproducible Masters and Transparencies

Unit 8 FAST FILE Resources
MiniLab Worksheet, p. 3
BioLab Worksheet, pp. 5–6
Reinforcement and Study Guide in English,
   pp. 7–8
Reinforcement and Study Guide in Spanish,
   pp. 11–12
Critical Thinking/Problem Solving, p. 16
Transparency Worksheets, pp. 17, 19–20, 21–22
**Reading Essentials for Biology,
Section 25.1**
Probeware Labs, pp. 21–24
🔆 **Section Focus Transparency 61**
🔆 **Basic Concepts Transparency 44**
🔆 **Reteaching Skills Transparency 38**

Technology

⬤ **Interactive Chalkboard CD-ROM: Section 25.1 Presentation** 🚩
⬤ TeacherWorks™ **CD-ROM** 🚩
MP3 **Guided Reading Audio Summaries MP3**

Unit 8 FAST FILE Resources
MiniLab Worksheet, p. 4
Reinforcement and Study Guide in English,
   pp. 9–10
Reinforcement and Study Guide in Spanish,
   pp. 13–14
Concept Mapping, p. 15
**Reading Essentials for Biology,
Section 25.2**
Laboratory Manual, pp. 159–162
🔆 **Section Focus Transparency 62**
🔆 **Basic Concepts Transparency 44**

⬤ **Interactive Chalkboard CD-ROM: Section 25.2 Presentation** 🚩
⬤ TeacherWorks™ **CD-ROM** 🚩
MP3 **Guided Reading Audio Summaries MP3**

Unit 8 FAST FILE Resources
Chapter Assessment, pp. 23–28
Student Recording Sheet, p. 29

The Princeton Review **Reviewing Biology,** pp. 49–50

⬤ **Interactive Chalkboard:** 🚩
Chapter 25 Assessment
⬤ **MindJogger Videoquizzes
DVD/VHS**
⬤ **ExamView® Pro Test Bank
CD-ROM**
⬤ TeacherWorks™ **CD-ROM** 🚩
⬤ **Succeeding on National Standards CD-ROM**

🖥 in.bdol.glencoe.com
/self_check_quiz
/vocabulary_puzzlemaker
/chapter_test
/standardized_test

🚩 Indicates materials created specifically for Indiana.

Short on Time?

 The BioDigest at the end of this unit can be used as a(n):

- preview to introduce important unit concepts.
- overview if time does not permit teaching the entire chapter.
- review of key unit concepts.

Understanding the Photo

Catostylus mosaicus, the brown blubber jellyfish, is common in the waters off the eastern coast of Australia. It can grow to 35 cm in diameter. This jellyfish has an unusual structure. Although its tentacles have stinging cells that can capture plankton, it has no mouth. Instead, there are many minute openings in the tentacles. This jellyfish also has a symbiotic relationship with a type of photosynthetic alga. Algae live within the jellyfish's body and supplement its food needs.

What is an animal?

What You'll Learn

- You will identify animal characteristics and distinguish them from those of other life forms.
- You will identify cell differentiation in the developmental stages of animals.
- You will identify and interpret body plans of animals.

Why It's Important

The animal kingdom includes diverse organisms, such as sponges, earthworms, clams, crickets, birds, and humans. An understanding of other animals will provide a better understanding of ourselves.

Understanding ▶ the Photo

Although they are different in appearance, these fishes and this jellyfish have common characteristics. They are multicellular organisms whose cells do not have cell walls. They also reproduce, respond, and must take in energy in the form of food. Scientists classify organisms with these characteristics as animals.

Biology Online

Visit in.bdol.glencoe.com to
- study the entire chapter online
- access Web Links for more information and activities on animals
- review content with the Interactive Tutor and self-check quizzes

672

 Two-Minute Chapter Launcher

Demo Ask students to observe two of the following animals in clear plastic containers: a hamster, an earthworm, a cricket, or a grasshopper. Ask them to list ways in which these animals are alike and how they are different. Remind students to treat live animals gently. **L2 ELL**

Indiana Academic Standards

Pages 672–673: B.1.16, B.1.30

Typical Animal Characteristics

 Indiana Standards Standard B.1.11 Describe that through biogenesis all organisms begin their life cycles as a single cell and that in multicellular organisms, successive generations of embryonic cells form by cell division.

SECTION PREVIEW

Objectives
Identify the characteristics of animals.

Identify cell differentiation in the development of a typical animal.

Sequence the development of a typical animal.

Review Vocabulary
autotroph: an organism that uses light energy or energy stored in chemical compounds to make energy-rich compounds (p. 46)

New Vocabulary
sessile
blastula
gastrula
ectoderm
endoderm
mesoderm
protostome
deuterostome

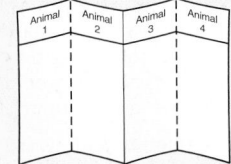

FOLDABLES
Study Organizer

Animals Make the following Foldable to help you understand what characteristics are common to all animals.

STEP 1 **Fold** a sheet of paper in half lengthwise twice.

STEP 2 **Fold** down 2.5 cm of paper from the top. (Hint: From the tip of your index finger to your middle knuckle is about 2.5 cm.)

STEP 3 **Open and draw** lines along all folds. **Label** the columns with the names of four different types of animals.

Animal 1 | Animal 2 | Animal 3 | Animal 4

Identifying Before reading Chapter 25, identify characteristics of each animal and list them in the corresponding column. After reading about the characteristics of animals, add any missing characteristics to your lists.

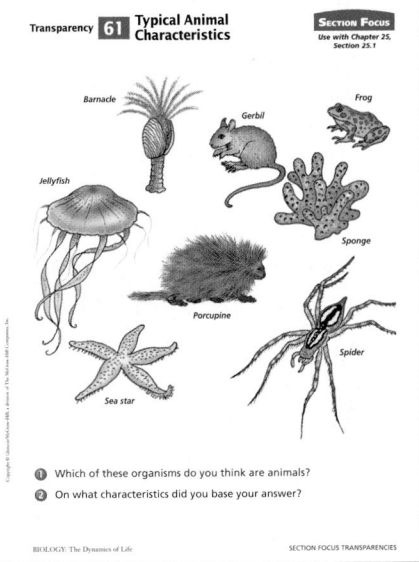

Transparency **61** Typical Animal Characteristics — SECTION FOCUS Use with Chapter 25, Section 25.1

① Which of these organisms do you think are animals?
② On what characteristics did you base your answer?

BIOLOGY: The Dynamics of Life — SECTION FOCUS TRANSPARENCIES

Characteristics of Animals

All animals have several characteristics in common. Animals are eukaryotic, multicellular organisms with ways of moving that help them reproduce, obtain food, and protect themselves. Most animals have specialized cells that form tissues and organs—such as nerves and muscles. Unlike plants, animals are composed of cells that do not have cell walls.

Animals obtain food

Examine the animals shown in *Figure 25.1.* One characteristic common to all animals is that they are heterotrophic, meaning they must consume food to obtain energy and nutrients. All animals depend either directly or indirectly on autotrophs for food.

Figure 25.1
Animals consume other organisms.

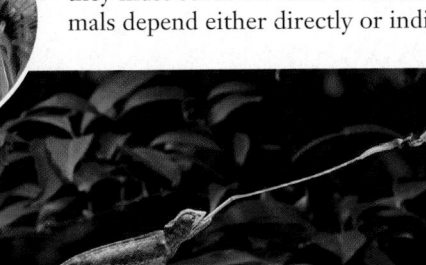

B A lizard consumes insects.

A Barnacles filter small organisms out of the water.

INTERACTIVE CHALKBOARD
with Image Bank

PowerPoint® Presentations
This CD-ROM is an editable Microsoft® PowerPoint® presentation that includes:
• Section presentations
• Section checks
• Image bank
• Hot links to Biology Online
• All transparencies

FOLDABLES™
For an additional Foldables activity idea, see the Chapter 25 Foldables page in *Unit 8 FAST FILE Resources.*

673

RESOURCE MANAGER

Unit 8 *FAST FILE* Resources
MiniLab Worksheet, p. 3
BioLab Worksheet, pp. 5–6
Reinforcement and Study Guide in English, pp. 7–8
Reinforcement and Study Guide in Spanish, pp. 11–12
Critical Thinking/Problem Solving, p. 16

Transparency Worksheets, pp. 17, 19–20, 21–22
Reading Essentials for Biology, Section 25.1
Probeware Labs, pp. 21–24
Section Focus Transparency 61
Basic Concepts Transparency 44
Reteaching Skills Transparency 38

2 Teach

CAREERS IN BIOLOGY

Marine Biologist

Would you enjoy spending your days studying the organisms found in the oceans? Perhaps you should become a marine biologist.

Skills for the Job
Many marine biologists go SCUBA diving in the oceans to find specimens, but they also spend time examining those organisms in labs and doing library research. They focus on topics such as the effects of temperature changes and pollution on ocean inhabitants. Many marine biologists work for government agencies, such as the National Oceanic and Atmospheric Administration (NOAA), and the Environmental Protection Agency (EPA). Some work for private industries, such as fisheries and environmental consulting firms. Other marine biologists teach and/or do research at colleges and universities. Most marine biologists have a master's degree or a doctorate, plus skill in analyzing data and solving problems.

For more careers in related fields, visit in.bdol.glencoe.com/careers

Scientists hypothesize that animals first evolved in water. Water is denser and contains less oxygen than air, but water usually contains more food. In water, some animals, such as barnacles and oysters, do not move from place to place and have adaptations that allow them to capture food from their water environment. Organisms that are permanently attached to a surface are called **sessile** (SE sul). They don't expend much energy to obtain food.

Some aquatic animals, such as the corals shown in *Figure 25.2A*, and sponges move about only during the early stages of their lives. They hatch from fertilized eggs into free-swimming larval forms. Most adults are sessile and attach themselves to rocks or other objects.

There is little suspended food in the air. Land animals use more oxygen and expend more energy to find food. The sidewinder snake and osprey shown in *Figure 25.2B* and *C*, can move about in their environment in an active search for food.

Animals digest food

Animals are heterotrophs that ingest their food; after ingestion, they must digest it. In some animals, digestion is carried out within individual cells; in other animals, digestion takes place in an internal cavity. Some of the food

Figure 25.2
Animals capture food in a variety of ways.

A Corals capture their food from the water as it moves over them. **Infer** *What types of organisms might be part of a coral's diet?*

B A sidewinder rattlesnake barely touches the ground as it follows the trail of its prey.

C The osprey can dive and snatch a fish from the waters of a lake or stream.

674 WHAT IS AN ANIMAL?

Figure 25.3
In animals such as planarians and earthworms, food is digested in a digestive tract.

Mouth

Extended pharynx

Digestive tract

A Planarians feed on small, live organisms or on the remains of larger animals. The planarian's digestive tract has only one opening, the pharynx, through which food enters and wastes exit.

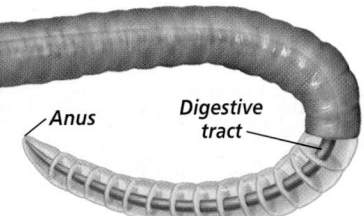

B Earthworms ingest soil and digest the organic matter contained in it. Soil enters the mouth and travels along the digestive tract in one direction. Indigestible waste is eliminated at the anus.

Anus

Digestive tract

that an animal consumes and digests is stored as fat or glycogen, a polysaccharide, and used when other food is not available.

Examine the digestive tracts of a flatworm and an earthworm in *Figure 25.3*. Notice that there is only one opening to the flatworm's digestive tract, a pharynx. An earthworm has a digestive tract with two openings, a mouth at one end and an anus at the other.

Animal cell adaptations

Most animal cells are differentiated and carry out different functions. Animals have specialized cells that enable them to sense and seek out food and mates, and allow them to identify and protect themselves from predators. Observe the animals in the *MiniLab* on this page. Can you identify any specialized cells in these animals? Find out about other specialized animal cells in the *Biotechnology* at the end of this chapter.

✓ **Reading Check** **Identify** three characteristics of the animal kingdom.

MiniLab 25.1

Observe and Infer

Observing Animal Characteristics Animals differ in size and shape, and can be found living in different habitats.

Procedure 🧪🥽🧤✋🔬

CAUTION: *Use caution when handling a microscope, glass slides, and coverslips.*

1. Copy the data table.
2. Add a few bristles from an old toothbrush to a glass slide. Add a drop of water containing rotifers to your slide. The drop should cover the bristles. Add a coverslip.
3. Observe the rotifers under low-power magnification.
4. Use the data table to record the characteristics that you were able to see. Describe the evidence for each trait.

Data Table		
Animal Characteristic	**Observed? (Yes or No)**	**Evidence**
Multicellular		
Feeding		
Movement		
Size in mm		

Analysis

1. **Describe** Are rotifers multicellular? Explain.
2. **Observe** Were you able to observe evidence of rotifers feeding? Explain.
3. **Infer** Are rotifers autotrophs or heterotrophs? Explain.

MiniLab 25.1

Purpose
Students will observe animal traits in rotifers.

Process Skills
classify, observe and infer, collect data, draw conclusions

Teaching Strategies
■ Rotifers are available from biological supply houses.
■ Rotifers are in the phylum Rotifera. These animals are used because students are unfamiliar with this phylum.
■ Remind students to treat live animals gently and wash their hands after the activity.

Expected Results
Students will observe movement and feeding. Students will infer that these animals are multicellular.

Analysis
1. Students won't see individual cells, so they infer that the rotifers are multicellular.
2. Student answers will vary. Most rotifers will be feeding on bacteria; the movement of their cilia implies that they are pulling water and food into their bodies.
3. They are not green, thus are probably not autotrophs.

Assessment
Knowledge Ask students to research rotifer classification and to write a report on their classification. Use the Performance Task Assessment List for Writing in Science in **PASC**, p. 159. **L2**

✓ **Reading Check** Student answers should include any three of the following: eukaryotic multicellular organisms, heterotrophic and digest food, means of moving to obtain food, reproduce, protect themselves; animal cells do not have cell walls, cells are differentiated to carry out functions.

CULTURAL DIVERSITY

Animals in a Cross-Cultural Perspective
Discuss the diverse views different societies and cultures have about animals in nature. Begin your discussion by asking students how animals are viewed and used in the United States today. Next, point out that not all cultures view animals in this way. For example, Native American traditions often portray animals as important as or even more important than humans. Obtain books about the legends and myths of different cultures, and discuss with students the role of animals in these stories.

Purpose

Students will determine that cytoplasm differences can influence development in frogs.

Process Skills

interpret scientific diagrams, compare and contrast, draw a conclusion, think critically, predict

Teaching Strategies

Explain to students that the normal pattern for cell division occurs as shown in the diagrams on the left. The last phase shown in both diagrams shows the larval stage of frog development.

Thinking Critically

1. When the gray crescent is present, normal development occurs. If the gray crescent is not present, development does not occur.
2. It is critical for normal embryo development.
3. One cell would develop.

Modified Assessment

Performance Have students use a dissecting microscope or hand lens to examine preserved frog eggs. Have them diagram what they observe and label the gray crescent. (Note: Preserved frog eggs are available from biological supply houses.) Use the Performance Task Assessment List for Scientific Drawing in **PASC**, p. 127. **L1** **ELL**

Development of Animals

Most animals develop from a fertilized egg cell called a zygote. But how does a zygote develop into many different kinds of cells that make up a snail, a fish, or a human? After fertilization, the zygote of different animal species all have similar, genetically determined stages of development.

Fertilization

Most animals reproduce sexually. Male animals produce sperm cells and female animals produce egg cells. Fertilization occurs when a sperm cell penetrates the egg cell, forming a new cell called a zygote. In animals, fertilization may be internal or external.

Cell division

The zygote divides by mitosis and cell division to form two cells in a process called cleavage. Find out how important this first cell division is in frog development by studying the *Problem-Solving Lab.* Once cell division has begun, the organism is known as an embryo. Recall that an embryo is an organism at an early stage of growth and development. The two cells that result from cleavage then divide to form four cells and so on, until a cell-covered, fluid-filled ball called a **blastula** (BLAS chuh luh) is formed. In some animals, such as a lancelet, the blastula is a single layer of cells surrounding a fluid-filled space. In other animals, such as frogs, there may be several layers of cells surrounding the space. The blastula is formed early in the development of an animal embryo. In sea urchin development, for example, the formation of a blastula is complete about ten hours after fertilization. In humans, the blastula forms about five days after fertilization.

Gastrulation

After blastula formation, cell division continues. The cells on one side of the blastula then move inward to form a **gastrula** (GAS truh luh)—a structure made up of two layers of cells with an opening at one end.

Problem-Solving Lab 25.1

Interpret Scientific Diagrams

How important is the first cell division in frog development?
The first division sometimes results in two cells with unequal amounts of cytoplasm. Does this have any impact on the development of an organism? It does in frogs.

Gray crescent

1st cleavage

Dies

Solve the Problem
In a frog cell, a small, specialized area forms in the cytoplasm just after fertilization. This area is called the gray crescent. Note its appearance in the diagram. Follow the changes in development as the first division of cytoplasm occurs equally through the gray crescent and unequally through the gray crescent.

Thinking Critically

1. **Explain** How does each set of diagrams illustrate the role of the gray crescent in early frog development?
2. **Infer** Answer the question posed at the beginning of this problem-solving lab.
3. **Predict** What would happen to a frog's development if the first cell division occurred on the horizontal plane rather than on the vertical plane?

676 WHAT IS AN ANIMAL?

TECH PREP

Spina Bifida: *Linguistic* Ask students to interview a doctor or another medical professional about spina bifida. Ask students to write a report of their findings and to prepare diagrams that show normal and abnormal stages of development. **L3**
COOP LEARN

Gastrula formation can be compared to the way a potter creates a cup or bowl from a lump of clay, as shown in *Figure 25.4*. First, the clay is formed into a ball. Then, the potter presses in on the top of the ball to form a cavity that becomes the interior of the bowl. In a similar way, the cells at one end of the blastula move inward, forming a cavity lined with a second layer of cells. The layer of cells on the outer surface of the gastrula is called the **ectoderm.** The layer of cells lining the inner surface is called the **endoderm.** The ectoderm cells of the gastrula continue to grow and divide, and eventually they develop into the skin and nervous tissue of the animal. The endoderm cells develop into the lining of the animal's digestive tract and into organs associated with digestion.

Formation of mesoderm

In some animals, the development of the gastrula progresses until a layer of cells called the mesoderm is formed. Mesoderm is found in the middle of the embryo; the term *meso* means "middle." The **mesoderm** (MEZ uh durm) is the third cell layer found in the developing embryo between the ectoderm and the endoderm. The mesoderm cells develop into the muscles, circulatory system, excretory system, and, in some animals, the respiratory system. Identify and review cell differentiation in the development of an animal as shown in *Figure 25.5* on the next page.

When the opening in the gastrula develops into the mouth, the animal is called a **protostome** (PROH tuh stohm). Snails, earthworms, and insects are examples of protostomes.

In other animals, such as sea stars, fishes, toads, snakes, birds, and humans, the mouth does not develop from the gastrula's opening. An animal whose mouth developed not from the opening, but from cells elsewhere on the gastrula is called a **deuterostome** (DEW tihr uh stohm).

Scientists hypothesize that protostome animals were the first to appear in evolutionary history, and that deuterostomes followed at a later time. Biologists today often classify an unknown organism by identifying its phylogeny. Recall that phylogeny is the evolutionary history of an organism. Determining whether an animal is a protostome or deuterostome can help biologists identify its group. Even though sea urchins, for example, are invertebrates and fishes are vertebrates, both are deuterostomes and are, therefore, more closely related than you might conclude from comparing their adult body structures.

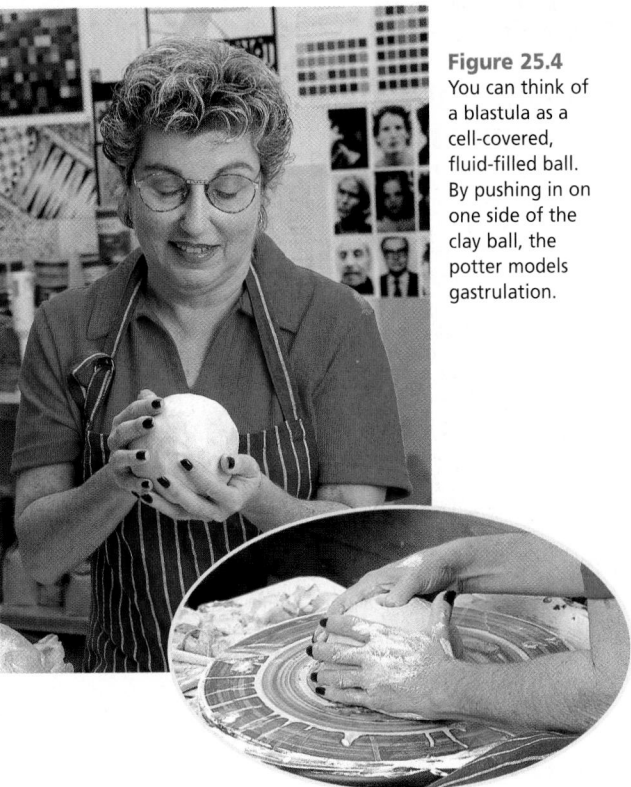

Figure 25.4
You can think of a blastula as a cell-covered, fluid-filled ball. By pushing in on one side of the clay ball, the potter models gastrulation.

Word Origin

protostome from the Greek words *protos,* meaning "first," and *stoma,* meaning "mouth"; deuterostome from the Greek words *deutero,* meaning "secondary," and *stoma,* meaning "mouth"

A protostome and a deuterostome differ in the location of the cells that become the organism's mouth.

Word Origin

Have students research to find and define other words that have "proto" as part of the root, such as *protoplasm, proton,* and *prototype.*

Biology Journal

Organs' Origins Provide students with diagrams of the human body showing bone, muscle, spinal cord, brain, kidneys, liver, lungs, and pancreas. Give them the following information: ectoderm produces brain, spinal cord, nerves, outer skin, eye lens, nose, and ears. Endoderm produces pancreas, liver, lungs, and lining of the digestive system. Mesoderm produces skeleton, muscles, excretory system, inner skin. Have them use colored pencils to shade parts of the body that develop from ectoderm yellow, parts that develop from endoderm green, and parts that develop from mesoderm red. **L1** **ELL**

Portfolio

Word Roots Have students work in pairs to look up words in the dictionary that begin with the prefixes *ecto-* and *endo-.* Ask students to make a list of the words. Have student pairs exchange lists and write their own definitions of the words. Then ask each student to compare actual definitions with their own definitions. **L2** **ELL** **COOP LEARN**

USING MODELS

Embryo Development Give students prepared salt dough (one part salt, one part flour, one part water). Have them cover a space on their desktops with a few paper towels and dip their fingers into flour so that the dough will not stick to them. Ask students to make cross-section models of a fertilized egg, a blastula, and a gastrula. They should make the stages in sequence, with one stage becoming the next stage, rather than lining up all three stages at once. They will not have to add more dough as the fertilized egg becomes the bastula because the total amount of cytoplasm does not increase as the early embryo develops. **L1** **ELL**

 Indiana Academic Standards

Pages 676–677: B.1.11

Purpose
Students study the stages of early embryonic development.

Teaching Strategies
Ask students to study the diagrams, then write a numbered list describing the developmental stages shown. They can use the list as a study guide.

Visual Learning
Have students describe the changes in appearance at each stage of development. **L1**

Critical Thinking
Cells continue to divide, becoming smaller and smaller with each cell division.

Inquiry
Activity Ask students to view prepared slides of sea urchin development. Ask them to identify slides that illustrate deuterostome development. Have students explain the significance of this type of development in illustrating how closely related sea urchins are to vertebrates. **L2**

The BioLab at the end of the chapter can be used at this point in the lesson.

Cell Differentiation in Animal Development

Figure 25.5
The fertilized eggs of most animals follow a similar pattern of development. From one fertilized egg cell, many divisions occur until a fluid-filled ball of cells forms. The ball folds inward and continues to develop. **Critical Thinking** *How do cells differentiate as an embryo develops?*

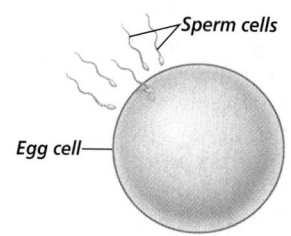

Sperm cells

Egg cell

A Fertilization A zygote is formed when an egg cell is fertilized by a sperm cell.

F Formation of mesoderm In protostomes, the mesoderm forms from cells that break away from the endoderm near the opening of the gastrula. In deuterostomes, the mesoderm forms from pouches of endoderm cells on the inside of the gastrula. After the formation of mesoderm, development continues with each cell layer differentiating into specialized tissues.

Endoderm

Ectoderm   *Mesoderm*

B First cell division The zygote divides by mitosis and cell division to form two cells. From this point, the developing organism is called an embryo.

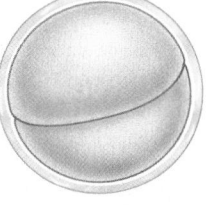

C Additional cell divisions Cell division continues. The eight-cell stage is shown here.

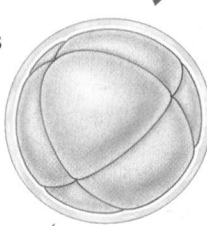

E Gastrulation As the embryo continues to grow, some of the cells of the blastula move inward, forming the gastrula. All animal embryos except sponges pass through this gastrula stage.

LM Magnification: 80×

D Formation of a blastula Continuous cell divisions result in a cell-covered, fluid-filled ball, the blastula. During these early developmental stages, the total amount of cytoplasm has not increased from the original cell.

Sea urchin blastula

678 WHAT IS AN ANIMAL?

Visually Impaired Obtain several old tennis balls or other types of hollow rubber balls. Have visually impaired students handle the balls and explain that the blastula appears just like the hollow balls. Then have these students hold the ball in one hand while pushing in on one side of the ball with their thumbs. Explain that now the balls represent the gastrula stage. Ask students to use their free hand to point to the parts of the ball that represent ectoderm and endoderm. **L1 ELL**

Indiana Academic Standards
Pages 678–679: B.1.1, B.1.11

678

LM Magnification: 1200×

Growth and development

Cells in developing embryos continue to differentiate and become specialized to perform different functions. Most animal embryos continue to develop over time, becoming juveniles that look like smaller versions of the adult animal. In some animals, such as insects and echinoderms, the embryo develops inside an egg into an intermediate stage called a larva (plural larvae). A larva often bears little resemblance to the adult animal. Inside the egg, the larva is surrounded by a membrane formed right after fertilization. When the egg hatches, the larva breaks through this fertilization membrane. Animals that

are generally sessile as adults, such as sea urchins, often have a free-swimming larval stage, as shown in *Figure 25.6*. You can observe development in fishes in the *BioLab* at the end of this chapter.

Adult animals

Once the juvenile or larval stage has passed, most animals continue to grow and develop into adults. This growth and development may take just a few days in some insects, or up to fourteen years in some mammals. Eventually the adult animals reach sexual maturity, mate, and the cycle begins again.

---

3 Assess

DAILY INTERVENTION

Check for Understanding
Intrapersonal Give students live insects in sealed, clear plastic containers. Ask them to list characteristics that make insects animals. Remind them to treat live animals gently. **L2**

Reteach
Kinesthetic Make clay models of stages of development. Ask students working in groups to place the models in sequence and describe what happens in each stage. **L1** **ELL**

Resources
For more practice, use *Reading Essentials for Biology*, Section 25.1.

Extension
Encourage students to visit a science museum that has displays about development. Have them make a photo essay of the exhibit that can be displayed in class. Have students include captions for the photos. **L2** **ELL**

 MODIFIED Assessment

Activity Ask students to write a note to a friend explaining what they do and do not understand about development. Have them exchange notes and help each other with areas of difficulty. **L1**

Section Assessment

Understanding Main Ideas
1. Identify and list the characteristics of a mouse that make it a member of the animal kingdom.
2. Explain why movement is an important characteristic of animals.
3. Compare and contrast a protostome and a deuterostome.
4. Identify cell differentiation in the development of an animal.
5. Describe gastrulation.

Thinking Critically
6. Name a land animal that is sessile. Why would this adaptation be a disadvantage to an animal in a land biome?

SKILL REVIEW
7. **Sequence** Make a concept map of animal development using the following stages, beginning with the earliest stage: gastrula, larva, adult, fertilized egg, blastula. For more help, refer to *Sequence* in the **Skill Handbook**.

 in.bdol.glencoe.com/self_check_quiz

25.1 TYPICAL ANIMAL CHARACTERISTICS **679**

Section Assessment

1. It is a multicellular heterotroph, moves to get food, and has cells without cell walls.
2. Animals must search for food and mates.
3. protostomes—the mouth develops from the opening in the gastrula; deuterostomes—the mouth develops elsewhere on the gastrula
4. Ectoderm—skin and the nervous system; endoderm—digestive organs and the digestive tract's lining; mesoderm—muscles, the circulatory and excretory systems, and in some animals, the respiratory system
5. Gastrulation occurs when cells of the blastula move inward and form an indentation on the surface of the blastula. It is now called a gastrula.
6. Scale insects mature as sessile animals after they pierce plant tissues with their mouths to feed on plant liquids. A sessile land animal could not locate a mate or find more food if its current food source disappeared.
7. fertilized egg, blastula, gastrula, larva, adult

1 Focus

INTERACTIVE CHALKBOARD
PowerPoint® Presentations

Bellringer
Section Focus Transparency 62

Transparency **62** Body Plans and Adaptations

SECTION FOCUS
Use with Chapter 25, Section 25.2

Group A

Group B

Group C

① How are shapes of the organisms in each group similar?

② How is the shape of each organism suited to the environment in which it lives?

BIOLOGY: The Dynamics of Life

SECTION FOCUS TRANSPARENCIES

Using an Analogy
Make and Use Tables Tables will vary depending on the animals students choose. Asymmetric animals include sponges and some corals; radially symmetric animals include sea stars, sand dollars, sea urchins, and hydra; bilaterally symmetric animals include spiders, grasshoppers, frogs, fishes, birds, and mammals.

Indiana Academic Standards

Pages 680–681: B.1.32

680

Section 25.2

SECTION PREVIEW

Objectives

Compare and contrast radial and bilateral symmetry with asymmetry.

Trace the phylogeny of animal body plans.

Distinguish among the body plans of acoelomate, pseudocoelomate, and coelomate animals.

Review Vocabulary
gastrula: an embryonic structure made up of two layers of cells with an opening at one end (p. 676)

New Vocabulary
symmetry
radial symmetry
bilateral symmetry
anterior
posterior
dorsal
ventral
acoelomate
pseudocoelom
coelom
exoskeleton
invertebrate
endoskeleton
vertebrate

Body Plans and Adaptations

Indiana Standards Standard B.1.15 Understand and explain that, in biological systems, structure and function must be considered together.

Form and Function

Using an Analogy Objects made by a potter can be many different shapes and sizes. There is a plan for making each piece of pottery according to its function. One plan results in a bowl, another in a vase, and still another in a plate. Animals' bodies also have plans—body shapes that are suited to a particular way of life. In this section, you will study animal body plans and see how a specific body plan is an adaptation to a particular environment.

Make and Use Tables *After you read about the different types of animal symmetry, make a table to categorize 25 animals according to their symmetry. Include animals that you are familiar with or have read about in this book. Compare your table to those of your classmates.*

What is symmetry?

Look at the animals shown in *Figure 25.7.* You know that all animals share certain characteristics, but these animals don't look like they have much in common. The sponge seems to have no particular shape, whereas the leopard has a head, body, tail, and two pairs of legs. The jellyfish doesn't have a head or tail, and is circular in form. Each animal can be described in terms of **symmetry** (SIH muh tree)—a term that describes the arrangement of body structures. Different kinds of symmetry enable animals to move about in different ways.

Asymmetry

Many sponges have an irregularly shaped body, as seen in *Figure 25.8A.* An animal that is irregular in shape has no symmetry or an asymmetrical body plan. Animals with no symmetry often are sessile organisms that do not move from place to place. Most adult sponges do not move about.

Figure 25.7
A sponge **(A)**, an Asian leopard **(B)**, and a jellyfish **(C)** all exhibit different kinds of symmetry.

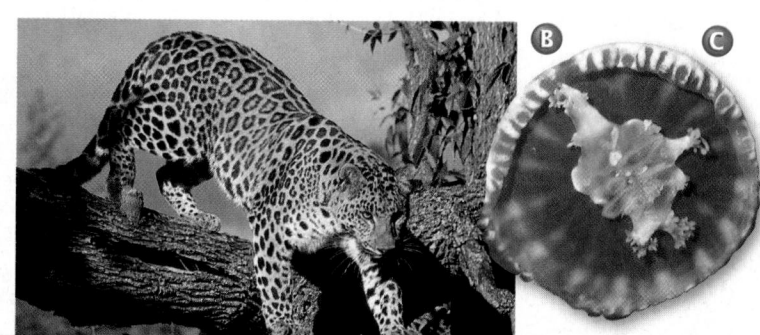

Ⓐ   Ⓑ   Ⓒ

RESOURCE MANAGER

Unit 8 *Fast File* Resources
MiniLab Worksheet, p. 4
Reinforcement and Study Guide in English, pp. 9–10
Reinforcement and Study Guide in Spanish, pp. 13–14
Concept Mapping, p. 15

Reading Essentials for Biology, Section 25.2
Laboratory Manual, pp. 159–162
Section Focus Transparency 62
Basic Concepts Transparency 44

Figure 25.8
All animals have body plans that enable them to survive in their surroundings.
Identify *What symmetry does a fish have? Explain.*

Dorsal

Anterior

Ventral

Posterior

A These irregularly shaped sponges are examples of animals with asymmetrical body plans.

B A hydra is an example of an animal with radial symmetry. It feeds on tiny animals by immobilizing them with venom from stinging cells that are along its tentacles.

C Bilaterally symmetrical animals, such as butterflies, have similar halves.

The bodies of most sponges consist of two layers of cells. Unlike all other animals, a sponge's embryonic development does not include the formation of an endoderm and mesoderm, or a gastrula stage. Fossil sponges first appeared in rocks dating back to more than 650 million years ago. They represent one of the oldest groups of animals on Earth—evidence that their two-layer body plan makes them well adapted for life in aquatic environments.

Radial symmetry

A hydra feeds on small animals it snares with its tentacles. A hydra has radial symmetry. Its tentacles radiate out from around its mouth. As shown in *Figure 25.8B*, animals with **radial** (RAY dee uhl) **symmetry** can be divided along any plane, through a central axis, into roughly equal halves.

Radial symmetry is an adaptation that enables an animal to detect and capture prey coming toward it from any direction.

Have you ever had your groceries double bagged at the store? The body plan of a hydra can be compared to a sack within a sack. These sacks are cell layers organized into tissues with distinct functions. A hydra develops from just two embryonic cell layers—ectoderm and endoderm.

Bilateral symmetry

The butterfly in *Figure 25.8C* has bilateral symmetry. An organism with **bilateral** (bi LA tuh rul) **symmetry** can be divided down its length into similar right and left halves. Bilaterally symmetrical animals can be divided in half only along one plane. In contrast, radially symmetrical animals can be divided along any vertical plane.

Activity

Visual-Spatial Bring in kitchen items such as bowls, vases, and a variety of spoons. Explain that each item is suited to a particular function. For example, the bowls hold soft or liquid foods, the spoons pick up or stir soft or liquid foods, and the vases hold flowers for display. Explain that, in a similar way, animals have structures that are suited to specific functions such as locomotion, food-getting, and circulating materials throughout their bodies.

Quick Demo

Symmetry Pass around the dried bodies of marine sponges, a live goldfish in a clear plastic container, and a large preserved jellyfish. Ask students to describe the shapes of the animals and explain if one side of the animal is equally balanced by the other. marine sponge, no; live goldfish, yes; preserved jellyfish, yes Explain to students that the quality they have just observed is called symmetry. **L1**

Caption Question Answer
Figure 25.8 bilateral symmetry; It can be divided down its center into similar left and right halves.

INCLUSION STRATEGIES

Visually Impaired Students who are visually impaired may benefit from handling a number of objects that are asymmetrical, radially symmetrical, or bilaterally symmetrical. First, explain to students what type of symmetry each object has, then give students new objects and have them determine symmetry. **L1**

Purpose
Students identify the type of body plans in three animals.

Process Skills
classify, observe and infer, compare and contrast, think critically

Teaching Strategies
Review the three types of body plans present in animals.

Thinking Critically
1. bilateral—body can be divided along its length into two equal halves; head and tail regions present, body cavity present, good muscular control
2. chair, pen, doll
3. asymmetry—body is irregular; does not move about, body consists of two cell layers
4. blob of clay, cottage cheese
5. radial—body can be divided along any plane through a central axis into equal halves; tentacles radiate from mouth, tissues present
6. wheel with spokes, open umbrella, apple corer

Assessment
Skill Have students prepare a concept map that uses the following terms: sponge, hydra, flatworm, roundworm, earthworm, radial symmetry, bilateral symmetry, asymmetry, pseudocoelomate, coelomate, acoelomate. Use the Performance Task Assessment List for Concept Map in **PASC**, p. 161. **L2**

In bilateral animals, the **anterior,** or head end, often has sensory organs. The **posterior** of these animals is the tail end. The **dorsal** (DOR sul), or upper surface, also looks different from the **ventral** (VEN trul), or lower surface. In animals that are upright or nearly so, the back is on the dorsal surface and the belly is on the ventral surface. Animals with bilateral symmetry can find food and mates and avoid predators because they have sensory organs and good muscular control. Test your ability to identify animal symmetry in *Problem-Solving Lab 25.2* on this page.

Bilateral Symmetry and Body Plans

Animals that are bilaterally symmetrical also share other important characteristics. All bilaterally symmetrical animals developed from three embryonic cell layers—ectoderm, endoderm, and mesoderm. Some bilaterally symmetrical animals also have fluid-filled spaces inside their bodies called body cavities in which internal organs are found. The development of fluid-filled body cavities made it possible for animals to grow larger because it allowed for the efficient circulation and transport of fluids, and support for organs and organ systems.

Acoelomates

Animals that develop from three cell layers—ectoderm, endoderm, and mesoderm—but have no body cavities are called **acoelomate** (ay SEE lum ate) animals. They have a digestive tract that extends throughout the body. Acoelomate animals may have been the first group of animals in which organs evolved.

Flatworms are bilaterally symmetrical animals with solid, compact bodies, as shown in *Figure 25.9*. Like other acoelomate animals, the organs of flatworms are embedded in the solid tissues of their bodies. A flattened body and branched digestive tract allow for the diffusion of nutrients, water, and oxygen to supply all body cells and to eliminate wastes.

Pseudocoelomates

A roundworm is an animal with bilateral symmetry. However, unlike a flatworm, the body of a roundworm

---

Problem-Solving Lab 25.2

Classify

Is symmetry associated with other animal traits? Animals show different patterns in their symmetry. Symmetry patterns are often associated with certain other characteristics or traits found in the animal.

Solve the Problem
Study these three animal diagrams. Determine the type of symmetry being shown.

Thinking Critically
1. **Identify** Animal A shows what type of symmetry? Explain your answer. Describe other traits associated with animal A.
2. **List** Name some objects other than animals that show the pattern of symmetry in A.
3. **Identify** Animal B shows what type of symmetry? Explain your answer. Describe other traits associated with animal B.
4. **List** Name some objects other than animals that show the pattern of symmetry in B.
5. **Identify** Animal C shows what type of symmetry? Explain your answer. Describe other traits associated with animal C.
6. **List** Name some objects other than animals that show the pattern of symmetry in C.

Additional Lab

Body Plans

Purpose
Students examine prepared cross-section slides of a hydra, flatworm, roundworm, and an earthworm to determine their body plan—acoelomate, pseudocoelomate, or coelomate.

Materials
microscope, prepared slides of cross sections of hydra, planarian, nematode, earthworm

Procedure
Give students the following directions.
1. Examine the cross-section slides.
2. Sketch, then label each cross section with the following: *Animal with Two Cell Layers, Pseudocoelomate Animal, Acoelomate Animal, Coelomate Animal,* and the names of organisms.

Analysis
1. Order the animals' body plans from least to most complex. hydra, planarian, nematode, earthworm

has a space that develops between the endoderm and mesoderm. It is called a **pseudocoelom** (soo duh SEE lum)—a fluid-filled body cavity partly lined with mesoderm.

Pseudocoelomates can move quickly. How? Think about the way your muscles work. The muscles in your arm lift your hand by pulling against your arm bones. If there were no rigid bones in your arms, your muscles would not be able to work. Although the roundworm has no bones, it does have a rigid, fluid-filled space, the pseudocoelom. Its muscles attach to the mesoderm and brace against the pseudocoelom. You can observe this movement in the *MiniLab* on this page.

Pseudocoelomates have a one-way digestive tract that has regions with specific functions. The mouth takes in food, the breakdown and absorption of food occurs in the middle section, and the anus expels wastes.

Figure 25.9
Animals with acoelomate bodies usually have a thin, flattened shape **(A)**. Pseudocoelomate animals are larger and thicker than their acoelomate ancestors **(B)**. Coelomates have complex internal organs **(C)**.

MiniLab 25.2

Observe and Infer

Check Out a Vinegar Eel Vinegar eels are roundworms with pseudocoeloms. They exhibit an interesting pattern of locomotion because they have only longitudinal (lengthwise) muscles.

LM Magnification: 50×

Vinegar eel

Procedure

CAUTION: *Use caution when handling a microscope and glassware.*

1. Prepare a wet mount of vinegar eels.
2. Observe them under low-power magnification.
3. Note their pattern of locomotion. Draw a series of diagrams that illustrate their pattern of movement.
4. Time, in seconds, how long it takes for one roundworm to move across the center of your field of view. Determine the diameter of your low-power field in mm. For help, refer to *Calculate Field of View* in the **Skill Handbook**. Time several animals and average their times, then calculate vinegar eel speed in mm/s.

Analysis

1. **Name** What type of symmetry is present in vinegar eels?
2. **Describe** What is the general pattern of locomotion for vinegar eels?
3. **Explain** How does the pseudocoelom aid vinegar eels in locomotion?
4. **Predict** Based on the speed of your vinegar eel, estimate the speed in mm/s for a flatworm. Explain your answer.

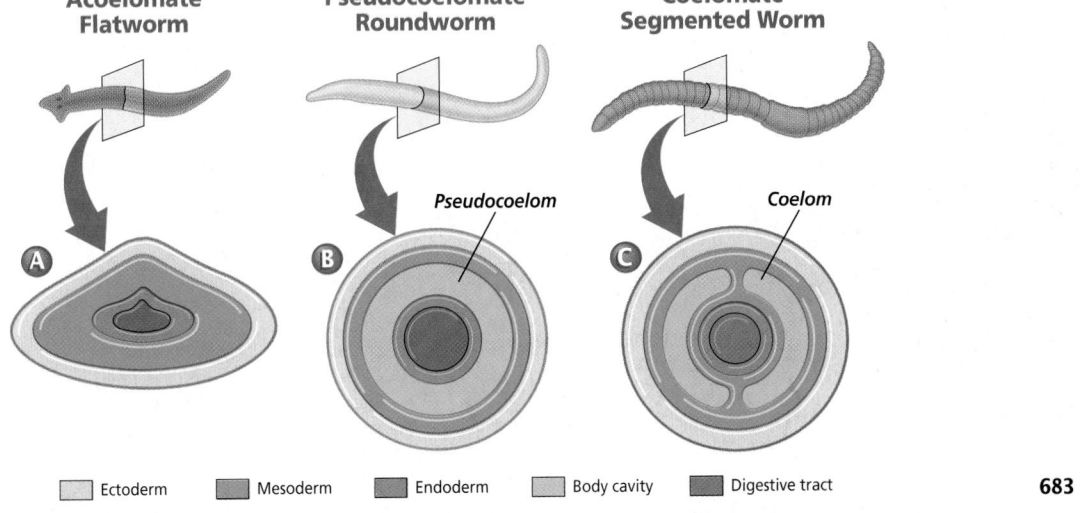

Acoelomate Flatworm

Pseudocoelomate Roundworm

Pseudocoelom

Coelomate Segmented Worm

Coelom

Ⓐ   Ⓑ   Ⓒ

☐ Ectoderm   ☐ Mesoderm   ☐ Endoderm   ☐ Body cavity   ☐ Digestive tract

683

MiniLab 25.2

Purpose

Students observe vinegar eels, *Turbatrix aceti*, and relate their pattern and speed of locomotion to a pseudocoelomate body plan.

Process Skills

collect data, observe and infer, predict

Teaching Strategies

- Use depression slides for wet mounts or add a few old toothbrush bristles to a regular slide to prevent crushing the roundworms.
- Review the meaning of "field of view." Remind students that to calculate speed, they must time the animal as it moves across their field of view.
- Remind students to treat live animals gently.

Expected Results

Students will observe the jerking contractions of vinegar eels.

Analysis

1. bilateral symmetry
2. series of jerky contractions
3. The body cavity is filled with fluid. Body muscles can brace and contract against this fluid.
4. The speed will range between 2 and 5 mm/s. A flatworm will move slower because it has no body cavity.

Modified Assessment

Portfolio Have students study vinegar eels under high-power magnification. Have them diagram and label body structures they observe. Use the Performance Task Assessment List for Scientific Drawing in **PASC**, p. 127. **L1** **ELL**

2. If you were to observe these animals' movements, predict what you might see. Explain in terms of their body plans. Students' descriptions should match those given in the chapter.

Assessment

Portfolio Ask students to summarize what they have learned about body plans in this lab. Have them consider the survival value of each type of body plan. Instruct them to put their summaries in their portfolios. Use the Performance Task Assessment List for Writing in Science in **PASC**, p. 159. **L2**

 Indiana Academic Standards

Pages 682–683: B.1.15

Reinforcement

Visual-Spatial Show students a live planarian in a deep-well projection slide (available from biological supply companies). Fill the well with pond or stream water. Use an overhead projector to project the swimming planarian onto a screen.

Next, place a small earthworm in a wet petri dish with a few small pebbles. Project it with your overhead projector. Ask students to relate the movements of both animals to their body plans.

Enrichment

Linguistic Have students write an account of the evolutionary development of the coelom. They should first determine the time period, explain how the coelom developed, identify animals with coeloms, and explain how the coelom has survival value. **L3**

Coelomates

The body cavity of an earthworm develops from a **coelom** (SEE lum), a fluid-filled space that is completely surrounded by mesoderm. Humans, insects, fishes, and many other animals have a coelomate body plan. The greatest diversity of animals is found among the coelomates.

Specialized organs and organ systems develop in the coelom. In coelomate animals, the digestive tract and other internal organs are attached by double layers of mesoderm and are suspended within the coelom. Like the pseudocoelom, the coelom cushions and protects the internal organs. It provides room for them to grow and move independently within an animal's body.

Animal Protection and Support

Over time, the development of body cavities resulted in a greater diversity of animal species. These diverse animal species became adapted to life in different environments. Some animals, such as mollusks, evolved hard shells that protected their soft bodies. Other animals, such as sponges, evolved hardened spicules between their cells that provided support.

Some animals developed exoskeletons. An **exoskeleton** is a hard covering on the outside of the body that provides a framework for support. Exoskeletons also protect soft body tissues, prevent water loss, and provide protection from predators. An exoskeleton is secreted by the epidermis and extends into the body, where it provides a place for muscle attachment. As an animal grows, it secretes a new exoskeleton and sheds the old one, as shown in *Figure 25.10.*

Exoskeletons are often found in invertebrates. An **invertebrate** is an animal that does not have a backbone. Many invertebrates, such as crabs, spiders, grasshoppers, dragonflies, and beetles, have exoskeletons.

Other animals have evolved different structures for support and protection. Invertebrates, such as sea urchins and sea stars, have an internal skeleton called an **endoskeleton.** It is covered by layers of cells and provides support for an animal's body. The endoskeleton protects internal organs and provides an internal brace for muscles to pull against. An endoskeleton may be made of calcium carbonate, as in sea stars; cartilage, as in sharks; or bone. Bony fishes, amphibians, reptiles, birds, and mammals all have endoskeletons made of bone.

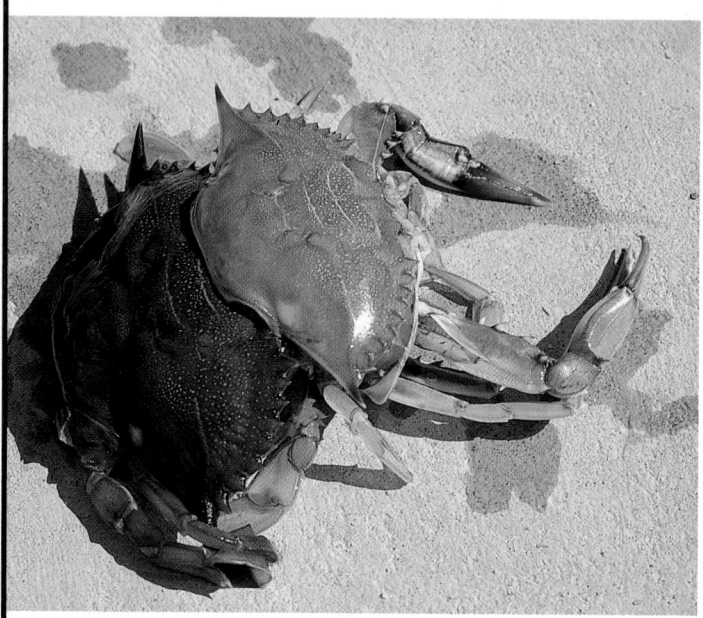

Figure 25.10
A new exoskeleton forms before a crab sheds its old one. Until the new exoskeleton expands and hardens, the crab is vulnerable to predators.

684 WHAT IS AN ANIMAL?

Indiana Academic Standards
Pages 684–685: B.1.15, B.1.32

Figure 25.11
Invertebrate animals such as an octopus (**A**) and a sea slug (**B**) have no backbones. Vertebrates with backbones include a monkey (**C**) and flamingos (**D**).

A **vertebrate** is an animal with an endoskeleton and a backbone. All vertebrates are bilaterally symmetrical. Examples of vertebrates include, fishes, amphibians, reptiles, birds, and mammals. *Figure 25.11* shows examples of invertebrate and vertebrate animals.

Origin of Animals

Most biologists agree that animals probably evolved from aquatic, colonial protists. Scientists trace this evolution back in time to late in the Precambrian. Although evidence suggests that bilaterally symmetrical animals might have appeared much later, many scientists agree that all the major animal body plans that exist today were already in existence at the beginning of the Cambrian Period, 543 million years ago. Since then, many new species have evolved but all known species have variations of the animal body plans developed during the Cambrian Period.

Section Assessment

Understanding Main Ideas
1. Compare and contrast radial and bilateral symmetry in animals. Give an example of each type.
2. Distinguish between the body plan of an acoelomate and a coelomate. Give an example of an animal with each type of body plan.
3. Explain how an adaptation such as an exoskeleton could be an advantage to animals in land biomes.
4. Compare movement in acoelomate and coelomate animals.

Thinking Critically
5. Explain the relationship between having a coelom and the development of complex organ systems.

SKILL REVIEW
6. **Get the Big Picture** Construct a table that compares the body plans of the sponge, hydra, flatworm, roundworm, and earthworm. For more help, refer to *Get the Big Picture* in the **Skill Handbook**.

 in.bdol.glencoe.com/self_check_quiz

25.2 BODY PLANS AND ADAPTATIONS **685**

INTERNET BioLab

Time Allotment
30 minutes on day 1; 15 minutes on days 2 through 5

Process Skills
interpret scientific illustrations, observe and infer, organize data, sequence, experiment

- Zebra fishes are available from pet shops or biological supply houses. Purchase six of each sex. Fishes must be young (between 6 and 24 months old). Remind students to treat live animals gently.
- Prepare an aquarium with filter, lights, timer, and heater. Marbles should be placed along the bottom. Embryos will fall between the marbles.
- Set timer and lights as follows: 14 hours light and 10 hours dark. Set the heater at 28.5°C.
- Feed fish flakes in the morning and brine shrimp or live blood worms in the afternoon.

Indiana Academic Standards
Pages 686–687: B.1.16

INTERNET BioLab

Before You Begin
The zebra fish (*Danio rerio*) is a common fresh-water fish sold in pet shops. They are ideal animals for study because they undergo embryonic developmental changes quickly and major stages can be observed within hours after fertilization.

Zebra Fish Development

PREPARATION

Problem
What do the developmental stages of the zebra fish look like?

Objectives
In this BioLab, you will:
- **Observe** stages of zebra fish development.
- **Record** all observations in a data table.
- **Use the Internet** to collect and compare data from other students.

Materials
zebra fishes (males and females)	petri dish	beaker
	wax pencil	dropper
prepared aquarium	bulb baster	
binocular microscope		

Safety Precautions
CAUTION: *Always wear safety goggles in the lab. Use caution when handling a binocular microscope and glassware.*

Skill Handbook
If you need help with this lab, refer to the **Skill Handbook**.

PROCEDURE

1. Copy the data table.
2. Use the bulb baster to transfer water and fish embryos from the aquarium to a beaker. Allow the embryos to settle to the bottom.
3. Use a wax pencil to write your name and class period on the edge of the lid of your petri dish. Use the dropper to half fill the bottom of your petri dish with aquarium water, and then to transfer several embryos from the beaker to your petri dish. Place the lid on your petri dish.
4. Your teacher will tell you the approximate time that fertilization occurred. Record the age of the embryos in your data table as hpf (hours past fertilization).
5. Observe the embryos under the microscope. In your data table, diagram what you observe.
6. Go to in.bdol.glencoe.com/internet_lab to post your data.

PROCEDURE

Teaching Strategies
- Use the baster to remove excess debris from the bottom of the tank on the evening prior to spawning.
- Females will release eggs about 30 min after the light comes on. Time this to correspond with your first morning class. Students may be able to see males following females along the bottom of the tank as eggs are released to fertilize them.
- Classes that occur later in the day may not be able to find early stages of embryonic development because fertilization took place in the morning. Embryonic development is rapid.
- Feeding is not necessary for the first week. Later, feed the young live paramecia.
- Use binocular microscopes to view embryo development.

7. Continue to observe your embryos daily for one week. Note when new organs appear and when movement is first seen. If you want to continue observing developmental changes, ask your teacher for instructions. **CAUTION:** *Wash your hands with soap and water immediately after each observation.*

8. CLEANUP AND DISPOSAL Clean all equipment as instructed by your teacher, and return everything to its proper place. Dispose of the water and embryos properly. Wash your hands thoroughly.

Data Table

Date	Age (hpf)	Diagram	Observations

ANALYZE AND CONCLUDE

1. **Explain** Why are zebra fishes ideal animals for studying embryonic development?

2. **Think Critically** Explain why you may not have been able to see stages such as a blastula or gastrula.

3. **Collect and Organize Data** Visit in.bdol.glencoe.com/internet_lab for links to internet sites that will help you complete sequences of the major changes during development of zebra fishes:

   a. between 1 and 10 hpf. Include labeled diagrams of these changes.

   b. between 10 and 28 hpf. Include labeled diagrams.

   c. between 28 and 72 hpf. Include labeled diagrams.

4. ERROR ANALYSIS Suggest how you could change the experiment's design to allow for observing blastula and gastrula stages.

Share Your Data

Find this BioLab using the link below and post your data in the data table provided for this activity. Using the additional data from other students on the Internet, answer the questions for this lab. Were there large variations in data posted by other students? What might have caused these differences?

 in.bdol.glencoe.com/internet_lab

ANALYZE AND CONCLUDE

1. They are inexpensive, easy to care for, form many embryos, and show rapid development.

2. The early stages occur rapidly after fertilization.

3. For questions a-c, student answers should agree with the information in Data and Observations. Encourage students to print out Internet diagrams and include them in their answers to this question.

4. ERROR ANALYSIS Students could reset the timer, or use embryos that were collected and preserved by an earlier class.

Assessment

Portfolio Ask students to prepare a report of their findings using their own data and diagrams as well as the diagrams available from their Internet sources. Use the Performance Task Assessment List for Writing in Science in **PASC**, p. 159. **L2**

Share Your Data

To navigate this Internet BioLab, go to **in.bdol.glencoe. com/internet_lab**. The advantage to having large numbers of trials in an experiment is that the results will be more accurate.

Data and Observations

Between 1–2 hpf: Dividing cells will appear above yolk sac.
Between 2–5 hpf: blastula formation
Between 5–10 hpf: Gastrulation formation is complete with appearance of somites.
Between 10–28 hpf: Tissues and organs form.
Between 28–72 hpf: Fins, gills, and mouth form.

CLEANUP AND DISPOSAL

Ask students to flush contents of petri dishes into sink with water and wash petri dishes, beaker, bulb baster, and dropper in warm soapy water and rinse well.

BIO TECHNOLOGY

Purpose

Students learn about the nature and function of stem cells, a method used to isolate stem cells, and their potential uses in medicine.

Background

Recent stem cell research involving rodents includes the use of stem cells to treat a condition in mice similar to Parkinson's disease, and the transplant of adult stem cells from mice brains into the bone marrow of other rodents, where the cells began creating red blood cells. Mouse stem cell research includes the restoration of movement in paralyzed mice following the injection of stem cells into spinal fluid.

Teaching Strategies

■ Define the term *differentiation*, and explain its importance in the development of a complex organism. Have students brainstorm different types of cells found in the human body. Ask students to explain advantages gained by an organism that has many different types of specialized cells.

■ Initially, students may believe that stem cells are found only in fetal tissue. Explain that scientists have discovered stem cells in adult organisms, including brain tissue, bone marrow, and fat deposits.

■ Have students consider how recent discoveries regarding the presence and versatility of stem cells in adults might influence public perception about stem cell research.

Mighty Mouse Cells

Around the world, researchers are beginning to understand the enormous potential of stem cells. It is hoped that better treatments or cures for diseases such as Parkinson's disease, leukemia, Alzheimer's disease, and diabetes will come from stem cell research. What makes stem cells so powerful and unique?

Putting stem cells to work Stem cells are undifferentiated cells that have the ability to produce more stem cells or produce specialized cells. Stem cells are found in embryos and in young and adult animals where they play key roles. For example, if you ever have damaged a muscle, your muscle stem cells helped with the repair. Blood stem cells work throughout your life to maintain the supply of specialized cell types found in your blood.

Somatic Cell Nuclear Transfer (SCNT) Biotechnologies are used to isolate and grow stem cells. In a process called somatic cell nuclear transfer, as illustrated at the right, the nucleus is removed from a normal animal egg cell. A somatic cell—any body cell other than an egg or sperm cell—is placed next to the egg cell without a nucleus and the two cells are made to fuse. The new cell undergoes many cell divisions and forms a blastocyst from which stem cells are taken.

Mouse stem cells to the rescue Because of ethical concerns, SCNT has only been done with mouse cells and recent studies have yielded interesting results. In 2001, researchers associated with the National Institutes of Health successfully used mouse stem cells to create insulin-producing cells. For people suffering from Type-1 diabetes, a condition in which the immune system mistakenly destroys cells that produce insulin, these results offer hope. In a study by scientists in England, mouse stem cells were used to create bone cells. This type of research could lead to new treatments for bone diseases, as well as improved bone grafts for treating serious bone injuries.

Future research Continued research promises greater understanding of stem cells. Once, researchers believed human stem cells could be found only in bone marrow, brain tissue, and fetal tissue. However, in a study conducted by researchers at the University of California, Los Angeles and the University of Pittsburgh, stem cells were found in human fat. Experiments with these fat cells produced types of muscle, bone, and cartilage cells. If these cells prove to be as versatile as many scientists expect them to be, their use in treating diseases could be unlimited. Some experts suggest stem cells might one day be used to grow new organs for transplant, and effectively treat many disorders by replacing diseased cells with healthy ones.

Egg · Nucleus removed

Somatic cell nuclear transfer

Fusion

Somatic cell

Blastocyst

Cultured stem cells

Applying Biotechnology

Think Critically Some diseases such as Alzheimer's disease and leukemia result in the gradual loss of healthy cells in specific parts of the body. Research a human disease that is caused by a gradual loss of healthy cells. Prepare a brief report about the disease and include how SCNT might be used to treat that disease.

 To learn more about stem cells, visit in.bdol.glencoe.com/biotechnology

Going Further

Research how technological advances in stem cell research also may be used in the development and testing of new drug therapies.

Applying Biotechnology

SCNT, using somatic cells from an ailing patient, could be used to create healthy cells to replace diseased ones. Stem cells obtained by this process could be coaxed into differentiating into the specific cell type needed, then transplanted back into the patient. One advantage is that because the nucleus of the somatic cell remains intact during the process, the new cells would be genetically identical to those of the person receiving the transplant, making it unlikely that the body would reject them.

STUDY GUIDE

Section 25.1

Typical Animal Characteristics

LM Magnification: 80×

Key Concepts

■ Animals are multicellular eukaryotes whose cells lack cell walls. Their cells are specialized to perform different functions.

■ All animals are heterotrophs that obtain and digest food.

■ At some point during its life, an animal can move from place to place. Most animals retain this ability.

■ Embryonic development of a fertilized egg cell by cell division and differentiation is similar among animal phyla. The sequence of developmental stages is:

1. formation of a blastula—a cell-covered, fluid-filled ball;

2. gastrulation—the inward movement of cells to form two cell layers, the endoderm and ectoderm;

3. formation of the mesoderm—the development of a cell layer between the endoderm and ectoderm.

Vocabulary

blastula (p. 676)
deuterostome (p. 677)
ectoderm (p. 677)
endoderm (p. 677)
gastrula (p. 676)
mesoderm (p. 677)
protostome (p. 677)
sessile (p. 674)

Section 25.2

Body Plans and Adaptations

Key Concepts

■ Animal adaptations include asymmetry, radial symmetry, or bilateral symmetry.

■ Flatworms and other acoelomates have flattened, solid bodies with no body cavities.

■ Animals such as roundworms have a pseudocoelom, a body cavity that develops between the endoderm and mesoderm.

■ A coelom is a fluid-filled body cavity that supports internal organs. Coelomate animals have internal organs suspended in a body cavity that is completely surrounded by mesoderm.

■ Exoskeletons provide a framework of support on the outside of the body. Endoskeletons provide internal support.

Vocabulary

acoelomate (p. 682)
anterior (p. 682)
bilateral symmetry (p. 681)
coelom (p. 684)
dorsal (p. 682)
endoskeleton (p. 684)
exoskeleton (p. 684)
invertebrate (p. 684)
posterior (p. 682)
pseudocoelom (p. 683)
radial symmetry (p. 681)
symmetry (p. 680)
ventral (p. 682)
vertebrate (p. 685)

 FOLDABLES
Study Organizer To help you review and identify characteristics of the animal kingdom, use the Organizational Study Fold on page 673.

 in.bdol.glencoe.com/vocabulary_puzzlemaker   CHAPTER 25 ASSESSMENT **689**

Chapter 25 Assessment

Key Concepts

Summary statements can be used by students to review the major concepts of the chapter.

 Biology Online

Visit in.bdol.glencoe.com
   /self_check_quiz
   /vocabulary_puzzlemaker
   /chapter_test
   /standardized_test

VOCABULARY PUZZLEMAKER

For additional help with vocabulary, have students access the Vocabulary PuzzleMaker online at in.bdol.glencoe.com/ vocabulary_puzzlemaker

FOLDABLES™

Have students use their Foldables to review the content of Section 25.1.

Use the ExamView®Pro Test Bank CD-ROM to:
● Create **multiple versions** of tests
● Create **modified** tests with one mouse click for **inclusion** students
● **Edit** existing questions and **add** your own questions
● Build tests aligned with state standards using built-in **State Curriculum Tags**
● Change **English** tests to **Spanish** with one mouse click and vice versa

 Indiana Academic Standards
Pages 688–689: B.1.1, B.1.15, B.1.16

Chapter 25 Assessment

 Questions and answers have been aligned and verified by The Princeton Review.

Vocabulary Review

1. mesoderm—the middle layer of cells in the gastrula; ectoderm—the outer cell layer of the gastrula
2. coelom—a fluid-filled space completely surrounded by mesoderm; pseudocoelom— a fluid-filled body cavity partly lined with mesoderm
3. blastula—a fluid-filled ball of cells in the early developmental stages of an embryo; gastrula—develops from the blastula when part of the ball of cells moves inward
4. Animals with radial symmetry can be divided into equal halves along any plane through a central axis. Bilaterally symmetrical animals can be divided down their length into similar halves.
5. protostome's mouth—from the opening in the gastrula; deuterostome's mouth— from an area of the gastrula other than the opening

Understanding Key Concepts

6. B	8. B	10. B
7. B	9. A	11. D

Constructed Response

12. The clay ball representing the blastula is solid rather than fluid-filled. The outside of the ball of clay does not move in to form the gastrula; instead a hole is made in the clay.
13. All, some, or none of the cells might survive and develop into embryos.
14. No, because this pattern is that of a protostome. A bird is a deuterostome.

Vocabulary Review

Review the Chapter 25 vocabulary words listed in the Study Guide on page 689. Distinguish between the vocabulary words in each pair.

1. mesoderm—ectoderm
2. coelom—pseudocoelom
3. blastula—gastrula
4. radial symmetry—bilateral symmetry
5. protostome—deuterostome

Understanding Key Concepts

6. Which of these organs develops from the ectoderm?
   A. stomach   C. intestines
   B. skin   D. liver
7. Animals that cannot make their own food are called _____.
   A. autotrophs   C. producers
   B. heterotrophs   D. photosynthetic
8. Coral larvae are _____ but adult forms are _____.
   A. haploid—diploid
   B. free-swimming—sessile
   C. acoelomates—coelomates
   D. protostomes—deuterostomes
9. Which of the following sentences does NOT describe an animal?
   A. It has cells with cell walls.
   B. It is a multicellular organism.
   C. It is a consumer.
   D. It has a digestive system that breaks down food.
10. Which animal shown below has radial symmetry?

A.
B.
C.
D.

Thinking Critically

15. leech; A leech and an earthworm are segmented worms with bilateral symmetry. A sea star has radial symmetry, an insect has legs, and a clam is not segmented.
16. Answers will vary. In general students would find that homeotic genes code

11. A fish has a fin on its upper surface. Because a fish has _____ symmetry, this fin is called the _____ fin.
   A. no—pectoral
   B. bilateral—anterior
   C. radial—posterior
   D. bilateral—dorsal

Constructed Response

12. **Open Ended** Look at *Figure 25.4.* Evaluate these models as to their adequacy in representing a blastula and gastrulation.
13. **Open Ended** Examine *Figure 25.5.* Predict what might happen if, at the 4-cell stage, the embryo cells separated.
14. **Open Ended** If the opening in the gastrula eventually develops into a mouth, could this animal be a bird? Explain.

Thinking Critically

15. **Differentiate** Which of these animals—sea star, insect, leech, or clam—shares the most characteristics with an earthworm? Explain.
16. **REAL WORLD BIOCHALLENGE** Homeotic or Hox genes regulate embryonic development in organisms. The Hox genes of organisms, such as zebra fishes, fruit flies, and roundworms, have been studied extensively. Visit **in.bdol.glencoe.com** to learn more about these genes. Present your research results as a poster or a multimedia presentation.
17. **Concept Map** Use the following terms to complete this concept map: blastula, ectoderm, gastrula, endoderm, mesoderm.

Animals develop from a
zygote
to a
1.
stage in which these tissues form
2.   3.
which forms the
4. —**during the**— 5. —**stage.**

 in.bdol.glencoe.com/chapter _test

for transcription factors that regulate development. Hox genes in simple and more complex organisms appear to be organized in the same way, indicating that they have similar functions in both types of animals.

17. 1. blastula; 2. endoderm; 3. ectoderm; 4. mesoderm; 5. gastrula

Chapter 25 Assessment

Part 1 Multiple Choice

When vertebrate eggs are developing, they go through the first meiotic division and then pause at metaphase of the second meiotic division until fertilization occurs before completing the second meiotic division. MPF, a protein, regulates the pause and continuation of meiosis after fertilization. Analyze the graph and answer questions 18–20.

MPF Levels During Meiosis

18. MPF is at high levels _____.
B.1.7
   A. at the beginning of the first meiotic division and at the beginning of the second meiotic division
   B. at the beginning of the first meiotic division and at metaphase of the second meiotic division
   C. only at the beginning of the first meiotic division
   D. only at metaphase of the second meiotic division

19. MPF also slows the beginning of the first
B.1.7, meiotic division to allow the egg to grow.
B.1.8 Therefore, at this time MPF levels are
_____.
   A. unchanged
   B. low
   C. high
   D. high and low

20. Which of the following statements best
B.1.7 describes the relationship between MPF and the slowing of meiosis in the developing egg?
   A. When MPF is high, meiosis progresses.
   B. MPF has no effect on slowing meiosis.
   C. MPF is necessary for mitosis.
   D. When MPF is high, meiosis slows down.

Study the diagram and answer questions 21–23.

Gastrula (5 hours after fertilization) / 18 hours after fertilization / 20 hours after fertilization / 1-day-old embryo

■ Ectoderm □ Mesoderm ▨ Yolk cell ▧ Heart or heart primordia

21. The cell layer from which the heart of the
B.1.1 zebra fish develops is the _____.
   A. endoderm   **C.** mesoderm
   B. ectoderm   **D.** yolk sac

22. One day after fertilization the zebra fish has _____.
   A. heart, tail, eyes, head
   B. heart, tail, fins, head
   C. no internal organs
   D. two cell layers in a gastrula

23. Twenty hours after fertilization the heart is _____.
   A. two chambered
   B. not divided into two chambers
   C. four chambered
   D. ectoderm

Part 2 Constructed Response/Grid In

Record your answers on your answer document.

24. Open Ended Describe the relationship between an animal's body plan and the environment
B.1.1, in which it lives. Give examples.
B.1.8
25. Open Ended Explain why the development of a body cavity enabled animals to move and feed more efficiently.

 in.bdol.glencoe.com/standardized_test

RUBRIC

For more help evaluating open-ended assessment questions, see the rubric on p. 9T.

End-of-Course Assessment Practice

18. B   **20.** D   **22.** A
19. C   **21.** C   **23.** B
24. Fishes have coeloms that their muscles can push against to seek prey. Acoelomate flatworms have thin bodies that aid diffusion through the cell layers.
25. Food moves into and wastes out of the cells of acoelomates by diffusion; coelomates have organs and/or organ systems that deliver food and take away wastes. Movement of acoelomates depends upon structures such as cilia, whereas coelomates have muscles for locomotion.

FAST FILE

Answer Sheet A practice answer sheet can be found on p. 29 of *Unit 8 FAST FILE Resources*.

Indiana Academic Standards

Pages 690–691: B.1.1, B.1.7, B.1.15, B.1.16

Chapter 26 Organizer

Section Objectives	National Science Standards	State/Local Standards	Advanced Lab and Demo Planning
Section 26.1 1/2 session 1. **Relate** the sessile life of sponges to their food-gathering adaptations. 2. **Describe** the reproductive adaptations of sponges.	UCP.1–3, UCP.5; A.1, A.2; C.1, C.4–6	**Indiana Standards** B.1.1, B.1.11, B.1.15	**Student Labs:** Additional Lab, p. 694: stereomicroscope, forceps, balance, wax marking pencil, 150-mL beakers, petri dish bottoms, sea sponges (grass, yellow, sheep's wool, hard head) Problem-Solving Lab 26.1, p. 695 **Teacher Demonstration:** Quick Demo, p. 696: dried skeletons of a variety of marine sponges
Section 26.2 1/2 session 3. **Analyze** the relationships among the classes of cnidarians. 4. **Sequence** the stages in the life cycle of a cnidarian. 5. **Evaluate** the adaptations of cnidarians for obtaining food.	UCP.1–5; A.1, A.2; C.1, C.3, C.4–6; F.4, F.5	**Indiana Standards** B.1.11, B.1.14, B.1.15, B.1.32, B.1.43	**Student Labs:** MiniLab 26.1, p. 702: dropper, hydra, watch glass, water, microscope, brine shrimp, petri dish, freshwater Problem-Solving Lab 26.2, p. 704 **Teacher Demonstration:** Quick Demo, p. 699: microprojector, prepared slides of discharged nematocysts
Section 26.3 1/2 session 6. **Distinguish** between the structural adaptations of parasitic flatworms and free-living planarians. 7. **Explain** how parasitic flatworms are adapted to their way of life.	UCP.1–3, UCP.5; C.1, C.4–6; F.1; G.1	**Indiana Standards** B.1.8, B.1.14, B.1.15, B.1.19	**Student Labs:** Problem-Solving Lab 26.3, p. 707 Investigate BioLab, p. 714: See materials list below. **Teacher Demonstration:** Quick Demo, p. 708: live planarian, water, slide projector
Section 26.4 1 1/2 sessions 8. **Compare and contrast** the structural adaptations of roundworms and flatworms. 9. **Identify** the characteristics of four roundworm parasites.	UCP.1–3, UCP.5; A.1, A.2; C.4–6; F.1, F.3–6; G.1–3	**Indiana Standards** B.1.1, B.1.14, B.1.15, B.1.17, B.1.43	**Student Labs:** MiniLab 26.2, p. 712: prepared slide of *Trichinella* larvae, microscope Problem-Solving Lab 26.4, p. 713
End of Chapter Assessment Student Edition Study Guide, p. 717 Content Assessment, pp. 718–719		**Indiana Standards** B.1.15, B.1.18, B.1.43	**Student Lab:** Investigate BioLab, p. 714: planarians, petri dish, distilled or bottled water, camel hair brush, chilled glass slide, dissecting microscope, marking pencil or labels, single-edged razor blade

Key to Teaching Strategies

L1 Level 1 activities should be appropriate for students with learning difficulties.

L2 Level 2 activities should be within the ability range of all students.

L3 Level 3 activities are designed for above-average students.

ELL ELL activities should be within the ability range of English Language Learners.

COOP LEARN Cooperative Learning activities are designed for small group work.

Legend

 Transparency   CD-ROM   🎵 MP3   📼 Videocassette   ⊙ DVD

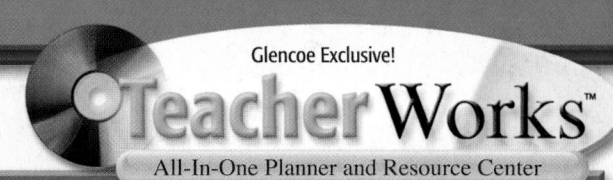

Glencoe Exclusive!
TeacherWorks™
All-In-One Planner and Resource Center

Reproducible Masters and Transparencies	Technology

Unit 8 FAST FILE Resources
Reinforcement and Study Guide in English, p. 37
Reinforcement and Study Guide in Spanish, p. 41
Concept Mapping, p. 45
Critical Thinking/Problem Solving, p. 46
Transparency Worksheets, pp. 47, 51–54
⎪ **Section Focus Transparency 63**
⎪ **Basic Concepts Transparencies 45, 46**

⊙ **Interactive Chalkboard CD-ROM: Section 26.1 Presentation** ▮
⊙ **TeacherWorks™ CD-ROM** ▮
🎵 **Guided Reading Audio Summaries MP3**

Unit 8 FAST FILE Resources
MiniLab Worksheet, p. 33
Reinforcement and Study Guide in English, p. 38
Reinforcement and Study Guide in Spanish, p. 42
Transparency Worksheets, pp. 48, 51–56
Laboratory Manual, pp. 163–164
⎪ **Section Focus Transparency 64**
⎪ **Basic Concepts Transparencies 45, 46, 47**

⊙ **Interactive Chalkboard CD-ROM: Section 26.2 Presentation** ▮
⊙ **TeacherWorks™ CD-ROM** ▮
🎵 **Guided Reading Audio Summaries MP3**

Unit 8 FAST FILE Resources
BioLab Worksheet, pp. 35–36
Reinforcement and Study Guide in English, p. 39
Reinforcement and Study Guide in Spanish, p. 43
Transparency Worksheets, pp. 49, 57–58
Laboratory Manual, pp. 165–166
⎪ **Section Focus Transparency 65**
⎪ **Reteaching Skills Transparency 39**

⊙ **Interactive Chalkboard CD-ROM: Section 26.3 Presentation** ▮
⊙ **TeacherWorks™ CD-ROM** ▮
🎵 **Guided Reading Audio Summaries MP3**

Unit 8 FAST FILE Resources
MiniLab Worksheet, p. 34
Reinforcement and Study Guide in English, p. 40
Reinforcement and Study Guide in Spanish, p. 44
Transparency Worksheet, p. 50
⎪ **Section Focus Transparency 66**

⊙ **Interactive Chalkboard CD-ROM: Section 26.4 Presentation** ▮
⊙ **TeacherWorks™ CD-ROM** ▮
🎵 **Guided Reading Audio Summaries MP3**

Unit 8 FAST FILE Resources
Chapter Assessment, pp. 59–64
Student Recording Sheet, p. 65

The Princeton Review **Reviewing Biology,** pp. 51–52

⊙ **Interactive Chalkboard:** ▮
Chapter 26 Assessment
⊙ **MindJogger Videoquizzes DVD/VHS**
⊙ **ExamView® Pro Test Bank CD-ROM**
⊙ **TeacherWorks™ CD-ROM** ▮
⊙ **Succeeding on National Standards CD-ROM**

🖥 in.bdol.glencoe.com
/self_check_quiz
/vocabulary_puzzlemaker
/chapter_test
/standardized_test

▮ Indicates materials created specifically for Indiana.

Sponges, Cnidarians, Flatworms, and Roundworms

Short on Time?

BIODIGEST The BioDigest at the end of this unit can be used as a(n):

- preview to introduce important unit concepts.
- overview if time does not permit teaching the entire chapter.
- review of key unit concepts.

Understanding the Photo

Marine flatworms have ruffled margins—the larger the animals, the greater the number of ruffles. Ruffles appear to undulate as the animal moves through the water. Except for black opaque forms, most marine flatworm species are somewhat transparent. Often, their organs can be seen through their epidermis. A female's ovaries can be seen as bright red or deep purple and affect the color of the worm's upper surface.

What You'll Learn

- You will identify and compare and contrast the characteristics of sponges, cnidarians, flatworms, and roundworms.
- You will describe and evaluate the significance of sponge, cnidarian, flatworm, and roundworm adaptations.

Why It's Important

Sponges and cnidarians are important to aquatic biomes. Flatworms and roundworms include many species that carry or cause diseases that affect both plants and animals.

Understanding ▶ the Photo

Marine flatworms, like this *Thysanozoon nigropapillosum*, move by rhythmic contractions of their longitudinal muscles. The colors and pigment patterns of marine flatworm species vary. This flatworm lives in the Red Sea, which is between the Arabian peninsula and northeast Africa.

Biology Online

Visit in.bdol.glencoe.com to
- study the entire chapter online
- access Web Links for more information and activities on sponges, cnidarians, flatworms, and roundworms
- review content with the Interactive Tutor and self-check quizzes

692

Two-Minute Chapter Launcher

Demo Have students observe a living member of the genus, *Spongilla*, with hand lenses. *Spongilla* species are freshwater sponges that grow attached to any hard object. Ask students to note the asymmetrical shape of the sponge and its many pores. Explain that all sponges have a large number of pores.

Indiana Academic Standards
Pages 692–693: B.1.15

Sponges

SECTION PREVIEW

Objectives
Relate the sessile life of sponges to their food-gathering adaptations.
Describe the reproductive adaptations of sponges.

Review Vocabulary
sessile: permanently attached to a surface (p. 674)

New Vocabulary
filter feeding
hermaphrodite
external fertilization
internal fertilization

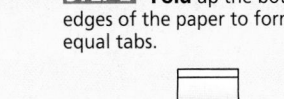
FOLDABLES™
Study Organizer

Sponges Make the following Foldable to help you learn the characteristics of sponges.

STEP 1 **Collect** 2 sheets of paper and layer them about 1.5 cm apart vertically. Keep the edges level.

STEP 2 **Fold** up the bottom edges of the paper to form 4 equal tabs.

STEP 3 **Fold** the papers and crease well to hold the tabs in place. Staple along the fold. **Label** each tab.

Sponges
Obtaining Food
Reproduction
Structural Adaptations

Organize Information As you read Section 26.1, list information on each tab about that sponge characteristic.

What is a sponge?

Sponges are asymmetrical aquatic animals that have a variety of colors, shapes, and sizes. Many are bright shades of red, orange, yellow, and green. Some sponges are ball shaped; others have many branches. Sponges can be smaller than a quarter or as large as a door. Although sponges do not resemble more familiar animals, they carry on the same life processes as all animals. *Figure 26.1* shows a natural sponge harvested from the ocean.

Sponges are pore-bearers

Sponges are classified in the invertebrate phylum Porifera, which means "pore bearer." More than 5000 species of sponges have been described. Most live in marine biomes, but about 150 species can be found in freshwater environments.

Sponges are mainly sessile organisms. Because most adult sponges can't travel in search of food, they get their food by a process called filter feeding. **Filter feeding** is a method in which an organism feeds by filtering small particles of food from water that pass by or through some part of the organism. How does a sponge get rid of its wastes?

Word Origin

porifera from the Greek word *poros,* meaning "passage," and the Latin word *ferre,* meaning "to carry"; Phylum Porifera includes animals with pores that allow water to flow through their bodies.

Figure 26.1
This bath sponge is dark brown or black in its natural habitat. After harvest, it is washed and dried in sunlight. The living material dies and is rinsed away. Only the sponge's pale, lightweight framework remains.

26.1 SPONGES **693**

1 Focus

INTERACTIVE CHALKBOARD
PowerPoint® Presentations

Bellringer
Section Focus Transparency 63

Transparency **63** Sponges

SECTION FOCUS
Use with Chapter 26, Section 26.1

Sponge

❶ What does the body shape of this sponge suggest about the way it gets food?

❷ What are the advantages and disadvantages of being permanently attached to a surface, as this sponge is?

BIOLOGY: The Dynamics of Life   SECTION FOCUS TRANSPARENCIES

INTERACTIVE CHALKBOARD
with Image Bank

PowerPoint® Presentations
This CD-ROM is an editable Microsoft® PowerPoint® presentation that includes:
• Section presentations
• Section checks
• Image bank
• Hot links to Biology Online
• All transparencies

Word Origin

Have students infer how the words *fare* and *ferry* are connected. Both words derive from words which mean "to bear" or "carry."

FOLDABLES™
For an additional Foldables activity idea, see the Chapter 26 Foldables page in *Unit 8 FAST FILE Resources.*

RESOURCE MANAGER

Unit 8 FAST FILE Resources
Reinforcement and Study Guide in English, p. 37
Reinforcement and Study Guide in Spanish, p. 41
Concept Mapping, p. 45
Critical Thinking/Problem Solving, p. 46
Transparency Worksheets, pp. 47, 51–54

Reading Essentials for Biology, Section 26.1
🖺 **Section Focus Transparency 63**
🖺 **Basic Concepts Transparencies 45, 46**

2 Teach

Purpose

Students will observe the basic features of a sponge and examine how it accomplishes filter feeding.

Teaching Strategies

Explain that sponges obtain food in a process called filter feeding.

Visual Learning

Point out that food particles in water are pulled into collar cells and digested. Nutrients from food are then distributed by amoebocytes to other body cells.

Critical Thinking

Sponges carry on the same life processes as all animals. They are multicellular eukaryotes that do not have cell walls around their cells.

Indiana Academic Standards

Pages 694–695: B.1.11, B.1.15

INSIDE STORY

A Sponge

Figure 26.2

Sponges have no tissues, organs, or organ systems. The body plan of a sponge is simple, being made up of only two layers of cells with no body cavity. Between these two layers is a jellylike substance that contains other cells as well as the components of the sponge's internal support system. Sponges have specialized cells that perform all the functions necessary to keep them alive.

Critical Thinking *Why are sponges classified as animals?*

Orange tube sponges

A Osculum Water and wastes are expelled through the osculum, the large opening at the top of the sponge. A sponge 1 cm in diameter and 10 cm tall can move more than 20 L of water through its body per day.

B Epithelial-like cells These cells are thin and flat. They contract in response to touch or to irritating chemicals. In so doing, they close pores in the sponge.

C Collar cell Lining the interior of sponges are collar cells. Each collar cell has a flagellum that whips back and forth, drawing water into the sponge.

D Pore cell Surrounding each pore is a pore cell. Pore cells allow water carrying food and oxygen into the sponge's body.

E Amoebocytes Located between the two cell layers of a sponge, amoebocytes carry nutrients to other cells, aid in reproduction, and produce chemicals that help make up the spicules of sponges.

F Spicules They are produced by cells derived from amoebocytes, and form the hard support systems of sponges. The small, needlelike structures located between the cell layers of a sponge are called spicules.

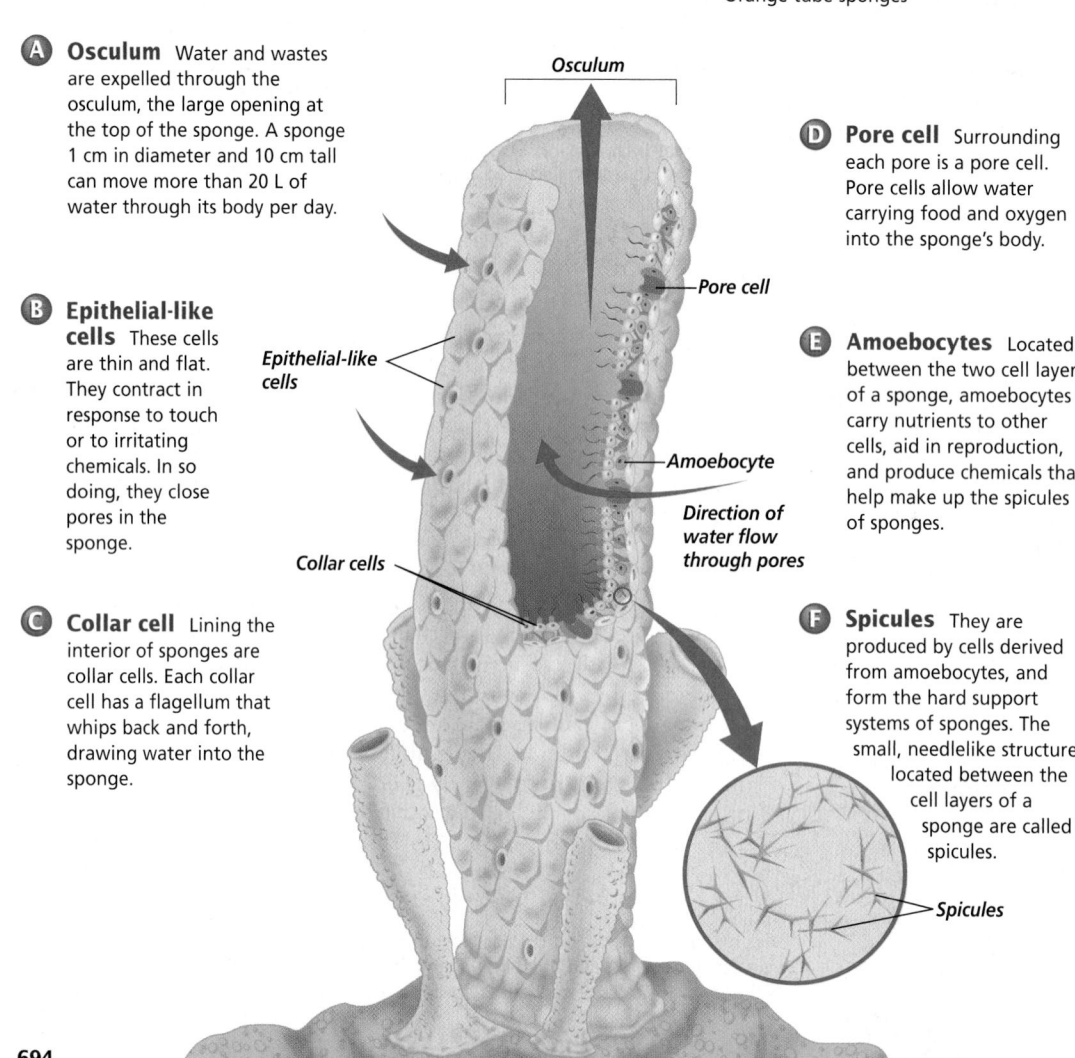

694

Additional Lab

Natural and Synthetic Sponges

Purpose

Students will compare the water-holding capacity and appearance of natural and synthetic sponges. Remind students to wash their hands after handling sponges.

Materials

stereomicroscope; forceps; balance; wax marking pencil; 150-mL beakers; petri dish bottoms; grass, yellow, sheep's wool, and hard head sea sponges (3-cm × 3-cm × 2-cm piece of each); four different types of unused synthetic sponges (3-cm × 3-cm × 2-cm piece of each)

Procedure

Give students the following directions.

1. Examine each piece of sponge under the microscope. Predict which type of sponge will hold more water.

2. Draw and label each sponge piece.

3. Place each sponge piece in a petri dish bottom and obtain the mass. Soak each sponge piece in a beaker of water for

Cell organization in sponges

Like all animals, sponges are multi-cellular, as shown in *Figure 26.2* on the opposite page. Their cells are differentiated to perform functions that help the animal survive. Read the *Problem-Solving Lab* on this page to find out how sponges survive in different environments. The functions of the different cell types are coordinated in a sponge, but sponges do not have tissues like those found in other animals. Tissues are groups of cells that are derived from the ectoderm, endoderm, and mesoderm in the embryo. Sponge embryos do not develop endoderm or mesoderm, so they do not have cells organized into tissues.

For some sponge species, if you took a living sponge and put it through a sieve, not only would the sponge's cells be alive and separated out, but these cells would come together to form new sponges. It can take several weeks for the sponge's cells to reorganize themselves.

Many biologists hypothesize that sponges evolved directly from colonial, flagellated protists, such as *Volvox*, described in Chapter 19. More importantly, sponges exhibit a major step in the evolution of animals—the change from a unicellular life to a division of labor among groups of organized cells.

Reproduction in sponges

Sponges can reproduce asexually and sexually. Depending on the species, asexual reproduction can be by budding, fragmentation, or the formation of gemmules. An external growth, called a bud, can form on a sponge. If a bud drops off, it can float away, settle, and grow into a sponge. Sometimes, buds do not break off. When this occurs, a colony of sponges forms, as shown in *Figure 26.3*. Often, fragments of a sponge break off and grow into new sponges.

Problem-Solving Lab 26.1

Apply Concepts

Why are there more species of marine sponges than freshwater sponges? Most sponges live in a marine biome. Is there an advantage for sponges to live in a marine biome rather than in a freshwater environment? A series of statements is provided below. Read them, then answer the questions that follow.

Solve the Problem

A. The internal tissues of marine organisms are isotonic with their surroundings.

B. Oceans do not have rapid changes in the velocity (rate of flow) of water.

C. Young marine animals often spend the early part of their life cycles as free-floating organisms.

Thinking Critically

1. **Describe** Based on statement A, how might a freshwater environment vary? How might this be a disadvantage for freshwater sponges?
2. **Describe** Based on statement B, how might a freshwater environment vary? How might this be a disadvantage for freshwater sponges?
3. **Infer** Using your collective answers, explain why few sponge species are found in freshwater environments.

Figure 26.3
Sponge colonies can form by asexual reproduction. **Infer** *How would these sponges compare genetically? Could they be considered clones?*

695

---

10 minutes and again obtain the mass of the sponge and petri dish.

4. Calculate the mass of the water absorbed by each sponge. Compare the data for all sponges.

Expected Results
Natural sponges have greater water-holding capacity than synthetic sponges.

Analysis
1. Which sponges, natural or synthetic, have greater water-holding capacity? natural sponges
2. Of what adaptive value is it for a sponge to be able to take in large amounts of water? They are filter feeders. Taking in more water increases the chances of taking in more food.

Reading Check Buds grow on living sponges, depend on them, and remain attached until they reach a size at which they can survive on their own. Gemmules are separate living particles formed when adult freshwater sponges die, from which new sponges develop.

Quick Demo

Sponge Frameworks
From a scientific supply house, obtain the dried frameworks of a variety of marine sponges. Ask students to examine them and describe how these animals would be different if they were alive. **L2** **ELL**

Biology Journal

Sponge Gemmules After observing prepared slides of sponge gemmules with a microscope, have students make drawings of gemmules in their journals. **L1** **ELL**

Indiana Academic Standards

Pages 696–697: B.1.1, B.1.11, B.1.15

Some freshwater sponges produce seedlike particles, called gemmules, in the fall when waters cool. The adult sponges die over the winter, but the gemmules survive and grow into new sponges in the spring when waters warm.

Reading Check **Compare and contrast** budding and the formation of gemmules.

Most sponges reproduce sexually. Some sponges have separate sexes, but most sponges are hermaphrodites. A **hermaphrodite** (hur MAF ruh dite) is an animal that can produce both eggs and sperm. Hermaphrodism increases the likelihood that fertilization will occur in sessile or slow-moving animals. Eggs and sperm form from amoebocytes. During reproduction, sperm released from one sponge can be carried by water currents to another sponge, where fertilization can occur.

Fertilization in sponges may be either external or internal. A few sponges have **external fertilization**—fertilization that occurs outside the animal's body. Most sponges have **internal fertilization,** in which eggs inside the animal's body are fertilized by sperm carried into the sponge with water. In sponges, the collar cells collect and transfer sperm to amoebocytes. The amoebocytes then transport the sperm to ripe eggs. Fertilization occurs and the result is the development of free-swimming, flagellated larvae, shown in *Figure 26.4.*

Figure 26.4
In sponges, part of the sexual reproductive process is the release of sperm to the surrounding water.

A Sperm are released into the water and can travel to other sponges.

B Fertilization is internal. Fertilized eggs develop into zygotes in the jellylike substance between cell layers. Zygotes become free-swimming larvae.

C The larvae swim from the body of the sponge on currents created by collar cells.

D A larva eventually settles on a surface and develops into an adult that can reproduce. Most sponges are mobile only in their larval stages.

CHALLENGE ACTIVITY

Sponge Chemicals Some sponges give off toxic chemicals that deter predators and the buildup of other sessile animals on their exterior surfaces. One of these chemicals, from a Caribbean sponge, is being used currently to treat cancer. Other chemicals produced by sponges are being used to fight fungal infections. Have interested students research this subject and write a report. **L3**

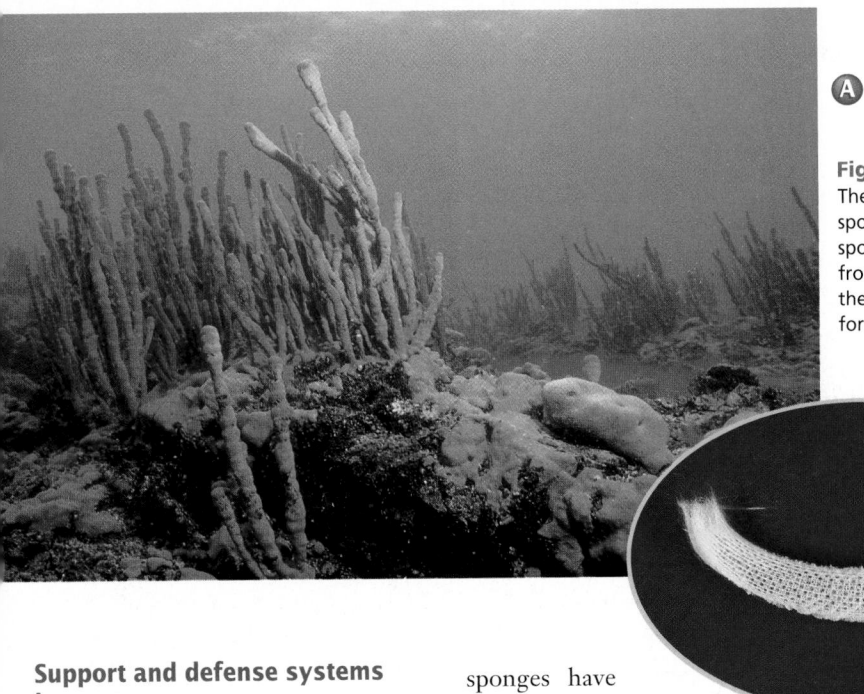

Figure 26.5
The spicules of freshwater sponges, such as these lake sponges **(A)**, protect them from predators. Spicules of the deep-water glass sponges form a rigid framework **(B)**.

Ⓑ

Support and defense systems in sponges

Sponges are soft-bodied invertebrates, that can be found at depths to about 8500 m. Their internal structure gives them support and can help protect them from predators. Some sponges have sharp, hard spicules located between the cell layers. Spicules may be made of glasslike material or of calcium carbonate. Some species, such as the lake sponges shown in *Figure 26.5*, have thousands of tiny, sharp, needlelike spicules that make them hard for animals to eat. Other

sponges have an internal framework made of silica or of spongin, a fibrous protein-like material. Sponges can be classified according to the shape and makeup of their spicules and/or frameworks.

Besides sharp spicules, some sponges may have other methods of defense. Some sponges contain chemicals that are toxic to fishes and to other predators. Scientists are studying sponge toxins to identify those that possibly could be used as medicines.

Section Assessment

Understanding Main Ideas
1. Explain how a sponge obtains food.
2. Explain how epithelial-like cells control filter feeding in sponges.
3. Compare and contrast sexual and asexual reproduction of sponges.
4. Describe the functions of amoebocytes in sponges.
5. Infer why hermaphrodism is a reproductive advantage for sessile organisms.

Thinking Critically
6. Compare and evaluate the adaptations of multicellular organisms, such as sponges, and unicellular organisms for obtaining food.

SKILL REVIEW
7. **Make and Use Tables** Make a table listing cell types and other sponge structures along with their functions. For more help, refer to *Make and Use Tables* in the **Skill Handbook**.

in.bdol.glencoe.com/self_check_quiz

Section Assessment

1. Sponges are filter feeders. They take water in and filter out the food.
2. Epithelial-like cells can contract and relax. This opens and closes pore cells.
3. Sexual reproduction—sperm from another sponge of the same species enters with water, travels to eggs where fertilization occurs; zygotes develop into larvae, which leave the sponge and eventually settle on a

surface, then they develop into adult sponges. Forms of asexual reproduction in sponges produce clones of the original sponge.
4. Amoebocytes carry food from collar cells to all body cells, carry sperm to eggs, and produce chemicals that help make up spicules.
5. In sessile or slow-moving organisms, hermaphrodism increases the chances

that eggs and sperm can unite to continue the species.
6. Division of labor among cells enables an organism to carry out life functions more efficiently than one cell can.
7. Students' tables should include collar cells, epithelial-like cells, pore cells, amoebocytes, spicules, and osculum, and their functions.

1 Focus

INTERACTIVE CHALKBOARD
PowerPoint® Presentations

Bellringer
Section Focus Transparency 64

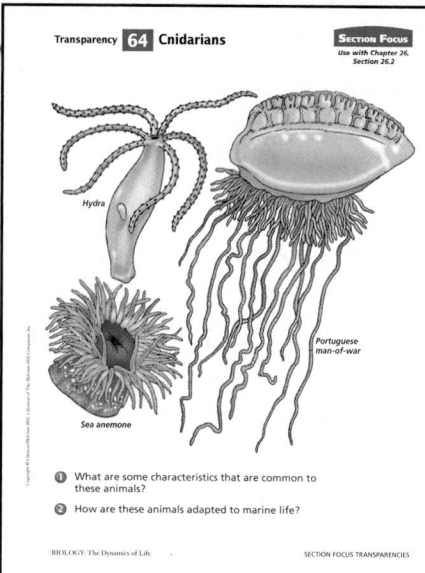

Transparency **64** Cnidarians | **SECTION FOCUS**
Use with Chapter 26, Section 26.2

Hydra

Portuguese man-of-war

Sea anemone

❶ What are some characteristics that are common to these animals?

❷ How are these animals adapted to marine life?

BIOLOGY: The Dynamics of Life · SECTION FOCUS TRANSPARENCIES

Finding Main Ideas

Outline If you find that some students struggle with making a traditional outline using Roman numerals, numbers, and upper-case and lowercase letters, ask them to make a list of the important points under each heading.

Indiana Academic Standards

Pages 698–699: B.1.15

698

Section 26.2

Cnidarians

Indiana Standards Standard B.1.15 Understand and explain that, in biological systems, structure and function must be considered together.

SECTION PREVIEW

Objectives
Analyze the relationships among the classes of cnidarians.

Sequence the stages in the life cycle of a cnidarian.

Evaluate the adaptations of cnidarians for obtaining food.

Review Vocabulary
endocytosis: a process where a cell engulfs materials with a portion of the cell's plasma membrane and releases the contents inside the cell (p. 200)

New Vocabulary
polyp
medusa
nematocyst
gastrovascular cavity
nerve net

Settlers and Floaters

Finding Main Ideas On a piece of paper, construct an outline about cnidarian characteristics, such as those of the corals shown here. Use the red and blue titles in this section as a guideline. As you read the paragraphs that follow the titles, add important information and vocabulary words to your outline.

Orange clump coral, *Tubastrea aurea*

Example:

I. What is a cnidarian?
  A. Body structure
    1. Radially symmetrical with one opening and two layers of cells
    2. Gas exchange occurs directly between cells and water
  B. Body form
    1. Polyp form has a tube-shaped body with a mouth surrounded by tentacles.

Use your outline to help you answer questions in the Section Assessment on page 705. For more help, refer to *Outline* in the **Skill Handbook.**

What is a cnidarian?

Cnidarians (ni DARE ee uns) are a group of invertebrates made up of more than 9000 species of jellyfishes, corals, sea anemones, and hydras. They can be found worldwide, and all but a few cnidarians live in marine biomes.

Body structure

Cnidarians are a diverse group of organisms but all have the same basic body structure, as shown in *Figure 26.6.* A cnidarian's body is radially symmetrical. It has one body opening and is made up of two layers of cells. The protective outer layer of cells develops from the ectoderm of the cnidarian embryo. The endoderm of the cnidarian embryo develops into the inner layer of cells. The two cell layers are organized into tissues with specific functions. For example, the inner layer is adapted mainly to assist in digestion.

Because a cnidarian's body is only two layers of cells, no cell is ever far from water. Oxygen dissolved in water can diffuse directly into body cells. Carbon dioxide and other wastes can move out of a cnidarian's body cells directly into the surrounding water.

Word Origin

cnidarian from the Greek word *knide,* meaning "nettle," a plant with stinging hairs; Cnidarians have stinging cells in their tentacles.

698 SPONGES, CNIDARIANS, FLATWORMS, AND ROUNDWORMS

RESOURCE MANAGER

Unit 8 *FAST FILE* Resources
MiniLab Worksheet, p. 33
Reinforcement and Study Guide in English, p. 38
Reinforcement and Study Guide in Spanish, p. 42
Transparency Worksheets, pp. 48, 51–56

Reading Essentials for Biology, Section 26.2
Laboratory Manual, pp. 163–164
Section Focus Transparency 64
Basic Concepts Transparencies 45, 46, 47

A Cnidarian

Figure 26.6

Cnidarians display a remarkable variety of colors, shapes and sizes. Some can be as small as the tip of a pencil. The flowerlike forms of sea anemones are often brilliant shades of red, purple, and blue. Most cnidarians have two distinct body forms during their life cycles. **Critical Thinking** *How is having poisonous stinging cells an advantage for a sessile organism?*

A **Polyp** A polyp is the sessile form of a cnidarian. Its mouth is surrounded by tentacles. Examples of polyps include sea anemones, corals, and hydras.

Tentacles

B **Medusa** A medusa is the free-swimming form of a cnidarian. It possesses an umbrella-shaped, floating body, called a bell, with the mouth on its underside.

A colony of hydras

Tentacles

Tentacles

Mouth

C **Tentacles** A ring of flexible, tubelike structures called tentacles surrounds the mouth of a cnidarian. Tentacles are used to capture food and vary greatly in length from several meters, like those of some jellyfishes, to a few millimeters, like those of hydras.

Nematocyst before discharge

Prey

Nematocyst after discharge

E **Bud** All cnidarians can reproduce both sexually and asexually. A polyp, such as a hydra, reproduces asexually by budding. Genetically, a bud is a clone of its parent.

Bud

D **Nematocysts** Stinging cells that contain nematocysts are located primarily at the tips of the tentacles. When prey touches the tentacles, the stinging cells discharge nematocysts that capture or paralyze the prey.

26.2 CNIDARIANS **699**

---

2 Teach

Purpose

Students will gain an understanding of the polyp and medusa forms of cnidarians, and learn about the tentacles and nematocysts common to these animals.

Teaching Strategies

Emphasize that polyps are sessile forms of cnidarians that live attached to a surface.

Visual Learning

Visual-Spatial Provide students with prepared slides of small cnidarian polyps and medusae. Have students observe the slides and make labeled drawings of their observations. **L2** **ELL**

Critical Thinking

A sessile organism cannot hunt for prey or move away from predators. Stinging cells help sessile organisms get food and escape predation.

Quick Demo

Viewing Nematocysts
Use a microprojector to show prepared slides of discharged nematocysts.

CULTURAL DIVERSITY

Hydra Myth: *Intrapersonal* Ask students to report about the Greek myth dealing with the water monster, Hydra. Students should indicate that Hydra had fatally poisonous breath and nine heads. Its center head was immortal. Each time Hercules cut off one head, two grew back. Have students identify parts of the myth that are scientifically accurate and those that are not. **L2**

Kinesthetic Have student groups make clay or salt-dough (one part salt, one part flour, one part water) models of the life cycle of a jellyfish. Tell them that when they are finished you will ask the group questions about the jellyfish life cycle. They will need to use their models to demonstrate their answers. Remind students to wear safety goggles and an apron when handling modeling materials. **L1** **ELL** **COOP LEARN**

Reinforcement

Make a transparency of Figure 26.7 with just the figures. White out the captions before you make your transparency and number each stage in the diagram. Ask students to make a list of corresponding numbers on a sheet of paper and describe each stage. **L2**

Biology Journal

Budding Hydra Have students examine prepared slides of budding hydra under a microscope. Ask them to make scientific drawings of the hydra in their biology journals. **L2** **ELL**

Body form

Most cnidarians undergo a change in body form during their life cycles. There are two body forms, the polyp and the medusa, as shown in *Figure 26.7*. A **polyp** (PAH lup) has a tube-shaped body with a mouth surrounded by tentacles. A **medusa** (mih DEW suh) has an umbrella-shaped body, called a bell, with tentacles that hang down. Its mouth is on the underside of the bell.

In cnidarians, one body form may be more observable than the other. In jellyfishes, the medusa is the body form usually observed. The jellyfish polyp is small and not easily seen. The polyp is the familiar body form of hydras. Its medusa form is small and delicate. Corals and sea anemones have only polyp forms.

Reproduction in cnidarians

All cnidarians have the ability to reproduce sexually and asexually. Sexual reproduction occurs in only one phase of the life cycle. It usually occurs in the medusa stage, unless there is no medusa stage then the polyp can reproduce sexually.

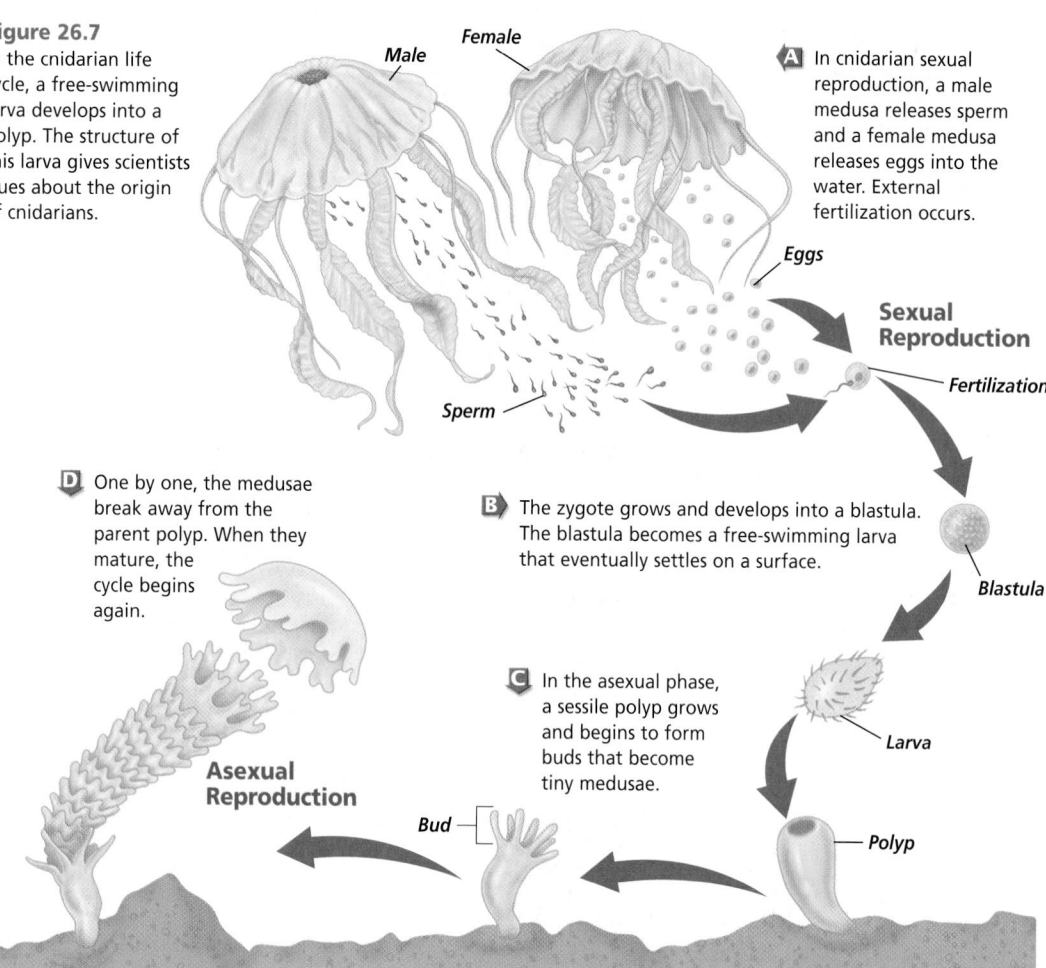

Figure 26.7
In the cnidarian life cycle, a free-swimming larva develops into a polyp. The structure of this larva gives scientists clues about the origin of cnidarians.

Male *Female*

A In cnidarian sexual reproduction, a male medusa releases sperm and a female medusa releases eggs into the water. External fertilization occurs.

Eggs

Sexual Reproduction

Fertilization

Sperm

D One by one, the medusae break away from the parent polyp. When they mature, the cycle begins again.

B The zygote grows and develops into a blastula. The blastula becomes a free-swimming larva that eventually settles on a surface.

Blastula

C In the asexual phase, a sessile polyp grows and begins to form buds that become tiny medusae.

Larva

Asexual Reproduction

Bud

Polyp

CHALLENGE ACTIVITY

Treating Jellyfish Stings: *Interpersonal*
Ask a group of students to contact first-aid stations on public beaches where jellyfishes are common. Have them prepare a report on the treatment given to victims of the stings of these animals. Ask students to demonstrate first-aid procedures for stings and explain why each procedure is performed. Students should write summaries for their portfolios. **L3** **ELL** **COOP LEARN**

The most common form of reproduction in cnidarians can be illustrated by the life cycle of a jellyfish, as shown in *Figure 26.7*. As you can see, the sexual medusa stage alternates with the asexual polyp stage, from generation to generation. Male medusae release sperm, and female medusae release eggs into the water where fertilization occurs. The resulting zygotes develop into embryos, and then into larvae. Recall that a larva is an intermediate stage in animal development. The free-swimming larva eventually settles and grows into a polyp that reproduces asexually to form new medusae. Even though these two stages alternate in a cnidarian's life cycle, this form of reproduction is not alternation of generations as in plants. In plants, one generation is diploid and the other is haploid. However, both cnidarian medusae and polyps are diploid animals.

Asexual reproduction can occur in either the polyp or medusa stage. Polyps reproduce asexually by a process known as budding, as shown in *Figure 26.8*. Cnidarians that remain in the polyp stage, such as hydras, corals and sea anemones, also can reproduce sexually as polyps.

Digestion in cnidarians

Cnidarians are predators that capture or poison their prey using nematocysts. A **nematocyst** (nih MA tuh sihst) is a capsule that contains a coiled, threadlike tube. The tube may be sticky or barbed, and it may contain toxic substances. Nematocysts are located in stinging cells that are on tentacles. In response to touch or chemicals in the environment, nematocysts are discharged like toy pop-guns, but much faster. Prey organisms are then taken in for digestion.

The origins of a digestive process, which is similar to that of animals that evolved later, are found in cnidarians.

Figure 26.8
The main form of reproduction in polyps is budding. During this process, small buds grow as extensions of the body wall (A). In some species, such as corals (B), a colony develops as the buds break away and settle nearby.

Figure 26.9
In addition to digestion, the gastrovascular cavity in a polyp (A) and a medusa (B) also function in circulation and gas exchange. **Compare** *How is this different from sponges?*

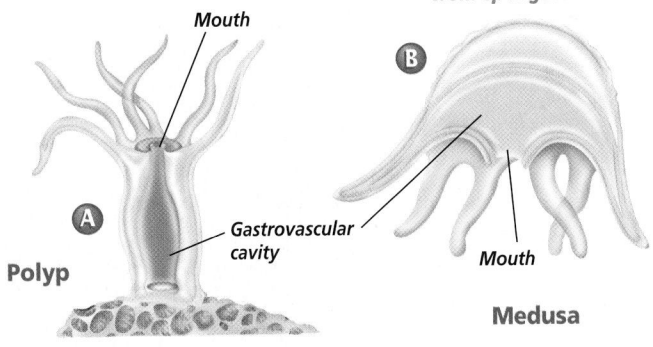

Mouth

Gastrovascular cavity

Polyp

Mouth

Medusa

26.2 CNIDARIANS **701**

Tying to Prior Knowledge

Review Figure 26.7 with students. Explain that larvae of cnidarians produced by sexual reproduction form in this way.

Display

Visual-Spatial Ask a group of students to prepare a bulletin board display of the life cycle of a jellyfish. Encourage them to use three-dimensional figures if possible. **L2 ELL COOP LEARN**

Inquiry

Discussion Ask each student group to design an experiment to determine the optimal water temperature for a hydra environment. Remind students to include a control and to plan to gather quantitative data. Ask groups to compare their experimental designs with one another and to discuss how and why experimental designs differ. **L2 COOP LEARN**

Caption Question Answer

Figure 26.9 In sponges, circulation results from the movement of collar-cell flagella. Gas exchange in sponges is a function of each cell.

PROJECT

Learning Disabled: *Visual-Spatial* Ask a group of students to visit a salt-water aquarium, either at a pet shop, restaurant, zoo, or marine park, and take photographs for a photo essay about sea anemones. You might also provide a preserved anemone for them to dissect. **L2 ELL**

 Indiana Academic Standards
Pages 700–701: B.1.11, B.1.15

Purpose

Students will observe the feeding behavior of hydra. Remind students they will be working with live animals, and to treat them gently. Have students wash their hands at the end of the MiniLab.

Process Skills

sequence, observe and infer, hypothesize, draw a conclusion

Teaching Strategies

■ Hydra are available from biological supply houses. Add pieces of broken glass to the original container the day before students observe the animals. Hydra will cling to glass fragments. Remove the glass and attached hydra with a forceps to aid in dispensing the animals.

■ Hatch brine shrimp from eggs 2 to 3 days prior to classroom need. Eggs are available from pet shops or biological supply houses. Follow the directions on the container for hatching. After hatching, shine a light at one edge of the tray—brine shrimp will move toward the light. Use a tea strainer to remove and rinse shrimp before feeding to hydra.

■ Students will not be able to see the release of nematocysts from the tentacles.

■ Binocular microscopes may be used, or use a 5× objective on the compound microscope if available.

Expected Results

Students will see the tentacles of hydra surround and capture brine shrimp. Food is then pushed by the tentacles into the animal's mouth.

Analysis

1. Nematocysts and tentacles work together to capture food.
2. Students' answers will vary depending on their original hypotheses.

Observe

Watching Hydra Feed Hydras are freshwater cnidarians. They have the typical polyp body plan and radial symmetry. Observe how they capture their food.

Procedure 〜🔬🧪☣

1 Use a dropper to place a hydra into a watch glass filled with water. Wait several minutes for the animal to adapt to its new surroundings. **CAUTION: Use caution when handling a microscope and glassware.**

Hydra eating copepod

2 Observe the hydra under low-power magnification.

3 Form a hypothesis as to how this animal obtains its food and/or catches its prey.

4 Place brine shrimp in a petri dish of freshwater to avoid introducing salt into the watch glass.

5 Add a drop of brine shrimp to the watch glass while continuing to observe the hydra through the microscope.

6 Note which structures the hydra uses to capture food.

7 Wash your hands after completing this investigation.

Analysis

1. **Describe** How does a hydra capture food?
2. **Explain** Was your hypothesis supported or rejected?
3. **Sequence** List the events that take place when a hydra captures and feeds upon its prey.
4. **Conclude** Do your observations support the fact that hydras have both nervous and muscular systems? Explain.

Figure 26.10
Physalia colonies are found primarily in tropical waters, but they sometimes drift into temperate waters where they can be washed up on shore.

702

3. prey organisms touch tentacles, nematocysts are released, prey is captured, tentacles push food into hydra's mouth
4. muscles move the tentacles, nervous system directs tentacles to trap and push food into mouth

Once captured by nematocysts, prey is brought to the mouth by contraction of the tentacles.

As shown in *Figure 26.9* on the previous page, the inner cell layer of cnidarians surrounds a space called a **gastrovascular** (gas troh VAS kyuh lur) **cavity.** Cells adapted for digestion line the gastrovascular cavity and release enzymes over captured prey. Any undigested materials are ejected back out through the mouth. You can observe a cnidarian feeding in the *MiniLab* on this page. Cnidarians are classified into groups partly based on whether or not there are divisions within the gastrovascular cavity, and if there are, how many divisions are present.

Nervous system in cnidarians

A cnidarian has a simple nervous system without a control center, such as a brain like that of other animals. In cnidarians, the nervous system consists of a **nerve net** that conducts impulses to and from all parts of the body. The impulses from the nerve net cause contractions of musclelike cells in the two cell layers. For example, the movement of tentacles when a cnidarian captures prey is the result of contractions of these musclelike cells.

Diversity of Cnidarians

There are four classes of cnidarians: Hydrozoa, Scyphozoa, Cubozoa, and Anthozoa. Cubozoans once were classified as scyphozoans.

Most hydrozoans form colonies

The class Hydrozoa includes two groups—the hydroids, such as hydra, and the siphonophores, including the Portuguese man-of-war. Most hydroids are marine animals that consist of branching polyp colonies formed

Modified Assessment

Portfolio Provide students with prepared slides of cnidarian nematocysts. Have them observe and diagram these cells under high-power magnification. Use the Performance Task Assessment List for Scientific Drawing in **PASC,** p. 127. **L1 ELL**

by budding, and are found attached to pilings, shells, and other surfaces. The siphonophores include floating colonies that drift about on the ocean's surface. Hydrozoans have open gastrovascular cavities with no internal divisions.

It's difficult to understand how the organism shown in *Figure 26.10* could be a closely associated group of individual animals. The Portuguese man-of-war, *Physalia*, is an example of a siphonophore hydrozoan colony. Each individual in a *Physalia* colony has a function that helps the entire organism survive. For example, just one individual forms a large, blue, gas-filled float. Regulation of gases in the float allows the colony to sink to lower depths or rise to the water's surface. Other polyps hanging from the float have functions, such as reproduction and feeding. The polyps all function together for the survival of the colony.

Scyphozoans are the jellyfishes

Have you ever seen a jellyfish like the one shown in *Figure 26.11?* The fragile and sometimes luminescent bodies of jellyfishes can be beautiful. Some jellyfishes are transparent, but others are pink, blue, or orange. The medusa form is the dominant stage in this class.

The gastrovascular cavity of scyphozoans has four internal divisions. Like other cnidarians, scyphozoans have musclelike cells in their outer cell layer that can contract. When these cells contract together, the bell contracts, which propels the animal through the water.

Jellyfishes can be found everywhere in the oceans, from arctic to tropical waters. They have been seen at depths of more than 3000 m. Swimmers should avoid jellyfishes because of their painful stings.

Figure 26.11
The jellyfish *Chrysaora hysoscella* has the common name compass jellyfish due to the radiating brown lines on its bell.

Most anthozoans build coral reefs

Anthozoans are cnidarians that exhibit only the polyp form. All anthozoans have many incomplete divisions in their gastrovascular cavities.

Sea anemones are anthozoans that live as individual animals, and are thought to live for centuries. They can be found in tropical, temperate, and arctic seas. Some tropical sea anemones may have a diameter of more than a meter.

Corals are anthozoans that live in colonies of polyps in warm ocean waters around the world. They secrete protective, cuplike calcium carbonate shelters around their soft bodies. Colonies of many coral species build the beautiful coral reefs that provide food and shelter for many other marine species. Corals that form reefs are known as hard corals. Other corals are known as soft corals because they do not build such structures. When a coral polyp dies, its shelter is left behind, which adds to the coral reef's structure.

26.2 CNIDARIANS **703**

Reinforcement
Be sure students understand that the Portuguese man-of-war is a colonial hydrozoan.

Visual Learning
Naturalist Show students examples of a variety of preserved sponges and cnidarians. Have them make a chart listing the type of animal, structural features they used to identify the animal, and adaptations the animal has that make it suited to its environment. **L1 ELL**

Biology Journal
Coral Art Ask students to design a postage stamp that will commemorate coral animals' importance and beauty. Give students colored markers and plain white paper. Remind them that little can be written on a postage stamp. Provide photos of corals. Have students place their designs in their journals. **L2**

INCLUSION STRATEGIES

English Language Learners Have students research the classes of cnidarians. Have each student make a concept map that includes the names of the classes of cnidarians, their economic importance, characteristics, and representative organisms of each class. Make sure they have included the classes Hydrozoa, Scyphozoa, and Anthozoa, and the following organisms: hydroids, siphonophores, jellyfishes, sea anemones, corals. **L2 ELL**

 Indiana Academic Standards

Pages 702–703: B.1.14, B.1.15

Purpose

Students will study two graphs that show how certain abiotic factors influence the location of coral species.

Process Skills

think critically, interpret data, compare and contrast, make and use graphs

Teaching Strategies

- Review the meaning of symbiosis and mutualism, abiotic and biotic factors.
- Suggest to students that they analyze each graph separately. However, point out that abiotic factors are interrelated.

Thinking Critically

1. abiotic—ocean depth, temperature; biotic—coral
2. The number of coral species decreases rapidly from 0 m to 15 m then it begins to level off.
3. Temperatures between 22°C and 30°C seem to be more favorable to coral diversity. Fewer species survive at temperatures below 22°C.
4. Student descriptions should include the following data: 10 m deep and 20 °C.

Assessment

Research Have students research how the building of a coral skeleton may also benefit from the presence of algae. **L2**

Indiana Academic Standards

Pages 704–705: B.1.11, B.1.15, B.1.32, B.1.43

Problem-Solving Lab 26.2

Interpret Data

What ocean conditions limit the number of coral species? All corals that build reefs have a mutualistic symbiotic relationship with zooxanthellae. Zooxanthellae within the coral carry on photosynthesis and provide some nutrients to the coral. Animals caught by the coral provide some nutrients to these protists.

Graph A

Number of species vs. Depth (m)

Graph B

Number of species vs. Temperature (°C)

Solve the Problem

Graph A shows the number of species present in coral reefs at certain depths. Graph B shows the number of species present at different temperatures. The effects of abiotic factors on organisms are usually related. For example, temperature and levels of illumination in an ocean vary with depth.

Thinking Critically

1. **Identify** What abiotic and biotic factors were studied in this ocean environment?
2. **Explain** In Graph A, what seems to be the correlation between number of coral species present and depth? Use actual numbers from the graph in your answers.
3. **Explain** In Graph B, what seems to be the correlation between number of species present and the temperature? Use actual numbers from the graph in your answer.
4. **Describe** Write a description of the environment that has 75 species of corals.

Figure 26.12
Corals feed by extending their tentacles outside their calcium carbonate cups **(A)**. If they are threatened, they can retreat back into the cups **(B)** until danger has passed.

The living portion of a coral reef is a thin, fragile layer that grows on top of the shelters left behind by previous generations. Coral reefs form slowly. It took thousands of years to form the reefs found today in tropical and subtropical waters. Find out more about the fragility of coral reefs by reading the *Biology and Society* feature at the end of this chapter.

A coral polyp extends its tentacles to feed, as shown in *Figure 26.12*. Although corals are often found in relatively shallow, nutrient-poor waters, they thrive because of their symbiotic relationship with microscopic, photosynthetic protists called zooxanthellae (zoh oh zan THEH lee). The zooxanthellae produce oxygen and food that the corals use, while using carbon dioxide and waste materials produced by the corals. These protists are primarily responsible for the bright colors found in coral reefs. Because the zooxanthellae are free-swimming, they sometimes leave the corals. Corals without these protists often die. You can find out how corals respond to changing environmental conditions in *Problem-Solving Lab 26.2*.

PROJECT

A Cnidarian Excursion Have student groups research the worldwide distribution of cnidarians. Ask each group to make a travel brochure for tourists who wish to see cnidarians. They should include all cnidarian groups in their brochure. **L2** **COOP LEARN**

Figure 26.13
Sponges and cnidarians evolved from a common ancestor early in geologic time. Sponges probably were the first to appear, followed by the classes of cnidarians.

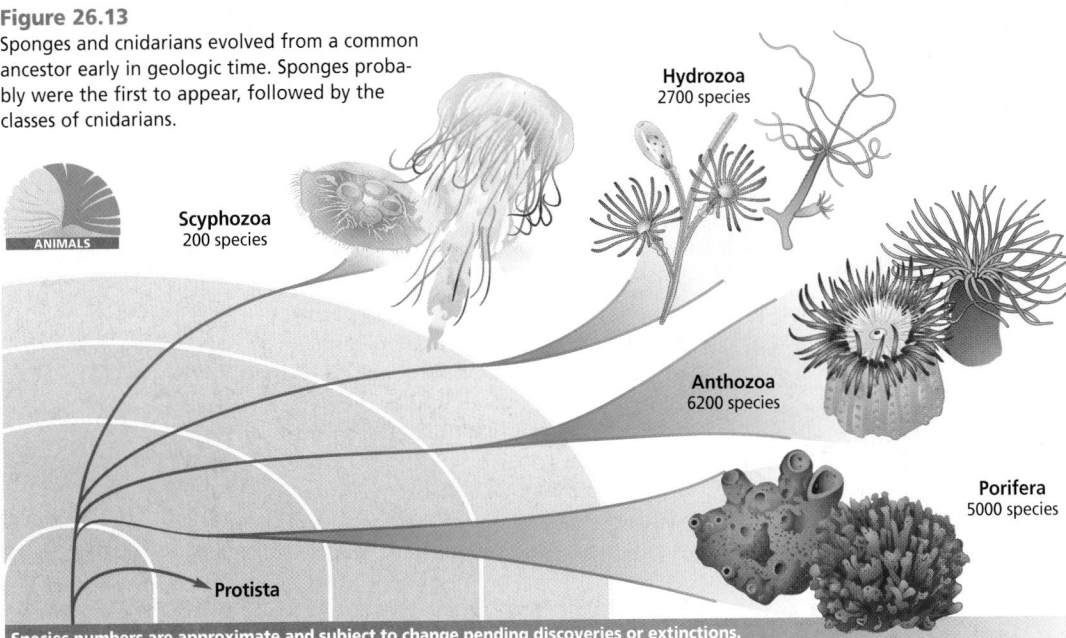

Species numbers are approximate and subject to change pending discoveries or extinctions.

ANIMALS

Scyphozoa
200 species

Hydrozoa
2700 species

Anthozoa
6200 species

Porifera
5000 species

Protista

Origins of Sponges and Cnidarians

As shown in *Figure 26.13,* sponges represent an old animal phylum. The earliest fossil evidence for sponges dates this group to late in the Precambrian, about 650 million years ago. Scientists infer that sponges may have evolved directly from a group of flagellated protists that today resemble the collar cells of sponges.

The earliest known cnidarians also date to the Precambrian, about 630 million years ago. Because cnidarians are soft-bodied animals, they do not preserve well as fossils, and their origins are not well understood. The earliest coral species were not reef builders, so reefs cannot be used to date early cnidarians. The larval form of cnidarians resembles protists, and because of this, scientists consider cnidarians to have evolved from protists.

Section Assessment

Understanding Main Ideas
1. Evaluate the adaptations of cnidarians for obtaining food.
2. Diagram and interpret the advantage of the reproductive cycle of a jellyfish.
3. What are the advantages of a two-layered body in cnidarians?
4. Distinguish between corals and other cnidarians.

Thinking Critically
5. Investigate and explain how destruction of a large coral reef would affect other ocean life.

SKILL REVIEW

6. **Get the Big Picture** In a table, list the three main groups of cnidarians, their characteristics, and a member of each group. For more help, refer to *Get the Big Picture* in the **Skill Handbook.**

 in.bdol.glencoe.com/self_check_quiz

26.2 CNIDARIANS **705**

---

3 Assess

DAILY INTERVENTION

Check for Understanding
Have students draw a hydra cross section and add arrows to show the exchange of oxygen and carbon dioxide and how food reaches all cells. **L1** **ELL**

Reteach
Interpersonal Draw a football field on the chalkboard. Divide the class into two teams. Ask questions about cnidarians. If a student answers correctly, advance the ball 10 yards toward that team's goalpost. If the answer is not correct, the question goes to the other team. The team that reaches its goalpost first wins. **L2** **COOP LEARN**

Resources
For more practice, use *Reading Essentials for Biology,* Section 26.2.

Extension

Have students write about the different ways that corals obtain food. Ask them to describe how each of these food-getting strategies are used during a 24-hour cycle. **L3**

✔ Assessment

Performance Have students observe the movements of a live hydra in a deep-well 35 mm projector slide on a slide projector. Ask them to review the adaptations of the hydra to its environment. Use the Performance Task Assessment List for Booklet or Pamphlet in **PASC,** p. 129. **L2**

Section Assessment

1. Because cnidarians are sessile or move on currents, they cannot chase prey. Nematocysts are an adaptation that allow cnidarians to efficiently capture prey from passing water. Tentacles move prey to the cnidarian's mouth. Corals also have photosynthetic zooxanthellae in their bodies that provide food for the coral.

2. Make sure students follow the steps shown in Figure 26.7.
3. The cell layers of cnidarians are organized into tissues, which enable an animal to be more efficient in carrying out life functions.
4. Corals secrete calcium carbonate shelters around their bodies.

5. Other ocean life will be destroyed because the marine life of the area is dependent upon coral reefs for food and habitats or niches.
6. Make sure students have listed the characteristics and examples of the three cnidarian groups.

1 Focus

INTERACTIVE CHALKBOARD
PowerPoint® Presentations

Bellringer
Section Focus Transparency 65

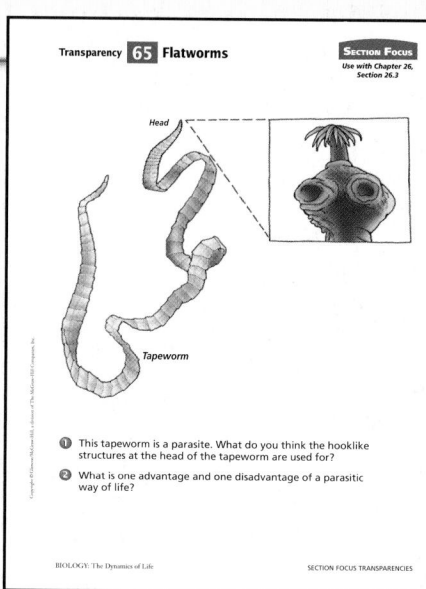

Transparency **65** Flatworms

SECTION FOCUS
Use with Chapter 26, Section 26.3

Head

Tapeworm

① This tapeworm is a parasite. What do you think the hooklike structures at the head of the tapeworm are used for?

② What is one advantage and one disadvantage of a parasitic way of life?

BIOLOGY: The Dynamics of Life
SECTION FOCUS TRANSPARENCIES

Using an Analogy

Compare and Contrast Advantages of parasitism: easy access to food; no need to move about to escape predators or find food or mates (most are hermaphrodites); Disadvantages of parasitism: cannot survive outside a host; when host dies, parasite dies; cannot move to another location if host becomes unsuitable due to disease or toxic substances taken in; Structural adaptations include hermaphrodism, digestive system absent or simple, and powerful specialized mouth structures.

Section 26.3

Flatworms

Indiana Standards Standard B.1.15 Understand and explain that, in biological systems, structure and function must be considered together.

SECTION PREVIEW

Objectives
Distinguish between the structural adaptations of parasitic flatworms and free-living planarians.

Explain how parasitic flatworms are adapted to their way of life.

Review Vocabulary
acoelomate: an animal that has three cell layers—ectoderm, endoderm, and mesoderm—but no body cavity (p. 682)

New Vocabulary
regeneration
pharynx
scolex
proglottid

This Is the Life

Using an Analogy Imagine the ultimate couch potato life. All of your needs are provided while you stay on the couch. Food and beverages are supplied constantly and wastes are taken away. Over time, however, you could become totally dependent on someone to supply all of your needs. This describes the parasitic life of a tapeworm, like the one shown to the right.

Compare and Contrast *As a class, compile two lists:* Advantages of Parasitism *and* Disadvantages of Parasitism. *Infer what structural adaptations are found in most parasites.*

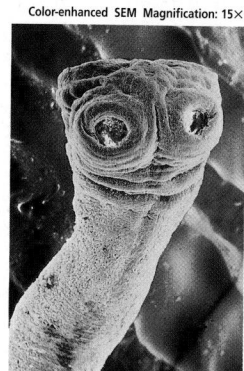
Color-enhanced SEM Magnification: 15×

Tapeworm scolex

What is a flatworm?

To most people, the word worm describes a spaghetti-shaped animal. Many animals have this general appearance, but are classified into different phyla. The least complex worms belong to the phylum Platyhelminthes (pla tee HEL min theez), as shown in *Figure 26.14*. These flatworms are acoelomates with thin, solid bodies. They range in size from 1 mm up to several meters. There are approximately 14 500 species of flatworms found in marine and freshwater environments and in moist habitats on land.

Figure 26.14
A tapeworm **(A)** is a parasite that invades and lives in a host organism. A fluke **(B)** usually requires two hosts in its complex life cycle. A planarian **(C)** is not parasitic, nor does it cause disease.

Ⓐ Ⓑ Ⓒ

LM Magnification: 10×

706 SPONGES, CNIDARIANS, FLATWORMS, AND ROUNDWORMS

RESOURCE MANAGER

Unit 8 *FAST FILE* Resources
BioLab Worksheet, pp. 35–36
Reinforcement and Study Guide in English, p. 39
Reinforcement and Study Guide in Spanish, p. 43
Transparency Worksheets, pp. 49, 57–58

Reading Essentials for Biology, Section 26.3
Laboratory Manual, pp. 165–166
Section Focus Transparency 65
Reteaching Skills Transparency 39

The most well-known members of this phylum are the parasitic tapeworms and flukes, which cause diseases in other animals, among them frogs and humans. The most commonly studied flatworms in biology classes are the free-living planarians. You can learn about the evolutionary relationships among these flatworm groups in the *Problem-Solving Lab* on this page.

Nervous control in planarians

Most of a planarian's nervous system is located in its head—a characteristic common to other bilaterally symmetrical animals. The nervous system enables a planarian to respond to stimuli in its environment. Some flatworms have a nerve net, and others have the beginnings of a central nervous system. A planarian's nervous system includes two nerve cords that run the length of the body, as shown in *Figure 26.15*. It also includes eyespots that can detect the presence or absence of light and sensory cells that can detect chemicals and movement in water. At the anterior end of the nerve cord is a small swelling called a ganglion (plural, ganglia). The ganglion receives messages from the eyespots and sensory pits, then communicates with the rest of the body along the nerve cords. Messages from the nerve cords trigger responses in a planarian's muscle cells.

Reproduction in planarians

Like many of the organisms studied in this chapter, most flatworms including planarians, are hermaphrodites. During sexual reproduction, individual planarians exchange sperm, which travel along special tubes to reach the eggs. Fertilization occurs internally. The zygotes are released in capsules into the water, where they hatch into tiny planarians.

Problem-Solving Lab 26.3

Predict

Which came first? There are three classes of flatworms. One class, Turbellaria, consists of free-living flatworms. The other two classes, Trematoda (flukes) and Cestoda (tapeworms), consist of parasitic organisms that often have mammal hosts, including humans.

Solve the Problem

Diagrams A, B, and C show a possible evolutionary relationship among the three classes. The class at the bottom of each diagram supposedly evolved first.

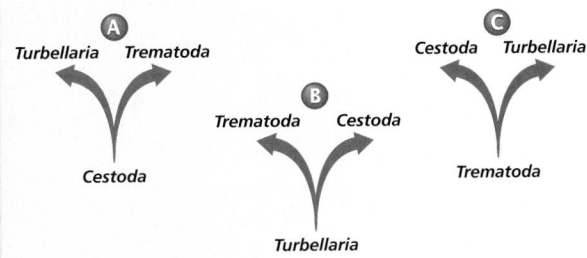

Thinking Critically

One of the three evolutionary patterns is correct. Choose the one that you consider to be correct. Explain your reasoning. Analyze, review, and critique your explanation as to its strengths and weaknesses using scientific information.

Figure 26.15
The simple nervous system of a planarian enables it to respond to stimuli in its environment.

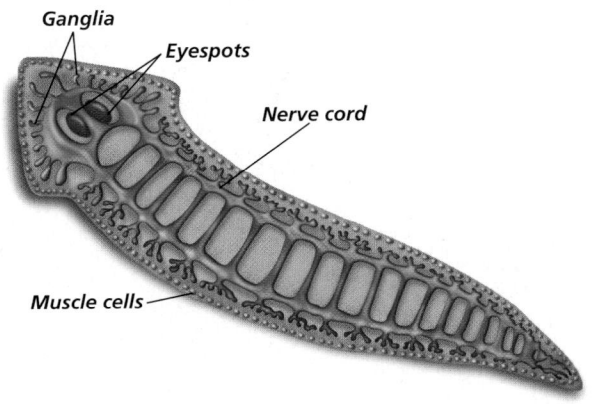

Ganglia
Eyespots
Nerve cord
Muscle cells

Problem-Solving Lab 26.3

Purpose

Students are to determine which class of flatworms evolved first.

Process Skills

think critically, predict

Teaching Strategies

- Students may need additional help in understanding the nature of the three diagrams.
- Student groups of 2 or 3 may work well for this activity.

Thinking Critically

Diagram B is correct. Student explanations may vary, but the main concept is that free-living classes of the flatworms evolved first. This class then evolved into the parasitic forms. It would be difficult to explain how a parasitic worm could evolve first with such a complex life cycle. If one assumes that flatworms evolved before mammals, then it would be impossible for the parasitic worms to have had any hosts available to them.

Assessment

Knowledge Ask students to describe those traits that flatworms do and do not share with cnidarians. Use the Performance Task Assessment List for Making Observations and Inferences in **PASC**, p. 89. **L2**

PROJECT

Planarian Behavior Have students design experiments that explore planarian behavior. They might investigate responses to food, touch, heat, cold, or other variables. Make sure they plan experiments in which there is only one variable, a control, and quantitative data to be collected. **L2** **ELL**

 Indiana Academic Standards

Pages 706–707: B.1.14, B.1.15, B.1.19, B.1.43

708

INSIDE STORY

A Planarian
Figure 26.16
If you've ever waded in a shallow stream and turned over some rocks, you may have found tiny, black organisms stuck to the bottom of the rocks. These organisms were most likely planarians. Planarians have many characteristics common to all species of flatworms. The bodies of planarians are flat, with both a dorsal and a ventral surface. All flatworms have bilateral symmetry.
Critical Thinking *Why is having a head an advantage to a swimming animal?*

LM Magnification: 10×

Planarian

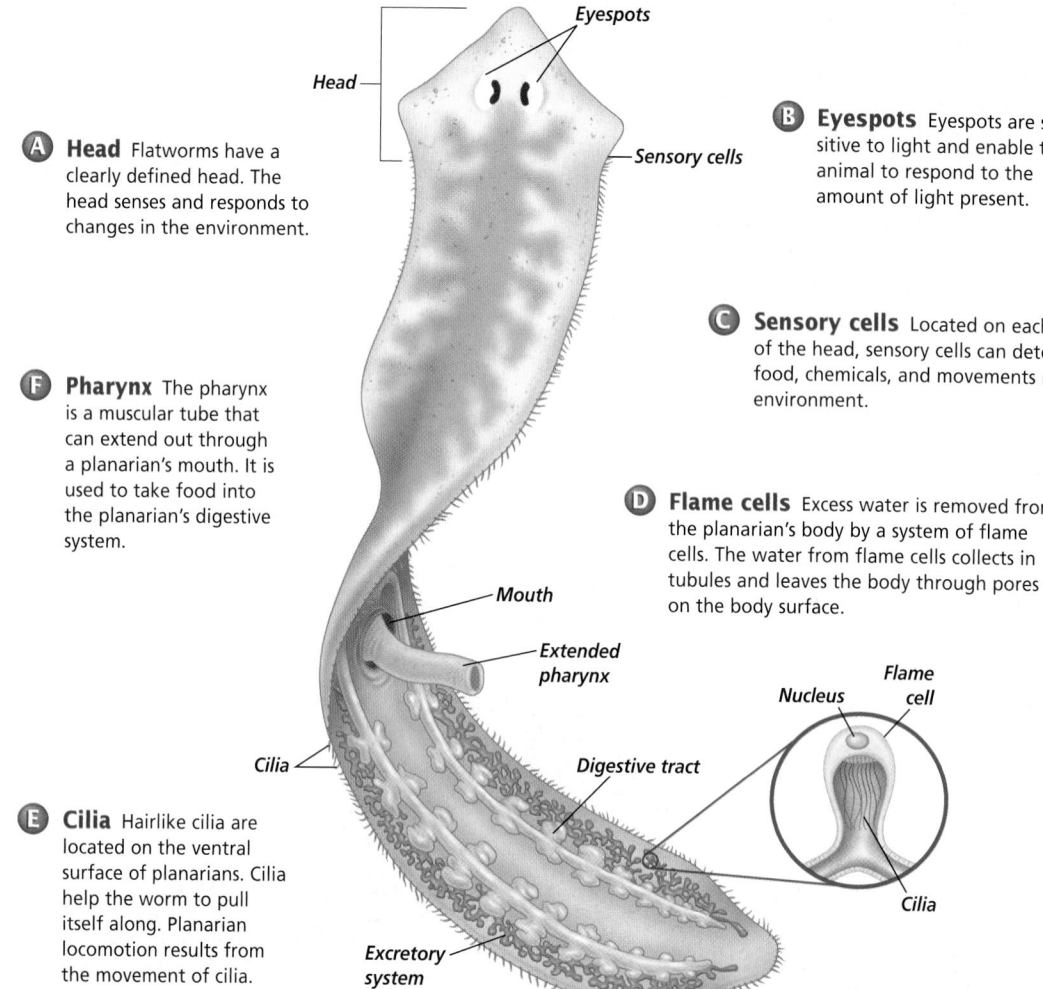

A **Head** Flatworms have a clearly defined head. The head senses and responds to changes in the environment.

F **Pharynx** The pharynx is a muscular tube that can extend out through a planarian's mouth. It is used to take food into the planarian's digestive system.

E **Cilia** Hairlike cilia are located on the ventral surface of planarians. Cilia help the worm to pull itself along. Planarian locomotion results from the movement of cilia.

B **Eyespots** Eyespots are sensitive to light and enable the animal to respond to the amount of light present.

C **Sensory cells** Located on each side of the head, sensory cells can detect food, chemicals, and movements in the environment.

D **Flame cells** Excess water is removed from the planarian's body by a system of flame cells. The water from flame cells collects in tubules and leaves the body through pores on the body surface.

Labels on figure: *Eyespots*, *Head*, *Sensory cells*, *Mouth*, *Extended pharynx*, *Cilia*, *Digestive tract*, *Excretory system*, *Nucleus*, *Flame cell*, *Cilia*

Planarians also can reproduce asexually. When a planarian is damaged, it has the ability to regenerate, or regrow, new body parts. **Regeneration** is the replacement or regrowth of missing body parts. Missing body parts are replaced through cell divisions. If a planarian is cut horizontally, the section containing the head will grow a new tail, and the tail section will grow a new head. Thus, a planarian that is damaged or cut into two pieces may grow into two new organisms—a form of asexual reproduction. The *BioLab* at the end of this chapter is about regeneration in planarians.

Feeding and digestion in planarians

A planarian feeds on dead or slow-moving organisms. It extends a tube-like, muscular organ, called the **pharynx** (FAHR inx), out of its mouth, as shown in *Figure 26.16*. Enzymes released by the pharynx begin digesting food outside the animal's body. Food particles are sucked into the digestive tract, where they are broken up. Cells lining the digestive tract obtain food by endocytosis. Food is thus digested in individual cells.

Feeding and digestion in parasitic flatworms

A parasitic flatworm is adapted to obtaining nutrients from inside the bodies of one or two hosts. Recall that a parasite is an organism that lives on or in another organism and depends upon that host organism for its food. Parasitic flatworms have mouthparts with hooks that keep the flatworm firmly attached inside its host. Because they are surrounded by nutrients, they do not need to move to seek out or find food. Parasitic flatworms do not have complex nervous or muscular tissue.

Tapeworm bodies have sections

The body of a tapeworm is made up of a knob-shaped head called a **scolex** (SKOH leks), and detachable, individual sections called proglottids, as shown in *Figure 26.17*. A **proglottid** (proh GLAH tihd) contains muscles, nerves, flame cells, and male and female reproductive organs. Each proglottid can contain up to 100 000 eggs. Some adult tapeworms that live in animal intestines can be more than 10 m in length and consist of 2000 proglottids.

Word Origin

scolex from the Greek word *skolek,* meaning "worm"; A scolex is the knob-shaped head of a tapeworm.

Figure 26.17
The scolex (**A**) is covered with hooks and suckers that attach to the intestinal lining of the host. Mature proglottids full of fertilized eggs (**B**) are shed. Eggs hatch when they are eaten by a secondary host.

Stained LM Magnification: 40×

LM Magnification: 5×

3 Assess

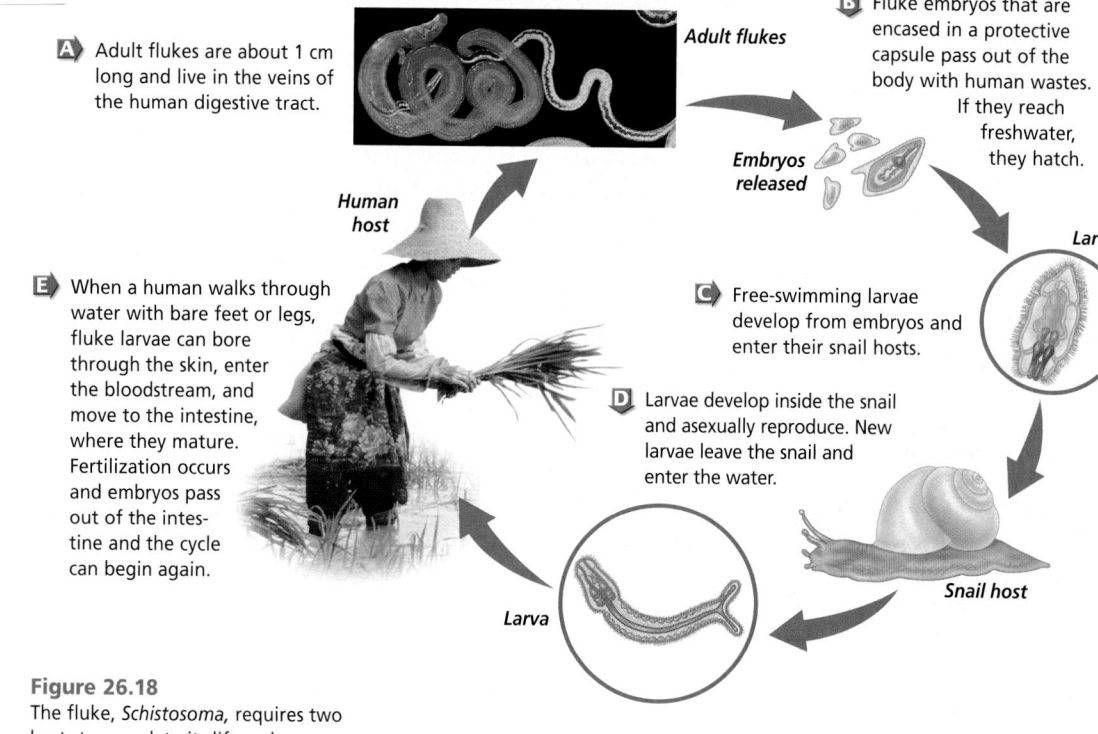

A Adult flukes are about 1 cm long and live in the veins of the human digestive tract.

Adult flukes

B Fluke embryos that are encased in a protective capsule pass out of the body with human wastes. If they reach freshwater, they hatch.

Embryos released

Larva

Human host

E When a human walks through water with bare feet or legs, fluke larvae can bore through the skin, enter the bloodstream, and move to the intestine, where they mature. Fertilization occurs and embryos pass out of the intestine and the cycle can begin again.

C Free-swimming larvae develop from embryos and enter their snail hosts.

D Larvae develop inside the snail and asexually reproduce. New larvae leave the snail and enter the water.

Snail host

Larva

Figure 26.18
The fluke, *Schistosoma*, requires two hosts to complete its life cycle.

The life cycle of a fluke

A fluke is a parasitic flatworm that spends part of its life in the internal organs of a vertebrate, such as a human or a sheep. It obtains its nutrition by feeding on cells, blood, and other fluids of the host organism. Flukes have complex life cycles that can include one, two, or more invertebrate and/or vertebrate hosts.

Blood flukes of the genus *Schistosoma*, as shown in **Figure 26.18,** cause a disease in humans known as schistosomiasis. Schistosomiasis is common in countries where rice is grown. Farmers must work in standing water in rice fields during planting and harvesting. Blood flukes are common where the secondary host, snails, also are found.

Section Assessment

Understanding Main Ideas
1. Diagram and label the structures of a planarian.
2. Explain why a tapeworm doesn't have a digestive system.
3. Discuss the adaptive advantage of a nervous system for a free-living flatworm.
4. Make a table to compare and contrast the body of a tapeworm and that of a planarian.

Thinking Critically
5. Examine the life cycle of a parasitic fluke, and suggest ways to prevent infection on a rice farm.

SKILL REVIEW

6. **Observe and Infer** How might an organism that has no mouth or digestive system interact with other organisms in its environment? For more help, refer to *Observe and Infer* in the **Skill Handbook.**

710 SPONGES, CNIDARIANS, FLATWORMS, AND ROUNDWORMS in.bdol.glencoe.com/self_check_quiz

Section Assessment

1. Make sure students have labeled the head, eyespots, sensory pits, cilia, flame cells, mouth, and pharynx.
2. They live in intestines surrounded by digested food.
3. It enables the worm to sense food and appropriate habitat as it swims.

4.

	Tapeworm	Planarian
Body plan	head and sections	head, no sections
Nervous system	nerves, flame cells	ganglia, nerve cord, eyespots, sensory cells
Digestive system	mouth with hooks, no digestive tract	mouth, pharynx, digestive tract
Reproduction	hermaphrodism	hermaphrodism, regeneration of organism

5. Workers could wear boots and gloves. Human wastes should be kept out of the water.
6. This organism would most likely be a parasite.

Section 26.4

SECTION PREVIEW

Objectives

Compare and contrast the structural adaptations of roundworms and flatworms.

Identify the characteristics of four roundworm parasites.

Review Vocabulary
pseudocoelom: fluid-filled body cavity partly lined with mesoderm (p. 683)

New Vocabulary
trichinosis

Roundworms

Public Health and Roundworms

Using Prior Knowledge

Have you ever been to the veterinarian to have your dog tested for heartworms? Perhaps you recall warnings about properly cooking pork products. It has been estimated that about one-third of the world's human population is affected by problems caused by roundworms.

Research *Contact your local health department or county extension service to learn what roundworm pests are common in your area. Research one of these roundworm pests. Collect information about its life cycle, ways to prevent its infection, recommended treatments for infection, and data regarding the number of reported infections during the previous year. On index cards, make a classroom reference file about roundworm pests.*

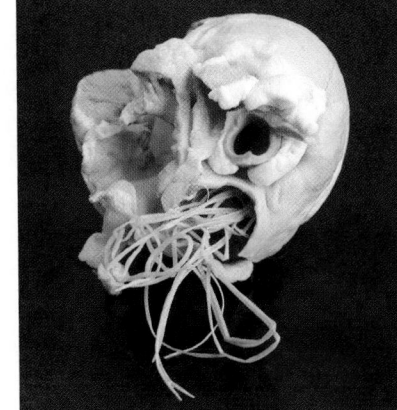

Dog heart infected with heartworms

What is a roundworm?

Roundworms belong to the phylum Nematoda. They are widely distributed, living in soil, animals, and both freshwater and marine environments. More than 12 000 species of roundworms are known to scientists. Most roundworm species are free-living, but many are parasitic. Nearly all plant and animal species are affected by parasitic roundworms.

Roundworms are tapered at both ends. They have a thick outer covering, which they shed four times as they grow, that protects them in harsh environments. Roundworms look like tiny, wriggling bits of thread. They lack circular muscles but have lengthwise muscles. As one muscle contracts, another muscle relaxes. This alternating contraction and relaxation of muscles causes roundworms to move in a thrashing fashion.

Roundworms have a pseudocoelom and are the simplest animals with a tubelike digestive system. Unlike flatworms, roundworms have two body openings—a mouth and an anus. The free-living species have well-developed sense organs, such as eyespots, although these are reduced in parasitic forms.

 Reading Check **Identify** the characteristics of the phylum Nematoda.

26.4 ROUNDWORMS **711**

Section 26.4

1 Focus

INTERACTIVE CHALKBOARD
PowerPoint® Presentations

Bellringer
Section Focus Transparency 66

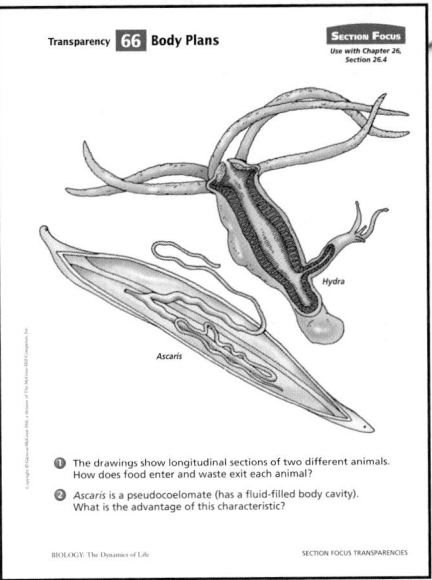

Transparency **66** Body Plans   SECTION FOCUS
Use with Chapter 26, Section 26.4

Hydra

Ascaris

❶ The drawings show longitudinal sections of two different animals. How does food enter and waste exit each animal?

❷ *Ascaris* is a pseudocoelomate (has a fluid-filled body cavity). What is the advantage of this characteristic?

BIOLOGY: The Dynamics of Life   SECTION FOCUS TRANSPARENCIES

Using Prior Knowledge

Research Student research will depend on geographic area and roundworm pest chosen. Be sure that students include documentation of facts.

 Reading Check Student responses should include all facts stated in the three paragraphs following "What is a roundworm?".

Word Origin

Have students identify the vocabulary word in this chapter that had "nema-" as a root.
nematocyst

RESOURCE MANAGER

Unit 8 *FAST FILE* Resources
MiniLab Worksheet, p. 34
Reinforcement and Study Guide in English, p. 40
Reinforcement and Study Guide in Spanish, p. 44
Transparency Worksheet, p. 50

Reading Essentials for Biology, Section 26.4
Section Focus Transparency 66

Indiana Academic Standards
Pages 710–711: B.1.14, B.1.15

2 Teach

Purpose

Students will observe the larval stage of *Trichinella* embedded in muscle tissue of its host.

Process Skills

observe and infer, measure in SI

Teaching Strategies

■ Prepared slides of *Trichinella* are available from biological supply houses.

■ Certain larvae will appear as round segments due to the plane through which the slice was made in preparing the slide.

Expected Results

Students will not be able to see *Trichinella* larvae without the aid of a microscope.

Analysis

1. microscopic, round, spiral
2. *Trichinella* larvae are microscopic and cannot be seen.
3. Samples of muscle tissue can be taken and viewed under a microscope.

Assessment

Portfolio Have students put their diagrams in their portfolios. Use the Performance Task Assessment List for Science Portfolio in **PASC**, p. 105. **L1**

Purpose

Students will analyze the life cycle of the black vine weevil and infer what time during its life cycle would be best to apply soil nematodes to kill it.

Process Skills

predict, interpret a scientific illustration, apply information, infer, identify, explain

---

MiniLab 26.2

Observe

Observing the Larval Stage of *Trichinella* You can observe the larval stage of a *Trichinella spiralis* embedded within swine muscle tissue. It will look like a curled up hot dog surrounded by muscle tissue.

Magnification: unavailable

Trichinella

Procedure

1. Examine a prepared slide of *Trichinella* larvae under the low-power magnification of your microscope.
2. Locate several larvae by looking for "spiral worms enclosed in a sac." All other tissue is muscle.
3. Estimate the size of the larva in μm (micrometers).
4. Diagram one larva. Indicate its size on the diagram.

Analysis

1. **Describe** What is the appearance of a *Trichinella* larva?
2. **Predict** Why might it be difficult to find larva embedded in muscle when meat inspectors use visual checking methods in packing houses to screen for *Trichinella* contamination?
3. **Infer** What might inspectors do to help detect *Trichinella* larvae?

Figure 26.19
Parasitic roundworms include, *Ascaris* **(A)**, hookworms **(B)**, and pinworms **(C)**. **Describe** *How do the means of infection differ among these organisms?*

Color-enhanced SEM Magnification: 100×

712

Diversity of Roundworms

Approximately half of the described roundworm species are parasites, and about 50 species infect humans.

Roundworm parasites of humans

Infection by *Ascaris* (ASS kuh ris), shown in **Figure 26.19**, is the most common roundworm infection in humans. It occurs worldwide but is more common in subtropical or tropical areas. Children become infected more often than adults do. Eggs of *Ascaris* are found in soil and enter a human's body through the mouth. The eggs hatch in the intestines, move into the bloodstream, and eventually to the lungs, where they are coughed up, swallowed, and begin the cycle again.

Pinworms are the most common human roundworm parasites in the United States. The highest incidence of infection is in children. Pinworms are highly contagious because eggs can survive for up to two weeks on surfaces. Its life cycle begins when live eggs are ingested. They mature in the host's intestinal tract. Female pinworms exit the host's anus—usually as the host sleeps—and lay eggs on nearby skin. These eggs fall onto bedding or other surfaces.

Trichinella causes a disease called **trichinosis** (trih keh NOH sis). This roundworm can be ingested in raw or undercooked pork, pork products, or wild game. Trichinosis can be controlled by properly cooking meat. Find out what these roundworms look like in *MiniLab 26.2*.

LM Magnification: 12×

Teaching Strategies

■ Remind students that the nematodes used are not harmful to plants, birds, mammals, or humans.

■ Show pictures of black vine weevils and their larvae to students.

Thinking Critically

August, September; Larvae would be hatching and the soil would be warm.

Assessment

Discussion Discuss with students the pros and cons of using nematodes to control insect pests. **L2**

Figure 26.20
Roundworm plant parasites usually enter the roots, forming cysts that inhibit the growth of the plant's vascular system.

Hookworm infections are common in humans in warm climates where they walk on contaminated soil in bare feet. Hookworms cause people to feel weak and tired due to blood loss.

Roundworm parasites of other organisms

About 1200 species of nematodes cause diseases in plants. Nematodes can infect and kill pine trees, cereal crops, and food plants such as potatoes. They are particularly attracted to plant roots, as shown in *Figure 26.20,* and cause a slow decline of the plant. They also can infect fungi and can form symbiotic associations with bacteria. Nematodes also can be used to control pests, as described in *Problem-Solving Lab 26.4.*

Problem-Solving Lab 26.4

Interpret Data

Can nematodes control weevil damage to plants? In the Pacific Northwest, the larvae of certain weevils feed on roots of woody shrubs, killing them in large numbers. Instead of using chemical pesticides, certain free-living nematodes can be used to kill weevil larvae. The nematodes must be introduced to the soil when it is warm and after the weevil larvae have recently hatched.

Solve the Problem
Study the life cycle of the black vine weevil, and infer what is the best time to apply soil nematodes to kill larvae.

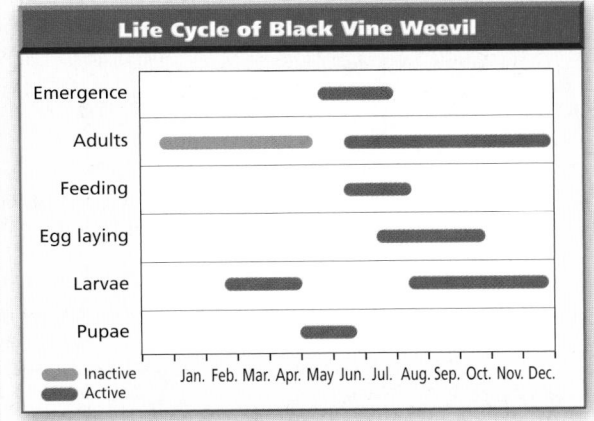

Life Cycle of Black Vine Weevil

Emergence
Adults
Feeding
Egg laying
Larvae
Pupae

Inactive
Active

Jan. Feb. Mar. Apr. May Jun. Jul. Aug. Sep. Oct. Nov. Dec.

Thinking Critically
Interpret Data What months would be best for application of soil nematodes to kill black vine weevil larvae? Explain.

3 Assess

DAILY INTERVENTION

Check for Understanding
Have students write true or false questions relating to roundworms. Review and explain the correct answers. **L2**

Reteach
Have students play bingo with a 16-square card with the name of a worm in each square. Read a list of statements and have students play bingo. **L2**

Resources
For more practice, use *Reading Essentials for Biology,* Section 26.4.

Extension
Ask students to do a videotape report on parasitic roundworms in humans. **L3**

✔ Assessment

Activity Set up stations around the classroom with photos or slides of the roundworms studied. Have students identify each worm. **L2 ELL**

Indiana Academic Standards

Pages 712–713: B.1.15, B.1.17, B.1.43

Section Assessment

Understanding Main Ideas
1. Compare and contrast the body structures of roundworms and flatworms.

2. Infer why children should be taught to wash their hands before eating.

3. Outline the method of infection of *Ascaris.*

4. Compare how humans are infected by a hookworm and by *Trichinella.*

Thinking Critically
5. An infection of pinworms is spreading among children at a preschool. Make a list of precautions that could be taken to stop its spread.

SKILL REVIEW

6. **Make and Use Tables** Make a table of the characteristics of four roundworm parasites, list their names, how the parasite is contracted, its action in the body, and means of prevention. For more help, refer to *Make and Use Tables* in the **Skill Handbook.**

 in.bdol.glencoe.com/self_check_quiz

Section Assessment

1. Roundworms have a pseudocoelom and two body openings. Flatworms are acoelomates with only one body opening.
2. to prevent infection by parasitic worms and bacteria

3. Student outlines should include information in this section about *Ascaris.*
4. Hookworm is contracted by walking barefoot on contaminated soil. *Trichinella* is contracted by eating contaminated, improperly cooked pork or wild game.

5. good personal hygiene, such as washing hands, clothing, and bedding
6. Make sure students' tables include information from pages 711–713.

INVESTIGATE
BioLab

Time Allotment

30 minutes the first day, 10 minutes every day for 2 weeks

Process Skills

collect data, experiment, think critically, observe and infer, organize data

Safety Precautions

■ Remind students to use razor blades carefully to avoid injury. Caution them to always cut in a direction down and away from the body.
■ Remind students they are working with live animals and to treat them gently.
■ Have students wash their hands after completing this BioLab.

Before You Begin

Certain animals have the ability to replace lost body parts through regeneration. In regeneration, organisms regrow missing parts. This process occurs in a number of different phyla throughout the animal kingdom. In this activity, you will observe regeneration in planarians. Planarians are able to form two new animals when one has been cut in half.

Observing Planarian Regeneration

PREPARATION

Problem

How can you determine if the flatworm *Dugesia* is capable of regeneration?

Objectives

In this BioLab, you will:
■ **Observe** the flatworm, *Dugesia*.
■ **Conduct** an experiment to determine if planarians are capable of regeneration.

Materials

planarians	chilled glass slide
petri dish	dissecting microscope
distilled or bottled water	marking pencil or labels
camel hair brush	single-edged razor blade

Safety Precautions

CAUTION: *Use extreme caution when cutting with a razor blade. Wash your hands both before and after working with planarians. Use care when handling a microscope and glassware.*

Skill Handbook

If you need help with this lab, refer to the **Skill Handbook**.

PREPARATION

Order planarians so that they arrive a day or two before they will be needed. Planarians are available from biological supply houses. Ask for the species, *Dugesia tigrina*.

Alternative Materials

■ Use a hand lens if binocular microscopes are not available.
■ A dropper or plastic pipette may be substituted for the camel hair brush.

PROCEDURE

1. Obtain a planarian and place it in a petri dish containing a small amount of distilled or bottled water. You can pick up a planarian easily with a small camel hair brush.
2. Use a dissecting microscope to observe the planarian. Locate the animal's head and tail region and its "eyes." Use Diagram **A** as a guide.
3. Move the animal onto a chilled glass slide. This will cause its muscles to relax.
4. Place the slide under the microscope. While looking through the microscope, use a single-edged razor blade to cut the animal in half across the midsection. Use Diagram **B** as a guide.

PROCEDURE

Teaching Strategies

■ Have students work in groups of 2 or 3.
■ Do not feed the planarians while they are undergoing regeneration. Replace any springwater lost through evaporation.

■ Store the regenerating pieces in a cool area (around 20°C) of the classroom and in subdued light.

Data and Observations

Students will observe the flatworms and will be able to see those structures shown in Figure A. Data table design will vary from student to student. Encourage students to diagram their observations. At the end of two weeks, students will observe that a new head has formed on the original tail section, and a new tail on the original head section.

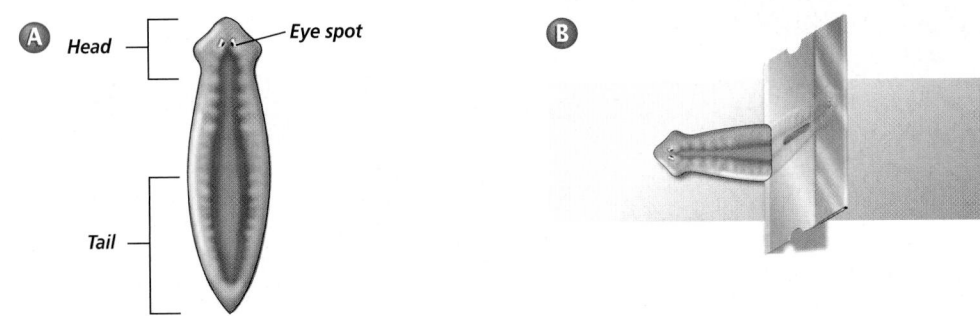

Ⓐ Head — Eye spot

Tail

Ⓑ

5. Remove the head end and return it to the petri dish filled with water. Put the lid on the dish and label the dish with the date, your name, and the word *Head*.

6. Add distilled or bottled water to a different petri dish and place the tail section in it. Put the lid on the dish, and label it as in step 5, except mark this dish *Tail*.

7. Repeat steps 3–6 with a second planarian.

8. Place the four petri dishes in an area designated by your teacher. Change the water in each petri dish every 3–4 days.

9. Prepare a data table that will allow you to record your observations of your planarians every other day for two weeks.

10. Observe your planarians under a dissecting microscope and record observations. Include diagrams and the number of days since starting the experiment in your data table.

11. **CLEANUP AND DISPOSAL** Clean all equipment as instructed by your teacher, and return everything to its proper place. Properly dispose of slides and planarians. Wash your hands thoroughly.

ANALYZE AND CONCLUDE

1. **State** To what phylum do flatworms belong? Are planarians free living or parasitic? What is your evidence?

2. **Observe** What new part did each original head piece regenerate? What new part did each original tail piece regenerate?

3. **Observe** Which section, head or tail, regenerated new parts faster?

4. **Infer** Is regeneration by mitosis or meiosis? Explain.

5. **Think Critically** What might be the advantage for an animal that can regenerate new body parts?

6. **Think Critically** Would the term "clone" be suitable in reference to the newly formed planarians? Explain your answer.

Apply Your Skill

Experiment Design an experiment that would test this hypothesis: If regenerating planarians are placed in a warmer environment, then the time needed for new parts to form would decrease.

 Web Links To find out more about regeneration, visit in.bdol.glencoe.com/regeneration

ANALYZE AND CONCLUDE

1. Planarians belong to the phylum Platyhelminthes. They are free-living and can be found in ponds and streams living on their own.

2. The head regenerated a new tail, and the tail regenerated a new head.

3. head section

4. mitosis; no formation of gametes

5. Answers may vary; there is no need to find a mate, able to replace lost body parts, faster than sexual reproduction, identical genetic make-up as original animal

6. Yes, clones form by mitosis. Regeneration in planarians is a type of cloning.

Assessment

Portfolio Have students write a report on their experimental findings. Be sure to have them include their data table with recorded results. Use the Performance Task Assessment List for Lab Report in **PASC**, p. 119. **L2**

Apply Your Skill

Experiment Have students redesign the experiment by making different types of cuts and/or making cuts at different locations on the animals' bodies.

CLEANUP AND DISPOSAL

🗑 Ask students to return razor blades to the designated container for washing. Have students wash their hands after cleaning up.

Purpose

Students learn about the importance of coral reefs, discover how they can be damaged, and explore methods for preventing damage.

Background

Corals contain zooxanthellae that can carry out photosynthesis. During the day, most corals withdraw into the safety of their cups and the zooxanthellae make food for them. At night, corals use their tentacles with nematocysts to capture planktonic organisms that drift by.

Teaching Strategies

Point out to students that, because most coral reefs lie in shallow waters near the shoreline, they are easily affected by coastal activities. The clearing of coastal land for development may increase erosion. Silt clouds the water and reduces the amount of sunlight available, limiting photosynthesis by zooxanthellae. Silt also can clog the mouths of the coral polyps, affecting their ability to feed at night.

Forming Your Opinion

Because coral reefs offer an enormous array of protected living spaces, the destruction of a reef would remove habitats needed by many species. Organisms that prey on any of those species would lose a food source. Coral reefs also slow waves, so the destruction of a reef could leave the shore subject to erosion from wave action.

Biology and Society

Why are the corals dying?

Coral reefs are some of Earth's most spectacularly beautiful and productive ecosystems. A reef is composed of hundreds of corals that together create a structure of brightly colored shapes and patterns. In the reef's cracks and crevices live a dazzling array of fishes and invertebrates. Coral reefs protect nearby shore areas from erosion by slowing incoming waves, thus, reducing the force that they can exert. But worldwide, coral reefs are increasingly being damaged and destroyed.

Physical damage to coral reefs Hurricanes can cause serious damage to coral reefs. Ships can run aground on reefs because they lie close to the water's surface. In some parts of the world, explosives are used to mine coral for building materials and fertilizers. Tropical aquarium fishes are sometimes collected by poisoning with cyanide, which stuns fishes and makes them easier to collect, but also kills corals. Collectors take pieces of coral for jewelry and souvenirs.

Damage from organisms In the 1970s, marine scientists began to realize that the world's coral reefs had diseases no one had seen before. Black band disease is caused by a cyanobacterium and two species of bacteria that combine to form a band of black filaments. This invading community slowly moves across the coral. White band disease causes the living tissue of a coral to peel away from its skeleton; the cause is uncertain.

Fishes, sea stars, and other organisms prey on corals and, as a result, damage coral reefs. Parrotfish eat corals causing excavations 1–2 cm deep. This condition is called white spot biting and was once thought to be rapid wasting disease.

Many of the world's coral reefs are losing their beautiful colors in a process called bleaching.

Healthy coral reef (above), and diseased reef (right)

The corals become gray or white in color. Some scientists hypothesize that coral bleaching is the result of a loss of zooxanthellae, the symbiotic protists that live in coral and give it much of its color as well as nutrients.

Perspectives Worldwide, coral reef health is declining. Most researchers hypothesize that coral diseases are on the increase because environmental changes, such as pollution in coastal runoff, higher water levels, or changes in ocean temperatures, make corals more vulnerable to opportunistic diseases.

Forming Your Opinion

Research Investigate the effects that the death of a coral reef might have on nearby ocean and coastal ecosystems. Prepare a bibliography about this topic.

 To find out more about coral reefs, visit in.bdol.glencoe.com/biology_society

Going Further

Intrapersonal A great deal of research on methods for protecting and restoring coral reefs occurs in the Florida Keys. Invite students to go to in.bdol.glencoe.com to find out about some of the problems and solutions scientists are exploring.

STUDY GUIDE

Section 26.1

Sponges

Key Concepts

- A sponge is an aquatic, sessile, asymmetrical, filter-feeding invertebrate.
- Sponges are made of four types of cells. Each cell type contributes to the survival of the organism.
- Most sponges are hermaphroditic with free-swimming larvae.

Vocabulary

external fertilization (p. 696)
filter feeding (p. 693)
hermaphrodite (p. 696)
internal fertilization (p. 696)

Section 26.2

Cnidarians

Key Concepts

- All cnidarians are radially symmetrical, aquatic invertebrates that display two basic forms: medusa and polyp.
- Cnidarians sting their prey with cells called nematocysts located on their tentacles.
- The three primary classes of cnidarians include the hydrozoans, hydras; scyphozoans, jellyfishes; and anthozoans, corals and anemones.

Vocabulary

gastrovascular cavity (p. 702)
medusa (p. 700)
nematocyst (p. 701)
nerve net (p. 702)
polyp (p. 700)

Section 26.3

Flatworms

LM Magnification: 10×

Key Concepts

- Flatworms are acoelomates with thin, solid bodies. They are grouped into three classes: free-living planarians, parasitic flukes, and tapeworms.
- Planarians have simple nervous and muscular systems. Flukes and tapeworms have structures adapted to their parasitic existence.

Vocabulary

pharynx (p. 709)
proglottid (p. 709)
regeneration (p. 709)
scolex (p. 709)

Section 26.4

Roundworms

LM Magnification: 12×

Key Concepts

- Roundworms are pseudocoelomate, cylindrical worms with lengthwise muscles, relatively complex digestive systems, and two body openings.
- Roundworms can be parasites of plants, fungi, and animals, including humans.

Vocabulary

trichinosis (p. 712)

FOLDABLES **Study Organizer** To help you review the diet, reproduction, structure, and adaptations of sponges, use the Organizational Study Fold on page 693.

in.bdol.glencoe.com/vocabulary_puzzlemaker

CHAPTER 26 ASSESSMENT **717**

Key Concepts

Summary statements can be used by students to review the major concepts of the chapter.

 Biology Online

Visit in.bdol.glencoe.com
/self_check_quiz
/vocabulary_puzzlemaker
/chapter_test
/standardized_test

VOCABULARY PUZZLEMAKER

 For additional help with vocabulary, have students access the Vocabulary PuzzleMaker online at in.bdol.glencoe.com/vocabulary_puzzlemaker

FOLDABLES™

Have students use their Foldables to review the content of Section 26.1. On the backs of their Foldables, have students analyze how sponges are adapted to their environments.

Use the ExamView®Pro Test Bank CD-ROM to:

- Create **multiple versions** of tests
- Create **modified** tests with one mouse click for **inclusion** students
- **Edit** existing questions and **add** your own questions
- Build tests aligned with state standards using built-in **State Curriculum Tags**
- Change **English** tests to **Spanish** with one mouse click and vice versa

 Indiana Academic Standards

Pages 716–717: B.1.1, B.1.15, B.1.43

Questions and answers have been aligned and verified by The Princeton Review.

Vocabulary Review

1. true
2. false—nematocyst
3. false—gastrovascular cavity
4. false—medusa
5. false—proglottid

Understanding Key Concepts

6. A   8. A
7. B   9. B

Constructed Response

10. Human wastes may be disposed of in such a way as to prevent fluke eggs from coming in contact with snails; or humans can avoid contact with water in which snails live.

11. Cilia on the ventral surface of a free-living flatworm help move it as it searches for food. Its head enables it to sense its environment as it moves forward. The pharynx can be extended through its mouth to suck up food. Parasitic flatworms have no means of locomotion. The hooks around its mouth keep the worm attached to its host. They do not have complex muscular, nervous, or digestive tissues because they receive nutrition from their host and do not move to find food.

Thinking Critically

12. Gulf of California, Hawaii, and Galápagos; Species B does not exist in the Gulf of California and the Galápagos. In Hawaii, there are fewer of species A and B than there are in reefs with more biodiversity.

13. Because species C appears in all of the reefs, even the

Vocabulary Review

Review the Chapter 26 vocabulary words listed in the Study Guide on page 717. Determine if each statement is true or false. If false, replace the underlined word with the correct vocabulary word.

1. Any animal that can produce both eggs and sperm is called a <u>hermaphrodite</u>.

2. A <u>medusa</u> is a capsule that contains a coiled threadlike tube that is used to capture and poison prey.

3. The <u>pharynx</u> is a space surrounded by the inner cell layer of a cnidarian in which digestion occurs.

4. The cnidarian body form that is umbrella-shaped with tentacles that hang down is called a <u>polyp</u>.

5. A <u>scolex</u> is a detachable, individual section of a tapeworm that contains muscles, nerves, flame cells, and male and female reproductive organs.

Understanding Key Concepts

6. Which of these cell types is found in sponges?
   A. collar   C. mesoderm
   B. endoderm   D. nematocyst

7. Of the following organisms, which one is a filter feeder?
   A. jellyfish   C. pinworm
   B. sponge   D. tapeworm

8. In cnidarians, medusae reproduce sexually to produce larvae, which develop into sessile _____.
   A. polyps   C. nematocysts
   B. tentacles   D. medusae

9. Acoelomate _____ have thin, solid bodies.
   A. roundworms   C. nematodes
   B. flatworms   D. hookworms

Constructed Response

10. **Open Ended** At what point(s) could the life cycle of a blood fluke be interrupted to prevent infestation of humans? Explain.

11. **Open Ended** How do the adaptations of a free-living flatworm and a parasitic flatworm differ? How do the adaptations of each ensure their long-term survival?

Thinking Critically

Use the diagram to answer question 12 and 13.

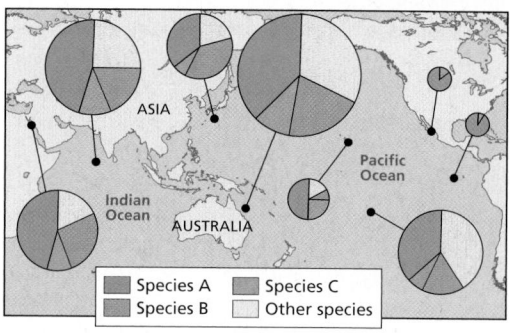

The map shows the worldwide distribution and biodiversity of coral reefs. The size of the circle is proportional to the total number of species that make up the reef.

12. **Interpret Data** Which three areas of Earth have the least biodiversity? How are species A, B, and C distributed in those areas?

13. **Infer** What might you infer about species C compared to the others? Why?

14. **REAL WORLD BIOCHALLENGE** Recent research shows that coral reefs suffer reduced diversity as a result of pollution, disease, warming water, hurricanes, and human destruction. Select an area of the world and investigate the health of the coral reefs found there. For information about your selected coral reefs, visit **in.bdol.glencoe.com**. What kinds of problems is the reef experiencing and why? Present the results of your research to your class in the form of a poster or a multimedia presentation.

 in.bdol.glencoe.com/chapter_test

ones with the least biodiversity, it must be more tolerant of adverse conditions and/or disease resistant.

14. Answers will vary depending on the area of the world selected.

RUBRIC

Evaluating Open-Ended Questions
Open-ended assessment questions are graded by using a multilevel rubric that guides you in assessing a student's knowledge of a particular concept. The following rubric is a sample scoring device.

Chapter 26 Assessment

End-of-Course Assessment Practice

All questions aligned and verified by The Princeton Review

Part 1 Multiple Choice

Use the table below to answer questions 15–17.

Effect of 1998 El Niño on Coral Reefs		
Region Destruction	Pre-1998 Coral Destruction	1998 Coral Destruction
Arabia	2%	33%
Indian Ocean (overall)	13%	46%
Australia, Papua New Guinea	1%	3%
Southeast Asia	16%	18%
Pacific Ocean (overall)	4%	5%
Caribbean	21%	1%
Global Total	11%	16%

15. The table shows coral destruction due to the 1998 El Niño warming was greatest in _____.

A. Arabia
B. the Caribbean
C. the Indian Ocean
D. Southeast Asia

16. Where did the warming effect of the 1998 El Niño have the least effect on coral?
A. Caribbean
B. Indian Ocean
C. Australia
D. Southeast Asia

17. _____ has suffered the least total destruction of coral.
A. Caribbean
B. Pacific Ocean
C. Australia
D. Arabia

Use the graph to answer questions 18 and 19.

Dimensions of Coral Reef Crevices

(graph: y-axis "Cavity area/entrance area" from 5 to 45; x-axis "Crevice diameter (m)" from 0.3 to 0.9)

Until recently, coral reef crevices that are less than 1.5 meters in diameter had not been studied as habitats for other organisms. The graph shows the relationship between crevice opening diameter and the ratio of internal cavity area to entrance area on a coral reef.

18. A group of scientists wants to survey all the life supported by a coral reef. It is important they study _____.
A. all crevices, large and small
B. only large crevices
C. only small crevices
D. only the reef surface

19. The size of a reef cavity with an opening of 0.7 m is _____ the cavity with an opening of 0.4 m.
A. larger than
B. smaller than
C. the same size as
D. smaller on the outside than

Part 2 Constructed Response/Grid In

Record your answers on your answer document.

20. Open Ended Mole crickets are pests of lawns and golf courses. Nematodes that often inhabit a cricket's digestive tract carry a bacterium that kills the cricket. As a greenskeeper for a golf course infested with mole crickets, what will you do to eliminate this pest?

21. Open Ended Synthetic optical fibers are important components of communication systems, but they degrade under water. A certain marine sponge produces light-conducting glass spicules that do not degrade when wet, therefore making them of high interest to optical fiber researchers. Assume you are a scientist interested in other properties of these sponge spicules. Describe an experiment you will do to compare the strength of sponge spicules to that of synthetic optical fibers.

 in.bdol.glencoe.com/standardized_test

CHAPTER 26 ASSESSMENT **719**

End-of-Course Assessment Practice

15. C **17.** C **19.** B
16. A **18.** A
20. You might use chemical pesticides or a biological control such as a nematode parasite.
21. Set up 200 synthetic optical fibers and 200 sponge spicules that are all the same length in an apparatus that will slowly apply measurable pressure to one side at a certain distance from the base of each spicule and fiber. Record the amount of pressure needed to break all the fibers and spicules. Accept answers that are based on good scientific reasoning.

FAST FILE

Answer Sheet A practice answer sheet can be found on p. 65 of *Unit 8 FAST FILE Resources.*

RUBRIC

SCORE	CRITERIA
4	A correct solution that is supported by well-developed, accurate explanations.
3	A generally correct solution, but may contain minor flaws in reasoning.

SCORE	CRITERIA
2	A partially correct interpretation and/or solution to the problem.
1	A correct solution with no supporting evidence or explanation.
0	An incorrect solution or no solution is given.

Indiana Academic Standards

Pages 718–719: B.1.15, B.1.18, B.1.43

Chapter 27 Organizer

Section Objectives	National Science Standards	State/Local Standards	Advanced Lab and Demo Planning
Section 27.1 1 session, 1/2 block 1. **Identify** the characteristics of mollusks. 2. **Compare** the adaptations of gastropod, bivalve, and cephalopod mollusks in their biomes.	UCP.1, UCP.2, UCP.5; A.1, A.2; C.3–6	**Indiana Standards** B.1.14, B.1.15, B.1.19, B.1.31	**Student Labs:** Problem-Solving Lab 27.1, p. 724 Additional Lab, p. 724: live land snails, clear plastic deli trays or large deli containers, wax marking pencils, lamp, crushed ice, ring stand, black construction paper, sandpaper, metric ruler MiniLab 27.1, p. 726 **Teacher Demonstration:** Quick Demo, p. 722: live land snail, petri dish, eraser of a pencil, lettuce
Section 27.2 2 sessions, 1 block 3. **Describe** the characteristics of segmented worms and their importance to the survival of these organisms. 4. **Compare and contrast** the classes of segmented worms.	UCP.1–5; A.1, A.2; C.3–6; D.2; E.1, E.2; F.1; G.1, G.2	**Indiana Standards** B.1.15, B.1.18, B.1.19, B.1.32	**Student Labs:** Problem-Solving Lab 27.2, p. 729 MiniLab 27.2, p. 730 Design Your Own BioLab, p. 734: See materials below.
End of Chapter Assessment Student Edition **Study Guide,** p. 737 **Content Assessment,** pp. 738–739		**Indiana Standards** B.1.14, B.1.15, B.1.17, B.1.19	**Student Lab:** Design Your Own BioLab, p. 734: live earthworms, glass pan, culture dishes, thermometer, dropper, ice, black paper, paper towels, sandpaper, warm tap water, water, penlight, ruler, cotton swabs, hand lens or stereomicroscope

Key to Teaching Strategies

L1 Level 1 activities should be appropriate for students with learning difficulties.

L2 Level 2 activities should be within the ability range of all students.

L3 Level 3 activities are designed for above-average students.

ELL ELL activities should be within the ability range of English Language Learners.

COOP LEARN Cooperative Learning activities are designed for small group work.

Legend

 Transparency   ⦿ CD-ROM   🎵 MP3   ▦ Videocassette   ⦿ DVD

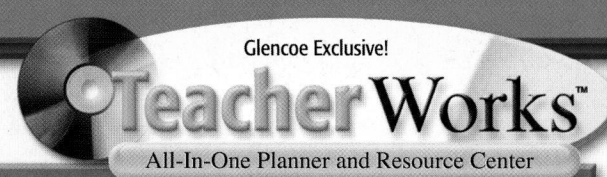
Glencoe Exclusive!
TeacherWorks™
All-In-One Planner and Resource Center

Reproducible Masters and Transparencies

Unit 8 *FAST FILE* Resources
MiniLab Worksheet, p. 69
Reinforcement and Study Guide in English, pp. 73–75
Reinforcement and Study Guide in Spanish, pp. 77–79
Transparency Worksheets, pp. 83, 85–88
Reading Essentials for Biology, Section 27.1
Laboratory Manual, pp. 167–170, 171–174
 Section Focus Transparency 67
Basic Concepts Transparency 48
Reteaching Skills Transparency 40

Unit 8 *FAST FILE* Resources
MiniLab Worksheet, p. 70
BioLab Worksheet, pp. 71–72
Reinforcement and Study Guide in English, p. 76
Reinforcement and Study Guide in Spanish, p. 80
Concept Mapping, p. 81
Critical Thinking/Problem Solving, p. 82
Transparency Worksheet, p. 84
Reading Essentials for Biology, Section 27.2
Section Focus Transparency 68

Unit 8 *FAST FILE* Resources
Chapter Assessment, pp. 89–94
Student Recording Sheet, p. 95

The Princeton Review **Reviewing Biology,** pp. 53–54

Technology

⦿ **Interactive Chalkboard CD-ROM: Section 27.1 Presentation**
⦿ **TeacherWorks™ CD-ROM**
🎵 **Guided Reading Audio Summaries MP3**

⦿ **Interactive Chalkboard CD-ROM: Section 27.2 Presentation**
⦿ **TeacherWorks™ CD-ROM**
🎵 **Guided Reading Audio Summaries MP3**
⦿ **Virtual Labs CD-ROM**
Virtual Lab: Earthworm Dissection

⦿ **Interactive Chalkboard: Chapter 27 Assessment**
⦿ **MindJogger Videoquizzes DVD/VHS**
⦿ **Exam*View*® Pro Test Bank CD-ROM**
⦿ **TeacherWorks™ CD-ROM**
⦿ **Succeeding on National Standards CD-ROM**

🖥 in.bdol.glencoe.com
/self_check_quiz
/vocabulary_puzzlemaker
/chapter_test
/standardized_test

Indicates materials created specifically for Indiana.

Chapter 27

Mollusks and Segmented Worms

Short on Time?

BIODIGEST The BioDigest at the end of this unit can be used as a(n):

- preview to introduce important unit concepts.
- overview if time does not permit teaching the entire chapter.
- review of key unit concepts.

What You'll Learn

- You will distinguish among the classes of mollusks and segmented worms.
- You will compare and contrast the adaptations of mollusks and segmented worms.

Why It's Important

Mollusks are an important food source for many animals, including humans. Some mollusks are filter feeders that clean impurities out of their watery environment. Earthworms turn, aerate, and fertilize the soil in which they live.

Understanding the Photo

Most mollusks and segmented worms are protected by a layer of mucus that covers their bodies. Snails secrete a mucous trail from glands in the foot. This mucous layer reduces friction and enables the snail to glide along the surface.

Understanding the Photo

Mucus is an important adaptation for some mollusks. These snails secrete a layer of mucus to reduce friction as they move along.

PowerPoint® Presentations

This CD-ROM is an editable Microsoft® PowerPoint® presentation that includes:
- Section presentations
- Section checks
- Image bank
- Hot links to Biology Online
- All transparencies

 Biology Online

Visit in.bdol.glencoe.com to
- study the entire chapter online
- access Web Links for more information and activities on mollusks and segmented worms
- review content with the Interactive Tutor and self-check quizzes

Two-Minute Chapter Launcher

Activity Display several seashells and have students infer what kinds of animals might have lived in them. Explain that the animals that lived in the shells are classified as mollusks. Make sure you have bivalve, gastropod, and chambered nautilus shells for examination.

If time permits, ask students who are familiar with seashores to explain what they know about the shells you have displayed. Ask others to explain what they know about snails based on their observations of snails in aquariums. **L2**

Section 27.1

Mollusks

Indiana Standards Standard B.1.15 Understand and explain that, in biological systems, structure and function must be considered together.

SECTION PREVIEW

Objectives
Identify the characteristics of mollusks.

Compare the adaptations of gastropod, bivalve, and cephalopod mollusks in their biomes.

Review Vocabulary
coelom: a fluid-filled body cavity completely surrounded by mesoderm (p. 684)

New Vocabulary
mantle
radula
open circulatory system
closed circulatory system
nephridia

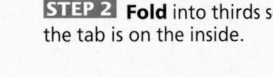
FOLDABLES™
Study Organizer

Mollusks Make the following Foldable to help you organize information on the three most common classes of mollusks.

STEP 1 **Fold** a vertical, 5-cm tab along the long edge of a sheet of paper.

STEP 2 **Fold** into thirds so the tab is on the inside.

STEP 3 **Open** the paper and **glue** the edges of the 5-cm tab to make a pocket. **Label** as shown.

Glue

Gastropods | Bivalves | Cephalopods

Identify and Describe As you read Chapter 27, collect notes and information about gastropods, bivalves, and cephalopods on 3 × 5-inch index cards or quarter sheets of notebook paper. Slide your notes into the appropriate pocket for quick reference.

What is a mollusk?

Figure 27.1
With at least 110 000 described species, phylum Mollusca is second in size only to insects and their relatives.

Slugs, snails, squids, and some animals that live in shells in the ocean or on the beach are all mollusks. These organisms belong to the phylum Mollusca. Members of this phylum range from the slow moving slug to the jet-propelled squid. Although most species live in the ocean, others live in freshwater and moist terrestrial habitats. Some aquatic mollusks, such as oysters, live much of their lives firmly attached to the ocean floor or to submerged docks or parts of boats. Others, such as the octopus, swim freely in the ocean. Land-dwelling slugs and snails can be found slowly moving over leaves on the forest floor. Examples of mollusks are shown in *Figure 27.1*.

A Snails, slugs, their shell-less relatives, and other one-shelled animals such as this limpet make up the largest class of mollusks.

B Predatory squids and octopuses are mollusks that have tentacles and do not have an external shell.

27.1 MOLLUSKS **721**

---

1 Focus

INTERACTIVE CHALKBOARD
PowerPoint® Presentations

Bellringer
Section Focus Transparency 67

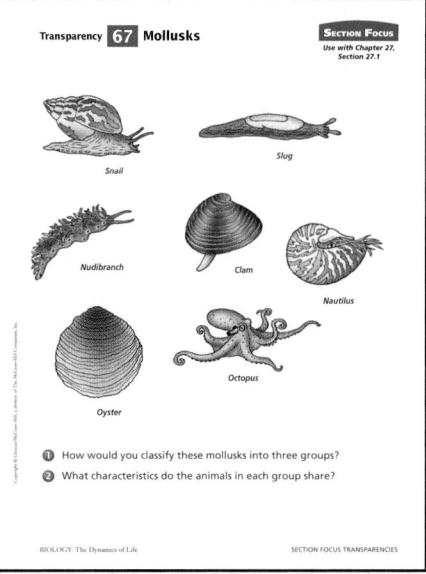
Transparency **67** Mollusks

SECTION FOCUS
Use with Chapter 27, Section 27.1

Snail

Slug

Nudibranch

Clam

Nautilus

Octopus

Oyster

① How would you classify these mollusks into three groups?
② What characteristics do the animals in each group share?

BIOLOGY: The Dynamics of Life   SECTION FOCUS TRANSPARENCIES

FOLDABLES™
For an additional Foldables activity idea, see the Chapter 27 Foldables page in *Unit 8 FAST FILE Resources.*

RESOURCE MANAGER

Unit 8 Fast File Resources
MiniLab Worksheet, p. 69
Reinforcement and Study Guide in English, pp. 73–75
Reinforcement and Study Guide in Spanish, pp. 77–79
Transparency Worksheets, pp. 83, 85–88

Reading Essentials for Biology, Section 27.1
Laboratory Manual, pp. 167–170, 171–174
Section Focus Transparency 67
Basic Concepts Transparency 48
Reteaching Skills Transparency 40

Indiana Academic Standards

Pages 720–721: B.1.15, B.1.31

2 Teach

Caption Question Answer
Figure 27.2 Both are mollusks with bilateral symmetry, a coelom, a digestive tract with two openings, and a mantle. A snail has a well-defined head, a large foot, and an external shell, whereas a squid does not have a well-defined head, it has tentacles instead of a foot, and its shell is small and internal.

✔Reading Check The mantle surrounds and protects the internal organs of a mollusk. The mantle also secretes the shell that protects the mollusk's body.

Figure 27.2
A mollusk has a soft body composed of a foot, a mantle, and a visceral mass that contains internal organs. Some mollusks also have a shell. **Evaluate** *Compare the similarities and differences in the structures of a snail and a squid.*

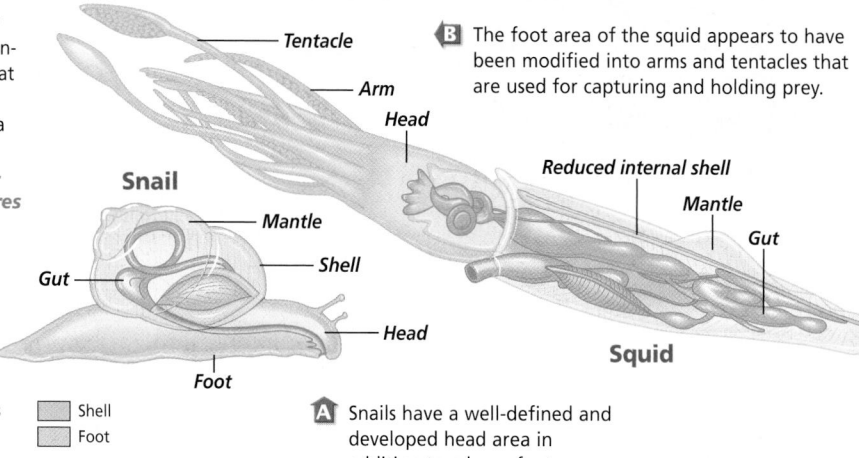

B The foot area of the squid appears to have been modified into arms and tentacles that are used for capturing and holding prey.

Tentacle — Arm — Head — Reduced internal shell — Mantle — Gut — Squid

Snail — Mantle — Shell — Gut — Head — Foot

| Visceral mass | Shell |
| Mantle | Foot |

A Snails have a well-defined and developed head area in addition to a large foot.

Word Origin

mollusk from the Latin word *molluscus,* meaning "soft"; Mollusks are animals with a digestive tract with two openings, a muscular foot, and a mantle.

Some mollusks have shells, and others, including slugs and squids, are adapted to life without a hard covering. All mollusks have bilateral symmetry, a coelom, a digestive tract with two openings, a muscular foot, and a mantle. The **mantle** (MAN tuhl) is a membrane that surrounds the internal organs of the mollusk. In shelled mollusks, the mantle secretes the shell.

Although mollusks look different from one another on the outside, they share many similarities on the inside. You can see the similarities and the differences in these body areas in *Figure 27.2* as you compare a snail and a squid.

✔Reading Check **Infer** how the mantle protects mollusks.

Figure 27.3
Look at the clam shell in this photo and locate the small hole on its edge. This tiny hole was made by the radula of a snail that ate the clam, leaving its shell behind to tell the tale of the clam's fate.

722

How mollusks obtain food

Have you ever watched a snail clean algae from the sides of an aquarium? Snails, like many mollusks, use a rasping structure called a radula to obtain food. A **radula** (RA juh luh), located within the mouth of a mollusk, is a tonguelike organ with rows of teeth. The radula is used to drill, scrape, grate, or cut food. *Figure 27.3* shows the results of the use of a radula. How does a radula cut food? Find out in *Figure 27.4.* Octopuses and squids are predators that use their radulas to tear up the food that they capture with their tentacles. Other mollusks are grazers and some are filter feeders. Bivalves do not have radulas; they filter food from the water.

Reproduction in mollusks

Mollusks reproduce sexually and most have separate sexes. In most aquatic species, eggs and sperm are released at the same time into the water, where external fertilization takes place. Many gastropods that live on land, and a few bivalves, are hermaphrodites and produce both eggs and sperm. Fertilization is internal.

A Snail

Figure 27.4

Snails belong to the largest class of mollusks, the gastropods. Gastropods include periwinkles, conches, whelks, limpets, abalones, and slugs. A snail moves by gliding along on a thin layer of mucus secreted by a gland in the foot. You may have seen the silvery trails of a snail in a garden. **Critical Thinking** *What other functions does mucus have for a snail?*

Snail

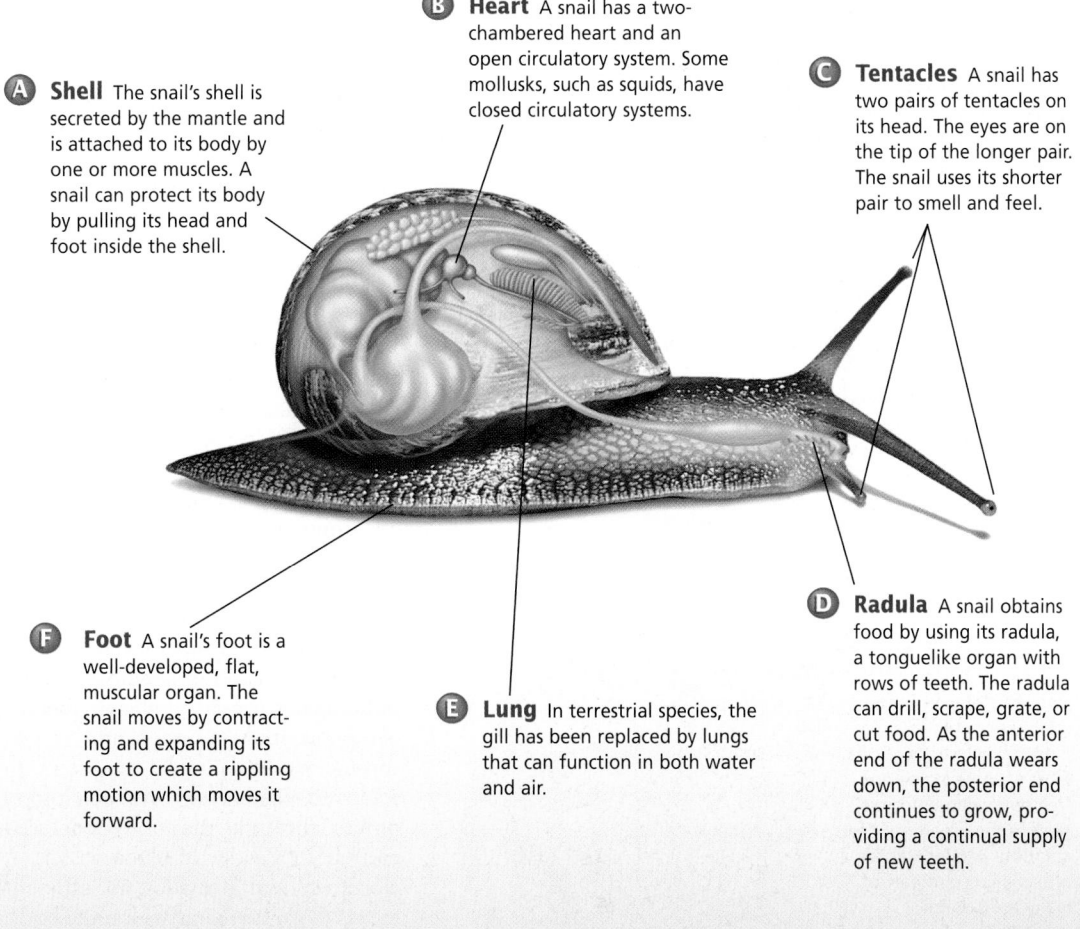

B Heart A snail has a two-chambered heart and an open circulatory system. Some mollusks, such as squids, have closed circulatory systems.

A Shell The snail's shell is secreted by the mantle and is attached to its body by one or more muscles. A snail can protect its body by pulling its head and foot inside the shell.

C Tentacles A snail has two pairs of tentacles on its head. The eyes are on the tip of the longer pair. The snail uses its shorter pair to smell and feel.

F Foot A snail's foot is a well-developed, flat, muscular organ. The snail moves by contracting and expanding its foot to create a rippling motion which moves it forward.

E Lung In terrestrial species, the gill has been replaced by lungs that can function in both water and air.

D Radula A snail obtains food by using its radula, a tonguelike organ with rows of teeth. The radula can drill, scrape, grate, or cut food. As the anterior end of the radula wears down, the posterior end continues to grow, providing a continual supply of new teeth.

27.1 MOLLUSKS **723**

Purpose

Students study the functions of the organs of a gastropod.

Teaching Strategies

■ Ask students to explain the functions of the snail's tentacles.

■ Explain that the snail moves by contracting and expanding its foot to glide along a layer of mucus.

■ Ask students to recall the differences between an open circulatory system and a closed circulatory system.

Visual Learning

Have students examine the features shown. Ask them to identify the external features on a live snail.

Critical Thinking

Mucus protects the snail's body, keeps it moist, and enables the snail to adhere to surfaces.

CULTURAL DIVERSITY

Pearl Cultivation In your lessons on mollusk biology, discuss with students how pearls are formed and describe the pearl cultivation industry in Japan. Since 1893, pearl farming has been one of Japan's most famous industries.

To add interest, introduce students to the ama women of Japan. The ama are diving women who collect pearls and valuable mollusks from the ocean. Diving women have operated in Japan for more than 2000 years. The divers take their name from the word *ama,* which in the ancient Japanese language meant "ocean" or "sky." The *ama* of Japan have been known to dive to depths greater than 50 meters hundreds of times daily without the use of snorkels or air tanks.

Indiana Academic Standards

Pages 722–723: B.1.15

Purpose
Students will study the life cycle of larval development in a fresh-water mussel.

Process Skills
think critically, analyze data, interpret scientific drawings

Teaching Strategies
Remind students that all mollusks do not follow the pattern of reproduction and development illustrated here.

Thinking Critically
1. sperm
2. They die.
3. They mature into juvenile clams.
4. Although the animal produces many glochidia, most do not find a suitable host and thus do not survive to adult stage.

Modified Assessment
Knowledge Provide students with a sample of glochidia but do not tell them what they are looking at. Have them examine glochidia under the microscope and identify what the organisms are. Preserved glochidia are available from biological supply houses. Use the Performance Task Assessment List for Making Observations and Inferences in **PASC**, p. 89. **L2** **ELL**

Problem-Solving Lab 27.1

Observe and Infer
How do freshwater clams reproduce?

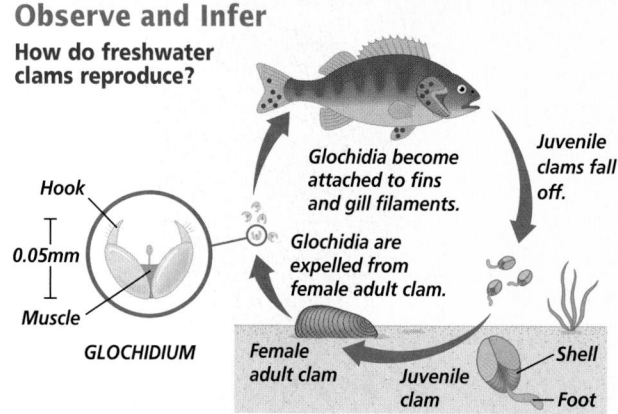

Hook

0.05mm

Muscle

GLOCHIDIUM

Glochidia become attached to fins and gill filaments.

Glochidia are expelled from female adult clam.

Juvenile clams fall off.

Female adult clam

Juvenile clam

Shell

Foot

Solve the Problem
Freshwater clams are either male or female. Immature larvae, called glochidia, are formed following fertilization within adult female clams' reproductive systems. Glochidia eventually are released in the surrounding water.

Thinking Critically
1. **Infer** What cell type must enter a female clam's body in order for glochidia to form?
2. **Hypothesize** Glochidia attach to and feed off of a specific fish host. What happens to glochidia if no host is available?
3. **Describe** How do glochidia change while attached to their host?
4. **Infer** It is estimated that a single clam can release over 1 000 000 glochidia. How might this be an adaptation to a life cycle that includes a parasitic stage?

Figure 27.5
One larval stage of most mollusks resembles a spinning top with tufts of cilia. Most of these larvae are free swimming before settling to the ocean floor for adult life. Mollusk larvae are an important part of many food chains.

Find out more about reproduction in mollusks by reading the *Problem-Solving Lab* on this page.

Although members of the phylum Mollusca have different appearances as adults, they all share similar developmental patterns. One larval stage of most mollusks is similar, as you can see in *Figure 27.5*.

Some marine mollusks have free-swimming larvae that propel themselves by cilia. Most marine snails and bivalves have another developmental stage called a veliger in which the beginnings of a foot, shell, and mantle can be seen.

Nervous control in mollusks
Mollusks have simple nervous systems that coordinate their movement and behavior. Some more advanced mollusks have a brain. Most mollusks have paired eyes that range from simple cups that detect light to the complex eyes of octopuses that have irises, pupils, and retinas similar to the eyes of humans.

Circulation in mollusks
Mollusks have a well-developed circulatory system that usually includes a two- or three-chambered heart. In most mollusks, the heart pumps blood through an open circulatory system. In an **open circulatory system,** the blood moves through vessels and into open spaces around the body organs. This adaptation exposes body organs directly to blood that contains nutrients and oxygen, and removes metabolic wastes. Some mollusks, such as octopuses, move nutrients and oxygen through a closed circulatory system. In a **closed circulatory system,** blood moves through the body enclosed entirely in a series of blood vessels. A closed system provides an efficient means of gas exchange within the body.

724 MOLLUSKS AND SEGMENTED WORMS

Additional Lab

Comparing Snail Speeds

Purpose
Students will compare the speed at which snails move under various environmental conditions.

Materials
live land snails, clear plastic deli trays or large deli containers, wax marking pencil, lamp, crushed ice, ring stand, black construction paper, sandpaper, metric ruler

Procedure
CAUTION: *Make sure students handle the snails in a humane manner. Have students wash their hands thoroughly with soap and water after completing the lab.*
1. Make a table for distances traveled by the snail on a smooth surface, a rough surface, in cold conditions, and in warm conditions.
2. Form a hypothesis about the conditions under which the snail will move the fastest.
3. With the wax marking pencil, mark an X in the middle of your tray. Place the snail on this X and measure how far it travels in 3 minutes.
4. Place a piece of black construction paper over the tray so that the snail is in

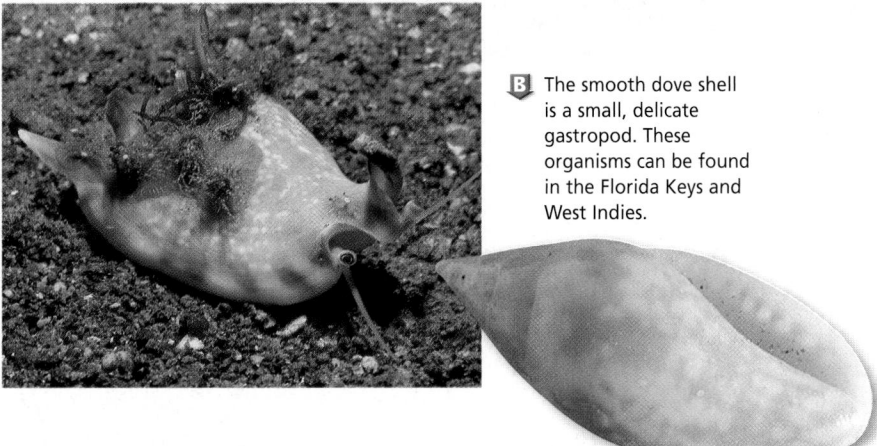

Figure 27.6
Shelled gastropods vary from petite, thin-shelled species to large animals with thick shells.

A The pink conch is a large gastropod with a thick shell.

B The smooth dove shell is a small, delicate gastropod. These organisms can be found in the Florida Keys and West Indies.

Respiration in mollusks

Most mollusks have respiratory structures called gills. Gills are specialized parts of the mantle that consist of a system of filamentous projections that contain a rich supply of blood for the transport of gases. Gills increase the surface area through which gases can diffuse. In land snails and slugs, the mantle cavity appears to have evolved into a primitive lung.

Excretion in mollusks

Mollusks are the oldest known animals to have evolved excretory structures called nephridia. **Nephridia** (nih FRIH dee uh) are organs that remove metabolic wastes from an animal's body. Mollusks have one or two nephridia that collect wastes from the coelom, which is located around the heart only. Wastes are discharged into the mantle cavity, and expelled from the body by the pumping of the gills.

Diversity of Mollusks

Phylum Mollusca is large and diverse. Three mollusk classes—Gastropoda, Bivalvia, and Cephalopoda—include the most common and well-known species.

Gastropods: One-shelled mollusks

The largest class of mollusks is Gastropoda, or the stomach-footed mollusks. The name comes from the way the animal's large foot is positioned under the rest of its body. Most species of gastropods have a shell. Other gastropod species, such as slugs, have no shell.

Shelled gastropods include snails, abalones, conches, periwinkles, whelks, limpets, cowries, and cones. They can be found in freshwater, saltwater, or moist terrestrial habitats. Shelled gastropods may be plant eaters, predators, or parasites. *Figure 27.6* shows two examples of shelled gastropods.

Instead of being protected by a shell, the body of a slug is protected by a thick layer of mucus. Colorful sea slugs, also called nudibranchs, are protected in another way. When certain species of sea slugs feed on jellyfishes, they incorporate the poisonous nematocysts of the jellyfish into their own tissues without causing these cells to discharge. Any fishes trying to eat the sea slugs are repelled when the nematocysts discharge into the unlucky predator. The bright colors of these gastropods warn predators of the potential danger, as shown in *Figure 27.7*.

Figure 27.7
Sea slugs such as this *Chromodoris* species live in the ocean. They eat hydras, sea anemones, and sea squirts. **Infer** *How does color benefit this sea slug?*

Purpose
Students will use a dichotomous key to identify mollusks based on their shells.

Process Skills
observe and infer, compare and contrast, classify, use a dichotomous key

Teaching Strategies
■ Make an overhead transparency of a dichotomous key. Use the transparency to demonstrate how a dichotomous key is used.
■ Ask students who collect shells to bring in their shell collections and identify the shells for their classmates.

Expected Results
Students will classify the pictured shells using the dichotomous key provided.

Analysis
1. A dichotomous key divides a group into smaller and smaller groups until each organism is identified.
2. easy: 1, 2, 3, 4; more difficult: 5, because it requires more interpretation and closer comparison

Modified Assessment
Skill Give students a simple dichotomous key for several shells. Ask them to use the key to identify the shells. Use the Performance Task Assessment List for Making and Using a Classification System in **PASC,** p. 121. **L1**

Physical Science Connection
(p. 727) In both cases, objects move as a result of the reaction force. A squid controls the direction of propulsion by orienting the siphon in a particular direction. A rocket engine forces the gases produced by the burning rocket fuel out of the back of the rocket. The gases, in turn, exert a force on the rocket in the forward direction.

MiniLab 27.1

Compare and Contrast

Identifying Mollusks Have you ever collected shells from a beach and wondered what they were? Use the following dichotomous key to determine the names of the shells.

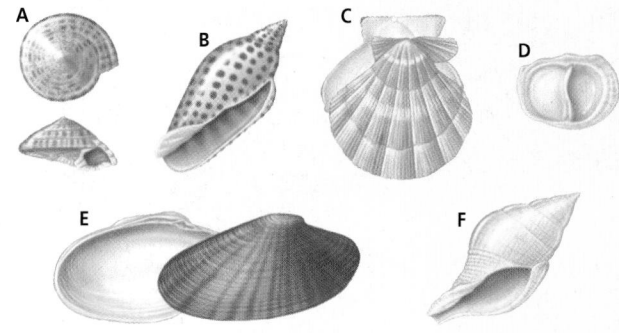

Procedure
■ To use a dichotomous key, begin with a choice from the first pair of descriptions.
■ Follow the instructions for the next choice. Notice that either a scientific name can be found at the end of each description, or directions will tell you to go on to another numbered set of choices.

1A	One shell	Gastropods see 2
1B	Two shells	Bivalves see 5
2A	Shelf inside shell	Common Atlantic slipper: *Crepidula fornicata*
2B	No shelf inside shell	see 3
3A	Flat coil	Sundial shell: *Architectonica nobilis*
3B	Thick coil	see 4
4A	Spotted surface	Junonia shell: *Scaphella junonia*
4B	Lined surface	Banded tulip shell: *Fasciolaria hunteria*
5A	Polished surface	Sunray shell: *Macrocallista nimbosa*
5B	Rough surface	Lion's paw shell: *Lyropecten nodosus*

Analysis
1. **Infer** How is a dichotomous key used to identify a variety of organisms?
2. **Evaluate** What shell features were easy to pick out using the key? What features were more difficult?

Figure 27.8
In bivalves, the mantle forms two siphons, one for incoming water and one for water that is excreted.

726 MOLLUSKS AND SEGMENTED WORMS

Bivalves: Two-shelled mollusks

Two-shelled mollusks such as clams, oysters, and scallops belong to the class Bivalvia, illustrated in *Figure 27.8.* Most bivalves are marine, but a few species live in freshwater habitats. Bivalves occur in a range of sizes. Some are less than 1 mm in length and others, such as the tropical giant clam, may be 1.5 m long. Bivalves have no distinct head or radula. Most use their large, muscular foot for burrowing in the mud or sand at the bottom of the ocean or a lake. A ligament, like a hinge, connects their two shells, called valves; strong muscles allow the valves to open and close over the soft body. See if you can identify the shells pictured in the *MiniLab* by using the dichotomous key given.

One of the main differences between gastropods and bivalves is that bivalves are filter feeders that obtain food by filtering small particles from the surrounding water. Bivalve mollusks have several adaptations for filter feeding, including gill cilia that beat to draw water in through an incurrent siphon. As water moves over the gills, food and sediments become trapped in mucus. Cilia that line the gills push food particles to the mouth. Cilia also act as sorting devices. Large particles, sediment, and anything else that is rejected is transported to the mantle where it is expelled through

---

CHALLENGE ACTIVITY

Bivalve Muscles Ask students to design an experiment to compare the strength of muscles in bivalves such as clams and scallops. Remind them to plan to collect quantitative data. Clam muscles should be stronger than scallop muscles.

Scallops have one adductor muscle that is used mainly for locomotion. Clams have two adductor muscles that are used mainly to hold their valves together. **L3**

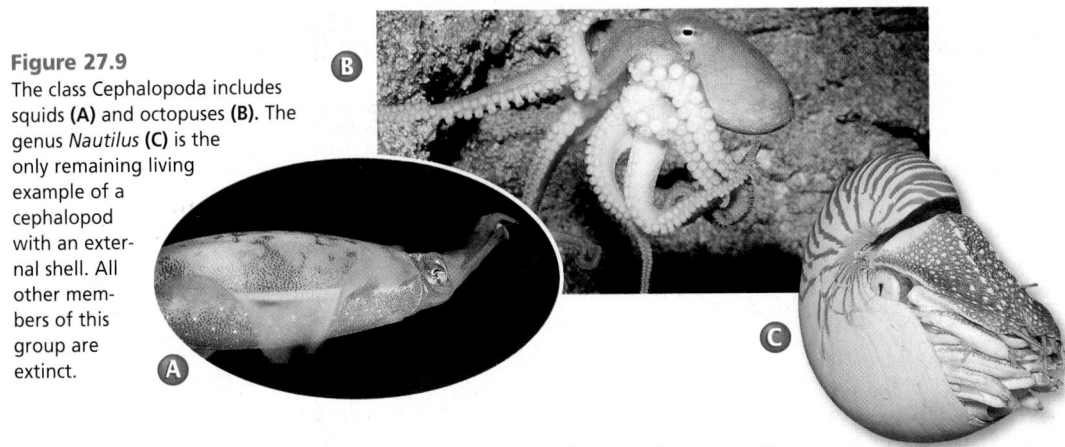

Figure 27.9
The class Cephalopoda includes squids **(A)** and octopuses **(B)**. The genus *Nautilus* **(C)** is the only remaining living example of a cephalopod with an external shell. All other members of this group are extinct.

the excurrent siphon, or to the foot, where it is eliminated from the animal's body.

Cephalopods: Head-footed mollusks

The head-footed mollusks are marine organisms in the class Cephalopoda. This class includes the octopus, squid, cuttlefish, and chambered nautilus, as shown in *Figure 27.9*. The only cephalopod with a shell is the chambered nautilus, but some species, such as the cuttlefish, have a reduced internal shell. Scientists consider the cephalopods to have the most complex structures and to be the most recently evolved of all mollusks.

In cephalopods, the foot has evolved into tentacles with suckers, hooks, or adhesive structures. Cephalopods

swim or walk over the ocean floor in pursuit of their prey, capturing it with their tentacles. Once tentacles have captured prey, it is brought to the mouth and bitten with beaklike jaws. Then the food is torn and pulled into the mouth by the radula.

Like bivalves, cephalopods have siphons that expel water. These mollusks can expel water forcefully in any direction, and move quickly by jet propulsion. Squids can attain speeds of 20 m per second using this system of movement. You may be aware that cephalopods use jet propulsion to escape from danger. Squids and octopuses also can release a dark fluid to cloud the water. This "ink" helps to confuse their predators so they can make a quick escape.

Physical Science Connection

Newton's third law For every force applied by an object, there is an equal but opposite force applied on the object. A squid expels water by pushing on the water. The water then pushes on the squid, propelling it in the direction opposite the water stream. Compare and contrast this example of Newton's third law with what happens during a rocket launch.

3 Assess

DAILY INTERVENTION

Check for Understanding
Have students explain how mollusks are more complex than other animals they have studied.

Reteach
Visual-Spatial Have students make a table describing mollusk traits with these headings: *Phylum, Representative Organisms, Symmetry, Habitat, Food Getting, Taking in Oxygen, Reproduction,* and *Protection.* **L2**

Resources
For more practice, use *Reading Essentials for Biology,* Section 27.1.

Extension

Ask students to prepare illustrated reports on pearl cultivation. **L1**

 Assessment

Portfolio Ask students to write a description of a habitat that is suited to a specific mollusk from each group. Have students explain how each organism is adapted to its habitat. **L2**

Indiana Academic Standards

Pages 726–727: B.1.15

Section Assessment

Understanding Main Ideas
1. Describe how mucus is important to some mollusks.
2. What adaptations make cephalopods effective predators in an aquatic biome?
3. Compare and contrast filter feeding with obtaining food by using a radula in an aquatic biome.
4. Compare how squids and sea slugs protect themselves in the marine biome.

Thinking Critically
5. How are the methods of movement for the snail, clam, and squid related to the structure of each one's foot?

SKILL REVIEW

6. **Get the Big Picture** Develop a classification key to identify the similarities and differences of the three classes of mollusks discussed. For more help, refer to *Get the Big Picture* in the **Skill Handbook**.

 in.bdol.glencoe.com/self_check_quiz

27.1 MOLLUSKS **727**

Section Assessment

1. Mucus protects some mollusks. It also enables mollusks to stick to surfaces and slide easily through their habitats.
2. jet-propulsion-type swimming, tentacles with suckers, large eyes with a well-developed nervous system, radula for tearing apart prey
3. A filter feeder takes in water and filters out food. The radula is a tonguelike organ that scrapes food from surfaces.
4. Squids protect themselves by their ability to move quickly away from danger. Sea slugs incorporate consumed toxic materials into their tissues.
5. The muscular foot of the snail secretes mucus on which the snail glides slowly.

The clam can burrow into sand with its muscular foot. The squid's foot is modified into tentacles that aid in movement.
6. Students' keys should include information found in the chapter under headings dealing with gastropods, bivalves, and cephalopods.

1 Focus

Bellringer
Section Focus Transparency 68

Transparency **68** Segmented Worms

Earthworm   *Roundworm*

① How does the body of the earthworm differ from that of the roundworm?

② How might this difference be an advantage?

BIOLOGY: The Dynamics of Life   SECTION FOCUS TRANSPARENCIES

Finding Main Ideas
Answers to Questions

1. The basic body plan of a segmented worm is a tube within a tube. The internal tube, which is suspended within the coelem, is the digestive tract.

2. Food and soil are taken in by the mouth, passed to the gizzard where they are ground, and then passed to the intestine. Undigested material and solid waste pass out of the body through the anus.

3. Most leeches suck blood or body fluids from the bodies of their hosts.

Indiana Academic Standards

Pages 728–729: B.1.15, B.1.19

Section 27.2

Segmented Worms

Indiana Standards Standard B.1.15 Understand and explain that, in biological systems, structure and function must be considered together.

SECTION PREVIEW

Objectives

Describe the characteristics of segmented worms and their importance to the survival of these organisms.

Compare and contrast the classes of segmented worms.

Review Vocabulary
parasitism: symbiotic relationship in which one organism benefits at the expense of the other species (p. 44)

New Vocabulary
setae
gizzard

Worms Are Nature's Gardeners

Finding Main Ideas As you read through the section about segmented worms, answer the following questions on a separate sheet of paper.

1. What is the basic body plan of a segmented worm?

2. Describe the digestive process of an earthworm.

3. Why are some leeches considered parasites?

Earthworm

What is a segmented worm?

Segmented worms are classified in the phylum Annelida. They include leeches and bristleworms, shown in *Figure 27.10*, as well as earthworms. Segmented worms are bilaterally symmetrical and have a coelom and two body openings. Some have a larval stage that is similar to the larval stages of certain mollusks, suggesting a common ancestor.

The basic body plan of segmented worms is a tube within a tube. The internal tube, suspended within the coelom, is the digestive tract. Food is taken in by the mouth, an opening in the anterior end of the worm, and wastes are released through the anus, an opening at the posterior end.

Most segmented worms have tiny bristles called **setae** (SEE tee) on each segment. The setae help segmented worms move by providing a way to anchor their bodies in the soil so each segment can move the animal along.

Segmented worms can be found in most environments, except in the frozen soil of the polar regions and the dry sand and soil of the deserts.

Figure 27.10
The phylum Annelida contains about 15 000 species.

A Leeches live in marine, freshwater, or terrestrial habitats. Suckers are found on one or both ends of the body.

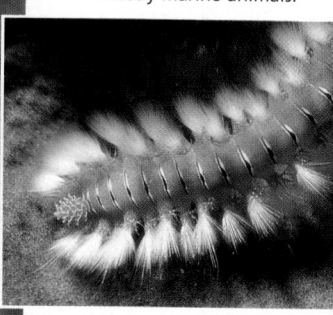

B Bristleworms have distinct heads, eyes, and tentacles. They are mostly marine animals.

728

RESOURCE MANAGER

Unit 8 Fast File Resources
MiniLab Worksheet, p. 70
BioLab Worksheet, pp. 71–72
Reinforcement and Study Guide in English, p. 76
Reinforcement and Study Guide in Spanish, p. 80

Concept Mapping, p. 81
Critical Thinking/Problem Solving, p. 82
Transparency Worksheet, p. 84
Reading Essentials for Biology, Section 27.2
Section Focus Transparency 68

Earthworms are just one of about 15 000 species of segmented worms that live in soil, freshwater, and the sea. Can you identify a segmented worm? Find out by reading the *Problem-Solving Lab* on this page.

Segmentation supports diversified functions

The most distinguishing characteristic of segmented worms is their cylindrical bodies that are divided into ringed segments, as seen in the worm in *Figure 27.11*. In most species, this segmentation continues internally as each segment is separated from the others by a body partition. Segmentation is an important adaptation for movement because each segment has its own muscles, allowing shortening and lengthening of the body.

Segmentation also allows for specialization of body tissues. Groups of segments may be adapted for a particular function. Certain segments have modifications for functions such as sensing and reproduction.

Nervous system

Segmented worms have simple nervous systems in which organs in anterior segments have become modified for sensing the environment. Some sensory organs are sensitive to light, and eyes with lenses and retinas have evolved in certain species. In some species there is a brain located in an anterior segment. Nerve cords connect the brain to nerve centers called ganglia, located in each segment. You can find out how earthworms respond to their environment in the *BioLab* at the end of this chapter.

Circulation and respiration

Segmented worms have a closed circulatory system. Blood carrying oxygen to and carbon dioxide from body cells

Problem-Solving Lab 27.2

Classify

When is it an annelid? You are on a zoological research expedition to South America. As the invertebrate specialist, you are asked by your fellow scientists to classify a number of animals.

Solve the Problem

Data Table	
Animal	**Characteristics**
A	Externally segmented body, no internal segments
B	No coelom, but has internal segments
C	Lives in water, has two body openings, sexes are separate
D	Backbone present, has digestive, circulatory, excretory systems
E	Both male and female reproductive organs present
F	Externally segmented body, has internal segments

Thinking Critically

Analyze Which are annelids, which are not, and which require more study to decide? Explain your answer for each animal.

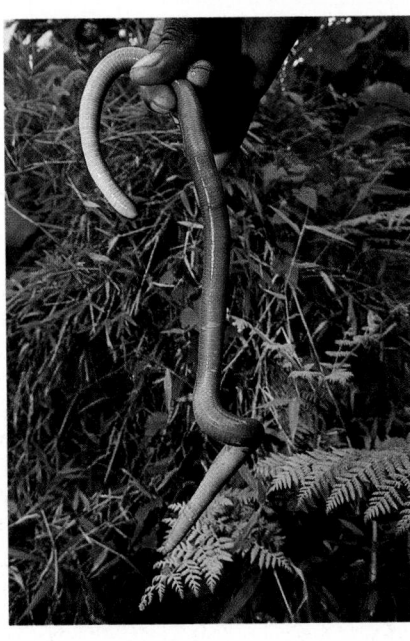

Figure 27.11
Segmentation is easily seen in earthworms. The giant earthworm of Australia can be more than 3 m long.
Infer *Why is segmentation an important adaptation?*

27.2 SEGMENTED WORMS **729**

2 Teach

Problem-Solving Lab 27.2

Purpose
Students will determine if certain traits are or are not associated with the phylum Annelida.

Process Skills
apply concepts, think critically, compare and contrast, draw a conclusion

Teaching Strategies
- Be sure that students have read the entire section on annelids before attempting to do this lab.
- Review any terms that may not be familiar to students.

Thinking Critically
A—Undecided; traits may apply to other phyla.
B—No; annelids have a coelom.
C—Undecided; traits may apply to other phyla as well as Annelida.
D—No; annelids are not vertebrates.
E—Undecided; traits may apply to other phyla as well as annelids.
F—Yes; true only of annelids

Assessment
Knowledge Ask students to list traits that are specific to Annelida and no other phyla. Ask students to list traits that are common to other phyla as well as Annelida. Use the Performance Task Assessment List for Making and Using a Classification System in **PASC**, p. 121. **L2**

Caption Question Answer
Figure 27.11 It allows for movement and specialization of body tissues.

DESIGN YOUR OWN BioLab

The BioLab at the end of the chapter can be used at this point in the lesson.

PROJECT

Earthworm Terrariums Ask each group of students to prepare a large jar as a terrarium for earthworms. Have them place rocks on the bottom for drainage. Then, have students alternate layers of moist sand and topsoil on top of the rocks. Have them add about six to eight worms to the jar, then cover the top layer of soil with dead leaves and grass. Instruct students to tape black paper to the outside of the jar. After several days, have them remove the paper and observe what happened to the leaves, grass, and soil layers. Have them also describe any tunnels they observe. **L1**
ELL **COOP LEARN**

MiniLab 27.2

Purpose

Students will use a diagram of an earthworm's internal anatomy to draw cross-section views.

Process Skills

analyze data, interpret scientific drawings, observe and infer

Teaching Strategies

- Review the meaning of a cross-section view. Use one small fireplace log cut longitudinally and another log cut in cross-sectional pieces to illustrate this concept.
- Point out to students that the segments are numbered.
- Make copies of an outline diagram of incomplete worm cross-sectional views for student use.

Expected Results

Student diagrams will reflect their ability to translate information from a longitudinal view to a cross-sectional view.

Analysis

Segment 8 will show muscles, esophagus, dorsal and ventral blood vessels, and nerve cord. Segment 14 will show crop, nephridia, blood vessels, nerve cord, and muscle layers.

Assessment

Skill Have students make cross-section diagrams of segments 3 and 16. Use the Performance Task Assessment List for Scientific Drawing in **PASC**, p. 127. `L2` `ELL`

✓ **Reading Check** Dry conditions might cause segmented worms to move to a location where there is more moisture because they exchange gases through their moist skin. If they cannot reach a moist area, they might die if their skin completely dries out.

MiniLab 27.2

Interpret Scientific Diagrams

A Different View of an Earthworm What does an earthworm look like internally? You could look at it many different ways—from the dorsal or ventral side, along the length of the animal (a longitudinal view), or in cross section through a segment.

Procedure

1. Diagram A illustrates a longitudinal dorsal view of the internal organs of an earthworm. Note that the segments are numbered.
2. Use Diagram B as a guide to how a cross section slice appears through segment 9.

1 2 3 4 5 6 7 8 9 10 11 12 13 14 15 16 — Brain — Pharynx — Esophagus — Blood vessel — Crop — Nephridia

— Muscle layers — Blood vessel — Esophagus — Nephridia — Ventral nerve cord

Analysis

Describe Make your own cross-section diagrams of segments 8 and 14. Label all the parts shown in your diagrams.

---

flows through vessels to reach all parts of the body. Segmented worms must live in water or in wet areas on land because they also exchange gases directly through their moist skin.

✓ **Reading Check** **Infer** how dry conditions affect segmented worms.

Digestion and excretion

Segmented worms have a complete internal digestive tract that runs the length of the body. Food and soil taken in by the mouth eventually pass to the **gizzard.** In the gizzard, a muscular sac and hard particles help grind soil and food before they pass into the intestine. Undigested material and solid wastes pass out the worm's body through the

---

anus. Segmented worms have two nephridia in almost every segment that collect waste products and transport them through the coelom and out of the body. Find out what an earthworm eats in *Figure 27.12.*

Reproduction in segmented worms

Earthworms and leeches are hermaphrodites, producing both eggs and sperm. During mating, two worms exchange sperm. Each worm forms a capsule for the eggs and sperm. The eggs are fertilized in the capsule, then the capsule slips off the worm and is left behind in the soil. In two to three weeks, young worms emerge from the eggs.

Bristleworms and their relatives have separate sexes and reproduce sexually. Usually eggs and sperm are released into the seawater, where fertilization takes place. Bristleworm larvae hatch in the sea and become part of the plankton. Once segment development begins, the worm settles to the bottom.

Diversity of Segmented Worms

The phylum Annelida includes three classes: class Oligochaeta, earthworms; class Polychaeta, bristleworms and their relatives; and class Hirudinea, leeches.

Earthworms

Earthworms are the most well-known annelids because they can be seen easily by most people. Although earthworms have a definite anterior and posterior section, they do not have a distinct head. Earthworms have only a few setae on each segment. What does an earthworm look like internally? You can find out in the *MiniLab* on this page.

TECH PREP

Earthworm Importance Ask a group of students to interview a farmer or an agriculture professor about the importance of earthworms in agriculture. Have them prepare a PowerPoint® presentation that could be presented to students at their local elementary school. `L2`

Virtual Lab

CD-ROM Students will examine the virtual anatomy of an earthworm in *Earthworm Dissection.*

An Earthworm

Figure 27.12
As an earthworm burrows through soil, it loosens, aerates, and fertilizes the soil. Burrows provide passageways for plant roots and improve drainage of the soil. **Critical Thinking** *In what way is segmentation an important advantage in earthworm movement?*

Earthworm

A **Mouth** An earthworm takes soil into its mouth, the beginning of the digestive tract.

B **Crop** The crop is a sac that holds soil temporarily before it is passed into the gizzard.

C **Gizzard** The gizzard grinds the organic matter, or food, into small pieces so that the nutrients in the food can be absorbed as it passes through the intestine. Undigested food and any remaining soil are eliminated through the anus.

G **Setae** An earthworm alternately contracts sets of longitudinal and circular muscles to move. First it contracts its longitudinal muscles on several segments, which bunch up. This causes tiny setae to protrude, anchoring the worm in the soil. Then the earthworm's circular muscles contract, the setae are withdrawn, and the worm moves forward.

D **Circulatory system** The closed circulatory system consists of enlarged blood vessels that are heavily muscled. When these muscles contract, they help pump blood through the system, much as a heart does in other animals.

E **Nervous system** An earthworm has a system of nerve fibers in each segment. These are connected by ventral nerve cords to a simple brain located near the mouth.

F **Nephridia** Nephridia are excretory structures that eliminate metabolic wastes from nearly every segment.

Purpose
Students will examine the internal structures of the earthworm and their functions.

Teaching Strategies
Ask students to write a paragraph that explains how earthworm bodies show more complexity than the bodies of flatworms and roundworms. Challenge your advanced students to make a table that compares earthworms with the free-living flatworms and roundworms. Students should include the following in their tables: digestion, locomotion, circulation, excretion, and sensory functions. **L3**

Visual Learning
Make photocopies of the Inside Story diagram without the labels and captions. Have students label and describe the functions of each structure on the photocopy as it is discussed. **L1** **ELL**

Critical Thinking
Earthworms have setae and muscles in each segment. They move by anchoring the setae in the ground, then contracting their muscles. The earthworm moves by alternately contracting and relaxing the muscles in each segment.

INCLUSION STRATEGIES

Visually Impaired: *Kinesthetic* For students who are visually impaired, provide an earthworm for them to hold while you point out the main features of its structure and behavior. Ask the students to explain how the earthworm's shape and texture make it adapted for life in the soil. **L1** **ELL**

Indiana Academic Standards

Pages 730–731: B.1.15, B.1.19

BIOTECHNOLOGY CAREERS

Microsurgeon

Would you like to be able to reattach an accident victim's hand? Then you might consider a career as a microsurgeon.

Skills for the Job

Microsurgeons use high-powered microscopes and three-dimensional computer technology to see and repair tiny nerves and blood vessels. A microsurgeon in ophthalmology might repair a retina, while other microsurgeons remove tumors deep within a brain, or transplant organs. Microsurgeons who reattach hands, feet, and ears often use leeches after surgery to improve blood flow through the reattached body part. Microsurgeons must complete four years of college, four years of medical school, three to five years of a residency program, and special training in microsurgery. They must also pass an examination to become certified.

 For more careers in related fields, visit
in.bdol.glencoe.com/careers

Figure 27.13
The fanworm traps food in the mucus on its "fans." Disturbances in the water, such as a change in the direction of the current or the passing by of an organism, cause these worms to quickly withdraw into their tubes.

Earthworms eat their way through soil. As they eat, they create spaces for air and water to flow through soil. As soil passes through their digestive tracts, nutrients are extracted and undigested materials pass out of the worms. Castings, the wastes of an earthworm, help fertilize soil.

Bristleworms and their relatives

The class Polychaeta includes bristleworms and their relatives—fanworms, shown in ***Figure 27.13,*** lug worms, plumed worms, and sea mice. Polychaetes are primarily marine organisms. Most body segments of a polychaete have many setae, hence the name. Polychaete means "many bristles." Most body segments of a polychaete also have a pair of appendages called parapodia, which can be used for swimming or crawling over corals and the bottom of the sea. Parapodia also function in gas exchange. A polychaete has a head with well-developed sense organs, including eyes.

Leeches

Leeches are segmented worms with flattened bodies and usually no setae. Most leeches live in freshwater streams or rivers. Unlike earthworms, many species are parasites that suck blood or other body fluids from the bodies of their hosts, which include ducks, turtles, fishes, and humans. Front and rear suckers enable leeches to attach themselves to their hosts.

You may cringe at the thought of being bitten by a leech, but the bite is not painful. This is because the saliva of the leech contains chemicals that act as an anesthetic. Other chemicals prevent the blood from clotting. A leech can ingest two to five times its own weight in one meal. Once fed, a leech will drop off its host. It may not eat again for months.

732 MOLLUSKS AND SEGMENTED WORMS

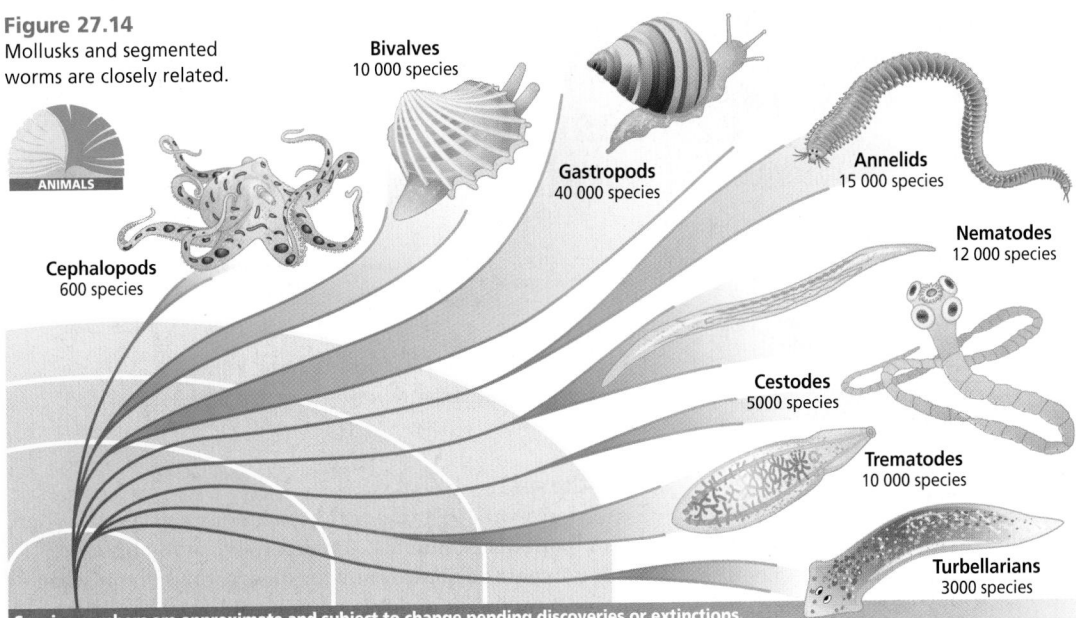

Figure 27.14
Mollusks and segmented worms are closely related.

ANIMALS

Bivalves
10 000 species

Gastropods
40 000 species

Cephalopods
600 species

Annelids
15 000 species

Nematodes
12 000 species

Cestodes
5000 species

Trematodes
10 000 species

Turbellarians
3000 species

Species numbers are approximate and subject to change pending discoveries or extinctions.

Origins of Mollusks and Segmented Worms

Fossil records show that mollusks lived in great numbers as long as 500 million years ago. Gastropod, bivalve, and cephalopod fossils have been found in Precambrian deposits. Some species, such as the chambered nautilus, appear to have changed very little from related species that lived long ago. Find out how fossil mollusks are used to determine the age of rocks in the *Connection to Earth Science* at the end of this chapter.

Annelids probably evolved in the sea, perhaps from larvae of ancestral flatworms. The fossil record for segmented worms is limited because segmented worms have almost no hard body parts. Tubes constructed by polychaetes are the most common fossils of this phylum. Some of these tubes appear in the fossil record as early as 540 million years ago, as you can see in *Figure 27.14*.

Section Assessment

Understanding Main Ideas
1. What is the most distinguishing characteristic of annelids? Why is it important?
2. Describe how bristleworms reproduce.
3. How do earthworms improve soil fertility?
4. Why are leeches classified in phylum Annelida?

Thinking Critically
5. Polychaetes actively swim, burrow, and crawl.

How do parapodia support the active life that most polychaetes pursue?

SKILL REVIEW
6. **Interpret Scientific Illustrations** Using *Figure 27.12*, interpret the function of the muscular system in the earthworm as the animal moves through the soil. For more help, refer to *Interpret Scientific Illustrations* in the **Skill Handbook**.

in.bdol.glencoe.com/self_check_quiz

27.2 SEGMENTED WORMS **733**

Section Assessment

1. Segmentation; each segment has its own muscles that lengthen and shorten for efficient movement; groups of segments may take on specific functions.
2. Bristleworms and their relatives have separate sexes and reproduce sexually. Eggs and sperm are released into the water, where fertilization takes place.
3. As an earthworm burrows through the soil, it loosens, aerates, and fertilizes the soil.
4. Leeches have segmented bodies just like other annelids.
5. Parapodia can be used for swimming or crawling and in gas exchange.
6. Circular muscles contract to move the worm forward. Longitudinal muscles contract to pull the worm's body along.

DESIGN YOUR OWN BioLab

Time Allotment
one or two class periods

Process Skills
observe and infer, compare and contrast, recognize cause and effect, form a hypothesis, interpret data, design an experiment, separate controls and variables

Safety Precautions
- Remind students to treat the earthworms in a humane manner at all times.
- Make sure that students wash their hands thoroughly with soap and water both before and after the experiment.

PREPARATION
Keep earthworms in the refrigerator overnight, but remove them two hours prior to the lab.

Possible Hypotheses
Students may hypothesize that the worms will move toward the dark, move faster on a rough surface, choose a moist surface over a dry surface, and prefer cool over warm conditions.

Indiana Academic Standards

Pages 734–735: B.1.18

DESIGN YOUR OWN BioLab

INQUIRY **Before You Begin**

An earthworm spends its time eating its way through soil, digesting organic matter, and passing inorganic matter through the digestive system and out of its body. Earthworms are dependent on soil for food and shelter. They respond to stimuli in a way that will ensure a continuous supply of food and a safe place in which to live. In this *BioLab*, you will design an experiment to determine the responses of earthworms to various stimuli.

How do earthworms respond to their environment?

PREPARATION

Problem
How do earthworms respond to light, different surfaces, moist and dry environments, and warm and cold environments?

Hypotheses
Place your worm in a tray with some moist soil. Watch your worm for about 5 minutes, and record what you observe. Make a hypothesis based on your observations about what the worm might do under conditions of light and dark, rough and smooth surfaces, moist and dry surfaces, and warm and cold conditions. Limit your investigation as time requires.

Objectives
In this BioLab, you will:
- **Measure** the sensitivity of earthworms to different stimuli, including light, water, and temperature.
- **Interpret** earthworm responses according to terms of adaptations that promote their survival.

Possible Materials
live earthworms	sandpaper
glass pan	warm tap water
culture dishes	water
thermometer or	penlight
temperature probe	ruler
dropper	cotton swabs
ice	hand lens or stereomicroscope
black paper	
paper towels	

Safety Precautions
CAUTION: *Be sure to treat the earthworm in a humane manner at all times. Wet your hands before handling earthworms. Always wear goggles in the lab.*

Skill Handbook
If you need help with this lab, refer to the **Skill Handbook**.

PLAN THE EXPERIMENT

Teaching Strategies
- To save time, have groups test only one or two variables and share their data.
- Review the terms *anterior*, *posterior*, *dorsal*, and *ventral*. Ask students to use these terms when recording their observations.

Possible Procedures
- To test which surface enables a worm to move fastest, students may decide to measure how far the worm moves in a given period on surfaces such as sandpaper, the bottom of the dry glass pan, the bottom of a wet glass pan, and on wet and dry paper towels.
- To test the worm's reaction to light, the bottom of a pan may be covered with soil. Part of the pan may be covered with a piece of black construction paper while a penlight is shone on the other side. The amount of time a worm spends in the light and dark sides of the container may then be measured.

PLAN THE EXPERIMENT

1. As a group, make a list of possible ways you might test your hypothesis. Keep the available materials in mind as you plan your procedure.

2. Be sure to design an experiment that will test one variable at a time. Plan to collect quantitative data. Make sure to incorporate a control.

3. Record your procedure and list materials and amounts you will need. Design and construct a data table for recording your findings.

Check the Plan
Discuss the following points with other group members.

1. What data will you collect, and how will they be recorded?

2. Does each test have one variable and a control? What are they?

3. Each test should include measurements of some kind. What are you measuring in each test?

4. How many trials will you run for each test?

5. *Make sure your teacher has approved your experimental plan before you proceed further.*

6. Carry out your experiment.

7. **CLEANUP AND DISPOSAL** Return earthworms to the container your teacher has provided. Wash your hands thoroughly with soap and water. Make wise choices about whether other lab materials should be disposed of or cleaned for reuse.

ANALYZE AND CONCLUDE

1. **Check Your Hypothesis** Which surface did the worm prefer? Explain.

2. **Interpret Observations** At which temperature was the worm most active? Explain.

3. **Observe and Infer** How did the earthworm respond to light? How did it respond to dry and moist environments? Of what survival value are these behaviors?

4. **Draw Conclusions** In general, what conditions do earthworms prefer?

5. **ERROR ANALYSIS** Analyze where errors may have occurred in your experiment.

Apply Your Skill

Project Based on your experiment, design another experiment that would help to answer a question that arose from your work. You might want to try other variables similar to the ones you used, or you might choose to investigate a completely different variable.

 Web Links To find out more about segmented worms, visit in.bdol.glencoe.com/segmented_worms

---

- To determine the worm's preference for heat or cold, the glass pan could be placed on top of two culture dishes—one containing warm tap water and the other containing ice.

Data and Observations
Most likely, earthworms will avoid light and extremes of temperature, move quickly on a rough surface, and prefer a moist surface.

CLEANUP AND DISPOSAL

Encourage students to make wise choices about reusing or disposing of lab materials. Students should dispose of used cotton swabs and paper towels. Other materials, such as the glass pans, should be washed, if needed, then returned to their designated places.

ANALYZE AND CONCLUDE

Student answers may vary.

1. a rough surface; the worm moves more easily on a rough surface

2. an intermediate temperature; an earthworm is ectothermic so its level of activity depends upon the surrounding temperature

3. moved away from light; preferred a moist environment; earthworms are safer from predators in the soil where it is dark, and earthworm's skin must remain moist or the animal will dry out and die

4. worms would prefer moist environments, intermediate temperatures, darkness, and rough surfaces

5. **ERROR ANALYSIS** earthworm unhealthy, cold, or too warm; too much handling of earthworm by other classes; environment not dark enough, not light enough, not moist enough; testing more than one variable at a time; inaccurate timing; sample size too small; too few trials

Assessment
Performance Ask students to design and then carry out an experiment to determine how earthworms respond to gravity. Remind students to use care when handling live animals. Use the Performance Task Assessment List for Designing an Experiment in **PASC**, p. 95. **L2**

Apply Your Skill

Project Have students design similar experiments for other invertebrates and compare their results with those obtained for the earthworm. **L3**

Purpose

Students will learn how mollusks can be used to determine ancient climates and environments as well as radiometric ages.

Teaching Strategies

■ Provide students with an assortment of fossil mollusk shells as well as living examples of these organisms. Allow students to use hand lenses to observe the diversity in these organisms, especially the shells. If actual specimens are not readily available, provide students with color photographs of mollusks.

Challenge students to classify the examples based on the relationship between the organisms' shells and soft body parts. Students should be able to identify organisms as belonging to the gastropod, bivalve, or cephalopod groups. **L2** **ELL**

■ Explain, if necessary, the method of absolute dating. Certain radioactive elements decay at a constant rate called a half-life. By measuring the amount of the original element left and the amount of its decay product, the age of a specimen can be determined.

■ Have a volunteer explain the observation made by Darwin. Students should recount that the shells were deposited in a body of water, probably an ocean. Earth processes, including uplift, caused this area of land, which was once below sea level, to be raised thousands of feet above the ocean's surface.

connection to Earth Science

Mollusks as Indicators

Although a few species of mollusks live on land, most mollusks are marine or freshwater organisms. How is it, then, that on one of his journeys to South America, Charles Darwin found aquatic mollusk shells thousands of feet above sea level? This observation by the famous naturalist helped to support Darwin's hypothesis that Earth has changed over time.

Mollusks once ruled Earth Mollusks first appear in Earth's fossil record more than 500 million years ago. By 30 million years later, these shelled creatures had become the dominant life form on Earth. Thousands of species of mollusks evolved to fill available niches. Yet, numerous species of mollusks became extinct at the close of

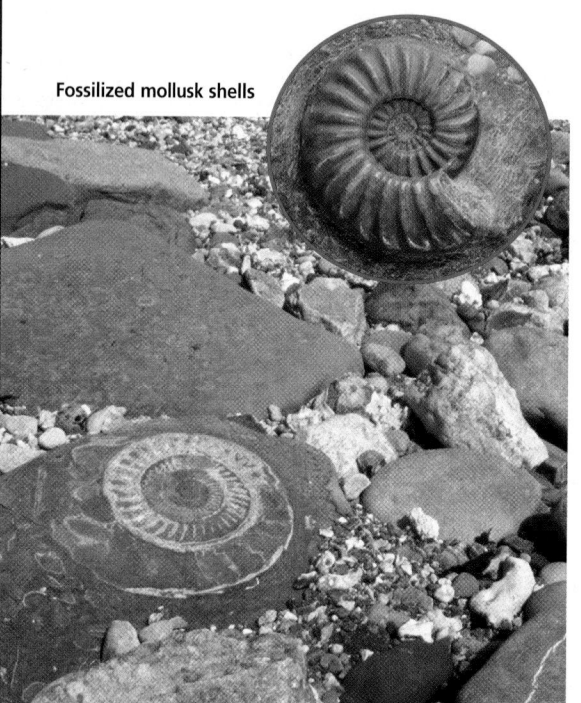

Fossilized mollusk shells

the Mesozoic Era about 65 million years ago. Today, the number of mollusk species is estimated at 110 000.

The present is the key to the past
Because mollusks are generally well preserved in the fossil record, abundant, easy to recognize, and widely distributed geographically, they are excellent index fossils. Index fossils, together with their modern relatives, can be used to hypothesize about ancient climates and environments.

Mollusk shells can also provide information about the biotic, physical, and chemical changes that occur in an ecosystem. Modern mollusks, for example, have been used to determine the source and distribution of various aquatic pollutants.

Mollusks as timekeepers Mollusks can also be thought of as marine timekeepers. A mollusk shell grows only along one edge. The pigmented patterns produced by the animal along this growing edge rarely change. Thus, the pattern produced is not only specific to the species but also is a space and time record of the shell-producing process of that particular organism.

Mollusk shells also can be used to estimate an age because these structures contain the element strontium. By measuring the amounts of different isotopes of strontium in the shell, scientists are able to closely estimate the age of the shell, and, by extension, the exact age of the rocks containing the shell.

Writing About Biology

Research Ammonites were early mollusks that lived from about 230 million years ago to about 65 million years ago. Ammonites are now extinct. Research to find out if these mollusks are good index fossils. Explain your answer.

 To find out more about mollusks and other index fossils, visit in.bdol.glencoe.com/earth_science

Writing About Biology

Most students should be able to deduce that ammonites are, in fact, excellent index fossils because they are readily preserved as fossils and lived for a geologically relatively short period of time.

STUDY GUIDE

Section 27.1

Mollusks

Key Concepts

- Mollusks have bilateral symmetry, a coelom, and a digestive tract with two openings. Many also have shells.

- Most gastropods, such as snails, have a shell, mantle, radula, an open circulatory system, gills, and nephridia. Gastropods without shells, such as slugs, are protected by a covering of mucus.

- Bivalve mollusks have paired shells, called valves, and are filter feeders. They have no radula. Clams and scallops are bivalves.

- Cephalopods have tentacles with suckers, beaklike jaws, a mouth with a radula, and a closed circulatory system. Cephalopods include the octopus, squid, and chambered nautilus.

Vocabulary

closed circulatory system (p. 724)
mantle (p. 722)
nephridia (p. 725)
open circulatory system (p. 724)
radula (p. 722)

Section 27.2

Segmented Worms

Key Concepts

- The phylum Annelida includes the earthworms, bristleworms and their relatives, and leeches. Annelids are bilaterally symmetrical and have a coelom and two body openings; some have larvae that look like the larvae of mollusks. Their bodies are cylindrical and segmented.

- Earthworms have complex digestive, excretory, muscular, and circulatory systems.

- Bristleworms and their relatives are mostly marine species. They have many setae and parapodia that are used for crawling along.

- Leeches are flattened, segmented worms. Most are aquatic parasites.

- Fossil remains of mollusks show that they first lived over 500 million years ago. Fossil records show that segmented worms first appeared 540 million years ago.

Vocabulary

gizzard (p. 730)
setae (p. 728)

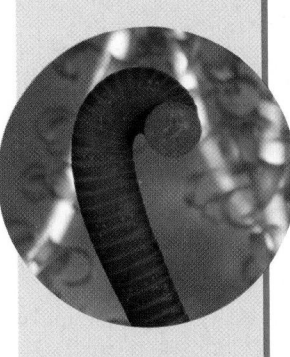

FOLDABLES
Study Organizer To help you review the diversity of mollusks, use the Organizational Study Fold on page 721.

 in.bdol.glencoe.com/vocabulary_puzzlemaker

CHAPTER 27 ASSESSMENT **737**

Key Concepts

Summary statements can be used by students to review the major concepts of the chapter.

Biology Online

Visit in.bdol.glencoe.com
/self_check_quiz
/vocabulary_puzzlemaker
/chapter_test
/standardized_test

VOCABULARY PUZZLEMAKER

For additional help with vocabulary, have students access the Vocabulary PuzzleMaker online at in.bdol.glencoe.com/vocabulary_puzzlemaker

FOLDABLES™

Have students use their Foldables to review the content of Section 27.1. On the back of the cards, have students analyze how each animal is adapted to its environment.

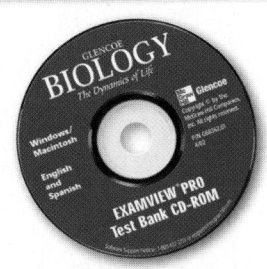

Use the Exam*View*®Pro Test Bank CD-ROM to:

- Create **multiple versions** of tests
- Create **modified** tests with one mouse click for **inclusion** students
- **Edit** existing questions and **add** your own questions
- Build tests aligned with state standards using built-in **State Curriculum Tags**
- Change **English** tests to **Spanish** with one mouse click and vice versa

 Indiana Academic Standards

Pages 736–737: B.1.15, B.1.32

The Princeton Review *Questions and answers have been aligned and verified by The Princeton Review.*

Vocabulary Review

1. mantle
2. gizzard
3. radula
4. nephridia
5. open circulatory system

Understanding Key Concepts

6. B		9. C	
7. C		10. C	
8. C		11. A	

Constructed Response

12. Gastropods can withdraw into their shells. Cephalopods, such as squids, can swim very fast, and the octopus can use its tentacles for defense.

13. Bristleworms, unlike earthworms, have separate sexes and reproduce sexually. Usually eggs and sperm are released into seawater, where fertilization takes place. In an aquatic environment, eggs and sperm can meet more easily than if they were released in the soil by earthworms of different sexes.

14. A snail protects itself by drawing into its shell, while an octopus secretes an inky liquid that can confuse a predator. A snail keeps its body moist with a covering of mucus, while an octopus remains moist in the water.

Thinking Critically

Vocabulary Review

Review the Chapter 27 vocabulary words listed in the Study Guide on page 737. Match the words with the definitions below.

1. membrane that surrounds the internal organs of a mollusk
2. sac with muscular walls and hard particles that grind soil before it passes into the intestine
3. in some mollusks, the rasping, tonguelike organ used to drill, scrape, grate, or cut food
4. organs that remove metabolic wastes from an animal's body
5. system where blood moves through vessels into open spaces around the body organs

Understanding Key Concepts

6. When an earthworm passes soil through its digestive tract, the soil does NOT go through the _____.
   A. stomach   C. gizzard
   B. nephridia   D. crop

7. Which of the following animals have setae?
   A. snails
   B. clams
   C. earthworms
   D. squids

8. Which of the following is a gastropod?

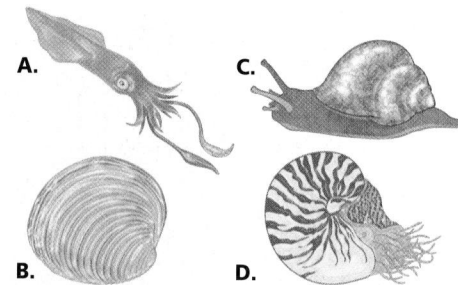

A.   C.

B.   D.

9. Which of the following word pairs are most closely related?
   A. filter feeding—radula
   B. scraping algae—siphon
   C. predation—tentacle
   D. nephridia—gizzard

10. Which of the following does NOT use a radula for feeding?
    A. snail   C. oyster
    B. slug   D. squid

11. Leeches that suck blood or other body fluids from their hosts are considered to be _____.
    A. parasites   C. filter feeders
    B. grazers   D. predators

Constructed Response

12. **Open Ended** Compare the protective adaptations of gastropods and cephalopods.

13. **Open Ended** Interpret the function of a bristleworm's reproductive system and relate it to its life in the aquatic biome.

14. **Open Ended** Compare the adaptations for survival in two different mollusks: a snail living on land and an octopus living in the ocean.

Thinking Critically

15. **Analyze** Fill in the table with key adaptations of the animals.

Data Table	Gastropods	Bivalves	Cephalopods
Getting food			
Circulation			
Excretion			
Protection			
Locomotion			

16. **REAL WORLD BIOCHALLENGE** Natural pearls are made by oysters in response to foreign material, such as a grain of sand lodging inside the shell. Pearls have been used as jewelry for centuries. Find out about the history of pearls and present-day pearl culture at **in.bdol.glencoe.com**. Visit a jeweler and ask to see and photograph marine and freshwater pearls. Prepare a poster or a multimedia presentation with your findings and present it to your class.

 in.bdol.glencoe.com/chapter_test

15.

	Gastropods	Bivalves	Cephalopods
Getting food	radula	filter feeding	tentacles
Circulation	open circulatory system	open circulatory system	closed circulatory system
Excretion	nephridia	nephridia	nephridia
Protection	shell, mucus	shell	inky substance, quick movement
Locomotion	muscular foot	muscular foot	jet propulsion, tentacles

16. Answers will vary depending on the part of the world in which the pearls are harvested.

17. The prey animal is not aware that it has been bitten by a leech.

18. The farm field would not have sufficient aeration and crop roots could not grow properly.

17. Infer A leech's saliva contains chemicals that act as an anesthetic. How does this benefit the leech?

18. Hypothesize What would happen to a farmer's field if all the earthworms were removed?

End-of-Course Assessment Practice

All questions aligned and verified by The Princeton Review

Part 1 Multiple Choice

Use the map to answer questions 19–21.

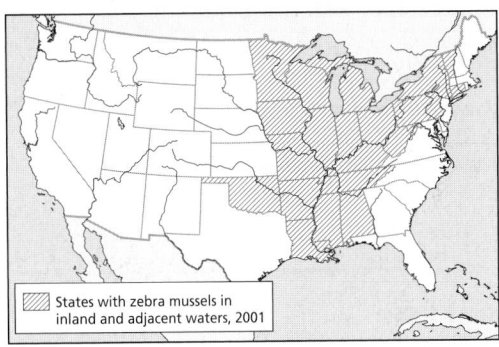

States with zebra mussels in inland and adjacent waters, 2001

19. The zebra mussel, a non-native mollusk, was first discovered in North America (Michigan and Ohio) in 1988. By 2001, zebra mussels had spread as far south as _____.
  A. Florida   C. Georgia
  B. Louisiana   D. Texas

20. By 2001, zebra mussels from Michigan and Ohio had invaded _____ additional states.
  A. 12   C. 14
  B. 8   D. 18

21. In 2001, you would NOT find zebra mussels in _____.
  A. Kansas
  B. Oklahoma
  C. West Virginia
  D. Wisconsin

Study the diagram and answer question 22.

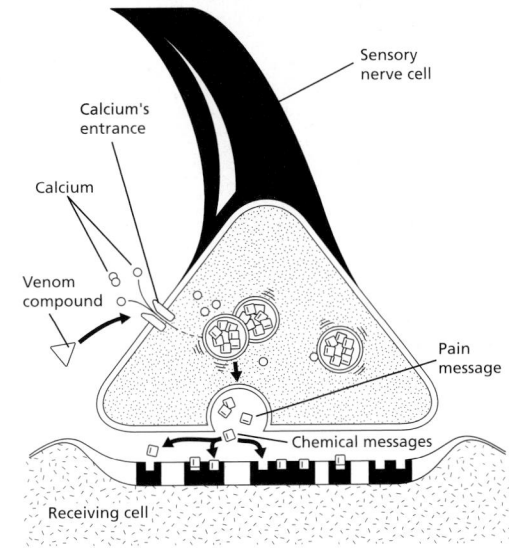

Sensory nerve cell
Calcium's entrance
Calcium
Venom compound
Pain message
Chemical messages
Receiving cell

22. Nerve cells send the chemical messages that produce pain. In the diagram, the chemical pain messages are squares activated by calcium, the round figures. Scientists studying the venom from sea slugs have found that in small quantities, the venom stops the pain signal from being sent. You might infer that the venom interrupts the signal at _____.
  A. calcium's entrance
  B. the pain message exit
  C. the receiving cell
  D. all of the above

Part 2 Constructed Response/Grid In

Record your answers or fill in the bubbles on your answer document using the correct place value.

23. Open Ended When temperatures increase and soil becomes drier, what happens to earthworms?

24. Grid In If a farmer's field has 75 earthworms per square meter, how many earthworms are in 4.5 square meters?

 in.bdol.glencoe.com/standardized_test

End-of-Course Assessment Practice

19. B   **21.** A
20. D   **22.** A
23. Earthworms move to a more suitable habitat or die.
24. 337.5

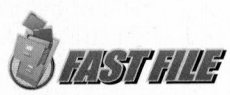 FAST FILE

Answer Sheet A practice answer sheet can be found on p. 95 of *Unit 8 FAST FILE Resources.*

RUBRIC

SCORE	CRITERIA
4	A correct solution that is supported by well-developed, accurate explanations.
3	A generally correct solution, but may contain minor flaws in reasoning.

SCORE	CRITERIA
2	A partially correct interpretation and/or solution to the problem.
1	A correct solution with no supporting evidence or explanation.
0	An incorrect solution or no solution is given.

 Indiana Academic Standards

Pages 738–739: B.1.14, B.1.15, B.1.17, B.1.19

Chapter 28 Organizer

Section Objectives	National Science Standards	State/Local Standards	Advanced Lab and Demo Planning
Section 28.1 1 session, 1/2 block 1. **Relate** the structural and behavioral adaptations of arthropods to their ability to live in different habitats. 2. **Analyze** the adaptations that make arthropods an evolutionarily successful phylum.	UCP.1–5; A.1, A.2; C.3–6; F.1, F.5	**Indiana Standards** B.1.14, B.1.15, B.1.16, B.1.19, B.1.43	**Student Labs:** Additional Lab, p. 742: bess beetles, cloth toweling, clear tape, heavy thread, balance, pennies, smooth tabletop, plastic petri dish MiniLab 28.1, p. 743: preserved lobster, forceps Problem-Solving Lab 28.1, p. 746 **Teacher Demonstration:** Quick Demo, p. 742: preserved or live arthropods, binocular microscopes or hand lenses
Section 28.2 2 sessions, 1 block 3. **Compare and contrast** the similarities and differences among the major groups of arthropods. 4. **Explain** the adaptations of insects that contribute to their success.	UCP.1–5; A.1, A.2; C.3–6; F.1–6; G.1–3	**Indiana Standards** B.1.11, B.1.15, B.1.17, B.1.19, B.1.31, B.1.32, B.1.38, B.1.43	**Student Labs:** MiniLab 28.2, p. 754: life stages of a grasshopper specimen, life stages of a moth specimen, forceps Design Your Own BioLab, p. 756: See materials below. **Teacher Demonstrations:** Quick Demo, p. 751: butterfly chrysalis, glass terrarium Quick Demo, p. 753: 2-L soft drink bottle, raw meat that has been exposed to flies
End of Chapter Assessment Student Edition **Study Guide,** p. 759 **Content Assessment,** pp. 760–761		**Indiana Standards** B.1.15, B.1.17, B.1.19, B.1.34, B.1.43	**Student Lab:** Design Your Own BioLab, p. 756: beakers or plastic bottles, labels or marking pencil, graduated cylinder, brine shrimp eggs, clear plastic trays, salt (noniodized), balance, water

Key to Teaching Strategies

L1 Level 1 activities should be appropriate for students with learning difficulties.

L2 Level 2 activities should be within the ability range of all students.

L3 Level 3 activities are designed for above-average students.

ELL ELL activities should be within the ability range of English Language Learners.

COOP LEARN Cooperative Learning activities are designed for small group work.

Legend

 Transparency   CD-ROM MP3 MP3 Videocassette DVD

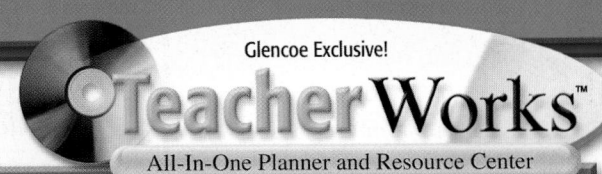

Glencoe Exclusive!
TeacherWorks™
All-In-One Planner and Resource Center

Reproducible Masters and Transparencies

Technology

Unit 8 FAST FILE Resources
MiniLab Worksheet, p. 99
Reinforcement and Study Guide in English,
pp. 107–108
Reinforcement and Study Guide in Spanish,
pp. 111–112
Transparency Worksheets, pp. 117, 119–122
**Reading Essentials for Biology,
Section 28.1**
Section Focus Transparency 69
Basic Concepts Transparency 49
Reteaching Skills Transparency 41

Interactive Chalkboard CD-ROM: Section 28.1 Presentation
TeacherWorks™ CD-ROM
Guided Reading Audio Summaries MP3
Virtual Labs CD-ROM
Virtual Lab: Classifying Arthropods

Unit 8 FAST FILE Resources
MiniLab Worksheet, p. 100
BioLab Worksheet, pp. 101–102
Real World BioApplications, pp. 103–104, 105–106
Reinforcement and Study Guide in English,
pp. 109–110
Reinforcement and Study Guide in Spanish,
pp. 113–114
Transparency Worksheets, pp. 118, 121–124
**Reading Essentials for Biology,
Section 28.2**
Laboratory Manual, pp. 175–178, 179–180
Inside Story Poster
Section Focus Transparency 70
Reteaching Skills Transparencies 41, 42

Interactive Chalkboard CD-ROM: Section 28.2 Presentation
TeacherWorks™ CD-ROM
Guided Reading Audio Summaries MP3

Unit 8 FAST FILE Resources
Chapter Assessment, pp. 125–130
Student Recording Sheet, p. 131

 The Princeton Review **Reviewing Biology,** pp. 55–56

**Interactive Chalkboard:
Chapter 28 Assessment**
**MindJogger Videoquizzes
DVD/VHS**
**ExamView® Pro Test Bank
CD-ROM**
TeacherWorks™ CD-ROM
Succeeding on National Standards CD-ROM

in.bdol.glencoe.com
/self_check_quiz
/vocabulary_puzzlemaker
/chapter_test
/standardized_test

Indicates materials created specifically for Indiana.

Arthropods

Short on Time?

BIODIGEST The BioDigest at the end of this unit can be used as a(n):

- preview to introduce important unit concepts.
- overview if time does not permit teaching the entire chapter.
- review of key unit concepts.

Understanding the Photo

Scorpions belong to the same class as spiders, Arachnida. Scorpions have only two body regions—an abdomen and a cephalothorax. The abdomen is divided into many segments ending in a long tail with a venomous stinger at the tip. Scorpions have six pairs of jointed appendages. The first pair is located near the mouth and is modified into pincers. The second pair is modified into claws, which are used for defense. The remaining four pairs of appendages have been adapted as legs.

PowerPoint® Presentations

This CD-ROM is an editable Microsoft® PowerPoint® presentation that includes:

- Section presentations
- Section checks
- Image bank
- Hot links to Biology Online
- All transparencies

What You'll Learn

- You will distinguish among the adaptations that have made arthropods the most abundant and diverse animal phylum on Earth.
- You will compare and contrast different classes of arthropods.

Why It's Important

Arthropods are adapted to fill many important niches in every ecosystem in the world. Because arthropods occupy so many niches, they have an impact on all living things, including humans.

Understanding ▶ the Photo

There are about one million known species of arthropods. Jointed appendages are one of the adaptations that make this group so diverse and successful. This desert hairy scorpion uses modified appendages, called pincers, to hold its prey while it injects the prey with venom.

 Biology Online

Visit in.bdol.glencoe.com to
- study the entire chapter online
- access Web Links for more information and activities on arthropods
- review content with the Interactive Tutor and self-check quizzes

740

Two-Minute Chapter Launcher

Demo Provide students with a live crayfish in a pan of water. Ask them to describe how the crayfish moves and to describe the structures of the crayfish that make this movement possible.

Students are likely to describe the legs of the crayfish and its finlike structures that enable movement in the water.

Compare movements of the crayfish on a dry surface and in the water. If time permits, ask students to place two different-sized crayfishes together in a small container and observe their behavior. They should hypothesize what benefit this behavior might have for survival of the species.

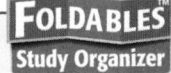
Characteristics of Arthropods

Indiana Standards Standard B.1.15 Understand and explain that, in biological systems, structure and function must be considered together.

SECTION PREVIEW

Objectives

Relate the structural and behavioral adaptations of arthropods to their ability to live in different habitats.

Analyze the adaptations that make arthropods an evolutionarily successful phylum.

Review Vocabulary

exoskeleton: a hard, waxy coating on the outside of some animals that provides support and protection (p. 684)

New Vocabulary

appendage
molting
cephalothorax
tracheal tube
spiracle
book lung
pheromone
simple eye
compound eye
mandible
Malpighian tubule
parthenogenesis

FOLDABLES™
Study Organizer

Arthropods Make the following Foldable to help you understand how arthropods are similar to and different from all other animals.

STEP 1 Fold a sheet of paper in half lengthwise.

STEP 2 Fold paper down 2.5 cm from the top. (Hint: From the tip of your index finger to your middle knuckle is about 2.5 cm.)

STEP 3 Open and draw lines along the 2.5-cm fold. **Label** as shown.

Similar | Different

Compare and Contrast As you read Chapter 28, summarize the characteristics of arthropods that are similar to all other animals in the left column and those characteristics of arthropods that are different in the right column.

What is an arthropod?

Arthropods pollinate many of the flowering plants on Earth. Some arthropods spread plant and animal diseases. Despite the enormous diversity of arthropods, they all share some common characteristics.

A typical arthropod is a segmented, coelomate invertebrate animal with bilateral symmetry, an exoskeleton, and jointed structures called appendages. An **appendage** (uh PEN dihj) is any structure, such as a leg or an antenna, that grows out of the body of an animal. In arthropods, appendages are adapted for a variety of purposes including sensing, walking, feeding, and mating. *Figure 28.1* shows some of these adaptations.

Figure 28.1
Developing jointed appendages was a major evolutionary step leading to the success of arthropods. **Infer** *How are jointed appendages beneficial to arthropods?*

A Spiders hold their prey with jointed mouthparts while feeding.

B The antennae of a moth are adapted for the senses of touch and smell.

741

1 Focus

Bellringer
Section Focus Transparency 69

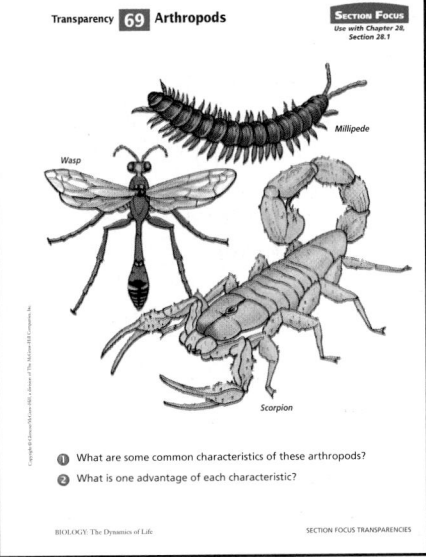

Transparency **69** Arthropods

SECTION FOCUS
Use with Chapter 28, Section 28.1

Millipede

Wasp

Scorpion

① What are some common characteristics of these arthropods?

② What is one advantage of each characteristic?

BIOLOGY: The Dynamics of Life   SECTION FOCUS TRANSPARENCIES

Caption Question Answer
Figure 28.1 Joints allow more flexibility in animals with hard exoskeletons, powerful movements of the appendages, and enable an appendage to be used in many different ways.

FOLDABLES™
For an additional Foldables activity idea, see the Chapter 28 Foldables page in *Unit 8 FAST FILE Resources.*

Indiana Academic Standards

Pages 740–741: B.1.43

2 Teach

Caption Question Answer
Figure 28.2 Exoskeletons would be too heavy and prevent movement by most arthropods.

Figure 28.2
When arthropods molt, the old exoskeleton is discarded after a new one is formed underneath. **Infer** *Why don't arthropods continue to molt and grow as large as mice?*

Word Origin

arthropod from the Greek words *arthron,* meaning "joint," and *pod,* meaning "foot"; Arthropods have jointed appendages.

cephalothorax from the Greek words *kephalo,* meaning "head," and *thorax,* meaning "breastplate"; The cephalothorax is the fused head and thorax of an arthropod.

Arthropods are the earliest known invertebrates to exhibit jointed appendages. Joints are advantageous because they allow more flexibility, especially in animals that have hard, rigid exoskeletons. Joints also allow powerful movements of appendages, and enable an appendage to be used in many different ways. For example, the second pair of appendages is used for mating in spiders and for seizing prey in scorpions.

Arthropod exoskeletons provide protection

The success of arthropods as a group can be attributed in part to the presence of an exoskeleton. The exoskeleton is a hard, thick, outer covering made of protein and chitin (KI tun). Chitin also is found in the cell walls of fungi and in other animals. In some species, the exoskeleton is a continuous covering over most of the body. In other species, the exoskeleton is made of separate plates held together by hinges. The exoskeleton protects and supports internal tissues and provides places for attachment of muscles. In many species that live on land, the exoskeleton is covered by a waxy layer that provides additional protection against water loss. In many aquatic species, the exoskeletons are reinforced with calcium carbonate.

Why arthropods must molt

Exoskeletons are an important adaptation for arthropods, but they also have their disadvantages. First, they are relatively heavy structures. The larger an arthropod is, the thicker and heavier its exoskeleton must be to support its larger muscles. Thus, the weight of the exoskeleton limits the size of arthropods. However, many terrestrial and flying arthropods have adapted to their habitats by having a thinner, lighter-weight exoskeleton, which offers less protection but allows the animal more freedom to fly and jump.

A second and more important disadvantage is that exoskeletons cannot grow, so they must be shed periodically. Shedding the old exoskeleton is called **molting.** Before an arthropod molts, a new, soft exoskeleton is formed beneath the old one. When the new exoskeleton is ready, the animal contracts muscles and takes in air or water. This causes the animal's body to swell until the old exoskeleton splits open, usually along the back. The animal then sheds its old exoskeleton, as shown in *Figure 28.2.* Before the new exoskeleton hardens, the animal puffs up as a result of increased blood circulation to all parts of its body. Many insects and spiders increase in size by also taking in air. Thus, the new exoskeleton hardens in a larger size, allowing some room for the animal to continue to grow.

Most arthropods molt four to seven times in their lives before they become adults. During molting, they are particularly vulnerable to predators. When the new exoskeleton is soft, arthropods cannot protect themselves from danger because they move by bracing muscles against the rigid exoskeleton. Therefore, many species hide or remain motionless for a few hours or days until the new exoskeleton hardens.

Additional Lab

Beetle Strength

Purpose
Students will observe and compare the pulling power of a beetle and a human.
Materials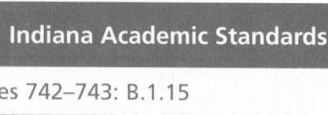

bess beetles, cloth toweling (30 cm²), clear tape, heavy thread (30 cm long), balance, pennies, smooth tabletop, plastic petri dish

Procedure
Give students the following directions.
1. Obtain the mass of the petri dish and the mass of the penny.
2. Place a beetle on its back in the petri dish and obtain the mass of the beetle and the dish. Calculate the mass of the beetle.
3. Make a slipknot loop on one end of the thread and put the loop over the head and body of the beetle so that it acts as a harness. Tape the ends of the thread inside the rim of the petri dish. Make a hypothesis about how many pennies the beetle will be able to pull on the petri dish sled.
4. Secure the cloth to the tabletop with tape. When the beetle begins to pull or

Segmentation in arthropods

Most arthropods are segmented, but they do not have as many segments as you have seen in segmented worms. In most groups of arthropods, segments have become fused into three body sections—head, thorax, and abdomen. In other groups, even these segments may be fused. Some arthropods have a head and a fused thorax and abdomen. In other groups, there is an abdomen and a fused head and thorax called a **cephalothorax** (se fuh luh THOR aks), as shown in *Figure 28.3B.*

Fusion of the body segments is related to movement and protection. Beetles and some other arthropod groups that have separate head and thorax regions are more flexible than those with fused regions. Many species, such as shrimps, lobsters, and crayfishes, have a cephalothorax, which protects the animal but which limits movement of the body regions. Take a closer look at the fused body segments of a lobster in the *MiniLab* on this page.

Figure 28.3
You can see the different body segments in these arthropods.

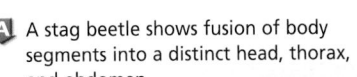
A stag beetle shows fusion of body segments into a distinct head, thorax, and abdomen.

B In the camel-backed shrimp, the head and thorax are fused into a cephalothorax. The animal also has an abdomen.

MiniLab 28.1

Compare and Contrast

Lobster Characteristics
There are more species of arthropods than all of the other animal species combined. This phylum includes a variety of adaptations that are not found in other animal phyla.

Lobster

Procedure

1. Examine a preserved lobster. **CAUTION:** *Wear disposable protective gloves and use a forceps when handling preserved material.*
2. Prepare a data table with the following arthropod traits listed: body segmentation, jointed appendages, exoskeleton, sense organs, jaws.
3. Observe the lobster. Fill in your data table, indicating which of the arthropod traits you observed.
4. Gently lift the edge of the body covering where the legs attach to the body. Look for feathery structures. These are gills and are part of the animal's respiratory system. **CAUTION:** *Wash hands with soap and water after handling preserved materials.*

Analysis

1. **Evaluate** Do lobsters have all of the traits listed above?
2. **Infer** Make a hypothesis as to how lobsters locate food.

MiniLab 28.1

Purpose
Students will observe a lobster as they are introduced to traits not seen in phyla studied previously.

Process Skills
compare and contrast, acquire information, classify, collect data, organize data

Safety Precautions
Remind students to use tongs, forceps, and/or protective gloves when handling specimens.

Teaching Strategies
- Living lobsters may be used in place of preserved specimens. Both preserved and living lobsters are available from biological supply houses.
- If living lobsters are used, caution students about being pinched by the animals' pincers.

Expected Results
All arthropod traits can be observed on the lobster.

Analysis
1. Yes, all traits listed are the major traits that characterize Arthropoda.
2. Student answers may vary: visually through their eyes; detection of odor or movement with antennae.

Assessment
Portfolio Ask students to write a short paragraph that describes the traits that differentiate the three major classes of arthropods from one another. Use the Performance Task Assessment List for Writing in Science from **PASC**, p. 159. L2

---

move the sled by walking, slowly add pennies to the petri dish, one at a time, until you find the maximum mass the beetle can pull. Do not prod the beetle.
5. Count and record the total number of pennies in the petri dish.
6. Record the relative pulling power of the insect by dividing the mass of the pennies by the mass of the beetle.

Expected Results
Students may find that beetles pull more pennies than they expected.

Analysis
Did your data support your hypothesis?
Some beetles can pull 15 or more pennies, more than most students will hypothesize.

Assessment
Performance Have students calculate how many grams they could pull if they had the same strength as their beetle. They should multiply their weight in grams by the pulling power of the beetle. Use the Performance Task Assessment List for Using Math in Science in **PASC**, p. 101. L2

Arthropod Habitats Ask student groups to list in their journals all the arthropods they know. Ask them to identify each arthropod's habitat: land, water, or air. Ask them why arthropods are able to live in so many different kinds of habitats and why there are so many different kinds of arthropods. **L2** **COOP LEARN**

✓**Reading Check** Aquatic arthropods exchange gases through gills, which extract oxygen from water and release carbon dioxide into the water. Most insects have tracheal tubes, branching networks of hollow air passages that carry air throughout the body. Most arachnids have book lungs, air-filled chambers that contain leaflike plates like the pages of a book.

Physical Science Connection

Demonstrate to students how the electric fields of light can be constrained to vibrate in the same direction. One sheet of polarizing filter allows light to vibrate in one direction. A second filter placed in front of the first will block the light when its polarization direction is oriented at ninety degrees with that of the first filter.

Figure 28.4
Arthropods have a wide variety of respiratory structures.

A Gills, with their large surface area, enable a large amount of blood-rich tissue to be exposed to water containing oxygen.

B Tracheal tubes are inside the body, thereby reducing water loss through the respiratory surface while carrying air close to each cell.

C Book lungs are folded membranes that increase the surface area of blood-rich tissue exposed to air.

Physical Science Connection

Polarized light Recall that light is an electromagnetic wave consisting of vibrating electric and magnetic fields. Light waves that have their electric fields vibrating in the same direction are said to be polarized. Sunlight scattered by the atmosphere becomes polarized. Some arthropods, such as bees, can detect this polarization, and use it to navigate by determining the position of the sun, even on cloudy days.

Arthropods have efficient gas exchange

Arthropods are generally quick, active animals. They crawl, run, climb, dig, swim, and fly. As you would expect, arthropods have efficient respiratory structures that ensure rapid oxygen delivery to cells. This large oxygen demand is needed to sustain the high levels of metabolism required for rapid movements.

Three types of respiratory structures have evolved in arthropods: gills, tracheal tubes, and book lungs. In some arthropods, air diffuses across the exoskeleton and body wall. For this to happen, the exoskeleton must be thin and permeable. Aquatic arthropods exchange gases through gills, which extract oxygen from water and release carbon dioxide into the water. Land arthropods have either a system of tracheal tubes or book lungs. Most insects have **tracheal** (TRAY kee ul) **tubes,** branching networks of hollow air passages that carry air throughout the body. Muscle activity helps pump the air through the tracheal tubes. Air enters and leaves the tracheal tubes through openings on the thorax and abdomen called **spiracles** (SPIHR ih kulz).

Most spiders and their relatives have **book lungs,** air-filled chambers that contain leaflike plates. The stacked plates of a book lung are arranged like pages of a book. All three types of respiration in arthropods are illustrated in *Figure 28.4.*

✓**Reading Check** **Describe** the three types of arthropod respiratory structures.

Arthropods have acute senses

Quick movements that are the result of strong muscular contractions enable arthropods to respond to a variety of stimuli. Movement, sound, and chemicals can be detected with great sensitivity by antennae, stalklike structures that detect changes in the environment.

Antennae are also used for sound and odor communication among animals. Have you ever watched as a group of ants carried home a small piece of food? The ants were able to work together as a group because they were communicating with each other

CHALLENGE ACTIVITY

Arthropod Respiration Arthropods have evolved efficient respiratory structures to deliver large amounts of oxygen to cells. Provide students with live or preserved arthropods that have gills, tracheal tubes, and book lungs. Ask students to explain and make diagrams about how these arthropods get oxygen. Have students describe how each method illustrates adaptations of these animals to their environments. **L3**

Indiana Academic Standards
Pages 744–745: B.1.14, B.1.15, B.1.19

by **pheromones** (FER uh mohnz), chemical odor signals given off by animals. Antennae sense the odors of pheromones, which signal animals to engage in a variety of behaviors. Some pheromones are used as scent trails, such as in the group-feeding behavior of ants, and many are important in the mating behavior of arthropods.

Accurate vision is also important to the active lives of arthropods. Most arthropods have one pair of large compound eyes and three to eight simple eyes. A **simple eye** is a visual structure with only one lens that is used for detecting light. A **compound eye** is a visual structure with many lenses. Each lens registers light from a tiny portion of the field of view. The total image that is formed is made up of thousands of parts. The multiple lenses of a flying arthropod, such as the dragonfly shown in *Figure 28.5*, enable it to analyze a fast-changing landscape during flight. Compound eyes can detect the movements of prey, mates, or predators, and can also detect colors.

Arthropod nervous systems are well developed

Arthropods have well-developed nervous systems that process information coming in from the sense organs. The nervous system consists of a double ventral nerve cord, an anterior brain, and several ganglia. Arthropods have ganglia that have become fused. These ganglia act as control centers for the body section in which they are located.

Arthropods have other complex body systems

Arthropod blood is pumped by a heart in an open circulatory system with vessels that carry blood away from the heart. The blood flows out of the vessels, bathes the tissues of the body, and returns to the heart through open body spaces.

Arthropods have a complete digestive system with a mouth, stomach, intestine, and anus, together with various glands that produce digestive enzymes. The mouthparts of most arthropod groups include one pair of jaws called **mandibles** (MAN duh bulz). The mandibles, together with other mouthparts, illustrated in *Figure 28.6*, are adapted for holding, chewing, sucking, or biting the various foods eaten by arthropods.

Most terrestrial arthropods excrete wastes through **Malpighian** (mal PIH gee un) **tubules.** In insects, the tubules are all located in the abdomen

Figure 28.5
The compound eyes of this dragonfly cover most of its head and consist of about 30 000 lenses. However, the images formed by compound eyes are unclear.

Figure 28.6
Mouthparts of arthropods exhibit tremendous variation among species.

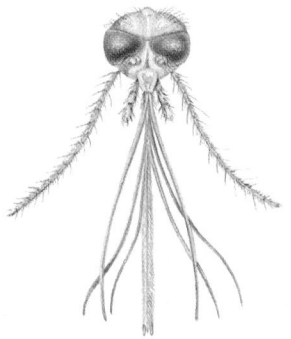

Ⓐ Sand flies and other insects that feed by drawing blood have piercing blades or needlelike mouthparts.

Ⓑ The rolled-up sucking tube of moths and butterflies can reach nectar at the bases of long, tubular flowers.

Ⓒ The sponging tongue of the housefly has an opening between its two lobes through which food is lapped.

28.1 CHARACTERISTICS OF ARTHROPODS **745**

3 Assess

Problem-Solving Lab 28.1

Use Numbers

How many are there? There are a lot of arthropod species on Earth. How does the number of arthropods compare with other animal species?

Numbers of Animal Species

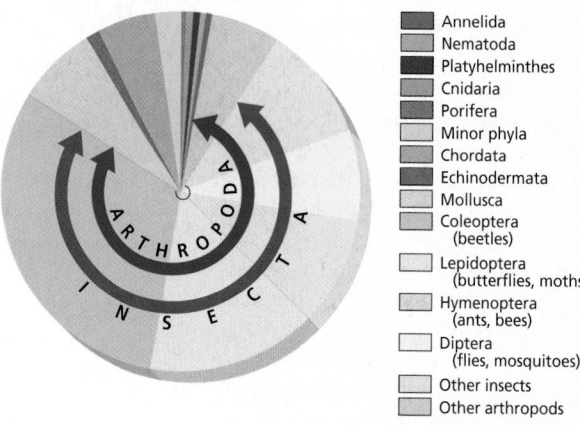

- Annelida
- Nematoda
- Platyhelminthes
- Cnidaria
- Porifera
- Minor phyla
- Chordata
- Echinodermata
- Mollusca
- Coleoptera (beetles)
- Lepidoptera (butterflies, moths)
- Hymenoptera (ants, bees)
- Diptera (flies, mosquitoes)
- Other insects
- Other arthropods

Solve the Problem
Examine the circle graph. Determine the number of species in each phylum or class by noting that each degree on the circle represents about 3000 species. (Note: You will need a protractor.)

Thinking Critically
1. **Analyze** About how many species of arthropods are known? What percentage of all animal species are arthropods?
2. **Analyze** Which class of arthropods makes up the larger category? How many species are in this class? What percentage of all arthropods is in this class? What percentage of all animal species is in this class?

rather than in each segment, as you have seen with nephridia in segmented worms. Malpighian tubules are attached to and empty into the intestine.

Another well-developed system in arthropods is the muscular system. In a human limb, muscles are attached to the outer surfaces of internal bones. In an arthropod limb, the muscles are attached to the inner surface of the exoskeleton. An arthropod muscle is attached to the exoskeleton on both sides of the joint.

Arthropods reproduce sexually

Most arthropod species have separate males and females and reproduce sexually. Fertilization is usually internal in land species but is often external in aquatic species. A few species, such as barnacles, are hermaphrodites, animals with both male and female reproductive organs. Some species, including bees, ants, aphids, and wasps, exhibit **parthenogenesis** (par thuh noh JE nuh sus), a form of asexual reproduction in which a new individual develops from an unfertilized egg.

Reproductive diversity is one reason there are more arthropod species than all other animal species combined. Find out how many species of arthropods there are by reading the *Problem-Solving Lab* on this page.

Section Assessment

Understanding Main Ideas
1. Describe the pathway taken by the blood as it circulates through an arthropod's body.
2. Describe two features that are common to arthropods.
3. What are the advantages and disadvantages of an exoskeleton?
4. How are compound eyes an adaptation to the way of life of some arthropods?

Thinking Critically
5. What characteristics of arthropods might explain why they are the most successful animals in terms of population sizes and numbers of species?

SKILL REVIEW
6. **Compare and Contrast** Compare the adaptations for gas exchange in aquatic and land arthropods. For more help, refer to *Compare and Contrast* in the **Skill Handbook**.

746 ARTHROPODS

 in.bdol.glencoe.com/self_check_quiz

Section Assessment

1. Blood is pumped by the heart through vessels. The blood flows out of the vessels, bathes the tissues of the body, and returns to the heart through open body spaces rather than through blood vessels.
2. jointed appendages, segmented bodies, exoskeletons
3. An exoskeleton is advantageous because it protects against water loss and injury. Disadvantages include its weight and inflexibility.
4. Compound eyes can detect the movements of prey, mates, or predators. The total image formed is made up of thousands of parts.
5. jointed appendages, exoskeletons, efficient gas exchange, wings in some, acute senses
6. Aquatic arthropods exchange gases through gills, which extract O_2 from water and release CO_2 into the water. Land arthropods have either tracheal tubes or book lungs. Tracheal tubes carry air throughout the body. Book lungs are chambers with leaflike plates for gas exchange.

Diversity of Arthropods

Indiana Standards Standard B.1.15 Understand and explain that, in biological systems, structure and function must be considered together.

SECTION PREVIEW

Objectives

Compare and contrast the similarities and differences among the major groups of arthropods.

Explain the adaptations of insects that contribute to their success.

Review Vocabulary
habitat: a place where an organism lives out its life (p. 42)

New Vocabulary
chelicerae
pedipalp
spinneret
metamorphosis
larva
pupa
nymph

Variety Is the Spice of Life

Using an Analogy You and your friends like the same things, except when you go out to eat. You want pizza, one friend wants tacos, and another friend is hungry for a burger. In the same way, all arthropods share common characteristics, but they have varied eating habits. Female mosquitoes drink blood. Other arthropods feed on nectar, dead organic matter, oil, and just about every other substance you can imagine.
Infer *What structures enable arthropods to eat varied diets? Explain.*

Female mosquito, *Aedes stimulans*

Bellringer
Section Focus Transparency 70

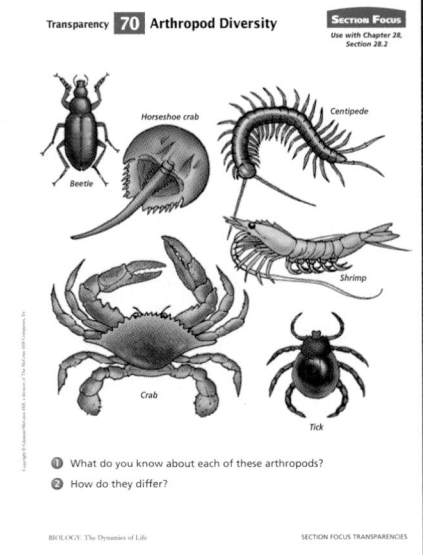

Transparency **70** Arthropod Diversity · SECTION FOCUS · Use with Chapter 28, Section 28.2

❶ What do you know about each of these arthropods?
❷ How do they differ?

BIOLOGY: The Dynamics of Life · SECTION FOCUS TRANSPARENCIES

Arachnids

Do you remember the last time you saw a spider? Did you draw back with a quick, fearful breath, or did you move a little closer, curious to see what it would do next? Of all 35 000 species of spiders, only about a dozen are dangerous to humans. In North America, you need to watch out for only the two species illustrated in *Figure 28.7*—the female black widow and the brown recluse.

What is an arachnid?

Spiders, scorpions, mites, and ticks belong to the class Arachnida (uh RAK nud uh). Spiders are the largest group of arachnids. Spiders and other arachnids have only two body regions—the cephalothorax and the abdomen. Arachnids have six pairs of jointed appendages.

Using an Analogy

Infer Mouthparts are modified to chew or take in a variety of foods. Legs are modified to capture prey or take in other materials. Digestive systems are modified to digest specific foods.

Word Origin

arachnid from the Greek word *arachne,* meaning "spider"; Spiders, and their relatives the scorpions, ticks, and mites, are arachnids.

Figure 28.7
The female black widow spider is shiny black with a red, hourglass-shaped spot on the underside of the abdomen **(A)**. The brown recluse is brown to yellow and has a violin-shaped mark on its head **(B)**. A bite from either spider will require prompt medical treatment.

RESOURCE MANAGER

Unit 8 *FAST FILE* Resources
MiniLab Worksheet, p. 100
BioLab Worksheet, pp. 101–102
Real World BioApplications, pp. 103–104, 105–106
Reinforcement and Study Guide in English, pp. 109–110
Reinforcement and Study Guide in Spanish, pp. 113–114

Transparency Worksheets, pp. 118, 121–124
Reading Essentials for Biology, Section 28.2
Laboratory Manual, pp. 175–178, 179–180
Inside Story Poster
 Section Focus Transparency 70
Reteaching Skills Transparencies 41, 42

Indiana Academic Standards

Pages 746–747: B.1.15, B.1.16

2 Teach

Caption Question Answer
Figure 28.8 Wash bedding regularly in hot water. Minimize window coverings and carpets. Clean and replace window and floor coverings regularly. Dust the home with specially treated cloths and mops that capture dust. A person allergic to dust mite droppings should not engage in cleaning activities and other activities that stir up dust.

Revealing Misconceptions

Many students think that pill bugs, also known as wood lice, are insects.

Uncover the Misconception

Pill bugs have all the characteristics of crustaceans even though they live on land. Pill bugs feed on detritus and fungi. They curl into a hard ball, like a "pill," when disturbed.

Demonstrate the Concept

Obtain pill bugs and have students look for crustacean characteristics: two pairs of antennae, two compound eyes, five pairs of walking legs. You may want to supply students with magnifying glasses to see these structures. Remind students of insect characteristics also.

Assess New Knowledge

Ask students to draw a diagram of a pill bug and ask them to point out its crustacean features.

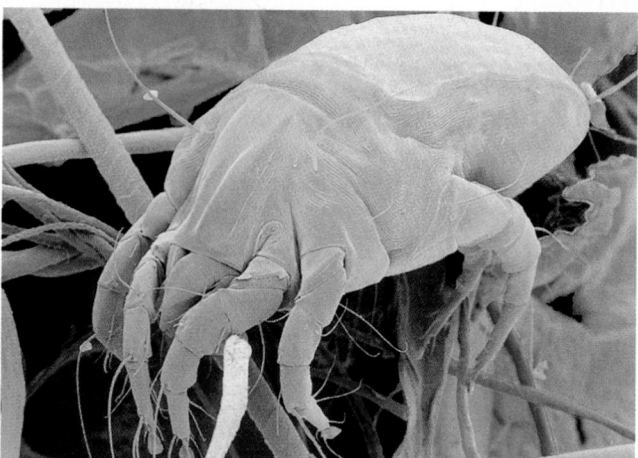

Color-enhanced SEM Magnification: 625×

Figure 28.8
Mites are distributed throughout the world and found in just about every habitat. House-dust mites feed on discarded skin cells that collect in dust on floors, in bedding, and on clothing. Some people are allergic to mite waste products. **Infer** *How might people who are allergic to dust mites reduce their exposure to the mite waste products?*

The first pair of appendages, called **chelicerae** (chih LIH suh ree), is located near the mouth. Chelicerae are often modified into pincers or fangs. Pincers are used to hold food, and fangs inject prey with poison. Spiders have no mandibles for chewing. Using a process of extracellular digestion, digestive enzymes from the spider's mouth liquefy the internal organs of the captured prey. The spider then sucks up the liquefied food.

The second pair of appendages, called the **pedipalps** (PE dih palpz), are adapted for handling food and for sensing. In male spiders, pedipalps are further modified to carry sperm during reproduction. The four remaining appendages in arachnids are adapted as legs for locomotion. Arachnids have no antennae.

Most people know spiders for their ability to make elaborate webs. Although all spiders spin silk, not all make webs. Spider silk is secreted by silk glands in the abdomen. As silk is secreted, it is spun into thread by structures called **spinnerets,** located at the rear of the spider. How does a spider catch its prey? Find out in *Figure 28.9* on the opposite page.

Ticks, mites, and scorpions: Spider relatives

Arachnida also includes ticks, mites, and scorpions. Ticks and mites differ from spiders in that they have only one body section, as shown in *Figure 28.8.* The head, thorax, and abdomen are completely fused. Ticks feed on blood from reptiles, birds, and mammals. They are small but capable of expanding up to 3 times or more of their original size after a blood meal. Ticks also can spread diseases.

Mites feed on fungi, plants, and animals. They are so small that they often are not visible to the unaided human eye. However, you can certainly feel their irritating bites. Like ticks, mites can transmit diseases.

Scorpions are easily recognized by their many abdominal body segments and enlarged pincers. They have a long tail with a venomous stinger at the tip. Scorpions live in warm, dry climates and eat insects and spiders. They use the poison in their stingers to paralyze large prey organisms.

Crustaceans

Crustaceans (krus TAY shuns) are the only arthropods that have two pairs of antennae for sensing. Some crustaceans have three body sections, and others have only two. All crustaceans have mandibles for crushing food and typically have two compound eyes, often located on movable stalks. Unlike the up-and-down movement of your jaws, crustacean mandibles open and close from side to side. Many crustaceans have five pairs of walking legs. A crustacean's walking legs are used for walking, seizing prey, and cleaning other appendages. The first pair of walking legs are often modified into strong claws for defense.

CHALLENGE ACTIVITY

Spider Poetry: *Linguistic* Have students work in pairs to write a limerick about a spider. Give them examples of limericks from anthologies of poetry and explain that a limerick is a humorous poem written in a special meter with five lines. Encourage them to include both humor and scientific accuracy in their limericks. **L3**

A Spider

Figure 28.9
The garden spider weaves an intricate and beautiful web, coats the threads with sticky droplets, and waits for a careless insect to get caught in them. Then the spider runs to wrap up and paralyze the insect, storing it for a future meal. Spiders are predatory animals, feeding almost exclusively on other arthropods. Many spiders build unique webs, which are effective in trapping flying insects. **Critical Thinking** *Explain how certain structures in spiders enable them to be effective predators.*

Garden spider

B Legs A spider's four pairs of walking legs are located on the cephalothorax.

C Cocoon Female spiders wrap their eggs in a silken sac or cocoon, where the eggs remain until they hatch. Some spiders lay their eggs and never see their young. Others carry the sac around with them until the eggs hatch.

A Simple eyes Spiders do not have compound eyes. They have six or eight simple eyes that, in most species, detect light but do not form images.

G Pedipalps A pair of pedipalps is used to hold and move food and also to function as sense organs. In males, pedipalps are bulbous and are used to carry sperm.

F Chelicerae Chelicerae are the two biting appendages of arachnids. In spiders, they are modified into fangs with poison glands located near the tips.

E Book lungs Gas exchange in spiders usually takes place in book lungs.

D Silk glands Spiders have seven types of silk glands, which first release silk as a liquid. The silk then passes through as many as 100 small tubes before being spun into thread by the spinnerets.

28.2 DIVERSITY OF ARTHROPODS **749**

INSIDE STORY

Purpose
Students learn about the structural and behavioral adaptations of spiders.

Teaching Strategies
- Explain to students that not all spiders spin webs. The tarantula is a fierce predator that stalks its prey and does not build webs. Such predators usually have thicker legs than web-building spiders.
- Have students create a table with these column heads: *Abdomen* and *Cephalothorax*. Beneath each head, have them list the structures of a spider that connect to that body part. **L2**

Visual Learning
As you point out each structure on the spider, have students use the caption to identify its function.

Critical Thinking
Fangs with poison glands enable spiders to paralyze and subdue their prey. Spiders build webs that snare prey.

CHALLENGE ACTIVITY

Spider Venom Spiders use their venom to paralyze or kill prey. However, their venom may have other uses for humans. Spider venom is being researched as an environmentally-friendly pesticide for crops such as cotton. Other research is focusing on medical uses in humans. Ask groups of students to report on the current medical research on venom from spiders. **L3**

 Indiana Academic Standards
Pages 748–749: B.1.15, B.1.43

749

Figure 28.10
Encased in armor plates, barnacles at first might not look like arthropods, but they have jointed limbs and their bodies inside the plates resemble those of their crustacean relatives.

Figure 28.11
A centipede may have from 15 to 181 body segments, each with one pair of legs (**A**). A millipede may have from 20 to more than 100 segments in its long abdomen, each with two spiracles and two pairs of legs (**B**).

Members of the class Crustacea include crabs, lobsters, shrimps, crayfishes, water fleas, pill bugs, and barnacles, shown in *Figure 28.10*. Most crustaceans are aquatic and exchange gases as water flows over feathery gills. Sow bugs and pill bugs, two of the few land crustaceans, must live where there is moisture, which aids in gas exchange. They are frequently found in damp areas around building foundations. You can observe crustaceans in the *BioLab* at the end of this chapter.

✓ **Reading Check** **Explain** the different uses of a crustacean's walking legs.

Centipedes and Millipedes

Centipedes, which belong to the class Chilopoda, and millipedes, members of the class Diplopoda, are shown in *Figure 28.11*. Like spiders, millipedes and centipedes have Malpighian tubules for excreting wastes. In contrast to spiders, centipedes and millipedes have tracheal tubes rather than book lungs for gas exchange.

If you have ever turned over a rock on a damp forest floor, you may have seen the flattened bodies of centipedes wriggling along on their many tiny, jointed legs. Centipedes are carnivorous and eat soil arthropods, snails, slugs, and worms. The bites of some centipedes are painful to humans.

A millipede eats mostly plants and dead material on damp forest floors. Millipedes do not bite, but they can spray foul-smelling fluids from their defensive stink glands. You may have seen their cylindrical bodies walking with a slow, graceful motion.

Horseshoe Crabs: Living Fossils

Horseshoe crabs are members of the class Merostomata. Of the three living genera, one, *Limulus*, is found along North America's East Coast,

750 ARTHROPODS

and two are found in the Asian tropics. Horseshoe crabs are considered to be living fossils; *Limulus* fossils have remained relatively unchanged since the Triassic Period about 220 million years ago.

Horseshoe crabs are heavily protected by an extensive exoskeleton and live in deep coastal waters. Shown in *Figure 28.12*, they forage on sandy or muddy ocean bottoms for algae, annelids, and mollusks. These arthropods migrate to shallow water in the spring, mating at night during high tide.

Figure 28.12
Horseshoe crabs have a semicircular exoskeleton and a long, pointed tail. They have four pairs of walking legs and five or six pairs of appendages that move water over their gills.

Insects

Have you ever launched an ambush on a fly with your rolled-up newspaper? You swat with great accuracy and speed, yet your prey is now firmly attached upside down on the kitchen ceiling. How does a fly do this?

The fly approaches the ceiling right-side up at a steep angle. Just before impact, it reaches up with its front legs. The forelegs grip the ceiling with tiny claws and sticky hairs, while the other legs swing up into position. The flight mechanism shuts off, and the fly is safely out of swatting distance. Adaptations that enable flies to land on ceilings are among the many that make insects the most successful arthropod group. How is the ability to fly an adaptive advantage to insects? Find out in *Figure 28.13* on the next page.

Flies, grasshoppers, lice, butterflies, bees, and beetles are just a few members of the class Insecta, by far the largest group of arthropods. Insects have three body segments and six legs. There are more species of insects than all other classes of animals combined. You can find out more about insects on pages 1080–1083 in the *Focus On*.

Insect reproduction

Insects usually mate once during their lifetime. The eggs usually are fertilized internally. Some insects exhibit parthenogenesis, reproducing from unfertilized eggs. In aphids, parthenogenesis produces all-female generations. Most insects lay a large number of eggs, which increases the chances that some offspring will survive long enough to reproduce. Many female insects are equipped with an appendage that can pierce through the surface of the ground or into wood. The female lays eggs in the hole.

Metamorphosis: Change in body shape and form

After eggs are laid, the insect embryo develops and the eggs hatch. In some wingless insects, such as silverfish, development is direct; the eggs hatch into miniature forms that look just like tiny adults. These insects go through successive molts until the adult size is reached. Many other species of insects undergo a series of major changes in body structure as they develop. In some cases, the adult insect bears little resemblance to its juvenile stage. This series of changes, controlled by chemical-substances in the animal, is called **metamorphosis** (me tuh MOR fuh sus).

Quick Demo

Observe a Chrysalis
Obtain a butterfly chrysalis from a biological supply company. Place it in a glass terrarium. Have students observe the chrysalis daily and make notes on any changes they see. **L1 ELL**

Struggling Learners
Present a slide show of a variety or arthropods. Review the characteristics of arthropods shown by each animal. Have students speculate about the likely habitat for each arthropod. **L1**

Display
Ask groups of students to design an arthropod that would be adapted to either water, soil, dry sand, the inside of trees, or living on another arthropod. Ask them to make sketches that show how their arthropods feed, defend themselves, and are adapted to their habitats. Display their sketches on the bulletin board. **L1 ELL**

CULTURAL DIVERSITY

Charles Henry Turner Have students report on the important contributions of African American biologist Charles Henry Turner (1867–1923) to our modern understanding of insect behavior. Turner's research included many species of insects, such as ants, bees, and cockroaches, and he often developed unique and interesting experimental techniques to study them. Turner was a very prolific scientist; between 1892 and 1923, he published 49 articles in the leading scientific journals of his time. **L2**

 Indiana Academic Standards

Pages 750–751: B.1.15, B.1.17, B.1.19, B.1.31

Purpose

Students will learn about the structural adaptations of grass-hoppers.

Teaching Strategies

■ Provide students with a live grasshopper in a large, clear container. Ask students to observe and describe its behavior. Have them examine the grasshopper under a stereo-scopic microscope and make a labeled sketch of its external body parts. Students should relate each structure to how the grasshopper is adapted to its environment. **L2**

■ Caution students that they are working with live animals and to treat them gently.

Visual Learning

Make an overhead transparency of the grasshopper with the labels covered. Ask students to label the lines pointing to grasshopper organs. Ask them to identify how each organ contributes to survival of the grasshopper. **L1** **ELL**

Critical Thinking

Grasshoppers have a complex nervous system consisting of a brain, a double ventral nerve cord, and several ganglia that act as control centers for other body sections.

A Grasshopper

Figure 28.13
Grasshoppers make rasping sounds either by rubbing their wings together or by rubbing small projections on their legs across a scraper on their wings. Most calls are made by males. Some aggressive calls are made when other males are close. Other calls attract females, and still others serve as an alarm to warn nearby grasshoppers of a predator in the area. Insects also use their wings to escape predators and to colonize new habitats. **Critical Thinking** *Do grasshoppers have a well-developed nervous system? Explain.*

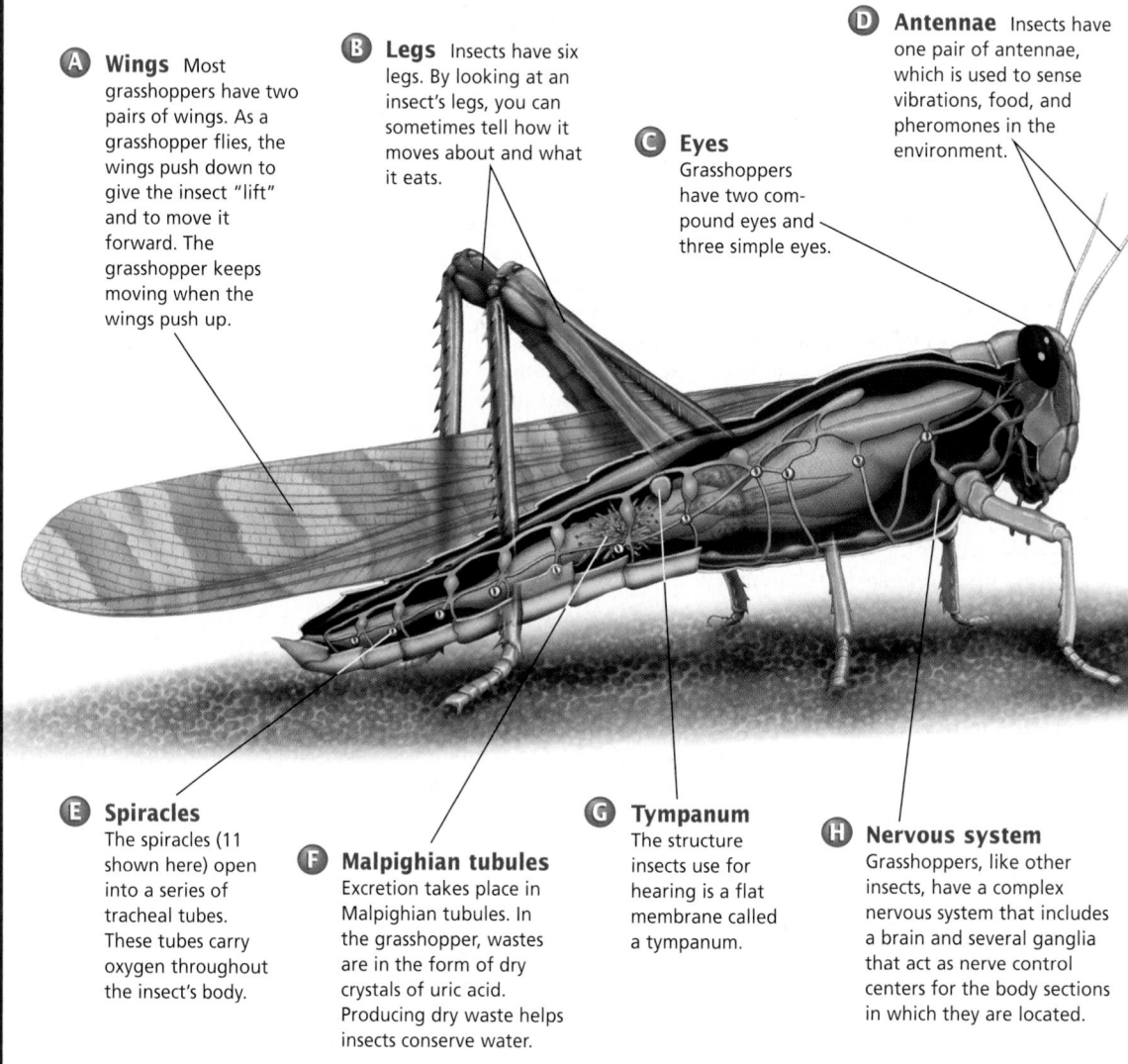

A **Wings** Most grasshoppers have two pairs of wings. As a grasshopper flies, the wings push down to give the insect "lift" and to move it forward. The grasshopper keeps moving when the wings push up.

B **Legs** Insects have six legs. By looking at an insect's legs, you can sometimes tell how it moves about and what it eats.

C **Eyes** Grasshoppers have two compound eyes and three simple eyes.

D **Antennae** Insects have one pair of antennae, which is used to sense vibrations, food, and pheromones in the environment.

E **Spiracles** The spiracles (11 shown here) open into a series of tracheal tubes. These tubes carry oxygen throughout the insect's body.

F **Malpighian tubules** Excretion takes place in Malpighian tubules. In the grasshopper, wastes are in the form of dry crystals of uric acid. Producing dry waste helps insects conserve water.

G **Tympanum** The structure insects use for hearing is a flat membrane called a tympanum.

H **Nervous system** Grasshoppers, like other insects, have a complex nervous system that includes a brain and several ganglia that act as nerve control centers for the body sections in which they are located.

752 ARTHROPODS

Identify Insects Ask student groups to make an insect light trap by putting a flashlight in a box with a 5 cm hole. They should set up their trap for several hours after dark and then cover the opening with tape and put the box into the freezer for an hour. This will immobilize the insects. Then have them empty their boxes, examine the insects with a hand lens, and identify the insects with a field guide. Have them count the number of each kind of insect trapped. Ask them to predict the diet and habitat of each insect based on their structural adaptations. **L2**
COOP LEARN

Figure 28.14
During complete metamorphosis, an insect undergoes a series of developmental changes from egg to adult.

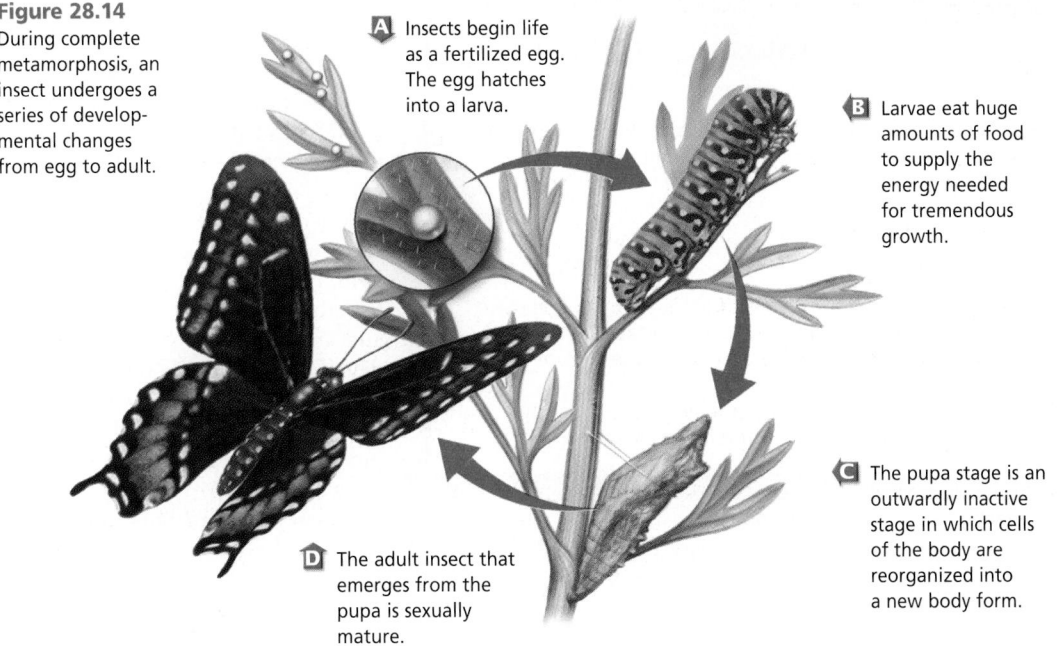

A Insects begin life as a fertilized egg. The egg hatches into a larva.

B Larvae eat huge amounts of food to supply the energy needed for tremendous growth.

C The pupa stage is an outwardly inactive stage in which cells of the body are reorganized into a new body form.

D The adult insect that emerges from the pupa is sexually mature.

Insects that undergo metamorphosis usually go through four stages on their way to adulthood: egg, larva, pupa, and adult. The **larva** is the free-living, wormlike stage of an insect, often called a caterpillar. As the larva eats and grows, it molts several times.

The **pupa** (PYEW puh) stage of insects is a period of reorganization in which the tissues and organs of the larva are broken down and replaced by adult tissues. Usually the insect does not move or feed during the pupa stage. After a period of time, a fully formed adult emerges from the pupa.

The series of changes that occur as an insect goes through the egg, larva, pupa, and adult stages is known as complete metamorphosis. In winged insects that undergo complete metamorphosis, the wings do not appear until the adult stage. More than 90 percent of insects undergo complete metamorphosis. The complete metamorphosis of a butterfly is illustrated in *Figure 28.14*. Other insects that undergo complete metamorphosis include ants, beetles, flies, and wasps.

Complete metamorphosis is an advantage for arthropods because larvae do not compete with adults for the same food. For example, butterfly larvae (caterpillars) feed on leaves, but adult butterflies feed on nectar from flowers. You can find out how destructive a caterpillar's diet can be in the *Biology and Society* feature at the end of this chapter.

Incomplete metamorphosis has three stages

Many insect species, as well as other arthropods, undergo a gradual or incomplete metamorphosis, in which the insect goes through only three stages of development.

Observe Fly Larvae Make a terrarium by using a 2-L soft drink bottle. Inside, place a small piece of raw meat that has been exposed to flies. Seal the terrarium. Have students observe and describe the larval stage of development of the flies that grow in the terrarium.

Enrichment
Linguistic Have each student prepare a report on the life cycle of the arthropod of their choice. **L2**

Project
Arthropod Origins Ask students to create a bulletin board display of arthropod origins. Instruct them to have one section of the bulletin board represent mollusk and annelid ancestors. Ask them to point out similarities and differences between these ancestors and present-day arthropods. **L2**

Inquiry
Activity Tell students that West Nile virus is transmitted by mosquitoes. Ask them to research information to find out how to control and help reduce the risk of West Nile virus in their community. Have them develop a public service announcement and poster that would alert the community about how to take action. They could contact the local Department of Health to determine what action has already been taken and devise a plan to determine the effectiveness of the action. **L3**

USING MODELS

Ideal Insects Supply students with clay or modeling dough and ask them to make a model and be prepared to describe the ideal insect adapted to an area that is very hot and dry during part of the year and very wet during another part of the year. Tell them that the temperature in the area remains constant all year. Students should use their knowledge of arthropods and insects to make their models. **L2**

Purpose

Students will compare and contrast patterns of metamorphosis.

Process Skills

compare and contrast, acquire information, collect data, hypothesize, observe and infer

Safety Precautions

Remind students to use tongs, forceps, and/or protective gloves when handling specimens. Students should wash their hands thoroughly with soap and water after completing the activity.

Teaching Strategies

■ You will have to mark the different stages of each life cycle so students can identify them.
■ Legs may be a good indicator of the stage being capable of movement. Mouthparts may provide evidence of feeding.

Expected Results

See data table below.

Analysis

1. A grasshopper has incomplete metamorphosis. The moth has complete metamorphosis.
2. The stages that were able to move are the only stages in which feeding occurs.
3. The nymph stage looks like a small adult, but it lacks wings and is sexually immature.

Modified Assessment

Knowledge Show students photos of different insects undergoing metamorphosis. Ask them to determine if the animal shown exhibits complete or incomplete metamorphosis. Use the Performance Task Assessment List for Making Observations and Inferences in **PASC,** p. 89. **L1**

MiniLab 28.2

Compare and Contrast

Comparing Patterns of Metamorphosis Insects undergo a series of developmental changes called metamorphosis. But not all insects follow the same pattern of metamorphosis.

Procedure

1. Copy the data table.
2. Examine the three life stages of a grasshopper. Complete the information called for in your data table. **CAUTION:** *Wear disposable protective gloves and use forceps to handle preserved insects.*
3. Examine the four life stages of a moth. Complete the information called for in your data table.

Data Table

Insect	Grasshopper			Moth			
Stage	Egg	Nymph	Adult	Egg	Larva	Pupa	Adult
Locomotion method							
Feeding method							
Able to reproduce							

Analysis

1. **Observe** What are the differences between the stages of metamorphosis of a grasshopper and those of a moth?
2. **Analyze** Correlate the ability to move with ability to feed.
3. **Compare** How are the nymph stage and the adult stage of the grasshopper similar?

These three stages are egg, nymph, and adult, as shown in *Figure 28.15.* A **nymph,** which hatches from an egg, has the same general appearance as the adult but is smaller. Nymphs may lack certain appendages, or have appendages not seen in adults, and they cannot reproduce. As the nymph eats and grows, it molts several times. With each molt, it begins to resemble the adult more. Wings begin to form, and an internal reproductive system develops. Gradually, the nymph becomes an adult. Grasshoppers and cockroaches are insects that undergo incomplete metamorphosis. You can compare the two types of metamorphosis in the *MiniLab* on this page.

Origins of Arthropods

Arthropods have been enormously successful in establishing themselves over the entire surface of Earth. Their ability to survive in just about every habitat is unequaled in the animal kingdom. The success of arthropods can be attributed in part to their varied life cycles, high reproductive output, and structural adaptations, such as small size, a hard exoskeleton, and jointed appendages. How did arthropods evolve?

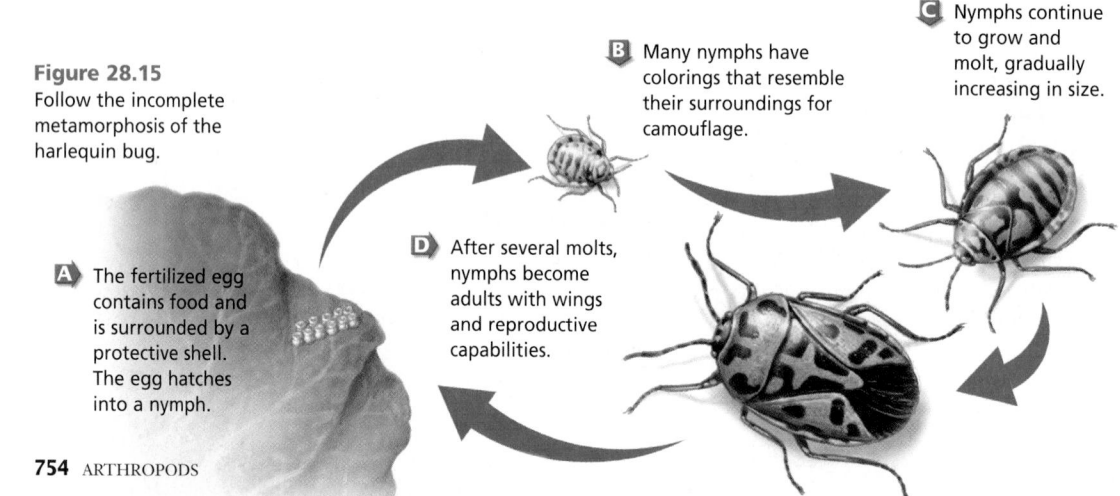

Figure 28.15
Follow the incomplete metamorphosis of the harlequin bug.

A The fertilized egg contains food and is surrounded by a protective shell. The egg hatches into a nymph.

B Many nymphs have colorings that resemble their surroundings for camouflage.

C Nymphs continue to grow and molt, gradually increasing in size.

D After several molts, nymphs become adults with wings and reproductive capabilities.

754 ARTHROPODS

Data Table

Insect	Grasshopper			Moth			
Stage	Egg	Nymph	Adult	Egg	Larva	Pupa	Adult
Locomotion method	no	yes	yes	no	yes	no	yes
Feeding method	no	yes	yes	no	yes	no	yes
Able to reproduce	no	no	yes	no	no	no	yes

Figure 28.16
The radiation of classes of arthropods shows their relationships.

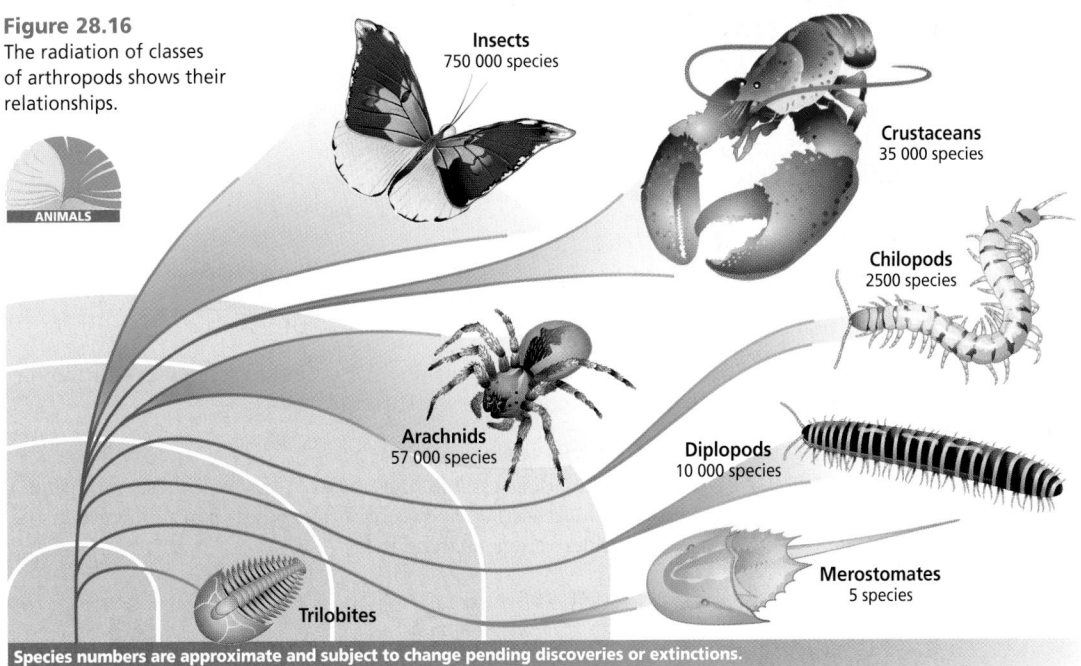

Insects
750 000 species

Crustaceans
35 000 species

Chilopods
2500 species

Arachnids
57 000 species

Diplopods
10 000 species

Merostomates
5 species

Trilobites

ANIMALS

Species numbers are approximate and subject to change pending discoveries or extinctions.

Arthropods most likely evolved from an ancestor of the annelids. As arthropods evolved, body segments fused and became adapted for certain functions such as locomotion, feeding, and sensing the environment. Segments in arthropods are more complex than in annelids, and arthropods have more developed nerve tissue and sensory organs, such as eyes.

The exoskeleton of arthropods provides protection for their soft bodies. Muscles in arthropods are arranged in bands associated with particular segments and portions of appendages. The circular muscles of annelids do not exist in arthropods. Because arthropods have many hard parts, much is known about their evolutionary history. The trilobites shown in *Figure 28.16* were once an important group of ancient arthropods, but they have been extinct for 248 million years.

Section Assessment

Understanding Main Ideas
1. Describe three major adaptations that contribute to the success of insects.

2. How are insects different from spiders?

3. Describe three sensory adaptations of insects.

4. Compare the stages of complete and incomplete metamorphosis.

Thinking Critically
5. Why might complete metamorphosis have greater adaptive value for an insect than incomplete metamorphosis?

SKILL REVIEW
6. **Get the Big Picture** Some plants produce substances that prevent insect larvae from forming pupae. How might this chemical production be a disadvantage to the plant? For more help, refer to *Get the Big Picture* in the **Skill Handbook.**

in.bdol.glencoe.com/self_check_quiz

28.2 DIVERSITY OF ARTHROPODS **755**

Section Assessment

1. varied life cycles, high reproductive output, small size, hard exoskeleton, jointed appendages
2. Spiders have two body regions, six pairs of appendages, book lungs, simple eyes, and spin silk. Insects generally have three body regions, three pairs of legs, one pair of antennae, spiracles, and compound eyes.
3. Insects have compound eyes, antennae, tympanums, and sensitive hairs over parts of the body.
4. Complete metamorphosis has four stages: egg, larva, pupa, and adult. Incomplete metamorphosis has three stages: egg, nymph, and adult.
5. Complete metamorphosis is an advantage because the larvae do not compete with adults for food.
6. Although the larval stage is most destructive to plants, many plants require the adult insects for pollination.

755

---

3 Assess

DAILY INTERVENTION

Check for Understanding
Give students a list of traits for an arthropod. Have them determine which arthropod class the traits describe. **L2**

Reteach
Have students make a chart on arthropod classes. Have them include an illustration in each column that shows the number of body sections, antennae positions, and numbers of legs. **L1**

Resources
For more practice, use *Reading Essentials for Biology,* Section 28.2.

Extension
Kinesthetic Have students use modeling clay and pipe cleaners to make models of centipedes and millipedes. **L1 ELL**

✓ MODIFIED Assessment

Performance Divide the class into two groups. Play the "Who am I?" game. A member of one group will call out clues, while a member of the second group guesses the class of the arthropod. A correct answer will earn the team one point. **L1 COOP LEARN**

Indiana Academic Standards

Pages 754–755: B.1.11, B.1.15, B.1.32

Time Allotment

one class period for set up, then 10 minutes per day for 3 days

Process Skills

collect data, identify and control variables, design an experiment, draw a conclusion, experiment, hypothesize, interpret data, observe and infer, organize data

Safety Precautions

Remind students to wear goggles to protect their eyes.

PREPARATION

■ Purchase brine shrimp eggs from a pet store or biological supply house.
■ Plan the experiment so that it starts on a Monday.
■ Plastic trays are available from the meat or produce department in most grocery stores.
■ Review the procedure for preparation of 1, 2, and 4% salt solutions.
■ Use noniodized table salt (kosher or sea salt). Check to make sure that iodine has not been added.

Possible Hypotheses

Students may hypothesize that hatching will not occur in any salt solution. Students may hypothesize that hatching will occur only in salt concentrations higher than 10% but lower than 20%.

PLAN THE EXPERIMENT

Teaching Strategies

■ Have students work in small groups of 3 or 4 students.
■ At the conclusion of the experiment, pool student data so students can see the results when a range of different salt concentrations are tested.
■ Judging the amount or degree of

756

 Before You Begin

Brine shrimp (*Artemia salina*) belong to the class Crustacea. They are excellent experimental animals because their eggs hatch into visible swimming larvae within a very short time. Using the name as a clue, where might these animals normally be found?

Will salt concentration affect brine shrimp hatching?

PREPARATION

Problem

How can you determine the optimum salt concentration for the hatching of brine shrimp eggs?

Hypotheses

Formulate a testable hypothesis. Your hypothesis might be that increased salt concentrations result in an increase in the number of eggs hatched.

Objectives

In this BioLab, you will:
■ **Analyze** how salt concentration may affect brine shrimp hatching.
■ **Interpret** your experimental findings.

Possible Materials

beakers or plastic bottles	clear plastic trays
labels or marking pencil	salt (noniodized)
graduated cylinder	balance
brine shrimp eggs	water

Safety Precautions

CAUTION: *Be sure to treat the brine shrimp in a humane manner at all times. Always wear goggles in the lab.*

Skill Handbook

If you need help with this lab, refer to the **Skill Handbook.**

PLAN THE EXPERIMENT

1. Decide on a way to test your group's hypothesis. Keep the available materials in mind as you plan your procedure. Be sure to include a control. For example, you might place brine shrimp eggs in two trays—one with the salt concentration of the water brine shrimp normally inhabit, and one with a different salt concentration.

hatching may be a problem. Brine shrimp hatchlings cannot be seen by the unaided human eye. Observing trays under a binocular microscope will allow students to make a qualitative assessment of the amount of hatching.

Possible Procedures

■ Students may prepare only 2 or 3

different salt concentrations. Make sure that the control dish contains only water and no salt.
■ Students will need to use the same amount of eggs in each tray. Counting eggs is difficult because of their small size. One suggestion is to touch the flat end of a toothpick to the eggs and transfer that same amount to each dish.

2. Decide how long you will make observations and how you will judge the extent of egg hatching.

3. Decide on the number of different salt water concentrations to use and what these concentrations will be. Review the steps needed to prepare solutions of different concentrations.

Check the Plan
Discuss the following points with other group members to decide on the final procedure for your experiment.

1. What is your single independent variable? Your dependent variable? What will be your control?

2. How much water will you add to each tray? How will you measure the same number of eggs to be used in each tray?

3. Will it be necessary to hold variables such as light and temperature constant?

4. What data will you collect and how will it be recorded?

5. *Make sure your teacher has approved your experimental plan before you proceed further.*

6. Carry out your experiment.

7. **CLEANUP AND DISPOSAL** Return the brine shrimp to your teacher. Wash your hands with soap and water after working with brine shrimp.

LM Magnification: 18×

Brine shrimp hatchling

ANALYZE AND CONCLUDE

1. **Interpret Data** Using specific numbers from your data, explain how salt concentration affects brine shrimp hatching.

2. **Draw a Conclusion** Was your hypothesis supported? Analyze the strengths and weaknesses of your hypothesis using your data.

3. **Identify and Control Variables** What were the independent and dependent variables? What were some of the variables that had to be held constant?

4. **Hypothesize** Formulate a hypothesis that explains why high salt concentrations may be harmful to brine shrimp hatching.

5. **Classify** Classify brine shrimp. Identify their kingdom, phylum, class, order, family, genus, and species.

Apply Your Skill

Project Design an experiment that you could perform to investigate the role that temperature plays in brine shrimp hatching. If you have all of the materials you will need, you may want to carry out the experiment.

Web Links To find out more about brine shrimp and other crustaceans, visit in.bdol.glencoe.com/crustaceans

28.2 DIVERSITY OF ARTHROPODS **757**

ANALYZE AND CONCLUDE

1. Students answers may vary; maximum hatching will occur at 1–4% salt concentration.

2. Student answers will vary depending upon their original hypothesis.

3. The independent variable was the salt concentration. The dependent variable was the number of eggs hatched. Other variables that had to be held constant were the temperature of the water, amount of water used, and number of eggs used.

4. Too high a salt concentration may result in water loss from the egg or larva, leading to dessication.

5. animal, Arthropoda, Crustacea, Anostraca, *Artemia salina*

Assessment

Skill Have students design an experiment that would determine how much time brine shrimp larvae spend in this stage. Use the Performance Task Assessment List for Designing an Experiment in **PASC**, p. 95. **L2**

Apply Your Skill

Project Have students carry out an experiment to determine if brine shrimp larvae respond in a similar manner to different colors of light. **L2**

■ Keep all trays at a temperature close to 21°C.

Data and Observations

Ideal salt concentrations for hatching will be in the 1–4% range. No salt present or concentrations higher than 4% may result in fewer larvae hatching.

CLEANUP AND DISPOSAL

 Encourage students to make wise choices about reusing or disposing of lab materials. When brine shrimp are no longer needed, they may be flushed with water into the lab sink drain.

Indiana Academic Standards

Pages 756–757: B.1.17

Biology and Society

Purpose

Students learn how gypsy moths spread, understand the problems gypsy moths pose for the economy and the environment, and explore solutions to those problems.

Teaching Strategies

■ Gypsy moth caterpillars feed on some three hundred different species of tree and shrub leaves, but have a preference for oak trees. Oak is a valuable hardwood in the timber business.

■ Since the females don't fly, gypsy moths spread only about thirteen miles each year. This spread is largely due to the caterpillars "ballooning" on silken threads in search of other food sources.

■ Egg masses laid on vehicles, tents, and other portable items have caused isolated outbreaks in areas previously unaffected by the gypsy moth.

Investigating the Issue

Natural pathogens can also be used to eradicate gypsy moths. Nucleopolyhedrosis virus (NPV) can collapse a gypsy moth outbreak. Entomophaga maimaiga (Em) is a fungus that is highly effective in wet conditions. However, both pathogens usually move into an area only after a major outbreak and are difficult to introduce as a preventative measure. Gypcheck, an EPA-approved formulation of NPV, is difficult and costly to produce. The only known way to import Em spores is to collect spore-containing soils or infected gypsy moth caterpillar cadavers and spread them around trees in infested areas.

One treatment that has proved effective against low-level populations is the spraying of pheromone flakes, which inundates an area with the scent that female gypsy moths emit to

Gypsy Moths Move Westward

Gypsy moths have wreaked havoc on American forests for nearly 150 years. Their gradual westward expansion is forcing more states to consider solutions to what is becoming a serious economic problem.

Perspectives When Frenchman Ettiene Leopold Trouvelot immigrated to the United States in 1856, he hoped to start a silk industry in suburban Boston. At the time, the gypsy moth was classified in the same genus as the silkworm, so he mistakenly thought they could produce silk. This classification was later proven wrong, but not before Trouvelot had imported thousands of eggs to his Medford, Massachusetts home.

As Trouvelot turned his attentions away from his failed silk business, his caterpillars took over Medford and spread throughout New England. By the time the devastating effects of the gypsy moth were first apparent, Trouvelot had returned to France.

During the next 130 years, the insects established themselves from Ontario, Canada, to North Carolina, and well into the Midwest, stripping the leaves from two million acres of hardwood forests every year.

The problem Gypsy moth caterpillars pose an environmental and economic threat. Healthy trees can survive one or two outbreaks, but survival rates drop after three consecutive years. Timber and tourism industries, among others, suffer when trees are destroyed. But eradicating the gypsy moth poses problems of its own.

The controversy Insecticides are among the most effective way of dealing with the moths, with *Bacillus thuringiensis* (thu rihn JEN sus) *kurstaki* (Btk) leading the attack. Btk is a naturally occurring soil bacteria that affects only moths and butterflies, and only in their larval stage. It is approved for use on food and grain

Gypsy moth with egg mass

Gypsy moth caterpillar

crops, including organic products, in the United States. Caterpillars eat vegetation sprayed with Btk and die within seven to ten days.

Btk does not only affect gypsy moth caterpillars. Hundreds of other moth and butterfly species have larval stages that coincide with that of the gypsy moth. Conservationists claim many rare and endangered species will be lost if Btk treatments become widespread. They also point out that the best Btk can do is slow the gypsy moth, not stop it entirely.

A difficult decision Some areas are choosing to fight the spread of the gypsy moth, risking the biodiversity of their regions. Others are letting nature take its course, losing acres of hardwood forests and animal habitat as a result. Meanwhile, the search for a solution continues.

Investigating the Issue

Form Your Opinion Research alternatives to Btk for eradicating gypsy moths. Form an opinion about which treatment you would choose, then explain your position in a report to your class.

 To find out more about gypsy moths, visit in.bdol.glencoe.com/biology_society

attract a mate. The males become confused and have difficulty finding a mate. If the gypsy moths cannot find a mate, they die off without producing any offspring.

Going Further

When Btk is used to control a gypsy moth population, it also has direct effects on other insect populations. These other insects might die or fail to reproduce. What effect would this have on the entire food chain?

STUDY GUIDE

Section 28.1

Characteristics of Arthropods

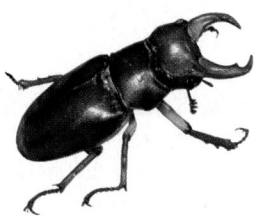

Key Concepts

- Phylum Arthropoda includes diverse groups of animals. However, arthropods have several characteristics in common. They are invertebrates with bilateral symmetry, they have exoskeletons and jointed appendages, and they undergo molting.
- Arthropods have varied life cycles and complex body systems.
- Arthropods are members of the most successful animal phylum in terms of diversity. This can be attributed in part to their structural and behavioral adaptations, which allow them to live on land, in water, or in air.

Vocabulary

appendage (p. 741)
book lung (p. 744)
cephalothorax (p. 743)
compound eye (p. 745)
mandible (p. 745)
Malpighian tubule (p. 745)
molting (p. 742)
parthenogenesis (p. 746)
pheromone (p. 745)
simple eye (p. 745)
spiracle (p. 744)
tracheal tube (p. 744)

Section 28.2

The Diversity of Arthropods

Key Concepts

- Arachnids include spiders, scorpions, mites, and ticks. Spiders have two body regions with four pairs of walking legs. They spin silk. Ticks and mites have one body section. They can spread diseases to animals and humans. Scorpions have many abdominal segments, enlarged pincers, and a venomous stinger at the end of the tail.
- Most crustaceans are aquatic and exchange gases in their gills. They include crabs, lobsters, shrimps, crayfishes, barnacles, and water fleas. Crustaceans typically have two or three body sections.
- Centipedes are carnivores with flattened, wormlike bodies. Millipedes are herbivores with cylindrical, wormlike bodies.
- Horseshoe crabs are considered to be living fossils, having remained relatively unchanged for millions of years.
- Insects are the most successful arthropod class in terms of diversity. They have many structural and behavioral adaptations that allow them to exploit all habitats.

Vocabulary

chelicerae (p. 748)
larva (p. 753)
metamorphosis (p. 751)
nymph (p. 754)
pedipalp (p. 748)
pupa (p. 753)
spinneret (p. 748)

FOLDABLES

Study Organizer To help you review the diversity of arthropods, use the Organizational Study Fold on page 741.

 in.bdol.glencoe.com/vocabulary_puzzlemaker

Key Concepts

Summary statements can be used by students to review the major concepts of the chapter.

Biology Online

Visit in.bdol.glencoe.com
/self_check_quiz
/vocabulary_puzzlemaker
/chapter_test
/standardized_test

VOCABULARY PUZZLEMAKER

For additional help with vocabulary, have students access the Vocabulary PuzzleMaker online at in.bdol.glencoe.com/ vocabulary_puzzlemaker

FOLDABLES™

Have students use their Foldables to review the content of Section 28.1.

Use the ExamView®Pro Test Bank CD-ROM to:

- Create **multiple versions** of tests
- Create **modified** tests with one mouse click for **inclusion** students
- **Edit** existing questions and **add** your own questions
- Build tests aligned with state standards using built-in **State Curriculum Tags**
- Change **English** tests to **Spanish** with one mouse click and vice versa

 Indiana Academic Standards

Pages 758–759: B.1.15, B.1.19, B.1.38

Chapter 28 Assessment

The Princeton Review **Questions and answers have been aligned and verified by The Princeton Review.**

Vocabulary Review

1. spiracles
2. pupa
3. pheromones
4. molting
5. appendage

Understanding Key Concepts

6. B	**9.** B	**12.** D
7. C	**10.** B	
8. D	**11.** C	

Constructed Response

13. An insect larva may eat crop plants, but an adult may pollinate the flowers.
14. The aphid would not need to find a mate as the unfertilized egg can develop into an adult.
15. The eyes would give the crustacean a greater field of view.

Thinking Critically

16. 1. appendages; 2. pedipalps; 3. chelicerae; 4. mandibles
17. Answers will vary depending on which insects students choose.
18. Pets can pick up ticks when they are outdoors in an area inhabited by ticks and deer.
19. Many plants that depend on insects for pollination would be unable to reproduce, so there would be fewer plants. Plants that are eaten by insects would increase in number if they are not dependent on insects for pollination.

Indiana Academic Standards

Pages 760–761: B.1.15, B.1.17, B.1.19, B.1.34, B.1.43

760

Vocabulary Review

Review the Chapter 28 vocabulary words listed in the Study Guide on page 759. Match the words with the definitions below.

1. openings on the thorax and abdomen through which air enters and leaves the tracheal tubes
2. stage of insect metamorphosis where tissues and organs are broken down and replaced by adult tissues
3. chemical odor signals given off by animals that signal them to engage in behaviors
4. the periodic shedding of an old exoskeleton
5. any structure, such as an antenna or a leg, that grows out of an animal's body

Understanding Key Concepts

6. Crustaceans are different from other arthropods because they have two _____ used for sensing.
   A. jointed appendages C. pedipalps
   B. pairs of antennae D. walking legs
7. Jointed appendages allow for greater _____ and more powerful movements.
   A. mobility C. flexibility
   B. molting D. camouflage
8. Which of the following structures are spiracles?

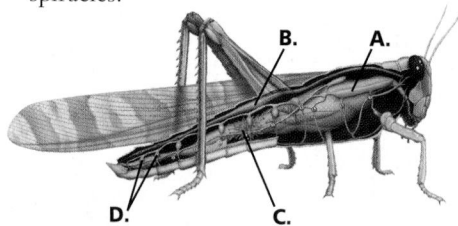

9. _____ are used by arthropods for gas exchange.
   A. Pedipalps C. Chelicerae
   B. Spiracles D. Spinnerets
10. A butterfly excretes wastes through _____.
   A. spinnerets C. spiracles
   B. Malpighian tubules D. tracheal tubes

11. Molting occurs when an arthropod sheds its old _____ and grows a new one.
   A. shell C. exoskeleton
   B. endoskeleton D. skin
12. The middle stage of incomplete metamorphosis is the _____.
   A. larva C. pupa
   B. egg D. nymph

Constructed Response

13. **Open Ended** Explain why many insects are pests to humans when they are larvae but are beneficial when they are adults.
14. **Open Ended** Why is it an adaptive advantage for aphids to exhibit parthenogenesis when they reproduce?
15. **Open Ended** Explain why it would be an advantage for a crustacean that has a cephalothorax to also have movable, stalked eyes.

Thinking Critically

16. **Concept Map** Complete the concept map by using the following vocabulary terms: appendages, mandibles, chelicerae, pedipalps.

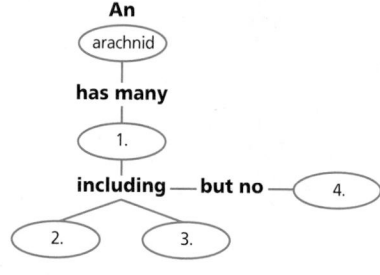

17. **REAL WORLD BIOCHALLENGE** Many arthropods make sounds. Researchers have discovered the mechanism of sound production in some arthropods. Visit **in.bdol.glencoe.com** to investigate the production of sound by a variety of arthropods, such as cicadas, ants, crickets, and snapping shrimp. Present the results of your research to your class in the form of a poster or multimedia presentation.

 in.bdol.glencoe.com/chapter_test

RUBRIC

Evaluating Open-Ended Questions
Open-ended assessment questions are graded by using a multilevel rubric that guides you in assessing a student's knowledge of a particular concept. The following rubric is a sample scoring device.

18. Infer How could household pets become infected with a disease usually found in deer?

19. Hypothesize What might happen to plant life if all insects were to die suddenly?

End-of-Course Assessment Practice

Use with pages 760–761 of the Student Edition

20. B **22.** A **24.** D
21. B **23.** B

25. The time of death of a body found outdoors can be determined by what kinds of insects are on the body. By examining chemicals in the insects, forensic entomologists can gain information about chemicals in the body at the time of death.

26. Because spiders eat insects, the populations of insects preyed upon by spiders increase. As particular insect populations increase, their predators increase. An unbalanced community is created as some of the insect populations that increase feed on plants that decrease, thereby changing the nature of the habitat and niches available for other animals.

End-of-Course Assessment Practice

All questions aligned and verified by *The Princeton Review*

Part 1 Multiple Choice
Use the map to answer questions 20 and 21.

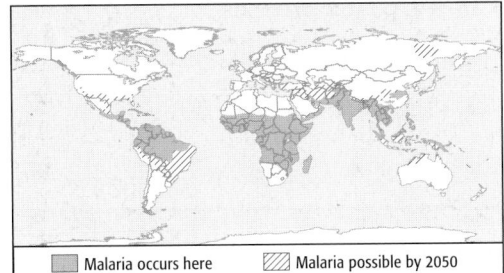

☐ Malaria occurs here ▨ Malaria possible by 2050

20. Some scientists predict that warming climate trends will continue, expanding suitable habitats for mosquitoes that transmit the disease-causing agent of malaria. What states might have suitable habitats by 2050 for malaria-carrying mosquitoes?
A. New England states and the Midwest
B. Florida, Texas, Louisiana, California, Washington
C. Minnesota, Michigan, Wisconsin
D. Alaska and Hawaii

21. Malaria mosquito habitats may expand to northern Australia and the southern United States because these areas may become _____.
A. cooler   **C.** wetter
B. warmer   **D.** drier

Study the graph and answer questions 22–24.

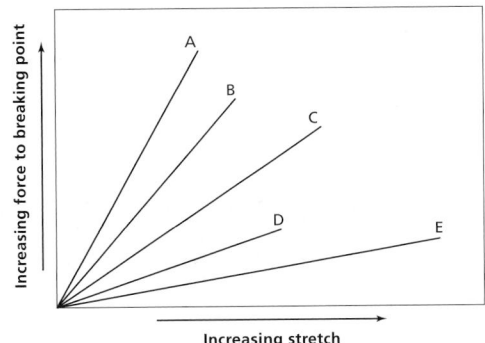

Force/Stretch Required to Break Silk of Various Spiders

Increasing force to breaking point

Increasing stretch

22. Which spider's silk stretched the most before breaking?
A. E   **C.** D
B. A   **D.** B

23. Which spider's silk requires a force greater than the others to break?
A. E   **C.** B
B. A   **D.** D

24. You want to make a fabric of spider silk that has a great deal of stretch. Which spider silk will you investigate first?
A. A   **C.** D
B. B   **D.** E

Part 2 Constructed Response/Grid in
Record your answers on your answer document.

25. Open Ended How can insects help criminal investigators solve crimes?

26. Open Ended What would happen to an ecological community if all spiders were eliminated?

 in.bdol.glencoe.com/standardized_test

 FAST FILE

Answer Sheet A practice answer sheet can be found on p. 131 of *Unit 8 FAST FILE Resources.*

RUBRIC

SCORE	CRITERIA
4	A correct solution that is supported by well-developed, accurate explanations.
3	A generally correct solution, but may contain minor flaws in reasoning.

SCORE	CRITERIA
2	A partially correct interpretation and/or solution to the problem.
1	A correct solution with no supporting evidence or explanation.
0	An incorrect solution or no solution is given.

Chapter 29 Organizer

Section Objectives	National Science Standards	State/Local Standards	Advanced Lab and Demo Planning
Section 29.1 1/2 session, 1/2 block 1. **Compare** similarities and differences among the classes of echinoderms. 2. **Interpret** the evidence biologists have for determining that echinoderms are close relatives of chordates.	UCP.1–5; A.1, A.2; C.3–6	**Indiana Standards** B.1.15, B.1.19, B.1.32, B.1.43	**Student Labs:** MiniLab 29.1, p. 764: slide of sea star pedicellariae, microscope Problem-Solving Lab 29.1, p. 768 **Teacher Demonstration:** Quick Demo, p. 765: dropper
Section 29.2 1 1/2 sessions, 1/2 block 3. **Summarize** the characteristics of chordates. 4. **Explain** how invertebrate chordates are related to vertebrates. 5. **Distinguish** between sea squirts and lancelets.	UCP.1–5; A.1, A.2; B.4; C.2, C.3, C.5, C.6; E.2; G.1, G.2	**Indiana Standards** B.1.15, B.1.19, B.1.32	**Student Labs:** Additional Lab, p. 772: compound microscope, prepared slides of sea urchin development, prepared slides of lancelets MiniLab 29.2, p. 773: preserved lancelet, glass slide, forceps, dissecting microscope Problem-Solving Lab 29.2, p. 775 Investigate BioLab, p. 776: See materials below. **Teacher Demonstration:** Quick Demo, p. 771: preserved or mounted specimens of tunicates and lancelets
End of Chapter Assessment **Student Edition** **Study Guide**, p. 779 **Content Assessment**, pp. 780–781		**Indiana Standards** B.1.15, B.1.19, B.1.43	**Student Lab:** Investigate BioLab, p. 776: preserved specimens of sea star, sea urchin, sand dollar, sea cucumber; forceps; culture or petri dish; toothpicks

Key to Teaching Strategies

L1 Level 1 activities should be appropriate for students with learning difficulties.

L2 Level 2 activities should be within the ability range of all students.

L3 Level 3 activities are designed for above-average students.

ELL ELL activities should be within the ability range of English Language Learners.

COOP LEARN Cooperative Learning activities are designed for small group work.

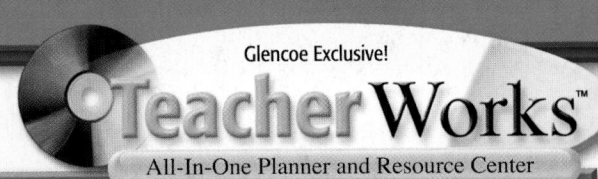

Glencoe Exclusive!
TeacherWorks™
All-In-One Planner and Resource Center

Reproducible Masters and Transparencies	Technology

Reproducible Masters and Transparencies

Unit 8 FAST FILE Resources
MiniLab Worksheet, p. 135
Reinforcement and Study Guide in English, pp. 139–141
Reinforcement and Study Guide in Spanish, pp. 143–145
Critical Thinking/Problem Solving, p. 148
Transparency Worksheets, pp. 149, 151–153
Reading Essentials for Biology, Section 29.1
Laboratory Manual, pp. 181–184, 185–186
Section Focus Transparency 71
Basic Concepts Transparencies 50, 51

Technology

◉ **Interactive Chalkboard CD-ROM: Section 29.1 Presentation**
◉ **TeacherWorks™ CD-ROM**
🎵 **Guided Reading Audio Summaries MP3**

Unit 8 FAST FILE Resources
MiniLab Worksheet, p. 136
BioLab Worksheet, pp. 137–138
Reinforcement and Study Guide in English, p. 142
Reinforcement and Study Guide in Spanish, p. 146
Concept Mapping, p. 147
Transparency Worksheets, pp. 150, 155–156
Reading Essentials for Biology, Section 29.2
Section Focus Transparency 72
Reteaching Skills Transparency 43

◉ **Interactive Chalkboard CD-ROM: Section 29.2 Presentation**
◉ **TeacherWorks™ CD-ROM**
🎵 **Guided Reading Audio Summaries MP3**

Unit 8 FAST FILE Resources
Chapter Assessment, pp. 157–162
Student Recording Sheet, p. 163

The Princeton Review **Reviewing Biology,** pp. 57–58

◉ **Interactive Chalkboard: Chapter 29 Assessment**
◉ **MindJogger Videoquizzes DVD/VHS**
◉ **ExamView® Pro Test Bank CD-ROM**
◉ **TeacherWorks™ CD-ROM**
◉ **Succeeding on National Standards CD-ROM**

in.bdol.glencoe.com
/self_check_quiz
/vocabulary_puzzlemaker
/chapter_test
/standardized_test

Indicates materials created specifically for Indiana.

Short on Time?

BIODIGEST The BioDigest at the end of this unit can be used as a(n):

- preview to introduce important unit concepts.
- overview if time does not permit teaching the entire chapter.
- review of key unit concepts.

Understanding the Photo

Sea stars are echinoderms belonging to the class Asteroidea. Echinoderms move by means of tube feet, and their bodies are covered by tiny, jawlike pincers. Most have a hard, spiny endoskeleton, radial symmetry, and bilaterally symmetrical larvae.

INTERACTIVE CHALKBOARD with Image Bank

PowerPoint® Presentations

This CD-ROM is an editable Microsoft® PowerPoint® presentation that includes:
- Section presentations
- Section checks
- Image bank
- Hot links to Biology Online
- All transparencies

Echinoderms and Invertebrate Chordates

What You'll Learn

- You will compare and contrast the adaptations of echinoderms.
- You will distinguish the features of chordates by examining invertebrate chordates.

Why It's Important

By studying how echinoderms and invertebrate chordates function, you will enhance your understanding of the beginnings of vertebrate evolution.

Understanding the Photo

Echinoderms obtain food by a variety of methods. They can be carnivores, herbivores, scavengers, or filter feeders. These sea stars are carnivorous echinoderms. They extend the stomach from the mouth and engulf mussels, filter-feeding mollusks.

 Biology Online

Visit in.bdol.glencoe.com to
- study the entire chapter online
- access Web Links for more information and activities on echinoderms and invertebrate chordates
- review content with the Interactive Tutor and self-check quizzes

---

 Two-Minute Chapter Launcher

Demo Use live or preserved sea stars or sea urchins to point out the physical characteristics of echinoderms. Elicit from students how the meaning of the term *echinoderm* relates to the features of animals in this group. *Echinoderm* means "spiny skin." The animals classified in this phylum have spinelike structures covering their bodies.

If time permits, have students observe and describe the movements of a live sea star by wetting a piece of clear, glasslike plastic with a solution similar to ocean water (available in pet shops), placing the sea star on the wet glasslike plastic, and observing the tube feet from underneath. You might also provide magnifiers to students.

Section 29.1

Echinoderms

Indiana Standards Standard B.1.15 Understand and explain that, in biological systems, structure and function must be considered together.

SECTION PREVIEW

Objectives

Compare similarities and differences among the classes of echinoderms.

Interpret the evidence biologists have for determining that echinoderms are close relatives of chordates.

Review Vocabulary
endoskeleton: internal skeleton of vertebrates and some invertebrates (p. 684)

New Vocabulary
ray
pedicellaria
water vascular system
madreporite
tube foot
ampulla

 FOLDABLES Study Organizer

Echinoderms Make the following Foldable to compare and contrast the characteristics of sea urchins and brittle stars.

STEP 1 Fold one sheet of paper lengthwise.

STEP 2 Fold into thirds.

STEP 3 Unfold and draw overlapping ovals. **Cut** the top sheet along the folds.

STEP 4 Label the ovals as shown.

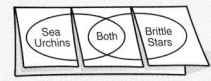
Sea Urchins | Both | Brittle Stars

Construct a Venn Diagram As you read Chapter 29, list the characteristics unique to sea urchins under the left tab, those unique to brittle stars under the right tab, and those characteristics common to both under the middle tab.

What is an echinoderm?

Members of the phylum Echinodermata have a number of unusual characteristics that easily distinguish them from members of any other animal phylum. Echinoderms move by means of hundreds of hydraulic, suction-cup-tipped appendages and have skin covered with tiny, jawlike pincers. Echinoderms (ih KI nuh durmz) are found in all the oceans of the world.

Echinoderms have endoskeletons

If you were to examine the skin of several different echinoderms, you would find that they all have a hard, spiny, or bumpy endoskeleton covered by a thin epidermis. The long, pointed spines on a sea urchin are obvious. Sea stars, sometimes called starfishes, may not appear spiny at first glance, but a close look reveals that their long, tapering arms, called **rays,** are covered with short, rounded spines. The spiny skin of a sea cucumber consists of soft tissue embedded with small, platelike structures that barely resemble spines. The endoskeleton of all echinoderms is made primarily of calcium carbonate, the compound that makes up limestone.

Some of the spines found on sea stars and sea urchins have become modified into pincerlike appendages called **pedicellariae** (PEH dih sih LAHR ee ay). An echinoderm uses its jawlike pedicellariae for protection and for cleaning the surface of its body. You can examine these structures in the *MiniLab* on the following page.

Word Origin

echinoderm from the Greek words *echinos,* meaning "spiny," and *derma,* meaning "skin"; Echinoderms are spiny-skinned animals.

pedicellariae from the Latin word *pediculus,* meaning "little foot"; Pedicellariae resemble little feet.

29.1 ECHINODERMS **763**

---

1 Focus
 INTERACTIVE CHALKBOARD PowerPoint® Presentations

Bellringer
Section Focus Transparency 71

Transparency **71** Echinoderms — SECTION FOCUS Use with Chapter 29, Section 29.1

Brittle star

Sand dollar

Sea urchin

① The word *echinoderm* comes from the Greek *echinos,* meaning "spiny," and *derm,* meaning "skin." Why do you think this name was given to this group of organisms?

② How is the radial symmetry of these saltwater animals an advantage?

BIOLOGY: The Dynamics of Life   SECTION FOCUS TRANSPARENCIES

Word Origin

Have students research to find and define other words using "derma" as part of the root, such as *dermatitis* and *dermatology.*

FOLDABLES™

For an additional Foldables activity idea, see the Chapter 29 Foldables page in *Unit 8 FAST FILE Resources.*

RESOURCE MANAGER

Unit 8 *FAST FILE* Resources
MiniLab Worksheet, p. 135
Reinforcement and Study Guide in English, pp. 139–141
Reinforcement and Study Guide in Spanish, pp. 143–145
Critical Thinking/Problem Solving, p. 148
Transparency Worksheets, pp. 149, 151–153

Reading Essentials for Biology, Section 29.1
Laboratory Manual, pp. 181–184, 185–186
Section Focus Transparency 71
Basic Concepts Transparencies 50, 51

 Indiana Academic Standards
Pages 762–763: B.1.15

2 Teach

Caption Question Answer

Figure 29.1 An animal with radial symmetry can get food from any direction. It also can detect danger coming from any direction, so it can either move or defend itself.

MiniLab 29.1

Purpose

Students will observe the pincherlike structure of pedicellariae.

Process Skills

observe and infer, compare and contrast, draw a conclusion

Teaching Strategies

Prepared slides are available from biological supply houses.

Expected Results

Students will observe that pedicellariae have a pincherlike appearance.

Analysis

1. Student answers will vary and may include pincherlike, plierslike, forcepslike.
2. allows animal to grasp objects, clean itself of debris, protection
3. These pincherlike organs allow the sea star to pinch potential predators when they touch the animal. Their shape also allows the sea star to clean itself by picking off materials that become stuck to its body.

Modified Assessment

Portfolio Have students put their diagrams in their portfolios. Use the Performance Task Assessment List for Science Portfolio in **PASC**, p. 177. **L1**

MiniLab 29.1

Observe and Infer

Examining Pedicellariae Echinoderms have tiny pincers on their skin called pedicellariae.

Procedure 🔬

1. Observe a slide of sea star pedicellariae under low-power magnification. **CAUTION:** *Use caution when working with a microscope and slides.*
2. Record the general appearance of one pedicellaria. What does it look like?
3. Make a diagram of one pedicellaria under low-power magnification.

Pedicellariae

Analysis

1. **Observe** Describe the general appearance of one pedicellaria.
2. **Infer** What is the function of this structure?
3. **Explain** How does the structure of pedicellariae assist in their function?

Figure 29.1
All echinoderms have radial symmetry as adults and an endoskeleton composed primarily of calcium carbonate. **Explain** *How does radial symmetry benefit an animal that cannot move fast?*

A A living sand dollar has an endoskeleton composed of flattened plates that are fused into a rigid framework.

B A sea lily's feathery rays are composed of calcified skeletal plates covered with an epidermis.

764

Echinoderms have radial symmetry

You may remember that radial symmetry is an advantage to animals that are stationary or move slowly. Radial symmetry enables these animals to sense potential food, predators, and other aspects of their environment from all directions. Observe the radial symmetry, as well as the various sizes and shapes of spines, of each echinoderm pictured in *Figure 29.1.*

The water vascular system

Another characteristic unique to echinoderms is the water vascular system that enables them to move, exchange gases, capture food, and excrete wastes. The **water vascular system** is a hydraulic system that operates under water pressure. Water enters and leaves the water vascular system of a sea star through the **madreporite** (mah druh POHR ite), a sievelike, disk-shaped opening on the upper surface of the echinoderm's body. This disk functions like the strainer that fits into a sink drain and keeps large particles out of the pipes.

INCLUSION STRATEGIES

Visually Impaired: *Kinesthetic* Provide visually impaired students with dried specimens of various echinoderms. Allow students to handle the specimens so they can feel the shapes, sizes, and characteristic spiny skins of these animals. **L1 ELL**

Look at the close-up of the underside of a sea star in *Figure 29.2*. You can see that tube feet run along a groove on the underside of each ray. **Tube feet** are hollow, thin-walled tubes that end in a suction cup. Tube feet look somewhat like miniature droppers. The round, muscular structure called the **ampulla** (AM pew lah) works something like the bulb of a dropper. The end of a tube foot works like a tiny suction cup. You can find out how tube feet help a sea star eat by looking at *Figure 29.4* on the next page. Each tube foot works independently of the others, and the animal moves along slowly by alternately pushing out and pulling in its tube feet. You can learn more about the operation of the water vascular system in the *Connection to Physics* at the end of this chapter.

Tube feet also function in gas exchange and excretion. Gases are exchanged and wastes are eliminated by diffusion through the thin walls of the tube feet.

Echinoderms have varied nutrition

All echinoderms have a mouth, stomach, and intestines, but their methods of obtaining food vary. Sea stars are carnivorous and prey on worms or on mollusks such as clams. Most sea urchins are herbivores and graze on algae. Brittle stars, sea lilies, and sea cucumbers feed on dead and decaying matter that drifts down to the ocean floor.

Echinoderms have a simple nervous system

Echinoderms have no head or brain, but they do have a central nerve ring that surrounds the mouth. Nerves extend from the nerve ring down each ray. Each radial nerve then branches into a nerve net that provides sensory information to the animal. Echinoderms have cells that detect light and touch, but most do not have sensory organs. Sea stars are an exception. A sea star's body consists of long, tapering rays that extend from the animal's central disk. A sensory organ known as an eyespot and consisting of a cluster of light-detecting cells is located at the tip of each arm, on the underside. Eyespots enable sea stars to detect the intensity of light. Most sea stars move toward light. Sea stars also have chemical receptors on their tube feet. When a sea star detects a chemical signal from a prey animal, it moves in the direction of the arm receiving the strongest signal.

Echinoderms have bilaterally symmetrical larvae

If you examine the larval stages of echinoderms, you will find that they have bilateral symmetry. The ciliated larva that develops from the fertilized egg of an echinoderm is shown in *Figure 29.3*. Through metamorphosis, the free-swimming larvae make dramatic changes in both body parts and in symmetry.

Echinoderms are deuterostomes

Recall that most invertebrates show protostome development. Echinoderms are deuterostomes. This pattern of development indicates a close relationship to chordates, which are also deuterostomes.

Figure 29.2
Tube feet enable sea stars and other echinoderms to creep along the ocean bottom or to pry open the shells of bivalves. **Infer** *What causes the suction a sea star uses to pry open shells?*

Figure 29.3
The larval stage of echinoderms is bilateral, even though the adult stage has radial symmetry. **Explain** *What does this characteristic show about echinoderms?*

Color-enhanced LM Magnification: 125×

Purpose

Students will learn about the structural and behavioral adaptations of a sea star.

Teaching Strategies

Ask students to observe a live sea star in action. They can use a hand lens to observe the tube feet as the sea star "walks" or "climbs" a surface of a marine aquarium. **L1** **ELL**

Visual Learning

Make photocopies of the Inside Story diagram without the labels of the structures. Number the parts and explain to students how each part functions and how the parts enable the sea star to survive in its environment. Have students use this information to label the diagram. **L1**

Critical Thinking

Radial symmetry enables animals that move slowly to sense and obtain potential food, escape predators, and sense other aspects of their environment from all directions.

Biology Journal

Sea Star Life Have students write an essay in which they describe one day in the life of a sea star. Allow a few students to read their essays. Have other students discuss which parts of the essays were scientific and which were creative fiction. **L3**

A Sea Star

Figure 29.4

If you ever tried to pull a sea star from a rock where it is attached, you would be impressed by how unyielding and rigid the animal seems to be. Yet at other times, the animal shows great flexibility, such as when it rights itself after being turned upside down. The rigidity or flexibility of a sea star is due to its endoskeleton.

Critical Thinking *How is radial symmetry useful to a sea star?*

Blood sea star

A Endoskeleton A sea star can quickly change from a rigid structure to a flexible one because it has an endoskeleton in the form of calcium carbonate plates just under its epidermis. The plates are connected by bands of soft tissue and muscle. When the muscles are contracted, the body becomes firm and rigid. When the muscles are relaxed, the body becomes flexible.

H Pedicellariae The pincerlike pedicellariae on the rays of the sea star keep the surface of its body clean.

Ray

B Madreporite Water flows in and out of the water vascular system through the madreporite.

Ring canal

Radial canal

G Anus Waste products of digestion are eliminated through the anus.

Nerve ring

Radial nerve

Ampullae

Mouth

F Stomach To eat, a sea star pushes its stomach out of its mouth and spreads the stomach over the food. Powerful enzymes secreted by the digestive gland turn solid food into a soupy liquid that the stomach can easily absorb. Then the sea star pulls the stomach back into its body.

C Tube feet The total suction action of tube feet, caused by the contraction and relaxation of the ampullae, is so strong that the sea star's muscles can open a clam or oyster shell.

Reproductive organ

Endoskeletal plates

D Eyespots Echinoderm eyespots distinguish between light and dark but do not form images.

E Digestive gland The digestive gland releases enzymes involved in digestion.

PROJECT

Echinoderm Display Ask a group of students to create a bulletin board display of echinoderms. Have them highlight the features of echinoderms. Ask them to find examples of everyday objects that show similar traits. Students may use sandpaper to model the texture of echinoderm skin. **L2** **ELL** **COOP LEARN**

Diversity of Echinoderms

Approximately 6000 species of echinoderms exist today. About one-fourth of these species are in the class Asteroidea (AS tuh ROY dee uh), to which the sea stars belong. The five other classes of living echinoderms are Ophiuroidea (OH fee uh ROY dee uh), the brittle stars; Echinoidea (eh kihn OY dee uh), the sea urchins and sand dollars; Holothuroidea (HOH loh thuh ROY dee uh), the sea cucumbers; Crinoidea (cry NOY dee uh), the sea lilies and feather stars; and Concentricycloidea (kon sen tri sy CLOY dee uh), the sea daisies. You can compare different echinoderms in the *BioLab* at the end of this chapter.

Sea stars

Sea stars may be the most familiar echinoderms. Most species of sea stars have five rays, but some have more. Some species may have more than 40 rays. You have already read about the characteristics of sea stars that make them a typical example of echinoderms.

Brittle stars

As their name implies, brittle stars are extremely fragile, *Figure 29.5*. If you try to pick up a brittle star, parts of its rays will break off in your hand. This adaptation helps the brittle star survive an attack by a predator. While the predator is busy with the broken-off ray, the brittle star can escape. A new ray will regenerate.

Brittle stars do not use their tube feet for locomotion. Instead, they propel themselves with the snake-like, slithering motion of their flexible rays. They use their tube feet to pass particles of food along the rays and into the mouth in the central disk.

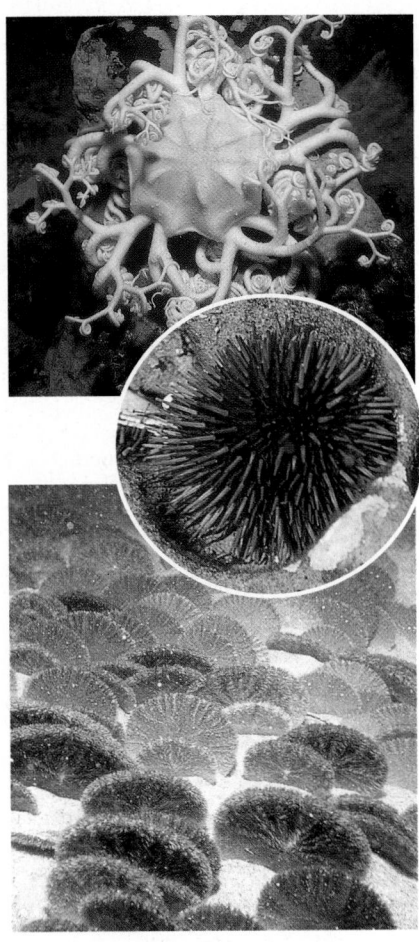

Figure 29.5
Echinoderms are adapted to life in a variety of habitats. **Explain** *What adaptations do you see here?*

A Basket stars, a kind of brittle star, live on the soft substrate found below deep ocean waters.

B Sea urchins often burrow into rocks to protect themselves from predators and rough water.

C Sand dollars burrow into sandy ocean bottom. They feed on tiny organic particles suspended in the water.

Sea urchins and sand dollars

Sea urchins and sand dollars are globe- or disk-shaped animals covered with spines, as *Figure 29.5* shows. They do not have rays. The circular, flat skeletons of sand dollars have a five-petaled flower pattern on the surface. A living sand dollar is covered with minute, hairlike spines that are lost when the animal dies. A sand dollar has tube feet that protrude from the petallike markings on its upper surface. These tube feet are modified into gills and are used for respiration. Tube feet on the animal's bottom surface aid in bringing food particles to the mouth.

29.1 ECHINODERMS **767**

Caption Question Answer
Figure 29.5 Spines help to protect the animals, and sea urchins can use their spines for burrowing. The rays of basket stars are flexible and enable the animal to easily hold prey.

INVESTIGATE BioLab The BioLab at the end of the chapter can be used at this point in the lesson.

Inquiry

Activity Biologists have discovered that brittle stars have crystal microlenses in their exoskeletons. They hypothesize that these microlenses enable brittle stars to detect light. Ask students to design a controlled experiment in which they plan to gather quantitative data that would enable them to tell if brittle stars can detect light with their microlenses. Tell students that they will not have to conduct this experiment. **L2**

CULTURAL DIVERSITY

Japan and the Sea Urchin Industry in the United States Sea urchins are prized in Japan as uni, a sushi delicacy. The Japanese value the sea urchin for the quality of its eggs, called roe. Today, sea urchins are harvested in Maine, California, and Alaska, as well as in other countries, and sent to Japan. Divers with permits collect sea urchins by hand. Urchin populations can be easily reduced by overfishing, so permit numbers are limited. Other measures, such as limiting areas open to sea urchin fishing, and hatchery replenishing of wild urchin stock are being considered to prevent population declines.

Indiana Academic Standards
Pages 766–767: B.1.15, B.1.19

Problem-Solving Lab 29.1

Purpose

Students will design an experiment to determine the stimulus for release of sea cucumber gametes.

Process Skills

design an experiment, identify and control variables

Teaching Strategies

Ask students to think of strategies that animals may use to ensure aquatic fertilization. Likely answers will include releasing large numbers of eggs and sperm, and releasing eggs and sperm at the same time.

Thinking Critically

To design another experiment, students may decide to keep a group of female sea cucumbers in aquariums, control all environmental variables, and then increase the period of light the sea cucumbers are exposed to for a set number of days to see if this causes the release of eggs.

Assessment

Portfolio Explain to students that sea stars have been found to spawn on the same day as sea cucumbers. Ask if this indicates that the stimulus for spawning is environmental or is in response to one male first releasing sperm. Ask students to write their responses in their portfolios. Use the Performance Task Assessment List for Making Observations and Inferences in **PASC,** p. 89. **L2**

✓**Reading Check** The spines protect the sea urchin from predators.

Problem-Solving Lab 29.1

Design an Experiment

What makes sea cucumbers release gametes? The orange sea cucumber often lives in groups of 40 or more per square meter. In the spring, these sea cucumbers produce large numbers of gametes (eggs and sperm), which they shed in the water all at the same time. The adaptive

Orange sea cucumber

value of such behavior is that fertilization of many eggs is assured. When one male releases sperm, the other sea cucumbers in the population, both male and female, also release their gametes. Biologists do not know whether the sea cucumbers release their gametes in response to a seasonal cue, such as increasing day length or increasing water temperature, or whether they do this in response to the release of sperm by one sea cucumber.

Solve the Problem

Design an experiment that will help to determine whether sea cucumbers release eggs and sperm in response to the release of sperm from one individual or in response to a seasonal cue.

Thinking Critically

Hypothesize If you find that female sea cucumbers release 200 eggs in the presence of male sperm and ten eggs in the presence of water that is warmer than the surrounding water, what would you do in your next experiment?

Figure 29.6
Sea cucumbers trap organic particles by sweeping their mucous-covered tentacles over the ocean bottom **(A).** Sea lilies and feather stars capture downward-drifting organic particles with their feathery rays **(B).**

Sea urchins look like living pincushions, bristling with long, usually pointed spines. The sea urchin's spines protect it from predators. Sea urchins have long, slender tube feet that, along with the spines, aid the animal in locomotion.

✓**Reading Check** **Explain** the functions of the spines of a sea urchin.

Sea cucumbers

Sea cucumbers are so called because of their vegetablelike appearance, shown in *Figure 29.6A.* Their leathery covering allows them flexibility as they move along the ocean floor. When sea cucumbers are threatened, they may expel a tangled, sticky mass of tubes through the anus, or they may rupture, releasing some internal organs that are regenerated in a few weeks. These actions confuse their predators, giving the sea cucumber an opportunity to move away. Sea cucumbers reproduce by shedding eggs and sperm into the water, where fertilization occurs. You can find out more about sea cucumber reproduction in the *Problem-Solving Lab* on this page.

Sea lilies and feather stars

Sea lilies and feather stars resemble plants in some ways, as shown in *Figure 29.6B.* Sea lilies are the only sessile echinoderms. Feather stars are sessile only in larval form. The adult feather star uses its feathery arms to swim from place to place.

Sea daisies

Two species of sea daisies were discovered in 1986 in deep waters off New Zealand. They are flat, disk-shaped animals less than 1 cm in diameter. Their tube feet are located around the edge of the disk rather than along radial lines, as in other echinoderms.

⊚ CHALLENGE ACTIVITY

Echinoderm Phylogeny: *Naturalist*
Provide students with echinoderm fossils. Include as many different kinds as possible and use photographs of fossils you don't have. Ask students to arrange the fossils and photographs to illustrate the phylogeny of this group. **L3**

Figure 29.7
Most echinoderms have been found as fossils from the early Paleozoic Era. Fossils of brittle stars are found beginning at a later period. Not much is known about the origin of sea daisies.

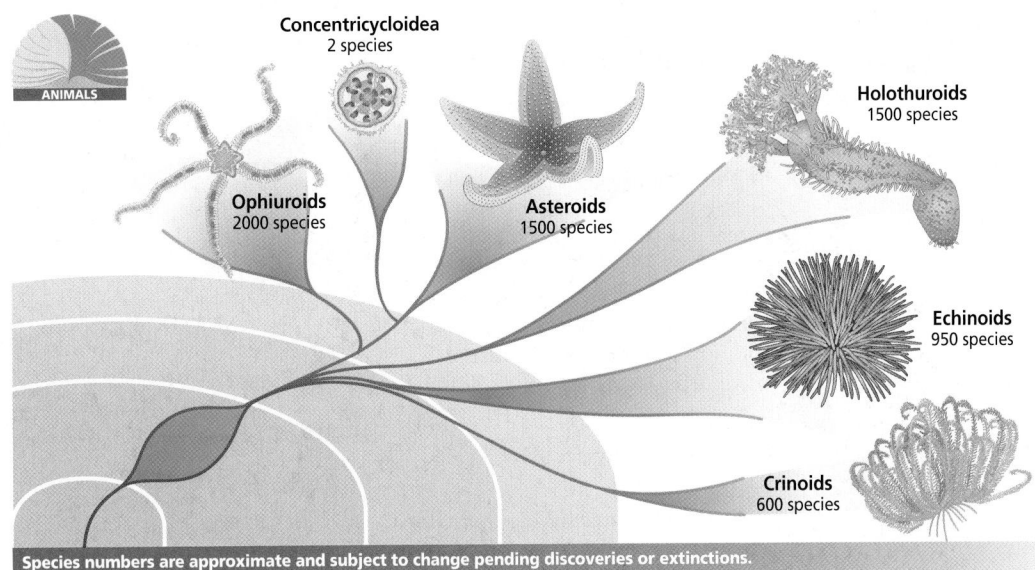

Concentricycloidea
2 species

Holothuroids
1500 species

Ophiuroids
2000 species

Asteroids
1500 species

Echinoids
950 species

Crinoids
600 species

Species numbers are approximate and subject to change pending discoveries or extinctions.

Origins of Echinoderms

The earliest echinoderms may have been bilaterally symmetrical as adults, and probably were attached to the ocean floor by stalks. Another view of the earliest echinoderms is that they were bilateral and free-swimming. Most invertebrates show protostome development, whereas deuterostome development appears mainly in chordates. The echinoderms represent the only major group of deuterostome inverte-brates. This pattern of development is one piece of evidence biologists have for placing echinoderms as the closest invertebrate relatives of the chordates.

Because the endoskeletons of echinoderms easily fossilize, there is a good record of this phylum. Echinoderms, as a group, date from the Paleozoic Era, as shown in *Figure 29.7*. More than 13 000 fossil species have been identified.

3 Assess

DAILY INTERVENTION

Check for Understanding
Naturalist Ask students to use Figure 29.7 to explain the phylogenetic history of echinoderms. **L2**

Reteach
Naturalist Give students photocopies of the inner, shaded part of the phylogenetic diagram in Figure 29.7. Have them place each class in its correct position. Ask them to list also the identifying features of each class. **L1**

Resources
For more practice, use *Reading Essentials for Biology*, Section 29.1.

Extension
Have students research and report on the relationship between the crown-of-thorns sea star and coral reefs. **L3**

 Assessment

Performance Have students prepare a demonstration for third graders that explains the water vascular system of a sea star. Ask them to present this demonstration to the class using a working model. **L2** **ELL**

Indiana Academic Standards
Pages 768–769: B.1.15, B.1.32, B.1.43

Section Assessment

Understanding Main Ideas

1. How does a sea star move? Explain in terms of the water vascular system of echinoderms.

2. Describe the differences in symmetry between larval echinoderms and adult echinoderms.

3. How are sea cucumbers different from other echinoderms?

4. What evidence suggests that echinoderms are closely related to chordates?

Thinking Critically

5. How do the various defense mechanisms among the echinoderm classes help deter predators?

SKILL REVIEW

6. **Get the Big Picture** Prepare a dichotomous key that distinguishes among classes of echinoderms. Include information on features you may find significant. For more help, refer to *Get the Big Picture* in the **Skill Handbook**.

in.bdol.glencoe.com/self_check_quiz

29.1 ECHINODERMS **769**

Section Assessment

1. A sea star moves by regulation of its water vascular system. Tube feet attach to a surface, the sea star moves itself forward, and the suction is released.

2. Larval echinoderms are bilaterally symmetrical, whereas adult echinoderms are radially symmetrical.

3. Sea cucumbers are tubular and have a leathery outer covering, which allows them flexibility, instead of hard plates.

4. Both echinoderms and chordates show deuterostome development.

5. The rigid endoskeleton helps protect echinoderms from their enemies. Spines and poison glands also protect echinoderms. Adult echinoderms move by walking, whereas larval forms are free swimming. If an echinoderm such as a sea star loses part of a ray, it can be regenerated. Sea cucumbers can expel their digestive tracts and grow new ones.

6. Students' keys will vary considerably, but all should utilize the branching nature of keys described in the Skill Handbook.

1 Focus

Bellringer
Section Focus Transparency 72

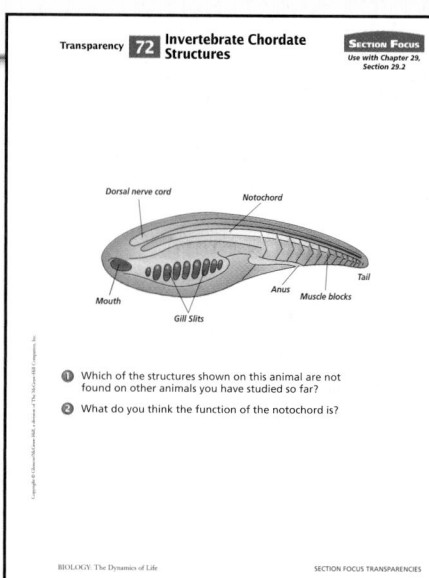

Transparency **72** Invertebrate Chordate Structures

SECTION FOCUS
Use with Chapter 29, Section 29.2

Dorsal nerve cord
Notochord
Mouth
Gill Slits
Anus
Muscle blocks
Tail

❶ Which of the structures shown on this animal are not found on other animals you have studied so far?

❷ What do you think the function of the notochord is?

BIOLOGY: The Dynamics of Life

SECTION FOCUS TRANSPARENCIES

Finding Main Ideas

Outline If some students struggle with the traditional outline using Roman numerals, upper and lower case letters, and numbers, ask these students to make a list of the important points under each red and blue title.

Invertebrate Chordates

Indiana Standards Standard B.1.15 Understand and explain that, in biological systems, structure and function must be considered together.

SECTION PREVIEW

Objectives

Summarize the characteristics of chordates.

Explain how invertebrate chordates are related to vertebrates.

Distinguish between sea squirts and lancelets.

Review Vocabulary

mesoderm: middle cell layer in the gastrula, between the ectoderm and endoderm (p. 677)

New Vocabulary

notochord
dorsal hollow nerve cord
pharyngeal pouch

How is a sea squirt your relative?

Finding Main Ideas On a piece of paper, construct an outline about invertebrate chordates. Use the red and blue titles in this section as a guideline. As you read the paragraphs that follow the titles, add important information and vocabulary words to your outline.

Example:

I. What is an invertebrate chordate?

  A. All chordates have a notochord.

  B. All chordates have a dorsal hollow nerve cord.

Use your outline to help you answer questions in the Section Assessment on page 775. For more help, refer to *Outline* in the **Skill Handbook.**

Sea squirt

What is an invertebrate chordate?

The chordates most familiar to you are the vertebrate chordates—chordates that have backbones, such as birds, fishes, and mammals, including humans. But the phylum Chordata (kor DAH tuh) includes three subphyla: Urochordata, the tunicates (sea squirts); Cephalochordata, the lancelets; and Vertebrata, the vertebrates. In this section you will examine the tunicates and lancelets—invertebrate chordates that have no backbones. You will study the vertebrate chordates in the next unit.

Invertebrate chordates may not look much like fishes, reptiles, or humans, but like all other chordates, they have a notochord, a dorsal hollow nerve cord, pharyngeal pouches, and a postanal tail at some time during their development. In addition, all chordates have bilateral symmetry, a well-developed coelom, and segmentation. The features shared by invertebrate and vertebrate chordates are illustrated in *Figure 29.8.* You can observe these features in invertebrate chordates in the *Problem-Solving Lab* later in this section.

Figure 29.8
Chordate characteristics—the notochord, dorsal hollow nerve cord, pharyngeal pouches, and a postanal tail—are shared by invertebrate as well as vertebrate chordates.

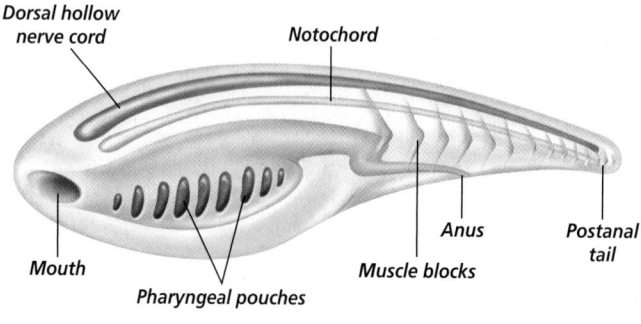

Dorsal hollow nerve cord
Notochord
Mouth
Pharyngeal pouches
Anus
Muscle blocks
Postanal tail

RESOURCE MANAGER

Unit 8 *FAST FILE* Resources
MiniLab Worksheet, p. 136
BioLab Worksheet, pp. 137–138
Reinforcement and Study Guide in English, p. 142
Reinforcement and Study Guide in Spanish, p. 146

Concept Mapping, p. 147
Transparency Worksheets, pp. 150, 155–156
Reading Essentials for Biology, Section 29.2
Section Focus Transparency 72
Reteaching Skills Transparency 43

All chordates have a notochord

The embryos of all chordates have a **notochord** (NOH tuh kord)—a long, semirigid, rodlike structure located between the digestive system and the dorsal hollow nerve cord. The notochord is made up of large, fluid-filled cells held within stiff, fibrous tissues. In invertebrate chordates, the notochord may be retained into adulthood. But in vertebrate chordates, this structure is replaced by a backbone. Invertebrate chordates do not develop a backbone.

The notochord develops just after the formation of a gastrula from mesoderm on what will be the dorsal side of the embryo. The notochord anchors internal muscles and enables invertebrate chordates to make rapid movements of the body. These movements propel the animal through the water at a great speed.

All chordates have a dorsal hollow nerve cord

The **dorsal hollow nerve cord** in chordates develops from a plate of ectoderm that rolls into a hollow tube. The sequence of development of the dorsal hollow nerve cord is illustrated in *Figure 29.9*. This tube is composed of cells surrounding a fluid-filled canal that lies above the notochord. In most adult chordates, the cells in the posterior portion of the dorsal hollow nerve cord develop into the spinal cord. The cells in the anterior portion develop into a brain. A pair of nerves connects the nerve cord to each block of muscles.

> **Word Origin**
>
> Chordata from the Latin word *chorda*, meaning "cord"; The phylum Chordata consists of animals with notochords.

Figure 29.9
After gastrulation, organs begin to form in a chordate embryo.

A The notochord is formed from mesoderm on the dorsal side of a developing embryo.

B The dorsal hollow nerve cord originates as a plate of dorsal ectoderm just above the developing notochord.

C The edges of this plate of ectoderm fold inward, eventually meeting to form a hollow tube surrounded by cells. The dorsal hollow nerve cord pinches off from the ectoderm and develops into the central nervous system of the animal.

D Cells migrate from the meeting margins of the neural tube and eventually form other organs, including bones and muscles.

Neural fold   Neural plate
Notochord
Ectoderm
Mesoderm
Endoderm
Dorsal hollow nerve cord
Notochord
Cells that form bones and muscle
Dorsal hollow nerve cord
Outer layer of ectoderm
Dorsal hollow nerve cord

2 Teach

Quick Demo

Tunicates and Lancelets Ask students to observe preserved or mounted specimens of tunicates and lancelets. Ask them if they can see any characteristics that link these animals to vertebrate chordates. Elicit whether the animals might have unseen characteristics that link them to vertebrate chordates. **L2**

Visual Learning
Have students explain how the Inside Story on development in Chapter 25 relates to Figure 29.9.

Struggling Learners
Have students run their fingers along their backs to feel their backbones. Explain that the backbone is unique to vertebrates and forms from the notochord—the structure that identifies all members of the phylum Chordata. Although all chordates have a notochord at some time during their development, not all chordates have backbones. **L1** **ELL**

USING MODELS

Modeling Sea Life Provide student groups with clay, modeling dough, or salt dough and ask them to make small models of a sea star, sea urchin, sand dollar, sea cucumber, lancelet, and tunicate. Ask students to describe the adaptations of each animal to its environment. **L2**

CHALLENGE ACTIVITY

Early Chordate Development Ask students to examine Figure 29.9 on page 771 and Figure 25.5 on page 678 and prepare a multimedia presentation that illustrates early chordate development. **L3**

Portfolio

Animal Nervous Systems Ask students to separate the following animals into groups based on the type of nervous system each has. Their lists should identify animals that have a ventral nerve cord, those that have a dorsal hollow nerve cord, and those that have some other nervous system arrangement: earthworm, snail, planarian, sea star, tunicate, clam, grasshopper, lancelet, spider, human. **L3**

Reading Check (p. 773) Larval tunicates are tadpole-shaped with a tail and are free swimming. Adult tunicates do not appear to have any shared chordate features except for gill slits.

Caption Question Answer
Figure 29.11 (p. 773) dorsal hollow nerve cord, postanal tail, notochord

Figure 29.10
Tunicate larvae are able to swim freely through the water **(A)**. As adults, tunicates become sessile filter feeders enclosed in a tough, baglike layer of tissue called a tunic **(B)**.

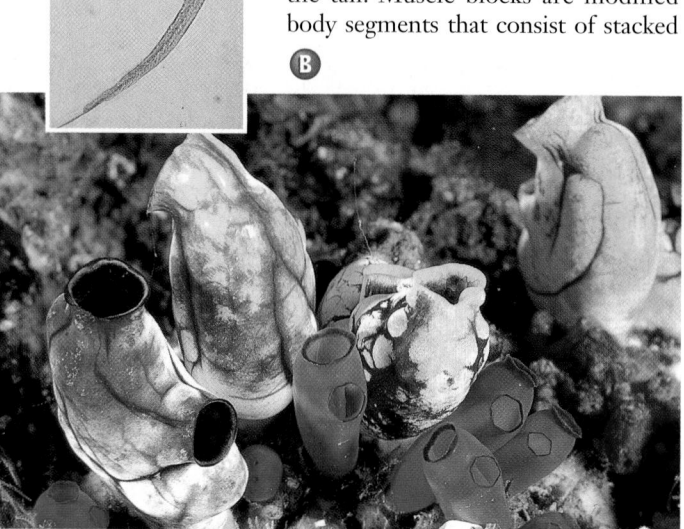

Color-enhanced LM
Magnification: 15×

All chordate embryos have pharyngeal pouches

The **pharyngeal pouches** of a chordate embryo are paired structures located in the pharyngeal region, behind the mouth. Many chordates have pharyngeal pouches only during embryonic development. In aquatic chordates, pharyngeal pouches develop openings called gill slits. Food is filtered out and gas exchange occurs as water flows through gill slits. In terrestrial chordates, pharyngeal pouches develop into other structures, such as the jaw, inner ear, and tonsils.

All chordates have a postanal tail

At some point in development, all chordates have a postanal tail. As you know, humans are chordates, and during the early development of the human embryo, there is a postanal tail that disappears as development continues. In most animals that have tails, the digestive system extends to the tip of the tail, where the anus is located. Chordates, however, usually have a tail that extends beyond the anus.

Muscle blocks aid in movement of the tail. Muscle blocks are modified body segments that consist of stacked muscle layers. Muscle blocks are anchored by the notochord, which gives the muscles a firm structure to pull against. As a result, chordates tend to be more muscular than members of other phyla. You can observe many of the chordate traits in a lancelet in the *MiniLab* on the next page.

Homeotic genes control development

Homeotic genes specify body organization and direct the development of tissues and organs in an embryo. Studies of chordate homeotic genes have helped scientists understand the process of development and the relationship of invertebrate chordates to vertebrate chordates.

Diversity of Invertebrate Chordates

The invertebrate chordates belong to two subphyla of the phylum chordata: subphylum Urochordata, the tunicates (TEW nuh kaytz), also called sea squirts, and subphylum Cephalochordata, the lancelets.

Tunicates are sea squirts

Members of the subphylum Urochordata are commonly called tunicates, or sea squirts. Although adult tunicates do not appear to have any shared chordate features, the larval stage, as shown in *Figure 29.10,* has a tail that makes it look similar to a tadpole. Tunicate larvae do not feed and are free swimming after hatching. They soon settle and attach themselves with a sucker to boats, rocks, and the ocean bottom. Many adult tunicates secrete a tunic, a tough sac made of cellulose, around their bodies. Colonies of tunicates sometimes secrete just one big tunic that has a common opening to the outside. You can find out how tunicates eat in *Figure 29.12* on page 774.

772 ECHINODERMS AND INVERTEBRATE CHORDATES

Additional Lab

Comparison of Sea Urchins and Lancelets

Purpose
Students will compare sea urchin larvae with adult lancelets.

Materials
compound microscope, prepared slides of sea urchin development, prepared slides of lancelets

Procedure
Give students the following directions.
1. Observe slides of the unfertilized sea urchin egg, zygote, 2-cell stage, 4-cell stage, 8-cell stage, blastula, gastrula, and sea urchin larvae. Use low-power magnification at first, then switch to high-power magnification.
2. Draw a diagram of each stage in the order listed. Label each diagram with the name of the stage.
3. Note how the size of the blastula compares with the size of the zygote. Note also the size of the cells at each stage.

Only the gill slits in adult tunicates indicate their chordate relationship. Adult tunicates are small, tubular animals that range in size from microscopic to several centimeters long. If you remove a tunicate from its sea home, it might squirt out a jet of water—hence the name *sea squirt*.

✓ Reading Check **Describe** which chordate features are present in larval and adult tunicates.

Lancelets are similar to fishes

Lancelets belong to the subphylum Cephalochordata. They are small, streamlined, and common marine animals, usually about 5 cm long, as *Figure 29.11* shows. They spend most of their time buried in the sand with only their heads sticking out. Like tunicates, lancelets are filter feeders. Unlike tunicates, however, lancelets retain all their chordate features throughout life.

Figure 29.11
Lancelets usually spend most of their time buried in the sand with only their heads sticking out so they can filter tiny morsels of food from the water (**A**). The lancelet's body looks very much like a typical chordate embryo (**B**). **Describe** *What chordate features are present in an adult lancelet?*

MiniLab 29.2

Observe

Examining a Lancelet *Branchiostoma californiensis* is a small, sea-dwelling lancelet. At first glance, it appears to be a fish. However, its structural parts and appearance are quite different.

Stained LM Magnification: unavailable

Procedure 🖐️🔬🧤📋

1 Place the lancelet onto a glass slide. **CAUTION:** *Wear disposable protective gloves and handle preserved material with forceps.*

2 Use a dissecting microscope to examine the animal. **CAUTION:** *Use care when working with a microscope and slides.*

3 Prepare a data table that will allow you to record the following: General body shape, Length in mm, Head region present, Fins and tail present, Nature of body covering, Sense organs such as eyes present, Habitat, Segmented body.

4 Indicate on your data table if the following can easily be observed: gill slits, notochord, dorsal hollow nerve cord.

Analysis

1. **Compare and Contrast** How does *Branchiostoma* differ structurally from a fish? How are its general appearance and habitat similar to those of a fish?

2. **Explain** Why weren't you able to see gills, a notochord, and a dorsal hollow nerve cord?

3. **Infer** Using its scientific name as a guide, where might the habitat of this species be located?

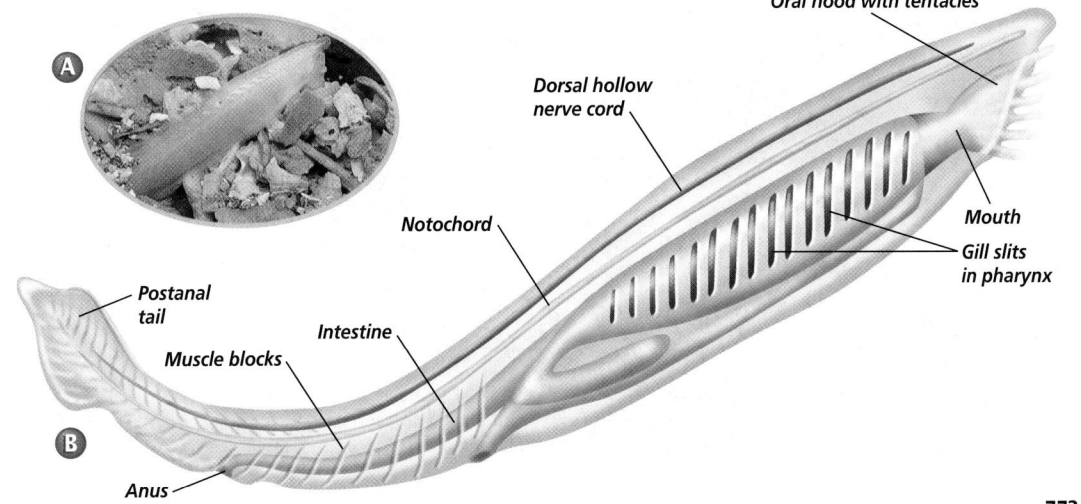

Oral hood with tentacles

Dorsal hollow nerve cord

Notochord

Postanal tail

Muscle blocks

Intestine

Anus

Mouth

Gill slits in pharynx

A

B

29.2 INVERTEBRATE CHORDATES **773**

MiniLab 29.2

Purpose
Students will observe the external appearance of lancelets.

Process Skills
compare and contrast, interpret data, make and use tables, measure in SI, observe and infer

Teaching Strategies
■ Specimens are available from biological supply houses.
■ A hand lens may be substituted for a binocular microscope.

Expected Results
Lancelets have a long, tubular body shape; length close to 50 mm, head region, tail-like posterior; smooth body; no sense organs. Students will not be able to see a notochord, gill slits, or a dorsal hollow nerve cord.

Analysis
1. It has no sense organs, gills, fins, or a distinct head. It looks like a fish because it has a streamlined shape and a tail. Both live in water.
2. These structures are all internal organs.
3. in the ocean along the coast of California

Assessment
Portfolio Have students write a paragraph explaining why lancelets are important in evolution. Use the Performance Task Assessment List for Writing in Science in **PASC**, p. 159. **L2**

---

4. Examine a prepared slide of a lancelet.
5. Find the following parts of the lancelet and label them on a diagram you make: dorsal hollow nerve cord, notochord, gill slits, postanal tail.
6. Note the fishlike form of the lancelet.

Expected Results
Students should see all of the features listed above.

Analysis
1. How does the size of the sea urchin blastula compare with that of the zygote? The blastula and the zygote are the same size. The cells become smaller as development proceeds.

2. What features of the lancelet place it in the phylum Chordata? dorsal hollow nerve cord, notochord, gill slits, postanal tail

Assessment
Skill Set up microscopes with slides showing features of lancelets and various stages of sea urchin development. Ask students to identify the part or sequence of development and state the importance of the part for chordates. Use the Performance Task Assessment List for Making Observations and Inferences in **PASC**, p.89. **L2**

Purpose

Students will learn about the structural and behavioral characteristics of tunicates.

Teaching Strategies

Ask students to compare the filter feeding of tunicates with the filter feeding of sponges and bivalves.

Visual Learning

■ Review with students the characteristics of tunicates that make them invertebrate chordates.

■ Show students live specimens of tunicates and have them compare the specimens with the diagram.

Critical Thinking

Sponges and tunicates are both filter feeders.

Problem-Solving Lab 29.2

Purpose

Students will interpret a cross-section slice of a lancelet.

Process Skills

interpret scientific illustrations, observe and infer, think critically

Teaching Strategies

■ Review the procedure for making a cross-section slice.

■ Review the orientation of the cross-section slice in relation to the whole animal. Use cross-sectional pieces of a fireplace log to illustrate the view and orientation.

Thinking Critically

1. pharyngeal pouches, notochord, dorsal hollow nerve cord; Student answers should agree that these are present.
2. Echinoderms would have tube feet and a water vascular system, but no notochord, dorsal hollow nerve cord, pharyngeal pouches, or muscle blocks.

INSIDE STORY

A Tunicate

Figure 29.12
Tunicates, or sea squirts, are a group of about 3000 species that live in the ocean. They may live near the shore or at great depths. They may live individually, or several animals may share a tunic to form a colony. **Critical Thinking** *In what ways are sponges and tunicates alike?*

Purple bell tunicate

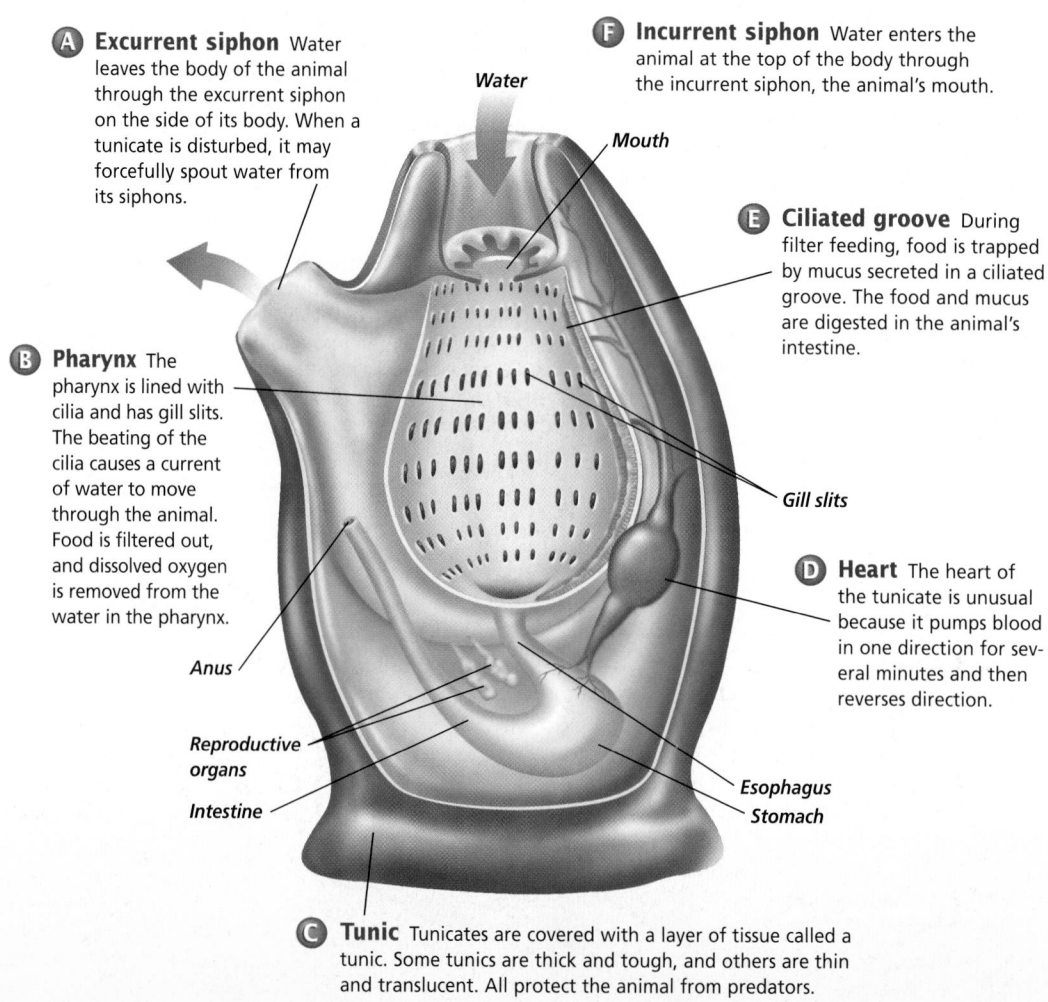

Ⓐ Excurrent siphon Water leaves the body of the animal through the excurrent siphon on the side of its body. When a tunicate is disturbed, it may forcefully spout water from its siphons.

Ⓕ Incurrent siphon Water enters the animal at the top of the body through the incurrent siphon, the animal's mouth.

Water

Mouth

Ⓔ Ciliated groove During filter feeding, food is trapped by mucus secreted in a ciliated groove. The food and mucus are digested in the animal's intestine.

Ⓑ Pharynx The pharynx is lined with cilia and has gill slits. The beating of the cilia causes a current of water to move through the animal. Food is filtered out, and dissolved oxygen is removed from the water in the pharynx.

Gill slits

Ⓓ Heart The heart of the tunicate is unusual because it pumps blood in one direction for several minutes and then reverses direction.

Anus

Reproductive organs

Intestine

Esophagus

Stomach

Ⓒ Tunic Tunicates are covered with a layer of tissue called a tunic. Some tunics are thick and tough, and others are thin and translucent. All protect the animal from predators.

774 ECHINODERMS AND INVERTEBRATE CHORDATES

---

3. An adult tunicate would have gill slits but no notochord or dorsal hollow nerve cord. A young developing tunicate has all of these structures.

Modified Assessment

Performance Ask students to draw a diagram of a longitudinal (lengthwise) view of a lancelet and label the gill slits, notochord, dorsal hollow nerve cord, and postanal tail. Use the Performance Task Assessment List for Scientific Drawing in **PASC**, p. 127. **L1**

Although lancelets look somewhat similar to fishes, they have only one layer of skin, with no pigment and no scales. Lancelets do not have a distinct head, but they do have light sensitive cells on the anterior end. They also have a hood that covers the mouth and the sensory tentacles surrounding it. The tentacles direct the water current and food particles toward the animal's mouth.

Origins of Invertebrate Chordates

Because sea squirts and lancelets have no bones, shells, or other hard parts, their fossil record is incomplete. Biologists are not sure where sea squirts and lancelets fit in the phylogeny of chordates. According to one hypothesis, echinoderms, invertebrate chordates, and vertebrates all arose from ancestral sessile animals that fed by capturing food in tentacles. Modern vertebrates probably arose from the free-swimming larval stages of ancestral invertebrate chordates. Recent discoveries of fossil forms of organisms that are similar to living lancelets in rocks 550 million years old show that invertebrate chordates probably existed before vertebrate chordates.

Problem-Solving Lab 29.2

Interpret Scientific Illustrations

What does a slice through an invertebrate chordate show? Why are tunicates and lancelets important? Being invertebrate chordates, they show three major structures that are present at some time during all chordate development.

Solve the Problem
The diagram at right shows a cross section of a lancelet. Determine what the various structures marked A–D are. Write your answers on a separate sheet of paper.

Thinking Critically
1. **Analyze** What three structures are present in all chordates at some time during their development? Does the cross-section diagram of the lancelet confirm your answer? Explain.
2. **Explain** How would you know that the cross section was not from an echinoderm?
3. **Infer** How might the cross section differ if it were taken from an adult tunicate? A young developing tunicate?

3 Assess

DAILY INTERVENTION

Check for Understanding
Ask students to list invertebrate chordate characteristics. **L1**

Reteach
Visual-Spatial Give student groups a large piece of paper. Have them diagram a lancelet and label its typical invertebrate chordate parts and their functions. **L2** **ELL**

Resources
For more practice, use *Reading Essentials for Biology,* Section 29.2.

Extension

Ask students to research the phyla Hemichordata and Chaetognatha. Ask them to report about the structural and behavioral adaptations of these animals and their evolutionary relationships with echinoderms and chordates. **L3**

MODIFIED Assessment

Knowledge Develop a table that compares lancelets and tunicates, discussing which features are common to vertebrates and invertebrates. **L1**

Section Assessment

Understanding Main Ideas
1. List the four features that are characteristic of chordates.
2. How are invertebrate chordates, such as lancelets, different from vertebrates, such as fishes and mammals?
3. Compare and contrast the physical features of sea squirts and lancelets.
4. How do sea squirts and lancelets protect themselves?

Thinking Critically
5. What features of chordates suggest that you are more closely related to invertebrate chordates than to echinoderms?

SKILL REVIEW
6. **Experiment** You have found some tadpolelike animals in the water near the seashore and you raise them in a laboratory. Design an experiment in which you will determine whether the animals are larvae or adults. For more help, refer to *Experiment* in the **Skill Handbook**.

 in.bdol.glencoe.com/self_check_quiz

29.2 INVERTEBRATE CHORDATES **775**

Indiana Academic Standards
Pages 774–775: B.1.15, B.1.19

Section Assessment

1. notochord, dorsal hollow nerve cord, pharyngeal pouches, postanal tail
2. In invertebrate chordates, the notochord is not replaced by a backbone.
3. Sea squirts are small, tubular, stationary filter feeders. Lancelets are shaped like fishes and can swim freely, but they spend most of their time buried

in the sand.
4. Sea squirts are covered with a thick tunic, and lancelets bury themselves in sand.
5. notochord, pharyngeal pouches, postanal tail, and dorsal hollow nerve cord

6. Watch the animals for several weeks to see if they change their body shape and symmetry. Watch for reproductive behavior or release of gametes.

Time Allotment
one class period

Process Skills
observe, compare and contrast, infer, describe, interpret, analyze

Safety Precautions
Caution students to wear goggles and protective gloves when handling preserved specimens.

Alternative Materials
If you live near a public aquarium or a seaside nature center, live specimens can be borrowed sometimes for classroom use and returned to the center afterward.

Before You Begin
Do all echinoderms have the same symmetry, shape, and body features? One way to answer this question is to examine a variety of echinoderms and note their similarities and differences. In this lab, you will make observations of a sea star, a sea urchin, a sea cucumber, and a sand dollar.

Observing and Comparing Echinoderms

Problem
How are sea stars, sea urchins, sea cucumbers, and sand dollars alike? How are they different from each other?

Objectives
In this BioLab, you will:
- **Observe, compare, and contrast** various echinoderms.
- **Draw** representative echinoderms.
- **List** the traits of four different echinoderms.
- **Infer** adaptations for life functions of echinoderms.

Materials
preserved specimens of sea star, sea urchin,
  sand dollar, sea cucumber
forceps
culture or petri dish
toothpicks

Safety Precautions
CAUTION: *Specimens are preserved and will be reused, so they must be kept intact. Wear disposable protective gloves and use forceps when handling preserved materials. Always wear goggles in the lab.*

Skill Handbook
If you need help with this lab, refer to the **Skill Handbook**.

1. Copy the data table.

Data Table

	Sea Star	Sea Urchin	Sand Dollar	Sea Cucumber
Outer covering	hard, bumpy	spiny	hard	leathery
Tube feet	yes	yes	yes	yes
Spines	no	yes	no	no
No. of body openings	2	2	2	2
Rays	yes	no	no	no
Type of symmetry	radial	radial	radial	radial

Teaching Strategies
- Rinse specimens thoroughly before giving them to students. They may be placed back in preservative for future use at the end of the day.
- You may want to have students work in groups and pass specimens from one group to another to limit how many specimens you would need to purchase.
- Depending on the preservative and how long the specimens have been preserved, tube feet may or may not be visible.

Data and Observations
See data table on next page.

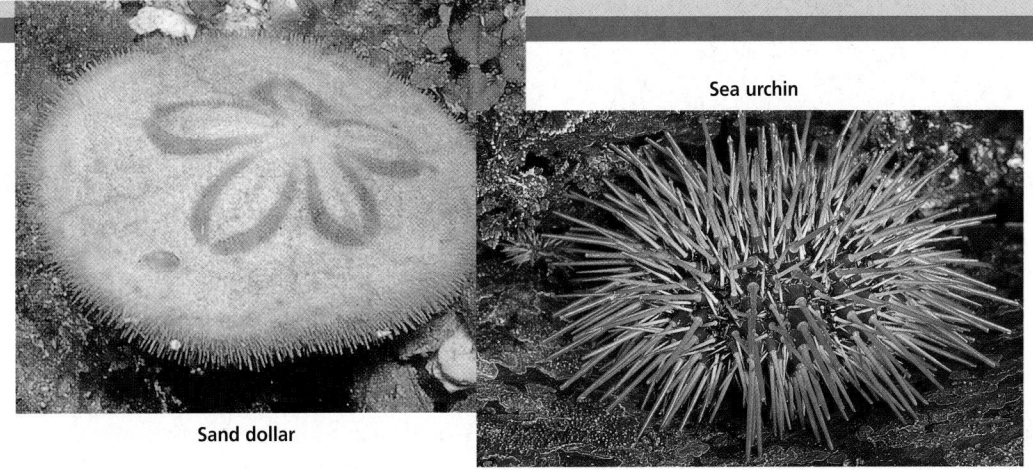

Sea urchin

Sand dollar

2. Examine the sand dollar, sea cucumber, sea star, and sea urchin and fill in the data table by describing the features listed.

3. Draw each of your specimens and label the external features you can see.

4. **CLEANUP AND DISPOSAL** Clean all equipment as instructed by your teacher, and return everything to its proper place for reuse. Wash your hands with soap and water after handling preserved specimens.

ANALYZE AND CONCLUDE

1. **Observe and Infer** Using your observations, compare the outer coverings of sea stars, sea urchins, sand dollars, and sea cucumbers. Explain how the coverings benefit the animals.

2. **Analyze** In what way are the echinoderms you examined alike externally? Explain how this adaptation benefits these animals.

3. **Infer** Tube feet are not visible on all the specimens you observed. Why not?

4. **Infer** The sea cucumber appears to be less like the other specimens you studied. Why is it classified as an echinoderm?

5. **Infer** Which of the echinoderms you studied may move the fastest? Explain.

6. **ERROR ANALYSIS** Preserved animal specimens may differ from living animals due to the preservation technique. Soft, fragile parts may not be preserved as well as hard, sturdy parts. Analyze your data table to see where errors may have occurred due to these differences.

Apply Your Skill

Project Obtain and view multimedia technology that shows live echinoderms. Summarize what you learned about echinoderms by watching them live as opposed to observing preserved specimens.

Web Links To find out more about echinoderms, visit in.bdol.glencoe.com/echinoderms

ANALYZE AND CONCLUDE

1. Sea stars have hard, bumpy outer coverings; sea urchins are spiny; sand dollars are hard; and sea cucumbers are leathery. The outer coverings protect the animals from predators and from the action of waves on the shoreline.

2. They all have radial symmetry—important for an animal that moves slowly to get food and escape predators. They all have two body openings, one for taking in food and one for expelling wastes—a more efficient digestive system than having one body opening.

3. Tube feet are fragile and do not have hard parts that can be preserved.

4. It has tube feet.

5. The sea star has rays in addition to tube feet that can aid in movement.

6. **ERROR ANALYSIS** Tube feet may not have been visible due to their fragile nature.

Assessment

Knowledge Ask students to draw an example of each of the echinoderms they studied and explain how each is adapted to its environment.

Apply Your Skill

Project Have students compare and contrast the characteristics of live and preserved echinoderms.

Data Table

	Sea Star	Sea Urchin	Sand Dollar	Sea Cucumber
Outer covering	hard, bumpy	spiny	hard	leathery
Tube feet	yes	yes	yes	yes
Spines	no	yes	no	no
Body openings	2	2	2	2
Rays	yes	no	no	no
Type of symmetry	radial	radial	radial	radial

connection to Physics

Hydraulics of Sea Stars

Many organisms use hydraulic systems to supply food and oxygen to, and remove wastes from, cells lying deep within the body. Hydraulics is a branch of science that is concerned with the practical applications of liquids in motion. In living systems, hydraulics is usually concerned with the use of water to operate systems that help organisms find food and move from place to place.

The sea star uses a unique hydraulic mechanism called the water vascular system for movement and for obtaining food. The water vascular system provides the water pressure that operates the tube feet of sea stars and other echinoderms.

The water vascular system On the upper surface of a sea star is a sievelike disk, the madreporite, which opens into a fluid-filled ring. Extending from the ring are long radial canals running along a groove on the underside of each of the sea star's rays. Many small lateral canals branch off from the sides of the radial canals. Each lateral canal ends in a hollow tube foot, as shown in *Figure 29.4* on page 766. The tube foot has a small muscular bulb at one end, the ampulla, and a short, thin-walled tube at the other end that is usually flattened into a sucker. Each ray of the sea star has many tube feet arranged in two or four rows on the bottom side of the ray. The tube feet are extended or retracted by hydraulic pressure in the water vascular system.

Mechanics of the water vascular system The entire water vascular system is filled with water and acts as a hydraulic system, allowing the sea star to move. The muscular ampulla contracts and relaxes with an action similar to the squeezing of a dropper bulb. When the muscles

Sea star opening a mollusk to feed

in the wall of the ampulla contract, a valve between the lateral canal and the ampulla closes so that water does not flow backwards into the radial canal. The pressure from the walls of the ampulla acts on the water, forcing it into the tube foot's sucker end, causing it to extend.

When the extended tube foot touches a rock or a mollusk shell, the center of the foot is retracted slightly. This creates a vacuum, enabling the tube foot to adhere to the rock or shell. The tip of the tube foot also secretes a sticky substance that helps it adhere. To move forward, muscles in the ampulla relax, and muscles in the tube foot wall contract. These actions shorten the tube foot and pull the sea star forward. Water is forced back into the relaxed ampulla. When the muscles in the ampulla contract, the tube foot extends again. This pattern of extension and retraction of tube feet results in continuous movement. It is the coordinated movement of many tube feet that enable the sea star to move slowly along the ocean floor.

Writing About Biology

Research Echinoderms are not the only animals to use water pressure for movement. Research to find out how scallops and earthworms also use hydraulic pressure for locomotion.

To find out more about hydraulic pressure systems, visit in.bdol.glencoe.com/physics

Writing About Biology

Scallops take in water and then clap their shells together, forcing water out quickly to move the animal in the opposite direction from the water flow. Earthworms have a hydrostatic skeleton (rigid, water-filled coelom) that their muscles brace against for movement through the soil.

STUDY GUIDE

Section 29.1

Echinoderms

Key Concepts

- Echinoderms have spines or bumps on their endoskeletons, radial symmetry, and water vascular systems. Most move by means of the suction action of tube feet.

- Echinoderms can be carnivorous, herbivorous, scavengers, or filter feeders.

- Echinoderms include sea stars, brittle stars, sea urchins, sand dollars, sea cucumbers, sea lilies, feather stars, and sea daisies.

- Deuterostome development is an indicator of the close phylogenetic relationship between echinoderms and chordates.

- A good fossil record of this phylum exists because the endoskeleton of echinoderms fossilizes easily.

Vocabulary
ampulla (p. 765)
madreporite (p. 764)
pedicellaria (p. 763)
ray (p. 763)
tube foot (p. 765)
water vascular system (p. 764)

Section 29.2

Invertebrate Chordates

Key Concepts

- All chordates have a dorsal hollow nerve cord, a notochord, pharyngeal pouches, and a postanal tail at some stage during development.

- All chordates also have bilateral symmetry, a well-developed coelom, and segmentation.

- Sea squirts and lancelets are invertebrate chordates.

- Vertebrate chordates may have evolved from larval stages of ancestral invertebrate chordates.

Vocabulary
dorsal hollow nerve cord (p. 771)
pharyngeal pouch (p. 772)
notochord (p. 771)

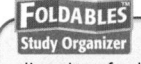
Study Organizer To help you review the diversity of echinoderms, use the Organizational Study Fold on page 763.

Key Concepts
Summary statements can be used by students to review the major concepts of the chapter.

Biology Online

Visit in.bdol.glencoe.com
/self_check_quiz
/vocabulary_puzzlemaker
/chapter_test
/standardized_test

VOCABULARY PUZZLEMAKER

For additional help with vocabulary, have students access the Vocabulary PuzzleMaker online at in.bdol.glencoe.com/vocabulary_puzzlemaker

FOLDABLES™
Have students use their Foldables to review the content of Section 29.1.

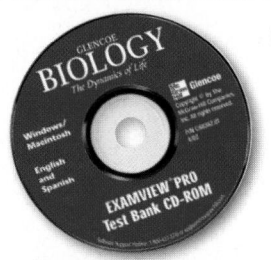

Use the ExamView®Pro Test Bank CD-ROM to:
- Create **multiple versions** of tests
- Create **modified** tests with one mouse click for **inclusion** students
- **Edit** existing questions and **add** your own questions
- Build tests aligned with state standards using built-in **State Curriculum Tags**
- Change **English** tests to **Spanish** with one mouse click and vice versa

Questions and answers have been aligned and verified by The Princeton Review.

Vocabulary Review

1. false—pedicellariae
2. true
3. false—dorsal hollow nerve cord
4. false—ampulla

Understanding Key Concepts

5. A   7. B
6. A   8. B

Constructed Response

9. Sea squirts are sessile filter feeders that are covered with a thick tunic to protect themselves.
10. Regeneration enables a sea star to survive and escape an attack by a predator. If a predator bites off a ray, the sea star can escape while the predator is feeding on that ray. A new ray will grow within weeks.
11. Most invertebrates show protostome development. Both echinoderms and chordates show deuterostome development, indicating a close relationship.

Thinking Critically

12. 1. water vascular system; 2. ampulla; 3. tube feet; 4. madreporite
13. Presentations will vary depending on what students find in their research and their own personal opinions.
14. The tube feet on the upper surface are modified to function as gills.
15. Lancelets are soft bodied and do not form lasting fossils.

Vocabulary Review

Review the Chapter 29 vocabulary words listed in the Study Guide on page 779. Determine if each statement is true or false. If false, replace the underlined word with the correct vocabulary word.

1. <u>Tube feet</u> are pincerlike appendages on echinoderms used for protection and cleaning.
2. The <u>pharyngeal pouches</u> are the paired openings found behind the mouth of all chordate embryos.
3. The <u>notochord</u> is the nerve cord found in all chordates that forms the spinal cord and brain.
4. The round, muscular structure on a tube foot is the <u>madreporite</u>.

Understanding Key Concepts

5. The water vascular system operates the tube feet of sea stars and other echinoderms by means of _____.
   A. water pressure **C.** water pumps
   B. water exchange **D.** water filtering
6. When a sea star loses a ray, it is replaced by the process of _____.
   A. regeneration **C.** metamorphosis
   B. reproduction **D.** parthenogenesis
7. The sand dollar in the diagram below exhibits what type of symmetry?
   A. bilateral symmetry **C.** asymmetry
   B. radial symmetry **D.** all of the above

8. Spines on sea stars and sea urchins are modified into pedicellariae used for _____.
   A. feeding **C.** breathing
   B. protection **D.** reproduction

Constructed Response

9. **Open Ended** How does a sessile animal such as a sea squirt protect itself?
10. **Open Ended** How is the ability of echinoderms to regenerate an adaptive advantage to these animals?
11. **Open Ended** In what ways are echinoderms more similar to vertebrates than to other invertebrates?

Thinking Critically

12. **Concept Map** Complete the concept map by using the following vocabulary terms: ampulla, madreporite, tube feet, water vascular system.

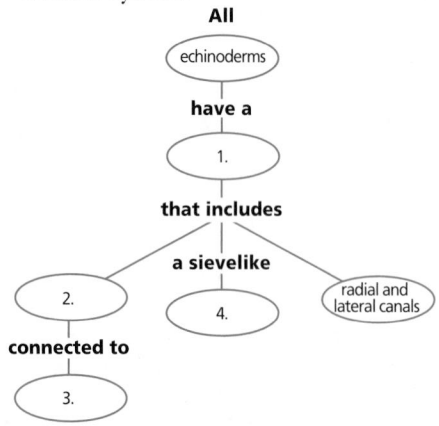

13. **REAL WORLD BIOCHALLENGE** Sea urchins are harvested on the coastlines of many states and imported to countries that consider sea urchin a gourmet food. Sea urchin populations have declined since harvesting began. Visit **in.bdol.glencoe.com** to investigate the controversy over continuing the harvesting. With other class members, stage a debate with assigned roles that will reveal the controversy. Roles should include a person who harvests sea urchins, a consumer, a scientist studying sea urchins, and a person wanting to protect sea urchins and their habitat.

 in.bdol.glencoe.com/chapter_test

14. Observe and Infer Explain why the tube feet of a sand dollar are located on its upper surface as well as on its bottom surface.

15. Explain Why is the fossil record incomplete for lancelets?

End-of Course Assessment Practice

16. B	**18.** C
17. A	**19.** B

Answer Sheet A practice answer sheet can be found on p. 163 of *Unit 8 FAST FILE Resources.*

End-of-Course Assessment Practice

The assessed Indiana standard appears next to the question.

All questions aligned and verified by *The Princeton Review*

Part 1 Multiple Choice

Use the graph below to answer question 16.

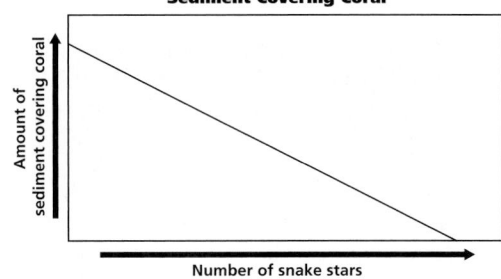

Relationship Between Snake Stars and Sediment Covering Coral

Amount of sediment covering coral

Number of snake stars

16. The snake star, a brittle star that looks snake-like, wraps itself around certain corals where it may stay for months. According to the graph, which phrase best describes the relationship between snake stars and the amount of sediment found on coral?
A. There is no relationship between snake stars and sediment.
B. As the number of snake stars increases, the amount of sediment decreases.
C. As the number of snake stars increases, the amount of sediment increases.
D. As the number of snake stars decreases, the amount of sediment decreases.

Study the diagram below and answer questions 17–19.

Tunicate larva

Larva of jawless vertebrate

17. The dorsal hollow nerve cords are the structures labeled _____.
A. 1 and 4   **C.** 3 and 6
B. 2 and 5   **D.** none of the above

18. The structures used for gas exchange are labeled _____.
B.1.15
A. 1 and 4   **C.** 3 and 6
B. 2 and 5   **D.** none of the above

19. The notochords are the structures labeled _____.
A. 1 and 4   **C.** 3 and 6
B. 2 and 5   **D.** none of the above

Part 2 Constructed Response/Grid In

Record your answers on your answer document.

20. Open Ended What might happen to a marine ecosystem in which fishes that eat sea urchins are overharvested? Explain.

21. Open Ended Infer why there are virtually no freshwater echinoderms.

 in.bdol.glencoe.com/standardized_test

RUBRIC

For more help evaluating open-ended assessment questions, see the rubric on p. 9T.

---

20. Sea urchins might increase in numbers, followed by a decrease in the algae on which they graze. The decrease in algae would also cause a decrease in the numbers of mollusks and other animals that feed on algae. Algae create a habitat for certain types of animals that would in turn decrease in numbers. Since algae produce oxygen released to the atmosphere, if enough algae are eliminated, the amount of oxygen in the atmosphere would decrease.

21. The marine biome is more consistent in its range of temperature, chemical makeup, and other habitat features than a freshwater habitat is. Echinoderms have not moved to freshwater as their adaptations are very specific to a marine biome. Other well-thought-out answers may also be accepted.

 Indiana Academic Standards

Pages 780–781: B.1.15, B.1.19, B.1.43

Prepare

Short on Time?

This BioDigest can be used as an overview of the invertebrate animal phyla. You may wish to use this unit summary to teach about invertebrates in place of the chapters in the invertebrate unit.

Key Concepts

Students learn about the phyla of invertebrates, which includes sponges, cnidarians, flatworms, roundworms, arthropods, and echinoderms, as well as the invertebrate chordates. They learn about cell organization in animals and observe differences in physical forms as organisms become more complex, with cells organized into tissues, and tissues organized into organs and organ systems.

1 Focus

Bellringer

Bring an assortment of live invertebrates into the classroom and have students examine them. Ask students to identify traits that these animals share. They should discover that invertebrates are animals without backbones. **L1**
ELL

Invertebrates

How are sponges, clams, sea urchins, and beetles alike? All of these animals are invertebrates—animals without backbones. The ancestors of all modern invertebrates had simple body plans. They lived in water and obtained food, oxygen, and other materials directly from their surroundings, just like present-day sponges, jellyfishes, and worms. Some invertebrates have external coverings such as shells and exoskeletons that provide protection and support.

Sponges

Sponges, phylum Porifera, are invertebrates made up of two cell layers. They have no tissues, organs, or organ systems. In general, sponges are asymmetrical. Most adult sponges are sessile—they do not move from place to place.

Direction of water flow

▲ Sponges are filter feeders. A sponge takes in water through pores in the sides of its body, filters out food, and releases the water through the opening at the top.

Prey

Nematocyst

▲ Jellyfishes and other cnidarians have nematocysts on their tentacles.

Cnidarians

Like sponges, cnidarians are made up of two cell layers and have only one body opening. The cell layers of a cnidarian, however, are organized into tissues with different functions. Cnidarians are named for stinging cells that contain nematocysts that are used to capture food. Jellyfishes, corals, sea anemones, and hydras belong to phylum Cnidaria.

RESOURCE MANAGER

Unit 8 *FAST FILE* Resources
Reinforcement and Study Guide in English, pp. 165–166
Reinforcement and Study Guide in Spanish, pp. 167–168
Student Recording Sheet, p. 169

Roundworms

Roundworms, phylum Nematoda, have a pseudocoelom and a tubelike digestive system with two body openings. Most roundworms are free-living, but many plants and animals are affected by parasitic roundworms.

Magnification: unavailable

▲ Flatworms have a head end with organs that sense the environment. Flatworms can detect light, chemicals, food, and movements in their surroundings.

▲ Plant-parasitic nematodes are one of the greatest threats to crops. They attack plant roots, stems, leaves, fruits, and seeds.

Flatworms

Flatworms, phylum Platyhelminthes, include free-living planarians, parasitic tapeworms, and parasitic flukes. Flatworms are bilaterally symmetrical animals with flattened solid bodies and no body cavities. Flatworms have one body opening through which food enters and wastes leave.

FOCUS ON ADAPTATIONS

Body Cavities

The type of body cavity an animal has determines how large it can grow and how it takes in food and eliminates wastes. Acoelomate animals, such as planarians, have no body cavity. Water and digested food particles travel through a solid body by the process of diffusion.

Animals such as roundworms have a pseudocoelom (soo duh SEE lum), a fluid-filled body cavity that is partly lined with mesoderm. Mesoderm is a layer of cells between the ectoderm and endoderm that differentiates into muscles, circulatory vessels, and reproductive organs. The pseudocoelom provides support for the attachment of muscles, making

movement more efficient. Earthworms have a coelom, a body cavity surrounded by mesoderm in which internal organs are suspended. The coelom acts as a watery skeleton against which muscles can work.

A pseudocoelomate roundworm

A coelomate segmented worm

An acoelomate flatworm

Digestive tract

783

2 Teach

Activity

Visual-Spatial Many of the invertebrate phyla are best observed in nature films. Select several nature films that highlight invertebrates. Ask students to list all the invertebrates they see in the films, and group the animals into phyla. Ask them to identify the characteristics they used to classify the animals. L2

Visual Learning

Interpersonal Ask student groups to make a labeled diagram of a planarian worm on the chalkboard. Ask them how the shape of a planarian reflects its living habits. Planarians are flattened, thereby enabling them to slip easily under rocks and debris in streams. L2 ELL COOP LEARN

Activity

Visual-Spatial Provide students with binocular microscopes, watch glasses, toothpicks, dropping pipettes, and a planarian worm culture. Ask them to place a few drops of water in the watch glass, then, using a toothpick, gently move a planarian to the watch glass. Have students observe the worm under the microscope and describe its movement.

Remind students to treat the planarian in a humane manner at all times. Have students wash their hands thoroughly with soap and water after completing the activity. L1 ELL

USING MODELS

Symmetry Ask students to find objects in the room that have bilateral and radial symmetry. Ask them to explain why they have identified particular objects as having one type of symmetry or another.

Objects such as a pencil and a test tube have radial symmetry. If an object

has radial symmetry, it can be divided along any plane through a central axis into roughly equal halves. Objects such as books and chairs have bilateral symmetry. If an object has bilateral symmetry, it can be divided along only one plane to form right and left halves that are mirror images. L2

Activity

Visual-Spatial Ask students to observe the movement of a live land snail. As the snail moves, ask students to describe its behavior when the antennae are touched with a cotton swab. **L1 ELL**

Microscope Activity

Ask students to observe the development of snail eggs with hand lenses or binocular microscopes.

Activity

Kinesthetic Ask students to set up a saltwater aquarium and add marine mollusks that can be obtained live from the supermarket. Clams, mussels, and oysters are generally available. Have students care for and make observations of their aquarium. **L2 ELL**

Mollusks

Slugs, snails, clams, squids, and octopuses are members of phylum Mollusca. All mollusks are bilaterally symmetrical and have a coelom, a digestive tract with two openings, a muscular foot for movement, and a mantle, which is a membrane that surrounds the internal organs. In shelled mollusks, the mantle secretes the shell.

Classes of Mollusks

There are three major classes of mollusks. Gastropods have one shell or no shell. Bivalves have two hinged shells called valves. Cephalopods have muscular tentacles and are capable of swimming by jet propulsion. All mollusks, except bivalves, have a rough, tonguelike organ called a radula used for obtaining food.

▼ Gastropods, such as snails, use their radulas to scrape algae from surfaces.

Bivalves, such ▶ as scallops, strain food from water by filtering it through their gills.

◀ Cephalopods, such as octopuses, are predators. They capture prey using the suckers on their long tentacles.

Leeches have ▶ flattened bodies and usually no setae. Most species are parasites that suck blood and body fluids from ducks, turtles, fishes, and mammals.

◀ Most bristleworms have a distinct head and a body with many setae.

Segmented Worms

Bristleworms, earthworms, and leeches are members of phylum Annelida, the segmented worms. Segmented worms are bilaterally symmetrical, coelomate animals that have segmented, cylindrical bodies with two body openings. Most annelids have setae, bristlelike hairs that extend from body segments, that help the worms move.

Segmentation is an adaptation that provides these animals with great flexibility. Each segment has its own muscles. Groups of segments have different functions, such as digestion or reproduction.

Classes of Segmented Worms

Phylum Annelida includes three classes: Hirudinae, the leeches; Oligochaeta, the earthworms; and Polychaeta, the bristleworms.

 CHALLENGE ACTIVITY

Invertebrate Advertisements Ask students to prepare a classified newspaper advertisement for a homesite for three animals, one in each of the classes of mollusks. Provide students with a page of the real estate section of the newspaper to review how such advertisements for homes are written. Students should be creative with their language but keep the precise habitat requirements of each animal in mind. **L3**

 Indiana Academic Standards

Pages 784–785: B.1.15, B.1.19

Arthropods

Arthropods are bilaterally symmetrical, coelomate invertebrates with tough outer coverings called exoskeletons. Exoskeletons protect and support their soft internal tissues and organs. They have jointed appendages that are used for walking, sensing, feeding, and mating. Jointed appendages allow for powerful and efficient movements.

Arthropod Diversity

Two out of three animals on Earth today are arthropods. The success of arthropods can be attributed to adaptations that provide efficient gas exchange, acute senses, and varied types of mouthparts for feeding. Arthropods include organisms such as spiders, crabs, lobsters, shrimps, crayfishes, centipedes, millipedes, and the enormously diverse group of insects.

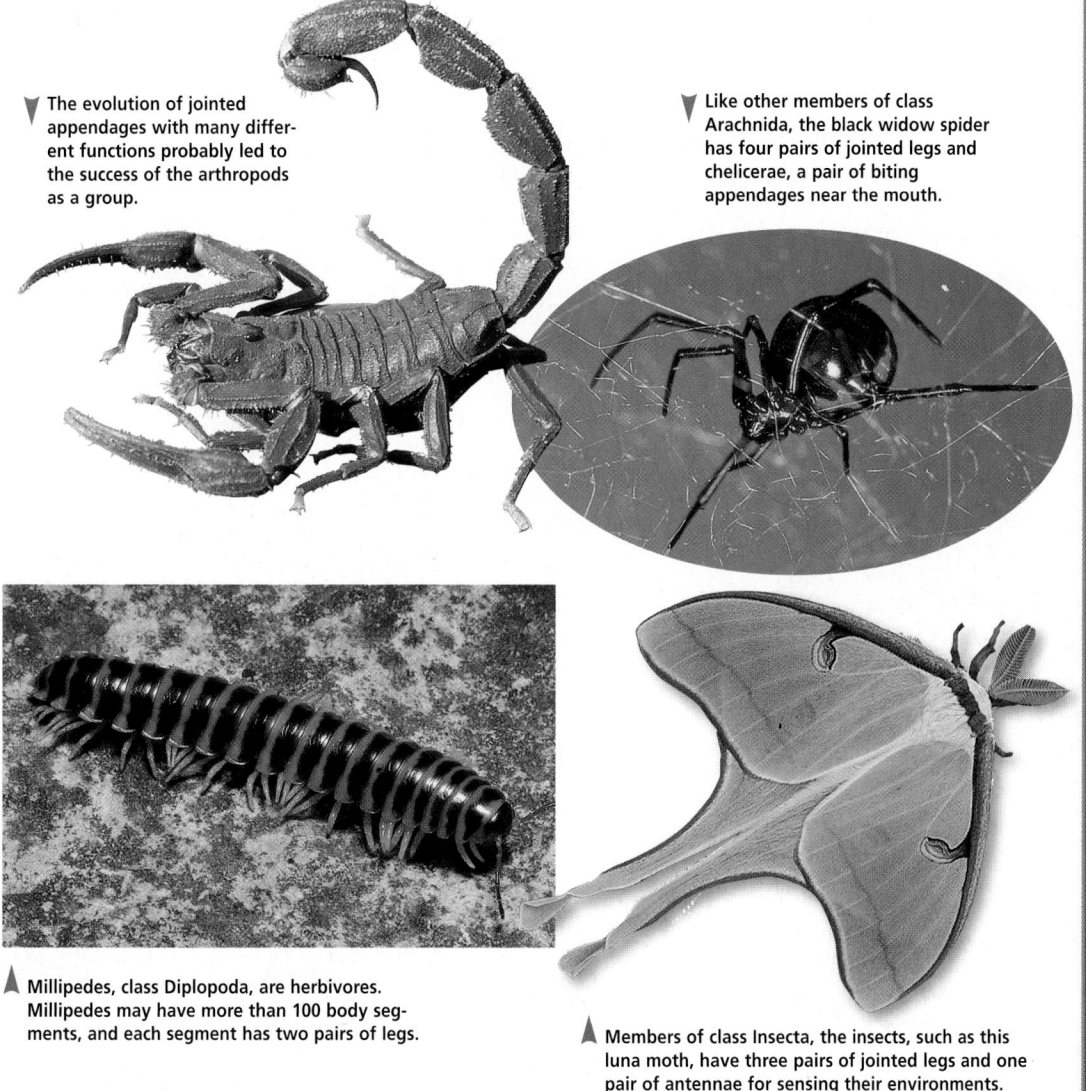

▼ The evolution of jointed appendages with many different functions probably led to the success of the arthropods as a group.

▼ Like other members of class Arachnida, the black widow spider has four pairs of jointed legs and chelicerae, a pair of biting appendages near the mouth.

⋏ Millipedes, class Diplopoda, are herbivores. Millipedes may have more than 100 body segments, and each segment has two pairs of legs.

⋏ Members of class Insecta, the insects, such as this luna moth, have three pairs of jointed legs and one pair of antennae for sensing their environments.

INVERTEBRATES **785**

Inquiry

Activity Give each group of students a live earthworm in one dish and a bristleworm in another dish. Ask them to observe their behavior and movements. Tell students to make a table that shows the similarities and differences between earthworms and bristleworms. Earthworms may be obtained from bait shops and bristleworms can be obtained from biological supply houses or bait shops near the sea.

Caution students to treat the earthworms and bristleworms in a humane manner at all times. Students should wet their hands before handling the worms. Make sure students wash their hands thoroughly with soap and water after handling the worms. **L2**

Quick Demo

Butterfly Diversity Borrow a collection of preserved butterflies from a nearby college or museum and call students' attention to the enormous variety in wing shapes, sizes, and colors. If preserved specimens are not available, then have students make correct-to-life-size cutouts of about one dozen different butterflies based on information in a field guide. **L2**

Visual Learning

Naturalist Ask students to examine the photographs of arthropods on this page and identify adaptations that enable each animal to survive in its habitat. **L1**

PROJECT

Classifying Mollusks as Food Have students obtain a menu from a local seafood restaurant. Ask students to construct a key to identify the gastropods, bivalves, and cephalopods listed on the menu. Have students summarize the importance of mollusks as a food source. **L2**

INCLUSION STRATEGIES

Visually Impaired Provide poster board cut-outs of flatworms, roundworms, and segmented worms. Ask visually impaired students to describe their tactile impressions of each worm. **L1**

Activity

Visual-Spatial Ask students to bring in jars of many types of arthropods. Number the jars and pass them from group to group, asking students to write the name of the arthropod and obvious arthropod features beside the name on a numbered list. For each arthropod, ask them to infer what features helped to make that particular arthropod successful. **L2**

Water Strider Show students a live water strider on the surface of pond water in a container with a large surface area. Ask students to hypothesize how the water strider stays on top of the water. *At the surface of water, water molecules are bound together by hydrogen bonds, giving the water high surface tension. Surface tension is the measure of how hard it is to break the surface of a liquid.* Ask them to identify adaptations the animal has that enables it to skate on the water surface. *light body weight distributed on widely set feet* **L2**

Activity

Have students design and conduct an experiment to determine the effect of temperature on the jumping ability of crickets. Remind students to handle the crickets in a humane manner at all times. Have students wash their hands thoroughly with soap and water after handling the crickets. *Students should find that crickets are sluggish in cold temperatures and more active in warm temperatures.* **L2**

Arthropod Origins

Arthropods most likely evolved from an ancestor of segmented worms; both groups show segmentation. However, an arthropod's segments are fused and have a greater complexity of structure than those of segmented worms. Because arthropods have exoskeletons, fossil arthropods are frequently found, and consequently more is known about their origins than about the phylogeny (fy LAH juh nee) of worms.

Arthropods
Largest class: Insecta, with 810 000 known species
Size ranges: Largest insects: tropical stick insect, length, 33 cm; Goliath beetle, mass, 100 g
Smallest insect: fairyfly wasp, length, 0.21 mm
Distribution: all habitats worldwide

FOCUS ON ADAPTATIONS

Insects

Staghorn beetle

Insects have many adaptations that have led to their success in the air, on land, in freshwater, and in salt water. For example, insects have complex mouthparts that are well adapted for chewing, sucking, piercing, biting, or lapping. Different species have mouthparts adapted to eating a variety of foods.

If you have ever been bitten by a mosquito, you know that mosquitoes have piercing mouthparts that cut through your skin to suck up blood. In contrast, butterflies and moths have long, coiled tongues that they extend deep into tubular flowers to sip nectar. Grasshoppers and many beetles have hard, sharp mandibles they use to cut off and chew leaves. But the heavy mandibles of staghorn beetles no

longer function as jaws; instead, they have become defensive weapons used for competition and mating purposes.

Different Foods for Different Stages

Because insects undergo metamorphosis, they often utilize different food sources at different times of the year. For example, monarch butterfly larvae feed on milkweed leaves, whereas the adults feed on milkweed flower nectar. Apple blossom weevil larvae feed on the stamens and pistils of unopened flower buds, but the adult weevils eat apple leaves. Some adult insects, such as mayflies, do not eat at all! Instead, they rely on food stored in the larval stage for energy to mate and lay eggs.

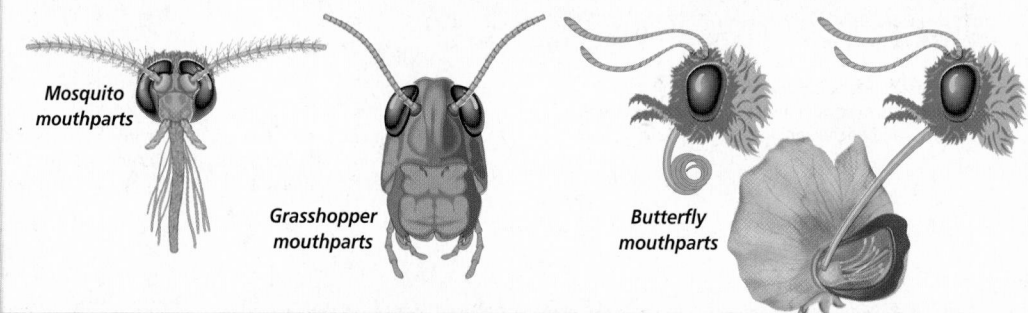

Mosquito mouthparts

Grasshopper mouthparts

Butterfly mouthparts

786

English Language Learners: *Kinesthetic* For students who are English language learners or are kinesthetic learners, purchase plastic arthropods. Ask them to work in groups and point out features of the arthropods as they pass them around the group. Features that they might be able to find include the head, thorax, abdomen, spiracles, claws, flippers, jointed legs, cephalothorax, antennae, mouthparts, pedipalps, chelicerae, compound and simple eyes, wings, tympanum, and mandibles. **L2**
ELL **COOP LEARN**

Echinoderms

Echinoderms, phylum Echinodermata, are radially symmetrical, coelomate animals with hard, bumpy, spiny endoskeletons covered by a thin epidermis. The endoskeleton is made primarily of calcium carbonate. Echinoderms move using a unique water vascular system with tiny, suction-cuplike tube feet. Some echinoderms have long spines also used in locomotion.

▼ Sea cucumbers have a leathery skin which gives them flexibility. Like most echinoderms, they move using tube feet.

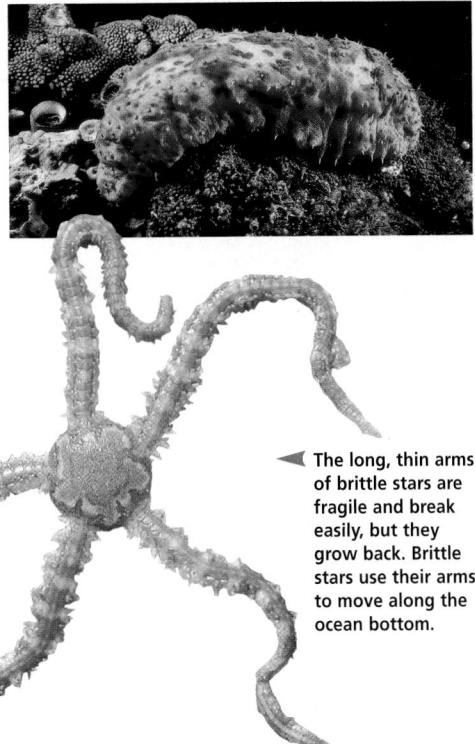

◄ The long, thin arms of brittle stars are fragile and break easily, but they grow back. Brittle stars use their arms to move along the ocean bottom.

Echinoderm Diversity

There are six living classes of echinoderms. They include sea stars, brittle stars, sea urchins, sea cucumbers, sand dollars, sea lilies, feather stars, and sea daisies.

Echinoderms have bilaterally symmetrical larvae and are deuterostomes, a feature that suggests a close relationship to the chordates.

Invertebrate Chordates

All chordates have, at one stage of their life cycles, a notochord, a dorsal hollow nerve cord, pharyngeal pouches, and a postanal tail. A notochord is a long, semirigid, rodlike structure along the dorsal side of these animals. The dorsal hollow nerve cord is a fluid-filled canal lying above the notochord. Pharyngeal pouches are paired openings in the pharynx that develop into gill slits in some invertebrate chordates, and are used to strain food from the water and for gas exchange. A muscular postanal tail is present in all chordates at some stage in their development. Muscle blocks aid in movement of the postanal tail. Muscle blocks are modified body segments consisting of stacked muscle layers.

Invertebrate chordates have all of these features at some point in their life cycles. The invertebrate chordates include the lancelets and the tunicates, also known as sea squirts.

▲ The lancelet is an invertebrate chordate. The lancelet's body is shaped like that of a fish even though it is a burrowing filter feeder.

INVERTEBRATES **787**

3 Assess

DAILY INTERVENTION

Check for Understanding
Naturalist Set up a lab practical with stations with preserved or live invertebrates. Ask students to identify the phylum and group within the phylum to which each animal belongs, and explain the visible features that helped them classify the invertebrates. **L2**

Reteach
Ask students to make a table in which they compare the characteristic features of invertebrate animals. **L1**

Extension

Ask students to make a collection of local insects and identify the features of these animals that make them adapted to the local environment. **L2** **ELL**

✔ Assessment

Portfolio Using large poster paper and markers, and their knowledge of invertebrate structure, have students design an invertebrate that is adapted to living in the school parking lot. Ask them to make a diagram and a list of adaptations. Have students include their posters in their portfolios. **L2**

🎯 CHALLENGE ACTIVITY

Hydraulics of Tube Feet Have students research the science of hydraulics. Have them describe how hydraulics helps to operate the tube feet of echinoderms. Have them compare and contrast this hydraulic system with other hydraulic systems in the plant or animal kingdom. **L3**

 Indiana Academic Standards

Pages 786–787: B.1.15, B.1.17

This page contains practice questions in the various formats that can be found on the most frequently given standardized tests.

Part 1 Multiple Choice

1. C	4. B	7. B
2. B	5. B	8. A
3. C	6. C	9. C

FAST FILE

Answer Sheet A practice answer sheet can be found on p. 169 of *Unit 8 FAST FILE Resources.*

Unit 8 Review
Standardized Test Practice

End-of-Course Assessment Practice

The assessed Indiana standard appears next to the question.

The Princeton Review **TEST-TAKING TIP**

What does the test expect of me?
Find out what concepts, objectives, or standards are being tested beforehand and keep those concepts in mind as you solve the questions. Stick to what the test is trying to test.

Part 1 Multiple Choice

1. Which of the following is used by segmented worms for movement? (B.1.15)
- **A.** chelicerae
- **B.** nematocysts
- **C.** setae
- **D.** water vascular system

2. An example of an animal with no body cavity is a(n) _____.
- **A.** sea star
- **B.** flatworm
- **C.** earthworm
- **D.** clam

Use the diagrams below to answer questions 3 and 4. The diagrams represent three different animal body plans.

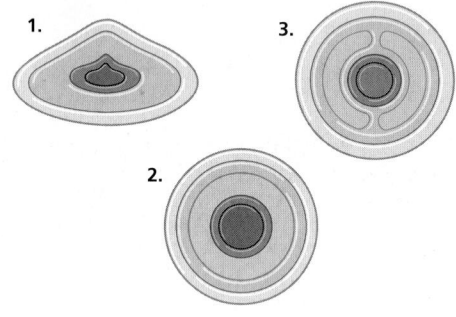

1.

3.

2.

3. Which body plan would be capable of more complex and powerful movements? (B.1.15)
- **A.** 1
- **B.** 2
- **C.** 3
- **D.** all of these

4. Which type of body plan belongs to pseudo-coelomate animals such as roundworms?
- **A.** 1
- **B.** 2
- **C.** 3
- **D.** all of these

---

5. An octopus belongs to phylum Mollusca because it has a mantle, bilateral symmetry, a digestive tract with two openings, and _____.
- **A.** an external shell
- **B.** a muscular foot
- **C.** a pseudocoelom
- **D.** segmentation

Use the diagrams below to answer questions 6–8. The diagram represents the life cycle for a beef tapeworm.

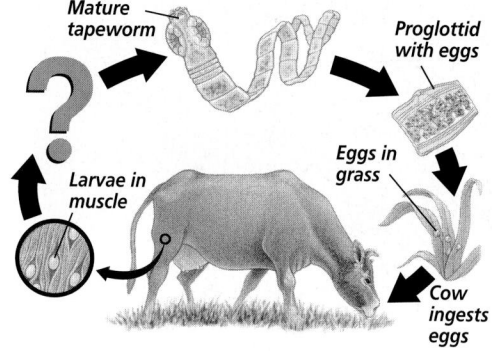

Mature tapeworm

Proglottid with eggs

Eggs in grass

Larvae in muscle

Cow ingests eggs

6. Which part of the life cycle for a beef tapeworm is missing?
- **A.** infection of the cow
- **B.** infection of the grass
- **C.** infection of the human host
- **D.** infection of the tapeworm

7. How do the tapeworm eggs get into the grass?
- **A.** from rainwater
- **B.** from feces of infected humans
- **C.** from snails
- **D.** from dead cows

8. Beef tapeworm larvae get into human hosts when humans _____.
- **A.** eat beef
- **B.** eat pork
- **C.** walk barefoot
- **D.** go swimming

9. Which of the following characteristics is unique to echinoderms?
- **A.** nematocycts
- **B.** jointed appendages
- **C.** a water vascular system
- **D.** filter feeding

Indiana Academic Standards

Pages 788–789: B.1.15, B.1.19

10. Asymmetrical organisms are often _____.
   A. free-swimming
   B. sessile
   C. photosynthetic
   D. autotrophic

11. Blood moves through vessels and into open
B.1.15 spaces around the body organs in a(n) _____.
   A. closed circulatory system
   B. water vascular system
   C. open circulatory system
   D. tracheal tube

Use the diagram below to answer questions 12–14. The diagram represents features shared by inverte-brate and vertebrate chordates.

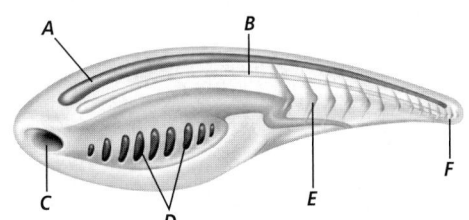

Part 2 Constructed Response/Grid In

Use the graph to answer questions 15–17. Record your answers or fill in the bubbles on the answer document using the correct place value.

15. Grid In How many more minutes does animal A spend in the light than animal B?

16. Grid In What is the average amount of time animals A, C, and E spend in the light?

17. Grid In What is the average amount of time animals D and E spend in the light?

18. Open Ended You are examining a free-living animal that has a thin, solid body with two surfaces. Into what phylum is this organism classified? Explain.

19. Open Ended Explain why asymmetrical animals, such as sponges, are often sessile.
B.1.15

20. Open Ended In what ways have wings been an adaptive advantage to the success of insects?
B.1.15

21. Open Ended Explain why worms are not as well represented in the fossil records as mollusks.

 in.bdol.glencoe.com/standardized_test

---

12. The structure labeled A in the diagram is the _____.
   A. postanal tail
   B. mouth
   C. dorsal hollow nerve cord
   D. notochord

13. The structure labeled E in the diagram is used
B.1.15 for _____.
   A. sensing the environment
   B. moving the tail
   C. support
   D. straining food from water

14. The structure labeled B in the diagram is the _____.
   A. postanal tail
   B. pharyngeal pouch
   C. dorsal hollow nerve cord
   D. notochord

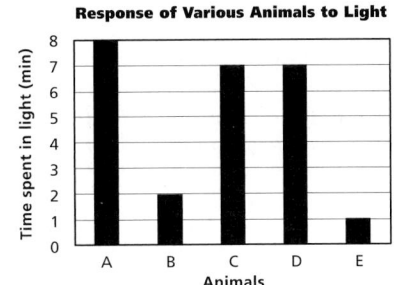

Response of Various Animals to Light

---

10. B	**13.** B	
11. C	**14.** D	
12. C		

Part 2 Constructed Response/Grid In

15. 6

16. 5

17. 4

18. It belongs to the phylum Platyhelminthes because it is a flatworm.

19. Asymmetrical organisms have no front end or back end; thus, they have little direction to their move-ment and cannot pursue food. They often wait for food to come to them—which works for a sessile animal.

20. Wings enable some arthro-pods to easily escape preda-tors, find food sources inaccessible to terrestrial arthropods, and move easily to other areas to find mates and nesting areas.

21. Soft-bodied worms do not fossilize as readily as mol-lusks, which have hard shells.

RUBRIC

For more help evaluating open-ended assessment questions, see the rubric on p. 9T.

Vertebrates

Unit Overview

Unit 9 presents information about the diversity of animals with backbones.

Chapter 30 reviews the evolutionary movement of animals from water to land environments. Students learn about the structure, adaptations, ecology, and physiology of fishes and amphibians.

Chapter 31 presents a study of reptiles and birds and their adaptations to their environments.

Chapter 32 introduces students to the diversity of mammals.

Chapter 33 explores the many types of animal behavior.

Introducing the Unit

Have examples of live vertebrates or vertebrate skeletons from different classes available for observation. Ask students to work in groups to make a table to compare and contrast the skeletons or animals. Vertebrate skeletons may be purchased from biological supply houses.

WebQuest A WebQuest is an inquiry-based online project in which all information used by students is obtained from the Web. Students evaluate the information to complete the activity. Access the Unit 9 WebQuest at **in.bdol.glencoe.com/webquest**

History & Biology

1680 • The first clocks with hands to indicate minutes are designed.

1600   1700

1671 • A torpedo fish, a type of electric ray, is dissected. The electric organ is examined, but scientists remain unaware that it produces electricity.

Torpedo fish

1735 • Carolus Linnaeus presents a system for classifying organisms based on structural similarities.

Vertebrates

What You'll Learn

Chapter 30
Fishes and Amphibians

Chapter 31
Reptiles and Birds

Chapter 32
Mammals

Chapter 33
Animal Behavior

Unit 9 Review
BioDigest & Standardized Test Practice

Indiana Standards
The following standards are covered in Unit 9:
B.1.14, B.1.15, B.1.16, B.1.17, B.1.18, B.1.19, B.1.31, B.1.32, B.1.34, B.1.36, B.1.41, B.1.43

Why It's Important

Animals classified as vertebrates have an internal skeleton and a backbone. These features, along with the development of lungs and, in most vertebrates, limbs, have allowed them to make the transition from life in water to life on land with great success.

Understanding the Photo ▶

Vertebrate animals have structural and physiological adaptations that allow them to live in all of Earth's biomes including arctic waters, deserts, rain forests, and mountain plateaus. Guanacos—relatives of camels, llamas, alpacas, and vicuñas—inhabit areas of Peru, Chile, and Argentina including the Andes at altitudes up to about 4000 m.

Time Line

Activity Have students research one of the events on the biology portion of the time line. Have them find more information about other scientific events at that time, the person who made the discovery, tools or technology available at that time, and the importance of the event. Students can present their findings in a multimedia presentation. **L2**

1845
The first inflatable rubber tire is invented.

1969
Neil Armstrong walks on the moon.

1800   1900   2000

1836
The first living species of lungfish is discovered in South America.

▲ Okapi

1901
Despite its zebra-like markings, the okapi is correctly identified as a relative of the giraffe.

1977
A woolly mammoth is found preserved in ice in the Soviet Union.

2002
Scientists announce the discovery of two new species of monkeys and a new species of parrot in the Amazon rain forest.

Unit 9

Advance Materials Planning

The following materials may need to be ordered a few weeks in advance of the planned activity.

Chapter 30

- **Additional Lab** (p. 798) aquarium setup, tropical fishes
- **MiniLab** (p. 806) living or preserved adult frog and tadpole
- **Quick Demo** (p. 805) live frog

Chapter 31

- **Quick Demo** (p. 818) live or mounted specimens of reptiles
- **MiniLab** (p. 827) contour and down feathers
- **Quick Demo** (p. 828) recording of bird calls and songs

Chapter 32

- **MiniLab** (p. 843) slide of longitudinal section of human canine tooth
- **Additional Lab** (p. 842) mouse, terrarium
- **MiniLab** (p. 845) owl pellets
- **Quick Demo** (p. 849) guide to animal tracks

Chapter 33

- **MiniLab** (p. 860) 6 isopods
- **Quick Demo** (p. 861) large sheet of clear, glasslike plastic
- **Additional Lab** (p. 864) glass terrarium or aquarium with cover, 1 female and 5 male field crickets
- **BioLab** (p. 874) snails

791

Unit Projects

Display

Visual-Spatial Have student groups do a census of animals on the school grounds or areas near the school. They should look for animals and their signs. Ask students to make a map of the area to scale, indicating where they found animals or their signs. **L2** **ELL** **COOP LEARN**

Using the Library

Intrapersonal Ask students to find out the habitat requirements of the animals found in their study area. **L2**

Modeling

Kinesthetic Have students make another map of the area showing how the area could be improved for wildlife living there. The map can be three-dimensional if materials are available. **L2**

791

Chapter 30 Organizer

Section Objectives	National Science Standards	State/Local Standards	Advanced Lab and Demo Planning
Section 30.1 1 1/2 sessions, 1/2 block 1. **Relate** the structural adaptations of fishes to their environments. 2. **Compare and contrast** the characteristics of the different groups of fishes. 3. **Interpret** the phylogeny of fishes.	UCP.1, UCP.2, UCP.4, UCP.5; A.1, A.2; C.3–6	**Indiana Standards** B.1.14, B.1.15, B.1.19, B.1.31, B.1.32	**Student Labs:** MiniLab 30.1, p. 795: slide of fish's gill, microscope Problem-Solving Lab 30.1, p. 796 Additional Lab, p. 798: aquarium setup, black and white gravel, tropical fishes (zebra, catfish, gourami), timer or stopwatch, black construction paper, masking tape **Teacher Demonstrations:** Quick Demo, p. 798: plastic package of ketchup, 2-L clear plastic bottle Quick Demo, p. 797: stereomicroscope
Section 30.2 2 sessions, 1 block 4. **Relate** the demands of a terrestrial environment to the adaptations of amphibians. 5. **Relate** the evolution of the three-chambered heart to the amphibian lifestyle.	UCP.1–5; A.1, A.2; B.3; C.1, C.3–6; E.2; F.1, F.3, F.4; G.1, G.2	**Indiana Standards** B.1.14, B.1.15, B.1.18, B.1.19, B.1.31, B.1.32	**Student Labs:** MiniLab 30.2, p. 806: living or preserved adult frog and tadpole Investigate BioLab, p. 810: See materials below. **Teacher Demonstration:** Quick Demo, p. 805: live frog
End of Chapter Assessment Student Edition **Study Guide,** p. 813 **Content Assessment,** pp. 814–815		**Indiana Standards** B.1.15, B.1.18, B.1.31, B.1.38	**Student Lab:** Investigate BioLab, p. 810: sample keys from guidebooks, field guides for amphibian identification

Key to Teaching Strategies

L1 Level 1 activities should be appropriate for students with learning difficulties.

L2 Level 2 activities should be within the ability range of all students.

L3 Level 3 activities are designed for above-average students.

ELL ELL activities should be within the ability range of English Language Learners.

COOP LEARN Cooperative Learning activities are designed for small group work.

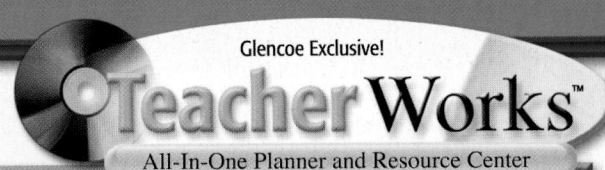

Glencoe Exclusive!
Teacher Works™
All-In-One Planner and Resource Center

Reproducible Masters and Transparencies

Technology

Unit 9 FAST FILE Resources
MiniLab Worksheet, pp. 3–4
Real World BioApplications, pp. 9–10
Reinforcement and Study Guide in English, pp. 11–12
Reinforcement and Study Guide in Spanish, pp. 15–16
Transparency Worksheets, pp. 21, 23–26
Reading Essentials for Biology, Section 30.1
Laboratory Manual, pp. 187–188
🔥 **Section Focus Transparency 73**
🔥 **Basic Concepts Transparencies 52, 53**

💿 **Interactive Chalkboard CD-ROM: Section 30.1 Presentation** ▮
💿 TeacherWorks™ **CD-ROM** ▮
 Guided Reading Audio Summaries MP3

Unit 9 FAST FILE Resources
MiniLab Worksheet, pp. 5–6
BioLab Worksheet, pp. 7–8
Reinforcement and Study Guide in English, pp. 13–14
Reinforcement and Study Guide in Spanish, pp. 17–18
Concept Mapping p. 19
Critical Thinking/Problem Solving p. 20
Transparency Worksheets, pp. 22, 25–26, 27–28
Reading Essentials for Biology, Section 30.2
Laboratory Manual, pp. 189–194
Inside Story Poster
🔥 **Section Focus Transparency 74**
🔥 **Basic Concepts Transparency 53**
🔥 **Reteaching Skills Transparency 44**

💿 **Interactive Chalkboard CD-ROM: Section 30.2 Presentation** ▮
💿 TeacherWorks™ **CD-ROM** ▮
 Guided Reading Audio Summaries MP3
💿 **Virtual Labs CD-ROM**
Virtual Lab: Frog Dissection

Unit 9 FAST FILE Resources
Chapter Assessment, pp. 29–34
Student Recording Sheet p. 35

The Princeton Review **Reviewing Biology,** pp. 59–60

💿 **Interactive Chalkboard:** ▮ **Chapter 30 Assessment**
💿 **MindJogger Videoquizzes DVD/VHS**
💿 **ExamView® Pro Test Bank CD-ROM**
💿 TeacherWorks™ **CD-ROM** ▮
💿 **Succeeding on National Standards CD-ROM**

🖱 in.bdol.glencoe.com
/self_check_quiz
/vocabulary_puzzlemaker
/chapter_test
/standardized_test

▮ Indicates materials created specifically for Indiana.

Fishes and Amphibians

Short on Time?

BIODIGEST The BioDigest at the end of this unit can be used as a(n):

- preview to introduce important unit concepts.
- overview if time does not permit teaching the entire chapter.
- review of key unit concepts.

What You'll Learn

- You will compare and contrast the adaptations of the different groups of fishes and amphibians.
- You will learn about the origin of modern fishes and amphibians.

Why It's Important

Fishes are the most diverse vertebrate group. Amphibians are adapted to live both in water and on land. The development of a bony endoskeleton in fishes and lungs in amphibians were major steps in animal evolution.

Understanding the Photo

There are about 35 species of seahorses worldwide. This one, *Hippocampus kuda*, can be found in the Indian Ocean. It can grow to about 30 cm but generally is about 10–12 cm. A seahorse feeds on plankton and brine shrimp which are sucked into its mouth. The suction is so strong that an audible sound is made.

Understanding the Photo

Seahorses are bony fishes. They swim upright and slowly move forward. An adaptation that allows them to capture prey is their long snout. It functions like a suction to draw in small organisms that pass by in the water. Seahorse species range in size from about 4 cm to 20 cm.

Biology Online

Visit in.bdol.glencoe.com to
- study the entire chapter online
- access Web Links for more information and activities on fishes and amphibians
- review content with the Interactive Tutor and self-check quizzes

792

 Two-Minute Chapter Launcher

Activity Remove hooks from a variety of fish-shaped lures that are made of the same material. Have students work in small groups and drop each lure into a 1000-mL graduated cylinder filled with water. Ask them to measure the time that it takes for each lure to reach the bottom of the cylinder. Ask students to correlate their results to the shape of each lure. Ask them what other variables might be important in their observations. Reinforce the importance of making accurate observations and collecting accurate data. **L2**

Section 30.1

Fishes

Indiana Standards Standard B.1.15 Understand and explain that, in biological systems, structure and function must be considered together.

SECTION PREVIEW

Objectives

Relate the structural adaptations of fishes to their environments.

Compare and contrast the characteristics of the different groups of fishes.

Interpret the phylogeny of fishes.

Review Vocabulary

vertebrate: an animal with a backbone (p. 685)

New Vocabulary

spawning
fin
lateral line system
scale
swim bladder
cartilage

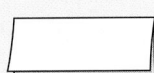

FOLDABLES Study Organizer

Fishes Make the following Foldable to help you organize information about the diversity and origins of fishes.

STEP 1 Fold a sheet of paper in half lengthwise. Make the back edge about 2 cm longer than the front edge.

STEP 2 Turn the paper so the fold is on the bottom. Then **fold** it into thirds.

STEP 3 Unfold and cut only the top layer along both folds to make three tabs.

STEP 4 Label the Foldable as shown.

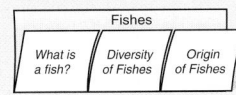

Fishes		
What is a fish?	Diversity of Fishes	Origin of Fishes

Answer Questions As you read Chapter 30, answer the question and fill in information about fishes behind the tabs.

What is a fish?

Fishes, like all vertebrates, are classified in the phylum Chordata. This phylum includes three subphyla: Urochordata, the tunicates; Cephalochordata, the lancelets; and Vertebrata, the vertebrates. Fishes belong to the subphylum Vertebrata. In addition to fishes, subphylum Vertebrata includes amphibians, reptiles, birds, and mammals. Recall from the previous chapter that all chordates have four traits in common—a notochord, pharyngeal pouches, postanal tail, and a dorsal hollow nerve cord. In vertebrates, the embryo's notochord is replaced by a backbone in adult animals. All vertebrates are bilaterally symmetrical coelomates that have endoskeletons, closed circulatory systems, nervous systems with complex brains and sense organs, and efficient respiratory systems.

Classes of fishes

Fishes can be grouped into four classes of the subphylum Vertebrata. The jawless fishes belong to the superclass Agnatha, which means "without jaws." Superclass Agnatha consists of two classes: class Myxini (mik SEE nee), hagfishes, and class Cephalaspidomorphi (se fa LAS pe do MOR fee), lampreys.

30.1 FISHES **793**

Section 30.1

1 Focus

INTERACTIVE CHALKBOARD
PowerPoint® Presentations

Bellringer
Section Focus Transparency 73

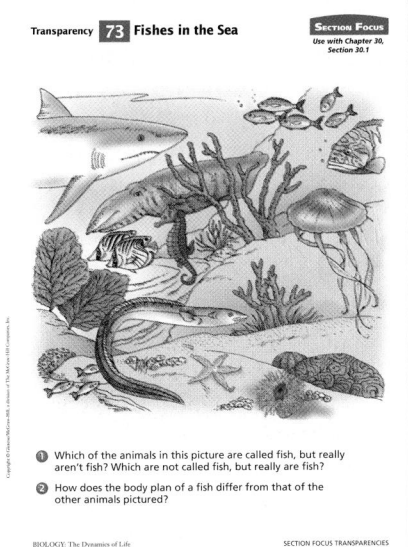

Transparency **73** Fishes in the Sea

SECTION FOCUS
Use with Chapter 30, Section 30.1

❶ Which of the animals in this picture are called fish, but really aren't fish? Which are not called fish, but really are fish?

❷ How does the body plan of a fish differ from that of the other animals pictured?

BIOLOGY: The Dynamics of Life   SECTION FOCUS TRANSPARENCIES

INTERACTIVE CHALKBOARD with Image Bank

PowerPoint® Presentations

This CD-ROM is an editable Microsoft® PowerPoint® presentation that includes:

• Section presentations
• Section checks
• Image bank
• Hot links to Biology Online
• All transparencies

FOLDABLES™

For an additional Foldables activity idea, see the Chapter 30 Foldables page in *Unit 9 FAST FILE Resources.*

RESOURCE MANAGER

Unit 9 *FAST FILE* Resources
  MiniLab Worksheet, pp. 3–4
  Real World BioApplications, pp. 9–10
  Reinforcement and Study Guide in English, pp. 11–12
  Reinforcement and Study Guide in Spanish, pp. 15–16

Transparency Worksheets, pp. 21, 23–26
Reading Essentials for Biology, Section 30.1
Laboratory Manual, pp. 187–188
Section Focus Transparency 73
Basic Concepts Transparencies 52, 53

 Indiana Academic Standards

Pages 792–793: B.1.15

2 Teach

Visual Learning

Figure 30.1 Have students look at the fishes shown in Figure 30.1. Ask them to list the adaptations that these fishes have to their habitat. fins, streamlined body, gills for obtaining oxygen dissolved in water **L1**

Chalkboard Example

Draw the two-chambered heart of a fish and the four-chambered heart of a mammal on the chalkboard. Briefly trace the path of blood through each heart and explain that the four-chambered heart is more efficient for an animal that must move quickly and maintain a constant body temperature.

✓ Reading Check All fishes reproduce sexually. Some release eggs and sperm into the water and fertilization is external. Other fishes have internal fertilization. Fish development can be either internal or external.

Indiana Academic Standards

Pages 794–795: B.1.15, B.1.19

Class Chondrichthyes (kahn DRIHK theez) is comprised of cartilaginous fishes, such as sharks and rays; and class Osteichthyes (ahs tee IHK theez) contains the bony fishes. Examples from the different classes are shown in *Figure 30.1.*

Fishes inhabit nearly every type of aquatic environment on Earth. They are found in freshwater and salt water and adapted to living in shallow, warm water and deeper, cold and lightless water.

Fishes breathe using gills

Fishes have gills made up of feathery gill filaments that contain tiny blood vessels. Gills are an important adaptation for fishes and other vertebrates that live in water. As a fish takes water in through its mouth, water passes over the gills and then out through slits at the side of the fish. Oxygen and carbon dioxide are exchanged through the capillaries in the gill filaments. You can find out more about the structure and function of gills in fishes in the *MiniLab* on the next page.

Fishes have two-chambered hearts

All fishes have two-chambered hearts, as shown in *Figure 30.2.* One chamber receives deoxygenated blood from the body tissues, and the second chamber pumps blood directly to the capillaries of the gills, where oxygen is picked up and carbon dioxide released. Oxygenated blood is carried from the gills to body tissues. Blood flow through the body of a fish is relatively slow because most of the heart's pumping action is used to push blood through the gills.

Fishes reproduce sexually

Although the method may vary, all fishes reproduce sexually. Fertilization and development is external in most fishes. Eggs and sperm can be released directly into the water, or deposited in more protected areas, such as on floating aquatic plants. Although most fishes produce large numbers of eggs at one time, hagfishes produce small numbers of relatively large eggs.

Figure 30.1
Examples of fishes include jawless fishes, cartilaginous fishes, and bony fishes.

 Most fishes you are familiar with are bony fishes, such as this swordfish.

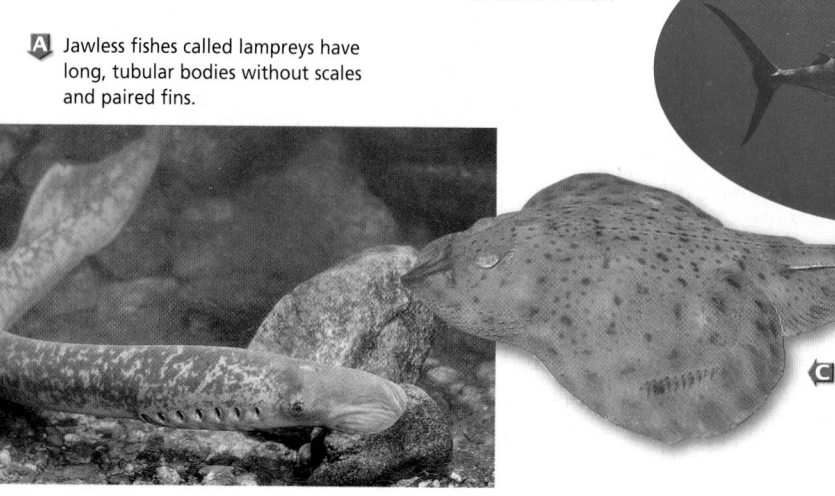

A Jawless fishes called lampreys have long, tubular bodies without scales and paired fins.

C Cartilaginous fishes called skates have a flattened body shape with large paired fins that enable them to "fly" over the ocean bottom as they search for food.

794 FISHES AND AMPHIBIANS

TECH PREP

Fish Farming Have a group of students visit a nearby fish farm or fish hatchery and make a multimedia presentation to the class. The presentation should include a description of the products, pricing, and costs of these businesses. **L2 ELL**

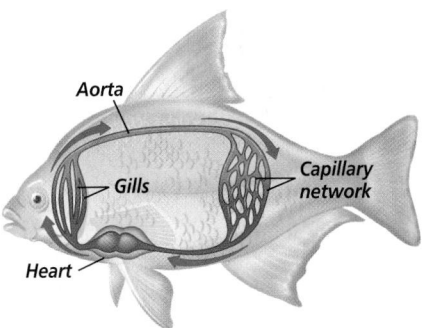

Figure 30.2
Blood in a fish flows in a one-way circuit throughout the body.

Cartilaginous fishes have internal fertilization. Skates deposit fertilized eggs on the ocean floor. Some female sharks and rays carry developing young inside their bodies. Because these young fishes are well developed when they are born, they have an increased chance of survival.

Most bony fishes have external fertilization and development. This type of external reproduction in fishes and some other animals is called **spawning.** During spawning, some female bony fishes, such as cod, produce as many as 9 million eggs, of which only a small percentage survive. In some bony fishes, such as guppies and mollies, fertilization and development is internal. Most fishes that produce millions of eggs provide no care for their offspring after spawning. In these species, only a few of the young survive to adulthood. Some fishes, such as the mouth-brooding cichlids, stay with their young after they hatch. When their young are threatened by predators, the parent fishes scoop them into their mouths for protection.

✓ Reading Check **Summarize** the different reproductive methods of cartilaginous and bony fishes.

MiniLab 30.1

Observe and Infer

Structure and Function of Fishes' Gills Fishes remove oxygen from the water by means of gills. Water enters a fish's mouth, moves over the gills and out through openings on the sides of the head. The gills are made up of thin filaments containing blood vessels. Inside the gills, blood moves in the opposite direction to the flow of water. When blood and water flow in opposite directions, the oxygen concentration difference between the water and the blood is large enough for oxygen to diffuse from water into blood.

Procedure

1. Examine a prepared slide of a fish's gill under the microscope. **CAUTION:** *Use care when working with microscopes and microscope slides.*
2. Draw and label a sketch of the gill filaments.

Analysis

1. **Observe and Infer** Why are the gills of fishes made up of very thin tissue?
2. **Predict** How might a fish adjust to water that suddenly has less oxygen?
3. **Explain** Some fishes have a mutualistic relationship with organisms, such as small shrimp, that "clean" gill filaments by feeding on parasites that live on the gill tissue. How is this relationship beneficial to each organism?

MiniLab 30.1

Purpose
Students will examine the microscopic structure of a fish's gills and analyze how structure is related to function.

Process Skills
identify, describe, interpret, sketch, analyze, predict, infer, observe, explain

Teaching Strategies
Review gill structure and function and gill covering (operculum) with students.

Expected Results
Students will see very thin gill filaments. Explain that the tissue has been stained for visibility.

Analysis
1. Thin tissue makes diffusion of oxygen more efficient.
2. A fish might take in more water, thus enabling gills to extract the amount of oxygen needed.
3. The shrimp benefits by eating the parasites. The fish benefits because without parasites on its gills, there is no tissue damage and the entire gill surface is exposed to water.

Assessment
Ask students to examine a fish from the fish market and compare the appearance of the gill structure of the fish with the microscopic structure they examined. **L2**

CULTURAL DIVERSITY

Samuel Milton Nabrit African American zoologist Samuel M. Nabrit conducted many experiments on tail regeneration in fishes. Nabrit earned a Ph.D. in Zoology in 1932 and became a researcher at Woods Hole Marine Biology Laboratory. Papers describing his work may be found in the *Journal of Experimental Zoology, Anatomical Record,* and *Biological Bulletin.* Nabrit is perhaps best known for his work toward promoting African Americans in science. He helped to organize the National Institute of Science in 1943, an organization designed to explore the teaching and research problems of African American scientists.

Purpose

Students will analyze the lateral line system of fishes.

Process Skills

describe, identify, analyze, infer, hypothesize, predict

Teaching Strategies

- This lab would be suited for cooperative groups.
- Show students photographs of the lateral lines of a variety of fishes.
- Review with students the vocabulary words associated with this lab.

Thinking Critically

1. Fishes might not be able to detect prey or approaching predators.
2. Vision would not assist fishes in detecting prey or approaching predators, so the lateral line system would be very important.
3. Fishes detect the movements of other fishes near them by means of their lateral line systems and respond accordingly.

Modified Assessment

Ask students to design a fish without a lateral line that could capture prey and detect predators. Form groups and ask students to use what they know about fishes and their creativity to design a fish. Direct each group to make an illustration with labels of their fish and describe the environment in which it lives. **L1** **COOP LEARN**

Think Critically

Why is having a lateral line system important? Aside from other senses, including sight and smell, most fishes also have a lateral line system.

Solve the Problem

The lateral line system runs along either side of a fish in its skin. Vibrations in the water cause the gelatin-like fluid in the lateral line system to move, which stimulates the receptor cells to send messages to the fish's brain. The fish receives information about the location of objects in the water such as coral, rocks, other fishes, and prey organisms.

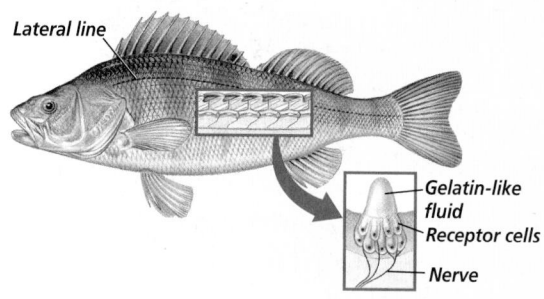

Lateral line
Gelatin-like fluid
Receptor cells
Nerve

Thinking Critically

1. **Infer** If a fish's lateral line system were damaged and unable to function, what effect could that have on the fish?
2. **Explain** Why might a lateral line system be important for fishes that live in the abyss, where there is no light?
3. **Hypothesize** Fishes in a school have the ability to change direction almost instantly. Form a hypothesis that explains how the lateral line system allows fishes to achieve this.

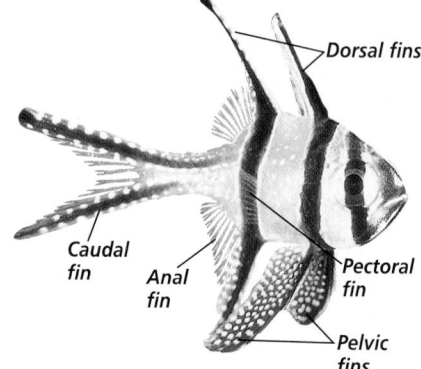

Figure 30.3
The paired fins of a fish include the pectoral fins and the pelvic fins. Fins found on the dorsal and ventral surfaces can include the dorsal fins and anal fin.

Dorsal fins
Caudal fin
Anal fin
Pectoral fin
Pelvic fins

Most fishes have paired fins

Fishes in the classes Chondrichthyes and Osteichthyes have paired fins. **Fins** are fan-shaped membranes that are used for balance, swimming, and steering. Fins are attached to and supported by the endoskeleton and are important in locomotion. The paired fins of fishes, illustrated in *Figure 30.3*, foreshadowed the development of limbs for movement on land and ultimately of wings for flying.

Fishes have developed sensory systems

All fishes have highly developed sensory systems. Cartilaginous and bony fishes have an adaptation called the lateral line system that enables them to sense objects and changes in their environment. The **lateral line system** is a line of fluid-filled canals running along the sides of a fish that enable it to detect movement and vibrations in the water. Find out more about the lateral line system by doing the *Problem-Solving Lab* on this page.

Fishes have eyes that allow them to see objects and contrasts between light and dark in the water as well. The amount of vision varies greatly among fishes. Some fishes that live in areas of the ocean where there is no light may have reduced, almost nonfunctional eyes.

Some fishes also have an extremely sensitive sense of smell and can detect small amounts of chemicals in the water. Sharks can follow a trail of blood through the water for several hundred meters. This ability helps them locate their prey.

Most fishes have scales

Cartilaginous and bony fishes have skin covered by intermittent or overlapping rows of scales. **Scales** are thin bony plates formed from the skin.

PROJECT

The Aquarium Ask students to prepare a written plan that identifies all materials needed to set up and maintain an aquarium, along with an explanation of why each material is needed. Allow students to set up and maintain their aquariums according to their plans. **L2**

Scales, shown in *Figure 30.4,* can be toothlike, diamond-shaped, cone-shaped, or round. Shark scales are similar to teeth found in other vertebrates. The age of some species of fishes can be estimated by counting annual growth rings in their scales.

Reading Check Describe the different shapes scales can have.

Jaws evolved in fishes

An important event in vertebrate evolution was the development of jaws in ancestral fishes. The advantage of jaws is that they enable an animal to grasp and crush its prey with great force. Jaws also allowed early fishes to prey on a greater variety of organisms. This, among other factors, explains why some early fishes were able to grow to such great size. *Figure 30.5* shows the evolution of jaws in fishes.

When you think of a shark, do you imagine gaping jaws and rows of razor-sharp teeth? Sharks have up to 20 rows of teeth that are continually replaced. Their teeth point backwards to prevent prey from escaping once caught. Sharks are among the most streamlined of all fishes and are well adapted for life as predators.

Figure 30.4
Fishes can be classified by the type of scales present. Diamond-shaped scales **(A)** are common to bony fishes, such as gars. Bony fishes, such as chinook salmon, have either cone-shaped or round scales **(B)**. Tooth-shaped scales **(C)** are characteristic of the sharks.

LM Magnification: 40×

Most fishes have bony skeletons

The majority of the world's fishes belong to the class Osteichthyes, the bony fishes. Bony fishes, a successful and widely distributed class, differ greatly in habitat, size, feeding behavior, and shape. All bony fishes have skeletons made of bone rather than cartilage as found in other classes of fishes. Bone is the hard, mineralized, living tissue that makes up the endoskeleton of most vertebrates.

Figure 30.5
Jaws evolved from the cartilaginous gill arches of early jawless fishes. Teeth evolved from skin.

Gill arches

Jawless, filter-feeding fish   Gill slits

Beginning of jaw formation

Gill slits

Gill arches

Skull   Jaws

Fish with jaws

30.1 FISHES **797**

Figure 30.6
Bony fishes vary in appearance, behavior, and way of life.

A Eels have a long, snakelike body and can wriggle through mud and crevices in search of food.

B Seahorses move slowly through the underwater forests of seaweed where they live. They are unusual in that the males brood their young in stomach pouches.

C Predatory bony fishes, such as this pike, have sleek bodies with powerful muscles and tail fins for fast swimming in freshwater lakes and rivers.

In general, the development of bone was important for the evolution of fishes and vertebrates. It allowed fishes to adapt to a variety of aquatic environments, as shown in *Figure 30.6,* and eventually to land.

Bony fishes have separate vertebrae that provide flexibility

The evolution of a backbone composed of separate, hard segments called vertebrae was significant in providing the major support structure of the vertebrate skeleton. Separate vertebrae provide great flexibility. This is especially important for fish locomotion, which involves continuous flexing of the backbone. You can see how modern bony fishes propel themselves through water in *Figure 30.*7. Some fishes are effective predators, in part because of the fast speeds they can attain as a result of having a flexible skeleton.

Bony fishes evolved swim bladders

Another key to the evolutionary success of bony fishes was the evolution of the swim bladder. A **swim bladder** is a thin-walled, internal sac found just below the backbone in most bony fishes. It can be filled with mostly oxygen or nitrogenous gases that diffuse out of a fish's blood. A fish with a

Figure 30.7
Most bony fishes swim in one of three ways.

A An eel moves its entire body in an S-shaped pattern.

B A mackerel flexes the posterior end of its body to accentuate the tail-fin movement.

C A tuna keeps its body rigid, moving only its powerful tail. Fishes that use this method move faster than all others.

798 FISHES AND AMPHIBIANS

swim bladder can control its depth by regulating the amount of gas in the bladder. The gas works like the gas in a blimp that allows the blimp to change its height above the ground.

Some fishes remove gases from the swim bladder by expelling them through a special duct that attaches the swim bladder to the esophagus. In fishes that do not have this duct their swim bladders empty when gases diffuse back into the blood.

Reading Check **Explain** the function of a swim bladder.

Diversity of Fishes

Fishes range in size from the tiny dwarf goby that is less than 1 cm long, to the huge whale shark that can reach a length of about 15 m—the length of two school buses.

Agnathans are jawless fishes

Lampreys and hagfishes belong to the superclass Agnatha. The skeletons of agnathans, as well as of sharks and their relatives, are made of a tough, flexible material called **cartilage.** Though they do not have jaws, they are voracious feeders. A hagfish, *Figure 30.8,* has a toothed mouth and feeds on dead or dying fishes.

It can drill a hole into a fish and suck out the blood and insides. Parasitic lampreys use their suckerlike mouths to attack other fishes. They use their sharp teeth to scrape away the flesh and then suck out the prey's blood.

Sharks and rays are cartilaginous fishes

Sharks, skates, and rays belong to the class Chondrichthyes, shown in *Figure 30.9.* These fishes, like agnathans, possess skeletons composed entirely of cartilage. Because living sharks, skates, and rays are similar to species that swam the seas more than 100 000 years ago, they are considered living fossils. Sharks are perhaps the most well-known predators of the oceans.

Figure 30.8
When touched, a hagfish's skin gives off a tremendous amount of mucus, which makes it so slimy it is nearly impossible to catch.

A The hammerhead shark is large and found in warm ocean water. It has two eyes that are at opposite ends of its flattened, extended skull.

Figure 30.9
Cartilaginous fishes include sharks, skates, and rays.

B Most rays are ocean bottom dwellers, but the Atlantic manta ray prefers to glide along just below the water's surface.

Reading Check The swim bladder allows a fish to change its depth in water when the amount of gas in the bladder changes.

Figure 30.10 Lobe-finned fishes and ray-finned fishes are the subclasses of the bony fishes.

A Lungfishes represent an ancient group of lobe-finned fishes. Lungfishes, such as this African lungfish, have both gills and lungs.

B The coelacanth, another type of lobe-finned fish, was thought to be extinct until living coelacanths were caught off the coast of Africa in 1938.

C You can easily see the rays that support the pectoral fins of this flying fish, an example of a ray-finned fish.

> **Physical Science Connection**
>
> **Buoyancy and density of fluids**
> A fluid—a liquid or a gas—exerts an upward, buoyant force on an object immersed in it. This buoyant force is equal to the weight of the fluid displaced by the object. The weight of fluid depends on the object's volume. When a fish's swim bladder is inflated, the volume of the fish increases and the buoyant force on the fish increases. How does this affect the depth of the fish in water?

Like sharks, most rays are predators and feed on or near the ocean floor. Rays have flat bodies and broad pectoral fins on their sides. By slowly flapping their fins up and down, rays can glide as they search for mollusks and crustaceans along the ocean floor. Some species of rays have sharp spines with poison glands on their long tails that they can use for defense. Other species of rays have organs that generate electricity, which can stun or kill both prey and predators.

Subclasses of bony fishes

Scientists recognize two subclasses of bony fishes—the lobe-finned fishes, including lungfishes, and the ray-finned fishes. *Figure 30.10* shows examples of these subclasses. The lobe-finned fishes are represented by seven living species: six species of lungfishes, which have both gills and

lungs, and the coelacanth, shown in *Figure 30.10B*. In the ray-finned fishes, such as catfish, perch, salmon, and cod, fins are fan-shaped membranes supported by stiff spines called rays. You can compare the interrelationships between the structures of a ray-finned fish in *Figure 30.11*.

Origins of Fishes

Scientists have identified fossils of fishes that existed during the late Cambrian Period, 500 million years ago. At this time, ostracoderms (OHS trah koh durmz), early jawless fishes, were the dominant vertebrates on Earth. Most ostracoderms became extinct at the end of the Devonian Period, about 354 million years ago. Present-day agnathans appear to be the direct descendants of ostracoderms.

CHALLENGE ACTIVITY

Marine versus Freshwater Fishes Have students who need an additional challenge research the differences in the physiology of marine and freshwater fishes. Students can focus on adaptations that fishes have to marine and freshwater biomes. Students can present their results to the class in the form of a multimedia presentation. See *BioChallenges and Enrichment* for additional projects and activities. **L3**

A Bony Fish

Figure 30.11
The bony fishes, class Osteichthyes, include some of the world's most familiar fishes, such as the bluegill, trout, minnow, bass, swordfish, and tuna. Though diverse in general appearance and behavior, bony fishes share some common adaptations with other fish classes. **Critical Thinking** *Explain how the different organ systems in bony fishes work together, allowing a fish to function in the water.*

Rainbow trout,
Oncorhynchus mykiss

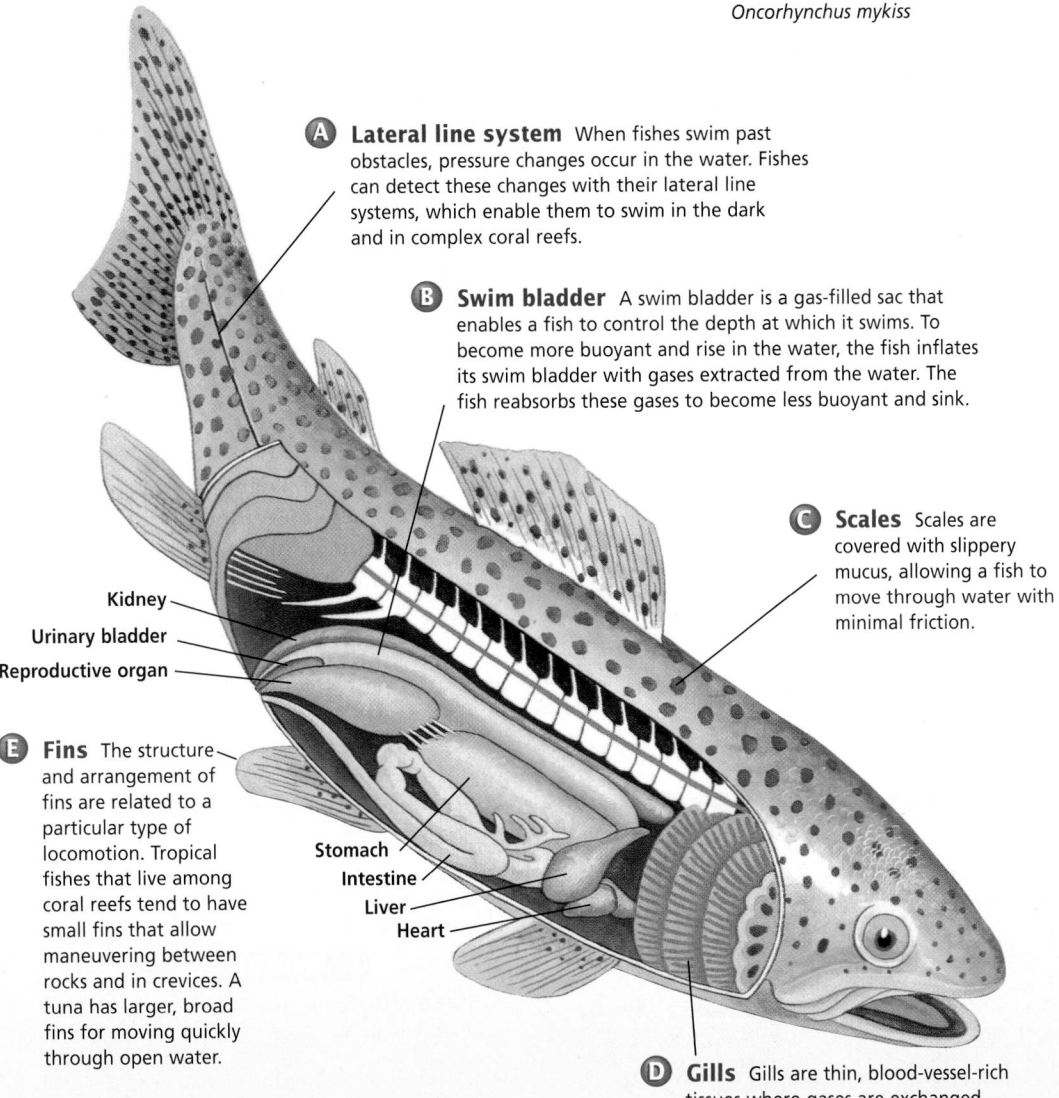

A Lateral line system When fishes swim past obstacles, pressure changes occur in the water. Fishes can detect these changes with their lateral line systems, which enable them to swim in the dark and in complex coral reefs.

B Swim bladder A swim bladder is a gas-filled sac that enables a fish to control the depth at which it swims. To become more buoyant and rise in the water, the fish inflates its swim bladder with gases extracted from the water. The fish reabsorbs these gases to become less buoyant and sink.

C Scales Scales are covered with slippery mucus, allowing a fish to move through water with minimal friction.

Kidney
Urinary bladder
Reproductive organ

E Fins The structure and arrangement of fins are related to a particular type of locomotion. Tropical fishes that live among coral reefs tend to have small fins that allow maneuvering between rocks and in crevices. A tuna has larger, broad fins for moving quickly through open water.

Stomach
Intestine
Liver
Heart

D Gills Gills are thin, blood-vessel-rich tissues where gases are exchanged.

30.1 FISHES **801**

Purpose
Students study features of bony fishes and examine the adaptive advantages of these features.

Teaching Strategies
On the chalkboard, make a table that compares the features of bony fishes with those of jawless and cartilaginous fishes.

Visual Learning
- Ask students to study the features shown. Have them identify the external features discussed on a live goldfish. **L2**
- Purchase a fish from a fish market that has not been cleaned. Carefully cut open the fish to show students the swim bladder. The swim bladder is very fragile, so be careful as you cut into the fish with a razor blade or scalpel.

Critical Thinking
The respiratory system of fishes consists of gills that exchange gases between the blood and the water. A fish's closed circulatory system has a two-chambered heart. Fishes have either bony or cartilaginous skeletons with fins that aid in swimming. Unique sensory structures adapted to an aquatic habitat include the lateral line system, sensitivity to chemicals in the water, and eyes that can detect contrasts between light and dark.

INCLUSION STRATEGIES

English Language Learners To help students who speak English as a second language, have them work with native English speakers and practice their English by explaining the terms and concepts in this section to their partners. **L2** **ELL**

3 Assess

Assessment

Knowledge Ask students to list fish adaptations for the following niches: live on a muddy pond bottom; feed on other fishes; feed on clams and other mollusks; live in coral reef crevices; live in dark deep water. **L2**

Extension

Ask students to speculate about why there are more fishes than other vertebrate types. Responses may state that all life began in the water and this environment has undergone fewer changes than have terrestrial habitats, thus reducing the risk of extinction because of the inability to adapt to new conditions. **L3**

802

Figure 30.12
Ostracoderms, the earliest vertebrate fossils known, were characterized by bony, external plates covering the body and a jawless mouth. **Infer** *How did these jawless ostracoderms obtain food?*

Heterostracan

Anaspid

Cephalaspid

Weighed down by heavy, bony external armor, ostracoderms, shown in **Figure 30.12**, were fearsome-looking animals that swam sluggishly over the murky seafloor. Although all ostracoderms had cartilaginous skeletons, they also had shields of bone covering their heads and necks. The development of bone in early vertebrates was an important evolutionary step because bone provides a place for muscle attachment, which improves locomotion. In ancestral fishes, bone that formed into plates provided protection as well.

Scientists hypothesize that the jawless ostracoderms were the common ancestors of all fishes. Modern cartilaginous and bony fishes evolved during the mid-Devonian Period. Lobe-finned fishes, such as coelacanths (SEE luh kanths), are another ancient group, appearing in the fossil record about 395 million years ago. They are characterized by lobelike, fleshy fins and live at great depths where they are difficult to find. The limblike skeletal structure of fleshy fins is thought to be an ancestral condition of all tetrapods (animals with four limbs). The earliest tetrapods discovered also had gills and therefore were still aquatic.

Section Assessment

Understanding Main Ideas
1. Identify three characteristics of fishes.
2. Compare how modern jawless fishes and cartilaginous fishes feed.
3. Identify the function of the circulatory system in fishes. Explain how it works.
4. Explain how a flexible skeleton is related to locomotion in fishes.

Thinking Critically
5. Why was the development of jaws an important step in the evolution of fishes?

SKILL REVIEW

6. **Summarize** Construct a diagram that shows the phylogeny of fishes and the development of important characteristics in their evolution. For more help, refer to *Summarize* in the **Skill Handbook**.

802 FISHES AND AMPHIBIANS

 in.bdol.glencoe.com/self_check_quiz

Section Assessment

1. They have scales, gills, and fins.
2. lampreys—parasites; hagfishes—scavengers; cartilaginous fishes—predators
3. exchanging gases and delivering nutrients to cells in fish tissues; A two-chambered heart pumps blood in a one-way circuit throughout the body.
4. Continuous flexing of the backbone enables fishes to move using muscles attached to the backbone.
5. Jaws enable fishes to grasp and crush prey with great force and to eat large chunks of food.
6. Student diagrams should correlate with information in the paragraphs following "Origins of Fishes."

Section 30.2

Amphibians

Indiana Standards Standard B.1.15 Understand and explain that, in biological systems, structure and function must be considered together.

A Double Life

Using Prior Knowledge
When you think of an amphibian, do you picture a jumping frog? Maybe a salamander sitting on a log? Perhaps you think of tadpoles in pond water. Amphibians are a diverse group of animals that can be found both on land and in water. In this section you will examine the characteristics of amphibians that allow them to spend at least part of their lives on land.

Infer *Make a list of characteristics that are necessary for an animal to live successfully on land.*

Pickerel frog (above) and tadpoles (inset)

SECTION PREVIEW

Objectives
Relate the demands of a terrestrial environment to the adaptations of amphibians.
Relate the evolution of the three-chambered heart to the amphibian lifestyle.

Review Vocabulary
metamorphosis: a series of changes in an organism controlled by chemical substances (p. 751)

New Vocabulary
ectotherm
vocal cord

What is an amphibian?

The striking transition from a completely aquatic larva to an air-breathing, semiterrestrial adult gives the class Amphibia (am FIHB ee uh) its name, which means "double life." The class Amphibia includes three orders: Caudata (kaw DAH tuh)—salamanders and newts, Anura (uh NUHR uh)—frogs and toads, and Apoda (uh POH duh)—legless caecilians, shown in *Figure 30.13*. Amphibians have thin, moist skin and most have four legs. Although most adult amphibians are capable of a terrestrial existence, nearly all of them rely on water for reproduction. Fertilization in most amphibians is external, and water is needed as a medium for transporting sperm. Amphibian eggs lack protective membranes and shells and must be laid in water or other moist areas. Review some adaptations that allow frogs to live a "double life" in *Figure 30.14* on the next page.

Figure 30.13
Caecilians, order Apoda, are long, limbless amphibians.

30.2 AMPHIBIANS **803**

---

1 Focus

INTERACTIVE CHALKBOARD
PowerPoint® Presentations

Bellringer
Section Focus Transparency 74

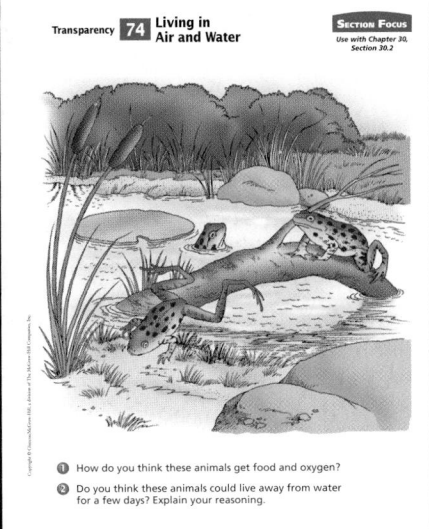

Transparency **74** Living in Air and Water — SECTION FOCUS — Use with Chapter 30, Section 30.2

① How do you think these animals get food and oxygen?
② Do you think these animals could live away from water for a few days? Explain your reasoning.

BIOLOGY: The Dynamics of Life — SECTION FOCUS TRANSPARENCIES

Using Prior Knowledge

Infer lungs for breathing air, protection to keep skin from drying out, skeleton and appendages that will support a body on land, ways to control internal temperature when temperatures on land vary more than in water

---

Indiana Academic Standards

Pages 802–803: B.1.15, B.1.18, B.1.31

2 Teach

Purpose

Students learn about the important features of frogs.

Teaching Strategies

■ Have a live frog available and wall charts that show internal and external frog anatomy. As each feature is discussed, point out that feature on the live frog and wall charts.

■ Divide students into teams and provide each with birthday blowers that have one side of hook-and-loop tape attached to the tip of each blower. Attach the other side of hook-and-loop tape to a small piece of ribbon. Have one student on each team move the ribbon "fly" while another student uses the blower "tongue" to try to catch the "fly." Ask students how this does and does not model a frog's tongue. **L1** **ELL COOP LEARN**

Visual Learning

■ Provide each student with an acetate transparency and markers. Have them trace the outline of the frog in Figure 30.14 on the acetate. Encourage students to label each of the structures shown in the diagram. **L1**

■ Ask students to use the transparencies they made to prepare a presentation about frogs for an elementary school science class. Have students outline the features to be covered in their presentations. **L2**

Critical Thinking

Both the lateral line and the tympanic membrane have sensory functions. In fishes, the lateral line senses movements in the water to which the fish responds. The tympanic membrane of a frog senses vibrations in the water and air to which the frog responds. It also can amplify sounds made by the frog.

A Frog

Figure 30.14
Many species of frogs look similar. As adults, they have short, bulbous bodies with no tails. This adaptation allows them to jump more easily. **Critical Thinking** *Compare and contrast the lateral line system of a fish to the tympanic membrane of a frog.*

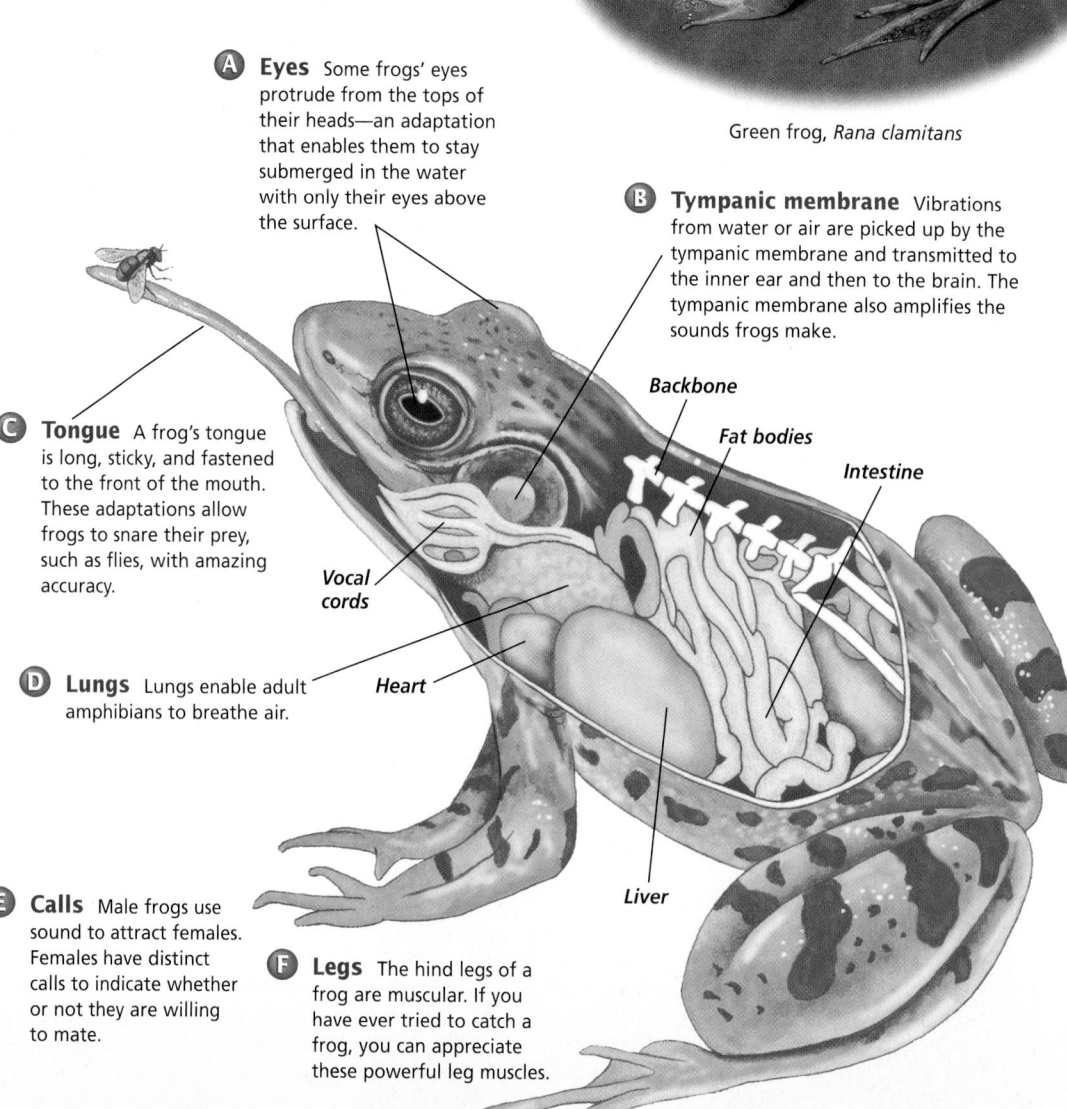

Green frog, *Rana clamitans*

A Eyes Some frogs' eyes protrude from the tops of their heads—an adaptation that enables them to stay submerged in the water with only their eyes above the surface.

B Tympanic membrane Vibrations from water or air are picked up by the tympanic membrane and transmitted to the inner ear and then to the brain. The tympanic membrane also amplifies the sounds frogs make.

C Tongue A frog's tongue is long, sticky, and fastened to the front of the mouth. These adaptations allow frogs to snare their prey, such as flies, with amazing accuracy.

D Lungs Lungs enable adult amphibians to breathe air.

E Calls Male frogs use sound to attract females. Females have distinct calls to indicate whether or not they are willing to mate.

F Legs The hind legs of a frog are muscular. If you have ever tried to catch a frog, you can appreciate these powerful leg muscles.

Backbone

Fat bodies

Intestine

Vocal cords

Heart

Liver

804 FISHES AND AMPHIBIANS

Frog Life Cycle Provide students with clay or modeling dough and instruct them to make models of the typical frog life cycle. Ask them to explain the internal changes taking place at each stage and explain how metamorphosis benefits frogs. **L2**

Amphibians are ectotherms

Amphibians are more common in regions that have warm temperatures all year because they are ectotherms. An **ectotherm** (EK tuh thurm) is an animal that has a variable body temperature and gets its heat from external sources. Because many biological processes require particular temperature ranges in order to occur, amphibians become dormant in regions that are too hot or cold for part of the year. During such times, many amphibians burrow into the mud and stay there until suitable conditions return.

Amphibians undergo metamorphosis

Unlike fishes, most amphibians go through the process of metamorphosis. Fertilized eggs hatch into tadpoles, the aquatic stage of most amphibians. You can compare tadpoles with adult frogs in the *MiniLab* on the next page. Tadpoles possess fins, gills, and a two-chambered heart as seen in fishes. As tadpoles grow into adult frogs and toads, they develop legs, lungs, and a three-chambered heart. *Figure 30.15* shows this life cycle.

Young salamanders resemble adults, but, as aquatic larvae, they have gills and usually have a tail fin. Most adult salamanders lack gills and fins. They breathe through their moist skin or with lungs. Salamanders in the family Plethodontidae have no lungs and breathe only through their skin. Completely terrestrial salamander species do not have a larval stage; the young hatch as smaller versions of adults. Most salamanders have four legs for moving about, but a few have only two front legs.

✔ **Reading Check** **Explain** the process of metamorphosis in amphibians.

Word Origin

parthenogenesis from the Greek word *parthenos,* meaning "virgin" and the Latin word *genesis,* meaning "birth"; Some amphibians, reptiles, and insects reproduce asexually through parthenogenesis. Insects usually produce all males, while reptiles and amphibians usually produce all females.

Figure 30.15
The amphibian life cycle can include an aquatic tadpole stage and a terrestrial adult stage.

Ⓐ *Fertilized eggs*

Ⓑ *Young, legless tadpoles live off yolk stored in their bodies.*

Ⓒ *Tadpoles with legs feed on plants in the water.*

Ⓓ *Young frogs have structures needed for life on land.*

Ⓔ *Adult frog*

Quick Demo

Frog Behavior Divide the class into groups. Give each group a live frog inside a large, clear container. Ask students to describe any behaviors they observe in the frog. Students are likely to describe the frog jumping, moving about, or breathing. Elicit from students how these activities may be suited to life on land. **L1**

✔**Reading Check** Fertilized eggs hatch into tadpoles that have fins, gills, and a two-chambered heart. As tadpoles develop into adults, they have legs, lungs, and a three-chambered heart.

Biology Journal
Mapping Amphibian Habitats Give students a blank world map and ask them to use an atlas of world wildlife to find out where various amphibians live. Have them color code their maps for various types of amphibians and place their maps in their journals. **L2** **ELL**

CHALLENGE ACTIVITY

Amphibians Have students research and create flowcharts that trace in detail the stages of the life cycles of a variety of amphibians, such as the blue-spotted salamander, plains spadefoot toad, or Surinam toad. Ask students to describe the features of each stage of the life cycle and how each feature benefits the organism at that stage. Have students create visual presentations of their research. **L3**

 Indiana Academic Standards

Pages 804–805: B.1.14, B.1.15, B.1.18

Purpose

Students will compare and contrast the appearance and traits of an adult frog and a tadpole.

Process Skills

compare and contrast, acquire information, recognize cause and effect, think critically

Teaching Strategies

■ Preserved materials are available from biological supply houses. Retain preserved specimens for the following year.

■ Place preserved materials on paper toweling or on trays.

■ Binocular microscopes may be used to observe the skin.

■ Provide references for the information regarding diet; larvae feed on algae, adults feed on insects, small fishes, and worms.

Expected Results

Tadpoles have a tail, gills, no tympanic membrane, and no limbs at early stages. Adults have lungs. All other traits are shared. Coloration of stages may vary with species being observed. Tadpoles feed on algae, adults on insects, worms, and small fishes. Tadpoles are confined to aquatic habitats; adults live both on land and in water.

Analysis

1. allows frog to escape predators, aids in swimming
2. Diffusion of oxygen occurs between lungs and air, and between gills and water.
3. A tadpole has a tail for swimming in water. An adult frog has legs for evading predators and swimming.
4. A tadpole has a small mouth for eating algae. An adult frog has a large mouth for eating small animals.
5. seeing food and predators
6. protective coloration from predators; Thin skin aids in gas exchange.

MiniLab 30.2

Compare and Contrast

Frog and Tadpole Adaptations An adult frog and its larval stage—a tadpole—are adapted to different habitats. How are the structures of a frog and a tadpole adapted to their environments?

Rana temporaria

Procedure

CAUTION: *Wear disposable gloves, and use a forceps when handling preserved specimens. Always wash your hands after working with live or preserved animals.*

1 Copy the data table.
2 Examine a living or preserved adult frog and larval (tadpole) stage.
3 Observe the first seven traits listed. Complete your data table for these observations.
4 Use references to fill in the information for the last three traits listed.

Data Table		
Trait or Information	Tadpole	Adult
Limbs present?		
Eyes present?		
Tympanic membrane present?		
Tail present?		
Mouth present?		
Nature of skin (color and texture)		
General size		
Respiratory organ type		
Diet		
Habitat		

Analysis

1. **Explain** How do hind leg muscles aid adult frog survival?
2. **Analyze** Correlate the type of respiratory organ in an adult and a tadpole with their differing habitats.
3. **Analyze** Correlate the type of appendages (arm, leg, tail) in an adult and a tadpole with their differing habitats.
4. **Analyze** Correlate mouth size in an adult and a tadpole with their differing diet.
5. **Explain** How do eyes aid in the survival of both stages?
6. **Think Critically** How can skin color and texture aid in adult frog survival?

Modified Assessment

Portfolio Have students locate references that describe the length of time for frog metamorphosis. Ask them to prepare a poster that compares length of metamorphosis for two frog species. Use the Performance Task Assessment List for Poster in **PASC**, p. 145. **L1**

Walking requires more energy

The laborious walking of early amphibians required a great deal of energy from food and large amounts of oxygen for aerobic respiration. The evolution of the three-chambered heart in amphibians ensured that cells received the proper amount of oxygen. This heart was an important evolutionary transition from the simple circulatory system of fishes.

In the three-chambered heart of amphibians, one chamber receives oxygen-rich blood from the lungs and skin, and another chamber receives oxygen-poor blood from the body tissues. Blood from both chambers then moves to the third chamber, which pumps oxygen-rich blood to body tissues and oxygen-poor blood back to the lungs and skin so it can pick up more oxygen. This results in some mixing of oxygen-rich and oxygen-poor blood in the amphibian heart and in blood vessels leading away from the heart. Thus, in amphibians, the skin is much more important than the lungs as an organ for gas exchange.

Because the skin of an amphibian must stay moist to exchange gases, most amphibians are limited to life on the water's edge or other moist areas. Some newts and salamanders remain totally aquatic. Amphibians, such as toads, have thicker skin, and although they live primarily on land, they still must return to water to reproduce.

Amphibian Diversity

Because most amphibians still complete part of their life cycle in water, they are limited to the edges of ponds, lakes, streams, and rivers or to areas that remain damp during part of the year. Although they may not be easily seen, amphibian species are numerous worldwide.

Frogs and toads belong to the order Anura

Frogs and toads are amphibians with no tails. Frogs have long hind legs and smooth, moist skin. Toads have short legs and bumpy, dry skin. Like fishes, frogs and toads have jaws and teeth. Adult frogs and toads are predators that eat invertebrates, such as insects and worms. Many species of frogs and toads secrete chemicals through their skin as a defense against predators. You can find out more about poisonous frogs in the *Connection to Chemistry* at the end of this chapter.

Frogs and toads also have vocal cords that are capable of producing a wide range of sounds. **Vocal cords** are sound-producing bands of tissue in the throat. As air moves over the vocal cords, they vibrate and cause molecules in the air to vibrate. In many male frogs, air passes over the vocal cords, then passes into a pair of vocal sacs lying underneath the throat, as shown in *Figure 30.16.*

Most frogs and toads spend part of their life cycle in water and part on land. They breathe through lungs or through their thin skins. As a result, frogs and toads often are among the first organisms to be exposed to pollutants in the air, on land, or in the water. Declining numbers of frog species, or deformities in local frogs, sometimes indicate the presence of pollutants in the environment.

✔ **Reading Check** **Analyze** the importance of environmental conditions to a frog's health.

Salamanders belong to the order Caudata

Unlike a frog or toad, a salamander has a long, slender body with a neck and tail. Salamanders resemble lizards, but have smooth, moist skin and lack claws. Some salamanders are

Figure 30.16
Most male frogs have throat pouches that, along with the tympanic membrane, increase the loudness of their calls. **Infer** *How might this adaptation benefit frogs?*

totally aquatic, and others live in damp places on land. They range in size from a few centimeters in length up to 1.5 m. The young hatch from eggs, look like small salamander adults, and are carnivorous.

Caecilians are limbless amphibians

Caecilians are burrowing amphibians, have no limbs, and have a short, or no, tail. Caecilians are primarily tropical animals with small eyes that often are blind. They eat earthworms and other invertebrates found in the soil. All caecilians have internal fertilization.

Origins of Amphibians

Imagine a time 360 million years ago when the inland, freshwater seas were filled with carnivorous fishes. One type of tetrapod had evolved that retained gills for breathing and a finned tail for swimming. Early tetrapods may have used their limbs to move on the bottom of marshlands filled with plants. In later fossils, the four limbs are found further below the body to lift it off the ground.

Using an Analogy

A frog senses sound and other vibrations by means of tympanic membranes—circular structures located just behind the eyes of the frog. The tympanic membrane vibrates much like the skin of a drum to alert the frog to sounds. Ask students to hypothesize why the sense of hearing is important to a frog. The sense of hearing is important to a frog for hearing the calls of mates and to avoid predators.

Caption Question Answer

Figure 30.16 Female members of the species that are far away will still be able to identify a male of their species.

The BioLab at the end of the chapter can be used at this point in the lesson.

✔ **Reading Check** Pollution in a frog's environment can produce deformities and result in a decline in numbers.

Resources

For additional high-interest activities, see the *Forensics and Biotechnology Lab Manual.*

 Indiana Academic Standards

Pages 806–807: B.1.15, B.1.18, B.1.19, B.1.32

808

Figure 30.17
Adaptation to life on land involves the positioning of limbs. The evolution of animal with four limbs led to the diversification of land vertebrates.

B Mammal bodies are raised above the ground with limbs that are positioned underneath the body. This position allows greater speed of locomotion, making mammals, such as this cheetah, the fastest-moving land animals.

A The salamander, an amphibian, has legs that extend at right angles to its body.

C Reptiles, such as this crocodile, have legs on the sides of their bodies, like amphibians, but the limbs have joints that enable them to bend and hold the body up off the ground.

Most likely, amphibians arose as their ability to breathe air through well-developed lungs evolved. The success of inhabiting the land depended on adaptations that would provide support, protect membranes involved in respiration, and provide efficient circulation.

Challenges of life on land

Life on land held many advantages for early amphibians. There was a large food supply, shelter, and no predators. In addition, there was much more oxygen in air than in water. However, land life also held many dangers. Unlike the temperature of water, which remains fairly constant, air temperatures can vary greatly. In addition, without the support of water, the body was clumsy and heavy. Some of the efforts by early amphibians to move on land probably were like movements of present-day salamanders. The legs of salamanders are set at right angles to the body. You can see in *Figure 30.17* why the bellies of these animals may have dragged on the ground.

Amphibians first appeared about 360 million years ago. Amphibians probably evolved from an aquatic tetrapod, as shown in *Figure 30.18*, around the middle of the Paleozoic Era. At that time, the climate on Earth is known to have become warm and wet, ideally suited for an adaptive radiation of amphibians. Able to breathe through their lungs, gills, or skin, amphibians became, for a time, the dominant vertebrates on land.

Figure 30.18
Transitional fossils of aquatic tetrapods from the Devonian Period show that they had amphibian characteristics, but they also retained some fishlike features.

Figure 30.19
The radiation of classes of fishes and orders of amphibians shows their relationships.

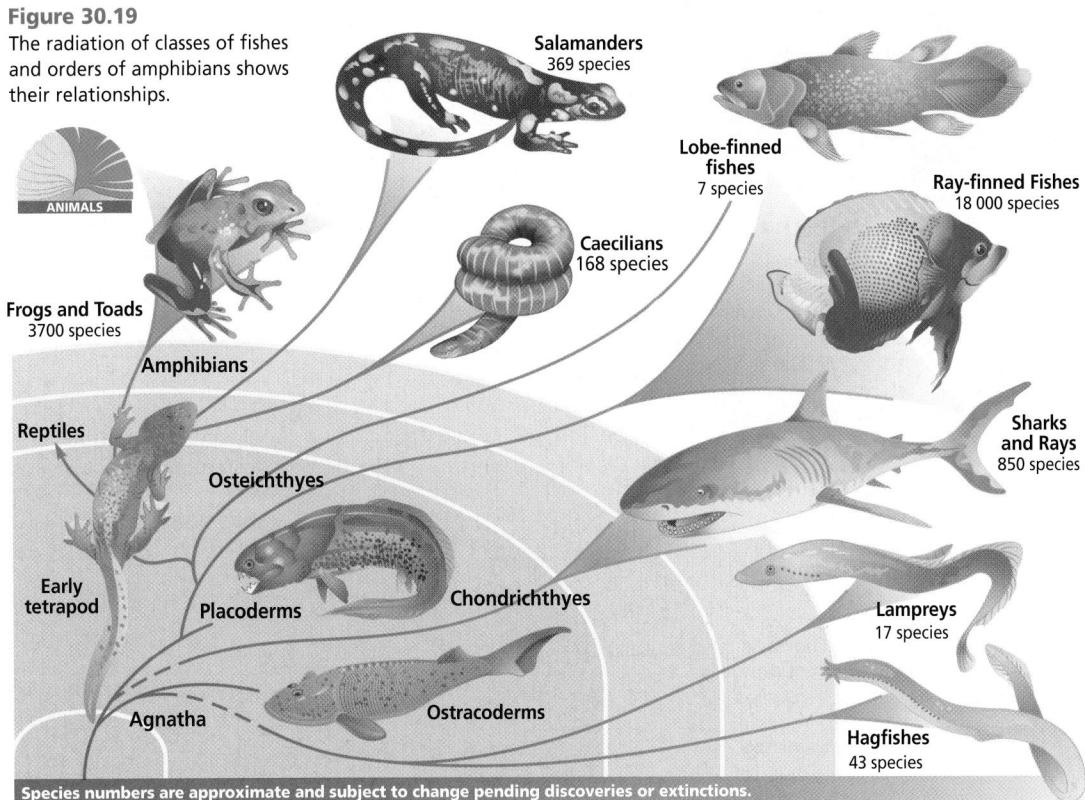

Salamanders
369 species

Lobe-finned fishes
7 species

Ray-finned Fishes
18 000 species

Caecilians
168 species

Frogs and Toads
3700 species

Amphibians

Sharks and Rays
850 species

Reptiles

Osteichthyes

Early tetrapod

Placoderms

Chondrichthyes

Lampreys
17 species

Agnatha

Ostracoderms

Hagfishes
43 species

Species numbers are approximate and subject to change pending discoveries or extinctions.

Recall that early vertebrates evolved from swimming fishes to aquatic tetrapods. Scientists have found fossil evidence that supports the hypothesis that limbs first evolved in aquatic animals. Some of these aquatic vertebrates had lungs and evolved into animals that crawled on the bottom of marshlands, and finally evolved to fully developed amphibians that could live on land. Although the fossil record for fishes and amphibians is incomplete, most scientists agree that the relationships shown in *Figure 30.19* represent the best fit for the available evidence.

Section Assessment

Understanding Main Ideas
1. Describe the events that may have led early animals to move to land.
2. Identify and describe three characteristics of amphibians.
3. List several reasons why amphibians are dependent on water.
4. Relate the demands of a terrestrial environment to the adaptations of amphibians.

Thinking Critically
5. How does a three-chambered heart enable amphibians to obtain the energy needed for movement on land?

SKILL REVIEW
6. **Get the Big Picture** Make a diagram that traces the evolutionary development of amphibians from lungfishes. For more help, refer to *Get the Big Picture* in the **Skill Handbook**.

 in.bdol.glencoe.com/self_check_quiz

30.2 AMPHIBIANS **809**

3 Assess

DAILY INTERVENTION

Check for Understanding
Have students make a table with these headings: *Trait, Anura,* and *Caudata.* Beneath *Trait,* list: *Symmetry, Habitat, Food Getting, Reproduction, Locomotion, Respiration, Protection, Examples.* Have them complete their tables. **L2**

Reteach
Prepare six sets of flash cards with a vocabulary term or an anatomical structure discussed in this section on one side and the meaning of the term or function of the structure on the other side. Have students work in groups to use the cards to review this section. **L1** **COOP LEARN**

Resources
For more practice, use *Reading Essentials for Biology,* Section 30.2.

Extension
Ask students to prepare a humorous cartoon that accurately portrays an aspect of a frog's environment, life history, or evolution. **L3** **ELL**

MODIFIED Assessment

Skill Have students write descriptions for an adapted toad that lives in a dry region where puddles form after rain and with hawks that prey on toads. Students' descriptions should include how the toad would obtain food, protect itself, reproduce, and reduce water loss from its body. **L1**

Section Assessment

1. Early tetrapods may have used limbs to move on the bottom of marshlands. Amphibians also arose when well-developed lungs evolved, allowing these organisms to breathe air.
2. three-chambered hearts, eggs without shells laid in water, smooth, moist skin
3. external fertilization, growth and development of eggs, development of larval stage
4. Many adult amphibians have lungs, legs for moving, and protection that keeps skin from drying out.
5. The heart is a more efficient pump, enabling oxygen to reach cells quickly, thereby enabling the animal to move quickly.
6. Amphibians first appeared about 360 million years ago, probably evolving from the lungfishes. Over time, the lungfishes evolved legs and feet suited to a land environment.

Time Allotment

one class period

Process Skills

design, construct, classify, analyze, compare and contrast, evaluate

PREPARATION

Gather examples of dichotomous keys and illustrations of amphibians.

PROCEDURE

Teaching Strategies

- Explain and demonstrate sample dichotomous keys to students. Explain that descriptions of features are in pairs, often with yes and no answers telling the user where to go to next in the key.
- Make sure to supply students with amphibian illustrations that include frogs, toads, salamanders, newts, caecilians, and sirenians.

INVESTIGATE
BioLab

Before You Begin

To help identify organisms, taxonomists have developed classification keys. A dichotomous key can consist of a set of questions for identifying organisms. When you use this type of a dichotomous key, you answer *yes* or *no* to a question based on the characteristics of the organism you are trying to identify. Depending on your answer, you are directed to another question that further narrows down the identification. When you have answered all the questions, you will arrive at the name of the organism or the group to which it belongs. In this lab, you will create a simple dichotomous key to help you identify different amphibians.

Making a Dichotomous Key for Amphibians

PREPARATION

Problem

How is a dichotomous key made?

Objectives

In this BioLab, you will:
- **Design and construct** a dichotomous key for amphibians.
- **Classify** organisms on the basis of structural characteristics.

Materials

sample keys from guidebooks
field guides for amphibian identification

Skill Handbook

If you need help with this lab, refer to the **Skill Handbook.**

PROCEDURE

1. Study the field guides for amphibians. Note characteristics, such as the number of legs present, length of hind legs, length of tail (if present), texture of skin, and the structure of gills (if present).

2. Make a list of *yes* or *no* questions based on the different characteristics of amphibians.

3. Begin with a broad question, then based on their answer, direct the user to another question that will further narrow down the identification of an organism.

4. Continue to construct your key using the question-and-answer system until the user can classify an organism into a particular group, such as family or genus.

5. Exchange dichotomous keys with another team. Use their key to classify some amphibians.

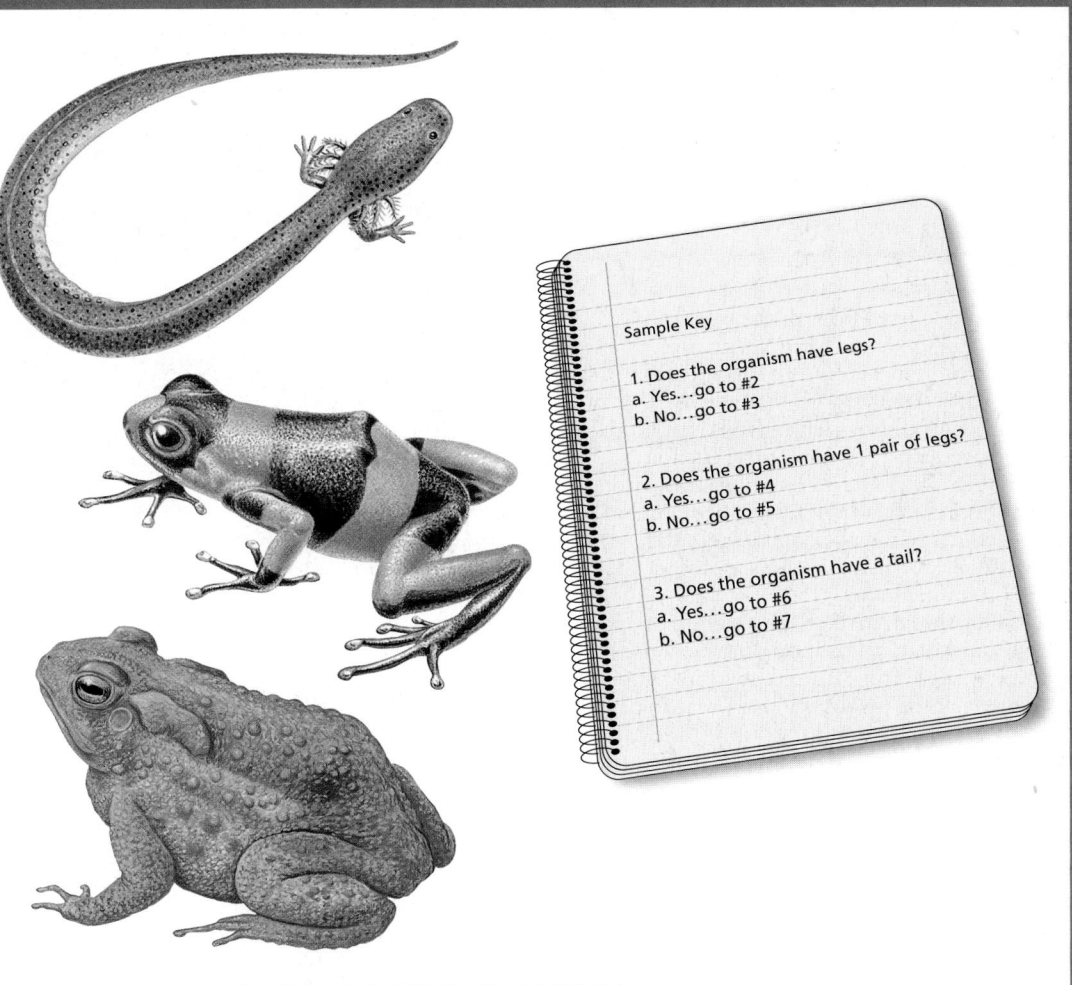

Sample Key

1. Does the organism have legs?
   a. Yes…go to #2
   b. No…go to #3

2. Does the organism have 1 pair of legs?
   a. Yes…go to #4
   b. No…go to #5

3. Does the organism have a tail?
   a. Yes…go to #6
   b. No…go to #7

ANALYZE AND CONCLUDE

1. **Compare and Contrast** Was the dichotomous key you constructed exactly like those of other students? Explain.

2. **Evaluate** What characteristics were most useful for making a classification key for amphibians? What characteristics were not useful for making your key?

3. **Think Critically** Why do keys typically offer two answer choices rather than a larger number of choices?

4. **ERROR ANALYSIS** Give reasons why another student might not be able to identify the group to which an amphibian belongs using your key.

Apply Your Skill

Field Investigation Find out which amphibians live near you, and make a dichotomous key specific for the amphibians in your area. Test the accuracy of your key by using it in the field to classify amphibians.

 Web Links To find out more about amphibians, visit
in.bdol.glencoe.com/amphibians

30.2 AMPHIBIANS **811**

ANALYZE AND CONCLUDE

1. The key of one group may or may not be like those of other groups. Some groups may have compared size or color first, and other body features later.

2. Toads have squat bodies, shorter legs, and dry, bumpy skins while frogs have smooth, wet skins and longer legs. Sirenians have only one pair of short legs. Salamanders and newts have two pairs of legs and a tail. Cecilians have no legs. Characteristics that are not useful are color, size, and other features such as presence or absence of eyes.

3. Having more than two choices would make it difficult to analyze organisms. Many keys are constructed so the choice is that the organism either has or does not have a particular trait.

4. **ERROR ANALYSIS** If keys are based on color or size of amphibians, the group to which they belong cannot be identified.

Assessment

Ask students to make a dichotomous key of fishes by using information at **in.bdol.glencoe.com** .
L2

Apply Your Skill

Field Investigation To learn which amphibians are found in your area, have students do library research, contact a wildlife agency, or go to **in.bdol.glencoe.com** .

connection to Chemistry

connection to Chemistry

Purpose

Students will study the nature of poisonous frogs and how their secretions affect cell chemistry of the prey.

Teaching Strategies

■ Review details of ion channels in cell membranes.

■ Have students diagram the two different actions frog toxins may have on cells. **L2**

■ Poisons from all species of poison arrow frogs are extremely toxic. The most toxic poison comes from *P. terribilis*. Barely 0.2 micrograms of its toxin can kill an adult human. Each golden poison frog can produce 200 micrograms of poison. Ask students to speculate about why these frogs are brightly colored. The color advertises their deadly condition to potential predators.

■ Have students research species of poison arrow frogs to find out which species are the most deadly. **L2**

■ Ask students whether scientists should lobby for tropical rain forest protection in view of the medical potential of some of these species.

Painkiller Frogs

The most colorful frogs in the world are found in South and Central America. These poisonous frogs, including 130 species of the Dendrobatidae family, range in size from 1 to 5 cm. Although all frogs have glands that produce secretions, these frogs secrete toxic chemicals through their skin. A predator will usually drop the foul-tasting frog when it feels the numbing or burning effects of the poison in its mouth.

The frogs advertise their poisonous personalities by bright coloration; they may be red or blue, solid colored, marked with stripes or spots, or have a mottled appearance. The poison secreted by these frogs is used by some native people to coat the tips of the darts that they use in their blow guns for hunting. Thus, these frogs are known as poison-arrow frogs.

The secretions of the poison-arrow frogs of the frog family Dendrobatidae are alkaloid toxins. The chemical structure of an alkaloid toxin includes a ring consisting of five carbon atoms and one nitrogen atom. The toxins secreted by poisonous frogs act on an ion channel between nerve and muscle cells. Normally, the channel is open to allow movement of sodium, potassium, and calcium ions. The toxins can block the flow of potassium and stop or prolong nerve impulse transmission and muscle contraction. One group of alkaloids affects the transport of calcium ions, which are responsible for muscle contraction. Current research indicates that these alkaloids may have clinical applications for muscle diseases and as painkillers.

Frog poison eases pain Recent research shows that a drug derived from the extract from some poison-arrow frogs, including *Epipedobates tricolor*, works as a powerful painkiller. The drug ABT-594 may have the same benefits as morphine, but not the side effects. Morphine is the primary drug used to treat the severe and

Poison-arrow frog, *Epipedobates tricolor*

Alkaloid toxin

unrelenting pain caused by cancer and serious injuries. Side effects of morphine include suppressed breathing and addiction. The "frog drug" does not interfere with breathing and does not appear to be addictive in initial testing. Another benefit of ABT-594 is that as it blocks pain, it does not block other sensations, such as touch or mild heat. One day, pain that you experience might be eased by a frog!

Researching in Biology

Evaluate the Impact of Research Research on newly discovered organisms, such as poisonous frogs, may result in drugs to treat specific disorders in humans. Evaluate the impact of this research on scientific thought and society. Identify diseases that could be treated using toxins from poisonous frogs.

 To find out more about poisonous frogs, visit in.bdol.glencoe.com/chemistry

Researching in Biology

Student answers will vary depending upon their research. Have students provide references for all of their research. Their evaluations of the impact on society should be based on information gathered and logically presented.

STUDY GUIDE

Section 30.1

Fishes

Key Concepts

- Fishes are vertebrates with backbones and nerve cords that have expanded into brains.

- Fishes belong to four classes: two classes of jawless fishes: lampreys and hagfishes, the cartilaginous sharks and rays, and the bony fishes. Bony fishes are made up of two groups: the lobe-finned fishes, including lungfishes, and the ray-finned fishes.

- Jawless, cartilaginous, and bony fishes may have evolved from ancient ostracoderms.

Vocabulary

cartilage (p. 799)
fin (p. 796)
lateral line system (p. 796)
scale (p. 796)
spawning (p. 795)
swim bladder (p. 798)

Fishes

Class	Organisms	Characteristics
Myxini	Hagfishes	Jawless, cartilaginous skeleton, gills
Cephalaspidomorphi	Lampreys	Jawless, cartilaginous skeleton, gills
Chondrichthyes	Sharks, skates, rays	Jaws, cartilaginous skeleton, paired fins, gills, scales, internal fertilization
Osteichthyes	Lobe-finned fishes, ray-finned fishes	Jaws, bony skeleton, paired fins, gills, scales, swim bladder

Section 30.2

Amphibians

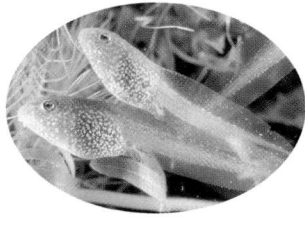

Key Concepts

- The class Amphibia includes three orders: Caudata—salamanders and newts, Anura—frogs and toads, and Apoda—legless caecilians.

- Adult amphibians have three-chambered hearts that provide oxygen to body tissues, but most gas exchange takes place through the skin.

- Land animals face problems of dehydration, gas exchange in the air, and support for heavy bodies. Amphibians possess adaptations suited for life on land.

- Amphibians probably evolved from ancient aquatic tetrapods.

Vocabulary

ectotherm (p. 805)
vocal cord (p. 807)

FOLDABLES
Study Organizer To help review information on fishes, use the Organizational Study Fold on page 793.

in.bdol.glencoe.com/vocabulary_puzzlemaker

Key Concepts

Summary statements can be used by students to review the major concepts of the chapter.

Biology Online

Visit in.bdol.glencoe.com
/self_check_quiz
/vocabulary_puzzlemaker
/chapter_test
/standardized_test

VOCABULARY PUZZLEMAKER

For additional help with vocabulary, have students access the Vocabulary PuzzleMaker online at in.bdol.glencoe.com/ vocabulary_puzzlemaker

FOLDABLES™

Have students use their Foldables to review the content of Section 30.1. On the back of their Foldables, have students analyze the environmental adaptations of each class of fishes.

Use the ExamView®Pro Test Bank CD-ROM to:
- Create **multiple versions** of tests
- Create **modified** tests with one mouse click for **inclusion** students
- **Edit** existing questions and **add** your own questions
- Build tests aligned with state standards using built-in **State Curriculum Tags**
- Change **English** tests to **Spanish** with one mouse click and vice versa

Indiana Academic Standards

Pages 812–813: B.1.15, B.1.18, B.1.19, B.1.32

Chapter 30 Assessment

Chapter 30 Assessment

 The Princeton Review **Questions and answers have been aligned and verified by The Princeton Review.**

Vocabulary Review

1. scale
2. swim bladder
3. fins
4. lateral line system

Understanding Key Concepts

5. C   7. A
6. A   8. A
9. 1. lateral line system;
   2. scales; 3. swim bladder

Constructed Response

10. Bone provides the support that land vertebrates need for locomotion.
11. Adaptations in body shape allow fishes to occupy and maneuver within different niche spaces.
12. Some use air in other parts of their bodies such as swallowing air, air pouches in the esophagus, or by swimming movements by muscles and fins.

Thinking Critically

13. internal fertilization and development: advantage—protection for fertilized egg, not as many gametes needed; disadvantage—male and female need be near each other and ready for reproduction; external fertilization: advantage—male needs to be where a female has laid eggs; disadvantage—eggs may be eaten or damaged
14. Answers will vary depending on students' Web searches.
15. Hypothesis: The waxy covering keeps the frog from drying out. Accept all reasonable answers provided that the experiment tests the hypothesis, has one variable, quantitative data

814

Vocabulary Review

Review the Chapter 30 vocabulary words listed in the Study Guide on page 813. Match the words with the definitions below.

1. thin bony plates formed from the skin of fish
2. thin-walled, internal sac found just below the backbone in bony fishes
3. fan-shaped membranes that are used for balance, swimming, and steering by fish
4. a line of fluid-filled canals running along the sides of a fish

Understanding Key Concepts

5. Which of the following characteristics do all vertebrates have at some point in their development?
   A. bilateral symmetry, exoskeletons, lungs
   B. lungs, postanal tail, backbone
   C. pharyngeal pouches, notochord, backbone
   D. closed circulatory systems, segmented bodies, external fertilization

6. In general, the respiratory system and circulatory system of fishes, as illustrated below, are composed of _____.
   A. gills and a two-chambered heart
   B. gills and a three-chambered heart
   C. gills and a four-chambered heart
   D. none of the above

7. How is the word *amphibia* related to the organisms classified in this group?
   A. Most amphibians spend part of their lives in water and part on land.
   B. Amphibians live their entire lives on land.
   C. Amphibians use swim bladders for breathing in water but use lungs on land.
   D. Many amphibians have a two-chambered heart that develops into a three-chambered heart when the animal matures.

is collected, and it incorporates a control.
16. Stocked species may be more aggressive feeders and create a diminished food supply for native fishes. Stocked fishes may be reproducing in greater numbers than native species.

---

8. Advantages to life on land for early amphibians included _____.
   A. more food and no predators
   B. greater temperature variations
   C. more food and more predators
   D. less oxygen in the air than water

9. Complete the following concept map by using the following vocabulary terms: lateral line system, scales, swim bladder.

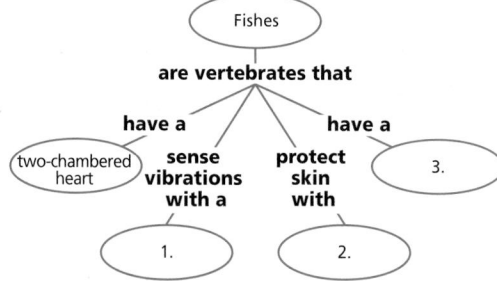

Constructed Response

10. **Open Ended** Relate the importance of the evolution of bone in fishes to the evolution of vertebrates.

11. **Open Ended** Relate the different types of body shapes of fishes to the habitat and behavior of fishes.

12. **Open Ended** Hypothesize how a fish without a swim bladder is able to maintain or vary its position in the water column.

Thinking Critically

13. **Writing in Biology** Compare and contrast the advantages and disadvantages of the different reproductive methods of fishes.

14. **REAL WORLD BIOCHALLENGE** There are several interpretations of how fishes can be classified. Visit **in.bdol.glencoe.com** to investigate the different ways fish groups are currently classified. Present the results of your research to your class in the form of a poster or multimedia presentation.

 in.bdol.glencoe.com/chapter_test

RUBRIC

Evaluating Open-Ended Questions
Open-ended assessment questions are graded by using a multilevel rubric that guides you in assessing a student's knowledge of a particular concept. The following rubric is a sample scoring device.

15. Design an Experiment Monkey frogs live in extremely dry regions of South America. They secrete wax from skin glands and spread the wax over their bodies. Form a hypothesis about the function of this wax, and design a controlled experiment that would test your hypothesis.

16. Writing in Biology Scientists do not know the ultimate effect of stocking freshwater ecosystems with fishes for food and sport. Decline of native species has been observed in areas where stocking occurs. Give possible reasons that explain why native species decline when new species are introduced.

End-of-Course Assessment Practice

The assessed Indiana standard appears next to the question.

All questions aligned and verified by *The Princeton Review*

Part 1 Multiple Choice

Use this diagram to answer question 17.

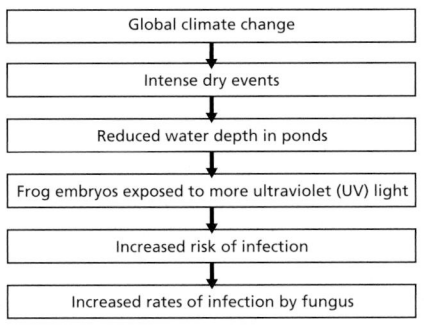

Global climate change
↓
Intense dry events
↓
Reduced water depth in ponds
↓
Frog embryos exposed to more ultraviolet (UV) light
↓
Increased risk of infection
↓
Increased rates of infection by fungus

17. The sequence that best describes amphibian decline is _____.
B.1.43
  A. fungus infection increases frogs' risk for damage by UV light caused by intense dryness
  B. intense dryness reduces pond depth, causing more exposure to UV light that increases risk for fungus infection
  C. intense dryness causes an increase in UV light that kills frogs
  D. increase in the depth of ponds causes more fungus infections in frogs

Use the following graph to answer questions 18–20.

Number of Frog Eggs Hatching at Various Temperatures in 5 Days.

18. How many eggs hatched at 20°C?
  A. 150   **C.** 95
  B. 120   **D.** 65

19. At which temperature did the fewest eggs hatch?
  A. 15°C   **C.** 25°C
  B. 20°C   **D.** 30°C

20. Based on the information presented in the graph, which temperature would you use for optimal hatching of eggs?
  A. 15°C   **C.** 25°C
  B. 20°C   **D.** 30°C

Part 2 Constructed Response/Grid In

Record your answers on your answer document.

21. Open Ended You are trying to find the optimum pH for hatching frog eggs. Design a controlled
B.1.17 experiment that would yield quantitative data.

22. Open Ended What might frogs be communicating when they make vocalizations? Explain why scientists use frog calls to identify different species of frogs.

 in.bdol.glencoe.com/standardized_test

End-of-Course Assessment Practice

17. B   **19.** A
18. C   **20.** C
21. Grow frog eggs in separate solutions with various pH levels. Count how many eggs hatch in each solution after a specific number of days.
22. Frogs' calls can announce their locations. The call is species specific, which ensures that a female and a male of the same species can mate. Because calls are species specific, scientists can use calls for frog identification.

 FAST FILE

Answer Sheet A practice answer sheet can be found on p. 35 of *Unit 9 FAST FILE Resources.*

RUBRIC

SCORE	CRITERIA
4	A correct solution that is supported by well-developed, accurate explanations.
3	A generally correct solution, but may contain minor flaws in reasoning.

SCORE	CRITERIA
2	A partially correct interpretation and/or solution to the problem.
1	A correct solution with no supporting evidence or explanation.
0	An incorrect solution or no solution is given.

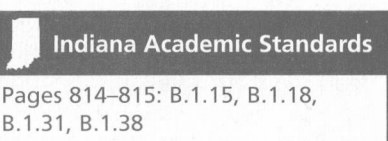 **Indiana Academic Standards**

Pages 814–815: B.1.15, B.1.18, B.1.31, B.1.38

Section Objectives	National Science Standards	State/Local Standards	Advanced Lab and Demo Planning
Section 31.1 1 1/2 sessions, 1/2 block 1. **Explain** how reptile adaptations make them suited to life on land. 2. **Compare** the characteristics of different groups of reptiles.	UCP.1–5; C.3–6	**Indiana Standards** B.1.14, B.1.15, B.1.18, B.1.19, B.1.31, B.1.32, B.1.34, B.1.43	**Student Lab:** Additional Lab, p. 818: thermometer, black paper, white paper, tape, lamp, metric ruler, 2 empty frozen juice containers with holes in one end, clay **Teacher Demonstration:** Quick Demo, p. 818: live or mounted specimens of reptiles
Section 31.2 2 1/2 sessions, 1 block 3. **Explain** how bird adaptations make them suited to life on land. 4. **Relate** bird adaptations to their ability to fly. 5. **Interpret** the phylogeny of birds.	UCP.1–5; A.1, A.2; C.3, C.5, C.6; F.1, F.3–6; G.1–3	**Indiana Standards** B.1.15, B.1.16, B.1.17, B.1.18, B.1.19, B.1.31, B.1.32, B.1.34, B.1.36, B.1.41, B.1.43	**Student Labs:** MiniLab 31.1, p. 827: contour feather, hand lens, down feather MiniLab 31.2, p. 830: several large plastic milk bottles, wires, seeds (sunflower seeds, hulled oats, cracked corn, wheat, thistle, millet) Problem-Solving Lab 31.1, p. 831 Design Your Own BioLab, p. 834: See materials below. **Teacher Demonstration:** Quick Demo, p. 828: recording of bird songs, including courtship, territorial, and distress calls
End of Chapter Assessment Student Edition **Study Guide**, p. 837 **Content Assessment**, pp. 838–839		**Indiana Standards** B.1.15, B.1.16, B.1.31, B.1.32	**Student Lab:** Design Your Own BioLab, p. 834: clay, ruler, string, hard-cooked egg, table tennis ball, golf ball, balance, protractor

Key to Teaching Strategies

L1 Level 1 activities should be appropriate for students with learning difficulties.

L2 Level 2 activities should be within the ability range of all students.

L3 Level 3 activities are designed for above-average students.

ELL ELL activities should be within the ability range of English Language Learners.

COOP LEARN Cooperative Learning activities are designed for small group work.

Legend

 Transparency   CD-ROM   🎵 MP3   ▭ Videocassette   ⊙ DVD

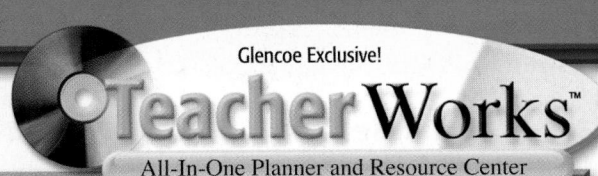

Glencoe Exclusive!
TeacherWorks™
All-In-One Planner and Resource Center

Reproducible Masters and Transparencies	Technology

Unit 9 FAST FILE Resources
Reinforcement and Study Guide in English, pp. 45–46
Reinforcement and Study Guide in Spanish, pp. 49–50
Transparency Worksheets, pp. 55, 57–60, 65–66
Reading Essentials for Biology, Section 31.1
Section Focus Transparency 75
Basic Concepts Transparencies 54, 55
Reteaching Skills Transparency 45

⊙ **Interactive Chalkboard CD-ROM: Section 31.1 Presentation**
⊙ **TeacherWorks™ CD-ROM**
🎵 **Guided Reading Audio Summaries MP3**
⊙ **Virtual Labs CD-ROM**
Virtual Lab: Dino Dig

Unit 9 FAST FILE Resources
MiniLab Worksheet, pp. 39, 40
BioLab Worksheet, pp. 41–42
Real World BioApplications, pp. 43–44
Reinforcement and Study Guide in English, pp. 47–48
Reinforcement and Study Guide in Spanish, pp. 51–52
Concept Mapping, p. 53
Critical Thinking/Problem Solving, p. 54
Transparency Worksheets, pp. 56, 61–64, 67–68
Reading Essentials for Biology, Section 31.2
Laboratory Manual, pp. 195–200, 201–204
Section Focus Transparency 76
Basic Concepts Transparencies 56, 57
Reteaching Skills Transparency 46

⊙ **Interactive Chalkboard CD-ROM: Section 31.2 Presentation**
⊙ **TeacherWorks™ CD-ROM**
🎵 **Guided Reading Audio Summaries MP3**

Unit 9 FAST FILE Resources
Chapter Assessment, pp. 69–74
Student Recording Sheet, p. 75

The Princeton Review **Reviewing Biology,** pp. 61–62

⊙ **Interactive Chalkboard: Chapter 31 Assessment**
⊙ **MindJogger Videoquizzes DVD/VHS**
⊙ **ExamView® Pro Test Bank CD-ROM**
⊙ **TeacherWorks™ CD-ROM**
⊙ **Succeeding on National Standards CD-ROM**

🖥 in.bdol.glencoe.com
/self_check_quiz
/vocabulary_puzzlemaker
/chapter_test
/standardized_test

Indicates materials created specifically for Indiana.

Short on Time?

 BIODIGEST The BioDigest at the end of this unit can be used as a(n):

- preview to introduce important unit concepts.
- overview if time does not permit teaching the entire chapter.
- review of key unit concepts.

Understanding the Photo

There are 11 species of barn owls—the only members of the family Tytonidae. Their reputation as excellent nocturnal hunters is because of their keen eyesight and acute hearing. A barn owl has no external ear structure. Instead, sound waves are directed to its internal ears because of its disc-shaped face, special feathers, and arrangement of facial feathers.

Reptiles and Birds

What You'll Learn

- You will compare and contrast various reptiles and birds.
- You will identify reptile and bird adaptations that make these groups successful.

Why It's Important

Studying reptiles, the first animals to become independent of water, can help you understand the adaptations required for life on land. Birds are unique in that they have feathers and wings—adaptations that contribute to birds living in a wide variety of habitats throughout the world.

Understanding ▶ the Photo

Birds of prey, such as this barn owl, use their keen eyesight to find their prey. Barn owls are nocturnal hunters of rodents. They are uncommon, but are easily identified because of the heart-shaped appearance of the face, small dark eyes, and long legs.

 Biology Online

Visit in.bdol.glencoe.com to
- study the entire chapter online
- access Web Links for more information and activities on reptiles and birds
- review content with the Interactive Tutor and self-check quizzes

816

Two-Minute Chapter Launcher

Demo Display reptilian skulls or skeletons. Have students compare and contrast them. For example, if displaying reptilian skulls, note the presence or absence of teeth and relate this feature to the reptile's diet. Point out the locations or absence of the appendages on the skeletons. Discuss the location of the appendages in relation to the reptile's life on land.

Section 31.1

Reptiles

Indiana Standards Standard B.1.15 Understand and explain that, in biological systems, structure and function must be considered together.

SECTION PREVIEW

Objectives

Explain how reptile adaptations make them suited to life on land.

Compare the characteristics of different groups of reptiles.

Review Vocabulary
embryo: the earliest stage of growth and development of both plants and animals (p. 402)

New Vocabulary
amniotic egg
Jacobson's organ

FOLDABLES™
Study Organizer

Reptiles Make the following Foldable to help you organize information about reptiles.

STEP 1 **Fold** a vertical sheet of paper from side to side. Make the back edge about 2 cm longer than the front edge.

STEP 2 **Turn** lengthwise and **fold** into thirds.

STEP 3 **Unfold and cut** only the top layer along both folds to make three tabs.

STEP 4 **Label** your Foldable as shown.

Reptiles
What is a reptile? | Diversity of Reptiles | Origin of Reptiles

Organize Information As you read Chapter 31, list characteristics of reptiles, as well as information about their diversity and origin, behind the appropriate tab.

What is a reptile?

Word Origin

reptile from the Latin word *repere*, meaning "to crawl"; A reptile is an ectothermic animal with dry skin and amniotic eggs.

At first glance, it may be difficult to determine how a legless snake is related to a tortoise. Snakes, turtles, alligators, and lizards are an extremely diverse group of animals, yet all share certain traits that place them in the class Reptilia.

Early reptiles, called the stem reptiles, as shown in ***Figure 31.1***, were the first animals to become adapted to life on land. All reptiles have adaptations that enable them to complete their life cycles entirely on land. These adaptations released the stem reptiles and other reptiles from the need to return to swamps, lakes, rivers, ponds, or oceans for reproduction.

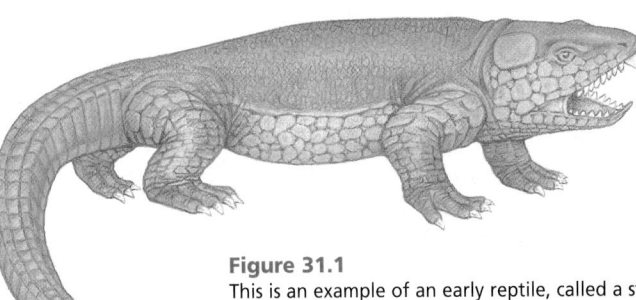

Figure 31.1
This is an example of an early reptile, called a stem reptile, that was probably an ancestor of the long-extinct dinosaurs as well as of today's living reptiles, birds, and mammals.

31.1 REPTILES **817**

---

1 Focus

INTERACTIVE CHALKBOARD
PowerPoint® Presentations

Bellringer
Section Focus Transparency 75

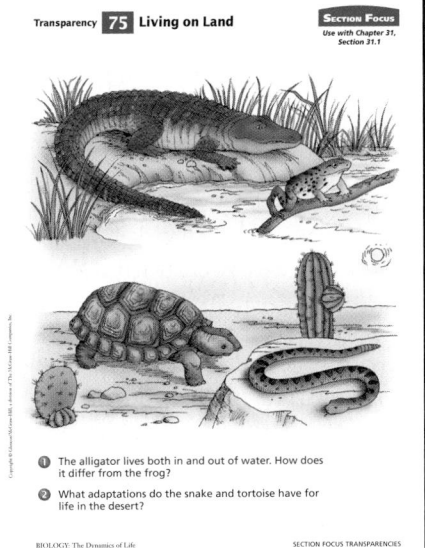

Transparency **75** Living on Land

SECTION FOCUS
Use with Chapter 31, Section 31.1

❶ The alligator lives both in and out of water. How does it differ from the frog?

❷ What adaptations do the snake and tortoise have for life in the desert?

BIOLOGY: The Dynamics of Life   SECTION FOCUS TRANSPARENCIES

INTERACTIVE CHALKBOARD
with Image Bank

PowerPoint® Presentations

This CD-ROM is an editable Microsoft® PowerPoint® presentation that includes:
- Section presentations
- Section checks
- Image bank
- Hot links to Biology Online
- All transparencies

FOLDABLES™

For an additional Foldables activity idea, see the Chapter 31 Foldables page in *Unit 9 FAST FILE Resources.*

---

2 Teach

Discussion

Ask students to share their experiences and feelings about reptiles, especially snakes. If they express fear, ask why they think that they have this fear. Point out that most primates show an instinctive fear of snakes. Ask students why they think this is so.

Caption Question Answer
Figure 31.2 Overlapping scales help to reduce the loss of water from the animal's skin.

Reptiles have scaly skin

Unlike the moist, thin skin of amphibians, reptiles have a dry, thick skin covered with scales. Scaly skin, as shown in *Figure 31.2,* prevents the loss of body moisture and provides additional protection from predators. Because gas exchange cannot occur through scaly skin, reptiles are dependent on lungs as their primary organ of gas exchange.

Reptiles reproduce on land

Most reptiles reproduce by laying eggs on land, as shown in *Figure 31.3.* Some snakes give live birth to well-developed young. Unlike amphibians, reptiles have no aquatic larval stage, so reptile young are not as vulnerable to water-dwelling predators.

Figure 31.2
Scales on a reptile's skin overlap like tiles on a roof.

A The scales of reptiles, unlike the separate glossy scales of fishes, are made of protein and are part of the skin itself. The scales are all connected to one another by hinges of skin.

Although all of these adaptations enabled reptiles to live successfully on land, the evolution of the amniotic (am nee AH tihk) egg was the adaptation that liberated reptiles from a dependence on water for reproduction. An **amniotic egg** provides nourishment to the embryo and contains membranes that protect it while it develops in a terrestrial environment. The egg functions as the embryo's total life-support system.

Skeletal changes in reptiles

Look again at *Figure 31.1.* This early reptile had legs that were placed more directly under the body rather than at right angles to the body as in early amphibians. This positioning of the legs provides greater body support and makes walking and running on land easier for most reptiles. They have a better chance of catching prey or avoiding other predators. Reptiles that have legs also have claws that help them obtain food and protect themselves. Additional evolutionary changes in the structure of the jaws and teeth of early reptiles allowed them to use other resources and niches on land.

Some reptiles have four-chambered hearts

Most reptiles, like amphibians, have three-chambered hearts. Some reptiles, notably the crocodilians, have a four-chambered heart that completely separates the supply of blood with oxygen from blood without oxygen. The separation enables more oxygen to reach body tissues. This separation is an adaptation that supports the higher level of energy use required by land animals.

B This snake is shedding. Old scaly skin is discarded after new skin grows beneath it.
Explain *How are overlapping scales an adaptation to life on land?*

818

Additional Lab

Body Color Adaptations

Purpose
Students observe how color affects the rate at which organisms absorb heat.

Materials
thermometer, black paper, white paper, tape, lamp, metric ruler, 2 empty frozen juice containers with holes in one end, clay

Procedure
Give students the following directions.
1. Make a data table for starting temperature, final temperature, and total temperature change for a black container and a white container.
2. Cover one container with black paper and the other with white paper. Tape the paper in place.
3. Place a thermometer into the hole in each container top and secure it with clay. Make sure the hole is tightly sealed.
4. Place both containers about 5 cm away from the bulb of a lamp. Do not turn on the lamp.
5. Record the starting temperature of both containers in your data table.
6. Develop a hypothesis as to which container will show a higher temperature at the end of 10 minutes.

An Amniotic Egg

Figure 31.3
The evolution of the amniotic egg was a major step in reptilian adaptations to land environments. Amniotic eggs enclose the embryo in amniotic fluid, provide a source of food in the yolk, and surround both embryo and food with membranes and a tough, leathery shell. These structures in the egg help prevent injury and dehydration of the embryo as it develops on land. **Critical Thinking** *How is the leathery covering of a reptile egg more suited to being laid deep in the sand than a hard-shelled bird egg would be?*

Hatchling turtle with egg tooth

(A) Amnion The amnion (AM nee ahn) is a membrane filled with fluid that surrounds the developing embryo. The fluid-filled amnion cushions the embryo and prevents dehydration.

(F) Egg tooth A reptile hatches by breaking its shell with the horny tooth on its snout. This egg tooth drops off shortly after hatching.

(B) Shell The reptile egg is encased in a leathery shell. Most reptiles lay their eggs in protected places beneath sand, earth, gravel, or bark.

(E) Chorion The chorion (KOR ee ahn) is a membrane that forms around the yolk, allantois, amnion, and embryo. It and the allantois allow gas exchange for respiration.

Embryo

(C) Yolk The main food supply for the embryo is the yolk, which is also attached to the embryo. The clear part of the egg is albumen (al BYEW mun), a source of additional food and water for the developing embryo.

Albumen

(D) Allantois The embryo's nitrogenous wastes are excreted into the allantois (uh LAN tuh wus), a membranous sac that is associated with the embryo's gut. When a reptile hatches, it leaves behind the allantois with its collected wastes.

Purpose
Students will study the amniotic egg and learn how this adaptation enabled reptiles to reproduce and live on land.

Teaching Strategies
■ Ask students to carefully open a raw chicken egg and note the shell, albumen, yolk, and the tough membrane inside the shell. Ask what parts of the egg shown in Figure 31.3 are missing from their egg. **L1 ELL**

■ **CAUTION:** *Students must wash their hands thoroughly with soap and water after handling uncooked eggs.*

Visual Learning
Challenge students to describe the differences between frog eggs and turtle eggs. The frog eggs are surrounded by a jellylike substance that must remain moist. The reptile eggs are covered by a shell. Ask how these differences might reflect the environment in which each of these animals live. Frogs must live near water for reproduction; reptiles do not depend upon water for reproduction.

Critical Thinking
Reptile eggs have a leathery, flexible shell. Bird eggs have a hard, but breakable, shell. Reptile eggs can withstand burial because they are flexible.

---

7. Turn on the lamp and allow it to shine on both containers for 10 minutes. Remind students not to touch the hot lamp.

8. Record the final temperature of both containers. Calculate the total change in temperature for each container and record it in your data table.

Expected Results
The black container will absorb more heat.

Analysis
1. Did black or white have the greater temperature change after 10 min? black

2. Did your data support your hypothesis? Explain. Yes, if students said that the black container would absorb more heat.

3. Which should absorb more light from the sun, a dark animal or a light animal? Why? Dark; dark colors absorb more light and heat up more quickly.

Assessment
Portfolio The ability to change skin color is an adaptation in many reptiles. Ask students to explain how this adaptation may help reptiles survive. They should include their explanation in their portfolios. Use the Performance Task Assessment List for Writing in Science in **PASC**, p. 159. **L2**

Interpersonal Ask a group of students to research the requirements for temperature, light, and diet for a lizard suited for terrarium life. Have them set up a terrarium and care for the lizard.
L2 **COOP LEARN**

✓ **Reading Check** They remain where it is cool during the hottest part of the day and seek the warmth of sunlight when temperatures are cool.

Biology Journal

Protecting Local Reptiles Ask students to contact their state or local division of wildlife to find out about programs underway to protect locally endangered reptiles. Ask them to prepare an illustrated report of their findings that identifies the endangered reptiles in their area. **L2**

Figure 31.4
Different reptiles regulate their body temperatures by a variety of behaviors.

A A desert horned lizard stays in the shade during the hottest part of a day.

B A bearded lizard suns itself to get warm.

All reptiles have internal fertilization. In most cases, the eggs are laid after fertilization and embryos develop after eggs are laid. Most reptiles lay their eggs under rocks, bark, grasses, or other surface materials, but a few dig holes or collect materials for a nest. Most reptiles provide no care for hatchlings, but female crocodiles have been observed guarding their nests from predators.

Reptiles are ectotherms

Even though reptiles are different from amphibians in many ways, they are similar in one way. Both amphibians and reptiles are ectotherms. They depend on an external heat source and behavior to maintain their body temperature within the range needed to perform life functions, such as digestion. In the cool morning, a turtle might pull itself out of the pond or swamp and bask on a log in the sunlight until noon. Then, when the temperature gets a little too

warm, the turtle may slip back into the cool water. *Figure 31.4* shows other examples of behavioral adjustment of body temperature in reptiles.

Because reptiles are dependent on heat from the environment, they do not inhabit extremely cold regions. Reptiles are common in temperate and tropical regions, where climates are warm, and in hot desert climates. Many species of reptiles become dormant during cold periods in moderately cold environments such as in the northern United States.

✓ **Reading Check** **Explain** how reptiles regulate body temperature through behavior.

How reptiles obtain food

Like other animals, reptiles have adaptations that enable them to find food and to sense the world around them. Most turtles and tortoises are too slow to be effective predators, but that doesn't mean they go hungry. Most are herbivores, and those that are predators prey on worms and mollusks. Snapping turtles, however, are extremely aggressive, attacking fishes and amphibians, and even pulling ducklings under water.

Lizards primarily eat insects. The marine iguana of the Galápagos Islands is one of the few herbivorous lizards, feeding on marine algae. The Komodo dragon, the largest lizard, is found on several islands in Indonesia, north of Australia. It is an efficient predator, sometimes even of humans. Although lizards such as the Komodo dragon may look slow, they are capable of bursts of speed, which they use to catch their prey.

INCLUSION STRATEGIES

Learning Disabled Have students make a cross-sectional model of an amniotic egg. They can use materials such as clay, plastic food wrap, and aluminum foil to represent membranes. **L1** **ELL**

Indiana Academic Standards

Pages 820–821: B.1.14, B.1.15, B.1.18, B.1.43

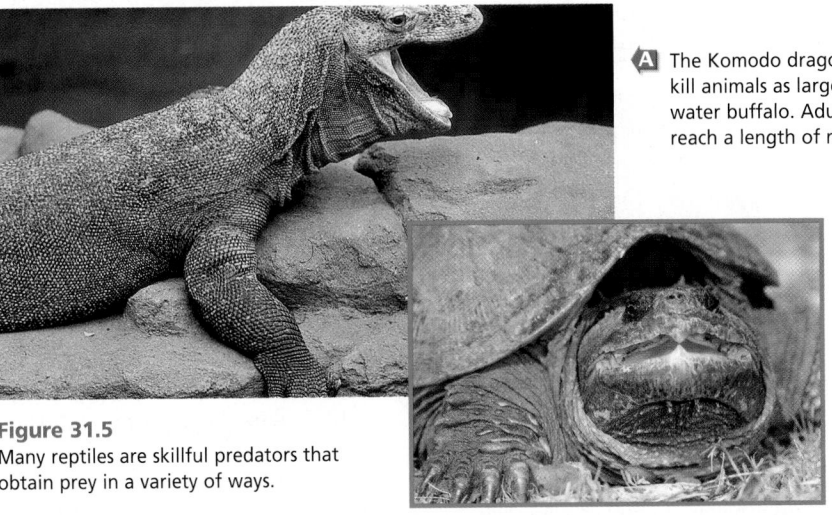

A The Komodo dragon is a predator that can kill animals as large as a deer or even a water buffalo. Adult Komodo dragons can reach a length of more than 3 m.

B The snapping turtle is common in North America. It has strong claws and a hooked beak that is sharp enough to bite through a person's fingers.

Figure 31.5
Many reptiles are skillful predators that obtain prey in a variety of ways.

Snakes are also effective predators. Some, like the rattlesnake, have poison fangs that they use to subdue or kill their prey. A constrictor wraps its body around its prey, tightening its grip each time the prey animal exhales. Two predatory reptiles are shown in *Figure 31.5*.

How reptiles use their sense organs

Reptiles have a variety of sense organs that help them detect danger or potential prey. How does a rattlesnake know that you are nearby?

The heads of some snakes, as shown in *Figure 31.6A*, have heat-sensitive organs or pits that enable them to detect tiny variations in air temperature brought about by the presence of warm-blooded animals.

Snakes and lizards are equipped with a keen sense of smell. Have you ever seen a snake flick out its tongue? The tongue is picking up molecules in the air. The snake draws its tongue back into its mouth and moves it past or inserts it into a pitlike structure called **Jacobson's organ**, described in *Figure 31.6B*.

Figure 31.6
Snakes have sense organs that enable them to detect prey or identify substances in their environment.

A A pair of heat-sensitive pits below their eyes enable rattlesnakes to detect prey in total darkness.

B The long, flexible tongues of snakes and lizards pick up molecules in the air and transfer them to the Jacobson's organ in the roof of the animal's mouth where special cells identify them.

Jacobson's organ

Tongue

821

Career Path

Courses in high school: art, photography, and biology
College: courses in art, art history, photography, and zoology
Other education sources: community art classes

Career Issue

Ask students if they think wildlife benefits or suffers when artists or photographers invade their habitats. Have the students provide examples to support their opinions.

For More Information

For more information on becoming a wildlife artist or photographer, contact the Wildlife Artists Association at www.wildlifeartistassoc.com, then communicate pertinent information to students.

Display

Visual-Spatial Assign groups of students orders of reptiles to research. Have them find the population distribution and prepare a map showing this distribution. Display these maps on the bulletin board. **L2 COOP LEARN**

CAREERS IN BIOLOGY

Wildlife Artist/ Photographer

If you are determined and patient, you can combine your love of nature and your artistic skills into a career as a wildlife artist or photographer.

Skills for the Job

Some wildlife artists/photographers spend weeks in the wilderness to find subjects for their art. Others draw, paint, or photograph animals in zoos or nature preserves. Becoming an artist or photographer depends more on your natural abilities than training, but art or photography courses can help strengthen your skills. Many wildlife artists also study biology or zoology so they can better understand their subjects. It can take years before artists are able to support themselves by selling their work, so many have another job, such as teaching art in a high school or college or giving private lessons.

For more careers in related fields, visit
in.bdol.glencoe.com/careers

Diversity of Reptiles

Gracefully gliding snakes and quickly darting lizards are grouped together in the order Squamata. Turtles, slowly plodding and carrying heavy shells, belong to the order Chelonia. Basking crocodiles and alligators, classified in the order Crocodilia, may look clumsy but are surprisingly quick hunters. Tuataras are lizardlike reptiles. They make up the fourth order of reptiles, Rhynchocephalia.

Figure 31.7
In the past, sailors killed Galápagos tortoises for food. As a result, their numbers declined rapidly.

Turtles have shells

Turtles are the only reptiles protected by a shell made up of two parts. The dorsal part of the shell is the carapace, and the ventral part of the shell is the plastron. The vertebrae and expanded ribs of turtles are fused to the inside of the carapace. Most turtles have a two-layer shell—a hard, bony inner layer and an outer layer of horny keratin. In a few species, the shell is a covering made of tough, leathery skin. Most turtles can draw their limbs, tail, and head into their shells for protection against predators. Although turtles have no teeth, they do have powerful jaws with a beaklike structure that is used to crush food.

Some turtles are aquatic, and some live on land. Turtles that live on land are called tortoises. Tortoises forage for fruit, berries, and insects. The largest tortoises in the world, shown in ***Figure 31.*7, are found on the Galápagos Islands off the coast of Ecuador.

Some adult marine turtles swim enormously long distances to lay their eggs. Like salmon, these turtles return from their feeding grounds to the place where they hatched. For example, green turtles travel from the coast of Brazil to Ascension Island in the Atlantic Ocean, a distance of more than 4000 km.

Crocodiles include the largest living reptiles

In contrast to marine turtles, crocodiles don't migrate to reproduce. They may spend their days alternately basking in the sun on a riverbank and floating like motionless logs. Only their eyes and nostrils remain above water. Crocodiles can be identified by their long, slender snouts, whereas alligators have short, broad snouts. Both animals have powerful jaws with sharp teeth that

---

PROJECT

Protecting the Environment Ask students to role play a citizen group debating the protection of a beach where endangered green sea turtles nest. Have them work in groups of 3 to 4 and assume the role indicated on a card you have prepared. Cards should identify the following roles: teenage surfer, mayor, condominium developer, beach home owner, turtle biologist, president of the Turtle Protection Society, beach concession owner, state wildlife protection officer. Have them research their assigned roles. Prior to role playing, students should prepare an outline of points that will be presented by the character he or she assumes. **L2 COOP LEARN**

Figure 31.8
Lizards have many structural and physiological adaptations that allow them to live in different habitats.

A Geckos are small, nocturnal lizards. They live in warm climates, such as those of the southern United States, West Africa, and Asia.

B The Gila monster of the southwestern United States and Mexico is a poisonous lizard.

can drag prey underwater and hold it there until it drowns. Another feature that makes these animals efficient predators is that, unlike other reptiles, they can continue to breathe air with their mouths full of food and water. The American alligator is found throughout many of the freshwater habitats of the southeastern United States. The American crocodile can be found only in salt water and estuarine habitats in southern Florida. The American alligator can reach a length of 5 m. Other crocodilians, such as the Nile crocodile of Africa, can grow even longer.

Both alligators and crocodiles lay eggs in nests on the ground. Unlike other reptiles, these animals stay close to their nests and guard them from predators. Several crocodilian species have been observed holding their newly hatched offspring gently in their mouths as they carried them to the safety of the water.

✓ Reading Check **Explain** how crocodiles and alligators reproduce.

Snakes and lizards have diverse forms

Lizards, like the ones shown in *Figure 31.8*, are found in many types of habitats throughout the world. Some live on the ground; some burrow; some live in trees; and some are aquatic. Many are adapted to hot, dry climates. Although a few species of lizards are limbless, most lizards have four legs.

Snakes, in contrast to most vertebrates, have no limbs and lack the bones to support limbs. Exceptions are pythons and boas, which retain bones of the pelvis. The many vertebrae of snakes permit fast undulations through grass and over rough terrain. Some snakes even swim and climb trees.

Snakes usually kill their prey in one of three ways. Remember that constrictors wrap themselves around their prey. Common constrictors include boas, pythons, and anacondas.

Venomous snakes use poison to paralyze or kill their prey. These include rattlesnakes, cobras, and vipers, which inject poison from venom glands.

Figure 31.9
Many poisonous snakes have hollow fangs for injecting venom. Venom can either paralyze or kill prey immediately.

Most snakes are neither constrictors nor poisonous. They get food by grabbing it with their mouths and swallowing it whole. Snakes eat rodents, amphibians, insects, fishes, eggs, and other reptiles, as shown in *Figure 31.9.*

The fourth order of reptiles, Rhynchocephalia, is represented by two living species of tuatara, one of which is shown in *Figure 31.10.* Tuataras are the only survivors of a primitive group of reptiles, most of which died out 100 million years ago.

Origins of Reptiles

You may have marveled at dinosaurs ever since you were very young. These animals were the most numerous land vertebrates during the Mesozoic Era. Some were the size of chickens, and others were the largest land dwellers that ever lived. Learn more about dinosaurs on pages 1084–1085 in the *Focus On.*

The ancestors of snakes and lizards are traced to a group of early reptiles, called scaly reptiles, that branched off from the ancient stem reptiles. The name "scaly reptiles" may be misleading because it implies that other reptiles lacked scales—which is not true. Although the evolutionary history of turtles is incomplete, scientists have suggested that they may also be descendants of stem reptiles. Dinosaurs and crocodiles are the third group to descend from stem reptiles, as you can see in *Figure 31.11.*

Although scientists used to think that birds arose as a separate group from this third branch, there is now much fossil evidence that leads biologists to suggest that birds are the living descendants of the dinosaurs.

Figure 31.10
Tuataras are found only in New Zealand. They have ancestral features, including teeth fused to the edge of the jaws, and a skull structure similar to that of early Permian reptiles.

824 REPTILES AND BIRDS

Figure 31.11
The radiation of orders of reptiles shows their relationships.

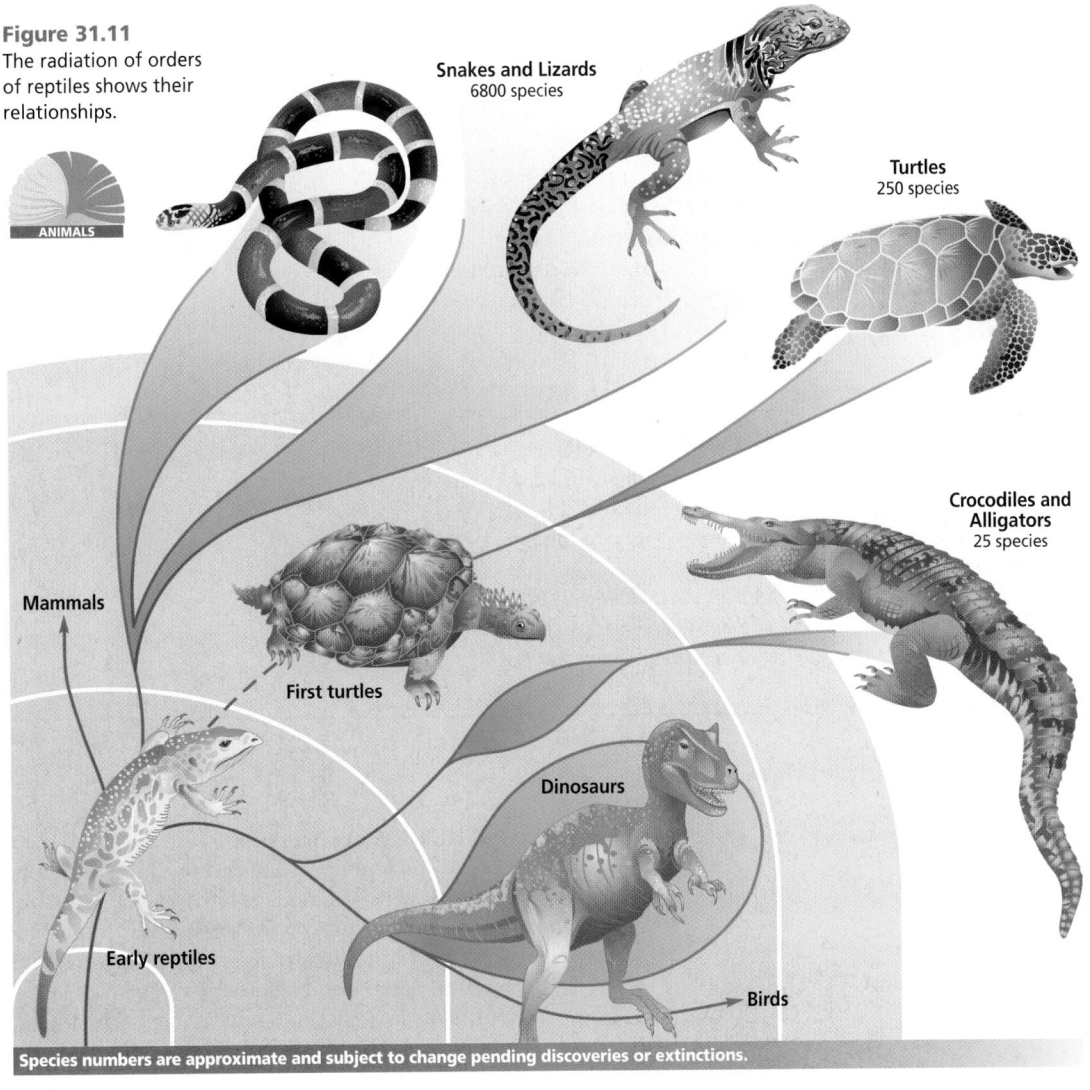

Snakes and Lizards
6800 species

Turtles
250 species

Crocodiles and Alligators
25 species

Mammals

First turtles

Dinosaurs

Early reptiles

Birds

Species numbers are approximate and subject to change pending discoveries or extinctions.

in.bdol.glencoe.com/self_check_quiz

Section Assessment

Understanding Main Ideas
1. Explain how the adaptations of early reptiles enabled these animals to live on land.
2. Describe two ways in which turtles protect themselves.
3. Describe how snakes use the Jacobson's organ for finding food.
4. Analyze the relationship between modern reptiles and dinosaurs.

Thinking Critically
5. Analyze how having a four-chambered heart benefits crocodiles and alligators on a daily basis.

SKILL REVIEW
6. **Classify** Set up a classification key that allows you to identify a reptile as a snake, lizard, turtle, or crocodile. For more help, refer to *Classify* in the **Skill Handbook**.

---

3 Assess

DAILY INTERVENTION

Check for Understanding
Naturalist Have students brainstorm to form a list of concepts they learned about reptiles. Ask students to classify each concept as being related to adaptations, characteristics, origins, or the evolution of reptiles. **L3**

Reteach
Visual-Spatial For each reptile group, have students develop a table with the following heads: *Representative Organisms, Habitat, Methods of Obtaining Food, Reproduction, Locomotion, Respiration,* and *Protection.* Have students complete their tables and then review them as a class. **L2**

Resources
For more practice, use *Reading Essentials for Biology,* Section 31.1.

Extension

Linguistic Ask a group of students to find a story that depicts reptiles in a negative way. Ask them to rewrite the story to depict reptiles in a positive way. Ask them to read the before and after versions of the story to the class. **L2**

MODIFIED Assessment

Activity Ask student groups to develop a television commercial in which a nonpoisonous reptile speaks about why it should not be feared. **L1**

Section Assessment

1. Early reptiles had legs that were located under the body rather than out to the sides, and they had clawed toes. This body structure and claws enhanced their movement on land.
2. Turtles can draw limbs, heads, and tails into their hard shells. Turtles may also use their powerful jaws to crush other animals.
3. The tongue picks up chemicals in the air. The snake then draws its tongue back into its mouth and moves it over or inserts it into the Jacobson's organ for identification.
4. They have the same reptilian features as dinosaurs—dry, thick scaly skin, clawed toes, and the amniotic egg.
5. A four-chambered heart keeps blood without oxygen separate from oxygenated blood. This means that more oxygen can reach tissues, which allows for a greater rate of cellular respiration and energy release.
6. Make sure that students start with general features of reptiles. Then, they should use the main features for each group.

825

1 Focus

Bellringer
Section Focus Transparency 76

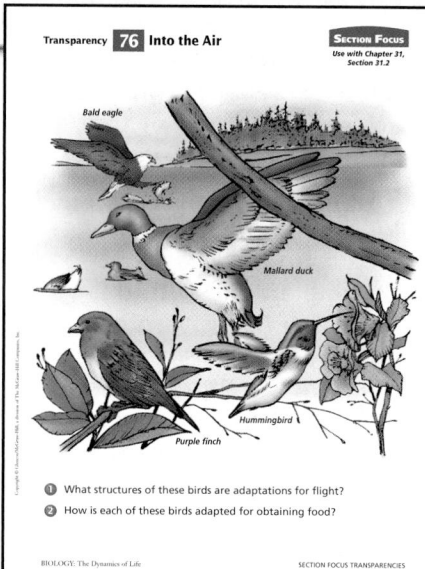

Transparency **76** Into the Air

SECTION FOCUS
Use with Chapter 31, Section 31.2

Bald eagle

Mallard duck

Hummingbird

Purple finch

① What structures of these birds are adaptations for flight?

② How is each of these birds adapted for obtaining food?

BIOLOGY: The Dynamics of Life

SECTION FOCUS TRANSPARENCIES

Using Prior Knowledge

Infer Modern birds have feathers, wings, lungs with air sacs, hollow bones, and beaks. They also are endotherms.

Section 31.2

Birds

Indiana Standards Standard B.1.15 Understand and explain that, in biological systems, structure and function must be considered together.

SECTION PREVIEW

Objectives

Explain how bird adaptations make them suited to life on land.

Relate bird adaptations to their ability to fly.

Interpret the phylogeny of birds.

Review Vocabulary
phylogeny: evolutionary history of a species based on comparative relationships of structures and comparisons of modern life forms with fossils (p. 452)

New Vocabulary
feather
sternum
endotherm
incubate

Fascinating Feathers

Using Prior Knowledge
Scientists use both physiological and structural characteristics to divide organisms into different groups. You already know how fishes, amphibians, and reptiles differ from each other. Just by looking at a bird, you can see that there are obvious differences between birds and reptiles.
Infer *What characteristics do birds have that make them different from reptiles?*

Robin

Chickadee

What is a bird?

After conquering the sea and land, vertebrates took to the air, where there was a huge source of insect food and a refuge from land-dwelling predators. The existence of more than 8600 species of modern birds, class Aves, shows that flight was a successful adaptation for survival. Birds inhabit a variety of environments around the world, including Antarctica, deserts, and tropical rain forests.

Biologists sometimes refer to birds as feathered dinosaurs. Fossil evidence seems to indicate that birds have evolved from small, two-legged dinosaurs called theropods, illustrated in *Figure 31.12*. Like reptiles, birds have clawed toes and protein scales on their feet. Fertilization is internal and shelled amniotic eggs are produced in both groups. Although some birds are flightless, all birds have feathers and wings.

Birds have feathers

A **feather**, shown in *Figure 31.13*, is a lightweight, modified protein scale that provides insulation and enables flight. You may have seen a bird running its bill or beak through

Figure 31.12
Most scientists agree that birds evolved from a group of reptiles called theropod dinosaurs, as shown in this artist's rendition. The skeletons of birds and theropods are similar.

Unit 9 *FAST FILE* **Resources**
MiniLab Worksheet, pp. 39, 40
BioLab Worksheet, pp. 41–42
Real World BioApplications, pp. 43–44
Reinforcement and Study Guide in English, pp. 47–48
Reinforcement and Study Guide in Spanish, pp. 51–52
Concept Mapping, p. 53
Critical Thinking/Problem Solving, p. 54

Transparency Worksheets, pp. 56, 61–64, 67–68
Reading Essentials for Biology, Section 31.2
Laboratory Manual, pp. 195–200, 201–204
 Section Focus Transparency 76
Basic Concepts Transparencies 56, 57
Reteaching Skills Transparency 46

 Indiana Academic Standards

Pages 826–827: B.1.15, B.1.16, B.1.19, B.1.31, B.1.32

its feathers while sitting on a tree branch or on the shore of a pond. This process, called preening, keeps the feathers in good condition for flight. During preening, a bird also uses its bill or beak to rub oil from a gland near the tail onto the feathers. This conditions feathers and helps them last longer. You can compare types of bird feathers in the *MiniLab* on this page.

Even with good care, feathers wear out and must be replaced. The shedding of old feathers and the growth of new ones is called molting. Most birds molt in late summer. However, most do not lose their feathers all at once and are able to fly while they are molting. Wing and tail feathers are usually lost in pairs so that the bird can maintain its balance in flight.

Birds have wings

A second adaptation for flight in birds is the modification of the front limbs into wings. Powerful flight muscles are attached to a large breastbone called the **sternum** and to the upper bone of each wing. The sternum looks like the keel of a sailing boat and is important because it supports the enormous thrust and power produced by the muscles as they move to generate the lift needed for flight.

Flight requires energy

Flight requires high levels of energy. Several factors are involved in maintaining these high energy levels. First, a bird's four-chambered, rapidly beating heart moves oxygenated blood quickly throughout the body. While sleeping, a chickadee's heart, for example, beats 500 times a minute. Compare this to an average human heart, which beats 70 times a minute. This efficient circulation supplies cells with the oxygen needed to produce energy.

MiniLab 31.1

Compare and Contrast

Comparing Feathers Birds have different kinds of feathers. Contour feathers used for flight are found on a bird's body, wings, and tail. Down feathers lie under the contour feathers and insulate the body.

Color-enhanced SEM
Magnification: 120×

Procedure

1. Examine a contour feather with a hand lens, and make a sketch of how the feather filaments are hooked together.
2. Examine a down feather with a hand lens. Draw a diagram of the filaments of the down feather.
3. Fan your face with each feather separately. Note how much air is moved past your face by each type of feather. **CAUTION: *Wash your hands with soap and water after handling animal material.***

Analysis

1. **Explain** How does the structure of a contour feather help a bird fly?
2. **Explain** How does the structure of a down feather keep a bird warm?
3. **Infer** What accounts for the differences you felt when fanning with each feather?

Figure 31.13
A feather's structure relates to its function.

A Fluffy down feathers have no hooks to hold the filaments together. Down feathers act as insulators to keep a bird warm.

B A large bird can have 25 000 or more contour feathers with a million tiny hooks that interlock and make the feathers hold together, making the bird's body streamlined for flight.

31.2 BIRDS **827**

USING MODELS

Simulating Flight Ask students to make a flip book of a flying bird. Have them cut eight 3 × 5 index cards in half and draw a sequence of a bird in flight on the 16 cards. Have them arrange the cards in sequence, and then flip through the cards quickly to observe the sequence of a bird flying. **L2** **ELL**

827

✓ **Reading Check** An endotherm is an animal that maintains a nearly constant body temperature that is independent of its environment's temperature.

Second, a bird's respiratory system supplies oxygenated air to the lungs when it inhales as well as when it exhales. A bird's respiratory system consists of lungs and anterior and posterior air sacs. You can see the path air follows in a bird's respiratory system in *Figure 31.14.* During inhalation, oxygenated air passes through the trachea and into the lungs, where gas exchange occurs. Most of the air, however, passes directly into the posterior air sacs. When a bird exhales deoxygenated air from the lungs, oxygenated air returns to the lungs from the posterior air sacs. At the next inhalation, deoxygenated air in the lungs passes into the anterior air sacs. Finally, at the next exhalation, air passes from the anterior air sacs out of the trachea. Thus, air follows a one-way path in a bird. Find out more about bird flight in *Figure 31.15.*

Figure 31.14
Birds require a great deal of oxygen because their large flight muscles expend huge amounts of ATP. Follow the arrows to see how air passes through a bird's respiratory system. Notice that when a bird inhales, inhalation cycles 1 and 2 occur simultaneously.

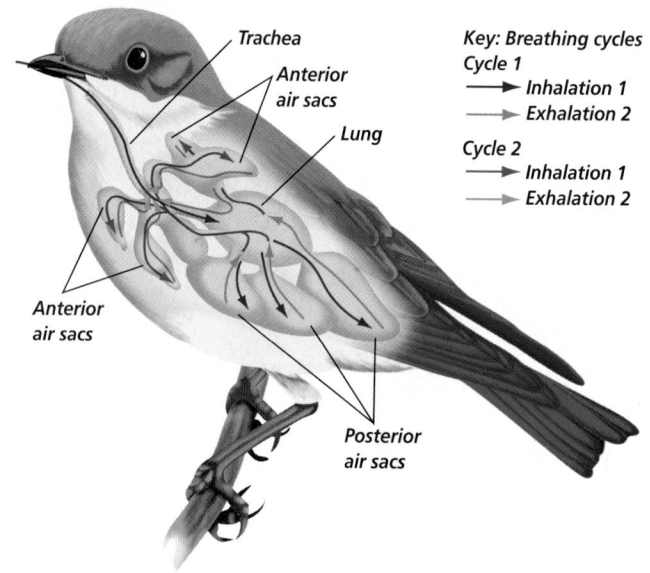

Trachea
Anterior air sacs
Lung
Anterior air sacs
Posterior air sacs

Key: Breathing cycles
Cycle 1
→ Inhalation 1
→ Exhalation 2
Cycle 2
→ Inhalation 1
→ Exhalation 2

Birds are endotherms

Birds are able to maintain the high energy levels needed for flight because they are endotherms. An **endotherm** is an animal that maintains a nearly constant body temperature that is not dependent on the environmental temperature.

Birds have a variety of ways to save or give off their body heat in order to maintain a nearly constant body temperature. Feathers reduce heat loss in cold temperatures. The feathers fluff up and trap a layer of air that limits the amount of heat lost. Responses to high temperatures include flattening the feathers and holding the wings away from the body. Birds also pant to increase respiratory heat loss.

A major advantage of being endothermic is that birds can live in all environments, from the hot tropics to the frigid Antarctic. However, birds and other endotherms must eat large amounts of food to sustain these higher levels of energy. Find out what kinds of food birds in your area prefer by doing the *MiniLab* on page 830.

✓ **Reading Check** **Describe** an endothermic animal.

Reproduction in birds

Birds, like reptiles, reproduce by internal fertilization and lay amniotic eggs usually inside a nest. Bird eggs are encased in a hard shell, unlike the leathery shell of a reptile. Bird nests may be made out of bits of straw and twigs, may consist of a depression scratched into the sand, or may be elaborate structures that are added to yearly. Whatever the type of nest, birds do not leave the eggs to hatch on their own. Instead, birds **incubate** or sit on their eggs to keep them warm. The eggs are turned periodically so that they develop properly.

Flight

Figure 31.15
Humans have always dreamed of being able to fly. The popularity of hang gliding and parachute jumping may reflect these dreams. For birds, the ability to fly is the result of complex selective pressures that led to the evolution of many adaptations. **Critical Thinking** *Although flying is the main form of locomotion for most birds, not all birds fly all the time. Some birds do not fly at all. What other forms of locomotion do birds use? Give specific examples.*

Male cardinal

A **Wings**
Birds have a variety of wing shapes and sizes. Some birds have longer, narrower wings adapted for soaring on updrafts, whereas others have shorter, broader wings adapted for quick, short flights among forest trees.

B **Hollow bones**
The hollow bones of birds are strengthened by bony crosspieces. The sternum is the large breastbone to which powerful flight muscles are attached.

F **Air sacs**
About 75 percent of the air inhaled by a bird passes directly into the air sacs rather than into the lungs. When a bird exhales, oxygenated air in the air sacs passes into the lungs. Birds receive oxygenated air when they breathe in and when they breathe out.

C **Beaks**
Birds have beaks, sometimes called bills, covered by a protein called keratin, but they do not have teeth.

Crop

Lung

Sternum

Intestine   *Gizzard*

E **Digestion**
The digestive system of a bird is adapted for dealing with large quantities of food that must be eaten to maintain the level of energy necessary for flight. Because birds have no teeth, many swallow small stones that help to grind up food in the gizzard.

D **Legs**
The legs of birds are made up of mostly skin, bone, and tendons. The feet are adapted to swimming, perching, walking, or catching prey.

Purpose
Students will gain an understanding of the adaptations that enable birds to fly.

Teaching Strategies
Obtain a turkey gizzard from a meat market. Use the gizzard to point out its thick muscles. Elicit reasons why the gizzard has such thick muscles. Always wash hands thoroughly with soap and water after handling biological specimens.

Visual Learning
- Obtain or borrow a mounted skeleton of a bird. Point out that the bones are thin but structurally strong. Point out the size of the sternum and ask students to compare the sternum of a bird with a human sternum.
- Obtain photographic slides of birds in flight. Ask students to examine wing shapes and determine type of flight unique to each bird. Explain that elliptical wings are adapted for quick movements. Wings that sweep back and taper to a slender tip promote high speed. Soaring birds have broad wings.

Critical Thinking
Some birds, such as ducks and geese, swim. Penguins dive through water to catch fishes and slide on their "bellies" across ice. Flightless birds, such as the ostrich, walk and run. Many other birds, such as robins and sparrows, hop or walk while on the ground. Woodpeckers and nuthatches can move up and down the trunks of trees.

CHALLENGE ACTIVITY

Speedy Birds: *Logical-Mathematical*
Ask students who have an interest in mathematics to make up a series of math problems dealing with wing beats for other students to solve. Provide students with the following data: number of wing beats per 10 seconds—crow 20, robin 23, pigeon 30, starling 45, chickadee 270, hummingbird 800. An example of a problem may be: If a crow, robin, pigeon, and starling each flew in the same direction at a starting speed of 48 km/h, how many times would each flap its wings if they flew 24 km? **L3**

DESIGN YOUR OWN **BioLab**

The BioLab at the end of the chapter can be used at this point in the lesson.

MiniLab 31.2

Purpose

Students will construct bird feeders and learn what types of foods birds prefer.

Process Skills

compare and contrast, recognize cause and effect, interpret data, classify

Teaching Strategies

■ Show photos or slides of common local birds.

■ Have students use binoculars to observe the birds that visit their feeders.

Expected Results

Depending on region, students may find cardinals, jays, woodpeckers, nuthatches, juncos, chickadees, sparrows, finches, tufted titmice, mourning doves, and many other local and migrating bird species.

Analysis

1. Sunflower seeds will attract a large variety of birds.
2. It is likely that birds will visit the same feeder over and over again until the feeder is empty.
3. Ideal bird food would have a mixture of a variety of seeds that would appeal to many different birds.

Modified Assessment

Knowledge Have each student write two questions about birds. Divide the class into pairs of students, and have them quiz each other. **L1**

MiniLab 31.2

Compare and Contrast

Feeding the Birds In the winter, it may be difficult for some birds to find food, especially if they live in an environment often blanketed with snow. Making a bird feeder and watching birds feed can be an enjoyable activity for you that may save some birds from starvation. If you do begin feeding birds in the winter, continue to feed them until natural food becomes available in the spring.

Procedure

1. Obtain several large, plastic milk bottles. Cut holes, about 10 cm in diameter, 5 cm from the base on opposite sides of each bottle.
2. Place small drainage holes in the bottom of each bottle. Hang the bottles from wires strung through small holes in the neck of each one.
3. Place a different kind of seed (sunflower seeds, hulled oats, cracked corn, wheat, thistle, millet) in different bottles. Add new seed when needed. **CAUTION:** *Always wash your hands with soap and water immediately after refilling the feeders.*
4. Use a bird guide to make a list of numbers and kinds of birds that frequent each feeder. Note the type of food offered.

Analysis

1. **Observe** What type of seed attracted the largest variety of bird types?
2. **Observe** Did any birds visit more than one feeder?
3. **Infer** What do you think an ideal bird food would be?

Figure 31.16
Examine these birds and infer where they live and how they are adapted to their environments.

Ptarmigan

Screech owls

Adélie penguins

In some species of birds, both parents take turns incubating eggs; in others, only one parent does so. Bird eggs are distinctive, and often the species of bird can be identified just by the color, size, and shape of an egg. You can find out more about the adaptive value of bird egg shape in the *BioLab* at the end of this chapter.

Diversity of Birds

Unlike reptiles, which take on a wide variety of forms from legless snakes to shelled turtles, birds are all very much alike in their basic form and structure. You have no difficulty recognizing a bird.

In spite of the basic uniformity of birds, they do exhibit specific adaptations, depending on the environment in which they live and the food they eat. As shown in *Figure 31.16*, ptarmigans have feathered legs and feet that serve as snowshoes in the winter, making it easier for the birds to walk in the snow. Penguins are flightless birds with wings and feet modified for swimming and a body surrounded with a thick layer of insulating fat. Large eyes, an acute sense of

PROJECT

Making a Flyway Map Provide students with a blank map of the world. Ask them to use field guides to find migration routes for the migrating birds of your area. Ask students to plot these data on their maps using a different color of pencil for each bird's route. **L1 ELL**

hearing, and sharp claws make owls well-adapted, nocturnal predators able to swoop with absolute precision onto their prey.

The shape of a bird's beak or bill gives clues to the kind of food the bird eats. Hummingbirds, for example, have long beaks that are used for obtaining nectar from flowers. Hawks, like the one shown in *Figure 31.17*, have curved beaks that are adapted for tearing apart their prey. Pelicans have huge bills with pouches that they use as nets for capturing fish. The short, stout beak of a cardinal is adapted to cracking seeds.

Many bird species are now threatened with extinction due to changes in their habitats. Read the *Problem-Solving Lab* to learn where birds are endangered. Then read the *Biology and Society* at the end of this chapter to learn how illegal trade in wildlife threatens birds and other animals.

Pelican

Hawk

Problem-Solving Lab 31.1

Analyze Information

Where are the most endangered bird species? More than 100 bird species have become extinct in the last 400 years.

Solve the Problem
Examine the world map. The key at the bottom right shows the number of bird species that are currently threatened with extinction. The numbers appearing on the map indicate the actual number of threatened bird species in specific countries.

Percent of threatened bird species	
	Fewer than 5%
	5 to 9.9%
	More than 10%

50
Hawaii
64
53
64
103
90
73
47 86
Philippines
104
Madagascar
Mauritius
New Zealand

Thinking Critically

1. **Use Numbers** If 50 species are threatened, what is the approximate number of bird species in the United States? (Hint: 2.5 percent of the bird species in the U.S. are threatened.)
2. **Estimate** It is estimated that about 11 percent or 1107 of the world's bird species are threatened. About how many bird species are there in the world?
3. **Observe** Hawaii, the Philippines, New Zealand, and Madagascar all show the highest percent of threatened species. What common geographical feature do these areas share?
4. **Infer** Use the map to support the fact that many areas have a lower number of threatened species and offer an explanation as to why this is so.

Figure 31.17
Different species of birds have differently shaped beaks. **Explain** *What can the shape of a bird's beak reveal about that bird?*

31.2 BIRDS **831**

Problem-Solving Lab 31.1

Purpose
Students will determine that a decline in bird species is most apparent on islands where there is habitat destruction.

Process Skills
think critically, recognize cause and effect, analyze information, apply concepts, use numbers, define operationally, predict

Teaching Strategies
■ Review the mathematics needed to calculate the total number of species if students know the number threatened.
■ Review the mathematics needed to calculate the total number of bird species.

Thinking Critically
1. 2000
2. about 10 000
3. All are islands.
4. Europe and Africa have low numbers of threatened species. These continents have large regions that species can move to when their natural habitats are destroyed.

Assessment
Performance Ask students to research the success of capture, breeding, and release programs for certain bird species in the United States, such as the whooping crane, and write a newspaper article describing these programs. Use the Performance Task Assessment List for Newspaper Article in **PASC**, p. 141. **L2**

Caption Question Answer
Figure 31.17 Bird beaks are adapted to eating different kinds of food.

 Indiana Academic Standards

Pages 830–831: B.1.15, B.1.16, B.1.34, B.1.36, B.1.43

3 Assess

Origins of Birds

Current thoughts about bird evolution are illustrated in *Figure 31.18*. Scientists hypothesize that today's birds are derived from an evolutionary line of dinosaurs that did not become extinct. *Figure 31.19* shows the earliest known bird in the fossil record, *Archaeopteryx*. At first, scientists thought that *Archaeopteryx* was a direct ancestor of modern birds; however, some paleontologists now

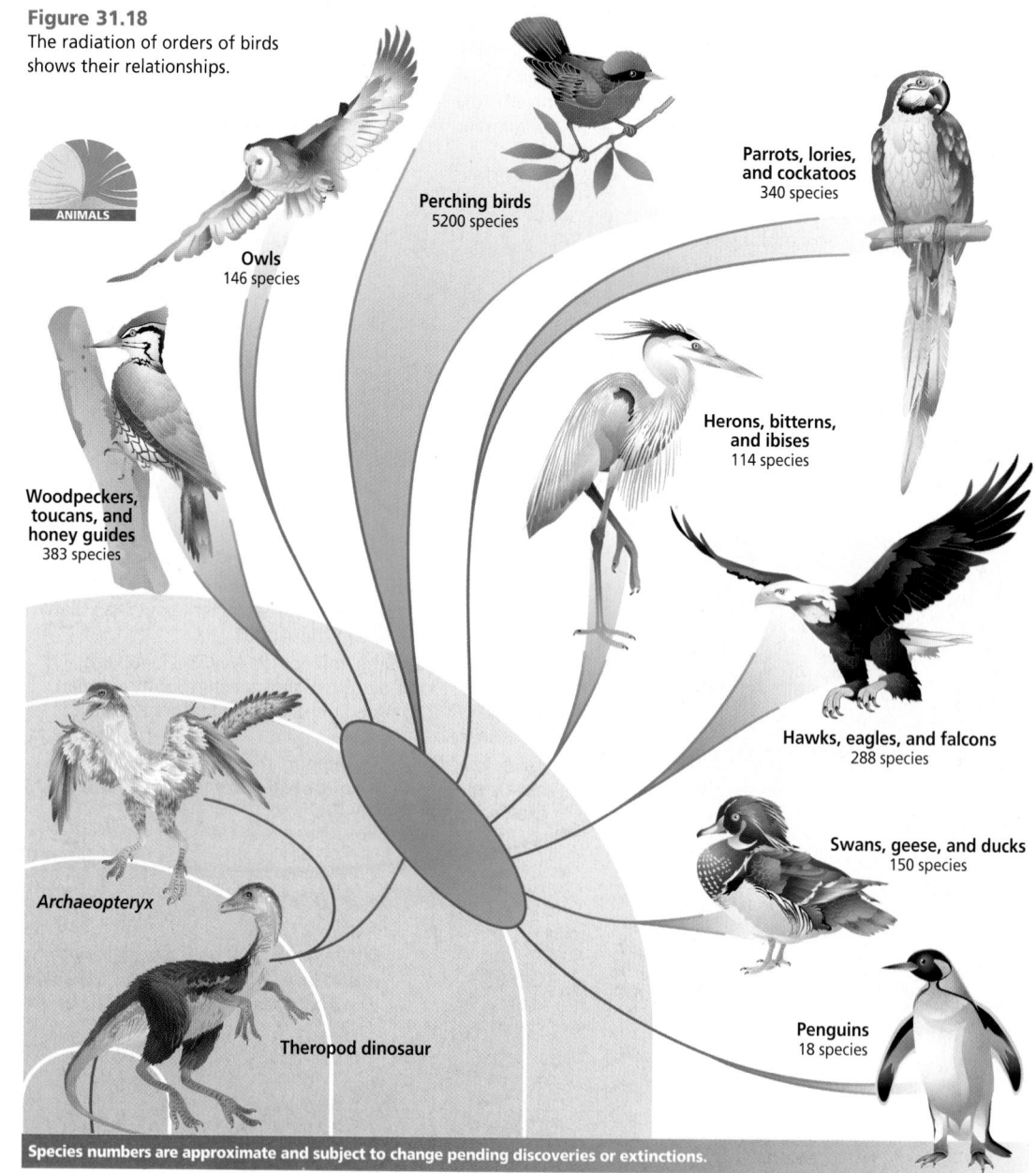

Figure 31.18
The radiation of orders of birds shows their relationships.

Owls
146 species

Perching birds
5200 species

Parrots, lories, and cockatoos
340 species

Herons, bitterns, and ibises
114 species

Woodpeckers, toucans, and honey guides
383 species

Hawks, eagles, and falcons
288 species

Archaeopteryx

Swans, geese, and ducks
150 species

Theropod dinosaur

Penguins
18 species

Species numbers are approximate and subject to change pending discoveries or extinctions.

832 REPTILES AND BIRDS

Figure 31.19
The fossil bones of *Archaeopteryx* show that it was definitely a bird, whereas those of *Caudipteryx zoui* indicate that it was a feathered theropod dinosaur.

Caudipteryx zoui

Archaeopteryx

Extension
Kinesthetic Obtain small birds such as Cornish game hens, chickens, or quail from a meat market or grocery store. The birds should be boiled and all meat removed from the bones. Have students carefully assemble the skeletons using sturdy glue and thin wire. Always wash hands thoroughly with soap and water after handling biological specimens. **L2** **ELL**

✔ **Assessment**

Performance Have groups of students sketch on sheets of butcher paper scale maps of the school grounds or a spot near the school. Have them add features to their maps that would make their areas more attractive to birds. Books about attracting birds in all types of environments from the inner city to the suburbs are available at libraries. **L2** **ELL** **COOP LEARN**

think that it most likely did not give rise to any other bird groups. *Archaeopteryx* was about the size of a crow and had feathers and wings like a modern bird. But it also had teeth, a long tail, and clawed front toes, much like a reptile.

Fossil finds in China support the idea that birds evolved from a theropod dinosaur. As illustrated in *Figure 31.19*, it was flightless and ran to capture prey. It was about 1 m tall and had feathers similar to those of modern birds. Scientists hypothesize that their feathers helped insulate the animal, or perhaps were adapted for camouflage or courtship behavior. Most scientists studying the origins of birds hypothesize that feathers evolved before flight.

But feathers aren't the only features shared by modern birds and some theropod dinosaurs. Both also have a sternum, a wishbone, shoulder blades, flexible wrists, and three fingers on each hand.

Section Assessment

Understanding Main Ideas
1. What features of birds enable them to live on land?
2. Describe how a bird's respiratory system works, and explain how air sacs improve a bird's ability to obtain the energy necessary for flight.
3. What is an endotherm? How does being an endotherm have adaptive value for birds that live in polar regions?
4. Analyze the relationship between modern birds and dinosaurs.

Thinking Critically
5. Large, flightless birds once were common in areas that did not have large, carnivorous predators. Many of these birds are now extinct. Form a hypothesis about the evolution and extinction of large, flightless birds.

SKILL REVIEW
6. **Get the Big Picture** Make a table that summarizes the adaptations birds have that enable them to fly. For more help, refer to *Get the Big Picture* in the **Skill Handbook**.

in.bdol.glencoe.com/self_check_quiz

31.2 BIRDS **833**

Section Assessment

1. lungs, wings, legs, beaks, internal fertilization, shelled, amniotic eggs, endothermic metabolism
2. Oxygen can enter a bird's circulatory system when it inhales and exhales. Inhalation results in oxygen entering the lungs then entering air sacs. When a bird exhales, oxygenated air in the air sacs passes into the lungs, thereby increasing the amount of oxygen available to the bird to generate energy needed for flight.
3. Endotherms can regulate their body temperature regardless of the environmental temperature.
4. Most scientists think that modern birds evolved from theropod dinosaurs.
5. Possible hypotheses: Large flightless birds evolved in regions where there were few large carnivores. Large flightless birds evolved where they were not the primary prey of carnivores.
6. Make sure students' tables include all the features listed on pages 826–828.

DESIGN YOUR OWN BioLab

Time Allotment
one class period

Process Skills
collect data, compare and contrast, identify and control variables, design an experiment, draw a conclusion, experiment, formulate models, hypothesize, interpret data, measure in SI, organize data

PREPARATION

Possible Hypothesis
If shape controls rolling, then different shapes will roll different distances and different shapes will form different patterns.

PLAN THE EXPERIMENT

Teaching Strategies
■ Students should work in groups of three or four with specific duties being assigned to each student within the group.
■ Balances may be shared among groups.
■ Class discussion at the conclusion would be meaningful to see the variety of hypotheses tested and conclusions reached.

Possible Procedures
■ To make egg models, students could mold clay around golf or table-tennis balls or real eggs.
■ The mass of the models can be kept fairly constant by adding or removing clay.

Indiana Academic Standards

Pages 834–835: B.1.31

DESIGN YOUR OWN BioLab

Which egg shape is best?

INQUIRY **Before You Begin**

Not all bird eggs have the same shape. An ostrich egg is almost totally round. Chicken eggs are almost a perfect oval on one end. Cliff-dwelling birds, such as the common guillemot (*Uria aalge*), have eggs that come almost to a point on one end. Why the variety of shapes? Is there any adaptive benefit to this variety of shapes? Could egg shape be related to where the bird nests?

PREPARATION

Problem
What shape would be best for an egg to reduce the distance it could roll if pushed from a nest on the ground or a cliff?

Hypotheses
There are several hypotheses that you can test. Your hypothesis might be that egg shape influences the distance an egg rolls, or that shape determines the tightness of circular rolling patterns.

Objectives
In this BioLab, you will:
■ **Design** an experiment to test your hypotheses.
■ **Model** different egg shapes and egg masses.
■ **Experiment** to test your hypothesis.
■ **Draw conclusions** based on your experimental data.

Possible Materials
clay	table-tennis ball
ruler	golf ball
string	balance
hard-cooked egg	protractor

Safety Precautions
CAUTION: *Always wear goggles in the lab. Never eat anything used in the lab.*

Skill Handbook
If you need help with this lab, refer to the **Skill Handbook.**

PLAN THE EXPERIMENT

1. Form a hypothesis and decide on a way to test your group's hypothesis. Keep the list of available materials in mind as you plan your procedure.

Data and Observations
Round eggs will roll the farthest. Eggs with greater mass will roll less far. Pointed eggs or oval eggs will roll in circular patterns and the total distance will be less than the total distance rolled by round eggs.

2. Consider the following questions as you design your experiment: How will you incorporate a control? How many egg shapes will you test? How will you model your egg shapes? How many trials will you perform? How might you keep egg models identical in mass? Where will you start to measure distance rolled?

Check the Plan
Discuss the following points with other group members to decide the final procedure for each of your experiments.
1. What is your independent and dependent variable?
2. How will you eliminate all other variables?
3. What data will you collect? How many trials will you run?
4. Will you need a data table and how might it be organized?
5. *Make sure your teacher has approved your experimental plan before you proceed further.*
6. Record your hypothesis and carry out your experiments.
7. CLEANUP AND DISPOSAL As you clean up after the lab, make wise choices about the disposal and recycling of lab materials.

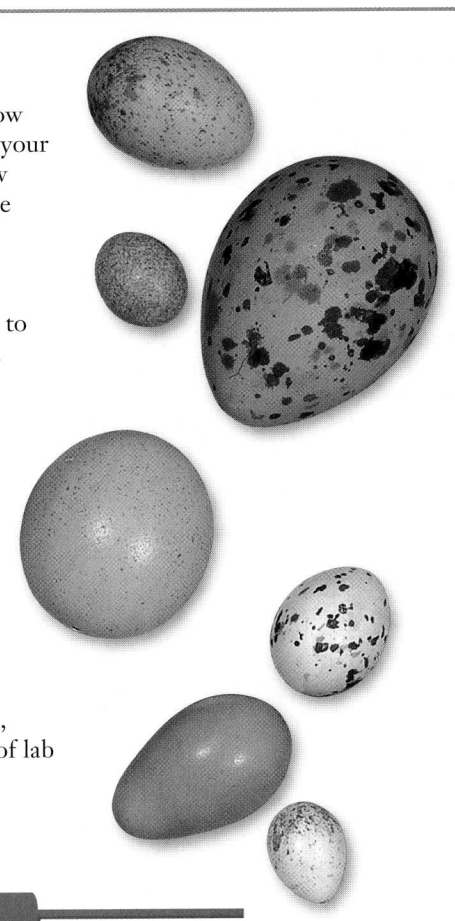

1. **Interpret Data** Describe your results after testing your hypothesis.
2. **Conclude** Do your data support your hypothesis? Explain using both quantitative and qualitative observations.
3. **Identify Variables** What were your independent and dependent variables?
4. **Conclude** In general, how does mass influence the distance an egg will roll? How does egg shape influence the distance an egg will roll or the pattern taken when it rolls?
5. **Predict** Predict why egg shape or mass may be helpful adaptations when considering the variety of bird habitats.
6. ERROR ANALYSIS Compare your data to that of other student groups. What revisions could be made to your hypothesis or experiment based on these comparisons?

Apply Your Skill

Knowledge Find out the chemical and physical nature of bird shells. Find out how and where birds produce a shell.

 Web Links To find out more about birds and bird eggs, visit in.bdol.glencoe.com/birds

31.2 BIRDS **835**

1. Student answers will vary. Example: Round eggs roll in straighter lines than oval or pointed eggs.
2. Student answers will vary. Example: Heavy round eggs rolled less distance (12 cm) than lighter round eggs (22 cm).
3. Student answers will vary. Example: independent variable, egg shape; dependent variable, distance rolled.
4. A greater mass will roll a shorter distance because, according to Newton's second law of motion ($f=ma$), when equal forces are applied to the two masses, the larger mass will have less acceleration. Oval or pointed eggs roll a shorter distance and form a circular path; the more pointed the end, the tighter the circular path.
5. Egg-shape adaptations ensure survival. For example, if rounded eggs of ground-nesting species roll out of the nest, it can be easily rolled back into it. Cliff-nesting species have pointed eggs that roll in circles, thus, if knocked out of the nest, they do not roll off the cliff.
6. ERROR ANALYSIS Students may have made errors in measuring the distance rolled. A small number of trials are not necessarily conclusive. Students used clay models of eggs that do not resemble birds' eggs on the inside. They might consider other materials that would be more like a bird's egg. Students might devise a more realistic nest edge.

Apply Your Skill

Knowledge Have students research the variety in egg shell coloration. Have them correlate this variety in coloration with natural selection and species survival. L3

Assessment
Knowledge Ask students to write a short report about how egg shape has adaptive value for birds. Use the Performance Task Assessment List for Lab Report in **PASC**, p. 119. L2

Biology and Society

Purpose

Encourage students to become aware of the illegal wildlife trade, and how consumer demand for wildlife and wildlife products drives the market for products made from threatened and endangered species.

Background

It may come as a surprise to some students that the United States is probably the largest single consumer of wildlife in the world. Many animals and wildlife products are bought and sold legally in the U.S., but many others are not. In a recent survey conducted by TRAFFIC, the wildlife trade monitoring organization supported by the World Wildlife Fund and the World Conservation Union (IUCN), packaged traditional medicines containing (or purporting to contain) tiger or rhino body parts were easy to find for sale in many large cities, even though the trade of such products is illegal.

Teaching Strategies

■ As a class project, contact the U.S. Fish and Wildlife Service for information about the illegal wildlife trade. Have students create posters showing ways in which people can help reduce the worldwide demand for products made from threatened and endangered animals and plants.

■ Visit a zoo that participates in a nationally accredited captive breeding program for threatened or endangered species.

Forming Your Opinion

Answers will vary depending on endangered species chosen.

Biology and Society

Illegal Wildlife Trade

In May 1998, the U.S. Fish and Wildlife Service with the assistance of several foreign law enforcement agencies, broke up an international smuggling ring. Their three-year investigation—code-named Operation Jungle Trade—ended in the arrest of smugglers operating in a dozen countries. In what illegal products were these criminals trafficking? Not diamonds or drugs, but in animals and rare birds.

Species for sale Some people pay large sums of money for parrots, tropical fishes, monkeys, snakes and lizards to add to their animal collections or to keep as exotic pets whether it is legal or not. Worldwide, millions of illegal wildlife products—from jewelry made from sea turtle shells to snow leopard coats and lizard skin belts—are bought and sold annually on the wildlife black market.

Unintended backing People can unknowingly support the illegal wildlife trade when they buy seashells, coral jewelry, or ivory trinkets that are sold as souvenirs in many countries. Also, buying fashion accessories made from animal skins can help finance illegal wildlife trade.

Many traditional remedies manufactured in certain countries are made with body parts from threatened species. Some users of traditional remedies believe strongly in the power of certain parts of animals or plants to enhance their physical attractiveness or treat health-related conditions. The fact that these parts come from endangered species and are traded on the black market may be unknown to the user.

Government action An international trade agreement called CITES (the Convention on International Trade in Endangered Species of Wild Fauna and Flora) was enacted in July 1975. Its purpose is to ensure that the buying and selling of wild animals and plants do not endanger their survival. CITES regulates the international trade of about 5 000 animal species and 25 000 plant species living or dead, and any part of or

Confiscated products from endangered species and a jaguar skin (inset)

products made from them. Currently, 160 governments are members of CITES. Despite this global agreement, the illegal wildlife trade is a multibillion-dollar-a-year business.

Perspectives The illegal wildlife trade is contributing to the near extinction of many species, and with every new extinction, Earth's biodiversity is decreased. Once a species is gone, illegal wildlife traders turn to a different species to fulfill the demands of the market. Education, stricter laws regulating all trade not just international trade, and better enforcement of current laws are needed in order to curtail the booming illegal wildlife trade.

Forming Your Opinion

Analyze the Issue Research one example of an endangered species that is traded illegally. How has this practice altered the equilibrium of the ecosystem in that area? What, if anything, is being done to further prevent illegal trading of the organism? Present your findings to your class as a multimedia presentation.

  To find out more about the illegal wildlife trade, visit in.bdol.glencoe.com/biology_society

Going Further

Linguistic Have students write an essay on the following question: Would you buy a product if you were aware that it was made from the body parts of an endangered species? Explain your response. **L2**

STUDY GUIDE

Section 31.1

Reptiles

Key Concepts

- Reptiles are ectotherms that have dry, scaly skins; legs under the body; internal fertilization; and amniotic eggs. Most reptiles have three-chambered hearts. Some reptiles have four-chambered hearts.

- Present-day reptiles belong to one of four groups. Turtles have shells and no teeth. Crocodiles and alligators have streamlined bodies and powerful, toothed jaws. Lizards have a variety of adaptations, including long bodies, tails, and short limbs. Snakes have no limbs. Tautaras are lizardlike reptiles with some primitive characteristics.

- The ancestors of present-day reptiles arose from ancient stem reptiles, which were also the ancestors of the dinosaurs.

Vocabulary

amniotic egg (p. 818)
Jacobson's organ (p. 821)

Section 31.2

Birds

Key Concepts

- Birds have adaptations for flight including feathers; a keel-shaped sternum; a four-chambered heart; endothermy; reinforced, hollow bones; a beak; and air sacs.

- Birds may be derived from a line of dinosaurs that did not become extinct.

- Female birds lay hard-shelled, amniotic eggs usually in a nest. Each bird species has unique eggs.

- Adaptations, such as beak shape and modified feet and wings, ensure the survival of birds in their specific habitats.

Vocabulary

endotherm (p. 828)
feather (p. 826)
incubate (p. 828)
sternum (p. 827)

Characteristics of Class Reptilia and Class Aves

Class	Organisms	Characteristics
Reptilia	Snakes, lizards, crocodiles, alligators, tuataras	Dry, scaly skin; ectothermic; four limbs (some limbless); three- or four-chambered heart; internal fertilization; leathery-shelled, amniotic egg
Aves	Cardinals, penguins, ostriches, owls	Feathers; wings; sternum; flight (most); endothermic; four-chambered heart; internal fertilization; hard-shelled, amniotic egg

FOLDABLES

Study Organizer To help you review reptiles, use the Organizational Study Fold on page 817.

in.bdol.glencoe.com/vocabulary_puzzlemaker

CHAPTER 31 ASSESSMENT **837**

Key Concepts

Summary statements can be used by students to review the major concepts of the chapter.

Biology Online

Visit in.bdol.glencoe.com
/self_check_quiz
/vocabulary_puzzlemaker
/chapter_test
/standardized_test

VOCABULARY PUZZLEMAKER

For additional help with vocabulary, have students access the Vocabulary PuzzleMaker online at in.bdol.glencoe.com/ vocabulary_puzzlemaker

FOLDABLES™

Have students use their Foldables to review the content of Section 31.1. On the back of each Foldable, analyze how a reptile's body form is adapted to its way of life.

Use the ExamView®Pro Test Bank CD-ROM to:

- Create **multiple versions** of tests
- Create **modified** tests with one mouse click for **inclusion** students
- **Edit** existing questions and **add** your own questions
- Build tests aligned with state standards using built-in **State Curriculum Tags**
- Change **English** tests to **Spanish** with one mouse click and vice versa

 Indiana Academic Standards

Pages 836–837: B.1.15, B.1.17, B.1.31, B.1.32, B.1.41

Vocabulary Review (answers)

1. true
2. false—sternum
3. false—feather
4. false—amniotic egg

Understanding Key Concepts (answers)

5. C   7. C
6. C   8. C
9. 1. endotherms; 2. sternum; 3. feathers

Constructed Response (answers)

10. If temperatures are higher, more males will be produced and populations ultimately reduced. If temperatures are lower, more females will be produced, which should increase the population.
11. Birds have lungs with air sacs that can deliver more oxygen to muscles that need high levels of energy for flight and a four-chambered heart.
12. *Caudipteryx* is a fossil dinosaur with feathers similar to those of modern birds. *Archaeopteryx* is the earliest fossil bird with feathers and wings.

Thinking Critically (answers)

13. The center of mass most likely would be more forward, as in birds, because theropod dinosaurs most likely evolved into birds.
14. Answers will vary depending on the species of turtle selected.
15. In one group of alligators, cover the domes with plastic so they cannot function. Another group of alligators should have domes uncov-

---

Vocabulary Review

Review the Chapter 31 vocabulary words listed in the Study Guide on page 837. Determine if each statement is true or false. If false, replace the underlined word with the correct vocabulary word.

1. <u>Jacobson's organ</u> is a sense organ in snakes that picks up and analyzes airborne chemicals.
2. A <u>feather</u> is a large breastbone that provides a site for muscle attachment.
3. A <u>sternum</u> is a lightweight, modified scale that provides insulation and enables flight.
4. An <u>endotherm</u> provides nourishment to the embryo and contains membranes that protect it while it develops in a terrestrial environment.

Understanding Key Concepts

5. What function does the amnion perform in an amniotic egg?
   A. collects the nitrogenous wastes of the embryo
   B. supplies food to the embryo
   C. cushions the embryo and prevents dehydration
   D. allows gas exchange during respiration
6. Which of the following is NOT an example of a reptile?
   A. turtle   C. penguin
   B. snake   D. tuatara
7. Three features that modern-day birds share are _____.
   A. endothermy; a three-chambered heart; dry, scaly skin
   B. endothermy, feathers, a three-chambered heart
   C. internal fertilization, amniotic eggs, feathers
   D. ectothermy, internal fertilization, hard-shelled eggs
8. Three features that modern-day reptiles share are _____.
   A. endothermy; a four-chambered heart; and dry, scaly skin
   B. endothermy, feathers, a three-chambered heart
   C. internal fertilization, an amniotic egg, leathery-shelled eggs
   D. ectothermy, internal fertilization, hard-shelled eggs that hatch inside the female

---

9. **Concept Map** Complete the concept map by using the following vocabulary terms: sternum, feathers, endotherms.

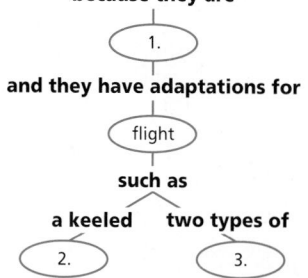

Constructed Response

10. **Open Ended** Nest temperature determines the gender of a reptile embryo. In alligators and crocodiles, low nest temperatures produce all female offspring. High nest temperatures produce all male offspring. Explain how this phenomenon could affect future populations of species in a particular area.
11. **Open Ended** Explain how a bird's circulatory and respiratory system interrelate to allow birds to achieve flight.
12. **Open Ended** Why are the fossils of *Archaeopteryx* and *Caudipteryx zoui* significant in explaining the evolutionary history of birds?

Thinking Critically

13. **Predict** Most dinosaurs had their center of mass near the hips, while most modern birds have their center of mass near the wings. Predict where the center of mass of theropod dinosaurs would be.
14. **REAL WORLD BioCHALLENGE** Visit in.bdol.glencoe.com to investigate the reasons for declining numbers of sea turtles. Select one species of sea turtle and design a pamphlet that describes your selected turtle, the reasons for decline, and the efforts that could be made to protect this species.

 in.bdol.glencoe.com/chapter_test

---

ered. Observe and count the number of responses of alligators turning their heads toward water dropping on the surface of the pond. Other answers may be accepted provided that there is a control group, one variable being tested, and quantitative data are being collected.

16. The bar-headed goose can move its huge wings quickly. Its wings have larger wing surface areas that reduce wind resistance. It can recirculate air through many air sacs to extract all the oxygen and have specialized hemoglobin that absorbs oxygen quickly.

15. Design an Experiment Alligator faces are covered with small, pigmented domes. Scientists hypothesize that the domes are extremely sensitive to small disturbances on the water's surface. Design an experiment that would test this hypothesis.

16. Infer Bar-headed geese migrate over the top of Mount Everest where oxygen levels are only one third of what they are at sea level. What parts of bar-headed geese bodies might have adaptations to survive in areas with low levels of oxygen?

End-of-Course Assessment Practice

17. A   **18.** B   **19.** D

20. The more eggs laid, the smaller the nestlings. Small nestlings do not require as much food.

21. The shelled eggs of the reptile are more protected than amphibian eggs, so they have a greater chance of hatching and surviving. Also, energy is conserved when fewer eggs are produced.

End-of-Course Assessment Practice

The assessed Indiana standard appears next to the question.

All questions aligned and verified by The Princeton Review

Part 1 Multiple Choice

Use the graph below to answer question 17.

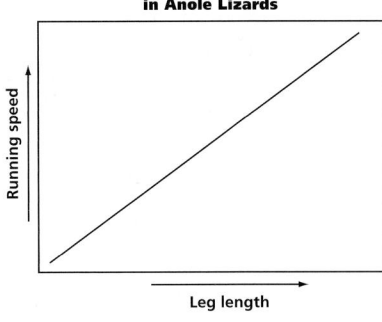
Running Speed Versus Leg Length in Anole Lizards

17. The relationship between running speed and leg length in anole lizards can best be described as which of the following:
A. As leg length increases, running speed increases.
B. As leg length decreases, running speed increases.
C. Leg length and running speed are not related.
D. Running speed decreases as leg length increases.

Use the graph below to answer questions 18 and 19.

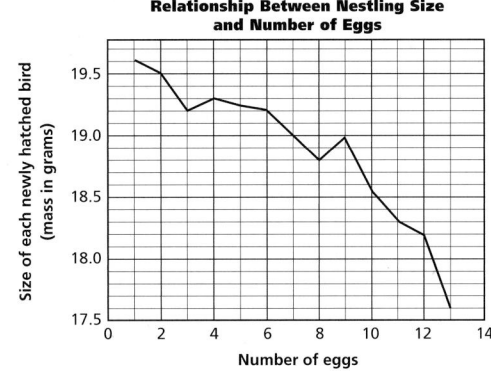
Relationship Between Nestling Size and Number of Eggs

18. If 13 eggs are laid, what is the mass of a newly hatched bird?
A. 17.5 g
B. 17.6 g
C. 18.1 g
D. 18.3 g

19. How many eggs were laid if the mass of a newly hatched bird is 18.8 g?
A. 5   C. 7
B. 6   D. 8

Part 2 Constructed Response/Grid In

Record your answers on your answer document.

20. **Open Ended** Describe the relationship between the number of eggs laid and the size of a newly hatched bird for the species described in questions 18 and 19. Explain why this occurs.

21. **Open Ended** Most reptiles lay between one and 200 eggs at a time. Amphibians lay thousands of
B.1.31 eggs at a time. Is there an adaptive advantage to laying fewer eggs on land?

 in.bdol.glencoe.com/standardized_test

CHAPTER 31 ASSESSMENT **839**

 FAST FILE

Answer Sheet A practice answer sheet can be found on p. 75 of *Unit 9 Fast File Resources.*

RUBRIC

For more help evaluating open-ended assessment questions, see the rubric on p. 9T.

Indiana Academic Standards

Pages 838–839: B.1.15, B.1.16, B.1.31, B.1.32

Chapter 32 Organizer

Section Objectives	National Science Standards	State/Local Standards	Advanced Lab and Demo Planning
Section 32.1 1 session, 1 block 1. **Distinguish** mammalian characteristics. 2. **Explain** how the characteristics of mammals enable them to adapt to most habitats on Earth.	UCP.1, UCP.2, UCP.5; A.1, A.2; C.4–6; F.1; G.1	**Indiana Standards** B.1.14, B.1.15, B.1.17, B.1.19, B.1.31	**Student Labs:** Additional Lab, p. 842: mouse, terrarium with 3–5 cm of sawdust or sand, objects for burying, timer MiniLab 32.1, p. 843: slide of a human tooth, microscope Problem-Solving Lab 32.1, p. 844 MiniLab 32.2, p. 845: owl pellet, paper toweling, forceps, microscope slide, coverslip, microscope **Teacher Demonstration:** Quick Demo, p. 845: glycerol, dog or cat hair, microscope, microscope slides, coverslips
Section 32.2 2 sessions, 1/2 block 3. **Distinguish** among the three groups of living mammals. 4. **Compare** reproduction in egg-laying, pouched, and placental mammals.	UCP.1, UCP.2, UCP.4, UCP.5; C.3–6	**Indiana Standards** B.1.15, B.1.17, B.1.31, B.1.32, B.1.41	**Student Lab:** Internet BioLab, p. 852: See materials below. **Teacher Demonstration:** Quick Demo, p. 849: guide to animal tracks
End of Chapter Assessment **Student Edition** **Study Guide,** p. 855 **Content Assessment,** pp. 856–857		**Indiana Standards** B.1.15, B.1.17, B.1.31, B.1.41	**Student Lab:** Internet BioLab, p. 852: access to the Internet

Key to Teaching Strategies

L1 Level 1 activities should be appropriate for students with learning difficulties.

L2 Level 2 activities should be within the ability range of all students.

L3 Level 3 activities are designed for above-average students.

ELL ELL activities should be within the ability range of English Language Learners.

COOP LEARN
Cooperative Learning activities are designed for small group work.

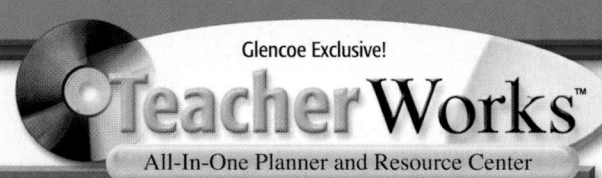

Glencoe Exclusive!
TeacherWorks™
All-In-One Planner and Resource Center

Reproducible Masters and Transparencies

Technology

Unit 9 FAST FILE Resources
MiniLab Worksheet, pp. 79, 80
Real World BioApplications, pp. 83–84
Reinforcement and Study Guide in English, pp. 85–86
Reinforcement and Study Guide in Spanish, pp. 89–90
Concept Mapping, p. 93
Critical Thinking/Problem Solving, p. 94
Transparency Worksheets, pp. 95, 97–102
Reading Essentials for Biology, Section 32.1
Laboratory Manual, pp. 205–208, 209–214
Section Focus Transparency 77
Basic Concepts Transparencies 58, 59
Reteaching Skills Transparency 47

● **Interactive Chalkboard CD-ROM: Section 32.1 Presentation**
● **TeacherWorks™ CD-ROM**
♫ **Guided Reading Audio Summaries MP3**

Unit 9 FAST FILE Resources
BioLab Worksheet, pp. 81–82
Reinforcement and Study Guide in English, pp. 87–88
Reinforcement and Study Guide in Spanish, pp. 91–92
Transparency Worksheets, p. 96
Reading Essentials for Biology, Section 32.2
Section Focus Transparency 78

● **Interactive Chalkboard CD-ROM: Section 32.2 Presentation**
● **TeacherWorks™ CD-ROM**
♫ **Guided Reading Audio Summaries MP3**

Unit 9 FAST FILE Resources
Chapter Assessment, pp. 103–108
Student Recording Sheet, p. 109

The Princeton Review **Reviewing Biology,** pp. 63–64

● **Interactive Chalkboard: Chapter 32 Assessment**
● **MindJogger Videoquizzes DVD/VHS**
● **ExamView® Pro Test Bank CD-ROM**
● **TeacherWorks™ CD-ROM**
● **Succeeding on National Standards CD-ROM**

⌨ **in.bdol.glencoe.com**
/self_check_quiz
/vocabulary_puzzlemaker
/chapter_test
/standardized_test

Indicates materials created specifically for Indiana.

Short on Time?

BIODIGEST The BioDigest at the end of this unit can be used as a(n):

- preview to introduce important unit concepts.
- overview if time does not permit teaching the entire chapter.
- review of key unit concepts.

Understanding the Photo

The earliest fossil records of giraffes date back to about 1.5 million years ago, and were found in Israel and Africa. Today, most giraffes live in savannas and open woodlands of eastern and southwestern Africa. A giraffe's neck can be over 1.5 m long, yet it only has seven vertebrae. Giraffes have valves in their blood vessels to ensure blood flow, even against gravity. Their vessels are also elastic to help relieve excess blood pressure when they lower their heads. A giraffe's gender can be determined by its stance while eating. Male giraffes eat from the highest branches, while females eat closer to the ground.

Mammals

What You'll Learn

- You will identify the characteristics of mammals.
- You will compare and contrast three groups of living mammals and examine their relationships to their ancient ancestors.

Why It's Important

Mammals play a major role in most ecosystems on Earth because they are one of the most successful groups of animals. Humans are mammals, so studying mammal characteristics provides information about humans as well.

Understanding ▶ the Photo

Giraffes are the tallest mammals. Newborn giraffes average 1.8 meters and can grow to be about 5.5 meters as adults. They have long legs and can run quickly—about 60 km/h. Their long legs, as well as their long necks, help them reach leaves in tall acacia trees.

Biology Online

Visit in.bdol.glencoe.com to
- study the entire chapter online
- access Web Links for more information and activities on mammals
- review content with the Interactive Tutor and self-check quizzes

840

 Two-Minute Chapter Launcher

Demo Show students a mouse, rat, gerbil, or hamster in its cage. Offer the animal food, and ask students to observe in groups its behavior for five minutes. Ask students to list the adaptations of the animal to its environment. Students may observe the animal carrying food back to its nest. The animal may sit back and hold food between its front feet when eating. The animal may scrape pieces off of the food with its front teeth.

 Indiana Academic Standards

Pages 840–841: B.1.15, B.1.17

Section 32.1

Mammal Characteristics

Indiana Standards Standard B.1.15 Understand and explain that, in biological systems, structure and function must be considered together.

Study Organizer

Mammals Make the following Foldable to help you identify main characteristics of mammals.

STEP 1 **Fold** a vertical sheet of notebook paper from side to side.

STEP 2 **Cut** along every fourth line of only the top layer to form tabs.

STEP 3 **Label** each tab.

Find Main Ideas As you read Chapter 32, list the main characteristics of mammals on the tabs. As you learn about the main characteristics, write a benefit of the adaptation under the tab for each.

SECTION PREVIEW

Objectives

Distinguish mammalian characteristics.

Explain how the characteristics of mammals enable them to adapt to most habitats on Earth.

Review Vocabulary
metabolism: all of the chemical reactions that occur within an organism (p. 147)

New Vocabulary
gland
mammary gland
diaphragm

Physical Science Connection

Movement of heat through hair Compared to solids or liquids, gases are poor conductors of heat. A layer of hair or fur on a mammal's skin contains many air pockets trapped between the hair shafts. Because air is a poor heat conductor, heat moves slowly through an air pocket. As a result, the rate at which heat is lost by the mammal is reduced.

What is a mammal?

Mammals, like birds, are endotherms. The ability to maintain a fairly constant body temperature enables mammals to live in almost every possible environment on Earth. Mammals have important characteristics not found in other animals. They have hair and produce milk to nurse their young. Mammals also have diaphragms, four-chambered hearts, specialized teeth, modified limbs, and highly developed brains.

Mammals have hair

Have you ever heard someone complain about a pet that is shedding its hair? There's no doubt that such a pet is a mammal because hair is present on all mammals at some point in their lives. Like feathers, mammalian hair, made out of the protein keratin, is also thought to have evolved from scales. The arrangement of hair provides insulation and waterproofing and thereby conserves body heat. If you have ever worn a wool sweater made from the hair of a sheep, you know how warm wool can be on a cold day. As shown in *Figure 32.1* on the next page, hair also serves other functions.

Although hair helps retain body heat, mammals also have internal feedback mechanisms that signal the body to cool off when it gets too warm. Mammals cool off by panting and through the action of sweat glands.

32.1 MAMMAL CHARACTERISTICS **841**

---

1 Focus

Bellringer
Section Focus Transparency 77

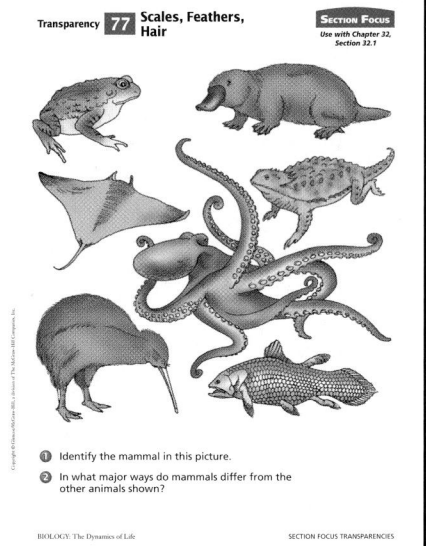

Transparency **77** Scales, Feathers, Hair

SECTION FOCUS
Use with Chapter 32, Section 32.1

① Identify the mammal in this picture.
② In what major ways do mammals differ from the other animals shown?

BIOLOGY: The Dynamics of Life   SECTION FOCUS TRANSPARENCIES

INTERACTIVE CHALKBOARD with Image Bank

PowerPoint® Presentations

This CD-ROM is an editable Microsoft® PowerPoint® presentation that includes:
- Section presentations
- Section checks
- Image bank
- Hot links to Biology Online
- All transparencies

FOLDABLES™
For an additional Foldables activity idea, see the Chapter 32 Foldables page in *Unit 9 FAST FILE Resources.*

RESOURCE MANAGER

Unit 9 *FAST FILE* Resources
MiniLab Worksheet, pp. 79, 80
Real World BioApplications, pp. 83–84
Reinforcement and Study Guide in English, pp. 85–86
Reinforcement and Study Guide in Spanish, pp. 89–90
Concept Mapping, p. 93
Critical Thinking/Problem Solving, p. 94

Transparency Worksheets, pp. 95, 97–102
Reading Essentials for Biology, Section 32.1
Laboratory Manual, pp. 205–208, 209–214
Section Focus Transparency 77
Basic Concepts Transparencies 58, 59
Reteaching Skills Transparency 47

2 Teach

Caption Question Answer
Figure 32.2 If the litter is larger and some of the litter is killed by prey, then there will still be animals left to become adults and reproduce.

Figure 32.1
Hair helps maintain a constant body temperature. It also serves a variety of other purposes.

A The sharp, barb-tipped quills of a porcupine are a type of modified hair.

B The black stripes of a tiger's fur aid in camouflaging this beautiful cat as it hunts for prey.

C The white patch of hair on the rump of the fleeing pronghorn signals danger to other members of the herd.

Panting releases water from the nose and mouth, which results in a loss of body heat. Sweat glands help regulate body temperature by secreting moisture onto the surface of the skin. As the moisture evaporates, it transfers heat from the body to the surrounding air.

Mammals nurse their young

Mammals have several types of **glands,** which are a group of cells that secrete fluids. They include glands that produce saliva, sweat, oil, digestive enzymes, hormones, milk, and scent.

You have already learned how sweat glands help keep a mammal cool.

Mammals also feed their young from **mammary** (MA muh ree) **glands,** possibly modified sweat glands, which produce and secrete milk, a liquid that is rich in fats, sugars, proteins, minerals, and vitamins. Mammals nurse their young until they are able to digest and absorb nutrients from solid foods. *Figure 32.2* shows that the number of young each mother has and the length of time she nurses her young vary among species.

Figure 32.2
Large mammals usually have few young. **Infer** *Why do mammals that are prey for many predators tend to have larger litters?*

A An Indian rhinoceros usually has one calf at a time. Calves begin to graze at two months of age.

B Mice have four to nine offspring in each litter, and up to 17 litters a year. The young nurse for just a few weeks.

842

Additional Lab

Burying Behavior

Purpose
Students will observe defensive burying behavior in mice and determine the types of objects that cause this behavior.

Safety Precautions

842

Materials
mouse, terrarium with 3–5 cm of sawdust or sand, objects for burying, timer

Preparation
When mice are confronted by potential predators such as snakes, they sometimes spray sand or soil at the predator. This behavior is called defensive burying. Defensive burying can be elicited by objects that resemble predators, as well as by predators themselves.

Procedure
Give students the following directions.
1. Make a data table that lists objects, the time it takes the mouse to start burying, and the time spent burying.
2. Develop a hypothesis about which objects a mouse will spend the most time burying.
3. Place one of the objects on the floor of the terrarium at the end farthest from

Respiration and circulation in mammals

Mammals need a high level of energy to maintain their endothermic metabolism. This energy level is sustained when large amounts of nutrients and oxygen enter the body and reach the cells.

The mammals' diaphragm helps expand the chest cavity to aid the flow of oxygen into their lungs. A **diaphragm** (DI uh fram) is the sheet of muscle located beneath the lungs that separates the chest cavity from the abdominal cavity, where other organs are located. Once in the lungs, oxygen diffuses into the blood. As the chest cavity returns to its resting position, air is released.

Mammals, like birds, have four-chambered hearts in which oxygenated blood is kept entirely separate from deoxygenated blood. This ensures that a good supply of nutrients and oxygen are delivered to cells which supports their endothermic metabolism. Circulation also removes waste products from cells and helps regulate body temperature. Blood helps keep a constant cellular environment, which maintains homeostasis.

Most mammals have specialized teeth

Teeth are a distinguishing feature of most mammals. Although fishes and reptiles have teeth, their teeth are relatively uniform and are used primarily for tearing, grasping, and holding prey.

Mammals with teeth have different kinds that are adapted to the type of food the animal eats. Think of the different tools you might use to build a piece of furniture, such as a chisel for scraping or a saw for cutting. Like a cabinetmaker's tools, teeth are shaped to match the types of jobs they do.

The pointed incisors of moles grasp and hold small prey. The chisel-like incisors of beavers are modified for gnawing. A lion's canines puncture and tear the flesh of its prey. Premolars and molars are used for slicing or shearing, crushing, and grinding. You can get a closer look at mammalian teeth in the *MiniLab* on this page. By examining the teeth of a mammal, a scientist can determine what kind of food it eats.

Many hoofed mammals have an adaptation called cud chewing that enables the cellulose in plant cell walls to be broken down into nutrients they can absorb and use.

MiniLab 32.1

Compare and Contrast

Anatomy of a Tooth Most mammals have teeth. Teeth are adapted to a mammal's diet.

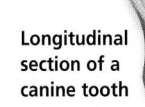
Longitudinal section of a canine tooth

Procedure

1. Examine a prepared longitudinal section view slide of a human tooth under low-power magnification. **CAUTION:** *Use caution when working with a microscope and slides.*
2. Locate the different areas—enamel, dentine, and pulp cavity—that form the tooth. Move the slide to see all areas.
3. Diagram the tooth as it appears under low power.

Analysis

1. **Explain** Most of the tooth you studied is composed of the root under the gums. How is the part above the gum adapted to the diet of humans?
2. **Interpret Scientific Illustrations** Examine the diagrams of mammal skulls and predict what kinds of food these mammals might eat based on the shape of their teeth.

Physical Science Connection

Teeth as simple machines Teeth and chisels are shaped like wedges. A wedge is a simple machine that increases an applied force and changes its direction. As a result, a downward force applied to a tooth is changed to a larger sideways force.

Purpose
Students will identify major areas of a mammalian tooth and analyze adaptations to what they eat.

Safety Precautions

Process Skills
interpret scientific diagrams, observe and infer, predict

Teaching Strategies
- Prepared slides are available from biological supply houses. You could use 35 mm slides or, instead of prepared slides, a microprojector or microvideo camera.
- Have students observe slides using dissecting microscopes, if available.

Expected Results
enamel layer—outermost, thinnest, compact, bonelike; dentine layer—thickest, compact, bonelike; pulp layer—innermost, least dense, appears vascular

Analysis
1. Humans do not have pointed canines; they do not use their teeth to tear flesh.
2. herbivore (top)—flat teeth adapted to chew plants; carnivore (bottom)—pointed canines adapted to tear meat

Assessment
Portfolio Have students draw longitudinal sections of all four types of human teeth. Use the Performance Task Assessment List for Scientific Drawing in **PASC**, p. 127. **L2** **ELL**

---

the animal. **CAUTION:** *Always use care when handling live animals. Wash hands thoroughly after completing your investigation.*

4. Note the time it takes for the mouse to begin burying behavior and the time it spends burying. Test one object at a time.
5. Fill out the data table. Make a bar graph to illustrate the total amount of time the mouse spent burying each object.

Analysis
1. Which objects did your mouse spend the most time burying? The least time? objects that looked more like predators; least like predators
2. How do your results compare with those of the class as a whole? Answers should be similar.
3. Do your data support your hypothesis? Data will support hypotheses that stated

"predatorlike" objects would cause more burying behavior.

Assessment
Performance Ask students to design and conduct an experiment that will determine the types of objects that cause more burying behavior. Use the Performance Task Assessment List for Assessing a Whole Experiment and Planning the Next Experiment in **PASC**, p. 105. **L2**

Purpose

Students compare the length of herbivore and carnivore digestive systems.

Process Skills

analyze information, compare and contrast, hypothesize, interpret data, predict, think critically

Teaching Strategies

You may wish to mention the need for several stomachs in ruminants to help with the digestion of cellulose.

Thinking Critically

1. Herbivores have a longer digestive system.
2. Answers may vary; hypotheses will be supported if students predicted herbivores have a longer digestive system.
3. The more difficult a food is to digest, the longer the digestive system will be.
4. Yes; for the comparison to be valid, one must compare animals of equal size. An animal of larger size, such as a lion, would have a much longer digestive system than a dog due to its larger size.

Assessment

Knowledge Have students predict which animal in each of the following pairs has the longest digestive tract, based on their diets: deer and lion, cat and rabbit, horse and bear. Use the Performance Task Assessment List for Analyzing the Data in **PASC,** p. 99. **L2**

 Indiana Academic Standards

Pages 844–845: B.1.15, B.1.31

844

Problem-Solving Lab 32.1

Analyze Information

Which animal has the longest digestive system? A mammal may be an herbivore, carnivore, or omnivore. Is there a relationship between length of a mammal's digestive tract and its diet? Make a hypothesis as to what that correlation might be.

Solve the Problem

The following data table provides general information on digestive tracts for several mammals.

Data Table			
Animal	**Length of Digestive Tract**	**Diet Category**	**Animal Mass**
Koala	305 cm	Herbivore	10 kg
Dog	135 cm	Carnivore	11 kg
Rabbit	272 cm	Herbivore	9 kg
Bobcat	145 cm	Carnivore	12 kg

Thinking Critically

1. **Analyze** What does the relationship between diet and digestive tract length appear to be?
2. **Interpret Data** Do the data support your hypothesis? Explain your answer.
3. **Formulate a Hypothesis** Explain the relationship between digestive tract length and difficulty in digesting food type. (Hint: Does cellulose take longer to digest?)
4. **Conclude** Was the mass of all animals relatively close when compared? Explain why mass is important.

C Premolars and molars are the predominant teeth in horses and other herbivores. These crushing and grinding teeth are covered with hard enamel.

844 MAMMALS

Have you ever seen cows slowly chewing while lying in a pasture? When plant material is swallowed, it moves into the first two of four pouches in the stomach where cellulose in the cell walls is broken down by bacteria. The partially digested food, called cud, is repeatedly brought back up into the mouth. After more chewing, the cud is swallowed again and when the food particles are small enough they are passed to the other stomach areas, where digestion continues. You can learn more about digestion in mammals in the *Problem-Solving Lab* on this page. The various types of teeth in different mammals can be seen in *Figure 32.3*.

Figure 32.3
Mammal groups are distinguished by number and types of teeth.

A Bears, like humans, have incisors, canines, premolars, and molars. Bears and humans are omnivores.

B Carnivores, such as this tiger, have canine teeth that stab and pierce food, and premolars and molars adapted for chewing.

Figure 32.4
The front limbs of moles are powerful and short, with large claws that enable them to dig through dirt. Bats have elongated finger bones that support the flight membranes of their wings.

Mammals have modified limbs

Mammals have several adaptations that help them meet their energy needs. For example, mammal limbs are adapted for a variety of methods of food gathering. Recall that primates use their opposable thumb to grasp objects—including fruits and other foods. *Figure 32.4* illustrates other limb modifications in mammals. You can see the bones of mammal limbs and other parts of mammalian skeletons in the *MiniLab* on this page. Refer to *Figure 32.5* on the next page for a summary of mammalian characteristics.

Mammals can learn

One reason mammals are successful is that they guard their young fiercely and teach them survival skills. Mammals can accomplish complex behaviors, such as learning and remembering what they have learned.

MiniLab 32.2

Observe

Mammal Skeletons Owls are predators. They feed on small mammals as well as on birds. After eating a meal, the tough indigestible parts of prey, such as bones, are regurgitated as pellets. The skeletons of a variety of small mammals can be studied by examining owl pellets.

Owl pellet

Procedure

1. Place an owl pellet onto a sheet of paper toweling.
2. Use a forceps to remove a small amount of the outer covering.
3. Prepare a wet mount of this material and observe under low-, then high-power magnification. Diagram what you see. Use forceps to open the pellet and remove all bones that are present. Look especially for skulls. (Note: Skulls may be small and certain parts, such as lower jaws, will be separated.)
4. Identify mammalian skulls using diagrams A and B as a guide.
5. Attempt to reconstruct the skeleton for an entire animal. You may wish to glue the skeletal pieces onto a piece of cardboard. Dispose of materials appropriately. **CAUTION:** *Wash your hands after handling animal materials.*

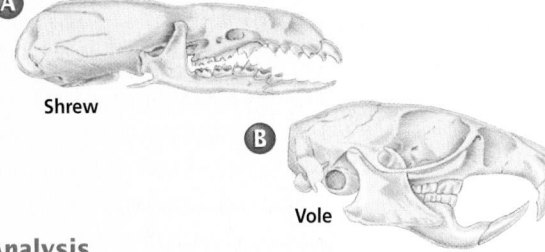

A Shrew

B Vole

Analysis

1. **Understand** What was the outer covering on the pellet? What does this tell you about the contents of the pellet? Explain.
2. **Interpret Data** How many vole and shrew skulls were present in your pellet?
3. **Explain** How were you able to differentiate the skulls of these two mammals?
4. **Predict** Are voles and shrews herbivores or carnivores based on appearance of their teeth? Explain.

MiniLab 32.2

Purpose
Students examine the disarticulated skeletons of small mammals in an owl pellet.

Process Skills
experiment, draw a conclusion, observe and infer, predict

Safety Precautions
Owl pellets purchased from biological supply companies have been autoclaved. If you use ones you or your students have collected they should be autoclaved to prevent disease.

Teaching Strategies
- Owl pellets are available from biological supply houses.
- Typically, there may be several disarticulated skeletons within each pellet. Small bird skeletons may also be present.

Cleanup and Disposal
Tell students to wrap their owl pellet remains in the paper towel and place them into the lab trash can. Have them wash their forceps and their hands in warm, soapy water and place the forceps in the container you have designated.

Expected Results
Hair comprises the outer covering of the pellet. Students will be able to differentiate between vole and shrew skulls.

Analysis
1. Hair; the prey must be a mammal if hair is present.
2. Answers may vary; there may be 1–4 skeletons per pellet.
3. by size and dentition patterns
4. Both are herbivores because they lack canines.

Modified Assessment
Portfolio Ask students to research the dental formula for adult humans and make a poster. The dental formula indicates the number of incisors, canines, premolars, and molars. Use the Performance Task Assessment List for Poster in **PASC**, p. 145. L1

Quick Demo

Compare and Contrast
Using glycerol instead of water, prepare slides of dog or cat hair. Ask students to compare and contrast guard hair with underfur. L2

USING MODELS

Provide students with jars with lids and masking tape to tape their thumbs to the palms of their hands. Have them try to open their jars without the use of their thumbs to demonstrate the importance of the opposable thumb. L1

INSIDE STORY

Purpose

Students will review the main characteristics of mammals.

Teaching Strategies

■ Ask students to prepare reports on various types of foxes. **L1**
■ Ask students to speculate about the adaptive advantage of the fox's bushy tail. **L2**

Visual Learning

Have students examine models that show the teeth of mammals that eat different foods. Next, ask them to identify the model with teeth similar to a fox.

Critical Thinking

The fox's hair provides insulation. Its sweat glands help cool it off.

CAREERS IN BIOLOGY

Career Path
Courses in high school: biology, math, English, physical education; for some positions, SCUBA certification
College: bachelor's degree in biological sciences or psychology; business management degree to manage a theme park; public speaking or drama experience

Career Issue

Some people feel that holding animals in small enclosures and teaching them "tricks" is wrong. Other people feel the more people know about these mammals, the more likely it is they will want to protect them in the wild.

For More Information

For more information on becoming an animal trainer, students can write to:

IMATA (International Marine Animal Trainers Association)
1200 S. Lake Shore Dr.
Chicago, IL 60605

Indiana Academic Standards
Pages 846–847: B.1.14, B.1.15, B.1.17, B.1.18, B.1.19

846

INSIDE STORY

A Mammal

Figure 32.5
A red fox, a member of the dog family, can be found in open country and forests throughout the United States. Red foxes are active at night, and feed on insects, birds, rodents, rabbits, berries, and fruit. **Critical Thinking** *Using the information given below, explain how a fox is able to maintain a constant body temperature.*

Red fox

A Glands Most mammals have sweat, oil, mammary, and scent glands in their skin. Sweat glands help mammals cool off. Oil glands lubricate the hair and skin. Foxes use their scent glands to mark new territories.

B Diaphragm The diaphragm is a muscle that helps the chest cavity expand to take in large amounts of oxygen used to maintain the high metabolism of all mammals. It separates the chest and abdominal cavities.

C Heart The four-chambered heart of mammals enables them to keep oxygenated and deoxygenated blood separate. This helps them maintain their high metabolism.

D Teeth A fox's teeth indicate what it eats and how it gets food. Its canines are used to puncture and tear the flesh of prey. Its molars slice and crush the flesh before swallowing.

F Hair Dense, soft underhair insulates the fox by trapping warm air next to its body. The coarse, long guard hairs protect against wear and may be colored for camouflage. The fox sheds its coat little by little during the summer.

E Mammary glands Like all female mammals, a female fox nourishes her young with milk from her mammary glands.

846 MAMMALS

CHALLENGE ACTIVITY

Mammal Photo Essay: *Visual-Spatial*
Have students take photographs of mammals and write a caption for each, indicating the food it eats, describing its habitat, and explaining its adaptations. Encourage students to use field guides to identify the mammal by common and scientific name. **L3**

TECH PREP

Agricultural Mammals Ask students to visit a dairy farm or sheep ranch and report on the latest techniques and strategies used in caring for and enhancing production of farm animals. If there are no farms nearby, provide library resources and information from a university cooperative extension unit. **L2**

Have you ever attended an aquarium show or watched a movie about performing dolphins and whales? Dolphins exhibit a wide variety of learned behaviors, including the behaviors performed for films or in aquarium shows.

Primates, including humans, are perhaps the most intelligent animals. Chimpanzees, for example, can use tools, illustrated in *Figure 32.6,* work machines, and use sign language to communicate with humans. Mammalian intelligence is a result of complex nervous systems and highly developed brains. The outer layer of a mammalian brain often is folded, forming ridges and grooves. These ridges and grooves increase the brain's active surface area.

Reading Check **Explain** what enables mammals to be intelligent.

Figure 32.6
A chimpanzee using a stick to get insects out of a tree trunk demonstrates that mammals other than humans are also intelligent enough to make and use tools.

Animal Trainer

If you seem to get along well with animals, consider a career as an animal trainer. A job as a trainer can be hard to find, but fun and rewarding.

Skills for the Job

Some animal trainers work in zoos or aquariums, teaching monkeys, parrots, seals, and other animals to perform specific behaviors. Some trainers work with race horses, and others teach police dogs to sniff out explosives or guide dogs to help people with physical limitations. Many trainers begin as animal keepers. A position at a dog obedience school may require only on-the-job experience, but if you want to train guide dogs, you must complete a three-year course of study. To train dolphins at a large aquarium, you must have a two- or four-year degree in psychology or biology. If you want to narrate the shows, you must also be a good public speaker.

For more careers in related fields, visit in.bdol.glencoe.com/careers

Section Assessment

Understanding Main Ideas
1. Name four characteristics of mammals.
2. Describe three mammal adaptations for obtaining and consuming food.
3. Identify and describe the relationship between internal feedback mechanisms and the maintenance of body temperatures.
4. How does intelligence benefit mammals?
5. Explain how the interrelationship between respiration and circulation sustains a mammal's metabolism.

Thinking Critically
6. Suppose you are a mammal that feeds on pine seeds and lives in a forest in a cold region. Describe the adaptations that would help you survive.

7. **Observe and Infer** On an archaeological dig, you find a skull about 5 cm long with two chisel-shaped front teeth and several flattened back teeth. Is this a skull from a mammal? Explain your answer. For more help, refer to *Observe and Infer* in the **Skill Handbook.**

in.bdol.glencoe.com/self_check_quiz

32.1 MAMMAL CHARACTERISTICS **847**

3 Assess

DAILY INTERVENTION

Check for Understanding
Linguistic Ask students to summarize in two paragraphs why mammals live everywhere. Have them include a discussion of mammals that live below the surface of Earth as well as in lakes, oceans, and deserts. **L2**

Reteach
Visual-Spatial Bring in a variety of pictures of the limbs of mammals. Ask students working in groups to examine the pictures and tell as much as they can about the life of that mammal based on the structure of its limbs. **L1**
COOP LEARN

Resources
For more practice, use *Reading Essentials for Biology,* Section 32.1.

Extension
Dolphins, sea lions, and beluga whales are being trained by the U.S. Navy to watch over Navy submarines while they are in harbor. Have students research the training of aquatic mammals for various tasks. **L3**

Assessment

Portfolio Ask students to draw the ideal mammal pet created by genetic engineering in the year 3000. **L1**

Reading Check Mammalian intelligence is a result of a complex nervous system and a highly developed brain.

Section Assessment

1. hair, mammary glands, diaphragm, and a uterus in the female
2. specialized teeth, modified limbs, endothermy
3. Internal feedback mechanisms signal the body to release heat through sweating and panting if body temperature rises.
4. They can learn, remember, communicate, and use tools.
5. Mammals take in oxygen that is circulated by an efficient 4-chambered heart. Oxygen is delivered to cells that use it to make energy.
6. forefeet with sharp claws that can hold a pinecone; sharp front teeth to get seeds inside; thick fur; short extremities including ears, legs, and nose; a long, bushy tail that can help with balance as the mammal moves in the trees and protects the face from cold as the animal sleeps
7. Yes. One mammal may have varied types of teeth in its skull.

1 Focus

INTERACTIVE CHALKBOARD
PowerPoint® Presentations

Bellringer
Section Focus Transparency 78

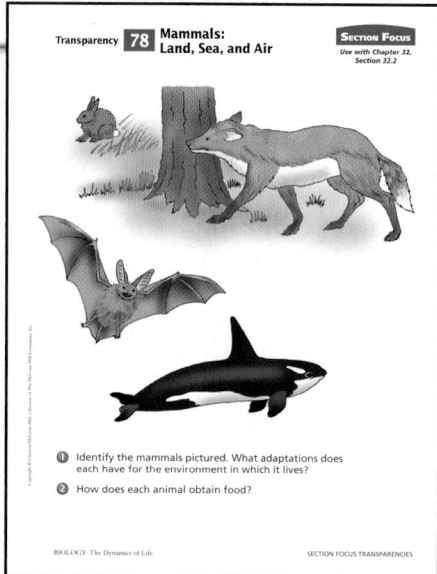

Transparency **78** Mammals: Land, Sea, and Air

SECTION FOCUS
Use with Chapter 32, Section 32.2

❶ Identify the mammals pictured. What adaptations does each have for the environment in which it lives?

❷ How does each animal obtain food?

BIOLOGY: The Dynamics of Life   SECTION FOCUS TRANSPARENCIES

Analyzing Mammalian Classification

Finding Main Ideas Make sure that students have used the red and blue headings to make their outlines. If struggling students have problems with the traditional outline using Roman numerals, upper and lower case letters, and numbers, have them make a list of the important points under each heading.

Caption Question Answer
Figure 32.7 Larger mammals have longer gestation times because it takes longer for the body systems of larger young to be fully functional.

Indiana Academic Standards

Pages 848–849: B.1.15, B.1.31

Section 32.2

Diversity of Mammals

Indiana Standards Standard B.1.15 Understand and explain that, in biological systems, structure and function must be considered together.

SECTION PREVIEW

Objectives

Distinguish among the three groups of living mammals.

Compare reproduction in egg-laying, pouched, and placental mammals.

Review Vocabulary
endangered species: a species in which the number of individuals falls so low that extinction is possible (p. 115)

New Vocabulary
placental mammal
uterus
placenta
gestation
marsupial
monotreme
therapsid

Analyzing Mammalian Classification

Finding Main Ideas On a piece of paper, construct an outline about mammal classification. Use the red and blue titles in this section as a guideline. As you read the paragraphs that follow the titles, add important information and vocabulary words to your outline.

Example:

I. Mammal Classification
  A. Placental mammals
    1.
  B. Pouched mammals
    1.
  C. Monotremes
    1.

Use your outline to help you answer questions in the section assessment on page 851. For more help, refer to *Outline* in the **Skill Handbook**.

Plains of America with bison

Figure 32.7
The length of gestation varies from species to species in placental mammals. These raccoon kits were born after nine weeks of gestation. Gestation of mice is 21 days, whereas gestation for a rhinoceros is about 14 to 16 months.
Hypothesize *Why do larger mammals have longer gestation times?*

Mammal Classification

Living in the United States, you are probably familiar with only one of the three subclasses, of the class Mammalia—placental mammals. Scientists place mammals into one of three subclasses based on their method of reproduction.

Placental mammals: A great success

Placental mammals give birth to young that have developed inside the mother's uterus until their body systems are fully functional and they can live independently of their mother's body. The **uterus** (YEWT uh rus) is a hollow, muscular organ in which offspring develop. Nourishment of the young inside the uterus occurs through an organ called the **placenta** (pluh SEN tuh), which develops during pregnancy. The placenta passes nutrients and oxygen to and removes wastes from the developing embryo. The time during which placental mammals develop inside the uterus is called **gestation** (jeh STAY shun). The kits shown in *Figure 32.*7 were born after a period of gestation.

848 MAMMALS

RESOURCE MANAGER

Unit 9 *Fast File* Resources
BioLab Worksheet, pp. 81–82
Reinforcement and Study Guide in English, pp. 87–88
Reinforcement and Study Guide in Spanish, pp. 91–92
Transparency Worksheets, p. 96

Reading Essentials for Biology, Section 32.2
Section Focus Transparency 78

Figure 32.8
In Australia and Tasmania, many marsupials fill niches that are occupied by placental mammals on other continents.

A The giant ant-eater of Mexico, a placental mammal, has a long, sticky tongue that it uses to collect ants and termites from their nests.

C The spotted cuscus of Australia, a marsupial, lives in trees. It is a solitary, nocturnal animal that eats fruit, leaves, bark, insects, small mammals, reptiles, and birds.

B The numbat, a marsupial, lives in Australia. It has a long, sticky tongue that it uses to eat termites and ants.

D The ring tailed lemur, a placental mammal, lives in trees on the island of Madagascar. It is active by day, and eats fruits, leaves, and occasionally insects.

Development inside the mother's body is an adaptation that played a major role in the success of mammals. It ensures that the offspring are protected from predators and the environment during the early stages of development.

About 90 percent of all mammals are placentals. You can learn more about placental mammals on pages 1086–1089 in the *Focus On*.

Pouched mammals: The marsupials

Marsupials make up the second subclass of mammals. A **marsupial** (mar SEW pee uhl) is a mammal in which the young have a short period of development within the mother's body, followed by a period of development inside a pouch made of skin and hair on the outside of the mother's body. You may have seen the only North American marsupial, the opossum. Most marsupials are found in Australia and surrounding islands. The theory of plate tectonics explains why most marsupials are found in Australia today. Scientists have found fossil marsupials on the continents that once made up Gondwana. These fossils support the idea that marsupials originated in South America, moved across Antarctica, and populated Australia before Gondwana broke up.

Ancestors of today's marsupials were able to populate the landmass that became Australia without having to share the area with the competitive placental mammals that evolved in other places. They successfully spread out and filled niches similar to those that placental mammals filled in all other parts of the world, as you can see in *Figure 32.8*. In fact, since humans introduced sheep, rabbits, and other placental mammals to

32.2 DIVERSITY OF MAMMALS **849**

Word Origin

gestation from the Latin word *gestare*, meaning "to bear"; Gestation is time during which a placental mammal develops in a uterus.

Quick Demo

Interpret Scientific Illustrations Provide students with guides to animal tracks. Ask them to pick an animal that lives in your area, trace the track pattern, and later see if they can find these tracks outdoors in wet and/or muddy or snowy areas. Point out that the shape of the track, size, numbers of toes, and claw marks will be significant in their identification of a track. **L2**

Word Origin

Ask students to do research to find out the origin of the word *marsupial.*

INTERNET BioLab The BioLab at the end of the chapter can be used at this point in the lesson.

Biology Journal

A Marsupial Adventure Have students make a travel brochure of a photo safari to Australia. They should describe the animals they promise to show tourists and include a map of their proposed travels. **L2**

Inquiry

Discussion Tiny fossils have been found in the hair of a prehistoric woolly mammoth frozen in the permafrost of Siberia. The tiny fossils were mosses, grass, beetles, and mites. Ask students to infer what kind of environment the woolly mammoth lived in. **L2**

 CHALLENGE ACTIVITY

Mammal Management Plan: *Logical-Mathematical* Ask students to look up survey methods for mammals in a wildlife management-techniques manual. Ask them to make a management plan for a particular mammal in your area that would ensure that their mammal has adequate habitat over the next 25 years. See *BioChallenges and Enrichment* for additional projects and activities. **L3**

Some students may think that unicorns are prehistoric mammals that lived some time during geologic history.

Uncover the Misconception

Explain that unicorns are mythological animals. Show students pictures of mythical unicorns. Often they are shown with wings.

Demonstrate the Concept

Ask a group of students to look up the role of the unicorn in myth and folklore and report their findings to the class.

Assess New Knowledge

Ask students to visit in.bdol.glencoe.com to find a hoofed mammal with two horns that might look like a unicorn if one of its horns broke off. Some think that these mammals may have originated the myths of unicorns.

☑ **Reading Check** Introduced placental mammals use the food supply that native marsupials normally use.

🏛 **Indiana Academic Standards**

Pages 850–851: B.1.32

850

Figure 32.9
Present-day monotremes include one species of platypus and two species of echidnas. This echidna species is found only in Australia and nearby islands **(A)**. The duck-billed platypus has several physical features that seem to belong to a variety of other animals **(B)**.

Australia, many of the native marsupial species have become threatened, endangered, or even extinct.

☑ **Reading Check** **Infer** why some marsupials have become threatened in Australia.

Monotremes: The egg layers

Do you think the animal shown in *Figure 32.9B* is a mammal? It has hair and mammary glands, yet it lays eggs. The duck-billed platypus is a **monotreme** (MA nuh treem), a mammal that reproduces by laying eggs.

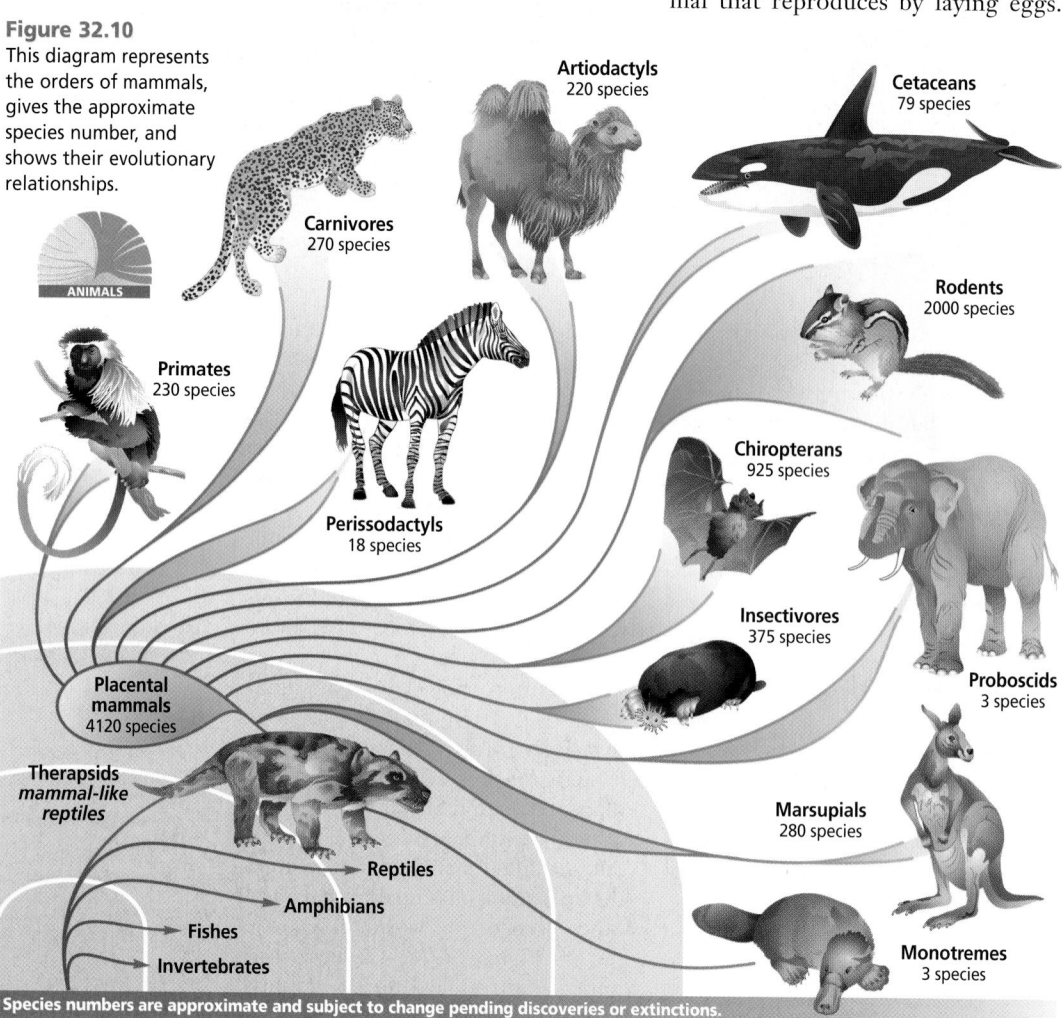

Figure 32.10
This diagram represents the orders of mammals, gives the approximate species number, and shows their evolutionary relationships.

ANIMALS

Carnivores
270 species

Artiodactyls
220 species

Cetaceans
79 species

Rodents
2000 species

Primates
230 species

Chiropterans
925 species

Perissodactyls
18 species

Insectivores
375 species

Proboscids
3 species

Placental mammals
4120 species

Therapsids
mammal-like reptiles

Marsupials
280 species

Reptiles

Amphibians

Fishes

Invertebrates

Monotremes
3 species

Species numbers are approximate and subject to change pending discoveries or extinctions.

Protecting Wild Mammals Mammals are perhaps the most exploited of all animals. African elephants, pandas, manatees, whales, and rhinos are just some of the mammals that are endangered.

As an example of how government intervention is essential for protecting endangered mammals, discuss with students the history of China's efforts to protect and breed pandas. Extend the discussion by asking students to bring in articles from recent newspapers and science magazines about the exploitation of mammals and conservation efforts to save them. **L2**

Spiny anteaters, also called echidnas, belong to this subclass as well. Monotremes are found only in Australia, Tasmania, and New Guinea. One of the two species of spiny anteaters can be found only in New Guinea. Only three species of monotremes are alive today.

The platypus, a mostly aquatic animal, has a broad, flat tail, much like that of a beaver. Its rubbery snout resembles the bill of a duck. The platypus has webbed front feet for swimming through water, but it also has sharp claws on its front and hind feet for digging and burrowing into the soil. Much of its body is covered with thick, brown fur.

The spiny anteater has coarse, brown hair, and its back and sides are covered with sharp spines that it can erect for defensive purposes when threatened by enemies. From its mouth, the anteater extends its long, sticky tongue to catch insects.

Origins of Mammals

Present-day mammal orders are shown in *Figure 32.10.* The first placental mammals appeared in the fossil record about 125 million years ago. Scientists trace the origins of placental mammals from a group of mouse-sized animals, such as *Eomaia* represented

in *Figure 32.11A,* to a group of reptilian ancestors called therapsids. **Therapsids** (ther AP sidz), represented in *Figure 32.11B,* had features of both reptiles and mammals. They existed between 270 and 180 million years ago.

The mass extinction of the dinosaurs at the end of the Mesozoic Era, along with the breaking apart of Pangaea and changes in climate, opened up new niches for early mammals to fill. The appearance of flowering plants at the end of this era supplied new living areas, food sources, and shelter. Some mammals that moved into the drier grasslands became fast-running grazers, browsers, and predators. The Cenozoic Era is sometimes called the golden age of mammals because of the dramatic increase in their numbers and diversity.

Figure 32.11
(A) *Eomaia* is the oldest placental mammal fossil discovered. Anatomical evidence shows that it may have lived in trees. **(B)** Therapsids were the ancestors of mammals. The lower jaw and middle ear bones of therapsids were like those of reptiles. However, they had straighter legs than reptiles and held them closer to the body.

Section Assessment

Understanding Main Ideas
1. Describe the characteristics of placental mammals.
2. Compare monotremes and marsupials.
3. Why are monotremes classified as mammals?
4. What are therapsids and what is their relationship to mammals?

Thinking Critically
5. There are several marsupial species in South America, but only one species is native to North

America. Make a hypothesis about the presence or absence of marsupial species in Europe. How could you test your hypothesis?

SKILL REVIEW

6. **Get the Big Picture** You find a mammal fossil and observe the following traits: hooves, flattened teeth, skeleton the size of a large dog. What can you infer about its way of life? For more help, refer to *Get the Big Picture* in the **Skill Handbook.**

 in.bdol.glencoe.com/self_check_quiz

Section Assessment

1. A placental mammal carries its young inside the uterus until development is nearly complete.
2. Monotremes lay eggs. Marsupials give birth to immature young that continue development in the mother's external pouch.
3. They have other mammalian characteristics, such as hair and mammary glands.
4. Therapsids are the reptilian ancestors of mammals.
5. Marsupials developed in South America and Australia, continents in Gondwana; Europe was part of

Laurasia. Students should infer that this suggests that there are no marsupials in Europe.
6. It is an herbivore that can run fast. It may have multiple stomachs and chew cud.

Time Allotment
one class period

Process Skills
make and use tables, observe, infer, compare and contrast, apply, make predictions, record data, use the Internet

---
PROCEDURE

Teaching Strategies
- Be sure to monitor carefully students' use of the Internet. Follow the Acceptable Use Policy of your school.
- If possible have students observe various breeds of dogs at a local animal shelter.
- You may want to review the difference between breeding dogs for certain characteristics and genetic engineering.
- If students have personal experience with particular kinds of dogs, you may want to have them relate this in a class discussion.

INTERNET
BioLab

Before You Begin
Dogs make great companions. They provide their owners with an opportunity to love and nurture another living thing. In return, they are loyal, offer protection to their owners, and are fun to have around. Dogs have been bred for a variety of reasons. Some are working dogs, such as herders, sporting dogs, sled dogs, and guide dogs. Others have been bred for racing, while others are show dogs. However, all of these breeds have the same basic dog characteristics.

Adaptations in Breeds of Dogs

PREPARATION

Problem
What adaptations are important to various breeds of dogs.

Objectives
In this BioLab, you will:
- **Observe** the characteristics of dogs.
- **Record** the adaptations of different dog breeds.
- **Use the Internet** to collect and compare data from other students.
- **Compare and contrast** the characteristics of breeds of dogs.

Materials
access to the Internet

Skill Handbook
If you need help with this lab, refer to the **Skill Handbook.**

PROCEDURE
---

1. Make a copy of the data table.
2. Visit **in.bdol.glencoe.com/internet_lab** to find links to sites that describe breeds of dogs.
3. Find pictures and descriptions of these dogs. Record the physical characteristics unique to each breed in the data table.

PROCEDURE

Data and Observations
Answers may vary.

Alaskan Malamute—fur with a woolly undercoat; powerful muscles through the chest, shoulders and legs; even temperament around other dogs; working dog

Australian Cattle Dog—muscular, agile, easily trained, adaptable, alert, and protective; herder

Collie—muscular, agile, easily trained, adaptable, alert, and protective; herder

German Shepherd—muscular, easily trained, non-aggressive, friendly, adaptable, protective; sporting dog

German Shorthaired Pointer—muscular, agile, easily trained, friendly, willing to please; sporting dog

Greyhound—muscular, sleek in shape, long legs, short hair and ears; sporting dog

Labrador Retriever—medium sized, agile, easily trained, friendly, willing to please; sporting dog

Dogs			
Breed	Physical Characteristics	Temperament	Classification
Alaskan Malamute			
Australian Cattle Dog			
Collie			
German Shepherd Dog			
German Shorthaired Pointer			
Greyhound			
Labrador Retriever			
Old English Sheepdog			
Samoyed			
Siberian Husky			
Whippet			

4. Record the temperaments of each breed in the data table.

5. Find links at **in.bdol.glencoe.com/internet_lab** to find information on dogs that are classified as working dogs, herding dogs, sporting dogs, and hounds.

6. Record the classification of each breed in the data table.

Rough Collie

ANALYZE AND CONCLUDE

1. **Compare and Contrast** Alaskan Malamutes, Greyhounds, Samoyeds, Siberian Huskys, and Whippets are all built for running. How are they similar and how are they different?

2. **Determine** Which dogs would make good guide dogs? Why?

3. **Explain** Why would a Collie make a good herder?

4. **Apply** Assume you work for a local nursing home and are asked to find a dog that could live in the home and be a good companion and perhaps even help some of the residents. Go to **in.bdol.glencoe.com/internet_lab** and select a breed of dog you think would be adapted for this work. Explain your reasoning.

Share Your Data

Find this BioLab using the link below, and post the data tables provided for this activity. Using the additional data from other students on the Internet, analyze the combined data and complete your table.

 in.bdol.glencoe.com/internet_lab

Old English Sheepdog—muscular, agile, easily trained, adaptable, alert, and protective; herder
Samoyed—fur with woolly undercoat; powerful muscles through the chest, shoulders and legs; even temperament around other dogs; working dog

Siberian Husky—fur with a woolly undercoat; powerful muscles through the chest, shoulders and legs; even temperament around other dogs; working dog
Whippet—sleek in shape, muscular, long legs, short hair and ears; sporting dog

ANALYZE AND CONCLUDE

1. Greyhounds and Whippets are sleek in shape, muscular, with long legs and short hair and ears that would prevent friction from slowing them down. Alaskan Malamutes, Samoyeds and Siberian Huskies have fur with a woolly undercoat, and powerful muscles through the chest, shoulders, and legs.

2. a dog that is easily maintained, medium sized, tolerant, non-aggressive, adaptable, intelligent, and has the ability to concentrate during training; German Shepherds and Labrador Retrievers have these traits.

3. Herding dogs need to be muscular, agile, intelligent, adaptable, alert, and protective. Collies have these traits.

4. A variety of selections might be appropriate, especially the guide dogs such as the Labrador and Golden Retriever as they are non-aggressive, easily trained, and friendly.

Assessment

Ask students to design the ideal dogs that would live on a northern sheep ranch and be able to pull a sled with supplemental food for the sheep in the winter. Provide students in their groups with a large sheet of paper and markers. They should be able to explain their ideal dog based on what they have learned in this lab. **L2**

Share Your Data

To navigate the Internet BioLabs, visit **in.bdol.glencoe.com/internet_lab**. Ask students to compare their results with those of students around the country. Explain.

Biology and Society

Purpose

Students will explore problems faced by modern zoos and analyze what critics say about zoos.

Teaching Strategies

- Ask students to recount why they think zoos should or should not be preserved. Have them consider a zoo's educational value and the opportunity it affords for the community.
- Explain that most zoos are financially unable to reform their programs to meet their new mission as wildlife conservationists. Ask what kind of fund-raising efforts are appropriate for zoos. They might solicit donations from people who visit the zoo and from people in the community. They might also raise money through the sale of books, magazines, or objects created to increase awareness about animals and about zoo functions.

Forming Your Opinion

One side should defend the idea that the zoo is a wildlife preserve helping to preserve endangered species by captive breeding. The other side should defend the idea that captive species promote species favoritism and that the money spent on zoos should be used to preserve natural wildlife habitats.

What should be the role of modern zoos?

Zoos were originally created for public entertainment. They began as a result of people's interest in exotic animals. The animals were kept in small cages with little attention given to their needs. Soon, however, people began to realize the animals needed more than food and basic shelter. Zoos began providing better surroundings for the animals, and giving the public information about animals and their natural habitat.

Modern zoos In modern zoos, animals are rarely kept in tiny cages. During the 20th century, zoos began providing a new experience for visitors by replacing the bars and walls of cages with protective moats and larger animal areas. But space is often limited so architects struggle to make exhibit areas look large and interesting to their inhabitants and visitors. Many zoos also have enrichment programs that provide animals with activities similar to those they would participate in if they were living in the wild. Zookeepers give animals games,

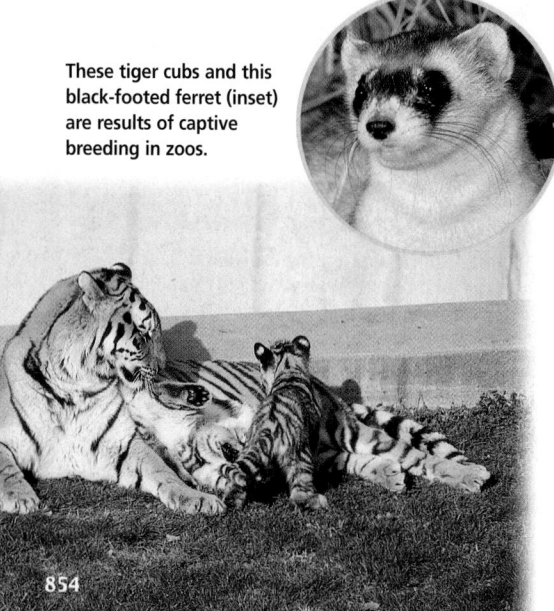

These tiger cubs and this black-footed ferret (inset) are results of captive breeding in zoos.

854

puzzles (such as fish stuffed into a block of ice for polar bears to dig out), slides, pools, and streams, as well as other items that simulate their natural environment.

Captive breeding Ensuring a future for the world's animals has become as much a priority for zoos as displaying them. Zoos use captive breeding to increase their populations. The animals below are results of captive breeding. Advances in captive breeding techniques, such as artificial insemination and in vitro fertilization, have drawn public attention to the potential for rescuing species. In some cases, captive breeding has meant the difference between survival and extinction of a species. However, there is not enough room in zoos to house many extra animals, and since some animals can be domesticated in as little as two generations, few species can survive in the wild after being raised for generations in captivity. Other limitations of captive breeding include inbreeding (which decreases the genetic diversity of the population), low fertility rates, lack of funding for programs, and diseases spread by contact with species not encountered in the wild.

Conservation Zoos also help preserve biodiversity through public education, professional training, research and support of conservation efforts in the wild. Some zoos and wildlife conservationists try to manage ecosystems and wildlife populations through research, establishing natural preserves, maintaining genetically diverse captive-breeding programs, developing educational programs, and many other activities. Scientists realize that wildlife species cannot be 'saved' in the long term by protecting them exclusively in zoos. Without sustainable, wild populations each species will end up inbred, and will eventually face extinction.

Forming Your Opinion

Debate the Issue What should be the role of modern zoos?

 To find out more about modern zoos, visit in.bdol.glencoe.com/biology_society

Going Further

If you have a local zoo, ask students to find out more about their zoo's captive-breeding programs or other ongoing research. **L2**

STUDY GUIDE

Section 32.1

Mammal Characteristics

Key Concepts

- Mammals are endotherms giving them the ability to maintain a fairly constant body temperature.
- Hair is present on all mammals at some point in their lives.
- Mammals feed their young from modified sweat glands called mammary glands.

- Mammals with teeth have different kinds of teeth that are adapted to the type of food they eat.
- Highly developed brains enable mammals to learn.

Vocabulary
diaphragm (p. 843)
gland (p. 842)
mammary gland (p. 842)

Section 32.2

Diversity of Mammals

Key Concepts

- Mammals are classified into three subclasses—placentals, marsupials, and monotremes—based on how they reproduce.

- Placental mammals carry young inside the uterus until their body systems are fully functional. Nourishment inside the uterus occurs through an organ called the placenta.
- Marsupials carry partially developed young in a pouch on the outside of the mother's body.
- Monotremes are egg-laying mammals found only in Australia, Tasmania, and New Guinea.

Vocabulary
gestation (p. 848)
marsupial (p. 849)
monotreme (p. 850)
placenta (p. 848)
placental mammal (p. 848)
therapsid (p. 851)
uterus (p. 848)

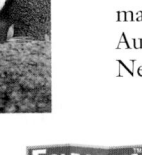

FOLDABLES
Study Organizer To help you review mammals, use the Organizational Study Fold on page 841.

 in.bdol.glencoe.com/vocabulary_puzzlemaker

Key Concepts

Summary statements can be used by students to review the major concepts of the chapter.

 Biology Online

Visit in.bdol.glencoe.com
/self_check_quiz
/vocabulary_puzzlemaker
/chapter_test
/standardized_test

VOCABULARY PUZZLEMAKER

 For additional help with vocabulary, have students access the Vocabulary PuzzleMaker online at in.bdol.glencoe.com/vocabulary_puzzlemaker

FOLDABLES™
Have students use their Foldables to review the content of Section 32.1.

Use the Exam*View*®Pro Test Bank CD-ROM to:
- Create **multiple versions** of tests
- Create **modified** tests with one mouse click for **inclusion** students
- **Edit** existing questions and **add** your own questions
- Build tests aligned with state standards using built-in **State Curriculum Tags**
- Change **English** tests to **Spanish** with one mouse click and vice versa

 Indiana Academic Standards
Pages 854–855: B.1.15, B.1.17, B.1.41

Chapter 32 Assessment

 The Princeton Review *Questions and answers have been aligned and verified by The Princeton Review.*

Vocabulary Review

1. uterus
2. monotreme
3. placenta
4. gestation
5. diaphragm

Understanding Key Concepts

6.	B	10.	A
7.	A	11.	A
8.	D	12.	B
9.	C	13.	B

Constructed Response

14. Animals that are endotherms can maintain their body temperature at a nearly constant level no matter what the environmental temperature.

15. Cover the seal's ears and eyes. Create a wake like prey fish in the water and count how many seals follow it compared to a control group that has eyes and ears uncovered. Other procedures would be acceptable provided that a control is incorporated and quantitative data are gathered.

16. 1. marsupials; 2. monotremes; 3. placental mammals; 4. placenta

Thinking Critically

17. Pamphlets will include various facts about grizzly bears.

18. Lower jaws, middle ear bones, and teeth of mammals are different from those of reptiles. Mammals have straighter legs placed underneath their body.

Vocabulary Review

Review the Chapter 32 vocabulary words listed in the Study Guide on page 855. Match the words with the definitions below.

1. the hollow, muscular organ in which the offspring of placental mammals develop
2. a mammal that reproduces by laying eggs
3. organ that provides food and oxygen to and removes waste from the young inside the uterus of placental mammals
4. time during which placental mammals develop inside the uterus
5. in mammals, a sheet of muscles located below the lungs that separates the chest cavity from the abdominal cavity

Understanding Key Concepts

6. Which of the following is NOT a characteristic of mammals?
   A. endothermic
   B. three-chambered heart
   C. hair
   D. mammary glands

7. Which of these is NOT an endothermic animal?
   A. rattlesnake   C. cat
   B. penguin   D. gorilla

8. Hair helps mammals by providing camouflage and helping them to maintain _____.
   A. evolution   C. reproduction
   B. running speed D. body temperature

9. _____ are examples of egg-laying mammals.
   A. Numbats and lemurs
   B. Anteaters and shrews
   C. Platypuses and spiny anteaters
   D. Seals and whales

10. Which pair of terms is most closely related?
    A. gland—secretion
    B. diaphragm—heart
    C. placenta—Golgi bodies
    D. gestation—molars

11. Which type of teeth pictured below would be most suited for feeding on grasses?

A.   C.

B.   D.

12. Like bird feathers, mammalian hair probably evolved from _____.
    A. teeth   C. claws
    B. scales   D. setae

13. _____ is a behavioral adaptation for cooling off a mammal's body.
    A. Running   C. Jogging
    B. Panting   D. Gnawing

Constructed Response

14. **Open Ended** How does endothermy enable mammals and birds to survive in the Arctic and in the Sahara of Africa?

15. **Open Ended** Biologists hypothesize that the whiskers of harbor seals are sensitive to the wakes their prey fish leave behind as they swim. Design an experiment to test this hypothesis.

16. **Concept Map** Complete the concept map by using the following vocabulary terms: marsupials, monotremes, placental mammals, placenta.

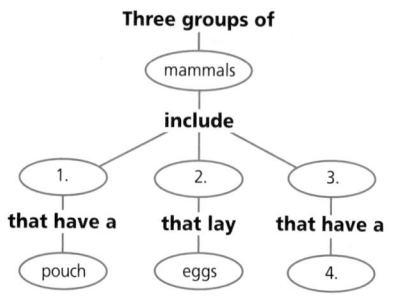

Three groups of

mammals

include

1.   2.   3.

that have a   **that lay**   **that have a**

pouch   eggs   4.

 in.bdol.glencoe.com/chapter_test

Thinking Critically

17. **REAL WORLD BioCHALLENGE** There are recovery efforts taking place in the lower 48 states to save the grizzly bear from extinction. In order for this to happen, there must be support by the public for endangered species protection. Visit **in.bdol.glencoe.com** to investigate this problem. Prepare a pamphlet that will educate the public about the grizzly bears' physical appearance, habitat, feeding habits, winter survival, management and restoration efforts, encounters with people, and what to do when hiking and camping in grizzly bear country. Present your pamphlet to your class.

18. **Differentiate** You find the skeleton of an animal. What features would indicate that it is a mammal rather than a reptile?

The assessed Indiana standard appears next to the question.

All questions aligned and verified by

End-of-Course Assessment Practice

Part 1 Multiple Choice

There are only 80–120 wild ocelots left in the United States. They are members of the cat family that require a thorn-scrub habitat. They live in south Texas, some are protected on the Laguna Atascosa National Wildlife Refuge and the Lower Rio Grande Valley National Wildlife Refuge. Examine the map and answer questions 19–21.

19. The best way to improve protection for
B.1.41 endangered ocelots would be to _____.
   A. educate people to the needs of wild animals and their role in the ecosystem
   B. have a short hunting season
   C. discontinue agriculture
   D. capture all ocelots and transport them to zoos

20. If ocelots disappear from south Texas,
B.1.41 _____.
   A. this wild population will rise in the future
   B. they can be easily replaced by zoo animals
   C. they will be extinct in the United States
   D. their disappearance will not be a problem for ecosystems since there are so few left

21. Ocelots are found in south Texas _____.
   A. exclusively on two wildlife refuges
   B. on wildlife refuges and areas outside the refuge
   C. exclusively on South Padre Island
   D. only of the seashore of south Texas

Part 2 Constructed Response/Grid In

Record your answers on your answer document.

22. **Open Ended** How does the development of young inside a uterus enable mammals to adapt to
B.1.31 environments that reptiles cannot?

23. **Open Ended** Mammals and insects are both considered to be extraordinarily successful animals.
B.1.31 Explain the criteria used in both cases that give them this distinction.

 in.bdol.glencoe.com/standardized_test

End-of Course Assessment Practice

19. A
20. C
21. B
22. Developing inside a uterus, young mammals are protected from environmental conditions, whereas the eggs of reptiles, developing externally, are subject to environmental conditions.
23. They both have enormous diversity of species and live in all environments.

FAST FILE

Answer Sheet A practice answer sheet can be found on p. 109 of *Unit 9 FAST FILE Resources*.

RUBRIC

SCORE	CRITERIA
4	A correct solution that is supported by well-developed, accurate explanations.
3	A generally correct solution, but may contain minor flaws in reasoning.

SCORE	CRITERIA
2	A partially correct interpretation and/or solution to the problem.
1	A correct solution with no supporting evidence or explanation.
0	An incorrect solution or no solution is given.

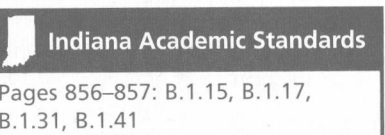

Indiana Academic Standards

Pages 856–857: B.1.15, B.1.17, B.1.31, B.1.41

Section Objectives	National Science Standards	State/Local Standards	Advanced Lab and Demo Planning
Section 33.1 1/2 session 1. **Distinguish** among the types of innate behavior. 2. **Demonstrate,** by example, the adaptive value of innate behavior.	UCP.1–5; A.1, A.2; C.2–4, C.6	**Indiana Standards** B.1.18, B.1.31, B.1.43	**Student Labs:** MiniLab 33.1, p. 860: plastic dish, moist paper toweling, black paper, tape, 6 isopods, lamp Problem-Solving Lab 33.1, p. 867 Additional Lab, p. 864: glass terrarium or aquarium tank with cover, sand, 1 female and 5 male field crickets, dry oatmeal in a jar lid, apple slices, clean sponge pieces soaked in water, 4 matchboxes, 5 jars with lids, 4 different colors of nail polish **Teacher Demonstration:** Quick Demo, p. 861: large piece of clear, glass-like plastic, notebook paper
Section 33.2 1 1/2 sessions 3. **Distinguish** among types of learned behavior. 4. **Demonstrate,** by example, types of learned behavior.	UCP.1–4; A.1, A.2; C.3, C.4, C.6; E.1, E.2; F.3–5; G.1, G.2	**Indiana Standards** B.1.18, B.1.43	**Student Labs:** MiniLab 33.2, p. 870: paper puzzle Problem-Solving Lab 33.2, p. 872 Investigate BioLab, p. 874: See materials below. **Teacher Demonstration:** Quick Demo, p. 871
End of Chapter Assessment Student Edition **Study Guide,** p. 877 **Content Assessment,** pp. 878–879		**Indiana Standards** B.1.31, B.1.43	**Student Lab:** Investigate BioLab, p. 874: snails, dropper, scissors, probe constructed from tape, rubber band, pencil, spring water, small dish, dissecting microscope

Key to Teaching Strategies

L1 Level 1 activities should be appropriate for students with learning difficulties.

L2 Level 2 activities should be within the ability range of all students.

L3 Level 3 activities are designed for above-average students.

ELL ELL activities should be within the ability range of English Language Learners.

COOP LEARN Cooperative Learning activities are designed for small group work.

Legend

🔦 Transparency   💿 CD-ROM   MP3   ▦ Videocassette   💿 DVD

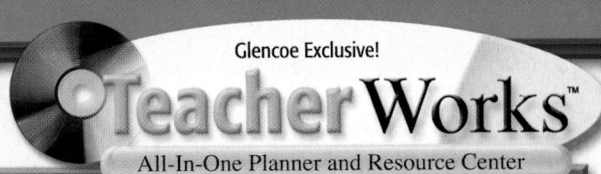

Glencoe Exclusive!

TeacherWorks™
All-In-One Planner and Resource Center

Reproducible Masters and Transparencies

Technology

Unit 9 FAST FILE Resources
    MiniLab Worksheet, p. 113
    Reinforcement and Study Guide in English,
      pp. 117–118
    Reinforcement and Study Guide in Spanish,
      pp. 121–122
    Concept Mapping, p. 125
    Critical Thinking/Problem Solving, p. 126
    Transparency Worksheet, p. 127
Reading Essentials for Biology, Section 33.1
Laboratory Manual, pp. 215–218
🔦 **Section Focus Transparency 79**

💿 **Interactive Chalkboard CD-ROM: Section 33.1 Presentation** ▪
💿 **TeacherWorks™ CD-ROM** ▪
📻 **Guided Reading Audio Summaries MP3**
💿 **Virtual Labs CD-ROM**
    Virtual Lab: Learned Behavior

Unit 9 FAST FILE Resources
    MiniLab Worksheet, p. 114
    BioLab Worksheet, pp. 115–116
    Reinforcement and Study Guide in English,
      pp. 119–120
    Reinforcement and Study Guide in Spanish,
      pp. 123–124
    Transparency Worksheets, pp. 128, 129–132
Reading Essentials for Biology, Section 33.2
Laboratory Manual, pp. 219–222
🔦 **Section Focus Transparency 80**
🔦 **Basic Concepts Transparency 60**
🔦 **Reteaching Skills Transparency 48**

💿 **Interactive Chalkboard CD-ROM: Section 33.2 Presentation** ▪
💿 **TeacherWorks™ CD-ROM** ▪
📻 **Guided Reading Audio Summaries MP3**

Unit 9 FAST FILE Resources
    Chapter Assessment, pp. 133–134
    Student Recording Sheet, p. 139

The Princeton Review **Reviewing Biology,** pp. 65–66

💿 **Interactive Chalkboard:**
    Chapter 33 Assessment ▪
💿 **MindJogger Videoquizzes**
    DVD/VHS
💿 **ExamView® Pro Test Bank**
    CD-ROM
💿 **TeacherWorks™ CD-ROM** ▪
💿 **Succeeding on National Standards CD-ROM**

🖱 **in.bdol.glencoe.com**
    /self_check_quiz
    /vocabulary_puzzlemaker
    /chapter_test
    /standardized_test

▪ Indicates materials created specifically for Indiana.

Chapter 33

Short on Time?

BIODIGEST The BioDigest at the end of this unit can be used as a(n):

- preview to introduce important unit concepts.
- overview if time does not permit teaching the entire chapter.
- review of key unit concepts.

Understanding the Photo

The queen bee is the largest in the hive. She has a pointed body and small wings. Her body is noticeably paler than the other bees in the hive, with less pronounced stripes on the abdomen. The queen bee emits pheromones that prevent other female bees from maturing sexually so the queen will remain dominant.

Animal Behavior

What You'll Learn

- You will distinguish between innate and learned behavior.
- You will identify the adaptive value of specific types of behavior.

Why It's Important

Animals have patterns of behavior that help them survive and reproduce. Some of these behavior patterns are inherited and some are learned. You will recognize that humans, like other animals, have both types of behavior, and that these behavior patterns enable you to survive as well.

Understanding ▶ the Photo

In a honeybee hive, a single queen lays all the eggs. Worker bees build combs, store pollen and nectar, feed the queen, and keep the hive ventilated and clean. The sole purpose of the drones is to mate with the queen. In this highly organized system, some behaviors are innate, while others are learned.

Biology Online

Visit in.bdol.glencoe.com to
- study the entire chapter online
- access Web Links for more information and activities on animal behavior
- review content with the Interactive Tutor and self-check quizzes

858

Two-Minute Chapter Launcher

Discussion Ask student volunteers to bring in a caged pet, such as a hamster or a gerbil, or a picture of an animal. Have the class list behaviors of the animal. Have student groups discuss the behaviors and place each in categories—those they think are learned and those they think are not learned. Have students edit their lists as you teach this chapter. **L2**

Indiana Academic Standards

Pages 858–859: B.1.18

Section 33.1

Innate Behavior

Indiana Standards Standard B.1.43 Understand that and describe how organisms are influenced by a particular combination of living and nonliving components of the environment.

1 Focus

Bellringer
Section Focus Transparency 79

SECTION PREVIEW

Objectives
Distinguish among the types of innate behavior.

Demonstrate, by example, the adaptive value of innate behavior.

Review Vocabulary
population: group of organisms of one species that interbreed and live in the same place at the same time (p. 38)

New Vocabulary
behavior
innate behavior
reflex
fight-or-flight response
instinct
courtship behavior
territory
aggressive behavior
dominance hierarchy
circadian rhythm
migration
hibernation
estivation

Do you exhibit innate behavior?

Finding Main Ideas Construct an outline about innate behavior. Use the red and blue titles in this section as a guideline. As you read the paragraphs that follow the titles, add important information and vocabulary words to your outline. An example follows.

I. Inherited Behavior
  A. Natural selection favors certain behaviors
    1. Individuals with behavior that makes them more successful at surviving and reproducing tend to produce more offspring than individuals without the behavior.
    2. Inherited behavior of animals is called innate behavior.
    3. Innate behaviors include fixed action patterns, automatic responses, and instincts.

Use your outline to help you answer questions in the Section Assessment on page 867. For more help, refer to *Outline* in the **Skill Handbook.**

Cedar waxwings and their nestlings

Finding Main Ideas

Outlining If some students have problems understanding how to create a traditional outline with Roman numerals, upper- and lowercase letters, and numbers, tell them to make a list of the important details under each red and blue title.

Figure 33.1
Animals respond to stimuli by exhibiting a variety of behaviors.

A Squirrels collect and store acorns and nuts in response to shorter day length and colder temperatures.

What is behavior?

A peacock displaying his colorful tail, a whale spending the winter months in the ocean off the coast of southern California, and a lizard seeking shade from the hot desert sun are all examples of animal behavior. **Behavior** is anything an animal does in response to a stimulus. A stimulus is an environmental change that directly influences the activity of an organism. The presence of a peahen stimulates a peacock to open its tail feathers and strut. Environmental cues, such as a change in day length, might be the stimulus that causes the whale to leave its summertime arctic habitat. Heat stimulates the lizard to seek shade. *Figure 33.1* shows two examples of stimuli that affect animal behavior.

B Spots that resemble the eyes of owls cause predatory birds to stop their pursuit of this insect.

859

PowerPoint® Presentations

This CD-ROM is an editable Microsoft® PowerPoint® presentation that includes:
• Section presentations
• Section checks
• Image bank
• Hot links to Biology Online
• All transparencies

RESOURCE MANAGER

Unit 9 *FAST FILE* **Resources**
MiniLab Worksheet, p. 113
Reinforcement and Study Guide in English, pp. 117–118
Reinforcement and Study Guide in Spanish, pp. 121–122
Concept Mapping, p. 125

Critical Thinking/Problem Solving, p. 126
Transparency Worksheet, p. 127
Reading Essentials for Biology, Section 33.1
Laboratory Manual, pp. 215–218
Section Focus Transparency 79

MiniLab 33.1

Purpose

Students will observe the innate response of an isopod to light.

Process Skills

experiment, collect data, analyze information, draw a conclusion

Safety Precautions

Have students wash their hands thoroughly with soap and water after handling lab specimens.

Teaching Strategies

- Isopods may be collected locally or purchased from biological supply houses.
- Use plastic or glass petri dishes for chambers or collect empty plastic food cartons. Cardboard boxes, such as shoe boxes, will also work. Use black construction paper to block light.
- Tape the toweling edges prior to moistening.
- If there is a problem of getting all isopods aligned at the center of the dish when first starting, use the species *Armadillidium* (available from supply houses). This species curls up into a ball when touched. Thus, curled up isopods can all be placed at the center at the same time.

Expected Results

Isopods will move toward low light.

Analysis

1. dark areas; majority of isopods were found under dark paper side
2. Explanations may vary, but the behavior is innate. This type of behavior would not have been learned during the experiment because isopods have this behavior as soon as they hatch and it may not be under their conscious control.
3. Isopods must remain moist to survive. Dark areas in nature are more likely to be moist

---

MiniLab 33.1

Experiment

Testing an Isopod's Response to Light Isopods, such as pill bugs and sow bugs, are common arthropods on sidewalks or patios. They are actually land crustaceans and respire through gill-like organs that must be kept moist at all times.

Procedure

1. Copy the data table.
2. Prepare a plastic dish using the diagram as a guide. Moisten the paper toweling.

Top of dish
Tape
Light source
Moist paper toweling
Black paper

3. Place six isopods in the center of the dish and quickly add the cover. Place the dish near a lamp or next to a classroom window with light. Have the light strike the dish as shown in the diagram. **CAUTION: Treat isopods gently.**
4. Wait five minutes and observe the dish. Count and record in your data table the number of isopods on the dark or light side. This is your "five minute observation."
5. Repeat step 4 three more times, waiting five minutes before each observation.

Data Table		
Observation in Minutes	Number of Isopods Present	
	Light Side	Dark Side
5		
10		
15		
20		
25		

Analysis

1. **Analyze** Do isopods tend to move toward light or dark areas? Support your answer with specific numbers from your data.
2. **Infer** Is the behavior of isopods toward light or darkness innate or learned? Explain your answer.
3. **Think Critically** What might be the adaptive advantage for the observed isopod behavior? Explain how natural selection may have influenced this isopod behavior.
4. **Make and Use Graphs** Prepare a bar graph that depicts your data.

Animals carry on many activities—such as getting food, avoiding predators, caring for young, finding shelter, and attracting mates—that enable them to survive and reproduce. These behavior patterns, therefore, have adaptive value. For example, a parent gull that is not incubating eggs or caring for chicks joins a noisy flock of gulls to dive for fishes. If the parent cannot catch a lot of fishes, not only will it die, but its chicks will not survive either. Therefore, this feeding behavior has adaptive value for the gull.

Inherited Behavior

Inheritance plays an important role in the ways animals behave. You don't expect a hummingbird to tunnel underground or a mouse to fly. Yet, why does a mouse run away when a cat appears? Why does a hummingbird fly south for the winter? These behavior patterns are genetically programmed. An animal's genetic make-up determines how that animal reacts to certain stimuli.

Natural selection favors certain behaviors

Often, a behavior exhibited by an animal species is the result of natural selection. The variability of behavior among individuals affects their ability to survive and reproduce. Individuals with behavior that makes them more successful at surviving and reproducing tend to produce more offspring than individuals without the behavior. These offspring will inherit the genetic basis for the successful behavior. You can observe the behavior of isopods in the *MiniLab* on this page.

Reading Check **Explain** how animal activities that enable them to survive and reproduce are a result of natural selection.

---

than light areas. Through natural selection, those isopods that innately moved toward dark areas survived and passed this genetic trait on to their offspring.

4. Students' bar graphs should depict the data they collected.

Assessment

Knowledge Ask students to describe the equipment and experimental procedure needed to test the hypothesis that isopods prefer dry rather than moist conditions. Use the Performance Task Assessment List for Designing an Experiment in **PASC**, p. 95. **L2**

Inherited behavior of animals is called **innate** (ih NAYT) **behavior.** A toad captures prey by flipping out its sticky tongue. To capture prey, a toad must first be able to detect and follow its movement. Toads have "insect detector" cells in the retinas of their eyes. As an insect moves across a toad's line of sight, the "insect detector" cells signal the brain of the prey's changing position, thus initiating an innate response; the toad's tongue flips out. *Figure 33.2* shows a toad that captured its prey using an innate behavior known as a fixed-action pattern. A fixed-action pattern is an unchangeable behavior pattern that, once initiated, continues until completed.

Genes form the basis of innate behavior

Through experiments, scientists have found that an animal's hormonal balance and its nervous system—especially the sense organs responsible for sight, touch, sound, or odor identification—affect how sensitive the individual is to certain stimuli. In fire ant colonies, a single gene influences the acceptance or rejection of the ant queen, thereby controlling the colony's social structure. Innate behavior includes fixed-action patterns, automatic responses, and instincts. You can observe the response of animals to certain stimuli in the *BioLab* at the end of this chapter.

Automatic Responses

What happens if something quickly passes in front of your eyes or if something is thrown at your face? Your first reaction is to blink and jerk back your head. Even if a protective clear shield is placed in front of you, you can't stop yourself from behaving this way when the object is thrown. This reaction is an example of the simplest form of innate

Figure 33.2
A toad can starve even though it is surrounded by dead insects because it cannot recognize non-moving animals as prey.

behavior, called a reflex. A **reflex** (REE fleks) is a simple, automatic response to a stimulus that involves no conscious control. *Figure 33.3* shows an example of a reflex.

The adaptive value of another automatic response is obvious. Think about a time when you were suddenly scared. Immediately, your heart began to beat faster. Your skin got cold and clammy, your respiration increased, and maybe you trembled. You were having a fight-or-flight response. A **fight-or-flight response** mobilizes the body for greater activity. Your body is being prepared to either fight or run from the danger. A fight-or-flight response is automatic and controlled by hormones and the nervous system.

Figure 33.3
Reflexes have survival value for animals. When you accidentally touch a hot stove, you jerk your hand away from the hot surface. The movement saves your body from serious injury.

Reflex Have students examine the blink response by asking them to hold a large piece of clear, glass-like plastic in front of their faces and try to keep their eyes open when a partner gently tosses a crumpled piece of notebook paper at the glass. **L1 ELL**

✓**Reading Check** (p. 860) When animals attract mates using certain behaviors, they increase the possibility of mating, thereby ensuring survival of the species.

Inquiry

Design an Experiment Ask students to hypothesize how different animals will respond to a loud noise. Have students design and carry out experiments and write their observations in their portfolios. Ask them to infer whether the behavior they observed is innate. **L2**

CHALLENGE ACTIVITY

Tend-and-Befriend Have interested students research what some scientists believe is the female response to stressful situations—tend-and-befriend. Have them compare the female response to that of males—fight-or-flight. When women experience stressful situations they are prone to protect and nurture their children and turn to social networks of support **L3**

 Indiana Academic Standards
Pages 860–861: B.1.31

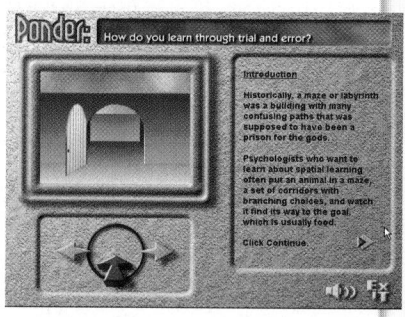
Caption Question Answer
Figure 33.4 The greylag goose's behavior is considered a fixed-action pattern because it is an unchangeable behavior pattern that, once initiated, continues until completed.

✔ **Reading Check** Flashing a species-specific light pattern is the courtship behavior of male fireflies. Female fireflies that are able to recognize the distinct light patterns of males of their species are able to mate and reproduce. Displaying and recognizing the light patterns are instinctive behaviors that have evolved through natural selection.

Word Origin

instinct from the Latin word *instinctus,* meaning "impulse"; An instinct is a complex pattern of innate behavior.

Figure 33.4
The female greylag goose instinctively retrieves an egg that she sees has rolled out of the nest. She does this by arching her neck around the stray egg and moving it like a hockey player advancing a puck. The female goose will retrieve many objects outside the nest, including baseballs and tin cans.
Explain *Why is this behavior considered a fixed-action pattern?*

Instinctive Behavior

Compare the fixed-action pattern of a toad capturing prey with a fight-or-flight response. Both are quick, automatic responses to stimuli. But some behaviors take a longer time because they involve more complex actions. An **instinct** (IHN stingt) is a complex pattern of innate behavior. Instinctive behavior begins when the animal recognizes a stimulus and continues until all parts of the behavior have been performed.

As shown in *Figure 33.4*, greylag geese instinctively retrieve eggs that have rolled from the nest. They will go through the motions of egg retrieval even if the eggs roll or are taken away until they are comfortably back on their nest. If they see the egg has not been retrieved they begin the process again.

Courtship behavior ensures reproduction

Much of an animal's courtship behavior is instinctive. **Courtship behavior** is the behavior that males and females of a species carry out before mating. Like other instinctive behaviors, courtship has evolved through natural selection. Imagine what would happen to the survival of a species if members were unable to recognize other members of that same species. Individuals often can recognize one another by the behavior patterns each performs. In courtship, behavior ensures that members of the same species find each other and mate. Obviously, such behavior has an adaptive value for the species. Different species of fireflies, for example, can be seen at dusk flashing distinct light patterns. However, female fireflies of one species respond only to those males exhibiting the species-correct flashing pattern.

Some courtship behaviors help prevent females from killing males before they have had the opportunity to mate. For example, in some spiders, the male is smaller than the female and risks the chance of being eaten if he approaches her. Before mating, the male in some species presents the female with an object, such as an insect wrapped in a silk web. While the female is unwrapping and eating the insect, the male is able to mate with her without being attacked. After mating, however, the male may be eaten by the female anyway.

In some species, such objects play an important role in allowing the female to exercise a choice as to which male to choose for a mating partner. The hanging fly, shown in *Figure 33.5*, is such a species.

✔ **Reading Check** **Explain** the results of natural selection in the courtship behavior of fireflies.

862 ANIMAL BEHAVIOR

 Indiana Academic Standards

Pages 862–863: B.1.31, B.1.43

Territoriality reduces competition

You may have seen a chipmunk chase another chipmunk away from seeds on the ground under a bird feeder. The chipmunk was defending its territory. A **territory** is a physical space an animal defends against other members of its species. It may contain the animal's breeding area, feeding area, and potential mates, or all three.

Animals that have territories will defend their space by driving away other individuals of the same species. For example, a male sea lion patrols the area of beach where his harem of female sea lions rests. He does not bother a neighboring male that has a harem of his own because both have marked their territories, and each respects the common boundaries. But if an unattached, young male tries to enter the sea lion's territory, the owner of the territory will attack and drive the intruder away from his harem.

Although it may not appear so, setting up territories actually reduces conflicts, controls population growth, and provides for efficient use of environmental resources. When animals space themselves out, they don't compete for the same resources within a limited space. This behavior improves the chances of survival of the young, and, therefore, survival of the species. If the male has selected an appropriate site and the young survive, they may inherit his ability to select an appropriate territory. Therefore, territorial behavior has survival value, not only for individuals, but also for the species. The male stickleback shown in *Figure 33.6* is another animal that exhibits territoriality, especially during breeding season.

Recall that pheromones are chemicals that communicate information among individuals of the same

Figure 33.5
Female hanging flies instinctively favor the male that supplies the largest object—in this case, a moth. The amount of sperm the female will accept from the male is determined by the size of the object.

species. Many animals produce pheromones to mark territorial boundaries. For example, wolf urine contains pheromones that warn other wolves to stay away. The male pronghorn antelope uses a pheromone secreted from facial glands. One advantage of using pheromones is that they work both day and night, and whether or not the animal that made the mark is present.

Figure 33.6
The male three-spined stickleback displays a red belly to other breeding males near his territory. The male instinctively responds to other red-bellied males by attacking and driving them away.

Visual Learning

Figure 33.7 Have students examine Figure 33.7 and explain how symbolic behavior contributes to survival.

Display

Ask a group of students to make a photo collage of aggressive behaviors of pets and other local animals. Have them post their display on the classroom bulletin board. **L2** **ELL** **COOP LEARN**

Chalkboard Example

Draw a diagram showing *pecking order* on the chalkboard. Use this diagram to explain how animals form a dominance hierarchy.

Indiana Academic Standards

Pages 864–865: B.1.43

Aggressive behavior threatens other animals

Animals occasionally engage in aggression. **Aggressive behavior** is used to intimidate another animal of the same species. Animals fight or threaten one another in order to defend their young, their territory, or a resource such as food. Aggressive behaviors, such as bird calling, teeth baring, or growling, deliver the message to keep away.

When a male bighorn sheep is threatened by another male moving into his territory, for example, he does not kill the invader. Animals of the same species rarely fight to the death. The fights are usually symbolic, as shown in *Figure 33.7*. Male bighorn sheep do not usually even injure one another. Why does aggressive behavior rarely result in serious injury? One answer is that the defeated individual shows signs of submission to the victor. These signs inhibit further aggression by the victor. Continued fighting might result in serious injury for the victor; thus, its best interests are served by stopping the fight.

Figure 33.7
In many species, such as bighorn sheep, individuals fight in relatively harmless ways among themselves.

Submission leads to dominance hierarchies

Do you have an older or younger sibling? Who wins when you argue? In animals, usually the oldest or strongest wins the argument. But what happens when several individuals are involved in the argument? Sometimes, aggressive behavior among several individuals results in a grouping in which there are different levels of dominant and submissive animals. A **dominance hierarchy** (DAH muh nunts • HI rar kee) is a form of social ranking within a group in which some individuals are more subordinate than others. Usually, one animal is the top-ranking, dominant individual. This animal might lead others to food, water, and shelter. A dominant male often sires most or all of the offspring. There might be several levels in the hierarchy, with individuals in each level subordinate to the one above. The ability to form a dominance hierarchy is innate, but the position each animal assumes may be learned.

Additional Lab

Cricket Hierarchies

Purpose
Students will observe crickets setting up a dominance hierarchy.

Safety Precautions
Have students wash their hands thoroughly with soap and water after handling lab specimens.

Materials
glass terrarium or aquarium with cover, sand, 1 female and 5 male field crickets, dry oatmeal in a jar lid, apple slices, clean sponge pieces soaked in water, 4 matchboxes, 5 jars with lids, 4 different colors of nail polish

Procedure
Give students the following directions.

1. Set up a terrarium with about 2 cm of sand in the bottom and numbered matchboxes in all 4 corners.

2. Place different colored spots of nail polish on the thoraxes of four male crickets. One male will not need polish. The female can be identified by her long

Figure 33.8
A variety of animals respond to the urge to migrate.

B Both the freshwater eel and all species of salmon migrate to their spawning grounds.

A Canadian and Alaskan caribou migrate from their winter homes in the taiga forests to the tundra for the summer.

C Adult monarch butterflies fly southward where they roost. In the spring, their young fly back north.

The term *pecking order* comes from a dominance hierarchy that is formed by chickens. The top-ranking chicken can peck any other chicken. The chicken lowest in the hierarchy is pecked at by all the other chickens in the group.

Behavior resulting from internal and external cues

Some instinctive behavior is exhibited in animals in response to internal, biological rhythms. Behavior based on a 24-hour day/night cycle is one example. Many animals, humans included, sleep at night and are awake during the day. Other animals, such as owls, reverse this pattern and are awake at night. A 24-hour, light-regulated, sleep/wake cycle of behavior is called a **circadian** (sur KAY dee uhn) **rhythm.** Circadian rhythms keep you alert during the day and help you relax at night. They may even wake you if you forget to set your alarm clock or on days that

you could sleep in. Circadian rhythms are controlled by genes, yet are also influenced by factors such as jet lag and shift work.

Rhythms also can occur on a yearly or seasonal cycle. Migration, for example, occurs on a seasonal cycle. **Migration** is the instinctive, seasonal movement of animals, shown in *Figure 33.8*. In North America, about two-thirds of bird species fly south in the fall to areas such as South America, where food is available during the winter. The birds fly north in the spring to areas where they breed during the summer. Whales migrate seasonally, as well. Change in day length is thought to stimulate the onset of migration in the same way that it controls the flowering of plants. You can find out how migrating turtles are tracked in the *Biotechnology* at the end of this chapter.

✓**Reading Check** **Infer** why some animals migrate.

33.1 INNATE BEHAVIOR **865**

---

ovipositor at the end of her abdomen.
3. Keep the crickets in separate jars for at least one day prior to beginning.
4. Place males in the terrarium and observe and record their behavior for 15 minutes.
5. Examine the crickets for about 10 minutes each day for 5 days. Note which becomes dominant and the behavior it exhibits.

Expected Results
One cricket will become dominant and the others will avoid him.
Analysis
1. What is the social ranking established by the crickets? dominance hierarchy
2. Describe the differences in behavior of the crickets before and after the hierarchy was established. Before: much aggression and chirping; after: other

crickets avoided the dominant male
Assessment
Performance Ask students to hypothesize how the crickets will respond to the female and then introduce her into the terrarium. The dominant male may mate with the female. Use the Performance Task Assessment List for Formulating a Hypothesis in **PASC**, p. 93. **L2**

Purpose

Students will determine that hibernation in squirrels is controlled by an internal annual biological clock.

Process Skills

think critically, analyze information, identify and control variables, design an experiment, interpret scientific illustrations

Teaching Strategies

- Point out that not all months of the year are listed.
- The dark bands correspond to periods of hibernation.
- Discuss human circadian patterns as an introduction to periods of hibernation.
- Help students determine the approximately annual cycle of behavior by noting the peaks of body weight and the time lapse between these peaks.

Thinking Critically

1. Squirrels spend about 120 days in hibernation and close to 200 days out of hibernation.
2. They were controlling variables by eliminating them from the experiment. Outside stimuli could provide clues as to when it might be time to hibernate.
3. to show that temperature was not influencing start of hibernation
4. Place newborn squirrels into identical experimental chambers, such as those used in the other experiments, and observe if squirrels hibernate at the proper time of the year.

Migration calls for remarkable strength and endurance. The arctic tern migrates between the arctic circle and the Antarctic, a one-way flight of almost 18 000 km.

Animals navigate in a variety of ways. Some use the positions of the sun and stars to navigate. They may use geographic clues, such as mountain ranges. Some bird species seem to be guided by Earth's magnetic field. You might think of this as being guided by an internal compass.

Animals that migrate might be responding to colder temperatures and shorter days, as well as to hormones. Young animals may learn when and where to migrate by following their parents. You can easily see why animals migrate from a cold place to a warmer place, yet most animals do not migrate. How many animals cope with winter is another example of instinctive behavior.

You know that many animals store food in burrows and nests. But other animals survive the winter by undergoing physiological changes that reduce their need for energy. Some mammals, such as bats and chipmunks, and a few other types of animals go into a deep sleep during parts of the cold winter months. This period of inactivity is called hibernation. **Hibernation** (hi bur NAY shun) is a state in which the body temperature drops substantially, oxygen consumption decreases, and breathing rates decline to a few breaths per minute. Hibernation conserves energy. Animals that hibernate typically eat vast amounts of food to build up body fat before entering hibernation. This fat fuels the animal's body while it is in this state. The golden-mantled ground squirrel shown in *Figure 33.9* is an example of an animal that hibernates. You can find out more about hibernation in the *Problem-Solving Lab* on the next page.

What happens to animals that live year-round in hot environments? Some of these animals respond in a way that is similar to hibernation. **Estivation** (es tuh VAY shun) is a state of reduced metabolism that occurs in animals living in conditions of intense heat. Desert animals appear to estivate sometimes in response to lack of food or periods of drought.

Figure 33.9
The golden-mantled ground squirrel has a normal body temperature of around 37°C. When the day length shortens in the fall, the ground squirrel's temperature drops to 5°C, and it goes into hibernation.

866 ANIMAL BEHAVIOR

Assessment

Skill Have students draw graphs that would illustrate the pattern of hibernation for squirrels that were born in the Andes Mountains of South America and then brought to the United States for experimentation to determine their year-long rhythms. Use the Performance Task Assessment List for Graph from Data in **PASC**, p. 111. **L3**

Figure 33.10
Australian long-necked turtles are among the reptiles and amphibians that respond to hot and dry summer conditions by estivating.

Australian long-necked turtles, shown in *Figure 33.10*, will estivate even when they are kept in a laboratory with constant food and water. Clearly, estivation is an innate behavior that depends on both internal and external cues.

Problem-Solving Lab 33.1

Design an Experiment

Is hibernation an innate or learned behavior? Circadian rhythms occur on an almost 24-hour cycle in certain organisms. The word *circadian* comes from Latin: *circa* ("about") and *dies* ("day").

Solve the Problem
Ground squirrels were placed in a room free from all outside stimuli. The room contained food and water, was kept at a temperature of 22°C, and a light remained on for 12 hours each day. Body mass was measured and recorded weekly. The graph shows the results of the experiment. The dark bands correspond to times when the squirrels were in hibernation.

Body Mass of Golden-Mantled Ground Squirrels

Thinking Critically
1. **Sequence** Describe the squirrels' cyclic pattern of activity.
2. **Lab Techniques** Why did scientists keep temperature, food and water, and light constant?
3. **Use Variables, Constants, and Controls** Why is it appropriate experimental procedure to repeat the experiment using different temperatures?
4. **Experiment** Suggest an experiment that supports the conclusion that this pattern of hibernation is genetic.

Section Assessment

Understanding Main Ideas
1. How is a reflex different from an instinct?
2. Explain by example two types of innate behavior.
3. Explain behaviors that reduce competition.

Thinking Critically
4. How is innate behavior an advantage to a species in which the young normally hatch after the mother has left?

 in.bdol.glencoe.com/self_check_quiz

SKILL REVIEW

5. **Experiment** Earthworms live in deep, long, and narrow burrows in moist soil. They leave their burrows at night and when it rains, because it is easier for them to move on a wet surface. Design an experiment to determine what stimulus causes an earthworm to return to its burrow. For more help, refer to *Experiment* in the **Skill Handbook**.

33.1 INNATE BEHAVIOR **867**

Section Assessment

1. A reflex is a simple physical response to a stimulus. An instinct is a complex pattern of innate behavior.
2. Courtship rituals in birds and migration in salmon have innate behavior components.
3. dominance hierarchy; symbolic aggressive behavior
4. Innate behaviors will enable the young to survive.
5. Students may hypothesize that earthworms return in response to light, heat, cold, touch, or water. Make sure their experimental designs test for only one variable, incorporate controls, and collect quantitative data.

1 Focus

INTERACTIVE CHALKBOARD
PowerPoint® Presentations

Bellringer
Section Focus Transparency 80

Transparency 80 Learning a Lesson

SECTION FOCUS
Use with Chapter 33, Section 33.2

❶ If the rat is placed in the maze several times, will it find the food in less time? Account for your conclusion.

❷ If the rat's behavior changes, is the change instinctive?

BIOLOGY: The Dynamics of Life   SECTION FOCUS TRANSPARENCIES

FOLDABLES™
For an additional Foldables activity idea, see the Chapter 33 Foldables page in *Unit 9 FAST FILE Resources.*

Indiana Academic Standards

Pages 868–869: B.1.43

Section 33.2

Learned Behavior

 Indiana Standards Standard B.1.43 Understand that and describe how organisms are influenced by a particular combination of living and nonliving components of the environment.

SECTION PREVIEW

Objectives

Distinguish among types of learned behavior.

Demonstrate, by example, types of learned behavior.

Review Vocabulary
pheromones: chemical signals given off by animals that signal animals to engage in specific behaviors (p. 745)

New Vocabulary
habituation
imprinting
trial-and-error learning
motivation
classical conditioning
insight
communication
language

FOLDABLES™
Study Organizer

Learned Behavior Make the following Foldable to help you understand the vocabulary terms in this chapter.

STEP 1 Fold a vertical sheet of notebook paper from side to side.

STEP 2 Cut along every third line of only the top layer to form tabs.

STEP 3 Label each tab.

Build Vocabulary As you read Section 33.2, list the vocabulary words about learned behavior on the tabs. As you learn the definitions, write them under the appropriate tab.

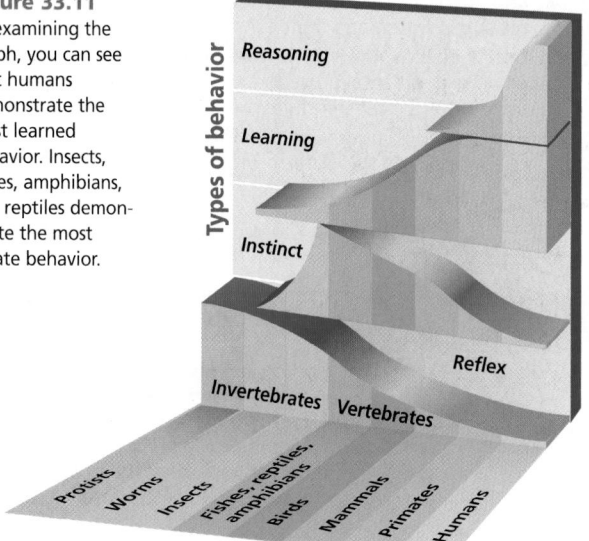

Figure 33.11
By examining the graph, you can see that humans demonstrate the most learned behavior. Insects, fishes, amphibians, and reptiles demonstrate the most innate behavior.

Comparison of Animal Behaviors

Types of behavior

Reasoning
Learning
Instinct
Reflex

Invertebrates   Vertebrates

Protists   Worms   Insects   Fishes, reptiles, amphibians   Birds   Mammals   Primates   Humans

What is learned behavior?

Learning, or learned behavior, takes place when behavior changes through practice or experience. The more complex an animal's brain, the more elaborate the patterns of its learned behavior. As you can see in *Figure 33.11,* innate behaviors are more common in invertebrates, and learned behaviors are more common in vertebrates. In humans, many behaviors are learned.

Learning has survival value for all animals in changing environments because it permits behavior to change in response to varied conditions. Learning allows an animal to adapt to change, an ability that is especially important for animals with long life spans. The longer that an animal lives, the greater the chance that its environment will change.

868 ANIMAL BEHAVIOR

RESOURCE MANAGER

Unit 9 *FAST FILE* Resources
MiniLab Worksheet, p. 114
BioLab Worksheet, pp. 115–116
Reinforcement and Study Guide in English, pp. 119–120
Reinforcement and Study Guide in Spanish, pp. 123–124
Transparency Worksheets, pp. 128, 129–132

Reading Essentials for Biology, Section 33.2
Laboratory Manual, pp. 219–222
🔖 **Section Focus Transparency 80**
🔖 **Basic Concepts Transparency 60**
🔖 **Reteaching Skills Transparency 48**

Kinds of Learned Behavior

Just as there are several types of innate behavior, there are several types of learned behavior. Some learned behavior is simple and some is complex. Which group of animals do you think carries out the most complex type of learned behavior?

Habituation: A simple form of learning

Horses normally shy away from an object that suddenly appears from the trees or bushes, yet after a while they disregard noisy cars that speed by the pasture honking their horns. This lack of response is called habituation. **Habituation** (huh bit choo AY shun) illustrated in *Figure 33.12*, occurs when an animal is repeatedly given a stimulus that is not associated with any punishment or reward. An animal has become habituated to a stimulus when it finally ceases to respond to the stimulus.

Imprinting: A permanent attachment

Have you ever seen young ducklings following their mother? This behavior is the result of imprinting. **Imprinting** is a form of learning in which an animal, at a specific critical time of its life, forms a social attachment to another object. Many kinds of birds and mammals do not innately know how to recognize members of their own species. Instead, they learn to make this distinction early in life. Imprinting takes place only during a specific period of time in the animal's life and is usually irreversible. For example, birds that leave the nest immediately after hatching, such as geese, imprint on their mother. They

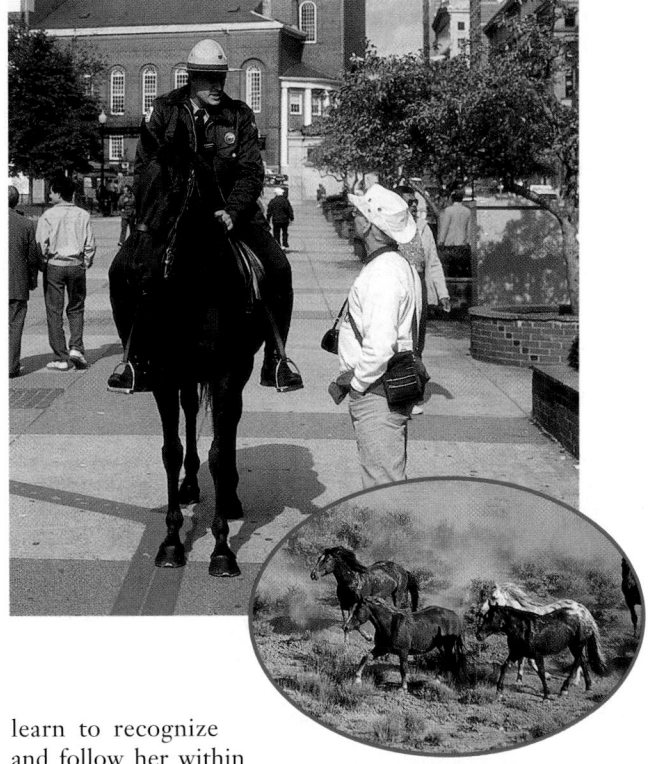

learn to recognize and follow her within a day of hatching.

In birds such as ducks, imprinting takes place during the first day or two after hatching. A duckling rapidly learns to recognize and follow the first conspicuous moving object it sees. Normally, that object is the duckling's mother. Learning to recognize their mother and follow her ensures that food and protection will always be nearby.

Learning by trial and error

Do you remember when you first learned how to ride a bicycle? You probably tried many times before being able to successfully complete the task. Nest building, like riding a bicycle, may be a learning experience. The first time a jackdaw builds a nest, it uses grass, bits of glass, stones, empty cans, old lightbulbs, and anything else it can find.

Figure 33.12
Habituation is a loss of sensitivity to certain stimuli. Young horses often are afraid of cars and noisy streets. Gradually, they become habituated to the city and ignore normal sights and sounds.

Visual Learning
Figure 33.12 Ask students to explain how each of the horses may become habituated to different stimuli.

 The BioLab at the end of the chapter can be used at this point in the lesson.

Reinforcement
Show students photos of mother animals and their young. Ask if they know how a mother is able to identify her own young and vice versa. Ask them to explain why imprinting would be important for animals in herds.

Biology Journal
Whale Communication Certain whales are known for their melodious songs. Play a recording of whale songs to the class. Ask students to describe in their journals the songs of the whales. Provide library resources and ask them to figure out whether the sounds the whales make are innate or learned. **L2**

CHALLENGE ACTIVITY

Do ants learn? Ask students to conduct an experiment to see if ants learn. They should set food farther away from an ant's nest at regular intervals. Ask students to determine if the ants learn to anticipate where food will be. Have students record their observations. **L3**

PROJECT

Imprinting Konrad Z. Lorenz has been called the "father of ethology." During the 1930s, he studied the behavior of birds and developed a theory of animal behavior that stressed its inherited aspects. Ask a group of students to present a skit about the work of Konrad Lorenz. **L2** **COOP LEARN**

Purpose

Students will conduct an experiment to test the nature of trial-and-error learning.

Process Skills

interpret data, think critically, collect data, draw a conclusion

Teaching Strategies

■ Have students work in teams of two. One can be the time keeper while the other does the puzzle. The time keeper should not watch the student doing the assembly but should be told when the assembler begins and completes the puzzle.

■ Prepare puzzle pieces in advance and place on card stock. Save puzzle pieces in plastic bags for students in later classes.

■ Enlarge puzzle pieces shown on the student page to approximately twice their size for your students.

Expected Results

Student times needed to complete the puzzle will decline with each trial.

Analysis

1. times decreased
2. The ability to work the puzzle was an example of learned behavior.
3. Student answers may vary. Imprinting and conditioning were not involved with this type of learning. Trial-and-error learning was operating with the initial solving of the puzzle, but later trials may have relied upon insight.

Assessment

Portfolio Ask students to describe how the experiment could be modified to introduce the aspect of motivation in solving the puzzle. Use the Performance Task Assessment List for Assessing a Whole Experiment and Planning the Next Experiment in **PASC**, p. 105. **L2**

870

Experiment

Solving a Puzzle You are given a bunch of keys and asked to open a door. How do you go about finding the right key? Several attempts are needed, and then finally, the door opens. The next time you are asked to perform the same task, can you go directly to the correct key? Chances are, you can. You have learned how to solve this problem.

Procedure

1 Copy the data table below.

2 Obtain a paper puzzle from your teacher.

3 Time how long it takes you to assemble the puzzle pieces into a perfect square.

4 Record the time it took and call this Trial 1.

5 Disassemble the square and mix the pieces.

6 Repeat step 3 for four more trials.

Data Table	
Trial	**Time Needed to Complete Square Puzzle**
1	
2	
3	
4	
5	

Analysis

1. **Interpret data** Explain how the time needed to complete the puzzle changed from Trial 1 to Trial 5.
2. **Infer** Was the final completion of the puzzle an example of innate or learned behavior? Explain your answer.
3. **Analyze** When solving the puzzle, what role might imprinting, trial and error, conditioning, and insight have played in improving your trial times?

Figure 33.13
Mice soon learn where grain is stored in a barn and are motivated by hunger to chew through the storage containers.

With experience, the bird finds that grasses and twigs make a better nest than do lightbulbs. The jackdaw has used **trial-and-error learning** in which an animal receives a reward for making a particular response. When an animal tries one solution and then another in the course of obtaining a reward, in this case a suitable nest, it is learning by trial and error. Find out for yourself how trial and error learning works in the *MiniLab* on this page.

Learning happens more quickly if there is a reason to learn or be successful. **Motivation** is an internal need that causes an animal to act, and it is necessary for learning to take place. In most animals, motivation often involves satisfying a physical need, such as hunger or thirst. If an animal isn't motivated, it won't learn. Animals that aren't hungry won't respond to a food reward. Mice living in a barn, shown in *Figure 33.13*, discover that they can eat all the grain they like if they first chew through the container in which the grain is stored.

CHALLENGE ACTIVITY

Rodent Behavior Have students construct a simple maze for small rodents such as mice and gerbils. Students should determine how many trials it takes for each type of rodent to learn the maze. Ask students to write a report on rodent learning for their portfolios. **L3** **COOP LEARN**

Figure 33.14

In the early 1900s, Ivan Pavlov, a Russian biologist, first demonstrated classical conditioning in dogs.

A Pavlov noted that dogs salivate when they smell food. Responding to the smell of food is a reflex, an example of innate behavior.

B By ringing a bell each time he presented food to a dog, Pavlov established an association between the food and the ringing bell.

C Eventually, the dog salivated at the sound of the bell alone. The dog had been conditioned to respond to a stimulus that it did not normally associate with food.

Classical conditioning: Learning by association

Suppose that when you first got a new kitten, it would meow as soon as it smelled the aroma of cat food in the can you were opening. After a few weeks, the sound of the can opener alone attracted your kitten, causing it to meow. Your kitten had become conditioned to respond to a stimulus other than the smell of food. **Classical conditioning** is learning by association. A well-known example of an early experiment in classical conditioning is illustrated in *Figure 33.14*.

Insight: The most complex type of learning

In a classic study of animal behavior, a chimpanzee was given two bamboo poles, neither of which was long enough to reach some fruit placed outside its cage. By connecting the two tapering short pieces to make one longer pole, the chimpanzee learned to solve the problem of how to reach the fruit. This type of learning is called insight. **Insight** is learning in which an animal uses previous experience to respond to a new situation.

Much of human learning is based on insight. When you were a baby, you learned a great deal by trial and error. As you grew older, you relied more on insight. Solving math problems is a daily instance of using insight. Probably your first experience with mathematics was when you learned to count. Based on your concept of numbers, you then learned to add, subtract, multiply, and divide. Years later, you continue to solve problems in mathematics based on your past experiences. When you encounter a problem you have never experienced before, you solve the problem through insight.

33.2 LEARNED BEHAVIOR **871**

Quick Demo

Habit Explain to students that doing something by habit has value because you don't waste time relearning the procedure each time you perform it. Ask students to write a set of directions for tying shoes. They should not tie or even look at shoes or laces as they write. Have them trade papers and then try to follow exactly the directions to tie one shoe. Ask them why it was difficult to describe how to tie a shoe. **L1**

✓**Reading Check** (p. 872)
Communication is an exchange of information that results in a change of behavior.

USING MODELS

Conditioning Ask student groups to design a step-by-step model training session to teach an animal by using conditioning. Those who have pets at home can test the model on a specific task to see if the model works. **L2**
COOP LEARN

TECH PREP

Imprinting Explain to students that biologists use puppets shaped like birds' heads to feed young birds raised in captivity. This is done to prevent them from imprinting on humans. Have students do research and make a puppet for feeding a young bird that may be raised in captivity.

Indiana Academic Standards

Pages 870–871: B.1.43

Purpose

Students will determine that the song of certain bird species is partially innate but mostly learned behavior.

Process Skills

analyze information, apply concepts, think critically, interpret scientific illustrations

Teaching Strategies

■ Advise students that the term "wild" refers to the sparrow raised in its natural surroundings.

■ Units along the left axis are kilocycles per second. Units along the bottom axis are in seconds of time.

Expected Results

Students will recognize that a small portion of the sparrow's song is innate, but the major portion of the song must be learned.

Analysis

1. Segment A is similar in both songs. Segments B and C are quite different.

2. Segment A appears to be innate; it would be impossible for the bird raised in isolation to have learned the first part of the song. Segments B and C must be learned because the bird raised in isolation cannot match these segments of the wild bird's song.

3. The majority of the bird's song appears to be learned because segments B and C are longer than segment A.

4. The bird will learn the correct sparrow song.

Assessment

Performance Have students design an experiment to test the hypothesis that birds raised in isolation will learn their proper song from a recording only immediately after hatching. Use the Performance Task Assessment List for Designing an Experiment in **PASC**, p. 95. 🄻2

872

Problem-Solving Lab 33.2

Interpret Data

Do birds learn how to sing? Do birds learn how to sing, or is this innate behavior? Most experimental evidence points to the fact that singing may be a combination of the two types of behavior, but in certain species, learning is critical in order to sing the species song correctly.

Solve the Problem

Bird sound spectrograms allow scientists to record and visually study the song patterns of birds. Using this tool, they recorded spectrograms for white-crowned sparrows. The top spectrogram is that of a wild white-crowned sparrow. The bottom spectrogram is that of a white-crowned sparrow hatched and raised in total isolation from all other birds. Segments of the song have been identified with the letters A–C.

Birds' Songs

Wild sparrow — A B C

Sparrow raised in isolation — A B C

Thinking Critically

1. **Compare and Contrast** In general, how do the two spectrograms compare?

2. **Read Graphs** Which segment of the sparrow's song may be innate? Learned? Explain your answers.

3. **Interpet Graphs** Does it appear that the majority of the sparrow's song is learned or innate? Explain your answer.

4. **Predict** In a different experiment, a recording of a white-crowned sparrow song was repeatedly played for a young bird raised in isolation. If a bird's song is mainly learned, predict the outcome of the experiment.

872

The Role of Communication

When you think about interactions among animals as a result of their behavior, you realize that some sort of communication has taken place. **Communication** is an exchange of information that results in a change of behavior. Black-headed gulls visually communicate their availability for mating with instinctive courtship behavior. The pat on the head from a dog's owner after the dog retrieves a stick signals a job well done.

✓ Reading Check **Define** the term *communication*.

Most animals communicate

Animals have several channels of communication open to them. They signal each other by sounds, sights, touches, or smells. Sounds vibrate in all directions and can be heard a long way from their sources. Sounds such as songs, roars, and calls communicate a lot of information quickly. For example, the song of a male cricket tells his sex, his location, his social status, and, because communication by sound is usually species specific, his species.

Signals that involve odors may be broadcast widely and carry a general message. Ants, shown in *Figure 33.15*, leave odor trails that are followed by other members of their nest. These odors are species specific. As you know, pheromones, such as those of moths, may be used to attract mates. Because only small amounts of pheromones are needed, other animals, especially predators, may be unable to detect the odor.

Figure 33.15
Ants follow chemical trails left by other ants to find food resources.

CULTURAL DIVERSITY

Bertram Fraser-Reid Discuss with students the important contributions of African American organic chemist, Bertram O. Fraser-Reid. His work involved synthesizing artificial insect pheromones as substitutes for dangerous insecticides. In Canada, the western pine beetle causes billions of dollars of damage to trees each year. Fraser-Reid reasoned that if he released artificial pheromones of female pine beetles in a part of the forest that contained no females, it might attract male pine beetles to the spot, thus preventing them from mating. Fraser-Reid's initial research laid the groundwork for future studies.

Using both innate and learned behavior

Some communication is a combination of both innate and learned behavior. In some species of songbirds, such as the one shown in *Figure 33.16*, males automatically sing when they reach sexual maturity. Their songs are specific to their species, and singing is innate behavior. Yet members of the same species that live in different regions learn different variations of the song. They learn to sing with a regional dialect. In other species, birds raised in isolation never learn to sing their species song. Find out more about the songs birds sing in the *Problem-Solving Lab* on the previous page.

Some animals use language

Language, the use of symbols to represent ideas, is present primarily in animals with complex nervous systems, memory, and insight. Humans, with the help of spoken and written language, can benefit from what other people and cultures have learned and don't have to experience everything for themselves. People can use the accumulated knowledge in the books shown in *Figure 33.17* to build new knowledge.

Figure 33.16
The Indigo bunting sings a high-pitched series of notes that descend the scale, then ascend again at the end of the song.

Figure 33.17
English and other languages are made up of words that have specific meanings. An amazing number of meanings can be communicated using words of any human language.

3 Assess

DAILY INTERVENTION

Check for Understanding
Write a list of behaviors on the chalkboard. Ask students to identify each as innate or learned. **L1**

Reteach
Interpersonal Have students play animal behavior charades. Write a number of behaviors on slips of paper. Have students draw a slip and act out the behavior. Class members will try to guess the name of the behavior and whether it is innate or learned. **L2** **ELL**
COOP LEARN

Resources
For more practice, use *Reading Essentials for Biology,* Section 33.2.

Extension

TECH PREP Ask students to accompany a wildlife specialist or a veterinarian on the job for a day. Have them report how knowledge of animal behavior is important to that particular job. **L2**

 Assessment

Portfolio Ask students to select a local animal species to observe. They should record behaviors and categorize them as innate, learned, or a combination of both. **L3**

Indiana Academic Standards

Pages 872–873: B.1.43

Section Assessment

Understanding Main Ideas

1. How is imprinting different from other types of learned behavior?

2. Compare and contrast trial-and-error learning and insight. Give an example of each.

3. Explain by example the difference between trial-and-error learning and classical conditioning.

4. What is the difference between communication and language?

5. How does an animal become habituated to a stimulus?

Thinking Critically

6. How does learning have survival value in a changing environment? Explain your answer by using an example from your daily life.

SKILL REVIEW

7. **Observe and Infer** Two dog trainers teach dogs to do tricks. One trainer gives her dog a food treat whenever the dog correctly performs the trick. The other trainer does not use treats. Which trainer will be more successful at dog training? Why? For more help, refer to *Observe and Infer* in the **Skill Handbook**.

in.bdol.glencoe.com/self_check_quiz

33.2 LEARNED BEHAVIOR **873**

Section Assessment

1. Imprinting takes place during a specific period of an animal's life. Other learned behaviors may develop later.

2. In trial-and-error learning, an animal tries different options while obtaining a reward for choosing a particular one. Learning to ride a bicycle is done by trial and error. Insight is learning while using previous experience in a new situation. Learning math uses insight.

3. You learn to ride a bicycle by trial-and-error learning; an animal may be conditioned to the sound of a can opener.

4. Communication is an exchange of information resulting in a change of behavior, whereas language is the use of symbols to represent ideas.

5. Habituation occurs when an animal has been repeatedly given a stimulus not associated with punishment or reward and it no longer responds to the stimulus.

6. Behavior can be modified to deal with a changing environment.

7. The dog will be more easily trained if it is rewarded when it responds correctly.

INVESTIGATE BioLab

Time Allotment
one class period

Process Skills
collect data, experiment, hypothesize, define operationally, observe and infer, conclude, think critically, use numbers

Safety Precautions
Have students wash their hands thoroughly with soap and water after handling lab specimens.

PREPARATION

No special housing or food are needed if snails are used almost immediately upon arrival from a supply house.

PROCEDURE

Teaching Strategies
- Small disposable plastic petri dishes (60 mm diameter × 15 mm deep) or Syracuse watch glasses are ideal.
- Allow students to prepare the probe. Substitute a wooden match or cotton swab for the pencil portion of the probe. Simply snip a rubber band in half to obtain the needed section.
- Have students work in small groups of three or four.

Troubleshooting
- Students must be able to tell front and rear ends of the snails. They are easy to tell apart macroscopically. Review the differences with students.
- Students must be cautioned about not striking the snail too hard with the rubber band probe.

Before You Begin
Land snails are members of the mollusk class Gastropoda. Land snails live on or near the ground, feed on decaying organic matter, and breathe with gills or, in some cases, with a simple lung. Land snails sense their environment with a pair of antennae and eyes. Snails are excellent organisms for behavioral studies because they show a variety of consistent responses to certain stimuli.

Behavior of a Snail

PREPARATION

Problem
How can you test the behavior of snails to touch stimuli?

Objectives
In this BioLab, you will:
- **Test** the response of snails to touch.
- **Measure** the time needed for habituation to occur after repeated touch stimuli.

Materials
snails	spring water
dropper	small dish
scissors	dissecting microscope
probe constructed from tape, rubber band, and pencil	

Safety Precautions
CAUTION: *Always wear goggles in the lab. Wash your hands with soap and water both before and after handling any animals. Use caution when working with live animals. Be careful not to harm the snails.*

Skill Handbook
If you need help with this lab, refer to the **Skill Handbook**.

PROCEDURE

1. Copy the data table.
2. Prepare a stimulator probe by taping a small piece of a cut rubber band to the tip of a pencil.
3. Cover the bottom of a small dish with spring water.

A land snail

4. Obtain a snail from your teacher and place it in the dish.
5. Use a dissecting microscope to examine and locate its head. Its head has two antennae that it can extend and retract.
6. Place the dish on your desk.

- Some stimulations will result in no response. Students should record exactly what they observe. Habituation will be difficult to achieve, if at all. Students will tire before the snail does.

Data and Observations
Both ends are sensitive to touch. Students may detect no response when performing a specific trial. Habituation will usually not occur.

7. Lightly touch the snail's anterior end using the end of the probe. Note if it responds (yes or no), and record any movement. Conduct a total of five trials.

8. Repeat step 7, touching the snail's posterior end.

9. Repeat step 7, touching the middle of the snail's body.

10. Test the snail's ability to become habituated.

   a. Continue to touch the snail's anterior end with the probe every 10 seconds until habituation occurs. Continue testing for a reasonable length of time if habituation does not occur.

   b. Count and record the number of stimulations needed for habituation.

11. **CLEANUP AND DISPOSAL** Return your snail to the area designated by your teacher. Clean all equipment and return everything to its proper place for reuse. Wash your hands thoroughly with soap and water.

Data Table

Body Area	Response to Touch		
Trial	Anterior	Posterior	Middle
1	Yes	Yes	Yes
2	Yes	Yes	Yes
3	Yes	Yes	Yes
4	Yes	Yes	Yes
5	Yes	Yes	Yes

Habituation Studies

Rate of Stimulation	Number of Stimulations Needed to Reach Habituation
every 10 seconds	Habituation usually does not occur. Snail may retreat into its shell.

ANALYZE AND CONCLUDE

1. **Hypothesize** Are the responses to touch shown by snails learned or innate? Explain your answer.

2. **Observe** Describe the direction that a snail moves when its anterior and posterior ends are stimulated. Does one end appear to be more sensitive than the other? Is the middle sensitive to touch? Is the speed of response slow or rapid?

3. **Explain** How is the behavior of responding to touch an adaptation for survival?

4. **Experiment** Why did you perform several trials for each experiment involving stimulation of the anterior, posterior, and middle of the snail?

5. **Define Operationally** Define the term *habituation*.

6. **ERROR ANALYSIS** Suppose you hypothesized that snails are quickly habituated to touch. Is this hypothesis supported by your data? Explain.

Apply Your Skill

Experiment Form a hypothesis regarding snail behavior when given a choice between light and dark conditions. Design and carry out an experiment to test your hypothesis.

 Web Links To find out more about animal behavior, visit in.bdol.glencoe.com/animal_behavior

ANALYZE AND CONCLUDE

1. Student answers may vary. These responses are innate because the animals lack a large enough brain to learn behavior; they do not have the opportunity to learn correct behavior because the first time they do not respond correctly, they may be eaten by a predator.

2. The snail moves backward when the anterior end is touched. The snail moves forward when the posterior end is touched. The anterior appears to be more sensitive to touch. The middle is less sensitive to touch.

3. The snail will move away from predators rapidly.

4. Student answers will vary; good experimental technique, failure to make contact with probe, etc.

5. Habituation is the lack of a response after repeated stimulation.

6. **ERROR ANALYSIS** Most students will find that habituation did not occur rapidly. This may be due in part to the inconsistency of the amount of pressure applied and the amount of time the probe was applied.

Apply Your Skill

Experiment Snails can also respond by withdrawing into their shells. Have students determine under what conditions snails withdraw rather than move away. **L1** **ELL**

CLEANUP AND DISPOSAL

Ask students to return their snails to the terrarium and wash and carefully rinse any soap from the dishes in which they tested their snails. Make sure students wash their hands with warm soapy water.

Assessment

Performance Ask students to plan an experiment that could be used to test a snail's response to rapid changes in light intensity. Use the Performance Task Assessment List for Designing an Experiment in **PASC**, p. 95. **L2**

Indiana Academic Standards

Pages 874–875: B.1.18, B.1.43

Purpose
Students become familiar with tagging and with satellite telemetry as methods of tracking animal migrations.

Background
Four species of sea turtles found along the U.S. coast are on the endangered species list: Kemp's ridley, hawksbill, Florida green, and leatherback. A fifth species, the loggerhead, is threatened.

The Florida green turtle nests from June to October, and a female will nest every two to four years. During a nesting year, the female will lay clutches of about 115 eggs at 12-day intervals.

Teaching Strategies
■ Have students locate the Caribbean Sea on a map. Point out that satellite tracking is especially useful for following the movements of animals that travel large distances.

■ Go over with students the definition of the word *telemetry*. Telemetry is the science of transmitting data over a distance via radio waves. It comes from the Greek words *tele*, meaning "distance," and *metron*, meaning "measure."

Applying Biotechnology

Students are likely to hypothesize that these areas are green turtle feeding grounds. The hypothesis could be tested by going to the area to see if turtles are feeding there, or by sampling the area for the presence of organisms on which the turtles are known to feed.

BIO TECHNOLOGY

Tracking Sea Turtles

Florida green turtle

The Florida green turtle (*Chelonia mydas mydas*) is an endangered species that nests on sandy beaches. It is found in temperate and tropical waters, including the southeastern coast of the United States. Like other sea turtles, the Florida green turtle spends virtually all of its life at sea; however, adult females visit beaches several times a year to lay their eggs.

Studying sea turtles presents a challenge because they spend so little time on land. Research is most easily conducted on the beach, where the nesting behavior of the females can be directly observed. These observations have provided important information about how to protect the nesting sites from human disturbance or predation. But more information about the Florida green turtle is needed because protecting an endangered species requires knowing what environmental factors are crucial to its survival.

Tagging To study these animals, researchers affix a small plastic or metal tag onto the flipper of a captured turtle. The tag is etched with an identification number. If the animal is captured again, the date and location are shared with other turtle researchers. But even when a tagged turtle is recaptured, the route the animal took to move from one location to another remains unknown.

Satellite tracking Recent improvements in satellite telemetry are making it possible for researchers to keep much better track of individual turtles as they swim from place to place. A transmitter the size of a small, portable cassette player is attached to the shell behind the turtle's neck. The battery-powered transmitter will work for six to ten months before it falls off. When the turtle comes to the surface to breathe, the transmitter broadcasts data in the form of a digital signal to an orbiting communications satellite. The satellite transmits the data to a receiving station on Earth.

The digital signal contains information about the turtle's latitude and longitude, the number of dives it made in the past 24 hours, the length of its most recent dive, and the temperature of the water. By plotting the location of data transmissions on a map, researchers can track the direction and speed in which the animal is moving.

Problems with satellite tracking Sometimes a transmitter stops working after just a few weeks, and there are problems with the data itself. Increasingly accurate information will become available as the technology improves and as more turtles are included in satellite tracking efforts.

Applying Biotechnology

Think Critically Telemetry data from a Florida green turtle indicate the animal has spent the past several days in an offshore location characterized by coral reefs and seagrass meadows. Past telemetry data from other green turtles indicate that these animals periodically interrupt their travels to stop at this location and at other coral reefs and seagrass meadows. Form a hypothesis that could explain this behavior. How could you test your hypothesis?

 To find out more about sea turtle migration, visit in.bdol.glencoe.com/biotechnology

Going Further

Invite students to learn more about the life cycle of the Florida green turtle, or to find out what other species of animals are currently being tracked via satellite telemetry.

STUDY GUIDE

Section 33.1

Innate Behavior

Key Concepts
- Behavior is anything an animal does in response to a stimulus.
- Many behaviors have adaptive value and are shaped by natural selection.
- Innate behavior is inherited. Innate behaviors include fixed-action patterns, automatic responses and instincts.
- Automatic responses include reflexes and fight-or-flight responses.
- An instinct is a complex pattern of innate behaviors.
- Behaviors such as courtship rituals, displays of aggressive behavior, territoriality, dominance hierarchies, hibernation, and migration are all forms of instinctive behavior.
  - Pecking order is an example of a dominance hierarchy.

Vocabulary
aggressive behavior (p. 864)
behavior (p. 859)
circadian rhythm (p. 865)
courtship behavior (p. 862)
dominance hierarchy (p. 864)
estivation (p. 866)
fight-or-flight response (p. 861)
hibernation (p. 866)
innate behavior (p. 861)
instinct (p. 862)
migration (p. 865)
reflex (p. 861)
territory (p. 863)

Section 33.2

Learned Behavior

Key Concepts
- Learning takes place when behavior changes through practice or experience.
- Learned behavior has adaptive value.
- Learning includes habituation, imprinting, trial and error, and classical conditioning.
- The most complex type of learning is learning by insight.
- Some animals use language, whereas most communicate by either visual, auditory, or chemical signals.

Vocabulary
communication (p. 872)
classical conditioning (p. 871)
habituation (p. 869)
imprinting (p. 869)
insight (p. 871)
language (p. 873)
motivation (p. 870)
trial-and-error learning (p. 870)

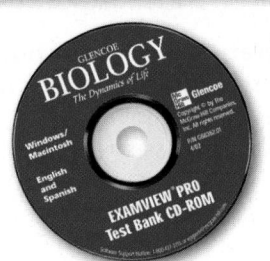

FOLDABLES **Study Organizer** To help you review animal behavior, use the Organizational Study Fold on page 868.

 in.bdol.glencoe.com/vocabulary_puzzlemaker

CHAPTER 33 ASSESSMENT **877**

Chapter 33 Assessment

Key Concepts
Summary statements can be used by students to review the major concepts of the chapter.

Biology Online

Visit in.bdol.glencoe.com
/self_check_quiz
/vocabulary_puzzlemaker
/chapter_test
/standardized_test

VOCABULARY PUZZLEMAKER

For additional help with vocabulary, have students access the Vocabulary PuzzleMaker online at in.bdol.glencoe.com/vocabulary_puzzlemaker

FOLDABLES™
Have students use their Foldables to review the content of Section 33.2. On the back of each tab, have them give an example of those that are learned behaviors.

Use the ExamView®Pro Test Bank CD-ROM to:
- Create **multiple versions** of tests
- Create **modified** tests with one mouse click for **inclusion** students
- **Edit** existing questions and **add** your own questions
- Build tests aligned with state standards using built-in **State Curriculum Tags**
- Change **English** tests to **Spanish** with one mouse click and vice versa

 Indiana Academic Standards
Pages 876–877: B.1.18, B.1.31

The Princeton Review **Questions and answers have been aligned and verified by The Princeton Review.**

Vocabulary Review

1. dominance hierarchy
2. imprinting
3. instinct
4. insight
5. territory

Understanding Key Concepts

6. B	8. D	10. C
7. A	9. C	11. B

Constructed Response

12. When animals exhibit certain behaviors that increase their likelihood of surviving—reproducing and passing on their variations to the next generation—the result is natural selection.

13. Ivan Pavlov observed dogs' natural behavior when food was presented. He hypothesized that the dogs could be conditioned to respond to the sound of a bell as if it were food. He designed an experiment to test his hypothesis. He rang a bell each time he fed a dog, then again when the dog smelled food. Finally, when he rang the bell with no food stimulus, the dog salivated. He concluded that the dog had been conditioned to respond to a stimulus that it did not normally associate with food.

14. They had learned not to fear large animals because there were no large predators on the islands.

Thinking Critically

15. They show alarm with the hawk model, but not with the goose because a hawk is a potential predator of the duckling, and the goose is

878

Vocabulary Review

Review the Chapter 33 vocabulary words listed in the Study Guide on page 877. Match the words with the definitions below.

1. innate behavior by which animals form a social ranking within a group in which some individuals are more subordinate than others; usually has one top-ranking individual

2. learned behavior in which an animal, at a specific critical time of its life, forms a social attachment to another object

3. complex innate behavior pattern that begins when an animal recognizes a stimulus and performs an action until all parts of the behavior have been formed

4. type of learning in which an animal uses previous experiences to respond to a new situation

5. physical space an animal defends against other members of its species; may contain an animal's breeding area, feeding area, potential mates, or all three

Understanding Key Concepts

6. Your adult dog is chewing on a bone when a puppy approaches. Your dog growls at the puppy. What type of behavior is your dog exhibiting?
   A. conditioning   C. habituation
   B. aggressive behavior   D. fighting

7. Animals with behavior that makes them more successful at surviving and reproducing tend to produce more _____.
   A. offspring   C. territory
   B. aggression   D. eggs

8. When a toad flips out its tongue to catch an insect flying past, it is exhibiting _____.
   A. learned behavior   C. territoriality
   B. courtship behavior D. innate behavior

9. Caribou are _____ when they move from their winter homes in the forests to the tundra for the summer.
   A. hibernating   C. migrating
   B. imprinting   D. learning

---

10. Establishing _____ reduces the need for aggressive behavior among members of the same species.
    A. reflexes   C. territories
    B. conditioning   D. habituation

11. Your cat exhibits _____ when it runs for its food dish upon hearing the can opener.
    A. insight   C. habituation
    B. conditioning   D. imprinting

Constructed Response

12. **Open Ended** Explain the result of natural selection in animal behavior.

13. **Open Ended** Explain how Ivan Pavlov used scientific methods to study classical conditioning.

14. **Recognize Cause and Effect** When Charles Darwin visited the Galápagos Islands in 1835, he was amazed that the animals would allow him to touch them. Hypothesize why they were not afraid.

Thinking Critically

15. **Compare and Contrast** Ducklings display an alarm reaction when a model of a hawk is flown over their heads and no alarm reaction when a model of a goose is flown over their heads. After several days, neither model causes any reaction. Compare the effects of the two models during the first two days with the effects of the same models two weeks later.

16. **REAL WORLD BIOCHALLENGE** Visit in.bdol.glencoe.com to investigate bee behavior and communication. Include historic discoveries about how bees communicate with other members of the hive as to where a new food source is. Also include the results of the most recent research about how bees measure the distance to a food source. Present the results of your research to your class in the form of a poster or multimedia presentation.

 in.bdol.glencoe.com/chapter_test

---

not. This is instinctive behavior. When there are no dangerous results, the ducklings become habituated to the hawk model.

16. Students' answers will vary depending on what journals they read.

17. 1. innate behavior;
    2. imprinting; 3. insight;
    4. habituation;
    5. conditioning

RUBRIC

Evaluating Open-Ended Questions
Open-ended assessment questions are graded by using a multilevel rubric that guides you in assessing a student's knowledge of a particular concept. The following rubric is a sample scoring device.

17. Concept Map
Complete the concept map by using the following vocabulary terms: innate behavior, imprinting, habituation, conditioning, insight.

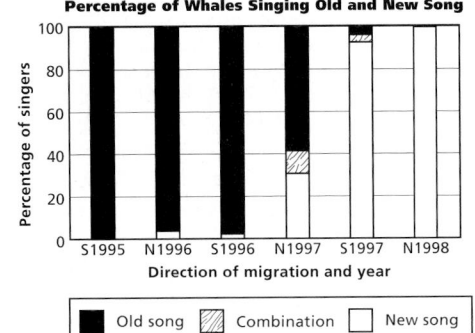

Animal behavior —includes— 1. —and— learned behavior

such as

2. 3. 4. 5.

The assessed Indiana standard appears next to the question.

End-of-Course Assessment Practice

All questions aligned and verified by The Princeton Review

Part 1 Multiple Choice

Study the graph and answer questions 18–19.

Recognition of Sheep Faces by Other Sheep

Average % correct (y-axis: 0, 25, 50, 75, 100)
Days after training (x-axis: 75–200, 201–400, 401–600, 601–800)

18. The recognition of sheep faces by other sheep can be described as _____.
A. more than 75% correct even after 800 days
B. less than 50% correct after 400 days
C. remembering 80 sheep after 800 days
D. remembering 800 sheep after 80 days

19. The ability of sheep to recognize faces may
B.1.31 be an adaptation to _____.
A. escaping predators
B. living in a herd
C. finding food
D. cold climate

On the east coast of Australia, humpback whales sing the same song while they migrate north and south. Use the graph to answer questions 20–21.

Percentage of Whales Singing Old and New Song

Percentage of singers (y-axis: 0, 20, 40, 60, 80, 100)
Direction of migration and year (x-axis: S1995, N1996, S1996, N1997, S1997, N1998)

Legend: ■ Old song ▨ Combination ☐ New song
N North   S South

20. In 1996, _____.
A. all whales sang the old song
B. all whales sang the new song
C. one or two whales sang a new song
D. no migration occurred

21. By 1998, all whales sang _____.
A. the new song
B. the old song
C. the old and new songs
D. the intermediate song

Part 2 Constructed Response/Grid In

Record your answers on your answer document.

22. Open Ended Some bird species give differing calls depending on the source of alarm. Other birds of the same species either scan the ground or the sky in response to the calls. Infer what the birds may be communicating.

23. Open Ended What would be the advantage of a dominance hierarchy in members of a species
B.1.31 that are not defending a territory?

 in.bdol.glencoe.com/standardized_test

RUBRIC

SCORE	CRITERIA
4	A correct solution that is supported by well-developed, accurate explanations.
3	A generally correct solution, but may contain minor flaws in reasoning.

SCORE	CRITERIA
2	A partially correct interpretation and/or solution to the problem.
1	A correct solution with no supporting evidence or explanation.
0	An incorrect solution or no solution is given.

Chapter 33 Assessment

End-of-Course Assessment Practice

18. A
19. B
20. C
21. A
22. They may be aggressive displays, courtship displays, playful displays, or an announcement of an event or place, such as a place to feed. Other well-thought-out answers may also be accepted.
23. A dominance hierarchy would reduce aggression at common feeding sites.

FAST FILE

Answer Sheet A practice answer sheet can be found on p. 139 of *Unit 9 FAST FILE Resources.*

Name _____ Date _____ Class _____

Chapter 33 Assessment
Student Recording Sheet

Use with pages 878–879 of the Student Edition

Vocabulary Review
Write the vocabulary words that match the definitions in your book.
1. _____ 4. _____
2. _____ 5. _____
3. _____

Understanding Key Concepts
Select the best answer from the choices given and fill in the corresponding oval.
6. A B C D   9. A B C D
7. A B C D   10. A B C D
8. A B C D   11. A B C D

Constructed Response
Record your answers for Questions 12 and 13 on a separate sheet of paper.

Thinking Critically
Record your answer for Question 14 on a separate sheet of paper.
15. REAL WORLD BIOCHALLENGE Follow your teacher's instructions for presenting your BioChallenge answer.
16. Fill in the correct terms to complete the concept map.
1. _____ 3. _____
2. _____ 4. _____

Standardized Test Practice
Part 1 Multiple Choice
Select the best answer from the choices given and fill in the corresponding oval.
17. A B C D   19. A B C D
18. A B C D   20. A B C D

Part 2 Constructed Response/Grid In
Record your answers for Questions 21 and 22 on a separate sheet of paper.

CHAPTER ASSESSMENT   CHAPTER 33 Animal Behavior 139

Indiana Academic Standards
Pages 878–879: B.1.31, B.1.43

879

Prepare

Short on Time?

This BioDigest can be used as an introduction to or as an overview of the vertebrate classes. You may wish to use this unit summary to teach about vertebrates in place of the chapters in the vertebrates unit.

Key Concepts

Students will study vertebrates by comparing and contrasting the features of fishes, amphibians, reptiles, birds, and mammals. Students learn that there are four classes of fishes as compared with one class each of amphibians, reptiles, birds, and mammals. Students will trace the evolution of vertebrates and identify the similar traits that are found within all the vertebrate classes. Students will see differences in form that correspond to adaptations to different habitats as vertebrate ancestors moved from life in the water to life on land.

1 Focus

Bellringer

Collect pictures of many different kinds of vertebrates and place them on the bulletin board. Number each picture. As students enter the classroom, have them take a sheet of notebook paper and list the names of the numbered animals. Ask students what all these animals have in common. They should be able to list some vertebrate characteristics, such as having a backbone. **L1**

Vertebrates

Like all chordates, vertebrates have a notochord, pharyngeal pouches, a dorsal hollow nerve cord, and postanal tail. However, in vertebrates the notochord is replaced during development by a backbone. All vertebrates are bilaterally symmetrical coelomate animals that have an endoskeleton, a closed circulatory system, an efficient respiratory system, and a complex brain and nervous system.

Fishes

All fishes are ectotherms, animals with body temperatures dependent upon an external heat source. Fishes have two-chambered hearts and breathe through gills. Fishes are grouped into four different classes.

Two Classes of Jawless Fishes

Lampreys and hagfishes make up the two classes of jawless fishes. Jawless fishes have endoskeletons made of cartilage, like sharks and rays, but they do not have jaws.

Cartilaginous Fishes

Sharks, skates, and rays are cartilaginous fishes. Fossil evidence shows that jaws first evolved in these fishes. Cartilaginous fishes have endoskeletons made of cartilage, paired fins, and a lateral line system that enables them to detect movement and vibrations in water.

Cartilaginous fishes such as this whitetip reef shark have internal fertilization. In some species of cartilaginous fishes, development of fertilized eggs is external; other species give live birth to well-developed young.

Bony Fishes

Most fish species belong to the bony fishes. All bony fishes have a bony skeleton, gills, paired fins, flattened bony scales, and a lateral line system. Bony fishes breathe by drawing water into their mouths, then passing it over gills where gas exchange occurs. They adjust their depth in the water by regulating the amount of gas that diffuses out of their blood into a swim bladder. Most bony fishes fertilize their eggs externally and leave the survival of the offspring to chance.

VITAL STATISTICS

Fishes

Size ranges: Largest: Whale shark, length, 15 m; smallest: Dwarf goby, length, 1 cm
Distribution: Freshwater, saltwater, and estuarine habitats worldwide
Unusual adaptations: Electric eels can deliver an electrical charge of 650 volts, which stuns or kills their prey. Some deep-sea fishes have their own bioluminescent lures to help capture prey.
Longest-lived: Lake sturgeon, 80 years
Numbers of species:
Class Myxini—hagfishes, 43 species
Class Cephalaspidomorphi—lampreys, 17 species
Class Chondrichthyes—cartilaginous fishes, 850 species
Class Osteichthyes—bony fishes, 18 007 species

RESOURCE MANAGER

Unit 9 *FAST FILE* Resources
   Reinforcement and Study Guide in English, pp. 141–142
   Reinforcement and Study Guide in Spanish, pp. 143–144
   Student Recording Sheet, p. 145

Amphibians

Amphibians are ectothermic vertebrates with three-chambered hearts, lungs, and thin, moist skin. Although they have lungs, most gas exchange in amphibians is carried out through the skin. As adults, the majority of amphibians live on land, however, many of these species rely on water for reproduction. Most amphibians go through metamorphosis, in which the young hatch into tadpoles, which gradually lose their tails and gills as they develop legs, lungs, and other adult structures.

Amphibian Classification

Amphibians are classified into three orders: Anura, frogs and toads; Caudata, salamanders and newts; and Apoda, legless caecilians. Frogs and toads have vocal cords that can produce a wide range of sounds. Frogs have thin, smooth, moist skin and toads have thick, bumpy skin with poison glands. Salamanders have long, slender bodies with a neck and tail. Caecilians are amphibians with long, wormlike bodies and no legs.

Like other amphibians, salamanders have smooth, moist skin and lack true claws on their toes. Salamanders are carnivorous, feeding on insects, worms, and small mollusks.

Caecilians are long, limbless amphibians adapted for burrowing and living underground.

VITAL STATISTICS

Amphibians

Size ranges: Largest: Goliath frog, length, 30 cm; Chinese giant salamander, length, 1.8 m; Smallest frog: *Psyllophryne didactyla*, length, 9.8 mm
Distribution: Tropical and temperate regions worldwide
Numbers of species:
Class Amphibia
    Order Anura—frogs and toads, 3700 species
    Order Caudata—salamanders and newts, 369 species
    Order Apoda—legless caecilians, 168 species

The tympanic membrane, or eardrum, is located behind and below the frog's eye. It transmits vibrations from the air or water to the frog's inner ear.

2 Teach
Field Trip
Naturalist Arrange a class trip to a local zoological park, nature center, or other park or natural area where students will be able to see representatives of the classes of vertebrates discussed in this unit. Ask students to list as many vertebrates as they see, then divide the animals into classes. Ask them to identify the characteristics they used to classify the animals. L2

Display
Visual-Spatial Ask students to prepare a bulletin board display of bony fishes by cutting out pictures of bony fishes from nature magazines. Fishes should be identified and each fish should have one part labeled, such as scales, lateral line, gills, and fins. L1 ELL

Biology Journal
Fun Facts Have students research to find out some fun facts about different amphibians. Students can record the results of their research in their journals and share them with the class. L2

PROJECT

Photo Essay Ask a group of students to go to a nearby zoo and take photographs of the animals. Have them present a photo essay to the class. Ask them to discuss whether each animal is endangered or threatened and any programs undertaken to support these animals. L2 COOP LEARN

 Indiana Academic Standards

Pages 880–881: B.1.15, B.1.17, B.1.19

881

Visual Learning

Direct students' attention to the photos of the snake and the crocodile. Using the photos and any previous knowledge, ask them to explain how the snake and the crocodile are alike and how they are different. They are both ectotherms with skin that is dry, thick, and covered with scales. They both have lungs and lay eggs with leathery shells. The snake does not have legs, whereas the crocodile has four legs. The snake has a three-chambered heart and the crocodile has a four-chambered heart.

Display

Visual-Spatial Have students prepare a bulletin board display of local reptiles. Have them do research to determine if there are any local endangered reptiles. **L1**

Vertebrates

Reptiles

Reptiles are ectotherms with dry, scaly skin and clawed toes. They include snakes, lizards, turtles, crocodiles, and alligators. With the exception of snakes, all reptiles have four legs that are positioned somewhat underneath their bodies. Most reptiles have a three-chambered heart, but crocodilians have a four-chambered heart in which oxygenated blood is kept entirely separate from blood without oxygen. The scaly skin of reptiles reduces the loss of body moisture on land, but scales also prevent the skin from absorbing or releasing gases to the air. Reptiles are entirely dependent upon lungs for this essential gas exchange.

◄ Constrictors, such as this emerald tree boa, hold prey with their mouths, then wrap coils around the prey's body. The snake tightens its coils, preventing inhalation, and the prey suffocates.

▲ All crocodilians have a strong, muscular jaw and teeth that are in sockets. Crocodiles generally have a narrower snout in comparison with alligators.

FOCUS ON ADAPTATIONS

The Amniotic Egg

Nile crocodile hatchling

Reptiles were the first group of vertebrates to live entirely on land. They evolved a thick, scaly skin that prevented water loss from body tissues. They evolved strong skeletons, with limbs positioned somewhat underneath their bodies. These limbs enabled them to move quickly on land, avoiding or seeking the sun as their body temperatures demanded. But perhaps their most important adaptation to life on land was the development of the amniotic egg.

Protecting the embryo An amniotic egg encloses the embryo in amniotic fluid; provides the yolk, a source of food for the embryo; and surrounds both the embryo and yolk with membranes and a tough, leathery shell. These structures in the egg help prevent

---

The shell of a turtle consists of bony plates covered with horny shields. A turtle can pull its head and legs into the shell to protect itself against predators.

All turtles, including this olive ridley, a marine species, lay eggs in nests they dig in the ground. After the eggs are laid, the female turtle covers them and leaves.

VITAL STATISTICS

Reptiles

Size ranges: Largest: Anaconda snake, length, 9 m; Leatherback turtle, mass, 680 kg; smallest: Thread snake, length, 1.3 cm

Distribution: Temperate and tropical forests, deserts, and grasslands, and freshwater, salt-water, and estuarine habitats worldwide

Reptile that causes most human death: King cobra, 7500 deaths per year

Numbers of species:
Class Reptilia
  Order Squamata—snakes and lizards, 6800 species
  Order Chelonia—turtles, 250 species
  Order Crocodilia—crocodiles and alligators, 25 species
  Order Rhynchocephalia—tuataras, 2 species

Internal Fertilization

All reptiles have internal fertilization and most species lay eggs. The development of the amniotic egg enabled reptiles to move away from a dependence upon water for reproduction. The amniotic egg provides nourishment to the embryo and protects it from drying out as it develops.

dehydration and injury to the embryo as it develops on land. Most reptiles lay their eggs in protected places beneath sand, soil, gravel, or bark.

Membranes inside the egg Membranes found inside the amniotic egg include the amnion, the chorion, and the allantois. The amnion is a membrane filled with fluid that surrounds the developing embryo. The embryo's nitrogenous wastes are excreted into a membranous sac called the allantois. The chorion surrounds the yolk, allantois, amnion, and embryo. With this egg, reptiles do not need water for reproduction. The evolution of the amniotic egg completed the move of tetrapods from water to land.

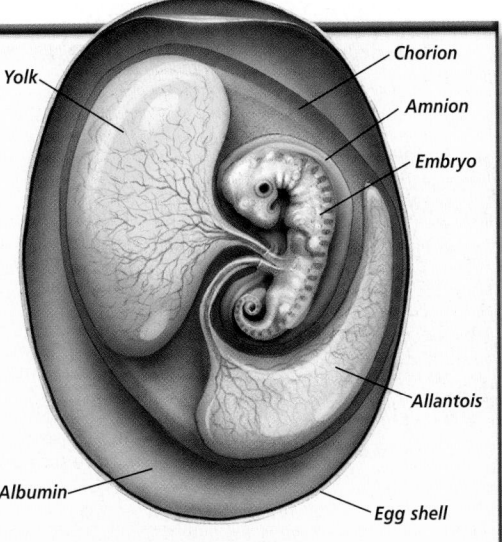

Yolk
Chorion
Amnion
Embryo
Allantois
Albumin
Egg shell

883

Inquiry

Reptile Misconceptions Ask students to research and report on misconceptions about reptiles, such as that all snakes are venomous, snakes sting with their tongues, snakes have cold, slimy skin, telling the age of a rattlesnake by counting its rattles, or telling the age of a turtle by counting the number of plates on the bottom of its shell. **L2**

✓ Assessment

Performance Have students sketch, on a sheet of butcher paper, a scale map of the school grounds or a spot near the school. Have them indicate how the area could be made more suitable for local wildlife. Have students work in groups to add features to their maps that would make the area more attractive to wildlife. Books about wildlife habitat restoration are available in libraries. **L2 ELL**

USING MODELS

Amniotic Egg Ask students to make and explain a model of an amniotic egg using the following materials: a small lump of clay, two small zipper-type plastic bags, two pill vials or plastic film containers, and a lunch-size paper bag. Possible model: The lump of clay represents the embryo. The pill vials, representing the yolk and the allantois, stick into the lump of clay. The clay with attached vials can be placed into one plastic bag that represents the amnion. The amniotic sac and its contents can be placed inside the other plastic bag, which represents the chorion. The chorion and its contents can be placed inside the paper bag, which represents the shell. **L1 ELL COOP LEARN**

Quick Demo

Bird Calls Play a recording of various types of bird songs and calls. Ask students to distinguish among distress calls, calls made to the young, courtship songs, and territorial calls. **L2**

Portfolio

Observing Feathers Provide students with contour and down bird feathers along with magnifying glasses. Feathers may be purchased from craft shops. Ask students to examine both feathers with the magnifying glass and draw diagrams of them in their journals. Ask them to hypothesize how the function of each feather differs. Down feathers keep birds warm by trapping warm air near their bodies. Contour feathers are used for flight. **L2**

Extension

Have students research more information about flightless birds. They can compile a profile of several different examples of flightless birds, including facts about the habitat, range, behavior, and special features of each species of bird, as well as theories explaining why the birds lost the ability to fly. **L2**

Birds

Birds are the only class of animals with feathers. Feathers, which are lightweight, modified scales, help insulate birds and enable them to fly. Birds have forelimbs that are modified into wings. Like reptiles, birds have scales on their feet and clawed toes; unlike reptiles, they are endotherms, animals that maintain a constant body temperature. Endotherms must eat frequently to provide the energy needed for producing body heat.

Penguins are flightless birds with wings and feet modified for swimming. A thick layer of insulating fat helps keep these penguins warm in the cold antarctic climate in which they live. This young emperor penguin may reach a height of 1 m and weigh nearly 34 kg.

The male peacock displays its tail feathers to attract the female peahen. Feathers keep birds warm, streamline them for flight, and are often important in courtship or camouflage.

Bird Flight

Birds have bones with cross braces that provide support for strong flight muscles. Birds also have a four-chambered heart and a unique respiratory system in which oxygen is available during both inhalation and exhalation.

FOCUS ON ADAPTATIONS

Bird Flight

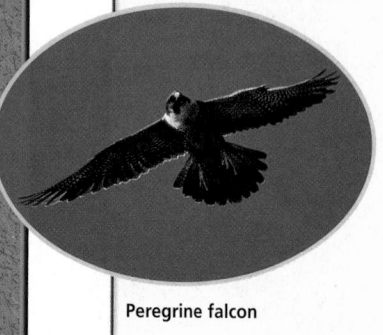

Peregrine falcon

What selection pressure may have resulted in bird flight? Maybe an early bird's need to escape from a predator caused it to run so fast its feet left the ground. Whatever caused birds to evolve an ability to fly, there must first have been adaptations that made flight possible. What are some of these adaptations? A bird that flies has a body that is lighter than that of an animal of equal size because it has little fat and air sacs throughout its body. It also has a beak instead of a heavy jaw with teeth, and its legs are made mostly of skin, bone, and tendons.

Efficient respiration Birds receive oxygenated air when they breathe in as well as when they breathe out. Air sacs enable birds to get more oxygen because 75 percent of the air inhaled by a

884

PROJECT

Endangered State Birds Have students do research to find out which endangered birds live in your state. Have them prepare a videotaped public service announcement about the birds' status with information about what can be done to enhance their chances of survival. **L3** **COOP LEARN**

Indiana Academic Standards

Pages 884–885: B.1.15, B.1.19, B.1.31

Nest Builders

Like reptiles, birds lay amniotic eggs. Unlike reptiles, birds incubate their eggs in nests, keeping eggs warm until the young birds hatch.

VITAL STATISTICS

Birds

Size ranges: Largest: Ostrich, height, 2.4 m, mass, 156 kg; smallest: Bee hummingbird, length, 57 mm, mass, 1.5 g

Distribution: Worldwide in all habitats.

Widest wingspan: Wandering albatross, 3.7 m

Fastest flyer: White-throated spinetail swift, 171 kph

Largest egg: Ostrich, length, 13.5 cm, mass, 1.5 kg

Longest yearly migration: Arctic tern, 40 000 km

Numbers of species:

Class Aves—8600 species in 27 present-day orders:

    Order Passeriformes—perching song birds, 5200 species

    Order Ciconiiformes—herons, bitterns, ibises, 114 species

    Order Anseriformes—swans, ducks, geese, 150 species

    Order Falconiformes—eagles, hawks, falcons, 288 species

The cedar waxwing is found in open woodlands, orchards, and backyards across the United States. They spend most of the year in flocks, descending upon orchards and eating until the fruit is gone.

Although some birds lay their eggs on the ground or rocks, most birds do construct some type of nest into which eggs are laid. Bald eagles build the largest nests, some of which are 2 m across and 2 tons in mass.

bird passes directly into posterior air sacs rather than into its lungs. When a bird exhales, oxygenated air in the sacs passes into its lungs, then into anterior air sacs and out through the trachea. This one-way flow of air provides the oxygen that birds need to power flight muscles.

Wings adapted for flight Flight is also supported by feathers that streamline a bird's body and shape the wings. Wing shape and size determine the type of flight a bird is capable of. Birds that fly through the branches of trees in a forest, such as finches, have elliptically shaped wings adapted to quick changes of direction. Wings of swallows and terns have shapes that sweep back and taper to a slender tip, promoting high speed in open areas. The broad wings of hawks, eagles, and owls provide strong lift and slow speeds. These birds are predators that carry prey while in flight.

Arctic tern

885

Visual Learning

Visual-Spatial Show students slides or pictures of birds in flight and ask them to hypothesize about what types of flight each bird could undertake: quick movements, high speeds, or soaring. Elliptical wings are adapted to quick movements. Wings that sweep back and taper to a slender tip promote high speed. Soaring birds have broad wings. **L1**

Activity

Kinesthetic Have students determine what kinds of birds live on school grounds. Look up specifications for houses for these birds and build bird houses to place on school grounds. **L1**

Portfolio

Create a Pet Ask students to use their creativity and knowledge of vertebrates to create their ideal vertebrate pet. They should write a description of this pet in their journals. Have them label a diagram with all the features unique to the vertebrate group to which their pet belongs. **L2**

CHALLENGE ACTIVITY

Bird Migration Have students who need an additional challenge research information about bird migration. What methods do birds use to determine their location and in which direction to fly in order to reach their final destination? Have students make a list of birds that migrate to or from the local area. Students also could make a map of one particular species' migration route. **L3**

Visual Learning

Show students slides of local mammals and ask them to point out how they are adapted to their habitats. Make sure they point out features that help them move, feed, and give them protection from predators and environmental elements.

Concept Development

In one year, 45 bears were killed on the roads of Florida. Accidents between large mammals and vehicles are common. Ask students to find out which large mammals are killed each year in their state. Ask them to find out what measures are being, or could be, taken to prevent these accidents.

Portfolio

Mammal Range Maps Give students field guides and blank maps of the United States. Ask them to make a list of local mammals. Have them look up each mammal on their list in the field guides and indicate the range of each animal on their maps. They should also make a color-coded key for their maps. **L2**

Inquiry

Monotremata Have students research to find out more information about both living and extinct species of egg-laying mammals. Students can make a chart showing the characteristics these animals have in common with reptiles, as well as which characteristics they share with mammals. **L2**

Indiana Academic Standards
Pages 886–887: B.1.15, B.1.17, B.1.18

Mammals

Mammals are endotherms that are named for their mammary glands, which produce milk to feed their young. Most mammals have hair that helps insulate their bodies and sweat glands that help keep them cool. Mammals need a high level of energy for maintaining body temperature and high speeds of locomotion. An efficient four-chambered heart and the muscular diaphragm beneath the lungs help to deliver the necessary oxygen for these activities.

Mammal Diversity

All mammals have internal fertilization, and the young begin development inside the mother's uterus. But from that point, developmental patterns in mammals diverge. Mammals are classified into three groups. Monotremes are mammals that lay eggs. Marsupials are mammals in which the young complete a second stage of development after birth in a pouch made of skin and hair on the outside of the mother's body. Placental mammals carry their young inside the uterus until development is nearly complete.

Female mammals, such as this moose, feed their young milk secreted from mammary glands. Mammals often care for their young until they become adults.

FOCUS ON ADAPTATIONS
Endothermy

Both birds and mammals are endotherms. Endotherms have internal processes that maintain a constant body temperature. Just as a thermostat controls the temperature of your home, internal processes cool endotherms if they are too warm, and warm them if they are too cool, thus maintaining homeostasis.

Adaptations A variety of adaptations enables mammals to maintain body temperature. Hair helps many mammals conserve heat. The thick coat of a polar bear is an adaptation to living in a cold climate. Small ears and an accumulation of body fat under the skin also help prevent heat loss. Small ears have less surface area than large ears from which body heat can escape.

Polar bear

886

PROJECT

Campaign to Save Mammals Ask students to develop a campaign to save a local mammal from extinction. They should prepare a list of recommendations, publicity in the form of commercials, bumper stickers, and flyers, and suggest an original idea to raise money to create a sanctuary. **L2**

Mammal Teeth

Mammals can be classified by the number and type of teeth they have. All mammals have diversified teeth used for different purposes. Incisors are used to cut food. Canines—long, pointed teeth—are used to stab or hold food. Molars and premolars have flat surfaces with ridges and are used to grind and chew food. By examining an animal's teeth, scientists can hypothesize what type of consumer it is.

Carnivores, such as wolves, have canine teeth that pierce food. Humans, who are omnivores, have incisors, canines, premolars, and molars in order to process many different kinds of food.

VITAL STATISTICS

Mammals

Size ranges: Largest: Blue whale, length, 30 m, mass, 190 metric tons; smallest: Etruscan shrew, length, 6 cm, mass, 1.5 g
Distribution: Worldwide in all habitats
Fastest: Cheetah, 110 kph
Longest-lived: Asiatic elephant, 80 years; humans, up to 120 years
Numbers of species:
Class Mammalia
   Order Monotremata—egg-laying mammals, 3 species
   Order Marsupialia—pouched mammals, 280 species
   Orders of Placental Mammals—4120 species

Grazing animals, such as this horse, rely on incisors to cut grasses and molars to grind and crush their food. Horses, like many other herbivores, lack canine teeth.

Fennec fox

Hibernation Many rodents hibernate during periods of extreme cold. During hibernation, the body temperature lowers. For example, when the surrounding temperature drops to about 0°C, a ground squirrel's temperature drops to 2°C, and it goes into hibernation, which conserves the animal's energy.

Estivation In hot desert environments, where water is limited, some small rodents survive without drinking. They obtain enough water from the foods they eat. Other desert mammals, such as the fennec fox, have large ears that aid in heat loss. During periods of intense heat, some desert mammals go into a state of reduced metabolism called estivation. As a result, the animal's body temperature is lowered and energy is conserved.

887

3 Assess

DAILY INTERVENTION

Check for Understanding
Show students a variety of mammal skulls or transparencies of mammal skulls you have made from field guides to mammals. Direct their attention to how teeth reflect what each animal eats. Ask them to make comparisons of teeth in carnivores and herbivores. Carnivores have sharp, pointed canines that enable them to tear apart prey. Herbivores have premolars and molars adapted to grinding the plant materials they eat.

Reteach
Show students slides or photos of the three groups of mammals and ask them to identify them by their features. **L1**

Extension

Rent a feature film in which a wild mammal or mammals play an important role. Ask students to identify important features of the mammals in the film. **L1**

✔ Assessment

Performance Ask students to design an experiment that would test the suitability of fat as insulation. Lard or cooking fat can be used in their experiments. **L2**

🎯 CHALLENGE ACTIVITY

Wildlife Management Have students who need an additional challenge develop a wildlife management plan for a particular mammal in your area. Based on numbers about the population that can be obtained from the local natural resources department, students should develop a management plan that will protect and maintain an appropriate habitat for 25 years. **L3**

This page contains practice questions in the various formats that can be found on the most frequently given standardized tests.

 Part 1 Multiple Choice

1. C   3. D   5. B
2. C   4. A

FAST FILE

Answer Sheet A practice answer sheet can be found on p. 145 of *Unit 9 FAST FILE Resources.*

Unit 9 Review   Standardized Test Practice

End-of-Course Assessment Practice   The assessed Indiana standard appears next to the question.

The Princeton Review **TEST-TAKING TIP**
If it Looks Too Good To Be True . . .

Beware of answer choices that seem obvious. Remember that only one answer choice of the several that you're offered for each question is correct. Check each answer carefully before finally selecting it.

Part 1 Multiple Choice

Use the information in the table to answer questions 1 and 2.

Behavior of Male Stickleback Fish	
Model Description	Frequency of Attack
Fish-shaped with no red belly	Low
Fish-shaped with a red belly	High
Lump of wax with red stripe at bottom	High

1. The bellies of male stickleback fish turn bright red during breeding season. In an experiment to test for triggers of aggressive behavior, several models were presented to live fish. Based on the results presented in the table, what can you conclude about the triggers for aggressive behavior in these fish?
   A. Aggressive behavior is exhibited when the fish recognizes another fish.
   B. Aggressive behavior is exhibited when the fish sees any type of foreign object.
   C. Aggressive behavior is exhibited when the fish recognizes the red belly.
   D. There is no pattern for aggressive behavior.

2. What is the independent variable in this experiment?
   A. the live fish used in the experiment
   B. the frequency of attacks
   C. the models of fish used in the experiment
   D. There is no independent variable.

888 UNIT 9 STANDARDIZED TEST PRACTICE

Use the information below and your knowledge of science to answer questions 3 and 4.

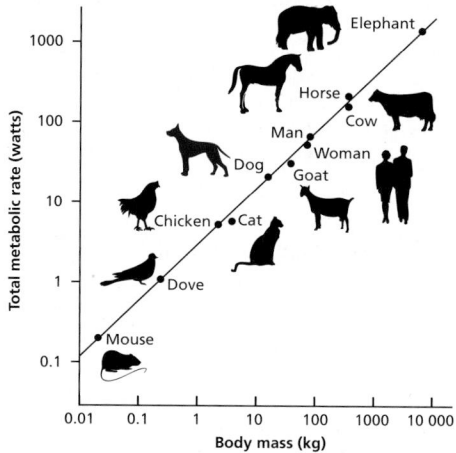

3. The best description of the relationship between body mass and total metabolic rate in animals is _____.
   A. as body mass increases, total metabolic rate decreases
   B. as body mass increases, total metabolic rate stays the same
   C. as total metabolic rate decreases, body mass decreases
   D. as body mass increases, total metabolic rate increases

4. Which title is appropriate for this graph?
   A. The Relationship Between Metabolic Rate and Body Size
   B. The Effect of Metabolic Rate on Body Size
   C. The Relationship Between Metabolic Rate and Life Span
   D. The Effect of Body Size on Metabolic Rate

5. The arctic fox lives further north than any other terrestrial mammal. The polar climate that occurs above the arctic circle is primarily due to which of the following?
   A. frequent El Niño events
   B. intensity of solar radiation at Earth's surface decreases as latitude increases
   C. ocean currents flow from north to south
   D. ocean currents flow from south to north

Indiana Academic Standards

Pages 888–889: B.1.15, B.1.32, B.1.43

Use the diagram below to answer questions 6 and 7.

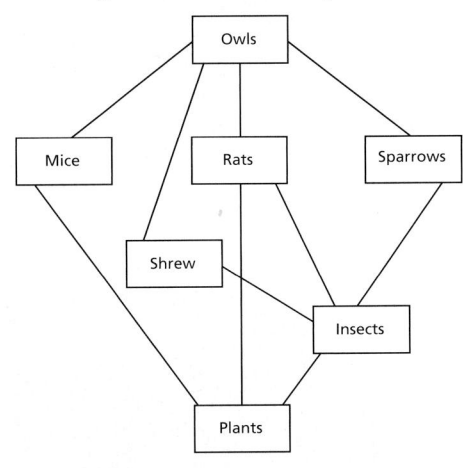

6. What effects could a drastic decline in the
B.1.43 insect population have?
  A. The numbers of shrew and sparrows will increase.
  B. The owls will eat more mice.
  C. The numbers of shrew and sparrows will remain the same.
  D. The number of rats will increase.

7. Which organism would be considered the top predator in this food web?
  A. shrew   **C.** mouse
  B. insect   **D.** owl

8. Fossil evidence has led scientists to believe that
B.1.31 modern birds evolved directly from _____.
  A. early reptiles
  B. therapod dinosaurs
  C. amphibians
  D. mammals

Use the graph to answer questions 9–11.

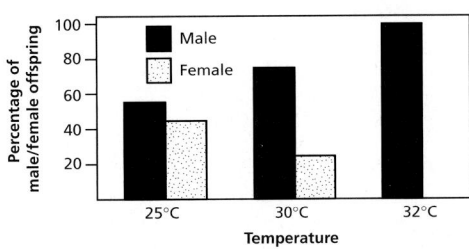

The graph shows the percentage of each gender in offspring of live-bearing lizards kept at different temperatures during gestation.

9. Which temperature(s) yielded the closest ratio of male and female offspring?
  A. 25°C   **C.** 32°C
  B. 30°C   **D.** all of the above

10. If a lizard had been kept at 28°C, predict what
B.1.43 percentage of the offspring would be female.
  A. 100   **C.** 50
  B. 70   **D.** 35

Part 2 Constructed Response/Grid In

Record your answers or fill in the bubbles on your answer document using the correct place value.

.43 11. Grid In If four lizards were born in the group at 30°C, how many of them would most likely be male?

12. Open Ended The egg case of a certain species of skate looks like a thin, leathery pod about 5 cm long with each of the four corners ending in a small, curved spike. Form a hypothesis that explains the function of these spikes.

13. Open Ended Tiny particles have been found in the hair of a prehistoric woolly mammoth frozen in
B.1.32 the permafrost of Siberia. The particles were of mosses, grasses, beetles, and mites. Make an inference about the environment in which this woolly mammoth lived.

14. Open Ended Wild western-lowland gorillas have been observed in the water making spectacular splash displays. Biologists hypothesize that the gorillas are using water to communicate. Infer what the gorillas may be communicating when they splash.

15. Open Ended The skin of a frog secretes mucus when it is injured or infected with microbes. Form a
B.1.17 hypothesis about the function of the mucus and design an experiment to test your hypothesis.

 in.bdol.glencoe.com/standardized_test

6. B   **8.** B   **10.** D
7. D   **9.** A

Part 2 Constructed Response/Grid In

11. 3

12. protection, locomotion, increasing water flow through the egg case; Its function is actually to increase the flow of water through the egg case, but other reasonable answers may be accepted.

13. This mammoth may have lived in grasslands that were wet during parts of the year since moss requires a wet environment. The small insects indicate that, at least for part of the year, the climate must have been moderate.

14. They may be aggressive displays, courtship displays, playful displays, or an announcement of an event or place, such as a place to feed. Other reasonable answers may also be accepted.

15. The mucus contains antimicrobial molecules that aid in fighting infection and healing. Other reasonable hypotheses may also be accepted.

RUBRIC

For more help evaluating open-ended assessment questions, see the rubric on p. 9T.

The Human Body

Unit Overview

Unit 10 describes the systems of the human body and how they interact with one another.

Chapter 34 describes the integumentary, skeletal, and muscular systems.

Chapter 35 covers the digestive and endocrine systems.

Chapter 36 presents the nervous system and the effects of drugs on body systems.

Chapter 37 describes the respiratory, circulatory, and urinary systems.

Chapter 38 focuses on human reproduction and development.

Chapter 39 outlines the structures and processes involved in immunity.

Introducing the Unit

Ask students which systems are important for a runner to succeed at a track meet. Which systems are involved in the excitement the runner feels before the race? Which systems are involved when the runner is racing?

 A WebQuest is an inquiry-based online project in which all information used by students is obtained from the Web. Students evaluate the information to complete the activity. Access the Unit 10 WebQuest at **in.bdol.glencoe.com/webquest**

 Indiana Academic Standards

Pages 890–891: B.1.19

890

Unit 10

The Human Body

History & Biology

1607 English colonists arrive in present-day Jamestown, Virginia, and establish the first permanent English settlement in America.

1600   *1700*

1628 William Harvey gives an accurate description of blood circulation.

Red blood cells ▲

1752 Experiments show that the gastric juices of the stomach chemically digest food.

What You'll Learn

Chapter 34
Protection, Support, and Locomotion

Chapter 35
The Digestive and Endocrine Systems

Chapter 36
The Nervous System

Chapter 37
Respiration, Circulation, and Excretion

Chapter 38
Reproduction and Development

Chapter 39
Immunity from Disease

Unit 10 Review
BioDigest & Standardized Test Practice

Indiana Standards
The following standards are covered in Unit 10:
B.1.1, B.1.3, B.1.7, B.1.8, B.1.9, B.1.10, B.1.11, B.1.14, B.1.15, B.1.16, B.1.17, B.1.19, B.1.20, B.1.21, B.1.41, B.1.43

Why It's Important

The organ systems of the human body coordinate to fulfill the body's basic survival needs. These include the uptake and distribution of oxygen, digestion of food, and the elimination of wastes. These systems also allow humans to complete complex behaviors such as writing or riding a bike.

Understanding the Photo ▶

The hurdlers in this photo are breathing fast and can feel the burn in their muscles as they compete. Running a race requires the coordination of many different body systems—systems that do not work independently but interact in hundreds of complex ways.

890 in.bdol.glencoe.com/webquest

Time Line

Activity Have students research more information about any of the time line entries or another "first" in medical/science history. Have students present a report on their findings including information about the scientist, the impact of his or her work on scientific thought and society, and if relevant, what type of technology was used. **L2**

1804 •
Lewis and Clark begin their exploration of the north-western United States.

1946 •
The United Nations, an international peace-keeping organization, has its first meeting.

1800

1900

2000

1847 •
An instrument that measures blood pressure is developed.

1875 •
The electrical activity of the brain is recorded for the first time.

◀ Alexander Fleming

1928 •
Alexander Fleming accidentally discovers the antibiotic penicillin.

1969 •
The first artificial heart is implanted into a human at a hospital in Texas.

1998 •
The world's first hand transplant is successfully performed.

891

Advance Materials Planning

The following materials may need to be ordered a few weeks in advance of the planned activity.

Chapter 34
■ **Additional Lab** (p. 896) slides of human skin

Chapter 35
■ **Chapter Launcher** (p. 916) iodine solution, amylase solution
■ **Quick Demo** (p. 920) pancreatic enzymes, Benedict's solution
■ **Quick Demo** (p. 930) human skull or large animal skull
■ **MiniLab 35.2** (p. 934) thyroid/parathyroid slides
■ **BioLab** (p. 936) iodine solution, amylase solution

Chapter 36
■ **BioLab** (p. 964) *Daphina*

Chapter 37
■ **Quick Demo** (p. 985) whole kidney

Chapter 38
■ **Quick Demo** (p. 997) and **Figure 38.7** (p. 1001) slide of cross section of testes
■ **Figure 38.7** (p. 1001) slide of cross section of ovaries
■ **MiniLab 38.1** (p. 1006) slide of human sperm, slide of human egg, and slide of sea star blastula
■ **Quick Demo** (p. 1007) slides of sea star development

Chapter 39
■ **Additional Lab** (p. 1032) bacterial culture and antibiotic disks
■ **MiniLab 39.2** (p. 1035) blood smear slides

Unit Projects

Using the Library
Linguistic Have student groups prepare a report on how an injury to one system structure—such as torn cartilage or a ruptured spleen—can disrupt the whole system. **L3** **COOP LEARN**

Interview
Interpersonal Have student groups interview a nurse or physician about a disease or disorder that affects mainly one body system. Have students present their findings in a report. **L2** **COOP LEARN**

Modeling
Kinesthetic Have student groups design and make a model of one body system, such as the nervous or endocrine system. They may use any materials they wish. **L2** **ELL**
COOP LEARN

Chapter 34 Organizer

Section Objectives	National Science Standards	State/Local Standards	Advanced Lab and Demo Planning
Section 34.1 1 session, 1/2 block 1. **Compare** the structure and functions of the epidermis and dermis. 2. **Identify** the role of the skin in responding to external stimuli. 3. **Outline** the healing process that takes place when the skin is injured.	UCP.1, UCP.2, UCP.5; A.1, A.2; C.5; F.1, F.5; G.1, G.2	**Indiana Standards** B.1.14, B.1.15, B.1.17, B.1.19, B.1.20	**Student Labs:** MiniLab 34.1, p. 895: non-toxic, washable-ink stamp pad, index card Problem Solving Lab 34.1, p. 896 Additional Lab, p. 896: microscope slide of human skin, microscope **Teacher Demonstration:** Quick Demo, p. 897
Section 34.2 2 sessions, 1 block 4. **Compare** the different types of movable joints. 5. **Describe** how bone is formed. 6. **Identify** the structure and functions of the skeletal system.	UCP.1, UCP.2, UCP.5; A.1, A.2; D.1; E.1; F.1, F.5, F.6; G.2	**Indiana Standards** B.1.14, B.1.15, B.1.16, B.1.19,	**Student Lab:** Problem Solving Lab 34.2, p. 903 **Teacher Demonstrations:** Quick Demo, p. 900: X rays Quick Demo, p. 902: beef bone
Section 34.3 2 sessions, 1 1/2 blocks 7. **Classify** the three types of muscles. 8. **Analyze** the structure of a myofibril. 9. **Interpret** the sliding filament theory.	UCP.1–3, UCP.5; A.1, A.2; B.6; C.1, C.5; E.1, E.2; F.1, F.5, F.6; G.1, G.2, G.3	**Indiana Standards** B.1.14, B.1.15, B.1.16, B.1.17, B.1.20	**Student Labs:** Problem-Solving Lab 34.3, p. 906 MiniLab 34.2, p. 907: ruler **Teacher Demonstration:** Quick Demo, p. 906: chicken feet
End of Chapter Assessment Student Edition **Study Guide,** p. 913 **Content Assessment,** pp. 914–915		**Indiana Standards** B.1.14, B.1.15, B.1.17, B.1.20	**Student Lab:** Design Your Own BioLab, p. 910: stopwatch or clock with second hand, graph paper, small weights

Key to Teaching Strategies

L1 Level 1 activities should be appropriate for students with learning difficulties.

L2 Level 2 activities should be within the ability range of all students.

L3 Level 3 activities are designed for above-average students.

ELL ELL activities should be within the ability range of English Language Learners.

COOP LEARN Cooperative Learning activities are designed for small group work.

Legend

 Transparency   CD-ROM   MP3   ▥ Videocassette   ⊙ DVD

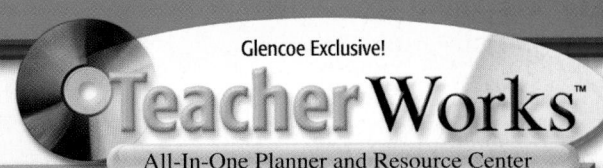
Glencoe Exclusive!
TeacherWorks™
All-In-One Planner and Resource Center

Reproducible Masters and Transparencies	Technology

Unit 10 FAST FILE Resources
MiniLab Worksheet, p. 3
Reinforcement and Study Guide in English, p. 11
Reinforcement and Study Guide in Spanish, p. 15
Concept Mapping, p. 19
Transparency Worksheets, pp. 21, 25–26
Section Focus Transparency 81
Basic Concepts Transparency 61

- **Interactive Chalkboard CD-ROM: Section 34.1 Presentation**
- TeacherWorks™ **CD-ROM**
- **Guided Reading Audio Summaries MP3**

Unit 10 FAST FILE Resources
Real World BioApplications, pp. 7–8
Reinforcement and Study Guide in English, pp. 12–13
Reinforcement and Study Guide in Spanish, pp. 16–17
Critical Thinking/Problem Solving, p. 20
Transparency Worksheets, pp. 22, 27–30
Laboratory Manual, pp. 223–226
Section Focus Transparency 82
Basic Concepts Transparencies 62, 63

- **Virtual Labs**
  Virtual Lab: Bones, the Body's Support
- **Interactive Chalkboard CD-ROM: Section 34.2 Presentation**
- TeacherWorks™ **CD-ROM**
- **Guided Reading Audio Summaries MP3**

Unit 10 FAST FILE Resources
MiniLab Worksheet, p. 4
BioLab Worksheet, pp. 5–6
Real World BioApplications, pp. 9–10
Reinforcement and Study Guide in English, p. 14
Reinforcement and Study Guide in Spanish, p. 18
Transparency Worksheets, pp. 23, 31–34
Probeware Labs, pp. 25–28
Inside Story Poster
Section Focus Transparency 83
Basic Concepts Transparency 64
Reteaching Skills Transparency 49

- **Interactive Chalkboard CD-ROM: Section 34.3 Presentation**
- TeacherWorks™ **CD-ROM**
- **Guided Reading Audio Summaries MP3**

Unit 10 FAST FILE Resources
Chapter Assessment, pp. 35–40
Student Recording Sheet, p. 41

The Princeton Review **Reviewing Biology,** pp. 67–68

- **Interactive Chalkboard: Chapter 34 Assessment**
- **MindJogger Videoquizzes DVD/VHS**
- **ExamView® Pro Test Bank CD-ROM**
- TeacherWorks™ **CD-ROM**
- **Succeeding on National Standards CD-ROM**

🖳 in.bdol.glencoe.com
/self_check_quiz
/vocabulary_puzzlemaker
/chapter_test
/standardized_test

▌ Indicates materials created specifically for Indiana.

Chapter 34

Protection, Support, and Locomotion

Short on Time?

BIODIGEST The BioDigest at the end of this unit can be used as a(n):

- preview to introduce important unit concepts.
- overview if time does not permit teaching the entire chapter.
- review of key unit concepts.

Understanding the Photo

During sports activities, the integumentary system plays an important role in cooling the body. The muscular system, using the skeletal system for support, is able to contract and provide movement.

What You'll Learn

- You will interpret the structure and functions of the integumentary system.
- You will identify the functions of the skeletal system.
- You will classify the different types of muscles in the body.

Why It's Important

Your skin, skeleton, and muscles work together to protect, support, and move your body. A knowledge of each system helps you understand how your body is able to accomplish such a variety of activities.

Understanding ▶ the Photo

The integration of the skeletal and muscular systems provides the support and power these athletes need to perform. The skin plays a role in regulating their body temperatures as they compete.

Biology Online

Visit in.bdol.glencoe.com **to**
- study the entire chapter online
- access Web Links for more information and activities on skin, bones, and muscles
- review content with the Interactive Tutor and self-check quizzes

892

Two-Minute Chapter Launcher

Demo Bounce a tennis ball or do some other kind of activity in front of the class. Ask students to explain how the skeletal and muscular systems are helping you perform this activity. As the students list various ways these systems help, write them on the board under two columns: skeletal and muscular. Use arrows to connect any answers that show connections between the systems, such as the muscles using the skeletal system for support and leverage. Ask students to consider the main functions of these two systems. How effectively would one system be able to function without the other? Have students think about examples such as a broken bone, a sprained joint, or a torn muscle. **L2**

Section 34.1

Skin: The Body's Protection

Indiana Standards Standard B.1.14 Recognize and explain that communication and/or interaction are required between cells to coordinate their diverse activities.

SECTION PREVIEW

Objectives
Compare the structures and functions of the epidermis and dermis.

Identify the role of the skin in responding to external stimuli.

Outline the healing process that takes place when the skin is injured.

Review Vocabulary
homeostasis: regulation of an organism's internal environment to maintain conditions suitable for its survival (p. 9)

New Vocabulary
epidermis
keratin
melanin
dermis
hair follicle

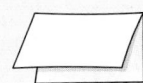
Study Organizer

Skin Structure and Function Make the following Foldable to help learn the structures and functions of the skin.

STEP 1 **Fold** a vertical sheet of paper in half from top to bottom.

STEP 2 **Fold** in half from side to side with the fold at the top.

STEP 3 **Unfold** the paper once. **Cut** only the fold of the top flap to make two tabs.

STEP 4 **Turn** the paper vertically and **label** the front tabs as shown.

Epidermis

Dermis

Read and Write As you read Chapter 34, draw and label the layers and structures of the skin under the appropriate tab. Describe one function for each of the labeled structures.

Transparency **81** To Cover, Contain, and Protect

SECTION FOCUS
Use with Chapter 34, Section 34.1

① Look at the title of this transparency. How does the polyethylene container in the picture satisfy these requirements?
② Do you think that polyethylene would be a satisfactory substitute for skin? Explain.

BIOLOGY: The Dynamics of Life   SECTION FOCUS TRANSPARENCIES

Structure and Functions of the Integumentary System

Skin, the main organ of the integumentary (inh TE gyuh MEN tuh ree) system, is composed of layers of the four types of body tissues: epithelial, connective, muscle, and nervous. Epithelial tissue, found in the outer layer of the skin, functions to cover surfaces of the body. Connective tissue, which consists of both tough and flexible protein fibers, serves as a sort of organic glue, holding your body together. Muscle tissues interact with hairs on the skin to respond to stimuli, such as cold and fright. Nervous tissue helps us detect external stimuli, such as pain or pressure. The skin is a flexible and responsive organ. Skin is composed of two principal layers—the epidermis and dermis. Each layer has a unique structure and performs a different function in the body.

Epidermis: The outer layer of skin

The **epidermis** is the outermost layer of the skin, and is made up of two parts—an exterior and interior portion. The exterior layer of the epidermis consists of 25 to 30 layers of dead, flattened cells that are continually being shed. Although dead, these cells still serve an important function as they contain a protein called **keratin** (KER uh tun). Keratin helps protect the living cell layers underneath from exposure to bacteria, heat, and chemicals.

Word Origin

epidermis from the Greek words *epi*, meaning "on," and *derma*, meaning "skin"; The epidermis covers other layers of skin.

with Image Bank

PowerPoint® Presentations
This CD-ROM is an editable Microsoft® PowerPoint® presentation that includes:
- Section presentations
- Section checks
- Image bank
- Hot links to Biology Online
- All transparencies

FOLDABLES™
For an additional Foldables activity idea, see the Chapter 34 Foldables page in *Unit 10 Fast File Resources.*

34.1 SKIN: THE BODY'S PROTECTION **893**

RESOURCE MANAGER

Unit 10 *FAST FILE* **Resources**
MiniLab Worksheet, p. 3
Reinforcement and Study Guide in English, p. 11
Reinforcement and Study Guide in Spanish, p. 15
Concept Mapping, p. 19
Transparency Worksheets, pp. 21, 25–26

Reading Essentials for Biology, Section 34.1
📖 **Section Focus Transparency 81**
📖 **Basic Concepts Transparency 61**

Indiana Academic Standards

Pages 892–893: B.1.14, B.1.15

2 Teach

Purpose

Students gain a further understanding of how structures of the skin perform their functions.

Teaching Strategies

■ Ask students to identify the primary function of hair. **L2**

■ Use the diagram to point out to students where pimples may form. in blocked hair follicles

Visual Learning

Set up the bulletin board display showing skin problems and challenge students to identify which skin structure is involved in each problem shown. **L2**

Critical Thinking

An injury to the top layers of epidermis would not bleed, because blood vessels are only found in the dermis layer.

Enrichment

Have students conduct research on artificial skin. Students should report how artificial skin is made and how its structure compares with that of natural skin. **L3**

Indiana Academic Standards

Pages 894–895: B.1.14, B.1.15

The Skin

Figure 34.1
The skin is an organ because it consists of tissues joined together to perform specific activities. It is the largest organ of the body; the average adult's skin covers one to two square meters. **Critical Thinking** *Would an injury to the top layers of the epidermis result in bleeding? Explain.*

LM Magnification: 65×

Melanin in cross section of skin cells

A Melanin
Differences in skin color are due to the amount of the pigment melanin produced by the cells. Melanin helps protect underlying cells by absorbing ultraviolet light, which can damage cells and lead to the development of skin cancer.

B Oil glands
Most oil glands are connected to hair follicles. Oil prevents hair from drying out and keeps the skin soft and pliable. It also inhibits the growth of certain bacteria.

C Hair
Hair's primary function is to protect the skin from injury and damage from solar rays. It also provides an insulating layer of air just above the surface of the skin.

Epidermis

Dermis

Subcutaneous layer

Sweat pore

Dead epidermis

Living epidermis

Touch receptor

Muscle

Hair follicle

Nerve

Fat tissue

Artery

Vein

D Elasticity
The connective tissue of the dermis contains many elastic fibers that allow the skin to return to its original shape after being stretched.

E Sweat glands
Sweat glands are located deep in the dermis and open up through pores onto the surface of the skin.

894 PROTECTION, SUPPORT, AND LOCOMOTION

USING MODELS

Modeling Skin Structure: *Kinesthetic* Have students use a variety of materials to create three-dimensional models of the skin. Use the illustrations found in Figure 34.1 as a guide. Students should include labels that identify each structure in their models as well as its function. **L2 ELL**
COOP LEARN

INCLUSION STRATEGIES

Learning Disabled: *Linguistic* Have students write a story about skin injury and healing from the viewpoint of the skin. Students should include the steps outlined in Figure 34.4 in their stories. **L1**

The interior layer of the epidermis contains living cells that continually divide to replace the dead cells. Some of these cells contain **melanin**, a pigment that colors the skin and helps protect body cells from damage by solar radiation. As the newly formed cells are pushed toward the skin's surface, the nuclei degenerate and the cells die. Once they reach the outermost epidermal layer, the cells are shed. This entire process takes about 28 days. Therefore, every four weeks, all cells of the epidermis are replaced by new cells.

Look at your fingertips. The epidermis on the fingers and palms of your hands, and on the toes and soles of your feet, contains ridges and grooves that are formed before birth. These epidermal ridges are important for gripping as they increase friction. As shown in *Figure 34.2,* footprints, as well as fingerprints, are often used to identify individuals as each person's pattern is unique. Make a set of your own fingerprints while doing the *MiniLab* on this page.

Dermis: The inner layer of skin

The second principal layer of the skin is the dermis. The **dermis** is the inner, thicker portion of the skin. The thickness of the dermis varies in different parts of the body, depending on the function of that part.

The dermis contains structures such as blood vessels, nerves, nerve endings, hair follicles, sweat glands, and oil glands. Why do some people have dark skin while others are pale? Find out by examining *Figure 34.1.* Beneath the dermis, the skin is attached to underlying tissues by the subcutaneous layer, which consists of fat and connective tissue. These fat deposits also help the body absorb impact, retain heat, and store food.

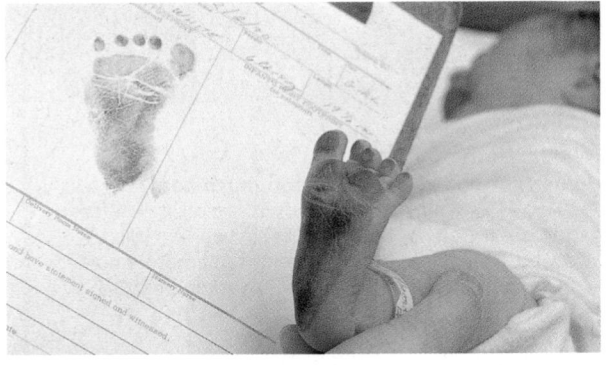

Figure 34.2
Babies' footprints are recorded at birth to establish an identification record for them in the future.

MiniLab 34.1

Compare

Examine Your Fingerprints Fingerprints form when the epidermis conforms to the shape of the dermis, which has small projections to increase its surface area.

Procedure

1. Press your thumb lightly on the surface of an ink pad.
2. Roll your thumb from left to right across the corner of an index card, then immediately lift your thumb straight up from the paper.
3. Repeat the steps above for your other four fingers, placing the prints in order across the card.
4. Examine your fingerprints with a magnifying lens, identifying the patterns by comparing them with the diagrams below.
5. Compare your fingerprints with those of your classmates.

Arch   Whorl   Loop   Combination

Analysis

1. **Observe** Are the fingerprint patterns on your fingers identical?
2. **Compare and Contrast** Do any of your fingerprints show the same patterns as those of a classmate?
3. **Infer** How can a fingerprint be used to identify a person?

MiniLab 34.1

Purpose

Students will observe, describe, and compare similarities and differences among fingerprint patterns to determine the uniqueness of such patterns.

Process Skills

observe and infer

Teaching Strategies

- Use non-toxic, washable-ink stamp pads for students to make fingerprints.
- For consistency when they make comparisons, have each student use the thumb and fingers of their right hand to make fingerprints.
- Have students begin by placing the left side of the thumb or finger on the card, and roll it completely over to the right side.
- Have students wash hands with soap and water after completing a set of fingerprints.

Expected Results

Each finger has a unique fingerprint and each individual has a unique set of fingerprints.

Analysis

1. No; however, the general patterns may be the same on different fingers.
2. It is possible that students may share patterns, but not identical fingerprints.
3. It is unique for each person.

Assessment

Performance Have students design an experiment to determine if the print patterns of toes are unique to each individual. Use the Performance Task Assessment List for Designing an Experiment in **PASC**, p. 95. L2

TECH PREP

Acne Treatments: *Interpersonal* Ask students to research various acne treatments. Have them record in their journals how these treatments prevent or treat acne. L2 ELL

Purpose
Students will analyze the series of events that occur in the body as internal body temperature increases.

Process Skills
think critically, recognize cause and effect, concept map, apply concepts, predict, sequence

Teaching Strategies
- Make sure that students are familiar with all the terms used in the lab, including *dilate* and *capillaries.*
- Verify that the concept of perspiring as a way of lowering body temperature is understood by students.
- This lab would be suitable for small cooperative groups.

Thinking Critically
1. skin (dermis and epidermis), nervous (brain), and circulatory (blood capillaries)
2. The brain is the structure that gives the signal to the sweat glands (to produce sweat) and to the capillaries (to dilate).
3. A change in body temperature causes an internal adjustment of various responses to bring the temperature back to its appropriate level.
4. cold causes body temperature to drop ⇒ brain detects drop in blood temperature ⇒ message sent to blood capillaries ⇒ capillaries constrict ⇒ heat not lost from skin ⇒ body warms

Assessment
Knowledge Ask students to explain why a person becomes flushed when he or she has a fever. What evidence do they have that body temperature is controlled automatically and not consciously? Use the Performance Task Assessment List for Formulating a Hypothesis in **PASC**, p. 93. **L2**

Recognize Cause and Effect

How does your body respond to too much heat? As you exercise vigorously, your body responds in several ways. One, you start to perspire. Two, the capillaries in your skin dilate. Both are reactions to a disruption of body temperature homeostasis. The body responds to internal feedback in order to restore homeostasis.

Solve the Problem
At right is a diagram of the events that take place in your body as it works to maintain homeostasis in response to a rise in internal temperature.

```
        Exercise
        causes
        body to
        heat up
       ↙        ↘
Brain detects    Heat stimulates
rise in blood    nerves in
temperature      skin
     ↓                ↓
Message sent to   Message sent
skin capillaries  to brain
     ↓                ↓
Capillaries      Message sent
dilate           to sweat glands
     ↓                ↓
Excess heat lost  Perspiration
through skin      occurs
       ↘        ↙
           Body
           cools
```

Thinking Critically
1. **Identify** Which systems work together to cool the body?
2. **Analyze** How is the brain directly in control of changing body temperature?
3. **Infer** Why is temperature regulation an example of an internal feedback system?
4. **Predict** Redraw and label the diagram to show the steps that would occur if your body temperature were too low.

Figure 34.3
This photomicrograph shows a cross section of human skin with hair follicles and hair.
Describe *What are the functions of hair?*

LM Magnification: 30×

Hair follicle

896

Hair, another structure of the integumentary system, grows out of narrow cavities in the dermis called **hair follicles,** as shown in *Figure 34.3.* As hair follicles develop, they are supplied with blood vessels and nerves and become attached to muscle tissue. Most hair follicles have an oil gland associated with them. When oil and dead cells block the opening of the hair follicle, pimples may form.

Functions of the integumentary system

One function of skin is to help maintain homeostasis by regulating your internal body temperature. When your body temperature rises, the many small blood vessels in the dermis dilate, blood flow increases, and body heat is lost by radiation. This mechanism also works in reverse. When you are cold, the blood vessels in the skin constrict and heat is conserved.

Another noticeable thing that happens to your skin as your body heats up is that it becomes wet. Glands in the dermis produce sweat in response to an increase in body temperature. As sweat evaporates, water changes state from liquid to vapor and heat is lost. The body cools as a result of the heat loss. Investigate further the role of skin in cooling the body by carrying out the *Problem-Solving Lab* on this page.

Of course, anyone who has ever stepped on a sharp object or been burned by a hot pot handle knows that skin also functions as a sense organ. Nerve cells in the dermis receive stimuli from the external environment and relay information about pressure, pain, and temperature to the brain.

Skin also plays a role in producing essential vitamins. When exposed to ultraviolet light, skin cells produce vitamin D, a nutrient that aids the absorption of calcium into the bloodstream. As a person's exposure to

Additional Lab

The Structure of Skin

Purpose
In this lab, students will observe the structure of human skin.

Preparation
You may choose to view the slides yourself before giving them to students to view.

Remind students to handle prepared slides with extreme caution.

Materials 🥽 👕 ✂️
microscope slide of human skin, microscope

Procedure
Give students the following directions.
1. Focus the human skin slide on low power. Then switch to high power.

sunlight varies, daily intake of vitamin D from dietary sources or supplements may be needed to meet requirements.

Skin also serves as a protective layer to underlying tissues. It shields the body from physical and chemical damage and from invasion by microbes. Cuts or other openings in the skin surface allow bacteria to enter the body, so they must be repaired quickly. *Figure 34.4* shows the stages involved in skin repair.

Figure 34.4
Healing the dermis after injury occurs in a series of stages.

Blood clot

A Blood flows out of the wound until a clot forms.

B A scab soon develops, creating a barrier between bacteria on the skin and underlying tissues.

Scab

Scab   *New skin cells*

C New skin cells begin repairing the wound from beneath. A scar may form if the wound is large.

Caption Question Answer
Figure 34.3 Hair's primary function is to protect the skin from injury and damage from solar rays. It also provides an insulating layer of air just above the surface of the skin.

---

2. Find the following structures: hair follicle, hair shaft, sweat gland, blood vessels, fat deposits, oil gland, and elastic fibers.

3. Notice that the outer portion of the dermis has numerous projections, similar to hills and valleys. These projections, or papillae, form no pattern except on the epidermis of the fingertips, palms, and soles of the feet, where they create parallel ridges that facilitate gripping

Analysis

1. **What structures form the fingerprints seen on fingers?** The outer portion of the dermis has projections, or papillae, that form the epidermal ridges seen in fingerprints.

2. **What is the function of the oil glands of the skin?** Oil secreted by the glands keeps hair from drying out and keeps the skin soft and pliable.

Assessment

Skill Have students draw, label, and color human skin as seen under the microscope. Students should place their drawings in their journals. Use the Performance Task Assessment List for Scientific Drawing in **PASC**, p. 127. **L2** **ELL**

Figure 34.5
As people age, their skin loses its elasticity and begins to wrinkle.

Skin Injury and Healing

If you've ever had a mild scrape, you know that it doesn't take long for the wound to heal. When the epidermis sustains a mild injury, such as a scrape, the deepest layer of epidermal cells divide to help fill in the gap left by the abrasion. If, however, the injury extends into the dermis, where blood vessels are found, bleeding usually occurs. The skin then goes through a series of stages to heal the damaged tissue. The first reaction of the body is to restore the continuity of the skin, that is, to close the break. Blood flowing from the wound soon clots. The wound is then closed by the formation of a scab, which prevents bacteria from entering the body. Dilated blood vessels then allow infection-fighting white blood cells to migrate to the wound site. Soon after, skin cells beneath the scab begin to multiply and fill in the gap. Eventually, the scab falls off to expose newly formed skin. If a wound is large, high amounts of dense connective tissue fibers used to close the wound may leave a scar.

Have you ever suffered a painful burn? Burns can result from exposure to the sun or contact with chemicals or hot objects. Burns are rated according to their severity.

First-degree burns, such as a mild sunburn, involve the death of epidermal cells and are characterized by redness and mild pain. First-degree burns usually heal in about one week without leaving a scar. Second-degree burns involve damage to skin cells of both the epidermis and the dermis and can result in blistering and scarring. The most severe burns are third-degree burns, which destroy both the epidermis and the dermis. With this type of burn, skin function is lost, and skin grafts may be required to replace lost skin. In some cases, healthy skin can be removed from another area of the patient's body and transplanted to a burned area.

As people get older, their skin changes. It becomes drier as glands decrease their production of lubricating skin oils—a mixture of fats, cholesterol, proteins, and inorganic salts. As shown in *Figure 34.5*, wrinkles may appear as the elasticity of the skin decreases. Although these changes are natural, they can be accelerated by prolonged exposure to ultraviolet rays from the sun.

✓**Reading Check** **Summarize** how the skin changes as people age.

Section Assessment

Understanding Main Ideas
1. Compare the structures and functions of the epidermis and the dermis.
2. Identify and interpret the functions of the integumentary system.
3. Compare how the skin interrelates with other organ systems to maintain a constant body temperature.
4. How does the skin respond to external stimuli?

Thinking Critically
5. How could third-degree burns over a significant portion of the skin affect the body as a whole?

SKILL REVIEW

6. **Sequence** Outline steps that occur as a cut in the skin heals. For more help, refer to *Sequence* in the **Skill Handbook.**

898 PROTECTION, SUPPORT, AND LOCOMOTION

 in.bdol.glencoe.com/self_check_quiz

Section Assessment

1. epidermis: layers of dead, flattened cells covering layers of live cells that continually divide; function: protection; dermis: thicker, contains blood vessels, nerves, nerve endings, hair follicles, glands; functions: detects external stimuli, produces sweat, hair, and oil

2. covers the body, detects external stimuli, temperature regulation, produces oil to prevent drying out, hair for protection and insulation

3. Skin nerve endings detect stimuli and signal the nervous system, which stimulates other body systems in response.

4. External nerve endings in skin detect temperature, pressure, and pain; nerve endings relay information to the brain for a response.

5. The body is susceptible to infection and drying out; if enough skin is damaged, it can become life threatening.

6. A blood clot forms. Blood vessels dilate and infection-fighting blood cells rush to the wound. Epidermal cells divide to fill in the wound.

Bones: The Body's Support

Indiana Standards Standard B.1.15 Understand and explain that, in biological systems, structure and function must be considered together.

SECTION PREVIEW

Objectives
Compare the different types of movable joints.
Describe how bone is formed.
Identify the structure and functions of the skeletal system.

Review Vocabulary
cartilage: tough, flexible material that makes up portions of bony-animal skeletons (p. 799)

New Vocabulary
axial skeleton
appendicular skeleton
joint
ligament
bursa
tendon
compact bone
osteocyte
spongy bone
osteoblast
red marrow
yellow marrow

The Body's Foundation

Finding Main Ideas On a piece of paper, construct an outline about the skeletal system. Use the red and blue titles in the section as a guideline. As you read the paragraphs that follow the titles, add important information and vocabulary words to your outline.

Example:
I. Skeletal System Structure
  A. Joints
    1. Ball-and-socket joint
    2. Pivot joint

Use your outline to help you answer questions in the Section Assessment on page 904. For more help, refer to *Outline* in the **Skill Handbook**.

As a baby develops in the uterus, its bones develop from cartilage. As a child grows, bones increase in both length and thickness.

Bellringer
Section Focus Transparency 82

Transparency **82** Flexible Support

SECTION FOCUS
Use with Chapter 34, Section 34.2

① Describe the range of motion that is possible in each object pictured.
② Identify a part of the human skeleton that can move like each of the objects.

BIOLOGY: The Dynamics of Life   SECTION FOCUS TRANSPARENCIES

Skeletal System Structure

The adult human skeleton contains about 206 bones. Its two main parts are shown in *Figure 34.6* on the next page. The **axial skeleton** includes the skull and the bones that support it, such as the vertebral column, the ribs, and the sternum. The **appendicular** (a pen DI kyuh lur) **skeleton** includes the bones of the arms and legs and structures associated with them, such as the shoulder and hip bones, wrists, ankles, fingers, and toes.

Joints: Where bones meet

Next time you open a door, notice how it is connected to the door frame. A metal joint positioned where the door and frame meet allows the door to move easily back and forth. In vertebrates, **joints** are found where two or more bones meet. Most joints facilitate the movement of bones in relation to one another. The joints of the skull, on the other hand, are fixed, as the bones of the skull don't move. These immovable joints are actually held together by the intergrowth of bone, or by fibrous cartilage.

Joints are often held together by ligaments. A **ligament** is a tough band of connective tissue that attaches one bone to another. Joints with large ranges of motion, such as the knee, typically have more ligaments surrounding them. In movable joints, the ends of bones are covered by cartilage.

34.2   BONES: THE BODY'S SUPPORT   **899**

Finding Main Ideas

Outline Review with students how to make an outline. Remind students that they can use the outline as a study tool at a later time.

Physical Science Connection

Possible answers include the knees, ankles, fingers, and head and neck. Bones serve as the rigid rods, joints are fulcrums, and muscles provide the input forces for the levers. Most levers in the human body are class three, which means that the input force is situated between the fulcrum and the output force.

Physical Science Connection

Joints and levers
Recall that a lever is a rod or plank that pivots on a fulcrum. A number of joints in your body serve as fulcrums. For example, your forearm is a lever that pivots on the elbow joint. The biceps muscle exerts an input force and the output force is exerted at your hand. Identify three other levers that are part of your body.

RESOURCE MANAGER

Unit 10 *FAST FILE* Resources
Real World BioApplications, pp. 7–8
Reinforcement and Study Guide in English, pp. 12–13
Reinforcement and Study Guide in Spanish, pp. 16–17
Critical Thinking/Problem Solving, p. 20
Transparency Worksheets, pp. 22, 27–30

Reading Essentials for Biology, Section 34.2
Laboratory Manual, pp. 223–226
 Section Focus Transparency 82
 Basic Concepts Transparencies 62, 63

 Indiana Academic Standards

Pages 898–899: B.1.14, B.1.15, B.1.17, B.1.20

Some students may think that the number of ribs found in male and female skeletons differs.

Uncover the Misconception

Explain to students that both males and females have an equal number of ribs.

Demonstrate the Concept

Using a male and female skeleton (or pictures of skeletons), have the students count the total number of ribs in both the female and male.

Assess New Knowledge

After the discussion of the misconception, ask students to compile a list of similarities and differences between male and female skeletons. similarities may include number of bones and types of bones; differences may include density of bones, overall size of skeleton, and curvature of hip bones

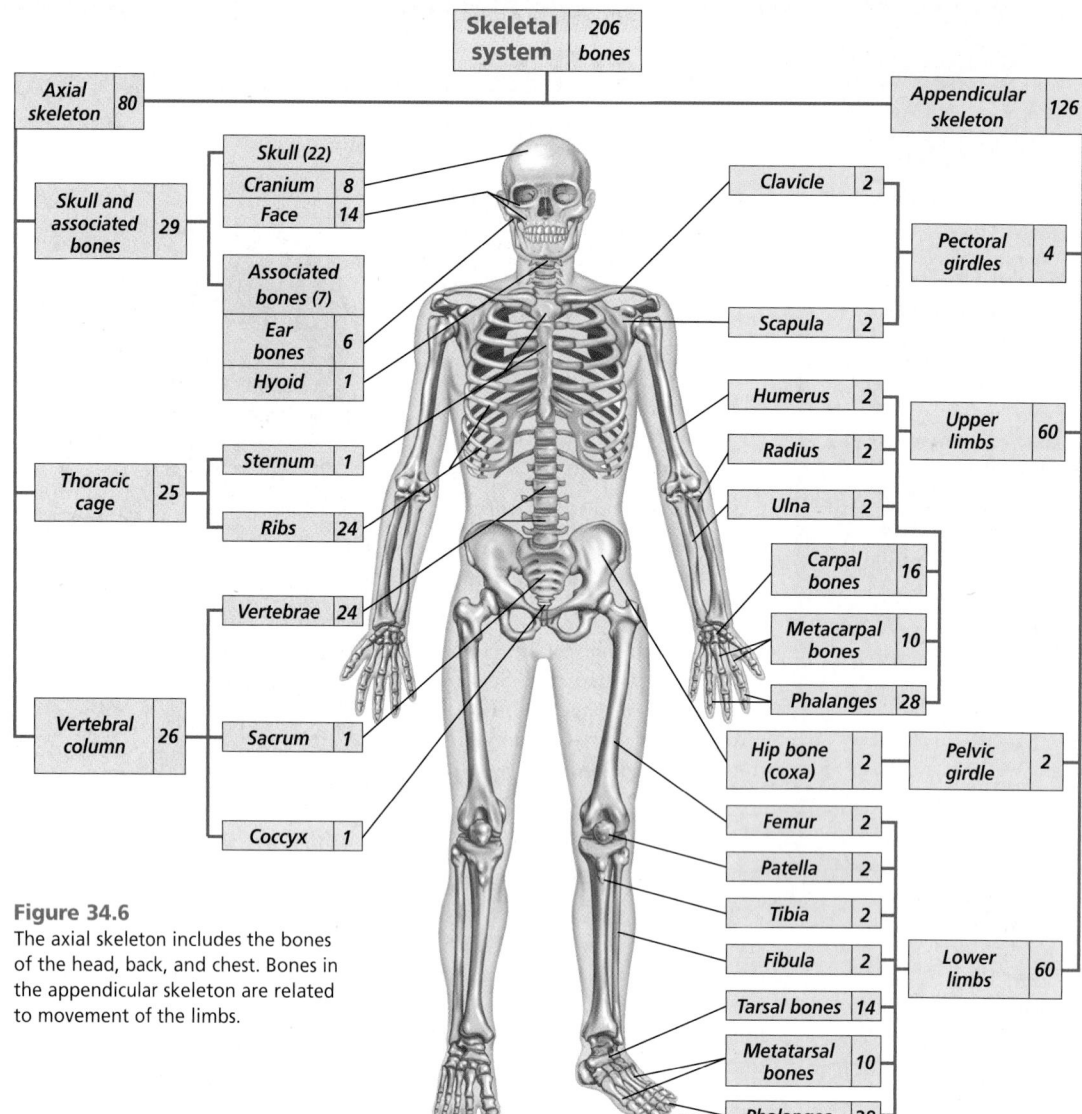

Figure 34.6
The axial skeleton includes the bones of the head, back, and chest. Bones in the appendicular skeleton are related to movement of the limbs.

This layer of cartilage allows for smooth movement between the bones. In addition, joints such as those of the shoulder and knee have fluid-filled sacs called **bursae** located on the outside of the joints. The bursae act to decrease friction and keep bones and tendons from rubbing against each other. **Tendons,** which are thick bands of connective tissue, attach muscles to bones. *Figure 34.*7 shows the different movable joints in the skeleton.

Forcible twisting of a joint, called a sprain, can result in injury to the bursae, ligaments, or tendons. A sprain most often occurs at joints with large ranges of motion such as the wrist, ankle, and knee.

Examining X rays Project X rays or hang them in windows on the day that you begin discussing the skeleton. Identify the bones shown in each X ray and the types of information X rays can reveal about bones.

Bone Strength: *Visual-Spatial* To demonstrate the strength of hollow bones, have students balance a heavy book on the open ends of two toilet paper tubes placed side by side. **L1** **ELL**

Figure 34.7
Body movements are made possible by joints that allow bones to move in several different directions.

A Ball-and-socket joints allow movement in all directions. The joints of the hips and shoulders are ball-and-socket joints; they allow you to swing your arms and legs around in many directions.

B Pivot joints allow bones to twist around each other. One example of a pivot joint is in your arm, between the ulna and the radius. It allows you to twist your lower arm around.

  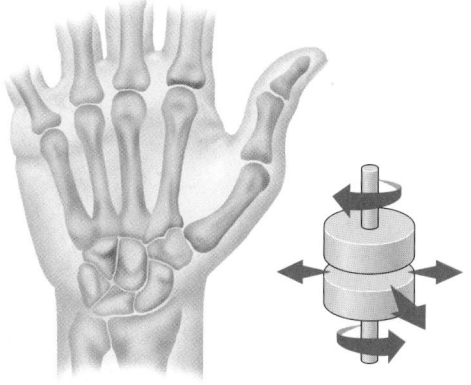

C Hinge joints are found in the elbows, knees, fingers, and toes. They allow back-and-forth movement like that of a door hinge.

D Gliding joints, found in the wrists and ankles, allow bones to slide past each other.

Besides injury, joints are also subject to disease. One common joint disease is arthritis, an inflammation of the joints. It can be caused by infections, aging, or injury. One kind of arthritis results in bone spurs, or outgrowths of bone, inside the joints. Such arthritis is especially painful, and often limits a person's ability to move his or her joints.

Compact and spongy bone

Although bones may appear uniform, they are actually composed of two different types of bone tissue: compact bone and spongy bone.

34.2   BONES: THE BODY'S SUPPORT   **901**

Using Science Terms

Discuss the derivation of the word *osteoporosis* with students. Ask students to find other terms in the chapter that make use of the prefix "osteo-". Ask them to explain how the prefix relates to the meaning of each term. **L1** **ELL**

Caption Question Answer

Figure 34.8 Osteons receive oxygen from small blood vessels running within the osteon systems. Nerve impulses travel on nerves in the osteon canals.

✓ **Reading Check** Growth in diameter occurs on the outer surface of the bone and growth in length occurs at the ends of bones in cartilage plates. Bone growth is due to osteoblast cells that deposit calcium salts and other ions.

Surrounding every bone is a layer of hard bone, or **compact bone.** Running the length of compact bone are tubular structures known as osteon or Haversian (ha VER zhen) systems, shown in *Figure 34.8*. Compact bone is made up of repeating units of osteon systems. Living bone cells, or **osteocytes** (AHS tee oh sitz), receive oxygen and nutrients from small blood vessels running within the osteon systems. Nerves in the canals conduct impulses to and from each bone cell. Compact bone surrounds less dense bone known as **spongy bone** because, like a sponge, it contains many holes and spaces.

Formation of Bone

The skeleton of a vertebrate embryo is made of cartilage. By the ninth week of human development, bone begins to replace cartilage. Blood vessels penetrate the membrane covering the cartilage and stimulate its cells to become potential bone cells called **osteoblasts** (AHS tee oh blastz). These potential bone cells secrete a protein called collagen in which minerals in the bloodstream begin to be deposited. The deposition of calcium salts and other ions hardens and the newly formed bone cells, now called osteocytes, are trapped. The adult skeleton is almost all bone, with cartilage found only in places where flexibility is

Figure 34.8
A bone has several components, including compact bone, spongy bone, and osteon systems. **Infer** *How do osteon systems receive oxygen? How do they receive nerve impulses?*

902 PROTECTION, SUPPORT, AND LOCOMOTION

needed—regions such as the nose tip, external ears, discs between vertebrae, and movable joint linings.

Bone growth

Your bones grow in both length and diameter. Growth in length occurs at the ends of bones in cartilage plates. Growth in diameter occurs on the outer surface of the bone. The increased production of sex hormones during your teen years causes the osteoblasts to divide more rapidly, resulting in a growth spurt. However, these same hormones will also cause the growth centers at the ends of your bones to degenerate. As these cells die, your growth will slow. After growth stops, bone-forming cells are involved in repair and maintenance of bone. Learn more about how bones age by doing the *Problem-Solving Lab* on this page.

✓ **Reading Check** **Explain** how bone growth occurs.

Skeletal System Functions

The primary function of your skeleton is to provide a framework for the tissues of your body. The skeleton also protects your internal organs, including your heart, lungs, and brain.

The arrangement of the human skeleton allows for efficient body movement. Muscles that move the body need firm points of attachment to pull against so they can work effectively. The skeleton provides these attachment points.

Bones also produce blood cells. **Red marrow**—found in the humerus, femur, sternum, ribs, vertebrae, and pelvis—is the production site for red blood cells, white blood cells, and cell fragments involved in blood clotting. **Yellow marrow,** found in many other bones, consists of stored fat as shown in *Figure 34.9*.

Problem-Solving Lab 34.2

Make and Use Tables

How does bone density differ between the sexes? Bone has a certain compactness or strength that can be measured in terms of the bone's mineral density. The higher the density of bone, the stronger it is. The lower the density of bone, the weaker it is.

Solve the Problem
Examine the chart's average values for bone density of males and females at different ages. The data are for the upper femur where it fits into the hip.

Average Bone Mineral Density		
Age	Female	Male
20	0.895	0.979
30	0.886	0.936
40	0.850	0.894
50	0.797	0.851
60	0.733	0.809
70	0.667	0.766
80	0.607	0.724

Thinking Critically

1. **Evaluate** What is the trend for bone density as a person ages?
2. **Analyze** Between the ages of 20 and 50, what percentage of bone density do females lose compared with males? What percentage is lost between the ages of 50 and 80 for either sex?
3. **Analyze** Which sex shows the greater change in bone density as it ages? Between which ages does the greatest change occur?
4. **Cause and Effect** The hormone in females that prevents bone density from decreasing begins to diminish at the age of 50. Does this correlate with the changes in bone density reported in the chart? Use specific numbers in your answer.

Figure 34.9
Bones can store fat for use in times of need.

Yellow bone marrow

Purpose
Students will compare bone density data for males and females at various ages.

Process Skills
make and use tables, use numbers, think critically, interpret data, compare and contrast

Teaching Strategies
■ Review the procedure for calculating percentages.
■ Remind students that prior to calculating all values called for in the Thinking Critically section, the amount of final bone density for an age group must be subtracted from the original bone density to arrive at the amount of bone density lost. Use amount of bone density lost compared with original bone density to calculate percent of bone density lost.

Example: Find the percent bone density lost for females between the ages of 20 and 50.

Step 1: $0.895 - 0.797$
$= 0.098$
Step 2: $0.098/0.895 \times 100 = 10.9\%$

Thinking Critically
1. Bone density decreases with age regardless of sex.
2. females from 20–50 = 10.9% males from 20–50 = 13.0%; females from 50–80 = 23.8% males from 50–80 = 14.9%
3. females, from age 50–80
4. Yes, from ages 20–50 a decrease in bone density of only 10.9% is measured for females, but from 50–80, the decrease is 23.8%.

Assessment
Knowledge Have students research the benefits of exercise on bone density. Challenge them to correlate their findings with the need for exercise by the elderly. Students should summarize their research in their journals. Use the Performance Task Assessment List for Writing in Science in **PASC**, p. 159. **L2**

(p. 904) Have students research how short wavelength electromagnetic radiation is used to treat cancer. X-rays are beamed on a cancerous growth in an attempt to destroy the tumor or prevent it from growing larger.

CHALLENGE ACTIVITY

Comparative Anatomy Have students who need an additional challenge compare the anatomy of the front limbs of a frog, bird, cat, whale, and bat with that of the human arm. Compare the number, shapes, and arrangements of bones. **L3**

3 Assess

Figure 34.10
The X ray on the left shows a leg bone that has completely fractured. The X ray on the right shows the bone (with a supporting rod) after it has healed. The arrow indicates the area where the break healed.

Physical Science Connection

Wave types X rays are electromagnetic waves. Unlike sound waves, electromagnetic waves can travel through space and consist of vibrating electric and magnetic fields. Microwaves, visible light, and ultraviolet rays are also electromagnetic waves with longer wavelengths than X rays.

Bones store minerals

Finally, your bones serve as storehouses for minerals, including calcium and phosphate. Calcium is needed to form strong, healthy bones and is therefore an important part of your diet. Sources of calcium include milk, yogurt, cheese, lettuce, spinach, and other assorted leafy vegetables.

Bone injury and disease

Bones tend to become more brittle as their composition changes with age. For example, a disease called osteoporosis (ahs tee oh puh ROH sus) involves a loss of bone volume and mineral content, causing the bones to become more porous and brittle. Osteoporosis is most common in older women because they produce lesser amounts of estrogen—a hormone that aids in bone formation.

When bones are broken, as shown by the X-ray images in *Figure 34.10,* a doctor moves them back into position and immobilizes them with a cast or splint until the bone tissue regrows. Read more about the use of X rays in the diagnosis of broken bones in the *Connection to Physics* at the end of this chapter.

Section Assessment

Understanding Main Ideas
1. Distinguish between the appendicular skeleton and the axial skeleton.
2. Compare and contrast the four main kinds of movable joints and provide an example of each.
3. How is compact bone structurally different from spongy bone?
4. Identify and interpret the functions of the skeletal system.

Thinking Critically
5. Why would it be impossible for bones to grow from within?

SKILL REVIEW

6. **Get the Big Picture** Outline the steps involved in bone formation and growth—from cartilage to the cessation of bone growth. For more help, refer to *Get the Big Picture* in the **Skill Handbook.**

904 PROTECTION, SUPPORT, AND LOCOMOTION

 in.bdol.glencoe.com/self_check_quiz

Section Assessment

1. axial skeleton: the skull and the bones that support it; appendicular skeleton: bones associated with the appendages
2. ball-and-socket joints: movement in all directions, hips and shoulders; pivot joints: allow twisting around each other, between radius and ulna; hinge joints: back-and-forth movement, elbows, knees, fingers, toes; gliding joints: allow bones to slide past each other, wrists
3. Compact bone is made up of osteon systems. Spongy bone contains holes.
4. The skeletal system provides a framework for the tissues of the body, produces blood cells, and stores minerals.
5. The structure of compact bone would not allow growth from the inside.
6. (1) embryo skeleton is cartilage; (2) bone begins to replace cartilage—osteoblasts secrete a material in which calcium salts and other ions are deposited and harden to form bone; (3) bones continue to grow in length from the ends, and in diameter from the outer surface until around age 20

Muscles for Locomotion

Indiana Standards Standard B.1.14 Recognize and explain that communication and/or interaction are required between cells to coordinate their diverse activities.

Classifying Muscles

Concept Map Copy the concept map onto a separate sheet of paper.

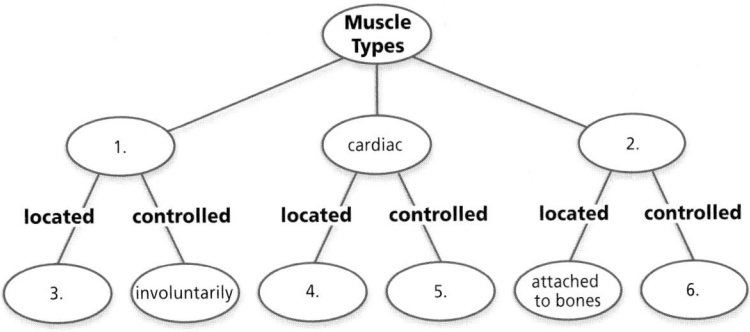

Organize Information As you read this section, complete the concept map to compare different types of muscles.

SECTION PREVIEW

Objectives

Classify the three types of muscles.

Analyze the structure of a myofibril.

Interpret the sliding filament theory.

Review Vocabulary
ATP: energy-storing molecule in cells composed of an adenosine molecule, a ribose sugar, and three phosphate groups (p. 222)

New Vocabulary
smooth muscle
involuntary muscle
cardiac muscle
skeletal muscle
voluntary muscle
myofibril
myosin
actin
sarcomere
sliding filament theory

Three Types of Muscles

Nearly half of your body mass is muscle. A muscle consists of groups of fibers, or cells, bound together. Almost all of the muscle fibers you will ever have were present at birth. *Figure 34.11* shows the three main kinds of muscles in your body. One type of tissue, **smooth muscle**, is found in the walls of your internal organs and blood vessels.

Figure 34.11
Muscles differ in structure and appearance.

LM Magnification: 100×

Color-enhanced TEM Magnification: 42 000×

Color-enhanced TEM Magnification: 1100×

A Smooth muscle fibers appear spindle-shaped under the microscope.

B Cardiac muscle fibers appear striated or striped when magnified.

C Skeletal muscle fibers also appear striated when magnified.

34.3   MUSCLES FOR LOCOMOTION **905**

1 Focus

INTERACTIVE CHALKBOARD
PowerPoint® Presentations

Bellringer
Section Focus Transparency 83

Transparency **83** Built to Move

SECTION FOCUS
Use with Chapter 34, Section 34.3

❶ How would the shape of this object change if the lower spring tightened? What would happen if the upper spring tightened instead?

❷ Where on your body is an apparatus similar to the one shown? What takes the place of a spring?

BIOLOGY: The Dynamics of Life   SECTION FOCUS TRANSPARENCIES

Concept Map

Organize Information After students have completed their reading and the concept map, give them a concept map filled in except for the bottom level. Have students fill in the missing answers as a quiz. 1. smooth; 2. skeletal; 3. walls of internal organs and blood vessels; 4. heart; 5. involuntarily; 6. voluntarily

---

RESOURCE MANAGER

Unit 10 *Fast File* Resources
MiniLab Worksheet, p. 4
BioLab Worksheet, pp. 5–6
Real World BioApplications, pp. 9–10
Reinforcement and Study Guide in English, p. 14
Reinforcement and Study Guide in Spanish, p. 18
Transparency Worksheets, pp. 23, 31–34

Reading Essentials for Biology, Section 34.3
Probeware Labs, pp. 25–28
Inside Story Poster
Section Focus Transparency 83
Basic Concepts Transparency 64
Reteaching Skills Transparency 49

Indiana Academic Standards

Pages 904–905: B.1.15, B.1.19

Quick Demo

Tendons and Muscles
Obtain some chicken feet from a butcher. Cut the upper end so that the tendons are free. Pull on each tendon to demonstrate the movement of the toes.

Problem-Solving Lab 34.3

Purpose
Students will compare the cells from different tissues: skin, bone, and muscle.

Process Skills
analyze, infer

Teaching Strategies
■ Allow students to work in pairs or small groups.
■ See the table below for possible student answers.

Thinking Critically
muscle tissue; sarcomeres showing actin and myosin filaments

Modified Assessment
Knowledge Quiz students using flash cards with descriptions of the different cell types. **L1**

(p. 907) Ask students to explain the difference between work and power. Power is the amount of work done divided by the time needed to do the work. The power needed to do a certain amount of work depends on the time over which the work is done. For example, the power needed to lift a 10-kg book bag 1 m high in 0.5 s is greater than the power needed to lift the book bag 1 m high in 2 s.

Problem-Solving Lab 34.3

Compare and Contrast

How are skin, bone, and muscle cells different? Cells that form skin (which includes epithelial cells), bone, and muscle are specialized to perform various functions. Each of these systems of the body contains different types of cells that work together to carry out the function of the tissue or organ.

Cell Structure and Function		
	Structure	Function
Skin		
Muscle		
Bone		

Solve the Problem
Using the text and figures on pages 894, 902, 905, and 908, prepare a table that compares and contrasts the structure and function of skin, muscle, and bone cells.

Thinking Critically
Infer Protein analysis of an unknown tissue sample yields a high level of myosin and actin. Is this sample skin, bone, or muscle? What structures could you look for in an electron microscope to confirm the identity of this tissue?

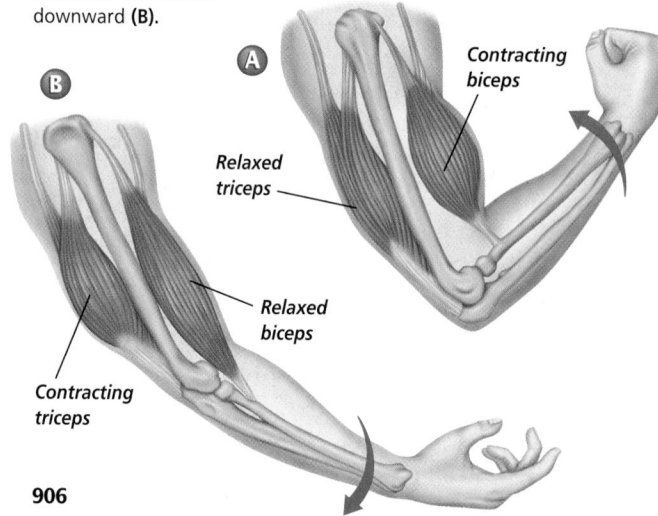

Figure 34.12
When the biceps muscle contracts, the lower arm is moved upward (**A**). When the triceps muscle on the back of the upper arm contracts, the lower arm moves downward (**B**).

906

Smooth muscle is made up of sheets of cells that are ideally shaped to form a lining for organs, such as the digestive tract and the reproductive tract. The most common function of smooth muscle is to squeeze, exerting pressure on the space inside the tube or organ it surrounds in order to move material through it. Examples include the movement of food through the digestive system and the movement of gametes through the reproductive system. Because contractions of smooth muscle are not under conscious control, smooth muscle is considered an **involuntary muscle.**

Another type of involuntary muscle is the **cardiac muscle,** which makes up your heart. Cardiac muscle fibers are interconnected and form a network that helps the heart muscle contract efficiently. Cardiac muscle is found only in the heart and is adapted to generate and conduct electrical impulses necessary for its rhythmic contraction.

The third type of muscle tissue, **skeletal muscle,** is the type that is attached to and moves your bones. The majority of the muscles in your body are skeletal muscles, and, as you know, you can control their contractions. A muscle that contracts under conscious control is called a **voluntary muscle.** Compare the structure and function of skin, muscle, and bone in the *Problem-Solving Lab* on this page.

Skeletal Muscle Contraction

Whether you are playing tennis, pushing a lawn mower, or writing, some muscles contract while others relax as the action is performed. *Figure 34.12* shows the movement of the lower arm as controlled by opposing muscles in the upper arm. The majority of skeletal muscles work in opposing pairs.

Cell Structure and Function		
	Structure	**Function**
Skin	Epidermal layer of flattened cells, dermal layer with blood vessels, connective tissue, hair follicles, sweat glands, nerves	Protects and covers body, regulates body temperature, produces Vitamin D
Muscle	Smooth, cardiac, and skeletal muscle types made of myofibrils divided into sarcomere units of actin and myosin	Contract to do work and move the body
Bone	Osteon systems of compact bone and spongy bone	Framework for body, protection of internal organs, muscle attachment, mineral storage

Muscle tissue is made up of muscle fibers, which are actually just very long, fused muscle cells. Each fiber is made up of smaller units called **myofibrils** (mi oh FI brulz). Myofibrils are themselves composed of even smaller protein filaments that can be either thick or thin. The thicker filaments are made of the protein **myosin,** and the thinner filaments are made of the protein **actin.** Each myofibril can be divided into sections called **sarcomeres** (SAR kuh meerz), the functional units of muscle. How do nerves signal muscles to contract? Find out in *Figure 34.13* on the next page.

The sliding filament theory currently offers the best explanation for how muscle contraction occurs. The **sliding filament theory** states that, when signaled, the actin filaments within each sarcomere slide toward one another, shortening the sarcomeres in a fiber and causing the muscle to contract. The myosin filaments, on the other hand, do not move. Learn more about the sliding filament theory and muscle contraction in the *MiniLab* on this page.

Muscle Strength and Exercise

How can you increase the strength of your muscles? Muscle strength does not depend on the number of fibers in a muscle. It has been shown that this number is basically fixed before you are born. Rather, muscle strength depends on the thickness of the fibers and on how many of them contract at one time. Regular exercise stresses muscle fibers slightly; to compensate for this added workload, the fibers increase in diameter by adding myofibrils.

Recall that ATP is produced during cellular respiration. Muscle cells are continually supplied with ATP from both aerobic and anaerobic processes. However, the aerobic respiration process dominates when adequate oxygen is delivered to muscle cells, such as when a muscle is at rest or during moderate activity. When an adequate supply of oxygen is unavailable, such as during vigorous activity, an anaerobic process—specifically lactic acid fermentation—becomes the primary source of ATP production.

✓ Reading Check **Identify** the two processes the body uses to produce ATP.

MiniLab 34.2

Interpret

Examining Muscle Contraction Sarcomeres in muscle fibers are composed of the protein filaments actin and myosin. The sliding action of these filaments in relation to one another results in muscle contraction.

Procedure

1. Look at diagrams A and B. Diagram A shows a sarcomere in a relaxed muscle. Diagram B shows a sarcomere in a contracted muscle.
2. Using a centimeter ruler, measure and record the length of a sarcomere, a myosin filament, and an actin filament in diagram A. Record your data in a table.
3. Repeat step 2 for diagram B.

Sarcomere

Ⓐ — *Myosin*

— *Actin*

Ⓑ

Analysis

1. **Evaluate** When a muscle contracts, do actin or myosin filaments shorten? Use your data to support your answer.
2. **Infer** How does the sarcomere shorten?

MiniLab 34.2

Purpose

Students will measure the length of a sarcomere during muscle relaxation and contraction.

Process Skills

acquire information, apply concepts, collect data, compare and contrast, formulate models, interpret data, measure in SI, predict

Teaching Strategies

■ Provide students with rulers.
■ Review vocabulary terms prior to the start of this activity.

Expected Results

Actin filaments slide over myosin filaments resulting in shortening of sarcomeres during contraction.

Analysis

1. Students will learn that actin and myosin do not change in length.
2. Actin filaments slide over myosin filaments, shortening the sarcomere.

Assessment

Knowledge Using the diagram of relaxed muscle, have students explain why skeletal muscle has a striated appearance when viewed under the microscope. Provide students with a slide of striated muscle tissue to verify their explanations. Use the Performance Task Assessment List for Making Observations and Inferences in **PASC**, p. 89. **L2**

✓ Reading Check aerobic cellular respiration and anaerobic cellular respiration

---

CHALLENGE ACTIVITY

Sports Medicine Ask advanced students to prepare and conduct an interview with a person who works in the field of sports medicine. Students should include questions on how their programs relate to muscle fitness and health. **L3**

INCLUSION STRATEGIES

English Language Learners: *Linguistic* Have students who are having difficulty make flash cards that show an anatomical term on one side of the card and its meaning and location on the other side. Have students work in pairs to review the cards. **L1 ELL**

Indiana Academic Standards

Pages 906–907: B.1.14, B.1.15

Purpose

Students gain further understanding of the way muscle cells contract.

Teaching Strategies

■ Have students describe the structure of skeletal muscle. **L2**

■ Ask students to describe the differences between actin and myosin filaments. **L2**

Visual Learning

Ask students what makes up a single muscle fiber. many myofibril units Elicit what chemical stimulates the formation of attachments between myosin and actin filaments. calcium

Critical Thinking

The nerve signal causes calcium to be released in the muscle. The calcium causes actin and myosin filaments to bind together. The actin filaments are then pulled inward, resulting in a muscle contraction.

Assessment

Knowledge Have students write a short summary of why lactic acid builds up in muscle cells during intense exercise. **L2**

The BioLab at the end of the chapter can be used at this point in the lesson.

Tying to Prior Knowledge

Point out that myofibrils of the muscles are a special type of microfilament, as discussed previously. This is a good time to review ATP, along with aerobic and anaerobic metabolism.

Indiana Academic Standards
Pages 908–909: B.1.14, B.1.15, B.1.16, B.1.17

908

A Muscle

Figure 34.13
Locomotion is made possible by the contraction and relaxation of muscles. The sliding filament theory of how muscles contract can be better understood by examining the detailed structure of a skeletal muscle.
Critical Thinking *How does a nerve signal cause a skeletal muscle to contract?*

A Muscle structure
When you tease apart a typical skeletal muscle and view it under a microscope, you can see that it consists of bundles of fibers. A single fiber is made up of myofibrils which, in turn, are made up of actin or myosin filaments. Each myofibril can be broken up into functional units called sarcomeres.

B Nerve signal
When a skeletal muscle receives a signal from a nerve, calcium is released inside the muscle fibers, causing them to contract.

C Contraction
The presence of calcium causes attachments to form between the thick myosin and thin actin filaments. The actin filaments are then pulled inward toward the center of each sarcomere, shortening the sarcomere and producing a muscle contraction. When the muscle relaxes, the filaments slide back into their original positions.

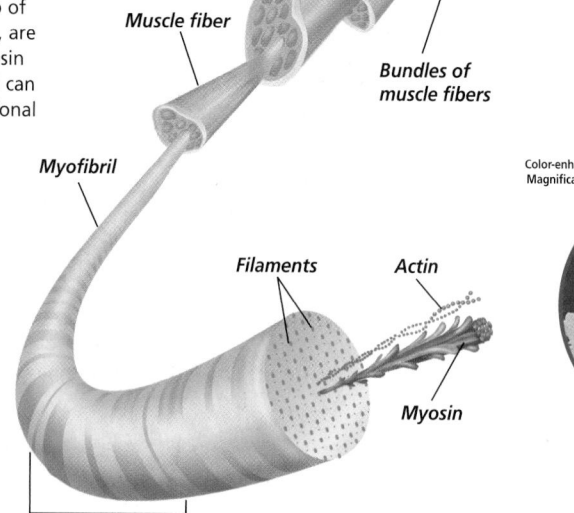

Bone
Tendon
Skeletal muscle
Muscle fiber
Bundles of muscle fibers

Color-enhanced SEM
Magnification: 580×

Skeletal muscle is responsible for moving your bones.

Myofibril
Filaments
Actin
Myosin
Sarcomere

Section of a striated muscle fiber
Actin
Myosin
Relaxed sarcomere
Contracted sarcomere

908 PROTECTION, SUPPORT, AND LOCOMOTION

Modeling Body Movement: *Visual-Spatial* Have students working in groups construct models to show how bones and muscles work together to move appendages. More advanced students may wish to work together to prepare a model that demonstrates the sliding filament theory. **L2 ELL COOP LEARN**

Physically Challenged Locate a physically challenged spokesperson who has a musculoskeletal disease and who is willing to speak to the class about the disorder. The focus of the discussion should be on the nature of the disease, restrictions the disease places on the person, and treatments for the disease.

Think about what happens when you are running in gym class or around the track at school. *Figure 34.14A* illustrates how an athlete's need for oxygen changes as the intensity of his or her workout increases. At some point, your muscles are not able to get oxygen fast enough to sustain aerobic respiration and produce adequate ATP. Thus, the amount of available ATP becomes limited. For your muscle cells to get the energy they need, they must rely on lactic acid fermentation as well. *Figure 34.14B* indicates how, at a certain intensity, the body shifts from aerobic respiration to the anaerobic process of lactic acid fermentation for its energy needs.

During exercise, lactic acid builds up in muscle cells. As the excess lactic acid is passed into the bloodstream, the blood becomes more acidic and rapid breathing is stimulated. As you catch your breath following exercise, adequate amounts of oxygen are supplied to your muscles and lactic acid is broken down. Regular exercise can result in improved performance of muscles. Do the *BioLab* at the end of the chapter to find out how muscle fatigue affects the amount of exercise your muscles can accomplish.

✓ **Reading Check** **Explain** what happens to lactic acid after exercise is completed.

Figure 34.14
Athletic trainers use information about muscle functioning during exercise to establish appropriate levels of intensity for training.

A As an individual increases the intensity of his or her workout, the need for oxygen goes up in predictable increments.

B During exercise, lactic acid concentrations can increase. **Infer** *What does an increase in the presence of lactic acid in the bloodstream indicate about the amount of oxygen available to muscle cells?*

✓ **Reading Check** Lactic acid is broken down as adequate amounts of oxygen are supplied to muscles.

Caption Question Answer
Figure 34.14 Muscle cells are not receiving enough oxygen to undergo aerobic respiration. They must use lactic acid fermentation to produce ATP.

3 Assess

Extension
Have interested students research diseases and disorders that affect the muscular system. Have them prepare a report on one of the disorders for their portfolios. **L3**

✓ **MODIFIED Assessment**

Performance Provide students with a diagram of muscles of the human body. Have students make a key to identify each type of muscle. **L1**

Section Assessment

Understanding Main Ideas
1. Compare the structure and interpret the functions of the three main types of muscles in the muscular system.
2. Summarize the sliding filament theory of muscle contraction.
3. How can exercise change muscle strength? How can it change muscle function?
4. What determines muscle strength?

Thinking Critically
5. Why would a disease that causes paralysis of smooth muscles be life threatening?

SKILL REVIEW
6. **Interpret Scientific Illustrations** Diagram the composition of muscle fibers as shown in *Figure 34.13*. For more help, refer to *Interpret Scientific Illustrations* in the **Skill Handbook**.

 in.bdol.glencoe.com/self_check_quiz

Section Assessment

1. Smooth muscle cells are spindle shaped and form the linings of organs. They apply pressure and squeeze. Cardiac muscle cells are striated and form a contraction network in the heart. Skeletal muscle cells are striated. They move the body.
2. Calcium is released into the muscle fiber, actin and myosin filaments form attachments, and the actin filaments are pulled inward toward the center of each sarcomere.
3. Exercise stresses muscles and causes fibers to increase in size and strength. Exercise cannot change muscle function.
4. Muscle strength depends on the thickness of the muscle fibers and how many of the fibers contract at one time.
5. Internal organs utilize smooth muscle to perform their functions, such as breathing and digestion.
6. The drawing should reflect that muscle fibers are made of tiny cylinders called myofibrils. Each myofibril is made of myosin and actin filaments arranged in a pattern within the sarcomere.

Time Allotment

one class period

Process Skills

observe and infer, communicate, measure in SI, predict, form a hypothesis, design an experiment

Safety Precautions

Warn students not to do any exercise they are uncomfortable with or that would exacerbate an existing physical condition. Students should not overexert themselves. Caution them to do exercises correctly and carefully so as not to sustain an injury. Be sure students are wearing clothing and footwear appropriate for exercise.

PREPARATION

Alternative Materials

Stopwatches are not necessary if a clock with a second hand is visible to all students.

Possible Hypotheses

- If a muscle becomes fatigued, then the muscle will not be able to do as much work.
- If a muscle becomes fatigued, its capacity to do work will not be diminished.

Indiana Academic Standards

Pages 910–911: B.1.16

PLAN THE EXPERIMENT

Teaching Strategies

- One student should act as timekeeper. The exerciser should count the number of times he or she can carry out the exercise in a given time period, such as 3 minutes.

- Trials should be performed as closely together as possible, so that little muscle rest occurs between trials.
- Place a sample graph on the chalkboard to help students prepare their graphs.

910

 Before You Begin

The movement of body parts results from the contraction and relaxation of muscles. In this process, muscles use energy from aerobic respiration and lactic acid fermentation. When exercise is continued for a long period of time, the waste products of fermentation accumulate and muscle fibers are stressed, causing fatigue. How does fatigue affect muscles? In this lab you will investigate the effects of fatigue on the ability of muscles to perform a task.

Does fatigue affect the ability to perform an exercise?

PREPARATION

Problem

How does fatigue affect the number of repetitions of an exercise you can accomplish?

Hypotheses

Hypothesize whether or not muscle fatigue has any effect on the amount of exercise muscles can accomplish. Consider whether fatigue occurs within minutes or hours.

Objectives

In this BioLab, you will:
- **Hypothesize** whether or not muscle fatigue affects the amount of exercise muscles can accomplish.
- **Measure** the amount of exercise done by a group of muscles.
- **Make a graph** to show the amount of exercise done by a group of muscles.

Possible Materials

stopwatch or clock
with second hand

graph paper
small weights

Safety Precautions

CAUTION: *Do not choose an exercise that is too difficult. Do not overexert yourself. Wear appropriate footwear and clothing for exercise.*

Skill Handbook

If you need help with this lab, refer to the **Skill Handbook**.

PLAN THE EXPERIMENT

1. Design a repetitive exercise for a particular group of muscles. Make sure you can count single repetitions of the exercise, for example, one jumping jack.

Possible Procedures

Students could choose an exercise such as jumping jacks, hopping or jogging in place, or stepping up and down from the bottom step of stairs. They should repeat the experiment 4 or 5 times so that the muscles become fatigued.

2. Work in pairs, with one member of the team being a timekeeper and the other member performing the exercise.

3. Compare your design with those of other groups.

Check the Plan
1. Be sure that the exercises are ones that can be done rapidly and cause a minimum of disruption to other groups in the classroom.

2. Consider how long you will do the activity and how often you will record measurements.

3. *Make sure your teacher has approved your experimental plan before you proceed further.*

4. Make a table in which you can record the number of exercise repetitions per time interval.

5. Carry out the experiment.

6. On a piece of graph paper, plot the number of repetitions on the vertical axis and the time intervals on the horizontal axis.

ANALYZE AND CONCLUDE

1. **Make Inferences** What effect did repeating the exercise over time have on the muscle group?

2. **Compare and Contrast** As you repeated the exercise over time, how did your muscles feel?

3. **Recognize Cause and Effect** What physiological factors are responsible for fatigue?

4. **Think Critically** How well do you think your fatigued muscles would work after 30 minutes of rest? Explain your answer.

5. **Hypothesize** Form a hypothesis about how different amounts of resistance would affect the rate of fatigue. Design an experiment to test your hypothesis. Identify the independent and dependent variables.

6. **ERROR ANALYSIS** Compare your results to those of other student groups. How can you explain the differences in results? If you were to perform this experiment again, how would you improve it?

Apply Your Skill

Project Design an experiment that will enable you to measure the strength of muscle contractions.

 Web Links To find out more about muscles, visit in.bdol.glencoe.com/muscles

ANALYZE AND CONCLUDE

1. The muscle groups became fatigued and the number of repetitions of the activity decreased as more trials were run.

2. The muscles felt tired and may even have begun to hurt toward the end. It became harder to do the activity and the strength of each contraction was reduced.

3. Cells are running out of oxygen and accumulating toxic products such as lactic acid and carbon dioxide as the muscles change to anaerobic processes.

4. Fatigued muscles should work as well after a rest of 30 minutes as they did before fatigue became a factor. The accumulated lactic acid has been broken down as the oxygen supply in the muscle cells has been replenished during the rest.

5. The greater the resistance, the more quickly fatigue will occur. One possible design would be to have a person do repetitions with increasing amounts of resistance with rest periods in between each increment. The independent variable is the amount of resistance. The dependent variable is the number of repetitions completed in a certain time period.

6. **ERROR ANALYSIS** Answers will vary. Differences may be explained by variations in types of activity and amount of individual exertion. Improvement answers will vary.

Data and Observations
Student graphs should show that the number of exercise repetitions goes down over time as the muscles become tired.

Apply Your Skill

Project Ask students how athletes such as marathon runners continue to exercise at a high level for hours. Why don't their muscles fatigue after a few minutes?

Assessment
Portfolio Have students place their laboratory reports, including their tables and graphs, in their journals. Use the Performance Task Assessment List for Science Journal in **PASC**, p. 175. **L2**

connection to Physics

Purpose

Students will learn about some uses of X rays in medicine.

Background

After Roentgen's (RENT ghun) discovery of X rays was made public, he was the recipient of many honors and awards including the Nobel Prize in Physics in 1901. X rays are sometimes referred to as *roentgenograms* in recognition of the man who discovered them.

Teaching Strategies

■ Ask students to share experiences about when they have had X rays taken. Ask students to explain why the X rays were needed.

■ Hang up X rays on the windows or show them on the overhead as you discuss the Connection to Physics. Point out how soft tissues do not show up on the X rays.

X Rays—The Painless Probe

X rays are a form of radiation emitted by X-ray tubes and by some astronomical objects such as stars. Machines that use X rays to view concealed objects are so common that you have probably had contact with one recently. Dentists use them to examine teeth, doctors to inspect bones and organs, and airports to look inside your carry-on and checked baggage.

Wilhelm Roentgen, a German physics professor, accidentally discovered the X ray in 1895. As he was studying cathode rays in a high-voltage vacuum tube, he noticed that a special screen lying nearby was giving off fluorescent light. He eventually determined that rays given off by the tube were able to penetrate the black box that enclosed it and strike the screen, causing it to glow. Because he did not know what these rays were, he called them X rays, "X" standing for "unknown." He made a film of his wife's hand, exposing the bones—the first permanent X ray of a human. Two months later, he published a short paper. Within a month of its publication, doctors in Europe and the U.S. were using X rays in their work.

Noninvasive diagnosis In medicine, X rays are passed through the body to photographic film. Bones and other dense objects show up as white areas on the film. As a result, the position and nature of a break is clearly visible. The contours of organs such as the stomach can be seen when a patient ingests a high-contrast liquid; other organs can be marked with special dyes.

Another practical application of X rays includes their use in tests that measure bone density. Recall that osteoporosis is a disease that results in bones becoming porous and brittle, causing them to fracture more easily. Bone density scans use X rays to measure the density of an

An X ray of Bertha Roentgen's hand (above). Bone scan of a 55 year-old female's hip (right).

individual's bones, such as those found in the hip and the spine. These scans are painless, low-risk scans that yield highly accurate results.

Radiation treatments As X rays bombard atoms of tissues, electrons are knocked from their orbits, resulting in damage to the exposed tissue cells. To protect healthy tissues, absorptive metals are used as shields. You've probably had a dental X ray where the dental assistant spread a heavy lead apron across your chest. The destructive nature of high doses of X rays has proven useful in the treatment of cancers, where cancerous cells are targeted and destroyed.

Researching in Biology

Research Evaluate the impact of X rays on scientific thought and society by researching how physicians diagnosed skeletal disorders prior to the invention of X rays. Investigate what other types of painless probes are available today, such as those used for facial recognition and iris scans.

 To find out more about X rays, visit in.bdol.glencoe.com/physics

912 PROTECTION, SUPPORT, AND LOCOMOTION

Researching in Biology

Prior to the invention of X rays, physicians had to make a diagnosis of a broken bone by touch. Bullets were located by exploring the wound using fingers or a metal probe. Students could include information on MRIs, PETs, CT scans, sonograms, and the newest technology of facial recognition and iris scans.

STUDY GUIDE

Section 34.1

Skin: The Body's Protection

Key Concepts

■ Skin is composed of the epidermis and dermis, with each layer performing various functions.

■ Skin regulates body temperature, protects the body, and functions as a sense organ.

■ Skin responds to injury by producing new cells and signaling a response to fight infection.

Vocabulary

dermis (p. 895)
epidermis (p. 893)
hair follicle (p. 896)
keratin (p. 893)
melanin (p. 895)

Section 34.2

Bones: The Body's Support

Key Concepts

■ The skeleton is made up of the axial and appendicular skeletons.

■ Joints allow movement between two or more bones where they meet.

■ Osteocytes are living bone cells.

■ Bones are formed from cartilage as a human embryo develops.

■ The skeleton supports the body, provides a place for muscle attachment, protects vital organs, manufactures blood cells, and serves as a storehouse for calcium and phosphorus.

Vocabulary

appendicular skeleton (p. 899)
axial skeleton (p. 899)
bursa (p. 900)
compact bone (p. 902)
joint (p. 899)
ligament (p. 899)
osteoblast (p. 902)
osteocyte (p. 902)
red marrow (p. 903)
spongy bone (p. 902)
tendon (p. 900)
yellow marrow (p. 903)

Section 34.3

Muscles for Locomotion

Key Concepts

■ There are three types of tissue: smooth, cardiac, and skeletal. Smooth muscle lines organs, contracting to move materials through the body. Cardiac muscle contracts rhythmically to keep the heart beating. Skeletal muscle is attached to bones and contracts to produce body movements.

■ Muscle tissue consists of muscle fibers, which can be divided into smaller units called myofibrils.

■ Muscles contract as filaments within the myofibrils slide toward one another.

Vocabulary

actin (p. 907)
cardiac muscle (p. 906)
involuntary muscle (p. 906)
myofibril (p. 907)
myosin (p. 907)
sarcomere (p. 907)
skeletal muscle (p. 906)
sliding filament theory (p. 907)
smooth muscle (p. 905)
voluntary muscle (p. 906)

FOLDABLES™
Study Organizer To help you review skin structure and function, use the Organizational Study Fold on page 893.

in.bdol.glencoe.com/vocabulary_puzzlemaker

Key Concepts

Summary statements can be used by students to review the major concepts of the chapter.

Biology Online

Visit in.bdol.glencoe.com
/self_check_quiz
/vocabulary_puzzlemaker
/chapter_test
/standardized_test

VOCABULARY PUZZLEMAKER

For additional help with vocabulary, have students access the Vocabulary PuzzleMaker online at in.bdol.glencoe.com/vocabulary_puzzlemaker

FOLDABLES™

Have students use their Foldables to review the content of Section 34.1. On the back of the paper, have students identify where the different tissue types of the body are located in the skin.

Use the ExamView®Pro Test Bank CD-ROM to:

● Create **multiple versions** of tests
● Create **modified** tests with one mouse click for **inclusion** students
● **Edit** existing questions and **add** your own questions
● Build tests aligned with state standards using built-in **State Curriculum Tags**
● Change **English** tests to **Spanish** with one mouse click and vice versa

Indiana Academic Standards

Pages 912–913: B.1.14, B.1.15, B.1.17, B.1.20

The Princeton Review **Questions and answers have been aligned and verified by The Princeton Review.**

Vocabulary Review

1. epidermis
2. ligaments
3. osteocytes
4. smooth muscle
5. myosin

Understanding Key Concepts

6. C   9. B
7. B   10. D
8. A

11. 1. skeletal muscles;
2. myofibrils; 3. myosin;
4. actin

Constructed Response

12. Muscles attach to the skeletal system and are able to develop force by pulling against the bone, causing movement.

13. Ligaments attach bone to bone across joints. Injury to the ligament could result in dislocation of a joint, not having full range of movement, pain, and swelling at the joint.

14. The sliding filament theory offers an explanation of how muscle fibers contract. Strengths: it has been modeled, tested, and validated with quantitative data in the laboratory; Weaknesses: as new data is collected and evaluated, the theory may need to be revised based on new findings.

Thinking Critically

15. Slide A: epidermis; protection; Slide B: either cardiac or skeletal muscle cell; Slide C: bone; support, movement, mineral storage, red blood cell production

16. Risk factors: sex hormone levels, diet, medications,

Vocabulary Review

Review the Chapter 34 vocabulary words listed in the Study Guide on page 913. Match the words with the definitions below.

1. the outermost layer of skin
2. tough bands of connective tissue that attach bone to bone
3. living cells of compact and spongy bone
4. type of muscle found in the walls of internal organs
5. protein that makes up the thick filaments of myofibrils

Understanding Key Concepts

6. Which of the following is a skin pigment that protects cells from solar radiation damage?
A. keratin   C. melanin
B. epidermis   D. dermis

7. Which of the following is nourished by blood vessels that run within this structure?
A. dermis
B. osteocyte
C. epidermis
D. sarcomere

Osteon system

8. All of the following are types of muscle except _____.
A. epidermal   C. smooth
B. cardiac   D. skeletal

9. Skin plays a role in _____.
A. storing calcium
B. regulating body temperature
C. manufacturing blood cells
D. supporting the body

10. The axial skeleton includes bones from _____.
A. the skull   C. the sternum
B. the ribs   D. all of the above

11. Complete the concept map by using the following vocabulary terms: actin, myofibrils, skeletal muscles, myosin.

1.
contain bundles of fibers made up of
2.
which are made of thick filaments of the protein / which are made of thin filaments of the protein
3.   4.

Constructed Response

12. **Open Ended** Compare the interrelations of the skeletal and muscular systems to each other and to the body as a whole.

13. **Open Ended** How could an injury to a ligament affect the function of the joint with which it is associated?

14. **Open Ended** Analyze, critique, and review the strengths and weaknesses of the sliding filament theory of muscle contraction.

Thinking Critically

15. **Infer** You view three tissue slides under the microscope. Slide A has an outer layer containing flat, dead cells. The cells of Slide B have nuclei and are striated. Slide C contains repeating circular units with capillaries at the center. Identify each slide as skin, bone, or muscle tissue, and explain the function of each.

16. **REAL WORLD BIOCHALLENGE** Osteoporosis is a health threat for many Americans. Visit **in.bdol.glencoe.com** to find out more information about this disease. What are the risk factors? Why are the elderly at greater risk for this disease? Analyze the importance of nutrition and exercise in the prevention of osteoporosis.

 in.bdol.glencoe.com/chapter_test

smoking, excessive alcohol use, inactive lifestyle, age, gender, body size, ethnicity and family history. The elderly are at risk because bones become less dense as people age. Adequate amounts of calcium in diet and regular weight-bearing exercise can help prevent the onset of osteoporosis.

17. Red bone marrow produces red blood cells, white blood cells, and clotting fragments. Tissues of the other systems would die from lack of oxygen or possible infections.

18. The continual rubbing on bare skin causes the epidermis to produce more cells.

17. Hypothesize How would the destruction of red bone marrow affect other systems within the body?

18. Infer During summer months many people go barefoot and the skin on their feet thickens. Why does this thickening occur?

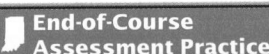 End-of-Course Assessment Practice

The assessed Indiana standard appears next to the question.

All questions aligned and verified by The Princeton Review

Part 1 Multiple Choice

Use the graph to answer questions 19–21.

Calcium Levels in Contracting Muscle

(y-axis: Muscle force and calcium levels; x-axis: Time (milliseconds) 10 30 50 70 90 110 130 150 170 190)

Curves labeled: Calcium level; Muscle force

19. The highest levels of calcium are found at approximately what time?
   A. 10 milliseconds   **C.** 30 milliseconds
   B. 50 milliseconds   **D.** 70 milliseconds

20. Which conclusion could be reached about the relationship between calcium and muscle contraction?
   A. Calcium is not involved in muscle contraction.
   B. Calcium is released after the muscle has finished contracting.
   C. Calcium is released before the muscle reaches its greatest force of contraction.
   D. Calcium is released the entire time the muscle contracts.

21. At what time is the force of the muscle contraction strongest?
   A. 10 milliseconds
   B. 50 milliseconds
   C. 30 milliseconds
   D. 70 milliseconds

Study the diagram and answer questions 22 and 23.

22. Which structure in the diagram is involved
B.1.15, in temperature regulation?
B.1.17
   A. 1   **C.** 3
   B. 2   **D.** 4

23. Which layer in the diagram above contains
B.1.15 melanin-producing cells?
   A. 1   **C.** 3
   B. 2   **D.** 4

Part 2 Constructed Response/Grid In

Record your answers on your answer document.

24. Open Ended What are the similarities and differences between first-degree burns,
B.1.17 second-degree burns, and third-degree burns? Include in your response information about which layers of the skin are damaged, symptoms, and treatment.

25. Open Ended Describe how muscle cells are supplied with energy during exercise.
B.1.16

 in.bdol.glencoe.com/standardized_test

CHAPTER 34 ASSESSMENT **915**

RUBRIC

For more help evaluating open-ended assessment questions, see the rubric on p. 9T.

End-of-Course Assessment Practice

19. C   **22.** A
20. C   **23.** C
21. D
24. First-degree burns involve the death of epidermal cells and are characterized by redness and mild pain. Second-degree burns involve damage to skin cells of the dermis and can result in blistering and scarring. Third-degree burns destroy both the epidermis and the dermis so skin function is lost. Skin grafts may be required to replace lost skin.
25. Muscle cells begin by undergoing aerobic respiration to produce ATP. If oxygen supplies are low, cells will switch to lactic acid fermentation to produce ATP.

 FAST FILE

Answer Sheet A practice answer sheet can be found on p. 41 of *Unit 10 FAST FILE Resources.*

 Indiana Academic Standards

Pages 914–915: B.1.14, B.1.15, B.1.16, B.1.17

Chapter 35 Organizer

Section Objectives	National Science Standards	State/Local Standards	Advanced Lab and Demo Planning
Section 35.1 1 session, 1/2 block 1. **Interpret** the different functions of the digestive system organs. 2. **Outline** the pathway food follows through the digestive tract. 3. **Identify** the role of enzymes in chemical digestion.	UCP.1, UCP.2, UCP.5; A.1, A.2; B.2, B.3, B.4; C.5; E.2; F.1; G.1	**Indiana Standards** B.1.15, B.1.16, B.1.19	**Student Labs:** Additional Lab, p. 920: liquid lactose digestive aid, glucose test paper, glucose solution, milk, graduated cylinders, droppers, test tubes Problem-Solving Lab 35.1, p. 922 **Teacher Demonstration:** Quick Demo, p. 920: 2 dialysis bags, 1–5% starch solution, 2 mL pancreatic enzymes, beaker, distilled water
Section 35.2 1/2 session 4. **Recognize** the contribution of the six classes of nutrients to body nutrition. 5. **Identify** the role of the liver in food storage. 6. **Relate** caloric intake to weight loss or gain.	UCP.1–3, UCP.5; A.1, A.2; B.2, B.3; C.5, C.6; F.1	**Indiana Standards** B.1.9, B.1.10, B.1.17, B.1.19	**Student Labs:** MiniLab 35.1, p. 927 Problem-Solving Lab 35.2, p. 928 **Teacher Demonstration:** Quick Demo, p. 925: various foods, grocery sacks (brown), water
Section 35.3 2 1/2 sessions, 1 block 7. **Describe** the internal feedback mechanism controlling hormone levels in the body. 8. **Contrast** the actions of steroid and amino acid hormones. 9. **Identify and interpret** the functions of some of the hormones secreted by endocrine glands.	UCP.1–3, UCP.5; A.1, A.2; B.2, B.3, B.6; C.1, C.5, C.6; F.1; G.1, G.2	**Indiana Standards** B.1.7, B.1.14	**Student Labs:** Problem-Solving Lab 35.3, p. 932 MiniLab 35.2, p. 934: microscope, thyroid and parathyroid endocrine gland tissue slides Investigate BioLab, p. 936: See materials below. **Teacher Demonstration:** Quick Demo, p. 930: human skull or large animal skull
End of Chapter Assessment Student Edition **Study Guide,** p. 939 **Content Assessment,** pp. 940–941		**Indiana Standards** B.1.6, B.1.7, B.1.10, B.1.14, B.1.15, B.1.19	**Student Lab:** Investigate BioLab, p. 936: variety of dry cereals, mortar and pestle, test tubes, test-tube racks, filter paper, funnel, balance, beaker, water, Bunsen burner or hot plate, graduated cylinder, iodine solution, dropper bottles, watch glasses, plastic droppers, amylase solution

Key to Teaching Strategies

L1 Level 1 activities should be appropriate for students with learning difficulties.

L2 Level 2 activities should be within the ability range of all students.

L3 Level 3 activities are designed for above-average students.

ELL ELL activities should be within the ability range of English Language Learners.

COOP LEARN
Cooperative Learning activities are designed for small group work.

Glencoe Exclusive!

TeacherWorks™
All-In-One Planner and Resource Center

Reproducible Masters and Transparencies	Technology

Unit 10 FAST FILE Resources
Real World BioApplications, pp. 49–50
Reinforcement and Study Guide in English, pp. 51–52
Reinforcement and Study Guide in Spanish, pp. 55–56
Transparency Worksheets, pp. 61, 67–68
🖊 **Section Focus Transparency 84**
🖊 **Reteaching Skills Transparency 50**

💿 **Interactive Chalkboard CD-ROM: Section 35.1 Presentation** 🚩
💿 TeacherWorks™ **CD-ROM** 🚩
📱 **Guided Reading Audio Summaries MP3**

Unit 10 FAST FILE Resources
MiniLab Worksheet, p. 45
Reinforcement and Study Guide in English, p. 53
Reinforcement and Study Guide in Spanish, p. 57
Concept Mapping, p. 59
Transparency Worksheets, pp. 62, 69–70
Laboratory Manual, pp. 227–230, 231–232
🖊 **Section Focus Transparency 85**
🖊 **Reteaching Skills Transparency 51**

💿 **Interactive Chalkboard CD-ROM: Section 35.2 Presentation** 🚩
💿 TeacherWorks™ **CD-ROM** 🚩
📱 **Guided Reading Audio Summaries MP3**

Unit 10 FAST FILE Resources
MiniLab Worksheet, p. 46
BioLab Worksheet, pp. 47–48
Reinforcement and Study Guide in English, p. 54
Reinforcement and Study Guide in Spanish, p. 58
Critical Thinking/Problem Solving, p. 60
Transparency Worksheets, pp. 63, 65–66
🖊 **Section Focus Transparency 86**
🖊 **Basic Concepts Transparency 65**

💿 **Interactive Chalkboard CD-ROM: Section 35.3 Presentation** 🚩
💿 TeacherWorks™ **CD-ROM** 🚩
📱 **Guided Reading Audio Summaries MP3**

Unit 10 FAST FILE Resources
Chapter Assessment, pp. 71–76
Student Recording Sheet, p. 77

The Princeton Review **Reviewing Biology,** pp. 69–70

💿 **Interactive Chalkboard:** 🚩 **Chapter 35 Assessment**
💿 **MindJogger Videoquizzes DVD/VHS**
💿 **ExamView® Pro Test Bank CD-ROM**
💿 TeacherWorks™ **CD-ROM** 🚩
💿 **Succeeding on National Standards CD-ROM**

🖥 in.bdol.glencoe.com
/self_check_quiz
/vocabulary_puzzlemaker
/chapter_test
/standardized_test

🚩 Indicates materials created specifically for Indiana.

Short on Time?

BIODIGEST The BioDigest at the end of this unit can be used as a(n):

- preview to introduce important unit concepts.
- overview if time does not permit teaching the entire chapter.
- review of key unit concepts.

Understanding the Photo

The photo illustrates the tubular nature of the digestive tract. Point out to students that this long tube contains cells specialized for digestion and absorption of food.

The Digestive and Endocrine Systems

What You'll Learn

- You will interpret the functions of the digestive system.
- You will outline the journey of a meal through the digestive system.
- You will identify different nutrients and their uses in the body.
- You will describe how internal feedback mechanisms regulate the release of hormones.
- You will analyze how endocrine hormones control internal body processes and help maintain homeostasis of the body.

Why It's Important

By examining the functions of your digestive and endocrine systems, you will understand how your body obtains energy from food and how it controls your behavior and development.

Understanding ▶ the Photo

Barium sulfate, a compound that absorbs X rays, provides contrast in this color-enhanced X ray of the large intestine and part of the small intestine.

Biology Online

Visit **in.bdol.glencoe.com** to
- study the entire chapter online
- access Web Links for more information and activities on the digestive and endocrine systems
- review content with the Interactive Tutor and self-check quizzes

916

Two-Minute Chapter Launcher

Demo Demonstrate the process of digestion by testing cracker crumbs for starch by adding a few drops of iodine to some ground crumbs in a watch glass. A dark brown/purple color indicates the presence of starch. To demonstrate the effects of saliva on the starch, add about 1 g of ground crackers to 1 mL of water. Add a small amount of amylase (available from biological supply companies) and let it sit for a minute. You can test for the breakdown of all of the starch by periodically using the iodine test. Ask students what the digestive process is doing to the starch in the crackers.

Section 35.1

Following Digestion of a Meal

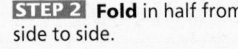
Indiana Standards Standard B.1.15 Understand and explain that, in biological systems, structure and function must be considered together.

SECTION PREVIEW

Objectives
Interpret the different functions of the digestive system organs.

Outline the pathway food follows through the digestive tract.

Identify the role of enzymes in chemical digestion.

Review Vocabulary
enzyme: type of protein found in all living things that increases the rate of chemical reactions (p. 161)

New Vocabulary
amylase
esophagus
peristalsis
epiglottis
stomach
pepsin
small intestine
pancreas
liver
bile
gallbladder
villus
large intestine
rectum

FOLDABLES
Study Organizer

Digestive System Make the following Foldable to help you learn more about the structures and functions of the digestive system.

STEP 1 **Draw** a mark at the midpoint of a sheet of paper along the side edge. Then **fold** the top and bottom edges in to touch the midpoint.

STEP 2 **Fold** in half from side to side.

STEP 3 **Open and cut** along the inside fold lines to form four tabs.

STEP 4 **Label** each tab as shown.

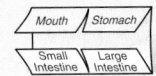

| Mouth | Stomach |
| Small Intestine | Large Intestine |

Identify As you read Chapter 35, list the functions of each of these digestive system structures beneath the appropriate tab.

Functions of the Digestive System

The main function of the digestive system is to disassemble the food you eat into its component molecules so that it can be used as energy for your body. In this sense, your digestive system can be thought of as a sort of disassembly line.

Digestion is accomplished through a number of steps. First, the system takes ingested food and begins moving it through the digestive tract. As it does so, it digests—or breaks down mechanically and chemically—the complex food molecules. Then, the system absorbs the digested food and distributes it to your cells. Finally, it eliminates undigested materials from your body. As you read about each digestive organ, use *Figure 35.1* on the next page to locate its position within the system.

The Mouth

The first stop along the digestive disassembly line is your mouth. Suppose it's lunchtime and you have just prepared a bacon, lettuce, and tomato sandwich. The first thing you do is bite off a piece and chew it.

35.1 FOLLOWING DIGESTION OF A MEAL **917**

1 Focus

INTERACTIVE CHALKBOARD
PowerPoint® Presentations

Bellringer
Section Focus Transparency 84

Transparency **84** Food Processors

SECTION FOCUS
Use with Chapter 35, Section 35.1

❶ What parts of the digestive system perform functions similar to the devices shown?

❷ What do you think is the overall function of the digestive system?

BIOLOGY: The Dynamics of Life   SECTION FOCUS TRANSPARENCIES

INTERACTIVE CHALKBOARD
with Image Bank

PowerPoint® Presentations
This CD-ROM is an editable Microsoft® PowerPoint® presentation that includes:
• Section presentations
• Section checks
• Image bank
• Hot links to Biology Online
• All transparencies

FOLDABLES™
For an additional Foldables activity idea, see the Chapter 35 Foldables page in *Unit 10 Fast File Resources*.

RESOURCE MANAGER

Unit 10 *Fast File* Resources
Real World BioApplications, pp. 49–50
Reinforcement and Study Guide in English, pp. 51–52
Reinforcement and Study Guide in Spanish, pp. 55–56
Transparency Worksheets, pp. 61, 67–68

Reading Essentials for Biology, Section 35.1
Section Focus Transparency 84
Reteaching Skills Transparency 50

Indiana Academic Standards
Pages 916–917: B.1.16, B.1.19

2 Teach

Caption Question Answer
Figure 35.1 The digestive system functions to break down food, both mechanically and chemically, so that nutrients can be absorbed and distributed to body cells. Undigested materials and waste products are eliminated from the body by the digestive system.

Revealing Misconceptions

Many students may believe that cavities are the greatest threat to teeth.

Uncover the Misconception

Ask students what they think is the biggest threat to teeth in the U.S. List their suggestions on the board or have them research to find the answer. periodontal disease

Demonstrate the Concept

Using either a model of the teeth and gums or a photograph, explain how periodontal disease affects the gums. Bacteria and the toxins they release irritate and inflame gums, causing them to bleed easily. As pockets of infection form, the gum begins to separate from the tooth. Left untreated, this infection can lead to destruction of the teeth and portions of the jawbone.

Assess New Knowledge

Have students work in groups to make a pamphlet they can distribute to middle or elementary grades presenting information about the dangers and prevention of periodontal disease.

918

Figure 35.1
All the digestive organs work together to break down food into simpler compounds that can be absorbed by the body.
Describe *Interpret the functions of the digestive system.*

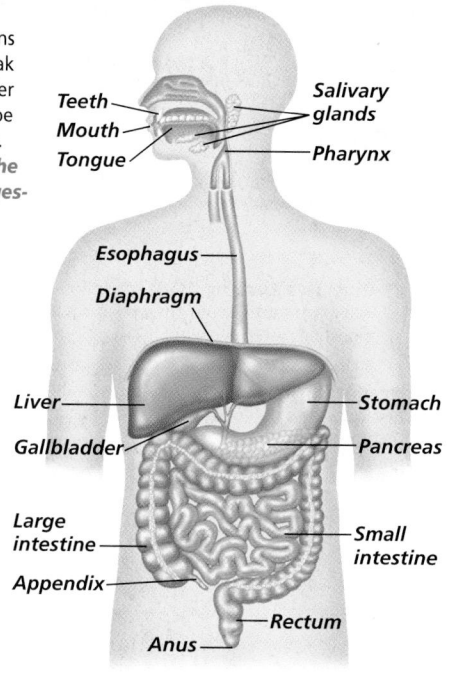

Physical Science Connection

Physical and chemical changes in matter Digestion involves both physical and chemical changes in matter. Describe the digestive processes that occur in the mouth. Classify each as a physical or a chemical change.

What happens as you chew?

As you chew, your tongue moves the food around and helps position it between your teeth. Chewing is a form of mechanical digestion, the physical process of breaking food into smaller pieces. Mechanical digestion prepares food particles for chemical digestion. Chemical digestion is the process of changing food on a molecular level through the action of enzymes. What purpose do the different structures inside your mouth serve? Find out by examining *Figure 35.2.*

Chemical digestion begins in the mouth

Some of the nutrients in your sandwich are starches, large molecules known as polysaccharides. As you chew your bite of sandwich, salivary glands in your mouth secrete saliva. Saliva contains a digestive enzyme, called **amylase,** which breaks down starch into smaller molecules such as di- or monosaccharides. In the stomach, amylase continues to digest starch in the swallowed food for about 30 minutes. *Table 35.1* lists some digestive enzymes that act to break food molecules apart.

Swallowing your food

Once you've thoroughly chewed your bite of sandwich, your tongue shapes it into a ball and moves it to the back of your mouth to be swallowed. Swallowing forces food from your mouth into your throat and from there into your **esophagus,** a muscular tube that connects your mouth to your stomach. Food moves down the esophagus by way of peristalsis. **Peristalsis** (per uh STAHL sus) is a series of involuntary smooth muscle contractions along the walls of the digestive tract.

Table 35.1 Digestive Enzymes			
Organ	**Enzyme**	**Molecules Digested**	**Product**
Salivary glands	Salivary amylase	Starch	Disaccharide
Stomach	Pepsin	Proteins	Peptides
Pancreas	Pancreatic amylase	Starch	Disaccharide
	Trypsin	Proteins	Peptides
	Pancreatic lipase	Fats	Fatty acids and glycerol
	Nucleases	Nucleic acids	Nucleotides
Small intestine	Maltase	Disaccharide	Monosaccharide
	Sucrase	Disaccharide	Monosaccharide
	Lactase	Disaccharide	Monosaccharide
	Peptidase	Peptides	Amino acids
	Nuclease	Nucleotides	Sugar and nitrogen bases

USING MODELS

Gastrointestinal Tract Using four different colors of yarn or string, make a length model of the esophagus, stomach, small intestine, and large intestine. To help students see the entire length of the digestive tract, tie each of the strings together in the correct order and wrap the string around the classroom. **L2**

CHALLENGE ACTIVITY

The Liver Students who need an additional challenge can research the various functions of the liver. Students can prepare an electronic presentation for the class on the major functions of the liver. **L3**

Your Mouth

Figure 35.2
Your mouth houses many structures involved in other functions besides digestion. Some of these structures protect against foreign materials invading your body; others help you taste the food you eat. **Critical Thinking** *Why is it important that the tongue is composed of skeletal muscles?*

A **Teeth** The incisors are adapted for cutting food. The cuspids, or canines, tear or shred food. The three sets of molars can crush and grind food. Often, there is not enough room for the third set of molars, called wisdom teeth, which then must be removed.

C **Tongue**
The tongue is attached to the floor of the mouth. It is made of numerous skeletal muscles covered with a mucous membrane.

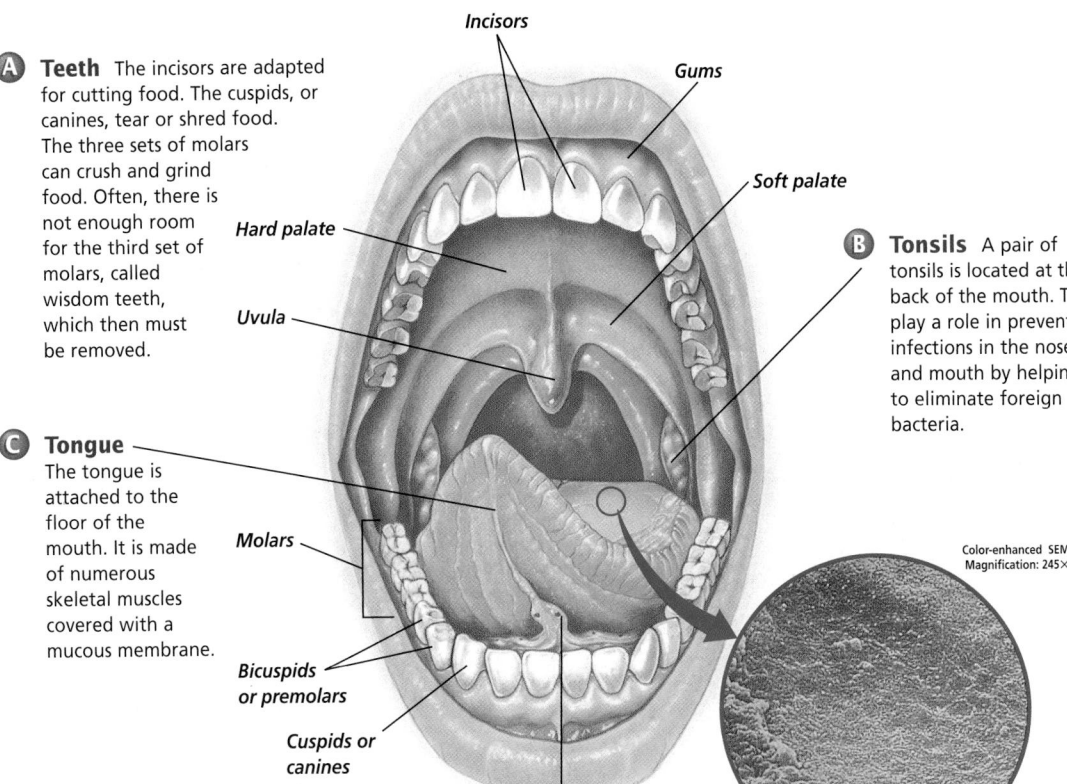

Incisors
Gums
Soft palate
Hard palate
Uvula
Molars
Bicuspids or premolars
Cuspids or canines
Opening of salivary gland duct

Color-enhanced SEM
Magnification: 245×

B **Tonsils** A pair of tonsils is located at the back of the mouth. They play a role in preventing infections in the nose and mouth by helping to eliminate foreign bacteria.

The tongue is covered by projections that contain numerous taste receptor cells like the ones shown here.

CROWN
NECK
ROOT

Enamel
Dentin
Pulp
Nerve
Root canal
Bone
Vascular supply

D **Structure of a tooth** Teeth are made mainly of dentin, a bonelike substance that gives a tooth its shape and strength. The dentin encloses a space filled with pulp, a tissue that contains blood vessels and nerves. The dentin of the crown is covered with an enamel that consists mostly of calcium salts. Tooth enamel is the hardest substance in the body.

35.1 FOLLOWING DIGESTION OF A MEAL **919**

Purpose
Students examine teeth and other structures of the mouth.

Teaching Strategies
Bring in models of animal skulls, including a human skull, to compare teeth.

Visual Learning
■ Point out the structures of the mouth shown in the diagram. As each structure is mentioned, have a volunteer read the description of the structure.
■ Ask students to name the four types of teeth shown. incisors, cuspids, bicuspids, and molars
■ Elicit from students the function of the tonsils and their location. The tonsils are located in the back of the mouth and function to remove bacteria that enter the mouth or nose.

Critical Thinking
Because it is composed of skeletal muscles, the tongue is capable of both voluntary and involuntary contractions that are important for control of tongue movements during chewing and swallowing, as well as during speech.

Portfolio
Primary Teeth Have students investigate how the number and location of primary teeth in humans differ from the secondary teeth. Ask students to diagram a mouth that shows only primary teeth. Have students identify the types of teeth shown in the diagram. **L2**

Physical Science Connection

(p. 918) Chewing and swallowing alter the form of your food without changing its identity—physical changes. Enzymes in saliva change the compounds in food to different compounds—chemical changes.

INCLUSION STRATEGIES

Learning Disabled: *Kinesthetic* Cut a 15-cm length of string and lay it fully stretched out on a desk. Use a second 15-cm piece of string to form a zigzag pattern. Have students observe the total horizontal distance between the two ends of each piece of string. Compare this to the increased surface area created by villi. **L1** **ELL**

 Indiana Academic Standards

Pages 918–919: B.1.15, B.1.16, B.1.19

919

Quick Demo

Digestion and Diffusion

To demonstrate both digestion and diffusion, fill a dialysis bag with 1–5% starch solution. In a second dialysis bag, add 2 mL of pancreatic enzymes and fill the remainder of the bag with starch solution. Allow each bag to sit in a beaker of distilled water for one day. Then, run a Benedict's test on the fluid in each beaker. Explain that the enzymes will speed the digestion of the starch to glucose, which diffuses out of the dialysis bag. The glucose will produce a positive Benedict's test.

Visual Learning

Have students look at Figure 35.4. Ask: What type of muscle makes up the walls of the stomach? smooth muscle

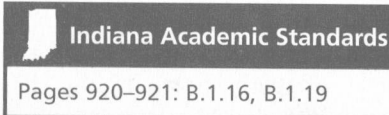

Indiana Academic Standards

Pages 920–921: B.1.16, B.1.19

Figure 35.3
Smooth muscle contractions are responsible for moving food through the digestive system.

From mouth — Food mass — To stomach

Longitudinal muscle

Circular muscle

Contraction

Contraction of circular muscles behind food mass

Contraction of longitudinal muscles ahead of food mass

Contraction in circular muscle layer forces food mass forward

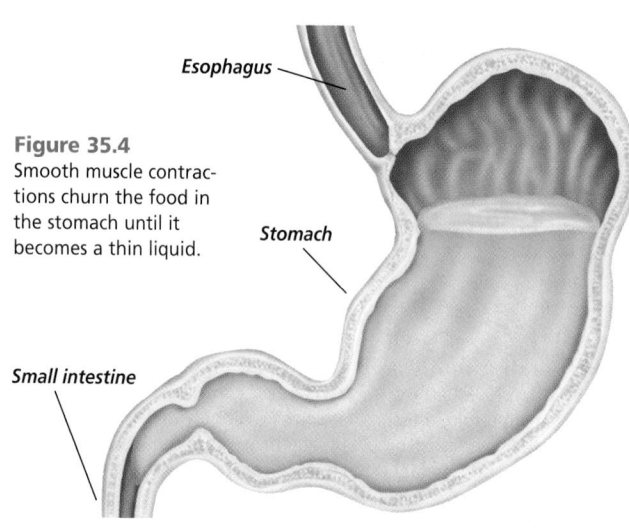

Esophagus

Figure 35.4
Smooth muscle contractions churn the food in the stomach until it becomes a thin liquid.

Stomach

Small intestine

Figure 35.3 shows how the food is moved along from the mouth to the stomach. The contractions occur in waves: first, circular muscles relax and longitudinal muscles contract; then circular muscles contract and longitudinal muscles relax.

When you swallow, the food enters the esophagus. Usually, a flap of cartilage called the **epiglottis** (ep uh GLAH tus) closes over the opening to the respiratory tract as you swallow, preventing food from entering. After the food passes into your esophagus, the epiglottis opens again. But if you talk or laugh as you swallow, the epiglottis may open, allowing food to enter the upper portion of the respiratory tract. Your response, a reflex, is to choke and cough, forcing the food out of the respiratory tube.

The Stomach

When the chewed food reaches the end of your esophagus, it enters the stomach. The **stomach** is a muscular, pouchlike enlargement of the digestive tract. Both physical and chemical digestion take place in the stomach.

Muscular churning

Three layers of involuntary muscles, lying across one another, are located within the wall of the stomach. When these muscles contract, as shown in *Figure 35.4*, they work to physically break down the swallowed food, creating smaller pieces. As the muscles continue to work the food pieces, they mix them with digestive juices produced by the stomach.

Chemical digestion in the stomach

The inner lining of the stomach contains millions of glands that secrete a mixture of chemicals called gastric juice. Gastric juice contains

---

Additional Lab

Digesting Lactose

Purpose
Students test whether a lactose digestive aid will digest lactose.

Safety Precautions
Remind students to handle test tubes with care and to dispose of any broken glass in the designated container.

Preparation
Do not use the tablet form of a lactose digestive aid; it tests positive for glucose. If you use liquid lactose digestive aid, test it for glucose first.

Materials
liquid lactose digestive aid, glucose test paper, glucose solution, milk, graduated cylinders, droppers, test tubes

Procedure
Give students the following directions.
1. Label four test tubes *1, 2, 3,* and *4*.
2. Place 2 mL of glucose in test tube *1*, 2 mL of milk in test tube *2*, 2 mL of milk

pepsin and hydrochloric acid. **Pepsin** is an enzyme that begins the chemical digestion of proteins in food. Pepsin works best in the acidic environment provided by hydrochloric acid, which increases the acidity of the stomach contents to pH 2.

How is the stomach lining protected from powerful digestive enzymes and strong acids? The stomach lining secretes mucus that forms a protective layer between it and the acidic environment of the stomach.

Food remains in your stomach for approximately two to four hours. When food is ready to leave the stomach, it is about the consistency of tomato soup. Peristaltic waves gradually become more vigorous and begin to force small amounts of liquid out of the lower end of the stomach and into the small intestine.

The Small Intestine

From your stomach, the liquid food moves into your **small intestine**, a muscular tube about 6 m long. This section of the intestine is called *small* not because of its length, but because of its narrow diameter—only 2.5 cm. Digestion of your meal is completed within the small intestine. Muscle contractions contribute to further mechanical breakdown of the food. At the same time, carbohydrates and proteins undergo further chemical digestion with the help of enzymes produced and secreted by the pancreas and liver.

✓ Reading Check **Explain** which types of digestion occur in the small intestine.

Chemical action

The first 25 cm of the small intestine is called the duodenum (doo ah DEE num). Most of the enzymes and chemicals that function in the duodenum enter it through ducts that collect juices from the pancreas, liver, and gallbladder. These organs, shown in *Figure 35.5*, play important roles in digestion, even though food does not pass directly through them.

Secretions of the pancreas

The **pancreas** is a soft, flattened gland that secretes both digestive enzymes and hormones, which you will learn more about in the last section of this chapter. The mixture of enzymes it secretes breaks down carbohydrates, proteins, and fats. Alkaline pancreatic juices also help to neutralize the acidity of the liquid food, stopping any further action of pepsin.

Secretions of the liver

The **liver** is a large, complex organ that has many functions. One of its functions is to produce bile. **Bile** is a chemical substance that helps break down fats. Once made in the liver, bile is stored in a small organ called the **gallbladder.**

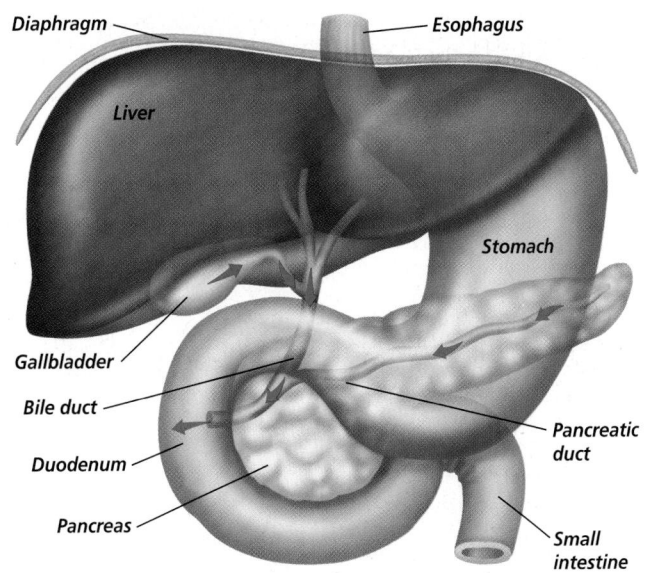

Diaphragm — Esophagus
Liver
Stomach
Gallbladder
Bile duct
Pancreatic duct
Duodenum
Pancreas
Small intestine

Figure 35.5
Both the pancreas and the liver produce chemicals needed for digestion in the small intestine.

✓ Reading Check Both chemical and mechanical digestion occur in the small intestine. Chemical digestion occurs due to the enzymes secreted by both the cells lining the duodenal wall and through the juices secreted from the pancreas, liver, and gallbladder. Mechanical digestion is due to the churning action from muscle contraction.

Inquiry

Activity Have students investigate why the stomach does not normally digest itself. How does the stomach protect itself from the digestive process? What happens if the stomach does allow holes in its lining, such as ulcers? What risk factors increase the likelihood of having ulcers? How are ulcers treated? **L2**

in test tube *3,* and 2 mL of the lactose digestive aid in test tube *4.*
3. Place 5 drops of the lactose digestive aid in test tube *3.*
4. Allow all tubes to sit for 5 minutes.
5. Using the glucose test paper, test each tube for glucose.

Analysis
1. What did the lactose digestive aid do to the lactose in milk? It broke down the lactose.
2. What is the function of test tubes *1, 2,* and *4?* They are controls.
3. How will a lactose digestive aid help people who cannot digest lactose? It will help break down the lactose present in dairy products.

Assessment
Portfolio Have students write a summary of the lab, including the answers to the Analysis questions, and add them to their portfolios. Use the Performance Task Assessment List for Lab Report in **PASC,** p. 119. **L2**

Purpose

Students compare the path of bile from the liver to the duodenum with and without the gallbladder.

Process Skills

analyze information, compare and contrast, draw a conclusion, interpret scientific illustrations, sequence, think critically

Teaching Strategies

Demonstrate the role of bile by adding a small amount of oil to a test tube of water. Shake it and have students note what happens to the oil after waiting a few minutes. (Oil reforms on top of the water.) Repeat the demonstration using liquid detergent to simulate bile. (Oil will remain as small droplets.)

Thinking Critically

1. liver; gallbladder
2. Bile physically changes fat into smaller droplets.
3. with a gallbladder: liver, hepatic duct, gallbladder, bile duct, duodenum; without a gallbladder: liver, hepatic duct, bile duct, duodenum
4. Only a small, but continuous, amount of bile reaches the duodenum. Large amounts needed to break up fats efficiently are not available.

Assessment

Performance Have students make a poster illustrating why gallstones cause discomfort. Gallstones can block the bile duct so that when the gallbladder contracts automatically (when fats are in the duodenum) it is not able to empty. Use the Performance Task Assessment List for Poster in **PASC**, p. 145. **L2**

Indiana Academic Standards

Pages 922–923: B.1.16, B.1.19

922

Sequence

How is digestion affected if the gallbladder is removed?
Many people have had their gallbladders surgically removed. What changes take place in digestion if the gallbladder is removed?

Solve the Problem

The following diagrams show the appearance of a normal liver and gallbladder (diagram A) and the appearance when the gallbladder has been removed (diagram B).

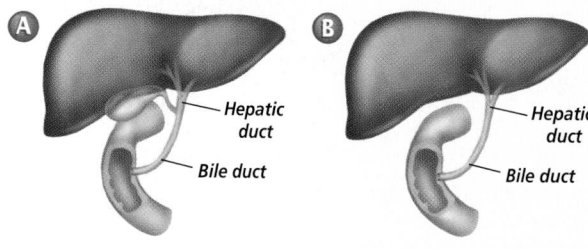

Hepatic duct

Bile duct

Hepatic duct

Bile duct

Thinking Critically

1. **Identify** Where is bile produced? Where is bile stored?
2. **Explain** How does bile affect fat?
3. **Sequence** Identify the pathway for bile from the liver to the duodenum in a person with a gallbladder and compare it to the sequence in a person with no gallbladder.
4. **Infer** The gallbladder is a muscular sac. It squeezes and discharges a large quantity of bile when fats are present in the duodenum. Explain why a person without a gallbladder is unable to digest fats as efficiently as someone who has a gallbladder.

Figure 35.6
Gallstones, seen in this color-enhanced X ray, can form in the gallbladder or bile duct. They consist mainly of crystallized bile salts.

Gallstones

922 THE DIGESTIVE AND ENDOCRINE SYSTEMS

From the gallbladder, bile passes into the duodenum. Bile causes further mechanical digestion by breaking apart large drops of fat into smaller droplets. If bile becomes too concentrated due to high levels of cholesterol in the diet, or if the gallbladder becomes inflamed, gallstones can form, as seen in *Figure 35.6*. Can a person live without a gallbladder? Find out in the *Problem-Solving Lab* on this page.

Absorption of food

Liquid food stays in your small intestine for three to five hours and is slowly moved along its length by peristalsis. As digested food moves through the intestine, it passes over thousands of tiny fingerlike structures called villi. A **villus** (plural, villi) is a single projection on the lining of the small intestine that functions in the absorption of digested food. The villi greatly increase the surface area of the small intestine, allowing for a greater absorption rate. Because the digested food is now in the form of small molecules, it can be absorbed directly into the cells of the villi, as shown in *Figure 35.7*. The food molecules then diffuse into the blood vessels of the villus and enter the bloodstream. The villi are the link between the digestive system and the circulatory system.

What happens to indigestible materials that remain in the digestive tract?

PROJECT

Meat Tenderizers Have students conduct research to find out how meat tenderizer works. Have them use the information they gather to design a demonstration that can be used to explain the process to others. Encourage students to write out the procedural steps for their demonstration and explain the purpose for each step. Finally, have students complete their demonstration with information that relates the function of meat tenderizer to its complementary organ of the digestive system. **L3** **COOP LEARN**

The Large Intestine

The indigestible material from your meal now passes into your **large intestine,** a muscular tube that is also called the colon. Although the large intestine is only about 1.5 m long, it is much wider than the small intestine—about 6.5 cm in diameter. The appendix, a tubelike extension off the large intestine thought to be an evolutionary remnant from our herbivorous ancestors, seems to serve no function in human digestion.

Water absorption

As the indigestible mixture passes through the large intestine, water and salts are absorbed by the intestinal walls, leaving behind a more solid material. In this way, the water is not wasted. A secondary function of the large intestine is vitamin synthesis. Anaerobic bacteria in the large intestine synthesize some B vitamins and vitamin K, which are absorbed as needed by the body. The presence of certain bacteria in the large intestine is beneficial in another way. Under normal conditions, these bacteria stop

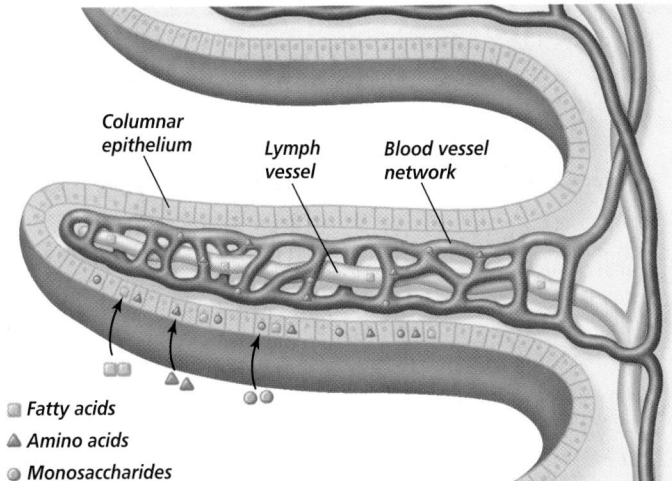

Columnar epithelium

Lymph vessel

Blood vessel network

■ Fatty acids
▲ Amino acids
● Monosaccharides

harmful bacteria from colonizing, reducing the risk of intestinal infections.

Reading Check **Identify and describe** the roles that bacteria play in maintaining health.

Elimination of wastes

After 18 to 24 hours in the large intestine, the remaining indigestible material, now called feces, reaches the rectum. The **rectum** is the last part of the digestive system. Feces are eliminated from the rectum through the anus. Your meal's entire journey through the digestive tract has taken between 24 and 33 hours.

Figure 35.7
Once food has been fully digested in the small intestine, it is in the form of molecules small enough to enter the body's bloodstream through projections called villi.

Reading Check Anaerobic bacteria in the large intestine synthesize some B vitamins and vitamin K. Recall from Chapter 18 that they also are part of the normal flora of the digestive tract.

3 Assess

DAILY INTERVENTION

Check for Understanding
Interpersonal Have a student name an organ of the digestive system. The next student must name a type of digestion that occurs in the organ. The next student must define this action by listing the enzymes or juices involved or defining the mechanical action. A fourth student should tell how the digestive action is controlled. Repeat for each digestive system organ. **L2**

Reteach
Visual-Spatial Have students prepare a chart of the digestive organs and the role of each in digestion. **L2**

Resources
For more practice, use *Reading Essentials for Biology,* Section 35.1.

Extension

Linguistic Have students research and report on cancers of the digestive tract and their possible causes and treatments. **L3**

✓ MODIFIED Assessment

Skill Have students label a digestive system diagram and identify the functions of each part. **L1**

Section Assessment

Understanding Main Ideas
1. Describe the functions of the digestive system and sequence the organs according to the order in which food passes through them.
2. Identify the effects of enzymes on food molecules. Which enzymes act on proteins?
3. How do villi of the small intestine increase the rate of nutrient absorption?
4. What role does the pancreas play in digestion?

Thinking Critically
5. How would chronic diarrhea affect homeostasis of the body?

SKILL REVIEW
6. **Get the Big Picture** Prepare a circle graph representing the time food remains in each part of the digestive tract. For more help, refer to *Get the Big Picture* in the **Skill Handbook.**

 in.bdol.glencoe.com/self_check_quiz

35.1 FOLLOWING DIGESTION OF A MEAL **923**

Section Assessment

1. functions: digest food, absorb nutrients, eliminate wastes; sequence: mouth, esophagus, stomach, small intestine, large intestine, rectum
2. Enzymes in digestive juices break down carbohydrates, proteins, and fats in food. Proteins are broken down in the stomach by pepsin and in the small intestine by trypsin and peptidases.
3. By increasing the total surface area, villi allow for increased absorption rates.
4. The pancreas secretes digestive enzymes, which break down carbohydrates, proteins, and fats.
5. Loose stool has an unusually high water content. Chronic diarrhea can result in dehydration and electrolyte imbalances. Fluids and electrolytes must be restored by drinking water and liquids that contain electrolytes regularly.
6. Students' graphs should show approximately these percentages: large intestine, 75%; small intestine, 13%; stomach, 11%; mouth and esophagus, 1%.

1 Focus

INTERACTIVE CHALKBOARD
PowerPoint® Presentations

Bellringer
Section Focus Transparency 85

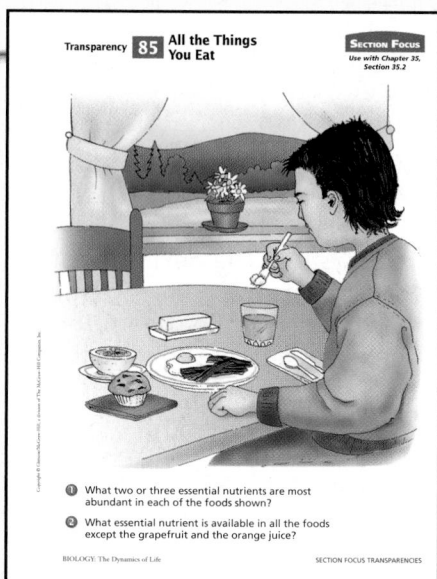

Transparency **85** All the Things You Eat

Section Focus
Use with Chapter 35, Section 35.2

❶ What two or three essential nutrients are most abundant in each of the foods shown?

❷ What essential nutrient is available in all the foods except the grapefruit and the orange juice?

BIOLOGY: The Dynamics of Life   SECTION FOCUS TRANSPARENCIES

Using Prior Knowledge

Evaluate Ask a volunteer to describe what he or she had for breakfast. Using the food pyramid, evaluate how well the meal fits into the pyramid. Have each student independently evaluate how well his or her last meal fit into the pyramid. **L1**

Indiana Academic Standards

Pages 924–925: B.1.9, B.1.10, B.1.19

Section 35.2

Nutrition

You Are What You Eat

Using Prior Knowledge In this section, you will learn about nutrition and the different molecules that your body uses for energy and those it needs to function properly. List the foods you eat in a day. Using the food pyramid as a guide, categorize them into different groups according to food type.
Evaluate How do your meals fit into this pyramid?

The food pyramid

Includes butter, oils, salad dressings, and soft drinks
☐ Fat
☑ Sugar

USE SPARINGLY
2–3 SERVINGS
2–3 SERVINGS
3–5 SERVINGS
2–4 SERVINGS
6–11 SERVINGS

The Vital Nutrients

Six basic kinds of nutrients can be found in foods: carbohydrates, fats, proteins, minerals, vitamins, and water. These substances are essential to proper body function. You supply your body with these nutrients when you eat foods from the five main food groups shown in *Figure 35.8*.

Carbohydrates

Perhaps your favorite food is pasta, fresh-baked bread, or corn on the cob. If so, your favorite food contains carbohydrates, important sources of energy for your body cells. Recall that carbohydrates are starches and sugars. Starches are complex carbohydrates found in bread, cereal, potatoes, rice, corn, beans, and pasta. Sugars are simple carbohydrates found mainly in fruits, such as plums, strawberries, and oranges.

During digestion, complex carbohydrates are broken down into simple sugars, such as glucose, fructose, and galactose. Absorbed into the bloodstream through the villi of the small intestine, these sugar molecules circulate to fuel body functions.

Figure 35.8
Select foods from each of the five food groups every day and you'll have a healthful diet that supplies the six essential nutrients your body needs.

924 THE DIGESTIVE AND ENDOCRINE SYSTEMS

RESOURCE MANAGER

Unit 10 *Fast File* Resources
MiniLab Worksheet, p. 45
Reinforcement and Study Guide in English, p. 53
Reinforcement and Study Guide in Spanish, p. 57
Concept Mapping, p. 59
Transparency Worksheets, pp. 62, 69–70

Reading Essentials for Biology, Section 35.2
Laboratory Manual, pp. 227–230, 231–232
Section Focus Transparency 85
Reteaching Skills Transparency 51

Some sugar is carried to the liver where it is stored as glycogen.

Cellulose, another complex carbohydrate, is found in all plant cell walls and is not digestible by humans. However, cellulose (also known as fiber) is still an important item to include in the diet as it helps in the elimination of wastes. Sources of fiber include bran, beans, and lettuce.

Fats

Many people think that eating fat means getting fat; however, fats are an essential nutrient. They provide energy for your body and are also used as building materials. Recall that fats are essential building blocks of the cell membrane. They are also needed to synthesize hormones, protect body organs against injury, and insulate the body from cold.

Sources of fat in the diet include meats, nuts, and dairy products, as well as cooking oils. In the digestive system, fats are broken down into fatty acids and glycerol and absorbed by the villi of the small intestine. Eventually, some of these fatty acids end up in the liver. The liver converts them to glycogen or stores them as fat throughout your body.

Proteins

Your body has many uses for proteins. Enzymes, antibodies, many hormones, and substances that help the blood to clot, are all proteins. Proteins form part of muscles and many cell structures, including the cell membrane.

During digestion, proteins are broken down into amino acids. After the amino acids have been absorbed by the small intestine, they enter the bloodstream and are carried to the liver. The liver can convert amino acids to fats or glucose, both of which can be used for energy. However, your body

uses amino acids for energy only if other energy sources are depleted. Most amino acids are absorbed by cells and used for protein synthesis. The human body needs 20 different amino acids to carry out protein synthesis, but it can make only 12 of them. The remaining 8 must be consumed in the diet and so are called essential amino acids. Sources of essential amino acids include meats, dried beans, whole grains, eggs, and dairy products.

Fluorine (F)
Dental cavity reduction
Fluoridated water

Iodine (I)
Formation of thyroid hormone
Seafood, eggs, iodized salt, milk group

Iron (Fe)
Formation of hemoglobin (carries oxygen to body cells) and cytochromes (ATP formation)
Liver, egg yolk, grain and meat groups, leafy vegetables

Sodium (Na)
Nerve activity, body pH regulation
Bacon, butter, table salt, vegetable group

Magnesium (Mg)
Muscle and nerve activity, bone formation, enzyme function
Fruit, vegetable, and grain groups

Calcium (Ca)
Teeth and bone formation, muscle and nerve activity, blood clotting
Milk and grain groups

Phosphorus (P)
Teeth and bone formation, blood pH, muscle and nerve activity, part of enzymes and nucleic acids
Milk, grain, and vegetable groups

Copper (Cu)
Development of red blood cells, formation of some respiratory enzymes
Grain group, liver

Potassium (K)
Nerve and muscle activity
Vegetable group, bananas

Sulfur (S)
Builds hair, nails, and skin, component of insulin
Grain and fruit groups, eggs, cheese

☐ Function ☐ Source

Figure 35.9
Minerals serve many vital functions. **Describe** *What are the functions of iron in the body?*

2 Teach

Caption Question Answer
Figure 35.9 Iron (Fe) is used in the formation of hemoglobin and cytochomes.

Enrichment

Interpersonal Have students work in groups to investigate and prepare a report on one vitamin deficiency, such as scurvy, beriberi, rickets, night blindness, polyneuritis, or pellagra. **L2**
COOP LEARN

Biology Journal

Cancer and Nutrients Have students research how antioxidants destroy free radicals that can damage cells and lead to cancer. Ask them to find out how vitamins C and E and beta-carotene destroy these antioxidants. **L3**

Purpose

Students evaluate the nutritional value of a food based on its label.

Process Skills

observe and infer, analyze, interpret data

Teaching Strategies

■ Explain the concept of daily value (DV) to students.

■ You may wish to have students work in pairs.

Expected Results

Students should discover that the soup represented is basically a healthy meal.

Analysis

1. Yes; sodium
2. A serving of soup contains about 39% of its Calories from saturated fat. (6 g/serving $\times$ 9 Cal/g = 54 Calories of saturated fat per serving. $54 \div 140 = 39\%$)
3. Basically yes, although the sodium content is high.

Modified Assessment

Performance Have students repeat the MiniLab for three foods found in their homes. Allow students having trouble with math to use a calculator. Use the Performance Task Assessment List for Carrying Out a Strategy and Collecting Data in **PASC**, p. 97. **L1**

Minerals and vitamins

When you think of minerals, you may picture substances that people mine, or extract from Earth. As shown in *Figure 35.9* on the previous page, the same minerals can also be extracted from foods and put to use by your body.

A **mineral** is an inorganic substance that serves as a building material or takes part in a chemical reaction in the body. Minerals make up about four percent of your total body weight, most of it in your skeleton. Although they serve many different functions within the body, minerals are not used as an energy source.

Unlike minerals, **vitamins** are organic nutrients that are required in small amounts to maintain growth and metabolism. The two main groups of vitamins are fat-soluble and water-soluble, as shown in *Table 35.2*. Although fat-soluble vitamins can be stored in the liver, the accumulation of excess amounts can prove toxic. Water-soluble vitamins cannot be stored in the body and so must be included regularly in the diet. *Table 35.2* lists foods that contain fat-soluble and water-soluble vitamins.

Vitamin D, a fat-soluble vitamin, is synthesized in your skin. Vitamin K and some B vitamins are made by bacteria in your large intestine. The rest of the vitamins must be consumed in your diet.

> **Word Origin**
>
> **vitamin** from the Latin word *vita*, meaning "life"; Vitamins are necessary for life.

Table 35.2 Vitamins

Vitamin	Function	Source
Fat-soluble		
A	Maintain health of epithelial cells; formation of light-absorbing pigment; growth of bones and teeth	Liver, broccoli, green and yellow vegetables, tomatoes, butter, egg yolk
D	Absorption of calcium and phosphorus in digestive tract	Egg yolk, shrimp, yeast, liver, fortified milk; produced in the skin upon exposure to ultraviolet rays in sunlight
E	Formation of DNA, RNA, and red blood cells	Leafy vegetables, milk, butter
K	Blood clotting	Green vegetables, tomatoes, produced by intestinal bacteria
Water-soluble		
B_1	Sugar metabolism; synthesis of neurotransmitters	Ham, eggs, green vegetables, chicken, raisins, seafood, soybeans, milk
B_2 (riboflavin)	Sugar and protein metabolism in cells of eyes, skin, intestines, blood	Green vegetables, meats, yeast, eggs
Niacin	Energy-releasing reactions; fat metabolism	Yeast, meats, liver, fish, whole-grain cereals, nuts
B_6	Fat metabolism	Salmon, yeast, tomatoes, corn, spinach, liver, yogurt, wheat bran, whole-grain cereals and bread
B_{12}	Red blood cell formation; metabolism of amino acids	Liver, milk, cheese, eggs, meats
Pantothenic acid	Aerobic respiration; synthesis of hormones	Milk, liver, yeast, green vegetables, whole-grain cereals and breads
Folic acid	Synthesis of DNA and RNA; production of red and white blood cells	Liver, leafy green vegetables, nuts, orange juice
Biotin	Aerobic respiration; fat metabolism	Yeast, liver, egg yolk
C	Protein metabolism; wound healing	Citrus fruits, tomatoes, leafy green vegetables, broccoli, potatoes, peppers

926 THE DIGESTIVE AND ENDOCRINE SYSTEMS

TECH PREP

Professional Nutritionist: *Linguistic*
Students interested in nutrition can interview a nutritionist working for a food company. They may ask what tests are carried out to determine the nutritional content of food produced by the company. **L2**

Water

Water is the most abundant substance in your body—between 45 and 75 percent of your total body mass. Water facilitates the chemical reactions in your body and is necessary for the breakdown of foods during digestion. Water is also an excellent solvent; oxygen and nutrients from food could not enter your cells if they did not first dissolve in water.

Recall that water absorbs and releases heat slowly. It is this characteristic that helps water maintain your body's internal temperature. A large amount of heat is needed to raise the temperature of water. Because the body contains so much water, it takes a lot of added energy to raise its internal temperature. Your body loses about 2.5 L of water per day through exhalation, sweat, and urine. As a result, water must be replaced constantly.

Calories and Metabolism

The energy content of food is measured in units of heat called **Calories,** each of which represents a kilocalorie, or 1000 calories (written with a small c). A calorie is the amount of heat required to raise the temperature of 1 mL of water by 1°C. Some foods, especially those with fats, contain more Calories than others. In general, 1 g of fat contains nine Calories, while 1 g of carbohydrate or protein contains four Calories. To learn more about Calories in meals, complete the *MiniLab* on this page.

The number of Calories needed each day varies from person to person, depending on metabolism, or rate at which energy is burned. As you will see in the next section, a major regulator of metabolic rate is a hormone from the thyroid gland.

MiniLab 35.1

Interpret Data

Evaluate a Bowl of Soup As a consumer, you are bombarded by advertising that promotes the nutritional benefits of specific food products. Choosing a food to eat on the basis of such ads may not make nutritional sense. By examining the product labels that list the ingredients of processed foods, you can learn about their actual nutritional content.

Data Table

Percentage of Daily Value (DV)	
Carbohydrates	60%
Fat	30%
Saturated fats	10%
Cholesterol	1.5%
Protein	10%
Total Calories	2000

NUTRITION FACTS
Serving Size: 2 cups (452g)
Servings Per Container: 1

Amount Per Serving	
Calories 140	Calories from Fat 54

	% Daily Value*
Total Fat 8g	12%
Saturated Fat 6g	30%
Cholesterol 20mg	7%
Sodium 1640 mg	68%
Total Carbohydrate 22g	7%
Dietary Fiber 5g	20%
Sugars 5g	
Protein 6g	

Vitamin A	50%	Vitamin C	4%
Calcium	2%	Iron	2%

* Percent Daily Values are based on a 2,000 calorie diet. Your daily values may be higher or lower depending on your calorie needs:

		Calories	2,000	2,500
Total Fat	Less than		65g	80g
Sat Fat	Less than		20g	25g
Cholesterol	Less than		300mg	300mg
Sodium	Less than		2,400mg	2,400mg
Total Carbohydrate			300g	375g
Fiber			25g	30g

Calories per gram:
Fat 9 • Carbohydrates 4 • Protein 4

Procedure
1. Examine the information in the table listing the daily value (DV) of various nutrients. DV expresses what percent of Calories should come from certain nutrients.
2. Examine the nutritional information on the soup can label, and compare it with the DV table.

Analysis
1. **Analyze** Does your bowl of soup provide more than 30 percent of any of the daily nutrients? Which ones?
2. **Use Numbers** Calculate the percentage of Calories in soup that are provided by saturated fat.
3. **Evaluate** Is this soup a nutritious meal? Explain.

A person's body mass, age, gender, and level of physical activity also affect metabolic rate. Generally, males need more Calories per day than females, teenagers need more than adults, and active people need more than inactive people.

 Reading Check **List** factors that can affect metabolic rate.

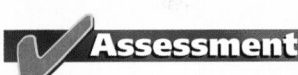 **Reading Check** Hormone levels, body mass, age, gender, and level of physical activity all affect metabolic rate.

3 Assess

DAILY INTERVENTION

Check for Understanding
Give the students a sample lunch that has nutritional deficiencies. Ask them to evaluate the lunch. Ask what nutrients are in excess and what nutrients should be added. Elicit what foods could provide these nutrients. **L1**

Reteach
Visual-Spatial Have students prepare a chart of the six nutrients. Have them identify the functions of these nutrients and identify foods that contain each. **L1**

Resources
For more practice, use *Reading Essentials for Biology,* Section 35.2.

Extension
Linguistic Have students interview a nutritionist to find out what criteria the nutritionist uses when planning meals that meet nutritional needs. **L2**

✔ Assessment

Portfolio Ask students to write a summary of which substances need to be included in a daily balanced diet and what each nutrient does. **L2**

Purpose

Students learn how to calculate Body Mass Index and determine whether or not a given weight is within accepted values.

Process Skills

think critically, apply concepts, collect data, interpret data, recognize cause and effect, use numbers

Teaching Strategies

■ Allow students to use calculators.

■ Review the technique for squaring a number.

■ For individuals under the age of 20, BMI guidelines are age- and gender-specific. Students who are interested in determining if they are at a healthy weight can visit
for more information about BMI guidelines.

Thinking Critically

1. BMI = 22.7; normal weight
2. The person could reduce his or her Calorie intake, and/or increase activity level.
3. His Calorie intake is in balance with his expenditure.
4. The test may overestimate the amount of body fat for a person who is well muscled, and may underestimate the amount of body fat for a person who is very thin but not well muscled.

Assessment

Portfolio Have student groups plan a general long-range program for a person to maintain a BMI below 25. Use the Performance Task Assessment List for Group Work in **PASC**, p. 169. **L3**

928

Problem-Solving Lab 35.2

Use Numbers

What is BMI? BMI is a reliable indicator of a healthy body weight for adult men and women based on height and weight. Approximately sixty percent of adults in the United States are considered overweight. Use the following equation to calculate a sample BMI.

Solve the Problem

Compute BMI, or Body Mass Index, using the following formula:

$$\frac{\text{weight (in pounds)}}{\text{height (in inches)}^2} \times 704.5 = \text{BMI}$$

The guidelines for adults from the National Institutes of Health are as follows:

A BMI
- 18.5 to 24.9 = normal weight
- 25 to 29.9 = overweight
- 30 or over = obese

Thinking Critically

1. **Evaluate** Calcuate the BMI for a person who is 5 feet 4 inches tall and weighs 132 pounds. According to the guidelines, is this person of normal weight, overweight, or obese?
2. **Recognize Cause and Effect** How might a person with a BMI of 27 reduce his or her BMI? Consider both nutritional intake and physical activity.
3. **Infer** Fred has a BMI of 22. How do you suppose his Calorie intake compares to his Calorie expenditure?
4. **Think Critically** What limits does the BMI test have? (Hint: A 6 foot tall, well-muscled athlete weighing 200 pounds would have a BMI of 27.)

Calories and health

What happens if a person consumes more Calories than his or her body can metabolize? When the energy taken in is greater than the energy expended, the extra energy is stored as body fat and a person gains weight. However, if a person eats fewer Calories than the body can metabolize, some of the body's stored energy is used and weight is lost.

Physicians have determined that many Americans are overweight. Being overweight or obese increases a person's risk for developing health problems such as high blood pressure, diabetes, and heart disease. Being underweight is also associated with health problems such as anemia, fatigue, and decreased ability to fight infection and disease. A simple way to determine if a person is at a healthy weight is to calculate his or her Body Mass Index (BMI). Calculate a sample BMI by doing the *Problem-Solving Lab* on this page.

Millions of people put themselves on diets every year in hopes of losing weight. While many diets are nutritionally sound, others prescribe eating habits that are not sensible and usually fail to produce the desired result. Read more about weight-loss products in the *Biology and Society* section at the end of this chapter.

Section Assessment

Understanding Main Ideas

1. Compare the functions of carbohydrates, fats, and proteins in the body.
2. Describe the role of the liver in the storage of carbohydrates, fats, and proteins.
3. Compare and contrast vitamins and minerals. Which vitamins and minerals can be found in milk?
4. What happens when a person takes in more food energy than his or her body needs?

Thinking Critically

5. Describe two effects dehydration can have on homeostasis of the body.

SKILL REVIEW

6. **Make and Use Tables** Using *Table 35.2* on page 926, analyze how a lack of vitamins A, D, K, and C in a person's diet could affect his or her health. For more help, refer to *Make and Use Tables* in the **Skill Handbook**.

928 THE DIGESTIVE AND ENDOCRINE SYSTEMS

 in.bdol.glencoe.com/self_check_quiz

Section Assessment

1. carbohydrates: sources of energy and are used for structure; fats: energy storage; proteins: structure, such as muscle, and also make up enzymes, antibodies, and many hormones
2. The liver stores glucose subunits and fatty acids in the form of glycogen. The liver can convert amino acids to fats or glucose to be used for energy.
3. vitamins: organic nutrients required in small amounts to maintain growth and metabolism; minerals: inorganic substances used as building materials or in a chemical reaction in the body; vitamins D, E, B$_1$, and B$_{12}$; pantothenic acid, iodine, calcium, phosphorus
4. When a person takes in more food energy than needed, the food energy will be stored as fat.
5. Water is needed for oxygen and nutrients to enter cells and to maintain body temperature.
6. A lack of Vitamin A, D, K, and C would cause problems with epithelial cells, vision, bones and teeth, blood clotting, wound healing, and protein metabolism.

The Endocrine System

Indiana Standards Standard B.1.14 Recognize and explain that communication and/or interaction are required between cells to coordinate their diverse activities.

SECTION PREVIEW

Objectives

Describe the internal feedback mechanism controlling hormone levels in the body.

Contrast the actions of steroid and amino acid hormones.

Identify and interpret the functions of some of the hormones secreted by endocrine glands.

Review Vocabulary
gland: in mammals, a cell or group of cells that secretes fluid (p. 842)

New Vocabulary
endocrine glands
hypothalamus
pituitary gland
target cell
receptor
negative feedback
 system
adrenal gland
thyroid gland
parathyroid glands

Internal Feedback

Concept Map Copy the concept map onto a separate sheet of paper.

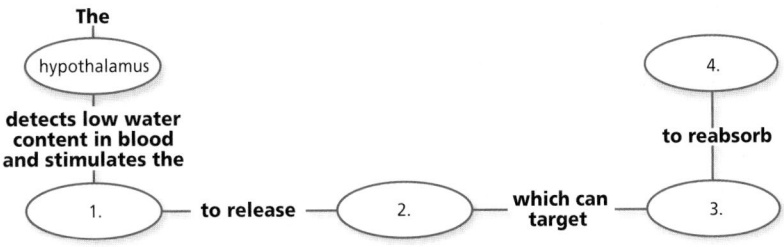

Organize Information As you read this section, complete the concept map about internal feedback in the endocrine system.

Control of the Body

Internal control of the body is directed by two systems: the nervous system, which you will learn more about later, and the endocrine system. The endocrine system is made up of a series of glands, called **endocrine glands,** that release chemicals directly into the bloodstream. These chemicals act as messengers, relaying information to other parts of the body. Ultimately, the functions of all body systems are controlled by the interaction between the nervous and endocrine systems.

Interaction of the nervous system and endocrine system

Much of the time, the endocrine system and the nervous system work together to maintain homeostasis within the body. Because there are two control systems within the body, coordination between the two systems is needed. The **hypothalamus** (hi poh THA luh mus) is the portion of the brain that connects the endocrine and nervous systems. The hypothalamus receives messages from other areas of the brain and from internal organs. When a change in homeostasis is detected, the hypothalamus stimulates the **pituitary** (pih TEW uh ter ee) **gland.** The pituitary gland, the main gland of the endocrine system, is located in the skull just beneath the hypothalamus. The pituitary gland is controlled by the hypothalamus, and the two are connected by nerves and blood vessels. In response to messages received by the hypothalamus, the pituitary gland releases its own chemicals or stimulates other glands to release theirs. Other endocrine glands under the control of the pituitary include the thyroid gland, the adrenal glands, and glands associated with reproduction.

35.3 THE ENDOCRINE SYSTEM **929**

Bellringer
Section Focus Transparency 86

Transparency **86** Negative Feedback

Concept Map

Organize Information 1. pituitary gland; 2. ADH; 3. kidney cells; 4. water

Word Origin

endocrine from the Greek words *endo,* meaning "within," and *krinein,* meaning "to separate"; The endocrine glands secrete hormones into the blood.

Word Origin

Have students research to find and define other words using "endo" as a part of the root, such as *endothelium* and *endoderm.*

Unit 10 *FAST FILE* **Resources**
MiniLab Worksheet, p. 46
BioLab Worksheet, pp. 47–48
Reinforcement and Study Guide in
 English, p. 54
Reinforcement and Study Guide in
 Spanish, p. 58
Critical Thinking/Problem Solving, p. 60

Transparency Worksheets, pp. 63,
 65–66
Reading Essentials for Biology,
 Section 35.3
Section Focus Transparency 86
Basic Concepts Transparency 65

Indiana Academic Standards

Pages 928–929: B.1.10, B.1.14,
B.1.17, B.1.19

2 Teach

Using Science Terms

Explain the meaning of the following terms: *Endo* is Greek for "within" and *crine* (krinein) is Greek for "to separate." Insulin gets its name from the Latin *insula*, meaning "island." Insulin is made in the small islands or islets of beta cells in the pancreas. *Hypo* is Greek for "under" and *thalamus* is Greek for "the inner room." The thalamus was an inner room in a Greek ship.

Caption Question Answer
Figure 35.10 The adrenal medulla secretes epinephrine and norepinephrine.

Endocrine control of the body

The chemicals secreted by endocrine glands into the bloodstream are called hormones. Recall that a hormone is a chemical released in one part of an organism that affects another part. Hormones convey information to other cells in your body, giving them instructions regarding your metabolism, growth, development, and behavior. Once released by the glands, the hormones travel in the bloodstream and then attach to specific binding sites found on the plasma membranes, or in the nuclei, of **target cells.** These binding sites on cells are called **receptors.** *Figure 35.10* summarizes the action of different endocrine glands.

Example of endocrine control

Human growth hormone (hGH) is a good example of an endocrine system hormone. When your body is actively growing, blood glucose levels are slightly lowered as the growing cells use up the sugar. This low blood glucose level is detected by the hypothalamus, which stimulates the production and release of hGH from the pituitary into the bloodstream. hGH binds to receptors on the plasma membranes of liver cells, stimulating the liver cells to release glucose into your blood. Your cells need the glucose in order to continue growing. *Figure 35.11* summarizes the control of hGH by the pituitary gland. This diagram also shows the types of hormones secreted by other human endocrine glands and some of the effects they have on the body.

Negative Feedback Control

If homeostasis is disrupted, endocrine glands can be stimulated by the nervous system, changes in blood chemistry, or by other hormones. Regulation of the endocrine system is controlled most often through one type of internal feedback mechanism called a **negative feedback system.** In a negative feedback system, the

Pituitary
Amino acid hormones
Controls adrenal gland, thyroid gland, ovaries, testes, mammary glands, stores hypothalamus hormones, and secretes growth hormone

Hypothalamus
Amino acid hormones
Controls pituitary and synthesizes antidiuretic hormone and oxytocin for uterus contraction during birth

Thyroid gland
Amino acid hormones
Secretes thyroxin to stimulate growth and metabolism and secretes calcitonin

Parathyroid gland
Amino acid hormones
Secretes parathyroid hormone

Ovary in female
Steroid hormones
Secretes female sex hormones

Adrenal medulla
Amino acid hormones
Secretes epinephrine and norepinephrine

Adrenal cortex
Steroid hormones
Secretes glucocorticoid and aldosterone

Testis in male
Steroid hormones
Secretes male sex hormones

■ Type of hormones released
  Function of gland

Figure 35.10
This diagram shows the principal human endocrine glands, the type of hormone(s) they secrete, and the action of the gland/hormone.
List *What are the hormones secreted by the adrenal medulla?*

930 THE DIGESTIVE AND ENDOCRINE SYSTEMS

hormones, or their effects, are fed back to inhibit the original signal. Once homeostasis is reached, the signal is stopped and the hormone is no longer released. The thermostat in your home is controlled by a similar negative feedback system. It maintains the room at a set temperature. When the temperature drops, the thermostat senses the reduction of thermal energy and signals the heater to increase its output. When the thermal energy of the room rises again to a certain point, the thermostat no longer stimulates the heater, which shuts off. When the temperature drops again, the process repeats itself. In this negative feedback system, the increase in temperature "feeds back" to signal the thermostat to stop stimulating thermal energy production.

✓ **Reading Check** **Relate** negative feedback systems to the maintenance of homeostasis.

Feedback control of hormones

The majority of endocrine glands operate under negative feedback systems. A gland synthesizes and secretes its hormone, which travels in the blood to target cells where the appropriate response occurs. Information regarding the hormone level or its effect on target cells is fed back, usually to the hypothalamus or pituitary gland, to regulate the gland's production of the hormone.

Control of blood water levels

Let's look at an example of a hormone that is controlled by a negative feedback system. After working out in the gym and building up a sweat, you are thirsty. This is because the water content of your blood has been reduced. The hypothalamus, which is able to sense the concentration of

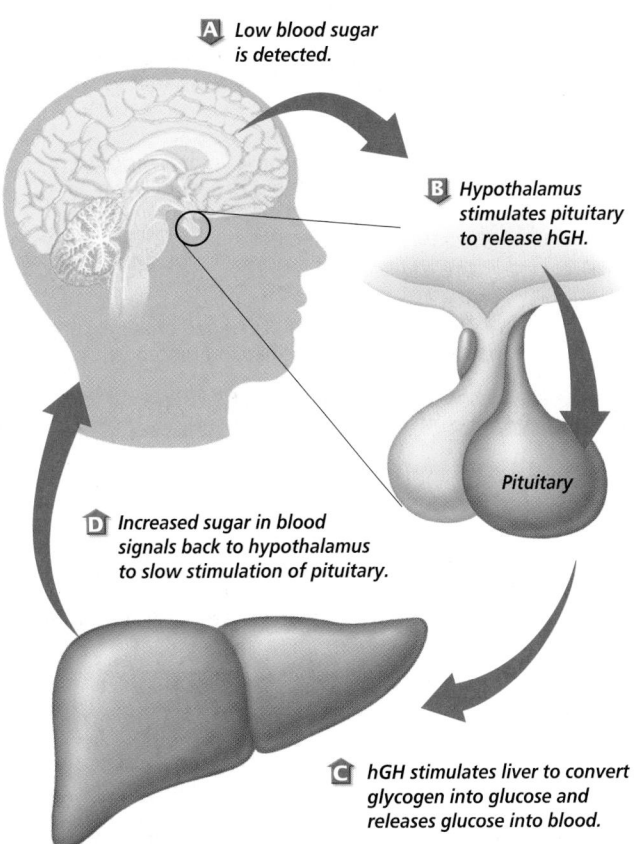

Ⓐ Low blood sugar is detected.

Ⓑ Hypothalamus stimulates pituitary to release hGH.

Pituitary

Ⓓ Increased sugar in blood signals back to hypothalamus to slow stimulation of pituitary.

Ⓒ hGH stimulates liver to convert glycogen into glucose and releases glucose into blood.

Figure 35.11
The hypothalamus and pituitary gland control the amount of human growth hormone (hGH) in your blood.

water in your blood, determines that your body is dehydrated. In response, it stimulates the pituitary gland to release antidiuretic (AN tih di yuh reh tihk) hormone (ADH).

ADH reduces the amount of water in your urine. It binds to receptors in kidney cells, promoting the reabsorption of water and reducing the amount of water excreted in urine. Information about blood water levels is constantly fed back to the hypothalamus so it can regulate the pituitary's release of ADH. If the body becomes overhydrated, the hypothalamus stops stimulating release of ADH.

Concept Development

Insulin-dependent diabetes is also called Type I, or juvenile, diabetes. One major complication of Type I diabetes is loss of vision due to cataracts. The excessive blood glucose chemically attaches to the lens proteins, clouding the lens. Type I diabetes often causes kidney damage, also. Noninsulin-dependent diabetes is called Type II diabetes. Because this type of diabetes is most common in people over the age of 35, it is sometimes called late-onset diabetes.

✓ **Reading Check** Negative feedback systems maintain homeostasis by monitoring certain factors, such as hormone level in the blood and relaying the information back to the source, such as the gland that produces the hormone, for adjustment of the hormone level. By constantly monitoring and adjusting the system, feedback systems maintain homeostasis.

⊙ CHALLENGE ACTIVITY

Human Growth Hormone Students who need additional challenges can find out more about genetic recombinant human growth hormone. They should find out how the hormone is synthesized commercially. They can write a position paper on whether people with normal amounts of growth hormone should be allowed to take human growth hormone to try to increase their growth. **L3**

Purpose

Students relate changes in blood insulin and glucagon levels during prolonged exercise to the body's need to get glucose to its cells.

Process Skills

recognize cause and effect, interpret data, analyze

Teaching Strategies

Ask students to list on the chalkboard the changes that occur in the body during exercise. Identify the changes that require increased glucose inside cells. **L1**

Thinking Critically

1. Exercise causes an increase in glucagon and a decrease in insulin in the blood.

2. As the muscle cells use more glucose, glucagon increases signaling the liver to release glucose. Insulin production, which signals storage of glucose in the liver, decreases.

3. Designs may vary but should include a demonstration of the fact that as muscle cells begin to contract, sugar level lowers in blood, glucagon secretion increases, and insulin secretion decreases. This causes sugar levels in the blood to raise.

Modified Assessment

Knowledge Ask students to summarize in their journals the effects of insulin and glucagon on blood glucose levels. Use the Performance Task Assessment List for Writing in Science in **PASC**, p. 159. **L1**

932

Interpret Data

How does exercise affect levels of insulin and glucagon?
Exercise represents an example of rapid fuel mobilization in the body. The body must gear up to supply great amounts of glucose and oxygen for muscle metabolism.

Solve the Problem

The graph here shows the effects of prolonged exercise, such as running a marathon, on blood insulin and glucagon levels.

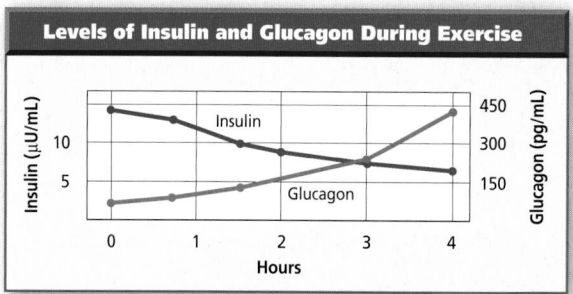

Levels of Insulin and Glucagon During Exercise

Thinking Critically

1. **Analyze** Examine the graph and explain how exercise affects the concentrations of insulin and glucagon in the blood.

2. **Recognize Cause and Effect** Relate the changes shown on the graph to what is occurring in muscle cells as well as to blood glucose levels.

3. **Sequence** Design a flowchart that shows the steps involved in maintaining homeostasis of blood glucose during exercise. Begin your flowchart with muscle cells.

Word Origin

adrenal from the Latin words *ad*, meaning "to" or "toward" and *renes*, meaning "the kidneys"; The adrenal glands are located on top of the kidneys.

Control of blood glucose levels

Another example of a negative feedback system involves the regulation of blood glucose levels. Unlike most other endocrine glands, the pancreas is not controlled by the pituitary gland. When you have just eaten and your blood glucose levels are high, your pancreas releases the hormone insulin. Then, insulin signals liver and

---

muscle cells to take in glucose, thus lowering blood glucose levels. When blood glucose levels become too low, another pancreatic hormone, glucagon, is released. Glucagon binds to liver cells, signaling them to release stored glycogen as glucose. Learn more about glucose storage and release by doing the *Problem-Solving Lab* on this page.

Hormone Action

Once hormones are released by an endocrine gland, they travel to target cells and cause a change. Hormones can be grouped into two basic types according to how they act on their target cells: steroid hormones and amino acid hormones.

Action of steroid hormones

Hormones that are made from lipids are called steroid hormones. Steroid hormones are lipid-soluble and therefore diffuse freely into cells through their plasma membranes, as shown in *Figure 35.12*. There they bind to a hormone receptor inside the cell. The hormone-receptor complex then travels to the nucleus where it activates the synthesis of specific messenger RNA molecules. The mRNA molecules move out to the cytoplasm where they guide the synthesis of the required proteins.

Action of amino acid hormones

The second group of hormones is made from amino acids. Recall that amino acids can be strung together in chains and that proteins are made from long chains of amino acids. Some hormones are short chains of amino acids and others are large chains. These amino acid hormones, once secreted into the bloodstream, bind to receptors embedded in the plasma membrane of the target cell,

---

PROJECT

Juvenile Diabetes Have students find out information about juvenile diabetes, including causes, symptoms, and current treatments. Students can present the results of their research to the class. **L2**

Cell membrane

Steroid hormone

New protein molecule

mRNA

Ribosome

Hormone-receptor complex

Nucleus

mRNA

DNA

Figure 35.12
Steroid hormones enter a cell (1), bind to a receptor (2), which in turn binds to DNA to stimulate protein synthesis (3).

as shown in *Figure 35.13*. From there, they open ion channels in the membrane, or route signals down from the surface of the membrane to activate enzymes inside the cell. The enzymes, in turn, alter the behavior of other molecules inside the cell. In both of these ways, the hormone is able to control what goes on inside the target cell.

Adrenal Hormones and Stress

You are sitting in math class and the teacher is about to hand out the semester test. Because this test is an important one, you have spent many hours studying for it. Like most of your classmates, you are a little nervous as the test is being passed down the row. Your heart is beating fast and your hands are a little sweaty. As you review the first problem, however, you begin to calm down because you know how to solve it.

The **adrenal glands** play an important role in preparing your body for stressful situations. The adrenal glands are located on top of the kidneys and consist of two parts—an inner portion and an outer portion.

The outer portion secretes steroid hormones, including glucocorticoids (glew ko KOR tuh koydz) and aldosterone (ahl DOS tuh rohn).

These steroid hormones cause an increase in available glucose and raise blood pressure. In this way, they help the body combat stresses such as fright, temperature extremes, bleeding, infection, disease, and even test anxiety.

Figure 35.13
When an amino acid hormone binds to the receptor on the cell membrane (1), it can open ion channels (2), or activate enzymes (3).

Amino acid hormone

Cell membrane

Hormone receptor

Enzyme (inactive)

Enzyme (active)

Ions

Ion channel

Nucleus

Enrichment
Have students identify causes of stress in their lives and bodily responses they notice as a result. increase in breathing rate, heart rate, alertness, a churning feeling in the stomach, or an increase in blood pressure List the stresses and responses on the chalkboard. Point out to students that such responses are under the control of the nervous system and hormones. **L2**

Inquiry
Activity Have students research possible reasons why the parathyroid glands may not function properly and how this would affect the body. Have students present their results to the class. **L2**

Quick Demo
Kidneys Using a whole kidney with adrenal gland attached, point out the gland and relate its position to the word origin of *adrenal* ("attached to the kidneys").

INCLUSION STRATEGIES
Learning Disabled Students can reinforce the difference between the action of steroid hormones and the action of amino acid hormones by making their own models. Students can use colored paper, marking pens, scissors, and tape to create models of the different hormone receptor complexes and the activity within the cell that results from the formation of the complex. **L1**

Indiana Academic Standards
Pages 932–933: B.1.7, B.1.14

Purpose

Students analyze a prepared slide of thyroid and parathyroid tissue.

Process Skills

compare and contrast, observe, apply concepts, hypothesize, interpret scientific illustrations

Teaching Strategies

■ Prepared slides of thyroid and parathyroid tissue are available from biological supply houses. It is cheaper to purchase the combined slide of both tissues rather than separate slides of each.

■ To further reduce costs, project one prepared slide onto a TV screen using a video camera.

Expected Results

Students will be able to differentiate between thyroid and parathyroid tissue.

Analysis

1. Student may notice that thyroid tissue contains many large spaces surrounded by a thin band while parathyroid tissue contains no large spaces or follicles.

2. a. thyroid
   b. stored hormones (thyroxine or calcitonin)
   c. It makes the hormones.

3. Both glands are located in the same general area of the neck. The parathyroids lie on the thyroid gland itself.

Assessment

Performance Ask students to research the cause and appearance of thyroid goiter. Provide students with prepared slides of normal thyroid tissue and thyroid tissue exhibiting a goiter. Have students compare and contrast the two tissues. Use the Performance Task Assessment List for Making Observations and Inferences in **PASC**, p. 89. **L2**

Observe

Compare Thyroid and Parathyroid Tissue Although their names seem somewhat similar, the thyroid and parathyroid glands perform rather different functions within the body.

Procedure

1. Copy the data table.
2. Use low-power magnification to examine a prepared slide of thyroid and parathyroid endocrine gland tissue. (Note: Both tissues appear on the same slide.) **CAUTION:** *Use caution when working with a microscope and prepared slides.*
3. The image on the right is a photograph of thyroid and parathyroid tissue. Use it as a guide in locating the two types of endocrine gland tissue under low power and in answering certain analysis questions.
4. Now locate each type of gland tissue under high-power magnification. Draw what you see in the data table. Then use what you learned in the chapter to identify the names of the hormones produced by each gland.

Color-enhanced LM Magnification: 16×

Parathyroid (A) and thyroid (B) tissue

Data Table		
Tissue	Drawing	Name of Hormone(s) Produced
Thyroid		
Parathyroid		

Analysis

1. **Compare and Contrast** Compare and contrast the microscopic appearance of parathyroid tissue to that of thyroid tissue.
2. a. **Observe** Which tissue type contains follicles (large liquid storage areas)?
   b. **Infer** What may be present within the follicles?
   c. **Think Critically** Hypothesize what function the thin layer of tissue that surrounds each follicle may have.
3. **Explain** How might you explain the fact that both thyroid and parathyroid tissue can be seen on the same slide?

The inner portion of the adrenal gland secretes two amino acid hormones: epinephrine (eh puh NEH frun)—often called adrenaline—and norepinephrine. Recall the fight-or-flight response discussed in the animal behavior chapter. During such a response, the hypothalamus relays impulses to the nervous system, which in turn stimulates the adrenal glands to increase their output of epinephrine and norepinephrine. These hormones increase heart rate, blood pressure, and rate of respiration; increase efficiency of muscle contractions; and increase blood sugar levels. If you have ever had to perform in front of a large audience, you may have experienced these symptoms, often referred to collectively as an "adrenaline rush." This is how the body prepares itself to face or flee a stressful situation.

Thyroid and Parathyroid Hormones

The **thyroid gland,** located in the neck, regulates metabolism, growth, and development. The main metabolic and growth hormone of the thyroid is thyroxine. This hormone affects the rate at which the body uses energy and determines your food intake requirements.

The thyroid gland also secretes calcitonin (kal suh TOH nun)—a hormone that regulates calcium levels in the blood. Calcium is a mineral the body needs for blood clotting, formation of bones and teeth, and normal nerve and muscle function. Calcitonin binds to the membranes of kidney cells and causes an increase in calcium excretion. Calcitonin also binds to bone-forming cells, causing them to increase calcium absorption and synthesize new bone.

 CHALLENGE ACTIVITY

Thyroid Gland Have students who need an additional challenge research information on hyperthyroidism and hypothyroidism. What are the causes and effects of these disorders? What treatments are currently available? Students can share their results with the class in the form of a multi-media presentation. **L3**

Another hormone involved in mineral regulation, parathyroid hormone (PTH), is produced by the **parathyroid glands,** which are attached to the thyroid gland. The release of PTH leads to an increase in the rate of calcium, phosphate, and magnesium absorption in the intestines. PTH causes the release of calcium and phosphate from bone tissue. It also increases the rate at which the kidneys remove calcium and magnesium from urine and return them to the blood.

The overall effect of parathyroid hormone and calcitonin hormone interaction in the body is shown in *Figure 35.14.* Take a closer look at thyroid and parathyroid tissue by completing the *MiniLab* on the previous page.

As you can see, hormones associated with the endocrine system are responsible for controlling many different functions in your body. Different hormones may play more important roles during some periods in your life than others. In any case, they remain the principal biological influence on your behavior and development.

 Reading Check **Describe** how blood calcium homeostasis is maintained within the body.

Figure 35.14
Calcitonin and parathyroid hormone (PTH) have opposite effects on blood calcium levels.

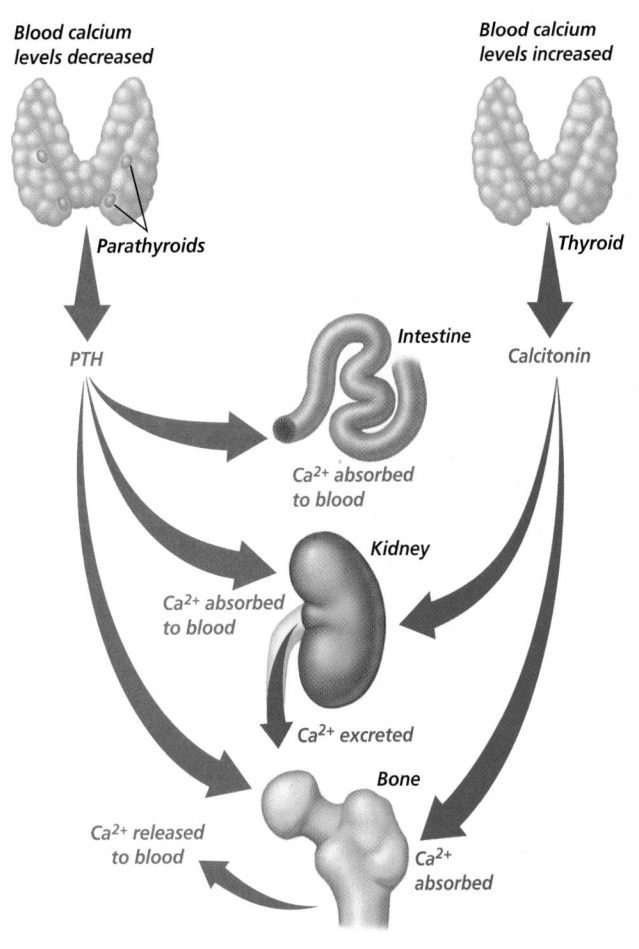

Blood calcium levels decreased

Blood calcium levels increased

Parathyroids

Thyroid

PTH

Intestine

Calcitonin

Ca²⁺ absorbed to blood

Kidney

Ca²⁺ absorbed to blood

Ca²⁺ excreted

Bone

Ca²⁺ released to blood

Ca²⁺ absorbed

---

3 Assess

DAILY INTERVENTION

Check for Understanding
Have students make a diagram that summarizes the control of calcium levels in the body. **L1** **ELL**

Reteach
Have students go around the room, with the first student naming a gland, the second naming a hormone secreted by that gland, and the third naming the function of the hormone. **L2**

Resources
For more practice, use *Reading Essentials for Biology,* Section 35.3.

Extension

Have students look up information on scientists who have discovered or synthesized endocrine hormones. F. G. Banting and C. H. Best discovered insulin. E. C. Kendall isolated thyroxine and cortisone. **L3**

 Assessment

Knowledge Ask students to summarize hormonal control of blood sugar levels. **L2**

 Reading Check Students' answers should be a synopsis of Figure 35.14.

Indiana Academic Standards

Pages 934–935: B.1.7, B.1.14

Section Assessment

Understanding Main Ideas
1. Identify and interpret the functions of the endocrine system.
2. Explain the interrelationship between the nervous system and the endocrine system.
3. Describe the relationship between a negative feedback system and the maintenance of homeostasis.
4. How does a steroid hormone affect its target cell? How does this action differ from how an amino acid hormone affects its target cell?

Thinking Critically
5. Hormones continually make adjustments in blood glucose levels. Why must blood glucose levels be kept fairly constant?

SKILL REVIEW
6. **Sequence** Create a flowchart that illustrates the internal feedback system the body uses to maintain blood glucose homeostasis. For more information, refer to *Sequence* in the **Skill Handbook.**

in.bdol.glencoe.com/self_check_quiz

35.3 THE ENDOCRINE SYSTEM **935**

Section Assessment

1. The endocrine system helps maintain homeostasis by releasing hormones in response to signals from the brain or body when homeostasis is disrupted.
2. The hypothalamus controls the pituitary, or master, endocrine gland.
3. In a negative feedback system, when a hormone reaches an appropriate level, it or its effects feed back to inhibit the release of more hormone.
4. A steriod hormone passes through the target cell membrane and activates protein synthesis. An amino acid hormone activates ion channels or enzyme pathways in the cell from its position on the membrane.
5. Glucose is the fuel for body cells and a constant level needs to be maintained for normal body functions.
6. As blood glucose levels increase, insulin is released and liver and muscle cells take in glucose. As blood glucose levels decrease, glucagon is released and glucose is released from the liver.

Time Allotment
one class period

Process Skills
make and use a table, interpret data, analyze

Safety Precautions
Caution students not to eat while in the laboratory and that iodine can irritate skin and eyes. Remind students to wash their hands upon completion of the laboratory cleanup.

PREPARATION

Order amylase or amylase solution from a biological supply house. To make amylase solution, place 1 g in 99 mL of water (1% solution). Purchase 4–5 boxes of breakfast cereal. You may want to include shredded wheat (non-sugar coated) as a cereal that has higher amounts of starch at the beginning of the experiment.

Before You Begin
The enzyme amylase is found in both salivary and pancreatic secretions. Amylase is used by the body to digest starch. When you eat foods that contain starch, such as breakfast cereals, salivary amylase immediately begins to digest these molecules. How long does it take for larger molecules of starch to be broken down into simple sugars? In this lab, you will investigate the relative rate of starch digestion by amylase.

The Action of the Enzyme Amylase on Breakfast Cereals

PREPARATION

Problem
How long does it take amylase to digest all of the starch in breakfast cereals?

Objectives
In this BioLab, you will:
- **Compare** the relative rate of starch digestion by amylase on three breakfast cereals.

Materials
variety of dry cereals	water
mortar and pestle	Bunsen burner or hot plate
test tubes	graduated cylinder
test tube racks	iodine solution in dropper bottles
filter paper	watch glasses
funnel	plastic droppers
balance	amylase solution
beaker	

Safety Precautions
CAUTION: *Never eat laboratory materials. Iodine can irritate and will stain skin.*

Skill Handbook
If you need help with this lab, refer to the **Skill Handbook.**

PROCEDURE

1. Copy the data table.
2. Label the breakfast cereals and three corresponding test tubes **A, B,** and **C.**

Data Table

Time (sec)	Presence of Starch		
	Cereal A	**Cereal B**	**Cereal C**
Initial test			
0			
30			
60			

PROCEDURE

Teaching Strategies
- Have students read through the entire lab with their equipment in front of them. Be sure they understand what to do at each step.

- Have students ask any questions they have about the procedure before beginning the experiment.

Data and Observations
Most cereals have both starch and simple sugar to start. Students should find the starch has rapidly disappeared in less than a minute or a few minutes at the most. Time will somewhat depend on how fine they grind their cereal and the amount of starch in the product to start.

3. Grind a small portion of each of the breakfast cereals to a powder using the mortar and pestle.

4. Place a piece of filter paper in the funnel. Place the funnel over test tube **A**.

5. Using the balance, measure out 0.5 g of ground cereal **A** and transfer it to the funnel.

6. Filter 10 mL of boiling water over the cereal and allow the filtrate to collect in the bottom of the test tube.

7. Repeat steps 4, 5, and 6 for cereals **B** and **C**. Rinse the funnel and replace the filter paper before each filtration.

8. Add 2 drops of the iodine solution to a watch glass, followed by 2 drops of filtrate **A**. A dark blue/black color indicates the presence of starch. Record your results.

9. Using a separate eyedropper for each solution, repeat step 8 on cereals **B** and **C**. Clean the watch glass between each test.

10. Add 2 mL of amylase solution to each filtrate. Immediately take a sample, and repeat steps 8 and 9 to retest for the presence of starch.

11. Test each filtrate every 30 seconds until all of the starch has been digested to simple sugars in each sample. Record your results.

12. **CLEANUP AND DISPOSAL** Clean all equipment as instructed by your teacher. Make wise choices as to the disposal or recycling of materials. Wash your hands thoroughly.

ANALYZE AND CONCLUDE

1. **Analyze** Did all of the breakfast cereals contain starch? What action did the amylase have on the starch?

2. **Observe and Infer** Which cereal was converted to simple sugars in the least amount of time? Infer what this indicates about the starch concentration of this cereal compared to the other cereals.

3. **Think Critically** Does the amount of starch versus simple sugars make a difference in the Calorie content of the cereal?

Apply Your Skill

Use Variables, Constants, and Controls Investigate the effect of temperature or pH on the action of amylase on one of the breakfast cereals.

 Web Links To find out more about digestive enzymes, visit in.bdol.glencoe.com/digestive_enzymes

35.3 THE ENDOCRINE SYSTEM **937**

ANALYZE AND CONCLUDE

1. Answers will vary but most cereals will contain starch. Amylase breaks down starch into simple sugars.

2. The cereal with the least starch will take the least amount of time.

3. No, 1 gram of carbohydrate, which includes both starch and simple sugars, yields 4 Calories of heat energy when broken down by the body.

Assessment
Portfolio Have students write summaries of the BioLab and include their summaries, their table, and their answers to the Analyze and Conclude questions in their portfolios. **L2**

Apply Your Skill

Use Variables, Constants, and Controls Students could repeat the lab experiment using cold water instead of boiling water. In separate experiments they could vary the pH of the water used for filtration and compare the results to those using water with a pH of 7.

CLEANUP AND DISPOSAL

 Iodine can be washed down the drain with a tenfold excess of water. Dispose of the boiling water for students or caution them about its potential harm.

Indiana Academic Standards

Pages 936–937: B.1.7

Biology and Society

Purpose

Students evaluate weight-loss products in light of what they know about good nutrition.

Background

Several years ago, nutritionists belonging to the Food and Nutrition Science Alliance (FANSA) put together a list of "warning signs" to help consumers evaluate various diet programs. Claims to watch out for include the following:

- Recommendations that promise a quick fix
- Claims that sound too good to be true
- Simplistic conclusions drawn from a complex study
- Recommendations based on a single study
- Recommendations made to help sell a product
- Recommendations from studies that ignore differences among individuals or groups

Teaching Strategies

- Invite a nutritionist to your classroom to talk about the risks of certain weight-loss products and to suggest strategies for designing healthy eating plans.
- Divide the class into three groups. Have each group research a weight-loss product and then present their findings regarding the likelihood that the product will result in safe, long-term weight loss.
- Lead the class in a discussion about societal pressures to be thin, and why Americans spend millions of dollars every year trying to lose weight.

Forming Your Opinion

Student answers will vary. Negative side effects could include nausea, vomiting, diarrhea, irregular heartbeat, and increased blood pressure.

Evaluate the Promise of Weight Loss as a Promotional Claim

Lose ten pounds in one week!" "Shed weight without going hungry!" "Burn fat while you sleep!"

The appeal of weight-loss products There are many weight-loss products available to the public. Some of these products are based on good nutrition and positive lifestyle changes, such as eating a well-balanced diet and incorporating a regular exercise program. Other products look like a fast and easy solution to a weight-loss problem. However, these products may not provide permanent results or may have negative side effects. How can you evaluate the promotional claims such as those seen in magazine and television advertisements or on a product label?

Read the fine print Many weight-loss products make claims in bold letters at the top of an advertisement or have a quote from someone claiming to have successfully lost weight using the product. However, in very small print at the bottom may be a qualifying statement such as "Results not typical" or "When used with a balanced diet and regular exercise."

Some weight-loss products may help some people lose a few pounds temporarily. However, for safe, long-term weight loss, nutritionists recommend a diet based on healthy eating habits: balanced, regular meals rich in fruits and vegetables, whole grains, sufficient protein, and small amounts of fat. Making lifestyle changes that incorporate regular exercise also allow for healthy weight loss and maintenance.

Forming Your Opinion

Evaluate Collect advertisements and product labels for three different weight-loss products that promise "miracle" results. Research how these products contribute to weight loss. What effects do these products have on the body that result in weight loss? Are there any negative side effects? Evaluate the promotional claims of these advertisements and product labels. Based on what you know about the importance of good nutrition and exercise on health, would you recommend the use of these particular products? Why or why not?

 To find out more about weight-loss products, visit in.bdol.glencoe.com/biology_society

Going Further

Have students visit in.bdol.glencoe.com to find out more information about the topic of weight loss or other health issues. **L2**

938

STUDY GUIDE

Section 35.1

Following Digestion of a Meal

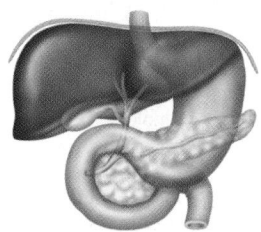

Key Concepts

- Digestion begins in the mouth with both mechanical and chemical action. The esophagus transports food from the mouth to the stomach.
- Chemical and mechanical digestion continue in the acidic environment of the stomach.
- In the small intestine, digestion is completed and food is absorbed. The liver and pancreas play key roles in digestion.
- The large intestine absorbs water before indigestible materials are eliminated.

Vocabulary

amylase (p. 918)
bile (p. 921)
epiglottis (p. 920)
esophagus (p. 918)
gallbladder (p. 921)
large intestine (p. 923)
liver (p. 921)
pancreas (p. 921)
pepsin (p. 921)
peristalsis (p. 918)
rectum (p. 923)
small intestine (p. 921)
stomach (p. 920)
villus (p. 922)

Section 35.2

Nutrition

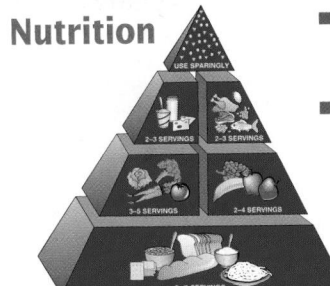

Key Concepts

- Carbohydrates are the body's main source of energy. Fats are used to store energy. Proteins are used as building materials.
- Minerals serve as structural materials or take part in chemical reactions. Vitamins are needed for growth and metabolism.
- Water facilitates chemical reactions in the body, acts as a solvent, and helps maintain internal body temperature.

Vocabulary

Calorie (p. 927)
mineral (p. 926)
vitamin (p. 926)

Section 35.3

The Endocrine System

New protein molecule
Cell membrane
Steroid hormone
mRNA
Ribosome
Hormone-receptor complex
Nucleus
mRNA
DNA

Key Concepts

- The endocrine glands work with the nervous system to regulate body functions.
- Blood hormone levels are controlled by a negative feedback system.
- Steroid hormones bind to receptors inside the target cells, and amino acid hormones bind to plasma membrane receptors.
- Hormones are involved in the regulation of blood glucose and calcium levels, as well as responses to stress.

Vocabulary

adrenal gland (p. 933)
endocrine glands (p. 929)
hypothalamus (p. 929)
negative feedback system (p. 930)
parathyroid glands (p. 935)
pituitary gland (p. 929)
receptor (p. 930)
target cell (p. 930)
thyroid gland (p. 934)

FOLDABLES
Study Organizer To help you review the digestive system, use the Organizational Study Fold on page 917.

in.bdol.glencoe.com/vocabulary_puzzlemaker

CHAPTER 35 ASSESSMENT **939**

Key Concepts

Summary statements can be used by students to review the major concepts of the chapter.

Biology Online

Visit in.bdol.glencoe.com
/self_check_quiz
/vocabulary_puzzlemaker
/chapter_test
/standardized_test

VOCABULARY PUZZLEMAKER

For additional help with vocabulary, have students access the Vocabulary PuzzleMaker online at in.bdol.glencoe.com/vocabulary_puzzlemaker

FOLDABLES™

Have students use their Foldables to review the content of Section 35.1.

Use the Exam*View*®Pro Test Bank CD-ROM to:

- Create **multiple versions** of tests
- Create **modified** tests with one mouse click for **inclusion** students
- **Edit** existing questions and **add** your own questions
- Build tests aligned with state standards using built-in **State Curriculum Tags**
- Change **English** tests to **Spanish** with one mouse click and vice versa

 Indiana Academic Standards

Pages 938–939: B.1.7, B.1.10, B.1.14, B.1.15, B.1.19

The Princeton Review **Questions and answers have been aligned and verified by The Princeton Review.**

Vocabulary Review

1. **amylase:** digestive enzyme found in saliva that breaks down starches in food; **bile:** chemical synthesized in the liver that helps breakdown fats in food

2. **epiglottis:** closes over the opening to the respiratory system when swallowing occurs; **esophagus:** muscular tube that connects the mouth with the stomach

3. **mineral:** inorganic substance that serves as a building material or in chemical reactions in the body; **vitamin:** organic nutrient required in small amounts to maintain growth and metabolism

4. **receptor:** binding site on a tissue; **target cell:** cell with receptors on plasma membrane or in nucleus

5. **hypothalamus:** portion of brain that connects endocrine and nervous systems; **pituitary gland:** main gland of the endocrine system

6. **thyroid gland:** regulates metabolism, growth, and development; **parathyroid glands:** involved in mineral regulation

Understanding Key Concepts

7. D	**10.** C	**13.** C
8. C	**11.** D	
9. A	**12.** C	

14. 1. Esophagus; 2. stomach; 3. small intestine; 4. liver; 5. bile; 6. gallbladder

Constructed Response

15. There would be a lack of pancreatic enzymes, which would cause incomplete food digestion in the small intestine and inadequate absorption of nutrients.

Vocabulary Review

Review the Chapter 35 vocabulary words listed in the Study Guide on page 939. Distinguish between the vocabulary words in each pair.

1. amylase—bile
2. epiglottis—esophagus
3. mineral—vitamin
4. receptor—target cell
5. hypothalamus—pituitary gland
6. thyroid gland—parathyroid glands

Understanding Key Concepts

7. Which of these is NOT a function of the digestive system?
   A. eliminating wastes
   B. absorbing nutrients
   C. digesting food
   D. regulating metabolism

8. Which structure prevents food from entering the respiratory tract?
   A. villus   C. epiglottis
   B. pancreas   D. stomach

9. Which of the following is located beneath the hypothalamus?
   A. pituitary gland
   B. adrenal glands
   C. thyroid gland
   D. parathyroid glands

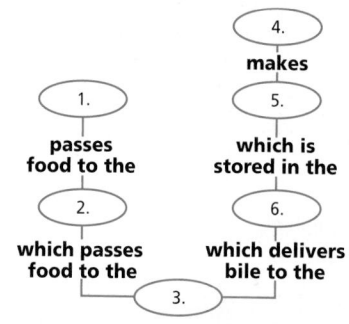

10. What unit is used to measure the energy content of food?
    A. temperature   C. Calorie
    B. gram   D. mass

11. The pancreas releases which of the following hormones?
    A. epinephrine, norepinephrine
    B. hGH, ADH
    C. thyroxine, calcitonin
    D. glucagon, insulin

12. What is the most abundant substance in the human body?
    A. carbohydrates   C. water
    B. vitamins   D. proteins

---

13. Which of these enzymes functions best in the acidic pH of the stomach?
    A. lipase   C. pepsin
    B. lactase   D. amylase

14. **Concept Map** Complete the concept map by using the following vocabulary terms: liver, bile, small intestine, stomach, esophagus, gallbladder.

```
                    ┌─────┐
                    │  4. │
                    └─────┘
                     makes
   ┌─────┐          ┌─────┐
   │  1. │          │  5. │
   └─────┘          └─────┘
   passes           which is
   food to the      stored in the
   ┌─────┐          ┌─────┐
   │  2. │          │  6. │
   └─────┘          └─────┘
   which passes     which delivers
   food to the      bile to the
        └────┬────────┘
          ┌─────┐
          │  3. │
          └─────┘
```

Constructed Response

15. **Open Ended** Patients with cystic fibrosis can have a blocked pancreatic duct. What effect will this have on digestion?

16. **Open Ended** People with Type 1 diabetes do not produce any insulin. What effect would this have on cells and metabolism if left untreated?

17. **Open Ended** How would the removal of the parathyroid glands affect muscle contraction? Explain how this could result in a disruption of homeostasis.

Thinking Critically

18. **Recognize Cause and Effect** How is the role of pancreatic hormones in glucose regulation important for homeostasis?

19. **REAL WORLD BIOCHALLENGE** Visit in.bdol.glencoe.com to find out more about the bacteria that live in the large intestines of humans. What species of bacteria are found in the large intestines of humans? How does each organism benefit from this relationship?

 in.bdol.glencoe.com/chapter_test

---

16. People with a lack of insulin have high blood glucose levels, and glucose does not enter cells as easily. Continuous uncontrolled lack of insulin can lead to kidney damage, blindness, and death.

17. Removal of the gland could greatly reduce blood calcium concentration and interfere with muscle contraction throughout the body.

Thinking Critically

18. The glucose concentration in the blood is maintained in a very narrow range. The pancreas releases insulin to remove glucose from the blood and glucagon to cause the release of glucose into the blood.

19. the Enterobacteriaceae family (such as *Escherichia coli*), *Bifidobacterium*,

20. Predict The thyroid gland needs the mineral iodine to function properly. Use your knowledge of the thyroid gland to predict the effects that an iodine deficiency could have on a person's health.

21. Design an Experiment Design an experiment to show that exercise can contribute to weight loss. Identify dependent and independent variables. What could account for variations in your results?

The assessed Indiana standard appears next to the question.

Eubacterium, Bacteroides, and *Enterococcus*; These bacteria produce some B vitamins and vitamin K as well as protect against infections by other organisms.

20. Without iodine, the thyroid gland cannot produce thyroxin. Growth and metabolic activity will be inhibited.

21. Experimental design may vary. Weight loss is the dependent variable and time is the independent variable. Reasons for variation may include the type of exercise, how long the individual exercises, etc.

End-of-Course Assessment Practice

All questions aligned and verified by The Princeton Review

Part 1 ▸ Multiple Choice
Use the diagram to answer questions 22–24.

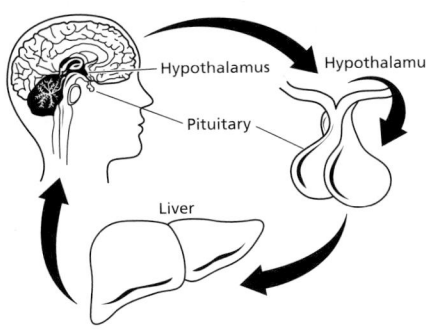

Hypothalamus

Hypothalamus

Pituitary

Liver

22. The diagram shows the control pathway of human growth hormone (hGH) in the blood. Which of the following stimulates the pituitary to release hGH?
B.1.17
  A. liver   **C.** hypothalamus
  B. pituitary gland   **D.** hGH

23. When the pituitary gland releases human growth hormone (hGH), what is the effect on the liver?
B.1.17
  A. stimulates the pituitary gland to release hGH
  B. stimulates the liver to convert glycogen into glucose
  C. stimulates the liver to store glucose
  D. decreases sugar level in blood

24. What stimulates the hypothalamus to initiate the entire sequence involving human growth hormone (hGH)?
B.1.17
  A. low blood glucose levels
  B. high blood glucose levels
  C. low levels of hGH
  D. high levels of hGH

Use the table to answer questions 25–27.

25. Using the table, calculate how many Calories of carbohydrates a person should be getting if he or she were consuming 2800 Calories of food energy per day.
  A. 1000 Cal   **C.** 1680 Cal
  B. 1550 Cal   **D.** 2000 Cal

Percentage of Daily Value (DV)	
Carbohydrates	60%
Fat	30%
Saturated fats	10%
Protein	10%
Total Calories	2000

26. If a person were using the table as a guideline to consume 50 g of protein per day (10% of the DV), calculate how many Calories of food energy that person is taking in each day. (1 g of protein = 4 Calories)
B.1.19
  A. 1000 Cal   **C.** 1600 Cal
  B. 1200 Cal   **D.** 2000 Cal

End-of-Course Assessment Practice

22. C   **24.** A   **26.** D
23. B   **25.** C

 FAST FILE

Answer Sheet A practice answer sheet can be found on p. 77 of *Unit 10 FAST FILE Resources.*

Part 2 ▸ Constructed Response/Grid In
Record your answers or fill in the bubbles on your answer document using the correct place value.

27. Grid In For a 2000-Calorie-per-day diet, calculate, in grams, the amount of carbohydrates, fats, and proteins that should be consumed using the Daily Values recommended by the FDA.
B.1.19
(Hint: 1 g of carbohydrate = 4 Calories, 1 g of fat = 9 Calories, 1 g of protein = 4 Calories)

28. Open Ended Achlorhydria is a condition in which the stomach fails to secrete hydrochloric acid. How would this condition affect digestion? If left untreated, how could this affect the body as a whole?

 in.bdol.glencoe.com/standardized_test

RUBRIC

For more help evaluating open-ended assessment questions, see the rubric on p. 9T.

27. carbohydrates: 300 g; fats: 66.6 g; protein: 50 g

28. Pepsin would not have the proper environment in which to function. Proteins would not be digested in the stomach. Less proteins would be absorbed in the small intestine, and less nutrients would reach cells.

Indiana Academic Standards

Pages 940–941: B.1.6, B.1.7, B.1.14, B.1.19

Chapter 36 Organizer

Section Objectives	National Science Standards	State/Local Standards	Advanced Lab and Demo Planning
Section 36.1 2 sessions, 1 block 1. **Analyze** how nerve impulses travel within the nervous system. 2. **Interpret** the functions of the major parts of the nervous system. 3. **Compare** voluntary responses and involuntary responses.	UCP.1, UCP.2, UCP.5; A.1, A.2; C.6; F.1, F.5	**Indiana Standards** B.1.14	**Student Labs:** MiniLab 36.1, p. 948: meterstick Additional Lab, p. 948: paper clips, metric ruler **Teacher Demonstrations:** Quick Demo, p. 945: cable Quick Demo, p. 949: rubber hammer
Section 36.2 1 session 4. **Define** the role of the senses in the human nervous system. 5. **Recognize** how senses detect chemical, light, and mechanical stimulation. 6. **Identify** ways in which the senses work together to gather information.	UCP.1, UCP.2, UCP.5; A.1, A.2; F.1, F.2; G.2	**Indiana Standards** B.1.14	**Student Lab:** Problem-Solving Lab 36.1, p. 954 **Teacher Demonstration:** Quick Demo, p. 952: cassette tape of various everyday sounds
Section 36.3 2 sessions, 1/2 block 7. **Recognize** the medicinal uses of drugs. 8. **Identify** the different classes of drugs. 9. **Interpret** the effects of drug misuse and abuse on the body.	UCP.1, UCP.2, UCP.3, UCP.5; A.1, A.2; C.5; F.1, F.5; G.1, G.2	**Indiana Standards** B.1.14	**Student Labs:** Problem-Solving Lab 36.2, p. 957 MiniLab 36.2, p. 959 Design Your Own BioLab, p. 964: See materials below. **Teacher Demonstration:** Quick Demo, p. 961: nonprescription drugs (aspirin, cough syrup, antacids)
End of Chapter Assessment Student Edition **Study Guide,** p. 967 **Content Assessment,** pp. 968–969		**Indiana Standards** B.1.14	**Student Lab:** Design Your Own BioLab, p. 964: aged tap water; *Daphnia* culture; dilute solutions of coffee, tea, cola, ethyl alcohol, tobacco, cold medicine; dropper; microscope; microscope slide

Key to Teaching Strategies

L1 Level 1 activities should be appropriate for students with learning difficulties.

L2 Level 2 activities should be within the ability range of all students.

L3 Level 3 activities are designed for above-average students.

ELL ELL activities should be within the ability range of English Language Learners.

COOP LEARN Cooperative Learning activities are designed for small group work.

Legend

 Transparency   CD-ROM   **MP3** MP3   ▭ Videocassette   ◉ DVD

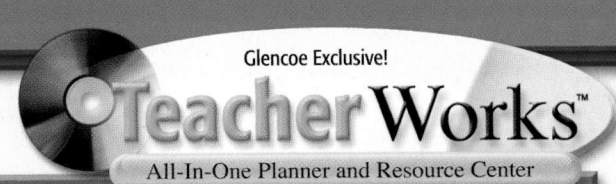

Glencoe Exclusive!
Teacher Works™
All-In-One Planner and Resource Center

Reproducible Masters and Transparencies	Technology

Unit 10 *Fast File* Resources
MiniLab Worksheet, p. 81
Reinforcement and Study Guide in English, pp. 89–90
Reinforcement and Study Guide in Spanish, pp. 93–94
Critical Thinking/Problem Solving, p. 98
Transparency Worksheets, pp. 99, 103–106
Probeware Labs, pp. 29–32
◉ **Section Focus Transparency 87**
◉ **Basic Concepts Transparency 66, 67**

◉ **Interactive Chalkboard CD-ROM: Section 36.1 Presentation**
◉ **TeacherWorks™ CD-ROM**
MP3 Guided Reading Audio Summaries MP3

Unit 10 *Fast File* Resources
Real World BioApplications, pp. 85–86
Reinforcement and Study Guide in English, p. 91
Reinforcement and Study Guide in Spanish, p. 95
Concept Mapping, p. 97
Transparency Worksheets, pp. 100, 107–114
Laboratory Manual, pp. 233–236
◉ **Section Focus Transparency 88**
◉ **Basic Concepts Transparencies 68, 69**
◉ **Reteaching Skills Transparencies 52, 53**

◉ **Interactive Chalkboard CD-ROM: Section 36.2 Presentation**
◉ **TeacherWorks™ CD-ROM**
MP3 Guided Reading Audio Summaries MP3

Unit 10 *Fast File* Resources
MiniLab Worksheet, p. 82
BioLab Worksheet, pp. 83–84
Real World BioApplications, pp. 87–88
Reinforcement and Study Guide in English, p. 92
Reinforcement and Study Guide in Spanish, p. 96
Transparency Worksheet, p. 101
◉ **Section Focus Transparency 89**

◉ **Interactive Chalkboard CD-ROM: Section 36.3 Presentation**
◉ **TeacherWorks™ CD-ROM**
MP3 Guided Reading Audio Summaries MP3

Unit 10 *Fast File* Resources
Chapter Assessment, pp. 115–120
Student Recording Sheet, p. 121

The Princeton Review **Reviewing Biology,** pp. 71–72

◉ **Interactive Chalkboard: Chapter 36 Assessment**
◉ **MindJogger Videoquizzes DVD/VHS**
◉ **Exam*View*® Pro Test Bank CD-ROM**
◉ **TeacherWorks™ CD-ROM**
◉ **Succeeding on National Standards CD-ROM**

🖥 in.bdol.glencoe.com
/self_check_quiz
/vocabulary_puzzlemaker
/chapter_test
/standardized_test

▌ Indicates materials created specifically for Indiana.

Short on Time?

BIODIGEST The BioDigest at the end of this unit can be used as a(n):

- preview to introduce important unit concepts.
- overview if time does not permit teaching the entire chapter.
- review of key unit concepts.

Understanding the Photo

Even though it appears the nervous system is working very hard during a time like a roller coaster ride and doing very little during sleep, the nervous system is always working to receive stimuli from the surroundings, interpret the stimuli, and react.

PowerPoint® Presentations

This CD-ROM is an editable Microsoft® PowerPoint® presentation that includes:

- Section presentations
- Section checks
- Image bank
- Hot links to Biology Online
- All transparencies

Chapter 36

The Nervous System

What You'll Learn

- You will relate the structure of a nerve cell to the transmission of a nerve signal.
- You will identify the senses and their signal pathways.
- You will compare and contrast various types of drugs and their effects on the nervous system.

Why It's Important

Your nervous system helps you perceive and react to the world around you. It controls vital involuntary processes such as respiration and digestion. By understanding how drugs affect the function of the nervous system, you will discover their role in treating medical disorders, and the danger they pose if misused.

► Understanding the Photo

These people feel the tingle of fear and excitement when they realize the height of the ride. Messages from the brain allow them to scream or smile as well as hold on tightly. It is the nervous system that interprets these messages and coordinates the responses of the body.

Biology Online

Visit **in.bdol.glencoe.com** to
- study the entire chapter online
- access Web Links for more information and activities on the nervous system
- review content with the Interactive Tutor and self-check quizzes

---

Two-Minute Chapter Launcher

Demo Create a loud noise by slamming a book on your desk. Use the students' reactions to begin a discussion of how the nervous system reacts to environmental stimuli. Ask the students what stimuli their brains were receiving and reacting to when you slammed the book.

What stimuli did your brain receive while slamming the book that the students did not receive (such as feeling the book)? In what ways did the students' bodies react? What systems were involved besides the nervous system?

The Nervous System

Indiana Standards Standard B.1.14 Recognize and explain that communication and/or interaction are required between cells to coordinate their diverse activities.

Cellular Communication

Using an Analogy When you use the telephone you communicate with a person in another location. You may know that your message is transmitted as an electrical impulse across telephone wires. Similar electrical impulses travel through your body, allowing some parts to communicate with others.

Sequence *As you read through this section, record the sequence of changes that occurs in a neuron when it is excited by a stimulus.*

Like telephone wires between homes, nerve cells relay messages within the human body.

Neurons: Basic Units of the Nervous System

The basic unit of structure and function in the nervous system is the neuron, or nerve cell. **Neurons** (NYU ronz) conduct impulses throughout the nervous system. As shown in *Figure 36.1,* a neuron is a long cell that consists of three regions: a cell body, dendrites, and an axon.

Dendrites (DEN drites) are branchlike extensions of the neuron that receive impulses and carry them toward the cell body. The **axon** is an extension of the neuron that carries impulses away from the cell body and toward other neurons, muscles, or glands.

Neurons fall into three categories: sensory neurons, motor neurons, and interneurons. Sensory neurons carry impulses from the body to the spinal cord and brain. Interneurons are found within the brain and spinal cord. They process incoming impulses and pass response impulses on to motor neurons. Motor neurons carry the response impulses away from the brain and spinal cord to a muscle or gland.

Figure 36.1
Dendrites and axons are extensions that branch out from the cell body of a neuron.

1 Focus

INTERACTIVE CHALKBOARD
PowerPoint® Presentations

Bellringer
Section Focus Transparency 87

Transparency **87** Take an Order

SECTION FOCUS
Use with Chapter 36, Section 36.1

① What action causes the boy's response?
② Give an example of a similar stimulus-response combination in the human body.

BIOLOGY: The Dynamics of Life   SECTION FOCUS TRANSPARENCIES

Using an Analogy

Sequence At rest, a neuron is polarized—the inside of the cell is more negative than the outside. As an impulse moves down a neuron, sodium channels open, sodium ions enter the cell, and the inside becomes more positively charged than the outside of the cell (depolarization). After the impulse passes, the sodium/potassium pump returns ions to normal concentrations and the neuron is repolarized.

Indiana Academic Standards

Pages 942–943: B.1.14

2 Teach

Visual Learning

Figure 36.2 Spend a few minutes reviewing the sequence of events involved in the nervous system's response to a stimulus. Ask students what path the nervous system would take to turn the head in response to a sound such as a honking car horn. The path would be the same except for the initial receptors, which would be located in the ear rather than in the skin.

Visual Learning

Figure 36.3 What effect does the Na⁺/K⁺ pump have on the charge of the normal resting neuron? It maintains a positive charge on the outside of the membrane and a negative charge within the membrane of a resting neuron.

Biology Journal

Nerve Analogy Have students write a paragraph that explains how a nerve is similar to a wire going from a controlling switch (stimulus) to a lightbulb. **L2**

Figure 36.2
The nervous system sorts and interprets incoming information before directing a response.

A Receptors in the skin sense a tap or other stimulus.

B Sensory neurons transmit the touch message.

C The message is interpreted by the brain. A response is sent to the motor neurons.

D Motor neurons transmit a response message to the neck muscles.

E The neck muscles are activated, causing the head to turn.

Figure 36.3
In a neuron at rest, the sodium/potassium pump (Na^+/K^+) and the presence of many negatively charged ions within a cell keeps the inside of a cell more negatively charged than the outside.

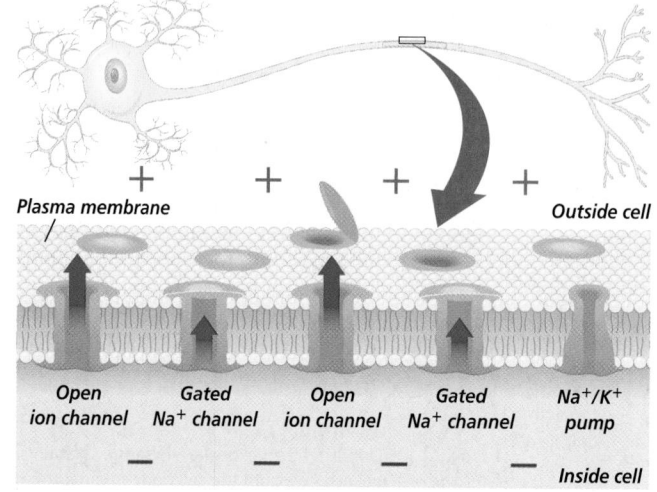

+   +   +   +

Plasma membrane   *Outside cell*

Open ion channel   Gated Na^+ channel   Open ion channel   Gated Na^+ channel Na^+/K^+ pump

−   −   −   −

Inside cell

Relaying an impulse

Suppose you're in a crowded, noisy store and you feel a tap on your shoulder. Turning your head, you see the smiling face of a good friend. How did the shoulder tap get your attention? The touch stimulated sensory receptors located in the skin of your shoulder to produce an impulse. The sensory impulse was carried to the spinal cord and then up to your brain. From your brain, an impulse was sent out to your motor neurons, which then transmitted the impulse to muscles in your neck. Your neck muscles then turned your head. *Figure 36.2* shows how a stimulus, such as a tap on the shoulder, is transmitted through your nervous system.

A neuron at rest

First, let's look at a resting neuron—one that is not transmitting an impulse. You have learned that the plasma membrane controls the concentration of ions in a cell. Because the plasma membrane of a neuron is more permeable to potassium ions (K^+) than it is to sodium ions (Na^+), more potassium ions exist inside of the cell membrane than outside it. Similarly, more sodium ions exist outside the cell membrane than inside of it.

The neuron membrane also contains an active transport system, called the sodium/potassium (Na^+/K^+) pump, which uses ATP to pump three sodium ions out of the cell for every two potassium ions it pumps in. As you can see in *Figure 36.3*, the action of the pump increases the concentration of positive charges on the outside of the membrane. In addition, the presence of many negatively charged proteins and organic phosphates means that the inside of the membrane is more negatively charged than the outside. Under these conditions, which exist when the cell is at rest,

---

Indiana Academic Standards

Pages 944–945: B.1.14

CHALLENGE ACTIVITY

Dissection Have students who need an additional challenge prepare a labeled dissection of a sheep brain. They should prepare whole brains and half brains, labeling areas discussed in this chapter. **L3**

the plasma membrane is said to be polarized. A polarized membrane has the potential to transmit an impulse.

How an impulse is transmitted

When a stimulus excites a neuron, gated sodium channels in the membrane open up and sodium ions rush into the cell. As the positive sodium ions build up inside the membrane, the inside of the cell becomes more positively charged than the outside. This change in charge, called depolarization, moves like a wave down the length of the axon, as seen in *Figure 36.4*. As the wave passes, gated channels and the Na^+/K^+ pump act to return the neuron to its resting state, with the inside of the cell negatively charged and the outside positively charged.

An impulse can move down the complete length of an axon only when stimulation of the neuron is strong enough. If the threshold level—the level at which depolarization occurs—is not reached, the impulse quickly dies out.

✓ **Reading Check** **Describe** the threshold level.

White matter and gray matter

Most axons are surrounded by a white covering of cells called the myelin sheath, shown previously in *Figure 36.1*. Like the plastic coating on an electric wire, the myelin sheath insulates the axon, hindering the movement of ions across its plasma membrane. The ions move quickly down the axon until they reach a gap in the sheath. Here, the ions pass through the plasma membrane of the nerve cell and depolarization occurs. As a result, the impulse jumps from gap to gap, greatly increasing the speed at which it travels.

Figure 36.4
A wave of depolarization moves down the axon of a neuron.

A Gated sodium channels open, allowing sodium ions to enter and make the inside of the cell positively charged and the outside negatively charged.

B As the impulse passes, gated sodium channels close, stopping the influx of sodium ions. Gated potassium channels open, letting potassium ions out of the cell. This action repolarizes the cell.

C As gated potassium channels close, the Na^+/K^+ pump restores the ion distribution.

36.1 THE NERVOUS SYSTEM **945**

Linguistic Have interested students read "Wide Hats and Narrow Minds" (from Stephen Jay Gould's *The Panda's Thumb*), which looks at the topic of brain size versus intelligence. **L3**

✓Reading Check To prevent a continual stimulation at the synapse, enzymes in the synapse break down the neurotransmitters shortly after transmission.

Caption Question Answer

Figure 36.5 At the end of the axon, vesicles of neurotransmitters are released, which diffuse across the synapse and bind with receptors on the end of the dendrite of the next neuron, stimulating an action potential in that neuron.

Physical Science Connection

Have students compare and contrast parallel and series circuits. In a parallel circuit, at least two pathways exist for electric current to flow through. In a series circuit, electric current follows a single path, so disruption of the path at any point causes the flow of current to stop.

Indiana Academic Standards

Pages 946–947: B.1.14

Physical Science Connection

Nerve impulses and parallel circuits Parallel circuits contain branched paths in which electric current can flow. Connections among neurons also can form branched paths. However, in a parallel circuit, the amount of charge that flows into and out of a junction must be equal. Neurons are different in that the strength of the impulse that moves through an excited neuron does not depend on the number of connections to other neurons.

The myelin sheath gives axons a white appearance. In the brain and spinal cord, masses of myelinated axons make up what is called "white matter." The absence of myelin in masses of neurons accounts for the grayish color of "gray matter" in the brain.

Connections between neurons

Although neurons lie end to end—axons to dendrites—they don't actually touch. A tiny space lies between one neuron's axon and another neuron's dendrites. This junction between neurons is called a **synapse.** Impulses traveling to and from the brain must move across the synaptic space that separates the axon and dendrites. How do they make this leap?

As an impulse reaches the end of an axon, calcium channels open, allowing calcium to enter the end of the axon. As shown in *Figure 36.5*, the calcium causes vesicles in the axon to fuse with the plasma membrane, releasing their chemicals into the synaptic space by exocytosis. These chemicals, called **neurotransmitters,** diffuse across the space to the dendrites of the next neuron. As the neurotransmitters reach the dendrites, they signal receptor sites to open the ion channels. These open channels change the polarity in the neuron, initiating a new impulse. Enzymes in the synapse typically break down the neurotransmitters shortly after transmission, preventing the continual firing of impulses.

✓Reading Check **Explain** what prevents the continual firing of impulses at the synapse.

The Central Nervous System

When you make a call to a friend, your call travels through wires to a control center where it is switched over to wires that connect with your friend's telephone. In the same manner, an impulse traveling through neurons in your body usually reaches the control center of the nervous system—your brain—before being rerouted. The brain and the spinal cord together make up the **central nervous system,** which coordinates all your body's activities.

Figure 36.5
As an impulse reaches the end of an axon, calcium channels open and calcium enters the end of the axon. **Explain** *How do nerve impulses move across a synapse?*

A Vesicle with neurotransmitters inside

B Vesicle fuses with membrane (exocytosis)

Axon

Ca^{2+}

Calcium channel Ca^{2+}

D Neurotransmitter diffuses across synapse and binds with receptor on dendrite

Synaptic space

C Neurotransmitters released into synapse

Ion channel

Dendrite

Dendrite

Axon

Impulse

Synapse

Impulse

Dendrite

Axon

946 THE NERVOUS SYSTEM

Two systems work together

Another division of your nervous system, called the **peripheral** (puh RIH frul) **nervous system,** is made up of all the nerves that carry messages to and from the central nervous system. It is similar to the telephone wires that run between a phone system's control center and the phones in individual homes. Together, the central nervous system (CNS) and the peripheral nervous system (PNS), shown in *Figure 36.6,* respond to stimuli from the external environment.

Anatomy of the brain

The brain is the control center of the entire nervous system. For descriptive purposes, it is useful to divide the brain into three main sections: the cerebrum, the cerebellum, and the brain stem.

The **cerebrum** (suh REE brum) is divided into two halves, called hemispheres, that are connected by bundles of nerves. Your conscious activities, intelligence, memory, language, skeletal muscle movements, and senses are all controlled by the cerebrum. The outer surface of the cerebrum, called the cerebral cortex, is made up of gray matter. The cerebral cortex contains countless folds and grooves that increase its total surface area. This increase in surface area played an important role in the evolution of human intelligence as greater surface area allowed more and more complex thought processes.

The **cerebellum** (ser uh BE lum), located at the back of your brain, controls your balance, posture, and coordination. If the cerebellum is injured, your movements become jerky.

The brain stem is made up of the medulla oblongata, the pons, and the midbrain. The **medulla oblongata** (muh DU luh • ah blon GAH tuh) is the

Figure 36.6
The human nervous system is made up of the CNS, in pink, and the PNS, in yellow. The brain and spinal cord are protected by the skull and the vertebrae, respectively.

Brain

Spinal cord

Cerebrum

Skull

Cerebellum

Medulla oblongata

Spinal cord

Vertebra

part of the brain that controls involuntary activities such as breathing and heart rate. The pons and midbrain act as pathways connecting various parts of the brain with each other. Read more about how the brain evolved on pages 1090–1091 in the *Focus On.* For the latest on technological advances in brain imaging, check out the *Biotechnology* section at the end of the chapter.

Enrichment

Linguistic The Chinese have used acupuncture as a complete system of medicine for thousands of years. The procedure involves inserting long, thin needles into specific areas of the patient's body. The needles are either rotated or electrical impulses are then sent down the length of the needles. Acupuncture is used to relieve pain, cure cancer, and everything in between. It is also currently being used in China as a form of anesthesia for patients undergoing surgery.

Have students research and report on ancient methods of acupuncture. How did the methods used then differ from those used today? The needles used to be turned to achieve the desired effect. Now electrical impulses are used instead. **L3**

Portfolio

Neuroscience Research Have students research and prepare a multimedia presentation for the class on one of the following topics: sleep, split-brain experiments, Alzheimer's disease, or amnesia. **L2**

Biology Journal

Neurology Have students who are interested in topics about the brain read *An Anthropologist on Mars* by Dr. Oliver Sacks. Students can write a summary of one of the stories in their journal. **L3**

INCLUSION STRATEGIES

Learning Disabled Ask students to list activities their bodies do without conscious thought. To get them started, have them consider what their bodies do while they are asleep. **L1**

TECH PREP

Exploring Nursing Have students interested in nursing contact a local hospital and arrange to shadow a nurse for an afternoon to find out more about what these professionals do. **L2**

Purpose

Students investigate how a distracting stimulus affects reaction time.

Process Skills

observe and infer, compare and contrast, recognize cause and effect, collect and organize data, interpret data, experiment, analyze

Teaching Strategies

If students find counting backwards awkward, have them whistle or sing a song as another kind of distraction.

Expected Results

A distraction should increase reaction time.

Analysis

1. As students learn to anticipate the drop, their reaction time should improve.
2. The distraction probably increased their reaction time.
3. Answers may include being tired, sick, hungry, or otherwise preoccupied.

Modified Assessment

Skill Have students verbally describe the sequence of events involved in their response to the falling meterstick. They should identify the stimulus (seeing the falling stick), the path of the impulse in their bodies, and the effect (grabbing the stick). Use the Performance Task Assessment List for Events Chain in **PASC**, p. 163. **L1**

The Peripheral Nervous System

Remember that the peripheral nervous system carries impulses between the body and the central nervous system. For example, when a stimulus is picked up by receptors in your skin, it initiates an impulse in the sensory neurons. The impulse is carried to the CNS. There, the impulse transfers to motor neurons that carry the impulse to a muscle.

The peripheral nervous system can be separated into two divisions—the somatic nervous system and the autonomic nervous system.

The somatic nervous system

The **somatic nervous system** is made up of 12 pairs of cranial nerves from the brain, 31 pairs of spinal nerves from the spinal cord, and all of their branches. These nerves are actually bundles of neuron axons bound together by connective tissue. The cell bodies of the neurons are found in clusters along the spinal column.

The nerves of the somatic system are part of the peripheral nervous system that relays information between your CNS and skeletal muscles. A response by the somatic nervous system to a stimulus usually is voluntary, meaning that you can decide whether or not to move body parts under the control of this system. Try the *MiniLab* on this page to find out how distractions can affect the time it takes you to respond to a stimulus.

Reflexes in the somatic system

Sometimes a stimulus results in an automatic, unconscious response within the somatic system. When you touch something hot, you automatically jerk your hand away. Such an action is a **reflex**, an automatic response to a stimulus. Rather than proceeding to the cerebrum or cerebellum for interpretation, a reflex impulse travels to the spinal column or brain stem where it causes an impulse to be sent directly back to a muscle. The brain becomes aware of the reflex only after it occurs. *Figure 36.7* on the next page shows the shortened route of a reflex impulse.

MiniLab 36.1

Experiment

Distractions and Reaction Time Have you ever tried to read while someone is talking to you? What effect does such a distracting stimulus have on your reaction time?

Procedure

1. Work with a partner. Sit facing your partner as he or she stands.
2. Have your partner hold the top of a meterstick above your hand. Hold your thumb and index finger about 2.5 cm away from either side of the lower end of the meterstick without touching it.
3. Tell your partner to drop the meterstick straight down between your fingers.
4. Catch the meterstick between your thumb and finger as soon as it begins to fall. Measure how far it falls before you catch it. Practice several times.
5. Run ten trials, recording the number of centimeters the meterstick drops each time. Average the results.
6. Repeat the experiment, this time counting backwards from 100 by fives (100, 95, 90, . . .) as you wait for your partner to release the meterstick.

Analysis

1. **Analyze** Did your reaction time improve with practice?
2. **Evaluate** How was your reaction time affected by the distraction (counting backwards)?
3. **Infer** What other factors, besides distractions, would increase reaction time?

Additional Lab

Skin Sensitivity

Purpose

Students determine the distance between sensory neurons.

Materials

paper clips in "U" shapes, metric ruler

Background

Certain areas of the skin contain sensory neurons that are packed closely together, other areas have neurons farther apart. When two different stimuli depolarize parts of the same neuron, the brain interprets them as if they were one stimulus.

Procedure

Give students the following directions.

1. Working with a partner, plan ten areas of the skin to test for the distance between sensory neurons.
2. Have your partner close his or her eyes. With the paper clip ends close together, test your partner by gently touching his or her skin with the opened paper clip.

Sensory neuron

Interneuron

Spinal cord *Motor neuron*

Flexor muscle contracts and withdraws part being stimulated

Direction of impulse

Pain receptors in skin

Figure 36.7
A simple reflex impulse involves one sensory neuron, one interneuron, and one motor neuron.

The autonomic nervous system

Imagine that you are spending the night alone in a creepy old house. Suddenly, a creak comes from the attic and you think you hear footsteps. Your heart begins to pound. Your breathing becomes rapid. Your thoughts race wildly as you try to figure out what to do—stay and confront the unknown, or run out of the house!

Your internal reactions to this scary situation are being controlled by your autonomic nervous system. The **autonomic nervous system** carries impulses from the CNS to internal organs. These impulses produce responses that are involuntary, or not under conscious control.

There are two divisions of the autonomic nervous system—the **sympathetic nervous system** and the parasympathetic nervous system. The sympathetic nervous system controls many internal functions during times of stress. When something frightens you, such as the rattlesnake shown in *Figure 36.8,*

the sympathetic nervous system causes the release of hormones, such as epinephrine and norepinephrine, that results in the fight-or-flight response.

The **parasympathetic nervous system** on the other hand, controls many of the body's internal functions when it is at rest. It is in control when you are relaxing after a picnic or reading quietly in your room. Both the sympathetic and parasympathetic systems send signals to the same internal organs. The resulting activity of the organ depends on the intensities of the opposing signals.

Figure 36.8
A fight-or-flight response to a rattlesnake will increase heart and breathing rates.

3 Assess

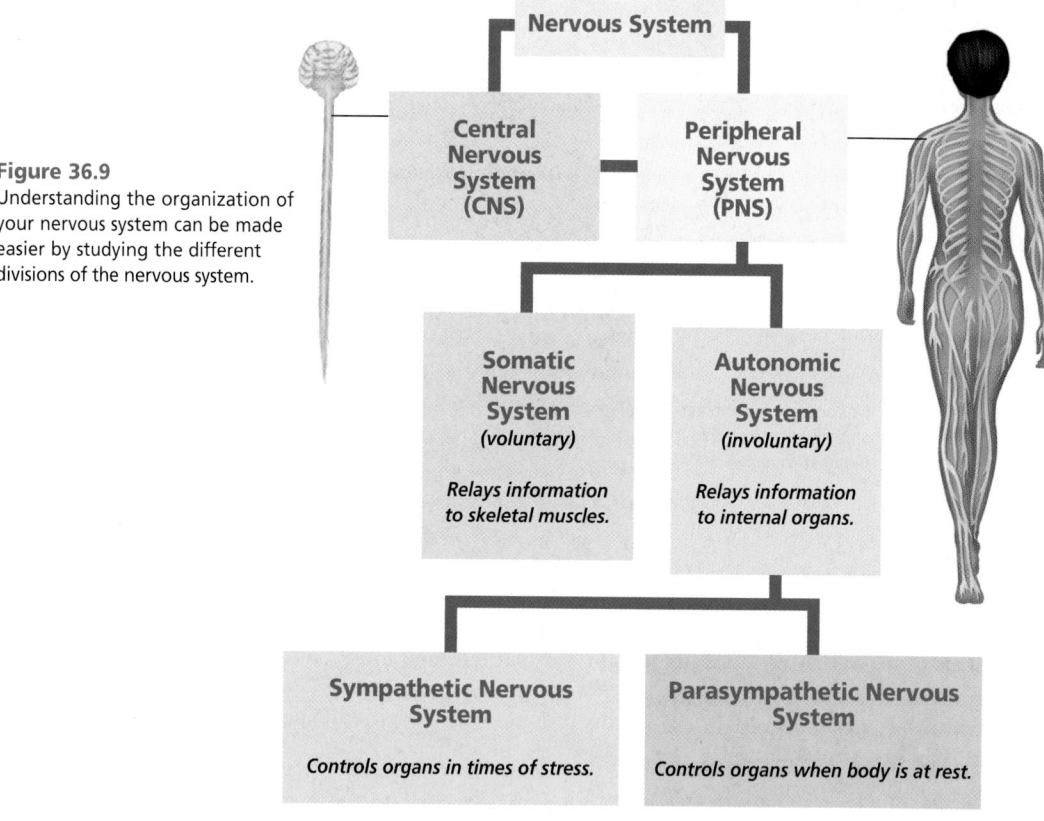

Figure 36.9
Understanding the organization of your nervous system can be made easier by studying the different divisions of the nervous system.

The different divisions and subsystems of your nervous system are summarized in *Figure 36.9*. Each division plays a key role in communication and control within your body.

Note that the sympathetic and parasympathetic systems are part of the autonomic nervous system. The autonomic and somatic systems are part of the PNS. The peripheral nervous system carries information to and from the CNS. Together, these two systems respond to stimuli from the external and internal environment.

Section Assessment

Understanding Main Ideas
1. Summarize how nerve impulses travel within the nervous system.

2. Interpret and compare the functions of the central and peripheral nervous systems.

3. Interpret the functions of the three major parts of the brain.

4. Compare and contrast voluntary responses and involuntary responses.

Thinking Critically
5. Why is it nearly impossible to stop a reflex from taking place?

SKILL REVIEW

6. **Get the Big Picture** Compare the interrelationships between the nervous system and other body systems in response to an external stimulus. For more help, refer to *Get the Big Picture* in the **Skill Handbook**.

 in.bdol.glencoe.com/self_check_quiz

Section Assessment

1. Nerve impulses travel down neurons and at the synapse, neurotransmitters are released. The neurotransmitters diffuse across the synapse and stimulate the next neuron impulse.

2. The CNS coordinates all the body's activities. The PNS carries impulses from the body to the CNS and carries impulses from the CNS to muscles and glands.

3. The cerebrum controls conscious activities, intelligence, memory, language, movement, and the senses. The cerebellum controls balance, posture, and coordination. The medulla oblongata mainly controls involuntary activities.

4. Voluntary responses are under the conscious control of the individual, whereas involuntary responses are not.

5. A reflex is an involuntary action that is not consciously controlled by the brain.

6. The nervous system controls and can modify the actions of all other systems of the body.

Section 36.2

The Senses

Indiana Standards Standard B.1.14 Recognize and explain that communication and/or interaction are required between cells to coordinate their diverse activities.

SECTION PREVIEW

Objectives

Define the role of the senses in the human nervous system.

Recognize how senses detect chemical, light, and mechanical stimulation.

Identify ways in which the senses work together to gather information.

Review Vocabulary
dermis: inner, thicker portion of the skin that contains nerves and nerve endings (p. 895)

New Vocabulary
taste bud
retina
rod
cone
cochlea
semicircular canals

 FOLDABLES™
Study Organizer

The Senses Make the following Foldable to help you organize information about the senses.

STEP 1 **Fold** a vertical sheet of paper from side to side. Make the back edge about 5cm longer than the front edge.

STEP 2 **Turn** lengthwise and **fold** into thirds, then **fold again** in half to make sixths.

STEP 3 **Unfold and cut** only the top layer along the five folds to make six tabs.

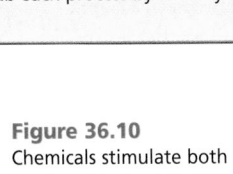

STEP 4 **Label** each tab as follows: *Smell, Taste, Sight, Hearing, Balance* and *Touch.* Label the top edge as *Senses.*

Read for Main Ideas As you read Chapter 36, record under the appropriate tab each process by which your body responds to stimuli.

Figure 36.10
Chemicals stimulate both smell and taste receptors.

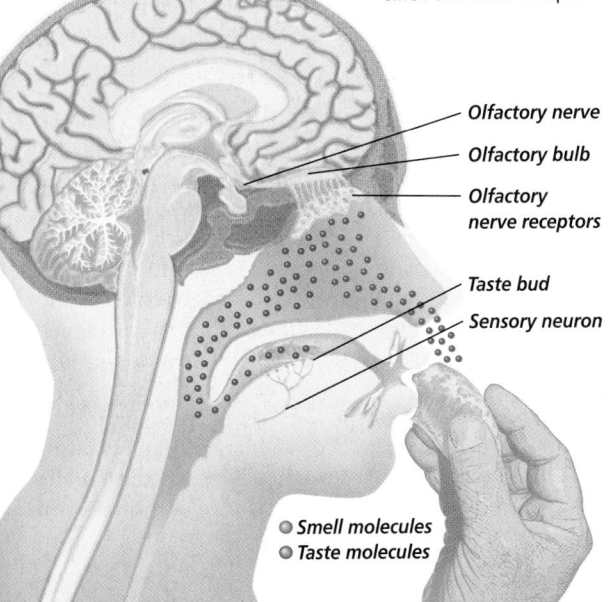

Olfactory nerve

Olfactory bulb

Olfactory nerve receptors

Taste bud

Sensory neuron

● Smell molecules
● Taste molecules

Sensing Chemicals

How are you able to smell and taste an orange? Chemical molecules of the orange contact receptors in your nose and mouth as you sniff and eat the fruit. The receptors for smell are hairlike nerve endings located in the upper portion of your nose, as shown in *Figure 36.10.* Chemicals acting on these nerve endings initiate impulses in the olfactory nerve, which is connected to your brain. In the brain, this signal is interpreted as a particular odor.

The senses of taste and smell are closely linked. Think about what your sense of taste is like when your nose is stuffed up and you can smell little, if anything. Because much of what you taste depends on your sense of smell, your sense of taste may also be dulled.

36.2   THE SENSES   **951**

1 Focus

 INTERACTIVE CHALKBOARD
PowerPoint® Presentations

Bellringer
Section Focus Transparency 88

Transparency **88** Common Senses

SECTION FOCUS
Use with Chapter 36, Section 36.2

① List the senses that you think the person in this scene is using.
② Identify the stimulus for each of the senses you listed in question 1.

BIOLOGY: The Dynamics of Life   SECTION FOCUS TRANSPARENCIES

Concept Development

Ask students what kind of information the sense organs keep the body informed of. They inform the body of changes that occur in the surroundings. What is the reason for keeping the body informed? So that it can respond to changes in the environment.

FOLDABLES™

For an additional Foldables activity idea, see the Chapter 36 Foldables page in *Unit 10 FAST FILE Resources.*

RESOURCE MANAGER

Unit 10 *FAST FILE* Resources
Real World BioApplications, pp. 85–86
Reinforcement and Study Guide in English, p. 91
Reinforcement and Study Guide in Spanish, p. 95
Concept Mapping, p. 97
Transparency Worksheets, pp. 100, 107–114

Reading Essentials for Biology, Section 36.2
Laboratory Manual, pp. 233–236
Section Focus Transparency 88
Basic Concepts Transparencies 68, 69
Reteaching Skills Transparencies 52, 53

 Indiana Academic Standards

Pages 950–951: B.1.14

2 Teach

✓ Reading Check Rods are receptor cells in the retina that are stimulated by dim light. Rods help detect shape and movement, but not color. Cones are receptor cells in the retina that are stimulated by bright light. Cones help detect sharp vision and color.

Inquiry

Activity Assign students the role of a part of the eye or ear. Ask students to line up and portray the eye sensing light or the ear hearing. The students should line up in the order of when the parts receive the signal. When their part plays a role, they can describe what their part does. **L2**

Enrichment

Invite an audiologist to speak to the class about sound levels, how they are measured, and damage that may result from high levels. Have the audiologist demonstrate how hearing is tested. **L2**

Figure 36.11
A cross section through the human eye shows the path light takes as it enters through the pupil.

You taste something when chemicals dissolved in saliva contact sensory receptors on your tongue called **taste buds.** Tastes that you experience can be divided into four basic categories: sour, salty, bitter, and sweet. As seen with the sequence of electrochemical changes a neuron undergoes as it is depolarized, each of the different tastes produces a similar change in the cells of taste buds. As these cells are depolarized, signals from your taste buds are sent to the cerebrum. There, the signal is interpreted and you notice a particular taste. A young adult has approximately 10 000 taste buds. As a person ages, his or her sense of smell becomes less sharp and taste buds may decrease in number or become less sensitive. This can result in a decreased sense of taste.

Sensing Light

How are you able to see? Your sense of sight depends on receptors in your eyes that respond to light energy. The **retina,** found at the back of the eye, is a thin layer of tissue made up of light receptors and sensory neurons. Light enters the eye through the pupil and is focused by the lens onto the back of the eye, where it strikes the retina. Follow the pathway of light to the retina in *Figure 36.11.*

The retina contains two types of light receptor cells—rods and cones. **Rods** are receptor cells adapted for vision in dim light. They help you detect shape and movement. **Cones** are receptor cells adapted for sharp vision in bright light. They also help you detect color.

At the back of the eye, retinal tissue comes together to form the optic nerve, which leads to the brain, where images are interpreted. Can you see as well with one eye as with two? To find out more about how the brain forms a visual image, look at *Figure 36.12.*

✓ Reading Check **Compare and contrast** rods and cones.

Sensing Mechanical Stimulation

How are you able to hear the leaves rustle and feel the grass as you relax in the park? These senses, hearing and touch, depend on receptors that respond to mechanical stimulation.

Your sense of hearing

Every sound causes the air around it to vibrate. These vibrations travel outward from the source in waves, called sound waves. Sound waves enter your outer ear and travel down to the end of the ear canal, where they strike a membrane called the eardrum and cause it to vibrate. The vibrations then pass to three small bones in the middle ear—the malleus, the incus, and the stapes. As the stapes vibrates, it causes the membrane of the oval window, a structure between the middle and inner ear, to move back and forth.

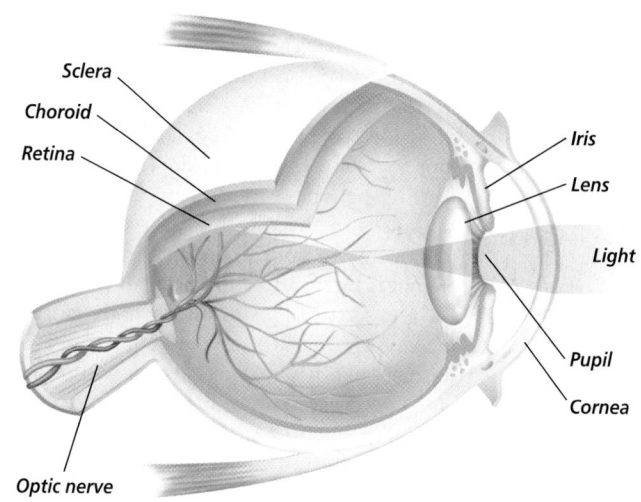

Sclera
Choroid
Retina
Iris
Lens
Light
Pupil
Cornea
Optic nerve

952 THE NERVOUS SYSTEM

The Eye

Figure 36.12
The light energy that reaches your retina is converted into nerve impulses, which are interpreted by your brain, allowing you to see the world around you. **Critical Thinking** *How would a person's vision be affected if his or her rod cells didn't function?*

Color-enhanced SEM
Magnification: 500×

Rod and cone cells

(A) Rod and cone cells Rod cells in the retina are excited by low levels of light. These cells convert light signals into nerve impulses and relay them to the brain. Your brain interprets the information as a black and white picture. Your cone cells respond to bright light. They provide the brain with information about color.

(B) Visual field Close one eye. Everything you can see with one eye open is the visual field of that eye. The visual field of each eye can be divided into two parts: a lateral, or outer portion, and a medial, or inner portion. As shown, the lateral half of the visual field projects onto the medial portion of the retina, and the medial half of the visual field projects onto the lateral portion of the retina.

Visual cortex in cerebrum

Optic nerve

Lens

Top view of brain

Retina

(D) Brain image projections The right half of the retina in each eye is connected to the right side of the visual cortex in the cerebrum. The left half of the retina is similarly connected to the left side of the visual cortex. Thus images entering the eye from the right half of each visual field project to the left half of the brain, and vice versa.

(C) Depth perception The visual fields of the eyes partially overlap, each eye seeing about two-thirds of the total field. This overlap allows your brain to judge the depth of your visual field.

36.2 THE SENSES **953**

Purpose

Students examine the function and structure of rods and cones and the divided projection of the visual field.

Teaching Strategies

- Ask students which cells are most active when they are reading color comics. cone cells
- Have students close one eye at a time and note the visual field they see out of each.
- Ask students to explain how they are able to judge depths using both eyes together. **L2**

Visual Learning

Dissect a cow or sheep eye. Cow and sheep eyes have a layer on the inner choroid coat that is not present in humans. Explain that this iridescent layer enhances night vision by reflecting some light back into the retina.

Critical Thinking

Because rod cells function in low levels of light, the person would be virtually blind in dimly lit areas.

Display

Visual-Spatial Obtain display models of the ear, eye, skin, or nose. Have students examine the models as they read about each sense. **L1** **ELL**

PROJECT

Comparing Eyes to Cameras Have students write an essay comparing the eye to a camera. They should include references to the lens, the aperture, the body, and the shutter of the camera. Students should include a copy of the essay in their journals. **L3**

 Indiana Academic Standards
Pages 952–953: B.1.14

Purpose

Students gain practice in determining whether statements are observations or inferences.

Process Skills

acquire information, define operationally, observe and infer, recognize cause and effect, think critically

Teaching Strategies

Refer students to the "Observe and Infer" section in the Skill Handbook at the back of this text. The entire report can also be accessed on the Internet.

Thinking Critically

1. Student choices must include a specific number. A definition of the word *quantitative* should also be included in their answer.
2. Student choices should not include a specific number. A definition of the word *qualitative* should also be included.
3. Students may cite sentences that include "may be" or "can." A definition of the word *inference* should also be included in their answer.
4. Student answers may include the wearing of protective hearing devices and reducing volume or exposure time.

Modified Assessment

Portfolio Explain the meaning of the term *decibel* and give students a listing of noise-causing agents and their decibel ratings. Have students prepare a poster based on the listing. Have them place the posters in their portfolios. Use the Performance Task Assessment List for Poster in **PASC,** p. 145. **L1**

Indiana Academic Standards

Pages 954–955: B.1.14

Problem-Solving Lab 36.1

Interpret and Analyze

When are loud sounds dangerous to our hearing? Observations may be described as either qualitative or quantitative. A qualitative observation about a woman's height might be that she is tall. A quantitative observation about the same person might be that she is 1.92 m tall.

Solve the Problem

"Hearing loss afflicts approximately 28 million people in the United States. Approximately 10 million of these impairments may be partially attributable to damage from exposure to loud sounds. Sounds that are sufficiently loud to damage sensitive inner ear structures can produce hearing loss that is not reversible. Very loud sounds of short duration, such as an explosion or gunfire, can produce immediate, severe, and permanent loss of hearing. Longer exposure to less intense but still hazardous sounds encountered in the workplace or during leisure activities, exacts a gradual toll on hearing sensitivity, initially without the victim's awareness. Live or recorded high-volume music, lawn-care equipment, and airplanes are examples of potentially hazardous noise."

—"Noise and Hearing Loss," NIH Consensus Statement, January 22–24, 1990

Thinking Critically

1. **Analyze** Choose and record two sentences or phrases from the passage above that provide examples of quantitative observations. Explain your selections.
2. **Analyze** Choose and record two sentences or phrases that provide examples of qualitative observations. Explain your selections.
3. **Infer** Choose and record one sentence or phrase that provides an example of an inference. Explain your selection.
4. **Think Critically** Suggest ways to minimize the type of noise exposure discussed in the last sentence.

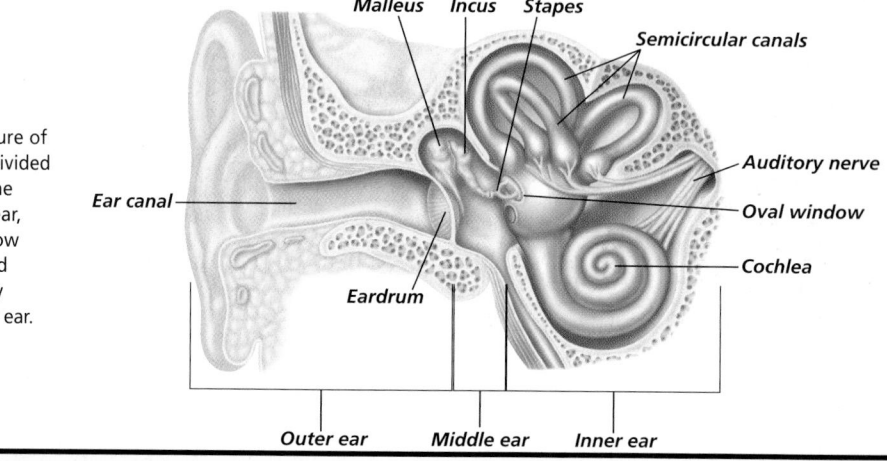

Figure 36.13
The internal structure of the human ear is divided into three areas: the outer ear, middle ear, and inner ear. Follow the pathway sound waves take as they move through your ear.

954

From here, the vibrations continue to travel deeper into the ear. The movement from the oval window causes fluid in the **cochlea,** a snail-shaped structure in the inner ear, to move. Inside the circular walls of the cochlea are structures that are lined with hair cells. The fluid in the cochlea moves like a wave against the hair cells causing them to bend.

The movement of the hairs produces electrical impulses, which travel along the auditory nerve to the sides of the cerebrum, where they are interpreted as sound. Trace the pathway of sound waves in *Figure 36.13*. Hearing loss can occur if the auditory nerve or the hair cells in the cochlea are damaged. To find out what impact loud sounds have on your hearing, do the *Problem-Solving Lab* on this page.

Your sense of balance

The inner ear also converts information about the position of your head into nerve impulses which travel to your brain, informing it about your body's equilibrium.

Maintaining balance is the function of your **semicircular canals.** Like the cochlea, the semicircular canals are also filled with a thick fluid and lined with

---

hair cells. When you tilt your head, the fluid moves, causing the hairs to bend. This movement stimulates the hair cells to produce impulses. Neurons from the semicircular canals carry the impulses to the brain, which sends an impulse to stimulate your neck muscles and readjust the position of your head.

✓ **Reading Check** **Explain** the function of the semicircular canals.

Your sense of touch

Like the ear, your skin also responds to mechanical stimulation with receptors that convert the stimulus into a nerve impulse. Receptors in the dermis of the skin respond to changes in temperature, pressure, and pain. It is with the help of these receptors, shown in *Figure 36.14*, that your body is able to respond to its external environment.

Although some receptors are found all over your body, those responsible for responding to particular stimuli are usually concentrated within certain areas of your body. For example, receptors that respond to light pressure are numerous in the dermis of your fingertips, eyelids, lips, the tip of your tongue, and the palms of your hands. When these receptors are stimulated, you perceive sensations of light touch.

Receptors that respond to heavier pressure are found inside your joints, in muscle tissue, and in certain

Figure 36.14
Many kinds of receptors are located throughout the skin. **Describe** *What types of sensations are perceived when the different receptors are stimulated?*

organs. They are also abundant on the skin of your palms and fingers and on the soles of your feet. When these receptors are stimulated, you perceive heavy pressure.

Free nerve endings extend into the lower layers of the epidermis. Free nerve endings act as receptors for itch, tickle, hot and cold, and pain sensations. Heat receptors are found deep in the dermis, while cold receptors are found closer to the surface of your skin. Pain receptors can be found in all tissues of the body except those in the brain.

✓ **Reading Check** The semicircular canals help the body maintain balance by recognizing the position of the head.

Caption Question Answer
Figure 36.14 Each type of skin receptor (temperature, pain, or pressure) sends a signal to the brain that is perceived according to the type of receptor.

3 Assess

Section Assessment

Understanding Main Ideas
1. Summarize the different types of messages the senses receive.
2. When you have a cold, why is it difficult to taste food?
3. Explain how your eyes detect light and images.
4. List the different types of receptors that are found in the skin.

Thinking Critically
5. Why might an ear infection lead to problems with balance?

SKILL REVIEW

6. **Sequence** List the sequence of structures through which sound waves pass to reach the auditory nerve. For more help, refer to *Sequence* in the **Skill Handbook**.

 in.bdol.glencoe.com/self_check_quiz

36.2 THE SENSES **955**

Section Assessment

1. The eyes respond to light. The ears respond to sound. Touch receptors respond to mechanical stimulation. The tongue and nose respond to chemicals.
2. The tasting of food involves both the sense of smell and the sense of taste.
3. Light stimulates the rod or cone cells in the retina, which transmit a signal to the brain by way of the optic nerve.
4. touch, temperature, pressure, and pain
5. Swelling associated with an ear infection could cause fluid in the ear to put pressure on the semicircular canals and cause the hairs in the canals to signal a false sense of balance in the brain.
6. outer ear, eardrum, malleus, incus, and stapes, fluid of cochlea, hairs of cochlea, auditory nerve to the brain

1 Focus

Bellringer

Section Focus Transparency 89

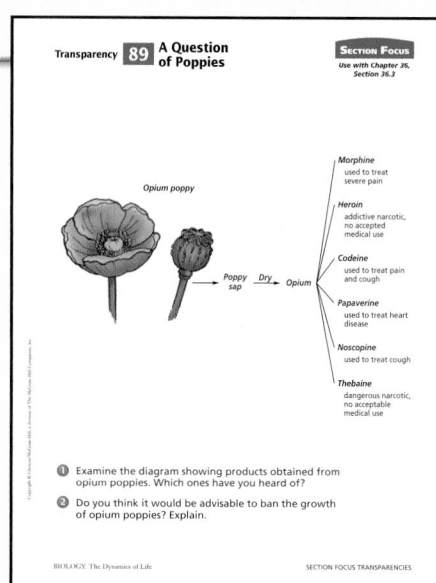

Transparency **89** A Question of Poppies

SECTION FOCUS
Use with Chapter 36, Section 36.3

Opium poppy

Poppy sap → *Dry* → *Opium*

Morphine
used to treat severe pain

Heroin
addictive narcotic, no accepted medical use

Codeine
used to treat pain and cough

Papaverine
used to treat heart disease

Noscopine
used to treat cough

Thebaine
dangerous narcotic, no acceptable medical use

① Examine the diagram showing products obtained from opium poppies. Which ones have you heard of?

② Do you think it would be advisable to ban the growth of opium poppies? Explain.

BIOLOGY: The Dynamics of Life

SECTION FOCUS TRANSPARENCIES

Finding Main Ideas

Outline Once students finish their outlines, have them brainstorm in groups and list as many types of medicinal categories of drugs that they can. Try to emphasize how drugs have extended life for many individuals, such as insulin for diabetics and antibiotics for infections. **L2**
COOP LEARN

Section 36.3

The Effects of Drugs

Indiana Standards Standard B.1.14 Recognize and explain that communication and/or interaction are required between cells to coordinate their diverse activities.

SECTION PREVIEW

Objectives

Recognize the medicinal uses of drugs.

Identify the different classes of drugs.

Interpret the effects of drug misuse and abuse on the body.

Review Vocabulary
receptors: specific binding sites found on the surface of or within a cell (p. 930)

New Vocabulary
drug
narcotic
stimulant
depressant
addiction
tolerance
withdrawal
hallucinogen

Drugs and the Nervous System

Finding Main Ideas On a piece of paper, construct an outline about the effects of drugs on the nervous system. Use the red and blue titles in the section as a guideline. As you read the paragraphs that follow the titles, add important information and vocabulary words to your outline.

Example:

 I. Drugs act on the body
  A. Drugs affect body functions
 II. Medicinal uses of drugs
  A. Relieving Pain
   1. Narcotics

Use your outline to help you answer questions in the Section Assessment on page 963. For more help, refer to *Outline* in the **Skill Handbook.**

Tobacco leaves, used to make cigarettes, contain the addictive drug nicotine.

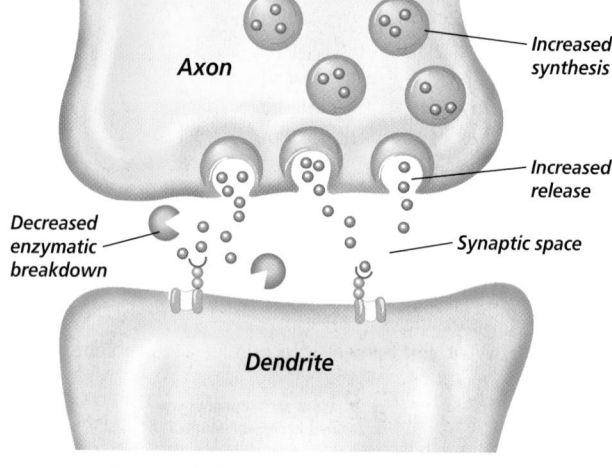

Axon

Increased synthesis

Increased release

Synaptic space

Decreased enzymatic breakdown

Dendrite

Figure 36.15
Drugs can increase neurotransmitter levels in the synapse by stimulating their synthesis, increasing their release, or by slowing their breakdown by enzymes.

956

Drugs Act on the Body

You probably hear the word *drug* used often, maybe even every day. A **drug** is a chemical that affects the body's functions. Most drugs interact with receptor sites on cells, probably the same ones used by neurotransmitters of the nervous system or hormones of the endocrine system. Some drugs increase the rate at which neurotransmitters are synthesized and released, or slow the rate at which they are broken down, as illustrated in *Figure 36.15.* Other drugs interfere with a neurotransmitter's ability to interact with its receptor. Explore how these different drugs work on neurotransmitters by doing the *Problem-Solving Lab* on the next page.

Medicinal Uses of Drugs

A medicine is a drug that, when taken into the body, helps prevent, cure, or relieve a medical problem. Some of the many kinds of medicines used to relieve medical conditions are discussed below.

Relieving pain

Headache, muscle ache, cramps—all are common pain sensations. You just studied how pain receptors in your body send signals to your brain. Medicines that relieve pain manipulate either the receptors that initiate the impulses or the central nervous system that receives them.

Pain relievers that do not cause a loss of consciousness are called analgesics. Some analgesics, like aspirin, work by inhibiting receptors at the site of pain from producing nerve impulses. Analgesics that work on the central nervous system are called **narcotics.** Many narcotics are made from the opium poppy flower, shown in *Figure 36.16.* Opiates, as they are called, can be useful in controlled medical therapy because these drugs are able to relieve severe pain from illness or injury.

✓ **Reading Check** **Describe** how medicines that relieve pain work.

Figure 36.16
Sticky sap from the fruit of an opium poppy is used to make drugs called opiates.

Problem-Solving Lab 36.2

Formulate Models

How do different drugs affect the levels of neurotransmitters in synapses? Drugs can act on neurotransmitters in a number of different ways. For example, they may block the release of the neurotransmitter from the axon of a neuron. They may also prevent the breakdown of the neurotransmitter by blocking the enzyme responsible for this action.

Solve the Problem
Examine the diagram shown here, which illustrates how neurotransmitters work.

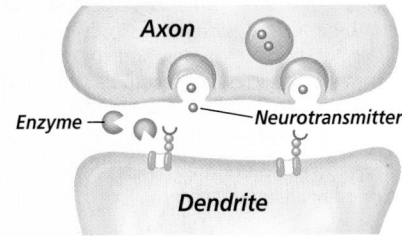

Thinking Critically
1. **Formulate Models** Draw models for two different drugs:
   a. Illustrate a drug that could block the enzyme from breaking down the neurotransmitter.
   b. Illustrate a drug that could block the release of the neurotransmitter from the axon.
2. **Evaluate** Evaluate your models according to their adequacy in representing the effects a drug can have on the transmission of an impulse across a synapse.
3. **Predict** Predict the effects of each drug on the body.

2 Teach

Problem-Solving Lab 36.2

Purpose
Students design drugs that will interfere with the action of neurotransmitters.

Process Skills
apply concepts, formulate models, hypothesize, interpret scientific illustrations, predict, recognize cause and effect, think critically

Teaching Strategies
■ Review the nature of the synapse and how neurotransmitters work normally.
■ Encourage students to consider the shapes of the neurotransmitter molecules, enzymes, and binding sites when designing their blockers.
■ Allow students to work in small groups.

Thinking Critically
1. Student models will vary.
2. Make sure that each one produces the effect described.
3. (a) Message will be transmitted for a longer period of time than normal; (b) Message will not be delivered to dendrite.

Assessment
Knowledge Have students make and interpret a diagram of neurotransmitter blockage. Use the Performance Task Assessment List for Scientific Drawing in **PASC,** p. 127. L2

✓ **Reading Check** They manipulate either the receptors that initiate pain impulses or the CNS that receives the impulses.

BIOTECHNOLOGY CAREERS

Pharmacist

Would you like to help people control or recover from illness by dispensing the latest medications developed through biotechnology? Then consider a career as a pharmacist.

Skills for the Job

Pharmacists read prescriptions written by doctors and other health professionals and carefully prepare containers with the correct medicine. (Few pharmacists still mix the medicine themselves; that is done by the drug manufacturer.) Pharmacists must know how drugs interact and guide people in avoiding harmful combinations. Besides drugstores, pharmacists work in hospitals and nursing homes, and for drug companies and government agencies. To become a pharmacist, you must complete a five-year bachelor's degree in pharmacy and pass a state examination.

 For more careers in related fields, visit in.bdol.glencoe.com/careers

Treating circulatory problems

Many drugs have been developed to treat heart and circulatory problems such as high blood pressure. These medicines are called cardiovascular drugs. In addition to treating high blood pressure, cardiovascular drugs may be used to normalize an irregular heartbeat, increase the heart's pumping capacity, or enlarge small blood vessels. Discover how various types of drugs can affect heart rate by doing the *BioLab* at the end of this chapter.

Treating nervous disorders

Several kinds of medicines are used to help relieve symptoms of nervous system problems. Among these medicines are stimulants and depressants.

Drugs that increase the activity of the central and sympathetic nervous systems are called **stimulants.**

Amphetamines (am FE tuh meenz) are synthetic stimulants that increase the output of CNS neurotransmitters. Amphetamines are seldom prescribed because they can lead to dependence. However, because they increase wakefulness and alertness, amphetamines are sometimes used to treat patients with sleep disorders.

Drugs that lower, or depress, the activity of the nervous system are called **depressants,** or sedatives. The primary medicinal uses of depressants are to encourage calmness and produce sleep. For some people, the symptoms of anxiety are so extreme that they interfere with the person's ability to function effectively. By slowing down the activities of the CNS, a depressant can temporarily relieve some of this anxiety.

The Misuse and Abuse of Drugs

The misuse or abuse of drugs can cause serious health problems—even death. Drug misuse occurs when a medicine is taken for an unintended use. For example, giving your prescription medicine to someone else, not following the prescribed dosage by taking too much or too little, and mixing medicines, are all instances of drug misuse. You must pay careful attention to the specific instructions given on the label of a drug you are taking. The *MiniLab* on the next page shows you how to analyze such a label.

Drug abuse is the inappropriate self-administration of a drug for nonmedical purposes. Drug abuse may involve use of an illegal drug, such as cocaine; use of an illegally obtained medicine, such as someone else's prescribed drugs; or excessive use of a legal drug, such as alcohol or nicotine. Drugs abused in this way can have powerful effects on the nervous system and other systems of the body, as described in *Figure 36.17*.

Addiction to drugs

When a person believes he or she needs a drug in order to feel good or function normally, that person is psychologically dependent on the drug. When a person's body develops a chemical need for the drug in order to function normally, the person is physiologically dependent. Psychological and physiological dependence are both forms of **addiction.**

Tolerance and withdrawal

When a drug user experiences tolerance to or withdrawal from a frequently used drug, that person is addicted to the drug. **Tolerance** occurs when a person needs larger or more frequent doses of a drug to achieve the same effect. The dosage increases are necessary because the body becomes less responsive to the drug. **Withdrawal** occurs when the person stops taking the drug and actually becomes ill.

Figure 36.17
The use of anabolic steroids without careful guidance from a physician is illegal. Some dangerous side effects of steroid abuse include cardiovascular disease, kidney damage, and cancer.

MiniLab 36.2

Analyze Information

Interpret a Drug Label One common misuse of drugs is not following the instructions that accompany them. Over-the-counter medicines can be harmful—even fatal—if they are not used as directed. The Food and Drug Administration requires that certain information about a drug be provided on its label to help the consumer use the medicine properly and safely.

Procedure

1 The photograph below shows a label from an over-the-counter drug. Read it carefully.

2 Make a data table like the one shown. Then fill in the table using information on the label.

Information from a Drug Label				
People with these conditions should avoid this drug	Possible Side Effects	This drug should not be taken with these medicines	Symptoms This Drug Will Relieve	Correct Dosage

Maximum Strength
12-Hour Extended Release Tablets
NASAL DECONGESTANT, ANTIHISTAMINE
EACH EXTENDED RELEASE TABLET CONTAINS:
75 mg Phenylpropanolamine Hydrochloride, USP
12 mg Brompheniramine Maleate, USP
INACTIVE INGREDIENTS: Dimethyl Polysiloxane Oil, Hydroxypropyl Methylcellulose, Lactose, Magnesium Stearate, Polyethylene Glycol, Talc, Titanium Dioxide, FD&C Blue No. 1 Aluminum Lake.
INDICATIONS: For temporary relief of nasal congestion due to the common cold, hay fever, or other upper respiratory allergies or associated with sinusitis; temporarily relieves running nose, sneezing, and itchy and watery eyes as may occur in allergic rhinitis (such as hay fever). Temporarily restores freer breathing through the nose.
DIRECTIONS: Adults and children 12 years of age and over: One tablet every 12 hours. DO NOT EXCEED 1 TABLET EVERY 12 HOURS, OR 2 TABLETS IN A 24-HOUR PERIOD.
WARNINGS: This product may cause excitability, especially in children. Do not take this product if you have high blood pressure, heart disease, diabetes, thyroid disease, asthma, emphysema, chronic pulmonary disease, shortness of breath, difficulty in breathing, glaucoma or difficulty in urination due to enlargement of the prostate gland, except under the advice and supervision of a physician. Do not give this product to children under 12 years, except under the advice and supervision of a physician. May cause drowsiness. Do not exceed recommended dosage because at higher doses nervousness, dizziness or sleeplessness

may occur. If symptoms do not improve within 7 days or are accompanied by fever, consult a physician before continuing use. Do not take if hypersensitive to any of the ingredients. As with any drug, if you are pregnant or nursing a baby, seek the advice of a health professional before using this product.
CAUTION: Avoid driving a motor vehicle or operating heavy machinery and avoid alcoholic beverages while taking this product.
DRUG INTERACTION PRECAUTION: Do not take this product if you are presently taking a prescription antihypertensive or antidepressant drug containing a monoamine oxidase inhibitor, except under the advice and supervision of a physician.
KEEP THIS AND ALL DRUGS OUT OF REACH OF CHILDREN. IN CASE OF ACCIDENTAL OVERDOSE, SEEK PROFESSIONAL ASSISTANCE OR CONTACT A POISON CONTROL CENTER IMMEDIATELY.
Store at Controlled Room Temperature, Between 15°C and 30°C (59°F and 86°F).
EACH TABLET INDIVIDUALLY SEALED FOR YOUR PROTECTION.
Made in USA

Analysis

1. **Evaluate** Evaluate the promotional claims on this product's label. What symptoms will this product relieve? What side effects can result from using this product? Is this product appropriate for everyone to use?

2. **Infer** Why should a person never take more than the recommended dosage?

MiniLab 36.2

Purpose
Students study information found on the labels of over-the-counter drugs.

Process Skills
observe and infer, analyze

Teaching Strategies
Have students look at the package labels of other over-the-counter drugs.

Expected Results
Student tables should show the following information: children under 12 years, people with high blood pressure, heart disease, diabetes, thyroid disease, asthma, or emphysema should avoid this drug; drowsiness is a possible side effect; should not be taken with antihypertensive or antidepressant drugs; will relieve nasal congestion associated with the common cold, hay fever, or sinusitis; the correct dosage is one tablet every 12 hours.

Analysis
1. See Expected Results for answers.
2. The recommended dosage is the one that has been tested and proven to be safe. Over-the-counter medicines are potentially harmful if not used as directed.

Assessment
Performance Ask students to repeat the MiniLab for other drug labels and include the tables in their portfolios. Use the Performance Task Assessment List for Carrying Out a Strategy and Collecting Data in **PASC,** p. 97. **L2** **ELL**

CULTURAL DIVERSITY

Solomon Carter Fuller Students may obtain a more thorough understanding of brain function by learning about common neuropathologies, such as Alzheimer's disease. During your discussions, emphasize the work of African American psychiatrist and researcher, Solomon Carter Fuller (1872–1953).

He was best known for expanding our medical knowledge in the fields of neuropathology and psychiatry. His research on degenerative diseases of the brain—including Alzheimer's disease—was considered pioneering work.

Enrichment

Researchers speculate that animals have learned to medicate themselves by feeding on certain plants. Zoopharmacognosy is the study of the use of medicinal plants by wild animals. This growing area of research involves observing wild animals (including chimpanzees and bears) as they eat plants known to have medicinal properties and noting the results.

In 1989, a primatologist from Kyoto University observed a lethargic chimpanzee that had diarrhea and discolored urine chewing on the bark and leaves of a plant called *Vernonia amygdalina*. The primatologist knew that the plant contained antibiotic and antiparasitic compounds. The day after eating the plant, the chimp had recovered fully.

Have students research ways in which their own pets use plants as medicine. Why do they think dogs and cats sometimes eat grass? **L3**

The BioLab at the end of the chapter can be used at this point in the lesson.

Figure 36.18
Babies born addicted to crack cocaine are usually low in birth weight, continually irritable, and may shake constantly.

Classes of Commonly Abused Drugs

Each class of drug produces its own special effect on the body, and its own particular symptoms of withdrawal. *Table 36.1* summarizes the health effects of some commonly abused drugs.

Stimulants: Cocaine, amphetamines, caffeine, and nicotine

You already know that stimulants increase the activity of the central nervous system and the sympathetic nervous system. Increased CNS stimulation can result in mild elevation of alertness, increased nervousness, anxiety, or even convulsions.

Cocaine stimulates the CNS by working on the part of the inner brain that governs emotions and basic drives, such as hunger and thirst. When these needs are met under normal circumstances, neurotransmitters—such as dopamine—are released to reward centers and the person experiences pleasure. Cocaine artificially increases levels of these neurotransmitters in the brain. As a result, false messages are sent to reward centers indicating that a basic drive has been satisfied. The user quickly feels a euphoric high called a rush. This sense of intense pleasure and satisfaction cannot be maintained, however, and soon the effects of the drug change. Physical hyperactivity follows. Often, anxiety and depression set in.

Cocaine also disrupts the body's circulatory system by interfering with the sympathetic nervous system. Although initially causing a slowing of the heart rate, it soon produces a great increase in heart rate and a narrowing of blood vessels, known as vasoconstriction. The result is high blood pressure. Heavy use of this drug compromises the immune system and often leads to heart abnormalities. Cocaine may affect more than just the individual who uses it. As *Figure 36.18* shows, babies of addicted mothers are sometimes born already dependent on this drug.

Amphetamines are stimulants that increase levels of CNS neurotransmitters. Like cocaine, amphetamines also cause vasoconstriction, a racing heart, and increased blood pressure. Other adverse side effects of amphetamine abuse include irregular heartbeat, chest pain, paranoia, hallucinations, and convulsions.

Not all stimulants are illegal. As shown in *Figure 36.19,* one stimulant in particular is as close as the nearest coffee maker or candy machine. Caffeine—a substance found in coffee, some carbonated soft drinks, cocoa,

Figure 36.19
Caffeine can trigger a condition called tachycardia, when the heart beats more than 100 times per minute.

CHALLENGE ACTIVITY

Neurotransmitters Have students who need an additional challenge research the relationship between drugs such as cocaine, nicotine, opiates, and alcohol and neurotransmitters such as dopamine, serotonin, GABA, enkephalin, and endorphins. Students can write a report and include a copy of it in their journals. **L3**

Indiana Academic Standards

Pages 960–961: B.1.14

Table 36.1 Commonly Abused Drugs

Category • Substance	Commercial or Street Name	Potential Health Hazards
Cannabinoid • Marijuana	• Grass, joints, pot, reefer, weed	Respiratory problems, impaired learning
Stimulants • Cocaine • Methylphenidate • Nicotine • Methamphetamine • MDMA	• Blow, coke, crack, rock • Ritalin, Skippy, vitamin R • Chew, cigarettes, cigars • Ice, speed, glass • Ecstasy, Eve	Increased heart rate and blood pressure, irregular heart beat, heart failure, and weight loss
Depressants • Benzodiazepines • Barbiturates	• Librium, Valium, Xanax, downers, sleeping pills • Barbs, red birds, yellows	Respiratory depression and arrest, lowered blood pressure, poor concentration
Hallucinogens • LSD	• Cubes, microdot	Chronic mental disorders, nausea, flashbacks
Opioids • Heroin	• H, junk, skag, smack	Respiratory depression and arrest, collapsed veins
Other • Inhalants • Anabolic steroids • Ketamine	• Paint thinners, gasoline, butane, nitrates, laughing gas • Juice • Special K, vitamin K	Headache, nausea, vomiting, unconsciousness, sudden death Liver and kidney cancer, acne, high blood pressure Respiratory depression and arrest, nausea, vomiting

and tea—is a CNS stimulant. Its effects include increased alertness and some mood elevation. Caffeine also causes an increase in heart rate and urine production, which can lead to dehydration.

Nicotine, a substance found in tobacco, is also a stimulant. By increasing the release of the hormone epinephrine, nicotine increases heart rate, blood pressure, breathing rate, and stomach acid secretion. Although nicotine is the addictive substance in tobacco, there are many other harmful chemicals found in tobacco products. Smoking cigarettes leads to an increased risk of lung cancer and cardiovascular disease. Use of chewing tobacco is associated with oral and throat cancers.

Depressants: Alcohol and barbiturates

As you already know, depressants slow down the activities of the CNS. All CNS depressants relieve anxiety, but most produce noticeable sedation.

One of the most widely abused drugs in the world today is alcohol. Easily produced from various grains and fruits, this depressant is distributed throughout a person's body via the bloodstream. Like other drugs, alcohol affects cellular communication by influencing the release of or interacting with receptors for several important neurotransmitters in the brain. Alcohol also appears to block the movement of sodium and calcium ions across the cell membrane, a process that is important in the transmission of impulses and the release of neurotransmitters.

Tolerance to the effects of alcohol develops as a result of heavy alcohol consumption. Addiction to alcohol—alcoholism—can cause the destruction of nerve cells and brain damage. A number of organ diseases are directly attributable to chronic alcohol use. For example, cirrhosis, a hardening of the tissues of the liver, is a common affliction of alcoholics.

Bioethics

Part of the procedure in getting a drug approved by the Food and Drug Administration (FDA) involves human drug tests. The deaths of participants in National Institute of Health (NIH) drug trials has raised questions as to the safety of these tests. Even though participants sign a consent form, desperately ill patients may be willing to place themselves in inordinately dangerous situations in hopes of helping to find a cure. As a result, researchers question whether these patients can be truly "informed" about the risks involved.

Ask students to research what consenting to drug testing by the FDA involves. Have students present their findings in a written report. Organize and moderate a classroom debate concerning the ethical issues involved in human drug testing. **L3**

Quick Demo

Over-The-Counter Comparison Bring various nonprescription drugs (such as aspirin, cough syrup, antacids, and so on) to hold up for the class. Compare such things as price, type of drug, type of packaging, and purpose of the drug.

CHALLENGE ACTIVITY

Alcohol in the Body Ask students who need an additional challenge to write a presentation on the effects of alcohol at various blood alcohol levels. Have them research how alcohol enters cells and what effects alcohol has on the brain and liver. **L3**

Barbiturates (bar BIH chuh ruts) are sedatives and anti-anxiety drugs. When barbiturates are used in excess, the user's respiratory and circulatory systems become depressed. Chronic use results in addiction.

Narcotics: Opiates

Most narcotics are opiates, derived from the opium poppy. They act directly on the brain. The most abused narcotic in the United States is heroin. It depresses the CNS, slows breathing, and lowers heart rate. Tolerance develops quickly, and withdrawal from heroin is painful.

Hallucinogens: Natural and synthetic

Natural hallucinogens have been known and used for thousands of years, but the abuse of hallucinogenic drugs did not become widespread in the United States until the 1960s,

when new synthetic versions became widely available.

Hallucinogens (huh LEW sun uh junz) stimulate the CNS—altering moods, thoughts, and sensory perceptions. The user sees, hears, feels, tastes, or smells things that are not actually there. This disorientation can impair the user's judgment and place him or her in a potentially dangerous situation. Hallucinogens also increase heart rate, blood pressure, respiratory rate, and body temperature, and sometimes cause sweating, salivation, nausea, and vomiting. After large enough doses, convulsions of the body may even occur.

Unlike the hallucinogens shown in *Figure 36.20,* LSD—or acid—is a synthetic drug. The mechanism by which LSD produces hallucinations is still debated, but it may involve the blocking of a CNS neurotransmitter.

Reading Check **Describe** the effects of hallucinogens on the body.

Figure 36.20
Some hallucinogens are found in nature.

A Mushrooms of the genus *Psilocybe* contain the CNS hallucinogen psilocybin. These mushrooms are considered sacred by certain Native American tribes, who use them in traditional religious rites.

B Ergot, a mold disease of cereal grains, contains a hallucinogen chemically related to LSD.

CHALLENGE ACTIVITY

Steroids Have students who need an additional challenge research more information on the effects of anabolic steroids on the body. Students can make a multimedia presentation of their results to the class. **L3**

Anabolic steroids

Anabolic steroids are synthetic drugs that are similar to the hormone testosterone. Like testosterone, anabolic steroids stimulate muscles to increase in size. Physicians use anabolic steroids in the treatment of hormone imbalances or diseases that result in a loss of muscle mass. Abuse of anabolic steroids is associated with infertility in men, high cholesterol, and extreme mood swings.

Breaking the Habit

Once a person has become addicted to a drug, breaking the habit can be very difficult. Recall that an addiction can involve both physiological and psychological dependencies. Besides the desire to break the addiction, studies have shown that people usually need both medical and psychological therapy—such as counseling—to be successful in their treatment. Support groups such as Alcoholics Anonymous allow addicts to share their experiences in an effort to maintain sobriety. Often, people going through the same recovery are able to offer the best support.

Nicotine replacement therapy

Nicotine replacement therapy is one example of a relatively successful drug treatment approach. People who are

Figure 36.21
To help break an addiction to tobacco, this patient is wearing a patch on his arm that releases small amounts of nicotine directly into his bloodstream.

trying to break their addiction to tobacco often go through stressful withdrawals when they stop smoking cigarettes. To ease the intensity of the withdrawal symptoms, patients wear adhesive patches that slowly release small amounts of nicotine into their bloodstream, as shown in *Figure 36.21*. Alternatively, pieces of nicotine-containing gum are chewed periodically to temporarily relieve cravings.

3 Assess

DAILY INTERVENTION

Check for Understanding
Linguistic Have students make a list of stimulants and depressants and write a paragraph about how these substances affect the body. **L2**

Reteach
Linguistic Have students write a paragraph explaining how nicotine replacement therapy helps smokers to stop smoking. **L2**

Resources
For more practice, use *Reading Essentials for Biology,* Section 36.3.

Extension

Have students research information about genetic susceptibility to alcoholism. **L2**

✔ Assessment

Knowledge Have one student name a drug from the chapter and a second student categorize the drug as a stimulant, depressant, narcotic, or hallucinogen. Have a third student list a side effect of the drug. Continue around the class until each student has been involved. **L2**

Understanding Main Ideas

1. How can drugs affect levels of neurotransmitters between neurons?

2. In what ways can drugs be used to treat a cardiovascular problem?

3. Identify the different classes of drugs. Give an example of each class.

4. How does nicotine affect the body?

Thinking Critically

5. Form a hypothesis as to how a person develops tolerance to a drug.

SKILL REVIEW

6. **Compare and Contrast** Distinguish between stimulants and depressants, comparing their effects on the body. For more help, refer to *Compare and Contrast* in the **Skill Handbook**.

Section Assessment

1. Drugs can increase or decrease the amount of neurotransmitters found between neurons.

2. Drugs are used to normalize an irregular heartbeat, increase the heart's pumping capacity, or enlarge small blood vessels.

3. Stimulants: cocaine, amphetamines, caffeine, and nicotine; Depressants: alcohol and barbiturates; Narcotics: opiates; Hallucinogens: LSD

4. Nicotine will stimulate the central nervous system, causing an increase in heart rate, blood pressure, and breathing rate.

5. Student answers may vary. Accept all reasonable hypotheses.

6. Stimulants increase the activity of the central and sympathetic nervous systems. Depressants decrease the activity of the central nervous system and increase activity of the parasympathetic nervous system.

Time Allotment
one class period

Process Skills
observe and infer, form a hypothesis, communicate, predict, interpret data, experiment, and analyze

Safety Precautions
Caution students not to drink any of the solutions tested and advise them to wash their hands at the conclusion of the lab.

Remind students that alcohol and tobacco are not legal for minors. Do not allow students to remove products from the classroom.

PREPARATION

Solutions
■ Ethyl alcohol—add 2 mL of ethyl alcohol to 98 mL of distilled water.
■ Nicotine—soak an unfiltered cigarette in 100 mL of warm distilled water for one hour; then filter the solution.
■ Prepare weak solutions of coffee and tea.
■ Dilute cola 1 part water to 1 part cola.
■ Cough medicine—add 2 mL of cough medicine to 98 mL of distilled water.

Possible Hypotheses
Students' hypotheses should categorize each drug according to whether it will increase, decrease, or not affect heart rate.

INQUIRY Before You Begin
Depending on their chemical composition, drugs affect different parts of your body. Stimulants and depressants are drugs that affect the central nervous system and the autonomic nervous system. Stimulants increase the activity of the sympathetic nervous system and cause an increase in your breathing rate and in your heart rate. Depressants decrease the activity of the sympathetic nervous system, reducing your breathing and heart rates. In this lab, you will investigate the effects that different drugs have on an organism's heart rate.

What drugs affect the heart rate of *Daphnia*?

PREPARATION

Problem
What legally available drugs are stimulants to the heart? What legal drugs are depressants? Because these drugs are legally available, are they less dangerous?

Hypotheses
Based on what you learned in this chapter, which of the drugs listed under Possible Materials do you think are stimulants? Which are depressants? How will they affect the heart rate in *Daphnia*? Make a hypothesis concerning how each of the drugs listed will affect heart rate.

Objectives
In this BioLab, you will:
■ **Measure** the resting heart rate in *Daphnia*.
■ **Compare** the resting heart rate with the heart rate when a drug is applied.

Possible Materials
aged tap water
Daphnia culture
dilute solutions of coffee, tea, cola, ethyl alcohol, tobacco, and cough medicine (containing dextromethorphan)

dropper
microscope
microscope slide

Safety Precautions
CAUTION: *Do not drink any of the solutions used in this lab. Always wear goggles in the lab. Use caution when working with a microscope, microscope slides, and glassware.*

Skill Handbook
If you need help with this lab, refer to the **Skill Handbook**.

PROCEDURE

Teaching Strategies
■ Age tap water by leaving it in a beaker overnight.
■ Set up a distribution station for all the solutions being tested.

■ *Daphnia* that are placed in the aged tap water after being tested with a drug can be reused again later.

Possible Procedures
Students should measure the resting heart rate of each *Daphnia* before adding several drops of one of the solutions and measuring the heart rate again.

1. Design an experiment to measure the effect on heart rate of four of the drug-containing substances in the Possible Materials list.

2. Design and construct a data table for recording your data.

Check the Plan

1. Be sure to consider what you will use as a control.

2. Plan to add two drops of a drug-containing substance directly to the slide.

3. When you are finished testing one drug, you will need to flush the used *Daphnia* with the solution into a beaker of aged tap water provided by your teacher. Plan to use a new *Daphnia* for each substance tested.

4. *Make sure your teacher has approved your experimental plan before you proceed further.*

5. Begin your experiment by using a dropper to place a single *Daphnia* on a slide. Observe the animal on low power and find its heart. **CAUTION:** *Wash your hands with soap and water immediately after making observations.*

6. **CLEANUP AND DISPOSAL** Collect the used *Daphnia* in a beaker of aged tap water and give them to your teacher. Make wise choices about the disposal or recycling of other materials.

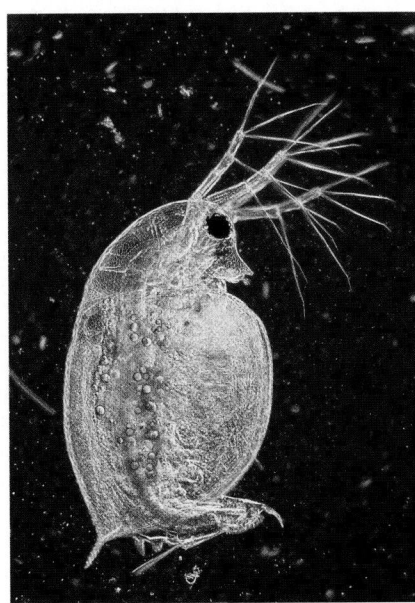

Daphnia

Color-enhanced SEM
Magnification: 1200×

ANALYZE AND CONCLUDE

1. **Infer** Examine your results and infer which drugs are stimulants. Which are depressants?

2. **Check Your Hypotheses** Compare your predicted results with the experimental data. Explain whether or not your data support your hypotheses regarding the drugs' effects.

3. **Draw Conclusions** How do the drugs affect the heart rate of this animal?

4. **ERROR ANALYSIS** Compare your data to that of other groups. How can you account for differences in results with other lab groups? How would you alter your experiment if you did it again?

Apply Your Skill

Use Variables, Constants, and Controls
Many other over-the-counter drugs are available. You may wish to test their effect on the heart rate of *Daphnia*.

 Web Links To find out more about drug effects, visit in.bdol.glencoe.com/drug_effects

36.3   THE EFFECTS OF DRUGS   **965**

ANALYZE AND CONCLUDE

1. Stimulants are coffee, tea, cola, and tobacco. Cough medicine may also be listed. Depressants are ethyl alcohol and cough medicine if it contains dextromethorphen hydrobromide.

2. Some students' hypotheses will be confirmed by their data; others' will be rejected.

3. Stimulants speed up the animal's heart rate. Depressants slow the heart rate.

4. **ERROR ANALYSIS** Answers will vary. Differences may be due to how much water was on the slide when they added the drug-containing substance. Different *Daphnia* may be more or less sensitive to the drug.

Assessment
Performance Have students each prepare a laboratory report that includes the experimental plan, the data table, and the answers to Analyze and Conclude, to be placed in their journals. Use the Performance Task Assessment List for Lab Report in **PASC**, p. 119. **L2**

Apply Your Skill

Use Variables, Constants, and Controls Have students compare the effects of four over-the-counter cough medicines on the heart rate of *Daphnia*. They should carefully make equal dilutions of each medicine after determining the concentration of the active drug in each (listed on the package). **L2**

Indiana Academic Standards

Pages 964–965: B.1.14

Data and Observations

Drug	Heart rate/min
No drug	240
Coffee	270
Cola	270
Tea	280
Ethyl alchohol	215
Tobacco	300
Cough medicine	Heart rate varies with brand

CLEANUP AND DISPOSAL

 The dilute solutions of the coffee, tea, cola, ethyl alcohol, tobacco, and cough medicine can be poured down the drain with lots of running water.

BIO TECHNOLOGY

Purpose

Students learn how radioactive isotopes are used in positron emission tomography (PET).

Background

To make use of PET scanners, patients are injected with short-lived radioisotopes such as C-11, N-13, or O-15. As the radioisotope circulates through the body, it emits positively charged particles called *positrons*. The positrons collide with electrons in body tissues, causing the release of gamma rays that are detected by PET receptors.

Teaching Strategies

PET scanners can be used to measure activities that involve circulation of chemicals or chemical reactions in the body. Ask students to list some body activities that doctors might be able to monitor with PET scanners.

Applying Biotechnology

PET scans allow scientists to observe the brain in action. Students may find a variety of examples of research being done using PET scans including studies on brain injury, vision, emotions, mental illness, and drug addiction. Research continues as to the exact manner in which the brain receives signals and reacts to different stimuli. As more is learned about brain function, new treatments for disease can be researched as well.

Scanning the Mind

Advancements in medical technology have led to instruments—such as X-ray and magnetic resonance imaging (MRI) machines—that can examine the human body in a noninvasive way. In addition to X rays and MRIs, another technology has been added to the medical toolbox—positron emission tomography (PET). This instrument is unique in that it allows a physician to view internal body tissues while they carry out their normal daily functions.

PET scanners are excellent tools for studying the human brain. By monitoring either the blood flow to an area or the amount of glucose being metabolized there, doctors are able to pinpoint active sections of the brain.

Here's how it works: The patient is injected with a compound containing radioactive isotopes. These isotopes emit detectable radiation and can be tracked by the sensitive PET scanner. Computers create a picture of brain activity by converting the energy emitted from the radioisotopes into a colorful map. The image indicates the location of an activity, such as glucose utilization, and its relative intensity in various regions.

Valuable research PET scanners are important in brain research, including the detection and diagnosis of brain tumors, the evaluation of damage due to stroke, and the mapping of brain functions. PET scans can also be used to see how learning takes place in the brain. The images on this page show activity in the left and right brains of two people. Each person was given a list of nouns and asked to visualize them. The unpracticed brain (top) had no previous experience with this exercise and thus was forced to engage in a high level of brain activity to perform the task. The practiced brain (bottom), by comparison, was able to picture the words with much less brain activity. Biologists can discover functions of different parts of the brain and their roles in learning.

PET scans

PET scans are also proving useful in the study of drug and alcohol addiction. Addicts can be given the addictive drug and then asked questions about their physical and emotional status while the scanner records metabolic activity in the brain. Researchers hope that information gained about how the brain works from the study of drug addiction will provide help in diagnosing and treating other illnesses such as manic-depressive psychosis and schizophrenia.

Applying Biotechnology

Evaluate Evaluate the impact of research done on the brain through PET scans. What effect has this had on scientific thought and society? What new information about the brain has been discovered through studies using a PET scan? How will this affect future diagnosis and treatment of brain diseases or disorders?

 To find out more about PET scans, visit in.bdol.glencoe.com/biotechnology

Going Further

Students can find out how PET scans are used to distinguish between the two types of breast tumors: those that have estrogen receptors and those that do not have estrogen receptors.

STUDY GUIDE

Section 36.1

The Nervous System

Key Concepts
- The neuron is the basic structural unit of the nervous system. Impulses move along a neuron in a wave of changing charges.
- The central nervous system consists of the brain and spinal cord.
- The peripheral nervous system relays messages to and from the central nervous system. It consists of the somatic and autonomic nervous systems.

Vocabulary
autonomic nervous system (p. 949)
axon (p. 943)
central nervous system (p. 946)
cerebellum (p. 947)
cerebrum (p. 947)
dendrite (p. 943)
medulla oblongata (p. 947)
neuron (p. 943)
neurotransmitter (p. 946)
parasympathetic nervous system (p. 949)
peripheral nervous system (p. 947)
reflex (p. 948)
somatic nervous system (p. 948)
sympathetic nervous system (p. 949)
synapse (p. 946)

Section 36.2

The Senses

Key Concepts
- The senses of taste and smell are responses to chemical stimulation.
- The sense of sight is a response to light stimulation.
- The senses of hearing, balance, and touch are responses to mechanical stimulation.

Vocabulary
cochlea (p. 954)
cones (p. 952)
retina (p. 952)
rods (p. 952)
semicircular canals (p. 954)
taste bud (p. 952)

Section 36.3

The Effects of Drugs

Key Concepts
- Drugs act on the body's nervous system.
- Some medicinal uses of drugs include relieving pain and treating cardiovascular problems and nervous disorders.
- The misuse of drugs involves taking a medicine for an unintended use. Drug abuse involves using a drug for a non-medical purpose.

Vocabulary
addiction (p. 959)
depressant (p. 958)
drug (p. 956)
hallucinogen (p. 962)
narcotic (p. 957)
stimulant (p. 958)
tolerance (p. 959)
withdrawal (p. 959)

FOLDABLES
Study Organizer To help you review the senses, use the Organizational Study Fold on page 951.

 in.bdol.glencoe.com/vocabulary_puzzlemaker

Key Concepts
Summary statements can be used by students to review the major concepts of the chapter.

 Biology Online

Visit in.bdol.glencoe.com
/self_check_quiz
/vocabulary_puzzlemaker
/chapter_test
/standardized_test

VOCABULARY PUZZLEMAKER

 For additional help with vocabulary, have students access the Vocabulary PuzzleMaker online at in.bdol.glencoe.com/vocabulary_puzzlemaker

FOLDABLES™
Have students use their Foldables to review the content of Section 36.2.

Use the ExamView®Pro Test Bank CD-ROM to:
- Create **multiple versions** of tests
- Create **modified** tests with one mouse click for **inclusion** students
- **Edit** existing questions and **add** your own questions
- Build tests aligned with state standards using built-in **State Curriculum Tags**
- Change **English** tests to **Spanish** with one mouse click and vice versa

 Indiana Academic Standards
Pages 966–967: B.1.14

967

Chapter 36 Assessment

The Princeton Review Questions and answers have been aligned and verified by The Princeton Review.

Vocabulary Review

1. cochlea, not part of a neuron
2. reflex, not a retinal cell
3. retina, not related to drugs
4. taste bud, not part of nerve impulse transmission
5. cerebrum, not a consequence of drug use
6. neuron, not a class of drugs

Understanding Key Concepts

7. D   9. A
8. C   10. A
11. 1. neurons; 2. dendrites; 3. axons; 4. neurotransmitters; 5. synapses

Constructed Response

12. The somatic nervous system is made of the 12 pairs of cranial nerves from the brain, the 31 pairs of spinal nerves from the spinal cord, and all their branches. These nerves contain both sensory and motor neurons. The autonomic nervous system carries impulses only from the central nervous system to internal organs to control involuntary responses.

13. Sensory receptors in skin, ears, eyes, and nose sense an external stimulus. Sensory neurons transmit an impulse to the spinal cord and/or brain. The message is interpreted and motor neurons carry a response back out to muscles or glands.

14. increased heart rate, increased breathing rate, and other reactions seen in the fight-or-flight response

Thinking Critically

15. A spinal cord injury causes damage to the nerves within the spinal canal affecting the ability of the nerves to send and receive messages from the brain to the body.

16. By blocking the opening of sodium channels, the nerve cells cannot depolarize and thus cannot initiate or transmit a nerve impulse to the brain to signal pain.

Vocabulary Review

Review the Chapter 36 vocabulary words listed in the Study Guide on page 967. For each set of vocabulary words, choose the one that does not belong. Explain why it does not belong.

1. axon—cochlea—dendrite
2. rods—cones—reflex
3. retina—depressant—stimulant
4. synapse—taste bud—neurotransmitter
5. tolerance—addiction—cerebrum
6. neuron—drug—hallucinogen

Understanding Key Concepts

7. Which of the following is NOT a type of neuron?
   A. interneuron
   B. sensory neuron
   C. motor neuron
   D. stimulus neuron

8. Which portion of the brain controls balance, posture, and coordination?
   A. pons
   B. medulla oblongata
   C. cerebellum
   D. cerebrum

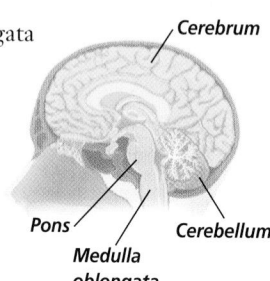

Cerebrum

Pons

Cerebellum

Medulla oblongata

9. Which part of the ear is involved in maintaining balance?
   A. semicircular canals
   B. oval window
   C. stapes
   D. cochlea

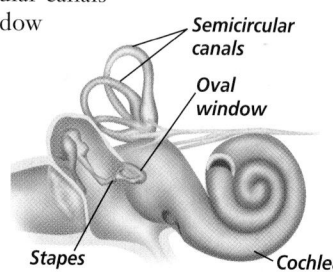

Semicircular canals

Oval window

Stapes   Cochlea

10. Which type of neuron carries impulses toward the brain?
    A. sensory   C. association
    B. motor   D. none of the above

11. Complete the concept map by using the following vocabulary terms: neurons, neurotransmitters, axons, dendrites, synapses.

1.

contain branchlike extensions called   contain long, single extensions called

2.   3.

release chemicals called

4.

which diffuse across

5.

Constructed Response

12. **Open Ended** Compare and contrast the somatic nervous system and the autonomic nervous system.

13. **Open Ended** Identify how the nervous system responds to external stimuli.

14. **Open Ended** The drug ephedrine is a sympathetic nervous system mimic drug. What could be the effects of this drug on the body?

Thinking Critically

15. **REAL WORLD BIOCHALLENGE** Visit in.bdol.glencoe.com to answer the following questions. What is a spinal cord injury? What treatments are available? What research is currently being done to help people overcome the effects of a spinal cord injury?

16. **Infer** Local anesthetics block the opening of sodium channels in nerve cells. Explain how this would affect the transmission of pain impulses.

 in.bdol.glencoe.com/chapter_test

RUBRIC

Evaluating Open-Ended Questions
Open-ended assessment questions are graded by using a multilevel rubric that guides you in assessing a student's knowledge of a particular concept. The following rubric is a sample scoring device.

17. Recognize Cause and Effect During a rough ferry crossing, the horizon seems to be moving up and down as you hold on to the railing. You begin to feel seasick. Explain what is happening in your body that might be causing you to feel this sensation.

18. Hypothesize Patients with multiple sclerosis lose the ability to control their movement. This is due to a continual loss of myelin sheaths on motor neurons. Form a hypothesis as to how this would cause these patients to lose control of their ability to move.

17. The semicircular canals are overstimulated as a result of all the movement.

18. One possible hypothesis is that without the myelin sheath, the motor neurons are unable to conduct a nerve impulse.

The assessed Indiana standard appears next to the question.

All questions aligned and verified by

End-of-Course Assessment Practice

Part 1 Multiple Choice

Use the diagram to answer questions 19–21.

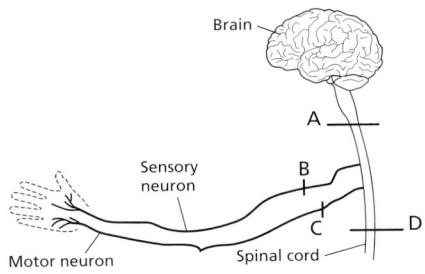

19. The diagram above shows four possible
B.1.17 blockages of nerve impulses at A, B, C, and D by an anesthetic. If the patient can move her hand but can't feel it, where is the blockage?
  A. A   **C.** C
  B. B   **D.** D

20. If the patient can feel a pinprick but cannot
B.1.17 move her hand, where is the blockage?
  A. A   **C.** C
  B. B   **D.** D

21. If the patient cannot feel a pinprick or move
B.1.17 her hand, where is the blockage?
  A. A   **C.** C
  B. B   **D.** D

Study the graph and answer questions 22–25.

22. What is the membrane potential of Neuron A when it is polarized?
  A. −80 mV   **C.** −55 mV
  B. −70 mV   **D.** +30 mV

23. What is the membrane potential of Neuron B when it is polarized?
  A. −80 mV   **C.** −55 mV
  B. −70 mV   **D.** +30 mV

24. What is the highest membrane potential reached by Neuron A while it is depolarized?
  A. −80 mV   **C.** −55 mV
  B. −70 mV   **D.** +30 mV

End-of-Course Assessment Practice

19. B   **21.** A   **23.** A
20. C   **22.** B   **24.** D
25. The threshold may not be reached and a nerve impulse may not be transmitted. Student answers will vary.
26. If hair cells are damaged they may no longer transmit impulses.

Answer Sheet A practice answer sheet can be found on p. 121 of *Unit 10 FAST FILE Resources.*

Part 2 Constructed Response/Grid In

Record your answers on your answer document.

25. Open Ended Neuron B is hyperpolarized, that is, it is more difficult for the threshold to be
B.1.15 reached. Explain how this condition would affect the transmission of nerve impulses in this neuron. Form a hypothesis about how the neuron became hyperpolarized.

26. Open Ended Exposure to loud noises, such as a jet engine, damages the hair cells in the
B.1.15 cochlea. Explain why extended exposure to loud noise results in hearing loss.

 in.bdol.glencoe.com/standardized_test

CHAPTER 36 ASSESSMENT **969**

RUBRIC

SCORE	CRITERIA
4	A correct solution that is supported by well-developed, accurate explanations.
3	A generally correct solution, but may contain minor flaws in reasoning.

SCORE	CRITERIA
2	A partially correct interpretation and/or solution to the problem.
1	A correct solution with no supporting evidence or explanation.
0	An incorrect solution or no solution is given.

Indiana Academic Standards

Pages 968–969: B.1.14

Chapter 37 Organizer

Section Objectives	National Science Standards	State/Local Standards	Advanced Lab and Demo Planning
Section 37.1 1 1/2 sessions, 1 block 1. **Identify** the structures involved in external respiration. 2. **Contrast** external and cellular respiration. 3. **Explain** the mechanics of breathing.	UCP.1, UCP.2, UCP.5; A.1, A.2; F.1	**Indiana Standards** B.1.14, B.1.19	**Student Labs:** Problem-Solving Lab 37.1, p. 973 Investigate BioLab, p. 988 See materials below. **Teacher Demonstration:** Quick Demo, p. 972: anatomical model of the respiratory organs
Section 37.2 1 1/2 sessions, 1 block 4. **Distinguish** among the various components of blood and among blood groups. 5. **Trace** the route blood takes through the body and heart. 6. **Explain** how heart rate is controlled.	UCP.1, UCP.2, UCP.5; A.1, A.2; F.1, F.5; G.1	**Indiana Standards** B.1.3, B.1.14, B.1.15, B.1.19, B.1.20, B.1.21	**Student Labs:** MiniLab 37.1, p. 981 Problem-Solving Lab 37.2, p. 983 Additional Lab, p. 982: distilled water, 250-mL flask, plastic straw, dropper bottle of phenolphthalein indicator, dropper bottle of 0.04% NaOH **Teacher Demonstration:** Quick Demo, p. 978: water, drinking glass
Section 37.3 2 sessions, 1 block 7. **Describe** the structures and functions of the urinary system. 8. **Explain** the kidneys' role in maintaining homeostasis.	UCP.1, UCP.2, UCP.3, UCP.5; A.1, A.2; F.1, F.5, F.6; G.1, G.2	**Indiana Standards** B.1.3, B.1.14, B.1.15, B.1.17, B.1.19, B.1.20	**Student Lab:** MiniLab 37.2, p. 987: grease pencil, glass slide, dropper, simulated "normal urine," simulated "abnormal urine," glucose test paper, forceps **Teacher Demonstration:** Quick Demo, p. 985: sheep kidney
End of Chapter Assessment Student Edition Study Guide, p. 991 Content Assessment, pp. 992–993		**Indiana Standards** B.1.14, B.1.15, B.1.19, B.1.20	**Student Lab:** Investigate BioLab, p. 988: round balloon, string (1 m), metric ruler, clock or watch with second hand

Key to Teaching Strategies

L1 Level 1 activities should be appropriate for students with learning difficulties.

L2 Level 2 activities should be within the ability range of all students.

L3 Level 3 activities are designed for above-average students.

ELL ELL activities should be within the ability range of English Language Learners.

COOP LEARN Cooperative Learning activities are designed for small group work.

Legend

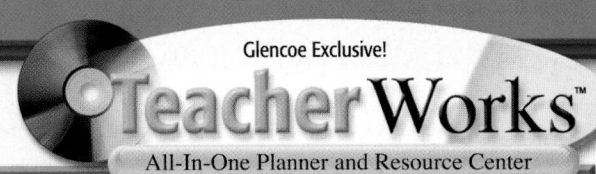

Glencoe Exclusive!
Teacher Works™
All-In-One Planner and Resource Center

Reproducible Masters and Transparencies	Technology

Reproducible Masters and Transparencies

Unit 10 FAST FILE Resources
BioLab Worksheet, pp. 129–130
Real World BioApplications, pp. 131–132
Reinforcement and Study Guide in English, p. 133
Reinforcement and Study Guide in Spanish, p. 137
Transparency Worksheet, p. 143
Section Focus Transparency 90

Technology

⊙ **Interactive Chalkboard CD-ROM: Section 37.1 Presentation**
⊙ TeacherWorks™ **CD-ROM**
Guided Reading Audio Summaries MP3

Unit 10 FAST FILE Resources
MiniLab Worksheet, pp. 125–126
Reinforcement and Study Guide in English, pp. 134–135
Reinforcement and Study Guide in Spanish, pp. 138–139
Concept Mapping, p. 141
Critical Thinking/Problem Solving, p. 142
Transparency Worksheets, pp. 144, 147–152, 155–156
Laboratory Manual, pp. 237–240
Probeware Labs, pp. 33–36, 37–40
Inside Story Poster
Section Focus Transparency 91
Basic Concepts Transparencies 70, 71, 72
Reteaching Skills Transparencies 54

⊙ **Interactive Chalkboard CD-ROM: Section 37.2 Presentation**
⊙ TeacherWorks™ **CD-ROM**
Guided Reading Audio Summaries MP3
⊙ **Virtual Labs CD-ROM**
Virtual Lab: Blood Pressure

Unit 10 FAST FILE Resources
MiniLab Worksheet, p. 127
Reinforcement and Study Guide in English, p. 136
Reinforcement and Study Guide in Spanish, p. 140
Transparency Worksheets, pp. 145, 153–154
Section Focus Transparency 92
Basic Concepts Transparency 73

⊙ **Interactive Chalkboard CD-ROM: Section 37.3 Presentation**
⊙ TeacherWorks™ **CD-ROM**
Guided Reading Audio Summaries MP3

Unit 10 FAST FILE Resources
Chapter Assessment, pp. 157–162
Student Recording Sheet, p. 163

The Princeton Review **Reviewing Biology,** pp. 73–74

⊙ **Interactive Chalkboard: Chapter 37 Assessment**
⊙ **MindJogger Videoquizzes DVD/VHS**
⊙ **ExamView® Pro Test Bank CD-ROM**
⊙ TeacherWorks™ **CD-ROM**
⊙ **Succeeding on National Standards CD-ROM**

    in.bdol.glencoe.com
/self_check_quiz
/vocabulary_puzzlemaker
/chapter_test
/standardized_test

Indicates materials created specifically for Indiana.

Short on Time?

BIODIGEST The BioDigest at the end of this unit can be used as a(n):

- preview to introduce important unit concepts.
- overview if time does not permit teaching the entire chapter.
- review of key unit concepts.

Understanding the Photo

As the climber works her way up this rock cliff, the respiratory and circulatory systems must meet the oxygen and nutrient demands of her cells and rid her body of products produced by the metabolism of glucose in her cells, especially her muscle cells.

PowerPoint® Presentations

This CD-ROM is an editable Microsoft® PowerPoint® presentation that includes:

- Section presentations
- Section checks
- Image bank
- Hot links to Biology Online
- All transparencies

Respiration, Circulation, and Excretion

What You'll Learn

- You will identify the functions of the respiratory system and explain the mechanics of breathing.
- You will describe the structure and function of the different types of blood cells and trace the pathway of blood circulation through the body.
- You will describe the structure and function of the urinary system.

Why It's Important

With a knowledge of how your circulatory, respiratory, and urinary systems function, you will understand how your cells receive, deliver, and remove materials to maintain your body's homeostasis.

Understanding ▶ the Photo

Coordination of the respiratory and circulatory systems allows blood to deliver much needed oxygen and nutrients to the hard-working cells of this climber.

Biology Online

Visit in.bdol.glencoe.com to
- study the entire chapter online
- access Web Links for more information and activities on respiration, circulation, and excretion
- review content with the Interactive Tutor and self-check quizzes

970

Two-Minute Chapter Launcher

Activity Have students calculate the daily heart output of a person whose heart beats 72 beats per minute with a blood volume of 70 mL per beat (72 beats per minute × 70 mL per beat × 60 minutes per hour × 24 hours per day = 7 257 600 mL/1000 = 7258 liters per day). Then ask them to calculate how much blood the heart beats per year (7258 liters per day × 365 days per year = 2 649 170 liters per year). Hold up a liter flask for students to get an idea of how much blood is in a liter. Have them think about how much blood this amazing pump circulates in a lifetime without mechanical repair! **L2**

The Respiratory System

Indiana Standards Standard B.1.19 Recognize and describe that metabolism consists of the production, modification, transport, and exchange of materials that are required for the maintenance of life.

SECTION PREVIEW

Objectives

Identify the structures involved in external respiration.

Contrast external and cellular respiration.

Explain the mechanics of breathing.

Review Vocabulary
diaphragm: sheet of muscles beneath the lungs that separates the chest cavity from the abdominal cavity (p. 843)

New Vocabulary
trachea
alveoli

FOLDABLES™
Study Organizer

Systems Make the following Foldable to help you organize information about the respiratory, circulatory, and urinary systems.

STEP 1 Fold one piece of paper lengthwise into thirds.

STEP 2 Fold the paper widthwise into fourths.

STEP 3 Unfold, lay the paper lengthwise, and draw lines along the folds.

STEP 4 Label your table as shown.

	Organs	Function
Respiratory system		
Circulatory system		
Urinary system		

Make a Table As you read Chapter 37, complete the table by describing the organs and functions of the respiratory, circulatory, and urinary systems.

Passageways and Lungs

Your respiratory system is made of a pair of lungs and a series of passageways, each one extending deeper into your body. These passageways include the nasal passages, the throat, the windpipe, and the bronchi. When you hear the term respiratory system, you probably think of breathing. However, breathing is just one of the functions that the respiratory system carries out. Respiration, the process of gas exchange, is another important function performed by the respiratory system. Respiration includes all of the mechanisms involved in getting oxygen to the cells of your body and getting rid of carbon dioxide. Recall that cellular respiration also involves the formation of ATP within the cells.

The path air takes

The first step in the process of respiration involves taking air into your body through your nose or mouth. Air flows into the pharynx, or throat, passes the epiglottis, and moves through the larynx. It then travels down the windpipe, or **trachea** (TRAY kee uh), a tubelike passageway that leads to two tubes, or bronchi (BRAHN ki) (singular, bronchus), which lead into the lungs. When you swallow food, the epiglottis covers the entrance to the trachea, which prevents food from getting into the air passages.

37.1 THE RESPIRATORY SYSTEM **971**

Physical Science Connection

Elements, compounds, and mixtures in everyday life
The atmosphere is a mixture of gases, liquids, and solids. The gases include nitrogen, oxygen, water vapor, argon, and carbon dioxide. Smoke and wind-blown dust particles are some of the solids found in air, and liquid water droplets are seen as clouds.

1 Focus

INTERACTIVE CHALKBOARD
PowerPoint® Presentations

Bellringer
Section Focus Transparency 90

Transparency **90** Take a Breath
SECTION FOCUS
Use with Chapter 37, Section 37.1

❶ What happens when the sides of the bellows are pulled apart? Why does that happen?

❷ What structures in the human body are comparable to the bellows and to the hands that push and pull on the bellows?

BIOLOGY: The Dynamics of Life   SECTION FOCUS TRANSPARENCIES

FOLDABLES™
For an additional Foldables activity idea, see the Chapter 37 Foldables page in *Unit 10 FAST FILE Resources.*

Physical Science Connection

Ask students to arrange the gases mentioned according to decreasing abundance in Earth's atmosphere. Then have them identify each as an element, compound, or mixture. nitrogen—element; oxygen—element; argon—element; carbon dioxide—compound; or water—compound (Abundance of water is variable.)

RESOURCE MANAGER

Unit 10 *FAST FILE* Resources
BioLab Worksheet, pp. 129–130
Real World BioApplications, pp. 131–132
Reinforcement and Study Guide in English, p. 133

Reinforcement and Study Guide in Spanish, p. 137
Transparency Worksheet, p. 143
Reading Essentials for Biology, Section 37.1
 Section Focus Transparency 90

Indiana Academic Standards

Pages 970–971: B.1.19

2 Teach

Respiratory System Use an anatomical model of the respiratory organs to point out the parts of the respiratory system as they are mentioned in the chapter.

Caption Question Answer
Figure 37.1 The functions of the respiratory system include breathing and gas exchange (oxygen, carbon dioxide) in the lungs and at the cells. Mucous membranes with cilia in the nasal cavity, trachea, and bronchi filter air to prevent foreign particles from reaching the lungs.

Caption Question Answer
Figure 37.2 When the diaphragm contracts and enlarges the chest cavity, the pressure in the lungs lowers.

Portfolio

Tracing the Path of Air Ask students to make a circular flowchart describing the pathway and processes involved in respiration. One-half of the circle should show events that take place as the diaphragm contracts, the other half should show events that take place as the diaphragm relaxes. Have them include the charts in their portfolios. **L2**

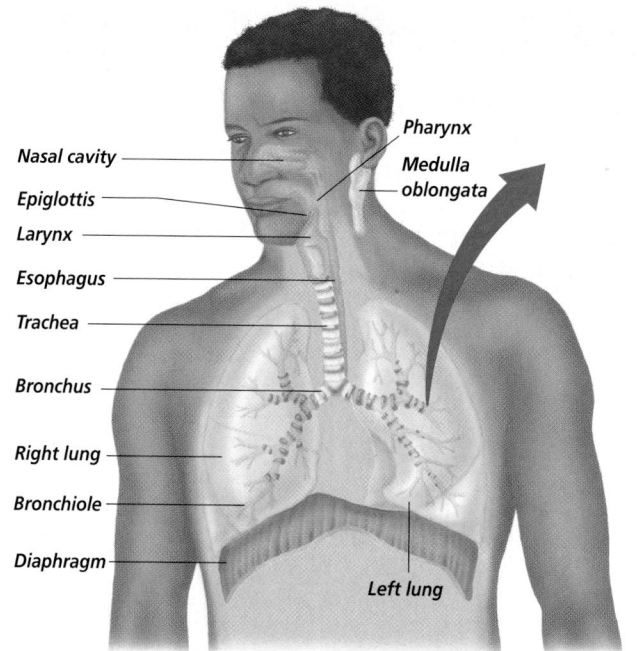

Figure 37.1
As air passes through the respiratory system, it travels through narrower and narrower passageways until it reaches the alveoli.
Explain *Interpret the functions of the respiratory system.*

Word Origin

alveoli from the Latin word *alveolus,* meaning "cavity" or "hollow"; The alveoli are small air sacs of the lung.

Cleaning dirty air

The air you breathe is far from clean. An individual living in an urban area breathes in millions of particles of foreign matter each day. To prevent most of this material from reaching the lungs, the nasal cavity, trachea, and bronchi are lined with ciliated cells that secrete mucus. The cilia constantly beat upward in the direction of your throat, where foreign material can be swallowed or expelled by coughing or sneezing. Follow the passage of air through the respiratory system in *Figure 37.1.*

Alveoli: The place of gas exchange

Like the branches of a tree, each bronchus branches into bronchioles, which in turn branch into numerous microscopic tubules that eventually open into thousands of thin-walled sacs called alveoli. **Alveoli** (al VEE uh li) are the sacs of the lungs where oxygen and carbon dioxide are exchanged by

diffusion between the air and blood. The clusters of alveoli are surrounded by networks of tiny blood vessels, or capillaries. Blood in these vessels has come from the cells of the body and contains wastes from cellular respiration. Diffusion of gases takes place easily because the wall of each alveolus, and the walls of each capillary, are only one cell thick. External respiration involves the exchange of oxygen or carbon dioxide between the air in the alveoli and the blood that circulates through the walls of the alveoli, and is shown in the inset portion of *Figure 37.1.*

Blood transport of gases

Once oxygen from the air diffuses into the blood vessels surrounding the alveoli, it is pumped by the heart to the body cells, where it is used for cellular respiration. In an earlier chapter, you learned that cellular respiration is the process by which cells use oxygen to break down glucose and release energy in the form of ATP. Carbon dioxide is

 CHALLENGE ACTIVITY

Blood Chemistry Have students who need an additional challenge investigate the carbonic acid-bicarbonate buffer system of the blood, which is important in maintaining body pH. Ask them to find out how carbon dioxide levels are medically tested in the body and what other arterial blood gas values are gathered. Ask them to investigate what types of things upset the acid-base balance of the body, such as hyperventilation and smoking. **L3**

a waste product of this process. The carbon dioxide diffuses into the blood, which carries it back to the lungs.

As a result, the blood that comes to the alveoli from the body's cells is high in carbon dioxide and low in oxygen. Carbon dioxide from the body diffuses from the blood into the air spaces in the alveoli. During exhalation, this carbon dioxide is removed from your body. At the same time, oxygen diffuses from the air in the alveoli into the blood, making the blood rich in oxygen. Use the *Problem-Solving Lab* on this page to find out more about how the composition of air changes as it passes through the lungs.

The Mechanics of Breathing

The action of your diaphragm and the muscles between your ribs enable you to breathe in and breathe out. *Figure 37.2* shows how air is drawn in or forced out of the lungs as a result of the diaphragm's position.

Figure 37.2
The diaphragm is located beneath the lungs.
Explain *How does the contraction of the diaphragm affect air pressure in the lungs?*

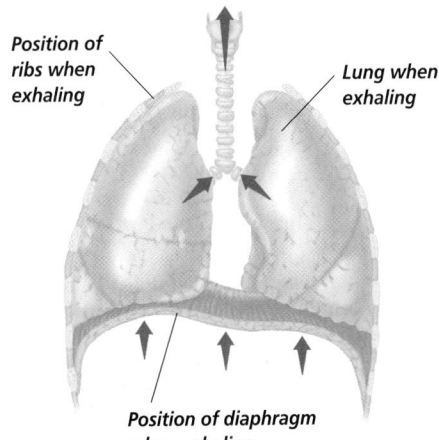

Position of ribs when exhaling

Lung when exhaling

Position of diaphragm when exhaling

A When relaxed, your diaphragm is positioned in a dome shape beneath your lungs, decreasing the volume of the chest cavity and forcing air out of the lungs.

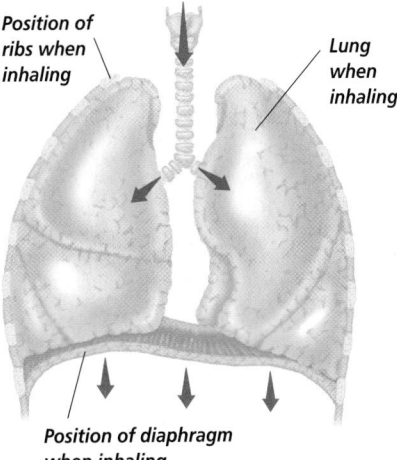

Position of ribs when inhaling

Lung when inhaling

Position of diaphragm when inhaling

B When contracting, the diaphragm flattens, enlarging the chest cavity and drawing air into the lungs.

Problem-Solving Lab 37.1

Interpret Data

How do inhaled and exhaled air compare? Air is composed of a number of different gases. As a result of cellular respiration, the percentages of some of the gases in air are altered by the time air is exhaled from the body.

Solve the Problem

Study the table below. It compares the relative percentages of gases in inhaled and exhaled air.

Comparison of Gases in Inhaled and Exhaled Air		
Gas	Inhaled Air	Exhaled Air
Nitrogen	78.00%	78.00%
Oxygen	21.00%	16.54%
Carbon dioxide	0.03%	4.49%
Other gases	0.97%	0.97%

Thinking Critically

1. **Interpret Data** What information about cellular respiration is conveyed by the data in the table?
2. **Sequence** Trace the pathway that a molecule of nitrogen follows when entering and leaving the lungs. (Note: Normally, nitrogen does enter the blood stream.)
3. **Explain** Why are carbon dioxide levels higher in air that is exhaled?

Problem-Solving Lab 37.1

Purpose

Students use data to support the conclusion that the body uses oxygen and produces carbon dioxide.

Process Skills

analyze information, think critically, compare and contrast, draw a conclusion, sequence

Teaching Strategies

- Tell students that "other gases" include inert gases such as helium, neon, and argon.
- Make certain students understand that the respiratory system delivers oxygen to the circulatory system for distribution throughout the body.

Thinking Critically

1. Cells take in oxygen and release carbon dioxide as a result of cellular respiration.
2. bronchus, bronchiole, alveoli, capillary network in alveoli, heart, circulatory system, heart, lung, capillary network, alveoli, bronchiole, bronchus, exhaled to air
3. Carbon dioxide is a waste produced by body cells that exits the body via the lungs.

Modified Assessment

Skill Ask students to draw the pathway oxygen follows inside the body. Use the Performance Task Assessment List for Events Chain in **PASC**, p. 163. **L1**

 INVESTIGATE BioLab

The BioLab at the end of the chapter can be used at this point in the lesson.

INCLUSION STRATEGIES

Visually/Hearing Impaired Pair visually impaired or hearing impaired students with other students. Have them use a model of the respiratory system to explain the mechanics of breathing. Have students point to or touch the various anatomical parts as they are discussed. **L2 ELL**

3 Assess

Extension

Have interested students find out what causes nitrogen narcosis. **L3**

MODIFIED Assessment

Skill Ask students to make a flowchart that describes the pathway of air as it moves into and out of the respiratory system. **L2**

CAREERS IN BIOLOGY

Career Path
Courses in high school: sciences and mathematics
College: two-year associate's or four-year bachelor's degree, or two- or three-year diploma program

For More Information
To learn more about becoming a nurse, students can contact:
American Nurses' Association
600 Maryland Ave. SW
Washington, DC 20024-2571

CAREERS IN BIOLOGY

Registered Nurse

If you want a fast-paced, hands-on career that puts your "people skills" to work, consider becoming a registered nurse.

Skills for the Job
Nurses give care, support, and advice as they help their patients get well or stay well. They may work in hospitals, doctors' offices, schools, nursing homes, rehabilitation centers, or public health agencies. Registered nurses (RNs) must complete a two-year associate degree program, a two- or three-year diploma program, or a four-year bachelor's degree. To become licensed, they must also pass a national test.

For more careers in related fields, visit in.bdol.glencoe.com/careers

When you inhale, the muscles between your ribs contract and your rib cage rises. At the same time, the diaphragm muscle contracts, becomes flattened, and moves lower in the chest cavity. These actions increase the space in the chest cavity, which creates a slight vacuum. Air rushes into your lungs because the air pressure outside your body is greater than the air pressure inside your lungs.

When you exhale, the muscles associated with the ribs relax, and your ribs drop down in the chest cavity. Your diaphragm relaxes, returning to its resting position. The relaxation of these muscles decreases the volume of the chest cavity and forces most of the air out of the alveoli.

The alveoli in healthy lungs are elastic, they stretch as you inhale and return to their original size as you exhale. The alveoli still contain a small amount of air after you exhale. Measure your breathing rate in the *BioLab* at the end of this chapter.

Control of Respiration

Breathing is usually an involuntary process. It is partially controlled by an internal feedback mechanism that involves signals being sent to the medulla oblongata about the chemistry of your blood. The medulla oblongata helps maintain homeostasis. It responds to higher levels of carbon dioxide in your blood by sending nerve signals to the rib muscles and diaphragm. The nerve signals cause these muscles to contract, and you inhale. When breathing becomes more rapid, as during exercise, a more rapid exchange of gases between air and blood occurs.

✔**Reading Check** **Describe** the relationship between an internal feedback mechanism and the rate of respiration.

Section Assessment

Understanding Main Ideas
1. Describe the path an oxygen molecule takes as it travels from your nose to a body cell. List each structure of the respiratory system through which it passes.
2. Describe how air in the respiratory tract is cleaned before it reaches the lungs.
3. Contrast external respiration and cellular respiration.
4. Explain the process by which gases are exchanged in the lungs.

Thinking Critically
5. During a temper tantrum, four-year-old Jamal tries to hold his breath. His parents are afraid that he will be harmed by this behavior. How will Jamal be affected by holding his breath?

SKILL REVIEW
6. **Sequence** What is the sequence of muscle actions that takes place during inhalation and exhalation? For more help, refer to *Sequence* in the **Skill Handbook**.

974 RESPIRATION, CIRCULATION, AND EXCRETION

 in.bdol.glencoe.com/self_check_quiz

Section Assessment

1. nose, pharynx, epiglottis, larynx, trachea, bronchi, alveoli, blood, cells
2. Particles are trapped in mucus. Cilia beat the mucus up the throat where it can be expelled or swallowed.
3. External respiration is the exchange of oxygen and carbon dioxide in the alveoli. Cellular respiration uses oxygen to break down glucose inside the cells.
4. In the alveoli, oxygen from the air diffuses into, and carbon dioxide diffuses out of the blood.
5. As carbon dioxide builds up in the blood, the child's medulla will stimulate his muscles to contract so that he inhales.
6. During inhalation, muscles between the ribs and the diaphragm contract. During exhalation, these muscles relax.

The Circulatory System

Indiana Standards Standard B.1.19 Recognize and describe that metabolism consists of the production, modification, transport, and exchange of materials that are required for the maintenance of life.

Vital Functions

Using Prior Knowledge You know that when you scrape your knee that blood will flow from the wound. What can you do to stop the bleeding? Applying direct pressure to the wound limits bleeding until the blood can clot. Forming clots is one function of the blood. Blood also carries oxygen from your lungs and nutrients from your digestive system to your cells, then hauls away cellular wastes. Together, your blood, your heart, and a network of blood vessels make up your circulatory system.

Infer *If the blood could not carry out its functions, how would this affect other cells in the body?*

A blood clot is composed of a network of fibers in which blood cells are trapped.

SECTION PREVIEW

Objectives
Distinguish among the various components of blood and among blood groups.

Trace the route blood takes through the body and heart.

Explain how heart rate is controlled.

Review Vocabulary
tissue: groups of cells that work together to perform a specific function (p. 210)

New Vocabulary
plasma
red blood cell
hemoglobin
white blood cell
platelet
antigen
antibody
artery
capillary
vein
atrium
ventricle
vena cava
aorta
pulse
blood pressure

Your Blood: Fluid Transport

Your blood is a tissue composed of fluid, cells, and fragments of cells. *Table 37.1* summarizes information about the components of human blood. The fluid portion of blood is called **plasma.** Plasma is straw colored and makes up about 55 percent of the total volume of blood. Blood cells—both red and white—and cell fragments are suspended in plasma.

Red blood cells: Oxygen carriers

The round, disk-shaped cells in blood are red blood cells. **Red blood cells** carry oxygen to body cells. They make up 44 percent of the total volume of your blood, and are produced in the red bone marrow of your ribs, humerus, femur, sternum, and other long bones.

Red blood cells in humans have nuclei only during an early stage in each cell's development. The nucleus is lost before the cell enters the bloodstream.

Table 37.1 Blood Components

Components	Characteristics
Red blood cells	Transport oxygen and some carbon dioxide; lack a nucleus; contain hemoglobin
White blood cells	Large; several different types; all contain nuclei; defend the body against disease
Platelets	Cell fragments needed for blood clotting
Plasma	Liquid; contains proteins; transports red and white blood cells, platelets, nutrients, enzymes, hormones, gases, and inorganic salts

37.2   THE CIRCULATORY SYSTEM   **975**

---

1 Focus

Bellringer
Section Focus Transparency 91

Using Prior Knowledge

Infer Blood delivers oxygen and nutrients to the cells and removes waste products from cellular respiration. Without this transportation system, cells of the body would die.

✔**Reading Check** (p. 974) The medulla monitors the level of carbon dioxide in your blood. When the level of carbon dioxide rises, the medulla signals the rib muscles and diaphragm to contract more rapidly, increasing breathing rate, which increases the rate the body releases carbon dioxide. This lowers the level of carbon dioxide in your blood.

RESOURCE MANAGER

Unit 10 *FAST FILE* Resources
MiniLab Worksheet, pp. 125–126
Reinforcement and Study Guide in English, pp. 134–135
Reinforcement and Study Guide in Spanish, pp. 138–139
Concept Mapping, p. 141
Critical Thinking/Problem Solving, p. 142
Transparency Worksheets, pp. 144, 147–152, 155–156

Reading Essentials for Biology, Section 37.2
Laboratory Manual, pp. 237–240
Probeware Labs, pp. 33–36, 37–40
Inside Story Poster
🔒 **Section Focus Transparency 91**
🔒 **Basic Concepts Transparencies 70, 71, 72**
🔒 **Reteaching Skills Transparencies 54**

 Indiana Academic Standards

Pages 974–975: B.1.3, B.1.14, B.1.19

2 Teach

Tying to Prior Knowledge

Review diffusion from Chapter 6. Relate this process to how oxygen and carbon dioxide get into the blood.

Portfolio

Summarizing Circulation Have students make a chart that lists the substances that blood carries to and from the heart. Have students identify how each substance is used by the body or the process that releases the substance as a waste product. **L2**

Assessment

Performance Have each student write two questions about blood transport. Arrange students in pairs and have them quiz each other. **L2**

Virtual Lab

CD-ROM Students will determine the major risk factors of hypertension in *Blood Pressure*.

Indiana Academic Standards

Pages 976–977: B.1.3, B.1.19, B.1.20

Figure 37.3
Red blood cells are disk-shaped cells that carry oxygen to tissue cells through thin-walled capillaries.

Side view

2.0 micrometers

Top view

7.5 micrometers

LM Magnification: 200×

Red blood cells remain active in the bloodstream for about 120 days, then they break down and are removed as waste. Old red blood cells are destroyed in your spleen, an organ of the lymphatic system, and in your liver.

Oxygen in the blood

How is oxygen carried by the blood? Red blood cells like those shown in *Figure 37.3* are equipped with an iron-containing protein molecule called **hemoglobin** (HEE muh gloh bun). Oxygen becomes loosely bound to the hemoglobin in blood cells that have entered the lungs.

Figure 37.4
Compared with red blood cells, white blood cells are larger in size and far fewer in number. White blood cells have a nucleus; mature red blood cells do not have a nucleus.

Stained LM Magnification: 250×

Red blood cell

White blood cells

These oxygenated blood cells carry oxygen from the lungs to the body's cells. As blood passes through body tissues with low oxygen concentrations, oxygen is released from the hemoglobin and diffuses into the tissues.

Carbon dioxide in the blood

Hemoglobin carries some carbon dioxide as well as oxygen. You have already learned that, once biological work has been done in a cell, wastes in the form of carbon dioxide diffuse into the blood and are carried in the bloodstream to the lungs. About 70 percent of this carbon dioxide combines with water in the blood plasma to form bicarbonate. The remaining 30 percent travels back to the lungs dissolved in the plasma or attached to hemoglobin molecules that have already released their oxygen into the tissues.

White blood cells: Infection fighters

White blood cells, shown in *Figure 37.4,* play a major role in protecting your body from foreign substances and from microscopic organisms that cause disease. They make up only one percent of the total volume of your blood.

976 RESPIRATION, CIRCULATION, AND EXCRETION

CULTURAL DIVERSITY

Carlos Monge and High-Altitude Physiology Carlos Monge (1884–1970) was a Peruvian scientist who studied the physiology of people who live at high altitudes. He was the founder of the Institute of Andean Biology and Pathology. Introduce students to Monge's research and major findings.

Discuss with students the physiological adaptations of people who live at high altitudes, such as the Aymara and Quechua Indians of South America. Have students relate these adaptations to the proper functioning of the respiratory system. **L2**

Blood clotting

Think about what happens when you cut yourself. If the cut is slight, you usually bleed for a short while, until the blood clots. That's because, in addition to red and white blood cells, your blood also contains small cell fragments called **platelets,** which help blood clot after an injury, as shown in *Figure 37.5.* Platelets help link together a sticky network of protein fibers called fibrin, which forms a web over the wound that traps escaping blood cells. Eventually, a dry, leathery scab forms. Platelets are produced from cells in bone marrow and have a short life span. They are removed from the blood by the spleen and liver after only about one week.

ABO Blood Groups

If a person is injured so severely that a massive amount of blood is lost, a transfusion of blood from a second person may be necessary. Whenever blood is transfused from one person to another, it is important to know to which blood group each person belongs. You have already learned about the four human blood groups—A, B, AB, and O. You inherited the characteristics of one of these blood groups from your parents. Sometimes, the term *blood type* is used to describe the blood group to which a person belongs. If your blood falls into group O, for example, you are said to have type O blood.

Blood surface antigens determine blood group

Differences in blood groups are due to the presence or absence of proteins, called antigens, on the membranes of red blood cells. **Antigens** are substances that stimulate an immune response in the body. As you'll learn in a later chapter, an immune response

defends the body against foreign proteins. The letters A and B stand for the types of blood surface antigens found on human red blood cells.

Blood plasma contains proteins, called **antibodies** (AN tih bahd eez), that are shaped to correspond with the different blood surface antigens. The antibody in the blood plasma reacts with its matching antigen on red blood cells if they are brought into contact with one another. This reaction results in clumped blood cells that can no longer function. Each blood group contains antibodies for the blood surface antigens found only in the other blood groups—not for antigens found on its own red blood cells.

For example, if you have type A blood, you have the A antigen on your red blood cells and the anti-B antibody in your plasma. If you had anti-A antibodies, they would react with your own type A red blood cells. What would happen if you had type A blood and anti-A was added to it by way of a transfusion of type B blood?

Figure 37.5
The whitish, globular structures shown adhering to red blood cells are platelets. **Describe** *What is the function of platelets?*

Color-enhanced SEM Magnification: 120×

37.2   THE CIRCULATORY SYSTEM   **977**

Reinforcement

A for *artery* and *A* for *away* is a mnemonic device that helps students remember that arteries carry blood away from the heart.

Concept Development

If Rh$^+$ antibodies produced by the mother cross the placenta and reach the Rh$^+$ blood of the fetus, the antibodies will destroy the red blood cells of the fetus. This is called hemolytic disease of the newborn (HDN) and can result in the death of the fetus.

Indiana Academic Standards

Pages 978–979: B.1.3, B.1.15, B.1.19, B.1.20, B.1.21

978

An antigen-antibody reaction would occur, resulting in clumped blood cells like those shown in *Figure 37.6B*. Clumped blood cells cannot carry oxygen or nutrients to body cells. Similarly, if you have type B blood, you have the B antigen on your red blood cells and the anti-A antibody in your blood plasma. *Figure 37.6C* illustrates the antigens and antibodies present in each blood group.

Rh factor

Another characteristic of red blood cells involves the presence or absence of an antigen called Rh, or Rhesus factor. Rh factor is an inherited characteristic. People are Rh positive (Rh$^+$) if they have the Rh antigen factor on their red blood cells. They are Rh negative (Rh$^-$) if they don't.

Rh factor can cause complications in some pregnancies. The problem begins when an Rh$^-$ mother becomes pregnant with an Rh$^+$ baby. At birth, the Rh$^+$ baby's blood mixes with the Rh$^-$ blood of the mother, as *Figure 37.7A* illustrates. Upon exposure to the baby's Rh$^+$ antigen factor, the mother will make anti-Rh$^+$ antibodies like those shown in *Figure 37.7B*. If the mother becomes pregnant again, these antibodies can cross the placenta. If the new fetus is Rh$^+$, the anti-Rh$^+$

Figure 37.6
Blood contains both antigens and antibodies.

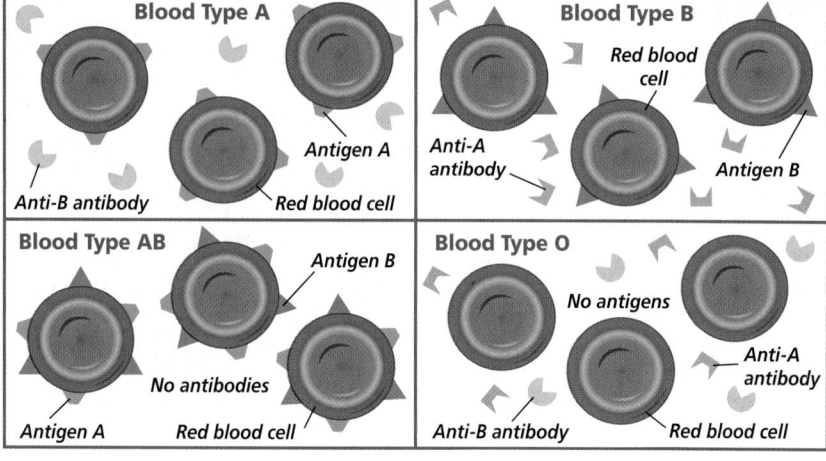

Stained LM Magnification: 82×

Ⓐ Normal blood is shown here. The plasma in your blood contains antibodies that do not react with the antigens on your own red blood cells.

Stained LM Magnification: 100×

Ⓑ The clumped blood illustrates an antibody-antigen reaction that could occur with an incorrect transfusion.

Ⓒ The four types of blood groups have different antigens and antibodies.

Blood Type A
Antigen A
Anti-B antibody
Red blood cell

Blood Type B
Red blood cell
Anti-A antibody
Antigen B

Blood Type AB
Antigen B
No antibodies
Antigen A
Red blood cell

Blood Type O
No antigens
Anti-A antibody
Anti-B antibody
Red blood cell

978

Figure 37.7
If a baby inherits Rh⁺ blood from the father and the mother is Rh⁻, problems can develop if the blood cells of mother and baby mix during birth.

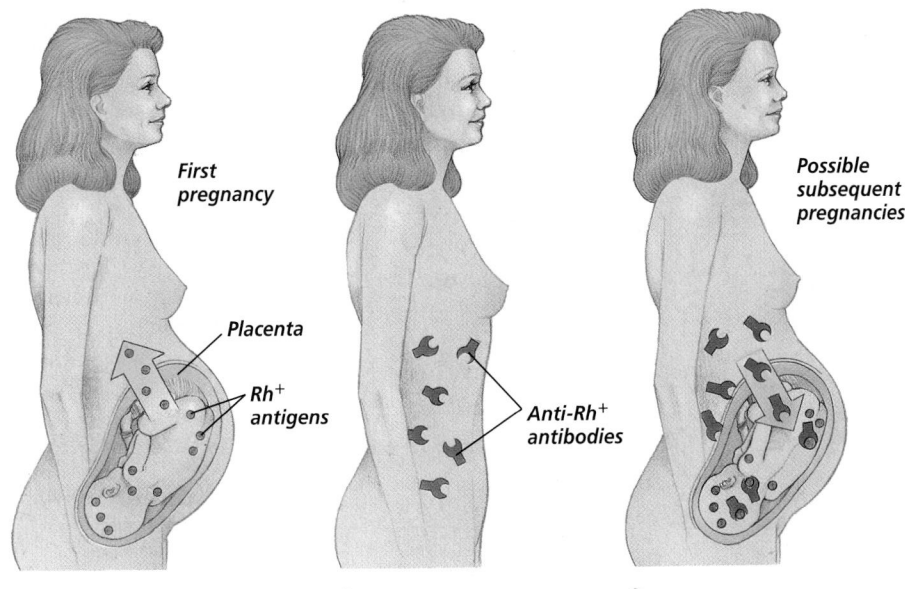

First pregnancy

Placenta

Rh⁺ antigens

Possible subsequent pregnancies

Anti-Rh⁺ antibodies

A Mother is exposed to Rh antigens at the birth of her Rh⁺ baby.

B Mother makes anti-Rh⁺ antibodies.

C During the mother's next pregnancy, Rh antibodies can cross the placenta and endanger the fetus.

antibodies from the mother will destroy red blood cells in the fetus, as shown in *Figure 37.7C.*

Prevention of this problem is possible. When the Rh⁺ fetus is 28 weeks old, and again shortly after the Rh⁺ baby is born, the Rh⁻ mother is given a substance that prevents the production of Rh antibodies in her blood. As a result, the next fetus will not be in danger.

Your Blood Vessels: Pathways of Circulation

Because blood is fluid, it must be channeled through blood vessels like those shown in *Figure 37.8.* The three main types of blood vessels are arteries, capillaries, and veins. Each is different in structure and function.

Arteries are large, thick-walled, muscular, elastic blood vessels that carry blood away from the heart.

Figure 37.8
Arteries carry blood away from the heart, whereas veins carry blood toward the heart. Capillaries form an extensive web in the tissues.

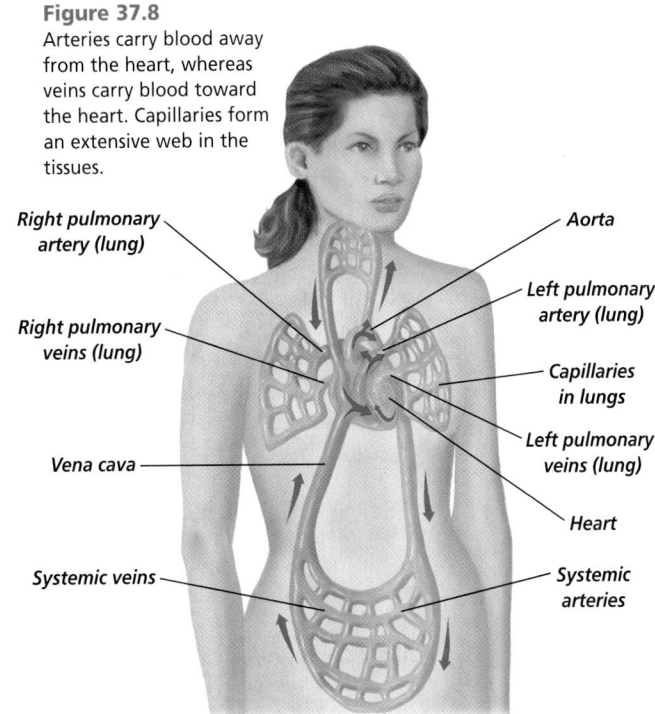

Right pulmonary artery (lung)

Right pulmonary veins (lung)

Vena cava

Systemic veins

Aorta

Left pulmonary artery (lung)

Capillaries in lungs

Left pulmonary veins (lung)

Heart

Systemic arteries

Figure 37.8 How are arteries different from veins? Arteries are much more muscular than veins. Veins contain valves to prevent blood from flowing backward.

Revealing Misconceptions

Arteries carry only oxygenated blood and veins carry only deoxygenated blood.

Uncover the Misconception

Ask students how arteries and veins are defined. Point out that arteries and veins are defined by the direction blood is flowing in them, not by the type of blood they are carrying.

Demonstrate the Concept

Using Figure 37.10, have students look at the pulmonary artery, which is leaving the heart, thus called an artery. Figure 37.10 shows this blood as blue because it is going to the lungs in order to receive oxygen. Point out the pulmonary veins, which are returning blood to the heart. The blood in these veins is colored red because the blood is oxygenated.

Assess New Knowledge

Provide students with a handout showing a simplified circulatory pathway, which includes various arteries and veins with lines drawn to them, similar to Figure 37.8, but without labels. Have students label whether a particular vessel is an artery or vein as a quiz.

PROJECT

Heart Health Survey Have students do research to determine what foods are healthy and unhealthy for the heart. Have them use this information to develop a survey that can be given to other students in the school. Ask students to conduct their surveys and evaluate the diets of high school students.

Have them use the results to answer the following questions. What foods do students eat that are high in saturated fats or cholesterol? How could students improve their diets? Are the school lunches served by your school good for your heart? **L2**

Inquiry

Activity Have students take their pulse rate for one minute. Record the data needed to calculate the class average. Use the class average to introduce and discuss the meaning of average, high and low pulse rates. **L1**

Biology Journal

Aspirin and the Circulatory System Have students research the use of aspirin as a means of preventing heart attack. Have them write reports to include in their journals. **L3**

Portfolio

Diagramming the Heart Have students draw, color, and label a diagram of the heart and lungs. Have them use a blue pencil to draw arrows that represent the pathway of deoxygenated blood, and a red pencil to draw arrows that represent the pathway of oxygenated blood. **L1**

Indiana Academic Standards

Pages 980–981: B.1.3, B.1.14, B.1.15, B.1.19, B.1.20

Figure 37.9
Veins contain one-way valves that work in conjunction with skeletal muscles.

Word Origin

vena cava from the Latin words *vena*, meaning "vein," and *cava*, meaning "empty"; Each vena cava empties blood into the heart.

The blood that they carry is under great pressure. As the heart contracts, it pushes blood through the arteries. Each artery's elastic walls expand slightly. As the heart relaxes, the artery shrinks a bit, which also helps push the blood forward. As a result, blood surges through the arteries in pulses that correspond with the rhythm of the heartbeat.

After the arteries branch off from the heart, they divide into smaller arteries that, in turn, divide into even smaller vessels called arterioles. Arterioles (ar TEER ee ohlz) enter tissues, where they branch into the smallest blood vessels, the capillaries. **Capillaries** (KA puh ler eez) are microscopic blood vessels with walls that are only one cell thick. These vessels are so tiny that red blood cells must move through them in single file. Capillaries form a dense network that reaches virtually every cell in the body. Thin capillary walls enable nutrients and gases to diffuse easily between blood cells and surrounding tissue cells.

As blood leaves the tissues, the capillaries join to form slightly larger vessels called venules. The venules merge to form **veins,** the large blood vessels

that carry blood from the tissues back toward the heart. Blood in veins is not under pressure as great as that in the arteries. In some veins, especially those in your arms and legs, blood travels uphill against gravity. These veins are equipped with valves that prevent blood from flowing backward. *Figure 37.9* shows how these valves function. When your skeletal muscles contract, the top valves open, and blood is forced toward the heart. When the skeletal muscles relax, the top valves close to prevent blood from flowing backward, away from the heart.

✔ **Reading Check** **Explain** why some veins have valves.

Your Heart: The Vital Pump

The thousands of blood vessels in your body would be of little use if there were not a way to move blood through them. The main function of the heart is to keep blood moving constantly throughout the body. Well adapted for its job, the heart is a large organ made of cardiac muscle cells that are rich in energy-producing mitochondria.

All mammalian hearts, including yours, have four chambers. The two upper chambers of the heart are the **atria.** The two lower chambers are the **ventricles.** The walls of each atrium are thinner and less muscular than those of each ventricle. As you will see, the ventricles perform more work than the atria, a factor that helps explain the thickness of their muscles. Each atrium pumps blood into the corresponding ventricle. The left ventricle pumps blood to the entire body, so its muscles are thicker than those of the right ventricle, which pumps blood to the lungs. As a result, your heart is somewhat lopsided.

◎ CHALLENGE ACTIVITY

Make a Model Students who need an additional challenge can build a simple model of the circulatory system using various sizes of aquarium tubing and a clear chamber for a heart. By making the arterial and venous sides separate, they can fill each side with red and blue water. See *BioChallenges and Enrichment* for additional projects and activities. **L3**

Blood's path through the heart

Blood enters the heart through the atria and leaves it through the ventricles. Both atria fill up with blood at the same time. The right atrium receives oxygen-poor blood from the head and body through two large veins called the **venae cavae** (vee nee • KAY vee) (singular, vena cava). The left atrium receives oxygen-rich blood from the lungs through four pulmonary veins. These veins are the only veins that carry blood rich in oxygen. After they have filled with blood, the two atria then contract, pushing the blood down into the two ventricles.

After the ventricles have filled with blood, they contract simultaneously. When the right ventricle contracts, it pushes the oxygen-poor blood from the right ventricle out of the heart and toward the lungs through the pulmonary arteries. These arteries are the only arteries that carry blood poor in oxygen. At the same time, the left ventricle forcefully pushes oxygen-rich blood from the left ventricle out of the heart through the **aorta** to the arteries of the body. The aorta is the largest blood vessel in the body. See *Figure 37.10* on the next page to learn how a drop of blood moves through the heart.

Heartbeat regulation

Each time the heart beats, a surge of blood flows from the left ventricle into the aorta and then into the arteries. Because the radial artery in the arm and carotid arteries near the jaw are fairly close to the surface of the body, the surge of blood can be felt as it moves through them. This surge of blood through an artery is called a **pulse.** Find out more about how the pulse is used to measure heart rate by conducting the *MiniLab* on this page.

MiniLab 37.1

Experiment

Checking Your Pulse The heart speeds up when the blood volume reaching your right atrium increases. It also speeds up when you exercise. The number of heartbeats per minute is your heart rate, which can be measured by taking your pulse.

Procedure

1. Copy the data table.
2. Have a classmate take your resting pulse for 60 seconds while you are sitting at your lab table or desk. Use the photo above as a guide to finding your radial pulse.
3. Record your pulse in the table.
4. Repeat steps 2 and 3 four more times, then calculate your average resting pulse rate. Switch roles and take your classmate's resting pulse.
5. Exercise by walking in place for one minute.
6. Have your classmate take your pulse for 60 seconds immediately after exercising. Record the value in the data table.
7. Repeat steps 5 and 6 four more times, then calculate your average pulse after exercise. Switch roles again with your classmate.

Data Table

Heart Rate (beats per minute)

Trial	Resting	After Exercise
1		
2		
3		
4		
5		
Total		
Average		

Analysis

1. **Explain** Why is your pulse a means of indirectly measuring heart rate?
2. **Describe** Use values from your data table to describe the changes that occur to your heart rate when exercising.
3. **Use Numbers** Suppose the amount of blood pumped by your left ventricle each time it contracts is 70 mL. Calculate your cardiac output (70 mL × heart rate per minute) while at rest and just after exercise.

MiniLab 37.1

Purpose

Students will measure their resting pulse and compare it with their pulse after exercise.

Process Skills

compare and contrast, hypothesize, experiment, analyze information, apply concepts, collect data, use numbers, recognize cause and effect

Teaching Strategies

- Excuse students with health or physical impairments from the exercise portion of this activity. Be sure students are wearing clothing and shoes appropriate for exercise.
- Help students find their radial or carotid pulse. Advise students not to use their thumb when taking a pulse.
- Pulse recording should begin as soon as exercising is finished.

Expected Results

Resting pulses will be around 80–90 beats per minute. After exercise, beats will be close to 120 per minute.

Analysis

1. A surge of blood through arteries corresponds with each ejection of blood from the heart.
2. Answers will vary. Average pulse after exercise is higher than resting pulse.
3. 70 mL × average resting pulse per minute = resting cardiac output in mL per minute; 70 mL × average exercising pulse per minute = cardiac output in mL per minute

Assessment

Performance Have students design and carry out an experiment that determines the time needed after exercise for heart rate to return to its resting rate. Use the Performance Task Assessment List for Designing an Experiment in **PASC**, p. 95. **L2**

USING MODELS

Circulation in the Heart Models of the heart are available from many biological supply companies or can be borrowed from the school health teacher. Go through the pathway blood follows as it goes through the heart. Be sure to emphasize that when the atria contract, blood moves from both atria into the corresponding ventricles. Discuss the oxygenation level of the blood in each chamber of the heart. **L2**

Purpose

Students will examine heart structure and function.

Teaching Strategies

■ Heart valves close due to blood pressure changes in the chambers, creating the characteristic lubb-dupp sounds that can be heard with a stethoscope. As the atria contract, blood passes into the ventricle through open valves. As the ventricles contract, pressure of the blood against the heart valves causes them to close.

■ Allow students to listen to their heartbeats with stethoscopes. The earpiece should be cleaned with alcohol before each use.

Visual Learning

■ Use a heart model to trace the pathway of blood as it flows through the heart.

■ A fetal heart has an opening between the two atria. Contrast how fetal heart circulation is different from adult heart circulation. Have students research "blue babies." **L2**

Critical Thinking

If blood flow is reduced to the heart, the heart muscle cells will have difficulty getting oxygen and nutrients and getting rid of carbon dioxide and waste products.

Indiana Academic Standards

Pages 982–983: B.1.14, B.1.15, B.1.19

Your Heart

Figure 37.10

Your heart is about 12 cm by 8 cm—roughly the size of your fist. It lies in your chest cavity, just behind the breastbone and between the lungs, and is essentially a large muscle completely under involuntary control. **Critical Thinking** *The cells in heart tissue receive oxygen and nutrients from a group of blood vessels located on the wall of the heart. How would the function of the heart be affected if bloodflow in these vessels was reduced?*

A The passage of blood If you were to trace the path of a drop of blood through the heart, you could begin with blood coming back from the body through a vena cava. The drop travels first into the right atrium, then into the right ventricle, and then through a pulmonary artery to one of the lungs. In the lungs, the blood drops off its carbon dioxide and picks up oxygen. Then it moves through a pulmonary vein to the left atrium, into the left ventricle, and finally out to the body through the aorta, eventually returning once more to the heart.

B Heart valves Between the atria and ventricles are one-way valves that keep blood from flowing back into the atria. Sets of valves also lie between the ventricles and the arteries that leave the heart.

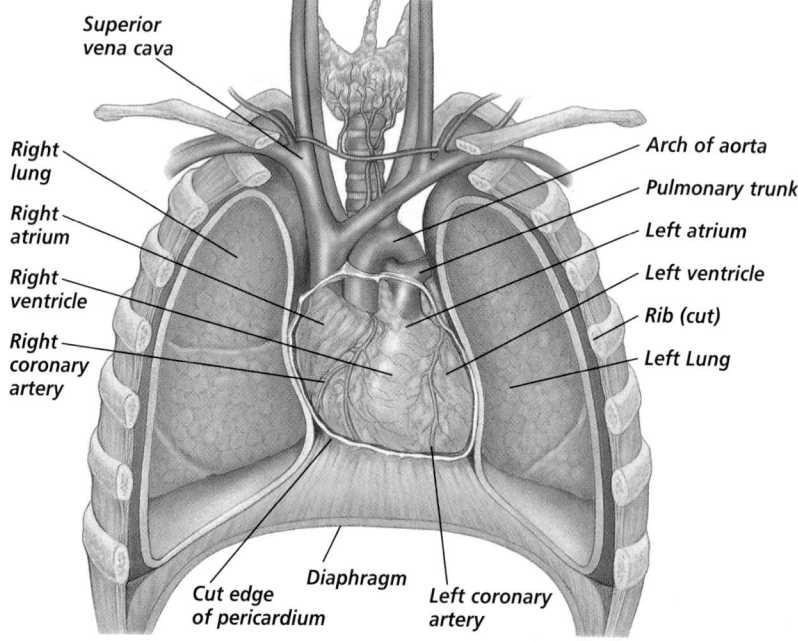

C Pericardium The heart is enclosed in a protective membrane called the pericardium.

Additional Lab

Exercise and CO₂

Purpose

Students will determine how exercise affects the amount of carbon dioxide exhaled.

Safety Precautions

CAUTION: *Wear goggles throughout the entire lab and cleanup. NaOH can cause burns. Always place the dropper back in the bottle. Flush all spills with excess water. If NaOH spills on skin or clothing, rinse off immediately and notify your teacher.*

Materials

distilled water, 250-mL flask, plastic straw, dropper bottle of phenolphthalein indicator, dropper bottle of 0.04% NaOH. For preparation instructions for NaOH solution, see page 17T of the Teacher Guide.

Procedure

1. Place 200 mL of distilled water in a 250-mL flask and add 5 drops of phenolphthalein indicator. This indicator is clear in the presence of an acid and pink in the presence of a base.

2. Add NaOH drop by drop to the flask while gently swirling until a faint pink color remains in the solution for one minute.

The heart rate is set by the pacemaker, a bundle of nerve cells located at the top of the right atrium. This pacemaker generates an electrical impulse that spreads over both atria. The impulse signals the two atria to contract at almost the same time. The impulse also triggers a second set of cells at the base of the right atrium to send the same electrical impulse over the ventricles, causing them to contract. These electrical signals can be measured and recorded by a machine called an electrocardio*graph*. This recording, shown in *Figure 37.11*, is called an electrocardio*gram* (ECG).

The ECG is an important tool used in diagnosing abnormal heart rhythms or patterns. Each peak or valley in the ECG tracing represents a particular electrical activity that takes place during a heartbeat. You can learn how ECG tracings are analyzed by carrying out the *Problem-Solving Lab* on this page.

Figure 37.11
The heart's pacemaker generates electrical signals that can be recorded on an ECG tracing. The sinoatrial node (pacemaker) causes both atria to contract simultaneously 70–80 impulses per minute. The atrioventricular node passes the impulse to the walls of the ventricles, which contract simultaneously.

Voltage (mV)

Atrial depolarization | Ventricular depolarization | Ventricular repolarization

0   0.1 0.2 0.3
Seconds

Problem-Solving Lab 37.2

Analyze Information

How are electrocardiograms analyzed? The electrical signals that regulate the pattern of heart muscle contraction and relaxation can be measured and recorded on an electrocardiograph.

Electrocardiograph

Solve the Problem
The electrocardiogram (ECG) in **Figure 37.11** is a tracing from a normal heart. The red, inked line is marked with letters that can be used to identify electrical impulses that occur during the heartbeat, such as P–Q and QRS. Segment P–Q represents the electrical charge that causes the atria to contract. Segment Q–T records the electrical charge that causes the ventricles to contract and repolarize. The blue, vertical lines of the graph paper represent units of time. The distance between heavy graph lines is equal to 0.1 seconds. The distance between light lines is equal to 0.02 seconds.

Thinking Critically
1. **Analyze** How long does it take for the electrical signal to travel through the atria? Through the ventricle?
2. **Infer** How would a physician interpret an ECG if the distances between T and P were much closer?

Sinoatrial node (Pacemaker)

Atrioventricular node

37.2   THE CIRCULATORY SYSTEM **983**

Problem-Solving Lab 37.2

Purpose
Students will determine the length of specific heart beat events by analyzing an ECG.

Process Skills
interpret data, interpret scientific illustrations, use numbers

Teaching Strategies
■ Students may be familiar with the older terminology of referring to the tracing as an EKG.
■ Review with students the procedure for calculating percent.
■ Remind students that the values being calculated from this ECG are average times.

Expected Results
Students will determine that atria are stimulated to contract first, for a short time, followed by ventricular contractions, which last slightly longer.

Analysis
1. atria: 0.12 seconds; ventricles: 0.20 seconds
2. The ECG would indicate that the heart is being stimulated to contract more rapidly.

Assessment
Skill Have students calculate pulse rate from the ECG by determining the total time that elapses between two atrial contractions, then dividing this number into 60. (60 sec/min ÷ 0.84 sec = 71 beats/ min). Use the Performance Task Assessment List for Using Math in Science in **PASC**, p. 101. L3

---

3. Exhale through the straw into the flask for 5 seconds, then remove your mouth from the straw and inhale for 5 seconds. Repeat until one minute has elapsed. **CAUTION: *Do not inhale through the straw.***
4. Again add NaOH drop by drop, while swirling the flask, until the solution again remains pink for one minute.
5. Record the number of drops of NaOH needed to produce the pink color.

6. Rinse the flask. Repeat steps 2 through 5 after jogging in place for 1 minute. Record the number of drops of NaOH needed after jogging. **CAUTION: *Wash hands with soap and water at the end of the lab***.

Analysis
1. Did the number of drops of NaOH needed increase or decrease after exercise? increase
2. NaOH neutralizes the carbonic acid formed by carbon dioxide and water.

Why is more carbon dioxide produced during exercise? As more energy is used, more carbon dioxide is produced.

Assessment
Performance Have students write a summary of the lab for their journal, including answers to the Analysis questions. Use the Performance Task Assessment List for Lab Report in **PASC**, p. 119. L2

3 Assess

Rubber cuff
Mercury column
Air control valve
Bulb

Figure 37.12
Blood pressure rises and falls with each heart beat. Pressure is exerted on all vessels throughout the body. However, blood vessels near the left ventricle are subjected to higher pressure than vessels that are farther away. Blood pressure usually is measured in the artery of the upper arm.

Blood Pressure

Systemic blood pressure (mm Hg)

Systolic pressure
Diastolic pressure

Aorta | Large arteries | Small arteries | Arterioles | Capillaries | Venules | Small veins | Large veins | Vena cavae

Distance from left ventricle ⟶

Blood pressure

A pulse beat represents the pressure that blood exerts as it pushes against the walls of an artery. **Blood pressure** is the force that the blood exerts on the blood vessels. As *Figure 37.12* shows, blood pressure rises and falls as the heart contracts and then relaxes.

Blood pressure rises sharply when the ventricles contract, pushing blood through the arteries. The high pressure is called systolic pressure. Blood pressure then drops dramatically as the ventricles relax. The lowest pressure occurs just before the ventricles contract again and is called diastolic pressure.

Control of the heart

Whereas the pacemaker controls the heartbeat, a portion of the brain called the medulla oblongata regulates the rate of the pacemaker, speeding or slowing its nerve impulses. If the heart beats too fast, sensory cells in arteries near the heart become stretched. Via the nervous system, these cells send a signal to the medulla oblongata, which in turn sends signals that slow the pacemaker. If the heart slows down too much, blood pressure in the arteries drops, signalling the medulla oblongata to speed up the pacemaker and increase the heart rate.

Section Assessment

Understanding Main Ideas

1. Summarize the distinguishing features and functions of each of the four components of blood: plasma, platelets, and red and white blood cells.

2. Compare and contrast an artery and a vein.

3. Outline the path taken by a red blood cell as it passes from the left atrium to the right ventricle of the heart.

4. Identify and interpret the functions of the circulatory system.

Thinking Critically

5. The level of carbon dioxide in the blood affects breathing rate. How would you expect high levels of carbon dioxide to affect the heart rate?

SKILL REVIEW

6. **Get the Big Picture** Compare how the nervous, respiratory, and circulatory systems interrelate to provide life support to body cells. How would homeostasis be affected if one of these systems could not function? For more help, refer to *Get the Big Picture* in the **Skill Handbook**.

984 RESPIRATION, CIRCULATION, AND EXCRETION

 in.bdol.glencoe.com/self_check_quiz

Section Assessment

1. plasma: fluid that carries blood cells, platelets, enzymes, hormones, gases, and inorganic salts; RBCs: no nucleus, contain hemoglobin, and transport oxygen; WBCs contain nuclei and defend against disease; platelets: cell fragments needed for blood clotting
2. An artery is a vessel that carries blood away from the heart. A vein is a vessel that carries blood toward the heart.
3. left atrium to left ventricle to arteries to arterioles to capillaries to venules to veins to right atrium to right ventricle
4. The circulatory system carries nutrients and oxygen to the body cells and delivers carbon dioxide to the lungs and waste products to the kidneys.
5. High levels of carbon dioxide increase the heart rate.
6. The nervous system controls the respiratory and circulatory systems. The circulatory and respiratory systems work together to bring oxygen to cells and take carbon dioxide to the lungs.

Section 37.3

The Urinary System

Indiana Standards Standard B.1.19 Recognize and describe that metabolism consists of the production, modification, transport, and exchange of materials that are required for the maintenance of life.

SECTION PREVIEW

Objectives
Describe the structures and functions of the urinary system.

Explain the kidneys' role in maintaining homeostasis.

Review Vocabulary
amino acids: basic building blocks of proteins (p. 161)

New Vocabulary
kidney
ureter
urinary bladder
nephron
urine
urethra

Waste Removal

Using an Analogy Sorting your CDs is a process similar to how the kidneys filter the blood. Some CDs you know you want to keep. Those are never even removed from the rack. Of the remaining CDs, some you will end up keeping, while others you may give away or sell. When blood enters the kidney, proteins and blood cells remain in the blood. Other substances, such as water and ions, are removed from the blood by a filter but may be reabsorbed later. Waste material is not reabsorbed and is excreted in the urine.

Explain *Why is it important that waste material be excreted from the body?*

Left and right ureters lead to the urinary bladder, as seen in a colorized X ray of the human urinary system.

Kidneys: Structure and Function

The urinary system is made up of two kidneys, a pair of ureters, the urinary bladder, and the urethra, which you can see in *Figure 37.13*. The **kidneys** filter the blood to remove wastes from it, thus maintaining the homeostasis of body fluids. Your kidneys are located just above the waist, behind the stomach. One kidney lies on each side of the spine, partially surrounded by ribs. Each kidney is connected to a tube called a **ureter,** which leads to the urinary bladder. The **urinary bladder** is a smooth muscle bag that stores a solution of wastes.

Nephron: The unit of the kidney

Each kidney is made up of about one million tiny filters. A filter is a device that removes impurities from a solution.

Figure 37.13
The paired kidneys are reddish-colored organs that resemble kidney beans in shape.

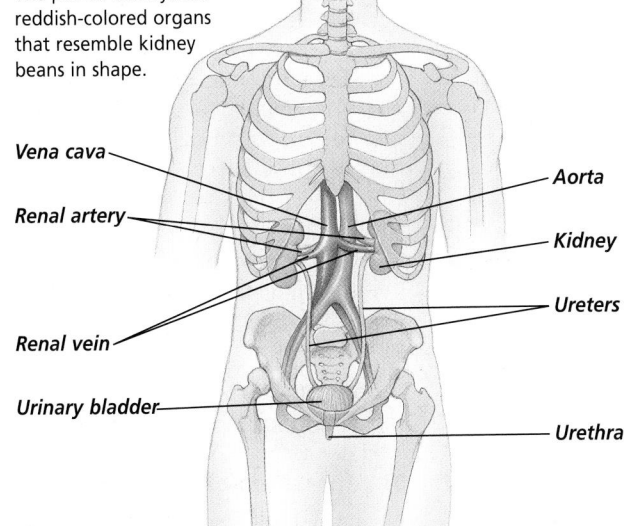

Vena cava
Renal artery
Aorta
Kidney
Ureters
Renal vein
Urinary bladder
Urethra

1 Focus

INTERACTIVE CHALKBOARD
PowerPoint® Presentations

Bellringer
Section Focus Transparency 92

Transparency **92** Saving and Discarding

SECTION FOCUS
Use with Chapter 37, Section 37.3

1. Follow the flow of blood through this diagram of the operation of the kidney. What, in general, is happening along the horizontal part of the diagram?

2. What substances are being conserved (saved) in the blood? What substances are being discarded?

BIOLOGY: The Dynamics of Life   SECTION FOCUS TRANSPARENCIES

Using an Analogy
Explain Waste material from digestive processes in the cells is toxic. If these molecules build up in the body, cells will die.

Quick Demo

Kidneys Slice a sheep kidney in half longitudinally. Identify the cortex and medulla. The cortex contains the nephrons. The medulla is a network of tubules and ducts that merge to form the ureter.

RESOURCE MANAGER

Unit 10 *Fast File* Resources
MiniLab Worksheet, p. 127
Reinforcement and Study Guide in English, p. 136
Reinforcement and Study Guide in Spanish, p. 140

Transparency Worksheets, pp. 145, 153–154
Reading Essentials for Biology, Section 37.3
📖 **Section Focus Transparency 92**
📖 **Basic Concepts Transparency 73**

Indiana Academic Standards

Pages 984–985: B.1.3, B.1.14, B.1.15, B.1.19, B.1.20

MiniLab 37.2

Purpose
Students will use commercial glucose testing paper to detect glucose in simulated urine.

Process Skills
collect data, draw a conclusion, experiment, interpret data, observe and infer, predict

Safety Precautions
Remind students to use care when handling glass slides and to wash their hands at the end of the lab.

Teaching Strategies
- Glucose test paper is available from drug stores or biological supply houses.
- To prepare abnormal urine, add 2 tsp. glucose and 2–3 drops of yellow food coloring to 500 mL water. To prepare normal urine, add 2–3 drops yellow food coloring to 500 mL water.

Expected Results
Test paper turns green in the presence of glucose. Water causes no color change.

Analysis
1. Any unknown that tests positive for glucose could indicate diabetes. High sugar intake may also result in glucose elimination in urine.
2. testing of normal and abnormal urine before testing of unknowns

Assessment
Performance Have students design an experiment to test the lowest glucose concentration that can be detected using glucose test paper. Use the Performance Task Assessment List for Designing an Experiment in **PASC**, p. 95. **L3**

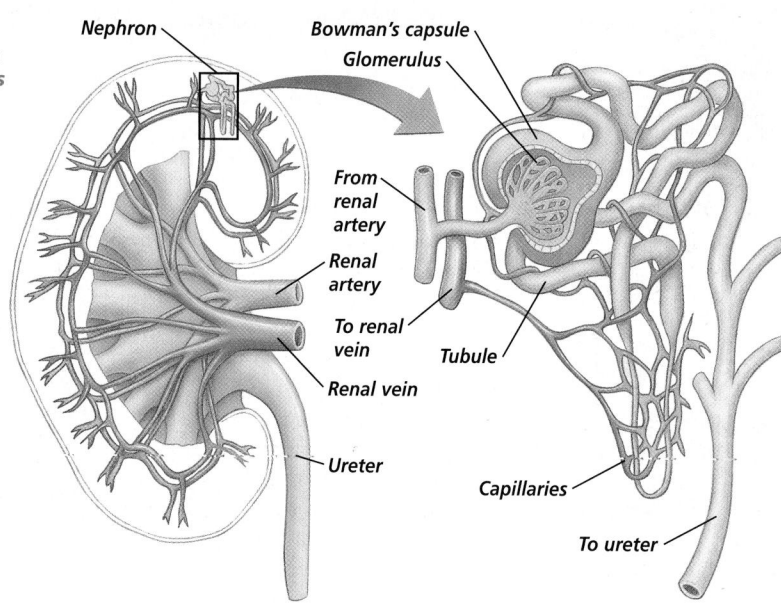

Figure 37.14 The kidneys filter wastes from the blood. **Explain** *How does blood enter and leave the kidneys?*

Labels: Nephron, Bowman's capsule, Glomerulus, From renal artery, Renal artery, To renal vein, Tubule, Renal vein, Ureter, Capillaries, To ureter

Word Origin
nephron from the Greek word *nephros,* meaning "kidney"; A nephron is a functional unit of a kidney.

Figure 37.15 Filtration and reabsorption take place in the nephron.

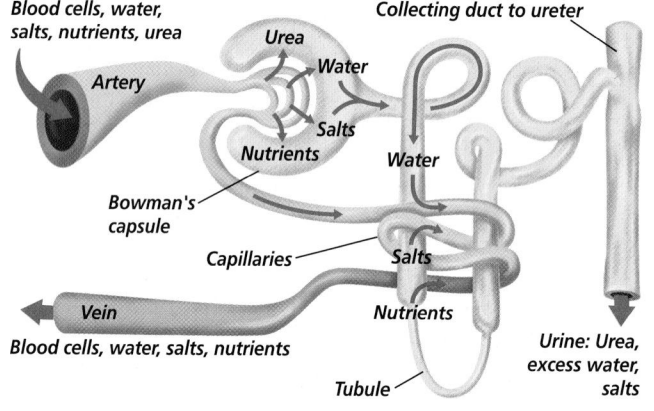

Labels: Blood cells, water, salts, nutrients, urea; Artery; Urea; Water; Salts; Nutrients; Bowman's capsule; Capillaries; Vein; Blood cells, water, salts, nutrients; Tubule; Water; Salts; Nutrients; Collecting duct to ureter; Urine: Urea, excess water, salts

Each filtering unit of the kidney is called a **nephron.** A nephron is shown in *Figure 37.14.*

Blood entering a nephron carries wastes produced by body cells. As blood enters the nephron, it is under high pressure and immediately flows into a bed of capillaries called the glomerulus. Because of the pressure, water, glucose, vitamins, amino acids, protein waste products (called urea), salts, and ions from the blood pass out of the capillaries into a part of the nephron called the Bowman's capsule. Blood cells and most proteins are too large to pass through the walls of a capillary, so these components stay within the blood vessels.

The liquid forced into the Bowman's capsule passes through a narrow, U-shaped tubule. As the liquid moves along the tubule, most of the ions and water, and all of the glucose and amino acids, are reabsorbed into the bloodstream. This reabsorption of substances is the process by which the body's water is conserved and homeostasis is maintained. Small molecules, including water, move back into the capillaries by diffusion. Other molecules and ions move back into the capillaries by active transport.

✔**Reading Check** **Explain** how molecules move across capillaries.

The formation of urine
The liquid that remains in the tubules—composed of waste molecules and excess water and ions—is **urine.**

986 RESPIRATION, CIRCULATION, AND EXCRETION

INCLUSION STRATEGIES

English Language Learners:
Interpersonal Have students in teams play Hangman or Password with the terms found in this section. Once a team gets the word, they must properly define the term to get the point. This will also help students who are having difficulty with the terms. **L1**
ELL

Caption Question Answer
Figure 37.14 Blood enters the kidney in the renal artery and leaves by the renal vein.

The production of urine is shown in *Figure 37.15*. You produce about 2 L of urine a day. This waste fluid flows out of the kidneys, through the ureter, and into the urinary bladder, where it may be stored. Urine passes from the urinary bladder out of the body through a tube called the **urethra** (yoo REE thruh).

The Urinary System and Homeostasis

The major waste products of cells are nitrogenous wastes, which come from the breakdown of proteins. These wastes include ammonia and urea. Both compounds are toxic to your body and, therefore, must be removed from the blood regularly.

In addition to removing these wastes, the kidneys control the level of sodium in blood by removing and reabsorbing sodium ions. This helps control the osmotic pressure of the blood. The kidneys also regulate the pH of blood by filtering out hydrogen ions and allowing bicarbonate to be reabsorbed back into the blood. Glucose is a sugar that is not usually filtered out of the blood by the kidneys. Individuals who have the disease known as diabetes have excess levels of glucose in their blood. The *MiniLab* on this page shows how urine is used to test for diabetes.

MiniLab 37.2

Experiment

Testing Simulated Urine for Glucose Glucose is normally not present in the urine. When the concentration of glucose becomes too high in the blood, as happens with diabetes, glucose is excreted in urine.

Procedure

1. Copy the data table.
2. Using a grease pencil, draw two circles on a glass slide. Mark one circle N, the other A.
3. Use a clean dropper to add two drops of simulated "normal urine" to circle N.
4. Use a clean dropper to add two drops of simulated "abnormal urine" to the circle marked A.
5. Hold a small strip of glucose test paper in a forceps and touch it to the liquid in the drop labeled N. Remove it, wait 30 seconds, and record the color. A green color means glucose is present. Use a new strip of glucose test paper to test drop A and record the color.
6. Test several simulated "unknown urine" samples for the presence of glucose. Use a clean slide for each test.

Data Table		
Simulated Urine Sample	Color of Test Paper	Glucose Present?
Normal (N)		
Abnormal (A)		
Unknown X		
Unknown Y		
Unknown Z		

Analysis

1. **Analyze** Which of the "unknown" samples could be from a person who has diabetes?
2. **Explain** Which part of the test procedure could be considered your control?

Reading Check (page 986)
Molecules move across capillaries by diffusion and active transport.

3 Assess

DAILY INTERVENTION

Check for Understanding
Have students trace the pathway of glucose, water, etc. through the kidney. **L1**

Reteach
Have students discuss the effect on the amount and concentration of urine of a meal rich in proteins, drinking large amounts of water, or high blood pressure. **L2**
COOP LEARN

Resources
For more practice, use *Reading Essentials for Biology,* Section 37.3.

Extension

Have students research how renin and angiotensin affect the kidneys. **L3**

Assessment

Portfolio Have students make a chart comparing the composition of blood plasma, the fluid inside the Bowman's capsule, and urine. **L2**

Indiana Academic Standards

Pages 986–987: B.1.14, B.1.15, B.1.17, B.1.19

Section Assessment

Understanding Main Ideas

1. Identify the organs that make up the urinary system and interpret the function of each.
2. What is the function of a nephron in the kidney? Describe what happens in the glomerulus, Bowman's capsule, and U-shaped tubule.
3. Identify the major components of urine, and explain why it is considered a waste fluid.
4. What is the kidney's role in maintaining homeostasis in the body?

Think Critically

5. During a routine physical, a urine test indicates the presence of proteins in the patient's urine. Explain what this could indicate about the patient's health.

SKILL REVIEW

6. **Sequence** Trace the sequence of urinary waste from a cell to the outside of the body. For more help, refer to *Sequence* in the **Skill Handbook**.

in.bdol.glencoe.com/self_check_quiz

37.3   THE URINARY SYSTEM   **987**

Section Assessment

1. kidneys: filter blood to remove waste; ureters: carry urine from kidneys to bladder; urinary bladder: stores urine; When the bladder contracts, urine flows out of the body through the urethra.
2. to filter wastes from the blood plasma; In glomerulus, water, glucose, vitamins, amino acids, protein waste products, salts and ions pass into Bowman's capsule; in U-shaped tubule, most of the ions and water and all of the glucose and amino acids are reabsorbed into the bloodstream.
3. urea, water, nitrogenous wastes, excess salt; contains toxic products from the metabolic breakdown of proteins
4. removes urinary waste; maintains blood pH, sodium levels, and osmotic balance
5. High blood pressure could force proteins into Bowman's capsule or the patient could have a kidney infection.
6. cell to blood to nephron to ureter to urinary bladder to urethra

987

Time Allotment

one class period

Process Skills

communicate, measure in SI, use numbers, interpret data, experiment, formulate a model

Safety Precautions

Provide plenty of balloons; students should not share balloons. Students with an allergy to latex should not come in contact with latex balloons.

PREPARATION

■ Ask students to bring calculators to lab for use in making calculations.
■ Use large-capacity balloons.

Alternative Materials

To decrease the number of balloons needed, cut a straw in half and use a rubber band to attach the balloon to the straw. Blow up the balloon through the straw, then replace only the straw for the next student.

PROCEDURE

Teaching Strategies

■ Explain that there are about 300 million alveoli in a human lung with a surface area of more than 50 m². Have students measure the classroom, calculate the number of square meters, and compare this figure with that of a human lung.

Before You Begin

The exchange of oxygen and carbon dioxide between the body and the atmosphere is external respiration. The amount of air inhaled and exhaled each minute during external respiration can be measured using a clinical machine called a spirometer. It also can be measured, although less accurately, using a balloon. In this lab you will calculate the total volume of air inhaled and exhaled each minute. This is done by finding the tidal volume, the volume of air in each breath, and multiplying it by the number of breaths per minute.

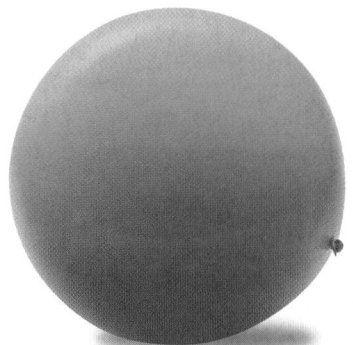

■ Have students work in pairs and, if time allows, reverse roles.

Measuring Respiration

PREPARATION

Problem

How can you measure respiratory rate and estimate tidal volume?

Objectives

In this BioLab, you will:
■ **Measure** resting breathing rate.
■ **Estimate** tidal volume by exhaling into a balloon.
■ **Calculate** the amount of air inhaled per minute.

Materials

round balloon   clock or watch with
string (1 m)   second hand
metric ruler

Safety Precautions 👓

CAUTION: *Always use laboratory materials appropriately.*

Skill Handbook

If you need help with this lab, refer to the **Skill Handbook**.

PROCEDURE

Part A: Breathing Rate at Rest

1. Copy Data Table 1.
2. Have your partner count the number of times you inhale in 30 s. Repeat this step two more times.
3. Calculate the average number of breaths. Multiply the result by two to get the average resting breathing rate in breaths per minute.

Data Table 1

Resting Breathing Rate	
Trial	**Inhalations in 30 s**
1	
2	
3	
Average number breaths	
Breaths per minute	

Data and Observations

Answers among students could vary greatly. Average breathing rate is 11 to 12 breaths per minute. Tidal volume should be approximately 500 mL. The amount of air inhaled should be 5 to 6 L per minute.

Part B: Estimating Tidal Volume

1. Copy Data Table 2.
2. Take a regular breath and exhale normally into the balloon. Pinch the balloon closed.
3. Have a partner fit the string around the balloon at the widest part.
4. Measure the length of the string, in centimeters, around the circumference of the balloon. Record this measurement.
5. Repeat steps 2–4 four more times.
6. Calculate the average circumference of the five measurements.
7. Calculate the average radius of the balloon by dividing the average circumference by 2π ($\pi = 3.14$).
8. Calculate the average tidal volume using the formula for determining the volume of a sphere. Use the average balloon radius for r and 3.14 for π. (Volume of a sphere $= \frac{4\pi r^3}{3}$)
9. Your calculated volume will be in cubic centimeters: $1 \text{ cm}^3 = 1 \text{ mL}$.

Data Table 2

Tidal Volume	
Trial	**String Measurement**
1	
2	
3	
4	
5	
Average circumference	
Average radius	
Average tidal volume	

Part C: Amount of Air Inhaled

1. Copy Data Table 3.
2. Multiply the average tidal volume by the average number of breaths per minute to calculate the amount of air you inhale per minute.
3. Divide the number of milliliters of air by 1000 to get the number of liters of air you inhale per minute.

Data Table 3

Amount of Air Inhaled	
mL/min	
L/min	

ANALYZE AND CONCLUDE

1. **Make Comparisons** Compare your average number of breaths per minute and tidal volume per minute with those of other students.
2. **Think Critically** An average adult inhales 6000 mL of air per minute. Compare your estimated average volume of air with this figure. What factors could account for any differences?
3. **Make Predictions** Predict what would happen to your resting breathing rate after exercise.
4. **ERROR ANALYSIS** List reasons that explain why there are differences between your results and those of other students. What changes could you make to this experiment to obtain more accurate results?

Apply Your Skill

Apply Concepts The largest amount of air that can be exhaled is called vital capacity. Determine your estimated average vital capacity by following a procedure similar to the one you used to determine average tidal volume.

 Web Links To find out more about respiratory volumes, visit
in.bdol.glencoe.com/respiration

ANALYZE AND CONCLUDE

1. Average breaths per minute and tidal volume per minute will differ among students.
2. Answers may vary from the average due to age, sex, size, and athletic condition.
3. After exercising, the breathing rate will be higher.
4. **ERROR ANALYSIS** Answers will vary but may include different individuals are expected to have somewhat different total volumes, differences from a real spirometer measurement could be due to differences in the elasticity of different balloons. By using a spirometer, the measurements would be much more accurate.

Assessment

Performance Have students write a summary of the lab, including the three tables and the answers to the Analyze and Conclude. Use the Performance Task Assessments List for Lab Report in **PASC,** p. 119. **L2**

Apply Your Skill

Apply Concepts Students can calculate their tidal volume after exercising and compare this with their tidal volume during rest. **L3**

Indiana Academic Standards

Pages 988–989: B.1.19

Biology and Society

Purpose

Students explore the connection between medical and social issues and learn about the need for organ donors

Background

There are two types of donors. Cadaveric donors are patients who have suffered brain death and will not survive. Living donors are healthy individuals willing to donate a kidney or a portion of their bone marrow. Humans can thrive with only a single kidney. Bone marrow is easily replaced by a healthy body.

Teaching Strategies

Explain to students that most donor organs come from individuals who have suffered massive injuries from which they can never recover. The body may continue to function for a time, but only if it is kept on artificial life support. A patient is never taken off life support if there is any hope of recovery, even if it means that his or her organs would become useless for transplanting.

Forming Your Opinion

Students may encounter a variety of opinions and beliefs. People who have received a donated organ, or know someone who has, are likely to encourage others to become donors. Some people may be uncomfortable talking about the subject. Students may discover that organ donation is one of the important decisions a family must make when one of its members has suffered brain death and is being kept alive by life support.

Finding Transplant Donors

The ability to replace a diseased heart, liver, kidney, pancreas, or other organ from a human donor has been an important advancement for medical science. Organs suitable for transplanting are scarce, and there are thousands of transplant patients waiting for them. Transplant recipients include children born with malformed hearts or digestive systems, patients suffering from severe liver or heart disease, burn victims in desperate need of skin grafts, or people whose kidneys have stopped functioning.

The waiting list A patient who is a good candidate for a transplant is placed on a waiting list. A national computer database keeps track of each patient's blood and tissue type, organ size, and other medical factors. When an organ becomes available, the computer produces a list of all the patients for whom the organ is medically suitable. Patients are ranked according to the severity of their illness, the length of time they have been waiting, and the distance between the donor and the transplant hospital.

Perspectives A donor organ must be transplanted within hours. Deciding who should receive an organ involves questions of medical urgency and logistics. Although over 20 000 successful organ transplants were performed in the United States in the year 2000, almost 80 000 people remained on the waiting list. One of the most important issues concerning organ transplantation today is the fact that there are more people awaiting organs than there are donor organs available.

Revising policies In 1998, the Department of Health and Human Services asked the national organization that coordinates the matching of organs with patients to revise their policies and make organs available to patients based on medical need regardless of location. If medically suitable recipients are selected based on geographic

Recovering transplant patient

location, a seriously ill patient who lives far from a large population center might have to wait longer than a patient who lives in a big city. However, if the most seriously ill patient is so far away that the transplant cannot be completed within the time limit, another patient must be selected. Policies regarding organ distribution and allocation are being revised to provide a set of medically objective measures by which recipients can be designated.

Forming Your Opinion

Analyze the Issue Research and analyze the medical and ethical considerations involved in organ donation and transplantation. What is your opinion on this issue? Organize a class discussion to share what you learned.

 To find out more about organ transplants, visit in.bdol.glencoe.com/biology_society

Going Further

Invite interested students to develop an education program to increase awareness in their community about the need for organ and tissue donors. **L3**

STUDY GUIDE

Section 37.1

The Respiratory System

Key Concepts

■ External respiration involves taking in air through the passageways of the respiratory system and exchanging gases in the alveoli of the lungs.

■ Breathing involves contraction of the diaphragm, the rush of air into the lungs, relaxation of the diaphragm, and air being pushed out of the lungs.

■ Breathing is partially controlled by the chemistry of the blood.

Vocabulary

alveoli (p. 972)
trachea (p. 971)

Section 37.2

The Circulatory System

Color-enhanced SEM Magnification: 120×

Key Concepts

■ Blood is composed of red and white blood cells, platelets, and plasma. Blood carries oxygen, carbon dioxide, and other substances through the body.

■ Blood cell antigens determine blood group and are important in blood transfusions.

■ Blood is carried by arteries, veins, and capillaries.

■ Blood is pushed through the vessels by the heart.

Vocabulary

antibody (p. 977)
antigen (p. 977)
aorta (p. 981)
artery (p. 979)
atrium (p. 980)
blood pressure (p. 984)
capillary (p. 980)
hemoglobin (p. 976)
plasma (p. 975)
platelet (p. 977)
pulse (p. 981)
red blood cell (p. 975)
vein (p. 980)
vena cava (p. 981)
ventricle (p. 980)
white blood cell
   (p. 976)

Section 37.3

The Urinary System

Key Concepts

■ The urinary system consists of the kidneys, ureters, the urinary bladder, and the urethra.

■ The nephrons of the kidneys filter wastes from the blood.

■ The urinary system helps maintain the homeostasis of body fluids.

Vocabulary

kidney (p. 985)
nephron (p. 986)
ureter (p. 985)
urethra (p. 987)
urinary bladder
   (p. 985)
urine (p. 986)

FOLDABLES™
Study Organizer To help you review the respiratory system, use the Organizational Study Fold on page 971.

 in.bdol.glencoe.com/vocabulary_puzzlemaker

Key Concepts

Summary statements can be used by students to review the major concepts of the chapter.

Biology Online

Visit in.bdol.glencoe.com
   /self_check_quiz
   /vocabulary_puzzlemaker
   /chapter_test
   /standardized_test

VOCABULARY PUZZLEMAKER

 For additional help with vocabulary, have students access the Vocabulary PuzzleMaker online at in.bdol.glencoe.com/vocabulary_puzzlemaker

FOLDABLES™

Have students use their Foldables to review the content of Section 37.1. On the back of their Foldables have students explain how the respiratory, circulatory, and urinary systems are interrelated.

Use the ExamView®Pro Test Bank CD-ROM to:

● Create **multiple versions** of tests
● Create **modified** tests with one mouse click for **inclusion** students
● **Edit** existing questions and **add** your own questions
● Build tests aligned with state standards using built-in **State Curriculum Tags**
● Change **English** tests to **Spanish** with one mouse click and vice versa

 Indiana Academic Standards

Pages 990–991: B.1.3, B.1.14, B.1.15, B.1.17, B.1.20

Chapter 37 Assessment

 The Princeton Review **Questions and answers have been aligned and verified by The Princeton Review.**

Vocabulary Review

1. aorta: artery that carries oxygenated blood away from the heart; vena cava: vein that carries deoxygenated blood from the body to the heart
2. artery: large vessel that carries blood away from the heart; vein: vessel that carries blood to the heart
3. red blood cell: carries oxygen to body cells; platelet: cell fragment involved in blood clotting
4. kidney: filters blood to remove waste; nephron: functional unit of the kidney
5. ureter: tube that connects the kidney to the bladder; urethra: tube through which urine leaves the body

Understanding Key Concepts

6. B   8. D
7. C   9. A
10. 1. left atrium; 2. left ventricle; 3. aorta; 4. arteries

Constructed Response

11. Diets high in saturated fats and cholesterol are associated with increased risk of atherosclerosis.
12. Most air pollution contains high levels of carbon monoxide and other toxic substances. Exercise would increase the amount of these toxic gases drawn into the lungs.
13. As glucose passes into the U-shaped tubules, it is reabsorbed into the bloodstream. In uncontrolled diabetes, all of the glucose in the U-shaped tubule cannot be reabsorbed, excess glucose is excreted in urine.

992

Vocabulary Review

Review the Chapter 37 vocabulary words listed in the Study Guide on page 991. Distinguish between the vocabulary words in each pair.

1. aorta—vena cava
2. artery—vein
3. red blood cell—platelet
4. kidney—nephron
5. ureter—urethra

Understanding Key Concepts

6. Homeostasis of blood osmotic pressure is maintained by which organ(s)?
   A. lungs   C. heart
   B. kidneys   D. liver

7. Breathing is an involuntary process controlled by which area of the brain?
   A. cerebrum
   B. cerebellum
   C. medulla oblongata
   D. hippocampus

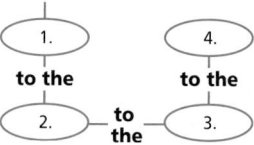

8. A person with Type O blood is given Type AB blood during a transfusion. Which of the following is a possible outcome from the transfusion?
   A. The anti-A antibodies in the recipient's blood will attack the A antigens in the donor's blood.
   B. The anti-B antibodies in the recipient's blood will attack the B antigens in the donor's blood.
   C. The donor cells will clump inside the recipient's body.
   D. all of the above

9. Emphysema is a condition that results in the destruction of alveoli in the lungs. What effects would this have on the body?
   A. lower levels of oxygen in the blood
   B. higher levels of oxygen in the blood
   C. lower levels of carbon dioxide in the blood
   D. no effect

Thinking Critically

14. Damage to the heart valves may cause leakage between the heart chambers causing the heart to work harder to move blood through.
15. heart enlargement and tissue damage, renal failure,

---

10. Complete the concept map using the following vocabulary terms: aorta, arteries, left atrium, left ventricle.

Blood moves from the pulmonary vein to the

1. _____ to the
2. _____ to the
4. _____ to the
3. _____

Constructed Response

11. **Open Ended** A diet low in saturated fats and cholesterol helps maintain elasticity and prevent clogging of the blood vessels. Why is this type of diet considered healthy for your heart?

12. **Open Ended** In some cities, citizens are advised to avoid heavy outdoor exercise when air pollution levels are high. Explain why it would be wise to heed such a warning.

13. **Open Ended** Explain what normally happens to glucose as blood passes through the kidney. Explain what happens to glucose in a patient with uncontrolled diabetes.

Thinking Critically

14. **Writing About Biology** When the *Streptococcus* bacterium that causes severe sore throats gets into the blood, damage to the valves of the heart can result. How might this damage affect heart function?

15. **REAL WORLD BIOCHALLENGE** Hypertension (high blood pressure) affects more than 50 million Americans. How does hypertension affect various organs of the body? What groups are at risk for hypertension? Analyze the importance of nutrition and exercise and each of their effects on hypertension. Visit **in.bdol.glencoe.com** to investigate the answers to these questions. Make a table to help organize and present your findings.

 in.bdol.glencoe.com/chapter_test

RUBRIC

For more help evaluating open-ended assessment questions, see the rubric on p. 9T.

16. Design an Experiment Design an experiment that would test the effect of various types of music on heartbeat rate. Include a hypothesis about which types of music may raise or lower heart rate.

17. Recognize Cause and Effect Compare how the respiratory, muscular, and nervous systems interrelate to accomplish the process of breathing. If there were a disruption in any one of these systems, how would it affect homeostasis in the body?

The assessed Indiana standard appears next to the question.

End-of-Course Assessment Practice

All questions aligned and verified by The Princeton Review

Part 1 Multiple Choice

Use the diagram to answer questions 18–21.

18. Which heart chamber pumps
B.1.15 blood to the lungs?
   A. 1   **C.** 3
   B. 2   **D.** 4

19. Where does blood go when
B.1.15 it leaves chamber 4?
   A. lungs   **C.** right atrium
   B. left atrium   **D.** aorta

20. Chamber 1 receives blood from which blood
B.1.15 vessel(s)?
   A. aorta   **C.** pulmonary arteries
   B. venae cavae   **D.** pulmonary veins

21. Which best describes the blood in chamber 3?
B.1.15 **A.** It is headed to the lungs to receive carbon dioxide.
   B. It is coming from the lungs after receiving carbon dioxide.
   C. It is headed to the lungs to receive oxygen.
   D. It is coming from the lungs after receiving oxygen.

Study the table and answer questions 22–24.

Blood Test Results			
Test	Normal Range	Patient A	Patient B
BUN	8–26 mg/dL		
WBC	5000–10 000/μL		7500/μL

BUN = Blood Urea Nitrogen (BUN is a measure of the amount of urea present in the blood.)
WBC = White Blood Cells

22. Patient A has been diagnosed with acute
B.1.15 kidney failure. Based on this information, what value could you expect his BUN to be?
   A. 4 mg/dL   **C.** 26 mg/dL
   B. 15 mg/dL   **D.** 35 mg/dL

23. Patient A's kidney failure has been caused by
B.1.17 a bacterial infection in his kidneys. Based on this information, what value could you expect his WBC count to be?
   A. 2000/μL   **C.** 10 000/μL
   B. 5000/μL   **D.** 20 000/μL

24. Patient B has healthy kidneys. Based on this
B.1.15 information, what value could you expect her BUN to be?
   A. 4 mg/dL   **C.** 28 mg/dL
   B. 15 mg/dL   **D.** 35 mg/dL

Part 2 Constructed Response/Grid In

Record your answers on your answer document.

25. Open Ended A blood test can be used to determine irregularities in many other systems of
B.1.15 the body including kidney function, liver function, and respiratory efficiency. Compare how the blood is interrelated with all other systems in the body. Include specific examples as part of your response.

26. Open Ended The bond formed between carbon monoxide and hemoglobin is over 200 times as
B.1.17, strong as the bond formed between oxygen and hemoglobin. Explain how exposure to carbon
B.1.19 monoxide can affect body homeostasis.

 in.bdol.glencoe.com/standardized_test

End-of-Course Assessment Practice

18. B   **20.** B   **22.** D   **24.** B
19. D   **21.** D   **23.** D

25. Blood delivers oxygen and nutrients to almost all body cells and carries away cellular wastes. Examples could include capillaries absorbing nutrients in the small intestine or taking up oxygen from the alveoli in the lungs. Wastes are removed from the blood by the kidneys.

26. When hemoglobin is bound to carbon monoxide, the oxygen carrying capacity of blood is reduced.

FAST FILE

Answer Sheet A practice answer sheet can be found on p. 163 of *Unit 10 FAST FILE Resources.*

---

strokes, hemorrhage, or aneurysm; Risk factors include family history of hypertension, advanced age, cigarette smoking, obesity, being glucose intolerant, and having a high sodium diet.

16. possible experiments: playing various types of music while taking pulse rate, and comparing pulse rate with music to pulse rate without music

17. The respiratory system exchanges gases with the blood. The diaphragm and rib muscles contract and relax to change the volume of the chest cavity. The nervous system controls the whole process, maintaining homeostasis. A disruption in any of these systems would affect the respiratory process.

Indiana Academic Standards

Pages 992–993: B.1.14, B.1.15, B.1.19, B.1.20

Section Objectives	National Science Standards	State/Local Standards	Advanced Lab and Demo Planning
Section 38.1 2 sessions, 1 1/2 blocks 1. **Identify** the structures and functions of the male and female reproductive systems. 2. **Summarize** the internal feedback control of reproductive hormones. 3. **Sequence** the stages of the menstrual cycle.	UCP.1–3, UCP.5; A.1, A.2; C.1; F.1, F.5	**Indiana Standards** B.1.7, B.1.8, B.1.11, B.1.14, B.1.15	**Student Labs:** Additional Lab, p. 998: graph paper, colored pencils (red, yellow, blue, green), data sheet Problem-Solving Lab 38.1, p. 1003 **Teacher Demonstration:** Quick Demo, p. 997: microscope projector, cross-section of the testis
Section 38.2 1/2 session, 1 block 4. **Describe** the processes of fertilization and implantation. 5. **Summarize** the events during each trimester of pregnancy.	UCP.1–3, UCP.5; A.1, A.2; E.2; F.1, F.5; G.1, G.2	**Indiana Standards** B.1.1, B.1.7, B.1.11, B.1.14, B.1.15, B.1.16, B.1.19, B.1.21	**Student Labs:** MiniLab 38.1, p. 1006: slide of human sperm, slide of human egg, slide of sea star blastula, microscope MiniLab 38.2, p. 1010 Problem-Solving Lab 38.2, p. 1011 **Teacher Demonstration:** Quick Demo, p. 1007: microscope projector, sea star embryos at various stages of development
Section 38.3 1 1/2 sessions, 1/2 block 6. **Describe** the three stages of birth. 7. **Summarize** the developmental stages of humans after they are born.	UCP.1–3, UCP.5; A.1, A.2; E.2; F.1, F.2, F.5; G.1–3	**Indiana Standards** B.1.7, B.1.11, B.1.15, B.1.16, B.1.19	**Teacher Demonstration:** Quick Demo, p. 1013: projector, photos or slides of newborn infants and elderly individuals Investigate BioLab, p. 1016: See materials below.
End of Chapter Assessment **Student Edition** **Study Guide,** p. 1019 **Content Assessment,** pp. 1020–1021		**Indiana Standards** B.1.7, B.1.11, B.1.14, B.1.15	**Student Lab:** Investigate BioLab, p. 1016: scissors, heavy paper, tracing paper

Key to Teaching Strategies

L1 Level 1 activities should be appropriate for students with learning difficulties.

L2 Level 2 activities should be within the ability range of all students.

L3 Level 3 activities are designed for above-average students.

ELL ELL activities should be within the ability range of English Language Learners.

COOP LEARN Cooperative Learning activities are designed for small group work.

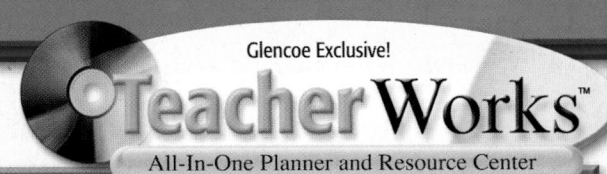

Glencoe Exclusive!
TeacherWorks™
All-In-One Planner and Resource Center

Reproducible Masters and Transparencies	Technology
Unit 10 FAST FILE Resources Reinforcement and Study Guide in English, pp. 173–174 Reinforcement and Study Guide in Spanish, pp. 177–178 Concept Mapping, p. 181 Critical Thinking/Problem Solving, p. 182 Transparency Worksheets, pp. 183, 187–192 **Reading Essentials for Biology, Section 38.1** **Section Focus Transparency 93** **Basic Concepts Transparencies 74, 75** **Reteaching Skills Transparency 55**	**Interactive Chalkboard CD-ROM: Section 38.1 Presentation** **TeacherWorks™ CD-ROM** **Guided Reading Audio Summaries MP3**
Unit 10 FAST FILE Resources MiniLab Worksheet, pp. 167, 168 BioLab Worksheet, pp. 169–170 Reinforcement and Study Guide in English, p. 175 Reinforcement and Study Guide in Spanish, p. 179 Transparency Worksheets, pp. 184, 193–195 **Reading Essentials for Biology, Section 38.2** **Section Focus Transparency 94** **Reteaching Skills Transparencies 56a, 56b**	**Interactive Chalkboard CD-ROM: Section 38.2 Presentation** **TeacherWorks™ CD-ROM** **Guided Reading Audio Summaries MP3**
Unit 10 FAST FILE Resources Real World BioApplications, pp. 171–172 Reinforcement and Study Guide in English, p. 176 Reinforcement and Study Guide in Spanish, p. 180 Transparency Worksheet, p. 185 **Reading Essentials for Biology, Section 38.3** **Section Focus Transparency 95**	**Interactive Chalkboard CD-ROM: Section 38.3 Presentation** **TeacherWorks™ CD-ROM** **Guided Reading Audio Summaries MP3**
Unit 10 FAST FILE Resources Chapter Assessment, pp. 197–202 Student Recording Sheet, p. 203 The Princeton Review **Reviewing Biology,** pp. 75–76	**Interactive Chalkboard: Chapter 38 Assessment** **MindJogger Videoquizzes DVD/VHS** **ExamView® Pro Test Bank CD-ROM** **TeacherWorks™ CD-ROM** **Succeeding on National Standards CD-ROM** in.bdol.glencoe.com /self_check_quiz /vocabulary_puzzlemaker /chapter_test /standardized_test

Indicates materials created specifically for Indiana.

Chapter 38

Reproduction and Development

Short on Time?

BIODIGEST The BioDigest at the end of this unit can be used as a(n):

- preview to introduce important unit concepts.
- overview if time does not permit teaching the entire chapter.
- review of key unit concepts.

Understanding the Photo

As sperm reach the egg, they collide with the egg and release enzymes from a packet called the acrosome found on their head end. These enzymes begin to digest the protective membrane surrounding the egg. Finally, one sperm is able to enter and fertilize the egg.

What You'll Learn

- You will identify and describe the anatomy, control, and functions of the male and female reproductive systems.
- You will distinguish the stages of development before birth.
- You will summarize the processes of birth, growth, and aging.

Why It's Important

As you grow and develop, your reproductive system is maturing. The human reproductive system prepares sex cells—sperm or eggs—which, when combined, ensure the continuation of our species.

Understanding ▶ the Photo

A human egg is shown surrounded by hundreds of sperm in this color-enhanced photograph from a scanning electron microscope. Only one sperm will penetrate the cell membrane to fertilize the egg.

Biology Online

Visit in.bdol.glencoe.com to
- study the entire chapter online
- access Web Links for more information on reproduction and development
- review content with the Interactive Tutor and self-check quizzes

Color-enhanced SEM Magnification: 3400×

Two-Minute Chapter Launcher

Activity Have students examine a photo of an SEM of a sperm. Help them to identify the visible cellular structures. head, midpiece, flagellum (tail), cell membrane; possibly also nucleus and mitochondria

Once students identify the structures, have them list each structure and infer what each of the cellular structures does. head: contains nucleus with DNA and packet of enzymes for digestion of egg

membrane; midpiece: contains mitochondria for cellular respiration; flagellum: propels sperm; cell membrane: controls what enters and leaves the sperm cell **L2**

Section 38.1

Human Reproductive Systems

Indiana Standards Standard B.1.14 Recognize and explain that communication and/or interaction are required between cells to coordinate their diverse activities.

SECTION PREVIEW

Objectives

Identify the structures and functions of the male and female reproductive systems.

Summarize the internal feedback control of reproductive hormones.

Sequence the stages of the menstrual cycle.

Review Vocabulary

meiosis: a type of cell division where one body cell produces four gametes, each containing half the number of chromosomes as the parent's body cell (p. 265)

New Vocabulary

scrotum
epididymis
vas deferens
seminal vesicle
prostate gland
bulbourethral gland
semen
puberty
oviduct
cervix
follicle
ovulation
menstrual cycle
corpus luteum

FOLDABLES™
Study Organizer

Reproductive Anatomy Make the following Foldable to help you organize information on the male and female reproductive systems.

STEP 1 **Draw** a mark at the midpoint of a vertical sheet of paper along the side edge.

STEP 2 **Fold** the outside edges in to touch at the midpoint mark.

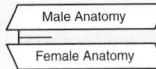
Male Anatomy
Female Anatomy

STEP 3 **Label** the tabs as shown.

Organize Information As you read Chapter 38, list the structures and functions of the male and female reproductive systems beneath the corresponding tabs.

Human Male Anatomy

The ultimate result of the reproductive process is the formation and union of egg and sperm, development of the fetus, and birth of the infant. The organs, glands, and hormones of the male reproductive system are instrumental in meeting this goal. Their main functions are the production of sperm—the male sex cells—and their delivery to the female.

Where sperm form

Sperm production takes place in the testes, which are located in the scrotum. The **scrotum** is a sac that contains the testes and is suspended directly behind the base of the penis. Before birth, the testes form in the embryo's abdomen and then descend into the scrotum. Because sperm can develop only in an environment with a temperature about 2–3°C lower than normal body temperature, the scrotum is positioned outside the abdomen. Muscles in the walls of the scrotum help maintain the proper temperature. The muscles contract in response to cold temperatures, pulling the scrotum closer to the body for warmth. The muscles relax in response to warm temperatures, lowering the scrotum to allow air to circulate and cool both testes and sperm. *Figure 38.1* on the next page shows the organs and glands of the male reproductive system.

38.1 HUMAN REPRODUCTIVE SYSTEMS **995**

1 Focus

INTERACTIVE
CHALKBOARD
PowerPoint® Presentations

Bellringer
Section Focus Transparency 93

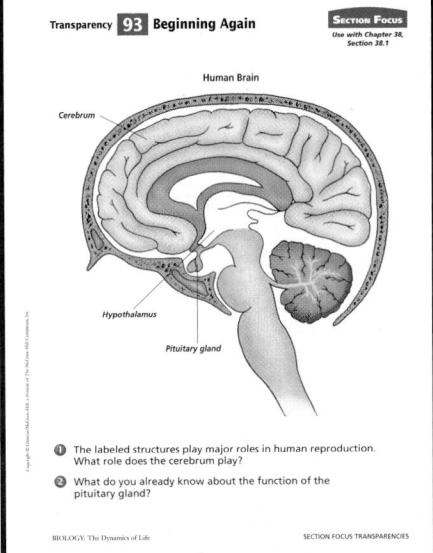

Transparency **93** Beginning Again

SECTION FOCUS
Use with Chapter 38, Section 38.1

Human Brain

Cerebrum

Hypothalamus

Pituitary gland

❶ The labeled structures play major roles in human reproduction. What role does the cerebrum play?

❷ What do you already know about the function of the pituitary gland?

BIOLOGY: The Dynamics of Life

SECTION FOCUS TRANSPARENCIES

INTERACTIVE
CHALKBOARD
with Image Bank

PowerPoint® Presentations

This CD-ROM is an editable Microsoft® PowerPoint® presentation that includes:

• Section presentations
• Section checks
• Image bank
• Hot links to Biology Online
• All transparencies

FOLDABLES™

For an additional Foldables activity idea, see the Chapter 38 Foldables page in *Unit 10 FAST FILE Resources.*

RESOURCE MANAGER

Unit 10 *FAST FILE* Resources
Reinforcement and Study Guide in English, pp. 173–174
Reinforcement and Study Guide in Spanish, pp. 177–178
Concept Mapping, p. 181
Critical Thinking/Problem Solving, p. 182
Transparency Worksheets, pp. 183, 187–192

Reading Essentials for Biology, Section 38.1
🖐 **Section Focus Transparency 93**
🖐 **Basic Concepts Transparencies 74, 75**
🖐 **Reteaching Skills Transparency 55**

Indiana Academic Standards

Pages 994–995: B.1.11

2 Teach

Tying to Prior Knowledge

Ask students to recall how sex cells are produced by meiosis. If necessary, remind them that meiosis produces haploid cells.

Visual Learning

Figure 38.1 Have students use the illustration of the male reproductive system to trace the path of sperm from the testes to the outside of the body. testes, epididymis, vas deferens, urethra **L1**

Caption Question Answer

Figure 38.2 The head of the sperm contains a nucleus and is covered by a cap containing enzymes that help penetrate the egg. Mitochondria in the midpiece provide energy for locomotion and the tail propels the sperm.

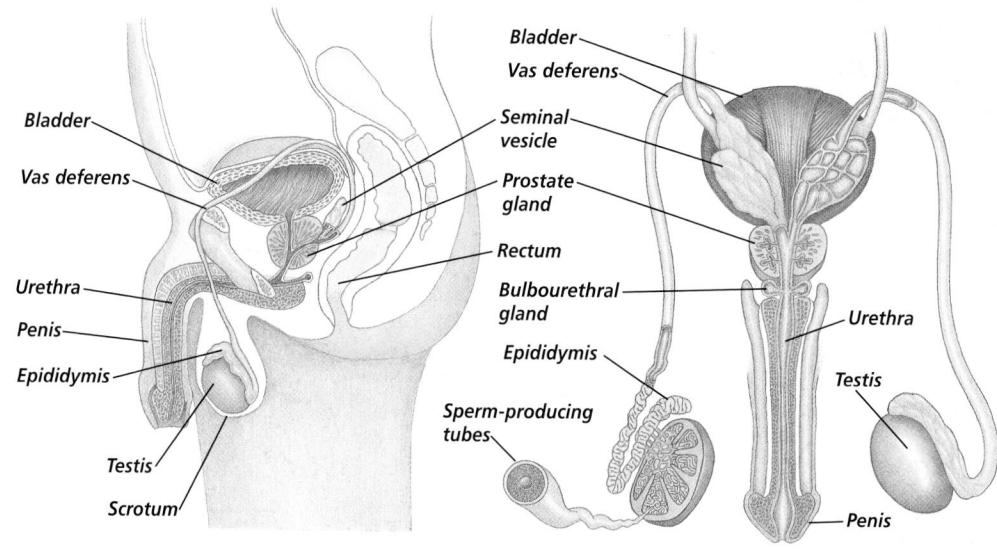

Figure 38.1
The organs and glands of the male reproductive system are shown in side and posterior views.

Within each testis is a fine network of highly coiled tubes. Sperm are produced by meiosis of the cells that line these tubes. Recall that meiosis produces haploid cells. When a single cell in the testis divides by meiosis, it produces four haploid cells. All four of these cells develop into mature sperm over a period of about 74 days. A sexually mature human male can produce about 300 million mature sperm per day, each day of his life.

As you can see in *Figure 38.2*, a sperm is highly adapted for reaching and entering the female egg. The head portion of a sperm contains the nucleus and is covered by a cap containing enzymes that help penetrate the egg. A number of mitochondria are found in the midpiece of the sperm; they provide energy for locomotion. The tail is a typical flagellum that propels the sperm along its way. Sperm usually live for about 48 hours inside the female reproductive tract.

How sperm leave the testes

Before the sperm mature, they move out of the testes through a series of coiled ducts that empty into a single tube called the epididymis. The **epididymis** (e puh DIH duh mus) is a coiled tube within the scrotum in which the sperm complete their maturation.

When sperm are released from the epididymis, they enter the vas deferens, where they are stored for as long as two or three months until they are released from the body.

Figure 38.2
A sperm is composed of a head, a midpiece, and a tail. **Describe** *How is a sperm cell adapted for its function?*

Magnification: unavailable

Midpiece (6 μm)

Fibrous sheath of flagellum

Head (5 μm)

Tail (55 μm)

Mitochondrial spiral

Nucleus

Cap

996 REPRODUCTION AND DEVELOPMENT

Indiana Academic Standards

Pages 996–997: B.1.11, B.1.15

INCLUSION STRATEGIES

Learning Disabled: *Visual-Spatial* Have students use tracing paper to trace the structures of the male reproductive system shown in Figure 38.1. Ask them to label each structure and write a description of its function beside the label. Have them include the diagrams they have created in their journals and use them as study tools. Students can quiz each other in pairs to review. **L1**

The **vas deferens** (VAS • DE fuh renz) is a duct that transports sperm from the epididymis toward the ejaculatory ducts and the urethra. Peristaltic contractions of the vas deferens force the sperm along. The urethra is a tube in the penis that transports sperm out of the male's body. The urethra also transports urine from the urinary bladder. A muscle located at the base of the bladder prevents urine and sperm from mixing.

Fluids that help transport sperm

As sperm travel from the testes, they mix with fluids that are secreted by several different glands. The **seminal vesicles** are a pair of glands located at the base of the urinary bladder. They secrete a mucouslike fluid into the vas deferens. The fluid is rich in the sugar fructose, which provides energy for the sperm cells.

The **prostate gland** is a single, doughnut-shaped structure that lies below the urinary bladder and surrounds the top portion of the urethra. The prostate secretes a thinner, alkaline fluid that helps sperm move and survive. Two tiny **bulbourethral** (bul boh yoo REE thrul) **glands** are located beneath the prostate. These glands secrete a clear, sticky, alkaline fluid that protects sperm by neutralizing the acidic environment of the male urethra and female vagina. The combination of sperm and all of these fluids is called **semen.**

Puberty in Males

In an earlier chapter, you learned that the glands of the endocrine system release hormones, which play a key role in the regulation of body functions, metabolism, and homeostasis. Hormones also control the development and activity of the male reproductive system.

Hormones and male puberty

In the early teen years, changes to a child's body begin to occur. Puberty begins. **Puberty** refers to the time when secondary sex characteristics begin to develop so that sexual maturity—the potential for sexual reproduction—is reached. *Figure 38.3* shows several males at a variety of ages. The physical transition of the body from child to young adult occurs during puberty. The changes associated with puberty are controlled by sex hormones secreted by the endocrine system.

Figure 38.3
As children go through puberty, changes that result in growth and sexual maturity occur.

997

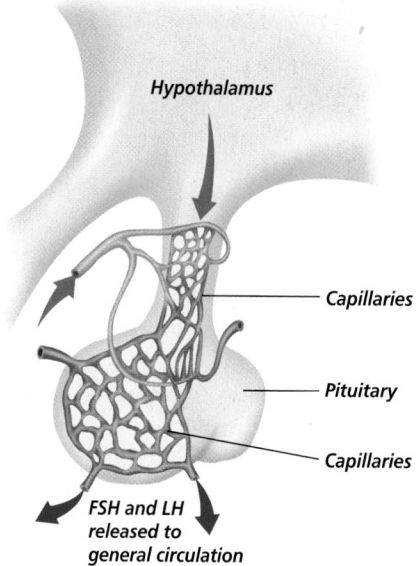

A In the hypothalamus, neurons secrete releasing and inhibiting hormones. These hormones travel to the pituitary gland, where they increase or decrease the secretion of FSH and LH.

B Release of FSH and LH from the pituitary gland stimulates production of sperm and of testosterone. As testosterone levels increase, production of FSH and LH slows. When sperm and testosterone levels drop, production of FSH and LH increases again.

Figure 38.4
The activity of the male reproductive system is controlled by the hypothalamus and the pituitary gland in the brain.

Hormones and the male reproductive system

In males, the onset of puberty causes the hypothalamus to produce several kinds of hormones that interact with the pituitary gland, which influences many physiological processes of the body. As shown in ***Figure 38.4A,*** the hypothalamus secretes a hormone that causes the pituitary gland to release two other hormones: follicle-stimulating hormone (FSH) and luteinizing (LEW ten i zing) hormone (LH). When released into the bloodstream, FSH and LH are transported to the testes. In the testes, FSH causes the production of sperm cells. LH causes endocrine cells in the testes to produce the male hormone, testosterone (teh STAHS tuh rohn), which in turn influences sperm cell production.

The levels of these hormones in the body are regulated by a negative-feedback system. As the testosterone levels in the blood increase, the production of FSH and LH is inhibited, or decreased. Increased production of sperm in the testis also feeds back into the system to inhibit production of FSH and LH, as ***Figure 38.4B*** illustrates. When testosterone levels in the blood drop, production of FSH and LH increases.

Testosterone is the steroid hormone responsible for the growth and development of secondary sex characteristics in a male. These characteristics include growth and maintenance of male sex organs; the production of sperm; an increase in body hair, especially on the face, under the arms, and in the pubic area; an increase in muscle mass; increased growth of the long bones of the arms and legs; and deepening of the voice.

Additional Lab

Tracking Hormone Levels

Purpose
Students will graph and analyze patterns of change that take place in female hormones during the menstrual cycle.

Materials
graph paper, colored pencils (red, yellow, blue, green), data sheet

Preparation
Prepare data sheets for students that include the information given here.

Data Table

Day	2	4	6	8	10	12	14	16	18	20	22	24	26	28
LH	17	17	17	17	17	46	35	20	19	18	17	16	14	13
FSH	14	14	14	13	10	8	15	8	7	7	6	6	6	7
Estrogen	4	4	5	6	10	13	13	10	9	10	11	11	11	8
Progesterone	1	1	1	1	1	1	2	4	7	12	14	14	9	3

Human Female Anatomy

The main functions of the female reproductive system are to produce eggs, which are the female sex cells, to receive sperm, and to provide an environment in which a fertilized egg can develop. Egg production takes place in the two ovaries. Each ovary is about the size and shape of an almond. One ovary is located on each side of the lower part of the abdomen.

As you can see in *Figure 38.5*, the open end of an oviduct is located close to each ovary. The **oviduct** is a tube that transports eggs from the ovary to the uterus. Peristaltic contractions of the muscles in the wall of the oviduct combine with beating cilia to move the egg through the tube.

You learned earlier that female mammals have a uterus in which the fetus develops during pregnancy. The human uterus is situated between the urinary bladder and the rectum and is the size and shape of an inverted pear. The uterine wall is composed of three layers: an outer layer of connective tissue; a thick, muscular middle layer; and a thin, inner lining called the endometrium (en doh MEE tree um). The lower end of the uterus, called the **cervix,** tapers to a narrow opening into the vagina, which is a passageway to the outside of the female's body.

Puberty in Females

As in males, puberty in females begins when the hypothalamus signals the pituitary to produce and release the hormones FSH and LH. These are the same hormones that are produced in males; however, in females, FSH stimulates the development of follicles in the ovary. A **follicle** is a group of epithelial cells that surround a developing egg cell. FSH also causes the release of the hormone estrogen from the ovary. Estrogen is the steroid hormone responsible for the secondary sex characteristics of females. These characteristics include the growth and maintenance of female sex organs, an increase in the growth rates of the long bones of the arms and legs, and a broadening of the hips.

Figure 38.5
The female reproductive system includes two ovaries, two oviducts—sometimes called fallopian tubes—the uterus, and the vagina.

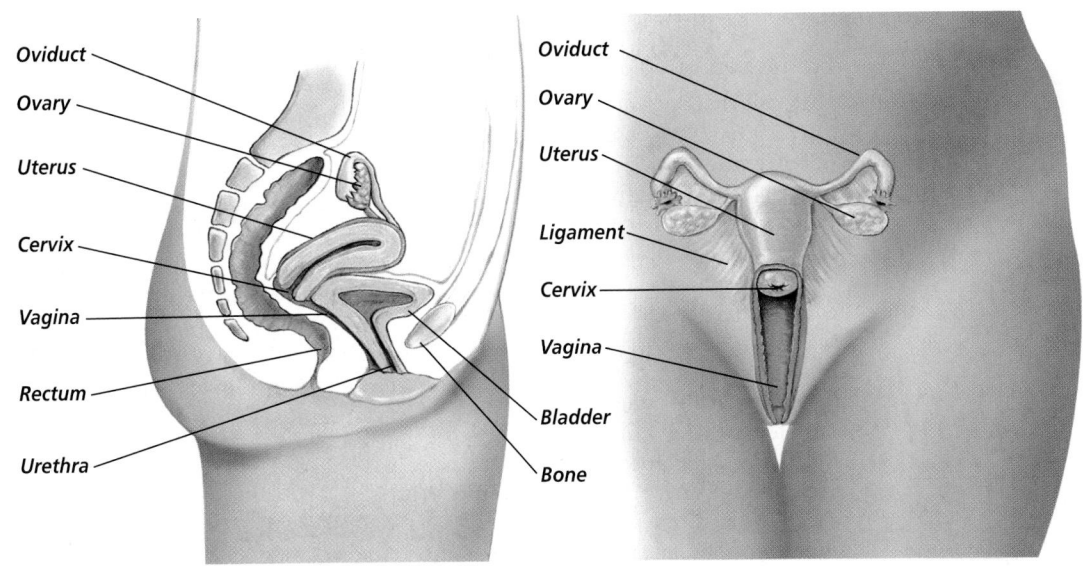

Oviduct

Ovary

Uterus

Cervix

Vagina

Rectum

Urethra

Oviduct

Ovary

Uterus

Ligament

Cervix

Vagina

Bladder

Bone

Magnification: unavailable

Ovulation

Figure 38.6
Once a female reaches puberty, follicles within her ovaries begin to mature and release an egg cell during each menstrual cycle.

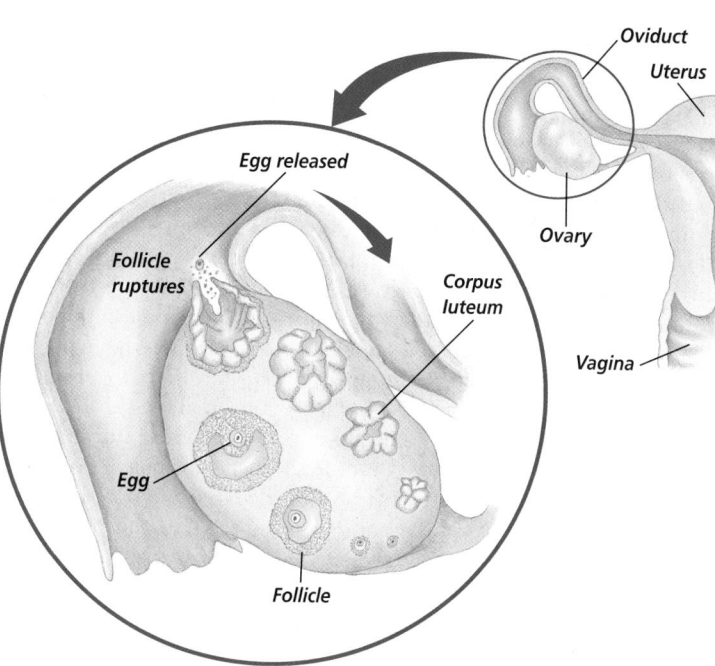

Oviduct
Uterus
Egg released
Follicle ruptures
Ovary
Corpus luteum
Vagina
Egg
Follicle

Other changes that take place include an increase in body hair, especially under the arms and in the pubic area; an increase in fat deposits in the breasts, buttocks, and thighs; and the onset of the menstrual cycle.

Production of eggs

Recall that sperm production does not begin in males until they reach puberty, after which time it continues for the rest of their lives. Egg production is different. Even before a female is born, her body begins to develop eggs. During this prenatal period, cells in her ovaries divide until the first stage of meiosis, prophase I, is reached. At this point, the cells go into a resting stage. At birth, a female's ovaries contain about two million of these potential eggs, which are called primary oocytes. Many of these break down, or degenerate. At puberty, a female's ovaries contain

about 40 000 primary oocytes. How does the production of sperm differ from the production of egg cells? To find out, look at *Figure 38*.7.

How eggs are released

About once a month, beginning at puberty, the process of meiosis starts up again in several of the prophase I cells. Each cell completes meiosis I and begins meiosis II. During meiosis II, one of the egg cells ruptures from the ovary and passes into the oviduct. The process of the egg rupturing through the ovary wall and moving into the oviduct is called **ovulation.** A total of about 400 eggs are ovulated during the reproductive life of a female. Fertilization, if it takes place, usually occurs in the oviduct. *Figure 38.6* shows the process leading to ovulation.

✓ Reading Check **Describe** the process of ovulation.

Sex Cell Production

Figure 38.7

As with many other animals, human sex cells are produced by meiosis. A mature male produces millions of swimming sperm cells each day. A mature female usually releases only one mature egg each month.

Critical Thinking *Compare and contrast the process by which eggs and sperm are produced and mature.*

Magnification: unavailable

Human egg surrounded by hundreds of sperm

Egg Formation

A **Egg production** In the fetal ovary, cells called oogonia (singular, oogonium) undergo a partial meiotic division to become primary oocytes. These cells are held at prophase in meiosis I until puberty.

Oogonium

Primary oocyte (2n)

First meiotic division

First polar body (degenerates)

Secondary oocyte (n)

Release into oviduct

B **Secondary oocyte formation** Beginning at puberty, FSH causes primary oocytes in one or more follicles to complete meiosis I. Unequal cell division forms a secondary oocyte and a small polar body that degenerates.

Sperm

Second meiotic division

Second polar body (degenerates)

Zygote

C **Ovulation** Usually, only one secondary oocyte is released from the ovary at ovulation. That oocyte will complete meiosis II only if fertilization takes place. Meiosis II produces a second polar body that degenerates.

Sperm Formation

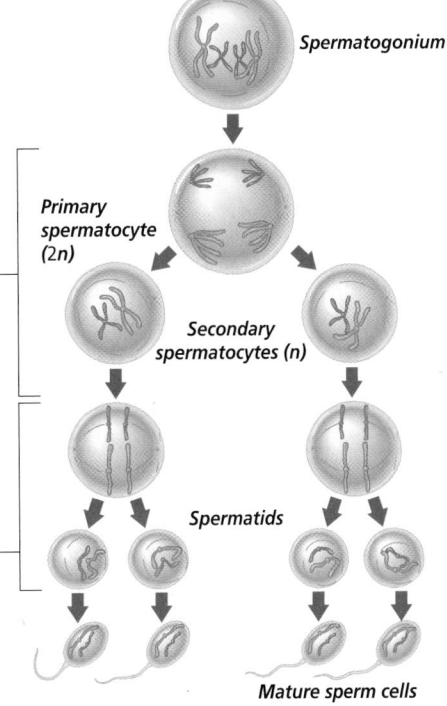

Spermatogonium

Primary spermatocyte (2n)

Secondary spermatocytes (n)

Spermatids

Mature sperm cells

D **Sperm production** Once puberty begins, cells within the testes called spermatogonia (singular, spermatogonium) undergo meiosis daily to produce primary spermatocytes. Meiosis I and meiosis II take place in the tubules of the testes. Secondary spermatocytes are produced at the end of meiosis I and spermatids, immature sperm cells, are produced at the end of meiosis II. Spermatids mature in the epididymis and mature sperm are stored in the vas deferens.

Purpose

Students will compare and contrast human egg production with sperm production.

Teaching Strategies

Have students identify similarities and differences in egg and sperm production. Egg production begins in the female fetus; sperm production begins in the male at puberty. Mature sperm are produced daily; mature eggs are produced only once a month.

Visual Learning

Using a microscope projector, show students a cross-section slide of an ovary. Point out developing follicles that contain a cell ready to complete meiosis (future egg cell). Project a cross-section of a testis, showing the sperm cells that result from meiosis.

Critical Thinking

Egg production starts in the fetal ovary, and one secondary oocyte finishes meiosis each month following puberty. The oogonium and secondary oocyte undergo unequal cell division, producing one large egg cell and three polar bodies, which will degenerate. Once puberty begins, many spermatogonia undergo meiosis daily, producing millions of sperm each day. Once produced, the sperm mature in the epididymis.

CHALLENGE ACTIVITY

Activity Have students who need an additional challenge prepare a table that compares and contrasts anatomy, sex cells, and puberty in males and females. Suggest they use the Make and Use Tables section of the **Skill Handbook** if they need help. **L3**

 Indiana Academic Standards

Pages 1000–1001: B.1.8, B.1.11, B.1.15

Figure 38.8
Changes in the uterine lining, follicles, and hormone levels take place during each phase of the menstrual cycle.

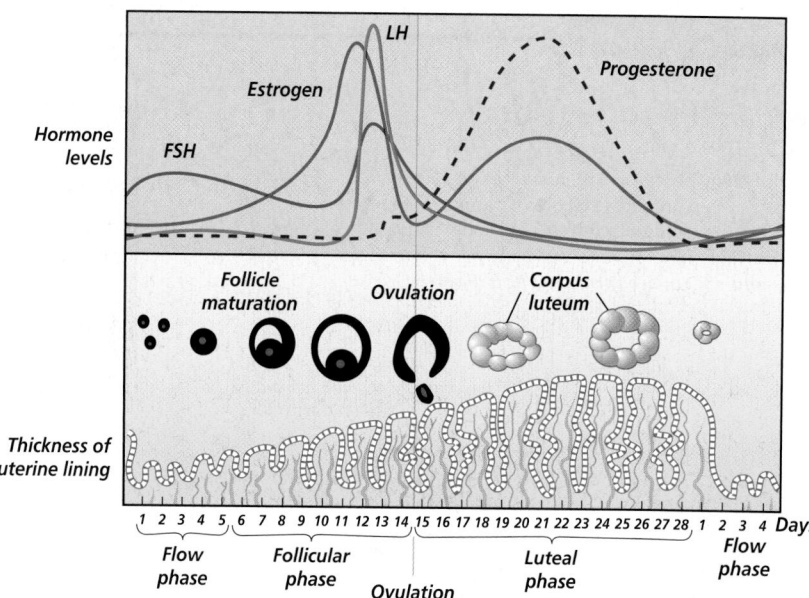

The Menstrual Cycle

The series of changes in the female reproductive system that includes producing an egg and preparing the uterus for receiving it is known as the **menstrual cycle.** The entire menstrual cycle repeats about once a month. Once an egg has been released during ovulation, the part of the follicle that remains in the ovary develops into a structure called the **corpus luteum.** The corpus luteum secretes the hormones estrogen and progesterone. Progesterone causes changes to occur in the lining of the uterus that prepare it for receiving a fertilized egg. The menstrual cycle begins during puberty and continues for 30 to 40 years, until menopause. At menopause, the female stops releasing eggs and the secretion of female hormones decreases.

The length of each menstrual cycle varies from female to female, but the average is 28 days. If the egg released at ovulation is not fertilized, the lining of the uterus is shed, causing some bleeding for a few days. The entire menstrual cycle can be divided into three phases: the flow phase, the follicular phase, and the luteal phase, illustrated in *Figure 38.8*. The timing of each phase of the menstrual cycle correlates with hormone output from the pituitary gland, changes in the ovary, and changes in the uterus. *Figure 38.9* shows how internal feedback controls hormone secretion during the menstrual cycle. Carry out the *Problem-Solving Lab* to find out how the phases of the menstrual cycle can vary in length.

Flow phase

Day 1 of the menstrual cycle is the day menstrual flow begins. Menstrual flow is the shedding of blood, tissue fluid, mucus, and epithelial cells that made up the lining of the uterus, the endometrium. This flow passes from the uterus through the cervix and the vagina to the outside of the body. Contractions of the uterine muscle help expel the uterine lining and can cause discomfort in some females.

Generally, menstrual flow ends by day 5 of the cycle. During the flow phase, the level of FSH in the blood begins to rise, and another follicle in one of the ovaries begins to mature as meiosis of the prophase I cell proceeds.

Follicular phase

The second phase of the menstrual cycle is more varied in length than the other phases. In a 28-day cycle, it lasts from about day 6 to day 14. As the follicle containing a primary oocyte continues to develop, it secretes estrogen, which stimulates the repair of the endometrial lining of the uterus. The endometrial cells undergo mitosis, and the lining thickens. The steady increase in estrogen also feeds back to the hypothalamus and pituitary gland, which slows the production of FSH and LH. Just before ovulation, estrogen levels peak, stimulating a sudden, sharp increase in the release of LH.

Ovulation occurs at about day 14. The sharp increase in LH causes the follicle to rupture, releasing the egg into the oviduct. At this time, the female's body temperature rises about 0.5°C.

Problem-Solving Lab 38.1

Apply Concepts

What happens when the menstrual cycle is not exactly 28 days? How does the number of days in each phase differ?

Solve the Problem

The graph compares menstrual cycles of different lengths. Study the graph and then answer the questions that follow.

M = flow phase   F = follicular phase   L = luteal phase

Thinking Critically

1. **Evaluate** Which phase does not vary in length, regardless of the total time for a cycle? Which hormones are associated with this phase?
2. **Infer** Offer a possible explanation for why the length of the follicular phase may vary.
3. **Explain** How would these events differ for the cycle during which a female becomes pregnant?

Figure 38.9
Internal feedback controls the levels of hormones in the female during her menstrual cycle. After ovulation, the corpus luteum secretes progesterone and some estrogen. High levels of progesterone inhibit the release of hormones from the hypothalamus and the pituitary gland. If fertilization does not occur, the corpus luteum degenerates and progesterone levels decrease. As progesterone levels decrease, the inhibition of the hypothalamus and the pituitary gland is blocked and the cycle begins again.

38.1 HUMAN REPRODUCTIVE SYSTEMS **1003**

Problem-Solving Lab 38.1

Purpose
Students will study similarities and differences among menstrual cycles of differing lengths of time.

Process Skills
analyze information, apply concepts, compare and contrast, think critically, draw a conclusion, interpret data, make and use graphs

Teaching Strategies
■ Make sure students are familiar with the three phases of the menstrual cycle.
■ Suggest that students refer to the graph and diagrams in Figures 38.8 and 38.9 for further information, if needed.

Thinking Critically
1. luteal phase; progesterone and estrogen
2. Student answers may vary. The three hormones interact, and may influence one another so as to alter the exact timing of the follicular phase.
3. The corpus luteum does not degenerate and continues to secrete hormones. The lining of the uterus is not shed, so there is no flow phase.

Modified Assessment
Skill Give students an unlabeled graph of the menstrual cycle similar to the one in Figure 38.8. Have them label the graph as a quiz. Use the Performance Task Assessment List for Graph from Data in **PASC**, p. 111. **L1**

PROJECT

Diagramming the Menstrual Cycle
Have students create flowcharts or concept maps showing the sequence of events that occurs during each phase of the menstrual cycle. Ask students to include information about all hormones involved in the regulation of the cycle. **L2**

 Indiana Academic Standards
Pages 1002–1003: B.1.7, B.1.14

1003

3 Assess

Unfertilized egg

Ovulation

Menstruation occurs

Fertilized egg

Ovulation

Embryo implants in uterine wall

Menstruation does not occur

Figure 38.10
Events that take place in the uterine wall after ovulation depend on whether or not fertilization has occurred.

In addition, the cells of the cervix produce large amounts of mucus. Some females also experience discomfort in the area of one or both ovaries around the time of ovulation.

Luteal phase

The last stage of the menstrual cycle, from days 15 to 28, is named the luteal phase, for the corpus luteum. During the luteal phase, LH stimulates the corpus luteum to develop from the ruptured follicle. The corpus luteum produces progesterone and some estrogen. Progesterone increases the blood supply of the endometrium, causing it to accumulate lipids and tissue fluid. These changes correspond to the arrival of a fertilized egg. Through negative feedback, progesterone prevents the production of LH.

If the egg is not fertilized, the rising levels of progesterone and estrogen from the corpus luteum cause the hypothalamus to inhibit the release of FSH and LH. The corpus luteum degenerates and stops secreting progesterone or estrogen. As hormone levels drop, the thick lining of the uterus begins to shed. If fertilization occurs, as shown in *Figure 38.10*, the endometrium begins secreting a fluid rich in nutrients for the embryo.

Section Assessment

Understanding Main Ideas
1. Identify the different structures, and interpret the functions of the male reproductive system.

2. Describe the relationship between internal feedback mechanisms and the regulation of male reproductive hormones.

3. Identify the different structures, and interpret the functions of the female reproductive system.

4. Sequence and describe the stages of the menstrual cycle.

Thinking Critically
5. What might happen to sperm production if a male has a high fever?

SKILL REVIEW
6. **Interpret Scientific Illustrations** Study *Figure 38.1*. Using the terms posterior, superior, and inferior, describe where the epididymis is located in relation to the vas deferens. Where is the prostate located in relation to the testes and bladder, respectively? For more help, refer to *Interpret Scientific Illustrations* in the **Skill Handbook**.

1004 REPRODUCTION AND DEVELOPMENT

 in.bdol.glencoe.com/self_check_quiz

Section Assessment

1. scrotum, testis, epididymis, vas deferens, urethra, penis, seminal vesicles, prostate gland, bulbourethral glands; production and storage of sperm and delivering sperm to the female
2. The hypothalamus produces releasing hormones, which cause FSH and LH to be secreted from the pituitary. FSH regulates sperm production and LH regulates testosterone production in the testes. As testosterone levels increase, the production of FSH and LH is inhibited by negative feedback.
3. ovary, oviduct, uterus, vagina; produce eggs, receive sperm, and provide an environment in which a fertilized egg can develop
4. flow phase: 1–5 days, shedding of the uterine lining; follicular phase: 6–14 days, follicle develops, endometrial and uterine linings increase, ovulation occurs; luteal phase: 15–28 days, old follicle becomes corpus luteum
5. Sperm may be killed by the high fever.
6. inferior to the vas deferens; superior to the testes and inferior to the bladder

Development Before Birth

Indiana Standards Standard B.1.11 Describe that through biogenesis all organisms begin their life cycles as a single cell and that in multicellular organisms, successive generations of embryonic cells form by cell division.

A Protected Environment

Using an Analogy Think about an astronaut within the protected environment of a space shuttle. All survival needs are met. Oxygen and food are provided as well as the opportunity to regulate temperature. In the same way, a human fetus is protected within the uterus. Survival needs are met through the exchange of oxygen, nutrients, and wastes between the mother and the developing fetus.

Organize Information *As you read the section, identify which structures are involved in the exchange of materials between the fetus and the mother.*

Like an astronaut in a space shuttle, a human fetus is protected inside a controlled environment.

Fertilization and Implantation

After an egg ruptures from a follicle, it is able to stay alive for about 24 hours. For fertilization to occur, sperm must be present in the oviduct at some point during those first hours after ovulation. Sperm enter the vagina of the female's reproductive system when strong, muscular contractions ejaculate semen from the male's penis. Between 300 and 500 million sperm are forced out of the male's penis and into the female's vagina during intercourse. Because sperm can live for 48 hours after ejaculation, fertilization can occur if intercourse occurs anywhere from a few days before to a day after ovulation.

One sperm plus one egg

How is it possible that, of the millions of sperm released into the vagina during ejaculation, only one fertilizes the mature egg? One reason is that the fluids secreted by the vagina are acidic and destroy most of the delicate sperm. Yet, some sperm survive because of the neutralizing effect of semen. The surviving sperm swim up the vagina into the uterus. Of the sperm that reach the uterus, only a few hundred pass into the two oviducts. The egg is present in one of them.

The head of the sperm contains enzymes that help the sperm penetrate the egg. Once one sperm has entered the egg, the electrical charge of the egg's membrane changes, preventing other sperm from entering the egg.

38.2 DEVELOPMENT BEFORE BIRTH **1005**

1 Focus

INTERACTIVE CHALKBOARD
PowerPoint® Presentations

Bellringer
Section Focus Transparency 94

Using an Analogy

Organize Information Using the chalkboard, compare and contrast an astronaut in a space shuttle or space suit and the human fetus protected inside the controlled uterine environment. Each is protected from the environment by a covering. Both the astronaut in space and the fetus move freely in the environment. The astronaut uses his or her lungs to acquire oxygen and discharge carbon dioxide, while the fetus receives oxygen from the umbilical cord and the umbilical cord takes carbon dioxide back to the mother's blood.

2 Teach

MiniLab 38.1

Purpose

Students will observe the structure of sperm, an egg, and a blastula.

Process Skills

observe and infer, use the microscope

Teaching Strategies

■ Students will need help finding eggs on the ovary slide.
■ A labeled picture from a human anatomy and physiology textbook would be helpful.

Expected Results

Students will examine sperm, an ovary slide for eggs, and a sea star blastula for various structures.

Analysis

1. Students should be able to find the sperm head, which contains the nucleus and DNA for fertilization; acrosome cap containing digestive enzymes; midpiece, which contains mitochondria; and flagellum for movement.
2. The follicle cells protect the egg and produce the hormones estrogen and progesterone.
3. After fertilization of the egg by the sperm, the zygote divides by mitosis to produce the multicellular blastula (called a blastocyst in humans).

Modified Assessment

Have students use colored pencils to draw and label the slides they view under the microscope. Have them identify the function of the structures labeled on the sperm cell. Use the Performance Task Assessment List for Lab Report in **PASC**, p. 119. **L1**

MiniLab 38.1

Observe and Infer

Examining Sperm, Egg, and Early Embryonic Development Sperm and egg cells are specialized for reproduction. The egg cell is produced with a large amount of cytoplasm and a special protective membrane. Sperm are specialized for their journey to join the egg. Once a sperm fertilizes the egg in the oviduct, the zygote begins to divide by repeated mitotic divisions to produce a blastocyst for implantation.

Color-enhanced SEM Magnification: 360×

Human blastocyst

Procedure

Carefully examine the prepared slides of a human sperm, human egg, and a sea star blastula. Compare the human sperm to *Figure 38.2*, the egg to *Figure 38.6*, and the blastula to the figure above. **CAUTION:** *Use care when working with a microscope and microscope slides.*

Analysis

1. **Compare** Which structures labeled in *Figure 38.2* are visible on the sperm slide? What is the function of each structure?
2. **Infer** What is the function of the cells of the follicle surrounding the egg?
3. **Explain** Where did the cells of the blastula come from?

The sperm's nucleus then combines with the egg's nucleus to form a zygote that contains a complete array of genetic information. Examine the structures of a sperm and egg cell by completing the *MiniLab* on this page.

The fertilized egg travels to the uterus

As the zygote passes down the oviduct, it begins to divide by repeated mitotic division. During its journey,

1006 REPRODUCTION AND DEVELOPMENT

pictured in *Figure 38.11*, the zygote obtains nutrients from fluids secreted by the mother. By the sixth day, the zygote passes into the uterus. Continuous cell divisions result in the formation of a hollow ball of cells called a blastocyst. *Blastocyst* is the term used when discussing human embryonic development. Recall that the term *blastula* is used for the embryonic development of other animals.

The blastocyst attaches to the uterine lining six days after fertilization. Attachment of the blastocyst to the lining of the uterus is called **implantation.** A small, inner mass of cells within the blastocyst will soon become a human embryo.

Embryonic Membranes and the Placenta

You have already learned about the importance of the amniotic egg to the evolutionary advancement of animals. Membranes that are similar to those of the amniotic egg form around the human embryo, protecting and nourishing it. The amnion is a thin, inner membrane filled with a clear, watery amniotic fluid. Amniotic fluid serves as a shock absorber and helps regulate the body temperature of the developing embryo.

The allantois membrane is an outgrowth of the digestive tract of the embryo. Blood vessels of the allantois form the **umbilical cord,** a ropelike structure that attaches the embryo to the wall of the uterus. The chorion is the outer membrane that surrounds the amniotic sac and the embryo within it. About 12 days after fertilization, fingerlike projections of the chorion, called chorionic villi, begin to grow into the uterine wall. The chorionic villi combine with part of the uterine lining to form the placenta, as shown in *Figure 38.12.*

CHALLENGE ACTIVITY

Fetal Development Have students who need an additional challenge research the medical techniques used to examine fetal development and genetics. Techniques may include ultrasound, amniocentesis, or chorionic villi sampling. **L3**

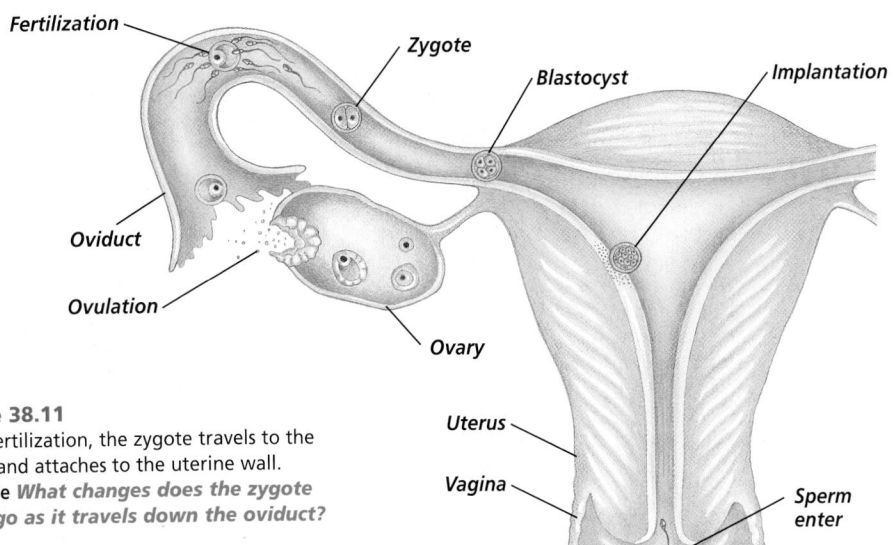

Figure 38.11
After fertilization, the zygote travels to the uterus and attaches to the uterine wall.
Describe *What changes does the zygote undergo as it travels down the oviduct?*

Fertilization
Zygote
Blastocyst
Implantation
Oviduct
Ovulation
Ovary
Uterus
Vagina
Sperm enter

Exchange between embryo and mother

To survive and grow, the embryo must obtain the proper nutrients and eliminate the wastes its cells produce. The placenta delivers nutrients to the embryo and carries wastes away.

In the placenta, blood vessels from the mother's uterine wall lie close to the blood vessels of the embryo's chorionic villi. Although they are close together, they are not directly connected to one another. Instead, oxygen and nutrients transported by the mother's blood diffuse into the blood vessels of the chorionic villi in the placenta. These vital substances are then carried by the blood in the umbilical cord to the embryo. In turn, waste products from the embryo travel in the umbilical blood vessels to the placenta. Here they diffuse out of the vessels in the chorionic villi into the blood of the mother. These waste products are then removed by the mother's excretory system.

Figure 38.12
A growing fetus exchanges nutrients, oxygen, and wastes with the mother through the placenta.

A As an embryo develops the chorionic villi begin to grow into the uterine wall.

B Nutrients, oxygen, and wastes diffuse across maternal and fetal blood vessels and are carried to and from the fetus through the umbilical cord.

C The placenta contains tissue from both mother and fetus.

Embryo
Chorionic villi
Chorion
Chorionic villus
Maternal blood
Umbilical cord
Fetal blood vessels
Maternal tissue of placenta
Umbilical cord
Placenta

INVESTIGATE BioLab The BioLab at the end of the chapter can be used at this point in the lesson.

Portfolio

Skill Ask students to prepare a time line that plots the changes that take place in a developing embryo and fetus. Have them use different-colored pencils to indicate clearly where each trimester of pregnancy begins and ends. **L2**

Discussion

Have students summarize the development of the human fetus. Discuss how changes in this orderly development may result in birth defects. **L2**

Figure 38.13
The embryo and fetus undergo significant changes during the first two trimesters of pregnancy.

 A five-week-old embryo is about 7 mm long. The heart—the large, red, circular structure protruding out of the embryo—begins as two muscular tubes. It starts to beat on about the 21st day of development. The arms and legs are beginning to bud, and the tissue that will form the eyes is beginning to darken.

Hormonal maintenance of pregnancy

Remember that estrogen, and especially progesterone, cause the uterine lining to thicken in preparation for implantation. Once the blastocyst implants, the chorionic membrane of the embryo starts to secrete the hormone human chorionic gonadotropin (hCG). This hormone keeps the corpus luteum alive so that it continues to secrete progesterone. Learn how this hormone is an indicator of pregnancy in the *BioLab* at the end of this chapter. By the third or fourth month, the placenta takes over for the corpus luteum, secreting enough estrogen and progesterone to maintain the pregnancy.

Fetal Development

When you think of an embryo growing within the mother's body, you may not realize that its development involves three different processes: growth, development, and cellular differentiation. Growth refers to the actual increase in the number of cells. Development follows as the multiplying cells move and arrange themselves into specific organs. In addition, each cell differentiates to perform specific tasks and functions. All three processes begin with fertilization.

Pregnancy in humans usually lasts about 280 days, calculated from the first day of the mother's last menstrual period. The baby actually develops for about 266 days, calculated from the time of fertilization to birth. This time span is divided into three trimesters, each about three months in length. Each trimester brings significant advancement in the development of the embryo and fetus.

Reading Check **Identify and describe** the three different processes involved in embryonic development.

1008 REPRODUCTION AND DEVELOPMENT

INCLUSION STRATEGIES

Learning Disabled Have students use modeling clay to show the changes a human egg undergoes from fertilization to implantation. Students should label the zygote and embryo stages, and summarize on index cards the changes and approximate time period involved between changes. Have students wear a lab apron and safety goggles when working with modeling materials. Have them wash their hands after working with the modeling materials. **L2** **ELL** **COOP LEARN**

B A two-month-old fetus is 4 cm long. The heart is fully formed, bones are beginning to harden, and nearly all muscles have appeared. As a result, the fetus can move spontaneously.

C A second-trimester fetus is 15 to 30 cm long. Its skin is covered by a white, fatty substance that protects it from the amniotic fluid. Movements are commonly felt by the mother as the fetus exercises its muscles.

First trimester:
Organ systems form

During the first trimester, all the organ systems of the embryo begin to form. A five-week embryo is shown in *Figure 38.13A*. During this time of development, the woman may not even realize she is pregnant. Yet, the first seven weeks following fertilization are critical because during this time, the embryo is more sensitive to outside influences—such as alcohol, tobacco, and other drugs that cause malformations—than at any other time. Other environmental factors that can adversely affect the health of a developing embryo include exposure to toxins, such as pesticides, or maternal infections such as chicken pox or measles. Lack of adequate amounts of folic acid, a vitamin found in green leafy vegetables, broccoli, and dried beans, is associated with neural tube defects. To find out how an expectant mother can help prevent one type of

birth defect, try the *Problem-Solving Lab* shown on page 1011.

By the eighth week, all the organ systems have been formed, and the embryo is now referred to as a fetus. You can see this stage of fetal development in *Figure 38.13B*. At the end of the first trimester, the fetus weighs about 28 g and is about 7.5 cm long from the top of its head to its buttocks. The gender of the fetus can be determined by the appearance of the external sex organs when viewed by ultrasound.

Second trimester:
A time of growth

For the most part, fetal development during the next three months is limited to body growth. Growth is rapid during the fourth month, but then slows by the beginning of the fifth month. During the fifth month, fetal movements can be felt by the mother. In the sixth month of development, the fetus's eyes open and eyelashes form.

DAILY INTERVENTION

Check for Understanding
Linguistic Ask students to describe orally how a fertilized egg changes after it is implanted in the uterus. L2

Reteach
Visual-Spatial Photocopy and distribute sketches showing fetal development in the later stages of pregnancy. Have students label the embryonic membranes and the placenta as you discuss them. L1

Resources
For more practice, use *Reading Essentials for Biology,* Section 38.2.

Extension

Linguistic Ask one member of each student group to interview his or her mother to find out what types of prenatal care and tests she received during her pregnancy. Ask students to record this information in their journals. L2
COOP LEARN

Assessment

Knowledge Ask students to write a summary of the role of the embryonic membranes and hormones during pregnancy. L2

 CHALLENGE ACTIVITY

Infertility Have students who need an additional challenge investigate the possible causes of infertility and the different treatments that are currently available. Students can include a written report of their findings in their journals. L3

 Indiana Academic Standards

Pages 1008–1009: B.1.1, B.1.7, B.1.14, B.1.16

MiniLab 38.2

Purpose
Students will graph and evaluate the growth of a human embryo.

Process Skills
make and use graphs, interpret data, analyze

Teaching Strategies
Be sure students recognize the change in units between the 6th and 7th weeks of development.

Expected Results
Graphs will show that the embryo grows fastest during the early periods of development.

Analysis
1. The embryo doubles in size during two 1-week periods: 3 to 4 weeks and 7 to 8 weeks.
2. All body systems are beginning to form.
3. 5th month

Assessment
Performance Have students write a summary of the MiniLab and place it in their journals along with the graph and the answers to the Analysis questions. Use the Performance Task Assessment List for Lab Report in **PASC,** p. 119. **L2**

✓**Reading Check** During the third trimester, the organ systems have developed sufficiently, allowing the fetus to function separately from the mother.

MiniLab 38.2

Make and Use Graphs

Making a Graph of Fetal Size You started out as a single cell. That cell divided by the process of mitosis to produce organ systems capable of maintaining an independent existence outside your mother's uterus. Growth in length is one of the many changes that occur as a fetus develops.

Growth of a Fetus		
Source of Sample	Time After Fertilization	Size
First trimester	3 weeks	3 mm
	4 weeks	6 mm
	6 weeks	12 mm
	7 weeks	2 cm
	8 weeks	4 cm
	9 weeks	5 cm
	3 months	7.5 cm
Second trimester	4 months	15 cm
	5 months	25 cm
	6 months	30 cm
Third trimester	7 months	35 cm
	8 months	40 cm
	9 months	51 cm

Procedure
1 Prepare a graph that plots time on the horizontal axis and length in centimeters on the vertical axis. Equally divide the horizontal axis into nine months. Then equally divide each of the first three months into four weeks.

2 Plot the data in the table above on your graph.

Analysis
1. **Interpret Data** When is the fastest period of growth?
2. **Explain** What structures are developing during this period of growth?
3. **Analyze** At what point does growth begin to slow down?

Figure 38.14
Genetic counselors use a variety of medical tests to provide couples with information about the risks of hereditary disorders.

1010

At this point, it is possible for the fetus to survive outside the uterus, but it would require a great amount of medical assistance, and the mortality rate is high. The fetus's metabolism cannot yet maintain a constant body temperature, and its lungs have not matured enough to provide a regular respiratory rate. *Figure 38.13C* shows a fetus during the second trimester. By the end of the second trimester, the fetus weighs about 650 g and is about 34 cm long.

Third trimester: Continued growth

During the last trimester, the mass of the fetus more than triples. The fetus continues to kick, stretch, and move freely within the amniotic cavity. During the eighth month, fat is deposited beneath the skin, which will help insulate the newborn. To examine the growth of a fetus, graph the data in the *MiniLab*.

During the final weeks of pregnancy, the fetus grows large enough to fill the space within the embryonic membranes. By the end of the third trimester, the fetus weighs about 3300 g and is about 51 cm long. All of its body systems have developed, and it can now survive independently outside the uterus.

✓**Reading Check** **Explain** how a fetus can survive independently at the end of the third trimester of pregnancy.

Genetic disorders can be predicted

With our increasing knowledge of human heredity and advancing technology, medical science is now better able to determine the risk that certain genetic disorders will occur in

---

━ TECH PREP ━

Genetic Counseling: *Linguistic* Have students interested in a career in genetic counseling visit with a local genetic counselor or school counselor to find out what a specialty in genetic counseling involves. **L2**

Indiana Academic Standards

Pages 1010–1011: B.1.11, B.1.15, B.1.16, B.1.21

individuals. Advances in the field of genetics have allowed scientists to identify genes that carry certain genetic disorders, such as cystic fibrosis, Huntington's disease, and Tay-Sachs disease. Early identification or detection of certain genetic disorders, such as phenylketonuria (PKU) and cystic fibrosis, is essential to the treatment of these disorders. As services, such as genetic counseling, become more available, some people may consider visiting a genetic counselor to discover additional information about their genetic makeup before having children.

A genetic counselor, like the one shown in *Figure 38.14,* has a medical background with additional training in genetics. Sometimes, a team of professionals works with potential parents. The team may include geneticists, clinical psychologists, social workers, and other consultants. A genetic counselor will start by recording the medical histories of both parents and their families. These histories may include pedigrees, biochemical analyses of blood, karyotypes, and DNA analysis. Once a counselor has collected and analyzed all the available information, he or she explains to the couple their risk factors for giving birth to children with genetic disorders.

✓ **Reading Check** **Describe** the role of a genetic counselor.

Problem-Solving Lab 38.2

Interpret Data

How can pregnant women reduce certain birth defects?
Ten of every 10 000 American babies are born with neural tube defects. One of the defects included in this group is known as spina bifida. This condition occurs if, during early embryonic development, the bones of the spine fail to form properly. As a result, the spinal cord forms outside of the spinal column rather than inside it. How can pregnant women decrease the occurrence of neural tube defects?

Solve the Problem
Research findings about how neural tube defects can be almost completely eliminated are provided in the table below. Folic acid is a vitamin found in green leafy vegetables, broccoli, and citrus fruits.

Effect of Folic Acid on Birth Defects	
Folic Acid Used Before or During Pregnancy	Neural Tube Defects per 1000 Births
Did use	0.9
Did not use	3.5

Thinking Critically
1. **Analyze** Analyze the importance of nutrition on the health of a developing embryo.
2. **Explain** Does the use of folic acid totally prevent neural tube defects? Use the data to support your answer.
3. **Infer** What additional questions might scientists want to ask regarding folic acid's role in fetal development?

in.bdol.glencoe.com/self_check_quiz

Section Assessment

Understanding Main Ideas
1. Describe the processes of fertilization and implantation.
2. What is the function of the placenta?
3. What is the function of the umbilical cord?
4. Why is an embryo most vulnerable to drugs and other harmful substances taken by its mother when it is between two and seven weeks old?

Thinking Critically
5. Compare the functions of human embryonic membranes with those inside a bird's egg.

SKILL REVIEW
6. **Sequence** Prepare a table listing the events in the three trimesters of pregnancy. For more help, refer to *Sequence* in the **Skill Handbook.**

Problem-Solving Lab 38.2

Problem-Solving Lab 38.2

Purpose
Students will learn that folic acid can reduce the incidence of certain birth defects.

Process Skills
analyze information, compare and contrast, draw a conclusion, think critically

Teaching Strategies
Explain that, during the third week of development, a groove forms in the embryo. Cells grow across the groove opening to form the neural tube, which will become the spine. Incomplete closure results in neural tube birth defects.

Thinking Critically
1. Folic acid is required to maintain growth and metabolism of the fetus. In this case, folic acid appears to help prevent neural tube defects.
2. No, the incidence of defects with folic acid is still 0.9.
3. Possible question: How does folic acid decrease incidence of neural tube defects?

Assessment
Performance Ask students to write an article informing people why pregnant women should receive plenty of folic acid. Use the Performance Task Assessment List for Newspaper Article in **PASC,** p. 141. **L2**

✓ **Reading Check** A genetic counselor explains test results and any risk factors present for giving birth to a child with genetic disorders.

Section Assessment

1. The sperm that reach the egg secrete enzymes to penetrate the egg. Once one sperm has entered the egg, the electrical charge of the egg's membrane changes and prevents other sperm from entering. The zygote divides many times and the blastocyst implants in the uterine lining six days after fertilization.
2. nutrient and waste exchange between the mother's and embryo's blood
3. The umbilical cord contains fetal blood vessels, which bring nutrients and oxygen to the fetus and return waste products back to the mother's blood.
4. This is when all body systems are forming.
5. both protect the developing embryo and allow for the exchange of materials
6. First trimester: organ systems start forming; partially formed heart begins beating. External sex organs become apparent. Second trimester: heart is fully formed; size increases; bones harden and fetus begins to move. Third trimester: Growth continues; fetus moves freely; eyes open.

1 Focus

Bellringer
Section Focus Transparency 95

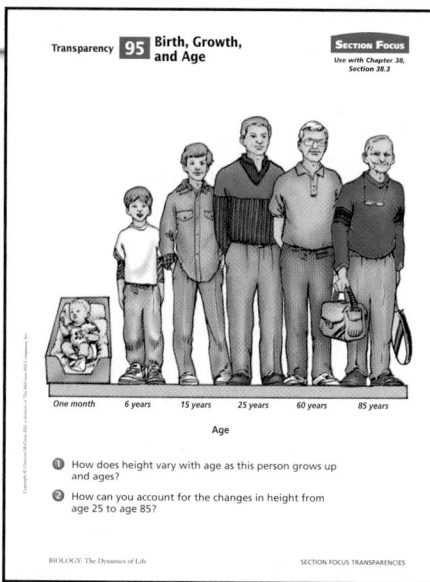

Transparency **95** Birth, Growth, and Age

SECTION FOCUS
Use with Chapter 38,
Section 38.3

One month   6 years   15 years   25 years   60 years   85 years

Age

❶ How does height vary with age as this person grows up and ages?

❷ How can you account for the changes in height from age 25 to age 85?

BIOLOGY: The Dynamics of Life   SECTION FOCUS TRANSPARENCIES

Using Prior Knowledge

Infer All organ systems are involved in growth of the human body. As the body grows, each of the organ systems enlarges. The growth is controlled primarily by human growth hormone, which acts mainly on the skeleton and skeletal muscles.

✓ Reading Check Oxytocin is the hormone that stimulates labor, or the contractions, of the uterine muscles.

Section 38.3

Birth, Growth, and Aging

Indiana Standards Standard B.1.15 Understand and explain that, in biological systems, structure and function must be considered together.

SECTION PREVIEW

Objectives

Describe the three stages of birth.

Summarize the developmental stages of humans after they are born.

Review Vocabulary

growth: increase in the amount of living material and formation of new structures in an organism (p. 8)

New Vocabulary

labor

Growing in Leaps and Bounds

Using Prior Knowledge You have undergone a great deal of growth and development since you were born. It may seem that you have grown a lot in the last few years. Yet the most rapid stage of growth in the life cycle of a human takes place within the uterus. From fertilization to birth, mass increases about 3000 times. Even so, although growth slows after birth, changes certainly do not stop.

Infer *Which organ systems are involved in growth of the human body?*

The human body changes throughout life.

Birth

Birth is the process by which a fetus is pushed out of the uterus and the mother's body and into the outside world, like the newborn in *Figure 38.15*. What triggers the onset of birth is not fully understood. Different hormones released from the pituitary gland, uterus, and placenta may all be involved in stimulating the uterus. Birth occurs in three recognizable stages: dilation, expulsion, and the placental stage.

Figure 38.15
A newborn infant continues growth and development outside the mother's body.

Dilation of the cervix

The physiological and physical changes a female goes through to give birth are called **labor.** Labor begins with a series of mild contractions of the uterine muscles. These contractions are stimulated by oxytocin, a hormone released by the pituitary. The contractions open, or dilate, the cervix to allow for passage of the baby, as shown in *Figure 38.16A*. As labor progresses, the contractions begin to occur at regular intervals and intensify as the time between them shortens. When the opening of the cervix is about 10 cm, it is fully dilated. Usually, the amniotic sac ruptures and the amniotic fluid is released through the vagina, which is also referred to as the birth canal.

✓ Reading Check **Describe** the role of the oxytocin in labor.

1012 REPRODUCTION AND DEVELOPMENT

RESOURCE MANAGER

Unit 10 *FAST FILE* Resources
Real World BioApplications, pp. 171–172
Reinforcement and Study Guide in English, p. 176
Reinforcement and Study Guide in Spanish, p. 180
Transparency Worksheet, p. 185

Reading Essentials for Biology,
Section 38.3
Section Focus Transparency 95

Expulsion of the baby

Expulsion occurs when the involuntary uterine contractions become so forceful that they push the baby through the cervix into the birth canal. The mother assists with expelling the baby by contracting her abdominal muscles in time with the uterine contractions. As shown in *Figure 38.16B*, the baby moves from the uterus, through the birth canal, and out of the mother's body. The expulsion stage usually lasts from 20 minutes to an hour.

Placental stage

As shown in *Figure 38.16C*, within ten to 15 minutes after the birth of the baby, the placenta separates from the uterine wall and is expelled with the remains of the embryonic membranes. Collectively, these materials are known as the afterbirth. The uterine muscles continue to contract forcefully, constricting uterine blood vessels to prevent the mother from bleeding excessively. After the baby is born, the umbilical cord is clamped and cut near the baby's abdomen. The bit of cord that is left eventually dries up and falls off, leaving an abdominal scar called the navel.

Growth and Aging

Once a baby is born, growth continues and learning begins. Human growth varies with age and is somewhat gender dependent.

A hormone controls growth

Human growth is regulated by human growth hormone (hGH), a protein secreted by the pituitary gland. Although hGH causes all body cells to grow, it acts principally on the skeleton and skeletal muscles. The hormone works by increasing the rate of protein synthesis and the metabolism of fat molecules. Other hormones that influence growth include thyroxin, estrogen, and testosterone.

Figure 38.16
The stages of birth are dilation, expulsion, and the placental stage.

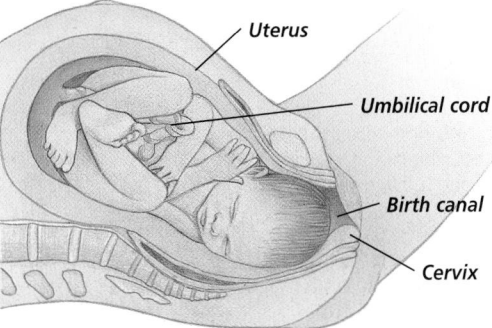

Uterus
Umbilical cord
Birth canal
Cervix

A Dilation Labor contractions open the cervix.

B Expulsion The baby rotates as it moves through the birth canal, making expulsion easier.

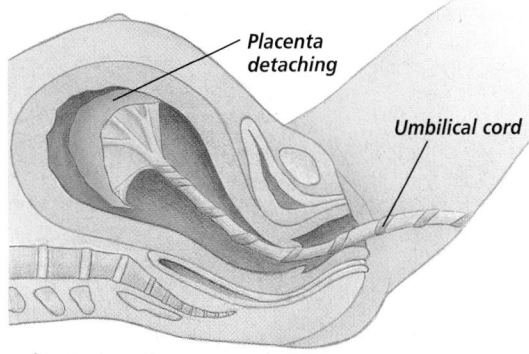

Placenta detaching
Umbilical cord

C Placental stage During the placental stage, the placenta and umbilical cord are expelled.

2 Teach

Quick Demo

Comparing Life Stages
Project photographs or slides of newborn infants and elderly individuals. Ask students to write down what they perceive as differences between the two.

Inquiry

Have students prepare interview questions to ask senior citizens. Questions should focus on the biology of aging as well as how senior citizens view aging. Collect questions from students and photocopy them. Distribute copies of all the questions to students and ask them to prepare a survey made up of ten questions. Have students use the survey to interview someone older than 65. Students should tally the results and present them to the class. **L2**

INCLUSION STRATEGIES

English Language Learners/Learning Disabled Have students prepare flash cards of the vocabulary terms from this chapter by writing the term on one side of the card and its definition on the other side. Have student groups review the terms and their meanings. **L1 ELL COOP LEARN**

 Indiana Academic Standards

Pages 1012–1013: B.1.15

Career Path
Courses in high school: sciences, mathematics, psychology
College: bachelor's degree to become a registered nurse; up to two years of training in midwifery

Career Issue
Tell students that some people think midwives should not be allowed to deliver babies without a doctor present. Invite the class to explore both sides of this issue.

For More Information
To learn more about becoming a midwife, students can contact:

American College of Nurse
   Midwives
818 Connecticut Avenue, NW
Suite 900
Washington, DC 20006

CAREERS IN BIOLOGY

Midwife

Giving birth can be one of the most exciting experiences life can offer. If you would like to help expectant mothers through the birth process, you might consider becoming a midwife.

Skills for the Job

Midwives have helped women give birth for thousands of years, sometimes with little training. However, today's midwives are professionally trained and well able to guide women with low-risk pregnancies safely through the birth process. Midwives first become registered nurses and then complete up to two years of clinical instruction in midwifery. They must also pass a national test and meet state requirements before they can become certified nurse-midwives. Many midwives work in hospitals or birthing centers; some help deliver babies at home. All midwives provide care, support, and monitoring throughout the pregnancy and afterward.

For more careers in related fields, visit in.bdol.glencoe.com/careers

The first stage of growth: Infancy

The first two years of life are known as infancy. During infancy, a child shows tremendous growth as well as an increase in physical coordination and mental development. Generally, an infant will double its birth weight by the time it is five months of age, and triple its weight in a year. By two years of age, most infants weigh approximately four times their birth weight. During this time, the infant learns to control its limbs, roll over, sit, crawl, and walk. By the end of infancy, the child also utters his or her first words.

From child to adult

Childhood is the period of growth and development that extends from infancy to adolescence, when puberty begins. Physically, the childhood years are a period of relatively steady growth. Mentally, a child develops the ability to reason and to solve problems.

Figure 38.17
Changes in the size and shape of the body are associated with growth. These photos show the changes that Shirley Temple Black has undergone as she has aged.

CULTURAL DIVERSITY

Rites of Passage In many cultures and religions, traditional celebrations mark the transition from childhood to adulthood. For example, in Mexican tradition, a girl celebrates her transition from childhood to adulthood on her fifteenth birthday in a celebration known as quinceanera. Discuss with students examples of initiation rites in various cultures. You may wish to have students research topics by asking them to identify a culture and then determine whether that culture has a traditional rite of passage.

Figure 38.18
In 1962, astronaut John Glenn made history as the first American to orbit Earth. He enthusiastically returned to space in 1998, at the age of 77, when he joined the crew of space shuttle *Discovery*.

DAILY INTERVENTION

Check for Understanding
Ask students to describe the aging process. **L2**

Reteach
Have students choose a system of the body and describe how it changes from birth through old age. **L2**

Resources
For more practice, use *Reading Essentials for Biology,* Section 38.3.

Extension

Ask students to research and report on current theories about infant learning. Encourage them to include illustrations in their reports. **L3**

 Assessment

Knowledge Ask students to choose a hormone discussed in this chapter and make a diagram of the negative-feedback loop for the hormone. **L2**

Adolescence follows childhood. At puberty, the onset of adolescence, there is often a growth spurt, sometimes quite a dramatic one. Increases of 5 to 8 cm of height in one year are not uncommon in teenage boys. During the teen years, adolescents reach their maximum physical stature, which is determined by heredity, nutrition, and their environment. By the time a young person reaches adulthood, his or her organs have reached their maximum mass, and physical growth is complete. You can see in *Figure 38.17* how the physical appearance of a person changes from birth to adulthood.

An adult ages

As an adult ages, his or her body undergoes many distinct changes. Metabolism and digestion become slower. The skin loses some of its elasticity, and less pigment is produced in the hair follicles; that is, the hair turns white. Bones often become thinner and more brittle, resulting in an increased risk of fracture. Stature may shorten because the disks between the vertebrae become compressed. Vision and hearing might diminish, but, as *Figure 38.18* shows, many people continue to be both intellectually and physically active as they grow older.

Section Assessment

Understanding Main Ideas
1. Identify and describe the three stages of birth.
2. How does the human growth hormone produce growth?
3. How does the human body change during childhood?
4. What changes to the body are usually associated with aging?

Thinking Critically
5. Compare the birth of a human baby with that of a marsupial mammal.

SKILL REVIEW
6. **Get the Big Picture** Create a table that shows the stages of growth and the changes that occur during each stage. For more help, refer to *Get the Big Picture* in the **Skill Handbook**.

 in.bdol.glencoe.com/self_check_quiz
38.3 BIRTH, GROWTH, AND AGING **1015**

Section Assessment

1. dilation: opening of the cervix; expulsion: muscular contractions push the baby through the cervix and birth canal; placental: placenta separates from the uterine wall and is expelled
2. Human growth hormone increases the rate of protein synthesis inside cells and the metabolism of fat molecules.
3. Muscle coordination, reasoning, and problem-solving abilities increase, and the body grows.
4. Metabolism and digestion slow. Skin loses elasticity and hair follicles lose pigment. Bones may become brittle. Vision and hearing may diminish.
5. Marsupials are born earlier in development. After birth, marsupials continue to develop within the mother's pouch.
6. infancy: growth, increase in physical coordination and mental development; childhood: child grows physically and gains ability to reason and solve problems; adolescence: reaches physical maturity, organs reach maximum mass; adult: physical and mental maturity have been reached

Time Allotment
one class period

Process Skills
acquire information, apply concepts, compare and contrast, draw a conclusion, formulate models, think critically

Safety Precautions
Remind students to use caution when working with scissors.

PREPARATION

To save class time, trace models A, B, and C onto tracing paper prior to class. Provide each student group with one set of tracing paper shapes to use in making their copies on heavy paper.

Indiana Academic Standards

Pages 1016–1017: B.1.7

Before You Begin
The chorion of an eight-day-old embryo produces a hormone called human chorionic gonadotropin (hCG). This hormone stimulates the corpus luteum to continue its production of progesterone, which in turn maintains the attachment of the embryo to the uterine lining. There is such a high concentration of hCG present in the blood of the mother that the kidneys excrete it in urine.

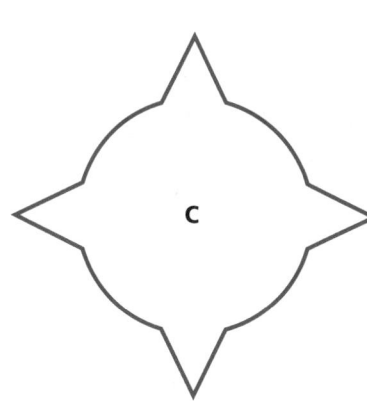

What hormone is produced by an embryo?

PREPARATION

Problem
How can you test a model for the presence of hCG?

Objectives
In this BioLab, you will:
- **Model** the chemicals used to test for the presence of hCG.
- **Interpret** the results of chemical reactions involving hCG in a pregnant and nonpregnant female.

Materials
scissors   heavy paper   tracing paper

Safety Precautions
CAUTION: *Use care when handling scissors.*

Skill Handbook
If you need help with this lab, refer to the **Skill Handbook**.

PROCEDURE

1. Copy the data table.
2. Copy models **A**, **B**, and **C** onto tracing paper.
3. Copy the tracings onto heavy paper and cut them out. You will need 4 models of **A**, 4 of **B**, and 1 of **C**.
4. Model **A** represents a molecule of the hCG hormone. Model **B** represents a chemical called anti-hCG hormone. Model **C** represents a chemical that has four hCG molecules attached to it.
5. Note that the shapes of hCG and anti-hCG join together like puzzle pieces. These two chemicals react, or join together, when both are present in a solution. The shapes of anti-hCG and chemical C also join, indicating that they chemically react when both are present. The combination of chemical C and anti-hCG is green. Chemical C without anti-hCG attached is colorless.
6. Model the following events for the "Not pregnant" condition. Record them in the data table using drawings of the models.

PROCEDURE

Teaching Strategies
- This lab simulates a home pregnancy test. Each manufacturer of home pregnancy tests has a variation on the final color and its interpretation.
- Students do not have to diagram all four molecules of chemical A and B on the data chart. However, they must diagram at least one to represent the concept of what is occurring.

Troubleshooting
- Remind students that each model represents a molecule. When two models fit together, this represents a chemical reaction.
- Students must realize that there is no hCG in the urine of a non-pregnant female.
- When joined together, hCG and anti-hCG cannot attach to chemical C.

Data Table

Condition	hCG in Urine?	+ Anti-hCG	= Joined hCG and Anti-hCG?	+ Chemical C with Anti-hCG?	Color
Not pregnant					
Pregnant					

   a. The hormone hCG is not present in the urine.

   b. Anti-hCG is added to a urine sample, then chemical C is added.

   c. Draw the resulting chemical in the data table, and indicate the color that appears.

7. Model the following events for the "Pregnant" condition. Record them in the data table using drawings of the models.

   a. The hormone hCG is present.

   b. Anti-hCG is added to urine, then chemical C is added.

   c. Draw the resulting chemical in the data table, and indicate the color that appears.

8. CLEANUP AND DISPOSAL Make wise choices about the disposal or recycling of materials used in this lab.

Color-enhanced TEM Magnification: 35×

Eight-day-old embryo

ANALYZE AND CONCLUDE

1. Analyze Explain the origin of hCG in a pregnant female.

2. Analyze Explain why hCG is absent in a nonpregnant female.

3. Conclude Describe the roles of anti-hCG and chemical C in both tests.

4. Observe and Infer Explain why anti-hCG is added to the sample before chemical C is added.

Apply Your Skill

Analyze Information Using references, look up the meaning of the words *chorionic* and *gonadotropin*. Explain why the name hCG suits this hormone.

Web Links To find out more about embryonic hormones, visit in.bdol.glencoe.com/hormones

---

ANALYZE AND CONCLUDE

1. The chorion begins to release hCG as early as eight days after fertilization.

2. There is no chorion to release hCG.

3. If pregnant, hCG joins with anti-hCG, preventing attachment to chemical C's hCG. No color appears. If not pregnant, anti-hCG attaches to chemical C's hCG and color appears.

4. To get an accurate result, hCG and anti-hCG must have a chance to bind before chemical C is added.

Assessment

Performance Have students prepare a puzzle-piece model to show how the presence of a hormone, such as FSH or estrogen, might be detected. Use the Performance Task Assessment List for Model in **PASC,** p. 123. **L2**

Apply Your Skill

Analyze Information Ask students who are interested to check on the meaning of "antigen-antibody reaction" and determine if the completed activity fits this description. **L3**

Data Table

Condition	hCG in urine?	+ Anti-hCG	= Joined hCG and anti-hCG?	+ Chemical C with anti-hCG?	Color
Not pregnant	—	⯇⯈ ⯆⯅	—	✦	Green
Pregnant		⯇⯈ ⯆⯅	⯇⯈ ⯆⯅	✦	Colorless

Purpose

Students will learn about the causes and effects of growth hormone deficiency and how scientists use recombinant DNA technology to treat this disorder.

Background

Growth hormone deficiency can be congenital where the pituitary gland or the hypothalamus is abnormal from birth. It also can be traced to severe head traumas or debilitating illnesses contracted during infancy or early childhood. Other cases result from craniopharyngioma, a tumor that can exert pressure on the pituitary gland or hypothalamus.

Teaching Strategies

- Using reference books as guides, have students sketch the pituitary gland in relation to the brain. Students should label the anterior and posterior lobes. Have them list the major hormones that are secreted by each lobe.
- Have students research the history of recombinant DNA technology. In particular, students can focus on the work of Drs. Stanley Cohen and Herb Boyer, who jointly launched the technique in the late 1970s.

Applying Biotechnology

Other applications of recombinant DNA technology include manufacturing insulin, interferons, interleukins, parathyroid hormone, and chemicals for treating hemophilia and anemia. Encourage students to use a variety of resources for their reports. Have each group present its report to the class.

BIO TECHNOLOGY

Human Growth Hormone

People grow from babies to adults. It's a normal part of life that is often taken for granted. However, some people either fail to grow or grow at slow rates. What can be done for them?

Up to 15 000 children in the United States suffer from growth hormone deficiency. This means that their pituitary glands produce low levels of human growth hormone (hGH). In some cases, hGH is not secreted at all. Children with a growth-hormone deficiency are small for their age. Their facial features resemble those of a younger child and they may have excessive body fat. Their limbs, however, are in proportion to their bodies.

Early attempts to help Between 1958 and 1985, doctors followed a logical course of treatment for growth hormone deficiency by giving the children injections of hGH. For the therapy to work, the hormone had to be extracted from human beings; growth hormones taken from other mammals would not be effective. The only available source of hGH was human cadavers. Thousands of children benefited from the treatment. Unfortunately, the supply of hGH was contaminated by the prion that causes mad-cow disease. Several young people died. The Food and Drug Administration (FDA) banned the treatment soon after.

What next? In 1985, using recombinant DNA technology, scientists were able to produce the first synthetic growth hormone. Because it was not taken from human bodies, there was little risk of disease. In the fall of 1985, the hormone received FDA approval.

How does it work? To create the synthetic growth hormone, scientists first had to sequence the DNA structure of hGH, which is made up of 191 amino acids. Once the gene code was determined, it was spliced into plasmids of bacteria.

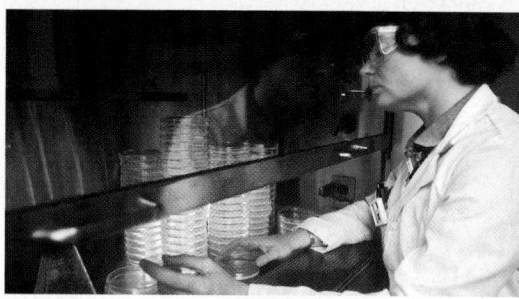

Bacteria with plasmids modified to produce hGH are grown in laboratory petri dishes.

Plasmids are circular DNA molecules within bacteria. The modified plasmids become genetic blueprints for hGH. Thus, when the bacteria multiply, they act as an hGH factory, replicating not only themselves but the hormone as well. In this way, hGH can be mass-produced.

How is it used? After the hormone is extracted from the bacteria, it is made into a powder. When mixed with liquid to form a solution, the hormone then can be injected into children with growth-hormone deficiency. Such children may receive anywhere from three to seven shots per week. The shots can be administered at home and results are nearly immediate. Within four months, children often grow at two to three times their previous rate. The growth rate eventually tapers off until the child achieves a normal height. At that point, treatment is stopped. Although there may be some side effects, overall, studies have found that the benefits of the treatment far outweigh the risks. Children who respond to treatment will likely reach their projected height.

Applying Biotechnology

Research Work in small groups to research other uses of recombinant DNA technology. Prepare a multimedia report explaining how these uses help replace deficient hormones in the human body. In your report, describe the diseases that are treated with recombinant DNA technology. How were they treated previously? Compare and contrast the benefits of the latest treatments to those of earlier ones.

 in.bdol.glencoe.com/biotechnology

Going Further

Tell students that synthesized hGH has some controversial uses. Namely, it is often marketed as an anti-aging remedy for adults. This use has not been approved by the FDA. Have students research the use of hGH as an anti-aging remedy. Analyze different hGH products available that advertise as anti-aging remedies. Do the product labels offer unrealistic promises? Are the claims on product labels backed by scientific data? As a class, discuss students' findings.

STUDY GUIDE

Section 38.1

Human Reproductive Systems

Magnification: unavailable

Key Concepts

■ The male reproductive system produces sperm and the female reproductive system produces eggs.

■ Through the control of the hypothalamus and pituitary, hormones act on the reproductive system as well as on other body systems. Hormone levels are regulated by negative feedback.

■ Changes in males and females at puberty are the result of the production of FSH, LH, and other sex hormones.

■ Under the control of hormones, the menstrual cycle produces a mature egg and prepares the uterus for receiving a fertilized egg.

Vocabulary

bulbourethral gland (p. 997)
cervix (p. 999)
corpus luteum (p. 1002)
epididymis (p. 996)
follicle (p. 999)
menstrual cycle (p. 1002)
oviduct (p. 999)
ovulation (p. 1000)
prostate gland (p. 997)
puberty (p. 997)
scrotum (p. 995)
semen (p. 997)
seminal vesicle (p. 997)
vas deferens (p. 997)

Section 38.2

Development Before Birth

Key Concepts

■ Fertilization occurs in the oviduct. The zygote undergoes mitotic division as it travels down the oviduct. The ball of cells that develops from the fertilized egg implants in the uterine wall.

■ The embryo changes from a small ball of cells to a well-developed fetus over the course of nine months.

■ The developing fetus is supported by oxygen and nutrients from the mother, exchanged through the umbilical cord.

Vocabulary

implantation (p. 1006)
umbilical cord (p. 1006)

Section 38.3

Birth, Growth, and Aging

Key Concepts

■ Birth involves dilation of the cervix, expulsion of the baby, and expulsion of the placenta.

■ Infancy, childhood, adolescence, and adulthood are the stages of human development. Human growth hormone (hGH) produces growth in all body cells, especially in cells of the skeleton and muscles.

Vocabulary

labor (p. 1012)

FOLDABLES™
Study Organizer To help you review reproductive anatomy, use the Organizational Study Fold on page 995.

 in.bdol.glencoe.com/vocabulary_puzzlemaker

Key Concepts

Summary statements can be used by students to review the major concepts of the chapter.

Biology Online

Visit **in.bdol.glencoe.com**
/self_check_quiz
/vocabulary_puzzlemaker
/chapter_test
/standardized_test

VOCABULARY PUZZLEMAKER

For additional help with vocabulary, have students access the Vocabulary PuzzleMaker online at in.bdol.glencoe.com/vocabulary_puzzlemaker

FOLDABLES™

Have students use their Foldables to review the content of Section 38.1. As students review the functions of reproductive structures, have them identify possible causes of infertility on the back of their Foldables.

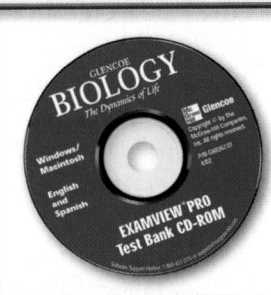

Use the Exam*View*®Pro Test Bank CD-ROM to:

● Create **multiple versions** of tests
● Create **modified** tests with one mouse click for **inclusion** students
● **Edit** existing questions and **add** your own questions
● Build tests aligned with state standards using built-in **State Curriculum Tags**
● Change **English** tests to **Spanish** with one mouse click and vice versa

 Indiana Academic Standards

Pages 1018–1019: B.1.7, B.1.11, B.1.15, B.1.16, B.1.19

Vocabulary Review

1. vas deferens   3. labor
2. implantation

Understanding Key Concepts

4. A   6. C   8. C
5. C   7. A   9. B
10. 1. ovulation; 2. follicle; 3. oviduct

Constructed Response

11. Muscles in the walls of the scrotum help maintain the proper temperature in the testis by regulating the distance of the testis from the body. Muscular peristaltic contractions in the vas deferens force the sperm along the vas deferens. Muscle contraction at the base of the bladder prevents urine and sperm from mixing.

12. Sperm cannot survive unless they are about 3°C lower than normal body temperature. If the testes remain in the body cavity, the sperm will not survive.

13. The endocrine system, through hormones, controls the female reproductive system. During puberty, this interaction causes the sexual maturation of the female as well as controls the monthly menstrual cycle until menopause.

Thinking Critically

14. Answers may vary. One hypothesis might include genetic control of aging. Experiments involving gene manipulation may provide insight on the genetic control of aging.

15. Category A: the possibility of fetal harm appears

1020

Vocabulary Review

Review the Chapter 38 vocabulary words listed in the Study Guide on page 1019. Match the words with the definitions below.

1. the duct that transports sperm from the epididymis toward the ejaculatory duct and urethra

2. attachment of the blastocyst to the lining of the uterus

3. the physiological and physical changes a female goes through to give birth

Understanding Key Concepts

4. Sperm production takes place in the _____.
   A. testes   C. vas deferens
   B. epididymis   D. seminal vesicles

5. Inhibition or decrease in the production of FSH and LH in males is triggered by which of the following?
   A. decreased blood levels of testosterone
   B. decreased production of sperm in the testes
   C. increased blood levels of testosterone
   D. when FSH and LH reach the testes

6. Ovulation is stimulated by the sharp increase of which of the following hormones?
   A. follicle stimulating hormone
   B. estrogen
   C. luteinizing hormone
   D. progesterone

7. Fertilization of an egg to form a zygote takes place in the _____.
   A. oviduct
   B. uterus
   C. vagina
   D. ovary

8. During which stage of human development does puberty occur?
   A. infancy   C. adolescence
   B. childhood   D. adulthood

---

9. What is the function of human chorionic gonadotropin (hCG)?
   A. hCG stimulates the uterus to secrete estrogen.
   B. hCG maintains the corpus luteum so it can secrete progesterone.
   C. hCG stimulates the placenta to secrete progesterone.
   D. hCG stimulates the hypothalamus to secrete luteinizing hormone.

10. Complete the concept map by using the following terms: follicle, ovulation, oviduct.

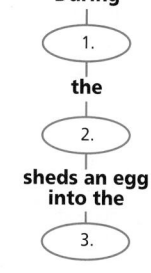

During
1.
the
2.
sheds an egg into the
3.

Constructed Response

11. **Open Ended** Explain the interrelationship between the muscular system and the male reproductive system. Include specific examples in your response.

12. **Open Ended** Normally, the testes descend into the scrotum during fetal development. If left untreated, what effects could undescended testes have on male fertility?

13. **Open Ended** Compare the interrelationships of the endocrine system and the female reproductive system. How does the interaction affect the body as a whole?

Thinking Critically

14. **Hypothesize** Form a hypothesis that explains the causes of the changes that occur as adults age. How could you test this hypothesis?

15. **REAL WORLD BIOCHALLENGE** Currently drugs are given an FDA pregnancy category rating. How are drugs rated for pregnancy? Find out more information by visiting **in.bdol.glencoe.com** .

 in.bdol.glencoe.com/chapter_test

---

remote. Category B: Animal studies have not demonstrated a fetal risk, but there are no controlled studies in pregnant women. Category C: Either animal studies have revealed adverse effects on the fetus and there are no controlled studies in women or studies in women, and animals are not available.

Category D: There is positive evidence of human fetal risk, but the benefits from use in pregnant women may be acceptable despite the risk. Category X: Studies in animals or human beings have demonstrated fetal abnormalities

16. An enlarged prostate may push on the bladder and constrict the flow

16. Infer How would an enlarged prostate gland affect urination? List possible symptoms of an enlarged prostate gland.

17. Recognize Cause and Effect How would an undersecretion of human growth hormone during childhood affect the body? What would be the effects of oversecretion?

End-of-Course Assessment Practice

The assessed Indiana standard appears next to the question.

All questions aligned and verified by **The Princeton Review**

Part 1 Multiple Choice

Use the diagram to answer questions 18–20.

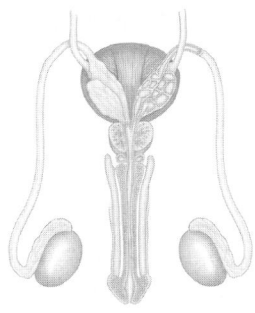

18. Which of these structures produces
B.1.15 testosterone?
A. testes
C. epididymus
B. prostate gland
D. vas deferens

19. Which of the following structures produce
B.1.15 the fluid portion of semen?
A. testes, prostate gland, bulbourethral glands
B. seminal vesicles, urethra, epididymus
C. prostate gland, bulbourethral glands, seminal vesicles
D. seminal vesicles, prostate gland, bladder

20. Testosterone influences which of the
B.1.17 following processes in males?
A. production of sperm
B. development of secondary sex characteristics
C. the production of FSH and LH
D. all of the above

Study the graph, and answer questions 21–24.

Cardiac Output and Heartbeat Rate During Pregnancy

The graph indicates changes in cardiac output and heartbeat in a woman over the course of her pregnancy.

21. During which week of pregnancy does cardiac output reach its highest level?
A. 6
C. 24
B. 20
D. 36

22. At its highest, heart rate increases by approximately what percentage?
A. 0
C. 20
B. 10
D. 25

23. What is the cardiac output of the mother at week 12?
A. 18
C. 28
B. 22
D. 30

Part 2 Constructed Response/Grid In

Record your answers on your answer document.

24. Open Ended Give possible explanations as to why cardiac output and heart rate increase in a
B.1.17 pregnant woman. How are these two values related?

25. Open Ended Explain how internal feedback controls the levels of hormones during the
B.1.17 menstrual cycle.

 in.bdol.glencoe.com/standardized_test

CHAPTER 38 ASSESSMENT **1021**

End-of-Course Assessment Practice

18. A **21.** D
19. C **22.** D
20. D **23.** B

24. The increase compensates for blood delivery to the developing fetus. As heartbeat rate increases, cardiac output increases.

25. The hypothalamus stimulates the pituitary to secrete FSH and LH. These hormones stimulate the ovary to produce estrogen and progesterone. Increases in progesterone and estrogen feed back to the pituitary and hypothalamus, inhibiting FSH and LH secretion.

 FAST FILE

Answer Sheet A practice answer sheet can be found on p. 203 of *Unit 10 FAST FILE Resources.*

of urine. Patients with an enlarged prostate may feel the urge to urinate more often, they may have trouble urinating and it may be painful.

17. Undersecretion of growth hormone will cause a deficiency in growth of the skeleton and muscles. Oversecretion will cause too

much growth of the skeleton and muscles.

RUBRIC

For more help evaluating open-ended assessment questions, see the rubric on p. 9T.

Indiana Academic Standards

Pages 1020–1021: B.1.7, B.1.11, B.1.14, B.1.15

Chapter 39 Organizer

Section Objectives	National Science Standards	State/Local Standards	Advanced Lab and Demo Planning
Section 39.1 1 session, 1/2 block 1. **Outline** the steps of Koch's postulates. 2. **Describe** how pathogens are transmitted. 3. **Explain** what causes the symptoms of a disease.	UCP.1, UCP.2, UCP.5; A.1, A.2; C.1, C.4; F.1, F.5; G.1–3	**Indiana Standards** B.1.17, B.1.20, B.1.43	**Student Labs:** Problem-Solving Lab 39.1, p. 1027 MiniLab 39.1, p. 1028: 4 plastic bags, fresh apple, rotten apple, cotton ball, alcohol **Teacher Demonstration:** Quick Demo, p. 1024: plate, nutrient agar
Section 39.2 2 sessions, 1/2 block 4. **Identify** the cells, tissues, and organs that make up the immune system. 5. **Compare** innate and acquired immune responses. 6. **Distinguish** between antibody and cellular immunity.	UCP.1–3, UCP.5; A.1, A.2; C.1, C.4; E.2; F.1, F.5, F.6; G.1–3	**Indiana Standards** B.1.15, B.1.20, B.1.41, B.1.43	**Student Labs:** Additional Lab, p. 1032: *E.coli* bacterial cultures, 3 types of antibiotic disks, sterile untreated disks, cotton swabs, forceps, ethanol, transparent tape, plates of nutrient agar, marking pen, incubator MiniLab 39.2, p. 1035: prepared slides of red and white blood cells, microscope Problem-Solving Lab 39.2, p. 1040 Internet BioLab, p. 1042: See materials below. **Teacher Demonstration:** Quick Demo, p. 1032: microprojector
End of Chapter Assessment Student Edition **Study Guide,** p. 1045 **Content Assessment,** pp. 1046–1047	UCP.1, UCP.2, UCP.5; C.1, C.4; F.1, F.5; G.1, G.3	**Indiana Standards** B.1.17, B.1.20, B.1.21, B.1.43	**Student Lab:** Internet BioLab, p. 1042: access to the Internet

Key to Teaching Strategies

L1 Level 1 activities should be appropriate for students with learning difficulties.

L2 Level 2 activities should be within the ability range of all students.

L3 Level 3 activities are designed for above-average students.

ELL ELL activities should be within the ability range of English Language Learners.

COOP LEARN Cooperative Learning activities are designed for small group work.

Legend

 Transparency   CD-ROM   MP3 📼 Videocassette ⊙ DVD

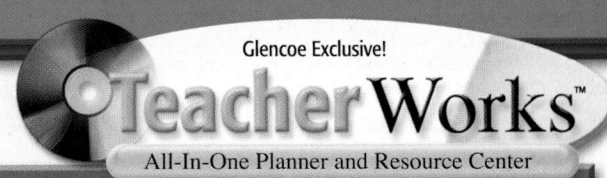
Glencoe Exclusive!
TeacherWorks™
All-In-One Planner and Resource Center

Reproducible Masters and Transparencies	Technology
Unit 10 FAST FILE Resources MiniLab Worksheet, p. 207 Reinforcement and Study Guide in English, p. 211 Reinforcement and Study Guide in Spanish, p. 215 Transparency Worksheets, pp. 221, 223–224 **Reading Essentials for Biology, Section 39.1** **Laboratory Manual,** pp. 249–252, 253–256 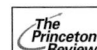 **Section Focus Transparency 96** **Basic Concepts Transparency 76**	⊙ **Interactive Chalkboard CD-ROM: Section 39.1 Presentation** ▮ ⊙ TeacherWorks™ **CD-ROM** ▮ **Guided Reading Audio Summaries MP3**

Unit 10 FAST FILE Resources
MiniLab Worksheet, p. 208
BioLab Worksheet, pp. 209–210
Reinforcement and Study Guide in English,
  pp. 212–214
Reinforcement and Study Guide in Spanish,
  pp. 216–218
Concept Mapping, p. 219
Critical Thinking/Problem Solving, p. 220
Transparency Worksheets, pp. 222, 225–227
Reading Essentials for Biology, Section 39.2
Section Focus Transparency 97
Basic Concepts Transparencies 77, 78a, 78b, 79
Reteaching Skills Transparencies 57, 58
	⊙ **Interactive Chalkboard CD-ROM: Section 39.2 Presentation** ▮
	⊙ TeacherWorks™ **CD-ROM** ▮
	Guided Reading Audio Summaries MP3

Unit 10 FAST FILE Resources
Chapter Assessment, pp. 237–242
Student Recording Sheet, p. 243
The Princeton Review **Reviewing Biology,** pp. 77–78
	⊙ **Interactive Chalkboard:** ▮
	  Chapter 39 Assessment
	⊙ **MindJogger Videoquizzes**
	  DVD/VHS
	⊙ **ExamView® Pro Test Bank**
	  CD-ROM
	⊙ TeacherWorks™ **CD-ROM** ▮
	⊙ **Succeeding on National Standards CD-ROM**
	
	in.bdol.glencoe.com
	/self_check_quiz
	/vocabulary_puzzlemaker
	/chapter_test
	/standardized_test

▮ Indicates materials created specifically for Indiana.

Chapter 39

Immunity from Disease

Short on Time?

BIODIGEST The BioDigest at the end of this unit can be used as a(n):

- preview to introduce important unit concepts.
- overview if time does not permit teaching the entire chapter.
- review of key unit concepts.

Understanding the Photo

A lymphocyte is a type of white blood cell that defends the body against foreign substances. Lymphocytes include B cells and T cells which are responsible for destroying bacteria as well as viruses and fungi. These cells can also be involved in autoimmune diseases such as rheumatoid arthritis and lupus.

What You'll Learn

- You will describe how infections are transmitted and what causes the symptoms of diseases.
- You will explain the various types of innate and acquired immune responses.
- You will compare antibody and cellular immunity.

Why It's Important

Your body constantly faces attack from disease-causing organisms. A knowledge of your immune system will help you understand how your body defends itself and works to maintain homeostasis.

Understanding ▶ the Photo

This color-enhanced lymphocyte, a type of white blood cell produced by the immune system, is attacking the rod-shaped bacteria that have invaded the body.

Biology Online

Visit in.bdol.glencoe.com to
- study the entire chapter online
- access Web Links for more information and activities on immunity
- review content with the Interactive Tutor and self-check quizzes

Color-enhanced SEM Magnification: 10 000×

1022

Two-Minute Chapter Launcher

Activity Ask how many students had at least one cold last year. Colds are caused by over 80 different viruses. Ask the students to describe what happened when the viruses attached to the cells of their nasal cavity. Use this to review the life cycle of a virus covered in Chapter 18 on pages 474–501. The viruses attach to the epithelial cells of the nasal cavity and inject their nucleic acid into the cell. The epithelial cell's metabolic machinery makes viral nucleic acids and viral proteins. The virus particles are assembled, and the host cells open and release new viral particles to infect more cells.

Section 39.1

The Nature of Disease

Indiana Standards Standard B.1.17 Understand that and describe how the maintenance of a relatively stable internal environment is required for the continuation of life and explain how stability is challenged by changing physical, chemical, and environmental conditions, as well as the presence of disease agents.

SECTION PREVIEW

Objectives

Outline the steps of Koch's postulates.

Describe how pathogens are transmitted.

Explain what causes the symptoms of a disease.

Review Vocabulary

virus: a disease-causing, nonliving particle composed of an inner core of nucleic acids surrounded by a capsid; replicates inside a living cell (p. 475)

New Vocabulary

pathogen
infectious disease
Koch's postulates
endemic disease
epidemic
antibiotic

Study Organizer

Disease Make the following Foldable to help you answer questions about disease.

STEP 1 **Fold** a vertical sheet of notebook paper from side to side.

STEP 2 **Cut** along every fifth line of only the top layer to form tabs.

STEP 3 **Label** the tabs with one question that relates to each of the red heads in the section. For example, "What causes disease?"

Answer Questions As you read Section 39.1, fill in your answers to the questions about disease beneath the appropriate tabs.

What is an infectious disease?

The cold virus causes a disease—a change that disrupts the homeostasis in the body. Disease-producing agents such as bacteria, protozoans, fungi, viruses, and other parasites are called **pathogens.** The main sources of pathogens are soil, contaminated water, and infected animals, including other people.

Not all microorganisms are pathogenic. In fact, the presence of some microorganisms in your body is beneficial. At birth, microorganisms establish themselves on your skin and in your upper respiratory system, lower urinary and reproductive tracts, and lower intestinal tract. *Figure 39.1* shows some common bacteria that live on your skin.

Figure 39.1
These bacteria establish a more-or-less permanent residence in or on your skin, but do not cause disease under normal conditions.

Color-enhanced SEM Magnification: 17 000×

Quick Demo

Bacterial Culture Touch the surface of a plate of nutrient agar with the palm of your hand or your fingertips, or have a student do so. Cover, tape closed, and incubate for 24–48 hours. Keeping the plate closed, show students the colonies of bacteria that grew on the agar.

INTERNET BioLab The BioLab at the end of the chapter can be used at this point in the lesson.

✓ Reading Check Diseases can be caused by pathogens, genetics (inherited), chemicals, malnutrition, and wear and tear on the body as it ages.

Biology Journal

Diseases and Their Causes Have students make a table that lists all the infectious diseases discussed in this section. As students read, have them fill in their tables with the cause of each disease, its vector (if applicable), and the body systems it infects. Have students use their tables as study tools. **L1**

Table 39.1 Human Infectious Disease			
Disease	**Cause**	**Affected Organ System**	**Transmission**
Smallpox	Virus	Skin	Droplet
Chicken pox	Virus	Skin	Droplet
Rabies	Virus	Nervous system	Animal bite
Poliomyelitis	Virus	Nervous system	Contaminated water
Colds	Viruses	Respiratory system	Direct contact
Influenza	Viruses	Respiratory system	Direct contact
HIV/AIDS	Virus	Immune system	Exchange of body fluids
Hepatitis B	Virus	Liver	Exchange of body fluids
Tetanus	Bacteria	Nervous system	Puncture wound
Food poisoning	Bacteria	Digestive system	Contaminated food/water
Strep throat	Bacteria	Respiratory system	Droplet
Diphtheria	Bacteria	Respiratory system	Droplet
Tuberculosis	Bacteria	Respiratory system	Droplet
Spinal meningitis	Bacteria	Nervous system	Droplet

Word Origin

pathogen from the Greek words *pathos*, meaning "to suffer," and *geneia*, meaning "producing"; Pathogens cause diseases.

These microorganisms have a symbiotic relationship with your body. Microorganisms that colonize the body help maintain equilibrium within the body by keeping harmful bacteria and other microorganisms from growing. If conditions change and the beneficial organisms are eliminated, pathogens can establish themselves and cause infection and disease. If the beneficial organisms enter areas of the body where they are not normally found or if a person becomes weakened or injured, these formerly harmless organisms can become potential pathogens.

Any disease caused by the presence of pathogens in the body is called an **infectious** (ihn FEK shus) **disease.** *Table 39.1* lists some of the infectious diseases that occur in humans.

Determining What Causes a Disease

One of the first problems scientists face when studying a disease is finding out what causes the disease. Not all diseases are caused by pathogens. Some disorders are inherited, such as

hemophilia (hee muh FIH lee uh), which is caused by a recessive allele on the X chromosome, and sickle-cell anemia. Others, such as osteoarthritis (ahs tee oh ar THRI tus), may be caused by wear and tear on the body as it ages. Some diseases, such as cirrhosis (suh ROH sihs), are caused by exposure to chemicals or toxins such as alcohol that destroy liver cells. Other diseases can be caused by malnutrition. Scurvy, which results in poor wound healing, swollen gums, and loosening of teeth, is caused by a deficiency of vitamin C. Pathogens cause infectious diseases and some cancers. In order to determine which pathogen causes a specific disease, scientists follow a standard set of procedures.

✓ Reading Check **List** the different causes of disease.

First pathogen identified

The first proof that pathogens actually cause disease came from the work of Robert Koch (KAHK) in 1876. Koch, a German physician, was looking for the cause of anthrax, a deadly disease that affects mainly

USING MODELS

Pathogen Reservoirs Bring in various examples of pathogen reservoirs (glasses, soft drink cans, combs, insects) as well as pictures of reservoirs, such as drinking fountains and toilets. Ask students to discuss the passage of diseases by inanimate objects. Ask students which objects would probably have the most organisms (most students will likely choose the drinking fountains and the toilets). In many cases, public drinking fountains and public toilets carry very few microorganisms because they are cleaned regularly. **L2**

cattle and sheep but can also occur in humans. Koch discovered a rod-shaped bacterium in the blood of cattle that had died of anthrax. He cultured the bacteria on nutrients and then injected samples of the culture into healthy animals. When these animals became sick and died, Koch isolated the bacteria in their blood and compared them with the bacteria he had originally isolated from anthrax victims. He found that the two sets of blood cultures contained the same bacteria.

A procedure to establish the cause of a disease

Koch established experimental steps, shown in *Figure 39.2,* for directly relating a specific pathogen to a specific disease. These steps, first published in 1884, are known today as **Koch's postulates:**

1. The pathogen must be found in the host in every case of the disease.

2. The pathogen must be isolated from the host and grown in a pure culture—that is, a culture containing no other organisms.
3. When the pathogen from the pure culture is placed in a healthy host, it must cause the disease.
4. The pathogen must be isolated from the new host and be shown to be the original pathogen.

Exceptions to Koch's postulates

Although Koch's postulates are useful in determining the cause of most diseases, some exceptions exist. Some organisms, such as the pathogenic bacterium that causes the sexually transmitted disease syphilis (SIH fuh lus), have never been grown on an artificial medium. Viral pathogens also cannot be cultured this way because they multiply only within cells. As a result, living tissue must be used as a culture medium for viruses.

Figure 39.2
Koch's postulates are steps used to identify an infectious pathogen.
Describe *What are some exceptions to Koch's postulates?*

Step 1

Infectious pathogen identified

Step 2

Pathogen grown in pure culture

Step 3

Pathogen injected into healthy animal

Healthy animal becomes sick

Step 4

Identical pathogen identified

Brainstorming

Have students discuss the importance of each step of Koch's postulates and how skipping any of them would affect the results of a search for the pathogen that causes a particular disease.

Discussion

Explain the term *plague* and ask why some people survived plagues while many others perished. A plague is an epidemic disease that results in a high number of deaths. Students may suggest that people in better health may have been more resistant to infection or possessed some unusual trait that prevented them from succumbing to infection. Accept all logical responses. Initiate a general discussion about the body's defenses to disease.

INCLUSION STRATEGIES

Learning Disabled: *Kinesthetic* Have students prepare a bulletin board with printed information about specific diseases. Brochures on diseases may be available from pharmaceutical companies, doctors' offices, or hospitals. Refer to the display as you discuss pathogens and diseases. **L1**

Indiana Academic Standards
Pages 1024–1025: B.1.17

Enrichment

Linguistic Have students research and report on the recent increase in tuberculosis (TB) infections in the United States.

Since 1986, TB infections have increased 20%, creating an urban epidemic. Tuberculosis is caused by an airborne bacteria. Infection can be latent or active. Once active, it infects the lungs and other vital organs and can cause death if not cured.

Among all the world's infectious diseases, TB remains one of the main causes of death. The re-emergence of TB in the United States has been attributed to several factors, which include an increase in the number of immigrants from areas of the world where TB is endemic such as Asia and Africa, the HIV/AIDS epidemic, an increase in the number of homeless people, and some patients' improper completion of the course of treatment prescribed to eradicate a TB infection. **L2**

Project

Antimicrobial Drugs Have students research the difference between drugs that are bactericidal and those that are bacteriostatic. Have students explain the different mechanisms by which these drugs help eliminate bacteria from the body. Bactericidal drugs kill bacteria, bacteriostatic drugs prevent bacteria from growing. These drugs usually work by inhibiting an essential process from occurring such as cell wall synthesis, protein synthesis, or nucleic acid synthesis. **L2**

The Spread of Infectious Diseases

For a disease to continue and spread, there must be a continual source of the disease organisms. This source can be either a living organism or an inanimate object on which the pathogen can survive.

Reservoirs of pathogens

The main source of human disease pathogens is the human body itself. In fact, the body can be a reservoir of disease-causing organisms. People may transmit pathogens directly or indirectly to other people. Sometimes, people can harbor pathogens without exhibiting any signs of the illness and unknowingly transmit the pathogens to others. These people are called carriers and are a significant reservoir of infectious diseases.

Other people may unknowingly pass on a disease during its first stage, before they begin to experience symptoms. This symptom-free period, while the pathogens are multiplying within the body, is called an incubation period. Humans can unknowingly pass on the pathogens that cause colds, streptococcal (strep tuh KAH kul) throat infections, and sexually transmitted diseases (STDs) such as gonorrhea (gah nuh REE uh) and AIDS during the incubation periods of these diseases.

Animals are other living reservoirs of microorganisms that cause disease in humans. For example, some types of influenza, commonly known as the flu, rabies, and Lyme disease are transmitted to humans from animals.

The major nonliving reservoirs of infectious diseases are soil and water. Soil harbors pathogens such as fungi and the bacterium that causes botulism, a type of food poisoning. Water contaminated by feces of humans and other animals is a reservoir for several pathogens, especially those responsible for intestinal diseases.

Figure 39.3
Diseases can be transmitted to humans from reservoirs in various ways.

A Common inanimate objects such as this glass of juice may harbor and transmit pathogens.

B Airborne transmission by droplets of water or dust spreads pathogens.

C Insects and other arthropods are the most common pathogen vectors.

1026 IMMUNITY FROM DISEASE

Transmission of disease

Pathogens can be transmitted to a host from reservoirs in four main ways: by direct contact, by an object, through the air, or by an intermediate organism called a vector. *Figure 39.3* illustrates several routes of transmission.

The common cold, influenza, and STDs are spread by direct contact. STDs, such as genital herpes and the virus that causes AIDS, are usually transmitted by the exchange of body fluids, especially during sexual intercourse.

Bacteria and other microorganisms can be present on nonliving objects such as money, toys, or towels. Transmission occurs when people unknowingly handle contaminated objects. This type of transmission can be prevented by thoroughly cleaning objects such as eating utensils and countertops that can harbor pathogens, and by washing your hands often throughout each day.

Airborne transmission of a disease can occur when a person coughs or sneezes, spreading pathogens contained in droplets of mucus into the air. *Streptococcus*, the bacterium that causes strep throat infections, and the virus that causes measles are two examples of disease-causing organisms that can be spread through the air.

Diseases transmitted by vectors are most commonly spread by insects and arthropods. Diseases such as malaria and the West Nile virus are transmitted by mosquitoes. Lyme disease and Rocky Mountain spotted fever are diseases that are transmitted by ticks. The bubonic plague—a disease that swept through Europe in the fourteenth century, killing up to one-quarter of the population—was caused by a bacterium that was transmitted from infected rats to humans by fleas. Flies also are significant vectors of disease. They transmit

pathogens when they land on infected materials, such as animal wastes, and then land on fresh food that is eaten by humans. A current international concern is the intentional spreading of disease organisms such as anthrax spores, as occurred in the fall of 2001 in the United States through contaminated mail. To learn more about how diseases are spread, refer to the *Problem-Solving Lab* here and the *MiniLab* on the next page.

Problem-Solving Lab 39.1

Design an Experiment

How does the herpes simplex virus spread?
Herpes (HER peez) simplex virus, which causes cold sores, infects a person for life, occasionally reproducing and then spreading to other cells in the body of its host. Scientists have been interested for a long time in how the herpes virus actually enters a cell.

Solve the Problem
Scientists have found that the herpes virus infects a cell in one of two possible ways. It may latch onto a cell receptor with its own glycoprotein spike, or it may use this spike to grab a growth factor molecule that latches onto the receptor, as shown in the diagram.

Thinking Critically
Experiment Design an experiment to determine the method by which the herpes virus enters a cell.

Problem-Solving Lab 39.1

Purpose
Students will design an experiment to determine how a virus enters a cell.

Process Skills
observe and infer, formulate models

Teaching Strategies
Ask students to include a control setup in their procedures.

Thinking Critically
Student answers will vary. One experiment might be to remove the growth factor from the cell to see if the virus can still get in. Another possibility would be to remove the receptor sites from the cell or to remove the glycoprotein spikes from the virus to see if the virus can still get in.

Assessment
Portfolio Ask students to write a summary of the lab. Have them include the summaries of their experimental designs in their portfolios. Use the Performance Task Assessment List for Lab Report in **PASC**, p. 119. L2

PROJECT

Health Careers Encourage students who are interested in health-related careers to set up an interview with members of the local Health Department to learn more about their roles in safeguarding community health. L2

 Indiana Academic Standards

Pages 1026–1027: B.1.17, B.1.43

Purpose

Students will examine how microbes are transmitted by direct contact.

Process Skills

use controls; collect, organize, and interpret data; experiment; analyze

Teaching Strategies

Point out that the brown area under the apple skin may be caused by bacteria.

Safety Precautions

Have students wash their hands after handling the rotting apples. All apples should be destroyed following the MiniLab.

Expected Results

Apples 2 and 3 will develop brown spots and decay. Apple 1 will show little or no change. Apple 4 will show little or no change, because the alcohol may have inhibited the decay.

Analysis

1. Apple 1 is a control.
2. Apple 2 decayed the most, Apple 3 had brown spots, and Apple 4 may have shown little or no change.
3. The alcohol may destroy some pathogens and help prevent infection.

Assessment

Performance Ask students to write a summary of the lab, including their results. Have them place their summaries and their answers to the Analysis questions in their journals. Use the Performance Task Assessment List for Lab Report in **PASC**, p. 119. **L2**

MiniLab 39.1

Experiment

Testing How Diseases Are Spread Microorganisms cannot travel over long distances by themselves. Unless they are somehow transferred from one animal or plant to another, infections will not spread. One method of transmission is by direct contact with an infected animal or plant.

Rotten apples

Procedure

1. Label four plastic bags 1 to 4.
2. Put a fresh apple in bag 1 and seal the bag.
3. Rub a rotting apple over the entire surface of the remaining three apples. The rotting apple is your source of pathogens. **CAUTION:** *Make sure to wash your hands with soap and water after handling the rotting apple.*
4. Put one of the apples in bag 2.
5. Put one of the apples in bag 3 and drop the bag to the floor from a height of about 2 m.
6. Use a cotton ball to spread alcohol over the last apple. Let the apple air-dry and then place it in bag 4.
7. Store all of the bags in a dark place for one week.
8. Without opening the sealed bags, compare the apples and record your observations. **CAUTION:** *Give all apples to your teacher for proper disposal.*

Analysis

1. **Explain** What was the purpose of the apple in bag 1?
2. **Describe** What happened to the rest of the apples?
3. **Infer** Why is it important to clean a wound with disinfectant?

What causes the symptoms of a disease?

When a pathogen invades your body, it encounters your immune system, which consists of individual cells, tissues, and organs that work together to protect the body against organisms that may cause infection or disease. If the pathogen overcomes the defenses of your immune system, it can metabolize and multiply, causing damage to the tissues it has invaded, and even killing host cells.

Damage to the host by viruses and bacteria

You already know that viruses cause damage by taking over a host cell's genetic and metabolic machinery. Many viruses also cause the eventual death of the cells they invade.

Most of the damage done to host cells by bacteria is inflicted by toxins. Toxins are poisonous substances that are sometimes produced by microorganisms. These poisons are transported by the blood and can cause serious and sometimes fatal effects. Toxins can inhibit protein synthesis in the host cell, destroy blood cells and blood vessels, produce fever, or cause spasms by disrupting the nervous system.

Figure 39.4
Before the days of modern medicine, wounded soldiers faced the additional, deadly danger of becoming infected with tetanus bacteria. **Infer** *What conditions of a battlefield are ideal for tetanus bacteria?*

1028 IMMUNITY FROM DISEASE

CHALLENGE ACTIVITY

Wartime Medicines Have students who need an additional challenge conduct research to find examples of medicines developed during wartime that have become important in treating civilians. Ask them to identify the reason the medicine was developed and explain what disease(s) it has been used to treat. **L3**

For example, the toxin produced by tetanus bacteria affects nerve cells and produces uncontrollable muscle contractions. If the condition is left untreated, paralysis and death occur. Tetanus bacteria are normally present in soil, and as *Figure 39.4* illustrates, a soldier could become infected with tetanus as a result of wounds received on the battlefield. If dirt transfers the bacteria into a deep wound on the body, the bacteria begin to produce the toxin in the wounded area. A small amount of this toxin, about the same amount as the ink used to make a period on this page, could kill 30 people.

Patterns of Diseases

The outbreak in 2003 of severe acute respiratory syndrome (SARS) spread to more than two dozen countries within a few months. Identifying a pathogen, its method of transmission, and the geographic distribution of the disease it causes are major concerns of government health departments. The Centers for Disease Control and Prevention, the central source of disease information in the United States, publishes a weekly report about the incidence of specific diseases.

Some diseases, such as typhoid fever, occur only occasionally in the United States. These periodic outbreaks often occur because someone traveling in a foreign country has brought the disease back home. On the other hand, many diseases are constantly present in the population. Such a disease is called an endemic disease. The common cold is an **endemic disease.**

Sometimes, an **epidemic** breaks out. An epidemic occurs when many people in a given area are afflicted with the same disease at about the same time. Influenza is a disease that often achieves epidemic status, sometimes spreading to many parts of the world. During the early 1950s, a polio epidemic spread across the United States. Victims of this disease were paralyzed or died when the polio virus attacked the nerve cells of the brain and spinal cord. Many survived only after being placed in an iron lung—a machine that allowed the patient to continue to breathe, as shown in *Figure 39.5.* You can learn more about emerging and re-emerging diseases in the *BioLab* at the end of the chapter.

Treating Diseases

A person who becomes sick often can be treated with medicinal drugs, such as antibiotics. An **antibiotic** is a substance produced by a microorganism that, in small amounts, will kill or inhibit the growth and reproduction of other microorganisms, especially bacteria. Antibiotics are produced naturally by various species of bacteria and fungi. Although antibiotics can be used to cure some bacterial infections, antibiotics do not have an effect on viruses.

Figure 39.5
During the early 1950s polio epidemic, many patients were placed in iron-lung machines like those shown here.

Figure 39.6
Penicillin is an antibiotic produced by a fungus **(A)**. Some types of bacteria, including *Streptococcus pneumoniae* are penicillin-resistant **(B)**.

Penicillin

Streptococcus pneumoniae

Color-enhanced SEM
Magnification 50 000×

Word Origin

antibiotic from the Greek words *anti*, meaning "against," and *bios*, meaning "life"; An antibiotic is given to control a bacterial infection.

With the continued use of antibiotics, bacteria can become resistant to the drugs. That means the drugs become ineffective. Penicillin, an antibiotic produced by a fungus, was used for the first time in the 1940s and is still one of the most effective antibiotics known. However, penicillin has now been in use for more than 50 years, and more and more types of bacteria have evolved that are resistant to it. Bacteria that are resistant to penicillin produce an enzyme that breaks down this antibiotic. Examples of penicillin-resistant bacteria include *Streptococcus pneumoniae*, shown in *Figure 39.6*, and the organism that causes the STD gonorrhea. The resistance of *Streptococcus pneumoniae* to penicillin is a problem because penicillin is the primary drug used to treat pneumonia, ear infections, and meningitis, all of which can be caused by this organism.

The use of antibiotics is only one way to fight infections. Your body also has its own built-in defense system—the immune system—that works to keep you healthy.

Section Assessment

Understanding Main Ideas
1. Outline and explain the steps of Koch's postulates.

2. What are the major reservoirs of pathogens?

3. List the different ways in which pathogens are transmitted.

4. How do pathogens, such as some bacteria and viruses, cause disease symptoms?

Thinking Critically
5. Sometimes patients contract a secondary infection while in the hospital. What possible ways could a disease be transmitted to a hospital patient?

SKILL REVIEW

6. **Experiment** Design an experiment that could determine whether a recently identified bacterium causes a type of pneumonia. For more help, refer to *Experiment* in the **Skill Handbook**.

1030 IMMUNITY FROM DISEASE

 in.bdol.glencoe.com/self_check_quiz

Section Assessment

1. The pathogen must be found in the host in every case of the disease. The pathogen must be isolated from the host and grown in pure culture. When the pathogen from the pure culture is placed in a healthy host, it must cause the disease. The pathogen must be isolated from the new host and be shown to be the original pathogen.
2. humans, animals, soil, and water
3. direct contact, through contaminated air, water, or inanimate object, or by a vector
4. Disease symptoms are often caused by bacterial toxins or death of body tissue.
5. by direct contact with employees or patients, through contaminated objects, or by airborne transmission
6. Grow suspected organisms in a pure culture, then inject them into another host. If that host develops the same disease, the organisms probably caused it. To be sure, isolate the organisms and compare with the original organisms.

SECTION PREVIEW

Objectives

Identify the cells, tissues, and organs that make up the immune system.

Compare innate and acquired immune responses.

Distinguish between antibody and cellular immunity.

Review Vocabulary
antibody: a protein in the blood plasma produced in reaction to antigens that reacts with and disables antigens (p. 977)

New Vocabulary
innate immunity
phagocyte
macrophage
pus
interferon
acquired immunity
tissue fluid
lymph
lymph node
lymphocyte
T cell
B cell
vaccine

Defense Against Infectious Diseases

Indiana Standards Standard B.1.20 Recognize that and describe how the human immune system is designed to protect against microscopic organisms and foreign substances that enter from outside the body…

Microscopic Enemies

Using an Analogy You can't see it, but a war is going on around these teenagers. In fact, the same sort of war is occurring around you. Millions of unseen enemies are present everywhere—in the air, on the ground, and even on your clothes. Defenders ready to protect you from the onset of attack are inside your body.

Infer *How does your body save you from the microscopic foes that cause infectious diseases? How do the body's defenses protect you from these unseen enemies?*

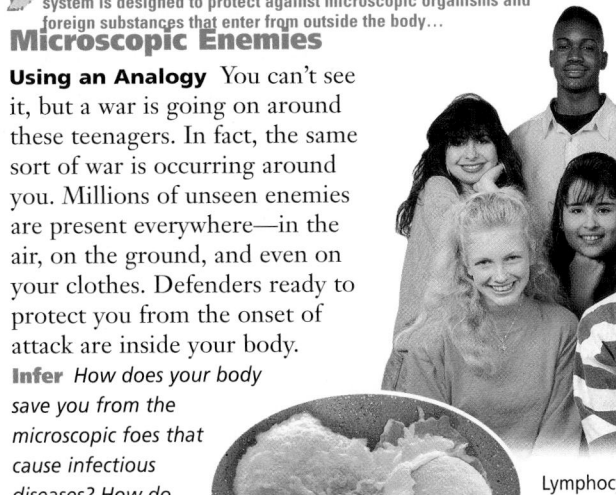

Lymphocytes (inset), types of white blood cells, help protect you from diseases.

Color-enhanced SEM Magnification: unavailable

Innate Immunity

Your body produces a variety of white blood cells that defend it against invasion by pathogens that are constantly bombarding you. No matter what pathogens are present, your immune system is always ready. The body's earliest lines of defense against any and all pathogens make up your nonspecific, **innate immunity.**

Skin and body secretions

When a potential pathogen contacts your body, often the first barrier it must penetrate is your skin. Like the walls of a castle, intact skin is a formidable physical barrier to the entrance of microorganisms.

In addition to the skin, pathogens also encounter your body's secretions of mucus, oil, sweat, tears, and saliva. The main function of mucus is to prevent various areas of the body from drying out. Because mucus is slightly viscous (thick), it also traps many microorganisms and other foreign substances that enter the respiratory and digestive tracts. Mucus is continually swallowed and passed to the stomach, where acidic gastric juice destroys most bacteria and their toxins. Sweat, tears, and saliva all contain the enzyme lysozyme, which is capable of breaking down the cell walls of some bacteria.

39.2 DEFENSE AGAINST INFECTIOUS DISEASES **1031**

1 Focus

INTERACTIVE CHALKBOARD
PowerPoint® Presentations

Bellringer
Section Focus Transparency 97

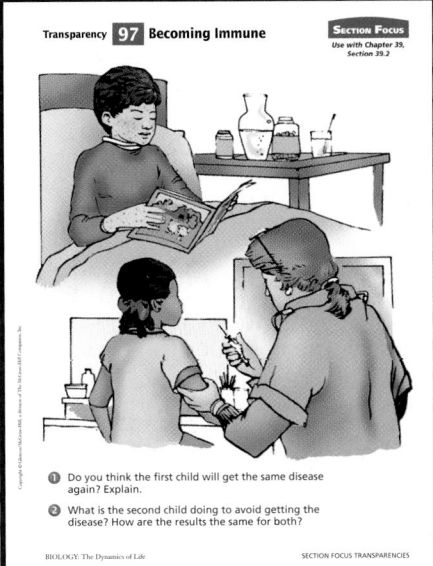

Transparency **97** Becoming Immune

SECTION FOCUS
Use with Chapter 39, Section 39.2

① Do you think the first child will get the same disease again? Explain.

② What is the second child doing to avoid getting the disease? How are the results the same for both?

BIOLOGY: The Dynamics of Life   SECTION FOCUS TRANSPARENCIES

Using an Analogy

Infer The body saves you from the microscopic foes by activating the immune system, which involves the innate, non-specific immunity and the acquired, specific immunity. Some of the main ways the immune system protects you is by phagocytic cells destroying pathogens, plasma cells producing antibodies, and cellular attack by T cells.

Indiana Academic Standards

Pages 1030–1031: B.1.17, B.1.20, B.1.43

2 Teach

Display

Assemble a bulletin board display of newspaper and magazine articles about AIDS. Refer to the articles when discussing AIDS and other viral infections.

Tying to Prior Knowledge

Ask students why, when a patient complains of a sore throat, the physician feels under the patient's chin and behind his or her ears and looks down the patient's throat. The doctor is looking for swollen lymph glands and for redness and blotchy white spots in the throat that would indicate a bacterial infection.

Figure 39.7
When tissues become inflamed, histamine release causes blood vessels to dilate (**A**). Tissue fluid leaks out of the vessels into the injured area, causing swelling (**B**).

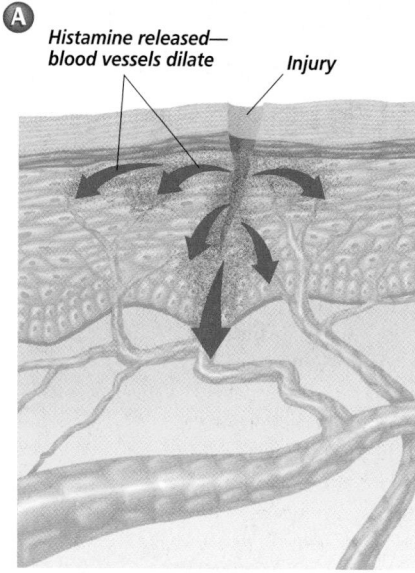

Histamine released— blood vessels dilate   Injury

Phagocytes   Swelling occurs   Tissue fluid moves into injured area   Pus

Inflammation of body tissues

If a pathogen manages to get past the skin and body secretions, your body has several other nonspecific defense mechanisms that can destroy the invader and restore homeostasis. Think about what happens when you get a splinter. If bacteria or other pathogens enter and damage body tissues, inflammation (ihn fluh MAY shun) results. Inflammation is characterized by four symptoms—redness, swelling, pain, and heat. As *Figure 39.7* shows, inflammation begins when damaged tissue cells called mast cells, and white blood cells called basophils release histamine (HIHS tuh meen). Histamine causes blood vessels in the injured area to dilate, which makes them more permeable to tissue fluid. These dilated blood vessels cause the redness of an inflamed area. Fluid that leaks from the vessels into the injured tissue helps the body destroy toxic agents and restore homeostasis. This increase in tissue fluid causes swelling and pain, and may also cause a local temperature increase. Inflammation can occur as a reaction to other types of injury as well as infections. Physical force, chemical substances, extreme temperatures, and radiation may also inflame body tissues.

Phagocytosis of pathogens

Pathogens that enter your body may encounter cells that carry on phagocytosis. Recall that phagocytosis occurs when a cell engulfs a particle. **Phagocytes** (FA guh sites) are white blood cells that destroy pathogens by surrounding and engulfing them. Phagocytes include monocytes, which develop into macrophages, neutrophils, and eosinophils. Macrophages are present in body tissues. The other types of phagocytes circulate in the blood.

Macrophages are white blood cells that provide the first defense against pathogens that have managed to enter the tissues. Macrophages, shown in *Figure 39.8*, are found in the tissues of the body. They are sometimes called giant scavengers, or big eaters, because of the manner in which they engulf pathogens or

---

Additional Lab

Antibiotics and Bacteria

Purpose
Students will determine which antibiotics are most effective in inhibiting bacterial growth.

Safety Precautions
Students should wear lab aprons, safety goggles, and disposable gloves. Do not open petri dishes after they have been sealed. Students should wash their hands after inoculating petri dishes and after making observations. Used petri dishes and toothpicks should be autoclaved before disposal.

Materials
E. coli bacterial culture, 3 types of antibiotic disks, sterile untreated disks, cotton swabs, forceps, ethanol, transparent tape, plates of nutrient agar, marking pen, incubator

Procedure
1. Use the marking pen to make a cross on the bottom of an agar plate, dividing it into four sections.

damaged cells. Lysosomal enzymes inside the macrophage digest the particles it has engulfed.

If the infection is not stopped by the tissue macrophages, another type of phagocyte, called a neutrophil, is attracted to the site. They also destroy pathogens by engulfing and digesting them.

If the infection is not stopped by tissue macrophages and neutrophils, there is a third method of defense. A different type of phagocyte begins to arrive on the scene. Monocytes are small, immature macrophages that circulate in the bloodstream. These cells squeeze through blood vessel walls to move into the infected area. Once they reach the site of the infection they mature and are now called macrophages. They then begin consuming pathogens and dead neutrophils by phagocytosis. Once the infection is over, some monocytes mature into tissue macrophages that remain in the area, prepared to fend off a new infection.

After a macrophage has destroyed large numbers of pathogens, dead neutrophils, and damaged tissue cells, it eventually dies. After a few days, infected tissue harbors a collection of live and dead white blood cells, multiplying and dead pathogens, and body fluids called **pus**. Pus formation usually continues until the infection subsides. Eventually, the pus is cleared away by macrophages.

Which white blood cells are involved in the body's defense against pathogens? Find out by looking at *Figure 39.9* on the following page and by carrying out the *MiniLab* on page 1035 to observe the different types of white blood cells.

Protective proteins

When an infection is caused by a virus, your body faces a problem. Phagocytes alone cannot destroy viruses. Recall that a virus multiplies within a host cell. A phagocyte that engulfs a virus will itself be destroyed if the virus multiplies within it. One way your body can counteract viral infections is with interferons. **Interferons** are proteins that protect cells from viruses. Interferons are host-cell specific. This means that human interferons will protect human cells from viruses but cannot protect cells of other species from the same virus.

Word Origin

phagocyte from the Greek words *phagein*, meaning "to eat," and *kytos*, meaning "hollow"; A phagocyte consumes foreign particles by engulfing them.

Reinforcement
Have students orally make an analogy between the reaction of the immune system and a battle scene. Ask them who or what might represent the skin, tissue macrophages, neutrophils, and monocytes.

Inquiry

The Common Cold Have students research and create a chart that shows the different types of viruses that can cause a cold. Have them answer the question: Why won't a single vaccine combat the common cold? A single vaccine cannot be effective against all of the different viruses that can cause a cold.

 Assessment

Knowledge Ask students to describe similarities between a macrophage and an amoeba. Both engulf particles by phagocytosis. **L2**

 Color-enhanced SEM Magnification: 4000×

Blood capillary

Macrophage

Connective tissue

Ⓐ

Ⓑ

Figure 39.8
Macrophages move out of blood vessels by squeezing between the cells of the vessel walls (**A**). Macrophages will attack anything they recognize as foreign, including microorganisms and dust particles that are breathed into the lungs (**B**).

1033

Indiana Academic Standards

Pages 1032–1033: B.1.15, B.1.20

2. Using a cotton swab, transfer some of the bacterial culture to the agar plate.

3. Spread the culture evenly over the surface of the agar plate using the cotton swab.

4. Dip the forceps into alcohol. Let them to air dry without touching any surface.

5. Use the forceps to transfer two antibiotic disks into each of three sections of the plate. Transfer two untreated disks to the fourth section of the plate. Label the bottom with the type of antibiotic used in each section.

6. Tape the plates closed and incubate for 48 hours at 37°C.

7. Look for regions of inhibition.

Analysis

1. Why were untreated disks placed in one section? This section was the control.

2. Did any of the antibiotics inhibit the growth of the bacteria? Answers will vary.

Assessment

Performance Have students design and perform another lab procedure using disks treated with antiseptics or soaps. Use the Performance Task Assessment List for Designing an Experiment in **PASC**, p. 95. **L2**

Purpose
Students visualize the various types of white blood cells and their role in the immune system.

Teaching Strategies
■ Review this page with students before and after completing MiniLab 39.2.
■ Have students prepare a table of the white blood cells that compares their characteristics, functions, and where they are found.
■ Have students discuss what would happen to the numbers of white blood cells during an infection. The number of white blood cells per milliliter of blood increases during an infection.

Visual Learning
Using a microscope projector, point out the various types of white blood cells on a blood smear slide.

Critical Thinking
Mature tissue macrophages are not found in the blood but out in the body tissues. Immature macrophages, called monocytes, are found in the bloodstream.

Immune Responses

Figure 39.9
White blood cells play a major role in protecting your body against disease. Many of these cells leave the bloodstream to fight disease organisms in the tissues. **Critical Thinking** *Why would you not expect to see tissue macrophages in a sample of blood cells?*

An abrasion breaks the protective barrier of the skin.

A Innate immune response
Macrophages are large, phagocytic white blood cells found in the tissues. They are the first to arrive at the site of an infection. *Basophils,* found in the blood, are not phagocytic. They are filled with granules that release histamine at an infection site. *Eosinophils* are also granular and also play a role in inflammation.

Color-enhanced SEM Magnification: unavailable   Stained LM Magnification: 400×   Stained LM Magnification: 400×

Macrophage   *Basophil*   *Eosinophil*

Color-enhanced TEM Magnification: 3000×

Color-enhanced TEM Magnification: 6600×

Color-enhanced LM Magnification: 750×

B Second wave of defenders A *neutrophil* (above) is a phagocytic white blood cell with a nucleus that has several lobes.

C Continued defense
After moving from the blood into an infected area, *monocytes* (above) mature into macrophages. Monocytes are two to three times larger than other blood cells and have large nuclei. They replenish the supply of tissue macrophages following an infection.

D Acquired immune response *Lymphocytes* (above) are cells with nuclei that nearly fill the cell. They include B cells and T cells and are involved in developing immunity to specific pathogens. Lymphocytes are found in the blood, spleen, thymus, lymph nodes, tonsils, and appendix.

CULTURAL DIVERSITY

Susumu Tonagawa and Immunity
Introduce students to the important contributions Japanese immunologist Susumu Tonagawa has made toward our understanding of the immune system. Tonagawa was able to show that somatic cells use a multi-step process to rearrange fragments from different genes, in different ways, to produce many different antibodies, proving that individuals inherit only a small number of genes that diversify in specialized somatic cells. For this work, Tonagawa received a Nobel prize in 1987.

Interferon is produced by a body cell that has been infected by the virus. The interferon diffuses to uninfected neighboring cells, which then produce antiviral proteins that can prevent the virus from multiplying.

Acquired Immunity

The cells of your innate immune system continually survey your body for foreign invaders. When a pathogen is detected, these cells begin defending your body right away. Meanwhile, as the infection continues, another type of immune response that counteracts the invading pathogen is also mobilized. Certain white blood cells gradually develop the ability to recognize a specific foreign substance. This acquired immune response enables these white blood cells to inactivate or destroy the pathogen. Defending against a specific pathogen by gradually building up a resistance to it is called **acquired immunity.**

Normally, the immune system recognizes components of the body as self, and foreign substances, called antigens, as nonself. Antigens are usually proteins present on the surfaces of whole organisms, such as bacteria, or on parts of organisms, such as the pollen grains of plants. An acquired immune response occurs when the immune system recognizes an antigen and responds to it by producing antibodies against it. Antigens are foreign substances that stimulate an immune response, and antibodies are proteins in the blood that correspond specifically to each antigen. The development of acquired immunity is the job of the lymphatic system. The process of acquiring immunity to a specific disease can take days or weeks.

The lymphatic system

Your lymphatic (lihm FA tihk) system not only helps the body defend itself against disease, but also maintains homeostasis by keeping body fluids at a constant level.

MiniLab 39.2

Observe and Infer

Distinguishing Blood Cells The human immune system includes five types of white blood cells in the bloodstream: basophils, neutrophils, monocytes, eosinophils, and lymphocytes.

Color-enhanced LM Magnification: 400×

A blood smear

Procedure

1. Copy the data table below.
2. Mount a prepared slide of blood cells on the microscope and focus on low power. Turn to high power and look for white blood cells. **CAUTION:** *Use care when working with microscope slides.*
3. Find a neutrophil, monocyte, eosinophil, and lymphocyte. You may see a basophil, although they are rare. Refer to *Figure 39.9* for photos of these cells.
4. Count a total of 50 white blood cells, and record how many of each type you see.
5. Calculate the percentage by multiplying the number of each cell type by two. Record the percentages. Diagram each cell type.

Data Table			
Type of White Blood Cell	Number Counted	Percent	Diagram
Neutrophil			
Monocyte			
Basophil			
Lymphocyte			
Eosinophil			

Analysis

1. **Summarize** Which type of white blood cell was most common? Second most common?
2. **Describe** How do red and white blood cells differ?

39.2 DEFENSE AGAINST INFECTIOUS DISEASES **1035**

MiniLab 39.2

Purpose
Students will determine the percentages of different kinds of white blood cells.

Process Skills
classify, observe and infer, compare and contrast, collect and organize data

Safety Precautions
Caution students to use care when working with prepared slides and microscopes. Special care should be taken when viewing slides under high power so the objective does not break the slide.

Teaching Strategies
It would be helpful for student identification to set up a prepared microscope slide showing both an eosinophil and a basophil.

Expected Results
The common percentages of white blood cells are: neutrophils, 60–70%; lymphocytes, 20–25%; monocytes, 3–8%; eosinophils, 2–4%; and basophils, 0.5–1%.

Analysis
1. neutrophils, lymphocytes
2. White blood cells have a nucleus; red blood cells don't.

Modified Assessment
Knowledge Quiz students by having them identify unlabeled photos of the different types of white blood cells. **L1**

CHALLENGE ACTIVITY

Research Have students who need an additional challenge research the difference between the two main groups into which white blood cells are categorized. Granulocytes include neutrophils, basophils, and eosinophils. They contain large granules in their cytoplasm that are visible under a light microscope after staining has occurred. Agranulocytes include monocytes and macrophages. Although these cells contain granules, they are not visible under a light microscope after staining. **L3**

1035

Discussion

Ask students to compare and contrast the functions of the circulatory system and the lymphatic system. Have students as a class discuss the two systems.

Enrichment

Have students research the life of David, the "bubble boy" of Houston, Texas, who lived in a sterile plastic bubble for all but 15 days of his life. He suffered from severe combined immune deficiency (SCID), a rare genetic disorder related to a dysfunction of the lymphocyte-producing cells of the bone marrow.

At birth, David was placed in a sterile plastic bubble. As he grew, he was placed in increasingly larger bubbles. At the age of 12, he left his bubble and underwent a bone marrow transplant using tissue from his sister. David died four months later, in February, 1984, of blood cancer. Encourage students to find out about current treatments, including gene therapy, for SCID. **L3**

Caption Question Answer
Figure 39.10 Students should be able to identify the various structures on the diagram.

✓ **Reading Check** Lymph is carried toward the heart in lymph veins. The veins converge to form two major lymph ducts which return the lymph to the bloodstream.

Figure 39.10
The lymphatic system is spread throughout the body. **Interpret Scientific Illustrations** *As you read about the various vessels, tissues, and organs of the lymphatic system, locate them on this diagram.*

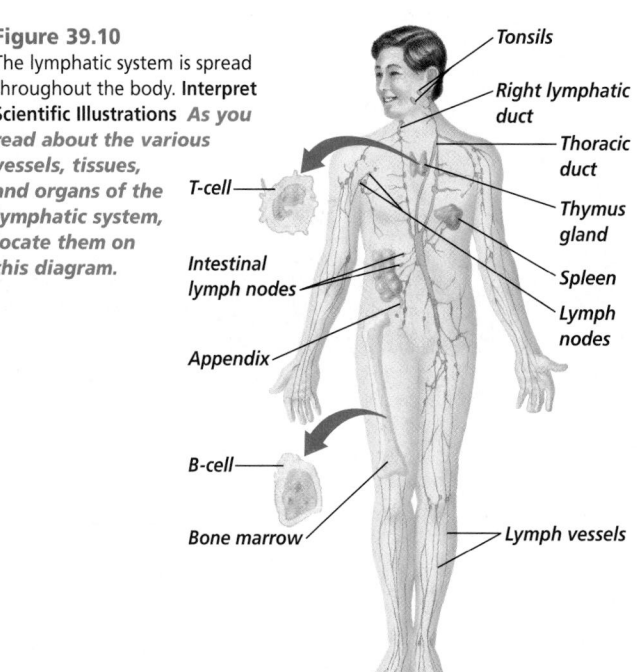

Figure 39.10 shows the major glands and vessels that make up the lymphatic system.

Your body's cells are constantly bathed with fluid. This **tissue fluid** is composed of water and dissolved substances that diffuse from the blood into the spaces between the cells that make up the surrounding tissues. This tissue fluid collects in

Figure 39.11
As lymph filters through a lymph node, the lymphocytes in the node trap and kill pathogens.

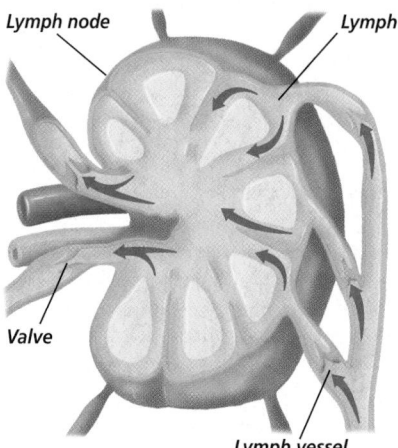

1036

open-ended lymph capillaries. Once the tissue fluid enters the lymph vessels, it is called **lymph.**

Lymph capillaries meet to form larger vessels called lymph veins. The flow of lymph is only toward the heart, so there are no lymph arteries. The lymph veins converge to form two major lymph ducts. These ducts return the lymph to the bloodstream in the shoulder area, after it has been filtered through various lymph glands.

✓ **Reading Check** **Describe** how lymph is circulated through the body.

Glands of the lymphatic system

At locations along the lymphatic system, the lymph vessels pass through lymph nodes. A **lymph node** is a small mass of tissue that contains lymphocytes and filters pathogens from the lymph, as shown in *Figure 39.11.* Lymph nodes are made of an interlaced network of connective tissue fibers that holds lymphocytes. A **lymphocyte** (LIHM fuh site) is a type of white blood cell that defends the body against foreign substances.

The tonsils are large clusters of lymph tissue located at the back of the mouth cavity and at the back of the throat. They form a protective ring around the openings of the nasal and oral cavities. Tonsils provide protection against bacteria and other pathogens that enter your nose and mouth.

The spleen is an organ that stores certain types of lymphocytes. It also filters out and destroys bacteria and worn-out red blood cells, and acts as a blood reservoir. Unlike lymph nodes, the spleen does not filter lymph.

Another important component of the lymphatic system is the thymus gland, which is located above the heart. The thymus gland stores immature lymphocytes until they mature and are released into the body's defense system.

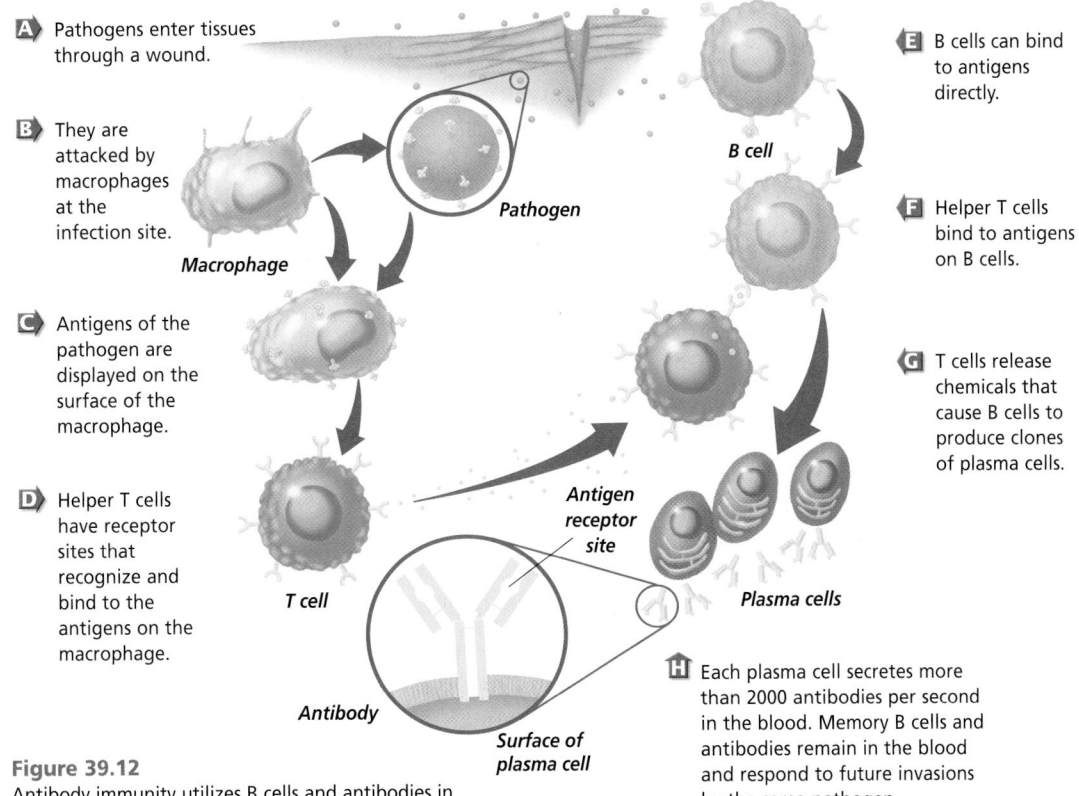

A Pathogens enter tissues through a wound.

B They are attacked by macrophages at the infection site.

Macrophage

Pathogen

C Antigens of the pathogen are displayed on the surface of the macrophage.

D Helper T cells have receptor sites that recognize and bind to the antigens on the macrophage.

T cell

Antibody

Surface of plasma cell

Antigen receptor site

E B cells can bind to antigens directly.

B cell

F Helper T cells bind to antigens on B cells.

G T cells release chemicals that cause B cells to produce clones of plasma cells.

Plasma cells

H Each plasma cell secretes more than 2000 antibodies per second in the blood. Memory B cells and antibodies remain in the blood and respond to future invasions by the same pathogen.

Figure 39.12
Antibody immunity utilizes B cells and antibodies in defending your body against invading pathogens.

Antibody Immunity

Acquired immunity involves the production of two kinds of immune responses: antibody immunity and cellular immunity. Antibody immunity is a type of chemical warfare within your body that involves several types of cells. Follow the steps of antibody immunity illustrated in *Figure 39.12*.

When a pathogen invades your body, it is first attacked by the cells of your innate immune system, as shown in *Figure 39.12A, B,* and *C*. If the infection is not controlled, then your body builds up acquired immunity to the antigen by producing antibodies to it. A type of lymphocyte called a T cell becomes involved. A **T cell** is a lymphocyte that is produced in bone marrow and processed in the thymus gland. Two kinds of T cells play different roles in immunity.

One kind of T cell, called a helper T cell, interacts with B cells, shown in *Figure 39.12D, E,* and *F*. A **B cell** is a lymphocyte that, when activated by a T cell, becomes a plasma cell and produces antibodies. B cells are produced in the bone marrow. Plasma cells, shown in *Figure 39.12G* and *H,* release antibodies into the bloodstream and tissue spaces. Some activated B cells do not become plasma cells but remain in the bloodstream as memory B cells. Memory B cells are ready and armed to respond rapidly if the same pathogen invades the body at a later time. The response to a second invasion is immediate and rapid, usually without any symptoms.

Enrichment

Have students research the successful eradication of smallpox. Smallpox was the first disease for which a vaccine was made and the first to be eradicated throughout the world through the use of vaccines.

The last known case of smallpox occurred in Somalia, Africa, in 1977. Smallpox was spread by droplets and caused lesions in layers of the skin that left disfiguring scars. This disease devastated Native American populations when European settlers brought it to America. **L3**

Reinforcement

Visual-Spatial Have students make a flowchart to show the sequence of events in cellular immunity as shown in Figure 39.13. **L2**

Assessment

Performance Have students use the text to develop a flowchart that traces the steps Jenner took to find a vaccine for smallpox. Then ask students to develop a second flowchart that describes the events that must have taken place in the immune system of the boy Jenner vaccinated. **L2**

Cellular Immunity

Like antibody immunity, cellular immunity also involves T cells with antigens on their surfaces. The T cells involved in cellular immunity are cytotoxic, or killer, T cells. T cells stored in the lymph nodes, spleen, and tonsils transform into cytotoxic T cells that are specific for a single antigen. However, unlike B cells, they do not form antibodies. Cytotoxic T cells differentiate and produce identical clones. They travel to the infection site and release enzymes directly into the pathogens, causing them to lyse and die. The steps in cellular immunity are illustrated in *Figure 39.13*.

The same cells that protect the body against pathogens can sometimes cause problems within the body. Sometimes the immune system overreacts to a harmless substance such as pollen. Mast cells release histamines in large amounts, causing the symptoms of an allergic reaction: sneezing, increased mucus production in the nasal passages, and redness. The immune system also can recognize its own cells as foreign and mistakenly attack the body's own tissues in what is referred to as an autoimmune disorder, such as lupus or rheumatoid arthritis. T cells and antibodies also can attack transplanted tissue, such as a transplanted kidney, that comes from a source outside the body.

Passive and Active Immunity

Acquired immunity to a disease may be either passive or active. Passive acquired immunity develops as a result of acquiring antibodies that are generated in another host. For example, prior to birth and during nursing, a human infant acquires passive immunity to disease from its mother.

Figure 39.13
Cellular immunity involves T cells that transform into cytotoxic T cells. These T cells release perforin, which pokes holes in cells invaded by pathogens.

Infected cells

Pathogen engulfed by

Foreign antigen

Perforin

Macrophage

Infected cell lyses

Displays antigens on surface and stimulates T cell

Attacks infected cells

Cytotoxic T cell

Helper T cell

Stimulates

Cytotoxic T cell

Stained SEM Magnification: 30 000×

1038 IMMUNITY FROM DISEASE

CHALLENGE ACTIVITY

Write a Play Have students who need an additional challenge write a short play that demonstrates aspects of the immune system and its responses. You may wish to have them perform the play and include a copy of it in their portfolios. **L3**

Table 39.2 Recommended Childhood Immunizations		
Immunization	**Agent**	**Protection Against**
Acellular DPT or Tetrammune	Bacteria	Diphtheria, pertussis (whooping cough), tetanus (lockjaw)
MMR	Virus	Measles, mumps, rubella
OPV	Virus	Poliomyelitis (polio)
HBV	Virus	Hepatitis B
HIB or Tetrammune	Bacteria	*Haemophilus influenzae B* (spinal meningitis)

Concept Development

Review the life cycle of a retrovirus. After discussing the AIDS epidemic, have students find out their school policy on educating students about AIDS and its prevention.

Active acquired immunity develops when your body is directly exposed to antigens and produces antibodies in response to those antigens.

✓**Reading Check** **Explain** the difference between passive acquired immunity and active acquired immunity.

Passive immunity

Passive immunity may develop in two ways. Natural passive immunity develops when antibodies are transferred from a mother to her unborn baby through the placenta or to a newborn infant through the mother's milk. Artificial passive immunity involves injecting into the body antibodies that come from an animal or a human who is already immune to the disease. For example, a person who is bitten by a snake might be injected with antibodies from a horse that is immune to the snake venom.

Active immunity

Active immunity is obtained naturally when a person is exposed to antigens. The body produces antibodies that correspond specifically to these antigens. Once the person recovers from the infection, he or she will usually be immune if exposed to the pathogen again.

Active immunity can be induced artificially by vaccines. A **vaccine** is a substance consisting of weakened, dead, or incomplete portions of pathogens or antigens that, when injected into the body, cause an immune response. Vaccines produce immunity because they prompt the body to react as if it were naturally infected. *Table 39.2* lists some common vaccines.

In the late 1790s, Edward Jenner, an English country doctor shown in *Figure 39.14,* demonstrated the first safe vaccination procedure. Jenner knew that dairy workers who acquired cowpox from infected cows were resistant to catching smallpox during epidemics. Cowpox is a disease similar to, but milder than, smallpox. To test whether immunity to cowpox also caused immunity to smallpox, Jenner infected a young boy with cowpox. The boy developed a mild cowpox infection. Six weeks later, Jenner scratched the skin of the boy with viruses from a smallpox victim.

Figure 39.14
This portrait shows Jenner vaccinating a young boy against smallpox. A worldwide attack on the disease through vaccinations brought an end to it. Because of the efforts of the World Health Organization, smallpox has been eliminated.

✓**Reading Check** Passive immunity involves acquiring antibodies produced in someone else, such as through an injection or a mother passing them through the placenta to her fetus. Active immunity is due to a person forming his or her own antibodies after being exposed to an antigen.

Biology Journal

The Nature of Scientific Discovery
Have students prepare a report on Louis Pasteur's work with rabies or Jonas Salk's and Albert Sabin's work with polio vaccines. **L2**

PROJECT

Vaccines Have students research details about the different types of vaccines, such as recombinant vaccines and nucleic acid vaccines, and the technology involved in manufacturing them. For which diseases are scientists currently researching the possibility of a vaccine? Students can record the results of their research in their journals. **L2**

INCLUSION STRATEGIES

Physically Challenged Ask students who are physically challenged by allergies or asthma to speak to the class about how the disorder affects their lives. **L2**

Indiana Academic Standards
Pages 1038–1039: B.1.15, B.1.20

Purpose

Students will determine that a person's immune system responds to a disease faster and more vigorously if he or she has been vaccinated against that disease.

Process Skills

analyze information, apply concepts, define operationally, compare and contrast, draw a conclusion, make and use graphs, recognize cause and effect, think critically

Teaching Strategies

- Remind students of the difference between a toxin and toxoid.
- Review the difference between antigen and antibody.

Thinking Critically

1. They illustrate acquired immunity. Innate immunity consists of skin barriers or body secretions. Acquired immunity is the process by which the body adapts to a specific antigen by forming antibodies against it.
2. A toxin is a poison released by a pathogen that may cause disease symptoms. A toxoid is a treated form of the toxin that does not harm the body but stimulates the immune system to form antibodies against the toxin.
3. Line A–B involves macrophages, T cells, and B cells. Line B–C probably involves memory B cells, plasma cells, and memory T cells.

Modified Assessment

Knowledge Provide students with a variety of antigen shapes and have students model the antibodies that would be formed by the immune system against each antigen shape. Use the Performance Task Assessment List for Model in **PASC**, p. 123.
L1 ELL

1040

The viruses for cowpox and smallpox are so similar that the immune system cannot tell them apart. The boy, therefore, did not get sick because he had artificially acquired active immunity to the disease. To learn more about how vaccines work, try the *Problem-Solving Lab* on this page.

Analyze Information

Get a Shot or Get the Disease? You probably have had injections for immunization. How do these shots prevent you from catching a particular disease?

Solve the Problem

Diphtheria toxoid is an inactivated form of the toxin produced by the bacterium *Corynebacterium diphtheriae*. The toxin causes the symptoms associated with the disease diphtheria. When injected into your body, the toxoid prompts the immune system to respond as if it were being attacked by the diphtheria toxin. The graph below shows the human body's response to receiving an immunization shot of the diphtheria toxoid and then to being infected later on with diphtheria.

Thinking Critically

1. **Explain** Are the events in the graph illustrating innate or acquired immunity?
2. **Describe** What is the difference between a toxin and a toxoid?
3. **Analyze** Which cells associated with the immune system are most likely involved with line A–B? With line B–C?

AIDS and the Immune System

In 1981, an unusual cluster of cases of a rare pneumonia caused by a protozoan appeared in the San Francisco area. Medical investigators soon related the appearance of this disease with the incidence of a rare form of skin cancer called Kaposi's sarcoma. Both diseases seemed associated with a general lack of function of the body's immune system.

By 1983, the pathogen causing this immune system disease had been identified as a retrovirus, now known as Human Immunodeficiency (ih myew noh dih FIH shun see) Virus, or HIV. HIV kills helper T cells and leads to the disorder known as Acquired Immune Deficiency Syndrome, or AIDS.

HIV is transmitted when blood or body fluids from an infected person are passed to another person through direct contact, or through contact with objects that have been contaminated by infected blood or other body fluids. Methods of transmission include intimate sexual contact, contaminated intravenous needles, and blood-to-blood contact, such as through transfusions of contaminated blood.

Since 1985, careful screening measures have been instituted by blood banks in the United States to help keep HIV-infected blood from being given to people who need transfusions. A pregnant woman infected with the virus can transmit it to her fetus. The virus can also be transmitted through breast milk.

Abstinence from intimate sexual contact provides protection from HIV and other sexually transmitted diseases. Among illegal drug users, HIV transmission can be prevented by not sharing needles.

CHALLENGE ACTIVITY

Types of Immunity Have students that need an additional challenge make concept maps that identify the different types of immunity and describe how they develop. Have students begin their concept maps with the terms *Passive Immunity* and *Active Immunity*. **L3**

Figure 39.15
HIV is a retrovirus with an outer envelope covered with knoblike attachment proteins. Researchers are studying these proteins to find ways to stop the spread of the virus in humans. The photo shows a T-lymphocyte with yellow-green HIV particles on its surface.

Proteins

RNA

Lipid coat

Color-enhanced SEM Magnification: 40 000×

DAILY INTERVENTION

Check for Understanding
Visual-Spatial Ask students to create a flowchart of B and T cell immune reactions. **L1**

Reteach
Have students prepare a table of the components of the lymphatic system and their functions. **L1**

Resources
For more practice, use *Reading Essentials for Biology,* Section 39.2.

Extension
Ask students to find out the current status of an AIDS vaccine. Have them look in the latest issues of medical and scientific journals. **L3**

 Assessment

Skill Have students explain how the AIDS virus overcomes both nonspecific and specific immunity. **L2**

The HIV virus in *Figure 39.15* is basically two copies of RNA wrapped in proteins, then further wrapped in a lipid coat. The knoblike outer proteins of the virus attach to a receptor on a helper T cell. The virus can then penetrate the cell, where it may remain inactive for months. HIV contains the enzyme reverse transcriptase, which allows the virus to use its RNA to synthesize viral DNA in the host cell.

The first symptoms of AIDS may not appear for eight to ten years after initial HIV infection. During this time, the virus reproduces and infects an increasing number of T cells. Infected persons may eventually develop AIDS. During the early stages of the disease, symptoms may include swollen lymph nodes, a loss of appetite and weight, fever, rashes, night sweats, and fatigue.

It is not known what percentage of persons infected with HIV will develop AIDS, but the majority of those untreated will. In most cases, as AIDS progresses, infectious diseases or certain forms of cancer take advantage of the body's weakened immune system and homeostasis is severely disrupted.

Section Assessment

Understanding Main Ideas
1. Identify the structures of and interpret the functions of the immune system.
2. Explain the difference between innate immunity and acquired immune responses.
3. What role do phagocytes play in defending the body against disease?
4. What role does a lymph node play in defending your body against microorganisms?

Thinking Critically
5. Why is it adaptive for memory cells to remain in the immune system after an invasion by pathogens?

SKILL REVIEW
6. **Get the Big Picture** Sequence the events that occur in the formation of antibody and cellular immunity. For more help, refer to *Get the Big Picture* in the **Skill Handbook**.

 in.bdol.glencoe.com/self_check_quiz

39.2 DEFENSE AGAINST INFECTIOUS DISEASES **1041**

 Indiana Academic Standards

Pages 1040–1041: B.1.15, B.1.20

Section Assessment

1. structures: lymphatic vessels, lymph nodes, tonsils, thymus gland, spleen, bone marrow, and appendix; functions: providing protection against foreign material, including pathogens, and bathing the tissue with lymph fluid
2. Innate immunity is a non-specific immunity that you are born with; acquired immunity is against a specific pathogen, which must be developed after exposure to the pathogen.
3. Phagocytes are white blood cells that ingest and destroy pathogens by surrounding and engulfing them.
4. A lymph node is a small mass of tissue that filters lymph and traps and destroys microorganisms.
5. Memory cells remain in case the body encounters the same antigen again. The second response will be rapid, before the antigen is able to cause disease.
6. Student answers should be a summary of Figures 39.12 and 39.13.

Time Allotment
one class period

Process Skills
acquire information, classify, collect data, communicate, compare and contrast, make and use tables, think critically, write about biology

Alternative Materials
Textbooks and materials from the school or public library may be substituted for internet information if computers are not available to all students.

INTERNET
BioLab

Before You Begin
Emerging diseases are those in which the incidence in humans has increased within the past 20 years or threatens to increase in the near future. These diseases may be new or a mutation of an existing organism, or may be an already identified disease that has spread to a new geographic area or population. Re-emerging diseases are ones that have increased in incidence after a time of decline. Disease agencies are constantly monitoring our world for these types of diseases.

Information on Emerging and Re-emerging Diseases

PREPARATION

Problem
How can you obtain current research information on emerging and re-emerging diseases?

Objectives
In this BioLab, you will:
- **Choose** five emerging and five re-emerging diseases for study.
- **Collect** data on the ten diseases and record in a table.

Materials
access to the Internet

Skill Handbook
If you need help with this lab, refer to the **Skill Handbook.**

PROCEDURE

1. Copy the two data tables on the next page.
2. Go to **in.bdol.glencoe.com/internet_lab** to find links that will provide you with information for this BioLab.
3. Choose five emerging and five re-emerging diseases you wish to investigate.
4. List the diseases in your data tables and fill in the rest of the columns.
5. Be sure to complete the last two rows of your data table that ask for current research findings and your sources of information.

PROCEDURE

Teaching Strategies
- You may wish to have students complete all or part of this activity at home if they have access to computers, or in the school library or computer center.
- Point out to students that their data tables will have to be expanded in size to accommodate all the information they obtain.
- Have students share their findings with classmates at the conclusion of the activity.

Data and Observations
Student data and observations will vary, depending on the diseases selected and the information resources used.

Data Table 1

Emerging Diseases	1	2	3	4	5
Disease name					
Organism responsible					
Classification of organism					
Mode of transmission					
Symptoms					
Treatment					
Current research					
Source of information					

Data Table 2

Re-emerging Diseases	1	2	3	4	5
Disease name					
Organism responsible					
Classification of organism					
Mode of transmission					
Symptoms					
Treatment					
Current research					
Source of information					

Color-enhanced TEM
Magnification: unavailable

Ebola virus

ANALYZE AND CONCLUDE

1. **Define** What is a pathogen? Provide several examples.
2. **Contrast** Describe the difference between an emerging and a re-emerging disease. Provide several examples of each.
3. **Think Critically** Hypothesize why a disease that was once on the decline might re-emerge.
4. **Apply Concepts** Compared with travel in the 1800s, how would current worldwide travel affect the transmission of disease?
5. **Use the Internet** What are some advantages and disadvantages of getting information on disease research by way of the Internet rather than from textbooks or an encyclopedia?

Share Your Data

Interpret Data Find this BioLab using the link below, and post your data in the data table provided for this activity. Using the additional data from other students on the Internet, analyze the data and complete your data tables.

 in.bdol.glencoe.com/internet_lab

1. A pathogen is a disease-producing agent. Pathogens include some bacteria, viruses, parasites, and some fungi.
2. Emerging diseases are ones that have increased in the past 20 years. Re-emerging diseases are ones that have increased in incidence after a time of decline.
3. Answers may vary, but might include a change in resistance to an organism or a change in the organism itself.
4. Because people travel much more and much faster today, diseases can be spread more easily from country to country, and continent to continent.
5. Advantages include the fact that information is relatively easy to find and a search can be done from one convenient place such as a home computer. Disadvantages include the fact the information may be unreliable and hard to verify.

Assessment

Skill Have students combine their lists of diseases so that a total of at least 20 diseases are included. Have students use the list to compare characteristics of viral versus bacterial diseases. Use the Performance Task Assessment List for Analyzing the Data in **PASC,** p. 99. **L2**

Share Your Data

To navigate the Internet BioLab, go to in.bdol.glencoe.com/internet_lab . Ask students to research current efforts to develop a cure for cancer or other diseases.

Biology and Society

Purpose

Students will examine the pros and cons of destroying the remaining smallpox cultures.

Teaching Strategies

■ Before reading the feature, have students review Section 39.1 and the role of viruses as causative agents of disease.

■ If possible, arrange for a representative from the local health department to visit the class. Ask the representative to discuss vaccines in general. Have students prepare questions beforehand.

■ After students have read the feature, have volunteers take turns listing on the chalkboard the advantages and disadvantages of destroying smallpox cultures.

■ Make sure students understand the meaning of "bioterrorism." The Centers for Disease Control and Prevention offers free information about bioterrorism and U.S. response plans.

Forming Your Opinion

Engage students in a class discussion on the limits of science. Point out that knowledge is the goal of science. However, science cannot answer ethical questions, such as those presented in the article. Have students brainstorm other ethical issues that arise in science, such as using animals for laboratory research. Then allow students to debate the smallpox issue. Encourage them to use scientific explanations in their arguments and to respect others' opinions.

Destroy or Preserve? The Debate over Smallpox

Color-enhanced TEM Magnification: 57 000×

The virus that causes smallpox has an envelope.

In 1980, the World Health Organization (WHO) announced an amazing victory in the field of health care—the first disease, smallpox, had been eradicated from the human population. Throughout history, this virus has killed an estimated 500 million people. Smallpox cultures still exist in two laboratories—one in the United States and the other in Russia. Now scientists must decide: Should these cultures be destroyed or preserved?

Smallpox is a highly contagious disease that infects internal organs and can cause blindness, disfigurement, and in 30 percent of cases, death. The only natural reservoir for the virus that causes smallpox is the human body. Smallpox was the first disease for which an effective vaccine was developed. Although vaccination offers protection, the United States and other developed countries stopped their smallpox vaccination programs decades ago. As a result, many people are not protected against the deadly disease. Destroying the virus would seemingly ensure that no one would ever again be infected by smallpox.

The anti-smallpox argument Proponents of destroying the cultures raise additional points. They note that the DNA sequence of the virus has been mapped. This should allow scientists to "reconstruct" the virus in the event that unknown reserves exist either in the natural environment or in other labs. The smallpox virus itself is not used in the vaccine. Some people feel these dangerous cultures should not be kept because it increases the risk that they may accidentally—or worse, deliberately—be let loose on the world.

The pro-smallpox argument Those in favor of preserving the smallpox cultures counter that no one can be absolutely certain that the virus has indeed been contained in only two laboratories.

1044 IMMUNITY FROM DISEASE

Other hidden cultures may exist. If so, destroying the known cultures will not necessarily protect the world against a smallpox outbreak. In addition, some scientists argue that a DNA map of the virus is insufficient for study purposes. In their opinion, it is crucial to study the virus intact because that is the best way to learn about—and develop strategies against—devastating diseases that attack the human body.

Perspectives The World Health Organization recognizes the complexity of the debate. WHO is made up of global representatives who, among other tasks, offer recommendations about health-care issues that affect the world at large. Since 1986, WHO has consistently stated that the smallpox cultures should be destroyed. However, fear of bioterrorism has risen steadily since that time. In 2002, WHO reversed its stance. Now, the organization says that the remaining cultures should be preserved until new vaccines or other treatments against smallpox are developed. This will also give scientists more time to study the virus.

Forming Your Opinion

Think Critically Review the arguments for and against the complete destruction of the smallpox virus. What ethical issues are involved? In your view, should the smallpox virus be destroyed or preserved? Organize a classroom debate about the issue.

 To find out more about the debate over smallpox, visit in.bdol.glencoe.com/biology_society

Going Further

Have students research the history of smallpox. Where and when did the greatest outbreaks occur? Tell students to make graphs that illustrate major epidemics of the disease. Afterwards, discuss how science benefited society by helping to eradicate the virus.

STUDY GUIDE

Section 39.1

The Nature of Disease

Key Concepts

- Infectious diseases are caused by the presence of pathogens in the body.
- The cause of an infection can be established by following Koch's postulates.
- Animals, including humans, and nonliving objects can serve as reservoirs of pathogens. Pathogens can be transmitted by direct contact, by a contaminated object, through the air, or by a vector.
- Symptoms of a disease are caused by direct damage to cells or by toxins produced by the pathogen.
- Some diseases occur periodically, whereas others are endemic. Occasionally, a disease reaches epidemic proportions.
- Some infectious diseases can be treated with antibiotics, but pathogens may become resistant to these drugs.

Vocabulary

antibiotic (p. 1029)
endemic disease (p. 1029)
epidemic (p. 1029)
infectious disease (p. 1024)
Koch's postulates (p. 1025)
pathogen (p. 1023)

Section 39.2

Defense Against Infectious Diseases

Color-enhanced SEM Magnification: 4000×

Key Concepts

- Innate immunity provides general protection against various pathogens.
- Innate immunity includes the physical barrier of the skin as well as mucus, lysozymes in sweat, oil, tears, and saliva, the inflammation response, phagocytosis, and interferons.
- Acquired immunity provides a way of fighting specific pathogens by recognizing invaders as nonself. It includes antibody and cellular immunity.
- The lymphatic system consists of the lymphatic vessels and the lymphatic organs: lymph nodes, tonsils, spleen, and thymus.
- Passive immunity develops as a result of acquiring antibodies generated in another host. Active acquired immunity develops when the body is directly exposed to antigens and produces antibodies in response.

Vocabulary

acquired immunity (p. 1035)
B cell (p. 1037)
innate immunity (p. 1031)
interferons (p. 1033)
lymph (p. 1036)
lymph node (p. 1036)
lymphocyte (p. 1036)
macrophage (p. 1032)
phagocyte (p. 1032)
pus (p. 1033)
T cell (p. 1037)
tissue fluid (p. 1036)
vaccine (p. 1039)

FOLDABLES
Study Organizer To help you review disease, use the Organizational Study Fold on page 1023.

in.bdol.glencoe.com/vocabulary_puzzlemaker

Key Concepts

Summary statements can be used by students to review the major concepts of the chapter.

Biology Online

Visit in.bdol.glencoe.com
/self_check_quiz
/vocabulary_puzzlemaker
/chapter_test
/standardized_test

VOCABULARY PUZZLEMAKER

For additional help with vocabulary, have students access the Vocabulary PuzzleMaker online at **in.bdol.glencoe.com/ vocabulary_puzzlemaker**

FOLDABLES™

Have students use their Foldables to review the content of Section 39.1.

Use the ExamView®Pro Test Bank CD-ROM to:
- Create **multiple versions** of tests
- Create **modified** tests with one mouse click for **inclusion** students
- **Edit** existing questions and **add** your own questions
- Build tests aligned with state standards using built-in **State Curriculum Tags**
- Change **English** tests to **Spanish** with one mouse click and vice versa

 Indiana Academic Standards

Pages 1044–1045: B.1.15, B.1.20, B.1.41, B.1.43

The Princeton Review **Questions and answers have been aligned and verified by The Princeton Review.**

Vocabulary Review

1. false—pathogen
2. false—endemic
3. false—acquired immunity
4. false—T cell

Understanding Key Concepts

5. A 　　　 7. A
6. D 　　　 8. B
9. 1. Koch's postulates; 2. infectious disease; 3. endemic; 4. epidemic

Constructed Response

10. The normal flora help keep harmful bacteria and other microorganisms from growing on or within the body. The normal flora of the intestinal tract also secrete some B vitamins. Bacteria that invade body tissues can set up a disease process by killing cells and secreting toxins, upsetting homeostasis.

11. Diseases, whether caused by pathogens, genetics, malnutrition, or chemicals, upset the natural balance of body function. Diseases upset chemical processes, cellular function, and may cause cell death. One example is the pathogen that causes tetanus, which secretes a toxin that affects nerve cell function and can result in uncontrollable muscle contractions, paralysis, and death.

12. The mother's antibodies to chicken pox crossed the placenta and are in the baby's blood, protecting the baby against chicken pox.

Thinking Critically

13. Someone who survived a disease would have antibodies to that disease in his or her serum.

Vocabulary Review

Review the Chapter 39 vocabulary words listed in the Study Guide on page 1045. Determine if each statement is true or false. If false, replace the underlined word with the correct vocabulary word.

1. An <u>antibiotic</u> is a disease-causing agent such as a bacterium or a virus.
2. A disease that is constantly present in a population is called an <u>epidemic</u>.
3. Defending against a specific pathogen by gradually building up a resistance to it is called <u>innate immunity</u>.
4. A <u>B cell</u> is a lymphocyte that is produced in bone marrow and processed in the thymus gland.

Understanding Key Concepts

5. Any disease caused by the presence of pathogens in the body is called a(n) _____.
   A. infectious disease
   B. endemic disease
   C. epidemic disease
   D. harmless disease

6. Which of the following is NOT an example of transmission of a disease by a vector?

   A.
   C.
   B.
   D.

7. _____ is a body response to an injury, characterized by redness, swelling, pain, and heat.
   A. Inflammation 　　 C. Sweating
   B. Fever 　　 D. Headache

---

8. A person is given an injection that contains antibodies against the hepatitis A virus. This is an example of which type of immunity?
   A. natural passive immunity
   B. artificial passive immunity
   C. natural active immunity
   D. artificial active immunity

9. Complete the concept map by using the following vocabulary terms: infectious disease, endemic, Koch's postulates, epidemic.

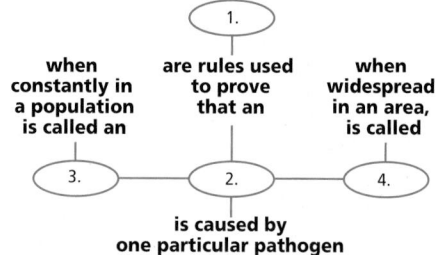

```
                    ┌─────┐
                    │  1. │
                    └─────┘
      when          are rules used      when
  constantly in       to prove       widespread
  a population         that an       in an area,
  is called an                       is called

  ┌─────┐         ┌─────┐          ┌─────┐
  │  3. │─────────│  2. │──────────│  4. │
  └─────┘         └─────┘          └─────┘

                 is caused by
            one particular pathogen
```

Constructed Response

10. **Open Ended** Summarize the role of microorganisms such as bacteria in maintaining and disrupting homeostasis in humans.

11. **Open Ended** Explain how disease is a failure of homeostasis. Include a specific example in your response.

12. **Open Ended** A new mother had chicken pox as a child. Why doesn't her newborn infant get the disease, even after being exposed to the virus that causes it?

Thinking Critically

13. **Infer** Why would it be helpful to an infected person's survival to receive an injection of blood serum from someone who has survived the same disease?

14. **REAL WORLD BIOCHALLENGE** Visit **in.bdol.glencoe.com** to research past episodes in which biological agents for warfare or terrorism have been used. What type of bioterrorism threats is the world currently preparing for? Give a multimedia presentation about your results to your class.

 in.bdol.glencoe.com/chapter_test

---

14. One historical example is the use of dried smallpox in warfare and terrorism. The U.S. is preparing for threats against diseases such as anthrax, Ebola fever, and smallpox.

15. The experiment would be a repeat of some of Koch's postulates, which would include isolating the organism from the parakeets and exposing the organisms to human cell cultures to show the susceptibility of the organisms to humans.

16. If a person were unable to produce B or T cells, he or she would not have specific immunity. The person would not likely be able to survive an infection, especially by a virus.

15. Design an Experiment Several weeks after buying a new pet parakeet, Johann became ill with flu-like symptoms. When he visited the pet store again, many of the parakeets were ill. Design an experiment that would determine if Johann had the same disease as the birds.

16. Infer Some hereditary disorders result in a person being unable to produce B cells or T cells. What effects would this have on a person's immunity? How would this affect the body overall?

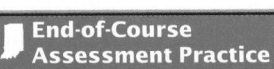
End-of-Course Assessment Practice

The assessed Indiana standard appears next to the question.

All questions aligned and verified by The Princeton Review

Part 1 Multiple Choice

Use the diagram to answer questions 17–19.

Macrophage

T cell

B cell

Plasma cell

17. When a pathogen enters the body, which
B.1.20 cells usually are the first to attack it?
A. macrophages
B. T cells
C. B cells
D. plasma cells

18. Which of the above cells are responsible for
B.1.20 antibody production?
A. macrophages
B. T cells
C. B cells
D. plasma cells

19. Which of the following cells are destroyed
B.1.20 in an AIDS infection?
A. macrophages
B. helper T cells
C. B cells
D. memory B cells

Study the graph and answer questions 20–22.

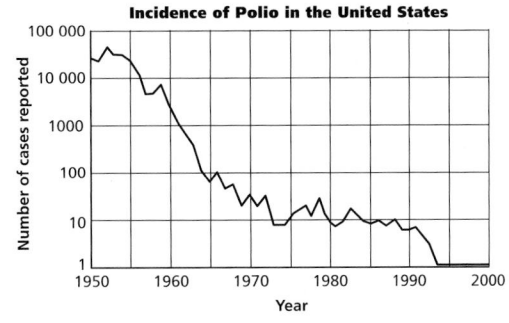
Incidence of Polio in the United States

20. During which ten-year period were the highest numbers of polio cases reported?
A. 1950s   C. 1970s
B. 1960s   D. 1980s

21. How many more cases of polio were reported in the year 1980 than in the year 2000?
A. 100   C. 9
B. 50   D. 0

Part 2 Constructed Response/Grid In

Record your answers on your answer document.

22. Open Ended Children in the United States began to get vaccinated against polio in 1954. A second
B.1.20 type of polio vaccine began to be used in 1963. Explain how vaccines provide immunity against disease. What could account for the cases of polio still occurring after the use of the vaccines?

23. Open Ended If the bacterium that causes tetanus is easily killed by penicillin, why doesn't
B.1.20 penicillin cure the disease tetanus?

 in.bdol.glencoe.com/standardized_test

CHAPTER 39 ASSESSMENT **1047**

End-of-Course Assessment Practice

17. A   **20.** A
18. D   **21.** C
19. B

22. Vaccines stimulate acquired immunity that will protect against the real disease. Very rarely, some of the viruses in the vaccine have mutated and are able to cause the disease polio. Polio also can occur in unvaccinated people.

23. The disease tetanus is caused by the toxin secreted by the bacteria. Antibiotics will kill the bacteria but will not inactivate any toxin that was secreted by the bacteria.

 FAST FILE

Answer Sheet A practice answer sheet can be found on p. 243 of *Unit 10 FAST FILE Resources.*

Prepare

Short on Time?

This BioDigest can be used as an introduction to or as an overview of the structures and functions of the human body systems. If time is limited, you may wish to use this unit summary to teach about human biology in place of the chapters in the human body unit.

Key Concepts

Students learn about the level of organization in body systems. They are then introduced to the structures and functions of the major body systems. Various vital statistics provide students with interesting facts about the body systems.

---

1 Focus

Bellringer

Using a large picture of a human body or a plastic model of a torso, ask students to name as many body systems as they can. Have students list organs under each body system. **L2** **ELL**

The Human Body

How do the human body systems function together? When an Olympic ice-skater performs on the ice, the cells, tissues, organs, and organ systems of the skater's body function together to help the athlete perform at his or her best and perhaps win a gold medal. All body systems must work together to make an award-winning performance possible.

Levels of Organization

All organisms are made of cells. In complex organisms, such as humans, most cells are organized into functional units called tissues. The four basic tissues of the human body are epithelium, muscle, connective, and nervous tissues. Epithelium covers the body and lines organs, vessels, and body cavities. Muscle tissue is contractile and is found attached to bones and in the walls of organs, such as the heart. Connective tissue is widely distributed throughout the body. It produces blood and provides support, binding, and storage. Nervous tissue transmits impulses that coordinate, regulate, and integrate body systems.

Tissues to Systems

Groups of tissues that perform specialized functions are called organs. Your stomach and eyes are examples of organs. Most organs contain all four basic tissue types. Each of the body's organs is part of an organ system. An organ system contains a group of organs that work together to carry out a major life function. The major organ systems of the human body are described in this BioDigest.

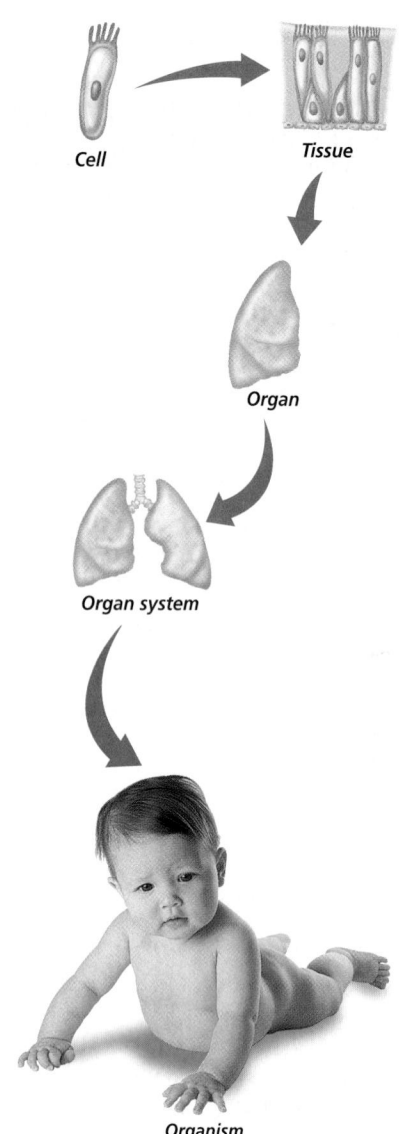

Levels of organization: cell, tissue, organ, organ system, organism

---

RESOURCE MANAGER

Unit 10 *FAST FILE* Resources
Reinforcement and Study Guide in English, pp. 245–246
Reinforcement and Study Guide in Spanish, pp. 247–248
Student Recording Sheet, p. 249

 Indiana Academic Standards

Pages 1048–1049: B.1.1, B.1.14, B.1.15, B.1.17

Skin

The skin and its associated structures, including hair, nails, sweat glands, and oil glands, are important in maintaining homeostasis in the body. The skin protects tissues and organs, helps regulate body temperature, produces vitamin D, and contains sensory receptors.

Skeletal System

The skeletal system consists of the axial skeleton and appendicular skeleton. The axial skeleton supports the head and includes the skull and the bones of the back and chest. The appendicular skeleton contains the bones associated with the limbs. The entire skeleton, which is made up of 206 bones, has many functions. It provides support for the softer, underlying tissues; provides a place for muscle attachment; protects vital organs; manufactures blood cells; and serves as a storehouse for calcium and phosphorus.

Joints: Where Bones Meet

The place where two bones meet is called a joint. Joints can be immovable, such as the joints in the skull, or movable, such as the shoulder joints. The shoulder joint is called a ball-and-socket joint; the elbow joint is a hinge joint. The wrists have gliding joints, and the neck has pivot joints.

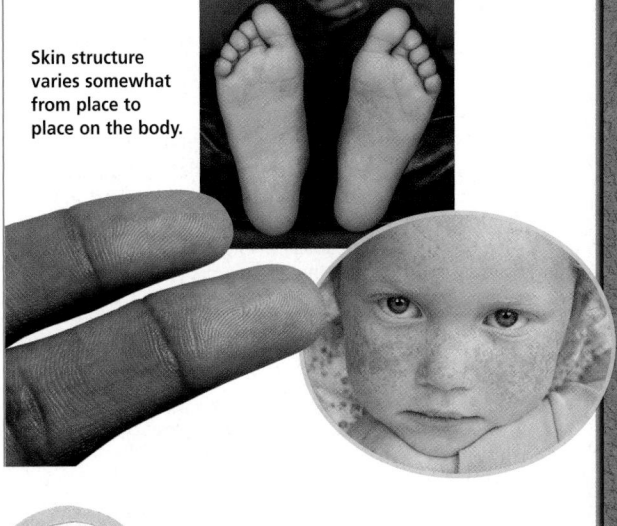

Skin structure varies somewhat from place to place on the body.

◀ The skeletal system consists of the axial (blue) and appendicular (yellow) skeletons.

Skull

Scapula
Sternum
Humerus
Radius
Carpals
Ribs
Pelvis
Ulna
Metacarpals
Femur
Patella
Phalanges
Tibia
Fibula
Phalanges
Metatarsals
Tarsals

1049

2 Teach

Visual Learning

Draw students' attention to the levels of organization diagram showing how cells are organized into tissues, organs, and organ systems. All systems together make up an organism.

Concept Development

Have students examine areas of their skin. The palms of the hands and soles of the feet contain no hairs. The fingertips contain large numbers of sensory nerve endings and ridges to help grip objects. Have students also note the different patterns and types of skin coloration.

Display

Have students prepare a bulletin board or posters using pictures cut out of magazines to illustrate the body systems. **L1**

USING MODELS

The Human Body: *Kinesthetic* A model human skeleton can be used to talk about the skeletal system and how skeletal muscles function. A model of a human torso can be used to demonstrate other body systems. Have students, in groups of two, quiz each other to identify the different bones of the skeletal system. Remove individual organs from the torso model and have students identify the organ, its function, and to which organ system it belongs. **L2 COOP LEARN**

Display

Prepare a bulletin board of magazine and newspaper articles of various disorders, sports injuries, and other problems relating to each body system.

Enrichment

Have a doctor from a sports medicine clinic speak to the class concerning fitness and the effects of sports injuries on the muscular system and other body systems.

Assessment

Skill Have students make a table comparing the three types of muscles. They should make columns for visual characteristics and where muscles are found. **L2**

Portfolio

Muscles Have students research topics related to muscles such as rigor mortis, hypotonia, hypertonia, muscular atrophy, and hypertrophy. Students should explain how each one of these conditions affects muscle tissue and overall function. Students can present the results of their research to the class and include a written report in their journals. **L2**

Muscular System

The muscular system includes three types of muscles: smooth, cardiac, and skeletal.

Smooth Muscle

Smooth muscles are found in the walls of hollow internal organs, such as inside the stomach or blood vessels. These muscles are not under conscious control and are called involuntary muscles. Smooth muscle contracts to exert pressure on the space inside the tube or organ it surrounds in order to move material through it.

During physical activity, almost every muscle can be involved, either voluntarily or by reflex actions.

Skeletal muscles allow body movement by being arranged in opposing pairs.

Pectoralis major

Biceps

Rectus abdominus

Sartorius

Rectus femoris

Gastrocnemius

Skeletal Muscle

Skeletal muscles are usually attached to bones and allow body movement. They can be controlled by conscious effort so they are called voluntary muscles. Skeletal muscle tissue is made up of long, threadlike cells, called fibers, which have alternating dark and light striations. Each fiber has many nuclei.

Heart Muscle

Cardiac muscle tissue is found only in the heart. These cells contain a single nucleus and have striations made up of organized protein filaments that are involved in contraction of the muscle. Like smooth muscle, cardiac muscle is involuntary muscle. Cardiac muscle has the unique ability to contract without first being stimulated by nervous tissue.

VITAL STATISTICS

Muscles

Most powerful skeletal muscle: The muscle you sit on is the gluteus maximus; it moves the thighbone away from the body and straightens the hip joint.
Longest muscle: The sartorius muscle runs from the waist to the knee and flexes the hip and knee.
A broad smile: A smile uses 17 facial muscles; a frown uses more than 40.

INCLUSION STRATEGIES

Hearing Impaired/Learning Disabled
Have students make flash cards with a body system named on one side of the card and its functions on the other side. Students can use the cards as a study aid. **L1 ELL**

Digestive System

The digestive system receives food and breaks it down so it can be absorbed by the body's cells. The digestive system also eliminates food materials that are not digested or absorbed. Foods are broken down into simpler molecules that can move through cell membranes and be transported to all parts of the body by the bloodstream or the lymphatic vessels. The digestive system includes the mouth, tongue, teeth, salivary glands, pharynx, esophagus, stomach, liver, gallbladder, pancreas, and small and large intestines.

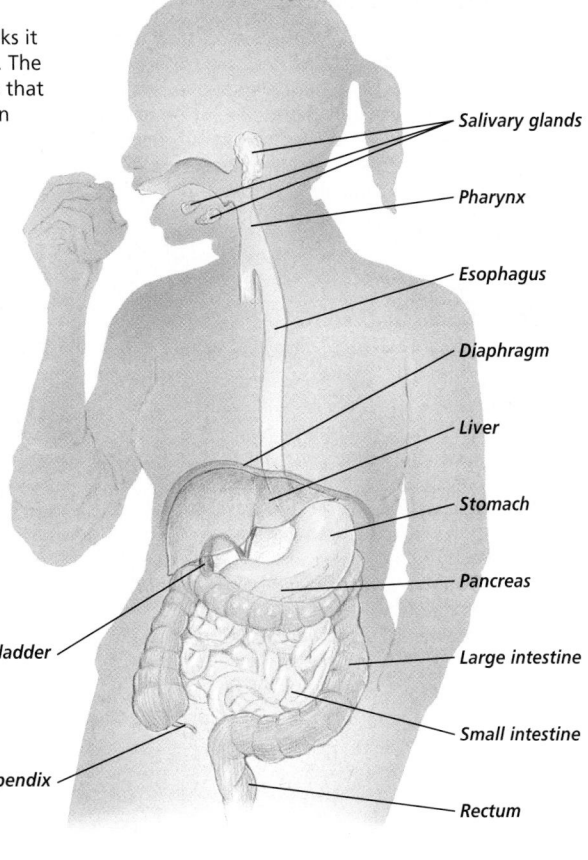

The digestive system breaks down food particles so that they can enter the body's cells.

Salivary glands

Pharynx

Esophagus

Diaphragm

Liver

Stomach

Pancreas

Gallbladder

Large intestine

Small intestine

Appendix

Rectum

Quick Demo

X Rays X rays of the skeletal system and barium X rays of the digestive system can be viewed by hanging them on classroom windows or projecting them with an overhead projector. Use the X rays to discuss the parts and functions of each of these systems.

Chalkboard Activity

Make a list of the items students have eaten in the last two days that would increase blood glucose levels. Discuss what happens in terms of insulin after the body takes in sugar.

Portfolio

Daily Calorie Intake Have students keep track of what they eat and all of their activities (including resting, sleeping, watching TV, etc.) for 48 hours. Students can use a Calorie guide to estimate their daily Calorie intake and an activity guide to calculate their Calorie usage. **L1**

FOCUS ON HEALTH

Blood Glucose Levels

Blood glucose levels rise as carbohydrates are digested and absorbed into the blood.

Levels of glucose in the blood are maintained all day long by hormones secreted by the pancreas. After a meal, the sugars from the food are transported into the blood, raising the blood glucose level. The sugars are either used immediately for activity or stored in the liver for later use. The pancreas secretes insulin, which helps the body's cells take up the sugar or convert it to glycogen in the liver for storage.

Between meals, when blood glucose levels go down, the pancreas secretes glucagon. Glucagon causes the glycogen in the liver to be broken down into glucose, which is then released into the bloodstream and made available to the body's cells. The control of blood sugar levels in the body is an example of a feedback mechanism that is vital for maintaining homeostasis.

1051

CHALLENGE ACTIVITY

Health Myths Have students look up health myths from the 1700–1800s. Ask them to prepare a presentation for the class. Have them lead the class in a discussion of present-day treatments and how our understanding of the human body has changed over time. Have students give examples of how technology has influenced this process. **L3**

Chalkboard Example

Draw a neuron on the chalkboard and label the parts. Using arrows, indicate the direction an impulse travels along a neuron. As you discuss transmission across the synapse, bring in the action of various drugs on the synapse. You can find more information in the chapter on the nervous system.

Inquiry

Activity Have students research and explain how a reflex occurs in the body. To demonstrate a protective reflex, have a student hold up a piece of transparent, glass-like plastic in front of his or her face. Have another student throw a soft, foam ball at the piece of plastic. The student behind the plastic will blink automatically, even if trying not to blink. **L2**

Biology Journal

Write a Skit Have students write a skit in their journal with a major player being the brain and how it interacts with and controls the body systems. **L2**

Endocrine System

The endocrine system controls all of the metabolic activities of body structures. This system includes all of the glands in the body that secrete chemical messengers called hormones. Hormones travel in the bloodstream to target cells, where they alter the metabolism of the target cell. Some of the major endocrine glands include the pituitary, thyroid, parathyroids, adrenals, pancreas, ovaries, and testes.

Nervous System

The organs of the nervous system include the brain, spinal cord, nerves, and sensory receptors. These organs contain nerve cells, called neurons, that conduct impulses. Nerve impulses allow the neurons to communicate with each other and with the cells of muscles and glands. Each impulse consists of an electrical charge that travels the length of a neuron's cell membrane.

Between two neurons there is a small gap called a synapse. When one neuron is stimulated, it releases chemicals called neurotransmitters into the synapse, which stimulates a change in electrical charge in the next neuron. Nerve impulses travel through the body this way, from neuron to neuron.

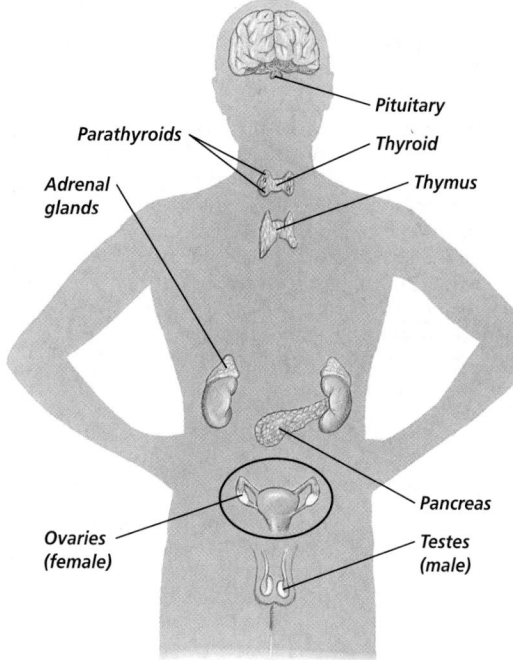

The major glands of the endocrine system secrete hormones that regulate growth, development, and metabolism.

Sensory Receptors

Some nerve cells act as sensory receptors that detect both external and internal stimuli. In response to a stimulus, these neurons carry impulses to the spinal cord and brain. The brain and spinal cord then send impulses to muscles or glands, stimulating them to contract or secrete hormones. This interconnection provides coordination between the nervous system and the endocrine system.

The central nervous system (brain and spinal cord) interprets and acts on information it receives from sensory neurons found throughout the body.

INCLUSION STRATEGIES

Visually Impaired Pair a visually impaired student with a peer to go over the organs of the respiratory and nervous systems using a model of a human torso. Ask the students to consider the functions of each organ. **L1** **ELL**

Indiana Academic Standards

Pages 1052–1053: B.1.14, B.1.19

The Human Body

Respiratory System

The organs of the respiratory system exchange gases between blood and the air. During inhalation, oxygen in the air passes into the blood from small air sacs called alveoli in the lungs. Body cells use oxygen to break down glucose to make ATP needed for metabolism.

Carbon dioxide (CO_2) is produced by the breakdown of glucose and is transported to the lungs by the blood. In the lungs, carbon dioxide diffuses out of the blood and into the alveoli. It is forced out of the lungs during exhalation. The major organs of the respiratory system are the nasal cavity, the pharynx, larynx, trachea, bronchi, and lungs.

- *Nasal cavity*
- *Epiglottis*
- *Larynx*
- *Trachea*
- *Right lung*
- *Bronchus*
- *Left lung*
- *Diaphragm*

▲ The respiratory system filters air as it passes into the nose, down the air passages, and into the lungs.

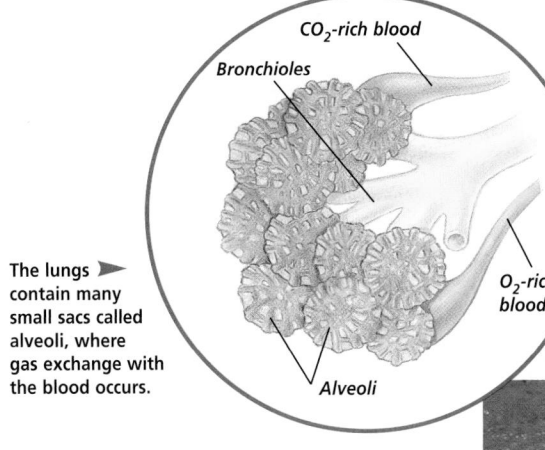

- *CO₂-rich blood*
- *Bronchioles*
- *O₂-rich blood*
- *Alveoli*

The lungs ▶ contain many small sacs called alveoli, where gas exchange with the blood occurs.

VITAL STATISTICS

Respiration

Breathing: At rest, humans inhale and exhale about 12 to 20 times per minute, moving about 15 L of air per minute, and inhaling 21.6 cubic meters of air each day.

Lungs: Lungs weigh about 2.2 kg each. The right lung has three lobes and the left lung has two lobes. There are 300 million alveoli in the lungs. Flattened out, they would cover 360 square meters.

Sneezes: A sneeze ejects particles at 165.76 km/hr.

▲ A swimmer comes up for air between strokes.

THE HUMAN BODY **1053**

Visual Learning

Review the process of diffusion using the detailed figure of alveoli. Discuss the diffusion of oxygen out of the alveoli into the blood, and carbon dioxide out of the blood into the alveoli.

Quick Demo

Breathing Rates Have students work in pairs. Have one student count the breathing rate of the other student, and vice versa. Compare individual (anonymous) breathing rates to the average breathing rate of the class. Discuss factors that could affect breathing rates, such as size, activity level when the breath rate is measured, and congestion from a cold or allergies. **L2** **ELL**

Enrichment

Have students choose a disease (infectious or noninfectious) of the respiratory system to research. **L3**

PROJECT

Tobacco and Cancer Many representatives of the tobacco industry claim there is no proof that use of tobacco causes cancer. After researching the issue, have students write an essay in their journals on how they would respond to the assertion that tobacco usage does not cause cancer. Students can use the results of their research to hold a class debate on this topic. **L2**

Quick Demo

Blood Pressure Ask the school nurse to demonstrate measuring blood pressure on a few students in the class.

Enrichment

Have students research the factors involved in the development of arteriosclerosis and its treatment. **L3**

Reinforcement

Interpersonal Play a body systems password game. Divide students into teams of two. One person on each team gives one-word clues to his or her partner, whose job is to guess the password with as few clues as possible. Each team plays against one other team. Each team works on a separate term and alternates giving clues to their partners. The first team to guess their word gets a point, then both teams go on to another password. Tally scores at the end of the game. **L2**
COOP LEARN

Enrichment

Have students research the various treatments for kidney disease, including portable kidney dialysis and kidney transplants. **L3**

Circulatory System

The circulatory system includes the heart, blood vessels (arteries, veins, and capillaries), and blood. The muscular heart pumps blood through the blood vessels. The blood carries oxygen from the lungs and nutrients from the digestive tract to all body cells. Blood also carries hormones to their target cells, carbon dioxide back to the lungs, and other waste products to the excretory system.

Urinary System

Metabolic waste products are created during the breakdown of amino acids. The urinary system removes these metabolic wastes from the blood, maintains the balance of water and salts in the blood, stores wastes in the form of urine, and transports urine out of the body.

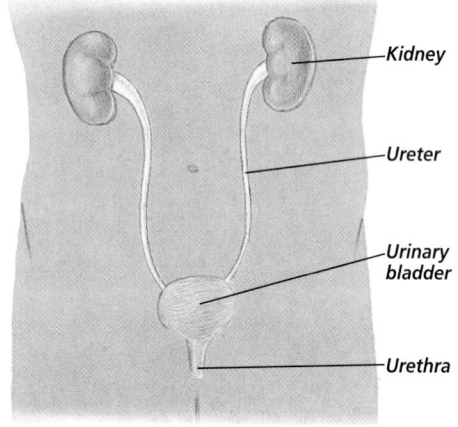

Kidney

Ureter

Urinary bladder

Urethra

The urinary system filters the blood, collects urine, and excretes urine from the body.

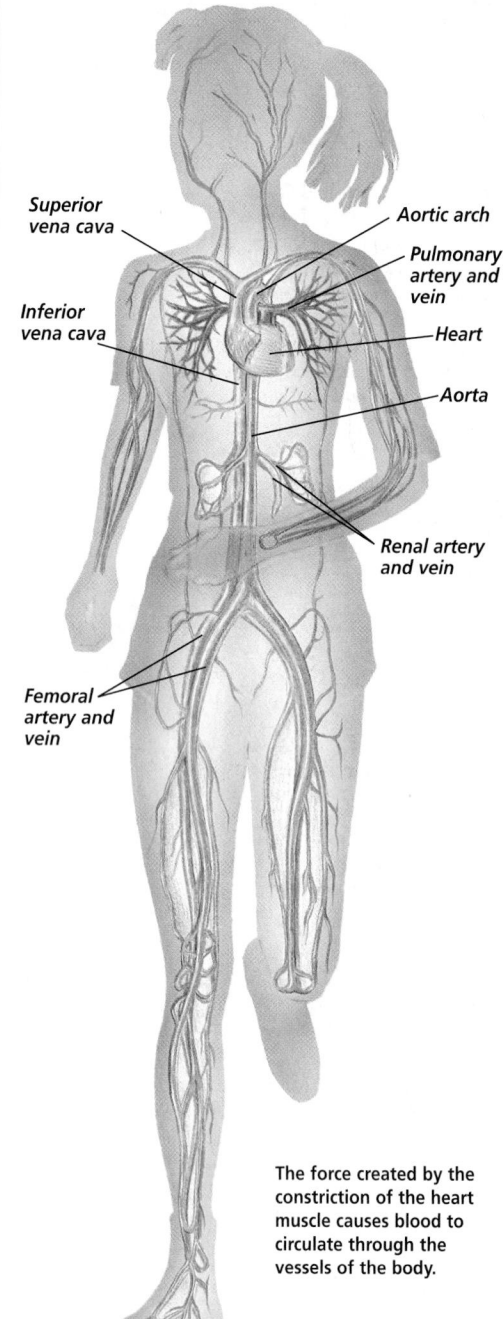

Superior vena cava

Aortic arch

Pulmonary artery and vein

Inferior vena cava

Heart

Aorta

Renal artery and vein

Femoral artery and vein

The force created by the constriction of the heart muscle causes blood to circulate through the vessels of the body.

PROJECT

Photo Essay Have students become familiar with the different body systems by asking groups of students to use pictures from medical or health journals to prepare a photo essay representing one body system. They should present their essays to the class with an oral explanation. **L2**
ELL **COOP LEARN**

Reproductive System

The reproductive system is involved in the production of gametes. The male reproductive system produces and maintains sperm cells and transfers them into the female reproductive tract. The female reproductive system produces and maintains egg cells, receives sperm cells, and supports the development of the fetus.

The male reproductive system

Prostate gland — Bladder
Bulbourethral gland — vas deferens
Epididymis — Seminal vesicle
Testis — Urethra
Scrotum — Penis

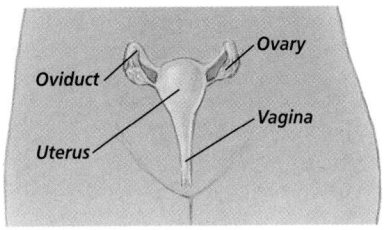

Ovary
Oviduct
Uterus — Vagina

The female reproductive system

Lymphatic System

Fluids leak out of capillaries and bathe body tissues. The lymphatic system transports this tissue fluid back into the bloodstream. The lymphatic system also plays an important role in immunity. As tissue fluids pass through lymphatic vessels and lymph nodes, disease-causing pathogens and other foreign substances are filtered out and destroyed.

Innate immunity involves the action of several types of white blood cells that protect the body against any type of pathogen. Macrophages and neutrophils engulf foreign substances that enter the body. If the infection persists, the lymphatic system becomes involved. The body develops an acquired immune response that defends against the specific pathogen.

Acquired immunity involves helper T cells that pass on chemical information about the pathogen to B cells. B cells produce antibodies that disarm or destroy the invaders. Some B cells remain in the body as memory B cells that recognize the antigens if they ever invade the body again. This process provides the body with acquired natural immunity against disease.

The lymphatic system includes lymph nodes, tonsils, the thymus gland, and spleen. T cells mature in the thymus. The spleen stores both T cells and B cells.

Tonsils

Thymus gland

Spleen

Appendix

Bone marrow

Lymph nodes

Lymph vessels

The lymphatic system provides protection against infections, such as colds and flu.

3 Assess

DAILY INTERVENTION

Check for Understanding
Provide groups of students with diagrams of the different human body systems. Have them use colored pencils to shade various organs of particular systems. For example, the components of the circulatory system could be colored red (oxygenated blood) and blue (nonoxygenated blood). **L1** **ELL**

Reteach
Students can be broken into groups that are assigned to summarize the components of each of the body's systems and present the summaries to the class. **L1**

Extension

Ask the school nurse to speak to the class on prevention of disease transmission and vaccination.

✓ Assessment

Knowledge Assign each student one component of a body system. Have students write a description of their assigned component and how it interacts with its body system and the entire organism. **L2**

PROJECT

Hormones and the Reproductive System Have students read information on how the endocrine system and reproductive system interact. Students can create a visual representation in the form of a chart or table showing how the endocrine system influences the reproductive system. **L2**

◎ CHALLENGE ACTIVITY

Health-Care Costs Have students who need an additional challenge research premature infant care costs. They can write a position paper on whether Americans should spend more or less on dramatic lifesaving measures and why. **L3**

Indiana Academic Standards
Pages 1054–1055: B.1.11, B.1.14, B.1.19, B.1.20

This page contains practice questions in the various formats that can be found on the most frequently given standardized tests.

Part 1 ▶ Multiple Choice

1. C	3. C	5. D
2. B	4. A	6. C

Answer Sheet A practice answer sheet can be found on p. 249 of *Unit 10 FAST FILE Resources.*

Unit 10 Review
Standardized Test Practice

End-of-Course Assessment Practice

The assessed Indiana standard appears next to the question.

The Princeton Review
TEST-TAKING TIP
Read the Instructions
No matter how many times you've taken a particular test or practiced for an exam, it's always a good idea to read through the directions provided at the beginning of each section. It only takes a moment.

Part 1 ▶ Multiple Choice

1. Which of the following is the correct sequence of increasing complexity when describing the levels of organization in the human body?
   A. organs, cells, tissues, organism, organ systems
   B. cells, organ systems, tissues, organism, organs
   C. cells, tissues, organs, organ systems, organism
   D. tissues, cells, organs, organ systems, organism

Use the figure below to answer question 2.

Osteocyte   Bone tissue   Osteon system   Long bone

2. Place the structures of the human body in order from least to most complex. **B.1.15**
   A. osteocyte, bone tissue, osteon system, long bone
   B. osteocyte, osteon system, bone tissue, long bone
   C. long bone, osteon system, bone tissue, osteocyte
   D. long bone, bone tissue, osteon system, osteocyte

3. Which of the following statements is NOT true regarding the skeletal system? **B.1.15**
   A. The skeletal system and the circulatory system interrelate because red blood cells, white blood cells, and platelets are produced in red bone marrow.
   B. The skeletal system and the muscular system interrelate because skeletal muscles are attached to bones in order to produce movement of the body.
   C. The skeletal system and the digestive system interrelate because bones release digestive juices that help break down food.
   D. The skeletal system functions to support the entire body and protect vital organs, such as the brain, heart, and lungs.

4. The functions of the digestive system include _____. **B.1.15**
   A. digesting food, absorbing nutrients, and eliminating undigested food and other wastes
   B. secreting hormones to control the metabolic activities of the body
   C. producing antibodies in response to antigens present in the body
   D. circulating blood containing oxygen throughout the body

5. Which of the following processes does NOT involve an internal feedback mechanism? **B.1.17**
   A. The release of insulin from the pancreas to maintain blood glucose levels.
   B. The release of antidiuretic hormone in response to a reduced concentration of water level in the blood.
   C. The release of calcitonin and parathyroid hormone to maintain proper levels of calcium in the blood.
   D. The release of carbon dioxide from the lungs during breathing.

6. In order for an impulse to be transmitted from one neuron to another, nerve cells release _____ at a synapse.
   A. hemoglobin   C. neurotransmitters
   B. luteinizing hormone D. antibodies

Indiana Academic Standards
Pages 1056–1057: B.1.15, B.1.16, B.1.17, B.1.19, B.1.20

Use the information below and your knowledge of science to answer questions 7–9.

Blood Pressure Fluctuation

7. **In which blood vessel is blood pressure the
B.1.15 greatest?**
   A. the aorta   C. the capillaries
   B. the arteries   D. the veins

8. **Which of the variables shown on the graph is
the dependent variable?**
   A. type of blood vessel   C. diastolic pressure
   B. systolic pressure   D. blood pressure

9. **The rate of blood flow would decrease if the
_____ of the blood increased.**
   A. momentum   C. viscosity
   B. conduction   D. polarization

10. **Which structure of the male reproductive
B.1.15 system produces sperm?**
   A. epididymis   C. testis
   B. scrotum   D. vas deferens

11. **In which structure of the female reproductive
B.1.15 system does a human embryo normally
develop?**
   A. ovary   C. placenta
   B. oviduct   D. uterus

12. **Failure of the urinary system to maintain
B.1.17 homeostasis in the body could result in all of
the following except _____.**
   A. high levels of nitrogenous waste products
      in the blood
   B. not enough nutrients reaching body cells
   C. the pH of the blood being abnormal
   D. irregularities in blood osmotic pressure

13. **The lymphatic system performs which of the
B.1.15 following functions?**
   A. transports tissue fluid back into the
      bloodstream
   B. carries oxygen and carbon dioxide to and
      from body cells
   C. controls the metabolic activities of body
      structures
   D. exchanges gases between blood and the air

14. **Which of the following statements regarding
B.1.20 B cells is NOT true?**
   A. B cells are part of innate immunity.
   B. B cells can form plasma cells that produce
      antibodies to attack foreign cells that
      invade the body.
   C. B cells can form memory cells that recognize
      antigens if they invade the body a second time.
   D. B cells are produced in the spleen.

Part 2 Constructed Response/Grid In

Record your answers on your answer document.

15. **Open Ended** Describe the differences between skeletal, smooth, and cardiac muscle. Include the func-
B.1.15 tions of each in your response.

16. **Open Ended** Explain how gas exchange occurs in the lungs. How does the respiratory system interre-
B.1.15 late with the circulatory system?

17. **Open Ended** Explain the functions of the male and female reproductive systems. How does fertiliza-
B.1.15 tion occur?

18. **Open Ended** Describe the structures and processes involved in innate immunity. How do these differ
B.1.20 from structures and processes involved in acquired immunity?

 in.bdol.glencoe.com/standardized_test

---

7. A   10. C   13. A
8. D   11. D   14. A
9. C   12. B

Part 2 Constructed Response/Grid In

15. Skeletal muscle is under voluntary control, found attached to bones, and involved in moving the body. Smooth muscle is under involuntary control, found in the walls of internal organs and blood vessels, and functions to move materials such as food and gametes through the body. Cardiac muscle is under involuntary control, located in the heart, and is able to generate impulses in order to keep the heart beating rhythmically.

16. Gas exchange occurs when oxygen and carbon dioxide diffuse across alveoli and capillary walls. The circulatory system carries newly oxygenated blood from the lungs to body cells and brings deoxygenated blood back to the lungs for gas exchange to occur.

17. The function of the male reproductive system is to produce and deliver sperm to the female reproductive system which produces eggs, receives sperm, and provides an environment in which a fertilized egg can develop. Fertilization occurs when one sperm penetrates an egg.

18. Structures involved in innate immunity include the skin and its secretions—mucus, sweat, tears, and saliva— which offer protection against all foreign invaders regardless of species. Inflammation and phagocytosis of pathogens by macrophages and neutrophils also provide innate immunity against infection. Acquired immunity occurs when the body defends itself against a specific pathogen using antibodies.

RUBRIC

For more help evaluating open-ended assessment questions, see the rubric on p. 9T.

1057

Student Resources

Contents

■ **NATIONAL GEOGRAPHIC** **FOCUS ON** These National Geographic articles provide in-depth coverage of interesting topics in biology. They are referenced within the chapters at point-of-use to support or extend the chapter content. For news about recent scientific discoveries and research, go to in.bdol.glencoe.com/news .

Focus On

Scientific Theories

Purpose

Students will learn from examples how theories are formed from repeated observations, comparative studies, and discussions among scientists over many decades.

Inquiry

Discussion Have students discuss the term *skepticism*, which means "an attitude of doubt; a method of suspended judgment." Discuss why this might be a valuable characteristic for a scientist to have.

Define the term *empirical* for students. It means "capable of being verified through experiment." Discuss why this term is used in connection with science. Knowledge gained through controlled experiments is empirical—based on verifiable investigation.

Teaching Strategies

■ Ask students to discuss what they know about dinosaurs. Ask them how they have learned about these amazing, extinct animals.

■ Have students put forward their own ideas on how dinosaurs lived from day to day. Ask them if their ideas are hypotheses, speculations, beliefs, or theories. Have them begin to distinguish among these different ideas by stating in a complete sentence what they know about another topic, such as computers.

■ If possible, visit a dinosaur display in a local museum, and have students make notes in their journals about the different theories of dinosaur behavior explained in the exhibits. **L2**

FOCUS ON Scientific Theories

IGUANODON

OBSERVE

People have been unearthing fossils for hundreds of years. The first person to reconstruct a dinosaur named it *Iguanodon*, (ih GWAH nuh dahn) meaning "iguana tooth," because its bones and teeth resembled those of an iguana. By 1842 these extinct animals were named *dinosaurs*, meaning "terrible lizards."

What is a scientific theory? In casual usage, "theory" means an unproven assumption about a set of facts. A scientific theory is an explanation of a natural phenomenon supported by a large body of scientific evidence obtained from various investigations and observations. The scientific process begins with observations of the natural world. These observations lead to hypotheses, data collection, and experimentation. If weaknesses are observed, hypotheses are rejected or modified and then tested again and again. When little evidence remains to cause a hypothesis to be rejected, it may become a theory. Follow the scientific process described here that led to new theories about dinoosaurs.

FIELD MUSEUM OF NATURAL HISTORY, CHICAGO

HADROSAUR

MAKE HYPOTHESES

Reptiles are ectotherms—animals with body temperatures influenced by their external environments. Early in the study of dinosaur fossils, many scientists assumed that because dinosaur skeletons resembled those of some modern reptiles, dinosaurs, too, must have been ectotherms. This assumption led scientists to conclude that many dinosaurs, being both huge and ectothermic, were slow-growing, slow-moving, and awkward on land.

Because the most complete dinosaur skeletons occurred in rocks formed at the bottom of bodies of water, scientists hypothesized that dinosaurs lived in water and that water helped to support their great weight. When skeletons of duck-billed dinosaurs, called *hadrosaurs*, were discovered, this hypothesis gained support. Hadrosaurs had broad, flat ducklike bills, which, scientists suggested, helped them collect and eat water plants.

1060 in.bdol.glencoe.com/news

 CHALLENGE ACTIVITY

History of Scientific Methods Students may think that the methods described in Chapter 1 have always been used by scientists. Have students research the history of the development of methods used by scientists in the past. Their research should include Isaac Newton, Galileo Galilei, and Roger Bacon. **L2**

BREAD PALM, CYCAD FAMILY

THINK CRITICALLY

In the 1960s, paleontologist (a scientist who studies fossils) Robert Bakker (right) hypothesized that dinosaurs were not sluggish ectotherms but fast-moving, land-dwelling endotherms—animals like birds and mammals. Bakker observed that many dinosaurs had feet and legs built for life on land. If hadrosaurs had led a semiaquatic life, Bakker reasoned, their feet would have been webbed with long, thin, widely spaced toes. But hadrosaurs had short, stubby toes and feet, obviously suited for land. In addition to Bakker's observations, studies of fossilized stomach contents revealed that hadrosaurs dined on the cones and leaves of cycads (above) and other land plants. After considering these data carefully, Bakker proposed that many dinosaurs were quick, agile endotherms that roamed Earth's ancient landscape.

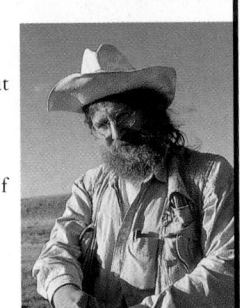

ROBERT BAKKER

COLLECT DATA

To test his hypotheses, Bakker intensified his research on dinosaur skeletons and bone structure. He found reports from the 1950s comparing thousands of cross sections of dinosaur bones with those of reptiles, birds, and mammals. These reports noted that many dinosaur bones were less dense than those of modern reptiles and riddled with channels for blood vessels. In short, many dinosaur bones resembled those of endotherms not ectotherms. Bakker confirmed his observations by collecting supporting evidence from other sources.

DINOSAUR BONE SHOWING
CHANNELS FOR BLOOD VESSELS
Magnification: 25×

FORM THEORIES

Bakker's hypotheses—supported by data gathered by other paleontologists and by dinosaur bones, growth patterns, and behavior—prompted scientists to reexamine theories about dinosaurs. Were some dinosaurs endotherms and others ectotherms? Did dinosaurs have their own unique physiology resembling neither reptiles nor mammals? Scientific theories about dinosaurs continue to evolve as new fossils are discovered and new tools to study those fossils are developed.

PALEONTOLOGIST WORKING ON FOSSIL

ROBERT BAKKER WITH
BRONTOSAUR BONE

EXPANDING Your View

1 **APPLY CONCEPTS** Robert Bakker's research led to a different theory regarding the physiology of dinosaurs. As new fossils are found and new tools developed to study them, paleontologists will continue to replace existing theories with newer ones. What kinds of scientific information or evidence can cause a scientific theory to be changed?

1061

Focus On

Biomes

Purpose

Students will associate terrestrial biomes with their geographic locations.

Background

The major biomes of the world are shown on this map. Latitude influences biomes because generally the closer to the equator, the warmer the area. Precipitation is also a major influence on the formation of biomes.

Teaching Strategies

- Ask students to name organisms that live in the different biomes.
- Remove a globe from its stand. Have one student gently pass it to another student. Have them stop and look at their right thumbs and record which biomes they are touching. Repeat 10 times. Most of the time, the thumbs will be on the ocean, helping students realize that oceans cover the greatest area.
- Show a video or slides for each biome.
- Discuss how air currents carrying moisture drop this moisture as precipitation as they approach a mountain. Therefore, one side of a mountain range has a lot of precipitation, and the other side is a desert.

WATER LILY

WATER

DESERT

FOCUS ON
Biomes

A biome is a large group of ecosystems that share the same type of mature climax community. When you think of a biome, you may imagine lions on an African grassland or monkeys in the rain forest. However, ecologists look at climax communities of plants rather than animals. Because plants don't migrate, they are a better indicator of the long-term characteristics of a biome. The number of biomes in the world is subject to change if climate changes. Some commonly accepted biomes are shown here.

GRASSLAND

TAIGA

60°N

30°N

EQUATOR

30°S

60°S

	WATER
	ICE
	TUNDRA
	TAIGA
	TEMPERATE/DECIDUOUS FOREST
	GRASSLAND
	DESERT
	TROPICAL RAIN FOREST

in.bdol.glencoe.com/news

INCLUSION STRATEGIES

Learning Disabled Use a globe to review the locations of Earth's equator, the tropics of Cancer and Capricorn, and the arctic and antarctic circles. Review the orientation of latitude lines on the globe and correlate these with those on a map. **L1** **ELL**

TEMPERATE/DECIDUOUS FOREST

BIOMES

Earth's surface is marvelously diverse. Millions of species find a home here. But their distribution is not random. As the world map shows, Earth's biomes exhibit tremendous variety.

In general, three factors—latitude, altitude, precipitation—determine which biome dominates a terrestrial location. A rainy, low-lying area near the equator will have a tropical rain forest as climax vegetation. A few kilometers away on a mountainside, ecologists may find plants typical of a biome thousands of kilometers to the north or south.

Look at the world map. Notice that Earth is more than two-thirds water. This water is mostly oceans, which make up the saltwater biome. Freshwater from precipitation makes up the other major water biome on land.

60°N

30°N

EQUATOR

30°S

60°S

TUNDRA

TROPICAL RAIN FOREST

EXPANDING Your View

1 **THINK CRITICALLY** Which biome do you think would recover most slowly from destruction arising from natural events or human causes? Explain.

2 **COMPARE AND CONTRAST** Think about the general pattern of biome types that exists from the equator to the poles. Do you think you would find a similar pattern if you climbed from the foot of a mountain in the tropics to its peak? Explain.

1063

Visual Learning

■ Have students identify the biome that makes up most of the area directly above the equator. tropical rain forest

■ Have students use the map to name the three biomes that occupy the greatest area on Earth. taiga, temperate/deciduous forest, and grassland Then ask them to identify the biome that occupies the smallest percentage of Earth's surface. tropical rain forest

■ Point out that the biomes that make up the United States, in order from largest to smallest, are temperate/deciduous forest, grassland, and desert.

Expanding Your View

1. A tropical rain forest. Because this biome contains the greatest species diversity, habitat destruction can result in extinction of large numbers of species.

2. Yes. Temperature decreases with an increase in altitude, just as it decreases with an increase in latitude.

Biology Journal

Biome Distribution Ask students to describe in their journals how terrestrial and marine biomes are distributed over the globe in relation to the equator. Have them estimate the percentages of land and water that appear above and below the equator. **L3**

PROJECT

Biome Tour Advise students that they are to lead a group of tourists to a biome they have thoroughly researched. Have them: (a) pick a specific biome as a destination; (b) suggest clothing the tourists should pack; (c) explain what the tourists should be prepared to see and experience. "Agents" should also prepare a brochure that will explain the ecology of the particular biome. List animals and plants tourists should expect to see and explain any environmental problems the biome might be experiencing. **L3**

Focus On
Microscopes

Purpose

Students will be provided with a historical perspective of the events that led to the development of the compound microscope, transmission electron microscope (TEM), and scanning electron microscope (SEM) and the uses of each microscope type.

Background

Magnifying lenses were developed hundreds of years ago but required live specimens. Further progress was delayed due to a lack of knowledge about how to prepare specimens.

Teaching Strategies

- Ask students whether they think the development of a successful microscope was delayed because of problems with creating lenses or a lack of knowledge about how to prepare specimens for study. Problems resulted more from a lack of knowledge about how to prepare specimens since lens construction dates back to the time of Galileo.

- Discuss the techniques involved in preparing specimens for electron microscopy studies, such as the use of metals for shadowing.

- Have students research the backgrounds and training of the individuals involved in the development of the microscope *or* the scientists who contributed to the development of the cell theory. **L3**

The invention and development of the light microscope some 300 years ago allowed scientists to see cells for the first time. Improvements have vastly increased the range of visibility of microscopes. Today researchers can use these powerful tools to study cells at the molecular level.

FOCUS ON Microscopes

THIS EARLY COMPOUND MICROSCOPE, housed in a gold-embossed leather case, was designed by English scientist Robert Hooke about 1665. Using it, he observed and made drawings of cork cells. Although the microscope has three lenses, they are of poor quality and Hooke could see little detail. ▶

ANTON VAN LEEUWENHOEK

◀ **THIS HISTORIC MICROSCOPE** — held by a modern researcher— was designed by Anton van Leeuwenhoek (above). By 1700, Dutch scientist, van Leeuwenhoek, had greatly improved the accuracy of microscopes. Grinding the lenses himself, van Leeuwenhoek built some 240 single-lens versions. He discovered—and described for the first time—red blood cells and bacteria, taken from scrapings from his teeth. By 1900, problems with lenses that had once limited image quality had been overcome, and the compound microscope had evolved essentially into its present form.

HOOKE'S MICROSCOPE

in.bdol.glencoe.com/microscopy

PROJECT

The Compound Microscope On a poster board or large sheet of paper, have students draw and label the parts of a compound microscope. Under each label, have them describe the function of the part. For the objective lenses, have students calculate and identify the power of magnification for an object viewed with each lens. Students could add photos taken of objects under microscopes as illustrations. Display posters around the room and refer to them when discussing microscopes. **L2** **ELL**

RED BLOOD CELLS
UNDER A COMPOUND
LIGHT MICROSCOPE
Magnification: 800×

HOW IT WORKS The magnifying power of a microscope is determined by multiplying the magnification of the eyepiece and the objective lens.

A **COMPOUND LIGHT MICROSCOPE** (above) uses two or more glass lenses to magnify objects. Light microscopes are used to look at living cells, such as red blood cells (top), small organisms, and preserved cells. Compound light microscopes can magnify up to about 1500 times.

RED BLOOD CELLS UNDER A
SCANNING ELECTRON MICROSCOPE
Magnification: 10 000×

SCANNING ELECTRON MICROSCOPE IMAGE OF A MOSQUITO
Magnification: 50×

SCANNING ELECTRON MICROSCOPE
An SEM sweeps a beam of electrons over the surface of a specimen, such as red blood cells (above), causing electrons to be emitted from the specimen. SEMs produce a realistic, three-dimensional picture—but only the surface of an object can be observed. An SEM can magnify only about 20 000 times without losing clarity.

SCANNING TUNNELING
MICROSCOPE IMAGE
OF A DNA FRAGMENT
Magnification: 2 000 000×

SCANNING TUNNELING MICROSCOPE
The STM revolutionized microscopy in the mid-1980s by allowing scientists to see atoms on an object's surface. A very fine metal probe is brought near a specimen. Electrons flow between the tip of the probe and atoms on the specimen's surface. As the probe follows surface contours, such as those on this DNA molecule (above), a computer creates a three-dimensional image. An STM can magnify up to one hundred million times.

RED BLOOD CELLS UNDER
A TRANSMISSION
ELECTRON MICROSCOPE
Magnification: 40 000×

◀ **TRANSMISSION ELECTRON MICROSCOPE** A TEM aims a beam of electrons through a specimen. Denser portions of an object allow fewer electrons to pass through. These denser areas appear darker in the image. Two-dimensional TEM images are used to study details of cells such as these red blood cells (above). A TEM can magnify hundreds of thousands of times.

RESEARCHER USING A TEM

EXPANDING Your View

① THINK CRITICALLY Which type of microscope should be used to examine the contents of a small bacterial cell? Why?

② COMPARE AND CONTRAST Compare and contrast the images seen with an SEM to those seen with a TEM.

Visual Learning

■ **Demonstration** Show students photomicrographs of the same organelle as it appears with a light microscope and an electron microscope. Also show them artists' sketches of cells and their organelles to aid students in recognizing two- and three-dimensional representations. Photomicrographs and drawings may be obtained from college-level texts.

■ **Display** Create a display consisting of pictures of the many types of early microscopes. Such pictures may be obtained from a museum or history of science text. Large displays of various types of modern microscopes are available from scientific supply houses. Use the pictures to contrast the location of the specimen, the methods of illumination, the types of lenses used, and how light passes through each (using light-ray optical diagrams). If possible, also show examples of specimens as they appear under each microscope.

Expanding Your View

1. A TEM should be used. It can magnify an object up to 500 000 times, unlike a compound light microscope, and can obtain images inside a cell, unlike an SEM or STM.
2. Images in the SEM are three-dimensional, while TEM images are two-dimensional. Images in the TEM can be magnified greater than those in the SEM.

INCLUSION STRATEGIES

Learning Disabled Students who have difficulty with mathematical concepts may need extra help with the SI calculations and measurements. Hands-on manipulations with metric rulers can increase their understanding of the mathematical concepts involved. Have students who are having difficulty with mathematics work cooperatively with students possessing strong math skills to make a variety of calculations related to microscopy. Calculations should include determining magnification, calculating field of view, and using the microscope as a measuring tool. **L1** **COOP LEARN**

NATIONAL GEOGRAPHIC

Focus On
Selective Breeding of Cats

Purpose
Students will gain some insight into the breeding of cats and the influence of cats on human life throughout history.

Background
Cats can be bred for a number of characteristics, including physical traits such as hair length or color. Temperament can also be selected by breeding. Certain breeds have a reputation for being quiet and loving, others for being noisy.

Teaching Strategies
- Make sure that students are familiar with the meaning of the terms *breed* and *selective breeding*.
- Ask students to bring in photographs of their pet cats. If any student's cat is a pure breed, have the student describe distinctive traits or qualities of the breed.

KITTENS (ABOVE AND BELOW) WITH DOMINANT WHITE MARKINGS ON FACE, PAWS, AND THROAT

FOCUS ON
Selective Breeding of Cats

Graceful, agile, and independent, cats are popular pets. In the United States alone, more than 55 million cats are kept as pets. Although the origin of the domestic cat is lost in antiquity, archeological evidence indicates that an association between cats and people existed as much as 3500 years ago in ancient Egypt. Unlike dogs, cattle, and many other domesticated animals, however, cats have only recently been bred selectively to exhibit specific traits. Currently, about 40 recognized breeds exist—developed by selectively mating cats having especially desirable or distinctive characteristics. Different breeds vary primarily in color, in length and texture of fur, and in temperament.

COLORFUL COATS
Cats come in many colors, but the most common coats are tabby (a striped or blotchy pattern), black, and orange. Cats with "orange" coats range in color from creamy yellow to dark ginger red. The genetic control of cat fur color is complex and only partially understood. Solid white fur is dominant to all other fur colors. Spots of white—especially on the face, throat, and paws—are also dominant to solid color coats. Some breeds such as the Siamese (below) have been bred for a light-colored body with dark legs, tail, ears, and face—the perfect frame for bright blue eyes.

SIAMESE

SOMALI—A LONGHAIRED ABYSSINIAN BREED—AT CAT SHOW

CULTURAL DIVERSITY

Cultural Taboos Against Inbreeding
Although inbreeding can result in high rates of stillbirths and offspring with congenital disorders, scientists are not sure whether taboos against inbreeding are culturally or naturally selected. Explain to students that taboos against inbreeding are not universal, indicating that their origins are cultural rather than genetic. However, individuals brought up in close proximity to each other, as family members, usually are less likely to develop a sexual interest in each other. This suggests that inbreeding taboos may have a biological component.

SCULPTURE OF EGYPTIAN GODDESS BASTET AS A CAT

SHORT VERSUS LONG

Cat breeds can be divided into two major groups: those with short hair and those with long. The Abyssinian—slender and regal-looking with large ears and almond-shaped eyes—is a popular short-haired breed. The ancestry of Abyssinians is unclear, but they may be descended from the sacred cats of ancient Egypt. Certainly, their similarity to Egyptian cat sculptures, such as the one at left, is striking. The American shorthair, on the other hand, is a sturdy muscular breed developed from cats that accompanied European settlers to the American colonies.

There are about a dozen breeds of longhaired cats, ranging from the large (up to 13.5 kg, or 30 pounds), shaggy Maine coon cat to the popular Persian. Persian cats (below) are prized for their extremely long fur that stands out from their bodies, especially on the neck, face, and tail. Hundreds of years of careful breeding have refined the distinct "powder puff" appearance of the modern Persian.

TRAITS AND TEMPERAMENTS

Some cats have been bred for special traits. The Manx (right), for example, is tailless. Manx cats trace their roots to the Isle of Man off the coast of England. With hind legs longer than front legs, Manx cats run with a rabbitlike, hopping gait. The breed known as Ragdoll gets its name from the fact that it relaxes its muscles and goes completely limp when picked up. Fearless and calm, the Ragdoll is a fairly new breed of cat, which originated in the United States in the 1960s. Different breeds of cats have different temperaments, or personalities. Siamese tend to be vocal and demanding. The Japanese bobtail—thought to bring good luck—is playful and adaptable. The elegant Abyssinian is known for being quiet and very affectionate.

SILVER MANX TABBY (ABOVE), AND WHITE PERSIAN GETTING GROOMED

EXPANDING Your View

1 THINK CRITICALLY The ancient Egyptians stored large amounts of grain to ensure there would be enough to eat if crops failed. Infer why ancient Egyptians may have been motivated to domesticate cats.

2 JOURNAL WRITING Research a domestic cat breed. In your journal, record the breed's history and specific traits for which it was bred.

1067

 CHALLENGE ACTIVITY

Taxonomy of Cats Have students research the lineage of domestic cats. They can design a chart or poster that traces the taxonomy of cats and shows non-domesticated relatives of cats. Students will require a basic understanding of levels of classification in order to do the project. **L3**

NATIONAL GEOGRAPHIC

Quick Demo

Plant Breeding Show students a variety of summer and winter squash. Have students discuss the similarities and differences of the squash. Explain that summer squash are all the same species, *Cucurbita pepo*, and that winter squash are also all the same species, *Cucurbita maxima*. Ask students to explain how people have achieved such a variety of squash. **L2**

Visual Learning

■ Make a bulletin-board display showing a variety of cat breeds. Have interested students research the history of some of these breeds. **L1**

■ Locate a local cat breeder and have the breeder bring in a cat to demonstrate how you would show a cat at a cat show.

Expanding Your View

1. Grain would attract rodents that would also carry diseases. Cats would keep the rodent population at a minimum.

2. Answers will vary depending on the breed selected. Check to see whether physical traits, such as hair length, hair color, or temperament, are mentioned.

Portfolio

Test Cross Have students draw Punnett squares to show a cat of unknown genotype and normal phenotype mated with one known to be homozygous for a recessive allele, *dd*, which causes a bone deformity. Half the offspring have normal bones; half have the deformity. **L2**

Focus On

Primates

Purpose

Students will learn about the characteristics of the major primate groups.

Background

By investigating the functional relationships between primate features, such as size, tooth structure, bone shape, and behavioral habits, the probable evolution of many anatomical differences can be better understood.

Teaching Strategies

- Discuss the characteristics of each group, emphasizing how each adaptation is important for its environment.
- Guide students to hypothesize how natural selection may have affected the groups' evolution.
- Discuss some of the methods used to analyze primate fossils, such as biomechanical studies to infer locomotion and scanning-electron microscopy to infer diet.

SQUIRREL MONKEY

FOCUS ON Primates

Catch the gaze of an orangutan and you'll be staring into a face very much like your own. Similarities between apes and humans are striking—expressive eyes, fingers that can grasp, keen intelligence, and complex social systems. The resemblance is no coincidence. Apes and other primates are humans' closest relatives. The Primate order is made up of 13 families, including *Hominidae,* to which *Homo sapiens,* our species, belongs.

STREPSIRRHINES ▶

These small, tree-dwelling animals look least like other primates. Their triangular faces, set off by large round eyes, lack muscles needed to make facial expressions that other primates use for communication. They can be as small as a mouse or as big as a large house cat. Perhaps the best known members of this group are the lemurs (right), which live only in Madagascar and neighboring islands off the coast of eastern Africa.

AYE-AYE

RING-TAILED LEMUR

OLD WORLD MONKEYS

MANDRILL

Monkeys found in Europe, Asia, and Africa are called Old World monkeys. They grow larger than New World monkeys and have no prehensile tail for grasping. Pads of tough skin on their rumps cushion them while they are seated. Among Old World monkeys, the mandrill (above) has the most colorful face. The Japanese macaque (right), or snow monkey, lives farther north than any other species of monkey.

JAPANESE MACAQUES

 1068 (in.bdol.glencoe.com/news)

INCLUSION STRATEGIES

Learning Disabled Have students define the following terms: *opposable thumb, binocular vision, strepsirrhine, anthropoid,* and *ape.* Have students circle the word in the following group that does not belong: New World monkey, opposable thumb, Old World monkey, ape, strepsirrhine. **L1 ELL**

CAPUCHINS

NEW WORLD MONKEYS ▲

Unlike their Old World counterparts, New World monkeys have prehensile tails. Sometimes compared to an extra hand, the tail can wrap around a tree limb and support the monkey's weight. Thus, the animal can dangle upside down to eat. The capuchins (above) of Central and South America have thumbs that can move to touch other fingers and help them pick up food.

ORANGUTAN

CHIMPANZEE

APES

Unlike monkeys, apes have no tails, and they are usually larger than monkeys. While monkeys run on all fours, apes walk on two legs with support from their hands. Chimpanzees (left), gibbons, gorillas, and orangutans (above) are all apes. Living in Africa and Asia, these primates have large brains and are considered to be more like humans than any other animal. They are subject to many of the same diseases as humans, can use simple tools, and some have been taught to communicate with humans using sign language.

EXPANDING Your View

1 **THINK CRITICALLY** Examine the photo of New World monkeys. How is having a tail an adaptive advantage for these primates?

2 **COMPARE AND CONTRAST** Which of the species in this feature probably live in trees? Explain your answer.

1069

Visual Learning

■ Prepare a video or slide presentation of one or more species of each primate group to provide detail about the groups' behaviors and ecologies.

■ Show pictures of primate fossils and discuss how each fossil provides evidence of primate evolution.

Expanding Your View

1. The tail aids in balance and allows them to grasp a branch and keep their hands free.

2. Long-tailed primates probably live in trees: strepsirrhines, New World monkeys, and some Old World monkeys.

Discussion Question

Fossil Problems A jaw fragment discovered in eastern Africa is 8 million years old. Scientists suggest that it might be from a primate ancestor of African apes and humans. What tests might you perform to verify this idea? analysis of skeletal structures, DNA sequences, and brain size **L2**

PROJECT

All About Primates Have student groups make presentations about particular species of primates. Student presentations can include models, posters, videos, or skits. Tell students that their presentations should include information regarding behavior, anatomy, ecology, taxonomy, evolution. Have students conclude with their thoughts on the above information and how it can relate to humans. **L3** **ELL** **COOP LEARN**

Focus On

Kingdoms of Life

Purpose

Students will learn the major differences among organisms in the six kingdoms. They will study the history of classification and different classification systems.

Background

Taxonomists work continually to improve the organizational system of about 1.5 million known species of organisms. Recent attempts at improvement include the division of prokaryotes into Kingdoms Archaebacteria and Eubacteria to better reflect the genetic differences of these two types of prokaryotes. Incorporating a taxon called domain, which is more inclusive than the kingdom taxon, into the modern classification system has been supported by some taxonomists. Such an organizational system would divide all known organisms into three domains that reflect today's knowledge about the evolutionary relationships of living things.

Biology Journal

Looking at Classification From a Historical Perspective Have students research the work of Aristotle, Linnaeus, Whittaker, and Woese and then write an essay that compares their work. **L3**

FOCUS ON Kingdoms of Life

PUFFIN

DROMEDARY

The great diversity of life on Earth—estimated at 3 to 10 million species and counting—can be overwhelming. To make sense of this bewildering array of living things, biologists use classification systems to group organisms in ways that highlight their similarities, differences, and relationships. The systematic grouping of living things originated in the 4th century B.C. But biological classification has changed a great deal over the years, as new tools and technologies have made it possible to examine organisms in increasing detail and trace their complex evolutionary pathways through time.

MOTH COLLECTION

ARISTOTLE RECOGNIZES PLANTS AND ANIMALS

Taxonomy, as the science of biological classification is called, began with the Greek philosopher Aristotle (384–322 B.C.). A keen observer of nature, Aristotle separated all living things into two major groups: plants and animals. He grouped plants into herbs, shrubs, and trees, and classified animals on the basis of size, where they lived—on the land or in the water, and how they moved. Although Aristotle's system of classification did little to reveal natural relationships among living things, it was widely accepted and used, with few modifications, into the Middle Ages.

CONEFLOWER

RHODODENDRON

OAK TREE

1070   in.bdol.glencoe.com/news

CHALLENGE ACTIVITY

Research Species Have students locate books, journals, magazines, and newspaper articles that estimate the numbers of species in each kingdom. Ask them to research the numbers and discuss how the numbers were derived. **L3**

LINNAEUS IDENTIFIES TWO KINGDOMS

Modern classification began with the work of John Ray (1627–1705), an English naturalist who outlined the idea of species. In the mid-1700s, Swedish botanist Carolus Linnaeus (1707–1778) picked up on this idea and developed a classification scheme that formed the basis of the system we use today. Linnaeus divided all living things between two kingdoms—plants and animals. But he subdivided these kingdoms into a hierarchy of smaller and more specific groups: classes, orders, genera, and species. Linnaeus placed organisms in these groups primarily on the basis of their physical similarities and differences.

QUEEN ANGELFISH

BARREL SPONGE WITH CRINOIDS

PROTISTS: THE THIRD KINGDOM

Linnaeus' classification system revolutionized taxonomy, but from the start there were problems. Organisms such as mushrooms and sponges resemble plants but do not make their own food. To which kingdom did they belong? As light microscopes improved, the situation became much more complex as biologists discovered a vast assortment of minute, primarily one-celled organisms. In 1866, German zoologist Ernst Haeckel (1834–1919) proposed giving these unicellular organisms—named protists—a kingdom of their own.

FLY AGARIC MUSHROOMS

PROKARYOTES AND FOUR KINGDOMS

The three-kingdom classification system persisted, however, until the middle of the 20th century when the electron microscope and advances in biochemistry made it possible to study living things at the subcellular level. These new tools revealed that there are two fundamentally different kinds of cells in the living world—prokaryotes and eukaryotes. Prokaryotes, such as the bacterium *Salmonella* (below left), lack the membrane-bound nuclei and most of the organelles characteristic of eukaryotic cells. All prokaryotes were then recognized as a separate kingdom that contained all the bacteria.

KELP (EUKARYOTE)

SALMONELLA (PROKARYOTE)
Magnification: 34 300×

VOLVOX (EUKARYOTE) Magnification: 15×

1071

Using Science Terms

On the chalkboard, write the names of the six kingdoms and the two words *eukaryote* and *prokaryote*. Have students use dictionaries to find the meanings of the Latin or Greek prefixes and suffixes in each word. Then ask them to explain how each name describes its group. **L1** **ELL**

Visual Learning

Have students make a bulletin board display from photos and illustrations, found in magazines or newspapers, of organisms from each kingdom. Group the visuals according to kingdom. **L1**

Struggling Learners

Have the students complete a time line about the historical evolution of biological classification. Provide students with a baseline of major events to include and a word bank of names and key terms. **L1** **ELL**

THE FIVE-KINGDOM SYSTEM

A flurry of ideas for new classification systems followed close on the heels of the discovery of prokaryotes. In 1969, American biologist R. H. Whittaker (1924–1980) proposed a five-kingdom system (right) that soon became universally accepted. The five kingdoms were Monera (bacteria), Protista (algae and other protists), Fungi (mushrooms, molds, and lichens), Plantae (mosses, ferns, and cone-bearing and flowering plants), and Animalia (invertebrate and vertebrate animals). The kingdom Monera included all the prokaryotes; the other four kingdoms consisted of eukaryotes. Fungi, plants, and animals were easily distinguished by their modes of nutrition. But the kingdom Protista was a grab bag, a diverse assortment of living things—some plantlike, some animal-like, some funguslike—that did not fit clearly into any of the other eukaryotic kingdoms.

EVOLUTIONARY RELATIONSHIPS

With the five-kingdom system in place, many taxonomists focused their research on reclassifying living things in terms of their evolutionary relationships rather than on their structural similarities. Present-day organisms, such as the millipede (below), were compared with extinct forms preserved in the fossil record, such as the trilobite (below right).

MILLIPEDE

New biochemical techniques made it possible to compare nucleotide sequences in genes and amino acid sequences in proteins from different organisms to determine how closely those organisms were related.

1072

WHITTAKER'S SYSTEM

PLANTS   FUNGI   ANIMALS

PROTISTS

EUKARYOTES

PROKARYOTES

MONERANS

CHALLENGE ACTIVITY

Observe Cells Have students use a microscope to observe a variety of prokaryotic and eukaryotic cells. Ask students to explain the differences they observe. **L3**

GRAND PRISMATIC SPRING, YELLOWSTONE NATIONAL PARK

THE SIXTH KINGDOM

In the 1970s, genetic tests showed that members of the kingdom Monera were far more diverse than anyone had suspected. One group of bacteria, originally called archaebacteria (ancient bacteria), seemed especially unusual. Archaebacteria, or archaeans, as most biologists now refer to them, often live in extreme environments—very hot or salty places—such as the Grand Prismatic Spring (left) in Yellowstone National Park. In 1996, researchers sequenced the archaean genome and discovered that these tiny cells are as different from bacteria as you are. A sixth kingdom was formed.

ARCHAEA
Magnification: 29 000×

DOMAINS

The discovery of the nature of Archaea led C. R. Woese and his colleagues at the University of Illinois to propose a new classification scheme (left) made up of three domains. The domain Bacteria has one kingdom, Eubacteria (true bacteria). The domain Archaea contains the kingdom Archaebacteria. The domain Eukarya consists of the kingdoms Protista, Fungi, Plantae, and Animalia.

The domain classification system takes into account more of the evolutionary history of organisms. Traditionally, the classification systems were weighted more toward physical characteristics of organisms, but the domain system is designed to show that there are vast differences between archaebacteria, eubacteria, and the other forms of life—fungi, animals, protists, and plants. These differences are not easy to see but are significant in terms of genetic makeup.

WOESE'S SYSTEM

DOMAIN	DOMAIN	DOMAIN
Bacteria	Archaea	Eukarya
KINGDOM Eubacteria	KINGDOM Archaebacteria	KINGDOMS Animalia Plantae Fungi Protista

EXPANDING Your View

1 **THINK CRITICALLY** How have technological advances, such as improved microscopes and new biochemical tests, changed biological classification?

2 **JOURNAL WRITING** The kingdom Protista contains very diverse organisms—from unicellular "animal-like" amoebas to multicellular "plantlike" giant kelp. In your journal, predict what might happen to the protist kingdom in the next few years as biologists study its members in more detail at biochemical and genetic levels.

1073

Enrichment

Have students identify which species of archaebacteria was sequenced. Current information suggests that archaebacteria may live in subsurface pores of rocks, as well as in other less severe environments. Ask how such data might affect the view of archaebacteria as "extremophiles."

Expanding Your View

1. Improved microscopes allow scientists to differentiate between prokaryotic and eukaryotic cells and among the cell organelles. Biochemical tests determine the presence of specific molecules in cells.

2. Answers will vary. Possible ideas are that organisms currently classified in Kingdom Protista may be reclassified into other kingdoms or that the subgroupings in Kingdom Protista may become additional kingdoms.

Going Further

Have students choose a kingdom to research. They should explore the kingdom's diversity by determining its number of phyla and listing representative organisms. Urge the students to include other information they discover. **L2**

Focus On

Viruses

Purpose

Students will compare and contrast the structures and shapes of viruses.

Background

The classification of viruses is based on the criteria of size, morphology, type of genetic material (DNA or RNA and double-stranded or single-stranded), and means of replication.

Teaching Strategies

Discuss with students the different ways viruses enter cells as illustrated by a bacteriophage and an enveloped virus.

MODEL OF AIDS VIRUS

FOCUS ON
Viruses

INVISIBLE INVADERS

Scientists have identified thousands of viruses. Some invade plants, others attack animals, and still others target bacteria.

In humans, viruses are responsible for chicken pox, warts, cold sores, and the common cold, as well as dreaded diseases such as rabies, influenza, hepatitis, and AIDS.

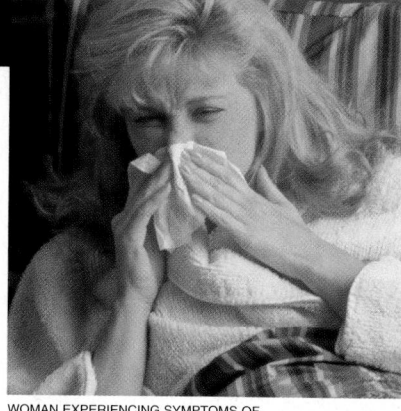

WOMAN EXPERIENCING SYMPTOMS OF THE COMMON COLD

STRUCTURE

A single drop of blood can contain billions of viruses. Despite their incredibly small size, many viruses, such as this tobacco mosaic virus (below), have complex structures. All viruses consist of a core of nucleic acid—either DNA or RNA—enclosed in a protein coat called a capsid. Both the type and arrangement of proteins in the capsid give different viruses characteristic shapes.

Viruses lurk everywhere—on computer keyboards, in bird droppings, under your fingernails—just waiting to get inside your body or some other living thing. Smaller than the smallest bacteria, viruses are not alive. By themselves, they cannot move, grow, or reproduce. But give viruses the chance to invade a living cell, and they will take over its metabolic machinery, reprogramming it to churn out more viruses to attack other cells.

POLIO VIRUS
Magnification:
85 000×

CAPSID   DNA

◀ MODEL OF TOBACCO MOSAIC VIRUS

ICOSAHEDRAL VIRUSES

Many animal viruses—such as polio (above) and adenovirus—have 20-sided, or icosahedral, capsids. Viewed under an electron microscope, icosahedral viruses look like perfectly symmetrical crystals.

USING MODELS

Build A Virus Have students research the structures of different viruses and construct models of the viruses using craft supplies. Make sure they label all of the structures on their models. **L3**

T-PHAGE

PHAGES

Bacteriophages, or phages for short, are viruses that infect bacteria. This T4-phage (top left), looks like a miniature lunar-landing module. It has a DNA-containing head, a protein tail, and protein tail fibers that attach to the surface of a bacterium. Once viruses are attached (left), the tail section contracts and pierces the cell wall, and viral DNA is injected into the host cell.

ENVELOPED VIRUSES

Some viruses, such as influenza and HIV (the virus that causes AIDS), are enclosed in an envelope composed of lipids, carbohydrates, and proteins. Envelope proteins (right) form spiky projections that help the virus gain entry to a host cell, much like keys fitting into a lock.

T-PHAGES, IN BLUE, INFECTING *E. COLI* BACTERIUM
Magnification: 90 000×

HELICAL VIRUSES

Helical viruses are shaped like tiny cylinders, with the viral genetic material spiraling down the center of a hollow protein tube. Tobacco mosaic virus (below), which infects plants (right), is a long helical virus.

TOBACCO MOSAIC VIRUS
Magnification: 30 000×

INFLUENZA VIRUS
Magnification: 17 150×

PLANT INFECTED BY TOBACCO MOSAIC VIRUS

DEADLY BEAUTY

Some viruses have irregular shapes. The Ebola virus (below), which causes massive internal bleeding in humans, has a twisted, worm-like form. A strain of Ebola virus from Zaire, Africa, is one of the most deadly viruses researchers have ever studied.

EBOLA VIRUS
Magnification: 19 000×

EXPANDING Your View

1 **THINK CRITICALLY** Describe why viruses like those that cause common colds are considered "more successful" than viruses such as Ebola.

2 **JOURNAL WRITING** Read *The Andromeda Strain* (1969) by Michael Crichton, a science fiction story about an alien virus that comes to Earth. In your journal, record your reactions to the book. What similarities did you notice between how scientists in the story handled the alien virus and how present-day scientists study viruses such as Ebola?

1075

Visual Learning

Have students make a video or computer presentation about a viral disease, such as mumps, Ebola, or rabies. Their presentations should include information about both the virus and the disease it causes. **L3**

Expanding Your View

1. They don't kill their hosts.
2. They used the highest level of containment when working with the virus, as do virologists who work with deadly and newly discovered viruses today.

Activity

Ask students to calculate the actual size of one of the tobacco mosaic viruses and one of the polio viruses by using a metric ruler to measure the size of the virus in the photo. Then, they should divide the measurement by the photo's magnification. **L2**

CHALLENGE ACTIVITY

Plant Viruses Students who need an additional challenge can do additional research on plant viruses. Have them make a table that lists the viruses' names, the plants they infect, and whether or not the viruses could directly or indirectly affect humans. **L3**

Focus On
Plants for People

Purpose
Students will discover the role of agriculture, silviculture, and horticulture in producing plants for food, shelter, medicine, and pleasure.

Background
Scientific names for species described in this feature are as follows: corn, *Zea mays*; rice, *Oryza sativa*; wheat, *Triticum darum var. vulgare*; potato, *Solanum tuberosum*; oats, *Avena sativa*; barley, *Hordeum vulgare*; sorghum, *Sorghum bicolor*.

Teaching Strategies
■ Have students read this feature. Then have them work in cooperative groups to prepare a table of all the plants described. Along the left side, have them list the crop species. Across the top, have them use the headings *Kingdom*, *Division*, *Class*, and *Family*. Advise students to refer to the Reference Handbook for help in the completion of their table. (Note: Not all plants are listed in the Reference Handbook.) **L1**
COOP LEARN

■ Have students write a short paragraph that describes the relative dependence of humans on plants as food sources. **L2**

FOCUS ON
Plants for People

Agriculture was perhaps the single most important development in human history. It is no accident that the beginnings of civilization occurred in productive farming areas. Today, many farmers grow just one crop called a monoculture. Monocultures enable farmers to use machinery for planting, cultivating, and harvesting. However, monocultures are very vulnerable to disease. Pest infestations can spread rapidly, wiping out an entire season's crop. To combat this problem, farmers have begun to use native species that are less susceptible to disease. Scientists are also using genetic engineering techniques to make cotton, corn, and other crop plants more insect resistant.

AGRICULTURE

CORN — Farmers in the United States use more acreage to grow corn than any other crop. Livestock consume most of the corn crop, but a significant portion also goes to manufacture starch, oil, sugar, meal, breakfast cereals, and alcohol.

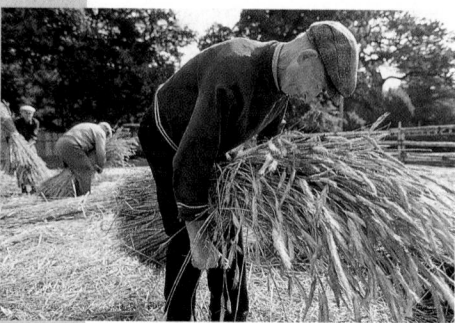
GATHERING WHEAT

WHEAT — Nearly one-third of all land in the world used for crop production is planted in wheat. Wheat probably originated in the Middle East and was an important food for the ancient Mesopotamian, Egyptian, and Indus civilizations.

RICE — Most humans equate rice with survival. In Asia, rice is the basis of almost all diets. More than 95 percent of the world's rice crop is used to feed humans. Rice is the only grain that can grow submerged in water.

RICE FIELDS

POTATO HARVEST

POTATOES — A South American native, the potato arrived in the United States via Europe. This nutritious root vegetable contains many essential amino acids. Potatoes also contain vitamins B and C and the minerals calcium and iron.

OATS — Oats make excellent food for both animals and humans. Containing from 10 to 16 percent protein, oats are low in fat and high in carbohydrates, proteins, B vitamins, fiber, and minerals. Native to northern Europe, oats grow well in poor soils as well as in cool, wet climates.

BARLEY — Barley was probably one of the first grain crops grown by humans. It was grown in the Middle East about 10 000 years ago. The world's fourth largest cereal crop, barley grows fast and is able to withstand harsh growing conditions in rugged climates such as Lapland and the Himalaya.

SORGHUM — Since prehistoric times, sorghum has been a major food crop in Africa. Because of its extensive root system, sorghum is especially drought resistant, providing food for people and hay for cattle.

SORGHUM CROP

1077

Teaching Strategies

- Supply students with blank maps of the United States. Ask them to color those areas that are primarily corn- and wheat-growing zones. Have them add labels to identify each crop. **L2**

- Supply students with a global outline map. Have them label on the map where early agriculture began—the Tigris and the Euphrates, Nile Valley, and Indus River region. **L2**

Tying to Prior Knowledge

Have students review the process of fermentation, and allow them to infer how corn can be used in the process to produce alcohol. Corn serves as the food source for yeast.

Enrichment

Intrapersonal Ask students to determine the differences between the wheat used for pasta (*T. durum*) and that used for bread (*T. vulgare*). Have them find out what some of the different physical properties are between the starches in these grains and why one is more suitable than the other for bread or pasta products. **L2**

Visual Learning

Visual-Spatial Obtain a copy of the USDA food pyramid. Ask students to examine the text and photos of the agricultural products shown here and determine where they fit in a daily balanced diet as described by the USDA food pyramid. How many parts of the food pyramid come from plants? How important are plants for human nutrition?

Background

Quinine, an antimalarial chemical derived from the bark of various species of *Cinchona*, was used by the Andean Indians before the European discovery of the New World.

Cinnamon quills, powder, and oil are derived from the stem bark of *Cinnamomum zeylanicum*. The tree is native to Southeast Asia.

Teaching Strategies

Have students work in cooperative groups to compile a list of different nuts that are from trees, and draw a map that shows where these are grown around the world. Responses may include almond, Brazil nut, cashew, hazelnut, pecan, pistachio, walnut, and chestnut. **L2** **COOP LEARN**

STRIPPING BARK FOR MEDICINAL USE

SILVICULTURE

Often confused with forestry, silviculture includes the growing of trees for lumber and paper and for food crops, such as apples and pecans. Oranges, walnuts, and olives are some of the foods grown on trees. Trees are also sources of medicines, such as aspirin, originally derived from the bark of the willow tree, and quinine, from the *Cinchona* tree, used to treat malaria. Trees help reduce air pollution and replenish the oxygen we breathe.

CHEMICALS AND SPICES — Wood is the source of many chemicals including wood alcohol, latex for rubber, and cellulose used to make paper. Charcoal and rayon as well as spices, such as cinnamon and cloves, also are tree products. Taxol, an extract from the bark of a Pacific Coast yew tree, is currently being used to fight cancer.

RESEARCH ON FRUIT TREES

LUMBER AND FUEL — When people think of forest products, they often think of lumber. A common building material, wood is easy to work with, durable, relatively abundant, and lightweight—making it ideal for home construction. Easy to transport and to store, wood is also a source of fuel throughout much of the world.

HARVESTED LOGS

HORTICULTURE

Many of the plants you are familiar with were originally brought from distant lands by naturalists and explorers. By preserving and cultivating these species, horticulturists gave us a legacy of beautiful and useful flowers and foods. Selective breeding, grafting, and more recently, genetic engineering are some methods used by plant scientists.

VEGETABLES — Vegetables were among the first plants cultivated by humans. Green cabbage, watercress, and radishes—members of the mustard family—were known to Egyptians and Romans in the Bronze Age. Root crops such as beets, carrots, sweet potatoes, and turnips are highly prized for fiber and nutrients and because they can be stored easily over winter.

FLOWERING BULBS

FRUIT MARKET

FLOWERS AND MEDICINAL PLANTS — Tulips, roses, scented herbs, and ornamentals of all kinds have been a source of pleasure for generations. Plants have been used for medicinal purposes for thousands of years. Today plants continue to be a major source of pharmaceuticals and herbal remedies.

FRUITS — The two main types of fruits are dry fruits and fleshy fruits. Acorns, walnuts, and pecans are among the dry fruits used as food by wildlife and humans. Fleshy fruits include pears, raspberries, apricots, and cherries.

EXPANDING Your View

1. **APPLY CONCEPTS** Take a piece of paper and make two columns. In the left column, list all of the products essential to your life that come from plants and/or agriculture. In the right column, list all of the essential products that do not come from plants and/or agriculture. Now write a paragraph summarizing the role of plants in your life.

1079

Activity

Kinesthetic Have students test a variety of plant roots for the presence of starch. Have them use thin slices of radish, turnip, and potato and add a few drops of iodine/potassium iodide solution to the root. A blue-black color indicates the presence of starch. As a control, have them add a drop of iodine solution to a small clump of corn starch. Ask them to write a report of their observations for their portfolios. **L2**

Expanding Your View

Except for communication, certain services, and products composed of metals, almost all human basic needs are tied to plants.

TECH PREP

Nutritional Value of Foods Have students prepare a chart comparing the fat and protein content of four of the foods mentioned in "Plants for People." Students should explain which foods would provide more energy and why. **L2**

Focus On

Insects

Purpose

Students will learn characteristics of insects and features of major groups of insects.

Background

Insects are essential to life, yet many are harmful. Their diversity in form makes insects not only successful, but also the largest animal group.

Teaching Strategies

■ Obtain a praying mantis egg case and have students make observations of hatching and development. Emphasize the adaptations that make the mantis an effective predator. **L1** **ELL**

■ Ask students to examine the mouthparts of preserved ants. Then have them design an experiment to determine food preferences of live ants. **L2**

■ Interested students can conduct the experiment on ant food preferences. **L3**

Enrichment

Insect Orders Have students prepare a chart of the insect orders. Some students can locate illustrations while others research information on each order, such as order characteristics, typical examples, and general comments. **L2**

COW KILLER ANT

FOCUS ON
Insects

Without insects, life as we know it would be impossible. Two-thirds of all flowering plants depend on insects to pollinate them. Insects also digest and degrade carrion, animal wastes, and plant matter. Their actions help fungi, bacteria, and other decomposers recycle nutrients and enrich the soil on which plants and all terrestrial organisms depend.

FLAME
SKIMMER
DRAGONFLIES

CHARACTERISTICS

Insects have three body divisions—head, thorax, abdomen—and six legs attached to the thorax. The abdomen has multiple segments, the last ones often possessing external reproductive organs.

Most adult insects have wings, usually one or two pairs. An insect's skin, or integument, is hard yet flexible, and waterproof. Many insects must molt in order to grow larger before metamorphosing into adult forms.

Because of their ability to fly, a rapid reproductive cycle, and a tough, external skeleton, insects are both resilient and successful.

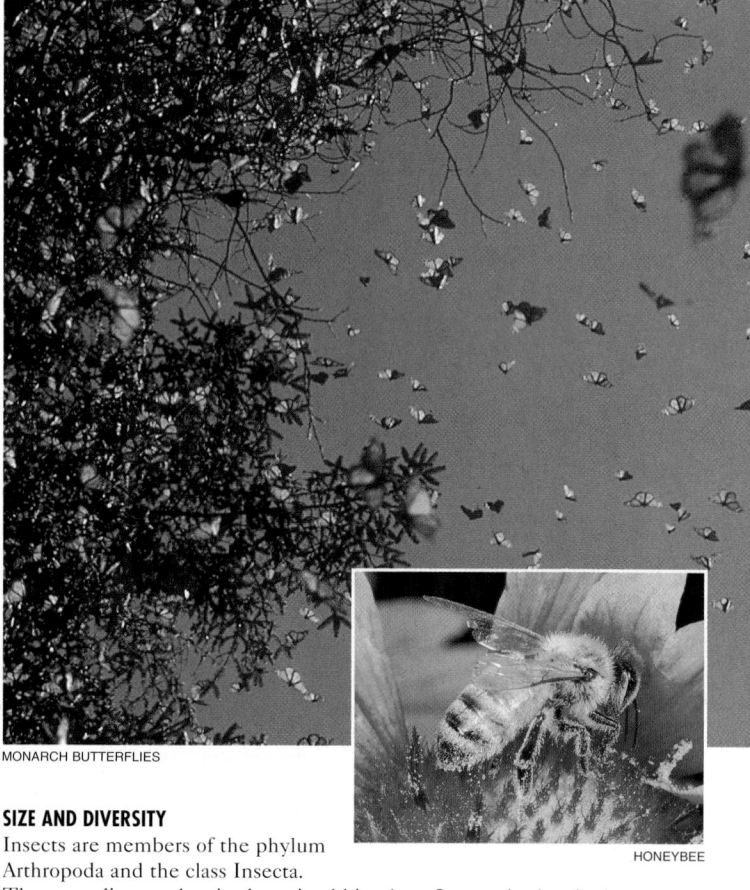

MONARCH BUTTERFLIES

HONEYBEE

SIZE AND DIVERSITY

Insects are members of the phylum Arthropoda and the class Insecta.

The most diverse class in the animal kingdom, Insecta is also the largest—it contains more species than all other animal groups combined.

1080 (in.bdol.glencoe.com/news)

PROJECT

Insect Scavenger Hunt: *Interpersonal*
Ask a group of students to prepare a class scavenger hunt for insects and signs of insects. The scavenger hunt should require that classmates observe various insect behaviors, such as movement and sound production, plus physical features of the insect and its habitat. Make sure the questions require that students actually observe the insect. For example: Describe two insect sounds that you hear outside. What insects are making these sounds? **L2** **COOP LEARN**

COMPOUND EYES OF GIANT RUDDER FLY

**NATIONAL
GEOGRAPHIC**

SENSE ORGANS

Insects gather information about their environment using a variety of sense organs that detect light, odors, sound, vibrations, temperature, and even humidity. Most adult insects have compound eyes, as well as two or three simple eyes on top of their heads. The compound eye of a large dragonfly contains a honeycomb of 30 000 lenses. The image from each lens is sent to the brain and somehow combined into a composite image, but we don't know exactly what such insects see. Some insects navigate by using sound waves or following odor trails. Katydids and crickets have "ears" on their front legs; houseflies have taste receptors on their feet.

KATYDID

ARCTIC WOOLLY BEAR CATERPILLAR

VERSATILITY

Some insects, such as the Arctic woolly bear caterpillar, can survive many months each year in subzero temperatures. Others, such as the monarch butterfly, migrate thousands of miles to warmer regions. Honeybees conserve heat in freezing temperatures by clumping into a ball that hums and churns all winter. Although some insects are plant pests, many others prey on their plant-munching relatives, and in so doing aid humans in the fight to control crop damage.

MOUTHPARTS

Insects get food by biting, lapping, and sucking. Some insects, such as grasshoppers and ants, have mouthparts for biting and chewing, with large mandibles for tearing into plant tissue or seizing prey. The powerful mandibles of bulldog ants, for example, are hinged at the sides of the head and bite inward—with great force—from side to side. Butterflies and honeybees have mouthparts shaped for lapping up nectar. Aphids and cicadas can pierce plant stems and then plant juices can be sucked like soda through a straw.

BLUE MORPHO
BUTTERFLY

BULLDOG ANT

1081

Enrichment

Kinesthetic Obtain preserved specimens of a variety of moths and butterflies and have students use a dissecting needle to unroll and measure the length of each proboscis. Have them hypothesize how proboscis length correlates with the type of flower each insect visits to sip nectar. **L2**

Visual Learning

Ask students to discuss their most positive and most negative experiences with insects. Ask if they have seen any insects similar to ones in the photos in this Focus On. Have them explain how the insects were similar to and different from the photos. **L1**

Biology Journal

Flea Collar Safety Ask students to contact a local veterinarian and report in their journals about the safety of flea collars for pets. Students should ask about the insecticides used, how the flea collar works, why the flea collars are not dangerous to the health of the pet, and alternatives to flea collars. **L2**

Inquiry

Discussion Have students discuss the positive contributions of insects in the world. Discussions should include the importance of bees, butterflies, and ants to all the other organisms of the world. **L2**

PROJECT

Mealworm Development Ask students to observe and record the development of a colony of mealworms as they develop from larvae to adults. Direct students to focus their attention on evidence suggesting molting has occurred. **L2**

Teaching Strategies

- Ask if any students ever caught and kept an insect in a jar. Ask why they did this and what they learned.
- Ask students to research the discovery of DDT and the factors that led to the banning of its use in the United States. **L3**
- Have students work in groups and imagine that they are a team of inventors with backgrounds in entomology. They have been given unlimited funding to design the ultimate device for insect control. Students should use their imaginations as well as scientific knowledge to make a model of their "bug catcher" and explain its function to the class. **L2** **COOP LEARN**

Biology Journal

Natural Pest Control Have students contact their local agricultural extension service to ask about Integrated Pest Management efforts in their area. Then have students write an advertisement for a gardening magazine to sell insects used for pest control using IPM techniques. **L2**

SOLDIER BEETLE

A SUPERLATIVE CRITTER

Some beetles can chew through metals, such as lead or zinc, or timber—not to mention whole fields of cotton. A leaf beetle in the Kalahari Desert produces a toxin powerful enough to fell an antelope. The American burying beetle can lift 200 times its weight. Among Earth's most recognizable beetles, fireflies light up summer evenings, and ladybugs control garden pests.

HARMFUL VERSUS HELPFUL

Some beetles damage crops and spread disease. Spotted cucumber beetles, for example, devour leaves and flowers of cucumbers, melons, and squashes. They can also spread bacterial diseases to the plants they attack.

Many other beetles, such as ladybugs (also known as ladybirds), should be welcome visitors anywhere. Gardeners, farmers, and fruit-growers release thousands of ladybugs into gardens, fields, and orchards as a first line of defense against insect pests, especially aphids. The bright red-orange of ladybug beetles is an unmistakable warning to potential predators that the beetles are extremely distasteful.

LEAF BEETLE

1082

LADYBUG BEETLES

SPOTTED CUCUMBER BEETLE

PROJECT

Insect Exhibit Have students develop a plan for constructing an insect exhibit for a zoo. They should choose insects, make a diagram of their exhibit, and explain how the insects must be cared for. **L2**

NATIONAL GEOGRAPHIC

NATIONAL GEOGRAPHIC

A SPECIAL NICHE

The Mesozoic Era is often identified as the age of dinosaurs. But the truly colossal event during this period in Earth's history was the proliferation of flowering plants. Primary pollinators of the era, beetles most likely fueled this explosion of color and fragrance. Beetles fill critical ecological niches as scavengers and as harvesters of caterpillars and other pests, which, left untended, would devour thousands of acres of crops and forest trees each year. When a beetle species faces extinction—as 12 species in the United States currently do—scientists see it as an early warning system alerting us to significant environmental change.

WEEVIL BEETLE

COLORADO POTATO BEETLE

BODY ARMOR

Many scientists consider beetles to be evolution's biggest success story and think that thousands of additional species remain undiscovered. Beetles—all 350 000 described species—presently account for approximately 1 in 4 known animal species. Beetles thrive in deserts, under tropical forest canopies, and in water. One key to beetles' adaptability is their "shell"—actually a pair of hardened wings called elytra. Elytra permit some beetles to live in deserts by sealing in moisture and other species to breathe underwater by trapping air. Many beetles are remarkably resistant to pesticides.

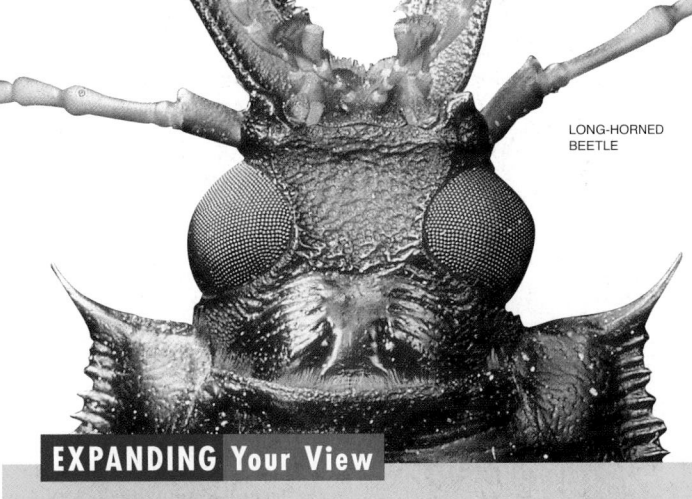

LONG-HORNED BEETLE

EXPANDING Your View

1 **THINK CRITICALLY** What are the advantages and disadvantages of an exoskeleton?

2 **JOURNAL WRITING** Research social behavior in insects and write a short essay to present to the class.

1083

Enrichment

Ask students to design and conduct an experiment to determine the ideal temperature for hatching and developing flour beetle eggs. L2

Expanding Your View

1. advantages of exoskeletons: protection, waterproofing; disadvantages: heavy, can't grow very large, must molt to grow
2. Students might present information on the social structure of bees in a hive or an ant colony.

◎ CHALLENGE ACTIVITY

Insect Population Ask students to sample one species of insect in a small area and then estimate the total number over a larger area. They should measure an area 1 m² and collect one type of insect, such as beetles. Then, knowing the size of the area, they can calculate how many insects of that type there are. Have students release the insects as soon as their calculations are complete. Have students predict how a sudden change in insect population number would impact the ecology of the area. L3

1083

Focus On

Dinosaurs

Purpose

Students learn about dinosaurs, including how they are classified. They explore theories about how dinosaurs became extinct.

Background

Most students will be familiar with dinosaurs such as *Stegosaurus*, *Apatosaurus*, *Tyrannosaurus*, and *Diplodocus*. However, they may not be aware of the different time periods during which each of the more familiar dinosaurs lived. Explain that some dinosaur species evolved, lived, and often went extinct as other dinosaur species became the dominant land animals. When scientists discuss the extinction of the dinosaurs, they are talking about the species that existed about 65 million years ago, not all the dinosaurs that lived and became extinct before that time.

Teaching Strategies

■ Arrange a class trip to a museum that has a dinosaur exhibit. Ask students to examine the skulls and feet of the dinosaurs on display and hypothesize what their habitats and diets might have been. **L1**

■ Have interested students research and report on animals that were not dinosaurs that lived at the same time as the dinosaurs. Suggestions include: the flying pterosaurs, fishlike plesiosaurs, and sailback reptiles such as *Dimetrodon*. **L2**

■ Have students develop a time line that traces the development of animals from the earliest reptiles to the beginning of the Age of Mammals. **L2**

EDMONTOSAURUS

FOCUS ON Dinosaurs

ORNITHISCHIANS

The ornithischians were the grazers of the Mesozoic Era. They are called "bird-hipped" because their hip bones (shown at left) angled backwards like those of modern birds. The ornithischians had diverse adaptations for eating plants and for defending themselves against their predatory relatives.

HYPSILOPHODON

Dinosaurs ruled the world for 130 million years, throughout the Mesozoic Era. Paleontologists have identified several hundred species of dinosaurs, and about a dozen new types are unearthed each year. Descended from ancient reptiles, dinosaurs are grouped into two general categories— ornithischians and saurischians— based on the structure of their hip bones.

PARASAUROLOPHUS

CORYTHOSAURUS

A FLEET-FOOTED HERBIVORE

Slender, graceful *Hypsilophodon* (above) was one of the fastest-moving ornithischians. With long hind legs adapted for running, this 1.5-meter herbivore probably was able to outdistance most predators with ease. *Hypsilophodon* had a sharp beak and small overlapping teeth suited for grinding leaves and other plant material.

BODY ARMOR

Many slow-moving ornithischians had elaborate body armor. Seven meters long and built like an armored tank, *Euoplocephalus* was a peaceful grazer that must have frustrated many a hungry carnivore. Its body was completely encased in bony plates—even the eyelids were bone-reinforced. It had a tail tipped with a massive bone "club." When threatened, *Euoplocephalus* could have hugged the ground and swung its club-studded tail from side to side to protect itself.

EUOPLOCEPHALUS

THE DUCKBILLS

There were many species of duck-billed dinosaurs. All had long tails, oddly shaped "bills," webbed fingers, and hooflike, three-toed hind feet. Despite the duckbills' webbed fingers, most paleontologists now think that duckbills lived on land. Some species, such as *Parasaurolophus* (left), had large, hollow crests on their heads that may have amplified whatever sounds these dinosaurs made. Fossil evidence indicates that duckbills were social animals that moved in herds and cared for their young.

1084　in.bdol.glencoe.com/news

COMPSOGNATHUS

FOOT OF LARGE THEROPOD

SAURISCHIANS

The "lizard-hipped" dinosaurs, or saurischians, had hip bones (shown below) like those of present-day lizards, with the pubic bone projecting forward. Two major groups of saurischians are the theropods, or three-toed carnivores, and the sauropods, or long-necked herbivores.

ALLOSAURUS

THE SMALLEST DINOSAUR

Less than a meter long, *Compsognathus* (above), which means "pretty-jawed," was the smallest of all dinosaurs. A delicate predator, this diminutive theropod probably hunted lizards and small mammals. A double-hinged jaw made it easy for *Compsognathus* to swallow its prey whole.

PALEONTOLOGIST SERENO AND TEAM IN NIGER

THE GIANT MEAT-EATERS

Big predatory theropods came in every imaginable shape and size. Fearsome *Allosaurus* and infamous *Tyrannosaurus* belong to this group, as does a new 12-meter-long dinosaur from the Sahara—*Suchomimus tenerensis*. Discovered in Niger in 1997 by a team of paleontologists led by Paul Sereno (shown in lower right of large photo), *Suchomimus* was a fish-eating predator with huge but narrow croc-odilelike jaws and powerful forelimbs with long thumb claws. Although *Suchomimus*, which means "crocodile mimic," was adapted to eating large fish, it probably stalked terrestrial prey as well.

SERENO AT THE NATIONAL GEOGRAPHIC SOCIETY WITH CAST SKULL OF *SUCHOMIMUS TENERENSIS*

BIG BROWSERS

The largest dinosaurs ever to roam Earth's surface were the long-tailed, long-necked, barrel-bodied sauropods such as *Seismosaurus*, *Diplodocus*, and *Apatosaurus*. These enormous plant-eaters—Seismosaurus was 36 meters long and weighed between 80 and 100 tons—could have browsed on leaves high in the treetops. Sauropods had small jaws and teeth. Their leafy meals were ground up in their stomachs with the help of sharp-edged pebbles, called gastroliths, that were probably swallowed along with their food.

APATOSAURUS

EXPANDING Your View

1 **THINK CRITICALLY** Compare and contrast the feeding adaptations of a plant-eating ornithischian and a meat-eating saurischian.

2 **JOURNAL WRITING** Using library resources and Web links at **in.bdol.glencoe.com**, research the hypothesis that dinosaurs disappeared as the result of a mass extinction caused by a giant meteor or asteroid colliding with Earth. Analyze, review, and critique the strengths and weaknesses of this hypothesis.

1085

Display

Interpersonal Prepare a large outline map of the world. Post the map on a classroom wall or bulletin board. Provide students with the resources necessary to identify where in the world different types of dinosaur fossils have been found. Have students work together to create a key that identifies each location according to dinosaur type on the map. **L2**
COOP LEARN

Misconception

Explain to students that movies often lead people to believe that humans and dinosaurs existed at the same time. Emphasize that dinosaurs became extinct at the end of the Cretaceous Period, 65 million years ago. Explain that humans have existed on Earth for fewer than 2 million years. Use these facts to demonstrate that humans and dinosaurs did not occupy Earth at the same time.

Expanding Your View

1. The ornithischians had adaptations, such as duckbills, that enabled them to eat plants. The saurischians were carnivores with heavy jaws and sharp teeth.

2. Dinosaurs became extinct at the end of the Cretaceous Period, 65 million years ago. This corresponds to the age of a meteorite that hit Earth near the Yucatan Peninsula in Mexico.

INCLUSION STRATEGIES

Visually Impaired Purchase scientifically accurate plastic dinosaur models. Allow visually impaired students to handle them to develop an understanding of the shapes and features of these animals. Help students estimate the true size of the actual organisms. **L1 ELL**

Focus On

Placental Mammals

Purpose

Students will examine the main orders of placental mammals.

Background

Once in their own order, the pinnipeds (seals, sea lions, and walruses) have been subsumed by order Carnivora. Scientists continue to refine their classification as more information becomes available. Besides the 12 orders shown here, the placental mammals also include the following orders: Dermoptera, the gliding lemurs (also called colugos); Pholidota, the scaly anteaters (also called pangolins); Tubulidentata, the aardvarks; Hyracoidea, the hyraxes; Scandentia, the tree shrews; and Macroscelidea, the elephant shrews.

Whales are divided into two subgroups based upon how they feed. One group of whales has teeth; this group includes the killer whales and dolphins shown here. These toothed whales feed on fishes, mollusks, and other aquatic mammals. The other subgroup of whales is made up of whales that have baleen rather than teeth. Baleen acts like a giant strainer that captures tiny organisms, such as krill, present in the water. As a baleen whale swims, it gulps water containing small organisms. As the water passes through the baleen, the organisms become trapped, becoming the whale's next meal.

JACKRABBIT

FOCUS ON

Placental Mammals

ORDER LAGOMORPHA
From a standstill, a jackrabbit can leap straight into the air. Rabbits, pikas, and hares belong to the lagomorph order. Most lagomorphs have hind legs suited for leaping. They also have two pairs of chisel-like incisors that grow throughout their lives.

Most of the more than 4300 species of mammals are placental mammals—whose young are nourished by a placenta while they complete development within the mother's uterus. At birth, however, newborn placental mammals vary widely. Some newborn gazelles can run fast enough to keep up with the herd within days of birth. Young kittens are blind and helpless. A human baby spends many years dependent on its parents before it can take care of itself. Many mammalogists recognize 18 orders of placental mammals, of which 12 are shown here.

CHIMPANZEE

ORDER PRIMATES
Chimpanzees communicate, walk upright, and make and use tools. Some unique characteristics of primates include opposable thumbs, flattened nails, excellent vision, and keen intelligence. Most primates also have complex social lives. Chimps—like orangutans, gorillas, and gibbons—are apes. Along with apes, lemurs, Old and New World monkeys, and humans are primates.

JAGUAR

ORDER CARNIVORA
Powerful and golden-eyed, the jaguar is the largest cat in North and South America. Like all carnivores, the jaguar has long, pointed canines to puncture and tear, and molars to cut and crush the flesh of prey. Some carnivores have claws that help them seize their prey. Most carnivores are meat eaters; some, such as bears and raccoons, consume plant material as well, and the panda mainly eats bamboo.

1086 (in.bdol.glencoe.com/news)

PROJECT

Endangered Mammals Provide students with a current list of endangered mammal species in the United States. Identify the state(s) in which each mammal is found. Have students write the names of the mammals in their correct state(s) on an outline map. Next, explain that the state in which a particular mammal lives wants to remove the animal from the endangered species list in order to develop the area for housing, malls, and businesses. Ask students to assume they are going to testify as expert mammalogists in favor of preserving the endangered animal's habitat. Have them present their testimony to the class. **L2**

AFRICAN CRESTED PORCUPINE

ORDER RODENTIA

Needle-sharp quills protect porcupines from enemies. The African crested porcupine—shown here eating a desert melon—is larger and heavier than its distant relatives in North and South America and has much longer quills. Porcupines, beavers, and chipmunks are rodents, along with rats and mice. Rodents, the largest order of mammals, live in all environments. Rodents have continuously growing, razor-sharp incisors, which they use to gnaw on hard seeds, bark, twigs, and roots.

BOTTLE-NOSED DOLPHINS

MANATEE

ORDER CETACEA

The bottle-nosed dolphin, a kind of toothed whale, uses squeaks, growls, whistles, and other sounds to communicate. Dolphins, porpoises, and whales—all members of the order Cetacea—have large complex brains. Little or no hair, streamlined bodies, dorsal fins, specialized forelimbs (flippers), extremely small or absent hind limbs, and the ability to breathe through blowholes on the tops of their heads are other characteristics they share.

ORDER SIRENIA

Slow-moving manatees cruise near the surface of warm, tropical waters and are often injured by speedboats. They can nap underwater for up to 15 minutes, but they must come to the surface to breathe. They have tails and front flippers like whales, distinct heads with a snout that points downward, and short necks. Manatees and dugongs, both of which are nicknamed "sea cows," belong to the order Sirenia, which includes only four species.

1087

Teaching Strategies

■ Ask students to solve the following problem: A little brown bat's diet consists of 20% mosquitoes. It eats 4 grams of food per night. How many mosquitoes does it eat in one night if a mosquito weighs 2.2 milligrams? 364 per night How many mosquitoes will it eat in one summer during June, July, and August? 33 488 per summer

■ Borrow a collection of mammal skulls from a local college or museum. Ask students to examine the teeth in each skull. In their groups, have them hypothesize about the type of food each mammal eats.

■ Have students working in groups create a photo essay that shows examples of mammals classified in each order discussed in this feature. Each group should focus on a different mammal order. Have students combine their materials into a class bulletin board display. **L2** **ELL** **COOP LEARN**

Visual Learning

Ask students to look at the jackrabbit and the porcupine on these two pages. Remind them that rodents include mice, rats, gerbils, squirrels, chipmunks, and so on. Ask students why they think rabbits are not included with the rodents in one order. There are differences in bone structure and teeth.

CHALLENGE ACTIVITY

Lemur Classification The Dermoptera, or gliding lemurs, at times have been placed into several different orders. Have students research gliding lemurs and find out and report on why they are not classified along with other lemurs into the order Primates. **L3**

Background

Armadillos are the only members of the order Edentata that live in the United States. Although the armadillo has hair, its most distinguishing feature is its hardened skin, which is arranged in a pattern of either six or nine bands around the armadillo's body. This tough, banded skin acts like a suit of armor to protect the armadillo from predators. When frightened, the animal rolls itself up into a tight ball, with its exterior armor protecting its head, limbs, and soft underbelly.

Most members of the order Artiodactyla live in plains and savannas, but others dwell in forests, and one group is semiaquatic. Within the order are some of the fastest-running mammals including antelope, but the order Artiodactyla also includes some slow and cumbersome species including pigs and hippopotamuses. Artiodactyls are native to all continents except Australia and Antarctica. The order contains a number of domesticated species such as sheep, goats, camels, llamas, pigs, and cows.

HAIRY-TAILED MOLE

ORDER INSECTIVORA

The hairy-tailed mole of North America seldom comes out of its tunnel. Designed for digging, the mole's front feet are powerful earth movers. Its eyes are nearly covered by thick, soft fur, and its eyesight is poor. Moles, shrews, and hedgehogs use their senses of smell, hearing, and touch to find food. Although they all mainly eat insects and most have pointed snouts and sharp claws for digging, insectivores have few other shared characteristics.

ORDER PERISSODACTYLA

The wild Przewalski (Pruz WOL skee) horses from Mongolia look similar to the ancestor of all modern horses. These hairy horses have thick legs and sturdy bodies. Zoos throughout the world have breeding programs to save this species. Hooved mammals with an odd number of toes, including horses, tapirs, and rhinos, belong to the order Perissodactyla. Most hoofed mammals are herbivores with molars for grinding.

PRZEWALSKI HORSES

ARMADILLO

ORDER XENARTHRA

Don't let their armor fool you—these are mammals. Plates of skin-covered bone protect most of the armadillo's body. But like anteaters and sloths—the other members of this order—armadillos are well equipped for digging. They lack incisors and canines and their molars are small cylinders without enamel. Xenarthras are found in Central and South America and in southern regions of North America.

1088

PROJECT

Lead and Mammal Development Mammalian development is adversely affected by high levels of lead. Mammal bones and teeth absorb lead because it is similar to calcium. When calcium is replaced by lead, toxic effects result. Have students research a study of California sea otters in which lead was found in their teeth. Have students create a poster that shows the pathway that lead takes from the environment into the bodies of the otters. Have them infer from the results of this otter study how lead could affect their own health. L3

1088

Focus On

Evolution of the Brain

Purpose

Students will explore the evolution of the brain by comparing the brains of different animals. They will also learn about brain structure and function.

Background

Functionally, the human brain can be divided into the lobes of the cerebrum (including the cerebral cortex), the cerebellum, and the brain stem—pons, midbrain, and medulla oblongata.

Over the course of human evolution, the human brain has tripled in size. Scientists surmise that the increase in brain size accompanied the developed use of tools and other skills that enabled our ancestors to live in a greater variety of habitats.

Teaching Strategies

■ Have students in groups draw a large outline of the brain on a piece of poster paper. Have them cut out magazine pictures that relate to the specializations of the brain and glue them on their outline. For instance, they could cut out eyes and place them in the occipital lobe to indicate that is where vision is interpreted. **L1**
COOP LEARN

■ Have students make scale models of the cerebrums in the different animals shown. Then have them compare the size of the cerebrum with the size of the animal. Which animal has the largest cerebrum for its body size? Which has the smallest? **L2**

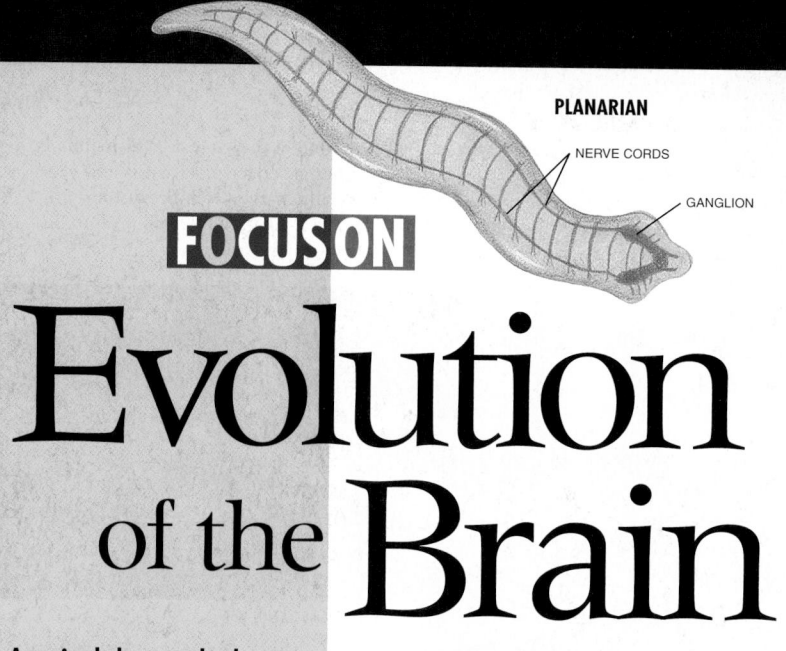

PLANARIAN
NERVE CORDS
GANGLION

FOCUS ON

Evolution of the Brain

As animals have evolved over hundreds of millions of years, there has been a tendency toward ever-increasing complexity in the nervous system, and especially, in the brain. Brains had their beginnings as relatively simple bundles of nerve cells. But over time, the brains of vertebrate animals have become more complex and specialized. Humans possess the most complex brain in the animal kingdom, a remarkable organ that enables us to reason, wonder, and dream.

THE EVOLVING BRAIN

Jumping ahead millions of years to when the vertebrates emerged, the five brains shown here illustrate how evolution has transformed a simple ganglion to a complex brain. As the brain evolved, areas that control senses, behavior, and coordination became predominant.

Notice that in humans the brain is proportionally much larger than it is in many other vertebrates and that the area dedicated to thinking, the cerebrum, covers and dominates everything else.

THE SIMPLEST BRAIN

Flatworms are the simplest animals that have an identifiable brain. A planarian, for example, has a mass of nerve tissue called a ganglion that lies beneath each eyespot. Extending back from these ganglia are long nerve cords that run the length of the body. Between the cords are cross connections that make the planarian nervous system look like a ladder.

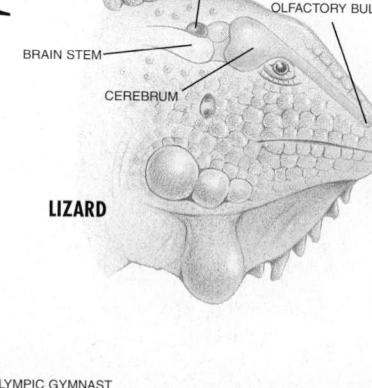

CEREBELLUM
OLFACTORY BULB
BRAIN STEM
CEREBRUM

LIZARD

OLYMPIC GYMNAST

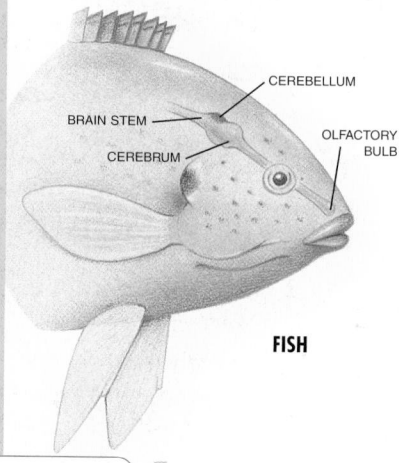

CEREBELLUM
BRAIN STEM
CEREBRUM
OLFACTORY BULB

FISH

in.bdol.glencoe.com/news

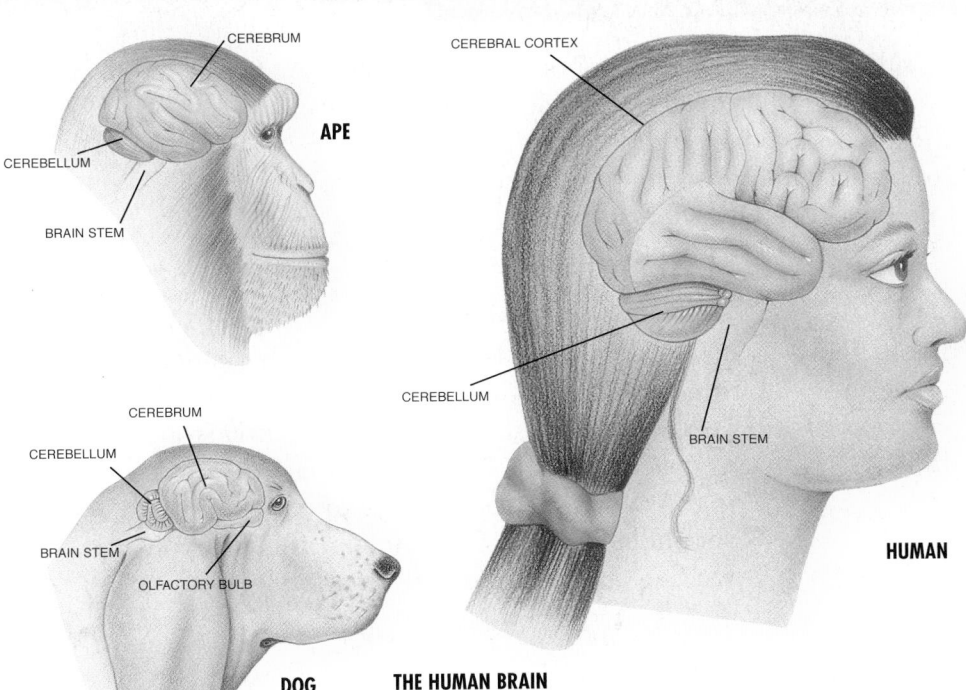

APE

CEREBRUM

CEREBELLUM

BRAIN STEM

CEREBRUM

CEREBELLUM

BRAIN STEM

OLFACTORY BULB

DOG

CEREBRAL CORTEX

CEREBELLUM

BRAIN STEM

HUMAN

HEARING WORDS

SEEING WORDS

SPEAKING WORDS

GENERATING WORDS

PET SCAN

GIRL PLAYING A VIOLIN

THE HUMAN BRAIN

The largest part of the human brain is the cerebrum. The cerebrum is divided into two hemispheres, left and right. But the feature that makes the cerebrum unique is an outer, folded layer less than 5 mm thick—the cerebral cortex. Because of the cortex, you can remember, reason, organize, communicate, understand, and create.

When you watch an Olympic gymnast perform on the balance beam, you are witnessing the work of a well-trained cerebellum. It is here that muscles are coordinated and the memories of physical skills are stored.

The brain stem consists of the medulla, pons, and midbrain. The brain stem regulates breathing, heart rate, circulation, and other vital body processes.

COMPLEX COORDINATION

The cerebral cortex may look like a uniform mass of nerve tissue. But different areas of the cortex receive and process different types of sensory, motor, and integrative nerve impulses. Using a technological tool known as a PET (positron emission tomography) scan (above left), scientists can pinpoint areas of increased metabolic activity in the brain. In so doing they can identify specific regions of the cortex that are involved in complex behaviors such as playing—from memory—a musical composition on the violin.

EXPANDING Your View

1. **THINK CRITICALLY** What are the advantages of having nervous tissue and sense organs concentrated in the head region?

2. **JOURNAL WRITING** In your journal, record your predictions about how a person's behavior might be affected by an injury to the cerebellum.

1091

Enrichment

Have students research the work of evolutionary biologists such as Niles Eldridge and Stephen Jay Gould. What facts are they able to base their work on? How much do they have to infer from fossil and other records?

Visual Learning

Visual-Spatial Display models or posters of various vertebrate brains. Point out the differences among the brains. **L1**

Tying to Prior Knowledge

Review the evolutionary sequence of the various phyla, paying special attention to the evolutionary tree of the vertebrates.

Expanding Your View

1. For animals that move in a forward direction, sights, sounds, and smells can be sensed more immediately.
2. The cerebellum coordinates physical skills, such as walking. Damage to this area of the brain could cause a person to have jerky, uncoordinated movements.

Going Further

Students interested in the evolution and function of the brain can read *Dragons of Eden*, by Carl Sagan.

ACTIVE READING AND STUDY SKILLS

Reading a science textbook is different than reading a novel. Reading science requires you to read slowly and carefully, paying close attention to details. The goal of reading a science textbook is to have a thorough understanding of what you read and to be able to retain the information presented. Here are some suggestions for reading *Biology: The Dynamics of Life*.

Preparing to Read

Before you begin reading your textbook, find a quiet and comfortable place to read. A good place to study allows you to focus on your work and better comprehend what you read.

Chapter Preview

Before you begin to read a new chapter, look through the chapter to see what subject matter is presented. Look at the chapter title and each section title. Ask yourself what you already know and what you would like to learn about these topics.

Section Objectives

Each section contains a list of objectives that tell you what you will learn. Try to recall what you already know about the objectives. When you finish reading each section, read the objectives again to check that you understand them.

Section Vocabulary

At the beginning of each section, there are two vocabulary lists. One reviews a vocabulary word and definition from a previous chapter. Another lists new vocabulary words. Before you read, write these words on a piece of paper. In your own words, write definitions of the words that are familiar to you. Check this list and fill in definitions for new words while you read.

Active Reading

Active reading is the process of thinking about what you are reading while you read. It requires you to read at a slower pace, frequently stopping to check that you understand what you are reading. As you practice this type of reading, you should be better able to understand what you are reading and retain the information longer.

Using Your Textbook

As an active reader, there are several textbook features you can use to check your understanding. For example, figures and tables are referenced in the textbook in ***boldface italic*** type.

When you come across a figure or table reference, stop. Study the figure or table. Notice any arrows or labels. Read the caption. Figures and tables often are summaries of important information and can be useful references when studying for quizzes and exams.

You will notice questions called *Reading Checks* throughout the text. Use them to make sure you understand the main idea of the previous paragraphs before you read on. If you cannot answer the question, go back and reread the paragraph.

Practice Problem 1 Create a checklist that you can use to remind yourself of things to do before you read that can help you be a more active reader. Sample answer: 1. Find a quiet place to study; 2. Preview section titles and objectives; 3. Try to recall previous knowledge; 4. List vocabulary words and fill in definitions of words I know.

SECTION PREVIEW

Objectives

Relate advances in microscope technology to discoveries about cells and cell structure.

Compare the operation of a compound light microscope with that of an electron microscope.

Identify the main ideas of the cell theory.

Review Vocabulary
organization: the orderly structure of cells in an organism (p. 7)

New Vocabulary
cell
compound light microscope
cell theory
electron microscope
organelle
prokaryote
eukaryote
nucleus

Concept Maps

While you read this textbook, you will be looking for important ideas, or concepts. One way to organize these concepts is to create a concept map. A concept map is similar to a road map but instead of showing relationships among locations, it shows relationships among concepts. Developing your own concept maps while you read will help you better understand and remember what you read. Three styles of concept maps that you might find useful are events chains, cycle maps, and network trees.

Events Chain An events-chain concept map is used to describe a sequence of events. These events could include the steps in a procedure or the stages of a process. When making an events-chain map, first identify the initiating event—the event that starts the sequence. Continue adding events in chronological order until you reach an outcome. An example of an events-chain map is shown below.

Practice Problem 2 Create an events-chain concept map to display the steps you take to get ready for school. Students' events chains should contain an initiating event and an outcome.

Cycle Map In a cycle concept map, the series of events do not produce a final outcome. The last event in the chain relates back to the initiating

event. Therefore, the cycle repeats itself. Follow the stages shown below in the cycle map of blood flow through the human circulatory system.

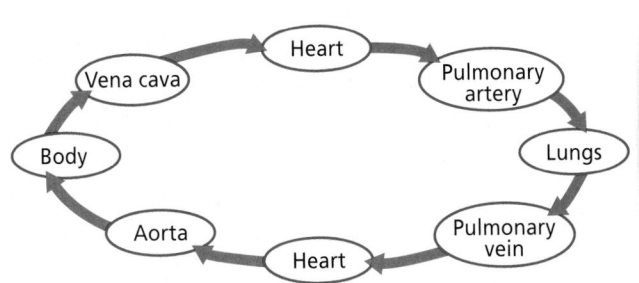

Network Tree A network tree concept map shows the relationship among concepts. Circled words, or concepts, are written in order from general to specific. In the network tree below, the most general concept is *Populations*. The next two concepts, *Autotrophs* and *Heterotrophs*, are subcategories of communities. The words written on the lines between the circles, called linking words, describe the relationships among the concepts. Together, the concepts and the linking words can form a sentence. For example, *Populations* are made up of *heterotrophs*, which include *carnivores* such as *lions*.

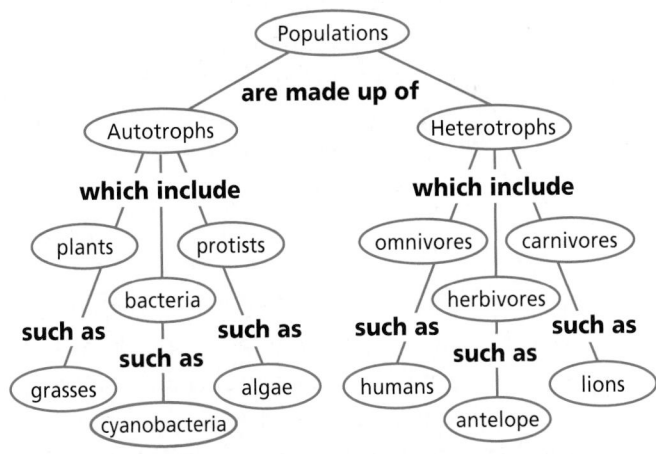

Practice Problem 3 Create a three-level network tree concept map about the different types of concept maps. Students' concept maps should contain main concepts in circles and linking words on connecting lines.

Foldables™

Instructions on how to create Foldable™ graphic organizers are featured in each chapter of the book. As you read the chapter, fill in the sections of your Foldable as part of your active reading process. When you finish reading a chapter, fill in any missing or incomplete information in your Foldable. Then use it to review for quizzes and exams on that topic. An example of a Foldable is shown below.

FOLDABLES
Study Organizer

The Cell Theory Make the following Foldable to help you organize the ideas of the cell theory.

STEP 1 **Collect** 2 sheets of paper and layer them about 1.5 cm apart vertically. Keep the edges level.

STEP 2 **Fold** up the bottom edges of the paper to form 4 equal tabs.

STEP 3 **Fold** the papers and crease well to hold the tabs in place. Staple along the fold. **Label** each tab with one of the main ideas of the cell theory.

Summarize After you read Section 7.1, summarize the three main ideas of the cell theory in your own words. Review the theory using the information provided and note its strengths and weaknesses.

Outline

Chapter and section headings provide a framework to start a chapter outline. As you read, add details under the heads to create an outline of the chapter that includes key concepts and vocabulary words. Use the chapter outline to learn the new material and to review for tests and quizzes.

Review for Understanding

Reviewing a chapter can be approached in two ways. One way is to memorize definitions and key concepts. If you've ever attempted this review method, you may have experienced sitting in an exam and drawing a blank when trying to think of an answer. Simply memorizing the information makes it difficult to remember it for very long.

Another way to review a chapter is to attempt to gain an understanding of it. If you study a process in biology, such as respiration, take the time to understand how each step in the process contributes to the end result—the release of energy that cells can use.

Get the Big Picture

When a new concept is introduced, it is important to learn how the idea fits into the "Big Picture." Ask yourself, "How does this new concept relate to the other things that I have learned?" Learning how concepts are interrelated increases your understanding of each part.

Using an Analogy

An analogy is a relationship between two different things that have some characteristics in common. For example, nerve cells can be analogous to telephone wires. Both use electric current to transmit signals from one location to another. Creating an analogy between something you are familiar with, such as telephone wires, and something new that you are learning about can make complex ideas easier to understand and remember.

When using an analogy, it is important to know how the two concepts are different. For example, if two wires are joined to make a single wire, the current in the single wire is the sum of the currents in the two wires. However, the current in a nerve cell does not depend on its connections to other nerve cells. All signals are transmitted with the same current. A nerve cell is either transmitting a signal or it's at rest.

Section and Chapter Assessments

Assessment questions allow you to test your knowledge at the end of a section or chapter. If you cannot answer a question, go back and reread the section of the chapter that discusses the material. If you are still having trouble, make a note to ask your teacher.

Understanding Scientific Terms

This list of prefixes, suffixes, and roots is provided to help you understand science terms used throughout this biology textbook. The list identifies whether the prefix, suffix, or root is of Greek (G) or Latin (L) origin. Also listed is the meaning of the prefix, suffix, or root and a science word in which it is used.

ORIGIN	MEANING	EXAMPLE
A		
ad (L)	to, toward	adaxial
aero (G)	air	aerobic
an (G)	without	anaerobic
ana (G)	up	anaphase
andro (G)	male	androcium
angio (G)	vessel	angiosperm
anth/o (G)	flower	anthophyte
anti (G)	against	antibody
aqu/a (L)	of water	aquatic
archae (G)	ancient	archaebacteria
arthro, artio (G)	jointed	arthropod
askos (G)	bag	ascospore
aster (G)	star	Asteroidea
autos (G)	self	autoimmune
B		
bi (L)	two	bipedal
bio (G)	life	biosphere
C		
carn (L)	flesh	carnivore
cephalo (G)	head	cephalopod
chlor (G)	light green	chlorophyll
chroma (G)	pigmented	chromosome
cide (L)	to kill	insecticide
circ (L)	circular	circadian
cocc/coccus (G)	small and round	streptococcus
con (L)	together	convergent
cyte (G)	cell	cytoplasm
D		
de (L)	remove	decompose
dendron (G)	tree	dendrite
dent (L)	tooth	edentate
derm (G)	skin	epidermis
di (G)	two	disaccharide
dia (G)	apart	diaphragm
dorm (L)	sleep	dormancy

ORIGIN	MEANING	EXAMPLE
E		
echino (G)	spiny	echinoderm
ec (G)	outer	ecosystem
endo (G)	within	endosperm
epi (G)	upon	epidermis
eu (G)	true	eukaryote
exo (G)	outside	exoskeleton
F		
fer (L)	to carry	conifer
G		
gastro (G)	stomach	gastropod
gen/(e)(o) (G)	kind	genotype
genesis (G)	to originate	oogenesis
gon (G)	reproductive	archegonium
gravi (L)	heavy	gravitropism
gymn/o (G)	naked	gymnosperm
gyn/e (G)	female	gynoecium
H		
hal(o) (G)	salt	halophyte
hapl(o) (G)	single	haploid
hemi (G)	half	hemisphere
hem(o) (G)	blood	hemoglobin
herb/a(i) (L)	vegetation	herbivore
heter/o (G)	different	heterotrophic
hom(e)/o (G)	same	homeostasis
hom (L)	human	hominid
hydr/o (G)	water	hydrolysis
I		
inter (L)	between	internode
intra (L)	within	intracellular
is/o (G)	equal	isotonic

ORIGIN	MEANING	EXAMPLE	ORIGIN	MEANING	EXAMPLE
K			pinna (L)	feather	pinnate
kary (G)	nucleus	eukaryote	plasm/o (G)	to form	plasmodium
kera (G)	hornlike	keratin	pod (G)	foot	gastropod
			poly (G)	many	polymer
L			post (L)	after	posterior
leuc/o (G)	white	leukocyte	pro (G) (L)	before	prokaryote
logy (G)	study of	biology	prot/o (G)	first	protocells
lymph/o (L)	water	lymphocyte	pseud/o (G)	false	pseudopodium
lysis (G)	break up	dialysis			
			R		
M			re (L)	back to original	reproduce
macr/o (G)	large	macromolecule	rhiz/o (G)	root	rhizoid
meg/a (G)	great	megaspore			
meso (G)	in the middle	mesophyll	**S**		
meta (G)	after	metaphase	scope (G)	to look	microscope
micr/o (G)	small	microscope	some (G)	body	lysosome
mon/o (G)	only one	monocotyledon	sperm (G)	seed	gymnosperm
morph/o (G)	form	morphology	stasis (G)	remain constant	homeostasis
			stom (G)	mouthlike opening	stomata
N			syn (G)	together	synapse
nema (G)	a thread	nematode			
neuro (G)	nerve	neuron	**T**		
nod (L)	knot	nodule	tel/o (G)	end	telophase
nomy(e) (G)	system of laws	taxonomy	terr (L)	of Earth	terrestrial
			therm (G)	heat	endotherm
O			thylak (G)	sack	thylakoid
olig/o (G)	small, few	oligochaete	trans (L)	across	transpiration
omni (L)	all	omnivore	trich (G)	hair	trichome
orni(s) (G)	bird	ornithology	trop/o (G)	a change	gravitropism
oste/o (G)	bone formation	osteocyte	trophic (G)	nourishment	heterotrophic
ov (L)	an egg	oviduct			
			U		
P			uni (L)	one	unicellular
pal(a)e/o (G)	ancient	paleontology			
para (G)	beside	parathyroid	**V**		
path/o (G)	suffering	pathogen	vacc/a (L)	cow	vaccine
ped (L)	foot	centipede	vore (L)	eat greedily	omnivore
per (L)	through	permeable			
peri (G)	around, about	peristalsis	**X**		
phag/o (G)	eating	phagocyte	xer/o (G)	dry	xerophyte
phot/o (G)	light	photosynthesis			
phyl (G)	race, class	phylogeny	**Z**		
phyll (G)	leaf	chlorophyll	zo/o (G)	living being	zoology
phyte (G)	plant	epiphyte	zygous (G)	two joined	homozygous

MATH AND PROBLEM-SOLVING SKILLS

Math Skills

Experimental data is often expressed using numbers and units. The following sections provide an overview of the common system of units and some calculations involving units.

Measure in SI

The International System of Measurement, abbreviated SI, is accepted as the standard for measurement throughout most of the world. The SI system contains seven base units. All other units of measurement can be derived from these base units by multiplying the units by factors of 10 or by combining units.

Table SH.1 SI Base Units		
Measurement	**Unit**	**Symbol**
Length	meter	m
Mass	kilogram	kg
Time	second	s
Electric current	ampere	A
Temperature	kelvin	K
Amount of substance	mole	mol
Intensity of light	candela	cd

When units are multiplied by factors of 10, new units are created. For example, if a base unit is multiplied by 1000, the new unit has the prefix *kilo*. One thousand meters is equal to 1 kilometer. Prefixes for some units are shown below.

Table SH.2 Common SI Prefixes		
Prefix	**Symbol**	**Equivalents**
mega	M	= 1 000 000 base units
kilo	k	= 1000 base units
hecto	h	= 100 base unit
deka	da	= 10 base units
deci	d	= 1×10^{-1} base units
centi	c	= 1×10^{-2} base units
milli	m	= 1×10^{-3} base units
micro	μ	= 1×10^{-6} base units
nano	n	= 1×10^{-9} base units
pico	p	= 1×10^{-12} base units

Some units are derived by combining base units. For example, units for volume are derived from units of length. A liter (L) is a cubic decimeter (dm^3, or $dm \times dm \times dm$). Units of density (g/L) are derived from units of mass (g) and units of volume (L).

To convert a given unit to a unit with a different factor of ten, multiply the unit by a conversion factor. A conversion factor is a ratio equal to one. The equivalents in Table SH.2 can be used to make such a ratio. For example, 1 km = 1000 m. Two conversion factors can be made from this equivalent.

$$\frac{1000 \text{ m}}{1 \text{ km}} = 1 \quad \text{and} \quad \frac{1 \text{ km}}{1000 \text{ m}} = 1$$

To convert one unit to another factor of 10, choose the conversion factor that has the unit you are converting from in the denominator.

$$1 \text{ km} \times \frac{1000 \text{ m}}{1 \text{ km}} = 1000 \text{ m}$$

A unit can be multiplied by several conversion factors to obtain the desired unit.

Practice Problem 4 How would you change 1000 milligrams to kilograms?

Convert Temperature

The following formulas can be used to convert between Fahrenheit and Celsius temperatures. Notice that each equation can be obtained by algebraically rearranging the other. Therefore, you only need to remember one of the equations.

Conversion of Fahrenheit to Celsius

$$°C = \frac{(°F) - 32}{1.8}$$

Conversion of Celsius to Fahrenheit

$$°F = 1.8(°C) + 32$$

Practice Problem 4 answer:

$$1000 \text{ mg} \times \frac{1 \text{ g}}{1000 \text{ mg}} \times \frac{1 \text{ kg}}{1000 \text{ g}} = 0.001 \text{ kg}$$

Calculate Magnification

Magnification describes how much larger an object appears when viewed through a microscope compared to the unaided eye. Look for numbers marked with an × on the eyepiece, the low-power objective, and the high-power objective. The × represents how many times the lens of each microscope part magnifies an object.

To calculate total magnification of any object viewed under your microscope, multiply the number on the eyepiece by the number on each objective. For example, if the eyepiece magnification is 4× and the low-power objective magnification is 10×, then the total magnification is 4 × 10, or 40, under low power. If the high-power objective magnification is 40×, the total magnification is 4 × 40, or 160×, under high power.

Practice Problem 5 Calculate the low-power and high-power magnification of a microscope that has an eyepiece with a magnification of 10×, a low-power objective of 40×, and a high-power objective of 60×. low power: 10 × 40 = 400; high power 10 × 60 = 600

Calculate Field of View

To measure the field of view of a microscope, you must use a unit called a micrometer (μm). There are 1000 micrometers in a millimeter. Place the millimeter-section of a plastic ruler over the central opening of your microscope stage. Using low power, locate the lines of the ruler in the center of the field of view. Move the ruler so that one of the lines representing a millimeter is visible at one edge of the field of view.

Remember that the distance between two lines is one millimeter, and estimate the diameter in millimeters of the field of view on low power. Use the conversion factor given above to calculate the

diameter in micrometers. For example, if the distance is 1.5 mm, then the diameter of the field of view at low power is

$$1.5 \text{ mm} \times 1000\frac{\mu m}{mm}, \text{ or } 1500 \text{ } \mu m.$$

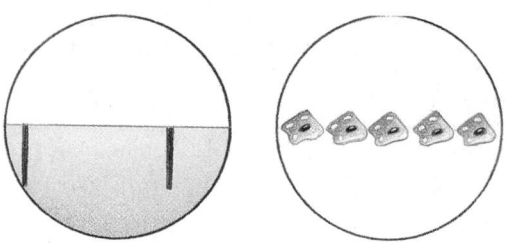

To calculate the diameter of the high-power field, divide the magnification of your high power (40×) by the magnification of the low power (10×), or 40 ÷ 10 = 4. Then, divide the diameter of the low-power field in micrometers (1500 μm) by this quotient (4). The result is the diameter of the high-power field in micrometers. In this example, the diameter of the high-power field is 1500 μm ÷ 4 = 375 μm.

You can calculate the diameters of microscopic specimens, such as pollen grains or amoebas, viewed under low and high power by estimating how many of them could fit end to end across the field of view. Divide the diameter of the field of view by the number of specimens.

If you want to know the actual size of any specimen shown in an electron micrograph in this textbook, follow these directions:

a. measure the diameter of the structure in millimeters,
b. multiply this number by 1000 μm/mm to convert the measurement to micrometers,
c. then divide this number by the magnification given next to the photograph.

Practice Problem 6

Calculate the actual size of one of the organisms shown in this electron micrograph.
Sample answer:

$$17 \text{ mm} \times 1000\frac{\mu m}{mm} = 17\ 000 \text{ } \mu m.$$

$$17\ 000 \text{ } \mu m \div 900 = 19 \text{ } \mu m.$$

Color-enhanced SEM Magnification: 900×

Make and Use Tables

Tables help organize data so that it can be interpreted more easily. Tables are composed of several components—a title describing the contents of the table, columns and rows that separate and organize information, and headings that describe the information in each column or row.

Table SH.3 Effect of Exercise on Heart Rate		
Pulse Taken	Individual Heart Rate	Class Average
At rest	73	72
After exercise	110	112
1 minute after exercise	94	90
5 minutes after exercise	76	75

Looking at this table, you should not only be able to pick out specific information, such as the class average heart rate after five minutes of exercise, but you should also notice trends.

Practice Problem 7 Did the exercise have an effect on the heart rate five minutes after exercise? How can you tell? The 5-minute heart rates were higher than the rest heart rates, and were therefore still affected by the exercise.

Make and Use Graphs

After scientists organize data in tables, they often display the data in graphs. A graph is a diagram that shows relationships among variables. Graphs make interpretation and analysis of data easier. The three basic types of graphs used in science are the line graph, the bar graph, and the circle graph.

Line Graphs A line graph is used to show the relationship between two variables. The independent variable is plotted on the horizontal axis, called the x-axis. The dependent variable is plotted on the vertical axis, called the y-axis. The dependent variable (y) changes as a result of a change in the independent variable (x).

Suppose a school started a peer-study program with a class of students to see how the program affected their science grades. The students' average science grades were collected and recorded every 30 days for the first four months of the school year. A table of their grades is shown below.

Table SH.4 Average Grades of Students in Study Program	
Time (days)	Average Science Grade
30	81%
60	85%
90	86%
120	89%

To make a graph of the grades of students in the program over a period of time, start by determining the dependent and independent variables. The average grade of the students in the program after each time increment is the dependent variable and is plotted on the y-axis. The independent variable, or the number of days, is plotted on the x-axis.

Plain or graph paper can be used to construct graphs. Draw a grid on your paper or a box around the squares that you intend to use on your graph paper. Give your graph a title and label each axis with a title and units. In this example, label the number of days on the x-axis. Because the lowest grade was 81% and the highest was 89%, you know that you will have to start numbering the y-axis at least at 81% and number to at least 89%. You decide to start numbering at 80% and number by twos spaced at equal distances to 90%.

Begin plotting points by locating 30 days on the *x*-axis and 81% on the *y*-axis. Where an imaginary vertical line from the *x*-axis and an imaginary horizontal line from the *y*-axis meet, place the first data point. Place other data points using the same process. After all the points are plotted, draw a "best fit" straight line through all of the points.

Average Grades of Students in Study Program

What if you want to compare the study group students' average grades with the average grades of another class? The data of the other class can be plotted on the same graph. Include a key with different lines indicating different sets of data.

Average Grades of Two Science Classes

Practice Problem 8 Which group began with the highest average grades? the regular class

Practice Problem 9 Which group's grades improved the most? By how many points did the study program students' grade average improve? the study students; 8 points

Bar Graphs A bar graph is similar to a line graph except it is used to show comparisons among data or to display data that do not continuously change. To make a bar graph, set up the *x*-axis and *y*-axis as you did for the line graph. Plot the data by drawing thick bars from the *x*-axis up to the *y*-axis data point.

Wing Vibration Rates in Insects

Look at the graph above. The independent variable is the type of insect. The dependent variable is the number of wing vibrations per second. It is easy to compare the number of wing vibrations per second of these insects when the data is plotted on a bar graph.

Practice Problem 10 How many more wing vibrations per second does the mosquito have than the insect with the least number of wing vibrations per second? 530 vibrations per second

Practice Problem 11 Which type of insect has the highest number of wing vibrations per second? Is this more than twice as fast as the housefly? Explain. mosquito; yes, doubling the vibration rate of the housefly yields 700, less than 750

Circle Graphs A circle graph consists of a circle divided into sections that represent parts of a whole. When all the sections are placed together, they equal 100 percent of the whole.

Suppose you want to make a circle graph to show the number of seeds that germinate in a package. You would first determine the total number of seeds and the number of seeds that germinate out of the total. You plant 143 seeds. Therefore, the whole circle represents this amount. You find that 129 seeds germinate. The seeds that germinate make up one section of the circle graph and the seeds that do not germinate make up another section.

To find out how much of the circle each section should cover, divide the number of seeds that germinate by the total number of seeds. Then multiply the answer by 360, the number of degrees in a circle. Round your answer to the nearest whole number. The sum of all of the segments of a circle graph should add up to 360°.

$$\text{segment of circle for seeds that germinated} =$$
$$\frac{\text{seeds that germinate}}{\text{total number of seeds}} = \frac{129}{143} \times 360° = 324.75° = 325°$$

$$\text{segment of circle for seeds that did not germinate} = 360° - 325° = 35°$$

To draw your circle graph, you will need a compass and a protractor. First, use the compass to draw a circle.

Then, draw a straight line from the center to the edge of the circle. Place your protractor on this line, and mark the point on the circle where a 35° angle will intersect the circle. Draw a straight line from the center of the circle to the intersection point. This is the section for the group of seeds that did not germinate. The other section represents the group of seeds that did germinate.

If your circle graph has more than two sections, you will need to construct a segment for

each entry. Place your protractor on the last line segment that you have drawn and mark off the appropriate angle. Draw a line segment from the center of the circle to the new mark on the circle. Continue this process until all of the segments have been drawn.

Next, determine the percentages of each part of the whole. Calculate percentages by dividing the part by the total and multiplying by 100. Repeat this calculation for each part.

$$\frac{\text{\% seeds that germinate}}{\text{total number of seeds}} = \frac{129}{143} \times 100 = 90.2\%$$

$$\text{\% seeds that do not germinate} = 100\% - 90.2\% = 9.8\%$$

Complete the graph by labeling the sections of the graph with percentages and giving the graph a title. Your completed graph should look similar to the one below.

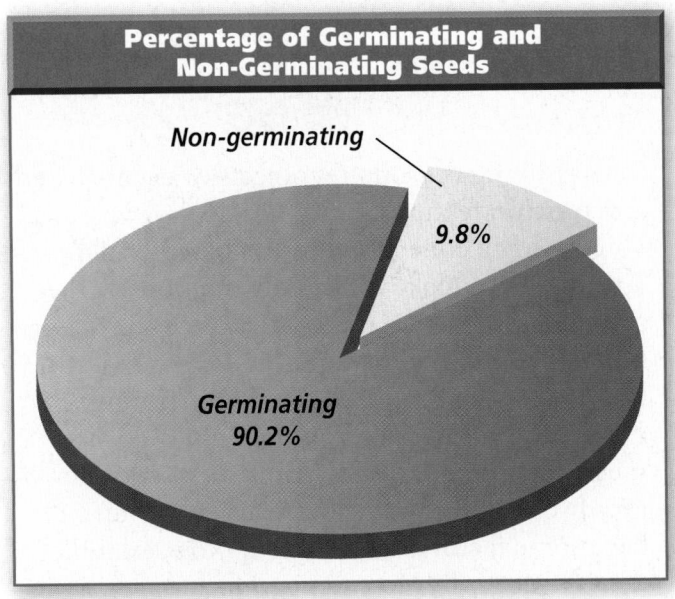

Practice Problem 12 There are 25 students in biology class. Construct a circle graph showing the percentage of students wearing each color of shirt. Five students are wearing blue shirts, eight are wearing white shirts, two are wearing yellow shirts, and 10 are wearing multicolor shirts. blue, 72°; white, 115°; yellow, 29°; and multicolor, 144°

Problem-Solving Skills

Scientists use a variety of problem-solving skills to identify problems and to propose hypotheses. The following problem-solving skills are used by all types of scientists.

Classify

You may not realize it, but you already use problem-solving skills. When you stack your favorite CDs into groups according to recording artist or when you separate your socks from your shirts, you are using the skill of classifying.

Classifying is grouping objects or events based on common features. For example, how would you classify a collection of CDs based on similarities? First, make careful observations of the group of items to be classified. Select one feature that is shared by some items in the group but not others. For example, you might classify dance CDs in one subgroup and alternative music CDs in another. You now have two subgroups. Ideally, the items in each subgroup will have some features in common. Now, examine the CDs for other features and form further subgroups. For example, the CDs you like to dance to could be subdivided into rap or pop subgroups. Continue to identify subgroups until the items can no longer be distinguished enough to identify them as distinct.

Practice Problem 13 How would you classify the following: terrier, canary, boxer, robin, parakeet, collie, and poodle? classification could be: birds and dogs, two legs and four legs, fur and feathers

All species may be classified in many different ways depending on the purpose of the classification. They are classified for identification or to show their evolutionary relationships. One is a general-purpose classification and the other is a phylogenetic classification.

Sequence

A sequence is an arrangement of things or events in a particular order. A common sequence with which you may be familiar is the sequence of the seasons in a temperate climate—spring, summer, autumn, winter. You also follow sequences of steps when you carry out a MiniLab or BioLab in this textbook. When you are asked to create a sequence of events, identify what comes first. Then decide what should come second. When you finish placing things or events in order, go back over the sequence to make sure each thing or event logically leads to the next.

Compare and Contrast

Observations can be analyzed and then organized by noting the similarities and differences between two or more objects or events. When you examine objects or events to determine similarities and differences, you are comparing and contrasting.

Practice Problem 14 Compare and contrast a leaf beetle and a weevil beetle. Make your observations on a piece of paper divided into two columns. List similarities in one column and differences in the other. After completing your lists, you might report your findings in a table or a graph.

Weevil beetle

Leaf beetle

Observe and Infer

Scientists try to make careful and accurate observations. Often they use instruments such as microscopes, binoculars, and tape recorders to extend their senses. Other instruments, such as thermometers and pan balances, are used to make measurements—numerical data that can be compared, checked, and repeated.

Scientists often use observations to make inferences. An inference is an attempt to explain observations. For example, if you observe a bird at a bird feeder, you might infer that the bird's nest is close by. But, the bird may just be passing through the area. To verify your inference, you should investigate further.

Investigating requires making thorough and accurate observations and records. Then, based on everything you know, try to explain what you observed. If possible, investigate further to determine whether your inference is correct.

Recognize Cause and Effect

Have you ever observed an event and then tried to determine how it came about? If so, you have observed an effect (the event) and inferred a cause for the effect.

Suppose that every time your teacher fed fish in a classroom aquarium, she tapped the food container on the edge. Then, one day she tapped the edge of the aquarium to make a point about an ecology lesson. You observed the fish swim to the surface of the aquarium to feed. You might infer that the tapping on the aquarium caused the fish to swim to the surface, expecting food. This is a logical inference based on observations.

Was there another cause for this effect that you may not have noticed? When scientists are unsure of the cause for an event, they often design experiments. Although your explanation is reasonable, you would have to perform an experiment to be certain that it was the tapping that caused the effect you observed.

Practice Problem 15 What are other possible explanations for the behavior of the fish? Have students list as many as they can think of.

Interpret Scientific Illustrations

Illustrations are included in your textbook to help you understand what you read. When you encounter an illustration, examine it carefully and read the caption and labels. Look at the illustrations of the roundworm and the segmented worm below. A cross section of both worms shows their internal structures. Think of a cross section as showing layers.

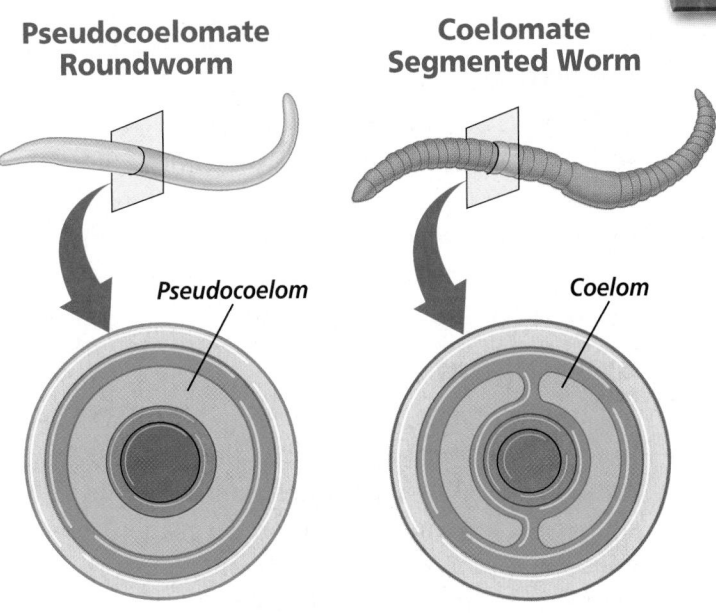

Pseudocoelomate Roundworm

Pseudocoelom

Coelomate Segmented Worm

Coelom

You will sometimes see terms that refer to the orientation of an organism. For example, the word dorsal refers to the upper side or back of an animal. Ventral refers to the lower side or belly of the animal. The illustration below shows both dorsal and ventral sides.

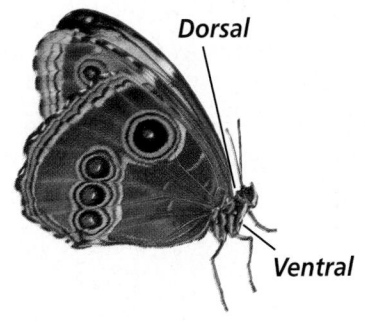

Dorsal

Ventral

LAB SKILLS AND TECHNIQUES

An important part of the work of a biologist is to make observations in nature and propose explanations for the observations. This process includes formulating testable hypotheses and then safely testing them. Good lab techniques, correct use of equipment, and safe lab procedures are part of this process.

Lab Skills

Biologists use a process that includes stating the problem, formulating a hypothesis, testing the hypothesis, and proposing an explanation for the event or observation in nature.

Hypothesize

Suppose you observe that your pet fish is less active after you change the water in the fish bowl. You might make a hypothesis to explain this behavior, such as: The number of fish movements in a given amount of time decreases with a decrease in water temperature.

Experiment

Once you state a hypothesis, you will want to find out whether or not it explains your observation. To be valid, a hypothesis must be able to be supported by experimentation. Consider how you would conduct an experiment to test the hypothesis about the effects of water temperature on fishes in an aquarium.

First, obtain five identical, clear glass containers, and fill each of them with the same amount of tap water. Leave the containers for a day to allow the water to come to room temperature. On the day of your experiment, measure and record the temperature of the water in the aquarium. Heat and cool the other containers, adjusting the water temperatures in the test containers so that two have higher temperatures and two have lower temperatures than the aquarium water temperature.

Place a fish from your aquarium in each container. Count the number of horizontal and vertical movements each fish makes during a five-minute period and record your data in a table. Your data table might look similar to the one below.

Table SH.5 Number of Fish Movements

Container	Temperature (°C)	Number of Movements
Aquarium	20	56
A	22	61
B	24	70
C	18	46
D	16	42

From your data, draw a conclusion about whether or not your results support your hypothesis. If they do not, state a new hypothesis and perform another test.

There is no number of experiments that can prove a hypothesis to be true without a shadow of a doubt. However, a hypothesis can be disproven with a single, repeatable experiment. If the results of many experiments done by many different scientists are consistent with the hypothesis, and if there are no repeatable experimental observations that disprove the hypothesis, the hypothesis may gain enough scientific support to become a theory. A theory is valid as long as no new experiments produce repeatable observations that are inconsistent with the theory.

Practice Problem 16 Do the data in the table support the hypothesis that different water temperatures affect fish activity? Explain your answer. Yes. The fish showed more activity in warmer water.

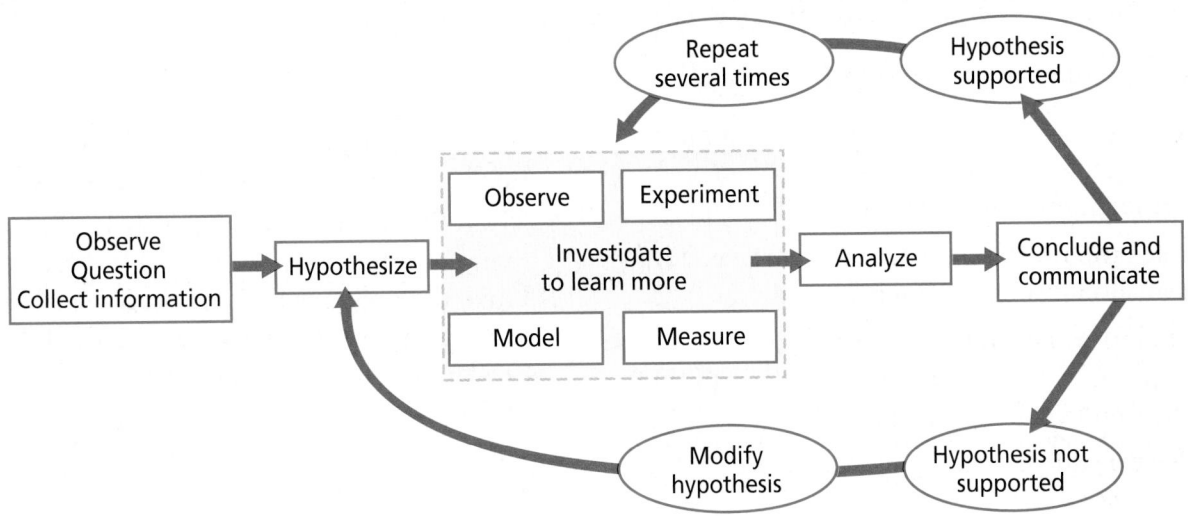

Use Variables, Constants, and Controls

When scientists perform experiments, they must be careful to manipulate or change only one condition at a time, keeping all other conditions in the experiment the same.

Independent Variable The condition that is systematically changed in an experiment is called the independent variable. In the fish experiment, the independent variable is temperature. All other conditions are kept constant. The constants in the fish experiment are the size and shape of the containers, the kind of fish, the amounts of water, and the time period. Scientists must be certain that only the independent variable (temperature) caused the change in the dependent variable (movement). All other factors must be constant in an experiment.

Dependent Variable The dependent variable is any change that results from changing the independent variable. In the fish experiment, the dependent variable is the number of movements of the fish.

Control Scientists can also use a control to be certain that the changes in the dependent variable would not have been observed with or without a change in the independent variable. A control is a sample that is treated exactly like the experimental group except that the independent variable is not applied. A common example of a controlled experiment is pharmaceutical testing. Part of a group of test subjects might receive a new pharmaceutical while the remainder receives a sugar tablet. This helps scientists determine whether or not the changes observed in the pharmaceutical test subjects were due to the pharmaceutical. Not all experiments require a control.

Practice Problem 17 Suppose that, in the previous goldfish experiment, there were several fish in the aquarium and you counted the number of movements of each fish during a fixed amount of time. The numbers of movements were: Fish 1: 53; Fish 2: 47; Fish 3: 59; Fish 4: 43; Fish 5: 69; Fish 6: 64. Upon repeating this experiment, you obtained similar results. Would this support your hypothesis that temperature affects fish activity? No. The fish in the aquarium were all the same temperature yet had varying numbers of movements.

Microscope Care and Use

1. Always carry the microscope by holding the arm of the microscope with one hand and supporting the base with the other hand.

2. Place the microscope on a flat surface. The arm should be positioned toward you.

3. Look through the eyepieces. Adjust the diaphragm so that light comes through the opening in the stage.

4. Place a slide on the stage so that the specimen is in the field of view. Hold it firmly in place by using the stage clips.

5. Always focus first with the coarse adjustment and the low-power objective lens. Once the object is in focus on low power, the high-power objective can be used. Use ONLY the fine adjustment to focus the high-power lens.

6. Store the microscope covered.

Eyepieces
Contain magnifying lenses to look through

Low-power objective
Contains the lens that is focused using coarse adjustment

Arm

Revolving nosepiece
Holds and turns the objectives into viewing position

Stage clips
Hold the microscope slide in place

High-power objectives
Contain lenses that are focused using fine adjustment only

Coarse adjustment
Focuses the image under low-power magnification

Stage
Platform used to support the microscope slide

Fine adjustment
Sharpens the image under high-power magnification

Diaphragm
Regulates the amount of light that passes through the specimen

Light source
Provides light for viewing the specimen

Safety Symbols

These safety symbols are used in laboratory and field investigations in this book to indicate possible hazards. Learn the meaning of each symbol and refer to this page often. *Remember to wash your hands thoroughly after completing lab procedures.*

SAFETY SYMBOLS	HAZARD	EXAMPLES	PRECAUTION	REMEDY
DISPOSAL	Special disposal procedures need to be followed.	certain chemicals, living organisms	Do not dispose of these materials in the sink or trash can.	Dispose of wastes as directed by your teacher.
BIOLOGICAL	Organisms or other biological materials that might be harmful to humans	bacteria, fungi, blood, unpreserved tissues, plant materials	Avoid skin contact with these materials. Wear mask or gloves.	Notify your teacher if you suspect contact with material. Wash hands thoroughly.
EXTREME TEMPERATURE	Objects that can burn skin by being too cold or too hot	boiling liquids, hot plates, dry ice, liquid nitrogen	Use proper protection when handling.	Go to your teacher for first aid.
SHARP OBJECT	Use of tools or glassware that can easily puncture or slice skin	razor blades, pins, scalpels, pointed tools, dissecting probes, broken glass	Practice common-sense behavior and follow guidelines for use of the tool.	Go to your teacher for first aid.
FUME	Possible danger to respiratory tract from fumes	ammonia, acetone, nail polish remover, heated sulfur, moth balls	Make sure there is good ventilation. Never smell fumes directly. Wear a mask.	Leave foul area and notify your teacher immediately.
ELECTRICAL	Possible danger from electrical shock or burn	improper grounding, liquid spills, short circuits, exposed wires	Double-check setup with teacher. Check condition of wires and apparatus.	Do not attempt to fix electrical problems. Notify your teacher immediately.
IRRITANT	Substances that can irritate the skin or mucous membranes of the respiratory tract	pollen, moth balls, steel wool, fiberglass, potassium permanganate	Wear dust mask and gloves. Practice extra care when handling these materials.	Go to your teacher for first aid.
CHEMICAL	Chemicals that can react with and destroy tissue and other materials	bleaches such as hydrogen peroxide; acids such as sulfuric acid, hydrochloric acid; bases such as ammonia, sodium hydroxide	Wear goggles, gloves, and an apron.	Immediately flush the affected area with water and notify your teacher.
TOXIC	Substance may be poisonous if touched, inhaled, or swallowed.	mercury, many metal compounds, iodine, poinsettia plant parts	Follow your teacher's instructions.	Always wash hands thoroughly after use. Go to your teacher for first aid.
OPEN FLAME	Open flame may ignite flammable chemicals, loose clothing, or hair.	alcohol, kerosene, potassium permanganate, hair, clothing	Tie back hair. Avoid wearing loose clothing. Avoid open flames when using flammable chemicals. Be aware of locations of fire safety equipment.	Notify your teacher immediately. Use fire safety equipment if applicable.

Eye Safety Proper eye protection should be worn at all times by anyone performing or observing science activities.

Clothing Protection This symbol appears when substances could stain or burn clothing.

Animal Safety This symbol appears when safety of animals and students must be ensured.

Radioactivity This symbol appears when radioactive materials are used.

Demonstrating Safe Lab Practices

The biology laboratory is a safe place to work if you follow standard safety procedures. Being responsible for your own safety helps to make the entire laboratory a safer place for everyone. When performing MiniLabs and BioLabs, read and apply the caution statements and safety symbols. Safety symbols are explained on the previous page. The safety guidelines and rules given here will help protect you and others during laboratory and field investigations.

Preventing Accidents

- Always wear chemical splash safety goggles (not glasses) in the laboratory. Goggles should fit snuggly against the face to prevent any liquid from entering the eyes. Put on your goggles before beginning the lab and wear them throughout the entire activity, cleanup, and hand washing. Only remove goggles with your teacher's permission.
- Wear protective aprons and the proper type of gloves as instructed by your teacher.
- Keep your hands away from your face and mouth while working in the laboratory.
- Do NOT wear sandals or other open-toed shoes in the lab.
- Remove jewelry on hands and wrists before doing lab work. Loose jewelry, such as chains and long necklaces, should be removed to prevent them from getting caught in equipment.
- Do NOT wear clothing that is loose enough to catch on anything. If clothing is loose, tape or tie it down.
- Tie back long hair to keep it away from flames and equipment.
- Do NOT use hair spray, mousse, or other flammable hair products just before or during laboratory work where an open flame is used. These products ignite easily.
- Eating, drinking, chewing gum, applying makeup, and smoking are prohibited in the laboratory.
- Students are expected to behave properly in the laboratory. Practical jokes and fooling around can lead to accidents and injury.
- Students should notify their teacher about allergies or other health conditions that they have which can affect their participation in a lab.

Making Wise Choices

- When obtaining consumable laboratory materials, carefully dispense only the amount you will use. If you dispense more than you will use, check with your teacher to determine if another student can use the excess.
- If you have consumable materials left over after completing an investigation, check with your teacher to determine the best choice for either recycling or disposing of the materials.

Working in the Laboratory and the Field

- Study all procedures before you begin a laboratory or field investigation. Ask questions if you do not understand any part of the procedure.
- Do NOT begin any activity until directed to do so by your teacher.
- Work ONLY on procedures assigned by your teacher. NEVER work alone in the laboratory.
- Do NOT handle equipment without permission. Use all lab equipment for their intended uses only.
- Collect and carry all equipment and materials to your work area before beginning the lab.
- Remain in your own work area unless given permission by your teacher to leave it. Keep your work area uncluttered.
- Learn and follow procedures for using specific laboratory equipment such as balances, microscopes, hot plates, and burners. Do not hesitate to ask for instructions about how to use any lab equipment.
- When heating or rinsing a container such as a test tube or flask, point it away from yourself and others.

- Do NOT taste, touch, or smell any chemical or substance unless instructed to do so by your teacher.
- If instructed to smell a substance in a container, hold the container a short distance away and fan vapors toward your nose.
- Do NOT substitute other chemicals/substances for those in the materials list unless instructed to do so by your teacher.
- Do NOT take any materials or chemicals outside of the laboratory.
- Stay out of storage areas unless you are instructed to be there and are supervised by your teacher.

Laboratory Cleanup

- Turn off all burners, gas valves, and water faucets before leaving the laboratory. Disconnect electrical devices.
- Clean all equipment as instructed by your teacher and return everything to the proper storage places.
- Dispose of all materials properly. Place disposable items in containers specifically marked for that type of item. Do not pour liquids down a drain unless your teacher instructs you to do so.
- Clean up your work and sink area.
- **Wash your hands thoroughly with soap and warm water after each activity and BEFORE removing your goggles.**

Emergencies

- **Inform the teacher immediately of _any_ mishap, such as fire, bodily injuries or burns, electrical shock, glassware breakage, and chemical or other spills.**
- In most instances, your teacher will clean up spills. Do NOT attempt to clean up spills unless you are given permission and instructions on how to do so.
- Know the location of the fire extinguisher, safety shower, eyewash, fire blanket, and first-aid kit. After receiving instruction, you can use the safety shower, eyewash, and fire blanket in an emergency without your teacher's permission. However, the fire extinguisher and the first-aid kit should only be used by your teacher or, in an extreme emergency, with your teacher's permission.
- If chemicals come into contact with your eyes or skin, notify your teacher immediately then flush your skin or eyes with large quantities of water.
- If someone is injured or becomes ill, only a professional medical provider or someone certified in first aid should perform first-aid procedures.

Six-Kingdom Classification

The classification used in this text combines information gathered from the systems of many different fields of biology. For example, phycologists, biologists who study algae, have developed their own system of classification, as have mycologists, biologists who study fungi. The naming of animals and plants is controlled by two completely different sets of rules. The six-kingdom system, although not ideal for reflecting the phylogeny of all life, is useful for showing relationships. Taxonomy is an area of biology that evolves just like the species it studies. In this Appendix, only the major phyla are listed, and one genus is named as an example. For more information about each taxon, refer to the chapter in the text in which the group is described.

Kingdom Eubacteria

Phylum Actinobacteria
Example: *Mycobacterium*
Phylum Omnibacteria
Example: *Salmonella*
Phylum Spirochaetae
Example: *Treponema*
Phylum Chloroxybacteria
Example: *Prochloron*
Phylum Cyanobacteria
Example: *Nostoc*

Kingdom Archaebacteria

Phylum Aphragmabacteria
Example: *Mycoplasma*
Phylum Halobacteria
Example: *Halobacterium*
Phylum Methanocreatrices
Example: *Methanobacillus*

Kingdom Protista

Phylum Rhizopoda
Example: *Amoeba*
Phylum Ciliophora
Example: *Paramecium*
Phylum Sporozoa
Example: *Plasmodium*
Phylum Zoomastigina
Example: *Trypanosoma*
Phylum Euglenophyta
Example: *Euglena*

Phylum Bacillariophyta
Example: *Navicula*
Phylum Dinoflagellata
Example: *Gonyaulax*
Phylum Rhodophyta
Example: *Chondrus*
Phylum Phaeophyta
Example: *Laminaria*
Phylum Chlorophyta
Example: *Ulva*
Phylum Acrasiomycota
Example: *Dictyostelium*
Phylum Myxomycota
Example: *Physarum*
Phylum Oomycota
Example: *Phytophthora*

Kingdom Fungi

Division Zygomycota
Example: *Rhizopus*
Division Ascomycota
Example: *Saccharomyces*
Division Basidiomycota
Example: *Amanita*
Division Deuteromycota
Example: *Penicillium*
Division Mycophycota
Example: *Cladonia*

Kingdom Plantae

Division Hepaticophyta
    Example: *Pellia*
Division Anthocerophyta
    Example: *Anthoceros*
Division Bryophyta
    Example: *Polytrichum*
Division Psilophyta
    Example: *Psilotum*
Division Lycophyta
    Example: *Lycopodium*
Division Arthrophyta
    Example: *Equisetum*

Division Pterophyta
    Example: *Polypodium*
Division Ginkgophyta
    Example: *Ginkgo*
Division Cycadophyta
    Example: *Cycas*
Division Coniferophyta
    Example: *Pinus*
Division Gnetophyta
    Example: *Welwitschia*
Division Anthophyta
    Example: *Rhododendron*

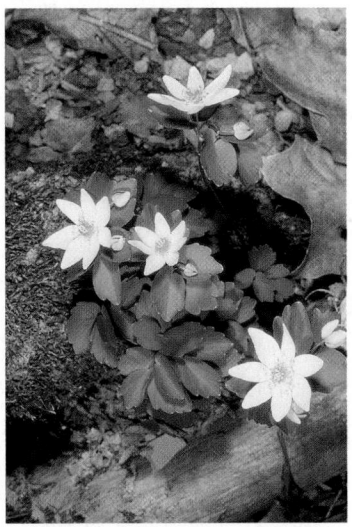

Kingdom Animalia

Phylum Porifera
    Example: *Spongilla*
Phylum Cnidaria
    Example: *Hydra*
Phylum Platyhelminthes
    Example: *Dugesia*
Phylum Nematoda
    Example: *Trichinella*
Phylum Mollusca
    Example: *Nautilus*
Phylum Annelida
    Example: *Hirudo*

Phylum Arthropoda
    Example: *Colias*
Phylum Echinodermata
    Example: *Cucumaria*
Phylum Chordata
Subphylum Urochordata
    Example: *Polycarpa*
Subphylum Cephalochordata
    Example: *Branchiostoma*
Subphylum Vertebrata
    Example: *Panthera*

Three-Domain Classification

Increasingly, biologists are classifying organisms into categories larger than kingdoms called domains. The three domains are: domain Bacteria, which includes the Kingdom Eubacteria; domain Archaea, which includes the Kingdom Archaebacteria; and the domain Eukarya, which includes protists, fungi, plants, and animals. With discoveries, this classification system may change.

DOMAIN	Bacteria	Archaea	Eukarya			
KINGDOM	Eubacteria	Archaebacteria	Protista	Fungi	Plantae	Animalia

The Periodic Table of Elements

Cómo usar el glosario en español:
1. Busca el término en inglés que desees encontrar.
2. El término en español, junto con la definición, se encuentran en la columna de la derecha.

Pronunciation Key

Use the following key to help you sound out words in the glossary.

a . . . . back (BAK)	ew . . . . food (FEWD)
ay . . . . day (DAY)	yoo . . . . pure (PYOOR)
ah . . . . father (FAH thur)	yew . . . . few (FYEW)
ow . . . . flower (FLOW ur)	uh . . . . comma (CAH muh)
ar . . . . car (CAR)	u (+ con) . . . . rub (RUB)
e . . . . less (LES)	sh . . . . shelf (SHELF)
ee . . . . leaf (LEEF)	ch . . . . nature (NAY chur)
ih . . . . trip (TRIHP)	g . . . . gift (GIHFT)
i (i + con + e) . . idea (i DEE uh)	j . . . . gem (JEM)
oh . . . . go (GOH)	ing . . . . sing (SING)
aw . . . . soft (SAWFT)	zh . . . . vision (VIH zhun)
or . . . . orbit (OR buht)	k . . . . cake (KAYK)
oy . . . . coin (COYN)	s . . . . seed, cent (SEED, SENT)
oo . . . . foot (FOOT)	z . . . . zone, raise (ZOHN, RAYZ)

A

English	Español
abiotic factors (ay bi AH tihk): (p. 37) nonliving parts of an organism's environment; air currents, temperature, moisture, light, and soil are examples.	**factores abióticos: (pág. 37)** Componentes inanimados del ambiente de un organismo, como las corrientes de aire, la temperatura, la humedad, la luz y el suelo.
acid: (p. 150) any substance that forms hydrogen ions (H^+) in water and has a pH below 7.	**ácido: (pág. 150)** Cualquier sustancia que forma iones hidrógeno (H^+) en el agua y tiene un pH menor de 7.
acid precipitation: (p. 118) rain, snow, sleet, or fog with a pH below 5.6; causes the deterioration of forests, lakes, statues, and buildings.	**precipitación ácida: (pág. 118)** Lluvia, nieve, granizo o neblina con un pH menor de 5.6; causa el deterioro de los bosques, los lagos, las estatuas y los edificios.
acoelomate (ay SEE lum ate): (p. 682) an animal with no body cavities.	**acelomado: (pág. 682)** Animales que carecen de cavidades corporales.
acquired immunity: (p. 1035) gradual build-up of resistance to a specific pathogen over time.	**inmunidad adquirida: (pág. 1035)** Aumento gradual de la resistencia a patógenos específicos a través del tiempo.
actin: (p. 907) structural protein in muscle cells that makes up the thin filaments of myofibrils; functions in muscle contraction.	**actina: (pág. 907)** Proteína estructural de las células de los músculos estriados que componen los filamentos finos de las miofibrillas; funcionan en la contracción muscular.
active transport: (p. 199) energy-expending process by which cells transport materials across the cell membrane against a concentration gradient.	**transporte activo: (pág. 199)** Proceso que requiere energía y mediante el cual la célula transporta materiales a través de la membrana celular contra un gradiente de concentración.
adaptation (a dap TAY shun): (p. 9) evolution of a structure, behavior, or internal process that enables an organism to respond to environmental factors and live to produce offspring.	**adaptación: (pág. 9)** Evolución de una estructura, comportamiento o proceso interno que permite a un organismo responder a los factores ambientales y sobrevivir para producir progenie.
adaptive radiation: (p. 412) divergent evolution in which ancestral species evolve into an array of species to fit a number of diverse habitats.	**radiación adaptativa: (pág. 412)** Evolución divergente en la cual la especie ancestral evoluciona y da origen a un grupo de especies adaptadas a ambientes diversos.
addiction: (p. 959) psychological and/or physiological drug dependence.	**adicción: (pág. 959)** Dependencia psicológica o fisiológica a una droga.
ADP (adenosine diphosphate): (p. 222) molecule formed from the breaking off of a phosphate group for ATP; results in a release of energy that is used for biological reactions.	**ADP (difosfato de adenosina): (pág. 222)** Molécula que se forma a partir de la pérdida de un grupo fosfato del ATP. Dicha pérdida resulta en la liberación de energía que se usa para las reacciones biológicas.

Glossary/Glosario

adrenal glands: (p. 933) pair of glands located on top of the kidneys that secrete hormones, such as adrenaline, that prepare the body for stressful situations.

aerobic: (p. 231) chemical reactions that require the presence of oxygen.

age structure: (p. 102) proportions of a population that are at different age levels.

aggressive behavior: (p. 864) innate behavior used to intimidate another animal of the same species in order to defend young, territory, or resources.

alcoholic fermentation: (p. 236) anaerobic process in which cells convert pyruvic acid into carbon dioxide and ethyl alcohol; carried out by many bacteria and fungi such as yeasts.

algae (AL jee): (p. 503) photosynthetic, plantlike, autotrophic protists.

allele (uh LEEL): (p. 256) alternative forms of a gene for each variation of a trait of an organism.

allelic frequency: (p. 405) percentage of any specific allele in a population's gene pool.

alternation of generations: (p. 516) type of life cycle found in some algae, fungi, and all plants where an organism alternates between a haploid (*n*) gametophyte generation and a diploid (*2n*) sporophyte generation.

alveoli (al VEE uh li): (p. 972) sacs in the lungs where oxygen diffuses into the blood and carbon dioxide diffuses into the air.

amino acids: (p. 161) basic building blocks of protein molecules.

amniotic egg (am nee AH tihk): (p. 818) major adaptation in land animals; amniotic sac encloses an embryo and provides nutrition and protection from the outside environment.

ampulla (AM pew lah): (p. 765) in echinoderms, the round, muscular structure on a tube foot that aids in locomotion.

amylase: (p. 918) digestive enzyme found in saliva and pancreatic juices; breaks starches into smaller molecules such as disaccharides and monosaccharides.

anaerobic: (p. 231) chemical reactions that do not require the presence of oxygen.

analogous structures: (p. 401) structures that do not have a common evolutionary origin but are similar in function.

anaphase: (p. 208) third phase of mitosis in which the centromeres split and the chromatid pairs of each chromosome are pulled apart by microtubules.

annual: (p. 595) anthophyte that lives for one year or less.

anterior: (p. 682) head end of bilateral animals where sensory organs are often located.

anther: (p. 641) pollen-producing structure located at the tip of a flower's stamen.

antheridium (an thuh RIH dee um): (p. 578) male reproductive structure in which sperm develop.

anthropoids (AN thruh poydz): (p. 424) humanlike primates that include New World monkeys, Old World monkeys, and hominoids.

glándulas adrenales: (pág. 933) Par de glándulas localizadas sobre los riñones que secretan hormonas, como la adrenalina, que preparan al cuerpo para las situaciones de tensión.

aeróbica: (pág. 231) Reacciones químicas que requieren la presencia de oxígeno.

estructura etaria: (pág. 102) Proporciones de una población que se encuentran en los diferentes estratos de edad.

comportamiento agresivo: (pág. 864) Comportamiento innato usado para intimidar a otros animales de la misma especie, en la defensa de las crías, el territorio o los recursos.

fermentación alcohólica: (pág. 236) Proceso anaeróbico en que las células convierten el ácido pirúvico a dióxido de carbono y alcohol etílico; la llevan a cabo muchas bacterias y hongos como las levaduras.

algas: (pág. 503) Protistas autótrofos fotosintéticos parecidos a plantas.

alelo: (pág. 256) Formas alternativas de un gene para cada variación de un rasgo de un organismo.

frecuencia alélica: (pág. 405) Porcentaje de un alelo específico en el caudal genético de una población.

alternancia de generaciones: (pág. 516) Tipo de ciclo de vida de algunas algas, hongos y todas las plantas en que el organismo alterna entre una generación gametofita haploide (*n*) y una generación esporofita diploide (*2n*).

alvéolos: (pág. 972) Sacos de los pulmones a través de los cuales el oxígeno se difunde hacia la sangre y el dióxido de carbono se difunde en el aire.

aminoácidos: (pág. 161) Componentes básicos de las moléculas de proteínas.

huevo amniótico: (pág. 818) Importante adaptación de los animales terrestres. El saco amniótico envuelve al embrión y le provee nutrición y protección del ambiente exterior.

ampolla: (pág. 765) En los equinodermos, la estructura muscular redonda del pie tubular que ayuda en la locomoción.

amilasa: (pág. 918) Enzima digestiva que se encuentra en la saliva y en los jugos pancreáticos. Descompone los almidones en moléculas más pequeñas como disacáridos y monosacáridos.

anaeróbico: (pág. 231) Reacciones químicas que no requieren la presencia de oxígeno.

estructuras análogas: (pág. 401) Estructuras que no tienen un origen evolutivo común, pero se parecen en su función.

anafase: (pág. 208) Tercera fase de la mitosis. En esta fase los centrómeros se separan y los pares de cromátides de cada cromosoma son separados por los microtúbulos.

anual: (pág. 595) Que vive por un año o menos.

anterior: (pág. 682) Extremo de la cabeza de un animal bilateral donde se localizan por lo general las estructuras sensoriales.

antera: (pág. 641) Estructura productora de polen localizada en la punta del estambre de la flor.

anteridio: (pág. 578) Estructura reproductora masculina en la cual se desarrollan los espermatozoides.

antropoide: (pág. 424) Primates parecidos a humanos que incluyen a los monos del Nuevo Mundo, los monos del Viejo Mundo y los hominoides.

antibiotics: (p. 1029) substances produced by a microorganism that, in small amounts, will kill or inhibit growth and reproduction of other microorganisms.

antibodies (AN tih bahd eez): (p. 977) proteins in the blood plasma produced in reaction to antigens that react with and disable antigens.

antigens: (p. 977) foreign substances that stimulate an immune response in the body.

aorta: (p. 981) largest blood vessel in the body; transports oxygen-rich blood from the left ventricle of the heart to the arteries.

aphotic zone: (p. 71) deep water that never receives sunlight.

apical meristem: (p. 611) regions of actively dividing cells near the tips of roots and stems; allows roots and stems to increase in length.

appendage (uh PEN dihj): (p. 741) any structure, such as a leg or an antenna, that grows out of an animal's body.

appendicular skeleton (a pen DIH kyuh lur): (p. 899) one of two main parts of the human skeleton, includes the bones of the arms and legs and associated structures, such as the shoulders and hip bones.

archaebacteria (ar kee bac TEER ee uh): (p. 384) chemosynthetic prokaryotes that live in harsh environments, such as deep-sea vents and hot springs.

archegonium (ar kih GOH nee um): (p. 578) female reproductive structure in which eggs develop.

artery: (p. 979) large, thick-walled muscular vessel that carries blood away from the heart.

artificial selection: (p. 395) process of breeding organisms with specific traits in order to produce offspring with identical traits.

ascospores: (p. 537) sexual spores of ascomycete fungi that develop within an ascus.

ascus: (p. 537) tiny, saclike structures in ascomycetes in which ascospores develop.

asexual reproduction: (p. 505) type of reproduction where one parent produces one or more identical offspring without the fusion of gametes.

atom: (p. 142) smallest particle of an element that has the characteristics of that element; basic building block of all matter.

ATP (adenosine triphosphate) (uh DEH nuh seen • tri FAHS fayt): (p. 222) energy-storing molecule in cells composed of an adenosine molecule, a ribose sugar and three phosphate groups; energy is stored in the molecule's chemical bonds and can be used quickly and easily by cells.

atria: (p. 980) two upper chambers of the mammalian heart through which blood enters.

australopithecine (ah stra loh PIH thuh sine): (p. 430) early African hominid, genus *Australopithecus*, that had both apelike and humanlike characteristics.

antibióticos: (pág. 1029) Sustancias producidas por microorganismos que, si se usan en pequeñas cantidades, son capaces de matar o inhibir el crecimiento y reproducción de otros microorganismos.

anticuerpos: (pág. 977) Proteínas del plasma sanguíneo que son producidas en reacción a la presencia de antígenos, los cuales reaccionan y destruyen a dichos antígenos.

antígenos: (pág. 977) Sustancias extrañas que estimulan la respuesta inmunológica del cuerpo.

aorta: (pág. 981) El vaso sanguíneo más grande del cuerpo; transporta sangre rica en oxígeno desde el ventrículo izquierdo del corazón hacia las arterias.

zona afótica: (pág. 71) Aguas profundas que nunca reciben luz solar.

meristemo apical: (pág. 611) Regiones de división celular activa localizadas cerca de los extremos de las raíces y los tallos; permiten que las raíces y los tallos se alarguen.

apéndice: (pág. 741) Cualquier estructura, como una pierna o una antena, que crece a partir del cuerpo del animal.

esqueleto apendicular: (pág. 899) Una de las dos partes principales del esqueleto humano, que incluye los huesos de los brazos y piernas y sus estructuras asociadas, como los huesos de los hombros y de las caderas.

arquebacterias: (pág. 384) Procariotas quimiosintéticos que viven en ambientes inhóspitos, como las fumarolas del océano profundo y las fuentes termales.

arquegonio: (pág. 578) Estructura reproductora femenina en la cual se desarrollan los óvulos.

arteria: (pág. 979) Vaso sanguíneo grande de paredes engrosadas que transporta la sangre desde el corazón.

selección artificial: (pág. 395) Proceso de cría de organismos que poseen rasgos específicos para producir progenies con rasgos idénticos.

ascosporas: (pág. 537) Esporas sexuales de los hongos ascomicetos las cuales se desarrollan dentro de los ascos.

ascos: (pág. 537) Estructuras diminutas con forma de saco de los ascomicetos dentro de los cuales se desarrollan las ascosporas.

reproducción asexual: (pág. 505) Tipo de reproducción en la cual un solo progenitor produce una o más crías idénticas sin la fusión de gametos.

átomo: (pág. 142) La partícula más pequeña de un elemento que mantiene las características de dicho elemento; estructura básica de toda la materia.

ATP (trifosfato de adenosina): (pág. 222) Moléculas que almacenan la energía de la célula, compuestas de una molécula de adenosina, un azúcar ribosa y tres grupos fosfato. La energía es almacenada en los enlaces químicos de la molécula y puede ser usada rápida y fácilmente por la célula.

aurículas: (pág. 980) Las dos cavidades superiores del corazón de los mamíferos a través de las cuales entra la sangre al corazón.

australopithecino: (pág. 430) Homínido africano temprano; género *Australopithecus*, que poseía tanto características de simio como de humano.

autonomic nervous system (ANS): (p. 949) in humans, portion of the peripheral nervous system that carries impulses from the central nervous system to internal organs; produces involuntary responses.

autosomes: (p. 318) pairs of matching homologous chromosomes in somatic cells.

autotrophs (AW tuh trohfs): (p. 46) organisms that use energy from the sun or energy stored in chemical compounds to manufacture their own nutrients.

auxins (AWK sunz): (p. 622) group of plant hormones that promote cell elongation.

axial skeleton: (p. 899) one of two main parts of the human skeleton, includes the skull and the bones that support it, such as the vertebral column, ribs, and sternum.

axon: (p. 943) a single cytoplasmic extension of a neuron; carries impulses away from a nerve cell.

sistema nervioso autónomo (SNA): (pág. 949) En los humanos, la porción del sistema nervioso periférico que lleva impulsos desde el sistema nervioso central hacia los órganos internos. Produce respuestas involuntarias.

autosomas: (pág. 318) Los pares de cromosomas homólogos de las células somáticas.

autótrofos: (pág. 46) Organismos que utilizan la energía del sol o la energía almacenada en los compuestos químicos para producir sus propios nutrientes.

auxinas: (pág. 622) Grupo de hormonas de las plantas que promueven el alargamiento de las células.

esqueleto axial: (pág. 899) Una de las dos partes principales del esqueleto humano; incluye el cráneo y los huesos que lo soportan, como la columna vertebral, las costillas y el esternón.

axón: (pág. 943) La extensión citoplasmática única de la neurona; transporta los impulsos a partir de esta célula hacia otra.

B

B cell: (p. 1037) a lymphocyte that, when activated by a T cell, becomes a plasma cell and produces antibodies.

bacteriophage (bak TIHR ee uh fayj): (p. 475) also called phages, viruses that infect and destroy bacteria.

base: (p. 150) any substance that forms hydroxide ions (OH^-) in water and has a pH above 7.

basidia (buh SIHD ee uh): (p. 538) club-shaped hyphae of basidiomycete fungi that produce spores.

basidiospores: (p. 538) spores produced in the basidia of basidiomycetes during sexual reproduction.

behavior: (p. 859) anything an animal does in response to a stimulus in its environment.

biennial: (p. 595) anthophyte that has a life span of two years.

bilateral symmetry (bi LA tuh rul): (p. 681) animals with a body plan that can be divided down its length into two similar right and left halves that form mirror images of each other.

bile: (p. 921) chemical substance produced by the liver and stored in the gallbladder that helps break down fats during digestion.

binary fission: (p. 489) asexual reproductive process in which one cell divides into two separate genetically identical cells.

binomial nomenclature: (p. 444) two-word system developed by Carolus Linnaeus to name species; first word identifies the genus of the organism, the second word is often a descriptive word that describes a characteristic of the organism.

biodiversity: (p. 111) variety of life in an area; usually measured as the number of species that live in an area.

biogenesis (bi oh JEN uh sus): (p. 381) idea that living organisms come only from other living organisms.

biological community: (p. 39) a community made up of interacting populations in a certain area at a certain time.

célula B: (pág. 1037) Linfocito que al ser activado por una célula T se convierte en una célula plasmática y produce anticuerpos.

bacteriófago: (pág. 475) También llamados fagos; virus que infectan y destruyen a las bacterias.

base: (pág. 150) Cualquier sustancia que forma iones hidróxido. (OH^-) en el agua y tiene un pH mayor de 7.

basidios: (pág. 538) Hifas en forma de bastón de los hongos basidiomicetos que producen esporas.

basidiosporas: (pág. 538) Esporas producidas en los basidios de los basidiomicetos durante la reproducción sexual.

comportamiento: (pág. 859) Cualquier actividad de un animal en respuesta a los estímulos ambientales.

bienal: (pág. 595) Antofita que tiene una vida de dos años.

simetría bilateral: (pág. 681) Aquellos animales que poseen un plán corporal en que, cuando el animal se divide en dos a lo largo, las mitades derecha e izquierda son similares.

bilis: (pág. 921) Sustancia química producida por el hígado y almacenada en la vesícula biliar que ayuda en la descomposición de las grasas durante la digestión.

fisión binaria: (pág. 489) Proceso de reproducción asexual en que una célula se divide en dos células separadas e idénticas genéticamente.

nomenclatura binaria: (pág. 444) El sistema de dos palabras desarrollado por Carlos Lineo para dar nombre a las especies; la primer palabra identifica el género del organismo, la segunda palabra es con frecuencia un término descriptivo de alguna característica del organismo.

biodiversidad: (pág. 111) La variedad de vida en un área; por lo común se mide como el número de especies que viven en un área.

biogénesis: (pág. 381) La idea de que los organismos vivos solo pueden provenir de otros organismos vivos.

comunidad biológica: (pág. 39) Comunidad compuesta de poblaciones que interactuan en cierta área en un tiempo dado.

biology: (p. 3) the study of life that seeks to provide an understanding of the natural world.

biomass: (p. 52) the total mass or weight of all living matter in a given area.

biome: (p. 70) group of ecosystems with the same climax communities; biomes on land are called terrestrial biomes, those in water are called aquatic biomes.

biomolecule: (p. 153) a large organic molecule found in living organisms; examples are carbohydrates, lipids, proteins, and nucleic acids.

biosphere (BI uh sfihr): (p. 36) portion of Earth that supports life; extends from high in the atmosphere to the bottom of the oceans.

biotic factors (by AH tihk): (p. 38) all the living organisms that inhabit an environment.

bipedal: (p. 428) ability to walk on two legs; leaves arms and hands free for other activities such as hunting, protecting young, and using tools.

birthrate: (p. 101) number of live births per 1000 population in a given year.

blastula (BLAS chuh luh): (p. 676) hollow ball of cells in a layer surrounding a fluid-filled space; an animal embryo after cleavage but before the formation of the gastrula.

blood pressure: (p. 984) force that blood exerts on blood vessels; rises and falls as the heart contracts and relaxes.

book lungs: (p. 744) gas exchange system found in some arthropods where air-filled chambers have plates of folded membranes that increase the surface area of tissue exposed to the air.

budding: (p. 533) type of asexual reproduction in unicellular yeasts and some other organisms in which a cell or group of cells pinch off from the parent to form a new individual.

bulbourethral glands (bul boh yoo REE thrul): (p. 997) glands located beneath the prostate that secrete a clear, sticky, alkaline fluid that protects sperm by neutralizing the acidic environment of the vagina.

bursa: (p. 900) fluid-filled sac located between the bones that absorb shock and keep bones from rubbing against each other.

biología: (pág. 3) El estudio de la vida; busca la comprensión del mundo natural.

biomasa: (pág. 52) La masa total o peso de toda la materia viva en un área dada.

bioma: (pág. 70) Grupo de ecosistemas con las mismas comunidades clímax; los biomas sobre la tierra firme se llaman biomas terrestres; los biomas en el agua se llaman biomas acuáticos.

biomolécula: (pág. 153) Molécula orgánica de gran tamaño en los seres vivos; ejemplos: carbohidratos, proteínas y ácidos nucleicos.

biosfera: (pág. 36) Porción de la Tierra que mantiene la vida; se extiende desde la parte alta de la atmósfera hasta el fondo de los océanos.

factores bióticos: (pág. 38) Los organismos vivos que habitan un ambiente.

bípedo: (pág. 428) La capacidad de caminar sobre dos extremidades, la cual deja los brazos y las manos libres para otras actividades, como la caza, la protección de las crías y el uso de herramientas.

índice de natalidad: (pág. 101) Número de nacimientos vivos por cada 1000 individuos de una poblacón en un año dado.

blástula: (pág. 676) Bola hueca formada por una capa de células que rodea un espacio interno lleno de fluido; el embrión de los animales después de la segmentación pero antes de la formación de la gástrula.

presión sanguínea: (pág. 984) La fuerza que ejerce la sangre contra las paredes de los vasos sanguíneos; sube y baja a medida que el corazón se contrae y se relaja.

filotráqueas: (pág. 744) Sistema de intercambio de gases que se encuentra en algunos artrópodos en que las cavidades llenas de aire tienen placas de membranas dobladas que aumentan el área de superficie del tejido expuesto al aire.

gemación: (pág. 533) Tipo de reproducción asexual en las levaduras unicelulares y otros organismos, en la cual una célula o grupo de células se separa de la célula progenitora y forma un nuevo individuo.

glándulas bulbouretrales: (pág. 997) Glándulas localizadas por debajo de la próstata, las cuales secretan un fluido claro y pegajoso de pH alcalino que protege a los espermatozoides neutralizando el ambiente ácido de la vagina.

bolsa: (pág. 900) Saco lleno de fluido localizado en los espacios entre los huesos que absorbe el impacto de los golpes y evita que los huesos se rocen unos contra otros.

C

Calorie: (p. 927) unit of heat used to measure the energy content of food, each Calorie represents a kilocalorie, or 1000 calories; a calorie is the amount of heat required to raise the temperature of 1 mL of water by 1°C.

Calvin cycle: (p. 228) series of reactions during the light-independent phase of photosynthesis in which simple sugars are formed from carbon dioxide using ATP and hydrogen from the light-dependent reactions.

Caloría: (pág. 927) Unidad de calor usada para medir el contenido energético de los alimentos; cada Caloría representa una kilocaloría ó 1000 calorías; una caloría es la cantidad de calor que se requiere para elevar en 1° C la temperatura de 1 mL de agua.

ciclo de Calvin: (pág. 228) La serie de reacciones que ocurren durante la etapa independiente de la luz de la fotosíntesis, en la cual se forman azúcares simples a partir del dióxido de carbono utilizando ATP e hidrógeno producidos durante las reacciones dependientes de la luz.

Glossary/Glosario

camouflage: (KA muh flahj): (p. 399) structural adaptation that enables species to blend with their surroundings; allows a species to avoid detection by predators.

cancer: (p. 211) uncontrolled cell division that may be caused by environmental factors and/or changes in enzyme production in the cell cycle.

capillaries (KA puh ler eez): (p. 980) microscopic blood vessels with walls only one cell thick that allow diffusion of gases and nutrients between the blood and surrounding tissues.

capsid: (p. 476) outer coat of proteins that surrounds a virus's inner core of nucleic acid; arrangement of capsid proteins determines the virus's shape.

captivity: (p. 125) when members of a species are held by people in zoos or other conservation facilities.

carbohydrate (car boh HI drayt): (p. 158) organic compound used by cells to store and release energy; composed of carbon, hydrogen, and oxygen.

cardiac muscle: (p. 906) type of involuntary muscle found only in the heart; composed of interconnected cardiac muscle fibers; adapted to generate and conduct electrical impulses for muscle contraction.

carrier: (p. 310) an individual heterozygous for a specific trait.

carrying capacity: (p. 93) number of organisms of one species that an environment can support indefinitely; populations below carrying capacity tend to increase; those above carrying capacity tend to decrease.

cartilage: (p. 799) tough flexible material making up the skeletons of agnathans, sharks, and their relatives, as well as portions of bony-animal skeletons.

cell: (p. 171) basic unit of all organisms; all living things are composed of cells.

cell cycle: (p. 204) continuous sequence of growth (interphase) and division (mitosis) in a cell.

cell theory: (p. 172) the theory that (1) all organisms are composed of one or more cells, (2) the cell is the basic unit of structure and organization of organisms, (3) all cells come from preexisting cells.

cell wall: (p. 179) fairly rigid structure located outside the plasma membrane of plants, fungi, most bacteria, and some protists; provides support and protection.

cellular respiration: (p. 231) chemical process where mitochondria break down food molecules to produce ATP; the three stages of cellular respiration are glycolysis, the citric acid cycle, and the electron transport chain.

central nervous system (CNS): (p. 946) in humans, the central control center of the nervous system made up of the brain and spinal cord.

camuflaje: (pág. 399) Adaptación estructural que permite a una especie confundirse con su ambiente; permite que una especie evite la depredación.

cáncer: (pág. 211) División celular fuera de control que puede ser causada por factores ambientales y/o cambios en la producción de enzimas durante el ciclo celular.

capilares: (pág. 980) Vasos sanguíneos microscópicos con paredes de solo una célula de grosor que permiten la difusión de gases y sustancias nutritivas entre la sangre y los tejidos circundantes.

cápsida: (pág. 476) Cobertura externa compuesta de proteínas que rodea el centro de los ácidos nucleicos de un virus; el arreglo de las proteínas de la cápsida determina la forma del virus.

cautiverio: (pág. 125) Cuando miembros de una especie son mantenidos en los zoológicos u otras instituciones con interés conservacionista.

carbohidrato: (pág. 158) Compuesto orgánico usado por las células para almacenar y liberar energía; está formado por carbono, hidrógeno y oxígeno.

músculo cardíaco: (pág. 906) Tipo de músculo involuntario que se encuentra solo en el corazón; está compuesto por fibras musculares cardíacas interconectadas; está adaptado para generar y transmitir impulsos nerviosos para la contracción muscular.

portador: (pág. 310) Individuo heterocigoto para un rasgo.

capacidad de carga: (pág. 93) Número de organismos de una especie que un ambiente puede mantener indefinidamente; las poblaciones que están por debajo de la capacidad de carga tienden a aumentar; aquellas que están sobre la capacidad de carga tienden a disminuir.

cartílago: (pág. 799) Material flexible y fuerte que compone el esqueleto de los agnatos, los tiburones y sus parientes, además de porciones del esqueleto de los animales con huesos.

célula: (pág. 171) Unidad básica de todos los organismos; todos los seres vivos están compuestos de células.

ciclo celular: (pág. 204) Secuencia continua de crecimiento (interfase) y división (mitosis) de una célula.

teoría celular: (pág. 172) Teoría que establece que (1) todos los organismos están compuestos por una o más células, (2) la célula es la unidad básica estructural y de organización de todos los organismos, (3) todas las células provienen de células preexistentes.

pared celular: (pág. 179) Estructura rígida localizada en la parte externa de la membrana celular de las plantas, hongos, la mayoría de las bacterias y algunos protistas; ofrece soporte y protección.

respiración celular: (pág. 231) Proceso químico durante el cual la mitocondria descompone las moléculas de alimento para producir ATP; las tres etapas de la respiración celular son la glicólisis, el ciclo del ácido cítrico y la cadena de transporte electrónico.

sistema nervioso central (SNC): (pág. 946) En los humanos, el centro de control central del sistema nervioso, compuesto por el cerebro y la médula espinal.

centrioles (SEN tree ohlz): **(p. 208)** in animal cells, a pair of small cylindrical structures composed of microtubules that duplicate during interphase and move to opposite ends of the cell during prophase.

centromere (SEN truh meer): **(p. 206)** cell structure that joins two sister chromatids of a chromosome.

cephalothorax (sef uh luh THOR aks): **(p. 743)** structure in some arthropods formed by the fusion of the head and thorax.

cerebellum (ser uh BE lum): **(p. 947)** rear portion of the brain; controls balance, posture and coordination.

cerebrum (suh REE brum): **(p. 947)** largest part of the brain, composed of two hemispheres connected by bundles of nerves; controls conscious activities, intelligence, memory, language, skeletal muscle movements, and the senses.

cervix: (p. 999) lower end of the uterus that tapers to a narrow opening into the vagina.

chelicerae (chih LIH suh ree): **(p. 748)** first pair of an arachnid's six pairs of appendages; located near the mouth, they are often modified into pincers or fangs.

chemosynthesis (kee moh SIHN thuh sus): **(p. 486)** autotrophic process where organisms obtain energy from the breakdown of inorganic compounds containing sulfur and nitrogen.

chitin (KITE un): **(p. 531)** complex carbohydrate that makes up the cell walls of fungi.

chlorophyll: (p. 226) light-absorbing pigment in plants and some protists that is required for photosynthesis; absorbs most wavelengths of light except for green.

chloroplasts: (p. 184) chlorophyll-containing organelles found in the cells of green plants and some protists; capture light energy and converted it to chemical energy.

chromatin (KROH muh tihn): **(p. 180)** long strands of DNA found in the eukaryotic cell nucleus; condense to form chromosomes.

chromosomal mutations: (p. 299) mutation that occurs at the chromosome level resulting in changes in the gene distribution to gametes during meiosis; caused when parts of chromosomes break off or rejoin incorrectly.

chromosomes (KROH muh sohmz): **(p. 203)** cell structures that carry the genetic material that is copied and passed from generation to generation of cells.

cilia (SIH lee uh): **(p. 187)** short, numerous, hairlike projections composed of pairs of microtubules; frequently aid in locomotion.

ciliates: (p. 506) group of protozoans of the phylum Ciliophora that have a covering of cilia that aids in locomotion.

circadian rhythm (sur KAY dee uhn): **(p. 865)** innate behavior based on the 24-hour cycle of the day; light-regulated; may determine when an animal sleeps and wakes.

centriolos: (pág. 208) En las células animales, un par de estructuras cilíndricas compuestas de microtúbulos que se duplican durante la interfase y se desplazan hacia extremos opuestos durante la profase.

centrómero: (pág. 206) Estructura celular que une a las dos cromátides hermanas de un cromosoma.

cefalotórax: (pág. 743) Estructura que se encuentra en algunos artrópodos, formada por la fusión de la cabeza y el tórax.

cerebelo: (pág. 947) Porción posterior del cerebro; controla el equilibrio, la postura y la coordinación.

cerebro: (pág. 947) La parte más grande de la masa cerebral, compuesto por dos hemisferios conectados por grupos de nervios; controla las actividades conscientes, la inteligencia, la memoria, el lenguaje, los movimientos de los músculos esqueléticos y los sentidos.

cérvix: (pág. 999) Extremo inferior del útero que se hace más angosto para formar la vagina.

quelíceros: (pág. 748) El primero de los seis pares de apéndices de los arácnidos; se localizan cerca de la boca y se encuentran con frecuencia modificados formando tenazas o colmillos.

quimiosíntesis: (pág. 486) Proceso autotrófico a través del cual los organismos obtienen energía de la descomposición de compuestos inorgánicos que contienen azufre y nitrógeno.

quitina: (pág. 531) Carbohidrato complejo que compone la pared celular de los hongos.

clorofila: (pág. 226) Pigmento que absorbe la luz, presente en las plantas y algunos protistas, que se requiere para la fotosíntesis; absorbe la mayoría de las longitudes de onda de luz excepto el verde.

cloroplastos: (pág. 184) Organelos que contienen clorofila; se encuentran en las células de las plantas verdes y algunos protistas; capturan la energía luminosa y la convierten en energía química.

cromatina: (pág. 180) Hebras largas de DNA que se encuentran en el núcleo de las células eucariotas. Al condensarse, forman los cromosomas.

mutaciones cromosómicas: (pág. 299) Mutaciones que ocurren a nivel cromosómico resultando en cambios en la distribución de los genes en los gametos durante la meiosis; suceden cuando partes de los cromosomas se separan y se vuelven a adherir en forma incorrecta.

cromosomas: (pág. 203) Estructuras celulares que portan el material genético el cual es copiado y transmitido de una generación de células a la siguiente.

cilios: (pág. 187) Proyecciones numerosas parecidas a vellos, compuestas de pares de microtúbulos; con frecuencia ayudan en la locomoción.

ciliados: (pág. 506) Grupo de protozoarios del filo Ciliophora que poseen un recubrimiento de cilios sobre sus cuerpos que les ayuda en la locomoción.

ritmo circadiano: (pág. 865) Comportamiento innato basado en el ciclo de 24 horas del día; regulado por la luz; puede determinar la hora en que el organismo se duerme y se despierta.

Glossary/
Glosario

citric acid cycle: (p. 232) in cellular respiration, series of chemical reactions that break down glucose and produce ATP; energizes electron carriers that pass the energized electrons on to the electron transport chain.

cladistics (kla DIHS tiks): (p. 452) biological classification system based on phylogeny; assumes that as groups of organisms diverge and evolve from a common ancestral group, they retain derived traits.

cladogram (KLA deh gram): (p. 452) branching diagram that models the phylogeny of a species based on the derived traits of a group of organisms.

class: (p. 449) taxonomic grouping of similar orders.

classical conditioning: (p. 871) learning by association.

classification: (p. 443) grouping of objects or information based on similarities.

climax community: (p. 68) a stable, mature community that undergoes little or no change in species over time.

clones: (p. 344) genetically identical copies of an organism or gene.

closed circulatory system: (p. 724) system in which blood moves through the body enclosed entirely in a series of blood vessels; provides an efficient means of gas exchange within the body.

cochlea: (p. 954) snail-shaped structure in the inner ear containing fluid and hairs; produces electrical impulses that the brain interprets as sound.

codominant alleles: (p. 317) pattern where phenotypes of both homozygote parents are produced in heterozygous offspring so that both alleles are equally expressed.

codon: (p. 292) set of three nitrogenous bases that represents an amino acid; order of nitrogenous bases in mRNA determines the type and order of amino acids in a protein.

coelom (SEE lum): (p. 684) fluid-filled body cavity completely surrounded by mesoderm.

collenchyma (coh LENG kuh muh): (p. 606) long, flexible plant cells with unevenly thickened cell walls; most common in actively growing tissues.

colony: (p. 515) group of unicellular or multicellular organisms that live together in a close association.

commensalism (kuh MEN suh lih zum): (p. 44) symbiotic relationship in which one species benefits and the other species is neither harmed nor benefited.

communication: (p. 872) exchange of information that results in a change of behavior.

community: (p. 39) collection of several interacting populations that inhabit a common environment.

compact bone: (p. 902) layer of protective hard bone tissue surrounding every bone; composed of repeating units of osteon systems.

companion cells: (p. 610) nucleated cells that help transport sugars and other organic compounds through the sieve cells of the phloem.

ciclo del ácido cítrico: (pág. 232) En la respiración celular, la serie de reacciones químicas que descomponen la glucosa y producen ATP; provee energía a los portadores de electrones que transfieren estos electrones energizados en la cadena de transporte electrónico.

cladística: (pág. 452) Sistema de clasificación biológica que se basa en la filogenia; asume que a medida que los grupos de organismos divergen y evolucionan a partir de un antepasado común, mantienen rasgos derivados.

cladograma: (pág. 452) Diagrama ramificado que representa la filogenia de una especie en base a los rasgos derivados de un grupo de organismos.

clase: (pág. 449) Agrupación taxonómica de órdenes similares.

condicionamiento clásico: (pág. 871) Aprendizaje por asociación.

clasificación: (pág. 443) La práctica de agrupar objetos o información de acuerdo con sus similitudes.

comunidad clímax: (pág. 68) Comunidad madura y estable que sufre poco o ningún cambio en su composición de especies.

clones: (pág. 344) Copias idénticas de la información genética de un organismo o de un gene.

sistema circulatorio cerrado: (pág. 724) Sistema en que la sangre se desplaza por el cuerpo completamente encerrada en una serie de vasos sanguíneos; provee una forma eficiente de intercambio gaseoso dentro del cuerpo.

cóclea: (pág. 954) Estructura con forma de caracol del oído interno que contiene fluido y vellos; produce impulsos eléctricos que el cerebro interpreta como sonidos.

alelos codominantes: (pág. 317) Patrón en que los fenotipos de ambos padres homocigotos se producen en el hijo heterocigoto, de tal forma que ambos alelos se expresan con igual intensidad.

codón: (pág. 292) Grupo de tres bases nitrogenadas que representa un aminoácido; el orden de las bases nitrogenadas en el mRNA determina el tipo y el orden de los aminoácidos en la proteína.

celoma: (pág. 684) Cavidad corporal llena de fluido que está rodeada completamente por el mesodermo.

colénquima: (pág. 606) Células vegetales largas y flexibles con paredes celulares de grosor variable; son más comunes en los tejidos en crecimiento.

colonia: (pág. 515) Grupo de organismos unicelulares o multicelulares que viven juntos en estrecha asociación.

comensalismo: (pág. 44) Relación simbiótica en la cual una de las especies se beneficia y la otra especie ni sufre daño ni se beneficia.

comunicación: (pág. 872) Intercambio de información que resulta en un cambio en el comportamiento.

comunidad: (pág. 39) Colección de varias poblaciones que interaccionan al habitar un ambiente común.

hueso compacto: (pág. 902) Capa protectora de tejido óseo compacto que rodea cada hueso; compuesto por unidades repetidas de sistemas de osteones.

células acompañantes: (pág. 610) Células nucleadas que ayudan a transportar azúcares y otros compuestos orgánicos a través de cuerpos de tubos cribosos del floema.

compound: (p. 145) substance composed of atoms of two or more different elements that are chemically combined.

compound eye: (p. 745) in arthropods, a visual system composed of multiple lenses; each lens registers light from a small portion of the field of view, creating an image composed of thousands of parts.

compound light microscope: (p. 171) instrument that uses light and a series of lenses to magnify objects in steps; can magnify an object up to 1500 times its original size.

conditioning: (p. 871) response to a stimulus learned by association with a specific action.

cones: (p. 567) in coniferophytes; scaly structures that support male and female reproductive structures; scaly structures produced by some seed plants that support male or female reproductive structures and are the sites of seed production. **(p. 952)** receptor cells in the retina adapted for sharp vision in bright light and color detection.

conidia (kuh NIHD ee uh): (p. 537) chains or clusters of asexual ascomycete spores that develop on the tips of conidiophores.

conidiophores (kuh NIHD ee uh forz): (p. 537) in ascomycetes, elongated, upright hyphae that produce conidia at their tips.

conjugation (kahn juh GAY shun): (p. 490) form of sexual reproduction in some bacteria where one bacterium transfers all or part of its genetic material to another through a bridgelike structure called a pilus.

conservation biology: (p. 121) field of biology that studies methods and implements plans to protect biodiversity.

control: (p. 13) in an experiment, the standard against which results are compared.

convergent evolution: (p. 413) evolution in which distantly related organisms evolve similar traits; occurs when unrelated species occupy similar environments.

cork cambium: (p. 611) lateral meristem that produces a tough protective covering for the surface of stems and roots.

corpus luteum: (p. 1002) part of an ovarian follicle that remains in the ovary after ovulation; produces estrogen and progesterone.

cortex: (p. 613) layer of ground tissue in the root that is involved in the transport of water and ions into the vascular tissue of the root.

cotyledons (kah tuh LEE dunz): (p. 589) structure of seed plant embryo that stores or absorbs food for the developing embryo.

courtship behavior: (p. 862) an instinctive behavior that males and females of a species carry out before mating.

covalent bond (koh VAY lunt): (p. 146) chemical bond formed when two atoms share electrons.

compuesto: (pág. 145) Sustancia formada por átomos de dos o más elementos diferentes que se encuentran combinados químicamente.

ojo compuesto: (pág. 745) En los artrópodos, sistema visual compuesto de lentes múltiples; cada lente absorbe la luz de una porción del campo visual, creándose una imagen formada por miles de partes.

microscopio de luz compuesto: (pág. 171) Instrumento que utiliza la luz y una serie de lentes para aumentar gradualmente el tamaño de los objetos; puede aumentar el tamaño de un objeto hasta 1500 veces su tamaño original.

condicionamiento: (pág. 871) Respuesta a un estímulo que se aprende por asociación con una acción específica.

conos: (pág. 567) Estructuras escamosas de las coniferofitas que contienen las estructuras reproductoras masculinas y femeninas y que son los sitios de producción de las semillas; **(pág. 952)** células receptoras en la retina adaptadas para la visión en luz brillante y para la detección del color.

conidios: (pág. 537) Cadenas o grupos de esporas asexuales de los ascomicetos que se desarrollan en los extremos de los conidióforos.

conidióforos: (pág. 537) En los ascomicetos, hifas alargadas que crecen en forma vertical y que producen conidios en los extremos.

conjugación: (pág. 490) Forma de reproducción sexual de algunas bacterias en la cual un individuo transfiere todo o parte de su material genético a otro individuo a través de una estructura parecida a un puente llamada pilo.

biología de la conservación: (pág. 121) Campo de la biología que estudia los métodos e implementa planes para proteger la biodiversidad.

control: (pág. 13) En un experimento, es la norma contra la cual se comparan los resultados.

evolución convergente: (pág. 413) Evolución en la cual organismos poco relacionados desarrollan rasgos similares; ocurre cuando especies no relacionadas ocupan ambientes similares.

cámbium suberoso: (pág. 611) Meristemo lateral que produce una capa protectora fuerte sobre la superficie de los tallos y las semillas.

cuerpo lúteo: (pág. 1002) Parte del folículo del ovario que permanece en el ovario después de la ovulación; produce estrógeno y progesterona.

corteza: (pág. 613) Capa de tejido fundamental en la raíz que participa en el transporte de agua y iones hacia el tejido vascular de la raíz.

cotiledones: (pág. 589) Estructura embrionaria de las plantas de semilla que almacena o absorbe alimento para el embrión en desarrollo.

comportamiento de cortejo: (pág. 862) Comportamiento instintivo que los machos y hembras de una especie llevan a cabo antes de aparearse.

enlace covalente: (pág. 146) Enlace químico que se forma cuando dos átomos comparten electrones.

Cro-Magnon/deoxyribonucleic acid (DNA)

Cro-Magnon (kroh MAG nun): (p. 434) modern form of *Homo sapiens* that spread throughout Europe between 35 000 to 40 000 years ago; were identical to modern humans in height, skull and tooth structure, and brain size.

crossing over: (p. 266) exchange of genetic material between nonsister chromatids from homologous chromosomes during prophase I of meiosis; results in new allele combinations.

cuticle (KYEWT ih kul): (p. 559) protective, waxy coating on the outer surface of the epidermis of most stems and leaves; important adaptation in reducing water loss.

cytokinesis (si toh kih NEE sus): (p. 209) cell process following meiosis or mitosis in which the cell's cytoplasm divides and separates into new cells.

cytokinins (si tuh KI nihnz): (p. 623) group of hormones that stimulate mitosis and cell division.

cytoplasm: (p. 181) clear, gelatinous fluid in cells that is the site of numerous chemical reactions; in eukaryotic cells, it suspends the cell's organelles.

cytoskeleton: (p. 185) cellular framework found within the cytoplasm composed of microtubules and microfilaments.

Cro-Magnon/ácido desoxirribonucleico (DNA)

Cro-Magnon: (pág. 434) Forma moderna de *Homo sapiens* que se extendió por Europa hace entre 35 000 y 40 000 años; eran idénticos a los humanos modernos en altura, estructura del cráneo y de los dientes y tamaño del cerebro.

entrecruzamiento: (pág. 266) Intercambio de material genético entre cromátides no hermanas de los cromosomas homólogos durante la profase I de la meiosis; resulta en nuevas combinaciones de alelos.

cutícula: (pág. 559) Cubierta cerosa protectora sobre la superficie externa de la epidermis de muchos tallos y hojas; es una importante adaptación para reducir la pérdida de agua.

citoquinesis: (pág. 209) Proceso celular que sigue a la meiosis o la mitosis y en el cual el citoplasma de la célula se divide y se separa para formar nuevas células.

citoquininas: (pág. 623) Grupo de hormonas que estimulan la mitosis y la división celular.

citoplasma: (pág. 181) Fluido gelatinoso de las células donde ocurren numerosas reacciones químicas. Es el fluido en el que se encuentran suspendidos los organelos de las células eucariotas.

citoesqueleto: (pág. 185) Armazón celular que se encuentra dentro del citoplasma, compuesto de microtúbulos y microfilamentos.

D

data: (p. 15) information obtained from experiments, sometimes called experimental results.

day-neutral plants: (p. 645) plants that flower over a range in the number of daylight hours.

death rate: (p. 101) number of deaths per 1000 population in a given year.

deciduous plants: (p. 592) plants that drop all of their leaves each fall or when water is scarce or unavailable; an adaptation for reducing water loss when water is unavailable.

decomposers: (p. 47) organisms, such as fungi and bacteria, that break down and absorb nutrients from dead organisms.

demography (de MAH gra fee): (p. 100) study of population characteristics such as growth rate, age structure, and geographic distribution.

dendrite (DEN drite): (p. 943) branchlike extension of a neuron; transports impulses toward the cell body.

density-dependent factor: (p. 97) limiting factors such as disease, parasites, or food availability that affect growth of a population.

density-independent factor: (p. 97) factor such as temperature, storms, floods, drought, or habitat disruption that affects all populations, regardless of their density.

deoxyribonucleic acid (DNA): (p. 163) a nucleic acid; the master copy of an organism's information code that contains the instructions used to form all of an organism's enzymes and structural proteins.

datos: (pág. 15) Información que se obtiene de los experimentos, llamada a veces resultados experimentales.

plantas de día neutro: (pág. 645) Plantas que pueden florecer en un amplio rango de número de horas de luz solar.

índice de mortalidad: (pág. 101) Número de muertes por cada 1000 individuos en una población en un año dado.

plantas caducas: (pág. 592) Plantas que pierden todas las hojas durante el otoño o cuando el agua escasea; adaptación para reducir la pérdida de agua cuando esta no está disponible.

descomponedores: (pág. 47) Organismos como los hongos y las bacterias que descomponen y absorben los nutrientes de organismos muertos.

demografía: (pág. 100) Estudio de las características de la población como la tasa de crecimiento, la estructura por edades y la distribución geográfica.

dendrita: (pág. 943) Extensión de la neurona que tiene forma ramificada; transporta los impulsos eléctricos hacia el cuerpo de la célula.

factor dependiente de la densidad: (pág. 97) Factores limitantes como las enfermedades, los parásitos o la disponibilidad de alimentos que afectan el crecimiento de una población.

factor independiente de la densidad: (pág. 97) Un factor, como la temperatura, las tormentas, las inundaciones, la sequía o la alteración del hábitat que afecta a todas las poblaciones, sin tomar en cuenta su densidad.

ácido desoxirribonucleico (DNA): (pág. 163) Ácido nucleico; la copia maestra del código de información de un organismo y que contiene las instrucciones que se usan para formar todas las enzimas y proteínas estructurales del organismo.

dependent variable: (p. 13) in an experiment, the condition that results from changes in the independent variable.

depressant: (p. 958) type of drug that lowers or depresses the activity of the nervous system.

dermis: (p. 895) inner, thicker portion of the skin that contains structures such as blood vessels, nerves, nerve endings, hair follicles, sweat glands, and oil glands.

desert: (p. 78) arid region with sparse to almost nonexistent plant life; the driest biome, usually receives less than 25 cm of precipitation annually.

deuterostome (DEW tihr uh stohm): (p. 677) animal whose mouth develops from cells other than those at the opening of the gastrula.

development: (p. 8) all of the changes that take place during the life of an organism; a characteristic of all living things.

diaphragm (DI uh fram): (p. 843) in mammals, the sheet of muscles located beneath the lungs that separates the chest cavity from the abdominal cavity; expands and contracts the chest cavity, which increases the amount of oxygen entering the body.

dicotyledon (di kah tuh LEE dun): (p. 595) class of anthophytes that have two seed leaves.

diffusion: (p. 155) net, random movement of particles from an area of higher concentration to an area of lower concentration, eventually resulting in even distribution.

diploid: (p. 263) cell with two of each kind of chromosome; is said to contain a diploid, or *2n*, number of chromosomes.

directional selection: (p. 408) natural selection that favors one of the extreme variations of a trait; can lead to rapid evolution in a population.

disruptive selection: (p. 408) natural selection that favors individuals with either extreme of a trait; tends to eliminate intermediate phenotypes.

divergent evolution: (p. 412) evolution in which species that once were similar to an ancestral species diverge; occurs when populations change as they adapt to different environmental conditions; eventually resulting in a new species.

division: (p. 449) taxonomic grouping of similar classes; term used instead of phyla by plant taxonomists.

DNA replication: (p. 284) process in which chromosomal DNA is copied before mitosis or meiosis.

dominance hierarchy (DAH muh nunts • HI rar kee): (p. 864) innate behavior by which animals form a social ranking within a group in which some individuals are more subordinate than others; usually has one top-ranking individual.

dominant: (p. 256) observed trait of an organism that masks the recessive form of a trait.

variable dependiente: (pág. 13) En un experimento, es la condición que resulta de los cambios introducidos en la variable independiente.

depresor: (pág. 958) Tipo de droga que baja o deprime la actividad del sistema nervioso.

dermis: (pág. 895) Porción de la piel más interna y más gruesa que contiene estructuras como vasos sanguíneos, nervios, terminaciones nerviosas, folículos pilosos, glándulas sudoríparas y glándulas sebáceas.

desierto: (pág. 78) Región árida con poca o ninguna vegetación; es el bioma más seco y en general recibe menos de 25 cm de precipitación al año.

deuterostomado: (pág. 677) Animal cuya boca se desarrolla de células que no son aquellas que se encuentran en la abertura de la gástrula.

desarrollo: (pág. 8) Todos los cambios que ocurren durante la vida de un organismo; una característica de todos los seres vivos.

diafragma: (pág. 843) En los mamíferos, lámina muscular localizada por debajo de los pulmones que separa la cavidad torácica de la cavidad abdominal; expande y contrae la cavidad torácica, lo que hace aumentar la cantidad de oxígeno que entra al cuerpo.

dicotiledónea: (pág. 595) Clase de las antofitas que posee dos cotiledones.

difusión: (pág. 155) Movimiento neto y al azar de partículas desde un área de mayor concentración hacia un área de menor concentración, lo que resulta a la postre en la distribución homogénea de las partículas.

diploide: (pág. 263) Aquella célula que posee dos de cada tipo de cromosomas, se dice que es diploide, o con un número *2n* de cromosomas.

selección direccional: (pág. 408) Selección natural que favorece una de las variantes extremas de un rasgo; puede conducir a la evolución rápida de una población.

selección disruptiva: (pág. 408) Selección natural que favorece aquellos individuos que presentan cualquiera de los extremos de un rasgo; tiende a eliminar los fenotipos intermedios.

evolución divergente: (pág. 412) Evolución en la cual especies que antes se parecían a un antepasado común comienzan a divergir; ocurre cuando las poblaciones cambian a medida que se adaptan a diferentes condiciones ambientales y con el tiempo resultan en nuevas especies.

división: (pág. 449) Agrupación taxonómica de clases similares; término utilizado por los taxónomos de plantas en lugar de filo.

replicación del DNA: (pág. 284) Proceso por medio del cual el DNA cromosomal es copiado antes de la mitosis o la meiosis.

jerarquía de dominación: (pág. 864) Comportamiento innato mediante el cual los animales forman un orden social dentro del grupo; en este tipo de jerarquía, algunos individuos son más subordinados que otros; existe por lo general un solo individuo de máximo rango.

dominante: (pág. 256) Rasgo expresado de un organismo que cubre la forma recesiva de dicho rasgo.

dormancy: (p. 654) period of inactivity in a mature seed prior to germination.

dorsal (DOR sul): (p. 682) upper surface of bilaterally symmetric animals.

dorsal hollow nerve cord: (p. 771) nerve cord found in all chordates that forms the spinal cord and brain.

double fertilization: (p. 651) anthophyte fertilization in which one sperm fertilizes the egg and the other sperm joins with the central cell; results in the formation of a diploid ($2n$) zygote and a triploid ($3n$) endosperm.

double helix: (p. 283) shape of a DNA molecule formed when two twisted DNA strands are coiled into a springlike structure and held together by hydrogen bonds between the bases.

doubling time: (p. 102) time needed for a population to double in size.

drug: (p. 956) chemical substance that affects body functions.

dynamic equilibrium: (p. 156) result of diffusion where there is continuous movement of particles but no overall change in concentration.

estado latente: (pág. 654) Período de inactividad de una semilla madura antes de la germinación.

dorsal: (pág. 682) La superficie superior de un animal con simetría bilateral.

cordón nervioso dorsal: (pág. 771) Cordón nervioso que se encuentra en todos los cordados y forma la espina dorsal y el cerebro.

fecundación doble: (pág. 651) Proceso de fecundación de las antofitas. En este proceso un espermatozoide fecunda el óvulo y el otro espermatozoide se une a la célula central; resulta en la formación de un cigoto diploide ($2n$) y un endosperma triploide ($3n$).

hélice doble: (pág. 283) La forma de la molécula de DNA; se forma cuando dos hebras enroscadas de DNA se enrollan juntas en una estructura parecida a un resorte y se mantienen juntas por medio de enlaces de hidrógeno entre las bases.

tiempo doble: (pág. 102) Tiempo de duplicación.

droga: (pág. 956) Sustancia química que afecta las funciones corporales.

equilibrio dinámico: (pág. 156) Resultado de la difusión donde hay un movimiento constante de partículas sin que ocurra un cambio en la concentración.

E

ecology: (p. 36) scientific study of interactions between organisms and their environments.

ecosystem: (p. 41) interactions among populations in a community; the community's physical surroundings, or abiotic factors.

ectoderm: (p. 677) layer of cells on the outer surface of the gastrula; eventually develops into the skin and nervous tissue of an animal.

ectotherm (EK tuh thurm): (p. 805) animal that has a variable body temperature and derives its heat from external sources.

edge effect: (p. 117) different environmental conditions that occur along the boundaries of an ecosystem.

egg: (p. 265) haploid female sex cell produced by meiosis.

electron microscope: (p. 172) instrument that uses a beam of electrons instead of light to magnify structures up to 500 000 times actual size; allows scientists to view structures within a cell.

electron transport chain: (p. 226) series of proteins embedded in a membrane along which energized electrons are transported; as electrons are passed from molecule to molecule, energy is released.

element: (p. 141) substance that can't be broken down into simpler chemical substances.

embryo: (p. 402) earliest stage of growth and development of both plants and animals; differences and similarities among embryos can provide evidence of evolution. **(p. 589)** the young diploid sporophyte of a plant.

emigration: (p. 102) movement of individuals from a population.

ecología: (pág. 36) Estudio científico de las interacciones entre los organismos y sus ambientes.

ecosistema: (pág. 41) Interacciones entre las poblaciones de una comunidad; el ambiente físico de la comunidad, o sea, los factores abióticos.

ectodermo: (pág. 677) Capa de células en la superficie externa de la gástrula; desarrolla a la postre la piel y el sistema nervioso de los animales.

animal de sangre fría: (pág. 805) Animal con temperatura corporal variable y que obtiene calor a partir de fuentes externas.

efecto de borde: (pág. 117) Las diferentes condiciones ambientales que ocurren en los límites de un ecosistema.

huevo, óvulo: (pág. 265) Célula sexual femenina haploide producida por medio de la meiosis.

microscopio electrónico: (pág. 172) Instrumento que utiliza un rayo de electrones en lugar de la luz para aumentar el tamaño de las estructuras hasta 500 000 veces; permite a los científicos observar estructuras dentro de la célula.

cadena de transporte de electrones: (pág. 226) Serie de proteínas inmersas en una membrana que se encargan de transportar electrones; a medida que los electrones pasan de una molécula a la siguiente, se libera energía.

elemento: (pág. 141) Sustancia que no puede ser descompuesta en sustancias químicas más simples.

embrión: (pág. 402) La etapa más temprana del crecimiento y desarrollo tanto de plantas como de animales; las diferencias y similitudes entre los embriones pueden dar evidencia sobre la evolución. **(pág. 589)** el esporofito joven de una planta.

emigración: (pág. 102) Movimiento de individuos desde una población.

endangered species: (p. 115) a species in which the number of individuals falls so low that extinction is possible.

endemic disease: (p. 1029) disease that is constantly present in a population.

endocrine glands: (p. 929) series of ductless glands that make up the endocrine system; release chemicals directly into the bloodstream where they relay messages to other parts of the body.

endocytosis (en doh si TOH sus): (p. 200) active transport process where a cell engulfs materials with a portion of the cell's plasma membrane and releases the contents inside of the cell.

endoderm: (p. 677) layer of cells on the inner surface of the gastrula; will eventually develop into the lining of the animal's digestive tract and organs associated with digestion.

endodermis: (p. 613) single layer of cells that forms a waterproof seal around a root's vascular tissue; controls the flow of water and dissolved minerals into the root.

endoplasmic reticulum (ER): (p. 181) organelle in eukaryotic cells with a series of highly folded membranes surrounded in cytoplasm; site of cellular chemical reactions; can either be rough (with ribosomes) or smooth (without ribosomes).

endoskeleton: (p. 684) internal skeleton; provides support, protects internal organs, and acts as an internal brace for muscles to pull against.

endosperm: (p. 651) food storage tissue in an anthophyte seed that supports development of the growing embryo.

endospore: (p. 491) structure formed by bacteria during unfavorable conditions that contains DNA and a small amount of cytoplasm encased by a protective outer covering; germinates during favorable conditions.

endotherm: (p. 828) animal that maintains a constant body temperature and is not dependent on the environmental temperature.

energy: (p. 9) the ability to cause change; organisms use energy to perform biological functions.

environment: (p. 8) biotic and abiotic surroundings to which an organism must constantly adjust; includes air, water, weather, temperature, other organisms, and many other factors.

enzymes: (p. 161) type of protein found in all living things that changes the rate of chemical reactions.

epidemic: (p. 1029) occurs when many people in a given area are afflicted with the same disease at about the same time.

epidermis: (p. 607) in plants, the outermost layer of flattened cells that covers and protects all parts of the plant. **(p. 893)** in humans and some other animals, the outermost protective layer composed of an outer layer of dead cells and an inner layer of living cells.

especie en peligro de extinción: (pág. 115) Una especie en la cual el número de individuos se reduce tanto que existe peligro de que se extinga.

enfermedad endémica: (pág. 1029) Enfermedad que se encuentra presente constantemente en una población.

glándulas endocrinas: (pág. 929) Serie de glándulas que no poseen conductos y que forman el sistema endocrino; liberan sustancias químicas directamente al torrente sanguíneo por medio del cual llevan mensajes a otras partes del cuerpo.

endocitosis: (pág. 200) Proceso de transporte activo en que la célula rodea y absorbe materiales utilizando una porción de la membrana citoplasmática y liberando su contenido dentro de la célula.

endodermo: (pág. 677) Capa de células de la parte interna de la gástrula; se desarrolla para formar el recubrimiento del tracto digestivo del animal y los órganos asociados a la digestión.

endodermis: (pág. 613) Estructura de una sola capa de células que forma un sello a prueba de agua alrededor del tejido vascular de la raíz; controla el flujo de agua y minerales disueltos hacia el interior de la raíz.

retículo endoplasmático: (pág. 181) Organelo de las células eucariotas que posee una serie de membranas muy dobladas rodeadas por citoplasma; sitio de reacciones químicas celulares; puede ser tanto rugoso (con ribosomas); como liso (sin ribosomas).

endoesqueleto: (pág. 684) Esqueleto interno que provee sostén, protege los órganos internos y actúa como un punto interno de apoyo sobre el cual pueden jalar los músculos.

endosperma: (pág. 651) Tejido de reserva de alimento de las semillas de las antofitas que ayuda al desarrollo del embrión en crecimiento.

endospora: (pág. 491) Estructura formada por bacterias durante condiciones desfavorables que contiene DNA y un pequeño volumen de citoplasma encerrado en una cubierta externa protectora; germina cuando las condiciones se vuelven favorables.

animal de sangre caliente: (pág. 828) Animal que mantiene una temperatura corporal constante y no depende de la temperatura ambiental.

energía: (pág. 9) La capacidad de producir un cambio; los organismos usan la energía para realizar sus funciones biológicas.

ambiente: (pág. 8) Los alrededores bióticos y abióticos a los cuales un organismo debe ajustarse constantemente; incluyen el aire, el agua, el clima, la temperatura, otros organismos y muchos otros factores.

enzimas: (pág. 161) Tipo de proteína presente en todos los seres vivos que modifica la tasa de las reacciones químicas.

epidemia: (pág. 1029) Ocurre cuando muchas personas de un área sufren la misma enfermedad más o menos al mismo tiempo.

epidermis: (pág. 607) En las plantas, la capa más externa de células aplanadas que protege todas las partes de la planta. **(pág. 893)** en los seres humanos y algunos otros animales, la capa protectora más externa compuesta por una capa exterior de células muertas y una capa interior de células vivas.

Glossary/Glosario

epididymis (e puh DIH duh mus): (p. 996) in human males, the coiled tube within the scrotum in which the sperm complete maturation.

epiglottis (ep uh GLAH tus): (p. 920) flap of cartilage that closes over the opening of the respiratory tract during swallowing; prevents food from entering the respiratory tract.

esophagus: (p. 918) muscular tube that connects the mouth to the stomach; moves food by peristalsis.

estivation (es tuh VAY shun): (p. 866) state of reduced metabolism that occurs in animals living in conditions of intense heat.

estuary (ES chuh wer ee): (p. 71) coastal body of water, partially surrounded by land, in which freshwater and salt water mix.

ethics: (p. 21) the moral principles and values held by humans.

ethylene (EH thuh leen): (p. 623) plant hormone that promotes the ripening of fruits.

eubacteria (yew bak TEER ee uh): (p. 457) group of prokaryotes with strong cell walls and a variety of structures, may be autotrophs (chemosynthetic or photosynthetic) or heterotrophs.

eukaryotes: (p. 173) unicellular or multicellular organisms, such as yeast, plants, and animals, composed of eukaryotic cells, which contain a true nucleus and membrane-bound organelles.

evolution (e vuh LEW shun): (p. 10) gradual change in a species through adaptations over time.

exocytosis: (p. 200) active transport process by which materials are secreted or expelled from a cell.

exoskeleton: (p. 684) hard covering on the outside of some animals, including spiders and mollusks; provides a framework for support, protects soft body tissues, and provides a place for muscle attachment.

exotic species: (p. 120) nonnative species in an area; may take over niches of native species in an area and eventually replace them.

experiment: (p. 13) procedure that tests a hypothesis by collecting information under controlled conditions.

exponential growth: (p. 93) growth pattern where a population grows faster as it increases in size; graph of a exponentially growing population resembles a J-shaped curve.

external fertilization: (p. 696) fertilization that occurs outside the animal's body.

extinction (ek STINGK shun): (p. 115) the disappearance of a species when the last of its members dies.

epidídimo: (pág. 996) En los machos humanos, el tubo enroscado dentro del escroto en que los espermatozoides terminan de madurar.

epiglotis: (pág. 920) Lámina de cartílago que al tragar, cierra la entrada del tracto respiratorio; evita que el alimento entre al tracto respiratorio.

esófago: (pág. 918) Tubo muscular que conecta la boca con el estómago; mueve el alimento por medio de la peristalsis.

estivación: (pág. 866) Estado de metabolismo reducido que ocurre en animales que viven bajo calores intensos.

estuario: (pág. 71) Masa de agua costera rodeada parcialmente por tierra en donde se mezcla el agua dulce con el agua salada.

ética: (pág. 21) Los principios y valores morales que los seres humanos mantienen.

etileno: (pág. 623) Hormona vegetal que promueve la maduración de los frutos.

eubacterias: (pág. 457) Grupo de procariotas con paredes celulares fuertes y una variedad de estructuras, pueden ser autótrofos. (quimiosintéticos o fotosintéticos) o heterótrofos.

eucariotas: (pág. 173) Organismos unicelulares o multicelulares, como las levaduras, las plantas y los animales, compuestos de células eucariotas, las cuales contienen un núcleo verdadero y organelos rodeados por membranas.

evolución: (pág. 10) Cambio gradual en una especie resultado de adaptaciones a lo largo del tiempo.

exocitosis: (pág. 200) Proceso de transporte activo por medio del cual los materiales son secretados o eliminados de la célula.

exoesqueleto: (pág. 684) Cubierta dura en la parte externa de algunos animales, incluyendo las arañas y los moluscos; provee una estructura de apoyo, protección para los tejidos suaves del cuerpo y proporciona sitios para que se adhieran los músculos.

especies exóticas: (pág. 120) Especies no nativas de un área; pueden tomar los nichos de las especies nativas de un área y a la postre reemplazarlas.

experimento: (pág. 13) Procedimiento que pone a prueba una hipótesis por medio de la recolección de información bajo condiciones controladas.

crecimiento exponencial: (pág. 93) Patrón de crecimiento en el cual la población crece más rápidamente a medida que aumenta su tamaño; la gráfica del crecimiento exponencial de una población se parece a una curva en forma de J.

fecundación externa: (pág. 696) Fecundación que ocurre fuera del cuerpo del animal.

extinción: (pág. 115) La desaparición de una especie; ocurre cuando el último miembro de una especie muere.

F

facilitated diffusion: (p. 198) passive transport of materials across a plasma membrane by transport proteins embedded in the plasma membrane.

feather: (p. 826) lightweight, modified scale found only on birds; provides insulation and enables flight.

fertilization: (p. 253) fusion of male and female gametes.

fetus: (p. 312) a developing mammal from nine weeks to birth.

fight-or-flight response: (p. 861) automatic response controlled by hormones that prepares the body to either fight or run from danger.

filter feeding: (p. 693) method in which food particles are filtered from water as it passes by or through some part of the organism.

fins: (p. 796) in fishes, fan-shaped membranes used for balance, swimming, and steering.

flagella (fluh JEL uh): (p. 187) long projections composed of microtubules; found on some cell surfaces; they help propel cells and organisms by a whiplike motion.

flagellates: (p. 506) protists that have one or more flagella.

fluid mosaic model: (p. 178) structural model of the plasma membrane where molecules are free to move sideways within a lipid bilayer.

follicle: (p. 999) in human females, group of epithelial cells that surround a developing egg cell.

food chain: (p. 49) simple model that shows how matter and energy move through an ecosystem.

food web: (p. 50) model that shows all the possible feeding relationships at each trophic level in a community.

fossil: (p. 370) physical evidence of an organism that lived long ago that scientists use to study the past; evidence may appear in rocks, amber, or ice.

fragmentation: (p. 515) type of asexual reproduction in algae where an individual breaks into pieces and each piece grows into a new individual.

frameshift mutation: (p. 299) mutation that occurs when a single base is added or deleted from DNA; causes a shift in the reading of codons by one base.

frond: (p. 567) in ferns leaves that grow upward from the rhizome; often divided into pinnae that are attached to a central rachis.

fruit: (p. 590) seed-containing ripened ovary of an anthophyte flower; may be fleshy or dry.

fungus: (p. 458) group of unicellular or multicellular heterotrophic eukaryotes that do not move from place to place; absorb nutrients from organic materials in the environment.

difusión facilitada: (pág. 198) Transporte pasivo de materiales a través de una membrana celular por medio de proteínas de transporte que se encuentran inmersas en la membrana.

pluma: (pág. 826) Escama modificada liviana que se encuentra solo en las aves; provee aislamiento y permite el vuelo.

fecundación: (pág. 253) Fusión de los gametos femenino y masculino.

feto: (pág. 312) Un mamífero en desarrollo desde las nueve semanas hasta el nacimiento.

respuesta de pelear o huir: (pág. 861) Respuesta automatizada controlada por las hormonas que preparan al cuerpo ya sea para pelear o para huir del peligro.

alimentación por filtración: (pág. 693) Método en que las partículas de alimento son filtradas del agua cuando esta pasa sobre o a través de una parte del organismo.

aletas: (pág. 796) En los peces, las membranas con forma de abanico que se usan para mantener el equilibrio, para nadar y para cambiar de dirección.

flagelos: (pág. 187) Proyecciones largas compuestas de microtúbulos; se las encuentra en la superficie de algunas células; ayudan a dar propulsión a las células y a los organismos con un movimiento como de látigo.

flagelados: (pág. 506) Protistas que tienen uno o más flagelos.

modelo del mosaico fluido: (pág. 178) Modelo estructural de la membrana celular en que las moléculas pueden moverse de lado a lado dentro la capa doble de lípidos.

folículo: (pág. 999) En las mujeres, grupo de células epiteliales que rodean a la célula óvulo en desarrollo.

cadena alimenticia: (pág. 49) Modelo sencillo que muestra la forma en que la materia y la energía se mueven a través del ecosistema.

red alimenticia: (pág. 50) Modelo que muestra todas las relaciones alimenticias posibles en cada nivel trófico en una comunidad.

fósil: (pág. 370) Prueba física de un organismo que vivió hace mucho tiempo que los científicos utilizan para estudiar el pasado; evidencia que puede aparecer en las rocas, el ámbar o el hielo.

fragmentación: (pág. 515) Tipo de reproducción asexual de las algas en que un individuo se rompe en trozos y cada trozo crece para formar un nuevo individuo.

mutación de cambio de estructura: (pág. 299) Mutación que ocurre cuando el DNA pierde o gana una sola base; hace que se desplace en una base el marco de lectura de los codones.

fronda: (pág. 567) Hojas de los helechos que crecen verticalmente desde el rizoma; se dividen a menudo en pinnas que se adhieren a un raquis central.

fruto: (pág. 590) Ovario maduro que contiene las semillas de la flor de una antofita; puede ser carnosa o seca.

hongo: (pág. 458) Grupo de eucariotas heterótrofos que pueden ser unicelulares o multicelulares, que no se mueven de un sitio a otro; absorben nutrientes de los materiales orgánicos del ambiente.

G

gallbladder: (p. 921) small organ that stores bile before the bile passes into the duodenum of the small intestine.

gametangium (ga muh TAN ghee uhm): (p. 536) structure that contains a haploid nucleus; formed by the fusion of haploid hyphae.

gametes: (p. 253) male and female sex cells; sperm and eggs.

gametophyte: (p. 516) haploid form of an organism in alternation of generations that produces gametes.

gastrovascular cavity (gas troh VAS kyuh lur): (p. 702) in cnidarians, a large cavity in which digestion takes place.

gastrula (GAS truh luh): (p. 676) animal embryo development stage where cells on one side of the blastula move inward forming a cavity of two or three layers of cells with an opening at one end.

gene: (p. 211) segment of DNA that controls the protein production and the cell cycle.

gene pool: (p. 405) all of the alleles in a population's genes.

gene splicing: (p. 352) in recombinant DNA technology, the rejoining of DNA fragments by vectors and other enzymes.

genetic drift: (p. 406) alteration of allelic frequencies in a population by chance events; results in disruption of genetic equilibrium.

genetic engineering: (p. 341) method of cutting DNA from one organism and inserting the DNA fragment into a host organism of the same or a different species.

genetic equilibrium: (p. 405) condition in which the frequency of alleles in a population remains the same over generations.

genetic recombination: (p. 270) major source of genetic variation among organisms caused by reassortment or crossing over during meiosis.

gene therapy: (p. 352) insertion of normal genes into human cells to correct genetic disorders.

genetics: (p. 253) branch of biology that studies heredity.

genotype (JEE noh tipe): (p. 258) combination of genes in an organism.

genus (JEE nus): (p. 444) first word of a two-part scientific name used to identify a group of similar species.

geographic isolation: (p. 409) occurs whenever a physical barrier divides a population, which results in individuals no longer being able to mate; can lead to the formation of a new species.

germination: (p. 654) beginning of the development of an embryo into a new plant.

gestation (jeh STAY shun): (p. 848) time during which placental mammals develop inside the uterus.

gibberellins (jih buh REH lunz): (p. 623) group of plant hormones that cause plants to grow taller by stimulating cell elongation.

vesícula biliar: (pág. 921) Pequeño órgano que almacena la bilis antes de que esta pase al duodeno del intestino delgado.

gametangio: (pág. 536) Estructura que contiene un núcleo haploide; se forma por la fusión de hifas haploides.

gametos: (pág. 253) Las células sexuales masculinas y femeninas; espermatozoides y óvulos.

gametofito: (pág. 516) Durante la alternación de generaciones, la forma haploide de un organismo que produce gametos.

cavidad gastrovascular: (pág. 702) En los cnidarios, una cavidad grande en la cual se lleva a cabo la digestión.

gástrula: (pág. 676) Etapa del desarrollo embrionario de los animales en la cual las células de un lado de la blástula se desplazan hacia adentro, formando una cavidad de dos o tres capas de células con una abertura en uno de los extremos.

gene: (pág. 211) Segmento del DNA que controla la producción de proteínas y el ciclo celular.

caudal de genes: (pág. 405) Todos los alelos de los genes de una población.

empalme de genes: (pág. 352) En la tecnología del DNA recombinante, la unión de fragmentos de DNA por medio de vectores y otras enzimas.

deriva genética: (pág. 406) Alteración al azar de las frecuencias alélicas de una población; resulta en una pérdida del equilibrio genético.

ingeniería genética: (pág. 341) Método de cortar el DNA de un organismo e insertar el fragmento en el DNA de otro organismo huésped de la misma especie o de una especie diferente.

equilibrio genético: (pág. 405) Condición en la cual las frecuencias de alelos de una población se mantienen iguales a través de las generaciones.

recombinación genética: (pág. 270) La fuente más importante de variabilidad entre los organismos causada por el reacomodo o el entrecruzamiento durante la meiosis.

terapia genética: (pág. 352) La inserción de genes normales en las células de un ser humano para corregir un trastorno genético.

genética: (pág. 253) La rama de la biología que estudia la herencia.

genotipo: (pág. 258) La combinación de genes en un organismo.

género: (pág. 444) La primera palabra del nombre de dos palabras usado para identificar un grupo de especies similares.

aislamiento geográfico: (pág. 409) Ocurre cuando una barrera física separa a una población, lo que resulta en la ausencia de apareamiento entre los individuos de tal población; puede conducir a la formación de una nueva especie.

germinación: (pág. 654) El comienzo del desarrollo del embrión en una nueva planta.

gestación (pág. 848) Período de tiempo durante el cual los mamíferos placentarios se desarrollan dentro del útero.

giberelinas: (pág. 623) Grupo de hormonas de las plantas que hacen que la planta se haga más alta al estimular el alargamiento de las células.

gizzard: (p. 730) sac with muscular walls and hard particles that grind soil before it passes into the intestine; common in birds and annelids such as earthworms.

gland: (p. 842) in mammals, a cell or group of cells that secretes fluids.

glycolysis (gli KAH lih sis): (p. 231) in cellular respiration, series of anaerobic chemical reactions in the cytoplasm that breaks down glucose into pyruvic acid; forms a net profit of two ATP molecules.

Golgi apparatus (GAWL jee): (p. 182) organelle in eukaryotic cells with a system of flattened tubular membranes; sorts and packs proteins and sends them to their appropriate destinations.

gradualism: (p. 411) idea that species originate through a gradual change of adaptations.

grasslands: (p. 79) biome composed of large communities covered with rich soil, grasses, and similar small plants; receives 25–75 cm of precipitation annually.

growth: (p. 8) increase in the amount of living material and formation of new structures in an organism; a characteristic of all living things.

guard cells: (p. 607) cells that control the opening and closing of the stomata; regulate the flow of water vapor from leaf tissue.

molleja: (pág. 730) Saco de paredes musculares y partículas duras que muele el suelo antes de que pase al intestino; es común en las aves y en anélidos como las lombrices de tierra.

glándula: (pág. 842) En los mamíferos, célula o grupo de células que secreta fluidos.

glicólisis: (pág. 231) En la respiración celular, la serie de reacciones químicas anaeróbicas del citoplasma las cuales descomponen la glucosa en ácido pirúvico; produce una ganancia neta de dos moléculas de ATP.

aparato de Golgi: (pág. 182) Organelo de las células eucariotas que consta de un sistema aplastado de membranas tubulares; se encarga de ordenar y acomodar las proteínas para enviarlas a su destino apropiado.

gradualismo: (pág. 411) La idea de que las especies se originan por medio del cambio gradual de adaptaciones.

praderas: (pág. 79) Bioma compuesto de grandes comunidades cubiertas por pastos y otras plantas pequeñas similares; tienen suelos fértiles y reciben entre 25 y 75 cm de precipitación al año.

crecimiento: (pág. 8) El aumento en la cantidad de material vivo y la formación de nuevas estructuras en un organismo; es una característica de todos los seres vivos.

células guardianas: (pág. 607) Células que controlan el cerrarse y el abrirse de los estomas; regulan el flujo de vapor de agua en los tejidos de la hoja.

H

habitat (HA buh tat): (p. 42) place where an organism lives out its life.

habitat corridors: (p. 123) natural strips of land that allow the migration of organisms from one wilderness area to another.

habitat degradation: (p. 118) damage to a habitat by air, water, and land pollution.

habitat fragmentation: (p. 117) separation of wilderness areas from each other; may cause problems for organisms that need large areas for food or mating.

habituation (huh bit choo AY shun): (p. 869) learned behavior that occurs when an animal is repeatedly given a stimulus not associated with any punishment or reward.

hair follicle: (p. 896) narrow cavities in the dermis from which hair grows.

hallucinogen (huh LEW sun uh jun): (p. 962) drug that stimulates the central nervous system so that the user becomes disoriented and sees, hears, feels, tastes, or smells things that are not there.

haploid: (p. 263) cell with one of each kind of chromosome; is said to contain a haploid or *n*, number of chromosomes.

haustoria (huh STOR ee uh): (p. 532) in parasitic fungi, hyphae that grow into host cells and absorb nutrients and minerals from the host.

hábitat: (pág. 42) Sitio donde un organismo vive toda su vida.

corredores de hábitat: (pág. 123) Franjas naturales de terreno que permiten la migración de los organismos de un área silvestre a otra.

degradación del hábitat: (pág. 118) Daño hecho a un hábitat por la contaminación del aire, del agua y del suelo.

fragmentación del hábitat: (pág. 117) Separación de las áreas silvestres; puede causar problemas a los organismos que requieren de grandes áreas para su alimentación o apareamiento.

habituación: (pág. 869) Comportamiento adquirido que ocurre cuando un animal recibe repetidamente un estímulo que no está asociado a un castigo o una recompensa.

folículos pilosos: (pág. 896) Cavidades angostas de la dermis de las cuales crece el pelo.

alucinógenos: (pág. 962) Droga que estimula al sistema nervioso central de tal forma que la persona sufre desorientación y ve, oye, siente, siente sabores u olores de cosas que no están presentes.

haploide: (pág. 263) Célula que tiene uno de cada tipo de cromosomas; se dice que contiene un número haploide, o *n*, de cromosomas.

haustorios: (pág. 532) En los hongos parásitos, las hifas que crecen hacia adentro de las células del huésped y absorbe los nutrientes y minerales del huésped.

Glossary/
Glosario

hemoglobin (HEE muh gloh bun): **(p. 976)** iron-containing protein molecule in red blood cells that binds to oxygen and carries it from the lungs to the body's cells.

heredity: (p. 253) passing on of characteristics from parents to offspring.

hermaphrodite (hur MAF ruh dite): **(p. 696)** an animal that can produce both eggs and sperm.

heterotrophs (HE tuh ruh trohfs): **(p. 47)** organisms that cannot make their own food and must feed on other organisms for energy and nutrients.

heterozygous (heh tuh roh ZI gus): **(p. 259)** when there are two different alleles for a trait.

hibernation (hi bur NAY shun): **(p. 866)** state of reduced metabolism occurring in animals that sleep during parts of cold winter months; an animal's temperature drops, oxygen consumption decreases, and breathing rate declines.

homeostasis (hoh mee oh STAY sus): **(p. 9)** organism's regulation of its internal environment to maintain conditions suitable for survival; a characteristic of all living things. **(p. 175)** process of maintaining equilibrium in cells' internal environments.

hominid (HAH mih nud): **(p. 428)** a group of bipedal primates that includes modern humans and their direct ancestors.

hominoid (HAH mih noyd): **(p. 428)** a group of primates that can walk upright on two legs; includes gorillas, chimpanzees, bonobos, and humans.

homologous chromosomes (hoh MAH luh gus): **(p. 264)** paired chromosomes with genes for the same traits arranged in the same order.

homologous structures: (p. 400) structures with common evolutionary origins; can be similar in arrangement, in function, or both; provides evidence of evolution from a common ancestor; forelimbs of crocodiles, whales, and birds are examples.

homozygous (hoh moh ZI gus): **(p. 258)** when there are two identical alleles for a trait.

hormone: (p. 622) chemical produced in one part of an organism and transported to another part, where it causes a physiological change.

host cell: (p. 475) living cell in which a virus replicates.

human genome: (p. 349) map of the approximately 80 000 genes on 46 human chromosomes that when mapped and sequenced, may provide information on the treatment or cure of genetic disorders.

hybrid: (p. 255) offspring formed by parents having different forms of a trait.

hydrogen bond: (p. 153) weak chemical bond formed by the attraction of positively charged hydrogen atoms to other negatively charged atoms.

hypertonic solution: (p. 196) in cells, solution in which the concentration of dissolved substances outside the cell is higher than the concentration inside the cell; causes a cell to shrink as water leaves the cell.

hemoglobina: (pág. 976) Molécula de proteína de los glóbulos rojos que contiene hierro que se enlaza al oxígeno y lo lleva desde los pulmones hasta las células del cuerpo.

herencia: (pág. 253) La transmisión de rasgos desde los progenitores hacia la progenie.

hermafrodita: (pág. 696) Animal que puede producir tanto óvulos como espermatozoides.

heterótrofos: (pág. 47) Organismos que no pueden producir su propio alimento y deben alimentarse de otros organismos para obtener energía y nutrientes.

heterocigoto: (pág. 259) Cuando existen dos alelos diferentes para el mismo rasgo.

hibernación: (pág. 866) Estado de metabolismo reducido que ocurre en los animales que duermen durante partes de los fríos meses de invierno; la temperatura del animal baja, el consumo de oxígeno disminuye y la tasa respiratoria se reduce.

homeostasis: (pág. 9) Regulación del organismo de su ambiente interno para mantener las condiciones adecuadas para la sobrevivencia; característica de todos los seres vivos. **(pág. 175)** el proceso que permite que las células mantengan el equilibrio de sus condiciones internas.

homínido: (pág. 428) Grupo de primates bípedos que incluye a los humanos y sus antepasados directos.

hominoido: (pág. 428) Grupo de primates que pueden caminar erguidos sobre dos piernas; incluye los gorilas, chimpancés, bonobos y a los humanos.

cromosomas homólogos: (pág. 264) Pares de cromosomas con genes para los mismos rasgos acomodados en el mismo orden.

estructuras homólogas: (pág. 400) Estructuras que tienen el mismo origen evolutivo; pueden ser similares en su localización, su función, o en ambas; proporcionan evidencias sobre la evolución a partir de un antepasado común; las extremidades delanteras de los cocodrilos, las ballenas y las aves son ejemplos.

homocigoto: (pág. 258) Cuando existen dos alelos idénticos para un rasgo.

hormona: (pág. 622) Compuesto químico producido en una parte del organismo y transportado a otra parte en donde causa un cambio fisiológico.

célula huésped: (pág. 475) Célula viva en la cual se replica un virus.

genoma humano: (pág. 349) Mapa de los aproximadamente 80 000 genes ubicados en los 46 cromosomas humanos, que cuando sean ubicados y puestos en secuencia, proveerán información para el tratamiento o la curación de los trastornos genéticos.

híbrido: (pág. 255) Progenie de progenitores que tienen formas diferentes para un rasgo.

enlace de hidrógeno: (pág. 153) Enlace químico débil formado por la atracción de los átomos de hidrógeno de carga positiva hacia átomos que tienen carga negativa.

solución hipertónica: (pág. 196) Ocurre cuando la solución que rodea a la célula tiene una concentración de sustancias disueltas mayor que la concentración dentro de la célula; ocasiona que la célula se encoja al perder agua hacia el ambiente.

hyphae (HI fee): **(p. 530)** threadlike filaments that are the basic structural units of multicellular fungi.

hypocotyl (HI poh kah tul): **(p. 655)** portion of the stem nearest the seed in a young plant.

hypothalamus (hi poh THA luh mus): **(p. 929)** portion of the brain that connects the endocrine and nervous systems, and controls the pituitary gland by sending messages to the pituitary, which then releases its own chemicals or stimulates other glands to release chemicals.

hypothesis (hi PAHTH us sus): **(p. 12)** explanation for a question or a problem that can be formally tested.

hypotonic solution: (p. 196) in cells, solution in which the concentration of dissolved substances is lower in the solution outside the cell than the concentration inside the cell; causes a cell to swell and possibly burst as water enters the cell.

hifas: (pág. 530) Filamentos parecidos a hebras que son la unidad estructural básica de los hongos multicelulares.

hipocótilo: (pág. 655) Porción del tallo más cercana a la semilla en plántulas.

hipotálamo: (pág. 929) Sección del cerebro que conecta los sistemas endocrino y nervioso y controla la glándula pituitaria por medio del envío de mensajes a la pituitaria, la cual libera entonces sus propias sustancias químicas o estimula a otras glándulas para que liberen sustancias química.

hipótesis: (pág. 12) Explicación para una pregunta o problema que puede ser puesta formalmente a prueba.

solución hipotónica: (pág. 196) Ocurre cuando la solución que rodea a la célula tiene una concentración de sustancias disueltas menor que dentro de la célula; ocasiona que la célula se hinche y puede llegar a estallar si entra una cantidad excesiva de agua.

immigration: (p. 102) movement of individuals into a population.

implantation: (p. 1006) in females, the attachment of a blastocyst to the lining of the uterus.

imprinting: (p. 869) learned behavior in which an animal, at a specific critical time of its life, forms a social attachment to another object; usually occurs early in life and allows an animal to recognize its mother and others of its species.

inbreeding: (p. 338) mating between closely related individuals; ensures that offspring are homozygous for most traits, but also brings out harmful, recessive traits.

incomplete dominance: (p. 315) inheritance pattern where the phenotype of a heterozygote is intermediate between those of the two homozygotes; neither allele of the pair is dominant but combine and display a new trait.

incubate: (p. 828) process of keeping eggs laid outside of the body warm; also involves periodic turning of the eggs to ensure proper development.

independent variable: (p. 13) in an experiment, the condition that is tested because it affects the outcome of the experiment.

infectious disease (ihn FEK shus): **(p. 1024)** any disease caused by pathogens in the body.

innate behavior (ih NAYT): **(p. 861)** an inherited behavior in animals; includes automatic responses and instinctive behaviors.

innate immunity (ih NAYT): **(p. 1031)** body's earliest lines of defense against any and all pathogens; includes skin and body secretions, inflammation of body tissues, and phagocytosis of pathogens.

insight: (p. 871) type of learning in which an animal uses previous experiences to respond to a new situation.

inmigración: (pág. 102) Ingreso de individuos a una población.

implantación: (pág. 1006) En las hembras es la fijación del blastocisto al revestimiento del útero.

impronta: (pág. 869) comportamiento aprendido en que un animal desarrolla un vínculo social con otro objeto, durante una etapa crítica de su desarrollo. En general, ocurre en etapas tempranas de la vida y permite que el animal reconozca a su madre y a otros miembros de su especie.

entrecruzamiento: (pág. 338) apareamiento entre parientes cercanos; permite obtener individuos homocigotos para la mayoría de los rasgos, pero también ocasiona la expresión de rasgos recesivos dañinos.

dominancia incompleta: (pág. 315) patrón hereditario en el cual el fenotipo de un individuo heterocigoto es intermedio entre los fenotipos de los homocigotos; ninguno de los alelos es dominante, sino que se combinan y originan un nuevo rasgo.

incubación: (pág. 828) proceso que permite mantener los huevos en una temperatura adecuada, fuera del cuerpo; incluye también la conducta de dar vuelta a los huevos periódicamente para asegurar un desarrollo adecuado.

variable independiente: (pág. 13) La condición que se prueba en un experimento porque afecta el resultado del experimento.

enfermedad infecciosa: (pág. 1024) Cualquier enfermedad causada por patógenos en el cuerpo.

comportamiento innato: (pág. 861) Comportamiento hereditario en los animales; incluye las respuestas automáticas y los comportamientos instintivos.

inmunidad innata: (pág. 1031) Son las más tempranas líneas de defensa del cuerpo contra los patógenos; incluye la piel y secreciones corporales, la respuesta inflamatoria y la fagocitosis de patógenos.

discernimiento: (pág. 871) Tipo de aprendizaje en el cual un animal usa experiencias previas para responder a nuevas situaciones.

instinct (IHN stingt): **(p. 862)** complex innate behavior pattern that begins when an animal recognizes a stimulus and continues until all parts of the behavior have been performed.

interferons: (p. 1033) host-cell specific proteins that protect cells from viruses.

internal fertilization: (p. 696) fertilization that occurs inside the female's body.

interphase: (p. 204) cell growth phase where a cell increases in size, carries on metabolism, and duplicates chromosomes prior to division.

intertidal zone: (p. 72) portion of the shoreline that lies between high tide and low tide lines.

invertebrate: (p. 684) animal that does not have a backbone.

involuntary muscle: (p. 906) muscle in which contractions are not under conscious control.

ion: (p. 147) atom or group of atoms that gain or lose electrons; has an electrical charge.

ionic bond: (p. 147) chemical bond formed by the attractive forces between two ions of opposite charge.

isomers (I suh murz): **(p. 158)** compounds with the same simple formula but different three-dimensional structures resulting in different physical and chemical properties.

isotonic solution: (p. 196) in cells, solution in which the concentration of dissolved substances in the solution is the same as the concentration of dissolved substances inside a cell.

isotopes (I suh tohps): **(p. 144)** atoms of the same element that have different numbers of neutrons in the nucleus.

instinto: (pág. 862) Patrón complejo de comportamiento innato que se inicia cuando el animal reconoce un estímulo determinado y se continúa hasta que todos los componentes del comportamiento son realizados.

interferonas: (pág. 1033) Proteínas específicas producidas por las células del huésped que protegen a las células contra virus.

fecundación interna: (pág. 696) Fecundación que ocurre dentro del cuerpo de la hembra.

interfase: (pág. 204) Fase del crecimiento de la célula, previa a la división celular, en la que la célula aumenta de tamaño, continúa realizando su metabolismo y duplica sus cromosomas.

zona intermareal: (pág. 72) Sección de la costa limitada por la marea alta y la marea baja.

invertebrado: (pág. 684) Animal que carece de columna vertebral.

músculo involuntario: (pág. 906) Músculo cuyas contracciones no están bajo control consciente.

ion: (pág. 147) Átomo o grupo de átomos que gana o pierde electrones; tiene carga eléctrica.

enlace iónico: (pág. 147) Enlace químico formado por la fuerza de atracción entre iones de cargas opuestas.

isómeros: (pág. 158) Compuesto que tienen la misma fórmula pero que tienen diferente estructura tridimensional, lo que les otorga diferentes propiedades físicas y químicas.

solución isotónica: (pág. 196) Ocurre cuando la solución que rodea a la célula tiene una concentración similar a la concentración de sustancias dentro de la célula.

isótopos: (pág. 144) Átomos de un mismo elemento que tienen diferente número de neutrones en el núcleo.

J

Jacobson's organ: (p. 821) in snakes, a pitlike sense organ on the roof of the mouth that picks up and analyzes airborne chemicals.

joints: (p. 899) point where two or more bones meet; can be fixed or facilitate movement of bones in relation to one another.

órgano de Jacobson: (pág. 821) Órgano sensorial de las serpientes, tiene forma de semilla y se localiza en el techo de la boca, se encarga de percibir y analizar las sustancias químicas en el aire.

articulaciones: (pág. 899) Sitios donde dos o más huesos se juntan; pueden ser fijas o facilitar el movimiento de un hueso en relación con los otros.

K

karyotype (KAYR ee uh tipe): **(p. 329)** chart of metaphase chromosome pairs arranged according to length and location of the centromere; used to pinpoint unusual chromosome numbers in cells.

keratin (KER uh tun): **(p. 893)** protein found in the exterior portion of the epidermis that helps protect living cells in the interior epidermis.

kidneys: (p. 985) organs of the vertebrate urinary system; remove wastes, control sodium levels of the blood, and regulate blood pH levels.

cariotipo: (pág. 329) Imagen de los cromosomas en metafase, organizados en parejas de acuerdo con su longitud y la posición del centrómero; se utiliza para resaltar números poco usuales de cromosomas en las células.

queratina: (pág. 893) Proteína que se encuentra en la parte exterior de la epidermis y que ayuda a proteger a las células vivas del interior de la epidermis.

riñones: (pág. 985) Órganos del sistema urinario de los vertebrados; elimina los desechos, controla el nivel de sodio en la sangre y regula el pH de la sangre.

kingdom: (p. 449) taxonomic grouping of similar phyla or divisions.

Koch's postulates: (p. 1025) experimental steps relating a specific pathogen to a specific disease.

reino: (pág. 449) Agrupación taxonómica que incluye filos o divisiones similares.

postulados de Koch: (pág. 1025) El conjunto de pasos a seguir para establecer una relación entre un patógeno y una enfermedad específica.

L

labor: (p. 1012) physiological and physical changes a female goes through during the birthing process.

lactic acid fermentation: (p. 236) series of anaerobic chemical reactions in which pyruvic acid uses NADH to form lactic acid and NAD^+, which is then used in glycolysis; supplies energy when oxygen for aerobic respiration is scarce.

language: (p. 873) use of symbols to represent ideas; usually present in animals with complex nervous systems, memory, and insight.

large intestine: (p. 923) muscular tube through which indigestible materials are passed to the rectum for excretion.

larva: (p. 753) in insects, the free-living, wormlike stage of metamorphosis, often called a caterpillar.

lateral line system: (p. 796) line of fluid-filled canals running along the sides of a fish that enable the fish to detect movement and vibrations in the water.

law of independent assortment: (p. 260) Mendelian principle stating that genes for different traits are inherited independently of each other.

law of segregation: (p. 257) Mendelian principle explaining that because each plant has two different alleles, it can produce two different types of gametes. During fertilization, male and female gametes randomly pair to produce four combinations of alleles.

leaf: (p. 561) the plant organ that grows from a stem in which photosynthesis usually occurs.

lichen (LI kun): (p. 542) organism formed from a symbiotic association between a fungus, usually an ascomycete, and a photosynthetic green alga or cyanobacteria.

life-history pattern: (p. 93) an organism's pattern of reproduction; may be rapid or slow.

ligament: (p. 899) tough band of connective tissue that attaches one bone to another; joints are often held together and enclosed by ligaments.

light-dependent reactions: (p. 225) phase of photosynthesis where light energy is converted to chemical energy in the form of ATP; results in the splitting of water and the release of oxygen.

light-independent reactions: (p. 225) phase of photosynthesis where energy from light-dependent reactions is used to produce glucose and additional ATP molecules.

limiting factor: (p. 65) any biotic or abiotic factor that restricts the existence, numbers, reproduction, or distribution of organisms.

parto: (pág. 1012) Cambios fisiológicos y físicos que ocurren cuando la mujer da a luz.

fermentación del ácido láctico: (pág. 236) Serie de reacciones químicas anaeróbicas en las cuales el ácido pirúvico utiliza NADH para formar ácido láctico y NAD^+, el cual es utilizado a continuación en la glicólisis; provee energía cuando el oxígeno para la respiración aeróbica es escaso.

lenguaje: (pág. 873) Uso de símbolos para representar ideas; está presente con frecuencia en animales que poseen sistemas nerviosos complejos, memoria y discernimiento.

intestino grueso: (pág. 923) Tubo muscular a través del cual pasan los materiales no digestibles hacia el recto para su eliminación.

larva: (pág. 753) En los insectos, la etapa de la metamorfosis parecida a un gusano que es de vida libre, llamada muchas veces oruga.

sistema de la línea lateral: (pág. 796) Línea de canales llenos de fluido que corren a lo largo de ambos lados de los peces y les permiten detectar el movimiento y las vibraciones en el agua.

ley de la distribución independiente: (pág. 260) Principio mendeliano que dice que los genes para rasgos diferentes se heredan independientemente unos de otros.

ley de la segregación: (pág. 257) Principio mendeliano que explica que, al tener dos alelos diferentes, cada planta puede producir dos tipos diferentes de gametos. Durante la fecundación, los gametos femenino y masculino se aparean al azar para producir cuatro combinaciones de alelos.

hoja: (pág. 561) Órgano de las plantas que crece desde el tallo y en el cual generalmente ocurre la fotosíntesis.

liquen: (pág. 542) Organismo que se forma a partir de la relación simbiótica entre un hongo, generalmente un ascomiceto y un alga verde fotosintética o una cianobacteria.

patrón de historia de vida: (pág. 93) Patrón reproductor de un organismo; puede ser rápido o lento.

ligamento: (pág. 899) Banda fuerte de tejido conectivo que adhiere un hueso al otro; las articulaciones están a menudo rodeadas y sostenidas en su lugar por los ligamentos.

reacciones dependientes de la luz: (pág. 225) Fase de la fotosíntesis en la cual la energía luminosa es convertida a energía química en forma de ATP; resulta en el rompimiento del agua y la liberación de oxígeno.

reacciones independientes de la luz: (pág. 225) Fase de la fotosíntesis en la cual la energía proveniente de las reacciones dependientes de la luz se utiliza para producir glucosa y moléculas adicionales de ATP.

factores limitantes: (pág. 65) Cualquier factor biótico o abiótico que restringe la existencia, el número, la reproducción y la distribución de los organismos.

Glossary/Glosario

linkage map: (p. 349) genetic map that shows the location of genes on a chromosome.

lipids: (p. 160) large organic compounds made mostly of carbon and hydrogen with a small amount of oxygen; examples are fats, oils, waxes, and steroids; are insoluble in water and used by cells for energy storage, insulation, and protective coatings, such as in membranes.

liver: (p. 921) large, complex organ of the digestive system that produces many chemicals for digestion, including bile.

long-day plants: (p. 644) plants that are induced to flower when the number of daylight hours is longer than its critical period.

lymph: (p. 1036) tissue fluids composed of water and dissolved substances from the blood that have collected and entered the lymph vessels.

lymph node: (p. 1036) small mass of tissue that contains lymphocytes and filters pathogens from the lymph; made of a network of connective tissue fibers that contain lymphocytes.

lymphocyte (LIHM fuh site): (p. 1036) type of white blood cell stored in lymph nodes that defends the body against foreign agents.

lysogenic cycle: (p. 479) viral replication cycle in which the virus's nucleic acid is integrated into the host cell's chromosome; a provirus is formed and replicated each time the host cell reproduces; the host cell is not killed until the lytic cycle is activated.

lysosomes: (p. 183) organelles that contain digestive enzymes; digest excess or worn out organelles, food particles, and engulfed viruses or bacteria.

lytic cycle (LIH tik): (p. 479) viral replication cycle in which a virus takes over a host cell's genetic material and uses the host cell's structures and energy to replicate until the host cell bursts, killing it.

mapa de enlace: (pág. 349) Mapa genético que muestra la posición de los genes en un cromosoma.

lípidos: (pág. 160) Compuestos orgánicos grandes formados principalmente de carbono e hidrógeno y pequeñas cantidades de oxígeno; ejemplos son las grasas, los aceites, las ceras y los esteroides; son insolubles en el agua y sirven a la célula para almacenar energía, para el aislamiento y como capa protectora, por ejemplo en las membranas.

hígado: (pág. 921) Órgano grande y complejo del sistema digestivo que produce muchas sustancias químicas para la digestión, incluyendo la bilis.

plantas de día largo: (pág. 644) Plantas que florecen cuando el número de horas de luz es mayor que su período crítico.

linfa: (pág. 1036) Fluidos de los tejidos compuestos de agua y sustancias disueltas provenientes de la sangre que han sido recogidas y han entrado a los vasos de la linfa.

ganglio linfático: (pág. 1036) Pequeña masa de tejido que contiene linfocitos y filtra a los patógenos de la linfa; está formado por una red de fibras de tejido conectivo que contienen linfocitos.

linfocito: (pág. 1036) Tipo de glóbulo blanco sanguíneo almacenado en los ganglios linfáticos que defiende al cuerpo contra los agentes externos.

ciclo lisogénico: (pág. 479) Ciclo de replicación de los virus en que los ácidos nucleicos del virus se integran al cromosoma de la célula huésped; el provirus se forma y es replicado cada vez que la célula huésped se reproduce; la célula huésped no es dañada hasta que se activa el ciclo lítico.

lisosomas: (pág. 183) Organelos que contienen enzimas digestivas; digieren los organelos gastados o extras, las partículas de alimento y rodean e ingieren los virus o las bacterias.

ciclo lítico: (pág. 479) Ciclo de replicación de los virus en que el virus toma posesión del material genético del huésped y utiliza las estructuras y la energía del huésped para replicarse a sí mismo hasta que la célula del huésped revienta, destruyéndola.

M

macrophages: (p. 1032) type of phagocyte that engulfs damaged cells or pathogens that have entered the body's tissues.

madreporite (mah druh POHR ite): (p. 764) in echinoderms, the sievelike, disk-shaped opening through which water flows in and out of the water vascular system; helps filter out large particles from entering the body.

Malpighian tubules (mal PIH gee un): (p. 745) in arthropods, tubules located in the abdomen that are attached to and empty waste into the intestine.

mammary glands (MA muh ree): (p. 842) modified sweat glands in female mammals, which produce and secrete milk to feed their young.

mandibles (MAN duh bulz): (p. 745) in most arthropods, mouthparts adapted for holding, chewing, sucking, or biting various foods.

macrófagos: (pág. 1032) Tipo de fagocito que rodea a las células dañadas o a los patógenos que han entrado a los tejidos del cuerpo.

madreporita: (pág. 764) En los equinodermos, la abertura con forma de disco y estructura parecida a un colador, a través de la cual entra y sale el agua del sistema vascular acuático; ayuda a filtrar las partículas grandes para que no entren en el cuerpo.

túbulos de Malpighi: (pág. 745) En los artrópodos, los túbulos localizados en el abdomen que están adheridos al intestino y en el cual vacían los desechos.

glándulas mamarias: (pág. 842) Glándulas sudoríparas modificadas que poseen las hembras de los mamíferos; producen y secretan leche para alimentar a las crías.

mandíbulas: (pág. 745) En la mayor parte de los artrópodos, las partes bucales adaptadas para sostener, masticar, chupar o morder el alimento.

mantle (MAN tuhl): **(p. 722)** a membrane that surrounds the internal organs of mollusks; in mollusks with shells, it secretes the shell.

marsupial (mar SEW pee uhl): **(p. 849)** subclass of mammals in which young develop for a short period in the uterus and complete their development outside of the mother's body inside a pouch made of skin and hair.

medulla oblongata (muh DU luh • ah blon GAH tuh): **(p. 947)** part of the brain stem that controls involuntary activities such as breathing and heart rate.

medusa (mih DEW suh): **(p. 700)** a cnidarian body form that is umbrella-shaped with tentacles that hang down.

megaspore: (p. 638) haploid spore formed by some plants that develops into a female gametophyte.

meiosis (mi OH sus): **(p. 265)** type of cell division where one body cell produces four gametes, each containing half the number of chromosomes as a parent's body cell.

melanin: (p. 895) pigment found in cells of the interior layer of the epidermis; protects cells from solar-radiation damage.

menstrual cycle: (p. 1002) in human females, the monthly cycle that includes the production of an egg, the preparation of the uterus to receive an egg, and the shedding of an egg if it remains unfertilized.

meristems: (p. 611) regions of actively dividing cells in plants.

mesoderm (MEZ uh durm): **(p. 677)** middle cell layer in the gastrula, between the ectoderm and the endoderm; develops into the muscles, circulatory system, excretory system, and in some animals, the respiratory system.

mesophyll (MEH zuh fihl): **(p. 618)** photosynthetic tissue of a leaf.

messenger RNA (mRNA): (p. 289) RNA that transports information from DNA in the nucleus to the cell's cytoplasm.

metabolism: (p. 147) all of the chemical reactions that occur within an organism.

metamorphosis (met uh MOR fuh sus): **(p. 751)** in insects, series of chemically-controlled changes in body structure from juvenile to adult; may be complete or incomplete.

metaphase: (p. 208) short second phase of mitosis where doubled chromosomes move to the equator of the spindle and chromatids are attached by centromeres to a separate spindle fiber.

microfilaments: (p. 185) thin, solid protein fibers that provide structural support for eukaryotic cells.

micropyle (MI kruh pile): **(p. 639)** the opening in the ovule through which the pollen tube enters.

microspore: (p. 638) haploid spore formed by some plants that develops into a male gametophyte.

microtubules: (p. 185) thin, hollow cylinders made of protein that provide structural support for eukaryotic cells.

manto: (pág. 722) Membrana que rodea los órganos internos de los moluscos; en los moluscos con concha, el manto produce la concha por secreción.

marsupial: (pág. 849) Subclase de los mamíferos en la cual las crías se desarrollan en el útero durante un corto período y completan su desarrollo fuera del cuerpo de la madre, dentro de una bolsa formada por piel y pelo.

bulbo raquídeo: (pág. 947) Parte del tronco encefálico que controla las actividades involuntarias como la respiración y el ritmo cardíaco.

medusa: (pág. 700) Forma corporal de los cnidarios que semeja un paraguas con tentáculos colgando hacia abajo.

megáspora: (pág. 638) Espora haploide producida por algunas plantas y que se convierte en el gametofito femenino.

meiosis: (pág. 265) Tipo de división celular en la cual las células del cuerpo producen gametos, cada uno de los cuales contiene la mitad del número de cromosomas de una célula corporal del progenitor.

melanina: (pág. 895) Pigmento que se encuentra en la capa interna de la epidermis; protege a las células del daño causado por la radiación solar.

ciclo menstrual: (pág. 1002) En las mujeres, el ciclo mensual que incluye la producción de un óvulo, la preparación del útero para recibir el óvulo y la descarga del óvulo si no ha sido fecundado.

meristemos: (pág. 611) Regiones de las plantas en las que las células se dividen activamente.

mesodermo: (pág. 677) Capa celular intermedia de la gástrula, entre el ectodermo y el endodermo; se desarrolla para formar los músculos, el sistema circulatorio, el sistema excretor y en algunos animales también el sistema respiratorio.

mesófilo: (pág. 618) Tejido fotosintético de la hoja.

RNA mensajero (mRNA): (pág. 289) RNA que transporta información desde el DNA en el núcleo hasta el citoplasma de la célula.

metabolismo: (pág. 147) Todas las reacciones químicas que ocurren dentro de un organismo.

metamorfosis: (pág. 751) En los insectos es la serie de cambios corporales controlados químicamente que cambian la estructura del cuerpo desde la forma juvenil hasta el adulto; puede ser completa o incompleta.

metafase: (pág. 208) La segunda fase de la mitosis en la cual los cromosomas se desplazan hacia el ecuador del huso y las cromátides se adhieren independientemente a las fibras del huso por medio de los centrómeros.

microfilamentos: (pág. 185) Fibras proteínicas largas y sólidas que proveen soporte estructural a las células eucariotas.

micrópilo: (pág. 639) Abertura en el óvulo a través de la cual entra el tubo polínico.

micróspora: (pág. 638) Espora haploide formada por algunas plantas y que se convierte en el gametofito masculino.

microtúbulos: (pág. 185) Cilindros angostos huecos formados por proteínas que dan apoyo estructural a las células eucariotas.

migration: (p. 865) instinctive seasonal movements of animals from place to place.

mimicry: (p. 398) structural adaptation that enables one species to resemble another species; may provide protection from predators or other advantages.

minerals: (p. 926) inorganic substances that are important for chemical reactions or as building materials in the body.

mitochondria: (p. 185) eukaryotic membrane-bound organelles that transform energy stored in food molecules; has a highly folded inner membrane that produces energy-storing molecules.

mitosis (mi TOH sus): (p. 204) period of nuclear cell division in which two daughter cells are formed, each containing a complete set of chromosomes.

mixture: (p. 148) combination of substances in which individual components retain their own properties.

molecule: (p. 146) group of atoms held together by covalent bonds; has no overall charge.

molting: (p. 742) in arthropods, the periodic shedding of an old exoskeleton.

monocotyledon (mah nuh kah tuh LEE dun): (p. 595) class of anthophytes that have one seed leaf.

monotreme (MAHN uh treem): (p. 850) subclass of mammals that have hair and mammary glands but reproduce by laying eggs.

motivation: (p. 870) internal need that causes an animal to act and that is necessary for learning to take place; often involves hunger or thirst.

multiple alleles: (p. 317) presence of more that two alleles for a genetic trait.

mutagen (MYEW tuh jun): (p. 300) any agent that can cause a change in DNA; includes high-energy radiation, chemicals, or high temperatures.

mutation: (p. 296) any change or random error in a DNA sequence.

mutualism (MYEW chuh wuh lih zum): (p. 44) a symbiotic relationship in which both species benefit.

mycelium (mi SEE lee um): (p. 530) in fungi, a complex network of branching hyphae; may serve to anchor the fungus, invade food sources, or form reproductive structures.

mycorrhiza (my kuh RHY zuh): (p. 540) mutualistic relationship in which a fungus lives symbiotically with a plant.

myofibril (mi oh FI brul): (p. 907) unit of muscle fibers composed of thick myosin protein filaments and thin actin protein filaments.

myosin: (p. 907) structural protein that makes up the thick filaments of myofibrils; functions in muscle contraction.

migración: (pág. 865) Desplazamientos estacionales instintivos de animales que se trasladan de un sitio a otro.

mimetismo: (pág. 398) Adaptación estructural que permite que una especie tenga un aspecto similar a otra especie; entre otras ventajas, puede ofrecer protección contra depredadores.

minerales: (pág. 926) Sustancias inorgánicas que son importantes en las reacciones químicas o como materiales de construcción del cuerpo.

mitocondrias: (pág. 185) Organelos eucariotas membranosos que transforman la energía almacenada en las moléculas de los alimentos; poseen una membrana interna con muchos dobleces que se encarga de producir las moléculas que almacenan la energía.

mitosis: (pág. 204) Período de la división nuclear en que se forman dos células hijas, cada una de las cuales contiene un grupo completo de cromosomas.

mezcla: (pág. 148) Combinación de sustancias en la que cada componente mantiene sus propiedades individuales.

molécula: (pág. 146) Grupo de átomos que se mantienen unidos por medio de enlaces covalentes; no posee carga neta.

muda: (pág. 742) En los artrópodos, el cambio periódico del exoesqueleto viejo.

monocotiledóneas: (pág. 595) Clase de las antofitas que tiene un solo cotiledón.

monotrema: (pág. 850) Subclase de los mamíferos que tiene pelo y glándulas mamarias pero se reproduce por medio de huevos.

motivación: (pág. 870) Necesidad interna que hace que un animal actúe y que es necesaria para el aprendizaje; con frecuencia involucra el hambre o la sed.

alelos múltiples: (pág. 317) Presencia de más de dos alelos para un rasgo genético.

mutágeno: (pág. 300) Cualquier agente capaz de causar un cambio en el DNA; incluye la radiación de alta energía, las sustancias químicas y las altas temperaturas.

mutación: (pág. 296) Cualquier cambio o error ocurrido al azar en la secuencia del DNA.

mutualismo: (pág. 44) Relación simbiótica en la cual las dos especies se benefician.

micelio: (pág. 530) En los hongos, la red compleja de hijas ramificadas; puede servir para adherir el hongo, invadir la fuente de alimento o formar estructuras reproductoras.

micorriza: (pág. 540) Relación mutualista en la cual un hongo vive de manera simbiótica con una planta.

miofibrilla: (pág. 907) Unidad de fibras musculares compuesta por filamentos gruesos de la proteína miosina y filamentos finos de la proteína actina.

miosina: (pág. 907) Proteína estructural que forma los filamentos gruesos de las miofibrillas; funciona en la contracción muscular.

N

NADP⁺ (nicotinamide adenine dinucleotide phosphate): (p. 227) electron carrier molecule; when carrying excited electrons it becomes NADPH.

narcotic: (p. 957) type of pain-relief drug that affects the central nervous system.

nastic movement: (p. 625) responsive movement of a plant not dependent on the direction of the stimulus.

natural selection: (p. 395) mechanism for change in populations; occurs when organisms with favorable variations survive, reproduce, and pass their variations to the next generation.

Neandertals: (p. 434) archaic *Homo sapiens* that lived from 35 000 to 100 000 years ago in Europe, Asia, and the Middle East; had thick bones and large faces with prominent noses and brains at least as large as those of modern humans.

negative feedback system: (p. 930) internal feedback mechanism in which a substance is fed back to inhibit the original signal and reduce production of a substance; examples include hormones in the endocrine system.

nematocyst (nih MA tuh sihst): (p. 701) in cnidarians, a capsule that contains a coiled, threadlike tube that may be sticky, barbed, or contain poisons; used in capturing prey.

nephridia (nih FRIH dee uh): (p. 725) organs that remove metabolic wastes from an animal's body.

nephron: (p. 986) individual filtering unit of the kidneys.

nerve net: (p. 702) simple netlike nervous system in cnidarians that conducts nerve impulses from all parts of the cnidarian's body.

neurons (NYU ronz): (p. 943) basic unit of structure and function in the nervous system; conducts impulses throughout the nervous system; composed of dendrites, a cell body, and an axon.

neurotransmitters: (p. 946) chemicals released from an axon that diffuse across a synapse to the next neuron's dendrites to initiate a new impulse.

niche (neesh): (p. 43) role or position a species has in its environment; includes all biotic and abiotic interactions as an animal meets its needs for survival and reproduction.

nitrogenous base: (p. 282) carbon ring structure found in DNA or RNA that contains one or more atoms of nitrogen; includes adenine, guanine, cytosine, thymine, and uracil.

nitrogen fixation: (p. 493) metabolic process in which bacteria use enzymes to convert atmospheric nitrogen (N_2) into ammonia (NH_3).

nondisjunction: (p. 271) failure of homologous chromosomes to separate properly during meiosis; results in gametes with too many or too few chromosomes.

NADP⁺ (sulfato dinucleótido de nicotinamida): (pág. 227) Molécula portadora de electrones; al acarrear electrones excitados se convierte en NADPH.

narcótico: (pág. 957) Tipo de droga para aliviar el dolor que afecta al sistema nervioso central.

movimiento nástico: (pág. 625) Movimiento de una planta que no depende de la dirección del estímulo.

selección natural: (pág. 395) Mecanismo de cambio en las poblaciones; ocurre cuando los organismos con variaciones favorables sobreviven, se reproducen y transfieren sus variaciones a la siguiente generación.

Neanderthal: (pág. 434) *Homo sapiens* antiguo que vivió hace entre 35 000 y 100 000 años en Europa, Asia y el Medio Este; tenía huesos gruesos y cara grande con nariz prominente y un cerebro por lo menos tan grande como los de los seres humanos actuales.

sistema de retroalimentación negativa: (pág. 930) Mecanismo interno de retroalimentación en el que una sustancia es enviada de regreso para inhibir la señal original y reducir la producción de una sustancia; ejemplos incluyen las hormonas del sistema endocrino.

nematocisto: (pág. 701) Es la cápsula de los cnidarios que contiene un tubo parecido a un hilo enroscado que puede ser pegajoso, con bárbulas o con veneno; se utiliza en la captura de las presas.

nefridios: (pág. 725) Órganos que eliminan los desechos metabólicos del cuerpo del animal.

nefrón: (pág. 986) Unidad individual de filtración de los riñones.

red nerviosa: (pág. 702) Sistema nervioso que forma una red sencilla en los cnidarios, el cual conduce los impulsos nerviosos desde todas partes del cuerpo de los cnidarios.

neuronas: (pág. 943) Unidades básicas de estructura y función del sistema nervioso; conducen los impulsos a través del sistema nervioso; están compuestas por las dendritas, el cuerpo celular y el axón.

neurotransmisores: (pág. 946) Sustancias químicas liberadas desde el axón que se difunden en el área de sinapsis hacia las dendritas de la próxima neurona para iniciar un nuevo impulso.

nicho: (pág. 43) La función o la posición de un organismo en su ambiente; incluye todas las interacciones bióticas y abióticas necesarias para que el organismo pueda satisfacer sus necesidades de sobrevivencia y reproducción.

base nitrogenada: (pág. 282) Estructura con un anillo de carbono que se encuentra en el DNA o el RNA y que contiene uno o más átomos de nitrógeno; incluye la adenina, la guanina, la citosina, la timina y el uracilo.

fijación del nitrógeno: (pág. 493) Proceso metabólico en que las bacterias utilizan enzimas para convertir el nitrógeno atmosférico (N_2) a amoniaco (NH_3).

falta de disyunción: (pág. 271) El fracaso de los cromosomas homólogos para separarse adecuadamente durante la meiosis; resulta en gametos con demasiados o muy pocos cromosomas.

nonvascular plants: (p. 562) plants that do not have vascular tissues.

notochord (NOHT uh kord): (p. 771) long, semirigid, rodlike structure found in all chordate embryos that is located between the digestive system and the dorsal hollow nerve cord.

nucleic acid (noo KLAY ihk): (p. 163) complex biomolecules, such as RNA and DNA, that store cellular information in cells in the form of a code.

nucleolus (noo klee OH lus): (p. 181) organelle in eukaryotic cell nucleus that produces ribosomes.

nucleotides: (p. 163) subunits of nucleic acid formed from a simple sugar, a phosphate group, and a nitrogenous base.

nucleus (NEW klee us): (p. 143) positively charged center of an atom composed of neutrons and positively charged protons, and surrounded by negatively charged electrons. (p. 174) in eukaryotic cells, the central membrane-bound organelle that manages cellular functions and contains DNA.

nymph: (p. 754) stage of incomplete metamorphosis where an insect hatching from an egg has the same general appearance as the adult insect but is smaller and sexually immature.

plantas no vasculares: (pág. 562) Plantas que no poseen tejidos vasculares.

notocordio: (pág. 771) Estructura parecida a un bastón largo y semirrígido que se encuentra en los embriones de todos los cordados y se localiza entre el sistema digestivo y el cordón nervioso dorsal hueco.

ácido nucleico: (pág. 163) Biomoléculas complejas, como el RNA y el DNA, que almacenan la información de las células por medio de un código.

nucléolo: (pág. 181) Organelo del núcleo de las células eucariotas que produce los ribosomas.

nucleótidos: (pág. 163) Subunidades de ácidos nucleicos formadas por un azúcar simple, un grupo fosfato y una base nitrogenada.

núcleo: (pág. 143) Centro del átomo con carga positiva compuesto por neutrones y protones de carga positiva, el cual está rodeado por electrones de carga negativa. (pág. 174) en las células eucariotas es el organelo membranoso central y está a cargo de las funciones celulares y contiene el DNA.

ninfa: (pág. 754) Etapa de la metamorfosis incompleta en la cual el insecto que sale del huevo tiene la misma apariencia general que el insecto adulto pero es más pequeño y sexualmente inmaduro.

O

obligate aerobes: (p. 491) bacteria that require oxygen for cellular respiration.

obligate anaerobes: (p. 491) bacteria that are killed by oxygen and can survive only in oxygen-free environments.

open circulatory system: (p. 724) system where blood moves through vessels into open spaces around the body organs.

opposable thumb: (p. 423) primate characteristic of having a thumb that can cross the palm and meet the other fingertips; enables animal to grasp and cling to objects.

order: (p. 449) taxonomic grouping of similar families.

organ system: (p. 210) multiple organs that work together to perform a specific life function.

organ: (p. 210) group of two or more tissues organized to perform complex activities within an organism.

organelles: (p. 173) membrane-bound structures with particular functions within eukaryotic cells.

organism: (p. 6) anything that possesses all the characteristics of life; all organisms have an orderly structure, produce offspring, grow, develop, and adjust to changes in the environment.

organization: (p. 7) orderly structure of cells in an organism; a characteristic of all living things.

osmosis (ahs MOH sus): (p. 195) diffusion of water across a selectively permeable membrane depending on the concentration of solutes on either side of the membrane.

aerobios obligados: (pág. 491) Bacterias que requieren oxígeno para la respiración celular.

anaerobios obligados: (pág. 491) Bacterias a las que destruye el oxígeno y que solo pueden sobrevivir en ambientes libres de oxígeno.

sistema circulatorio abierto: (pág. 724) Sistema en que la sangre se mueve a lo largo de vasos y en espacios abiertos alrededor de los órganos.

pulgar oponible: (pág. 423) Característica de los primates que les permite cruzar el pulgar sobre la palma de la mano y tocar las puntas de los otros dedos; le permite al animal agarrar y sostenerse de objetos.

orden: (pág. 449) Agrupación taxonómica de familias similares.

sistema de órganos: (pág. 210) Órganos múltiples que trabajan juntos para llevar a cabo una actividad vital específica.

órgano: (pág. 210) Grupo de dos o más tejidos organizados para llevar a cabo actividades complejas dentro del organismo.

organelos: (pág. 173) Estructuras membranosas con funciones específicas localizadas dentro de las células eucariotas.

organismo: (pág. 6) Cualquier cosa que posea todas las características de la vida; todos los organismos tienen una estructura ordenada, producen progenies, crecen, se desarrollan y se adaptan a los cambios del ambiente.

organización: (pág. 7) Estructura ordenada de las células en un organismo; es una característica de todos los seres vivos.

osmosis: (pág. 195) Difusión del agua a través de una membrana de permeabilidad selectiva que depende de la concentración de solutos en cualquiera de los dos lados de la membrana.

osteoblasts (AHS tee oh blastz): (p. 902) potential bone-forming cells that secrete collagen in which minerals in the bloodstream can be deposited.

osteocytes: (AHS tee oh sitz): (p. 902) newly formed bone cells.

ovary: (p. 643) in plants, the bottom portion of a flowers's pistil that contains one or more ovules each containing one egg.

oviduct: (p. 999) in females, the tube that transports eggs from the ovary to the uterus.

ovulation: (p. 1000) in females, the process of an egg rupturing through the ovary wall and moving into the oviduct.

ovule: (p. 588) in seed plants, the sporophyte structure surrounding the developing female gametophyte; forms the seed after fertilization.

ozone layer: (p. 118) layer of the atmosphere that helps to protect living organisms on Earth's surface from damaging doses of ultraviolet radiation from the sun.

osteoblastos: (pág. 902) Células que potencialmente pueden formar hueso; secretan colágeno en el cual se pueden depositar los minerales de la sangre.

osteocitos: (pág. 902) Células óseas de reciente formación.

ovario: (pág. 643) En las plantas es la porción inferior del pistilo que contiene uno o más huevos, cada uno de los cuales contiene un óvulo.

oviducto: (pág. 999) Es el tubo que transporta los óvulos desde el ovario hasta el útero en las hembras.

ovulación: (pág. 1000) En las mujeres, el proceso de salida de un óvulo a través de la pared del ovario y su entrada al oviducto.

óvulo: (pág. 588) En las plantas con semillas, la estructura del esporofito que rodea el gametofito femenino en desarrollo; forma la semilla después de la fecundación.

capa de ozono: (pág. 118) Capa de la atmósfera que ayuda a proteger a los organismos vivos en la superficie de la Tierra de dosis dañinas de radiación ultravioleta proveniente del sol.

P

pancreas: (p. 921) soft, flattened gland that secretes digestive enzymes and hormones; products help break down carbohydrates, proteins, and fats.

parasitism (PER uh suh tih zum): (p. 44) symbiotic relationship in which one organism benefits at the expense of another, usually another species.

parasympathetic nervous system (PNS): (p. 949) division of the autonomic nervous system that controls many of the body's internal functions when the body is at rest.

parathyroid glands: (p. 935) produce parathyroid hormone (PTH), which is involved in the regulation of minerals in the body.

parenchyma (puh RENG kuh muh): (p. 605) most abundant type of plant cell; spherical cells with thin, flexible cell walls and a large central vacuole; important for storage and food production.

parthenogenesis (par thuh noh JE nuh sus): (p. 746) type of asexual reproduction in which a new individual develops from an unfertilized egg.

passive transport: (p. 198) movement of particles across cell membranes by diffusion or osmosis; the cell uses no energy to move particles across the membrane.

pathogens: (p. 1023) disease-producing agents such as bacteria, protozoans, fungi, viruses, and other parasites.

pedicellariae (PEH dih sih LAHR ee ay): (p. 763) pincerlike appendages on echinoderms used for protection and cleaning.

pedigree: (p. 309) graphic representation of genetic inheritance used by geneticists to map genetic traits.

páncreas: (pág. 921) Glándula suave y aplanada que secreta enzimas digestivas y hormonas; sus productos ayudan en la digestión de los carbohidratos, las proteínas y las grasas.

parasitismo: (pág. 44) Relación simbiótica en la cual un organismo se beneficia de otro, a menudo de otra especie.

sistema nervioso parasimpático (SNP): (pág. 949) División del sistema nervioso autónomo que controla muchas de las funciones internas del cuerpo cuando este está en reposo.

glándulas paratiroides: (pág. 935) Producen la hormona paratiroides (PTH), la cual participa en la regulación de minerales en el cuerpo.

parénquima: (pág. 605) El tipo más abundante de célula vegetal; formado por células esféricas con paredes celulares delgadas y flexibles, y una gran vacuola central; es importante para el almacenamiento y la producción de alimento.

partenogénesis: (pág. 746) Tipo de reproducción asexual en la cual un nuevo individuo se desarrolla a partir de un óvulo no fecundado.

transporte pasivo: (pág. 198) Movimiento de partículas a través de las membranas celulares por medio de la difusión o la osmosis; la célula no utiliza energía para mover las partículas a través de la membrana.

patógenos: (pág. 1023) Agentes productores de enfermedades, como las bacterias, los protozoarios, los hongos, los virus y otros parásitos.

pedicelarios: (pág. 763) Apéndices con forma de pinzas de los equinodermos los cuales los usan para protección y para el aseo.

árbol genealógico: (pág. 309) Representación gráfica de la herencia genética que usan los genetistas para hacer mapas de los rasgos genéticos.

pedipalps (PE dih palpz): (p. 748) second pair of an arachnid's six pairs of appendages that are often adapted for handling food and sensing.

pepsin: (p. 921) enzyme found in gastric juices; begins the chemical digestion of proteins in food; most effective in acidic environments.

peptide bond: (p. 161) covalent bond formed between amino acids.

perennial: (p. 596) anthophyte that lives for several years.

pericycle: (p. 614) in plants, the layer of cells just within the endodermis that gives rise to lateral roots.

peripheral nervous system (puh RIH frul) (PNS): (p. 947) division of the nervous system made up of all the nerves that carry messages to and from the central nervous system.

peristalsis (per uh STAHL sus): (p. 918) series of involuntary smooth muscle contractions along the walls of the digestive tract that move food through the digestive tract.

permafrost: (p. 76) layer of permanently frozen ground that lies underneath the topsoil of the tundra.

petals: (p. 641) leaflike flower organs, usually brightly colored structures at the top of a flower stem.

petiole (PE tee ohl): (p. 618) in plants, the stalk that joins the leaf blade to the stem.

pH: (p. 150) measure of how acidic or basic a solution is; the scale ranges from below 0 to above 14; solution with pH above 7 is basic and a pH below 7 is acidic.

phagocytes (FAG uh sites): (p. 1032) white blood cells that destroy pathogens by surrounding and engulfing them; include macrophages, neutrophils, monocytes, and eosinophils.

pharyngeal pouches: (p. 772) paired openings located in the pharynx behind the mouth of a chordate embryo.

pharynx (FAHR inx): (p. 709) in planarians, the tubelike, muscular organ that extends from the mouth; aids in feeding and digestion.

phenotype (FEE nuh tipe): (p. 258) outward appearance of an organism, regardless of its genes.

pheromones (FER uh mohnz): (p. 745) chemical signals given off by animals that signal animals to engage in specific behaviors.

phloem: (p. 610) vascular plant tissue made up of tubular cells joined end to end; transports sugars to all parts of the plant.

phospholipids (fahs foh LIH pids): (p. 176) lipids with an attached phosphate group; plasma membranes are composed of phospholipid bilayer with embedded proteins.

photic zone: (p. 71) portion of the marine biome that is shallow enough for sunlight to penetrate.

photolysis (fo TAH luh sis): (p. 227) reaction taking place in the thylakoid membranes of a chloroplast during light-dependent reactions where two molecules of water are split to form oxygen, hydrogen ions, and electrons.

photoperiodism: (p. 644) flowering plant response to differences in the length of day and night.

pedipalpos: (pág. 748) Segundo par de los seis pares de apéndices de los arácnidos que a menudo están adaptados para manipular el alimento y para la percepción.

pepsina: (pág. 921) Enzima que se encuentra en los jugos gástricos; comienza la digestión química de las proteínas en el alimento; es más eficiente en medios ácidos.

enlace peptídico: (pág. 161) Enlace covalente formado entre aminoácidos.

perenne: (pág. 596) Que vive varios años.

periciclo: (pág. 614) En las plantas, la capa de células apenas dentro de la epidermis que origina las raíces laterales.

sistema nervioso periférico (SNP): (pág. 947) División del sistema nervioso compuesta por los nervios que transportan mensajes desde y hacia el sistema nervioso central.

peristalsis: (pág. 918) Serie de contracciones involuntarias del músculo liso a lo largo de las paredes del tracto digestivo que hace que se mueva el alimento a lo largo del tracto digestivo.

permagel: (pág. 76) Capa de suelo congelado en forma permanente que se encuentra bajo el suelo superficial de la tundra.

pétalos: (pág. 641) Órganos de la planta parecidos a hojas que a menudo forman estructuras de colores brillantes en la parte superior del tallo de la flor.

peciolo: (pág. 618) En las plantas, el pedúnculo delgado que une a la hoja con el tallo.

pH: (pág. 150) Medida de la acidez o la basicidad de una solución; la escala varía entre menos de 0 a más de 14. Las soluciones con pH mayor que 7 son básicas y las soluciones con pH menor que 7 son ácidas.

fagocitos: (pág. 1032) Glóbulos blancos sanguíneos que destruyen a los patógenos rodeándolos y tragándoselos; incluye a los macrófagos, los neutrófilos, los monocitos y los eosinófilos.

bolsas faríngeas: (pág. 772) abertura par faríngea que se ubicada detrás de la boca de un embri ón cordado.

faringe: (pág. 709) En las planarias, el órgano muscular parecido a un tubo que se extiende desde la boca; ayuda en la alimentación y la digestión.

fenotipo: (pág. 258) Apariencia externa de un organismo, sin tomar en cuenta sus genes.

feromonas: (pág. 745) Señales químicas que los animales emiten que dirige a otros animales a comportarse de cierta manera.

floema: (pág. 610) Tejido vascular de las plantas formado por células tubulares unidas en sus extremos; transporta azúcares hacia todas las partes de la planta.

fosfolípidos: (pág. 176) Lípidos que tienen un grupo fosfato adherido; las membranas celulares están compuestas de una capa doble de fosfolípidos con proteínas inmersas.

zona fótica: (pág. 71) Porción del bioma marino que es suficientemente bajo para permitir la penetración de la luz solar.

fotólisis: (pág. 227) Reacción que sucede en las membranas tilacoides del cloroplasto durante las reacciones dependientes de la luz, en la cual dos moléculas de agua se rompen y forman oxígeno, iones de hidrógeno y electrones.

fotoperiodicidad: (pág. 644) Respuesta de las plantas de flor a las diferencias en la duración del día y de la noche.

photosynthesis: (p. 225) process by which autotrophs, such as algae and plants, trap energy from sunlight with chlorophyll and use this energy to convert carbon dioxide and water into simple sugars.

phylogeny (fy LAH juh nee): (p. 452) evolutionary history of a species based on comparative relationships of structures and comparisons of modern life forms with fossils.

phylum (FI lum): (p. 449) taxonomic grouping of similar classes.

pigments: (p. 226) molecules that absorb specific wavelengths of sunlight.

pistil: (p. 643) female reproductive organ of a flower.

pituitary gland (pih TEW uh ter ee): (p. 929) main gland of the endocrine system that controls many other endocrine glands.

placenta (pluh SEN tuh): (p. 848) organ that provides food and oxygen to and removes waste from young inside the uterus of placental mammals.

placental mammals: (p. 848) mammals that give birth to young that have developed inside the mother's uterus until their body systems are fully functional and they can live independently of their mother's body.

plankton: (p. 73) small organisms that drift and float in the waters of the photic zone; includes both autotrophic and heterotrophic organisms, their eggs, and the juvenile stages of many marine animals.

plasma: (p. 975) fluid portion of the blood that makes up about 55 percent of the total volume of the blood; contains red and white blood cells.

plasma membrane: (p. 175) flexible boundary between the cell and its environment; allows materials such as water and nutrients to enter and waste products to leave.

plasmid: (p. 343) small ring of DNA found in a bacterial cell that is used as a biological vector.

plasmodium (plaz MOH dee um): (p. 518) in plasmodial slime molds, the mass of cytoplasm that contains many diploid nuclei but no cell walls or membranes.

plastids: (p. 184) group of plant organelles that are used for storage of starches, lipids, or pigments.

plate tectonics (tek TAH nihks): (p. 379) geological explanation for the movement of continents over Earth's thick, liquid interior.

platelets: (p. 977) small cell fragments in the blood that help blood clot after an injury.

point mutation: (p. 298) mutation in a DNA sequence; occurs from a change in a single base pair.

polar molecule: (p. 152) molecule with an unequal distribution of charge, resulting in the molecule having a positive end and a negative end.

polar nuclei: (p. 648) two nuclei in the center of the egg sac of a flowering plant that become the triploid ($3n$) endosperm when joined with a sperm during double fertilization.

fotosíntesis: (pág. 225) Proceso por medio del cual los organismos autótrofos, como las algas y las plantas, atrapan la energía solar por medio de la clorofila y utilizan esta energía para convertir el dióxido de carbono y el agua en azúcares simples.

filogenia: (pág. 452) Historia evolutiva de una especie que se basa en las comparaciones de las relaciones de sus estructuras y comparaciones de las formas de vida modernas con los fósiles.

filo: (pág. 449) Agrupación taxonómica de clases similares.

pigmentos: (pág. 226) Moléculas que absorben longitudes de onda específicas de la luz solar.

pistilo: (pág. 643) Órgano reproductor femenino de la flor.

glándula pituitaria: (pág. 929) Glándula principal del sistema endocrino que controla a muchas otras glándulas endocrinas.

placenta: (pág. 848) Órgano que provee alimento y oxígeno a la cría en desarrollo en el útero de los mamíferos placentarios, además de eliminar sus desechos.

mamífero placentario: (pág. 848) Mamífero que pare a las crías, desarrolladas dentro del útero de la hembra, cuando los sistemas corporales de las crías son completamente funcionales y pueden vivir independientemente de la madre.

plancton: (pág. 73) Pequeños organismos que flotan y derivan en las aguas de la zona fótica; incluye organismos autótrofos y heterótrofos así como sus huevecillos y los estadios juveniles de muchos animales marinos.

plasma: (pág. 975) Porción fluida de la sangre que forma el 55 por ciento del volumen total de la sangre; contiene glóbulos blancos, glóbulos rojos y plaquetas.

membrana plasmática: (pág. 175) Frontera flexible entre una célula y su ambiente; permite que los materiales como el agua y los nutrientes entren y los desechos salgan de la célula.

plasmidio: (pág. 343) Pequeño anillo de DNA que se encuentra en las células bacterianas y se usa como vector biológico.

plasmodio: (pág. 518) En los hongos plasmódicos, la masa de citoplasma que contiene muchos núcleos diploides pero no tiene membranas o paredes celulares.

plastidios: (pág. 184) Grupo de organelos de las plantas que se usan para almacenar almidón, lípidos o pigmentos.

tectónica de placas: (pág. 379) Explicación geológica del movimiento de los continentes sobre el denso interior líquido de la Tierra.

plaquetas: (pág. 977) Pequeños fragmentos celulares de la sangre que ayudan en la coagulación después de una herida.

mutación de punto: (pág. 298) Mutación en la secuencia del DNA; es resultado del cambio en una sola base.

molécula polar: (pág. 152) Molécula con una distribución desigual de cargas, lo que resulta en que la molécula tiene un extremo positivo y otro negativo.

núcleo polar: (pág. 648) Dos de los núcleos en el centro del saco embrionario de las plantas con flores, se convierten en el endosperma triploide (3n) cuando se unen al espermatozoide durante la doble fecundación.

Glossary/Glosario

pollen grain: (p. 588) in seed plants, structure in which the male gametophyte develops; consists of sperm cells, nutrients, and a protective outer covering.

pollination: (p. 254) from male reproductive organs to female reproductive organs of plants, usually within the same species.

polygenic inheritance: (p. 320) inheritance pattern of a trait controlled by two or more genes; genes may be on the same or different chromosomes.

polymer: (p. 158) large molecule formed when many smaller molecules bond together.

polyp (PAH lup): (p. 700) a cnidarian body form that is tube-shaped with a mouth surrounded by tentacles.

polyploid: (p. 410) any species with multiple sets of the normal set of chromosomes; results from errors during mitosis or meiosis.

population: (p. 38) group of organisms all of the same species, which interbreed and live in the same place at the same time.

posterior: (p. 682) tail end of bilaterally symmetric animals.

prehensile tail (pree HEN sul): (p. 425) long muscular tail used as a fifth limb for grasping and wrapping around objects; characteristic of many New World monkeys.

primary succession: (p. 67) colonization of barren land by pioneer organisms.

primates: (p. 421) group of mammals including lemurs, monkeys, apes, and humans that evolved from a common ancestor; shared characteristics include a rounded head, a flattened face, fingernails, flexible shoulder joints, opposable thumbs or big toes, and a large, complex brain.

prion: (p. 482) a virus-like infectious agent composed of only protein, with no genetic material.

proglottid (proh GLAH tihd): (p. 709) a section of a tapeworm that contains muscles, nerves, flame cells, and reproductive organs.

prokaryotes: (p. 173) unicellular organisms, such as bacteria, each of which is composed of a prokaryotic cell. Prokaryotic cells lack internal membrane-bound structures.

prophase: (p. 206) first and longest phase of mitosis where chromatin coils into visible chromosomes.

prostate gland: (p. 997) in human males, single gland that lies below the bladder and surrounds the top portion of the urethra; secretes a thin, alkaline fluid that helps sperm move and survive.

protein: (p. 160) large, complex polymer essential to all life composed of carbon, hydrogen, oxygen, nitrogen, and sometimes sulfur; provides structure for tissues and organs and helps carry out cell metabolism.

grano de polen: (pág. 588) En las plantas con semilla, la estructura en la cual se desarrolla el gametofito masculino; consta de células espermáticas, nutrientes y una cubierta protectora externa.

polinización: (pág. 254) Transferencia de los granos de polen desde el órgano reproductor masculino hacia el órgano reproductor femenino de las plantas, generalmente de la misma especie.

herencia poligénica: (pág. 320) Patrón de herencia en el que los rasgos son controlados por dos o más genes; los genes pueden estar en el mismo o en diferentes cromosomas.

polímero: (pág. 158) Molécula grande formada por la unión de muchas moléculas pequeñas.

pólipo: (pág. 700) Forma corporal que semeja un tubo y que presenta una boca rodeada de tentáculos.

poliploide: (pág. 410) Que tiene grupos múltiples del número normal de cromosomas; es el resultado de fallas durante la mitosis o la meiosis.

población: (pág. 38) Grupo de organismos, todos ellos de la misma especie, que se entrecruzan y viven en el mismo sitio al mismo tiempo.

posterior: (pág. 682) Extremo de la cola de los animales con simetría bilateral.

cola prensil: (pág. 425) Cola muscular larga usada como quinta extremidad para agarrarse y enrollar alrededor de los objetos; es característica de muchos monos del Nuevo Mundo.

sucesión primaria: (pág. 67) Colonización de terrenos desnudos por organismos pioneros.

primate: (pág. 421) Grupo de mamíferos que incluye los lémures, los monos, los simios y los seres humanos que evolucionaron de un antepasado común; las características que comparten incluyen la cabeza redondeada, la cara aplastada, uñas, articulaciones flexibles en los hombros, pulgar o dedo gordo oponible y un cerebro grande y complejo.

prión: (pág. 482) agente infeccioso semejante a un virus; está formado por proteínas y carece de material genético.

proglótido: (pág. 709) Sección de una tenia que contiene músculos, nervios, bulbos ciliados y órganos reproductores.

procariotas: (pág. 173) Organismos unicelulares, como las bacterias, compuestos por células procariotas. Las células procariotas carecen de estructuras internas rodeadas por membranas.

profase: (pág. 206) La primera y más prolongada fase de la mitosis en la cual la cromatina se enrosca para formar cromosomas visibles.

glándula prostática: (pág. 997) En los hombres, la glándula única que se localiza debajo de la vejiga y rodea la porción superior de la uretra; secreta un fluido poco denso alcalino que ayuda al movimiento y la sobrevivencia de los espermatozoides.

proteína: (pág. 160) Polímero grande y complejo, esencial en todos los seres vivos y que está compuesto por carbono, hidrógeno, oxígeno, nitrógeno y algunas veces azufre; provee estructura a los tejidos y órganos y ayuda a realizar el metabolismo celular.

prothallus (proh THA lus): (p. 582) fern gametophyte.

protist: (p. 458) diverse group of multicullular or unicellular eukaryotes that lack complex organ systems and live in moist environments; may be autotrophic or heterotrophic.

protocell: (p. 383) large, ordered structure, enclosed by a membrane, that carries out some life activities, such as growth and division.

protonema (proh tuh NEE muh): (p. 635) in mosses, a small, green filament of haploid cells that develops from a spore; develops into the gametophyte.

protostome (PROH tuh stohm): (p. 677) animal with a mouth that develops from the opening in the gastrula.

protozoan (proh tuh ZOH uhn): (p. 503) unicellular, heterotrophic, animal-like protist.

provirus: (p. 479) viral DNA that is integrated into a host cell's chromosome and replicated each time the host cell replicates.

pseudocoelom (soo duh SEE lum): (p. 683) fluid-filled body cavity partly lined with mesoderm.

pseudopodia (sew duh POH dee uh): (p. 504) in protozoans, cytoplasm-containing extensions of the plasma membrane; aid in locomotion and feeding.

puberty: (p. 997) in humans, the period when secondary sex characteristics begin to appear; changes are controlled by sex hormones secreted by the endocrine system.

pulse: (p. 981) surge of blood through an artery that can be felt on the surface of the body.

punctuated equilibrium: (p. 411) idea that periods of speciation occur relatively quickly with long periods of genetic equilibrium in between.

pupa (PYEW puh): (p. 753) stage of insect metamorphosis where tissues and organs are broken down and replaced by adult tissues; larva emerges from pupa as a mature adult.

pus: (p. 1033) collection of dead macrophages and body fluids that forms in infected tissues.

prótalo: (pág. 582) Gametofito de los helechos.

protista: (pág. 458) Grupo diverso de eucariotas unicelulares y multicelulares que carecen de sistemas de órganos complejos y viven en ambientes húmedos; pueden ser autótrofos o heterótrofos.

protocélula: (pág. 383) Estructura ordenada grande encerrada por una membrana, que puede llevar a cabo algunas de las actividades vitales, como el crecimiento y la división.

protonema: (pág. 635) En los musgos, el filamento corto y verde de las células haploides que se desarrolla a partir de una espora; se convierte en el gametofito.

protostomado: (pág. 677) Animal con una boca que se desarrolla a partir de la abertura de la gástrula.

protozoario: (pág. 503) Protista unicelular heterótrofo parecido a un animal.

provirus: (pág. 479) DNA viral que se integra al cromosoma de la célula huésped y es replicado cada vez que la célula huésped se replica.

seudoceloma: (pág. 683) Cavidad corporal llena de fluido que está parcialmente rodeada por mesodermo.

seudópodos: (pág. 504) En los protozoarios, extensiones de la membrana celular que contienen citoplasma; ayudan en la locomoción y en la alimentación.

pubertad: (pág. 997) En los seres humanos, el período en que comienzan a aparecer las características sexuales secundarias; las hormonas sexuales secretadas por el sistema endocrino controlan los cambios.

pulso: (pág. 981) Flujo de sangre a través de una arteria, el cual puede sentirse a través de la superficie del cuerpo.

equilibrio interrumpido: (pág. 411) La idea de que los períodos de especiación ocurren relativamente rápido, separados por largos períodos de equilibrio genético.

pupa: (pág. 753) Etapa de la metamorfosis de un insecto en la cual los tejidos y órganos son desintegrados y reemplazados por tejidos adultos; la larva emerge de la pupa como un adulto maduro.

pus: (pág. 1033) Colección de macrófagos muertos y fluidos corporales que se forma en los tejidos infectados.

R

radial symmetry (RAY dee uhl): (p. 681) an animal's body plan that can be divided along any plane, through a central axis, into roughly equal halves.

radicle (RA dih kul): (p. 655) embryonic root of an anthophyte embryo; the first part of the young sporophyte to emerge during germination.

radula (RA juh luh): (p. 722) in some snails and mollusks, the rasping, tonguelike organ used to drill, scrape, grate, or cut food.

rays: (p. 763) long tapered arms of some echinoderms that are covered with short, rounded spines.

receptors: (p. 930) binding sites on target cells that bind with specific hormones.

simetría radial: (pág. 681) Plan corporal de los animales cuyos cuerpos pueden dividirse con un eje central a través de cualquier plano y formar dos partes relativamente iguales.

radícula: (pág. 655) Raíz embrionaria del embrión de las antofitas; la primera parte del esporofito joven que emerge durante la germinación.

rádula: (pág. 722) En algunos caracoles y moluscos, el órgano raspador parecido a una lengua que se usa para hacer hoyos, raspar, moler o cortar el alimento.

rayos: (pág. 763) Brazos largos que se estrechan en los extremos pertenecientes los equinodermos que están cubiertos por espinas redondas y cortas.

receptores: (pág. 930) Sitios de adherencia en las células asignadas en donde se enlazan hormonas específicas.

recessive: (p. 256) trait of an organism that can be masked by the dominant form of a trait.

recombinant DNA (ree KAHM buh nunt): (p. 341) DNA made by recombining fragments of DNA from different sources.

rectum: (p. 923) last part of the digestive system through which feces passes before it exits the body through the anus.

red blood cells: (p. 975) round, disk-shaped cells in the blood that carry oxygen to body cells; make up 44 percent of the total volume of the blood.

red marrow: (p. 903) marrow found in the humerus, femur, sternum, ribs, vertebrae, and pelvis that produces red blood cells, white blood cells, and cell fragments involved in blood clotting.

reflex (REE fleks): (p. 861) simple, automatic response in an animal that involves no conscious control; usually acts to protect an animal from serious injury. **(p. 948)** automatic response to a stimulus; reflex stimulus travels to the spinal column and sent directly back to the muscle.

regeneration: (p. 709) replacement or regrowth of missing body parts.

reintroduction programs: (p. 124) programs that release organisms into an area where their species once lived in hopes of reestablishing naturally reproducing populations.

reproduction: (p. 7) production of offspring by an organism; a characteristic of all living things.

reproductive isolation: (p. 410) occurs when formerly interbreeding organisms can no longer produce fertile offspring due to an incompatibility of their genetic material or by differences in mating behavior.

response: (p. 9) an organism's reaction to a change in its internal or external environment.

restriction enzymes: (p. 342) DNA-cutting enzymes that can cut both strands of a DNA molecule at a specific nucleotide sequence.

retina: (p. 952) thin layer of tissue found at the back of the eye made up of light receptors and sensory neurons.

retrovirus (reh tro VY rus): (p. 481) type of viral replication where a virus uses reverse transcriptase to make DNA from viral RNA; the retroviral DNA is then integrated into the host cell's chromosome.

reverse transcriptase (trans KRIHP tayz): (p. 481) enzyme carried in the capsid of a retrovirus that helps produce viral DNA from viral RNA.

rhizoids (RI zoydz): (p. 535) fungal hyphae that penetrate food and anchor a mycelium; secrete enzymes for extracellular digestion and absorb nutrients.

rhizome: (p. 585) thick, underground stem of a fern and other vascular plants; often functions as an organ for food storage.

ribonucleic acid (RNA): (p. 163) a nucleic acid that forms a copy of DNA for use in making proteins.

recesivo: (pág. 256) Rasgo de un organismo que puede ser encubierto por la forma dominante del rasgo.

DNA recombinante: (pág. 341) DNA que se produce al combinar fragmentos de DNA de diferentes fuentes.

recto: (pág. 923) La última parte del sistema digestivo a través de la cual pasan las heces antes de salir al exterior a través del ano.

glóbulos rojos: (pág. 975) Células sanguíneas redondas con forma de disco que llevan el oxígeno a las células del cuerpo; forman el 44 por ciento del volumen total de la sangre.

médula roja: (pág. 903) Médula que se encuentra en el húmero, el fémur, el esternón, las costillas, las vértebras y la pelvis que produce glóbulos rojos, glóbulos blancos y fragmentos celulares que participan en la coagulación de la sangre.

reflejo: (pág. 861) Respuesta simple automática de un animal que no está bajo control consciente. a menudo actúa para proteger al animal de daños serios. **(pág. 948)** respuesta automática a un estímulo; el estímulo reflejo viaja a la médula espinal y es devuelto directamente al músculo.

regeneración: (pág. 709) Reemplazo o crecimiento nuevo de partes corporales perdidas.

programas de reintroducción: (pág. 124) Programas en los cuales se liberan organismos en áreas donde la especie solía vivir con la esperanza de restablecer poblaciones que se reproduzcan en forma natural.

reproducción: (pág. 7) La producción de crías por un organismo; es una característica de todos los seres vivos.

aislamiento reproductor: (pág. 410) Ocurre cuando organismos que solían reproducirse con éxito no pueden ya producir crías fértiles debido a una incompatibilidad de su material genético o por diferencias en su comportamiento de apareamiento.

respuesta: (pág. 9) La reacción de un organismo a un cambio en su ambiente interno o externo.

enzimas restrictivas: (pág. 342) Enzimas cortadoras del DNA que pueden cortar ambas hebras de la molécula de DNA cuando encuentran una secuencia específica de nucleótidos.

retina: (pág. 952) Capa delgada de tejido que se localiza en la parte trasera del ojo, la cual está compuesta de receptores de luz y neuronas sensoriales.

retrovirus: (pág. 481) Tipo de replicación viral que utiliza la transcriptasa inversa para formar DNA a partir de RNA viral; el DNA del retrovirus es luego integrado al cromosoma de la célula huésped.

transcriptasa inversa: (pág. 481) Enzima presente en la cápsida de un retrovirus que ayuda a producir DNA viral a partir de RNA viral.

rizoides: (pág. 535) Hifas de los hongos que penetran el alimento y anclan el micelio; secretan enzimas para la digestión extracelular y absorben los nutrientes.

rizoma: (pág. 585) Tallo grueso subterráneo de helechos y otras plantas vasculares; funciona a menudo como órgano de almacenamiento de alimentos.

ácido ribonucleico (RNA): (pág. 163) Ácido nucleico que forma una copia de DNA para uso en la elaboración de proteínas.

ribosomal RNA (rRNA): (p. 290) RNA that makes up the ribosomes; clamps onto mRNA and uses its information to assemble amino acids in the correct order.

ribosomes: (p. 181) nonmembrane-bound organelles in the nucleus where proteins are assembled.

rods: (p. 952) receptor cells in the retina that are adapted for vision in dim light; also help detect shape and movement.

root: (p. 561) plant organ that absorbs water and minerals usually from soil; contains vascular tissues; anchors plant; can be a storage organ.

root cap: (p. 615) tough, protective layer of parenchyma cells that covers the tip of a root.

RNA ribosomal (rRNA): (pág. 290) RNA que forma los ribosomas; se adhiere al RNA mensajero y utiliza su información para armar los aminoácidos en el orden correcto.

ribosomas: (pág. 181) Organelos nucleares no membranosos en los que se arman las proteínas.

bastones: (pág. 952) Células receptoras de la retina que están adaptadas para la visión en luz baja; también ayudan a detectar la forma y el movimiento.

raíz: (pág. 561) Órgano de las plantas que absorbe el agua y los minerales, generalmente del suelo; contiene tejidos vasculares; sujeta la planta al suelo; puede servir como órgano de almacenamiento.

piloriza: (pág. 615) Capa dura protectora de células del parénquima que cubre la punta de las raíces.

S

safety symbol: (p. 15) symbol that warns you about a danger that may exist from chemicals, electricity, heat, or experimental procedures.

sarcomere (SAR kuh meer): (p. 907) each section of a myofibril in muscle.

scales: (p. 796) thin bony plates that come in a variety of shapes and sizes formed from the skin of many fishes and reptiles.

scavengers: (p. 47) animals that feed on animals that have already died.

scientific methods: (p. 11) procedures that biologists and other scientists use to gather information and answer questions; include observing and hypothesizing, experimenting, and gathering and interpreting results.

sclerenchyma (skle RENG kuh muh): (p. 606) plant cells with thick, rigid cell walls; provide support for the plant and are a major component of vascular tissue.

scolex (SKOH leks): (p. 709) knob-shaped head of a tapeworm.

scrotum: (p. 995) in males, the sac suspended directly behind the base of the penis that contains the testes.

secondary succession: (p. 68) sequence of changes that take place after a community is disrupted by natural disasters or human actions.

seed: (p. 562) a plant organ of seed plants consisting of an embryo, a food supply, and a protective coat; protects the embryo from drying out and also can aid in dispersal.

selective permeability: (p. 175) feature of the plasma membrane that maintains homeostasis within a cell by allowing some molecules into the cell while keeping others out.

semen: (p. 997) combination of sperm and fluids from the seminal vesicles, prostate gland, and bulbourethral glands.

símbolo de seguridad: (pág. 15) Símbolo que te advierte acerca de algún peligro, ya sean sustancias químicas, la electricidad, el calor o las maniobras realizadas durante el procedimiento experimental.

sarcómero: (pág. 907) Cada sección de una miofibrilla muscular.

escamas: (pág. 796) Las placas óseas de diferentes formas y tamaños que se forman a partir de la piel de muchos peces y reptiles.

carroñero: (pág. 47) Animales que se alimentan de animales muertos.

métodos científicos: (pág. 11) Procedimientos que los biólogos y otros científicos utilizan para reunir información y contestar preguntas; incluyen la observación, la formación de hipótesis, la experimentación y la recolección y análisis de los resultados.

esclerénquima: (pág. 606) Célula vegetal que tiene paredes celulares gruesas y rígidas; provee soporte a la planta y es uno de los componentes más importantes del tejido vascular.

escólex: (pág. 709) La cabeza con forma de perilla que poseen las tenias.

escroto: (pág. 995) En los machos, el saco que contiene los testículos y situado directamente detrás de la base del pene.

sucesión secundaria: (pág. 68) Secuencia de cambios en las comunidades que suceden después de que la comunidad ha sufrido disturbios debido a los desastres naturales o las acciones humanas.

semilla: (pág. 562) Órgano de las plantas con semilla que consta del embrión, una fuente de alimento y una capa protectora; protege al embrión de la desecación y puede también ayudar en la dispersión.

permeabilidad selectiva: (pág. 175) Característica de la membrana celular que mantiene la homeostasis dentro de la célula al permitir la entrada de algunas moléculas y detener el paso de otras.

semen: (pág. 997) Combinación de los espermatozoides con fluidos producidos por las vesículas seminales, la glándula próstata y las glándulas bulbouretrales.

Glossary/Glosario

semicircular canals: (p. 954) structures in the inner ear containing fluid and hairs that help the body maintain balance.

seminal vesicles: (p. 997) in males, pair of glands located at the base of the urinary bladder that secrete a mucouslike fluid into the vas deferens.

sepals: (p. 641) leaflike, usually green structures encircle the top of a flower stem below the petals.

sessile (SE sul): **(p. 674)** organism that is permanently attached to a surface.

setae (SEE tee): **(p. 728)** tiny bristles that help segmented worms move by anchoring their bodies in the soil so each segment can move the animal along.

sex chromosomes: (p. 318) in humans, the 23rd pair of chromosomes; determine the sex of an individual and carry sex-linked characteristics.

sex-linked traits: (p. 325) traits controlled by genes located on sex chromosomes.

sexual reproduction: (p. 266) pattern of reproduction that involves the production and subsequent fusion of haploid sex cells.

short-day plant: (p. 644) a plant that is induced to flower when the number of daylight hours is shorter than its critical period.

sieve tube members: (p. 610) tubular cells in phloem; each cell lacks a nucleus.

simple eye: (p. 745) visual structure in arthropods that uses one lens to detect light and focus.

sink: (p. 617) any part of a plant that stores sugars produced during photosynthesis.

sister chromatids: (p. 206) identical halves of a duplicated parent chromosome formed during the prophase stage of mitosis; the halves are held together by a centromere.

skeletal muscle: (p. 906) a type of voluntary muscle that is attached to and moves the bones of the skeleton.

sliding filament theory: (p. 907) theory that actin filaments slide toward each other during muscle contraction while the myosin filaments do not move.

small intestine: (p. 921) muscular tube about 6 m long where digestion is completed; connects the stomach and the large intestine.

smooth muscle: (p. 905) type of involuntary muscle found in the walls of internal organs and blood vessels; most common function is to squeeze, exerting pressure inside the tube or organ it surrounds.

solution: (p. 149) mixture in which one or more substances (solutes) are distributed evenly in another substance (solvent).

somatic nervous system: (p. 948) portion of the nervous system composed of cranial nerves, spinal nerves, and all of their branches; voluntary pathway that relays information mainly between the skin, the CNS, and skeletal muscles.

canales semicirculares: (pág. 954) Estructuras en la parte interna del oído que contiene fluido y vellos que ayudan al cuerpo a mantener el equilibrio.

vesículas seminales: (pág. 997) En los machos, el par de glándulas localizadas en la base de la vejiga urinaria que secretan un fluido denso a menudo hacia los vasos deferentes.

sépalos: (pág. 641) Estructuras parecidas a hojas y generalmente de color verde que rodean la parte superior del tallo de la flor, por debajo de los pétalos.

sésil: (pág. 674) Organismo que permanece adherido a una superficie.

setas: (pág. 728) Pequeñas espinas o cerdas que ayudan a que los gusanos segmentados se muevan, anclando el cuerpo en el suelo para que cada segmento del animal avance.

cromosomas sexuales: (pág. 318) En los seres humanos, corresponde al cromosoma número 23; determina el sexo del individuo y porta las características sexuales secundarias.

rasgos ligados al sexo: (pág. 325) Rasgos controlados por genes que se encuentran en los cromosomas sexuales.

reproducción sexual: (pág. 266) Patrón de reproducción que implica la producción y luego la fusión de células sexuales haploides.

plantas de día corto: (pág. 644) Plantas que florecen cuando el número de horas de día es menor que su período crítico.

miembros de los tubos cribosos: (pág. 610) Células tubulares del floema que carecen de núcleo.

ojo simple: (pág. 745) Estructura visual de los artrópodos que utiliza un lente para detectar la luz y para enfocar.

depósito: (pág. 617) Cualquier parte de la planta que almacena azúcares producidos durante la fotosíntesis.

cromátides hermanas: (pág. 206) Mitades idénticas de un cromosoma progenitor que se ha duplicado que se forman durante la etapa de profase de la mitosis; las mitades se mantienen unidas por medio de los centrómeros.

músculo esquelético: (pág. 906) Tipo de músculo voluntario que se encuentra adherido a los huesos del esqueleto, a los cuales mueve.

teoría del filamento deslizante: (pág. 907) Teoría que dice que los filamentos de actina se deslizan unos hacia otros durante la contracción muscular, mientras que los filamentos de miosina no se mueven.

intestino delgado: (pág. 921) Tubo muscular de unos 6 metros de largo en el cual se completa la digestión; conecta el estómago con el intestino grueso.

músculo liso: (pág. 905) Tipo de músculo involuntario que se encuentra en las paredes de los órganos internos y los vasos sanguíneos; su función más común es la de apretar, poniendo presión dentro del tubo u órgano que rodea.

solución: (pág. 149) Mezcla en la cual una o más sustancias (solutos) están distribuidos en forma homogénea en otra sustancia (disolvente).

sistema nervioso somático: (pág. 948) Porción del sistema nervioso compuesto por los nervios craneales, los nervios de la espina dorsal y todas sus ramificaciones; es la ruta voluntaria que pasa la información sobre todo entre la piel, el CNS y los músculos esqueléticos.

sorus: (p. 586) clusters of sporangia usually found on the surface of fern fronds.

spawning: (p. 795) method of reproduction in fishes and some other animals where a large number of eggs are fertilized outside of the body.

speciation (spee shee AY shun): (p. 409) process of evolution of new species that occurs when members of similar populations no longer interbreed to produce fertile offspring within their natural environment.

species (SPEE sheez): (p. 7) group of organisms that can interbreed and produce fertile offspring in nature.

specific epithet: (p. 444) the second word of a species name.

sperm: (p. 265) haploid male sex cells produced by meiosis.

spindle: (p. 208) cell structures composed of microtubule fibers; forms between the centrioles during prophase and shorten during anaphase, pulling apart sister chromatids.

spinnerets: (p. 748) silk-producing glands located at the rear of a spider.

spiracles (SPIHR ih kulz): (p. 744) in arthropods, openings on the thorax and abdomen through which air enters and leaves the tracheal tubes.

spongy bone: (p. 902) soft bone containing many holes and spaces surrounded by a layer of more dense compact bone.

spontaneous generation: (p. 380) mistaken idea that life can arise from nonliving materials.

sporangium (spuh RAN jee uhm): (p. 533) in fungi, a sac or case of hyphae in which spores are produced.

spore: (p. 508) type of haploid (*n*) reproductive cell with a hard outer coat that forms a new organism without the fusion of gametes.

sporophyte: (p. 516) in algae and plants, the diploid (*2n*) form of an organism in alternation of generations that produces spores.

sporozoans: (p. 508) group of parasitic protozoans of the phylum Sporozoa that reproduce by spore production.

stabilizing selection: (p. 408) natural selection that favors average individuals in a population; results in a decline in population variation.

stamen: (p. 641) male reproductive organ of a flower consisting of an anther and a filament.

stem: (p. 561) plant organ that provides support and growth; contains tissues that transport food, water, and other materials; organ from which leaves grow. Can serve as a food storage organ; green stems can carry out photosynthesis.

sternum: (p. 827) large breastbone that provides a site for muscle attachment; provides support for the thrust and power produced by birds as they generate motion for flight.

stimulant: (p. 958) drug that increases the activity of the central and sympathetic nervous systems.

soros: (pág. 586) Grupos de esporangios que a menudo se encuentran en la superficie de las frondas de los helechos.

desove: (pág. 795) Método de reproducción de los peces y de algunos otros animales en que un gran número de huevos son fecundados fuera del cuerpo del individuo.

especiación: (pág. 409) Proceso de la evolución de nuevas especies, ocurre cuando los miembros de poblaciones similares no pueden ya reproducirse y producir progenie fértil dentro de su ambiente natural.

especie: (pág. 7) Grupo de organismos que pueden cruzarse y producir progenies fértiles bajo condiciones naturales.

epíteto específico: (pág. 444) La segunda palabra del nombre de una especie.

espermatozoide: (pág. 265) Células haploides masculinas producidas por medio de la meiosis.

huso: (pág. 208) Estructura celular compuesta por fibras de microtúbulos; se forma entre los centriolos durante la profase y se acorta durante la anafase, separando a las cromátides hermanas.

hileras: (pág. 748) Glándulas productoras de seda localizadas en la parte posterior de las arañas.

espiráculos: (pág. 744) En los artrópodos, las aberturas en el tórax y el abdomen a través de las cuales el aire entra y sale de los tubos traqueales.

hueso esponjoso: (pág. 902) Hueso suave con muchos hoyos y espacios, rodeados por una capa más densa de hueso compacto.

generación espontánea: (pág. 380) Idea errada de que la vida puede generarse a partir de materiales inanimados.

esporangio: (pág. 533) En los hongos, un saco o envoltura en las hifas en donde se producen las esporas.

espora: (pág. 508) Tipo de célula reproductora haploide (*n*) con una cubierta protectora capaz de formar un nuevo organismo sin la fusión de gametos.

esporofito: (pág. 516) En las algas y las plantas, la forma diploide (*2n*) del organismo productora de esporas durante la alternancia de generaciones.

esporozoarios: (pág. 508) Grupo de protozoarios parasíticos del filo Sporozoa que se reproducen por medio de la producción de esporas.

selección estabilizadora: (pág. 408) Selección natural que favorece a los individuos promedio de una población; resulta en la caída de la variabilidad de la población.

estambre: (pág. 641) Órgano reproductor masculino de la flor formado por la antera y el filamento.

tallo: (pág. 641) Órgano de las plantas que proporciona soporte a la planta, que contiene tejidos que transportan alimentos, agua y otros materiales, y a partir del cual crecen las hojas; puede servir también como órgano de almacenamiento de alimentos; los tallos de color verde pueden realizar fotosíntesis.

esternón: (pág. 827) Hueso pectoral grande que provee sitio para la fijación de músculos; proporciona el punto de apoyo para el impulso y el poder generado por el ave cuando aletea para volar.

estimulante: (pág. 958) Droga que aumenta la actividad de los sistemas nerviosos central y simpático.

stimulus: (p. 9) anything in an organism's internal or external environment that causes the organism to react.

stolons (STOH lunz): (p. 535) fungal hyphae that grow horizontally along a surface and rapidly produce a mycelium.

stomach: (p. 920) muscular, pouchlike enlargement of the digestive tract where chemical and physical digestion take place.

stomata (STOH mah tuh): (p. 607) openings in leaf tissues that control gas exchange.

strobilus (stroh BIH lus): (p. 582) compact cluster of spore-bearing leaves produced by some non-seed vascular plants.

succession (suk SESH un): (p. 67) orderly, natural changes, and species replacements that take place in communities of an ecosystem over time.

sustainable use: (p. 123) philosophy that promotes letting people use resources in wilderness areas in ways that will not damage the ecosystem.

swim bladder: (p. 798) thin-walled, internal sac found just below the backbone in bony fishes; helps fishes control their swimming depth.

symbiosis (sihm bee OH sus): (p. 44) permanent, close association between two or more organisms of different species.

symmetry (SIH muh tree): (p. 680) a term that describes the arrangement of body structures.

sympathetic nervous system: (p. 949) division of the autonomic nervous system that controls many of the body's internal functions during times of stress.

synapse: (p. 946) tiny space between one neuron's axon and another neuron's dendrites over which a nerve impulse must pass.

estímulo: (pág. 9) Cualquier condición del ambiente interno o externo de un organismo que ocasiona una reacción en el organismo.

estolones: (pág. 535) Hifas de los hongos que crecen en forma horizontal a lo largo de la superficie y rápidamente producen el micelio.

estómago: (pág. 920) Agrandamiento muscular, en forma de bolsa, del tracto digestivo en que se lleva a cabo la digestión química y la física.

estomas: (pág. 607) Aberturas en los tejidos de las hojas que regulan el intercambio gaseoso.

estróbilo: (pág. 582) Grupo compacto de hojas productoras de esporas producido por algunas plantas vasculares sin semillas.

sucesión: (pág. 67) Cambios naturales y ordenados y el reemplazo de especies que ocurren en las comunidades de un ecosistema a lo largo del tiempo.

uso sostenible: (pág. 123) Filosofía que promueve el uso por los seres humanos de los recursos de las áreas silvestres de tal manera que el ecosistema no sufra daños.

vejiga natatoria: (pág. 798) Saco interno de paredes delgadas que se encuentra debajo de la columna vertebral de los peces óseos; ayuda a los peces a controlar la profundidad a la que nadan.

simbiosis: (pág. 44) Asociación estrecha permanente entre dos o más organismos de diferentes especies.

simetría: (pág. 680) Término que describe la colocación de las estructuras corporales.

sistema nervioso simpático: (pág. 949) División del sistema nervioso autónomo que controla muchas de las funciones internas del cuerpo durante los períodos de estrés.

sinapsis: (pág. 946) Espacios diminutos entre el axón de una neurona y las dendritas de otra a través de los cuales debe pasar el impulso nervioso.

T

T cell: (p. 1037) lymphocyte produced in bone marrow and processed in the thymus that plays a role in immunity; includes helper T cells and killer T cells.

taiga (TI guh): (p. 77) biome just south of the tundra; characterized by a boreal or northern coniferous forest composed of larch, fir, hemlock, and spruce trees and acidic, mineral-poor topsoils.

target cells: (p. 930) cells that have receptors on their plasma membranes or in their nuclei for specific endocrine hormones.

taste buds: (p. 952) sensory receptors located on the tongue that result in taste perception.

taxonomy (tak SAH nuh mee): (p. 443) branch of biology that groups and names organisms based on studies of their shared characteristics; biologists who study taxonomy are called taxonomists.

technology (tek NAH luh jee): (p. 22) application of scientific research to society's needs and problems.

telophase: (p. 209) final phase of mitosis during which new cells prepare for their own independent existence.

célula T: (pág. 1037) Linfocito producido en la médula ósea y procesado en el timo, el cual juega un papel en la inmunidad; incluye las células T ayudantes y las células T asesinas.

taiga: (pág. 77) Bioma localizado directamente al sur de la tundra; se caracteriza por la presencia de un bosque boreal (o norteño) de coníferas compuesto por pinos, cipreses, pinabetos y abetos y suelos ácidos pobres en minerales.

células blanco: (pág. 930) Células que poseen receptores en sus membranas celulares o en sus núcleos para hormonas endocrinas específicas.

papilas gustativas: (pág. 952) Receptores sensoriales localizados en la lengua responsables de la percepción del gusto.

taxonomía: (pág. 443) Rama de la biología que agrupa y da nombre a los organismos en base a sus características compartidas; los biólogos que estudian la taxonomía se llaman taxónomos.

tecnología: (pág. 22) Aplicación de la investigación científica a los problemas y necesidades de la sociedad.

telofase: (pág. 209) Fase final de la mitosis durante la cual las nuevas células se preparan para su existencia independiente.

temperate/deciduous forest: (p. 80) biome composed of forests of broad-leaved hardwood trees that lose their foliage annually; receives 70–150 cm of precipitation annually.

tendons: (p. 900) thick bands of connective tissue that attach muscles to bones.

territory: (p. 863) physical space an animal defends against other members of its species; may contain an animal's breeding area, feeding area, potential mates, or all three.

test cross: (p. 339) mating of an individual of unknown genotypes with an individual of known genotype; can help determine the unknown genotype of the parent.

thallus: (p. 514) body structure produced by some plants and some other organisms that lacks roots, stems, and leaves.

theory: (p. 18) explanation of natural phenomenon supported by a large body of scientific evidence obtained from many different investigations and observations.

therapsids (ther AP sidz): (p. 851) reptilian ancestors of mammals that had features of both reptiles and mammals.

threatened species: (p. 116) when the population of a species is likely to become endangered.

thyroid gland: (p. 934) gland located in the neck; regulates metabolism, growth, and development.

tissue: (p. 210) groups of cells that work together to perform a specific function.

tissue fluid: (p. 1036) fluid that bathes the cells of the body; formed when water and dissolved substances diffuse from the blood into the spaces between the cells that make up the surrounding tissues.

tolerance: (p. 959) as the body becomes less responsive to a drug and an individual needs larger or more frequent doses of the drug to achieve the same effect. **(p. 66)** the ability of an organism to withstand fluctuations in biotic and abiotic environmental factors.

toxin: (p. 492) poison produced by a bacterium.

trachea (TRAY kee uh): (p. 971) tubelike passageway for air flow that connects with two bronchi tubes that lead into the lungs.

tracheal tubes (TRAY kee ul): (p. 744) hollow passages in some arthropods that transport air throughout the body.

tracheids (TRA kee uhdz): (p. 608) tubular cells in the xylem that have tapered ends and are dead at maturity.

trait: (p. 253) characteristic that is inherited; can be either dominant or recessive.

transcription (trans KRIHP shun): (p. 290) process in the cell nucleus where enzymes make an RNA copy of a DNA strand.

transfer RNA (tRNA): (p. 290) RNA that transports amino acids to the ribosomes to be assembled into proteins.

bosques templados/caducifolios: (pág. 80) Bioma compuesto de bosques de árboles de madera dura y hojas anchas que pierden su follaje cada año; reciben entre 70 y 150 cm de precipitación al año.

tendones: (pág. 900) Bandas gruesas de tejido conectivo que adhieren los músculos a los huesos.

territorio: (pág. 863) Espacio físico que un animal defiende contra otros miembros de su especie; puede contener el área donde se construyen los nidos, el área de alimentación, donde encuentran posibles parejas o todos los anteriores.

cruce de prueba: (pág. 339) Cruce de individuos de genotipo desconocido con un individuo de genotipo conocido; puede ayudar a determinar el genotipo desconocido de uno de los progenitores.

talo: (pág. 514) Estructura corporal producida por algunas plantas y otros organismos que carecen de raíces, tallos y hojas.

teoría: (pág. 18) Explicación de un fenómeno natural que tiene el apoyo de un gran cuerpo de evidencia científica obtenida de muchos experimentos y observaciones diferentes.

terápsidos: (pág. 851) Reptiles que se consideran antepasados de los mamíferos que tenían características tanto de reptiles como de mamíferos.

especies amenazadas: (pág. 116) Ocurre cuando la población de una especie se encuentra a punto de desaparecer.

glándula tiroides: (pág. 934) Glándula que está localizada en el cuello; regula el metabolismo, el crecimiento y el desarrollo.

tejido: (pág. 210) Grupo de células que trabajan juntas para llevar a cabo una función específica.

fluido tisular: (pág. 1036) Fluido que baña las células del cuerpo; se forma cuando el agua y las sustancias disueltas pasan por difusión desde la sangre hacia los espacios entre las células que componen el tejido circundante.

tolerancia: (pág. 959) Sucede a medida que el cuerpo se vuelve menos sensible a una droga y el individuo necesita dosis más altas y más frecuentes de la droga para lograr el mismo efecto. **(pág. 66)** la capacidad de un organismo de soportar fluctuaciones en los factores bióticos y abióticos del ambiente.

toxina: (pág. 492) Veneno producido por una bacteria.

tráquea: (pág. 971) Pasaje tubular para el flujo de aire que se conecta con los dos bronquios que llegan a los pulmones.

conducto traqueal: (pág. 744) Pasajes huecos que tienen algunos artrópodos y que usan para transportar aire a las diferentes partes del cuerpo.

traqueidas: (pág. 608) Células tubulares del xilema que tienen extremos angostos y que en su madurez son células muertas.

rasgo: (pág. 253) Característica heredada; puede ser dominante o recesiva.

transcripción: (pág. 290) Proceso que ocurre en el núcleo de la célula, en que las enzimas hacen una copia de RNA a partir de una hebra de DNA.

RNA de transferencia (tRNA): (pág. 290) El RNA que transporta los aminoácidos a los ribosomas para armar las proteínas.

Glossary/Glosario

transgenic organisms: (p. 341) organisms that contain functional recombinant DNA from a different organism.

translation: (p. 293) process of converting information in mRNA into a sequence of amino acids in a protein.

translocation (trans loh KAY shun): (p. 617) movement of sugars in the phloem of a plant.

transpiration: (p. 619) in plants, the loss of water through stomata.

transport proteins: (p. 178) proteins that span the plasma membrane creating a selectively permeable membrane that regulates which molecules enter and leave a cell.

trial-and-error: (p. 870) type of learning in which an animal receives a reward for making a particular response.

trichinosis (trih ken NOH sis): (p. 712) a disease caused by the roundworm *Trichinella* that can be ingested in raw or undercooked pork, pork products, or wild game.

trichomes (TRI kohmz): (p. 607) hairlike projections that extend from a plant's epidermis; help reduce water evaporation and may provide protection from herbivores.

trophic level (TROH fihk): (p. 50) organism that represents a feeding step in the movement of energy and materials through an ecosystem.

tropical rain forests: (p. 81) biome near the equator with warm temperatures, wet weather, and lush plant growth; receives at least 200 cm of rain annually; contains more species of organisms than any other biome.

tropism: (p. 624) growth response of a plant to an external stimulus.

tube feet: (p. 765) in echinoderms, hollow, thin-walled tubes that end in a suction cup; part of the water vascular system, they also aid in locomotion, gas exchange, and excretion.

tundra (TUN druh): (p. 76) biome that surrounds the north and south poles; treeless land with long summer days and short periods of winter sunlight; characterized by permafrost.

organismos transgénicos: (pág. 341) Organismos que contienen DNA recombinante en estado funcional, proveniente de organismos diferentes.

traducción: (pág. 293) Proceso de conversión de la información del RNAm a la secuencia de aminoácidos de una proteína.

translocación: (pág. 617) Transporte de azúcares por el floema de la planta.

transpiración: (pág. 619) En las plantas es la pérdida de agua a través de los estomas.

proteínas de transporte: (pág. 178) Proteínas que cubren la membrana celular creando una membrana que es permeable en forma selectiva para regular las entrada y salida de las moléculas.

por tanteos: (pág. 870) Tipo de aprendizaje en que el animal recibe una recompensa al dar una respuesta en particular.

triquinosis: (pág. 712) Enfermedad causada por la *Trichinella*, un gusano redondo que puede ser ingerido al comer carne de cerdo cruda o mal cocinada, productos fabricados con carne de cerdo o la carne de animales silvestres.

tricomas: (pág. 607) Proyecciones parecidas a pelos que se extienden desde la epidermis de la planta; ayudan a reducir la evaporación del agua y pueden ofrecer protección contra los herbívoros.

nivel trófico: (pág. 50) Representa uno de los niveles en el movimiento de energía y materiales a través del ecosistema.

bosques pluviales tropicales: (pág. 81) Bioma cercano al ecuador con temperaturas cálidas, clima húmedo y crecimiento vegetal exuberante; recibe por lo menos 200 cm de lluvia al año; contiene más especies de organismos que ningún otro bioma.

tropismo: (pág. 624) Crecimiento de una planta en respuesta a estímulos externos.

patas ambulacrales: (pág. 765) En los equinodermos, los tubos huecos de paredes delgadas que terminan en una copa de succión; como parte del sistema vascular acuático, ayudan en la locomoción, el intercambio de gases y la excreción.

tundra: (pág. 76) Bioma que rodea el polo norte y el polo sur; es una tierra sin árboles con largos días de verano y cortos períodos de luz en invierno; se caracteriza por la presencia de permagel.

U

umbilical cord: (p. 1006) ropelike structure that attaches the embryo to the wall of the uterus; supplies a developing embryo with oxygen and nutrients and removes waste products.

ureter: (p. 985) tube that transports urine from each kidney to the urinary bladder.

urethra (yoo REE thruh): (p. 987) tube through which urine is passed from the urinary bladder to the outside of the body.

urinary bladder: (p. 985) smooth muscle bag that stores urine until it is expelled from the body.

cordón umbilical: (pág. 1006) Estructura parecida a una cuerda que ata al embrión a la pared del útero; provee al embrión en desarrollo de oxígeno y nutrientes y elimina los productos de desecho.

uréter: (pág. 985) Tubo que transporta la orina desde cada riñón hacia la vejiga urinaria.

uretra: (pág. 987) Tubo a través del cual la orina es llevada desde la vejiga urinaria hacia el exterior del cuerpo.

vejiga urinaria: (pág. 985) Bolsa de músculo liso que almacena la orina hasta que es evacuada del cuerpo.

urine: (p. 986) liquid composed of wastes that is filtered from the blood by the kidneys, stored in the urinary bladder, and eliminated through the urethra.

uterus (YEWT uh rus): (p. 848) in females, the hollow, muscular organ in which the offspring of placental mammals develop.

orina: (pág. 986) Líquido compuesto de productos de desecho que es filtrado de la sangre por los riñones, almacenado en la vejiga urinaria y eliminado a través de la uretra.

útero: (pág. 848) En las hembras, el órgano muscular hueco en donde se desarrollan las crías de los mamíferos placentarios.

V

vaccine: (p. 1039) substance consisting of weakened, dead, or incomplete portions of pathogens or antigens that produce an immune response when injected into the body.

vacuole: (p. 183) membrane-bound space in the cytoplasm of cells used for the temporary storage of materials.

vas deferens (VAS • DE fuh renz): (p. 997) in males, duct that transports sperm from the epididymis towards the ejaculatory ducts of the urethra.

vascular cambium: (p. 611) lateral meristem that produces new xylem and phloem cells in the stem and roots.

vascular plants: (p. 562) plants that have vascular tissues; enables taller growth and survival on land.

vascular tissues (VAS kyuh lur): (p. 562) tissues found in vascular plants composed of tubelike, elongated cells through which water, food, and other materials are transported throughout the plant; include xylem and phloem.

vector: (p. 342) means by which DNA from another species can be carried into the host cell; may be biological or mechanical.

vegetative reproduction: (p. 634) type of asexual reproduction in plants where a new plant is produced from existing plant organs or parts of organs.

veins: (p. 980) large blood vessels that carry blood toward the heart.

venae cavae (vee nee • KAY vee): (p. 981) two large veins that fill the right atrium of the mammalian heart with oxygen-poor blood from the head and body.

ventral (VEN trul): (p. 682) lower surface of bilaterally symmetric animals.

ventricles: (p. 980) two lower chambers of the mammalian heart; receive blood from the atria and send it to the lungs and body.

vertebrate: (p. 685) an animal with an endoskeleton and a backbone.

vessel elements: (p. 608) hollow, tubular cells in the xylem; conduct water and dissolve minerals from the roots to the stem; have open ends through which water passes freely from cell to cell.

vestigial structure (veh STIH jee ul): (p. 401) a structure in a present-day organism that no longer serves its natural purpose, but was probably useful to an ancestor; provides evidence of evolution.

vacuna: (pág. 1039) Sustancia compuesta de patógenos muertos o debilitados, de sus fragmentos, o de antígenos, que producen una respuesta inmunológica cuando se inyectan dentro del cuerpo.

vacuola: (pág. 183) Espacio en el citoplasma de las células rodeado por una membrana y que se utiliza para el almacenamiento temporal de materiales.

conductos deferentes: (pág. 997) En los machos, conductos que transportan los espermatozoides desde el epidídimo hacia los conductos eyaculatorios de la uretra.

cámbium vascular: (pág. 611) Meristemo lateral que produce células nuevas del xilema y el floema en los tallos y las raíces.

plantas vasculares: (pág. 562) Plantas que poseen tejidos vasculares; permite la existencia de plantas más altas y la supervivencia en ambientes terrestres.

tejidos vasculares: (pág. 562) Tejidos que se encuentran en las plantas vasculares, compuestos de células alargadas con forma de tubos a lo largo de las cuales el agua, los alimentos y otros materiales son transportados a través de la planta; incluyen el xilema y el floema.

vector: (pág. 342) Vehículo por medio del cual el DNA de otra especie puede ser llevado a la célula huésped; puede ser biológico o mecánico.

reproducción vegetativa: (pág. 634) Tipo de reproducción asexual de las plantas en el cual se produce una nueva planta a partir de órganos o partes del órgano de una planta.

venas: (pág. 980) Vasos sanguíneos grandes que llevan sangre hacia el corazón.

venas cavas: (pág. 981) Son las dos grandes venas en los mamíferos que llevan la sangre pobre en oxígeno a la aurícula derecha, desde la cabeza y el resto del cuerpo.

ventral: (pág. 682) La superficie inferior de los animales con simetría bilateral.

ventrículos: (pág. 980) Las dos cavidades inferiores del corazón de los mamíferos; reciben la sangre proveniente de las aurículas y la envían a los pulmones y al resto del cuerpo.

vertebrados: (pág. 685) Animal que posee endoesqueleto y columna vertebral.

elementos acanalados: (pág. 608) Células huecas tubulares del xilema; conducen agua y minerales disueltos desde las raíces hasta el tallo; tienen los extremos abiertos a través de los cuales el agua puede pasar libremente de una célula a la siguiente.

estructura vestigial: (pág. 401) Estructura corporal de un organismo que ya no cumple con su función natural, pero que fue probablemente útil a alguno de sus ancestros; nos proporciona evidencia sobre la evolución.

villus: (p. 922) single projection on the lining of the small intestine that functions in the absorption of digested food; they increase the surface area of the small intestine and increase the absorption rate.

viroid: (p. 482) a virus-like infectious agent that is composed of only a single, circular strand of RNA.

viruses: (p. 475) disease-causing, nonliving particles composed of an inner core of nucleic acids surrounded by a capsid; replicate inside living cells called host cells.

vitamins: (p. 926) organic nutrients required in small amounts to maintain growth and metabolism; are either fat-soluble or fat-insoluble vitamins.

vocal cords: (p. 807) sound-producing bands of tissue in the throat that produce sound as air passes over them.

voluntary muscle: (p. 906) muscle that contracts under conscious control.

microvellosidad: (pág. 922) Proyección individual del recubrimiento del intestino delgado que funciona en la absorción del alimento digerido; aumenta el área de superficie del intestino delgado lo que aumenta la tasa de absorción.

viroide: (pág. 482) Agente infeccioso semejante a un virus que está compuesto por una fibra circular de RNA.

virus: (pág. 475) Partículas no vivas causantes de enfermedades, compuestas de un centro interno de ácidos nucleicos rodeado por una cápsida; se replica dentro de células vivas llamadas células huésped.

vitaminas: (pág. 926) Sustancias nutritivas orgánicas que se requieren en pequeñas cantidades para mantener el crecimiento y el metabolismo; pueden ser liposolubles o insolubles en lípidos.

cuerdas vocales: (pág. 807) Bandas de tejido localizadas en la garganta que son capaces de producir sonido cuando el aire pasa sobre ellas.

músculo voluntario: (pág. 906) Músculos que se contraen bajo control consciente.

W

water vascular system: (p. 764) in echinoderms, the hydraulic system that operates under water pressure; aids in locomotion, gas exchange, and excretion.

white blood cells: (p. 976) large, nucleated blood cells that play a major role in protecting the body from foreign substances and microscopic organisms; make up only one percent of the total volume of the blood.

withdrawal: (p. 959) psychological response or physiological illness that occurs when a person stops taking a drug.

sistema vascular acuático: (pág. 764) Se encuentra en los equinodermos; sistema hidráulico que funciona bajo el efecto de la presión del agua; ayuda a la locomoción, el intercambio de gases y la excreción.

glóbulos blancos: (pág. 976) Células sanguíneas nucleadas que juegan un papel importante en la protección del cuerpo contra las sustancias extrañas y los organismos microscópicos; componen solamente el uno por ciento del volumen total de la sangre.

síndrome de abstinencia: (pág. 959) Respuesta psicológica o enfermedad fisiológica que ocurre cuando una persona deja de tomar una droga.

X

xylem: (p. 608) vascular plant tissue composed of tubular cells that transport water and dissolved minerals from the roots to the rest of the plant.

xilema: (pág. 608) Tejido de las plantas vasculares compuesto de células tubulares que transportan el agua y los minerales disueltos desde las raíces hacia el resto de la planta.

Y

yellow marrow: (p. 903) marrow composed of stored fats found in many bones.

médula amarilla: (pág. 903) Médula que se encuentra en muchos huesos, compuesta por grasas almacenadas.

Z

zygospores (ZI guh sporz): (p. 536) thick-walled spores of zygomycetes that can withstand unfavorable conditions.

zygote (ZI goht): (p. 253) diploid cell formed when a sperm fertilizes an egg.

cigosporas: (pág. 536) Esporas de paredes gruesas de los cigomicetos capaces de soportar condiciones desfavorables.

cigoto: (pág. 253) Célula diploide que se forma cuando el espermatozoide fecunda el óvulo.

Index

Index Key

Italic numbers = illustration/photo   **Bold numbers = vocabulary term**

A

A blood type, 324, *325*, 977–978

A vitamin, 926 table

AB blood type, 324, *325*, 977

Abdomen (arthropod), 743, 1080

Abiotic factor, 37, 41, 132: affect on coral numbers. *See* Problem-Solving Lab; affect on food production. *See* Problem-Solving Lab; salt tolerance of seeds. *See* MiniLab

ABO blood groups, 324, 977–978. *See also* Inside Story

Accidents, prevent lab, 1108

Acetabularia, 180 lab

Acetyl-CoA, 232, *233*, 247

Acetylsalicylic acid (aspirin). *See* Aspirin; Connection to Health

Acid, 150, 151, 151 lab

Acid-base chemistry, 149–151: determine pH. *See* MiniLab; pH scale and, *150–151*

Acoelomate, 682, *683*, 783

Acquire Information, 235 lab

Acquired Immune Deficiency Syndrome. *See* AIDS (Acquired Immune Deficiency Syndrome)

Acquired Immunity, *1034,* **1035**–1040, 1055: active, 1039–1040; antibody immunity, 1037–1038; cellular immunity, 1038; lymphatic system and, 1035–1037; passive, 1038–1039

Acrasiomycota, 1110

Actin, 907, *908*

Active immunity, 1039–1040

Active reading, 1092

Active site, *162,* 245. *See also* Enzyme

Active transport, 199, 199 table, 247: release of viruses by, 480–481; sodium/potassium pump and, 944–945

Adaptation, 9, 397–398: behavior as, 859–860; camouflage as, *398,* 399. *See also* MiniLab; as characteristic of life, 9–10, 30; natural selection of. *See* Problem-Solving Lab; physiological, 399; structural, *396,* 397–398

Adaptive radiation, 412–413, 469

Addiction, 959

Adenine (A), 282: pairing of in DNA, 282, *283,* 361. *See also* Problem-Solving Lab

Adenosine diphosphate (ADP), 222, *223*

Adenosine monophosphate (AMP), 222

Adenosine triphosphate (ATP), 222–224, 247: Calvin cycle and. *See* Inside Story; cellular respiration and, 231, 232, *233,* 234; comparing respiration and fermentation and. *See* Problem-Solving Lab; muscles and exercise and, 907, 909; photosynthesis and, 225, 227

Adenovirus, 475, 1074

ADH (antidiuretic hormone), 931

Adolescence, 1015

ADP. *See* Adenosine diphosphate (ADP)

Adrenal. *See* Word Origin

Adrenal glands, 929, *930,* **933**–934, 1052

Adrenal hormones, *930,* 933–934

Adrenaline, 934

Adulthood: animal development and, 679; human development and, 1015

Advertisements: test promotional claims. *See* Problem-Solving Lab; weight loss products. *See* Biology and Society

Aerial root, 613

Aerobic, 231

Aerobic respiration. *See* Cellular respiration

AFM. *See* Atomic force microscope (AFM)

Afterbirth, 1013

Age: gene expression and, 322

Age of Mammals, 466

Age structure, 102, *103*

Aggressive behavior, 864

Aging, 1015: bone injury and disease and, 904, 1015; causes of, 297; skin and, 898, 1015

Agnathan. *See* Jawless fishes

Agriculture, 1076–1077: herbicide resistant crops, 347 lab, 348; importance of biodiversity to, 114; organic farming and. *See* Biology and Society; recombinant DNA technology and, 348, 358

AIDS (Acquired Immune Deficiency Syndrome), 352, 356, 481, 482, 1026, 1027, 1040–1041, 1074, 1075. *See also* HIV (Human Immunodeficiency Virus)

Air bladder, 514

Air pollution, 118: lichen as indicators of, 542

Air sac, 828, *829*

Alaskan malamute: test cross of, *340*

Alcohol, 961: test for presence of. *See* MiniLab

Alcoholic fermentation, 235, **236:** of apple juice. *See* MiniLab; lactic acid fermentation vs., 235 table

Alcoholism, 961

Aldosterone, 933

Algae, 503, 504, 510–516, 552–553: alternation of generation in, 516; brown algae, 514–515; characteristics, 510. *See also* MiniLab; diatoms, 512–513, 524; dinoflagellates, 513; euglenoids, 511–512; green algae, 515–516; lichen and, 542; red algae, 514; unicellular, 510, 511

Allantois, *819,* 883, 1006

Alleles, 256. *See also* Allelic frequency; Genetics; Heredity: ABO blood group. *See* Inside Story; chance of inheriting. *See* Problem-Solving Lab; codominant, 316–317, 323–324; convention for recording, 257; dominant, 256–257; multiple, 317, 324. *See also* Problem-Solving Lab; Punnett squares and, 260–261; recessive, 256–257; Word Origin. *See* Word Origin

Allelic frequency, 405: genetic drift and, 406, 468; Hardy-Weinberg principle and. *See* Connection to Math; migration/emigration from populations and, 406–407, 468; mutation and, 406, 468; natural selection and, 407–409, 468. *See also* BioLab, Internet

Allergic reaction, 1038

Alligator, 817, 822, 823, 825, 882. *See also* Reptile

Alternate leaf arrangement, 618

Alternation of generation, 516, 562–563, 633–634, 664: compare plant gametophytes and sporophytes. *See* Problem-Solving Lab; in green algae, 516; History & Biology, 556–557; in nonvascular plants, 577–578, 581–582; trend in size of plant gametophytes and sporophytes. *See* Problem-Solving Lab

Alveoli, 972, *973.* *See also* Word Origin

Amber, 370 table

Amino acid hormones, 932–933

Amino acids, 161: compare human proteins with other primates. *See* MiniLab; DNA as ultimate code for, 288, 289; genetic code for from mRNA, 291–293. *See also* Problem-Solving Lab; human nutrition and, 925; protein chain formation by, 295; similarity of and evolutionary relationships, 402–403; translation of from mRNA, 293, *294,* 295, 362. *See also* MiniLab

Index

Index

Index

Index

Index

Index

Index

Index

D

Index

Index

Index

Index

H

Index

Index

Index

Index

Index

Index

Pregnancy: birth process, 1012–1013; embryonic membranes and placenta, 1006–1008; environmental factors affecting, 1009. *See also* Problem-Solving Lab; fetal development during (trimesters), 1008–1010; graph of fetal size. *See* MiniLab; hormones and, 1008. *See also* BioLab, Investigate; implantation of egg in uterus, 1006; Rhesus (Rh) factor and, 978–979

Prehensile tail, 425, *469*

Premolars, 843, 887

Pressure: diffusion and, 155

Primary oocyte, 1000, *1001*

Primary succession, 67–68: pioneer species, 134–135, 542. *See also* MiniLab; secondary succession vs.. *See* Problem-Solving Lab

Primate, 421, 468, 1086. *See also* Focus On; Inside Story: anthropoids, *423,* 424–426, 468; characteristics of, 421, *422,* 423, 468; compare human proteins with. *See* MiniLab; compare infant and adult. *See* Problem-Solving Lab; compare skulls of. *See* BioLab, Investigate; human origins and. *See* Human origins; monkeys. *See* Monkey; opposable thumbs, *422, 423. See also* MiniLab; origins of, 423–427, 468

Primordial soup, 382, 388. *See also* Biology and Society; Word Origin

Princeton Review: Standardized Test Practice, 29, 63, 89, 109, 131, 136–137, 169, 193, 219, 243, 248–249, 279, 307, 335, 359, 364–365, 391, 419, 441, 465, 501, 527, 554–555, 575, 631, 663, 668–669, 691, 719, 739, 761, 781, 788–789, 815, 839, 857, 879, 888–889, 915, 941, 969, 993, 1021, 1047, 1056–1057; Test-Taking Tip, 31, 136, 248, 364, 470, 554, 668, 788, 888, 1056

Prion, 482, 500

Pro-. *See* Word Origin

Probability, 261–262, 262 lab

Probeware, 274, 544, 734

Probiscidea (order), 1089

Problem-Solving Lab: abiotic factors and food production, 37 lab; analysis of promotional claims, 16 lab; arthropod species, number of, 746 lab; atomic nucleus diagram, 145 lab; bacterial reproduction rates, 95 lab; birth defects, 1011 lab; Body Mass Index (BMI), 928 lab; body temperature regulation in humans, 896 lab; botulism (food poisoning), 492 lab; bryophyte distribution, 578 lab; cancer, incidence of, 212 lab; cell control by nucleus, 180 lab; cell division in frog development, 676 lab; cell size limits, 203 lab; cellular respiration or fermentation, 235 lab; chances of inheriting a trait,

311 lab; chestnut blight, 534 lab; classify annelids, 729 lab; classify organisms (red wolf) as separate species, 447 lab; compare gametophytes and sporophytes, 563 lab; compare infant and adult primates, 426 lab; compare mosses, ferns, and conifers, 640 lab; compare skin, bone, and muscle cells, 906 lab; control weevil damage with nematodes, 713 lab; density of bone, 903 lab; density of water and ice, 154 lab; determine genotype by test cross, 339 lab; digestive enzymes in paramecia, 508 lab; digestive system length in mammals, 844 lab; distinguish between primary and secondary succession, 68 lab; DNA fingerprinting, 353 lab; Duchenne's muscular dystrophy, inheritance of, 326 lab; Earth's history, model, 384; electrocardiograms (ECG), 983 lab; endangered bird species, 831 lab; evolutionary relationships among flatworm classes, 707 lab; extinction and land area, 115 lab; floral structure variation, 644 lab; fossil ferns in Antarctica, 372 lab; freshwater clam reproduction, 724 lab; gallbladder, digestion and, 922 lab; gases in inhaled vs. exhaled air, 973 lab; graphs, information from, 20 lab; hearing damage, 954 lab; hibernation, 867 lab; homologous chromosomes, 264 lab; human population growth trends, 102 lab; insulin and glucagon levels, exercise and, 932 lab; invertebrate chordate cross section, 775 lab; kingdoms, number of species in each, 456 lab; lateral line system in fishes, 796 lab; length of cell cycle, 204 lab; lichen structure, 542 lab; marine and freshwater sponges, 695 lab; menstrual cycle length, variation in, 1003 lab; multiple alleles and rabbit coat color, 318 lab; mutation resulting in sickle-cell anemia, 299 lab; natural selection, observe, 397 lab; Neanderthals and humans, similarities between, 433 lab; neurotransmitters, effect of drugs on, 957 lab; nucleotide pairing in DNA, 283 lab; number of nitrogen bases that code for amino acids, 291 lab; ocean conditions limiting coral numbers, 704 lab; oxygen in tide pools, 73 lab; photosynthesis and light intensity, 226 lab; phototropic response to light, 624 lab; plasma membrane as selective barrier, 176 lab; plasmodial slime mold life cycle, 518 lab; ratios in Mendel's monohybrid cross, 262 lab; red tides of dinoflagellates, 514 lab; reintroduction programs, 124 lab; release of sea cucumber gametes, 768 lab; singing, learned or innate?, 872 lab; size of gametophytes and sporophytes, 567 lab; spread of herpes simplex, 1027 lab; storage of energy as fat, 222 lab; symmetry, identify type of, 682 lab;

transpiration rate, factors affecting, 619 lab; trophic level information, 50 lab; vaccination for diphtheria, 1040 lab; vascular tissue interruption, 611 lab; verify gene transfer, 347 lab; virus, determine type of, 480 lab; water and fertilization in non-seed vascular plants, 584 lab

Procedures: investigation. *See* BioLab, Design Your Own; BioLab, Internet; BioLab, Investigate; MiniLab; plan and implement. *See* BioLab, Design Your Own

Producer. *See* Autotroph

Product labeling: evaluate a bowl of soup. *See* MiniLab; interpret drug labels. *See* MiniLab; test for presence of alcohol. *See* MiniLab; test promotional claims. *See* Problem-Solving Lab; weight loss products. *See* Biology and Society

Productivity, 70

Progesterone, 1002, 1004, 1008

Proglottid, 709

Prokaryote, 173, 174, 187 table, 245, 456–457, 484, 1071: archaebacteria. *See* Archaebacteria; bacteria. *See* Bacteria; endosymbiont theory and, 384–385, 467; eubacteria. *See* Eubacteria; eukaryotes vs., 173, 174, 187 table; origins, 383, 384, 466, 467; translation in cytoplasm of, 293

Promotional claims: analysis of commercial product. *See* Problem-Solving Lab; evaluate a bowl of soup. *See* MiniLab; interpret drug labels. *See* MiniLab; of weight loss products. *See* Biology and Society

Prop root, 612–613

Prophase (mitotic), 206, *207,* 208, 247

Prophase I (meiotic), 266, *267,* 268

Prophase II (meiotic), *267,* 269

Prostate gland, 997

Protein, 160–161, 163, 245, 281: compare human with other primates. *See* MiniLab; control of cell cycle by (cyclins), 211; enzymes. *See* Enzyme; human nutrition and, 925; information on in DNA, 281, 288; interferons, 1033, 1035; molecular clocks and. *See* Biotechnology; mutations in DNA and, 298–299. *See also* MiniLab; Problem-Solving Lab; plasma membrane, 177, 178; synthesis of by ribosomes, 181–182; three-dimensional shape of, 161; transcription and, 290–292, 362. *See also* BioLab, Investigate; MiniLab; translation of from mRNA, 293, 294, 295, 362. *See also* MiniLab; transport, 178, 198, 199

Prothallus, 582, 636

Index

Index

Index

Index

Index

Index

Index

Index

Index

Magnification Key

Magnifications listed are the magnifications at which images were originally photographed.
LM–Light Microscope
SEM–Scanning Electron Microscope
TEM–Transmission Electron Microscope

Art Credits

Glencoe would like to acknowledge the artists and agencies who participated in illustrating this program: Felipe Passalacqua; James Shough & Associates; John Edwards; Laurie O'Keefe; Morgan Cain; Nancy Heim/158 Street Design Group; Ortelius Design; Precision Graphics; Rolin Graphics; Susan Moore/Lisa Freeman Inc.; Tom Gagliano; Tom Kennedy/Romark Illustration; Wildlife Art; Zoo Botanica

Photo Credits

Cover (front back) Gerard Lacz/Animals Animals; **xxvi** Ed Eckstein/CORBIS; **xxvi–1** Carr Clifton/Minden Pictures; **1** Bettmann/CORBIS; **2** Roy Toft; **4** (tl)Steve Kaufman/DRK Photo, (tr)John Gerlach/DRK Photo, (bl)Norbert Wu/Mo Yung Productions, (br)Jeffrey Lepore/Photo Researchers; **5** (t)Bob Daemmrich, (b)William J. Weber/Visuals Unlimited; **6** (t)John Sohlden/Visuals Unlimited, (b)Kjell B. Sandved/Photo Researchers; **7** (t)O.S.F./Animals Animals, (b)Tom McHugh/Photo Researchers; **8** (t)Tom Bean/DRK Photo, (b)John Gerlach/DRK Photo; **9** (t)John Gerlach/DRK Photo, (r)Tom Brakefield/DRK Photo; **10** (l)Sam Fried/Photo Researchers, (r)Renee Lynn/Photo Researchers; **11** M.C. Chamberlain/DRK Photo; **12** Gerry Ellis/ENP Images; **13** (t)The Ohio State University/OARDC, (b)Tom Brakefield/DRK Photo; **14** KS Studios; **15** (t)Robert Essel, NYC/CORBIS, (b)Gerard Mare/Petit Format/Photo Researchers; **16** KS Studios; **17** (t)Science VU/Visuals Unlimited, (b)KS Studios; **18** Gregory G. Dimijian/Photo Researchers; **19** Aaron Haupt; **20** M. Abbey/Photo Researchers; **21** (l)Art Wolfe, (r)Luiz C. Marigo/Peter Arnold, Inc.; **22** Will & Deni McIntyre/Photo Researchers; **23** Richard Hamilton Smith/CORBIS; **24** James H. Robinson/Photo Researchers; **26** (t)Jeff Greenberg/Visuals Unlimited, (b)KS Studios; **27** (t)Steve E. Ross/Photo Researchers, (c)Gerry Ellis/ENP Images, (b)Luiz C. Marigo/Peter Arnold, Inc.; **28** Carolyn A. McKeone/Photo Researchers; **30** Arthur C. Twomey/Photo Researchers; **32–33** Carr Clifton/Minden Pictures; **33** U.S. Fish and Wildlife Service/Joseph Hautman; **34** Gregory K. Scott/Photo Researchers; **35** Joe McDonald/DRK Photo; **36** (l)David Sieren/Visuals Unlimited, (r)Marc Epstein/DRK Photo; **37** Jim Brandenburg/Minden Pictures; **38** Michael Habicht/Earth Scenes; **39** Larry Ulrich; **40** (tl tr)Barbara Gerlach/DRK Photo, (c)IFA/Peter Arnold, Inc., (bl)Earth Satellite Corporation/Science Photo Library/Photo Researchers, (br)Frans Lanting/Minden Pictures; **41** (l)Michael P. Gadomski/Photo Researchers, (r)Carolina Biological Supply/Phototake, NYC; **42** (tl)John D. Cunningham/Visuals Unlimited, (bl)Breck P. Kent/Animals Animals; **42–43** Matt Meadows; **43** (tr)Stanley Breeden/DRK Photo, (br)Zig Leszcznski/Animals Animals; **44** Michael Fogden/DRK Photo; **45** (l)Eastcott/Momatiuk/Earth Scenes, (r)Donald Specker/Animals Animals; **46** Hans Pfletschingel/Peter Arnold, Inc.; **47** M.P. Kahl/DRK Photo; **54** Matt Meadows; **55** Michael P. Gadomski/Photo Researchers; **58** M. Abbey/Visuals Unlimited; **59** Biophoto Associates/Photo Researchers; **61** (t)Zig Leszcznski/Animals Animals, (b)Hans Pfletschingel/Peter Arnold, Inc.; **64** Breck P. Kent/Earth Scenes; **65** John D. Cunningham/Visuals Unlimited; **66** Jeff Lepore/Photo Researchers; **67** (l)V. Ahmadjian/Visuals Unlimited, (r)William H. Mullins/Photo Researchers; **69** Richard Thom/Visuals Unlimited; **70** Tom Bean/DRK Photo; **71** Altitude (Y. Arthus-Bertrand)/Peter Arnold, Inc.; **72** Norbert Wu/Peter Arnold, Inc.; **73** Science VU/Visuals Unlimited; **76** (t)Johnny Johnson, (bl)Joe McDonald/Visuals Unlimited, (br)Tom McHugh/Photo Researchers; **77** (t)Beth Davidow/Visuals Unlimited, (bl)Tom & Pat Leeson/DRK Photo, (bc)Alan D. Carey/Photo Researchers, (br)Johnny Johnson; **78** (t)Zig Leszczynski/Earth Scenes, (bl)Joe McDonald/DRK Photo, (br)Kennan Ward/DRK Photo; **79** (t)Steve Kaufman/Peter Arnold, Inc., (b)Tom Bean/DRK Photo; **80** (t)Barbara Cushman Rowell/DRK Photo, (bl)Jeff Lepore/Photo Researchers, (bc)M.H. Sharp/Photo Researchers, (br)Joe McDonald/Visuals Unlimited; **81** Gregory G. Dimijian/Photo Researchers; **83** (l)Lynn M. Stone/Photo Researchers, (c)Kevin Schafer/Peter Arnold, Inc., (r)Ray Coleman/Visuals Unlimited; **84** Bob Daemmrich; **86** (t)Porterfield-Chickering/Photo Researchers, (b)William J. Weber/Visuals Unlimited; **87** (t)Richard Thom/Visuals Unlimited, (b)Barbara Cushman Rowell/DRK Photo; **88** Simon Fraser/Science Photo Library/Photo Researchers; **90** Art Wolfe/Photo Researchers; **91** Biophoto Associates/Photo Researchers; **92** KS Studios; **94** Francois Gohier/Photo Researchers; **95** (t)Blair Seitz/Photo Researchers, (b)Rod Planck/Photo Researchers; **96** (tl)Envision/B.W. Hoffman, (tr)Jim Kieffer/Peter Arnold, Inc.; **97** Robert McLeroy/*San Antonio Express*/CORBIS Sygma; **98** (l)Stephen J. Krasemann/Peter Arnold, Inc., (r)Robert Wilson/Animals Animals; **99** (l)Marcie Griffen/Animals Animals, (r)KS Studios; **100** Tom Van Sant/Geosphere Project, Santa Monica, CA.SPL/Photo Researchers; **104** Aaron Haupt; **106** Aaron Haupt; **107** Thomas Kitchin/Tom Stack & Associates; **110** Michio Hoshino/Minden Pictures; **111** (l)Gary Gray/DRK Photo, (r)Envision/B.W. Hoffman; **112** Envision/George Mattei; **113** Norm Thomas/Photo Researchers; **114** (l)Tom & Pat Leeson/Photo Researchers, (c)Patti Murray/Earth Scenes, (r)Don & Pat Valenti/DRK Photo; **115** (l)Tom McHugh/Photo Researchers, (r)Doug Perrine/DRK Photo; **116** Steve Wolper/DRK Photo; **117** Michael Fredericks, Jr./Animals Animals; **118** Will & Deni McIntyre/Photo Researchers; **119** (l)Doug Sokell/Tom Stack & Associates, (r)Matt Meadows; **120** (l)G. Carleton Ray/Photo Researchers, (r)Scott Camazine/Photo Researchers; **121** (t)Jeff Lepore/Photo Researchers, (b)Victoria McCormick/Animals Animals; **122** Matt Meadows; **123** (t)Charlie Heidecker/Visuals Unlimited, (bl)Tony Morrison/South American Pictures, (br)KS Studios; **124** (t)M.C. Chamberlain/DRK Photo, (b)Alan D. Carey/Photo Researchers; **125** Sid Greenberg/Photo Researchers; **126** (tl)George Calef/DRK Photo, (tr)Aldo Brando/Peter Arnold, Inc., (b)Renee Stockdale/Animals Animals; **127** (t)Renee Stockdale/Animals Animals, (b)Fred Bruemmer/DRK Photo; **129** (t)Michael Sewell/Peter Arnold, Inc., (b)Jeff Lepore/Photo Researchers; **132** (t)Fred Bavendam/Minden Pictures, (c)Nigel J. Dennis/Photo Researchers, (bl)D.R. Specker/Animals Animals, (br)W. Gregory Brown/Animals Animals; **133** (t)Dana White/ImageQuest, (b)Doug Sokell/Visuals Unlimited; **134** (t)J & B Photographers/Animals Animals, (b)Doug Sokell/Visuals Unlimited; **135** (t)Bruce Watkins/Animals Animals, (b)Envision/B.W. Hoffman; **138** Science

Museum/Science & Society Picture Library, **138–139** Biophoto Associates/Science Source/Photo Researchers; **140** Robert Lubeck/Animals Animals/Earth Scenes; **141** Jeffrey Rotman/Photo Researchers; **142** (l)A.B. Joyce/Photo Researchers, (r)F. Stuart Westmoreland/Photo Researchers; **144** (tl)Elaine Shay, (tc)Ross Frid/Photo Researchers, (tr)Photolibrary/Photolibrary/PictureQuest, (b)Matt Meadows/Peter Arnold, Inc.; **145** Chip Clark; **146** Michael P. Gadomski/Photo Researchers; **148** Matt Meadows; **149** Aaron Haupt; **150** (tl–tr)Mark Steinmetz, Mark Burnett, J. Sekowski, Mark Burnett, Aaron Haupt, (b)Aaron Haupt; **151** (l)Elaine Shay, (c r)Aaron Haupt; **152** Jim Steinberg/Photo Researchers; **154** (t)Matt Meadows, (b)Aaron Haupt; **155** Aaron Haupt; **159** (t c)Aaron Haupt, (b)C. Allan Morgan/Peter Arnold, Inc.; **160** (tl b)Aaron Haupt, (tr)Elaine Shay; **161** William S. Lea; **164** Matt Meadows; **165** Matt Meadows; **166** Gabridge/Custom Medical Stock Photo; **170** Biophoto Associates/Photo Researchers; **172** (t)Francesc Muntada/CORBIS, (b)Cabisco/Visuals Unlimited; **173** George Musil/Visuals Unlimited; **175** Kristen Brochmann/Fundamental Photographs; **176** C.C. Lockwood/DRK Photo; **179** (t)Aaron Haupt, (b)Courtesy Biao Ding, The Ohio State University; **180** D.E. Akin/Visuals Unlimited; **181** Don W. Fawcett/Visuals Unlimited; **182** R. Bolander and Don W. Fawcett/Visuals Unlimited; **183** (t)Don W. Fawcett/Visuals Unlimited, (bl)Biophoto Associates/Photo Researchers, (br)David M. Phillips/Visuals Unlimited; **184** Jeremy Burgess/Science Photo Library/Photo Researchers; **185** Keith R. Porter/Photo Researchers; **189** Breck P. Kent/Animals Animals; **190** (l)SSEC/University of Wisconsin, Madison, (r)Alfred Pasieka/Science Source/Photo Researchers; **193** R. Bolander and Don W. Fawcett/Visuals Unlimited; **194** Jean Claude Revy/Phototake, NYC; **197** Joseph Kurantsin-Mills, M.Sc.Ph.D; **198** KS Studios; **202** Michael Abbey/Visuals Unlimited; **207** (t ct b)Ed Reschke/Peter Arnold, Inc., (cb)Carolina Biological Supply/Phototake, NYC; **208** Barry King, University of California, School of Medicine/Biological Photo Service; **209** (t)Ed Reschke/Peter Arnold, Inc., (b)David M. Phillips/Visuals Unlimited; **211** Luis M. De La Maza, PhD.M.D./Phototake, NYC; **213** Bob Mullenix/KS Studios; **216** Dixie Knight/Medichrome/The Stock Shop; **217** Luis M. De La Maza, PhD.M.D./Phototake, NYC; **218** Ed Reschke/Peter Arnold, Inc.; **220** Johann Schumacher/Peter Arnold, Inc.; **221** (t)Aaron Haupt, (b)Tom McHugh/Photo Researchers; **222** Mel Victor/The Stock Shop; **224** (t)Dr. K.S. Kim/Peter Arnold, Inc., (b)National Geographic Society Image Collection; **226** (t)Matt Meadows, (b)James Westwater; **228** Bettmann/CORBIS-UPI; **229** Dr. Jeremy Burgess/Science Photo Library/Photo Researchers; **230** Matt Meadows; **231** Michael Keller/CORBIS; **233** Profs. P. Motta & T. Naguro/Science Photo Library/Custom Medical Stock Photo; **235** Gerard Vandystadt/Vandystadt Agency/Photo Researchers; **236** Matt Meadows; **237** (l)file photo, (r)George Robbins; **238** Matt Meadows; **239** Runk-Schoenberger/Grant Heilman Photography; **240** (t)Robert Calentine/Visuals Unlimited, (inset)Dan Gotshall/Visuals Unlimited; **241** (t)Tom McHugh/Photo Researchers, (b)Matt Meadows; **244** (t)Michael Rosenfelf/Tony Stone Images, (b)Science VU/Visuals Unlimited; **245** (t)Dr. Kari Lounatmaa/Science Photo Library/Photo Researchers, (b)Moredun Animal Health, Ltd./Science Photo Library/Photo Researchers; **246** (l)Biophoto Associates/Photo Researchers, (r)Dr. Gopel Murti/Phototake, NYC; **250** Science Photo Library/Photo Researchers; **250–251** Tom Brakefield/CORBIS; **251** (tl)Omi-kron/Science Source/Photo Researchers, (tr)CNRI/Phototake, NYC; **252** Dr. G.G. Dimijian/Photo Researchers; **257** Dwight R. Kuhn; **263** Biophoto Associates/Photo Researchers; **265** (tl)Rob & Ann Simpson/Visuals Unlimited, (tr)Aaron Haupt, (b)Robert J. Ellison/Photo Researchers; **267** (clockwise from top) (1–4 7 9)John D. Cunningham/Visuals Unlimited, (5 6 8)Carolina Biological Supply/Phototake, NYC; **271** R.B. Satterthwaite; **272** B. John/Cabisco/Visuals Unlimited; **273** Bildarchiv Okapi/Photo Researchers; **274** Matt Meadows; **275** Ray Pfortner/Peter Arnold, Inc.; **276** R.W. VanNorman/Visuals Unlimited; **280** Robert Harding World Imagery/Alamy Images; **281** (t)Aaron Haupt, (inset)CNRI/Phototake, NYC; **283** Dan Richardson/The Stock Shop; **285 286** Dr. Gopel Murti/Science Photo Library/Photo Researchers; **296** Richard Katris; **297** (tl)SIU/Visuals Unlimited, (tr)Visuals Unlimited, (b)Grace Moore/The Stock Shop/Medichrome; **301** Tom Tracy/The Stock Shop/Medichrome; **303** Matt Meadows; **304** Photo Researchers; **305** Dr. Gopal Murti/Science Photo Library/Photo Researchers; **308** Stewart Cohen/Index Stock Imagery; **311** Biophoto Associates/Science Source/Photo Researchers; **313** (tl)Runk-Schoenberger/Grant Heilman Photography, (tr)David M. Dennis/Tom Stack & Associates, (c)Aaron Haupt, (b)L.J. Davenport/Visuals Unlimited; **315** Aaron Haupt; **317** (tl)Larry Lefever/Grant Heilman Photography, (bl)Steve Maslowski, (bc)Mark E. Gibson/Visuals Unlimited, (br)Aaron Haupt; **319** Dr. Jeremy Burgess/Science Photo Library/Photo Researchers; **321** (tl)Eastcott/Momatiuk/Animals Animals, (tr)Ralph Reinhold/Animals Animals, (b)Frank Oberle/ImageQuest; **322** (l)Visuals Unlimited, (c)Grant Heilman/Grant Heilman Photography, (r)Aaron Haupt; **323** (t)Aaron Haupt, (inset)Chris Pinchbeck/ImageQuest; **324** Stanley Flegler/Visuals Unlimited; **325** Custom Medical Stock Photo; **327** SIU/Visuals Unlimited; **328** Brent Turner/BLT Productions; **329** Biophoto Associates/Photo Researchers; **330** Aaron Haupt; **331** Carolina Biological Supply/Phototake, NYC; **332** Science VU/Visuals Unlimited; **333** (t)Grant Heilman/Grant Heilman Photography, (b)Stanley Flegler/Visuals Unlimited; **335** Lester V. Bergman/CORBIS; **336** Milo Burcham; **338** (t)Frank Gorski/Peter Arnold, Inc., (b)Bill Engel/ImageQuest; **339** Mak-1; **341** Courtesy Keith Woods; **343** Francis Leroy, Biocosmos/Science Photo Library/Custom Medical Stock Photo; **345** Bruce Burkhardt/CORBIS; **346** Jean Claude Revy/Phototake, NYC; **349** George Wilder/Visuals Unlimited; **350** Aaron Haupt; **351** (t)Drs. T. Tied & D. Ward/Peter Arnold, Inc., (b)Tim Courlas; **354** Crown Studios; **356** Science VU/Visuals Unlimited; **357** Biophoto Associates/Photo Researchers; **360** (t)Omikron/Photo Researchers, (b)Bettmann/CORBIS; **366** Breck P. Kent/Earth Scenes; **366–367** Daryl Balfour/Getty Images; **367** J. Breckett/D. Fannin/American Museum of Natural History; **368** Soames Summerhays/Photo Researchers; **370** (1)T.A. Wiewandt/DRK Photo, (2)Breck P. Kent/Earth Scenes, (3)Michael Collier, (4)John Gerlach/DRK Photo, (5)Jeff J. Daly/Visuals Unlimited; **371** (t)Jan Hinsch/Science Photo Library/Photo Researchers, (b)Patti Murray/Earth Scenes, (c)Gilbert S. Grant/Photo Researchers; **372** Louie Psihoyos/Matrix; **373** (t)Louis Psihoyos/Matrix, (b)Associated Press/The Mesa Tribune; **374** Kathy Sloane/Photo Researchers; **376** J. William Schopf/UCLA; **377** (t)Fred Bavendam/Peter Arnold, Inc., (b)Ken Lucas/Visuals Unlimited; **378** (l)Louis Psihoyos/Matrix, (r)Michael Dick/Animals Animals; **380** Fletcher & Baylis/Photo Researchers; **383** Sidney Fox/Visuals Unlimited; **384** George Gerster/Comstock; **386** (l)file photo, (r)Matt Meadows; **388** Roger Ressmeyer/Starlight; **389** Jeff J. Daly/Visuals Unlimited; **392** D. Lyon/Bruce Coleman, Inc.; **394** (t)Frans Lanting/Photo Researchers, (tr)Tom Brakefield/DRK Photo, (b)Barbara Cushman Rowell/DRK Photo; **397** M.W. Tweedie/Photo Researchers; **398** (l)R. Calentine/Visuals Unlimited, (c)John Colwell/Grant Heilman Photography, (r)S.L. & J.T. Collins/Photo Researchers; **401** (t)Dave Watts/Tom Stack & Associates, (b)Stephen Dalton/Photo Researchers; **404** (l)Rod Planck/Tom

A BIOLOGIST'S GUIDE TO THE PERIODIC TABLE

Element ──── Hydrogen
Atomic number ──── 1
Symbol ──── H ──── State of matter
Atomic mass ──── 1.008

- Gas
- Liquid
- Solid
- Synthetic

An acid is a substance that forms hydrogen ions (H⁺) in water. Some life processes, such as the chemical digestion of food in the stomach, require a highly acidic environment.

The movement of sodium and potassium ions across the plasma membranes of neurons transmits nerve impulses.

Magnesium is part of chlorophyll. In animals, it is essential for muscle and nerve activity and enzyme function.

The iron ions in hemoglobin bind to oxygen molecules in the lungs. The hemoglobin then delivers the oxygen to other parts of the body.

Calcium is needed for blood clotting, formation of bones and teeth, and normal nerve and muscle function.

Very small quantities of cesium-137, a radioactive isotope of cesium, are used to treat some types of cancer.

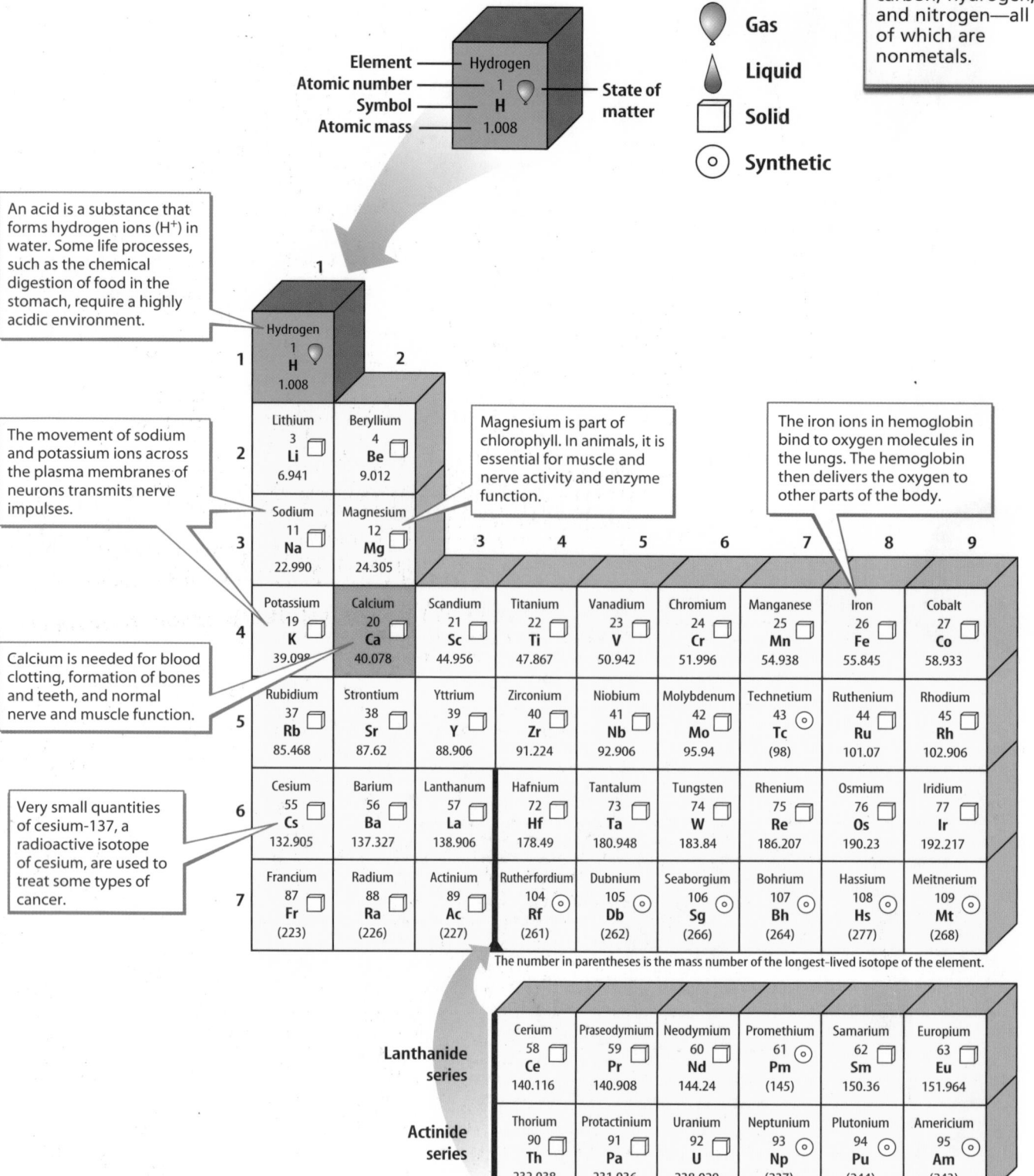

The number in parentheses is the mass number of the longest-lived isotope of the element.